AN ADVANCED TREATISE ON PHYSICAL CHEMISTRY

AN ADVANCED TREATISE ON PHYSICAL CHEMISTRY

VOLUME ONE

Fundamental Principles

The Properties of Gases

by

J. R. PARTINGTON
M.B.E., D.Sc.
Emeritus Professor of Chemistry in the University of London

1724

LONGMANS

LONGMANS, GREEN AND CO LTD
48 Grosvenor Street, London W1

Associated companies, branches and representatives throughout the world

First published 1949
New impression 1967

Printed and bound in Great Britain by William Clowes and Sons Limited, London and Beccles

PREFACE

The present book is intended to form part of a comprehensive treatise on Physical Chemistry in three or four volumes. The treatment lays emphasis on the experimental side, which has been rather neglected in some recent works on Physical Chemistry. In addition to descriptions of apparatus and experimental methods, collections of numerical data are given, including material not easily accessible and scattered through a large number of publications. Very full references to the literature are given; these cover periodical publications, proceedings of academies, books, dissertations, and all sources which were thought useful, and include most of the interesting classical publications as well as more recent work, in the case of Vol. I to the end of 1948. The text aims at being concise yet readable, and all points which are likely to offer difficulty are carefully explained.

Although the book is comprehensive it also aims at being intelligible, the title " Advanced " referring rather to the size and scope of the work than to its difficulty. For this reason the mathematical parts have been treated with great care. The Mathematical Introduction, together with special sections in the text dealing with more advanced mathematical apparatus, should enable a reader having only a very elementary knowledge of mathematics to acquire what is necessary. At the same time, the developments of statistical mechanics and wave mechanics are fully utilised, and the text is modern and comprehensive from this point of view. The symbols used are uniform, a full list of these being given, and equations as given in the literature have been reproduced in accordance with this systematic symbol list.

Although the relevant theory is fully dealt with in all parts, details of speculative material or formulae which contain undeterminable quantities and are without practical significance are omitted. There are, however, literature references to most of these. The space so set free has been used in assembling empirical or semi-empirical formulae which are likely to be of interest to laboratory workers, or to chemists or engineers engaged in large-scale work, who often require quantitative data not available which can be calculated with sufficient approximation for their needs by means of such formulae. The book, therefore, diverges from a tendency to treat the subject round a few theoretical ideas which may or may not be correct, and so to neglect a large mass of important practical material lying outside the immediate interest. Only those who, like the author, have had to search for such aids to research can fully appreciate their value.

The present volume begins with a Mathematical Introduction containing a condensed treatment of the parts of that subject required, commencing with the elements of the calculus (no knowledge of which, or of trigonometry, is assumed), and ending with differential equations and Fourier's series (spherical harmonics and other special functions being taken up in the later section on Wave Mechanics). This is followed by accounts of the principles of Thermodynamics, the Kinetic Theory of Gases, Statistical Mechanics, and Wave Mechanics. This fundamental theory is followed by sections on Thermometry, High and Low Temperatures, and a long section on the Properties of Gases, dealing with pressure-volume-temperature relations, characteristic equations and critical phenomena, density and molecular weight, specific heat, viscosity, thermal conductivity, diffusion, and the properties of gases at very low pressures. The second volume, which is in the press, deals with the corresponding properties of liquids and solids. After this brief statement of the character of the book, some indication of its plan and of some special features which have formed a part of its contents may be given.

The time has long gone when the great Continental masters found the inclination to present a detailed integration of the subject in which they laboured; the treatises of Berzelius, Dumas, Liebig, and Kekulé, to name only a few, stand as lasting monuments to the energy and genius of their authors. In the preface to his famous work,[1] Thomas Thomson noted that the production of such works was regarded in Britain as " a piece of drudgery, below the dignity of a philosopher." This spirit, still very much in evidence in the land of its birth, seems to have spread to the New World.[2] The modern style perhaps began in Lavoisier's " Traité Élémentaire de Chimie " (Paris, 1789), in which a limited amount of material, mostly the author's own work, is skilfully arranged around his own theories (many of which are erroneous) to give a more readable and attractive volume than one which covers a more extensive field. Books of this kind are well suited to beginners, but the more advanced require something more substantial. Opinions differ widely as to what is then most desirable. Every teacher who has not himself written a book has decided opinions as to what such a book should contain—usually one or two favourite topics which are " not properly understood " by others—and how it should be written, but no two opinions agree sufficiently to help an author in his task. Some authorities [3] believe that " our graduate student body is very heterogeneous as to objectives and abilities and it may well be doubted whether there is any real place for text-books in the graduate field. Timely monographs, covering more limited fields, would seem preferable." Reference has been made [4] to " German . . . thoroughness, which means the attempt to get into the book at least a reference to every article no matter how obscure the source, or how worthless the material," as contrasted with " the American tradition " of a " treatise or monograph " which " deals, in general, with the material with which the author has had intimate personal contact," and is " sure to be fully charged with its author's personality and prejudices." The " heavy diet offered by up-to-date Teutonic or pseudo-Teutonic treatises " is also deplored.[5] The present work, it may be confessed, to some extent continues pseudo-Teutonic traditions, formerly held in more respect,[6] and will be found unsuited to the needs of many classes of readers.

A word of praise has been given [7] to those who resist " the temptation, so insidious to the Teutonic mind, to write a ponderous 'Handbuch' in many instalments," although innumerable references to such works abound in present-day literature, and they do, in fact, seem to fill some need. Those who dig deeply in this mine of ready-made material for their slimmer and more attractive volumes mostly omit to say where they have been for their material, and, if they

[1] " A System of Chemistry," Edinburgh, 1802, **1**, pref.
[2] Huntress, *Chem. Eng. News*, 1949, **27**, 76.
[3] Kraus, *J.A.C.S.*, 1936, **58**, 537.
[4] MacInnes, *J.A.C.S.*, 1926, **48**, 538; Waters, *Nature*, 1946, **157**, 605: references " included with Teutonic frequency."
[5] Kendall, *J.A.C.S.*, 1926, **48**, 1778.
[6] P. F. Frankland, *B.A. Rep.*, 1901, 584.
[7] Forbes, *J.A.C.S.*, 1922, **44**, 1602.

give references, usually reproduce those of their unnamed sources, all the inaccuracies being carefully copied. It is, however, a mistake to assume that a capacity to present a field of science as a whole, and not merely a small part in which the author himself has worked, is incompatible with originality when this is joined with versatility; of Thomas Young (1773–1829), whose originality was of such a high order that most of his speculations, now commonplaces of scientific theory, were wholly beyond his contemporaries, it was said [1] that the " ample pages of the 'Encyclopædia Britannica' provided a fitting storehouse for arranging the treasures of his truly encyclopædical mind, and an opportunity of allaying that thirst for labour which haunted him throughout life as a passion."

There is no real need for a comprehensive work to contain " a hodge-podge of everything the authors have ever heard about, unilluminated by any clear understanding of the theoretical basis upon which they are proceeding "; nor for it to be " the work of minor scientists who hurry into print with the complicated applications of theories they do not understand." [2] It is not necessary, nor is it always desirable, to have a theoretical basis for *all* scientific knowledge, and those who have passed beyond the elementary stage know quite well how much valuable material will not fit in the shop-window display of the systematiser, yet often proves very handy in everyday laboratory or works experience. There is in the present volume an unusually large amount of such material in tables of data or empirical equations, and only those who have been faced with the urgent need to find some approximate value of a quantity can realise how much better such figures or equations are than theoretical formulae which contain unknown, and perhaps unknowable, constants. In any case, the material cannot be said to have been hurried into print. For many years the author has had to deliver courses of lectures and to supervise the work of research students, and in such work has required information not easily found in the standard treatises. In many cases the theoretical apparatus needed was found in a very abstract and unnecessarily mathematical form, and had to be reduced to a shape in which it was intelligible and useful to chemists who were not mathematicians. A large field had to be traversed and a body of information slowly came into being which is now presented in a systematic form. Whether it will be as useful to others must be judged by the readers. Those who have at their disposal all the large treatises and complete sets of journals, and have the ability to find in them rapidly all the information they need, will probably judge the book of little value and may well make no use of it. Those less favourably situated may find it of use, and it is mainly intended for such readers. It will not, therefore, be a valid criticism to say that all the information in it can be found in a better form elsewhere.

It is emphasised that the work deals with Physical Chemistry, not Chemical Physics or Mathematical Physics. Van't Hoff [3] defined Physical Chemistry as " the science devoted to the introduction of physical knowledge into chemistry, with the aim of being useful to the latter," and it is so understood here. The treatment is often mathematical, but the mathematics is a means to an end, and not the primary interest in the treatment. Even as late as 1889 it could be said,[4] with some justification, that: " Chemistry, being more concrete, is less exact than physics; mathematical methods can scarcely as yet be applied to purely

1 Anon., *Edin. N. Phil. J.*, 1855, **2**, 149.
2 Tolman, *J.A.C.S.*, 1930, **52**, 3742.
3 *J. Phys. Chem.*, 1905, **9**, 81.
4 Muir, " Principles of Chemistry," Cambridge, 1889, 5.

chemical data." It is true that, long before, in 1789, in his Koenigsberg Inaugural Dissertation, " De Usu Matheseos in Chymia," Richter said that " chemistry belongs in its greatest part to applied mathematics," [1] and in his later work, " Anfangsgründe der Stöchyometrie, oder Messkunst chemischer Elemente " (1792), he complained that " the most prominent chemists occupy themselves little with mathematics, and the mathematicians feel that they have little business in the province of chemistry," so that he began the book by expounding the elements of arithmetic and algebra. The first part of Richter's statement is not so true now as it was, but the second part still remains, unfortunately, very nearly correct.

It is now impossible to make any progress in Physical Chemistry without a knowledge of the calculus. As Ostwald [2] said: " Of course one can with the help of more or less cumbrous mathematical apparatus give an ' elementary ' proof of almost everything; but experience has shown that such diffuse page-long calculations are of no real aid in the comprehension of the subject." Whilst a treatment which " cannot get rid of the confused train of equations which constantly veil a positive comprehension of the results of the analysis " [3] is unsuited to the needs of chemists, the attempt to express mathematical operations in words (as found for example in Maxwell's " Theory of Heat ") is no more successful, and " to most people, analysis without equations and geometry without figures are particularly trying." [4] The need to express the physico-chemical problem to be solved in a form amenable to mathematical treatment always presents difficulties to the pure mathematician, and it is now no longer true, as it might have been for de Morgan,[5] that " Kant's space and time and Berkeley's matter are sufficient outfit for the mathematician." It has been said [6] that " the fall of a stone cannot be represented without employing the calculus, and it is hardly likely that the more complex problems of chemical reactions will prove any easier."

The form in which mathematics may be introduced can vary. Although a great experimenter [7] appealed for " learning put lightly like powder in jam," it has also been said [6] that " some object to being made to consume enormous quantities of jam to get a little valuable medicine." Most teachers agree that: [8] " Even those who have taken college mathematics commonly have difficulty in thinking of a derivative as anything else than the slope of a curve or of an integral as anything except the area under a curve. Most of them have trouble when the independent variable is time or temperature, or pressure or volume, or mole fraction."

Many topics are probably beyond the capacity of the " average " student, and teachers should not spend too much energy on his peculiar difficulties. It has been said [9] that " a very small—but not insignificant—minority of the very large number of those who have ' had ' courses in thermodynamics ever use it readily," and the teacher should remember that very few of his hearers will make any use of material he has tried with so much trouble and care to make

1 For a similar view, see Crum Brown, *B.A. Rep.*, 1874, 45.
2 " Outlines of General Chemistry," 1895, pref. v.
3 Pictet, *Phil. Mag.*, 1876, **1**, 477.
4 Barus, *J. Phys. Chem.*, 1905, **9**, 420.
5 *Trans. Cambr. Phil. Soc.*, 1871, **11**, 165 (read in 1864).
6 Partington, *J. Phys. Chem.*, 1924, **28**, 1007.
7 H. B. Dixon, in Mellor, " Higher Mathematics for Students of Chemistry and Physics, with Special Reference to Practical Work," 1902, pref.
8 Grinell Jones, *J.A.C.S.*, 1940, **62**, 456.
9 Johnston, *J.A.C.S.*, 1927, **49**, 1609.

intelligible and accurate; they will go to the text-books. The present book, therefore, contains the material of many undelivered as well as delivered lectures.

Much of the book was written during the war period, and in more than one case a visit to a library during an air-raid alert proved a trying experience. The manuscript was kept together, and during the worst hours it was taken to basements or shelters and, in a suitcase, served as a seat for the author. In such circumstances, chances of error are bound to occur, but it is hoped that the carefully revised text as finally printed shows little sign of the unfavourable times during which some of it was first written down.

In the older treatises on Physical Chemistry, such as Ostwald's " Lehrbuch der allgemeinen Chemie," a proper balance between theory and experiment was observed, but the later tendency has been to write books more and more devoted to the mathematical theory, without any regard being paid to experimental methods or their results, which are introduced merely for the purpose of proving or disproving the theories set out. Although such a book is much easier to write (and probably to read) than one in which experimental methods are described, it is little suited to the needs of physical chemists concerned with the development of the science.[1] The descriptions of experimental methods are, necessarily, brief, but enough is said to indicate the methods which have been used in investigations, and to point the way to the possibility of their adaptation to new problems or to improvements of them. The literature references will enable anyone to obtain full details of the methods.

The " advanced " character of the work implies that the principal aim has been to give information to those in search of it, and not to train students or even to " make readers think." It has no educational pretensions, except perhaps one. What is, apparently, an ideal of education as understood in some circles [2] is to " produce an attitude of scepticism and unreceptiveness." This attitude is natural and requires conscious and constant checking rather than inculcation. A cursory study of the history of science may be of some value in refuting such a suggestion as the above, since the acceptance of new ideas such as the theory of electrolytic dissociation and the quantum theory led to rapid and fruitful advances which left the sceptics far in the rear. Some new ideas prove to be mistaken, but the harm done in taking them up and working in the directions they suggest is much outweighed by the positive gain resulting from an open and receptive attitude towards original thought. It is believed that no careful reader of the book can be left in any doubt as to the truth of this assertion.

One tendency which has been avoided is to " build " the discussion of a topic around a theory which has been selected from among many alternatives. This is a favourite method in many modern treatments, and usually gains commendation on the ground that everything becomes " clear," and a mass of experimental data can be " co-ordinated " and reduced to a comprehensible unity. In reading through literature, old and new, many such attempts have been encountered, and in a large number of cases they have since foundered on newer experimental data, so that the discussion gives a completely distorted and inaccurate view of the subject. It is hoped that readers who believe that some such procedure should have been adopted, and feel impatient with a less elegant

[1] Demorest, *J.A.C.S.*, 1930, **52**, 4177: " there is all too great a tendency to neglect the facts and deal too much in theory in present-day pedagogy and book writing."

[2] Dr. R. H. Thouless, Lecturer in Psychology in Cambridge University, quoted in *Cambridge Daily News*, 21 August, 1944.

treatment, will bear in mind that an author who has read far more literature than they have may have good reasons for his own procedure.

The relation between theory and experiment can have two aspects. In one, the interest is in theory, and the experiments are regarded merely as verifying it. In the second, theory is regarded as providing equations by means of which experimental results can be calculated and interpreted, equations which are not capable of experimental test being of little interest. The second view is generally adopted in this book. According to Sosman,[1] " the pragmatic philosopher prefers to base his electromagnetics upon a piece of lodestone and a stroked cat; they can always be depended upon . . . even though one's notions of magnetic and electric fields have changed."

It has been truly said [2] that: " If one is interested in the theoretical side of a subject, it is necessary to go back a good many years in the journal literature. As a broad statement, only those things get into text-books which fit into the existing theory." These are usually known as " significant " or " timely." Another tendency is to confine the treatment almost entirely to very modern work, and completely ignore all the classical researches. It has been remarked [3] that, in a book of about 200 pages on the phase rule, the name of Gibbs is not once mentioned. Many older papers contain important material which has long been forgotten; some of it has had a revival of interest since its rediscovery in later years. It has been said [4] that " a good idea at the wrong time or by the wrong man, which is perhaps the same thing, is apparently as much wasted as though it had never occurred." Whether this is better or worse than a poor idea at the right time is a debatable question.

Day and Sosman [5] remarked that, in the history of science, " instances can be brought forward in about equal number, on the one hand of good theoretical judgment which disregarded existing data and was afterwards justified by the results of more exact measurement, and on the other hand of apparent discrepancies in experimental results which, though carefully explained away by the experimenter himself, subsequently proved his experimental accuracy to have been better than his judgment."

In some cases, great extensions in the literature of a particular topic occurred during the preparation of the book. In such cases, the bibliography has usually been brought up to date, but it would not have been possible to extend the text without deranging the whole plan of the book. The responsibility for such new information must necessarily rest with the authors of the references cited.[6]

Since the author is interested in the history of science the treatment in a section often begins with a short historical survey. Many of these cost much trouble in preparation, since the original sources were often inaccessible, and modern literature, when it mentioned the pioneers at all, did so with inaccurate statements of the literature and its content. All inaccuracies found were corrected without special mention unless it seemed necessary. A zealous urge to the correction of other authors is a failing which is tiresome in print. The historical sections are quite small and may not be to the taste of all readers, yet Ostwald [7] correctly said: " It cannot be too often emphasised how much

1 In " Temperature. Its Measurement and Control," New York, 1941, 43.
2 Bancroft, *J. Phys. Chem.*, 1929, **33**, 320.
3 *J.A.C.S.*, 1927, **49**, 1607.
4 Bancroft, *J. Phys. Chem.*, 1924, **28**, 262.
5 In Glazebrook, " Dict. of Applied Physics," 1922, **1**, 864.
6 Cf. Kohlrausch, *Ann. Phys.*, 1906, **20**, 798.
7 ***Z. phys. Chem.***, 1899, **28**, 187.

better a fact or relation stays in the memory when some sort of personal touch can be attached to it."

Since the author read most of the literature, checked most of the references, and wrote all the text, he has little to add in the way of acknowledgments. His son, Dr. R. G. Partington, is responsible for the ingenious mnemonic of Maxwell's equations on pages 189–90. Mr. A. F. J. Light gave valuable assistance in checking many references in the earlier stages of the work, and both he and the author met with great courtesy and help from the officials of the many libraries used, with only one exception. Mr. B. Fullman, of the British Non-Ferrous Metals Research Association, very kindly obtained otherwise inaccessible publications and directed attention to several valuable papers which otherwise would have escaped notice. It is inevitable that many more such papers have been passed over through ignorance, although the author looked through several complete sets of journals and the relevant sections of *Chemical Abstracts* from their commencement. Thanks are due to Mr. Higham and Mr. J. C. Longman, who gave the author every help and encouragement in difficult times. The compositors of Messrs. Clowes deserve mention for the very skilful and accurate way in which they dealt with the difficult copy.

CAMBRIDGE AND LONDON, *June 1949.*

CONTENTS

LIST OF LITERATURE ABBREVIATIONS

In the footnote references a uniform plan has been followed. In the case of periodicals, the year and volume number usually fix the volume exactly, and the specification of the series in the case of journals such as the *Annales de Chimie*, the *Journal de Physique*, the *Annalen der Physik*, etc., which begin a new numbering of the volumes in each series, is unnecessary. In some cases, such as the *Annalen der Physik*, a continuous enumeration of the volumes appears on the title-pages as well as those of the separate series numbers, but this was not usually continued, and would be inconvenient. In at least one case, the *American Journal of Science*, the continuous enumeration was suddenly adopted in place of the previous series numbers, and (since the latter had been dropped), this has then been used. In some cases a journal has changed its name, sometimes more than once. The format has not been given either for books or journals, except when it is necessary; in one case an octavo and a quarto appeared side by side with the same title, but are quite separate publications. In some cases (e.g. *Proceedings* and *Philosophical Transactions* of the Royal Society, *Zeitschrift für physikalische Chemie*) an A and a B series are involved; to avoid unnecessary repetition only the B series is specified, the A series (mostly used) being without letter. In other cases (e.g. *Gazzetta Chimica Italiana*) there are two parts to each volume, which are denoted by i and ii; in others (e.g. *Sitzungsberichte der Akademie der Wissenschaften in Wien*) there are class numbers and letters, denoted by II A, etc.; in case an Academy issues publications dealing with scientific and linguistic matters, only the former is understood. It is believed that no difficulty will be found in any case in tracing the reference.[1]

In quoting names of authors, initials are not usually given; these can be found by turning up the publication. An exception is often made in the case of books by authors with names such as Smith, for convenience in consulting library catalogues. References which are grouped are usually in order of *date*, but an exception is made in some very long reference groups, where the order is that of authors' names. There is much to be said for the first practice, since it makes clear the priority of discovery, a matter which is not always obvious in modern accounts. It should not be necessary to say that every reference given has been checked with the original whenever this was possible. In some cases, however, when the abstract of a paper in an easily accessible abstract journal was unusually good, a reference to this is given as well as the original. A very large proportion of the references have been seen by the author personally, but in spite of every effort, recent Russian journals and nearly all Japanese journals of the war period proved to be unobtainable. In such cases, when the paper seemed from the abstract to be interesting, a reference is given even though it could not be checked.

In the case of very long papers, two page references are often given, one for the first page of the paper and the second (in brackets) for the page on which the statement in the text is to be found. In some works of reference the actual page in a paper is quoted, so that many apparently different references are

[1] The pitfalls in citing literature, and the confusion in numbering volumes of journals, etc., are feelingly described by Mohr, *Z. anal. Chem.*, 1870, **9**, 236.

really to the same paper. This has led to error in authors who have quoted from such works and have never seen the originals. A surprisingly large number of references given in standard works were found to be incorrect, usually in exactly the same form in different books, and in some cases quotations in inverted commas were not found in papers, sometimes not in any form, in others in a different form and sense. It is hardly necessary to say that references which gave the most trouble in locating were the least important to the modern worker.

In the case of book titles, a reasonably complete form has been given, such words as " An Elementary Treatise on . . ." being often omitted. In old books, the full title sometimes practically fills the title-page. The place of publication has usually been given, but if the title is English and no place is specified, London is to be understood, and if in French, Paris. A full list of journal abbreviations is given below. It is believed that any worker interested in a particular theory or experimental method should, by an afternoon's work in a good library, be able to acquire a useful foundation for a knowledge of the subject. He is strongly recommended to see *all* the references which he can, since it is only in this way that a comprehensive picture of the subject can be gained. Some references contain valuable bibliographies of the subject, and this has mostly been noted. For work later than the date of the volume, a study of the subject index of *British Abstracts* or *Chemical Abstracts*, the *Zentralblatt*, and *Science Abstracts* will provide an opening into the literature, and on consulting the originals many new references will be found.

Since the statement of cross-references by page numbers would have been an enormous additional task after the page-proofs had been made up, all such references are by paragraph and section. There are seven main sections, shown in the table of Contents, each with its own paragraph numbers. The section number will be found on the inner margin of the left-hand page, and the paragraph number on the inner margin of the right-hand page, so that the place can be found very quickly. Equations are numbered in each paragraph, so that (5), § 8.VI B means equation (5) in paragraph 8 of section VI B. The subject of the main section is given on the left-hand page, and that of the paragraph on the right-hand page. The figure (illustration) numbers are also separate in each sub-section. A glance at a few pages of the book will make this simple system quite clear. A subject index is provided, but an author index would have been of little use, since some names would occur in it so many times that it would have taken a very long time to turn them all up in the text.

The book contains 18,145 separate references to literature (some of which are repeated in dealing with different topics), distributed among countries of publication of the sources as follows:

Germany, 6012
Great Britain and Ireland, 4139
The United States of America, 3701
France, 1779
Holland, 1070
Switzerland, 289
Austria, 213
Russia, 198
Italy, 175
Japan, 124
Belgium, 87
Canada, 61
Spain, 61
Sweden, 54
India, 44
Poland, 41
Denmark, 29
Australia, 18
New Zealand, 11
Rumania, 7
Czechoslovakia, 6
Finland, 6
Norway, 6
Brazil, 4
China, 4
Argentina, 3
South Africa, 2
Latvia, 1

Since in many sections (e.g. in Section IV), American references greatly outweigh all others, and often run on for pages, the magnitudes of the first three items are of considerable interest.

Abhl. Akad. Munich. Abhandlungen der mathematisch-physikalischen Klasse der Königlich Bayrischen Akademie der Wissenschaften, Munich.

Abhl. d. D. Bunsen Ges. Abhandlungen der Deutschen Bunsen Gesellschaft, Halle.

Abhl. K. Akad. [*Wiss.*] *Berlin.* Abhandlungen der Kgl. Akademie der Wissenschaften zu Berlin, physikalisch-mathematische Klasse, Berlin.

Abhl. Phys. Techn. Reichsanst. See *Wiss. Abhl.*

Acta Chem. Scand. Acta Chemica Scandinavica, Copenhagen.

Acta Comment. Univ. Dorpatensis. Acta et Commentationes Universitatis Dorpatensis.

Acta Erudit. Acta Eruditorum, Leipzig.

Acta Phys. Polon. Acta Physica Polonica, Warsaw.

Acta Physicochim. U.R.S.S. Acta Physicochimica U.R.S.S.

Acta Soc. Sci. Fenn. Acta Societatio Scientiarum Fennicae, Helsingfors.

Acta Univ. Latviensis. Acta Universitatis Latviensis, Riga.

Alembic Club Repr[*ints*]. Alembic Club Reprints, Edinburgh.

Amer. Chem. Abstr. Chemical Abstracts, published by the American Chemical Society, Easton, Pa.

Amer. Chem. J. American Chemical Journal, Baltimore.

Amer. Inst. Min. Met. Eng. See *Trans. Amer. Inst. Min. Met. Eng.*

Amer. Inst. Min. Met. Eng. Contrib. American Institute of Mining and Metallurgical Engineers, Contributions, New York.

Amer. Inst. Min. Met. Eng. Techn. Publ. American Institute of Mining and Metallurgical Engineers, Technical Publication, New York.

Amer. J. Pharm. American Journal of Pharmacy, Philadelphia, Pa.

Amer. J. Phys. American Journal of Physics, Lancaster, Pa.

Amer. J. Sci. American Journal of Science, New Haven.

An. Acad. Brasil Cienc. Anais Academia Brasileira de Ciencias, Rio de Janeiro.

An. Assoc. Quim. Brasil. Anais de Associacão Química de Brasil, Sao Paulo.

An. Fis. Quim. Anales de la Real Sociedad Española de Física y Química, Madrid.

An. Soc. Cient. Argentina. Anales de la Sociedad Cientifica Argentina, Buenos Aires.

Anal. Chem. See *Ind. Eng. Chem. Anal.*

Analyst. The Analyst, London.

Angew. Chem. See *Z. angew. Chem.*

Ann. Annalen der Chemie (Liebig's Annalen), Leipzig.

Ann. Acad. Sci. Fenn. Annales Academiae Scientiarum Fennicae, Helsingfors.

Ann. Chim. Annales de Chimie (formerly combined with Annales de Physique), Paris.

Ann. Chim. Anal. [*Appl.*]. Annales de Chimie Analytique et de Chimie Appliqué, *Paris.*

Ann. Chim. Appl. Annali di Chimica Applicata, Rome.

Ann. de l'École Norm. Annales Scientifique de l'École Normale Supérieure, Paris.

Ann. de Phys. Annales de Physique, Paris (see *Ann. Chim.*).

Ann. des Mines. Annales des Mines, Paris.

Ann. Entomol. Soc. Amer. Annals of the Entomological Society of America, Columbus, Ohio.

Ann. Ergzb. Annalen der Chemie Ergänzungsbände.
Ann. Fac. Sci. Toulouse. Annales de la Faculté des Sciences de Toulouse.
Ann. Mines. See *Ann. des Mines.*
Ann. Phil. Annals of Philosophy, London.
Ann. Phys. Annalen der Physik, Leipzig (several series; formerly Annalen der Physik und Chemie, etc.).
Ann. Phys. Beibl. Beiblätter zu den Annalen der Physik (1881–1919), Leipzig (continued as *Phys. Ber.*).
Ann. Phys. Boltzmann Festschr. Ludwig Boltzmann Festschrift gewidmet, Leipzig, 1904 (uniform with volumes of Annalen der Physik).
Ann. Phys. Ergzb. Annalen der Physik Ergänzungsbände.
Ann. Phys. Pogg. Jubelband. Annalen der Physik. Poggendorff Jubelband, Berlin, 1874.
Ann. Rep. C[hem]. S[oc.]. Annual Reports of the Chemical Society, London.
Ann. Sci. Univ. Jassy. Annales Scientifique de l'Université de Jassy, Jassy, Rumania.
Annals New York Acad. Sci. Annals of the New York Academy of Sciences.
Annals of Sci[ence]. Annals of Science, London.
Annali di Chimica. Annali di Chimica e Storia Naturali, edit. Brugnatelli, Pavia.
Appl. Sci. Res. Applied Science Research.
Apotheker Ztg. Apothekerzeitung, Berlin.
Arch. di Fisiol. Archivio di Fisiologia, Florence.
Arch. exp. Path. Pharm. Archiv für experimentelle Pathologie und Pharmakologie, Leipzig.
Arch. Mus. Teyler. Archives du Musée Teyler, Haarlem.
Arch. Néerl. Archives Néerlandais des Sciences Exactes et Naturelles, Series III (Sciences exactes), The Hague, Holland.
Arch. Pharm. Archiv der Pharmazie, Leipzig.
Arch. Sci. Phys. Nat. Archives des Sciences Physiques et Naturelles, Geneva (continuation of *Bibl. Univ.*).
Arch. Techn. Messen. Archiv für technisches Messen, Munich.
Archiv Eisenhüttenw. Archiv für das Eisenhüttenwesen, Düsseldorf.
Archiv Gesch. Naturwiss. Technik. Archiv für die Geschichte der Naturwissenschaft und der Technik, Leipzig.
Archiv Mat. Naturvidenskab. Christiania. Archiv for Mathematik og Naturvidenskab, Christiania.
Arkiv Kem. Min. Geol. Arkiv för Kemi, Mineralogi och Geologi, Stockholm.
Arkiv Mat. Astron. Fys. Arkiv för Matematik, Astronomi och Fysik, Stockholm.
Astrophys. J. The Astrophysical Journal, Chicago.
Atti Accad. Ital. [R. Sci.] fis. mat. [nat.]. Atti della Reale Accademia d'Italia. Memoria della Classe di Scienze Fisiche, Matematiche e Naturali, Rome.
Atti Accad. Torino. Atti della Reale Accademia delle Scienze di Torino, Turin.
Atti Accad. Veneto. Atti del Reale Instituto Veneto di Scienze, Lettere ed Arti, Venice.
Atti Congr. Naz. Chim. Pura Applic. Atti del Congresso Nazionale di Chimica Pura ed Applicata, Rome.
Atti R. Accad. Lincei. Atti della Reale Accademia dei Lincei, Rendiconti Classe di Scienza Fisiche, Matematiche e Naturali, Rome.
Austral. J. Sci. Res. Australian Journal of Scientific Research, Ser. A, Physical Sciences, East Melbourne.

Avhl. Norsk. Videns. Akad. Oslo. Avhandlinger uitgitt av det Norske Videnskaps-Akademie i Oslo.

B.A. Rep. British Association for the Advancement of Science, Reports, London.

B.A. Rep. Coll. Chem. Reports on Colloid Chemistry, British Association for the Advancement of Science, London.

Beitr. Kryst. Min. Beiträge zur Krystallographie und Mineralogie, Heidelberg.

Bell Syst. Techn. J. Bell System Technical Journal, New York.

Bell Telephone Syst. Techn. Monogr. Bell Telephone System Technical Monographs, New York.

Bell Telephone Syst. Techn. Publ. Bell Telephone System Technical Publications, New York.

Ber. Berichte der Deutschen chemischen Gesellschaft, Berlin (name changed to Chemische Berichte).

Ber. D. Phys. Ges. See *Z. Phys.*

Ber. Oberhess. Ges. Natur- u. Heilkde. Berichte der Oberhessischen Gesellschaft für Natur- und Heilkunde, Giessen.

Berlin Ber. Sitzungsberichte der [Königlich] Preussischen Akademie der Wissenschaften, Physikalisch-mathematische Klasse, Berlin.

Berlin. klin. Wochenschr. Berliner klinische Wochenschrift, Berlin (continued as Klinische Wochenschrift).

Bibl. Univ. Bibliothèque Universelle de Gèneve, Geneva.

Bihang Kgl. Svensk. Vet. Akad. Handl. Bihang till Kongliga Svenska Vetenskaps-Akademiens Handlinger, Stockholm.

Biochem. J. The Biochemical Journal, Liverpool.

Biochem. Z. Biochemische Zeitschrift, Berlin.

Biodynamica. St. Louis, Missouri.

Bol. Acad. Cienc. Argentina. Boletin de la Academia Nacional de Ciencias de la República Argentina, Córdoba.

Brennstoff Chem. Brennstoff-Chemie, Essen.

Brit. Chem. Abstr. British Abstracts, Bureau of Abstracts, London.

Brit. Pat. British Patent.

Bul. Soc. Chim. Roman. Buletinul Societăţii de Chimie (din România), Bucarest.

Bull. Soc. Roman. de Stiinte. Buletinul de Chimie pură și applicată, Societatea Română de Stiinte (formerly Buletinul Societăţii Române de Stiinte).

Bull. Soc. Stiinte Cluj. Buletinul Societăţii de Stiinte din Cluj, Cluj, Rumania.

Bull. Acad. Polon. Bulletin Internationale de l'Académie Polonaise des Sciences et Lettres, Section A, Cracow (formerly Bulletin Internationale de l'Académie des Sciences de Cracovie).

Bull. Acad. Roy. Belg. Bulletin de l'Académie Royale de Belgique, Classe des Sciences, Brussels.

Bull. Acad. [*Sci.*] *St. Petersb.* Bulletin de l'Académie Impériale des Sciences de St. Petersbourg, St. Petersburg (continued as *Bull. Acad. Sci. Russe*).

Bull. Acad. Sci. Russe. Bulletin de l'Académie des Sciences de Russie, Petrograd.

Bull. Acad. Sci. U.R.S.S. Bulletin de l'Académie des Sciences de l'U.R.S.S.

Bull. Amer. Inst. Min. Met. Eng. Bulletin of the American Institute of Mining and Metallurgical Engineers, New York.

Bull. Assoc. Chim. Bulletin de l'Association des Chimistes de Sucrerie et de Distillerie de France et des Colonies, Paris.

Bull. Chem. Soc. Japan. Bulletin of the Chemical Society of Japan, Tokyo.

Bull. Eng. Expt. Stat. Univ. Illinois. Bulletin Illinois University Engineering Experimental Station.

Bull. Inst. Phys. Chem. Res. Tokyo. Bulletin of the Institute of Physical and Chemical Research, Tokyo.
Bull. Inst. Intern. Froid. Bulletin Institut Internationale du Froid, Paris.
Bull. Nat. Res. Counc. Bulletin of the National Research Council, Washington.
Bull. Sect. Sci. Acad. Roum[*aine*]. Bulletin de la Section Scientifique de l'Académie Roumaine, Bucarest.
Bull. Sci. Pharmacol. Bulletin des Sciences Pharmacologiques, Paris.
Bull. Soc. Chim. Bulletin de la Société Chimique de France, Paris.
Bull. Soc. Chim. Belg. Bulletin de la Société Chimique de Belgique, Brussels (since 1944 Bulletin des Sociétés Chimiques Belges, Liége).
Bull. Soc. Chim. Biol. Bulletin de la Société de Chimie Biologique, Paris.
Bull. Soc. Encourag[*em.*]. *Ind.* [*Nat.*]. Bulletin de la Société d'Encouragement pour l'Industrie Nationale, Paris.
Bull. Soc. Geol. Bulletin de la Société Géologique de France, Paris.
Bull. Soc. Imp. Naturalistes de Moscow. Bulletin de la Société Impériale des Naturalistes de Moscow, Moscow.
Bull. Soc. Ind. Min. Bulletin de la Société de l'Industrie Minérale de St. Étienne, Paris.
Bull. Soc. Int[*ernat.*]. *Elec.* Bulletin de la Société Internationale des Électriciens, Paris.
Bull. Soc. Min. Bulletin de la Société Française de Minéralogie, Paris.
Bull. Soc. Philomath. Bulletin de la Société Philomathique, Paris.
Bull. Soc. Phys. Bulletin de la Société Française de Physique, Paris.
Bull. Soc. Phys. Séances. Bulletin de la Société Française de Physique, Séances, Paris.
Bull. Soc. Roy. Sci. Liége. Bulletin de la Société Royale des Sciences de Liége.
Bull. Soc. Sci. Cluj. See *Bul. Soc. Stiinte Cluj.*
Bull. Univ. Illinois Eng. Expt. Station. Bulletin of the University of Illinois Engineering Experimental Station.
Bull. U.S. Geol. Survey. Bulletins of the United States of Geological Survey (Department of the Interior), Washington.
Bur. Mines Bull. Bureau of Mines Bulletin, Washington.
Bur. Mines Rep. Invest. Bureau of Mines Reports of Investigations, Washington.
Bur. Mines Techn. Paper. Bureau of Mines Technical Papers, Washington.
Bur. Stand. Bull. Bulletin of the Bureau of Standards, Washington.
Bur. Stand. Circ. Bureau of Standards Circulars, Washington.
Bur. Stand. J. Res. Journal of Research of the National Bureau of Standards, Washington.
Bur. Stand. Misc. Publ. Bureau of Standards Miscellaneous Publications, Washington.
Cambr. and Dublin Math. J. Cambridge and Dublin Mathematical Journal.
Cambr. Math. J. Cambridge Mathematical Journal (continued as *Cambr. and Dublin Math. J.*), Cambridge.
Canad. Chem. J. Canadian Chemical Journal, Toronto (name changed 1921 to *Canad. Chem. Met.*).
Canad. Chem. Met. Canadian Chemistry and Metallurgy, Toronto (continued as Canadian Chemistry and Process Industries).
Canad. Chem. Process. Ind. Canadian Chemistry and Process Industries, Toronto.
Canad. J. Res. Canadian Journal of Research, Ottawa.
Carl's Repert. d. Phys. See *Repert. Phys.*

Carnegie Inst. Publ. Carnegie Institution of Washington Publications.
Centr. Min. Centralblatt für Mineralogie, Geologie und Paläontologie, Sects. A (Mineralogie und Petrographie) and B (Geologie und Paläontologie), Stuttgart.
Centr. Zuckerind. Centralblatt für die Zuckerindustrie, Magdeburg.
Chaleur et Ind. Chaleur et Industrie, Paris.
Chem. Age. Chemical Age, London.
Chem. App. Chemische Apparatur, Leipzig.
Chem. and Ind. Chemistry and Industry, London.
Chem. Ber. See *Ber.*
Chem. Centr. Chemisches Centralblatt (name changed to Chemisches Zentralblatt), Berlin.
Chem. Eng. Chemical Engineering, New York (continued as *Chem. Met. Eng.*).
Chem. Eng. Mining Rev. Chemical Engineering and Mining Review, Sydney.
Chem. Eng. News. Chemical Engineering News (American Chemical Society).
Chem. Fabr. Die chemische Fabrik, Berlin.
Chem. Gazette. Chemical Gazette, London.
Chem. Listy. Chemické Listy, Prague.
Chem. Met. Eng. Chemical and Metallurgical Engineering, New York.
Chem. News. Chemical News, London.
Chem. Obzor. Chemický Obzor, Prague.
Chem. Rev. Chemical Reviews, Baltimore.
Chem. Techn. Die Chemische Technik, Berlin.
Chem. Trade J. Chemical Trade Journal and Chemical Engineer, London.
Chem. Weekbl. Chemisch Weekblad, Amsterdam.
Chem. Zentr. See *Chem. Centr.*
Chem. Ztg. Chemiker-Zeitung, Cöthen.
Chemist-Analyst. The Chemist-Analyst, Phillipsburg, N.J.
Chim. e Ind. Chimica e l'Industria, Milan.
Chim. et Ind. Chimie et Industrie, Paris.
Chinese Chem. J. Chinese Chemical Journal.
Chinese J. Phys. Chinese Journal of Physics.
Chymia. Chymia, Annual Studies in the History of Chemistry, Philadelphia, Pa.
Civilingenieur. Freiburg.
Coll. Czech. Chem. Comm. Collection of Czechoslovak Chemical Communications, Prague.
Coll. Rep. See *B.A. Rep. Coll. Chem.*
Comm. Kodak Res. Lab. Communications of the Kodak Research Laboratory, Rochester, New York.
Comm. Leiden. Communications from the Physical [Kamerlingh Onnes] Laboratory of the University of Leiden, Leiden.
Comment. Phys. Math. Soc. Sci. Fenn. Societas Scientiarum Fennica Commentationes Physico-Mathematicae, Helsingfors.
Compt. Rend. Comptes Rendus hebdomadaires des Séances de l'Académie des Sciences, Paris.
Compt. Rend. Soc. Biol. Comptes Rendus des Séances de la Société de Biologie, Paris.
Compt. Rend. U.R.S.S. Comptes Rendus de l'Académie des Sciences de l'U.R.S.S.
Conf. Lab. de Friedel. Conférences faites au Laboratoire de M. Friedel, 4 vols., Paris, 1888–94.

Congrès Internat. Électricité. Procès-Verbaux Congrès Internationaux, Paris, 1900–02.
Congrès Internat. Phys. Congrès International de Physique, Paris, 1900–02.
Conseil Solvay. Institut Internationale de Chimie Solvay, Conseil de Chimie. Rapports et Discussions, Paris.
Cosmos, Paris.
Current Sci. Current Science, Bangalore.
Dansk. Vidensk. Selsk. Forhl. Det Kongelige Danske Videnskabernes Selskab Forhandlinger, Copenhagen.
Deutsch. Apothek. Ztg. Deutsche Apotheker Zeitung, Berlin.
Die Chemie. Berlin.
Die Technik. Berlin.
Die Wissenschaft, Brunswick.
Dingl. J. Dingler's Polytechnisches Journal, Berlin.
Discuss. Faraday Soc. Discussion, Faraday Society.
Dissert. Dissertation.
D.S.I.R. Fuel Res. Paper. Department of Scientific and Industrial Research, London, Fuel Research Paper.
Éclair. Élec. Éclairage Électrique, Paris.
Edin. J. Sci. Edinburgh Journal of Science, Edinburgh.
Edin. N. Phil. J. Edinburgh New Philosophical Journal, Edinburgh.
Elec[*tr.*]. *Rev.* Electrical Review, London.
Elec. World. Electrical World, New York.
Electrician. The Electrician, London.
Electrochem. and Metall. Ind. Electrochemical and Metallurgical Industry, New York.
Elektrochem. Z. Elektrochemische Zeitschrift, Berlin.
Electronics, New York.
Elektrotechn. Z. Electrotechnische Zeitschrift, Berlin.
Elster-Geitel Festschr. Arbeiten aus den Gebieten der Physik, Mathematik, Chemie, Festschrift Julius Elster und Hans Geitel, Brunswick, 1915.
" Ency. Brit." Encyclopædia Britannica.
Endeavour, London.
Energia Termica, Milan.
Eng. Boiler House Review. Engineering and Boiler House Review, London.
Eng. Mining J. Engineering and Mining Journal, New York.
Engineer. The Engineer, London.
Engineering, London.
" Enzykl. d. math. Wiss." Enzyklopädie der mathematischen Wissenschaften, Leipzig.
Ergebn. [*d.*] *exakt. Naturwiss.* Ergebnisse der exakten Naturwissenschaften, Berlin.
Essays and Obs. Phys. and Lit. Essays and Observations Physical and Literary Read before a Society in Edinburgh, and published by them, Edinburgh.
Experientia, Basel.
Farbe u. Lack. Farbe und Lack, Hanover.
Foreign Petrol. Techn. Foreign Petroleum Technology, Linden, New Jersey.
Forhl. Vidensk.-Selsk. Christiania. Forhandlinger i Videnskabs-Selskabet i Christiania, Christiania.
Forschungen u[*nd*]. *Fortschritte.* Forschungen und Fortschritte, Berlin.
Forschungsarb. Gebiet Ingenieurw. (also other abbreviations). Mitteilungen über Forschungsarbeiten auf dem Gebiet des Ingenieurwesens, Berlin.

Fortschr. Phys. Fortschritte der Physik, Berlin, 1846–1919; continued as Physikalische Berichte.

Fysisk Tidsskr. Fysisk Tidsskrift, Copenhagen.

Gas Age, New York.

Gas Ind. Die Gas-Industrie, Halle.

Gas J. Gas Journal, London.

Gas Research Board Comm. Gas Research Board Communication, London.

Gas u. Wasserfach. Das Gas- und Wasserfach, Munich.

Gas World, London.

Gazz. Gazzetta Chimica Italiana, Rome.

Gen. Elec. Rev. General Electric Review, Schenectady, N.Y.

Germ. Pat. German Patent.

" Ges. Abhl." Gesamte (or Gesammelte) Abhandlungen.

Gesundh. Ing. Gesundheits-Ingenieur, Munich.

Giorn. Chim. Ind. Appl. Giornale di Chimica Industriale ed Applicata, Milan.

Glas u. Apparat. Glas und Apparat, Weimar.

Glastechn. Ber. Glastechnische Berichte, Frankfurt.

Gött Nachr. Nachrichten der Akademie der Wissenschaften zu Göttingen, Mathematisch-physikalische Klasse, Berlin.

Hand u. Jahrb. [d., der] chem. Phys[ik]. Hand- und Jahrbücher der chemischen Physik, Leipzig.

Heidelberg Ber. Sitzungsberichte der Heidelberger Akademie der Wissenschaften, Mathematisch-naturwissenschaftliche Klasse, Heidelberg.

Helv. Chim. Acta. Helvetica Chimica Acta, Basel.

Helv. Phys. Acta. Helvetica Physica Acta, Basel.

Hist. Acad. Berlin. Histoire de l'Académie Royale des Sciences et des Belles Lettres de Berlin.

Hist. Acad. Sci. (Paris). Histoire de l'Académie Royale des Sciences, Paris.

Illum. Eng. Illuminating Engineer, London.

Ind. Eng. Chem. Industrial and Engineering Chemistry (to vol. 14, 1924, Journal of Industrial and Engineering Chemistry).

Ind. Eng. Chem. Anal. Industrial and Engineering Chemistry, Analytical (name changed in 1948 to Analytical Chemistry).

Indian J. Agric. Sci. Indian Journal of Agricultural Science, Delhi.

Indian J. Phys. Indian Journal of Physics, Calcutta.

Industria Chimica. L'Industria Chimica, Turin.

Instruments, Pittsburg, Pa.

Int. Kongr. angew. Chem. Kongress für angewandte Chemie, Berlin, 1903.

Internat. Congr. Refrig. Proceedings of the International Congress of Refrigeration, The Hague.

Iron Age, New York.

Iron and Steel Carnegie Schol. Mem. Iron and Steel Institute (London) Carnegie Scholarship Memoirs, London.

Isis. Ghent, etc.

J.A.C.S. Journal of the American Chemical Society, Easton, Pa.

J. Acoust. Soc. Amer. Journal of the Acoustical Society of America, Lancaster, Pa.

J. Amer. Ceram. Soc. Journal of the American Ceramic Society, Easton, Pa.

J. Amer. Inst. Elec. Eng. Journal of the American Institute of Electrical Engineers, New York.

J. Amer. Orient. Soc. Journal of the American Oriental Society, New York.

J. Amer. Soc. Mech. Eng. Journal of the American Society of Mechanical Engineers (name changed to Mechanical Engineering).
J. Amer. Soc. Refrig. Eng. Journal of the American Society of Refrigerating Engineers, New York.
J. Appl. Mechan[*ics*]. Journal of Applied Mechanics, issued as part of the Transactions of the American Society of Mechanical Engineers, New York.
J. Appl. Phys. Journal of Applied Physics, Lancaster, Pa.
J. Appl. Phys. Moscow. Journal of Applied Physics, Moscow.
J. Asiat. Journal Asiatique, Paris.
J. Chem. Educ. Journal of Chemical Education, Easton, Pa.
J. Chem. Ind. U.S.S.R. Journal of Chemical Industry of the U.S.S.R., Moscow.
J. Chem. Phys. The Journal of Chemical Physics, American Institute of Physics, Lancaster, Pa.
J. Chem. Phys. (Schweigger). Journal für Chemie und Physik, Nürnberg, etc. (continued as *J. prakt. Chem.*).
J.C.S. Journal of the Chemical Society, London.
J. Chem. Soc. Japan. Journal of the Chemical Society of Japan, Tokyo.
J. Chim. Phys. Journal de Chimie Physique, Geneva, and (from 1906) Paris.
J. Chinese Chem. Soc. Journal of the Chinese Chemical Society.
J. Colloid Sci. Journal of Colloid Science, New York.
J. de l'École Polytechn. Journal de l'École Polytechnique, Paris.
J. [*de*] *Math.* (Liouville). Journal des Mathématiques pures et appliquées, Paris.
J. de Phys. Journal de Physique théorique et appliqué, continued as Journal de Physique et le Radium, Paris.
J. der Pharmacie. Journal der Pharmacie, Leipzig (1794–1817).
J. der Phys. Journal der Physik (preceded Annalen der Physik), edit. Gren, Halle and Leipzig.
J. Exptl. Theor. Phys. U.S.S.R. Journal of Experimental and Theoretical Physics, U.S.S.R.
J. f. Math. (Crelle). See *J. reine angew. Math.* (Crelle).
J. Franklin Inst. Journal of the Franklin Institute, Philadelphia.
J. Gasbeleucht. Journal für Gasbeleuchtung, Munich (name changed 1922 to Gas- und Wasserfach).
J. Gas Lighting. Journal of Gas Lighting and Water Supply, London (name changed to Gas Journal).
J. Gen. Chem. U.S.S.R. Journal of General Chemistry, U.S.S.R.
J. Gen. Physiol. Journal of General Physiology, Baltimore.
J. Imp. Coll. Chem. Eng. Soc. Journal of the Imperial College Chemical Engineering Society, London.
J. Indian Chem. Soc. Journal of the Indian Chemical Society, Calcutta.
J. Indian Inst. Sci. Journal of the Indian Institute of Science, Bangalore.
J. Inst. Elec. Eng. Journal of the Institution of Electrical Engineers, London.
J. Inst. Fuel. Journal of the Institute of Fuel, London.
J. Inst. Met. Journal of the Institute of Metals, London.
J. Inst. Petrol. Journal of the Institute of Petroleum, London.
J. Inst. Petrol. Techn. Journal of the Institution of Petroleum Technologists, London.
J. Iron Steel Inst. Journal of the Iron and Steel Institute, London.
J. Math. See *J. de Math.*
J. Math. Phys. Mass. Inst. [*Techn.*]. Journal of Mathematics and Physics, Massachusetts Institute of Technology, Cambridge, Mass.

J. Oil. Colour Chem. Assoc. Journal of the Oil and Colour Chemists Association, London.

J. Opt. Soc. Amer. Journal of the Optical Society of America, Lancaster, Pa.

J. Pharm. Chim. Journal de Pharmacie et de Chimie, Paris.

J. Phys. Chem. The Journal of Physical Chemistry, Ithaca, N.Y., and Baltimore.

J. Phys. Chem. U.S.S.R. Journal of Physical Chemistry, U.S.S.R.

J. Phys. U.S.S.R. Journal of Physics, U.S.S.R.

J. prakt. Chem. Journal für praktische Chemie, Leipzig.

J. Proc. Roy. Soc. N.S. Wales. Journal and Proceedings of the Royal Society of New South Wales, Sydney.

J. reine angew. Math. (Crelle). Journal für die reine und angewandte Mathematik (Crelle's Journal), Berlin.

J. Rheol[*ogy*]. Journal of Rheology, Easton, Pa.

J. Roy. Astron. Soc. Canada. Journal of the Royal Astronomical Society of Canada, Richmond Hills, Ontario.

J. Roy. Inst. Journal of the Royal Institution of Great Britain, London.

J. Roy. Soc. Arts. Journal of the Royal Society of Arts, London.

J. Roy. Soc. N.S. Wales. Journal of the Royal Society of New South Wales, Sydney.

J. Roy. Techn. Coll. Glasgow. Journal of the Royal Technical College, Glasgow.

J. Russ. Phys. Chem. Soc. Journal of the Russian Physical-Chemical Society, Moscow. (C=Chemistry Section, P=Physics Section.)

J.S.C.I. Journal of the Society of Chemical Industry, London.

J. Soc. Arts. See *J. Roy. Soc. Arts.*

J. Sci. Hiroshima Univ. Journal of Science of the Hiroshima University, Hiroshima, Japan.

J. Sci. Instr. Journal of Scientific Instruments and of Physics in Industry, London.

J. Soc. Chem. Ind. [*J.S.C.I.*] *Japan.* Journal of the Society of Chemical Industry, Japan, Tokyo.

J. Soc. Dyers Colourists. Journal of the Society of Dyers and Colourists, Bradford.

J. Soc. Glass Technol. Journal of the Society of Glass Technology, Sheffield.

J. Techn. Phys. U.S.S.R. Journal of Technical Physics, U.S.S.R.

J. Text. Inst. Journal of the Textile Institute, Manchester.

J. Univ. Bombay. Journal of the University of Bombay, Bombay.

J. Usines Gaz. Journal des Usines à Gaz, Paris.

J. Wash. Acad. [*Sci.*]. Journal of the Washington Academy of Sciences, Washington.

J. Western Soc. Eng. Journal of the Western Society of Engineers, Oak Park, Ill.

Jahrb. f. Berg- u. Hütten-Wesen in Sachsen. Jahrbuch für Berg- und Hütten-Wesen in Sachsen, Freiberg.

Jahrb. Radioakt. Elektronik. Jahrbuch der Radioaktivität und Elektronik (combined 1924 with Physikalische Zeitschrift), Leipzig.

Jahresb. Jahresbericht über die Fortschritte der Chemie und verwandter Theile anderer Wissenschaften, var. editors, Giessen and Brunswick.

Jahres-Ber. Jahres-Bericht über die Fortschritte der Chemie und Mineralogie, by J. Berzelius, transl. by F. Wöhler, Tübingen.

Jern-Kontorets Annaler, Stockholm.

K. Norsk[e]. Vidensk. Selsk. Forhl. Kongelige Norske Videnskabernes Selskabs Forhandlinger, Trondhjem.

K. Svensk. [Vet.] Akad. Handl. Kongliga Svenska Vetenskaps-Akademiens Handlingar, Uppsala and Stockholm.

K[gl.]. Dansk. Videns[k.]. Selsk[ab]. Mat. fys. Meddel. Det Kongelige Danske Videnskabernes Selskab Matematisk-Fysiske Meddelelser, Copenhagen.

Kgl. Dansk. Videns. Selsk[ab.]. Skrift. Det Kongelige Danske Videnskabernes Selskab. Skrifter Naturvidenskabelig og Mathematisk Afdeling, Copenhagen.

Klassiker. See Ostwald.

Koll. Beih. Kolloidchemische Beihefte, Dresden (name changed to Kolloidbeihefte).

Koll. Z. Kolloid Zeitschrift, Dresden and Frankfurt.

Kosmos (Lwow).

Landolt-Börnstein " Tabellen ". Landolt-Börnstein, Physikalisch-chemische Tabellen.

Le Radium, Paris.

Le Vide, Paris.

Leipzig Ber. Berichte über die Verhandlungen der Sächsischen Akademie der Wissenschaften zu Leipzig, Mathemathisch-physische Klasse, Leipzig.

Licht u. Lampe. Licht und Lampe, Berlin.

Lingnan Sci. J. Lingnan Science Journal, Lingnan University, Canton, China.

L'Industrie Chim. L'Industrie Chimique, Paris.

Manch. Mem. Memoirs and Proceedings of the Manchester Literary and Philosophical Society, Manchester.

Marburg Ber. Sitzungsberichte der Gesellschaft zur Beförderung der gesamten Naturwissenschaften zu Marburg, Marburg.

Math. Ann. Mathematische Annalen, Leipzig.

Mech. Eng. N.Y. Mechanical Engineering, New York.

Meddel. Nobelinst. Meddelanden från K. Svenska Vetenskapsakademiens Nobelinstitut, Uppsala, etc.

Mém. Acad. Sci. Mémoires de l'Académie des Sciences de l'Institut de France, Paris.

Mém. Acad. Roy. Belg. Mémoires de l'Académie Royale des Sciences, des Lettres et des Beaux-Arts de Belgique, quarto, and octavo, Brussels.

Mém. Acad. St. Petersb. Mémoires de l'Académie Impériale des Sciences de St. Petersbourg.

Mem. Accad. Lincei. Memorie della Reale Accademie Nazionale dei Lincei, Classe di scienze fisiche, Rome.

Mem. Accad. Torino. Memorie della Reale Accademia di Scienza di Torino, Turin.

Mem. Coll. Sci. Kyoto Imp. Univ. Memoirs of the College of Science Kyoto Imperial University, Kyoto.

Mém. Couronn. Acad. Roy. Bruxelles. Mémoires Couronnés de l'Académie Royale des Sciences etc. de Bruxelles, Brussels.

Mém. Couronn. et de Sav. étrang. Acad. Roy. Bruxelles. Mémoires Couronnés et Mémoirs des Savants étrangers. Académie Royale des Sciences, Brussels.

Mém. de l'Inst. Mémoires de l'Institut de France, Paris.

Mém. div. Sav. [Étrangères] Acad. Sci. Mémoires présentés par divers Savants à l'Académie des Sciences de l'Institut de France, Paris.

Mém. Divers Sav. St. Petersbourg Acad. Mémoirs présentés à l'Académie Impériale des Sciences de St. Petersbourg par divers Savans et lus dans ses Assembleés, St. Petersburg (1831–1859).

Mém. Poudres. Mémoires des Poudres et Salpêtres, Paris.

Mém. Soc. Arcueil. Mémoires de Physique et de Chimie de la Société d'Arcueil, Paris.

Mém. Soc. Phys. Nat. (Geneva). Mémoires de la Société de Physique et d'Histoire Naturelle de Genève, Geneva.

Mém. Soc. Sci. Phys. Nat. Bordeaux. Mémoires de la Société des Sciences Physiques et Naturelles de Bordeaux, Bordeaux.

Messenger of Math. Messenger of Mathematics, Cambridge.

Metal Progr. Metal Progress, Cleveland, Ohio.

Metals Tech. Metals Technology, American Institute of Mining and Metallurgical Engineers, Technical Publication, New York.

Met. Chem. Eng. Metallurgical and Chemical Engineering, New York.

Metall. u. Erz. Metall und Erz, Halle.

Metallographist, Boston.

Metallurgia, Manchester.

Metallurgie, Halle.

Metallwirtsch. Metallwirtschaft, Berlin.

Meteorol. Z. Meteorologische Zeitschrift, Brunswick.

Mikrochem. Mikrochemie, Vienna.

Min. and Met. Invest. U.S. Bur. Mines Carnegie Inst. Boards Co-oper. Mining and Metallurgical Investigations under the Auspices of the U.S. Bureau of Mines Carnegie Institute of Technology and Mining and Metallurgical Advisory Boards, Pittsburg, Pa.

Mineral. Mag. Mineralogical Magazine and Journal of the Mineralogical Society, London.

Mining and Met. Mining and Metallurgy, New York.

" Misc. Sci. Papers." Miscellaneous Scientific Papers.

Mitt. K. Wilh. Inst. Eisenforsch. Düsseldorf. Mitteilungen aus dem Kaiser-Wilhelm-Institut für Eisenforschung zu Düsseldorf, Düsseldorf.

Mitt. Kgl. Materialsprüfungsamt. Mitteilungen aus dem Königlichen Materialprüfungsamt zu Gross-Lichterfelde, Berlin-Dahlem.

Monatsh. Monatshefte für Chemie und verwandte Teile anderer Wissenschaften, Vienna.

Monatsh. Math. Phys. Monatshefte für Mathematik und Physik, Vienna.

Month. Not. Roy. Astron. Soc. Monthly Notices of the Royal Astronomical Society, London.

Munich Ber. Sitzungsberichte der Königlichen Bayerischen Akademie der Wissenschaften zu München, Mathematisch-physikalische Klasse, Munich.

N. J. der Phys. [Gren]. Neues Journal der Physik, edit, Gren, Leipzig (see *J. der Phys.*).

N. Jahrb. Min. Neues Jahrbuch für Mineralogie, Geologie, und Paläontologie, Stuttgart.

N. Jahrb. Min. B. Bd. Neues Jahrbuch für Mineralogie etc., Beilage Band, Stuttgart.

N. Zeal. J. Sci. Tech. New Zealand Journal of Science and Technology, Wellington.

Nat. Petrol. News. National Petroleum News, Cleveland, Ohio.

Natural Gas and Gasoline J. Natural Gas and Gasoline Journal, Buffalo.

Nature, London.

Naturwiss. Die Naturwissenschaften, Berlin.
Natuurw. Tijdschr. Natuurwetenschappelijk Tijdschrift, Antwerp.
Nederl Tijdschr. Natuurkde. Nederlands Tijdschrift voor Natuurkunde, The Hague.
Nernst. Festschr. Nernst Festschrift (supplement to *Z. phys. Chem.*).
Nicholson's J. Nicholson's Journal, London.
Norg. Geol. Undersökels. Norges Geologiske Undersøkelse, Oslo.
Nouv. Mém. Acad. Berlin. Nouveaux Mémoires de l'Académie Royale des Sciences et des Belles-Lettres de Berlin, Berlin, 1770–86.
Nova Acta Leopold[*ina*]. Nova Acta Academiae Caesareae Leopoldina-Carolinae Germanicae Naturae Curiosorum, Halle.
Nova Acta Soc. Reg. Upsal. Nova Acta Regiae Societatis Scientiarum Upsaliensis, Uppsala.
Nova Acta Upsal. See above.
Novi Comment. Acad. [*Imp.*] *Petropol.* Novi Commentarii, Académie Impériale des Sciences de St. Pétersbourg, 1747–75.
Nuov. Cim. Il Nuovo Cimento, Pisa and Bologna.
Nuov. Mém. Acad. Berlin. Nouveau Mémoires de l'Académie Royale des Sciences et des Belles Lettres de Berlin.
Obs. sur la Phys. Observations sur la Physique (edit. Rozier), Paris (later Journal de Physique).
Oel u. Kohle. Öl und Kohle, Berlin.
Oesterr. Chem. Ztg. Oesterreichische Chemiker-Zeitung, Vienna.
Ov. K. Dansk. Videns. Selsk. Forhl. Oversigt over det Kongelige Danske Videnskabernes Selskabs Forhandlinger, Copenhagen.
Öfv. Finska Vet. Soc. Förhl. Öfversigt af Finska Vetenskaps-Societetens Förhandlingar, Helsingfors.
Öfversigt af K. Vetensk. Akad. Förhandl. Oefversigt af K. Vetenskaps Akademiens Förhandlingar, Stockholm.
Oil and Soap, Chicago.
Oil Gas J. Oil and Gas Journal, Tulsa, Oklahoma.
Onnes Festschr. Onnes Festschrift, Leiden, 1922.
Oriris. Bruges.
Österr. Chem. Ztg. Oesterreichische Chemiker-Zeitung, Vienna.
Ostwald's *Klassiker.* Ostwald's Klassiker der exakten Wissenschaften, Leipzig.
Paper Trade J. Paper Trade Journal, New York and Chicago.
Petrol. Refiner. Petroleum Refiner.
Petroleum (German). *Petrol. Z.* Petroleum, Zeitschrift für das gesamte Interesse der Mineralöl Industrie, Berlin.
Phil. Mag. Philosophical Magazine, London,
Phil. Trans. Philosophical Transactions of the Royal Society, London. Section A unless B stated.
Phil. Trans. abdgd. Philosophical Transactions. Abridged by Hutton, Shaw, and Pearson. 18 vols., London, 1809.
Philipp. J. Sci. Philippine Journal of Science, Manila.
Photogr. J. Photographic Journal, London.
Phys. Ber. Physikalische Berichte, Brunswick.
Phys. Rev. Physical Review, Ithaca, N.Y., and Lancaster, Pa.
Phys. Rev. Suppl. Physical Review Supplement, Minneapolis.
Phys. Z. Physikalische Zeitschrift, Leipzig.
Physica. Physica. The Hague.

Physical Memoirs (Phys. Soc.). Physical Memoirs published by the Physical Society, London.

Physics, Minneapolis.

Proc. Amer. Acad. Proceedings of the American Academy of Arts and Sciences, Boston.

Proc. Amer. Gas Assoc. Proceedings of the American Gas Association, New York.

Proc. Amer. Petrol. Inst. Proceedings of the American Petroleum Institute, New York.

Proc. Amer. Phil. Soc. Proceedings of the American Philosophical Society, Philadelphia.

Proc. Amer. Soc. Testing Mater. Proceedings of the American Society for Testing Materials, Philadelphia.

Proc. Cambr. Phil. Soc. Proceedings of the Cambridge Philosophical Society, Cambridge.

Proc. Chem. Soc. Proceedings of the Chemical Society, London.

Proc. Durham Phil. Soc. Proceedings of the Durham Philosophical Society, Durham.

Proc. Edin. Math. Soc. Proceedings of the Edinburgh Mathematical Society, Edinburgh.

Proc. Imp. Acad. Japan. Proceedings of the Imperial Academy of Japan, Tokyo.

Proc. Imp. Acad. Tokyo. See above.

Proc. Indian Acad. [*Sci.*]. Proceedings of the Indian Academy of Sciences, Bangalore.

Prov. XV Indian Sci. Congr. Proceedings of the XV Indian Science Congress, Calcutta.

Proc. Inst. Mech. Eng. Proceedings of the Institution of Mechanical Engineers, London.

Proc. Iowa Acad. [*Sci.*]. Proceedings of the Iowa Academy of Science, Des Moines.

Proc. K. Akad. Wetens. Amsterdam. Koninklijke Akademie van Wetenschappen te Amsterdam, Proceedings of the Section of Sciences, Amsterdam.

Proc. Leeds Phil. Soc. Proceedings of the Leeds Philosophical and Literary Society, Leeds.

Proc. Lond[*on*]. *Math. Soc.* Proceedings of the London Mathematical Society, London.

Proc. Math. Soc. London. See above.

Proc. Nat. Acad. Proceedings of the National Academy of Sciences of the United States of America, Washington.

Proc. Nat. Inst. Sci. India. Proceedings of the National Institute of Science, Delhi.

Proc. Nova Scotia Inst. Sci. Proceedings and Transactions of the Nova Scotian Institute of Science, Halifax, N.S.

Proc. Oklahoma Acad. Sci. Proceedings of the Oklahoma Academy of Science, publ. in University of Oklahoma Bulletin, Norman, Oklahoma.

Proc. Phil. Soc. Glasgow. Proceedings of the Philosophical Society of Glasgow, Glasgow.

Proc. Phys. Soc. The Proceedings of the Physical Society, London.

Proc. Phys. Math. Soc. Japan. Proceedings of the Physico-Mathematical Society of Japan, Tokyo.

Proc. Phys. Math. Soc. Tokyo. See above.

Proc. Roy. Dublin Soc. The Scientific Proceedings of the Royal Dublin Society, Dublin.

Proc. Roy. Inst. Proceedings of the Royal Institution of Great Britain, London.

Proc. Roy. Irish. Acad. Proceedings of the Royal Irish Academy, Dublin.

Proc. Roy. Soc. Proceedings of the Royal Society, London. (Section A unless B stated).

Proc. Roy. Soc. Edin. Proceedings of the Royal Society of Edinburgh, Edinburgh.

Proc. Roy. Soc. N. S. Wales. See *J. Proc. Roy. Soc. N. S. Wales.*

Proc. Soc. Chem. Ind. Victoria. Proceedings of the Society of Chemical Industry, Victoria.

Proc. Wash. Acad. [*Sci.*]. Proceedings of the Washington Academy of Science, Washington.

Prometheus, Leipzig.

Przem. Chem. Przemysl Chemiczny, Warsaw.

Q. J. Geol. Soc. The Quarterly Journal of the Geological Society of London.

Quart. J. Math. Quarterly Journal of Mathematics, Oxford.

Quart. J. Sci. The Quarterly Journal of Science, London.

Quart. Rev. Chem. Soc. Quarterly Reviews, London, The Chemical Society.

R. Accad. Napoli. See *Rend. Accad. Fis. Mat. Napoli.*

R. R. Inst. Lombardo. Rendiconti Real Instituto Lombardo di Scienze e Lettere, Milan.

Rap[*port*]. *Cons. Phys. Solvay.* See *Conseil Solvay.*

Rec. Trav. Chim. Recueil des Travaux Chimiques des Pays-Bas, Amsterdam.

Refrig. Eng. Refrigerating Engineering, New York.

Rend. Acad. Fis. Mat. Napoli. Rendiconti dell'Academia delle Scienze Fisiche e Matematiche (Classe della Società Reale di Napoli), Naples.

R[*end.*]. *Fis. Mat. Accad. Napoli.* See above.

Rep. Progr. Phys. Reports on Progress in Physics, The Physical Society, London.

Repert. [*d.*] *Phys.* Repertorium der Physik, edit. Carl, etc., Berlin.

Research, London.

Rev. Acad. Cienc. Madrid. Revista de la Real Academia de Ciencias, Madrid.

Rev. Gén. Sci. Revue Générale des Sciences Pures et Appliquées, Paris.

Rev. Mod. Phys. Reviews of Modern Physics, Lancaster, Pa.

Rev. Philosoph. Revue Philosophique, Paris.

Rev. Opt. Revue d'Optique, Théorique et Instrumentale, Paris.

Rev. Sci. Revue Scientifique, Paris.

Rev. Sci. Instr. The Review of Scientific Instruments, Lancaster, Pa.

Rev. Univ[*ers.*]. *Mines.* Revue Universelle des Mines, etc., Paris.

Rheol. Bull. Rheology Bulletin, New York.

Ricerca Sci. La Ricerca Scientifica, Rome.

Riv. Fis. Mat. Sci. Nat. Rivista di Fisica, Matematica e Scienze Naturale, Pavia.

Rivista Nuov. Cim. Rivista del Nuovo Cimento, Bologna.

Roczn. Chem. Roczniki Chemji, Warsaw.

Rozpravy. Rozpravy České Akademie Ved a Umění, Prague.

Safety in Mines Res. Board. Safety in Mines Research Board, Papers, London.

Samml. chem. und chem.-techn. Vorträge. Sammlung chemischer und chemisch-technischer Vorträge, Stuttgart.

School Sci. Rev. School Science Review, London.

Sci. Abstr. Science Abstracts, London.

Sci. and Culture. Science and Culture, Calcutta.
Sci. Pap. Inst. Phys. Chem. Res. Tokyo. Scientific Papers of the Institute of Physical and Chemical Research, Tokyo.
" Sci. Papers." Scientific Papers.
Sci. Progr. Science Progress, London.
Sci. Rep. Tôhoku Imp. Univ. Science Reports of the Tôhoku Imperial University, Tokyo.
Science, Lancaster, Pa.
Scientia, Milan.
Scientific Memoirs (Harper). Scientific Memoirs, publ. Harper, New York.
Scientific Memoirs (Taylor). Scientific Memoirs, edit. Taylor, etc., London, 1836–53.
Sexagint. The Sexagint being a Collection of Papers dedicated to Professor Yukichi Osaka, Kyoto, 1927.
Siebert Festschr. (Hanau). Siebert Festschrift, Hanau.
Sitzb. phys. ökonom. Ges. Königsberg. Sitzungsbericht der physikalisch-ökonomischen Gesellschaft zu Königsberg, Königsberg.
Smithsonian Contributions to Knowledge, Smithsonian Institution, Washington.
Smithsonian Misc. Coll. Smithsonian Miscellaneous Collections, Smithsonian Institution, Washington.
Soc. France Phys. Séances. Société Française de Physique Bulletin des Séances, Paris, 1902–10.
Sow. Phys. Z. Physikalische Zeitschrift der Sowjetunion.
Sprechsaal, Coburg.
Stahl u. Eisen. Stahl und Eisen, Düsseldorf.
Suomen Kemist. Suomen Kemistilehti, Helsinki.
Svensk Kem. Tid. Svensk Kemisk Tidskrift, Stockholm.
Techn. Phys. U.S.S.R. Technical Physics of the U.S.S.R., Leningrad.
Techn. Rep. Tôhoku Imp. Univ. Technical Reports of the Tôhoku Imperial University, Tokyo.
Technique Moderne, Paris.
Tekn. Tidskr. (Kem.). Teknicsk Tidsskrift (Kemi), Stockholm.
Textile Res. J. Textile Research Journal, Lancaster, Pa.
Thonindustr. Ztg. Thonindustrie Zeitung, Berlin.
Trans. Amer. Electrochem. Soc. Transactions of the American Electrochemical Society, New York.
Trans. Amer. Inst. Chem. Eng. Transactions of the American Institute of Chemical Engineers, New York.
Trans. Amer. Inst. Elec. Eng. Transactions of the American Institute of Electrical Engineers, New York.
Trans. Amer. Inst. Metals. Transactions of the American Institute of Metals, Buffalo.
Trans. Amer. Inst. Min. [Met.] Eng. Transactions of the American Institute of Mining and Metallurgical Engineers, New York.
Trans. Amer. Phil. Soc. Transactions of the American Philosophical Society, Philadelphia.
Trans. Amer. Soc. Civil Eng. Transactions of the American Society of Civil Engineers, New York.
Trans. Amer. Soc. Mech. Eng. Transactions of the American Society of Mechanical Engineers, New York.
Trans. Amer. Soc. Metals. Transactions of the American Society for Metals, Cleveland, Ohio.

Trans. Cambr. Phil. Soc. Transactions of the Cambridge Philosophical Society, Cambridge.
Trans. Ceram. Soc. Transactions of the Ceramic Society, Stoke on Trent (continued as British Ceramic Society Transactions).
Trans. Connect[icut]. Acad. Transactions of the Connecticut Academy of Arts and Sciences, New Haven.
Trans. Faraday Soc. Transactions of the Faraday Society, London.
Trans. Illum. Eng. Soc. Transactions of the Illuminating Engineering Society, Baltimore (continued as Illuminating Engineering).
Trans. Inst. Chem. Eng. Transactions of the Institution of Chemical Engineers, London.
Trans. Inst. Min. Met. Transactions of the Institution of Mining and Metallurgy, London.
Trans. Inst. Rubber Ind. Transactions of the Institution of the Rubber Industry, London.
Trans. Nat. Inst. Sci. India. Transactions of the National Institute of Sciences of India, Bangalore.
Trans. Opt. Soc. Transactions of the Optical Society, London.
Trans. Roy. Dublin Soc. Scientific Transactions of the Royal Dublin Society, Dublin.
Trans. Roy. Soc. Canada. Transactions of the Royal Society of Canada, Toronto.
Trans. Roy. Soc. Edin. Transactions of the Royal Society of Edinburgh.
Trans. Roy. Soc. S. Africa. Transactions of the Royal Society of South Africa, Cape Town.
Trav. et Mém. Bur. Internat. Poids et Mes. Travaux et Mémoires du Bureau Internationale des Poids et Mesures, Paris.
Trav. et Mém, Fac. Lille. Travaux et Mémoirs de la Faculté des Sciences de l'Université, Lille.
Trav. Inst. Métrol. Stand. U.R.S.S.. Travaux el l'Institut de Métrologie et de Standardisation de l'U.R.S.S.
Ukrain. Chem. J. Ukrainian Chemical Journal, Kharkov.
Univ. Wisc. Bull., Eng. Ser. University of Wisconsin Bulletin, Engineering Series.
U.S. Bur. Mines Bull. Bureau of Mines Bulletin, Washington.
U.S. Dept. Agric. Techn. Bull. United States Department of Agriculture Technical Bulletin, Washington.
U.S. Geol. Survey Bull. United States Geological Survey Bulletin, Washington.
U.S. Pat. United States Patent.
Verhl. d. D. Phys. Ges. Verhandlungen der Deutschen Physikalischen Gesellschaft, Berlin-Charlottenburg.
Verhl. d. Naturforsch. Ges. Basel. Verhandlungen der Naturforschenden Gesellschaft in Basel, Basel.
Verhl. d. Vereins z. Beförd. d. Gewerbfl. Verhandlungen des Vereins zur Beförderung des Gewerbfleisses in Preussen, Berlin.
Verhl. K. Akad. Wetens. Amsterdam. Verhandelingen der Koninklijke Akademie van Wetenschappen, Amsterdam.
Verhl. Naturhist.-Med. Vereins Heidelberg. Verhandlungen des Naturhistorischen-Medizinischen Vereins zu Heidelberg, Heidelberg.
Verslag. K. Akad. Wetens. Amsterdam. Verslag van de Gewone Vergaderingen der Wis- en Natuurkundige Afdelling Koninklijke Akademie van Wetenschappen te Amsterdam, Amsterdam. (Commenced as Verslagen en Mededeelingen der Koninklijk Akademie van Wetenschappen.)

Wärme- und Kälte-Techn. Wärme- und Kälte-Technik, Berlin.
Westinghouse Eng. Westinghouse Engineer, Pittsburg, Pa.
Wien Anz. Anzeiger der Kaiserlichen Akademie der Wissenschaften zu Wien, mathematisch-naturwissenschaftliche Klasse, Vienna.
Wien Ber. Sitzungsberichte der mathematisch-naturwissenschaftlichen Klasse der Kaiserlichen Akademie der Wissenschaften zu Wien, Vienna.
Wire Ind. Wire Industry, London.
" Wiss-Abhl." Wissenschaftliche Abhandlungen.
Wiss-Abhl. Phys.-tech. Reichsanst. Wissenschaftliche Abhandlungen der Physikalisch-technischen Reichsanstalt, Berlin.
Wis. Natuurkde. Tijdschr. Wis- en Natuurkundig Tijdschrift, Ghent.
Wiss. Veröff[*entl.*]. *Siemens-Konzern.* Wissenschaftliche Veröffentlichungen aus dem Siemens Konzern, Berlin; continued as:
Wiss. Veröffentl. Siemens-Werken. Wissenschaftliche Veröffentlichungen aus dem Siemens Werken, Berlin.
Yale J. Biol. Med. Yale Journal of Biology and Medicine, New Haven.
Z. anal. Chem. Zeitschrift für analytische Chemie, Munich.
Z. angew. Chem. Zeitschrift für angewandte Chemie, Leipzig (since 1932, Angewandte Chemie).
Z. angew. Math. [*Mech.*]. Zeitschrift für angewandte Mathematik und Mechanik, Berlin.
Z. anorg. Chem. Zeitschrift für anorganische und allgemeine Chemie, Leipzig.
Z. Elektrochem. Zeitschrift für Elektrochemie, Halle.
Z. f. Chem. Zeitschrift für Chemie, Göttingen.
Z. f. Phys. und verwandte Wiss. Zeitschrift für Physik und verwandte Wissenschaften.
Z. ges. Kälte-Ind. Zeitschrift für die gesamte Kälte-Industrie, Berlin.
Z. Instr. Zeitschrift für Instrumentenkunde, Berlin.
Z. kompr. flüss. Gase. Zeitschrift für komprimierte und flüssige Gase, Weimar.
Z. Krist. See *Z. Kryst.*
Z. Kryst. Zeitschrift für Krystallographie, Leipzig (name changed, 1921, to Zeitschrift für Kristallographie).
Z. Math. Phys. (Schlömilch). Zeitschrift für Mathematik und Physik, edit. Schlömilch, etc., Leipzig.
Z. Metallkde. Zeitschrift für Metallkunde, Berlin.
Z. Naturforsch. Zeitschrift für Naturforschung (parts A and B), Tübingen.
Z. Phys. Zeitschrift für Physik (formerly Berichte der Deutschen Physikalischen Gesellschaft), Berlin.
Z. phys. Chem. Zeitschrift für physikalische Chemie Stöchiometrie und Verwandtschaftslehre, Leipzig (Section A unless B stated).
Z. phys. chem. Unterr. Zeitschrift für den physikalischen und chemischen Unterricht, Berlin.
Z. physiol. Chem. Zeitschrift für die physiologische Chemie, Leipzig.
Z. Sauerstoff Stickstoff Ind. Zeitschrift für Sauerstoff-Stickstoff-Industrie, Halle (name changed to Die Gas-Industrie).
Z. techn. Phys. Zeitschrift für technische Physik, Leipzig.
Z. Verein D. Ing[*enieure*]. Zeitschrift des Vereins Deutscher Ingenieure, Berlin.
Z. Verein. D. Zuckerind. Zeitschrift des Vereins der Deutschen Zuckerindustrie, Berlin.
Z. wiss. Photogr. Zeitschrift für wissenschaftliche Photographie, Photophysik und Photochemie, Leipzig.
Zavodskaya Lab. Zavodskaya Laboratoriya, Moscow.

LIST OF SYMBOLS

This list incorporates the relevant symbols from the recommended list[1] and also includes other symbols in common use. Symbols used in the meanings given in round brackets were proposed by the British Standards Institute for engineering symbols and those in square brackets for electrical engineering symbols; they are not generally used in the present work. The didactic and aesthetic value of well-chosen symbols was emphasised by Leibniz[2] in 1678.

A.	Ångström unit $=10^{-8}$ cm.
A	atomic weight; surface area; moment of inertia; compressibility coefficient; ($1/\boldsymbol{J}$, where $\boldsymbol{J}$=mechanical equivalent of heat); {alternative symbol for free energy}.
atm.	atmosphere.
a	activity; van der Waals's and Berthelot's constants: pressure factor; cells in phase space; radius; constant of Morse equation; accommodation coefficient.
B	beta function.
B	moment of inertia; [susceptance; magnetic flux density]; virial coefficient.
B	magnetic induction.
b	van der Waals's and Berthelot's constants; [susceptance].
C, c	specific heat; concentration; velocity; statistical constant; moment of inertia; (modulus of shearing rigidity of elasticity); [capacitance]; Sutherland's constant; chemical constant.
c.g.s.	centimetre-gram-second unit.
cm.	centimetre.
c_v, c_p	specific heat at constant volume (pressure) per g.

1 "Report of a Joint Committee of the Chemical Society, the Faraday Society, and the Physical Society on Symbols for Thermodynamical and Physico-Chemical Quantities," London, 1937 (symbols in { } brackets are given in the above list as alternatives); for earlier lists of symbols, see Nernst *et al.*, *Z. Elektrochem.*, 1903, **9**, 685; Luther, *ibid.*, 1906, **12**, 97; Hering, *J. Franklin Inst.*, 1910, **170**, 194; 1911, **171**, 129 (long list); Anon., *Trans. Faraday Soc.*, 1910, **5**, 252; *Verhl. d. D. Phys. Ges.*, 1910, **12**, 476; 1913, **15**, 143 (AEF= Aufschluss für Einheiten und Formelgrössen); Neesen, *Phys. Z.*, 1913, **14**, 167; Strecker, *ibid.*, 1914, **15**, 113; Report of Committee, *Proc. Phys. Soc.*, 1914, **26**, 381; Martens, *Verhl. d. D. Phys. Ges.*, 1914, **16**, 97; Lash Miller, *Chem. Rev.*, 1924, **1**, 293; Partington, "Chemical Thermodynamics," 1924, 263; Harned and Owen, "The Physical Chemistry of Electrolytic Solutions," New York, 1943, pp. xiii–xxvii; for numerical values of universal constants, Karrer, *J. Franklin Inst.*, 1923, **196**, 79; Birge, *Reports on Progress in Physics*, 1941, **8**, 90; *J.C.S.* 1946, 219; Schmidt, *Naturwiss.*, 1947, **34**, 62.

A list of symbols in *Ind. Eng. Chem.*, 1947, **39**, 438, is similar to that given here, except that no black letters are used, latent heat is λ instead of $\boldsymbol{l}$, coefficient of linear expansion is α and of volume expansion β, quantity of heat is Q, c_p/c_v is k or κ, thermal diffusivity is α, viscosity is μ, kinematic viscosity ν, and British thermal unit B.t.u.

The pictorial symbols proposed by Walker, *Nature*, 1908, **78**, 271, would require over 200 new types for printing.

2 "In signis spectanda est commoditas ad inveniendum, quae maxima est, quoties rei naturam intimam paucis exprimunt ad velut pingunt, ita enim mirifice imminuitur cogitandi labor"; in "Der Briefwechsel von Gottfried Wilhelm Leibniz mit Mathematikern," edit. Gerhardt, Berlin, 1899, **1**, 375.

C_v, C_p	molecular heat at constant volume (pressure) (per mol).
c	velocity of light in vacuum.
$\sqrt{\overline{c^2}}$	root mean square velocity.
D	differential operator.
D′	integral operator.
d	differential.
$\mathrm{d}y/\mathrm{d}x$	total differential coefficient of y with respect to x.
$(\mathrm{d}y/\mathrm{d}x)_z$	partial differential coefficient of y with respect to x when z is constant.
d	diameter; density.
D	density; heat of dilution; dielectric constant; energy of dissociation; spectrum symbol; [electrostatic flux density]; diffusivity.
D_0	limiting density.
E	energy; Young's modulus; [e.m.f.].
e	base of natural logarithms=2·7182818 . . .; (*subscript*) evaporation.
e	electromotive force[1]; (direct strain); emissivity.
$\boldsymbol{e}$	positive electronic charge.
F	free energy=$E-TS$; number of degrees of freedom; spectrum symbol; (aggregate shearing force); force.
$\boldsymbol{F}$	faraday=charge in coulombs per g. equivalent of an ion.
f, F	function.
f	(*subscript*) fusion.
f	activity coefficient; fugacity; force constant; acceleration; (modulus of rupture); {partition function}; van der Waals's vapour pressure constant.
G	statistical weight.
G	available energy=$E-TS+PV$; [conductance].
g.	gram.
g.cal.	gram calorie.
g, ḡ	gas functions.
g	gaseous state; statistical weight; osmotic coefficient; [conductance]; acceleration of gravity.
H	Hessian functional determinant; Hermite polynomial.
H	heat content or enthalpy=$E+PV$; (quantity of heat); [magnetic field strength]; Hamiltonian function.
H	magnetic field strength.
h	constant of activity equation; small increment of x; Δh=heat change per electrochemical g. equivalent; height.
$\boldsymbol{h}$	Planck's constant.
I	ionic strength; moment of inertia; integration constant; ionisation energy; intensity of magnetisation; (heat content [$=H$]); [current strength]; light intensity.
i	(*subscript*) irreversible; van't Hoff's factor; vapour pressure (or chemical) constant; $\sqrt{-1}$.
i_s	nuclear spin quantum number.
J	Jacobian functional determinant.
J	rotational quantum number; [intensity of magnetisation]; integral.

[1] The recommended list gives E, but this would occur in equations containing the symbol E for energy.

J mechanical equivalent of heat; (moment of inertia (polar)).
j activity function; inner quantum number; [$\sqrt{-1}$].
j_s electronic spin quantum number.
K. absolute temperature.
K equilibrium constant; rotational quantum number; (bulk modulus of elasticity [$=\epsilon$]); radius of gyration; radiation intensity; internal pressure.
k.cal. kilogram calorie.
kw kilowatt.
kwh kilowatt-hour.
$\boldsymbol{k}$ distribution coefficient; general symbol for a constant; thermal conductivity; modulus of expansion; small increment of y.
k Boltzmann's constant$=\boldsymbol{R}/N$.
L Laguerre polynomial.
L latent heat per mol; heat of solution; [self inductance]; Lagrangian function.
L_e, L_f, L_s, L_d latent heats of evaporation, fusion, sublimation and dissociation per mol.
L_s heat of solution.
l liquid state; latent heat per g.; serial quantum number; direction cosine; mean free path.
l_e, l_f, l_s, l_d latent heats of evaporation, fusion, sublimation and dissociation. per g.
l_i internal latent heat.
l_p latent heat of pressure change.
l_v latent heat of expansion.
l_x generalised latent heat; heat of solution.
Lim limit.
ln natural logarithm ($=2{\cdot}3026\ \log_{10}$).
MΩ megohm.
M molecular weight; [mutual inductance]; magnetic moment; mass.
m. metre.
ml. millilitre.[1]
mm. millimetre.
mμ millimicron$=10^{-3}\mu$.
mA [milliampere].
m mass; molality; direction cosine; ($1/m$, Poisson's ratio); magnetic quantum number (m_l).
N mol fraction; number of particles; (modulus of shearing rigidity or elasticity); normalising factor.
N_L Loschmidt's number.
$\boldsymbol{N}$ Avogadro's number.
$N!$ factorial $N=N(N-1)(N-2)\ldots 2.1$.
$\boldsymbol{n}$ number of mols; number of components; wave number; direction cosine; refractive index.
ø ørsted.
P spherical harmonic function.

[1] Except in very accurate specifications of larger volumes, the difference between the centimetre cube or cm.^{3} and the millilitre ($=1{\cdot}00028$ cm.^{3}) is insignificant. The old symbol c.c. for millilitre is not used.

P, p	pressure (gas or osmotic); spectrum symbol; generalised momentum; (aggregate normal force, total pressure); (intensity of normal stress); polarisation (electric).
$[P]$	parachor.
p_c	critical pressure.
p_r	reduced pressure$=p/p_c$.
Q	quantity of electricity; minus q; (quantity of heat).
q	heat *entering* a system (positive); (*subscript*) adiabatic change; generalised position coordinate; (intensity of shear stress).
(q)	heat *absorbed* in a cycle.
q_s, q_d	heats of solution and dilution.
R	radial function.
R	radius of curvature; [resistance]; molar refractivity; reflectivity; resisting force.
$[R]$	rheochor.
$\boldsymbol{R}$	gas constant per mol.
r	radius; distance; (*subscript*) reversible; number of phases; (radius of curvature); gas constant per g.
S	tesseral harmonic function.
S	entropy; solubility; spectrum symbol; (specific gravity); (*subscript*) isentropic change.
$S_0{}^{\mathrm{G}}$	entropy constant.
s	(*subscript*) sublimation.
s	solid; solubility; symmetry factor; spin quantum number; (intensity of shear stress); distance.
T	absolute temperature; (twisting moment); period; kinetic energy.
T_b	boiling-point (abs.).
T_c	critical temperature (abs.).
T_m	melting-point (abs.).
T_r	reduced temperature$=T/T_c$.
t	time; temperature.
t_c	critical temperature.
U	velocity of sound; {alternative symbol for energy}.
u	velocity; velocity component$=\mathrm{d}x/\mathrm{d}t=\dot{x}$.
V	volume; electrical potential; potential energy; velocity; [potential difference].
V_m	molar volume.
v	volume; velocity component$=\mathrm{d}y/\mathrm{d}t=\dot{y}$; velocity; (specific volume); vibrational quantum number.
v_c	critical volume.
v_r	reduced volume$=v/v_c$.
W	thermodynamic probability; weight.
w	work *done* by a system (positive); velocity component$=\mathrm{d}z/\mathrm{d}t=\dot{z}$; weight.
(w)	work *done* in a cycle.
w_T	maximum work$=-\triangle F$.
w'_T	available (net) work$=-\triangle G$.
X	force component in x-direction; generalised force; [reactance].
$\bar{X}$	partial molar quantity.[1]

[1] Except for this use (Lewis and Randall), and $\bar{g}$, a barred symbol denotes an *average* value; note that $\overline{c^2}$ is different from $\bar{c}^2$.

x	distance along x axis; generalised coordinate; anharmonicity constant; $\beta\nu/T$; angle; mol fraction.
Y	surface spherical harmonic.
Y	force component in y-direction; [admittance $Y=G+jB$ ($j=\sqrt{-1}$)].
y	distance along y axis; number of faradays transferred in electrochemical change.
Z	force component in z-direction; state sum (" partition function "); atomic number; nuclear charge; collision number; [impedance$=R+jX$ ($j=\sqrt{-1}$)].
z	distance along z axis; valency of an ion.
α	reversible change; coefficient of expansion; degree of dissociation; constant in Nernst's equation; angle; polarisability; most probable velocity of molecules.
β	irreversible change; coefficient of tension; Duhem-Margules constant; activity constant; constant in Nernst's equation; frequency coefficient$=\boldsymbol{h}/\boldsymbol{k}$ in $\beta\nu/T$; Bunsen's absorption coefficient.
Γ	surface concentration excess; gamma function.
γ	ratio of specific heats c_p/c_v; thermal coefficients; activity coefficients; [surface tension].
Δ	finite increment; spectrum symbol.
ΔT_{mb},	molar elevation of boiling-point.
ΔT_{mf},	molar *depression* of freezing point.
δ	small increment; lattice constant.
∂	Jacobi symbol for partial differentiation (if $z=f(x, y)$, $\partial z/\partial x=(dz/dx)_y$, etc.).
ϵ	elasticity; energy of a particle, etc.; energy quantum; coefficient of external friction.
ζ	coefficient of slip.
η	thermodynamic efficiency; coefficient of viscosity.
Θ	surface zonal harmonic function.
Θ	Debye characteristic temperature; quadrupole moment.
θ	temperature on any scale, e.g. on the Centigrade scale; angle; (torsional strain; absolute temperature).
ϑ	reduced temperature$=T/T_c$; theta operator.
κ	compressibility; Debye-Hückel parameter; [permittivity (dielectric constant)]; conductivity (specific conductance); magnetic susceptibility (volume).
λ	compressibility coefficient; variable of extent; Lagrangian multiplier; wave-length; equivalent conductivity; root of equation; Ostwald's solubility coefficient.
μ	chemical potential; Poisson's ratio; integrating factor; Lagrangian multiplier$=1/\boldsymbol{k}T$; dipole moment; wave number; (coefficient of friction; refractive index); [permeability]; reduced mass; cos x; micron$=10^{-3}$ mm.; molecular conductivity.
μF	microfarad.
ν	stoichiometric coefficient; frequency (also $\tilde{\nu}$).
ν'	wave number.
ξ	concentration in mol/lit.

Π	product; hydrostatic pressure; spectrum symbol.
π	ratio of circumference to diameter of a circle=3·1416...; reduced pressure=p/p_c.
ρ	density of matter g./ml.; of energy erg/cm.^{3}; resistivity (specific resistance); radius of curvature.
ρ_c	critical density=$1/v_c$.
ρ_r	reduced density=ρ/ρ_c.
Σ	sum; system; spectrum symbol.
σ	surface tension; atomic or molecular diameter; $\sigma=\boldsymbol{h}^2/8\pi^2\boldsymbol{I}\boldsymbol{k}T$; system; (Poisson's ratio); Stefan-Boltzmann constant; specific heat of saturated liquid or vapour.
τ	reciprocal of reduced temperature=$1/\vartheta$; [temperature]; average life; $d\tau$ volume element.
Φ	spherical harmonic function.
$\mathit{\Phi}$	[flux (magnetic)]; co-volume.
$\Phi(C_p)$	partial molar heat capacity.
$\Phi(E)$	partial molar expansibility.
$\Phi(K)$	apparent partial molar compressibility.
$\Phi(V)$	apparent partial molar volume.
ϕ	function; reduced volume=v/v_c; valency factor; angle; (entropy, direct shear); phase difference; co-volume; fluidity.
Ψ	wave function; (electric flux).
ψ	wave function; space-filling number.
χ	magnetic susceptibility (mass).
Ω	ohm.
ω	angular velocity; wave number; Batschinsky's constant.
$\tilde{\omega}$	frequency.
$\int$	integration.
$\oint$	integration round a cycle.
$\simeq$	approximate equality.
∇	del or nabla; Laplacian operator, $\nabla=\partial/\partial x+\partial/\partial y+\partial/\partial z$; del squared, $\nabla^2=\partial^2/\partial x^2+\partial^2/\partial y^2+\partial^2/\partial z^2$.

THE GREEK ALPHABET

A	α	alpha	N	ν	nu
B	β	beta	Ξ	ξ	xi
Γ	γ	gamma	O	o	omicron
Δ	δ	delta	Π	π, ϖ	pi
E	ϵ	epsilon	P	ρ	rho
Z	ζ	zeta	Σ	σ, ς	sigma
H	η	eta	T	τ	tau
Θ	θ, ϑ	theta	Y	υ	upsilon
I	ι	iota	Φ	ϕ	phi
K	κ	kappa	X	χ	chi
Λ	λ	lambda	Ψ	ψ	psi
M	μ	mu	Ω	ω	omega

FUNDAMENTAL PHYSICO-CHEMICAL CONSTANTS

The values of the fundamental physical constants[1] have undergone revision in recent years, and cannot be said to be satisfactorily established at present.[2] The following table gives three sets of figures, proposed by Birge (1941),[3] Kaye and Laby (1948), and Du Mond and Cohen (1948). All values are on the chemical scale of atomic weights O=16·0000.

[1] J. J. Thomson, *Phil. Mag.*, 1897, **44**, 293; 1898, **46**, 528; Wiechert, *Sitzb. phys. ökonom. Ges. Königsberg*, 1897, **38**; *Ann. Phys.*, 1897, **61**, 544; 1897, **62**, 596; 1898, **65**, 431; Kaufmann and Aschkinass, *ibid.*, 1897, **62**, 588; Simon, *ibid.*, 1899, **69**, 589; Townsend, *Phil. Mag.*, 1898, **45**, 125; Wilson, *ibid.*, 1903, **5**, 429; Planck, " Vorlesungen über die Theorie der Wärmestrahlung," Leipzig, 1906, 162; Sirk, *Wien Ber.*, 1908, **117**, II A, 1159; *Ann. Phys.*, 1908, **25**, 894; Millikan, *Phys. Rev.*, 1908, **26**, 197; 1909, **29**, 560; 1911, **32**, 348; *Phil. Mag.*, 1910, **19**, 209; Rutherford and Geiger, *Proc. Roy. Soc.*, 1908, **81**, 141, 161; *Phys. Z.*, 1908, **10**, 1; Regener, *Verhl. d. D. Phys. Ges.*, 1908, **10**, 78; Perrin, *Ann. Chim.*, 1909, **18**, 5; " Les Atomes," 1914, 154, 174, 244, 281; Ehrenfest, *Ann. Phys.*, 1918, **56**, 1; Ladenburg, *Jahrb. Radioakt. Elektronik*, 1921, **17**, 93, 273; Porter and Hedges, *Trans. Faraday Soc.*, 1922, **18**, 91; *Phil. Mag.*, 1922, **44**, 641; Schrader, *Phys. Rev.*, 1922, **19**, 422; Palmer, *J. Opt. Soc. Amer.*, 1923, 7, 873; Gerlach, " Materie, Elektrizität, Energie," Dresden and Leipzig, 1923, 49; Millikan, *Phys. Rev.*, 1923, **21**, 217; Ladenburg, in Landolt-Börnstein, " Tabellen," 1923, **2**, 8011; Ray, *Z. phys. Chem.*, 1923, **128**, 182; Wolf, *Ann. Phys.*, 1927, **83**, 849; Wilson, *Phys. Rev.*, 1929, **34**, 1493; Bäcklin, *Nature*, 1929, **123**, 409; Compton, *J. Franklin Inst.*, 1929, **208**, 605; Bearden, *Proc. Nat. Acad.*, 1929, **15**, 528; Millikan, *Science*, 1929, **69**, 481; Birge, *Phys. Rev. Suppl.*, 1929, **1**, 1; *Phys. Rev.*, 1929, **33**, 265; Sunier, *J. Chem. Educ.*, 1929, **6**, 299; Feder, *Ann. Phys.*, 1929, **1**, 497; Grotrian, *Naturwiss.*, 1929, **17**, 201; Olpin, *Phys. Rev.*, 1930, **36**, 251; Bond, *Phil. Mag.*, 1930, **10**, 994; Cork, *Phys. Rev.*, 1930, **35**, 128; Shiba, *Sci. Pap. Inst. Phys. Chem. Res. Tokyo*, 1932, **19**, 97; Kirchner, *Ann. Phys.*, 1932, **13**, 59; Ladenburg, *ibid.*, 1933, **16**, 468; Birge, *Science*, 1934, **77**, 438; *Phys. Rev.*, 1935, **48**, 918; Söderman, *Nova Acta Soc. Reg. Upsal.*, 1935, **9**, No. 8; Schaitberger, *Ann. Phys.*, 1935, **24**, 84; Ladenburg, *Ann. Phys.*, 1936, **27**, 458; Birge, *Phys. Rev.*, 1936, **49**, 204; Robinson, *Rep. Progr. Phys.*, 1936, **2**, 247; 1937, **4**, 212; Van Friesen, *Proc. Roy. Soc.*, 1937, **160**, 424; Birge, *Phys. Rev.*, 1937, **52**, 241; Ishida, Fulkushima, and Suetsugu, *Sci. Pap. Inst. Phys. Chem. Res. Tokyo*, 1937, **32**, 57; Shiba, *ibid.*, 1938, **34**, 1308; Millikan, *Ann. Phys.*, 1938, **32**, 34, 520; Wensel, *Bur. Stand. J. Res.*, 1939, **22**, 375; Dunnington, *Rev. Mod. Phys.*, 1939, **11**, 65; Goedicke, *Ann. Phys.*, 1939, **36**, 47; Du Mond, *Phys. Rev.*, 1939, **56**, 153; Darwin, *Proc. Phys. Soc.*, 1940, **52**, 202; Ohlin, *Arkiv Mat. Astron. Fys.*, 1940, **27** B, No. 10; Bearden, *J. Appl. Phys.*, 1941, **12**, 395; Birge, *Rev. Mod. Phys.*, 1941, **13**, 233; *Phys. Rev.*, 1941, **60**, 766; *Rep. Progr. Phys.*, 1941, **8**, 90; Hopper and Laby, *Proc. Roy. Soc.*, 1941, **178**, 243; De Groot, *Nederl. Tijdschr. Natuurkde.*, 1942, **9**, 497; *Amer. Chem. Abstr.*, 1944, **38**, 3884; Eddington, *Proc. Phys. Soc.*, 1942, **54**, 491; Laby, *Nature*, 1942, **150**, 648; Panofsky, Green, and Du Mond, *Phys. Rev.*, 1942, **62**, 214; Benford, *ibid.*, 1943, **63**, 212; Birge, *ibid.*, 1943, **63**, 213; *Amer. J. Phys.*, 1945, **13**, 63; Du Mond and Cohen, *Rev. Mod. Phys.*, 1948, **20**, 82; Kaye and Laby, " Tables of Physical and Chemical Constants," 10th edit., 1948, 7, 71, 81, 121, 129, 139. Some remarkable numerical relations between fundamental constants collected by Mills, *J. Phys. Chem.*, 1932, **36**, 1089, were criticised by Birge, *Science*, 1932, **75**, 383.

[2] A point at issue is the electrochemical equivalent of F. The older value as found by gravimetric methods with the silver coulometer differs appreciably from that found more recently by volumetric analysis with the iodine coulometer. The second seems likely to be less accurate, and Birge's procedure of taking a mean value is open to criticism. The values of the absolute temperature of 0° C. and of the acceleration of gravity g are far from certain.

[3] Birge, *Amer. J. Phys.*, 1945, **13**, 63, changed the value of N from $6{\cdot}0228\times10^{23}$ to $6{\cdot}02338\times10^{23}$, which affects many of the other constants in his list; see Du Mond and Cohen, *Rev. Mod. Phys.*, 1948, **20**, 82.

	Birge	Du Mond and Cohen	Kaye and Laby
Avogadro's number N	$6{\cdot}0228 \times 10^{23}$	$6{\cdot}0235 \times 10^{23}$	$6{\cdot}0226 \times 10^{23}$
Faraday F e.m.u. equiv.$^{-1}$	9648·77	9649·6	9648·0
,, intern. cmb. equiv.$^{-1}$ ...	96501·2	—	96493·7
Electronic charge e e.s.u.	$4{\cdot}8025 \times 10^{-10}$	$4{\cdot}8024 \times 10^{-10}$	$4{\cdot}8023 \times 10^{-10}$
,, e.m.u.	$1{\cdot}60203 \times 10^{-20}$	$1{\cdot}60199 \times 10^{-20}$	$1{\cdot}6020 \times 10^{-20}$
Molar Volume[1] of ideal gas V_{mi} cm.^{3} mol^{-1}.	$22{\cdot}4146 \times 10^3$	$22{\cdot}4146 \times 10^3$	$22{\cdot}4151 \times 10^3$
Molar Gas Constant[1] R erg mol^{-1} deg.$^{-1}$.	$8{\cdot}31436 \times 10^7$	$8{\cdot}31436 \times 10^7$	$8{\cdot}3145 \times 10^7$
Boltzmann's constant k erg deg.$^{-1}$	$1{\cdot}38047 \times 10^{-16}$	$1{\cdot}38032 \times 10^{-16}$	$1{\cdot}3806 \times 10^{-16}$
Planck's constant h erg sec. ...	$6{\cdot}624 \times 10^{-27}$	$6{\cdot}6234 \times 10^{-27}$	$6{\cdot}622 \times 10^{-27}$
Velocity of light c cm. sec.$^{-1}$ ...	$2{\cdot}99776 \times 10^{10}$	$2{\cdot}99776 \times 10^{10}$	$2{\cdot}99774 \times 10^{10}$
Mass of electron m_e g.	$9{\cdot}1066 \times 10^{-28}$	$9{\cdot}1055 \times 10^{-28}$	—
Ratio e/m_e for electron e.s.u. g.$^{-1}$	$5{\cdot}2736 \times 10^{17}$	$5{\cdot}2741 \times 10^{17}$	$5{\cdot}2727 \times 10^{17}$
Mechanical equiv. of heat J intern. joule 15° g.cal.$^{-1}$	4·1847	—	4·1846
Absolute temperature of 0° C. ...	273·16	[273·16]	273·16

Electrical units adopted by the National Physical Laboratory:

1 ohm=1·00049 abs. ohm; 1 watt=1·00019 abs. watt; 1 volt=1·00034 abs. volt; 1 henry=1·00049 abs. henry; 1 amp.=0·99985 abs. amp.; 1 farad=0·99951 abs. farad.

The Bureau of Standards has adopted: [2]

1 ohm=1·000495 abs. ohm; 1 volt=1·000330 abs. volt; 1 amp.=0·999835 abs. amp.

[1] With $g=980{\cdot}665$ cm. sec.$^{-2}$. The value of R in l. atm. deg.$^{-1}$ mol^{-1} adopted by Birge and by Du Mond and Cohen is $8{\cdot}20544 \times 10^{-2}$. Kaye and Laby take $8{\cdot}2063 \times 10^{-2}$.

[2] Curtis, *Bur. Stand. J. Res.*, 1944, **33**, 235; Du Mond and Cohen, *Rev. Mod. Phys.*, 1948, **20**, 82.

SECTION I

MATHEMATICAL INTRODUCTION

As explained in the Preface, the present book is preceded by a summary of the mathematical methods used later in the text. In dealing with the mathematics which could reasonably be assumed to be unfamiliar to ordinary science students (some, in fact, to honours mathematics students), it was necessary to decide how much of the simpler fundamental material could be assumed to be known. This will vary with different readers; some will know a good deal and some very little, and in the end it seemed desirable to begin with the simplest things. In this way, very elementary calculus and trigonometry are dealt with, but more advanced matters are soon encountered. Those readers who are good at calculus and trigonometry will pass over the elementary parts, but should remember that many readers are not good at these things, and a start further along the road would have left them far behind.

The mathematics required by the physical chemist, it has been said:[1] "is not the kind of mathematics that boys are usually taught at school; it is not the kind of mathematics that medical and science candidates have to pass at a preliminary or first B.Sc. examination; it is mathematics *for use*. It bears to what we may call examination mathematics the same sort of relation that French and German *for use* bear to much of our school French and German, and the way to learn it is to work with it."

A drawback of many text-books which the author himself felt when a student is the undue curtailment of the intermediate steps in the mathematics: most mathematicians seem to fear being thought too elementary. It has been said[2] that: "Some teachers can bridge the common gaps of text-books and can supply the easy-stage background so often taken for granted—generally without warrant." This is particularly the case in thermodynamics, and in other fields integration by parts is carried out in the background and the result only presented, whereas in the author's experience this manipulation, simple as it is, is one which presents difficulty to most students of chemistry. Many students are also unable to recognise in special cases, where the symbols are different, the standard mathematical forms with which they are otherwise familiar: they do not see, e.g. that:

$$\int\frac{\mathrm{d}v}{v^{\gamma}}=\frac{1}{1-\gamma}v^{1-\gamma}+\text{const.}$$

is simply an example of the standard integral:

$$\int x^{n}\mathrm{d}x=\frac{1}{n+1}x^{n+1}+\text{const.},$$

unless it is pointed out to them, and, if they are serious students, could waste

[1] Crum Brown, Presidential Address, *J.C.S.*, 1892, **61**, 474; L. H. Adams, *J. Wash. Acad. Sci.*, 1926, 266.

[2] Mack, *J.A.C.S.*, 1939, **61**, 1298.

much time and effort in understanding this very simple calculation.[1] It is most desirable that a chemistry student should have a special course of mathematics suited to his needs, otherwise, as has been said,[2] he will have no time to learn chemistry.

At the risk of being slightly rude, the author will point out two types of mathematical treatment which are particularly wearying to the *average* physical chemist. In the first, many formulae are developed not one of which is expressed in terms of measurable quantities, and not one of which is capable of application to or test by experimental results. A formula of any use must contain only measurable quantities as independent variables. In the second type of treatment, some simple formula in common use is shown to be only an approximation of a more general formula, which cannot be expressed in usable form; in this case, the first formula is usually stigmatised as " unsound " or " theoretically incorrect," without any attempt being made to show that the terms it neglects are of very minor importance. Some authors seem to find satisfaction in repeatedly deriving results which are well known, and in emphasising the " elegance " of the new bottles for the old wine. Another fault is that: " the cumbrous phraseology of precise usage, which often involve long parentheses, is frequently unnecessary and confusing. This insistence on precision in all cases is not unlike a demand that all weighings should be made with the utmost accuracy, whether or not the final figures have significance." [3] The tendency to labour at length in showing how not to make mistakes which no one in his senses could make, in which " a man of straw is thoroughly demolished," [4] is also a tiresome conceit.

One of the main drawbacks of a " strict " mathematical treatment, emphasised by Clausius,[5] is that it necessarily lays most emphasis on the difficulties of the mathematical processes themselves, which have little importance for the physical principles involved, the latter appearing more satisfactorily in a simplified treatment: in other words, it stresses what might be called the pathology of mathematics. The simpler treatment is not only more understandable, but is scientifically preferable. The strict treatment is, in almost all cases, solely concerned with the value of some numerical coefficient and not with the symbolical part of the equation. By the time a subject has reached the stage of needing a " strict " proof, it has usually moved on into new fields.

There is no suggestion of impertinence in the above; it is not mathematicians who are in question, but their imitators. All the same, it seems that high mathematicians have been known to " disdain mere experimental information from humble ' dirt ' physicists." [6]

Almost every young reader should now have at his disposal a working knowledge of the calculus. The book, however, is intended to be of use also to other classes of readers, who may have had no instruction in higher mathematics in their student days, and who have found no time or inclination to learn

[1] This example also illustrates the general undesirability of rigid adherence to a set of " approved " symbols; it is only when a student has learnt to feel at home with *any* symbols that he moves freely through the literature of a subject, where a single quantity, such as entropy, has many symbols such as S, ϕ, η, etc. As Guye, *J. Chim. Phys.*, 1917, **15**, 360, said, the over-systematisers have shown " un âpreté et une passion qui ont généralement paru excessives."

[2] Guye, *J. Chim. Phys.*, 1921, **19**, 143.

[3] Mark, *J.A.C.S.*, 1933, **55**, 862.

[4] Beattie, *J.A.C.S.*, 1937, **59**, 770.

[5] Die kinetische Theorie der Gase, in " Die mechanische Wärmetheorie," Brunswick, 1889–91, **3**, 110.

[6] Du Mond, *Phys. Rev.*, 1939, **56**, 153.

it for themselves. There are many chemists in industry and elsewhere, leaders in their own fields, who are not at ease with even the simpler parts of higher mathematics. Even research students, in the author's experience, have not the facility in mathematics which might be expected. For all such readers a short mathematical introduction has been provided, which, starting from the simplest mathematics, leads rapidly to those parts of the calculus and simple differential equations which are used in the book. This section is not intended for readers who have an adequate knowledge of higher mathematics, who can proceed straight to the text. It has been said [1] that: " 'a little learning' is not 'a dangerous thing' in itself, but becomes so when its possessor is ignorant of its littleness." It should hardly be necessary to say that no one will reasonably expect an adequate treatise on mathematics in a few pages of a book on physical chemistry. What has mostly been done is to divest the material needed of those long and, to the practical scientist, often unnecessary discussions which are so vital to the mathematician; as one might say,[2] the matter is presented with the "apes and peacocks thrown overboard." It may be true that: [3] "The examination of natural phenomena is best effected with the minimum of assumption of any kind; and instead of demanding a theory, it would be better to ask how we could dispense with one. It is juster and wiser to adhere to facts than attempt to transcend them." Another aspect of this idea is Larmor's [4] statement that "the infinite variety of nature can be only partially enchained in symbols." The great French mathematician Fourier, whose work was literally rescued by physicists from mathematical oblivion, said: [5] ". . . la vérité qu'on se proposait de découvrir n'est pas moins cachée dans les formules d'Analyse quelle ne l'était dans la question physique ellemême." The danger of operating with mathematical symbols without understanding their intimate relation to the experimental material is very real.[6]

In many ways mathematical analysis is a help to the intellect, and if the mind were more powerful it could dispense with it. The train of abstract thought is mathematically developed in short steps, a process which preserves continuity, and enables us to leave the path and return to it again after an interruption of thought. The previous steps are marked in symbols, which relieve us of the necessity of thinking out the whole sequence in one effort, and of carrying in the mind more than it is capable of bearing unless aided by such artificial memory. The mathematical apparatus plays the same part as any particular language in expressing the imagery of a poet, and although, like language, it may have a beauty and intellectual value of its own, it is in no way identical with the conceptions it serves to record in its peculiar, and often cumbrous, way. On the other hand, a mathematical symbol may, to one who knows its meaning, express something which would take many hours to state in ordinary language ("plain English").[7] If seems as if, "with truly creative intellects, the result is always earlier than the proof," [8] and that no amount of steady plodding along the lines of school-desk mathematics can replace the "leap in the dark" which is inseparable from the working of genius.

A much closer approach to "truth" is often attainable in chemistry without

1 Rankine, "Miscellaneous Scientific Papers," 1881, 432.
2 T. L. Davis, *J.A.C.S.*, 1928, **50**, 3396.
3 E. J. Mills, *Phil. Mag.*, 1876, **1**, 12.
4 "Mathematical and Physical Papers," Cambridge, 1929, **2**, 412.
5 "Oeuvres," 1888, **1**, 9 ("Théorie Analytique de la Chaleur," 1822).
6 Planck, *Phys. Z.*, 1909, **10**, 195.
7 L. H. Adams, *J. Wash. Acad. Sci.*, 1926, **16**, 266.
8 Ostwald, "Lehrbuch der allgemeinen Chemie," 1911, **2**, ii, 159.

mathematics than with it. In physics, it has been said[1]: " We have no guarantee whatever that nature is so constructed that it can be adequately described in terms of mechanical or electrical models: it is much more probable that our most fundamental relationships can only be expressed mathematically, if at all." It would, however, be highly inconvenient so to describe, e.g. the simple operation of peeling a potato, whereas an attempt could be made to describe it so that anyone who did not know how to do it could perform the operation after a little practice. The same applies to innumerable chemical preparations. A large part of chemistry is much too complicated and difficult to offer a successful field for the application of mathematical methods, and chemistry cannot afford to wait for this to catch it up. After all, the chemists knew that the benzene molecule was a flat hexagonal ring long before this had been shown by the X-rays, and the concepts of valency and chemical bonds were reached over half a century before wave mechanics had come into existence, and is trying to represent them in mathematical symbols.

The point of view presented is that chemistry is a science which can make fruitful use of physics and mathematics, but is one which has profitably gone its own way, and cannot, even now, submit to be a mere appendage to other sciences. Many will disagree with this, and are entitled to their opinions.[2]

Unless an experimenter has a clear idea of the exact nature of a problem, he will rarely find a mathematician who is able or willing to solve it for him. He must, in general, have arrived at a differential equation or have his ideas clarified up to the point where a mathematician can so represent them. The problems presented to mathematicians by chemists ignorant of higher mathematics are sometimes in a totally unsuitable form, and are often incapable of mathematical treatment. In one case the experimenter had ten independent variables, and hence ten equations would be necessary for solution, but the worker had only one set of results, he not having grasped the simple point that one thing must be varied at a time, the others being kept constant. Even Newton could do nothing with such material. The modern trend of science tends to eliminate the " meaningless question," e.g. of the type:[3] (*a*) Is an electron a particle or a wave? (*b*) When will a radium atom disintegrate? (*c*) What is the molecular weight of diamond? (*d*) What is the temperature of a hydrogen molecule in the gas at 0° C.?

The idea that a science is not " scientific " unless it is mathematical is an old error of the schools going back to Plato. The Greeks emphasised the importance of mathematics, and they never wanted followers. They were fairly good at descriptive biology, but they knew nothing of chemistry. In chemistry the notion is wrong. Many of the greatest chemists either knew very little mathematics or disliked the subject. Emil Fischer, Baeyer, and W. H. Perkin, junr., produced work of outstanding eminence without the use of mathematics. Even some physicists have not been good mathematicians, the outstanding example being Faraday.

Faraday had no mathematical training and in a curious note jotted down on a card he says:[4] " Pique about mathematics in chemists, and resolution to support the character of experiment—as better for the mass. Hence origin of the title *Exp. researches*." He knew the value of mathematics, and counselled Tyndall

[1] Langmuir, *J.A.C.S.*, 1929, **51**, 2847.

[2] On the influence of mathematical speculation on chemistry, see Le Chatelier, *Chim. et Ind.*, 1920, 3, 555.

[3] Langmuir, *op. cit.*

[4] Quoted in S. P. Thompson, " Michael Faraday—His Life and Work," 1898, 239.

to work out his experimental results " so that the mathematicians may be able to take it up." [1] His own long series of *Experimental Researches* contain no mathematical symbols, yet Maxwell, after reading them, was able to say: [2] " When I had translated . . . Faraday's ideas into a mathematical form, I found that in general the results of the two methods coincided . . . also that several of the most fertile methods of research discovered by the mathematicians could be expressed much better in terms of ideas derived from Faraday than in their original form. . . . The way in which Faraday made use of his lines of force in co-ordinating the phenomena of electric induction shows him to have been a mathematician of high order, and one from whom the mathematicians of the future may derive valuable and fertile methods."

It is not only in reducing to brief compass the long series of experimental results that Maxwell's mathematical restatement of Faraday's theory was illuminating; it had also a creative function, since his equations contained the implication of electromagnetic waves, which were afterwards discovered experimentally by Hertz along the way pointed out by these mathematical equations. Huxley [3] compared mathematics with a mill which grinds up what is put into it: " What you get out depends on what you put in," and " pages of formulae will not get a definite result from loose data." This is true, yet Maxwell's equations can give all the results of experiment beforehand; a more striking example is the recent prediction of the existence of ortho- and para-hydrogen molecules, which followed from theoretical equations and, otherwise, would probably still remain unknown.[4]

There have not been lacking cases in which mathematicians have failed to understand new mathematical methods applied to scientific problems. Lord Kelvin [5] tells how Fourier's method was considered to be incorrect by some mathematicians, and Clausius [6] reports that a professor of mathematics criticised thermodynamics as " an abuse of analysis, and bungling nonsense, . . . nothing more than a rotten nut, which looks well from the outside, but in reality contains nothing whatever." It was therefore necessary for Clausius to explain in his book the elementary theory of perfect differentials, which had escaped the attention of the mathematician. There are examples of this type available in modern literature.[7] The opposite error is also met with.

The writer well remembers being told, in 1913, by a leading English physicist, that the formulae of the quantum theory were nothing but lucky empirical equations, with no theoretical foundation whatever.

It seemed necessary to mitigate as fully as might be the objections of reasonable critics that it was useless to give so much space to elementary mathematics which could much better be learnt from standard books on the subject. A short selection of these works on mathematics is given below.

1. *History and General.*

Ball, W. W. R., A Short Account of the History of Mathematics, 1915; Mathematical Recreations and Essays, 1919; Cajori, F., History of Mathematics, New York, 1894, 2nd

[1] Quoted in S. P. Thompson, " Michael Faraday—His Life and Work," 1898, 280,

[2] *Ibid.*, 217, 284; see the Preface to Maxwell's " Treatise on Electricity and Magnetism," Oxford, 1873, where he also says: " I shall avoid, as much as I can, those questions which, though they have elicited the skill of mathematicians, have not enlarged our knowledge of science."

[3] " Collected Essays," 1894, **8**, 333.

[4] Whitehead, *Phil. Mag.*, 1942, **33**, 353.

[5] " Mathematical and Physical Papers," Cambridge, 1882, **1**, 1.

[6] " The Mechanical Theory of Heat," transl. by W. R. Browne, 1879, 339.

[7] See e.g. Fowler and Sterne, *Rev. Mod. Phys.*, 1932, **4**, 707, for an amusing case.

edit., 1922; Sir T. Heath, A History of Greek Mathematics, 2 vols., Cambridge, 1921; Tropfke, J., Geschichte der Elementar-Mathematik, Berlin, 1940; Bowley, A. L., A General Course of Pure Mathematics from Indices to Solid Geometry, Oxford, 1913; Brown, F. G. W., Higher Mathematics, 1926; Cracknell, A. G., Practical Mathematics, 1925; Hardy, G. H., A Course of Pure Mathematics, Cambridge, 9th edit., 1946.

2. *Algebra.*

Briggs, W., and Bryan, G. H., The Tutorial Algebra, Advanced Course, 1903, revised by Walker, G., 1942; Burnside, W. S., and Panton, A. W., The Theory of Equations, 5th edit., 1904; Chrystal, G., Algebra, Part I, 5th edit., 1920; Part II, 2nd edit., 1922; Hall, H. S., and Knight, S. R., Higher Algebra, 4th edit., 1904; Milne, W. P., Higher Algebra, 1913; Smith, C., A Treatise on Algebra, 5th edit., 1920; Todhunter, I., Elementary Treatise on the Theory of Equations, 1882; Weber, H., and Wellstein, J., Encyclopädie der Elementarmathematik, 3 vols., Leipzig, 1903–7.

3. *Series and Limits.*

Bromwich, J. T. I., An Introduction to the Theory of Infinite Series, 1908, 2nd edit., 1926; Leathem, J. G., Elements of the Mathematical Theory of Limits, 1925.

4. *Exponentials.*

Du Bray, M., Exponentials Made Easy, 1921; see also under *Algebra* and *Calculus*.

5. *Theory of Functions.*

Bowman, F., Introduction to Bessel Functions, 1938; Cayley, A., An Elementary Treatise on Elliptic Functions, 1876, 2nd edit., 1895; Forsythe, A. R., Theory of Functions of a Complex Variable, 3rd edit., Cambridge, 1918; Gray, A., and Mathews, G. B., A Treatise on Bessel Functions, 1922; Greenhill, A. G., The Applications of Elliptic Functions, 1892; Harkness, J., and Morley, F., Treatise on the Theory of Functions, 1893; Hobson, E. W., The Theory of Functions of a Real Variable and the Theory of Fourier's Series, 3rd edit., 2 vols., Cambridge, 1926–7; Macrobert, T. M., Functions of a Complex Variable, 1917; Magnus, W., and Oberhettinger, F., Formeln und Sätze für die speziellen Funktionen der mathematischen Physik, Berlin, 1943; Neville, E. H., Jacobian Elliptic Functions, Oxford, 1944; Titchmarsh, E. C., The Theory of Functions, Oxford, 1932, 2nd edit., 1939; Whittaker, E. T., A Course of Modern Analysis, Cambridge, 1902, enlarged by Watson, G. N., 4th edit., 1927.

6. *Trigonometry.*

Briggs, W., and Bryan, G. H., The Tutorial Trigonometry, 3rd edit., 1928; Hobson, E. W., Trigonometry, 7th edit., Cambridge, 1928; Hobson, E. W., and Jessop, C. M., An Elementary Treatise on Plane Trigonometry, Cambridge, 1910; Loney, S. L., Plane Trigonometry, Parts I and II; Todhunter, I., Plane Trigonometry, 8th edit., 1880, revised by Hogg, R. W., 1919.

7. *Coordinate Geometry.*

Baker, W. M., Algebraic Geometry, 9th edit., 1926; Briggs, W., and Bryan, G. H., The Right Line and Circle; Frost, P., Elementary Treatise on Curve Tracing, 1872, revised by Bell, R. J. T., 1918; Gibson, G. A., and Pinkerton, P., Elements of Analytical Geometry, 1929; Grieve, A. B., Analytical Geometry of Conic Sections and Elementary Solid Figures, 1925; Loney, S. L., Elements of Coordinate Geometry, 1924; Smith, C., An Elementary Treatise on Conic Sections by the Methods of Coordinate Geometry, 1914; Todhunter, I., A Treatise on Plane Coordinate Geometry, 5th edit., 1874.

8. *Solid Geometry.*

Bell, R. J. T., Coordinate Geometry of Three Dimensions, 1920; Frost, P., Solid Geometry, 1886; Salmon, G., and Rogers, R. A. P., A Treatise on the Analytic Geometry of Three Dimensions, 2 vols., 1915–28; Smith, C., An Elementary Treatise on Solid Geometry, 6th edit., 1897.

9. *Calculus.*

Bacon, H. M., Differential and Integral Calculus, New York, 1942; Bertrand, G. L. F., Traité de Calcul Différentiel, 1864; *idem.*, Traité de Calcul Intégral, 1870; Bisacre, F. F. P., Applied Calculus, 1922; Burington, R. S., and Torrance, C. C., Higher Mathematics with Applications to Science and Engineering, New York, 1939; Carey, F. S., Infinitesimal Calculus, 1925; Carslaw, H. S., An Introduction to the Infinitesimal Calculus, 2nd edit., 1919; Caunt,

G. W., An Introduction to the Infinitesimal Calculus with Applications to Mechanics and Physics, Oxford, 1914; Chaundy, T., The Differential Calculus, Oxford, 1935; Edser, E., Differential and Integral Calculus for Beginners, 1901, 1909; Edwards, J., The Differential Calculus, 3rd edit., 1918; Differential Calculus for Beginners, 1893, 1919; A Treatise on the Integral Calculus, 2 vols, 1921–2; Integral Calculus for Beginners, 1894, 1898, 1919; Gibson, G. A., Elementary Treatise on the Calculus, 1906, 1919; An Introduction to the Calculus, 1906; Greenhill, A. G., Differential and Integral Calculus, 3rd edit., 1896; Johnson, W. W., An Elementary Treatise on the Differential Calculus founded on the Method of Rates, New York, 1904; Lamb, H., An Elementary Course of Infinitesimal Calculus, 3rd edit., Cambridge, 1919 (omits material in 2nd edit., 1902); Lodge, A., Differential Calculus for Beginners, 2nd edit., 1905, 4th edit., 1913; Integral Calculus for Beginners, 1905, 3rd edit., 1920; Lorentz, H., Lehrbuch der Differential- und Integralrechnung, transl. [from Dutch] by Schmidt, G. C., 4th edit., Leipzig, 1922; Love, A. E. H., Elements of the Differential and Integral Calculus, Cambridge, 1909; Mercer, J. W., The Calculus for Beginners, Cambridge, 1910; Middlemiss, R. R., Differential and Integral Calculus, 2nd edit., New York, 1946; Morgan, A. de, The Differential and Integral Calculus, 1842; Murray, D. A., Differential and Integral Calculus, 1927; Perry, J., The Calculus for Engineers, 1897; Price, B., Treatise on Infinitesimal Calculus, 4 vols., Oxford, 1857–89; Smith, R. H.. The Calculus for Engineers and Physicists, 2nd edit., 1908; Sokolnikoff, I. S., Advanced Calculus, New York, 1939; *idem* and Sokolnikoff, E. S., Higher Mathematics for Engineers and Physicists, New York, 1934, 2nd edit., 1941; Stewart, C. A., Advanced Calculus, 2nd edit., 1946; Stoney, J., Calculus for Engineering Students, 1919; Taylor, F. G., An Introduction to the Differential and Integral Calculus and Differential Equations, 1923; Thompson, S. P., Calculus Made Easy, 2nd edit., 1919; Todhunter, I., A Treatise on the Differential Calculus, 1919; A Treatise on the Integral Calculus, 5th edit., 1878, 1919; Williamson, B., An Elementary Treatise on the Differential Calculus, 7th edit., 1889 (reprinted); An Elementary Treatise on the Integral Calculus, 8th edit., 1906 (reprinted).

10. *Differential Equations.*

Airey, G. B., Elementary Treatise on Partial Differential Equations, 1866, 2nd edit., 1873; Bateman, H., Differential Equations, 1918; Boole, G., Treatise on Differential Equations, 1877, and Supplement, 1865; Forsythe, A. R., A Treatise on Differential Equations, 4th edit., 1914, 6th edit., 1929; Foster, P. F., and Baker, J. F., Differential Equations of Engineering and Science, Oxford, 1929; Frank, P., and von Mises, R., Differentialgleichungen der Physik, 1930; Green, S. L., An Introduction to Differential Equations, 1945; Hitchcock, F. L., and Robinson, C. S., Differential Equations in Applied Chemistry, New York, 2nd edit., 1936; Hort, W., Die Differentialgleichungen der Technik und Physik, 4th edit., Leipzig, 1944; Ince, E. L., Ordinary Differential Equations, 1927; Johnson, W. W., A Treatise on Ordinary and Partial Differential Equations, 3rd edit., 1891; Kamke, E., Gewöhnliche Differentialgleichungen, 3rd edit., Leipzig, 1944; Murray, D. A., Introductory Course in Differential equations, 22nd impress., 1927; Piaggio, H. T. H., An Elementary Treatise on Differential Equations, 6th edit., 1928.

11. *Fourier's Series.*

Byerly, W. E., An Elementary Treatise on Fourier's Series and Spherical, Cylindrical, and Ellipsoidal Harmonics, Boston, 1893; Carslaw, H. S., Fourier's Series and Integrals, 3rd edit., 1930; Eagle, A., A Practical Treatise on Fourier's Series and Harmonic Analysis, 1925; Fourier, J. B. J. de, The Analytical Theory of Heat, transl. Freeman, A., Cambridge, 1878 (reprint, New York, 1945); Hobson, E. W., The Theory of Functions of a Real Variable and the Theory of Fourier's Series, Cambridge, 3rd edit., 2 vols, 1926–7; Titchmarsh, E. C., Introduction to the Theory of Fourier Integrals, Oxford, 1937.

12. *Spherical Harmonics.*

Byerly, W. E., An Elementary Treatise on Fourier's Series and Spherical, Cylindrical, and Ellipsoidal Harmonics, Boston, 1893; Ferrers, N. M., An Elementary Treatise on Spherical Harmonics, 1877; Hobson, E. W., The Theory of Spherical and Ellipsoidal Harmonics, Cambridge, 1931; Macrobert, T. M., Spherical Harmonics, 1927; Ramsey, A. S., An Introduction to the Theory of Newtonian Attractions, Cambridge, 1940; Stratton, J. A., Morse, P. M., Chu, L. J., and Hunter, R. A., Elliptic, Cylinder, and Spheroidal Wave Functions, New York, 1941.

13. *General Treatises on the Applications of Higher Mathematics to Physics and Chemistry.*

Brillouin, L., Notions Élémentaires de Mathematiques pour les Sciences Expérimentales, 1935; Brown, F. G. W., Higher Mathematics for Students of Engineering and Science, 1926;

Chini, L., Lezioni sull'integrazione della equazioni differenziali, ad uso de gli studenti di Chimica, Livorno, 1921; Cibraria, M., Corso di Matematica per i Chimici ed i Naturalisti, Turin, 1937; Courant, R., and Hilbert, D., Die Methoden der mathematischen Physik, Berlin, 1937 (new edit., 2 vols., New York, 1944); Daniels, F., Mathematical Preparation for Physical Chemistry, New York, 1928; Doherty, R. E., and Keller, F. G., Mathematics of Modern Engineering, vol. **1**, New York, 1936; Eucken, A., Jette, E. R., and La Mer, V. K., Fundamentals of Physical Chemistry, New York, 1925, pp. 1–34; Gay, L., Les Mathématiques du Chimiste, Paris, 1926; Helm, G., Grundlagen der höheren Mathematik, Leipzig, 1910; Jeffreys, H., and Jeffreys, B. S., Methods of Mathematical Physics, Cambridge, 1946; Margenau, H., and Murphy, G. M., The Mathematics of Physics and Chemistry, New York, 1943; Mellor, J. W., Higher Mathematics for Students of Chemistry and Physics, 4th edit., 1931; Partington, J. R., Higher Mathematics for Chemical Students, 4th edit., 1931; Riemann, G. F. B., Partielle Differentialgleichungen und deren Anwendungen auf physikalische Fragen, edit. Hattendorf, Brunswick, 1882, reprinted 1938; Wüllner, A., Lehrbuch der Experimentalphysik, Leipzig, 1895, **1**, 312; Sherwood, T. K., and Reed, C. E., Applied Mathematics in Chemical Engineering, New York, 1939; Sokolnikoff, I. S., and E. S., Higher Mathematics for Engineers and Physicists, 1934, 2nd edit., 1941; Thirring, H. (editor), in Geiger, H., and Scheel, K., Handbuch der Physik, 1928, **3**.

14. *Method of Least Squares, Computation, etc.*

Chauvenet, W., Manual of Spherical and Practical Astronomy with Appendix on the Method of Least Squares [also published separately], Philadelphia, 2 vols., 1873; Cox and Matuschak, *J. Phys. Chem.*, 1941, **45**, 362 (least squares); Crumpler, T. B., and Yoe, J. H., Chemical Computations and Errors, New York, 1940; Deming, *Phil. Mag.*, 1931, **11**, 146 (least squares); Egloff and Kuder, *J. Phys. Chem.*, 1942, **46**, 926 (bibl. of theory of errors); Holman, S. W., Computation Rules and Logarithms, with Tables of other useful Functions, New York, 1896; Johnson, W. W., The Theory of Errors and the Method of Least Squares, New York, 1892; Lipka, J., Graphical and Mechanical Computation, New York, 1918; Merriman, M., Method of Least Squares, New York, 1891; Running, T. R., Empirical Formulas, New York, 1917.

15. *Determinants and Theory of Groups.*

Burnside, W., Theory of Groups of Finite Order, Cambridge, 1911; Cullis, C. E., Matrices and Determinants, 3 vols., Cambridge, 1914–25; Muir, T., Theory of Determinants in the Historical Order of Development, 4 vols., 1906–23; Turnbull, H. W., The Theory of Determinants, Matrices, and Invariants, 1928.

16. *Vector Analysis.*

Coffin, J. G., Vector Analysis, New York, 1909, 2nd edit., 1912; Henrici, O., and Turner, G. C., Vectors and Rotors, 1903; Runge, C., Vector Analysis, 1923; Shaw, J. B., Vector Calculus with Applications to Physics, 1922; Weatherburn, C. E., Elementary Vector Analysis, 1925; Wilson, E. B., Vector Analysis, New York, 1902.

17. *Calculus of Variations.*

Bliss, G. A., Lectures on the Calculus of Variations, Chicago, 1946; Bolza, O., Vorlesungen über Variationsrechnung, Leipzig and Berlin, 1909; Carll, L. B., Treatise on the Calculus of Variations, New York, 1881, London, 1885; Forsythe, A. R., Calculus of Variations, Cambridge, 1927; Grüss, G., Variationsrechnung, Leipzig, 1938; Jellett, J. H., An Elementary Treatise on the Calculus of Variations, Dublin, 1850; *idem*, Die Grundlehren der Variationsrechnung, transl. Schnuse, C. H., Brunswick, 1860; Todhunter, I., History of the Progress of the Calculus of Variations, 1861.

THE DIFFERENTIAL CALCULUS

§ 1. Functions

Suppose that a variable magnitude x (e.g. the volume of a given mass of gas at a fixed temperature, $x=v$) has a range of values which can be fixed arbitrarily, then x is called an *independent variable.* For each value of x in this interval let another magnitude y (e.g., the pressure of the gas, $y=p$) assume one or more *definite* values, then y is called the *dependent variable.* The relation between x and y is expressed by saying [1] that y is a *function* of x. If there is only one value of y for each value of x, y is called a *single valued* or *uniform* function; otherwise it is called *multi-valued* or *multiform*. By way of notation (symbolic representation) the functional dependence is represented [2] by $y=\mathrm{f}(x)$, read "y is a function of x." Some writers [3] use fx for f(x), and f is often replaced by F, ϕ, ψ, etc. The letters x, y, z (or immediately preceding ones, such as u, v, w) or Greek letters ξ, η, ζ (etc.) are generally used for variables, and a, b, c (etc.) or α, β, γ (etc.) for constants, although k is a common general symbol for a constant. The pressure p of a gas at constant temperature is a single-valued function of the volume v, the exact form of the functional dependence being given by Boyle's law: $p=\mathrm{f}(v)=k/v=kv^{-1}$. The pressure of a fixed mass of a gas depends on the temperature θ as well as on the volume v, i.e. p is a function of *two* independent variables: $p=\mathrm{F}(v, \theta)$, and in this case Boyle's and Charles's laws show that if θ is in °C.: $p=(k/v)(1+\theta/273)$, where k is a constant depending on the nature of the gas and its mass. In general, y may be a function of several independent variables: $y=\mathrm{f}(u, v, w, \ldots)$. In experiments, the dependence of y on each independent variable is found by keeping all the others constant.

If the function can be given in the form $y=\mathrm{f}(x)$, it is called an *explicit function*, but if it is in the form $\mathrm{f}(x, y)=0$, y is called an *implicit function* of x.

§ 2. Continuity

In Fig. 1.I the curve AB runs from start to finish without a break, but CD′DE breaks suddenly at the point D′, recommencing at D. The curve AB is *continuous*, whilst CD′DE is *discontinuous*. If each curve is regarded as the graph of a given function: $y=\mathrm{f}(x)$, then two kinds of functions must be recognised: (i) *continuous functions*, typified by AB, and (ii) *discontinuous functions*, typified by CD′DE.

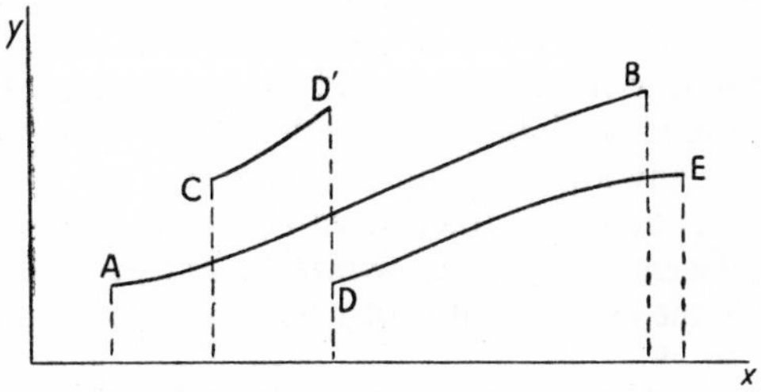

FIG. 1.I. Continuity and Discontinuity

A criterion of a continuous function [4] which expresses *analytically* (i.e. in symbols) what is shown graphically (i.e. *geometrically*) by these curves reads as follows. Let f(x) be the value of the function when the independent variable x has *any* given value x in the range from x_1 to x_2, and let $\mathrm{f}(x+h)$ be its value when x has the value $x+h$, h being a *small increment* of x; e.g. if $x_1=0$,

[1] The name is due to Leibniz (1692), the definition to John Bernoulli (1718), and the symbol f(x) to Euler (1734). For an interesting account of the development of the meaning of "function," see Hobson, "Theory of Functions of a Real Variable," 2nd edit., Cambridge, 1921–6, **1**, 256; Burnside and Panton, "Theory of Functions," Dublin, 1904–18; Harkness and Morley, "A Treatise on the Theory of Functions," 1893, 51; the value of y must be *definite*: a value of x which makes y infinite is excluded. The independent variable is sometimes called the *argument* of the function.

[2] The letters f, F, etc., are printed in roman type: see the "Report of a Joint Committee of the Chemical Society, the Faraday Society, and the Physical Society on Symbols for Thermodynamical and Physico-Chemical Quantities and Conventions relating to their Use," 1937, obtainable from the three Societies named.

[3] E.g. Greenhill, "Differential and Integral Calculus," 1896, 2, and many older authors, such as Poisson.

[4] The concept and name are due to Leibniz (1687); a "strict" definition, given by Bolzano (1817), is that used in the text.

$x_2=10$, let $x=4$ and $h=0{\cdot}01$, so that $x+h=4{\cdot}01$. If $f(x)=x^2$, the function then has the values 16 and 16·0801. If a value of h, which is not zero, can be chosen which makes the absolute value of $f(x+h)-f(x)$ (i.e. its numerical value with a positive sign) smaller than *any* number arbitrarily chosen, but not zero, then $f(x)$ is a continuous function of x over the range x_1 to x_2. It may be that the function is continuous for *all* values of x.

There are various kinds of functions. *Algebraic functions* are obtained by performing with x and known constants, k, etc., any finite number of operations of addition, subtraction, multiplication, division, and extraction of integral (whole number) roots, e.g. $2x$, x^2, $\sqrt{x}$, $\sqrt[3]{x}$. If the operations include the first four only, the function is called a *rational function*, and can always be reduced to the form $F(x)/f(x)$, where $F(x)$ and $f(x)$ are *rational integral functions*, each having a finite number of terms of the form Ax^m, where A is a constant and m a positive or negative integer (whole number). The rational integral function $y=f(x)=a+bx$, where a and b are constants, is a *linear function*, since the graph of y against x is a straight line.

A function of x which is not an algebraic function is called a *transcendental function*, e.g. $\cos x$, or e^x, or $\log x$. These are considered later.

§ 3. Limits

If a variable which changes according to some assigned law can be made to *approach* a fixed constant value as nearly as may be wished, without ever becoming actually equal to it, this constant value is called the *limiting value*, or *limit*, of the variable.[1]

In the fraction $y=(2x+3)/(x+1)$, y is a variable which changes with x according to the equation. Divide the numerator and denominator by x: $y=(2+3/x)/(1+1/x)$. If x is steadily increased, $3/x$ and $1/x$ steadily decrease, and if x increases beyond any assigned value, however great, or as is said, "x tends to infinity" (denoted by $x\to\infty$), then $3/x$ and $1/x$ both become smaller than any assigned values, however small, or as is said, "tend to zero." Thus the value of the fraction can be made as close to 2 as may be wished by taking x sufficiently large. In symbols: $(2x+3)/(x+1)\to 2$ when $x\to\infty$. By definition 2 is the limiting value of y when x tends to infinity, or:

$$\lim_{x\to\infty} (2x+3)/(x+1)=2.$$

It should be noted that ∞ does not denote a definite number, and it should not, strictly speaking, ever be said that anything is "equal" to infinity, although good mathematicians often write $x=\infty$, etc., the meaning being kept in mind.[2] Zero is, of course, a definite number, and it is *strictly* correct to write $x=0$. If ? denotes an *indeterminate* magnitude, the value of which cannot be the object of quantitative investigation, then: $\infty+\infty=\infty$, $\infty-\infty=?$, $n\times 0=0$, $0\times 0=0$, $n\times\infty=\infty$, $0/0=?$, $n/0=\infty$, $0/n=0$, $\infty/0=\infty$, $0/\infty=0$, $n/\infty=0$, $\infty/n=\infty$, $\infty/\infty=?$. These are *orders* of infinity. The lowest order is the *enumerable infinity*, such as the series of natural numbers, or any set of objects which can be enumerated. A higher order is the *non-enumerable infinity* or *infinity of the power of the continuum*, represented by the number of points in any finite portion of a continuum, and immensely larger than the enumerable infinity.

[1] This idea of a limit seems to be due to Wallis, "Arithmetica Infinitorum," Oxford, 1656.

[2] See de Morgan, *Trans. Cambr. Phil. Soc.*, 1871, **11**, 145 (read 1864: "On Infinity and on the Sign of Equality).”

§ 4. Differentials

The limitations of elementary mathematics appear in dealing with *continuous* changes. If an object moves with a *constant velocity* of 10 cm. per sec. (or cm./sec., or cm. sec.$^{-1}$), then after 5 secs. it will have gone $5\times 10=50$ cm. Conversely, if an object moves with a *constant* velocity u, this is found by dividing [1] the distance s travelled by the time t as $u=s/t$. If the velocity is not constant an *average value* over a small interval is found by dividing the small distance δs travelled in that instant by the very small time interval δt: $u=\delta s/\delta t$. The ratio $\delta s/\delta t$ becomes more accurately equal to the velocity *at an instant* the nearer δt approaches zero. The symbols δs and δt do not mean s or t multiplied by δ, any more than log x means log multiplied by x, but are symbols for the *very small changes*, or *increments*, of s and t. The accurate velocity is the *limit* of $\delta s/\delta t$ when $\delta t\to 0$; it is denoted by:

$$u=\lim_{\delta t\to 0}(\delta s/\delta t)=\mathrm{d}s/\mathrm{d}t,$$

where ds and dt are called *differentials*, or *infinitesimals*. The limiting value of the *ratio*, ds/dt, is called a *differential coefficent*. Since both δs and δt become zero together when $\delta t\to 0$, Bishop Berkeley [2] satirically called them " the ghosts of departed quantities," but there is no ambiguity in what they mean.

In the case of the fall of a body from a fixed point, the distance s travelled in a time t is given by $s=\frac{1}{2}gt^2$, where g=acceleration of gravity. In the next very small interval of time δt, let the fall be through a further small distance δs, making a total fall $(s+\delta s)$ in a time $(t+\delta t)$:

$$\therefore\ (s+\delta s)=\tfrac{1}{2}g(t+\delta t)^2=\tfrac{1}{2}gt^2+gt\delta t+\tfrac{1}{2}g(\delta t)^2.$$

Subtract $s=\frac{1}{2}gt^2$, therefore $\delta s=gt\delta t+\frac{1}{2}g(\delta t)^2$. If δt is very small (e.g. 0·01), $(\delta t)^2$ is of the *second order of smallness* (0·0001), and can be neglected in comparison with the other terms, $\therefore\ \delta s=gt\delta t$, $\therefore\ \mathrm{d}s=gt\mathrm{d}t$ when $\delta t\to 0$, $\therefore\ \mathrm{d}s/\mathrm{d}t=gt$.

The velocity at an instant t secs. after the start of fall is thus $g\times t$. It should be noticed that the " neglect " of the term containing $(\delta t)^2$ makes the result more, not less, accurate, and the retention of differentials of higher order till the end of a calculation is a pure waste of time.[3] The mathematical concept of continuity also appears to be a fiction, since *every* process occurring in nature, when closely scrutinised, is actually discontinuous, and should be represented by differentials which always remain finite. The transition from these to " differential coefficients " or " derived functions " (see below) is a mathematical fiction which has no counterpart in physical processes.

The *approximations with finite small quantities* given below should be noted, as they are very useful in practice. If a, b, c, d are *small compared with unity*,

[1] The very convenient *solidus* notation for division, e.g. s/t, was introduced by Stokes, " Math. and Phys. Papers," Cambridge, 1880, **1**, preface. It is best not used in *writing* equations, but only in printing.

[2] " The Analyst, or a Discourse addressed to an Infidel Mathematician," London, 1734; in " Collected Works," Oxford, 1901, 3, 44.

[3] Ball, " A Short . . . History of Mathematics," 1912, 410, quotes Lagrange as saying: " . . . when we have grasped the spirit of the infinitesimal method . . . we may employ infinitely small quantities as a sure and valuable method of shortening and simplifying our proofs." The usual school-teaching procedure of insisting that dy and dx must never be separated in dy/dx, and then freely separating them in more advanced work, including d/dx itself as an operator, seems as strange to the author as it did to Augustus de Morgan, " Differential and Integral Calculus," 1842, 198. In the case of *partial* differential coefficients (§ 25) the variables must not usually be separated, for if $z=\mathrm{f}(x, y)$, $(\partial z/\partial x)/(\partial z/\partial y)$ is not $\partial y/\partial x$ but $-\partial y/\partial x$.

then (the symbol $\simeq$ denoting " is approximately equal to," i.e. with approximation sufficient in the equation in which it appears):

$$(1\pm a)(1\pm b)(1\pm c)(1\pm d)\simeq 1\pm a\pm b\pm c\pm d$$

$$\frac{(1\pm a)(1\pm b)}{(1\pm c)(1\pm d)}\simeq 1\pm a\pm b\mp c\mp d$$

$$\frac{1}{1\pm a}\simeq 1\mp a$$

$$(1\pm a)^n\simeq 1\pm na$$

[with the special cases: $(1\pm a)^2=1\pm 2a$, $(1\pm a)^3=1\pm 3a$, $\sqrt{(1\pm a)}=(1\pm a)^{1/2}\simeq 1\pm\frac{1}{2}a$, $\sqrt[3]{(1\pm a)}=(1\pm a)^{1/3}\simeq 1\pm\frac{1}{3}a$]

$$\sqrt{(ab)}\simeq\tfrac{1}{2}(a+b)$$

$$e^a\simeq 1+a$$

$$x^a\simeq 1+a\ln x$$

$$\ln(1+a)\simeq a-\tfrac{1}{2}a^2$$

(where ln denotes the natural logarithm to the base e: see § 12). If 1 is replaced by a constant, m, the expression is first reduced to one of the above cases by division: $1/(m+a)=1/(1+a/m)m\simeq(1-a/m)/m$, etc.

There is nothing more to *understand* about a differential or a differential coefficient than has been given above, and if sufficient time were available it could always be found by this method. An enormous saving of time and trouble is gained, however, by learning a few simple rules, which follow. Although any multiplication sum can be worked by successive additions, this does not justify a neglect to learn the rules of multiplication. In modern works, the *differential coefficient* is often called a *derived function* or a *derivative*,[1] but the operation of finding it is always called *differentiation*.[2]

§ 5. Meaning of Differential Coefficient

Just as ds/dt in the above example gives the *velocity*, or *rate of change* of distance with time, so if y is a function of x, denoted by $y=f(x)$, the value of dy/dx, for *a particular value of* x, gives the rate of change of y with x, when x has this value. When y is *increasing* with x, then dy/dx is positive; when y is *decreasing* as x increases, then dy/dx is negative. When the graph of $y=f(x)$ is considered, another interesting meaning of dy/dx appears.

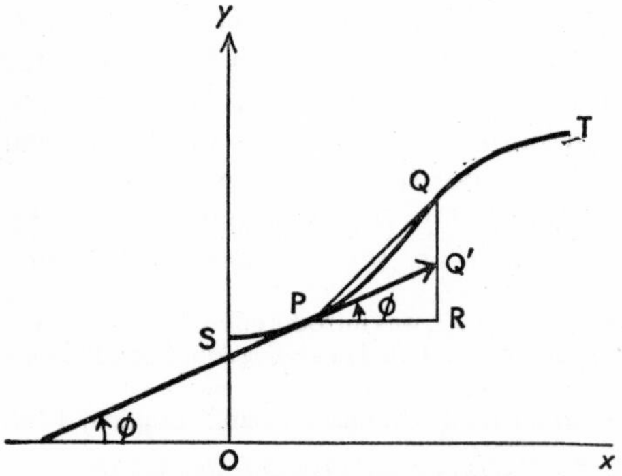

FIG. 2.I. Gradient of a Curve

Let PQ (Fig. 2.I) be part of the curve SPQT representing the function $y=f(x)$. Through the points P and Q draw PR and QR parallel to the axes, and join PQ. Let

[1] See the rigorous definition in Hobson, " Theory of Functions of a Real Variable," 2nd edit., Cambridge, 1921–6, **1**, 330. The name " derivative " is due to Leibniz (1677) (" Leibnizens mathematische Schriften," edit. Gerhardt, Berlin, 1849, **1**, 156; see § 56), the symbol $f'(x)$ to Lagrange (1797).

[2] Riemann, " Partielle Differentialgleichungen," 1938, 214, has "Derivirten" for derivative, i.e. " the derived."

PR=δx and RQ=δy. Then $\delta y/\delta x$=RQ/PR=tan QPR, is the *gradient* (or *slope*) of the *secant* PQ. If Q moves along the curve until it coincides with P, the secant PQ becomes the *tangent* PQ′ to the curve at the point P, and $\delta x \to 0$; hence the value of $\delta y/\delta x$ becomes $\mathrm{d}y/\mathrm{d}x$=RQ′/PR, which now measures the gradient of the tangent [1] to the curve at P, or (as is said) the *gradient of the curve* at P. If ϕ is the angle (measured in radians: see § 40), positive when measured counter-clockwise, which the positive direction of the tangent line at P makes with the positive direction of the x axis, then:

$$\mathrm{d}y/\mathrm{d}x=\tan\phi.$$

Since limit PR/RQ=limit $\delta x/\delta y$=PR/RQ′=$1/(\mathrm{d}y/\mathrm{d}x)$, therefore $\mathrm{d}x/\mathrm{d}y=1/(\mathrm{d}y/\mathrm{d}x)$.

§ 6. Rules of Differentiation

The process or operation of finding the *differential*, or *differential coefficient*, of a given function is called *differentiation*. Thus, if $s=\frac{1}{2}gt^2$, then $\mathrm{d}s/\mathrm{d}t=gt$ is found by " differentiating s with respect to t." In general, the result of differentiating y=f(x) with respect to x will depend on the " form " of the function. Before taking up special forms, some *general rules* relating to sums, products, and quotients of functions will be useful. Suppose u, v, and w are separate different continuous [2] functions of x, which can be denoted by:

$$u=\mathrm{f}_1(x),\quad v=\mathrm{f}_2(x),\quad w=\mathrm{f}_3(x);$$

$$\text{or}\quad u=\mathrm{f}(x),\quad v=\mathrm{F}(x),\quad w=\phi(x),\ \text{etc.,}$$

and let k be a constant.

(1) Since the rate of change of k is zero, it follows that:

$$\mathrm{d}k=0 \quad . \quad . \quad . \quad . \quad . \quad . \quad . \quad . \quad . \quad . \quad . \quad (1)$$

or *the differential of a constant is zero*. This is often a neater way of showing that a quantity is constant than by writing " k is constant ", e.g. the condition of an isothermal change, in which the temperature θ is constant, is expressed by the equation $\mathrm{d}\theta=0$.

(2) Let $y=ku$ be the product of a constant k and a function u=f(x) of x. If x changes by δx, let u change by δu. Then y becomes $y+\delta y=k(u+\delta u)$, and by subtracting $y=ku$ it follows that $\delta y=k\delta u$; or in the limit, when $\delta x \to 0$:

$$\mathrm{d}y=k\mathrm{d}u \quad . \quad . \quad . \quad . \quad . \quad . \quad . \quad . \quad . \quad . \quad (2)$$

i.e. $\mathrm{d}(ku)=k\mathrm{d}u$. Division by the increment $\mathrm{d}x$ which has produced the increments $\mathrm{d}u$ and $\mathrm{d}y$ gives:

$$\mathrm{d}y/\mathrm{d}x=k(\mathrm{d}u/\mathrm{d}x) \quad . \quad . \quad . \quad . \quad . \quad . \quad . \quad . \quad (2a)$$

The differential of a function multiplied by a constant is equal to the constant multiplied by the differential of the function.

[1] Note the distinction between the *tangent line* PQ′ and the *trigonometrical tangent* of the angle ϕ, denoted by tan ϕ. On calculation of tangents to $y=c+ax+bx^2$ by the method of least squares, see Gucker and Brennan, *J.A.C.S.*, 1932, **54**, 881.

[2] A function which has a differential coefficient, or is " differentiable," must be continuous, but some continuous functions have no differential coefficient; roughly speaking, if $\mathrm{d}y/\mathrm{d}x$ is interpreted as the gradient of a curve (§ 5), and the curve consists of an infinite number of infinitesimally small " saw-teeth," its gradient at any point is indeterminate: see Harkness and Morley, " A Treatise on the Theory of Functions," 1893, 58; Hobson, " Theory of Functions of a Real Variable," Cambridge, 1907, 264, 620; 2nd edit., 1921, **1**, 330; 1926, **2**, 389.

(3) *The differential of a sum of functions.* Let $y=u+v+w+\ldots$

$$\therefore\ y+\delta y=(u+\delta u)+(v+\delta v)+(w+\delta w)+\ldots$$

$$\therefore\ \delta y=\delta u+\delta v+\delta w+\ldots$$

$$\text{or } \mathrm{d}y=\mathrm{d}u+\mathrm{d}v+\mathrm{d}w+\ldots$$

$$\therefore\ \mathrm{d}(u+v+w+\ldots)=\mathrm{d}u+\mathrm{d}v+\mathrm{d}w+\ldots \quad (3)$$

$$\text{or } \mathrm{d}y/\mathrm{d}x=\mathrm{d}u/\mathrm{d}x+\mathrm{d}v/\mathrm{d}x+\mathrm{d}w/\mathrm{d}x+\ldots \quad (3a)$$

Any of the signs may be negative, when, for example, $\mathrm{d}(u-v)=\mathrm{d}u-\mathrm{d}v$, etc.

The differential of a sum of functions is equal to the sum of the differentials of the functions.

(4) *The differential of a product of functions.* Consider first the product of *two* functions, $y=uv$,

$$\therefore\ y+\delta y=(u+\delta u)(v+\delta v)$$

$$=uv+u\delta v+v\delta u+\delta u\delta v$$

$$\therefore\ \delta y=u\delta v+v\delta u+\delta u\delta v.$$

The term $\delta u\delta v$ is a small quantity of the second order which vanishes in the limit:

$$\therefore\ \mathrm{d}y=\mathrm{d}(uv)=u\mathrm{d}v+v\mathrm{d}u \quad (4)$$

$$\text{or } \mathrm{d}y/\mathrm{d}x=u(\mathrm{d}v/\mathrm{d}x)+v(\mathrm{d}u/\mathrm{d}x) \quad (4a)$$

The differential of the product of two functions is equal to the first function multiplied by the differential of the second plus the second function multiplied by the differential of the first.

If $y=uvw$, it is easy to show, similarly, that:

$$\mathrm{d}y=vw\mathrm{d}u+uw\mathrm{d}v+uv\mathrm{d}w,$$

and so on, for any number of functions. (An easier way of obtaining this equation is given in § 15.)

(5) *The differential of a quotient of two functions.* This is a special case of (4). Let $y=u/v$, therefore $u=yv$,

$$\therefore\ (u+\delta u)=(y+\delta y)(v+\delta v),$$

$$\therefore\ \delta u=y\delta v+v\delta y+\delta v\delta y$$

$$\therefore\ \mathrm{d}u=y\mathrm{d}v+v\mathrm{d}y,$$

as in (4). Hence:

$$\mathrm{d}y=(\mathrm{d}u-y\mathrm{d}v)/v=[\mathrm{d}u-(u/v)\mathrm{d}v]/v=(v\mathrm{d}u-u\mathrm{d}v)/v^2$$

$$\therefore\ \mathrm{d}y=\mathrm{d}(u/v)=(v\mathrm{d}u-u\mathrm{d}v)/v^2 \quad (5)$$

$$\text{or } \mathrm{d}y/\mathrm{d}x=[v(\mathrm{d}u/\mathrm{d}x)-u(\mathrm{d}v/\mathrm{d}x)]/v^2 \quad (5a)$$

It would be cumbersome to put this simple result into words. (A simpler way of finding (5) is to write $y=uv^{-1}$ and use (4) in conjunction with the rule for v^n (where $n=-1$) given in § 7.)

The notation $\mathrm{d}y/\mathrm{d}x$ is due to Leibniz.[1] Other symbols are y_1, y', or $\mathrm{D}y$;

[1] The differential method (" Algorithmo, ut ita dicam, calculi hujus, quem voco *differentialem* ") and notation were explained by Leibniz in a letter to Oldenburg intended for Newton, of June 1677 (see " Leibnizens mathematische Schriften," edit. Gerhardt, Berlin, 1849, **1**, 154), and published in 1684 (*Acta Erudit.*, 1684, 467); in 1686 (*ibid.*, 1686, 292) he called it " calculo meo differentiali." He published the integral sign ∫ notation in 1694 (*ibid.*, 1694, 364), but it appears in his MS. in 1675 (he did not communicate it to Newton: see " Leibnizens mathematische Schriften," edit. Gerhardt, 1849, **1**, 159). Newton referred vaguely to his fluxional method in an anagram in a letter to Oldenburg, intended for Leibniz, in October 1676; he did not publish his method in the " Principia " (1687): his " Methodus Fluxionum,"

or, if $y=f(x)$, dy/dx is denoted by $f'(x)$ or $Df(x)$. Newton used the "pricked" letter $\dot{y}$, formerly called the *fluxion* of y, and this is still used for a velocity: $\dot{x}=dx/dt$. The symbol d/dx or D may be regarded as an *operator* which acts on the function $f(x)$ to produce the function $f'(x)$.

§ 7. Differentiation of a Power of *x*

Let $y=x^n$, where n may be positive or negative, integral or fractional. If $y=x^2$:

$$y+\delta y=(x+\delta x)^2=x^2+2x\delta x+(\delta x)^2$$

$$\therefore\ dy=2xdx \quad \text{or} \quad dy/dx=2x.$$

If $y=x^3$:

$$y+\delta y=(x+\delta x)^3=x^3+3x^2\delta x+3x(\delta x)^2+(\delta x)^3$$

$$\therefore\ dy=3x^2dx \quad \text{or} \quad dy/dx=3x^2.$$

From these results it could be guessed that when $y=x^n$:

$$dy=nx^{n-1}dx \quad \text{or} \quad dy/dx=nx^{n-1}$$

and this can be proved as follows.[1]

(i) If n is a *positive integer*, $y=x^n=xxx\ldots$ to n factors, therefore from case (4) § 6:

$$dy=x^{n-1}dx+x^{n-1}dx+\ \ldots \text{ to } n \text{ terms}$$

$$\therefore\ dy=nx^{n-1}dx \quad \text{or} \quad dy/dx=nx^{n-1}.$$

(ii) If n is a *positive fraction* r/s, where r and s are positive integers, put $x=z^s$. Then $x^{r/s}=z^r$

$$\therefore\ d(x^{r/s})=dz^r=rz^{r-1}dz.$$

$$\text{But } dx=sz^{s-1}dz \quad \therefore\ dz=(1/s)z^{1-s}dx,$$

$$\therefore\ d(x^{r/s})=rz^{r-s}(1/s)dx=(r/s)x^{(r-s)/s}dx=(r/s)x^{r/s-1}dx.$$

$$\therefore\ dx^n=nx^{n-1}dx.$$

(iii) If n is a *negative integer or fraction*, put $n=-m$, where m is positive. Then, by (i) and (ii), $dx^n=d(1/x^m)$, and by the rule for differentiation of a quotient, (5) § 6, with $u=1$, $v=x^m$, this is

$$(vdu-udv)/v^2=-udv/v^2=-mx^{m-1}/x^{2m}=-mx^{-m-1}dx=nx^{n-1}dx.$$

(iv) The case when n is a surd (Latin *surdus*, deaf), such as $\sqrt{2}$ or $\sqrt{3}$, is best dealt with by logarithmic differentiation (§ 15), writing $\ln y=n \ln x$, where x is positive. Thus the formula $dx^n/dx=nx^{n-1}$ holds for all the above cases. This, together with the rules in § 6, will serve to differentiate any *algebraic function* (§ 2), $F(x)/f(x)$. E.g. if:

$$y=(x^2+3x+2)/(x+3)$$

$$\text{put } u=x^2+3x+2 \quad \therefore\ du=(2x+3)dx$$

$$\text{and } v=x+3 \quad \therefore\ dv=dx$$

written in 1671, was not published until 1736. Leibniz's symbols were generally used on the Continent, Newton's were used practically only by conservative English mathematicians. (See Love, art. Infinitesimal Calculus, "Ency. Brit.," 11th edit., 1910, **14**, 535; Fleckenstein, *Experientia*, 1946, **2**, 262.)

[1] Greenhill, "Differential and Integral Calculus," 1896, 4; Serret and Scheffers, "Lehrbuch der Differential- und Integralrechnung," 1908, **1**, 58; the common proof uses the Binomial Theorem (§ 33) and assumes its convergency.

$$\therefore \ \mathrm{d}y=\frac{v\mathrm{d}u-u\mathrm{d}v}{v^2}=\frac{(x+3)(2x+3)\mathrm{d}x-(x^2+3x+2)\mathrm{d}x}{(x+3)^2}$$

$$=\frac{x^2+6x+7}{x^2+6x+9}\mathrm{d}x.$$

If $y=u/v=uv^{-1}$

$$\mathrm{d}y/\mathrm{d}x=u(\mathrm{d}v^{-1}/\mathrm{d}x)+v^{-1}(\mathrm{d}u/\mathrm{d}x)=-(u/v^2)(\mathrm{d}v/\mathrm{d}x)+(1/v)(\mathrm{d}u/\mathrm{d}x)$$

$$=(v.\mathrm{d}u/\mathrm{d}x-u.\mathrm{d}v/\mathrm{d}x)/v^2,$$ as in (5a), § 6.

§ 8. Differentiation of a Function of a Function

Let $y=\sqrt{(1+x^2)}=(1+x^2)^{1/2}$, then y is a function of x^2 which is itself a function of x. Put $1+x^2=u$, therefore $y=u^{1/2}$, and, from § 7:

$$\mathrm{d}y=\tfrac{1}{2}u^{1/2-1}\mathrm{d}u=\tfrac{1}{2}u^{-1/2}\mathrm{d}u.$$

But $\mathrm{d}u=\mathrm{d}(1+x^2)=\mathrm{d}(x^2)=2x\mathrm{d}x$,

$$\therefore \ \mathrm{d}y=\tfrac{1}{2}u^{-1/2}\,.\,2x\mathrm{d}x=(1+x^2)^{-1/2}x\mathrm{d}x=[x/\sqrt{(1+x^2)}]\mathrm{d}x.$$

All cases of this kind may be dealt with by a similar substitution.

In general, if $y=\mathrm{F}(u)$, where $u=\mathrm{f}(x)$, then:

$$\frac{\mathrm{d}y}{\mathrm{d}x}=\frac{\mathrm{dF}(u)}{\mathrm{d}u}\cdot\frac{\mathrm{d}u}{\mathrm{d}x},$$

or $\mathrm{d}y=\mathrm{F}'(u)\mathrm{f}'(x)\mathrm{d}x$.

Example. $y=\sqrt{[(1+x+x^2)/(1-x+x^2)]}$. Put $1+x+x^2=u$ and $1-x+x^2=v$, therefore $\mathrm{d}u=(2x+1)\mathrm{d}x$ and $\mathrm{d}v=(2x-1)\mathrm{d}x$.

$y^2=u/v \quad \therefore \ 2y\mathrm{d}y=(v\mathrm{d}u-u\mathrm{d}v)/v^2$ from (5), § 6,

$$v\mathrm{d}u=(1-x+x^2)(2x+1)\mathrm{d}x=(1+x-x^2+2x^3)\mathrm{d}x$$

$$u\mathrm{d}v=(1+x+x^2)(2x-1)\mathrm{d}x=(-1+x+x^2+2x^3)\mathrm{d}x$$

$$\therefore \ v\mathrm{d}u-u\mathrm{d}v=(2-2x^2)\mathrm{d}x=2(1-x^2)\mathrm{d}x,$$

$$\therefore \ \mathrm{d}y=\frac{2(1-x^2)\mathrm{d}x}{2y(1-x+x^2)^2}=\frac{(1-x^2)(1-x+x^2)^{1/2}}{(1+x+x^2)^{1/2}(1-x+x^2)^2}\mathrm{d}x$$

$$=\frac{1-x^2}{(1+x+x^2)^{1/2}(1-x+x^2)^{3/2}}\mathrm{d}x.$$

It should be noted that *implicit functions* (§ 1) may be differentiated directly. E.g. if:

$$ax^2+2hxy+by^2+2gx+2fy+c=0,$$

then $2ax+2hy+2hx(\mathrm{d}y/\mathrm{d}x)+2by(\mathrm{d}y/\mathrm{d}x)+2g+2f(\mathrm{d}y/\mathrm{d}x)=0$,

from which $\mathrm{d}y/\mathrm{d}x$ may be found as usual by algebra as:

$$\mathrm{d}y/\mathrm{d}x=(ax+hy+g)/(hx+by+f).$$

§ 9. Maximum and Minimum Values

Certain functions, with continuous increase of the independent variable x, either rise to a maximum value and then decrease again, or else fall to a minimum value and then increase again. A *maximum value* of a function for a value

$x=x_1$ is a value *algebraically* greater than all values *in the immediate neighbourhood of* x_1, and a *minimum value* is a value *algebraically* less than all values *in the immediate neighbourhood of* x_1.

Consider the curve $y=f(x)$ in Fig. 3.I, and notice the sign of the gradient or slope (see Fig. 2.I) dy/dx as the tangent-line rolls round the crest A and the trough C. Let ϕ be the angle between the tangent and the x axis (see § 5). At a_1 the tangent-line makes a positive angle ($\phi>0$) with the x axis:

$$\therefore \tan\phi = dy/dx \text{ is } \textit{positive.}$$

At A the tangent-line is parallel to the x-axis ($\phi=0$):

$$\therefore \tan\phi = dy/dx \text{ is } \textit{zero.}$$

At a_2 the tangent-line makes a negative angle with the x axis ($\phi<0$):

$$\therefore \tan\phi = dy/dx \text{ is } \textit{negative.}$$

The changes in sign of $dy/dx=\tan\phi$ as the tangent-line rolls round a *crest*, corresponding with a *maximum value* of the function $y=f(x)$, are $[+]\to[0]\to[-]$;

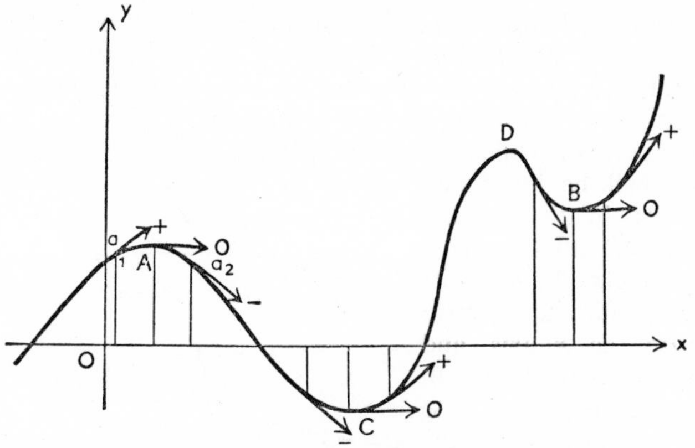

FIG. 3.I. Maximum and Minimum Values

and those when the tangent-line rolls round a *trough*, corresponding with a *minimum value* of the function, are $[-]\to[0]\to[+]$.

Thus, (i) for both a maximum and a minimum value of $y=f(x)$, the value of $dy/dx=f'(x)$ is zero; and (ii) as x increases through the value for which y is a maximum or a minimum, dy/dx undergoes the above changes of sign.

Example. If $y=3x^2+2x-6$, $dy/dx=6x+2$. For a maximum or minimum, $dy/dx=0$, therefore $x=-1/3=-0{\cdot}333...$ If $x=-0{\cdot}4$ (algebraically *less* than $-1/3$),

$$dy/dx=-(6\times 0{\cdot}4)+2=-0{\cdot}4.$$

If $x=-0{\cdot}2$ (algebraically *greater* than $-1/3$),

$$dy/dx=-(6\times 0{\cdot}2)+2=+0{\cdot}8.$$

Hence the change of sign is $[-]\to[0]\to[+]$, corresponding with a *minimum*. This result is confirmed by plotting the graph of the function $y=3x^2+2x-6$. The principle of the method goes back to Fermat (1638); the discrimination between maximum, minimum, and point of inflexion (see below) is due to Leibniz (1684).

It is assumed above that dy/dx or $f'(x)$ is a *continuous* function of x in passing through a maximum or minimum point, but this may not be the case. In

Fig. 4.I, ABCDEFG is the graph of a continuous function f(x), with a gradient f′(x) which is discontinuous at B, C, D, E, and F. The value of f′(x) changes from $+\infty$ to $-\infty$ in passing B, from $-\infty$ to $+\infty$ in passing C; f′(x) changes discontinuously from a positive to a negative value on passing D, from a negative to a positive value in passing E, and at F from one positive value to a different positive value. In no case does dy/dx or f′(x) become zero at the maxima B, D, and F, or the minima C and E. Such exceptional cases are not often met with, but it should be realised that the condition f′(x)=0 for a maximum or minimum breaks down when f′(x) is infinite or discontinuous.

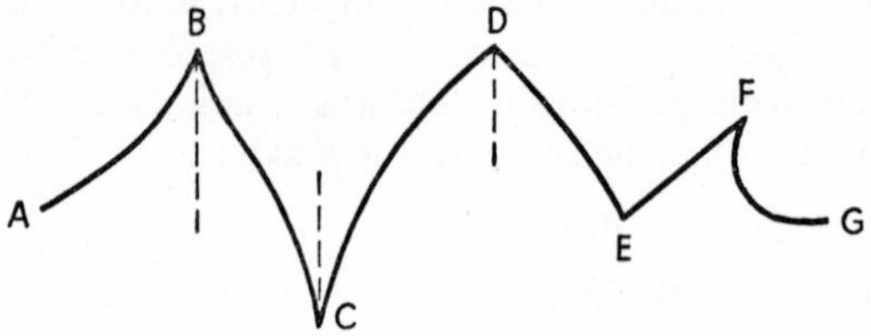

FIG. 4.I. Discontinuities of dy/dx

§ 10. Point of Inflexion

If the value of dy/dx does not change sign in passing through the zero value, i.e. if the criterion becomes $[+]\rightarrow[0]\rightarrow[+]$, or $[-]\rightarrow[0]\rightarrow[-]$, the curve becomes parallel to the axis at that point, but then continues *in the same direction* as at first. At the given point there is a *change of curvature*, and the point at which this occurs is called a *point of inflexion*. It is not necessary that the tangent-line shall be horizontal at this point; in the general case a point of inflexion is a point where a curve *crosses* its tangent-line. Before it, the curve is concave to the x axis, and after it, convex (cases A and B, Fig. 5.I), or else the reverse (case C), and there is no need for the tangent to become parallel to the x axis (dy/dx=0), as in case A; in cases B and C this does not happen.

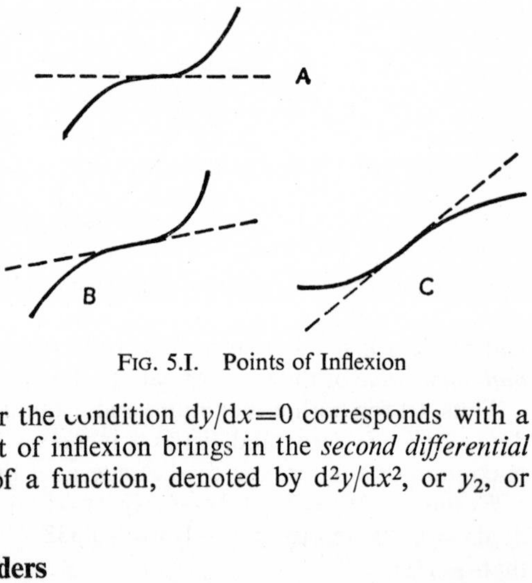

FIG. 5.I. Points of Inflexion

The consideration as to whether the condition dy/dx=0 corresponds with a maximum, a minimum, or a point of inflexion brings in the *second differential coefficient*, or *second derivative*, of a function, denoted by d^2y/dx^2, or y_2, or y'', or f″(x).

§ 11. Differentials of Higher Orders

The result of differentiating a function of x with respect to x is, in general, another function of x, except when the first is a linear function of x (§ 2), when the result of differentiation is a constant. The differential coefficient can thus usually be differentiated again with respect to x, giving what is called the *second differential coefficient*, and the process may be repeatable to give the third, fourth, etc., differential coefficients. These are denoted by:

$$\frac{d}{dx}\left(\frac{dy}{dx}\right)=\frac{d^2y}{dx^2} \text{ (read " d two } y\text{, d } x \text{ squared ")}$$

$$\frac{d}{dx}\left(\frac{d^2y}{dx^2}\right)=\frac{d^3y}{dx^3}, \text{ etc., or generally } \frac{d^ny}{dx^n}.$$

In function notation the successive differential coefficients are denoted by $y', y'', y''', \ldots y^n$; or $f'(x), f''(x), f'''(x), \ldots f^n(x)$, the last being sometimes written $f^{(n)}(x)$ to distinguish it from the n-th power of $f(x)$. Another notation is $y_1, y_2, y_3, \ldots y_n$. Higher differentials were used by Leibniz in 1684 (§ 6).

If $y=x^3+4x^2-6x+2$, then $y'=3x^2+8x-6$, $y''=6x+8$, $y'''=6$, and all higher derivations are zero. It is easily seen that $f^{(m)}x^m=m(m-1)(m-2) \ldots 2.1=m!$ (factorial m) and all higher derivatives are zero.

Since at a *maximum* value of y the value of dy/dx goes from a positive value through zero to a negative value, its rate of increase with x, that is, d^2y/dx^2, is negative, or $d^2y/dx^2<0$.

For a *minimum*, the change of dy/dx is in the opposite sense, hence $d^2y/dx^2>0$. At a *point of inflexion*, dy/dx does not change sign, and at that point dy/dx " pauses " for an instant, and then goes on with unchanged sign, so that $d^2y/dx^2=0$; *in this case it is not necessary that* dy/dx *shall be zero*, although it may be.

In the example in § 9, $y=3x^2+2x+6$, $dy/dx=6x+2$, therefore there is a maximum or minimum value of y when $x=-1/3$. Since $d^2y/dx^2=6$, which is *positive*, the value is a *minimum*.

Since dx/dt represents a *velocity*, or rate of change of position, d^2x/dt^2, i.e. $(d/dt)(dx/dt)$, is a rate of change of velocity, or an *acceleration*. Hence (§ 6) $\dot{x}$=velocity, $\ddot{x}$=acceleration, the " pricking " of the letter in fluxional notation denoting differentiation, in this case with respect to time.

If d/dx or D dnotes the *operator* for acting on $f(x)$ or y to produce $f'(x)$, then d^2/dx^2 or D^2, etc., denote operators producing $f''(x)$, etc. In the differential notation, $d(dy)$ is denoted by d^2y. The reason for writing $(dx)^2$ or dx^2 in d^2y/dx^2 is seen by remembering that:

$$dy=f'(x)dx,$$

$$\text{and } d^2y=d[f'(x)]dx=[f''(x)dx]dx=f''(x)dx^2;$$

$$\text{hence } f''(x)=d^2y/dx^2,$$

and similarly for higher derivatives, dx being always a *constant* increment of x.

It may be noted that, as d^2y/dx^2 measures the rate of change of the gradient dy/dx, it gives a measure of the *curvature* of a curve. It will be shown that the *radius of curvature* ρ (see § 48) of a plane curve is given by:

$$\rho=[1+(dy/dx)^2]^{3/2}/(d^2y/dx^2),$$

and when dy/dx is very small, i.e. the curve is only slightly inclined to the x axis (e.g. with a deflected horizontal beam), $1/\rho=d^2y/dx^2$.

§ 12. The Exponential Function

In this section a simple working knowledge of the use of *logarithms* and the properties of *indices* or *powers*, or *exponents*, is assumed. In elementary algebra, a^m is defined as the product of m factors each equal to a: $a^m=a\,.\,a\,.\,a \ldots$ to m factors, where the *index* m is a positive integer, and a is any positive or negative, integral or fractional, quantity. It is then shown that if m and n are positive integers:

$$a^m \times a^n=a^{m+n} \quad \ldots \quad (1)$$

$$a^m/a^n=a^{m-n} \quad \ldots \quad (2)$$

$$(a^m)^n=a^{mn} \quad \ldots \quad (3)$$

$$(ab)^m=a^m b^m \quad \ldots \quad (4)$$

$$(a/b)^m=a^m/b^m \quad \ldots \quad (5)$$

If these results are *assumed* to hold for fractional, zero, and negative exponents:

$$a^{m/n}=(a^m)^{1/n}=\sqrt[n]{a^m} \quad . \quad . \quad . \quad . \quad . \quad . \quad . \quad . \quad (6)$$

where m and n are positive integers,

$$a^m \times a^0=a^{m+0}=a^m \quad \therefore \; a^0=1 \quad . \quad . \quad . \quad . \quad . \quad . \quad (7)$$

$$a^{-m} \times a^m=a^0=1 \quad \therefore \; a^{-m}=1/a^m \quad . \quad . \quad . \quad . \quad . \quad . \quad (8)$$

Ostwald [1] proposed to write powers of 10 ($a=10$) by giving the exponent in brackets: $3\times10^{10}=3(10)$, $0{\cdot}0008=8(-4)$, but this has not been adopted.

Any function in which the *independent variable* x is in the index (or exponent) is called an *exponential function*, the general type being a^x, where a is a constant:

$$y=a^x.$$

If a is a fixed positive quantity greater than unity, then if x ranges from $-\infty$ to $+\infty$, y will range from $a^{-\infty}=1/a^{\infty}=0$, to $a^{\infty}=+\infty$. If a series of indices x and powers $a^x=y$ are tabulated for a given fixed value of a, then the *indices* constitute a *table of logarithms* of the corresponding numbers in the table of powers, a being called the *base of the logarithms.*

Every positive number N can be expressed as a power of some other fixed positive number a, viz. $+N=a^x$, where x may be positive, negative, integral or fractional. If $a=10$, then $N=10^x$, when x is called the *logarithm to the base* 10 of N, or the common logarithm of N; i.e. x is the power to which 10 must be raised to give N, and $x=\log_{10} N$. Tables of logarithms to the base 10 were published by H. Briggs in 1617. Multiplication is then equivalent to adding logarithms, and division to subtracting them, as is easily seen. E.g., $15=10^{1{\cdot}1761}$ and $28=10^{1{\cdot}4472}$, therefore $15\times28=10^{1{\cdot}1761}\times10^{1{\cdot}4472}=10^{1{\cdot}1761+1{\cdot}4472}=10^{2{\cdot}6233}$. The number of which $2{\cdot}6233$ is the logarithm is 420, i.e. $10^{2{\cdot}6233}=420$, hence $15\times28=420$.

Instead of $a=10$, any other positive number could be taken as a base for a table of logarithms, which would then be different from the common logarithms. If $a=2{\cdot}718281828...=\mathrm{e}$, $N=(2{\cdot}718281828...)^x=\mathrm{e}^x$, and $x=\log_e N$.

A " logarithm to the base e " is called a *natural*, or a *hyperbolic*, or a *Naperian logarithm* (after John Napier, 1550–1617, who in 1614 used logarithms closely related to these, approximately to the base 1/e); the symbol e is due to Euler, who also introduced the general use of the symbol π in the same year, 1739. Besides the symbol $\log_e$, it is sometimes written " lg," or (by mathematicians only) " log "; but the most compact symbol is that proposed by Ostwald,[2] viz. ln, which will be used consistently.

Since $N=10^{\log_{10}N}=\mathrm{e}^{\ln N}=(2{\cdot}718281828...)^{\ln N}$, and $2{\cdot}718281828...$, or e, is less than 10, it follows that $\ln N$ is larger than $\log_{10} N$. For all values of N the two logarithms are in a constant ratio.

Let $\log_a N=A$ and $\log_b N=B$, a and b being the bases of two systems of logarithms. Then $N=a^A=b^B$, $\therefore\ a=b^{B/A}$, $\therefore\ \log_a a=1=\log_a b^{B/A}=(B/A)\log_a b$, $\therefore\ \log_a b=A/B=(\log_a N)/(\log_b N)$, $\therefore\ \log_a N=\log_b N\times\log_a b$.

Let $a=10$ and $b=\mathrm{e}$, then $\log_{10} N=\ln N\times\log_{10}\mathrm{e}=\ln N\times\log_{10}(2{\cdot}718281828...)=\ln N\times0{\cdot}43429448....$ This number is denoted by μ, hence $\log_{10} N=\mu \ln N$,

[1] *Z. phys. Chem.*, 1910, **71**, 128.

[2] " Lehrbuch der allgemeinen Chemie," 1893, **2**, 491. Tables of e^x: Newman, *Trans, Cambr. Phil. Soc.*, 1877, **13**, 145; 1883, **14**, 237; Glaisher, *ibid.*, 1877, **13**, 243; Partington, " Higher Mathematics," 1931, 273; Burington, " Handbook of Mathematical Tables and Formulas," Sandusky, Ohio, 1941, 240; " Handbook of Chemistry and Physics," Chem. Rubber Publishing Co., Cleveland, Ohio, 1941, 139. Table of e^{-x}: Gruner, *Jahrb. Radioakt. Elektronik*, 1906, **3**, 120.

or $\ln N=(1/\mu)\log_{10} N=\log_{10} N\times 2{\cdot}3025851$.... The values $\mu=0{\cdot}4343$ and $1/\mu=2{\cdot}3026$ are usually sufficiently accurate, and should be remembered. A short table of values of e^x and of $\ln x$ is:

x	0	0·25	0·5	1·0	1·5	2·0	3·0	4·0	5·0	10
e^x	1·0	1·284	1·649	2·718	4·482	7·389	20·086	54·59	148·4	22026
e^{-x}	1·0	0·779	0·607	0·368	0·223	0·135	0·0498	0·0183	0·0067	$0{\cdot}0_4 45$
$\ln x$	$-\infty$	−1·386	−0·693	0	0·405	0·693	1·099	1·386	1·609	2·303
$\log_{10} x$	$-\infty$	−0·602	−0·301	0	0·176	0·301	0·477	0·602	0·699	1·000

Such special tables are unnecessary, since values of e^x (and $e^{-x}=1/e^x$) and $\ln x$ can be found from ordinary logarithm tables as follows.

Let $y=e^x$. Then $\ln y=2{\cdot}3026 \log y$, $\log y=0{\cdot}4343 \ln y$, and the multiplication can be performed by logarithms. Taking x as the given number, multiply it by 0·4343 and find the number (anti-logarithm) corresponding with the result. This is the value of e^x. E.g. to find $e^{-5\cdot 460}$, find (by the use of logarithms) that $-5{\cdot}460\times 0{\cdot}4343=-3{\cdot}054=\bar{4}{\cdot}946$. Anti-logarithm $\bar{4}{\cdot}946=0{\cdot}0008831$, therefore $e^{-5\cdot 460}=0{\cdot}0008831$. The reader is advised to draw the graphs of e^x, e^{-x} $(=1/e^x)$, and $\ln x$ from the table.

§ 13. Differentiation of the Exponential Function [1]

Let $y=a^x$, $\therefore\ y+dy=a^{(x+dx)}$,

$$\therefore\ dy=a^{(x+dx)}-a^x=a^x(a^{dx}-1).$$

Since $a^{dx}-1$ is a function of a and dx, and vanishes when $dx=0$, it may be assumed to contain dx as a factor and to be of the form $A dx$, where A is a function of a, and hence a constant, which is to be determined. Hence:

$$d(a)^x=a^x A dx \quad \ldots\ldots\ldots \quad (1)$$

The value of A is determined by that of a. Choose a value of a which makes $A=1$, and denote this value of a by e. Then e^x is usually called *the* exponential function, and:

$$d(e^x)=e^x dx \quad \text{or} \quad de^x/dx=e^x \quad \ldots\ldots \quad (2)$$

The fundamental property of the exponential function is that *its derived function is equal to the function itself.* It must now be shown that the value of e is, in fact, 2·718281828..., as given in § 12. It is assumed, and justified later in § 33, that $e^x=f(x)$ can be represented, to any desired degree of accuracy, by an infinite series of integral positive powers of x, or (mathematically expressed) that " e^x can be expanded in an infinite power series ":

$$e^x=a_0+a_1x+a_2x^2+a_3x^3+\ \ldots \quad \ldots\ldots \quad (3)$$

It is also assumed that differentiation of e^x is equivalent to differentiation of this series term by term (which is not generally true for any infinite series):

$$\therefore\ de^x/dx=a_1+2a_2x+3a_3x^2+\ \ldots\ldots\ldots \quad (4)$$

[1] The treatment in Lodge, " Differential Calculus for Beginners," 1905, 54 f., is followed. It seems to date from de Morgan, " Differential and Integral Calculus," 1842, 56, 75. It is easily made " strict," and is much to be preferred to the usual method involving the use of the Binomial Theorem: see Lamb, " An Elementary Course of Infinitesimal Calculus," 3rd edit., Cambridge, 1927, 72 f.

Since $de^x/dx=e^x$ by (2), the two series (3) and (4) are identical, and coefficients of like powers of x in them are equal:

$$\therefore\ a_1=a_0,\quad a_2=\tfrac{1}{2}a_1,\quad a_3=\tfrac{1}{3}a_2, \text{ etc.}$$

Since $e^x=1$ when $x=0$, by (7), § 12, it follows from (3) that $a_0=1$, hence $a_1=1$, $a_2=\frac{1}{2}$, $a_3=1/3\,.\,2$, etc.

If the continued product $1\,.\,2\,.\,3\,.\,4\,.\,.\,.\,n$ is denoted by $\underline{|n}$ or $n!$ (read [1] " factorial n ") it follows that:

$$e^x=1+x+x^2/2!+x^3/3!+x^4/4!+\ \dots\ +x^r/r!+\ \dots \text{ to infinity} \quad (5)$$

This *exponential series* was published by Newton in 1669. Put $x=1$, then:

$$e=1+1+\frac{1}{1\,.\,2}+\frac{1}{1\,.\,2\,.\,3}+\frac{1}{1\,.\,2\,.\,3\,.\,4}+\frac{1}{1\,.\,2\,.\,3\,.\,4\,.\,5}+\ \dots$$

$$=2+0{\cdot}5+0{\cdot}1666+0{\cdot}0417+0{\cdot}00833+\ \dots$$

The value correct to nine places of decimals is 2·718281828, i.e. 2·7 (a part which must always be remembered) followed by the figures 1828 twice repeated. Thus, e is the same as the base of natural logarithms in § 12.

To find A in (1), let $a^x=e^{bx}$, therefore $a=e^b$, and $b=\ln a$,

$$\therefore\ da^x=d(e^{bx})=e^{bx}d(bx)=be^{bx}dx=\ln a\,.\,a^x dx,$$

so that $A=\ln a$. Hence:

$$da^x=a^x \ln a\, dx \quad (6)$$

From the series for e^x:

$$e^x=1+x/1!+x^2/2!+x^3/3!+\ \dots$$

that for a^x is found by putting bx for x and writing $a=e^b$, $\therefore\ b=\ln a$. Hence:

$$a^x=e^{bx}=e^b\,.\,e^x=e^{x\ln a}$$

$$\therefore\ a^x=1+(1/1!)x\ln a+(1/2!)x^2(\ln a)^2+(1/3!)x^3(\ln a)^3+\ \dots \quad (7)$$

In the author's experience, many students find difficulty in working with exponential functions (which are neglected in school mathematics). They should remember the following *Rules*:

(i) The function e^x is like the ordinary a^m of elementary algebra except that a now has a particular value e, equal to 2·718281828 . . ., and m instead of a constant number is a variable number, x.

(ii) A logarithm to the base e is like a common logarithm, except that its base is e instead of 10, and since e is less than 10, *the logarithm to the base* e *is larger than the common logarithm*; it is 2·3026 times the latter. This should always be remembered; the " common " or " vulgar " logarithm is " meaner " or smaller than the natural logarithm.

(iii) The reason for choosing the base e is that the result of the differentiation of e^x by x is to be e^x itself. Thus, if $f(x)=e^x$, $df(x)/dx=f(x)$, i.e. the function e^x is increasing with x at a rate equal to itself. In general, a function a^x increases with x at a rate *proportional* to itself, the factor of proportionality being $\ln a$.

(iv) Any expression involving a logarithm may be converted into one involving an exponential function, or vice versa. For, if $y=e^x$ then $\ln y=x$, and if $u=f(x)$ is put instead of x, viz. $y=e^u=e^{f(x)}$, then $\ln y=u=f(x)$.

Thus the rule is: *to convert a logarithmic expression into an exponential one, drop the* ln *and raise the other side of the equation to an exponent of* e. This

[1] In *writing*, factorials are always denoted by $\underline{|n}$, and this is used in some books. The notation $n!$ is due to Kramp.

applies however complicated the function may be. With long or complicated exponents e^u or $e^{f(x)}$ may be written exp u or exp[f(x)], read "exponential function of u [or of f(x)]," and having exactly the same meaning. The notation[1] $\ln^{-1}u$ for e^u is little used.

A function which has been used[2] to represent many physico-chemical processes is: $y-d=K/(1+Ce^{rx})$, where d, K, C, and r are constants.

The Gomperz[3] function: $y=Ke^{-e^{-x}}$, has been used in statistical investigations.

(v) A constant k can always be represented as $k=e^{\lambda}$, where λ is another constant. For example, the ordinary equation for a unimolecular reaction is $\ln[a/(a-x)]=kt$, where a=concentration at time $t=0$, $a-x$=concentration after a time t, and k is the velocity coefficient, a constant. Put $a=c_0$, $a-x=c$, the two concentrations, then:

$$\ln(c_0/c)=kt \quad \therefore\ c_0/c=e^{kt}, \quad \therefore\ c/c_0=1/e^{kt}=e^{-kt},$$

$$\therefore\ c=c_0e^{-kt} \quad \ldots\ldots\ldots \quad (8)$$

The two equations express exactly the same result. By differentiation with respect to time (if necessary, put $kt=u$):

$$dc/dt=d(c_0e^{-kt})/dt$$
$$=-kc_0e^{-kt}=-kc,$$

which shows that c is decreasing at a rate *proportional* to itself, which is the law of mass action for a unimolecular reaction. If c_0 is put equal to e^{λ}, equation (8) can be written: $c=e^{\lambda-kt}$.

The exponential function represents what Lord Kelvin[4] called the *Compound Interest Law*, in which *a magnitude is increasing at a rate proportional to itself.* The most general type of exponential function of one independent variable x is $y=y_0e^{kx}$, where k and y_0 are constants. Since $e^0=1$, y_0 is the value of y where $x=0$ (i.e. y_0 is the initial value of y). By differentiation: $dy/dx=ky_0e^{kx}=ky$, therefore $(1/y)(dy/dx)=k$, so that k is the *proportional* rate of increase of y with x.

§ 14. Differentiation of a Logarithm

Let $y=\ln x$, $\therefore\ x=e^y$ $\therefore\ dx=e^y dy=x dy$ $\therefore\ dy/dx=1/x$, or:

$$d\ln x/dx=1/x.$$

This result is of the very highest importance, and must be carefully remembered. If $y=\ln u$, where u=f(x), $d\ln u/du=1/u$, therefore $d\ln u=du/u$. But $du=df(x)dx=f'(x)dx$:

$$\therefore\ d\ln u/dx=d\ln f(x)/dx=f'(x)/f(x).$$

This result is also of great importance: it shows that if an expression obtained by differentiation of a function is of such a fractional form that the numerator is the differential coefficient of the denominator, the original function differentiated was the logarithm of the denominator (with, possibly, a constant added, which disappears in differentiation, since $d\ln k=0$).

1 Greenhill, "Differential and Integral Calculus," 1896, 57. The use of exp u instead of e^u, when u is a concise expression, is generally considered pedantic.

2 Reed and Berkson, *J. Phys. Chem.*, 1929, **33**, 760.

3 Gomperz, *Phil. Trans.*, 1825, **115**, 513; de Witt, *Ind. Eng. Chem.*, 1943, **35**, 695.

4 Art. Elasticity in "Ency. Brit.," 9th edit., 1878; "Math. and Phys. Papers," 1890, **3**, 27.

§ 15. Logarithmic Differentiation

The differentiation of an expression containing products or powers of functions is often much easier if logarithms are first taken and the sum of the logarithms then differentiated. Let $y=uvw$,

$$\therefore\ \ln y=\ln u+\ln v+\ln w,$$
$$\therefore\ \mathrm{d}y/y=\mathrm{d}u/u+\mathrm{d}v/v+\mathrm{d}w/w,$$
$$\therefore\ \mathrm{d}y=y\mathrm{d}u/u+y\mathrm{d}v/v+y\mathrm{d}w/w$$
$$=vw\mathrm{d}u+uw\mathrm{d}v+uv\mathrm{d}w,$$

a result found with more difficulty in § 7.

If $y=x^n$, then $\ln y=n\ln x$, therefore $\mathrm{d}y/y=n\mathrm{d}x/x$, therefore $\mathrm{d}y/\mathrm{d}x=ny/x=nx^{n-1}$, as found in § 7.

§ 16. Two Important Limits

It is required to show that:

(i) xe^{-x} when $x\to\infty$, i.e. $\lim\limits_{x\to\infty} xe^{-x}$, is 0;

(ii) $x\ln x$ when $x\to 0$, i.e. $\lim\limits_{x\to 0} x\ln x$, is 0.

In (i), when $x\to\infty$, $\mathrm{e}^{-x}=1/\mathrm{e}^{x}\to 1/\infty\to 0$, and the function assumes the *indeterminate form* $\infty\times 0$ (see § 3). In (ii), when $x\to 0$, $\ln x\to-\infty$ (see § 12), and the function assumes the indeterminate form $-\infty\times 0$. Finite limiting values of both functions can, however, be found by the following rule (*L'Hôpital's theorem*, 1696). If u/v is the ratio of two functions of x, both of which are 0 or ∞ when $x=a$, the value of u/v when $x=a$ (i.e., an indeterminate form $0/0$ or ∞/∞ by direct substitution) is given by differentiating u and v with respect to x, and then putting $x=a$ in the ratio $(\mathrm{d}u/\mathrm{d}x)/(\mathrm{d}v/\mathrm{d}x)$. In the first case, when $x=a$, $u=0$, and $v=0$, and when $x=a+\mathrm{d}x$, $u=0+\mathrm{d}u$, and $v=0+\mathrm{d}v$. Hence the limiting value of u/v when $\mathrm{d}x\to 0$ (i.e. $x\to a$) is the value of $\mathrm{d}u/\mathrm{d}v$, or $(\mathrm{d}u/\mathrm{d}x)/(\mathrm{d}v/\mathrm{d}x)$, when $x=a$. In the second case, write u/o as $(1/v)/(1/u)$ and proceed as above.

(i) $x\mathrm{e}^{-x}=x/\mathrm{e}^{x}=u/v$; thus $\mathrm{d}u=\mathrm{d}x$ and $\mathrm{d}v=\mathrm{e}^{x}\mathrm{d}x$, therefore $\mathrm{d}u/\mathrm{d}v=1/\mathrm{e}^{x}$, and when $x\to\infty$ this is zero.

(ii) $x\ln x=\ln x/x^{-1}=u/v$; thus $\mathrm{d}u=\mathrm{d}\ln x=\mathrm{d}x/x$, and $\mathrm{d}v=\mathrm{d}(x^{-1})=-x^{-2}\mathrm{d}x$, therefore $u/v=\mathrm{d}u/\mathrm{d}v=-x$, and when $x=0$, this is zero.

THE INTEGRAL CALCULUS

§ 17. Integration

The *Differential Calculus* provides a process, called *differentiation*, by means of which the *rate of change* $\mathrm{d}f(x)/\mathrm{d}x$ of a function $f(x)$ of x can be found. The *Integral Calculus* provides a means, called *integration*, by which the *original function* is recovered if its rate of change, or differential coefficient, is known. Integration thus involves " the memory of differentiation," [1] and it depends more on skill than on rules. Newton, who called a differential coefficient a " fluxion," called its integral a " fluent."

The symbol $\mathrm{d}/\mathrm{d}x$ or D denotes an *operator* which, acting on the function $f(x)$, with or without an additive constant C, produces the derived function

[1] De Morgan, *Trans. Cambr. Phil. Soc.*, 1844, **8**, 188.

$f'(x)$; i.e. if $y=f(x)$, $dy/dx=Dy=f'(x)$, therefore $dy=f'(x)dx$. Evidently also $d(y+C)=dy=f'(x)dx$, where C is any constant.

Integration is denoted by the symbol ∫ (the old form of the small letter s), and, since $y+C=\int f'(x)dx$, it may be regarded as *the inverse of differentiation.* Alternatively, integration may be regarded (see § 20) as *a process of summation* (as originally by Newton): $y=\Sigma dy=\Sigma f'(x)dx$, where, instead of adding *finite* quantities, to which the symbol Σ properly applies, *infinitesimal* values of dy are added, which approach the limit zero, when $\Sigma f'(x)dx$ passes into $\int f'(x)dx$. In this case, C is the value of y for any particular value of x, say x_0, i.e. the initial value of y or $f(x)$, and the *integral* $\int dy=\int f'(x)dx$ then adds on the *increase* of y as x increases from x_0 to x. This is denoted by:

$$y-y_0=\int_{x_0}^{x} f'(x)dx \quad . \quad . \quad . \quad . \quad . \quad . \quad . \quad . \quad (1)$$

and is found by *subtracting* the value of the integral for $x=x_0$ from the value for $x=x$, the constant C thus disappearing. The values x_0 and x are called the *limits* of the integral, and an integral with two specified limits is called a *definite integral,* since the indefinite constant C (corresponding with an unspecified lower limit x_0) has disappeared. (The word " limit " is used here in a sense different from that in § 3.)

An integral without limits of integration (such as those shown below, and in § 18) is called an *indefinite integral.* An integral with a specified lower limit but an unspecified upper limit is sometimes called a *corrected integral.* The name " integral " is due to James Bernoulli (1690), the process and the sign ∫ are due to Leibniz (1686; see § 6).

If any expression to be integrated can be put in the form du, where u is a function of x, the integral is $u+C$. If this cannot be done, but a series of numerical values of y corresponding with values of x is given, an approximate value of the integral can be found graphically or by applying certain rules (e.g., Simpson's rule) given in the text-books. The name " definite integral " is often used (e.g. by Riemann, " Partielle Differentialgleichungen," 1938) for those integrals which can be evaluated only between certain definite limits, and the indefinite integrals of which cannot be found. Examples of these are given in Section III.

The following *General Theorems on Integration* follow at once from the General Theorems on Differentiation in § 6. Let u and v be functions of x and k a constant. Then:

$$\int k du=k\int du=ku+C \quad . \quad . \quad . \quad . \quad . \quad . \quad . \quad . \quad . \quad (2)$$

$$\int(du+dv)=\int d(u+v)=u+v+C \quad . \quad . \quad . \quad . \quad . \quad . \quad (3)$$

$$\int d(uv)=\int(u dv+v du) \quad . \quad . \quad . \quad . \quad . \quad . \quad . \quad (4)$$

$$\therefore \int u dv=uv-\int v du+C \quad . \quad . \quad . \quad . \quad . \quad . \quad . \quad . \quad (5)$$

§ 18. Some Important Integrals

The following special results of integration follow from the previous results of differentiation.

From § 7:

$$\int x^n dx=\frac{1}{n+1}\int d(x^{n+1})=\frac{x^{n+1}}{n+1}+C \quad . \quad . \quad . \quad . \quad . \quad (1)$$

except when $n=-1$.

From § 14:

$$\int x^{-1}dx=\int dx/x=\int d\ \ln x=\ln x+C \quad . \ . \ . \ . \ . \quad (2)$$

Equation (2) can be found as a special case of (1) as follows. From (7), § 13:

$$(a^x-1)/x=\ln a+\tfrac{1}{2}x(\ln a)^2+\ \ldots$$

Change a to x and x to n, then when n approaches zero: $(x^n-1)/n=\ln x$. Put $y=(x/a)^{-m}$, where a is an arbitrary constant, then:

$$\int_a^x y dx=\int_a^x (x/a)^{-m}dx=\int_a^x (x/a)^{-m}a d(x/a)$$

$$=\frac{a}{1-m}\left(\frac{x}{a}\right)^{1-m}-\frac{a}{1-m}$$

$$=\frac{a}{1-m}[(x/a)^{1-m}-1].$$

Expand as above, putting $x/a=x$, therefore $a=1$, and $1-m=n$, then when n approaches zero, or m approaches -1, the integral becomes $\ln x$.

From § 13:

$$\int e^x dx=\int d(e^x)=e^x+C \quad . \ . \ . \ . \ . \ . \ . \ . \ . \quad (3)$$

To find the integral of $e^{\alpha x}$, where α is a constant, put $\alpha x=u$ and see § 8:

$$d(e^{\alpha x})=\alpha e^{\alpha x}dx, \quad \therefore\ e^{\alpha x}dx=(1/\alpha)d(e^{\alpha x})$$

$$\therefore\ \int e^{\alpha x}dx=(1/\alpha)\int d(e^{\alpha x})=(1/\alpha)e^{\alpha x}+C \quad . \ . \ . \ . \ . \ . \ . \ . \quad (4)$$

$$\int e^{-x}dx=-\int d(e^{-x})=-e^{-x}+C \quad . \ . \ . \ . \ . \ . \ . \ . \ . \quad (5)$$

$$\int e^{-\alpha x}dx=(1/\alpha)\int d(e^{-\alpha x})=-(1/\alpha)e^{-\alpha x}+C \quad . \ . \ . \ . \ . \quad (6)$$

The two following integrals are found by writing $x+a=u$ and $(a-x)=v$, when $du=dx$ and $dv=-dx$:

$$\int\frac{dx}{x+a}=\int\frac{du}{u}=\ln u+C=\ln(x+a)+C \quad . \ . \ . \ . \quad (7)$$

$$\int\frac{dx}{a-x}=-\int\frac{dv}{v}=-\ln v+C=-\ln(a-x)+C \quad . \ . \ . \quad (8)$$

Useful *Tables of Integrals* [1] are available. The integration of various algebraic, exponential, and trigonometrical expressions usually involves a previous reduction to a standard form, this generally requiring skill which is acquired only by working many examples found in the regular text-books. As G. A. Gibson said: [2] "Most of the difficulty beginners find in integration is due to a deficiency of power in . . . elementary algebraic and trigonometric transformations."

§ 19. Integration by Parts

Equation (5), § 17:

$$\int u dv=uv-\int v du+C \quad . \ . \ . \ . \ . \ . \ . \ . \ . \quad (1)$$

is the basis of the very important method of *integration by parts*, due to Leibniz (the idea goes back to Pascal, 1659), which is used when it is possible to pick out

[1] Bierens de Haan, "Nouvelles Tables d'Intégrales Définies," Leyden, 1867; Pierce, "A Short Table of Integrals," Boston, 1910; Dwight, "Mathematical Tables," New York, 1941; Dwight, "Tables of Integrals and other Mathematical Data," New York, 1934; Burington, "Handbook of Mathematical Tables and Formulas," Sandusky, Ohio, 1941. Chapter vii on Integration in General in Greenhill's "Differential and Integral Calculus," 1896, 383 f., gives a good selection of standard forms and methods.

[2] "An Elementary Treatise on the Calculus," 1933, 296.

of the expression to be integrated a factor which is recognised as the differential of a function.

E.g.: $$\int x^2 e^{\alpha x} dx.$$

By inspection, $de^{\alpha x} = (1/\alpha)d(e^{\alpha x})$, from (4), § 18,

$$\therefore \; dv = e^{\alpha x}dx \quad \text{and} \quad u = x^2 \text{ are chosen for (1).}$$

Then, $v = (1/\alpha)e^{\alpha x}$ (the constant C is added later), and $du = 2xdx$,

$$\therefore \; \int x^2 e^{\alpha x}dx = (1/\alpha)x^2 e^{\alpha x} - (1/\alpha)\int e^{\alpha x} \,.\, 2xdx + C.$$

To find the integral on the right, put $dv = e^{\alpha x}dx$ and $u = 2x$,

$$\therefore \; v = (1/\alpha)e^{\alpha x} \quad \text{and} \quad du = 2dx$$

$$\therefore \; \int 2xe^{\alpha x}dx = (1/\alpha)e^{\alpha x} \,.\, 2x - (2/\alpha)\int e^{\alpha x}dx$$
$$= (2/\alpha)e^{\alpha x}x - (2/\alpha^2)e^{\alpha x},$$

$$\therefore \; \int x^2 e^{\alpha x}dx = (1/\alpha)x^2 e^{\alpha x} - (2/\alpha)xe^{\alpha x} + (2/\alpha^2)e^{\alpha x}$$
$$= (e^{\alpha x}/\alpha)(x^2 - 2x + 2/\alpha) + C.$$

The rule is that *one factor is integrated and the other differentiated*, and after some practice, the successive steps can be written down at once.

An important special case is $\int \ln x \,.\, dx$. Integrate dx and differentiate $\ln x$ (giving dx/x):

$$\therefore \; \int \ln x dx = x \ln x - \int x d(\ln x) = x \ln x - \int dx$$
$$= x \ln x - x + C.$$

Values of the so-called *integral logarithm*, li $x = \int dx/\ln x$, are tabulated by Ekholm.[1]

§ 20. Definite Integral as the Limit of a Sum

An important meaning of a definite integral is that of a limit of a sum (§ 17), e.g. a sum of infinitesimal strips giving the *value of an area*. In Fig. 6.I, let PQ represent $y = f'(x)$ and divide the area under PQ into a large number of very narrow strips, each of width dx. Each strip is approximately[2] a rectangle of area $ydx = f'(x)dx$. The whole area between the curve PQ, the ordinates y_0 and y_n, and the axis of x is the limit of the sum of all the strips when the width of each strip becomes vanishingly small, i.e.[3]:

$$\textit{area} = \int_{x_0}^{x_n} f'(x)dx = f(x_n) - f(x_0),$$

where $f(x)$ is the function from which $f'(x)dx$ is formed by differentiation. Actually, the area of each strip is replaced in the sum by:

$$f'(x)dx = f(x+dx) - f(x)$$

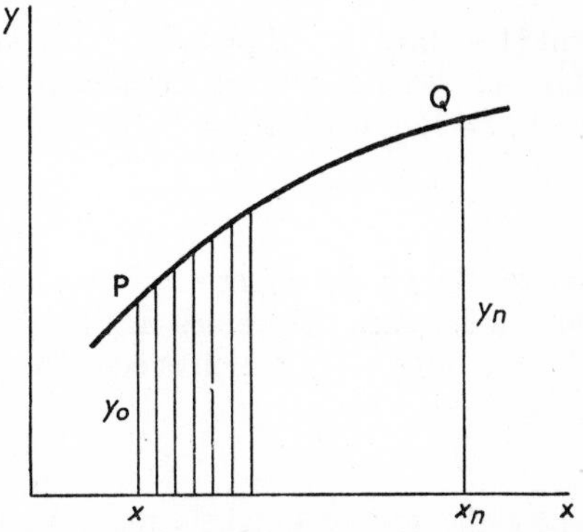

FIG. 6.I. Definite Integral as Limit of a Sum

[1] *Arkiv Mat. Astron. Fys.*, 1908, **4**, No. 29.

[2] The top of each strip is bevelled off to the shape of the curve, but the fragment of the rectangle missing is so small compared with the rest that it is quite negligible, and becomes accurately zero when dx, the width of the strip, tends to the limit zero. A symbolic "proof" of this is merely clothing the idea in mathematical dress.

[3] The notation is due to Fourier; on graphical integration, see Runge, *Z. techn. Phys.*, 1924, **5**, 161.

and on adding all these contributions, only the difference between the final value and the initial value, $f(x_n)-f(x_0)$, remains, all the intermediate values cancelling with opposite signs. Since integration finds the values of areas, including " squaring the circle," its old name was *quadrature*. It should be noted that the value of an integral can be found *graphically* by plotting $f'(x)$ against x and counting the squares on the graph paper, or cutting out the figure and weighing.

Besides *areas*, the definite integral can sometimes be used in finding *volumes*. The following example shows this and also brings in some additional notation used with integrals.

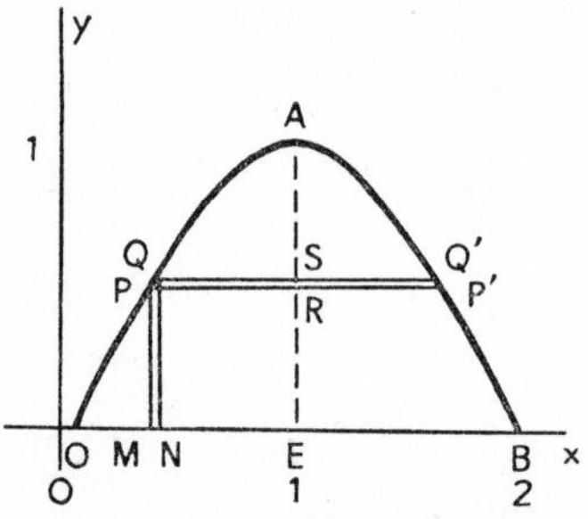

FIG. 7.I. Volume of a Paraboloid

Example. The parabola $y=2x-x^2$ (Fig. 7.I) is rotated about a line AE through its vertex. Find the volume of the parabolic hill between the curve and the plane containing the x axis. The parabola is symmetrical about the ordinate AE ($y=1$) at $x=1$. The volume can be found in two ways.

(i) *The circular slab method.*[1] Imagine the solid divided into thin circular slabs or slices by planes at right angles to AE, a section being shown by PQQ'P'. Let the coordinates of P be (x, y) and those of Q be $(x+dx, y+dy)$. The volume of the slab (neglecting infinitisemals of higher orders, due to the slight slope of its boundary) is (since $dy=(2-2x)dx$):

$$\pi(PR)^2 . RS=\pi(1-x)^2 . dy=\pi(1-x)^2 . (2-2x)dx$$
$$=2\pi(1-x)^3dx.$$

The volume V of the paraboloid is the sum of the volumes of the slabs and is got by integrating between the limits $x=0$ and $x=1$ (*not* $x=2$),

$$\therefore \quad V=2\pi\int_0^1(1-x)^3dx.$$

Put $(1-x)=z \quad \therefore \ dx=-dz$. *The limits of integration must always be suitably adjusted when a new independent variable is introduced*, and in this case when $x=0$, $z=1$, and when $x=1$, $z=0$;

$$\therefore \quad V=-2\pi\int_1^0 z^3dz.$$

Interchanging the upper and lower limits changes the sign of a definite integral; if I_0 and I_1 are the values in the present case for $z=0$ and $z=1$, the integral above is $-(I_0-I_1)$, which is equal to (I_1-I_0);

$$\therefore \quad V=2\pi\int_0^1 z^3dz=2\pi\left[\tfrac{1}{4}z^4\right]_0^1$$

where the square brackets mean that the value inside for $z=0$ is to be subtracted from the value for $z=1$;

$$\therefore \quad V=2\pi(\tfrac{1}{4}-0)=\pi/2 \text{ unit cubes.}^2$$

(ii) *The hollow cylinder method.* Strips such as PQNM revolved about the vertical axis AE form a number of thin hollow cylinders, the limit of the sum of

[1] The idea goes back to Archimedes.

[2] The enthusiast in " dimensions " (see § 11.II) will be interested in seeing that the number π here seems to have the dimensions of volume. It has been gravely asserted, *Trans. Faraday Soc.*, 1940, **36**, 139, to have other " dimensions."

the volumes of which is the volume of the paraboloid. The volume of the cylinder is:

$$2\pi \mathrm{PR}\,.\,\mathrm{PM}\,.\,\mathrm{MN} = \textit{girth} \times \textit{height} \times \textit{thickness}$$
$$= 2\pi(1-x)\,.\,(2x-x^2)\,.\,\mathrm{d}x$$
$$= 2\pi(2x-3x^2+x^3)\mathrm{d}x,$$

$$\therefore\ V = 2\pi\int_0^1 (2x-3x^2+x^3)\mathrm{d}x = \Big[2\pi(x^2-x^3+\tfrac{1}{4}x^4\Big]_0^1 = \pi/2, \text{ as before.}$$

Example. (This uses trigonometrical material discussed later.) To find $\int_0^a \sqrt{(a^2-x^2)}\,.\,\mathrm{d}x$, put $x=a\sin\phi$, then $\mathrm{d}x=a\cos\phi\,.\,\mathrm{d}\phi$. When $x=0$, $\sin\phi=0$, therefore the lower limit remains 0; but when $\phi=\frac{1}{2}\pi$, $x=a$ (since $\sin\frac{1}{2}\pi=1$), and the upper limit must be changed from a to $\frac{1}{2}\pi$. Hence:

$$\int_0^a \sqrt{(a^2-x^2)}.\mathrm{d}x = \int_0^{\pi/2} \sqrt{(a^2-a^2\sin^2\phi)}.a\cos\phi.\mathrm{d}\phi = \int_0^{\pi/2} a\sqrt{(1-\sin^2\phi)}.a\cos\phi.\mathrm{d}\phi$$
$$= \int_0^{\pi/2} a^2\cos^2\phi\,.\,\mathrm{d}\phi = \tfrac{1}{2}a^2\int_0^{\pi/2}(1+\cos 2\phi)\mathrm{d}\phi \text{ from (10), § 41}$$
$$= \tfrac{1}{2}a^2\int_0^{\pi/2}\mathrm{d}\phi + \tfrac{1}{2}a^2\int_0^{\pi/2}\cos 2\phi\,.\,\mathrm{d}\phi$$
$$= \tfrac{1}{2}a^2\int_0^{\pi/2}\mathrm{d}\phi + \tfrac{1}{2}a^2\int_0^{\pi/2}\tfrac{1}{2}\mathrm{d}(\sin 2\phi), \text{ from (1), § 42}$$
$$= \tfrac{1}{2}a^2\Big[\phi\Big]_0^{\pi/2} + \tfrac{1}{4}a^2\Big[\sin 2\phi\Big]_0^{\pi/2} = \pi a^2/4,$$

since $\sin 0=0$ and $\sin\pi=0$.

This is the solution of "squaring the circle," the latter being defined by the curve $x^2+y^2=a^2$ (a=radius), therefore $y=\sqrt{(a^2-x^2)}$. If y is integrated from 0 to a, a quadrant of the circular area (also swept out by the radius revolving from 0 to $\frac{1}{2}\pi=90°$) is found, hence the whole area is πa^2.

If the equation of the circle is given in polar coordinates (Fig. 8.I): $r=2a\cos\theta$, the area is given by letting the radius vector r move from the direction OP′ to the direction OP, i.e. over the angle from $-\frac{1}{2}\pi$ to the angle $+\frac{1}{2}\pi$:

$$\int_{-\pi/2}^{\pi/2}\tfrac{1}{2}r^2\mathrm{d}\theta = 2a^2\int_{-\pi/2}^{\pi/2}\cos^2\theta\,.\,\mathrm{d}\theta =$$
$$a^2\int_{-\pi/2}^{\pi/2}(1+\cos 2\theta)\mathrm{d}\theta = \pi a^2,$$

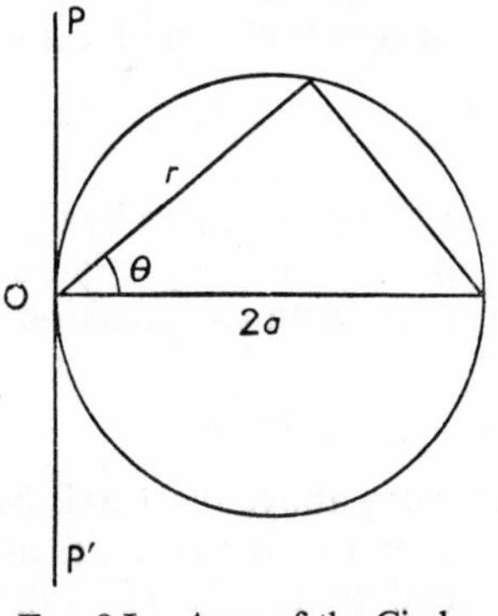

FIG. 8.I. Area of the Circle

the area of any small triangle between two positions of r making an angle of $\mathrm{d}\theta$ being $\frac{1}{2}$(height)×(base)$=\frac{1}{2}r\,.\,r\mathrm{d}\theta$, very nearly (§ 8.III).

It should be noted that the value of a definite integral is determined by its limits, so that the particular letter used to denote the variable is immaterial. Thus, the integral $\int_1^0 z^3\mathrm{d}z$ used in the first example could have been written

$\int_1^0 x^3dx$ or $\int_1^0 y^3dy$, and the integral $\int_0^{\pi/2} \cos 2\phi \, . \, d\phi$ in the example above could have been written $\int_0^{\pi/2} \cos 2x \, . \, dx$, etc.

§ 21. Some Properties of Definite Integrals

The following properties of the definite integral are very important.

$$\int_a^b f(x)dx = -\int_b^a f(x)dx \quad . \quad . \quad . \quad . \quad . \quad . \quad . \quad . \quad (1)$$

since if $\int f(x)dx = F(x)$, the first integral is $F(b) - F(a)$, and the second $F(a) - F(b)$. This implies that a *sign* must be attributed to an area: if it is traced out in the direction of *increasing* x it is positive, if in the direction of decreasing x it is negative.

$$\int_a^c f(x)dx = \int_a^b f(x)dx + \int_b^c f(x)dx \quad . \quad . \quad . \quad . \quad . \quad . \quad (2)$$

This result is obvious; it merely implies a temporary pause somewhere in the work of adding the elements of the integral.

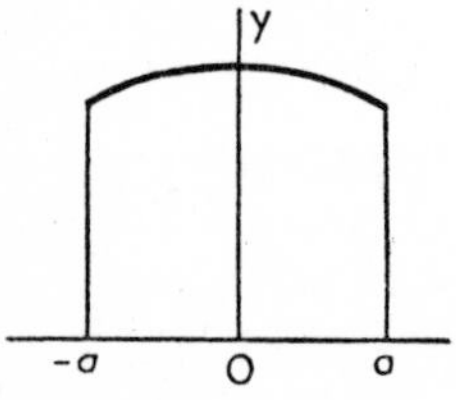

FIG. 9.I. Even Function

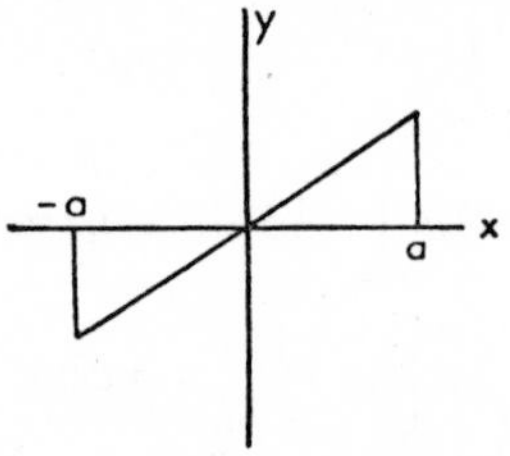

FIG. 10.I. Odd Function

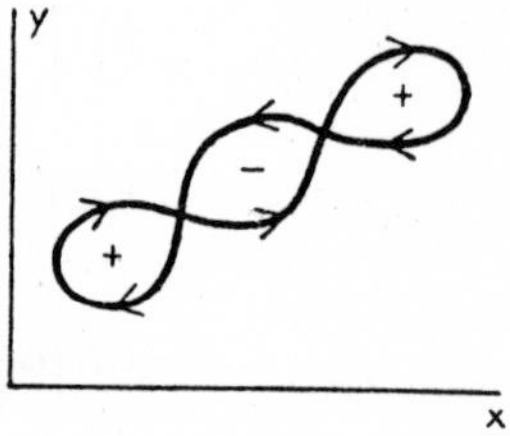

FIG. 11.I. Sign of an Area

If the area lies wholly above or below the x axis, and $f(x) = f(-x)$, i.e. $f(x)$ is an *even* function of x (like x^2), then (Fig. 9.I):

$$\int_{-a}^a f(x)dx = 2\int_0^a f(x)dx \quad . \quad . \quad . \quad . \quad . \quad . \quad . \quad . \quad (3)$$

the area represented by the first integral being bisected by the y axis.

If the area lies partly above and partly below the x axis, and $f(x) = -f(-x)$, i.e. $f(x)$ is an *odd* function of x (e.g. x), then (Fig. 10.I):

$$\int_{-a}^a f(x)dx = 0 \quad . \quad . \quad . \quad . \quad . \quad . \quad . \quad . \quad . \quad (4)$$

the area above the x axis being equal to the area below it.

If part of the area lies above and part below the x axis, the total area represented by the integral is the sum of the areas above the axis less the sum of the areas below the axis, the separate areas being found by separate integrations between the appropriate limits. . . . . (5)

If the curve forms a closed *loop* (or *cycle*), or several such loops (Fig. 11.I), each loop traced out *clockwise* encloses a *positive* area (the area under the upper curve being *numerically* greater than that under the lower curve, and the area of the loop being the *algebraic* difference of the areas), and if traced out *counter-clockwise* it encloses a *negative* area. It should be noted that this is not a "convention," like the sign of an angle, but is a necessary result. . . (6)

§ 22. Multiple Integrals [1]

In Fig. 12.I let $y=f(x)$ and let x and $x+dx$ be the x-coordinates of P and Q. Thus NM$=dx$. The area of the strip PQMN in the limit is ydx. The area ABDC is $\int ydx=\int f(x)dx$, taken between the limits of x corresponding with A and B. Suppose this cut from the paper, and let σ be the mass of the paper per unit area, then the mass of the figure is $\sigma\int f(x)dx$. If, however, the mass per unit area varies from point to point, so that σ is a function of the position of a point, or $\sigma=\phi(x, y)$, this process fails. Now take a small rectangle fgkh of height dy on the strip; its mass is

$$\sigma dxdy=\phi(x, y)dxdy,$$

the values of x and y in $\phi(x, y)$ being the average values over the very small area fgkh. The mass of the strip PQMN is

$$\int[\phi(x, y)dx]dy=[\int\phi(x, y)dy]dx,$$

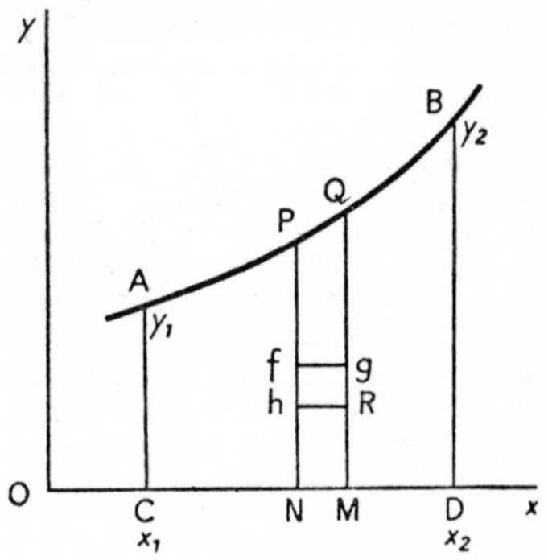

FIG. 12.I. Representation of a Surface Integral

the integration being with respect to y, with x (and hence dx) kept constant, the limits of y being 0 and the ordinate of P. The mass of the area ABDC is now found by adding the masses of all the strips, which corresponds with an integration of the above with respect to x from $x=x_1$ to $x=x_2$, y being now supposed to vary in the first integral from its value y_1 corresponding with A, to its value y_2 corresponding with B. The whole mass is thus:

$$\int_{x_1}^{x_2}\left[\int_{y_1}^{y_2}\phi(x, y)dy\right]dx.$$

This is a *double* (or *surface*) *integral*, and the standard notation [2] is:

$$\int_{x_1}^{x_2}\int_{y_1}^{y_2}\phi(x, y)dxdy \quad . \quad . \quad . \quad . \quad . \quad . \quad . \quad . \quad (1)$$

which indicates that $\phi(x, y)$ is first integrated with respect to y from y_1 to y_2, keeping x constant, and the result (which is now expressed in terms of the *limits* of y, i.e. *constants*, and the *variable* x) is then integrated with respect to x from x_1 to x_2, keeping y constant.

If a third (z) axis is added, in a direction forward from the plane of the paper in the so-called *right-handed* (or " English ") *system* (used, since Maxwell's time, in all physical discussions),[3] then it is possible to represent a volume by a *volume* or *triple integral.* The volume of an elementary parallelepiped [4]

[1] See e.g. Sokolnikoff, " Advanced Calculus," New York, 1939, 130.

[2] The notation varies, but the above seems generally used. The integrations are carried out in order beginning with the differential on the *right*, and the integral signs are in the same order as the differentials.

[3] Maxwell, " A Treatise on Electricity and Magnetism," 3rd edit., Oxford, 1892, **1**, 26. The left-handed, or " Continental " axes, with the z axis passing backwards through the plane of the paper, is used in most mathematical books. The standard position is with the z axis vertical, the y axis in the plane of the paper, and in the right-handed system the x axis to the right-hand, looking from the origin along the positive y axis (or to the right of the zy plane), or, in the left-handed system, to the left-hand. The planes through the axes divide space into eight cubical *octants.*

[4] Greek παραλληλεπίπεδον (in Euclid), from παράλληλος (parallel), ἐπί (upon), and πέδον, the ground: misspelled parallel*o*piped by convention.

parallel to the z axis is $z\mathrm{d}x\mathrm{d}y$ (Fig. 13.I, where the whole coordinate system is tilted forward), and if this is divided into rectangular elements of sides dx, dy, dz, and volume $\mathrm{d}x\mathrm{d}y\mathrm{d}z$, the density ρ per unit volume being variable, $\rho=\phi(x, y, z)$, the whole mass is easily seen to be given by:

$$\iiint\phi(x, y, z)\mathrm{d}x\mathrm{d}y\mathrm{d}z \quad . \quad (2)$$

with suitable limits for x, y, and z.

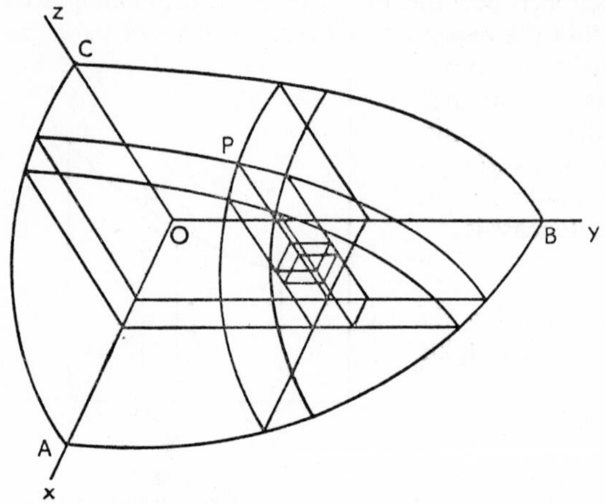

FIG. 13.I. Representation of a Volume Integral

With four, five, six, . . . n variables, *quadruple*, *quintuple*, *sextuple*, . . . *n-tuple* integrals are obtained. In such cases, a geometrical representation in three-dimensional space is impossible, but there is no difficulty in imagining the integration to be carried out in n-dimensional space. In ordinary mathematical books the triple integral is usually the highest considered, but sextuple and even octuple integrals are very common in the kinetic theory of gases (see, e.g., § 22.III). To avoid the alarming appearance of:

$$\iiiiiint f(x, y, z, u, v, w)\mathrm{d}x\mathrm{d}y\mathrm{d}z\mathrm{d}u\mathrm{d}v\mathrm{d}w,$$

two integral signs may be used, with a number in brackets between to show how many integral signs should be written, e.g., $\int . (6) . \int$, but it is usual in Continental works to represent the n-dimensional volume element $\mathrm{d}x\mathrm{d}y\mathrm{d}z\mathrm{d}u\mathrm{d}v\mathrm{d}w$ . . . by dτ, and the n-tuple integration by $\int\mathrm{d}\tau$, and this notation will often be used. Polar, or other, coordinates may replace rectangular coordinates when convenient.

Example. To find the volume of a sphere. Take the coordinate system in Fig. 14.I, but use polar coordinates as shown (with $a=r$). The small arc on the sphere between two radii of length r inclined at an angle dθ is rdθ; if these radii are prolonged by dr, a small area $r\mathrm{d}\theta\mathrm{d}r$ is formed. If this is revolved around the z axis through an angle 2π, whereby a circle of circumference $2\pi r \sin\theta$ is formed, a solid ring of volume $2\pi r \sin\theta r\mathrm{d}\theta\mathrm{d}r$ is formed. If, however, it is revolved through the angle dϕ, the volume of the elementary parallelepiped formed is d$\phi/2\pi$ times this, viz. $r^2 \sin\theta\mathrm{d}\phi\mathrm{d}\theta\mathrm{d}r$. The whole volume is evidently:

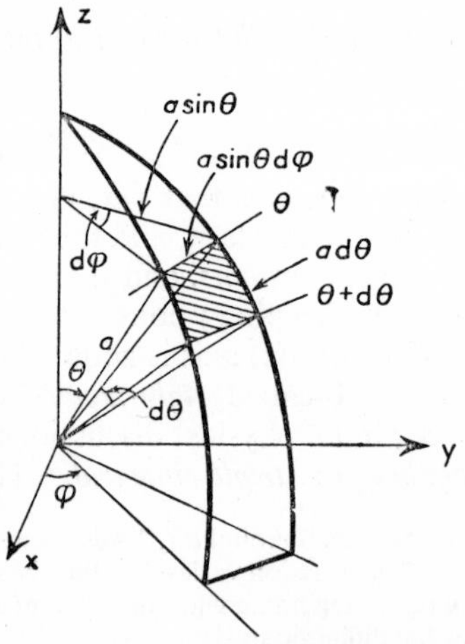

FIG. 14.I. Polar Coordinates for Volume of Sphere

$$v=\iiint r^2 \sin\theta\mathrm{d}\phi\mathrm{d}\theta\mathrm{d}r.$$

Integrate first with respect to r from 0 to a, the radius of the sphere, then

$\int_0^a r^2 \mathrm{d}r = a^3/3$. In the other two integrations it is convenient to limit the volume to one-eighth of the sphere, i.e. in one octant. Then the limits of θ are 0 and $\frac{1}{2}\pi$,

$$\therefore\ v = \iint_0^{\pi/2} (a^3/3) \sin\theta \mathrm{d}\phi \mathrm{d}\theta$$

$$= (a^3/3) \iint_0^{\pi/2} \sin\theta \mathrm{d}\phi \mathrm{d}\theta = (a^3/3) \int \mathrm{d}\phi$$

since $\int \sin\theta \mathrm{d}\theta = -\cos\theta$, and $\cos 0 = 1$, $\cos \frac{1}{2}\pi = 0$.

The limits of ϕ are also 0 and $\frac{1}{2}\pi$:

$$\therefore\ v = (a^3/3) \int_0^{\pi/2} \mathrm{d}\phi = \pi a^3/6,$$

and the volume of the whole sphere is $8 \times (\pi a^3/6) = (4/3)\pi a^3$.

§ 23. Partial Fractions

An important method used in the integration of rational algebraic functions (§ 2) is resolution into *partial fractions*, which is best illustrated by a few examples.[1]

Let $\dfrac{1}{(a-x)(b-x)} = \dfrac{A}{a-x} + \dfrac{B}{b-x}$ for all values of x. Multiply by $(a-x)$:

$$\frac{1}{b-x} = A + B\frac{a-x}{b-x}.$$

Put $x=a$, then $A = 1/(b-a)$ or $A = -1/(a-b)$ if the letters are kept in cyclic order (a, b, c). Similarly, by multiplying by $(b-x)$ and putting $x=b$ it is found that $B = 1/(a-b)$:

$$\therefore\ \frac{1}{(a-x)(b-x)} = \frac{1}{a-b}\left[\frac{1}{b-x} - \frac{1}{a-x}\right]$$

and

$$\int \frac{\mathrm{d}x}{(a-x)(b-x)} = \frac{1}{a-b}[\ln(a-x) - \ln(b-x] = \frac{1}{a-b} \ln \frac{a-x}{b-x}.$$

Similarly, it is shown that:

$$\frac{1}{(a-x)(b-x)(c-x)} = -\frac{1}{(a-b)(c-a)(a-x)} - \frac{1}{(a-b)(b-c)(b-x)}$$
$$-\frac{1}{(b-c)(c-a)(c-x)}.$$

Let $\dfrac{1}{(x^2+x+1)(x-1)(x-2)} = \dfrac{A}{x-1} + \dfrac{B}{x-2} + \dfrac{Cx+D.}{x^2+x+1.}$ In this case x^2+x+1 cannot be resolved into real factors. Multiply by the denominator on the left:

$$1 = A(x-2)(x^2+x+1) + B(x-1)(x^2+x+1) + (Cx+D)(x-1)(x-2).$$

By putting $x=2$ and $x=1$, in succession, find $\mathrm{B} = \frac{1}{7}$ and $A = -\frac{1}{3}$. By substituting these in the equation, and giving x *any* two values in succession, simultaneous equations are obtained, which may be solved to find C and D. Such expressions as x^2+x+1 may also be split into linear factors of the form $(x+ia)(x-ia)$,

[1] For further details, see e.g. C. Smith, "Treatise on Algebra," Ch. xxiii.; Chrystal, "Algebra," 1886, **1**, 147; Todhunter, "Integral Calculus," 1878 23.

where $i=\sqrt{(-1)}$, and De Moivre's Theorem (§ 46) used to remove the imaginary quantities.[1]

It is useful to remember that if a rational integral function of x vanishes when $x=a$, then $(x-a)$ is a factor. This is not true for functions in general: e^{-1/x^2} vanishes when $x=0$, but is not divisible by any positive power of x.

§ 24. Some Remarks

In its applications to finding lengths of curves, areas, and volumes, the Integral Calculus *defines* these lengths, areas, and volumes as the limiting values of sums, and if such limiting values do not exist, the curve is said by mathematicians [2] to have no length, etc. The length of the cutting edge of a very fine saw, e.g. does not " exist " mathematically when the width of the teeth decreases without limit, although the saw-edge remains a saw-edge. The trouble would seem rather to lie in the mathematics than in the saw, and in the recent developments of the quantum theory, some violence has had to be done to cherished mathematical creeds in order to make progress on the physical side; in revenge, many firmly rooted physical (and even philosophical) beliefs have been profoundly disturbed by the pure mathematics of the quantum theory.

In some cases, the very proper attempts by mathematicians to obtain rigour in definitions seem to the non-mathematical scientist at times overstrained. When it is said, for example,[3] that: " a collection of definite distinct objects which is regarded as a single whole is called an aggregate," some difficulty may be felt in understanding what is meant by a " collection " and how it differs from an " aggregate."

A schoolboy would make little progress with arithmetic if he were required to busy himself with the theory of numbers, and a beginner in calculus is advised [4] to leave the " fundamentals " (theories of continuity and limits) until he has had some practice in the methods of the subject. A chemist knows that " strict " definitions of *element* and *compound* are difficult, and never troubles beginners with them. Experimental science is not much concerned with " definitions."

PARTIAL DIFFERENTIAL COEFFICIENTS

§ 25. Partial Differential Coefficients

Let $u=f(x, y)$ be a continuous [5] function of two variables, x and y, which are first regarded as independent. This may be differentiated with respect to x on the assumption that y is kept constant, giving what may be denoted by $(du/dx)_y$, and it may be differentiated with respect to y on the assumption that

[1] See e.g. Edwards, " Differential Calculus for Beginners," 1893, 56.

[2] Hobson, " Theory of Functions of a Real Variable," Cambridge, 1907, 37; Borel, *Rev. Gén. Sci.*, 1912, **23**, 842.

[3] Hobson, *op. cit.*, 149.

[4] The late Sir Horace Lamb advised his students, in the author's time in Manchester, to leave the first chapters of his " Infinitesimal Calculus " alone until they had become proficient in the elementary rules of differentiation and integration.

[5] It may be noticed that if $f(x, y)$ is a continuous function of x when $x=x_1$, and a continuous function of y when $y=y_1$, it is *not* necessarily a continuous function of x and y at x_1, y_1; e.g., $xy/(x^2+y^2)$ is continuous in either x or y when $x=0$ or $y=0$, but not when *both* are zero. Even Cauchy, the father of modern " rigour," fell into this trap. See Harkness and Morley, " A Treatise on the Theory of Functions," 1893, 61, and Hobson, " Theory of Functions of a Real Variable," 1907, 301 f. The detailed theory is really quite difficult, and no attempt can be made here to deal with matters of great concern to mathematicians.

x is kept constant, giving $(du/dy)_x$. E.g. if $u=ax^2+by^2$, then $(du/dx)_y=2ax$ and $(du/dy)_x=2by$. Again, let $pv=RT$ (the ideal gas equation; R=const.), or $p=RT/v$, then $(dp/dv)_T=-RT/v^2$, and $(dp/dT)_v=R/v$. If $-v(dp/dv)=$ elasticity ϵ, show that the *isothermal* elasticity of an ideal gas is equal to the pressure: $\epsilon_T=p$.

The differential coefficients just found, $(du/dx)_y$ and $(du/dy)_x$, are called the *partial differential coefficients* (or *partial derivatives*) of the function $u=f(x, y)$ with respect to x and y, respectively. They are also denoted [1] by $\partial u/\partial x$, $\partial u/\partial y$, by [2] d_yu/dx and d_xu/dy, by D_xu and D_yu, and by $f'_x(x, y)$ and $f'_y(x, y)$. In mathematical books, "Jacobi's symbols," $\partial u/\partial x$, $\partial u/\partial y$ and $\partial u/\partial z$ are commonly used when there are three variables, two of which are understood to be kept constant in each case.

Let δu be the small change of u consequent on the changes δx and δy of the variables x and y. Then :

$$\begin{aligned}\delta u&=f(x+\delta x, y+\delta y)-f(x, y)\\&=f(x+\delta x, y+\delta y)-f(x, y+\delta y)+f(x, y+\delta y)-f(x, y)\\&=\frac{f(x+\delta x, y+\delta y)-f(x, y+\delta y)}{\delta x}\delta x+\frac{f(x, y+\delta y)-f(x, y)}{\delta y}\delta y.\end{aligned}$$

If both δx and δy tend to zero, then:

$$\frac{f(x+\delta x, y+\delta y)-f(x, y+\delta y)}{\delta x}=f'_x(x, y+\delta y)=f'_x(x, y)$$

$$\frac{f(x, y+\delta y)-f(x, y)}{\delta y}=f'_y(x, y)$$

$$\therefore\ du=f'_x(x, y)dx+f'_y(x, y)dy$$

or, in the alternative notation:

$$du=(du/dx)_y dx+(du/dy)_x dy \quad . \quad . \quad . \quad . \quad . \quad . \quad . \quad (1)$$

If x and y are both functions of another variable t (sometimes called a *parameter*), then dx and dy are their variations consequent on a change of t by dt, and by division of (1) by dt:

$$du/dt=(du/dx)_y(dx/dt)+(du/dy)_x(dy/dt)$$

or

$$\frac{du}{dt}=\frac{\partial u}{\partial x}\frac{dx}{dt}+\frac{\partial u}{\partial y}\frac{dy}{dt} \quad . \quad . \quad . \quad . \quad . \quad . \quad . \quad . \quad (2)$$

If $t=x$, so that $y=f(x)$, and u is thus a function of *one* variable x, then $dx/dt=1$, and (2) becomes:

$$\frac{du}{dx}=\frac{\partial u}{\partial x}+\frac{\partial u}{\partial y}\frac{dy}{dx} \quad . \quad . \quad . \quad . \quad . \quad . \quad . \quad . \quad (3)$$

in which $\partial u/\partial x$ results from a change of an explicitly named variable x only, whilst du/dx is the change of u due both to the change of x and to the change of

[1] Apparently first by Legendre in 1786, then by Euler, "Institutionum Calculi Integralis." St. Petersburg, 1792. They are usually referred to Jacobi (1841), and are exclusively used by mathematicians. They are, however, ambiguous and unsuitable when several independent variables are involved, as in thermodynamics.

[2] Clausius, "Mechanical Theory of Heat," 1879, 177. An alternative hybrid notation, $\partial u/\partial_y x$, $\partial u/\partial_x y$, etc., proposed by Perry, *Nature*, 1902, **66**, 53, 271, 520, is cumbersome, and that suggested by Muir, *ibid.*, 1902, **66**, 271, 520, is even less convenient.

y consequent on this; $\partial u/\partial x$ is a *partial*, and du/dx a *total, differential coefficient*. In differential notation (3) becomes:

$$du = (\partial u/\partial x)dx + (\partial u/\partial y)dy \quad \ldots \ldots \quad (4)$$

and du in (4) is called a *total, complete*, or *perfect* differential.

For more than two variables, say x, y, and z, the same procedure gives:

$$\frac{du}{dt} = \frac{\partial u}{\partial x}\frac{dx}{dt} + \frac{\partial u}{\partial y}\frac{dy}{dt} + \frac{\partial u}{\partial z}\frac{dz}{dt} \quad \ldots \ldots \quad (5)$$

$$du = \frac{\partial u}{\partial x}dx + \frac{\partial u}{\partial y}dy + \frac{\partial u}{\partial z}dz \quad \ldots \ldots \quad (6)$$

It is important to notice that (4) and (6) are true whether the variables x and y, or x, y, and z are all independent or are functions of one or more independent variables, all functions and all first partial derivatives being supposed continuous.[1] For if x y, and z are functions of *two* independent variables (parameters), say s and t, then $u = f(s, t)$ and:

$$du = (\partial u/\partial s)ds + (\partial u/\partial t)dt \quad \ldots \ldots \quad (7)$$

$$dx = \frac{\partial x}{\partial s}ds + \frac{\partial x}{\partial t}dt, \qquad dy = \frac{\partial y}{\partial s}ds + \frac{\partial y}{\partial t}dt, \qquad dz = \frac{\partial z}{\partial s}ds + \frac{\partial z}{\partial t}dt \quad . \quad (8)$$

Equation (5) can now be replaced by the *two* equations:

$$\frac{\partial u}{\partial s} = \frac{\partial u}{\partial x}\frac{\partial x}{\partial s} + \frac{\partial u}{\partial y}\frac{\partial y}{\partial s} + \frac{\partial u}{\partial z}\frac{\partial z}{\partial s} \quad \ldots \ldots \quad (a)$$

$$\frac{\partial u}{\partial t} = \frac{\partial u}{\partial x}\frac{\partial x}{\partial t} + \frac{\partial u}{\partial y}\frac{\partial y}{\partial t} + \frac{\partial u}{\partial z}\frac{\partial z}{\partial t} \quad \ldots \ldots \quad (b)$$

Multiply (a) by ds and (b) by dt and add:

$$\therefore \frac{\partial u}{\partial s}ds + \frac{\partial u}{\partial t}dt = \frac{\partial u}{\partial x}\left(\frac{\partial x}{\partial s}ds + \frac{\partial x}{\partial t}dt\right) + \frac{\partial u}{\partial y}\left(\frac{\partial y}{\partial s}ds + \frac{\partial y}{\partial t}dt\right) + \frac{\partial u}{\partial z}\left(\frac{\partial z}{\partial s}ds + \frac{\partial z}{\partial t}dt\right)$$

$$= \frac{\partial u}{\partial x}dx + \frac{\partial u}{\partial y}dy + \frac{\partial u}{\partial z}dz \quad \ldots \ldots \quad (9)$$

from (8). Comparison of (7) and (9) gives:

$$du = (\partial u/\partial x)dx + (\partial u/\partial y)dy + (\partial u/\partial z)dz \quad \ldots \quad (10)$$

which is the same as (6), in which x, y, and z were all supposed to be independent variables, while here they are all functions of *two* independent variables, s and t.[2] Thus it is possible to write:

$$du = (\partial u/\partial x_1)dx_1 + (\partial u/\partial x_2)dx_2 + (\partial u/\partial x_3)dx_3 + \ldots$$

whether each x is an independent or a dependent variable.

There is one point relating to partial differential coefficients which needs care. In (4) put $du = 0$, then:

$$(du/dx)_y dx + (du/dy)_x dy = 0.$$

Transpose and divide by dx, then:

$$(du/dy)_x (dy/dx)_u = -(du/dx)_y,$$

[1] It is a common mistake in non-mathematical works to suppose that x, y, and z must be *independent* variables.

[2] See Forbes and Fuoss, *J.A.C.S.*, 1927, **49**, 142.

since putting $du=0$ means that u is constant, hence dy/dx must be written $(dy/dx)_u$. Hence:

$$(dy/dx)_u = -(du/dx)_y/(du/dy)_x \quad . \quad . \quad . \quad . \quad . \quad . \quad (11)$$

and not with a positive sign, as might have been expected. In actual work, du is divided out of the quotient on the right, giving dy/dx, but the sign must be changed. " Cancelling " in differential coefficients is misleading when these are partial. This example is very common in thermodynamics. Clarity is best attained by using the old notation with brackets, rather than the modern symbols with ∂.

§ 26. Higher Partial Derivatives

Since $(du/dx)_y$ and $(du/dy)_x$ are usually functions of x and y, they can be differentiated again with respect to these variables, and four partial second differential coefficients are so obtained:

$$\frac{d}{dx}(du/dx)_y = (d^2u/dx^2)_y, \text{ also denoted by } \partial^2u/\partial x^2, \text{ or } u_{xx}, \text{ or } f_{xx},$$

$$\frac{d}{dy}(du/dy)_x = (d^2u/dy^2)_x, \text{ also denoted by } \partial^2u/\partial y^2, \text{ or } u_{yy}, \text{ or } f_{yy},$$

$$\frac{d}{dx}[(du/dy]_x]_y = (d^2u/dydx)_y, \text{ also denoted by } \partial^2u/\partial y\partial x, \text{ or } u_{yx}, \text{ or } f_{yx},$$

$$\frac{d}{dy}[(du/dx)_y]_x = (d^2u/dxdy)_x, \text{ also denoted by } \partial^2u/\partial x dy, \text{ or } u_{xy}, \text{ or } f_{xy}.$$

(Note the *order* of differentiation in $\partial^2u/\partial y\partial x$ and $\partial^2u/\partial x\partial y$.) If, however, u is a continuous function of x and y, it can be shown [1] (the proof is rather involved), and can be checked by taking examples, that:

$$\partial^2u/\partial y\partial x = \partial^2u/\partial x\partial y \quad . \quad . \quad . \quad . \quad . \quad . \quad . \quad . \quad (1)$$

i.e. the result is independent of the order of differentiation, so that there are only three, not four, second derivates, the third and fourth being identical. The same result holds for higher derivatives, e.g. $\partial^3u/\partial y\partial x^2 = \partial^3u/\partial x^2\partial y$, etc.

It may be mentioned that if $z=f(x, y)$, the partial differential coefficients are sometimes denoted by special symbols:

$$\partial z/\partial x = p \qquad \partial z/\partial y = q$$

$$\partial^2z/\partial x^2 = r \qquad \partial^2z/\partial x\partial y = s \qquad \partial^2z/\partial y^2 = t.$$

A problem which frequently arises is to find d^2u/dt^2 when u is a function of two variables x and y, each of which is a function of a third variable (sometimes called a *parameter*) t:

Let $u=f(x, y)$, $x=\phi(t)$, $y=\psi(t)$

$$\therefore \frac{du}{dt} = \frac{\partial u}{\partial x}\frac{dx}{dt} + \frac{\partial u}{\partial y}\frac{dy}{dt} \quad . \quad . \quad . \quad . \quad . \quad . \quad . \quad . \quad . \quad . \quad . \quad . \quad (2)$$

$$\therefore \frac{d^2u}{dt^2} = \frac{d}{dt}\left(\frac{du}{dt}\right) = \frac{\partial u}{\partial x}\frac{d^2x}{dt^2} + \frac{dx}{dt}\frac{d}{dt}\left(\frac{\partial u}{\partial x}\right) + \frac{\partial u}{\partial y}\frac{d^2y}{dt^2} + \frac{dy}{dt}\frac{d}{dt}\left(\frac{\partial u}{\partial y}\right) \quad . \quad (3)$$

by (4a), § 6.

[1] See e.g. Gibson, " An Elementary Treatise on the Calculus," 1933, 221.

Since $\partial u/\partial x$ and $\partial u/\partial y$ are functions of x and y, by using these instead of u in (2):

$$\frac{\mathrm{d}}{\mathrm{d}t}\left(\frac{\partial u}{\partial x}\right)=\frac{\partial^2 u}{\partial x^2}\frac{\mathrm{d}x}{\mathrm{d}t}+\frac{\partial^2 u}{\partial y\partial x}\frac{\mathrm{d}y}{\mathrm{d}t},$$

$$\frac{\mathrm{d}}{\mathrm{d}t}\left(\frac{\partial u}{\partial y}\right)=\frac{\partial^2 u}{\partial x\partial y}\frac{\mathrm{d}x}{\mathrm{d}t}+\frac{\partial^2 u}{\partial y^2}\frac{\mathrm{d}y}{\mathrm{d}t}.$$

Substitute these values in (2) and put $\partial^2 u/\partial y\partial x=\partial^2 u/\partial x\partial y$, then

$$\frac{\mathrm{d}^2 u}{\mathrm{d}t^2}=\frac{\partial u}{\partial x}\frac{\mathrm{d}^2 x}{\mathrm{d}t^2}+\frac{\partial u}{\partial y}\frac{\mathrm{d}^2 y}{\mathrm{d}t^2}+\frac{\partial^2 u}{\partial x^2}\left(\frac{\mathrm{d}x}{\mathrm{d}t}\right)^2+2\frac{\partial^2 u}{\partial x\partial y}\frac{\mathrm{d}x}{\mathrm{d}t}\frac{\mathrm{d}y}{\mathrm{d}t}+\frac{\partial^2 u}{\partial y^2}\left(\frac{\mathrm{d}y}{\mathrm{d}t}\right)^2 \quad . \quad (4)$$

which is the result required.

§ 27. Perfect (or Complete) Differentials

Let $\mathrm{f}(x, y)$ and $\phi(x, y)$ be two functions of the independent variables x and y, and suppose that if x and y suffer small variations, the equation:

$$\mathrm{d}u=\mathrm{f}(x, y)\mathrm{d}x+\phi(x, y)\mathrm{d}y \quad . \quad . \quad . \quad . \quad . \quad . \quad . \quad (1)$$

defines $\mathrm{d}u$ in terms of $\mathrm{d}x$ and $\mathrm{d}y$.

It does not follow that $\mathrm{d}u$ is a differential of a function $u=\mathrm{F}(x, y)$ of x and y considered as independent variables. In some cases it is, in others it is not. When $\mathrm{d}u$ is the differential of a function of x and y a condition must be fulfilled by the functions $\mathrm{f}(x, y)$ and $\phi(x, y)$. In this case:

$$\mathrm{d}u=(\partial u/\partial x)\mathrm{d}x+(\partial u/\partial y)\mathrm{d}y \quad . \quad . \quad . \quad . \quad . \quad . \quad . \quad . \quad (2)$$

and by comparing (1) and (2), the condition that u in (1) is a function of x and y is seen to be:

$$\mathrm{f}(x, y)=\partial u/\partial x \quad \text{and} \quad \phi(x, y)=\partial u/\partial y \quad . \quad . \quad . \quad . \quad . \quad (3)$$

If u is a continuous function of x and y it has been stated in (1), § 26, that:

$$\partial^2 u/\partial y\partial x=\partial^2 u/\partial x\partial y \quad . \quad . \quad . \quad . \quad . \quad . \quad . \quad . \quad (4)$$

From (3) and (4) it follows that:

$$\frac{\partial}{\partial y}\mathrm{f}(x, y)=\frac{\partial}{\partial x}\phi(x, y) \quad . \quad . \quad . \quad . \quad . \quad . \quad . \quad . \quad . \quad (5)$$

is a *necessary* condition that $\mathrm{d}u$ in (1) is the differential of a function of x and y, say $u=\mathrm{F}(x, y)$. In this case, $\mathrm{d}u$ is a *perfect* (or *complete*, or *total*) differential (§ 25), and equation (5) is called *Euler's*[1] *criterion* (1734–5). The proof that it is also a *sufficient* condition (i.e. that no other condition is needed) for a perfect differential is simple,[2] but need not be given here.

E.g. $(3y^2x-x^2)\mathrm{d}y+(y^3-2xy)\mathrm{d}x$ is a perfect differential, because

$$(\partial/\partial x)(3y^2x-x^2)=3y^2-2x \quad \text{is equal to} \quad (\partial/\partial y)(y^3-2xy)=3y^2-2x.$$

$$\mathrm{F}(x, y) \quad \text{in this case is} \quad y^3-x^2y, \quad \text{since} \quad (\mathrm{d}/\mathrm{d}y)(y^3-x^2y)=3y^2-x^2,$$

$$\text{and} \quad (\mathrm{d}/\mathrm{d}x)(y^3-x^2y)=y^3-2xy;$$

$$\text{and} \quad (3y^2x-x^2)\mathrm{d}y+(y^3-2xy)\mathrm{d}x=\mathrm{d}(y^3-x^2y).$$

[1] Pronounced " Oyler's."

[2] See § 60, and e.g. Johnson, "Differential Equations," 1891, 22; Hobson, "Theory of Functions of a Real Variable," Cambridge, 1907, 317 (where the result is generalised for higher derivatives).

But $y\mathrm{d}x-(x+y^2)\mathrm{d}y$ is not a perfect differential, since $(\partial/\partial y)y=1$ and $(\partial/\partial x)(x+y^2)=y^2$. There is no function of x and y from which $y\mathrm{d}x-(x+y^2)\mathrm{d}y$ can be found by differentiation, and the coefficients of $\mathrm{d}x$ and $\mathrm{d}y$ are quite arbitrary functions.

If (5) is satisfied, the expression on the right of (1) is immediately integrable, since it is a complete differential of some function $\mathrm{F}(x, y)$ of x and y, in which these are treated as independent variables, and such that:

$$(\partial/\partial x)\mathrm{F}(x, y)=\mathrm{f}(x) \quad \text{and} \quad (\partial/\partial y)\mathrm{F}(x, y)=\phi(x) \quad . \quad . \quad . \quad (6)$$

Hence from (1):

$$u=\mathrm{F}(x, y)+\text{const.} \quad . \quad . \quad . \quad . \quad . \quad . \quad . \quad . \quad . \quad (7)$$

But if (5) is not satisfied, (1) cannot be integrated so as to give the solution (7). If, however, *some relation exists between x and y*, so that they are no longer independent, but one can be expressed as a function of the other, then integration again becomes possible. For if:

$$\mathrm{f}(x, y)=0 \quad . \quad . \quad . \quad . \quad . \quad . \quad . \quad . \quad . \quad . \quad (8)$$

x or y can be eliminated from (1), giving, e.g.:

$$\mathrm{d}u+\psi(x)\mathrm{d}x$$

$$\therefore\ u=\mathrm{F}(x)+\text{const.} \quad . \quad . \quad . \quad . \quad . \quad . \quad . \quad . \quad (9)$$

and (8) and (9) *together* may be regarded as forming a solution of (1).

E.g. if $\mathrm{d}u=(2x^2-3xy)\mathrm{d}x+3x^2\mathrm{d}y$, the expression on the right is not a perfect differential. If, however, the relation $y=4x^2$, i.e. $(y-4x^2)=\mathrm{f}(x, y)=0$, exists, then $\mathrm{d}y=8x\mathrm{d}x$, and:

$$\mathrm{d}u=(2x^2-12x^3)\mathrm{d}x+24x^3\mathrm{d}x=(12x^3-2x^2)\mathrm{d}x,$$

$$\therefore\ u=3x^4-\tfrac{2}{3}x^3+\text{const.}$$

The distinction between perfect and non-perfect differentials is of great importance in the integration of expressions such as (1). For, if it is assumed that $\mathrm{F}(x, y)$ in (7) is a single-valued function of the coordinates x and y, and that the initial and final positions of a point representing the value of the function in the plane of x, y coordinates are known points, (x_1, y_1) and (x_2, y_2), then the *change* in the value of the function u (which may be regarded as plotted on a third axis at right angles to the x, y plane) will be $\mathrm{F}(x_2, y_2)-\mathrm{F}(x_1, y_1)$, and is thus independent of the values of x and y lying between x_1, y_1, and x_2, y_2, i.e. of the path of integration, or of the way in which a point passes from its initial to its final position.

In the second case it is quite otherwise. Of the two equations (8) and (9), the first may be regarded as the equation of a curve, and since the form of the second depends upon it, the change of u during the motion of the point in the x, y plane is determinate only when the *whole* of the path is known, since an infinite number of possible curves may pass through the initial and final points, (x_1, y_1) and (x_2, y_2). If the point describes a closed *loop* or *cycle*, so that $x_2=x_1$, and $y_2=y_1$, then in the first case the change of u is zero, but in the second case it may have any positive or negative value. These important results may be illustrated by two examples.

Example 1. Let

$$\mathrm{d}u=y^2\mathrm{d}x+2xy\mathrm{d}y \quad . \quad . \quad . \quad . \quad . \quad . \quad . \quad . \quad . \quad (10)$$

Since $\mathrm{d}(y^2)/\mathrm{d}y=2y$ and $\mathrm{d}(2xy)/\mathrm{d}x=2y$, it follows from (5) that $\mathrm{d}u$ is a perfect differential d[F(x, y)]. In Fig. 15.I let A represent u_1 (for $x_1=-a$, $y_1=b$) and B represent u_2 (for $x_2=a$, $y_2=b$). Then it will be shown that the change of u in passing from A to B is the same if the integration of (10) is carried out along any one of three arbitrarily chosen paths: (i) the straight line AB, (ii) the circular arc AB, (iii) the broken line AOB.

(i) The *straight line* AB satisfies the equation $y=b=$const., therefore dy=0, therefore from (10), d$u=y^2$d$x=b^2$dx,

$$\therefore \int_A^B du=\int_{x_1}^{x_2} du=\int_{x_1}^{x_2} b^2 dx=b^2(x_2-x_1)=b^2(a+a)=2ab^2.$$

(ii) The *broken line* is represented by *two* equations:

$$y=-(b/a)x \text{ along AO} \quad \text{and} \quad y=(b/a)x \text{ along OB},$$

since the equation of any straight line is $y=x\tan\theta+c$, and in this case $c=0$ and $\tan\theta$ has the values $-b/a$ and $+b/a$. Thus d$y=-(b/a)$dx or (b/a)dx.

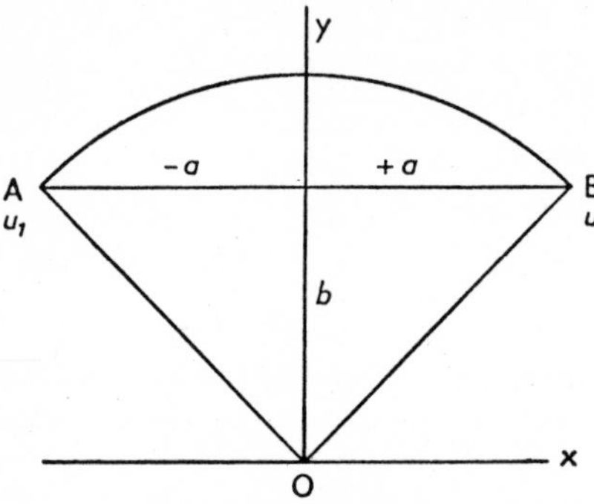

FIG. 15.I. Integration along Two Different Paths

Along AO:

$$du=y^2dx+2xydy=(b^2/a^2)x^2dx+2x^2(b^2/a^2)dx,$$

$$\therefore du=3(b^2/a^2)x^2dx,$$

$$\therefore \int_{x_1}^{x_2} du=3(b^2/a^2)\int_{x_1}^{x_2} x^2dx=(b^2/a^2)(x_2^3-x_1^3)=(b^2/a^2)a^3=b^2a$$

since $x_1=-a$ and $x_2=0$.

Along OB, similarly:

$$\int_{x_1}^{x_2} du=b^2a,$$

therefore the sum for AO+OB$=b^2a+b^2a=2b^2a$, as in (i).

(iii) Along the *circular arc* (radius r) the equation of the circle of radius r is:

$$x^2+y^2=r^2=a^2+b^2,$$

$$\therefore y^2=a^2+b^2-x^2, \quad \therefore 2ydy=-2xdx$$

$$\therefore dy=-(x/y)dx,$$

$$\therefore du=y^2dx+2xydy=(a^2+b^2-x^2)dx-2x^2dx$$

(since $2ydy=-2xdx \quad \therefore 2xydy=-2x^2dx$).

$$\therefore du=(a^2+b^2-3x^2)dx,$$

$$\therefore \int du=\int(a^2+b^2-3x^2)dx=a^2x+b^2x-x^3$$

$$\therefore \int_{x_1}^{x_2} du=2ab^2, \text{ as in (i) and (ii), since } x_1=-a \text{ and } x_2=a.$$

Example 2. Now take the case:

$$du=y^2dx+xydy \quad . \; . \; . \; . \; . \; . \; . \; . \; . \quad \textbf{(11)}$$

Since d(y^2)/d$y=2y$ and d(xy)/d$x=y$ it follows from (5) that (11) is not a perfect differential. Integrate (11) along the straight line AB and along the broken line AOB as before.

(i) Along AB: $y=b$, therefore d$u=b^2$dx

$$\therefore \int_{x_1}^{x_2} du=b^2\int_{x_1}^{x_2} dx=2ab^2.$$

(ii) Along AOB: $y=-(b/a)x$ and $y=(b/a)x$.

Along AO:

$$du=y^2dx+xydy=(b^2/a^2)x^2dx+(b^2/a^2)x^2dx=2(b^2/a^2)x^2dx$$

$$\therefore \int_{x_1}^{x_2} du=2(b^2/a^2)\int_{-a}^{0} x^2dx=\tfrac{2}{3}(b^2/a^2)a^3=\tfrac{2}{3}ab^2.$$

Along OB:

$$du=2(b^2/a^2)x^2dx,$$

$$\therefore \int_{x_1}^{x_2} du=2(b^2/a^2)\int_{0}^{a} x^2dx=\tfrac{2}{3}ab^2,$$

$\therefore$ along AO and OB the integral is:

$$\tfrac{2}{3}ab^2+\tfrac{2}{3}ab^2=\tfrac{4}{3}ab^2,$$

which is different from that along AB, so that the value of the integral now depends on the path of integration.

§ 28. The Operator ∇^2

If u is a function of the three variables x, y, z, the expression:

$$\partial^2u/\partial x^2+\partial^2u/\partial y^2+\partial^2u/\partial z^2 \quad . \; . \; . \; . \; . \; . \; . \; . \quad (1)$$

may be regarded as formed by operating on the function u with the *operator*:

$$\partial^2/\partial x^2+\partial^2/\partial y^2+\partial^2/\partial z^2 \quad . \; . \; . \; . \; . \; . \; . \; . \quad (2)$$

i.e. $(\partial^2/\partial x^2+\partial^2/\partial y^2+\partial^2/\partial z^2)u=\partial^2u/\partial x^2+\partial^2u/\partial y^2+\partial^2u/\partial z^2.$

The operator (2) is generally denoted by the symbol ∇^2 (" del squared "),[1] and (1) is therefore written ∇^2u.

It is frequently required to transform the expression

$$\nabla^2u=\partial^2u/\partial x^2+\partial^2u/\partial y^2+\partial^2u/\partial z^2$$

into *polar coordinates*, in which r, θ, and ϕ replace Cartesian coordinates according to the scheme (see § 22):

$$x=r\sin\theta\cos\phi;\; y=r\sin\theta\sin\phi;\; z=r\cos\theta.$$

The transformation is neatly effected in two steps as follows: [2]

$$\text{Put } x=\rho\cos\phi, \text{ and } y=\rho\sin\phi, \text{ but retain } z \quad . \; . \; . \; . \; . \; . \quad (a)$$

$$z=r\cos\theta, \text{ and } \rho=r\sin\theta, \text{ but retain } \phi \quad . \; . \; . \; . \; . \; . \; . \quad (b)$$

$$\therefore \rho=\sqrt{(x^2+y^2)} \quad \text{and} \quad \phi=\tan^{-1}(y/x),$$

$$\therefore d\rho=(xdx+ydy)/\sqrt{(x^2+y^2)},\; d\phi=(xdy-ydx)/(x^2+y^2) \text{ (§ 44)},$$

$$\therefore \partial\rho/\partial x=\cos\phi,\; \partial\phi/\partial x=-\sin\phi/\rho,\; \partial\rho/\partial y=\sin\phi,\; \partial\phi/\partial y=\cos\phi/\rho$$

1 The symbol ∇ was named " nabla " (" from a supposed resemblance to an Assyrian harp ") by representative British and American physicists in 1884: see Hathaway, *Phys. Rev.*, 1902, **15**, 127; the name " del," used by E. B. Wilson, " Vector Analysis founded upon the Lectures of J. Willard Gibbs," New York, 1902, 138, is now common. In Continental works ∇^2 is very often denoted by Δ. The expression (1) was used by Laplace in 1787; *Mém. Acad. Sci.*, 1787 (1789), 249 (252).

2 Serret and Scheffers, " Lehrbuch der Differential- und Integralrechnung," 4th–5th edit., Leipzig, 1908, **1**, 163. A more direct " physical " derivation of (7) is given by Lord Kelvin, " Mathematical and Physical Papers," 1884, **1**, 41, and (still more directly) by Riemann, " Partielle Differentialgleichungen," 1938, 177. The treatment in the present paragraph assumes a knowledge of trigonometric functions, discussed later.

$$\frac{\partial u}{\partial x}=\frac{\partial u}{\partial \rho}\frac{\partial \rho}{\partial x}+\frac{\partial u}{\partial \phi}\frac{\partial \phi}{\partial x}=\frac{\partial u}{\partial \rho}\cos\phi-\frac{\partial u}{\partial \phi}\frac{\sin\phi}{\rho} \quad . \quad . \quad . \quad . \quad (3)$$

$$\frac{\partial u}{\partial y}=\frac{\partial u}{\partial \rho}\frac{\partial \rho}{\partial y}+\frac{\partial u}{\partial \phi}\frac{\partial \phi}{\partial y}=\frac{\partial u}{\partial \rho}\sin\phi+\frac{\partial u}{\partial \phi}\frac{\cos\phi}{\rho} \quad . \quad . \quad . \quad . \quad . \quad (4)$$

Since these equations hold for *any* function of x, y, and z, u in (3) can be replaced by $\partial u/\partial x$, and in (4) by $\partial u/\partial y$:

$$\therefore\ \frac{\partial^2 u}{\partial x^2}=\frac{\partial}{\partial \rho}\left(\frac{\partial u}{\partial x}\right)\cos\phi-\frac{\partial}{\partial \phi}\left(\frac{\partial u}{\partial x}\right)\frac{\sin\phi}{\rho}$$

$$\frac{\partial^2 u}{\partial y^2}=\frac{\partial}{\partial \rho}\left(\frac{\partial u}{\partial y}\right)\sin\phi+\frac{\partial}{\partial \phi}\left(\frac{\partial u}{\partial y}\right)\frac{\cos\phi}{\rho}.$$

Since ϕ is constant in partial differentiation by ρ:

$$\frac{\partial^2 u}{\partial x^2}=\frac{\partial}{\partial \rho}\left(\frac{\partial u}{\partial x}\cos\phi\right)+\frac{1}{\rho}\frac{\partial}{\partial \phi}\left(-\frac{\partial u}{\partial x}\sin\phi\right)+\frac{\partial u}{\partial x}\frac{\cos\phi}{\rho}$$

$$\frac{\partial^2 u}{\partial y^2}=\frac{\partial}{\partial \rho}\left(\frac{\partial u}{\partial y}\sin\phi\right)+\frac{1}{\rho}\frac{\partial}{\partial \phi}\left(\frac{\partial u}{\partial y}\cos\phi\right)+\frac{\partial u}{\partial y}\frac{\sin\phi}{\rho}.$$

Add these two equations and, from (3) and (4), put:

$$(\partial u/\partial x)\cos\phi+(\partial u/\partial y)\sin\phi=\partial u/\partial \rho$$

$$-(\partial u/\partial x)\sin\phi+(\partial u/\partial y)\cos\phi=(1/\rho)(\partial u/\partial \phi)$$

$$\therefore\ \frac{\partial^2 u}{\partial x^2}+\frac{\partial^2 u}{\partial y^2}=\frac{\partial^2 u}{\partial \rho^2}+\frac{1}{\rho^2}\frac{\partial^2 u}{\partial \phi^2}+\frac{1}{\rho}\frac{\partial u}{\partial \rho} \quad . \quad . \quad . \quad . \quad . \quad (5)$$

$$\therefore\ \nabla^2 u=\frac{\partial^2 u}{\partial \rho^2}+\frac{1}{\rho^2}\frac{\partial^2 u}{\partial \phi^2}+\frac{1}{\rho}\frac{\partial u}{\partial \rho}+\frac{\partial^2 u}{\partial z^2} \quad . \quad . \quad . \quad . \quad . \quad (6)$$

Since equations (b) on p. 41 follow from (a) if x, y, ρ, ϕ are replaced by z, ρ, r, θ, it follows by analogy that (5) will give:

$$\frac{\partial^2 u}{\partial z^2}+\frac{\partial^2 u}{\partial \rho^2}=\frac{\partial^2 u}{\partial r^2}+\frac{1}{r^2}\frac{\partial^2 u}{\partial \theta^2}+\frac{1}{r}\frac{\partial u}{\partial r}$$

and from (4) the analogous equation:

$$\partial u/\partial \rho=(\partial u/\partial r)\sin\theta+(\partial u/\partial \theta)(\cos\theta/r)$$

is found. Thence (6) becomes:

$$\nabla^2 u=\frac{\partial^2 u}{\partial r^2}+\frac{1}{r^2}\frac{\partial^2 u}{\partial \theta^2}+\frac{1}{r}\frac{\partial u}{\partial r}+\frac{1}{\rho^2}\frac{\partial^2 u}{\partial \phi^2}+\frac{\partial u}{\partial r}\frac{\sin\theta}{\rho}+\frac{\partial u}{\partial \theta}\frac{\cos\theta}{r\rho}.$$

Now put $\rho=r\sin\theta$, and obtain the required equation:

$$\nabla^2 u=\frac{\partial^2 u}{\partial r^2}+\frac{2}{r}\frac{\partial u}{\partial r}+\frac{1}{r^2}\frac{\partial^2 u}{\partial \theta^2}+\frac{\cos\theta}{r^2\sin\theta}\frac{\partial u}{\partial \theta}+\frac{1}{r^2\sin^2\theta}\frac{\partial^2 u}{\partial \phi^2} \quad . \quad . \quad (7)$$

Since
$$\frac{\partial}{\partial \theta}\left(\sin\theta\frac{\partial u}{\partial \theta}\right)=\sin\theta\frac{\partial^2 u}{\partial \theta^2}+\cos\theta\frac{\partial u}{\partial \theta}$$

and
$$\frac{\partial^2}{\partial r^2}(ru)=r\frac{\partial^2 u}{\partial r^2}+2\frac{\partial u}{\partial r}$$

equation (7) can be written in the alternative forms:

$$\nabla^2 u = \frac{\partial^2 u}{\partial r^2} + \frac{2}{r}\frac{\partial u}{\partial r} + \frac{1}{r^2 \sin\theta}\frac{\partial}{\partial\theta}\left(\sin\theta\frac{\partial u}{\partial\theta}\right) + \frac{1}{r^2\sin^2\theta}\frac{\partial^2 u}{\partial\phi^2} \quad . \quad . \quad (8)$$

$$r^2\nabla^2 u = r\frac{\partial^2(ru)}{\partial r^2} + \frac{1}{\sin\theta}\frac{\partial}{\partial\theta}\left(\sin\theta\frac{\partial u}{\partial\theta}\right) + \frac{1}{\sin^2\theta}\frac{\partial^2 u}{\partial\phi^2} \quad . \quad . \quad . \quad . \quad (9)$$

§ 29. Jacobians and Hessians

If $x=\mathrm{f}(u, v)$ and $y=\mathrm{F}(u, v)$ are variables given explicitly as functions of two other variables, u and v, then if z is some function of x and y, $z=\phi(x, y)$:

$$\frac{\partial z}{\partial u} = \frac{\partial z}{\partial x}\frac{\partial \mathrm{f}}{\partial u} + \frac{\partial z}{\partial y}\frac{\partial \mathrm{F}}{\partial u}$$

$$\frac{\partial z}{\partial v} = \frac{\partial z}{\partial x}\frac{\partial \mathrm{f}}{\partial v} + \frac{\partial z}{\partial y}\frac{\partial \mathrm{F}}{\partial v}$$

The expression $\frac{\partial x}{\partial u}\frac{\partial y}{\partial v} - \frac{\partial x}{\partial v}\frac{\partial y}{\partial u}$ is called the *Jacobian* (Jacobi, 1841) of x and y with respect to u and v and is denoted by $\frac{\partial(x, y)}{\partial(u, v)}$ or $\mathrm{J}(x, y)$. Hence

$$\frac{\partial z}{\partial x} = \frac{\partial(z, \mathrm{F})}{\partial(u, v)} \Big/ \frac{\partial(\mathrm{f}, \mathrm{F})}{\partial(u, v)}; \quad \frac{\partial z}{\partial y} = \frac{\partial(\mathrm{f}, z)}{\partial(u, v)} \Big/ \frac{\partial(\mathrm{f}, \mathrm{F})}{\partial(u, v)}.$$

More generally, if u, v, w be functions of the independent variables x, y, z, the Jacobian is compactly written in *functional determinant* form:

$$\frac{\partial(u, v, w)}{\partial(x, y, z)} \equiv \mathrm{J}(u, v, w) \equiv \begin{vmatrix} \frac{\partial u}{\partial x} & \frac{\partial u}{\partial y} & \frac{\partial u}{\partial z} \\ \frac{\partial v}{\partial x} & \frac{\partial v}{\partial y} & \frac{\partial v}{\partial z} \\ \frac{\partial w}{\partial x} & \frac{\partial w}{\partial y} & \frac{\partial w}{\partial z} \end{vmatrix}$$

the determinant being expanded as explained in text-books on algebra,[1] or in special works. The first symbol is due to Donkin (1854).

If the functions u, v, w, are differential coefficients of another function, V: $u=\partial V/\partial x$, $v=\partial V/\partial y$, $w=\partial V/\partial z$, the determinant:

$$\frac{\partial(\partial V/\partial x, \partial V/\partial y, \partial V/\partial z)}{\partial(x, y, z)} \equiv \mathrm{H}(V) \equiv \begin{vmatrix} \frac{\partial^2 V}{\partial x^2} & \frac{\partial^2 V}{\partial x\partial y} & \frac{\partial^2 V}{\partial x\partial z} \\ \frac{\partial^2 V}{\partial y\partial x} & \frac{\partial^2 V}{\partial y^2} & \frac{\partial^2 V}{\partial y\partial z} \\ \frac{\partial^2 V}{\partial z\partial x} & \frac{\partial^2 V}{\partial z\partial y} & \frac{\partial^2 V}{\partial z^2} \end{vmatrix}$$

is called the *Hessian* of V (O. Hesse, 1844).

If $u_1, u_2, \ldots, u_n$ are n functions of the independent variables $x_1, x_2, \ldots, x_x$, the determinant:

$$\begin{vmatrix} \partial u_1/\partial x_1 & \partial u_1/\partial x_2 \ldots & \partial u_1/\partial x_n \\ \partial u_2/\partial x_1 & \partial u_2/\partial x_2 \ldots & \partial u_2/\partial x_n \\ \ldots & \ldots & \ldots \\ \partial u_n/\partial x_1 & \partial u_n/\partial x_2 \ldots & \partial u_n/\partial x_n \end{vmatrix}$$

is called a *Wronskian*.

[1] Briggs and Bryan, "Tutorial Algebra," revised by Walker, 1944, 2, 374.

These determinants[1] are used in transforming multiple integrals and in the theory of differential equations.

§ 30. Euler's Theorem on Homogeneous Functions

A mathematical theorem due to Euler[2] is used in the more mathematical treatment of thermodynamics and other subjects. A function:

$$F(x_1, x_2, \ldots x_n) \quad \ldots \quad (1)$$

of the n variables[3] $x_1, x_2, \ldots x_n$, is said to be *homogeneous* and of the mth *degree* with respect to these variables when the identity:

$$F(kx_1, kx_2, \ldots kx_n)=k^m F(x_1, x_2, \ldots x_n) \quad \ldots \quad (2)$$

is verified for all values of $x_1, x_2, \ldots x_n$, and k. Thus, $x^2+2xy+y^2$ is homogeneous and of the second degree, since if xk and yk are substituted for x and y it becomes $k^2(x^2+2xy+y^2)$. Thus, if :

$$F[k(x_1+\delta x_1), kx_2, \ldots kx_n]=k^m F(x_1+\delta x_1, x_2, \ldots x_n)$$

then $(1/k\delta x_1)\{F[k(x_1+\delta x_1), kx_2, \ldots kx_n]-F(kx_1, kx_2, \ldots kx_n)\}$. (3)

$$=k^{m-1}(1/\delta x_1)[F(x_1+\delta x_1, x_2, \ldots x_n)-F(x_1, x_2, \ldots x_n)] \quad . \quad (4)$$

or, proceeding to the limit $\delta x_1 \to 0$, when (3) and (4) become partial differential coefficients:

$$\frac{\partial F(kx_1, kx_2, \ldots kx_n)}{\partial(kx_1)}=k^{m-1}\frac{\partial F(x_1, x_2, \ldots x_n)}{\partial x_1} \quad . \quad . \quad (5)$$

Differentiate both sides of (2) with respect to k, put $kx_1=u_1$, etc., and write $F(kx_1, kx_2, kx_3, \ldots , kx_n)=F_k$. Then:

$$\partial F_k/\partial k=(\partial F_k/\partial u_1)(\partial u_1/\partial k)+(\partial F_k/\partial u_2)(\partial u_2/\partial k)+ \ldots +(\partial F_k/\partial u_n)(\partial u_n/\partial k)$$
$$=x_1[\partial F_k/\partial(kx_1)]+x_2[\partial F_k/\partial(kx_2)]+ \ldots +x_n[\partial F_k/\partial(kx_n)]$$
$$=mk^{m-1}F(x_1, x_2, \ldots, x_n),$$

from (2) and the result $(x=k)$ that $dx^m/dx=mx^{m-1}$. Hence from (5):

$$x_1\frac{\partial F(x_1, x_2, \ldots x_n)}{\partial x_1}+x_2\frac{\partial F(x_1, x_2, \ldots x_n)}{\partial x_2}+ \ldots +x_n\frac{\partial F(x_1, x_2, \ldots x_n)}{\partial x_n}$$
$$=mF(x_1, x_2, \ldots x_n) \quad . \quad . \quad (6)$$

which is Euler's Theorem.[4] Three important special cases are:

(i) F is a homogeneous function of *zero degree*:

$$\Sigma x_1 \partial F/\partial x_1=0 \quad \ldots \quad (7)$$

[1] See Williamson, "Differential Calculus," 1887, 414, 432; "Integral Calculus," 1888, 320; Forsyth, "Differential Equations," 1914, 12.

[2] This must not be confused with Euler's criterion, given in § 27.

[3] For example, $x_1=x$, $x_2=y$, $x_3=z$, etc.

[4] For alternative proofs see e.g. Partington, "Text Book of Thermodynamics," 1913, 360; Gibson, "Elementary Treatise on the Calculus," 1933, 412; Williamson, "Elementary Treatise on the Differential Calculus," 1887, 123; Haas, in "A Commentary on the Scientific Writings of J. W. Gibbs," New Haven, 1936, **2**, 302. It may be noted that a rational integral homogeneous algebraic function of the mth degree is sometimes called a *quantic*.

(ii) F is a homogeneous function of the *first degree* (not necessarily linear):

$$\Sigma x_1 \partial F/\partial x_1 = F \quad . \; . \; . \; . \; . \; . \; . \; . \; . \quad (8)$$

(iii) F is a homogeneous function of the *second degree*:

$$\Sigma x_1 \partial F/\partial x_1 = 2F \quad . \; . \; . \; . \; . \; . \; . \; . \; . \quad (9)$$

§ 31. Mean Value Theorem and Rolle's Theorem

If x is any number lying between a and b ($a \leqslant x \leqslant b$) then $x-a$ and $b-a$ are of the same sign whether a is less or greater than b. E.g. if $a=1$, $x=2$, and $b=3$, then $x-a=1$ and $b-a=2$; if $a=3$, $x=2$, $b=1$, then $x-a=-1$ and $b-a=-2$, and so on. Hence $(x-a)/(b-a)$ is a *positive* proper fraction, θ, and $x=a+\theta(b-a)$. Suppose $b=a+h$, therefore $b-a=h$, and $x=a+\theta h$.

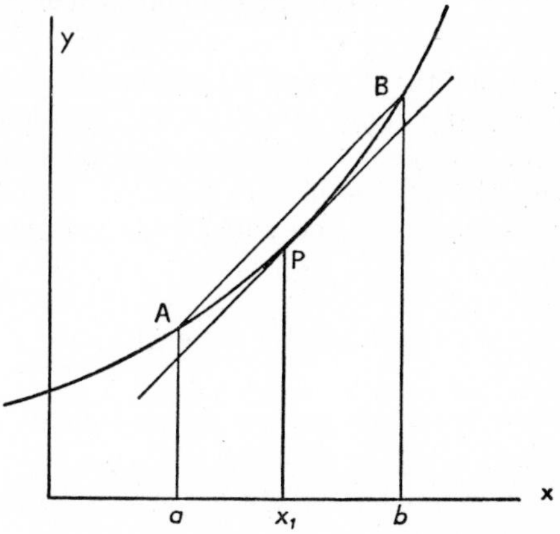

FIG. 16.I. The Mean Value Theorem

Now consider any curve $y=f(x)$, Fig. 16.I, and take two points A [$x=a$, $y=f(a)$] and B [$x=b$, $y=f(b)$] on it. Join AB. The gradient of the *chord* AB is $[f(b)-f(a)]/(b-a)$. It is assumed as obvious that there is at least one point P [$x=x_1$, $y=f(x_1)$] on the curve between A and B such that the *tangent* to the curve at P is parallel to, i.e. has the same gradient as, the chord AB. The gradient of the tangent is $dy/dx = f'(x_1)$; hence:

$$[f(b)-f(a)]/(b-a) = f'(x_1) \quad . \; . \; . \; . \; . \; . \; . \quad (1)$$

This is called the *Mean Value Theorem*. Thus:

$$[f(a+h)-f(a)]/h = f'(a+\theta h) \quad . \; . \; . \; . \; . \; . \; . \quad (2)$$

If a continuous function $f(x)$ vanishes when $x=a$ and also when $x=b$, then its derived function $f'(x)=df(x)/dx$, if it is also continuous, must vanish for some value of x between a and b (*Rolle's Theorem*).[1]

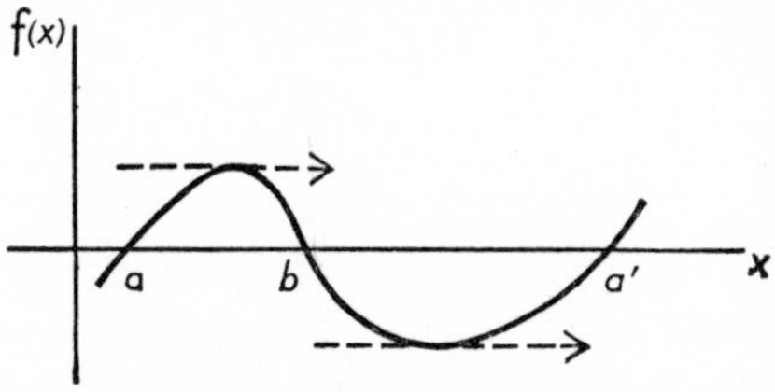

FIG. 17.I. Rolle's Theorem

This is sufficiently obvious for our purposes on inspection of Fig. 17.I, whence it is seen that, if $f(x)$ has the value 0 for the two values a and b (or b and a') (one of which may be 0), it has a maximum or minimum value between them, and for this value the tangent is parallel to the x axis, or $f'(x)=0$.

§ 32. Taylor's Theorem

The *binomial series* in Algebra and the *exponential series* (§ 13) are special cases of a general form of the *expansion of a function in a power series* which is

[1] "Traité d'Algèbre," Paris, 1690; Lagrange in 1797 spoke of it as: "ce beau théorème nouveau"!

called *Taylor's Theorem,* first published by Brook Taylor in his " Methodus Incrementorum " in 1715 as a corollary from a theorem in finite differences. The theorem may be stated as follows. Let $f(x+h)$ be any function of x *which is capable of expansion in a convergent series of positive integral powers of x* (when the function is called *regular*), then:

$$\left.\begin{aligned} f(x+h) &= f(x)+h\,.\,\frac{df(x)}{dx}+\frac{h^2}{2!}\cdot\frac{d^2f(x)}{dx^2}+\ldots+\frac{h^n}{n!}\,\frac{d^nf(x)}{dx^n}+\ldots \\ &= f(x)+hf'(x)+\frac{h^2}{2!}f''(x)+\frac{h^3}{3!}f'''(x)+\ldots \end{aligned}\right\} \quad (1)$$

provided that $f(x)$ and its differential coefficients (or derivatives) are continuous within the range of values of x considered. A proof[1] of Taylor's Theorem is as follows. Let the function $f(x+z)$ and all its derivatives up to the nth inclusive: $f'(x+z)$, $f''(x+z)$, . . . $f^n(x+z)$, be finite and continuous within the values $z=0$ and $z=h$ of the variable increment z. Then it will be proved that:

$$f(x+h)=f(x)+hf'(x)+\frac{h^2}{2!}f''(x)+\ldots+\frac{h^{n-1}}{(n-1)!}f^{n-1}(x)+\frac{h^n}{n!}f^n(x+\theta h)$$

where θ is some positive proper fraction (i.e. less than 1). Assume:

$$f(x+h)=f(x)+hf'(x)+\frac{h^2}{2!}f''(x)+\ldots+\frac{h^{n-1}}{(n-1)!}f^{n-1}(x)+\frac{h^n}{n!}R \quad . \quad (2)$$

where R is a function of x and h. It is to be proved that the remainder $R=f^n(x+\theta h)$. Let the function:

$$\phi(z)=f(x+z)-zf'(x)-\frac{z^2}{2!}f''(x)-\ldots-\frac{z^{n-1}}{(n-1)!}f^{n-1}(x)-\frac{z^n}{n!}R$$

be differentiated n times with respect to z, keeping x constant:

$$\begin{aligned} &f'(x+z)-f'(x)-zf''(x)-\ldots-\frac{z^{n-2}}{(n-2)!}f^{n-1}(x)-\frac{z^{n-1}}{(n-1)!}R=\phi'(z) \\ &f''(x+z)\qquad -f''(x)-\ldots-\frac{z^{n-2}}{(n-3)!}f^{n-1}(x)-\frac{z^{n-2}}{(n-2)!}R=\phi''(z) \\ &\ldots \qquad\qquad\qquad\qquad\qquad\qquad\qquad\qquad \ldots \\ &f^{n-1}(x+z)\qquad\qquad\qquad\qquad -f^{n-1}(x)\qquad -zR=\phi^{n-1}(z) \\ &f^n(x+z)\qquad\qquad\qquad\qquad\qquad\qquad\qquad\qquad -R=\phi^n(z) \end{aligned}$$

All the functions $\phi(z)$, $\phi'(z)$, . . . $\phi^n(z)$ are finite and continuous between the values 0 and h of the variable z, and $\phi(0)$, $\phi'(0)$, . . . $\phi^{n-1}(0)$, found by putting $z=0$ *after* differentiation, are evidently all zero; also, from (2), $\phi(h)=0$. If $\phi(z)$ is continuous between 0 and h, Rolle's Theorem (§ 31) shows that it must have a maximum or minimum value for some value of z between 0 and h,

[1] For an adequate consideration of Taylor's Theorem see e.g. Hobson, " Theory of Functions of a Real Variable," Cambridge, 1907, 501. Most mathematical works are, very properly, more concerned with exceptions to the validity of Taylor's Theorem than with its applications; the interest is then, it has been said, in the " pathology of functions." With certain restrictions, it holds for the complex variable $z=x+iy$, where $i=\sqrt{-1}$.

say h_1 for which $\phi'(z)=0$. Hence $\phi'(z)=0$ for some value h_1 of z between 0 and h $(h_1<h)$. Further differentiation gives, similarly:

$$\phi''(z)=0 \text{ for some value } h_2 \text{ of } z \text{ between 0 and } h_1\ (h_2<h_1),$$

$$\therefore\ \phi'''(z)=0 \text{ for some value } h_3 \text{ of } z \text{ between 0 and } h_3\ (h_3<h_2).$$

$$\ldots \qquad \ldots$$

$$\therefore\ \phi^n(z)=0 \text{ for some value } h_n \text{ of } z \text{ between 0 and } h_n\ (h_n<h_{n-1}).$$

Thus:
$$f^n(x+h_n)-R=0.$$

Since $h_n<h_{n-1}<h_{n-2}< \ldots <h_2<h_1<h$, it is possible to put $h_n=\theta h$, where θ is some positive proper fraction, therefore $R=f^n(x+\theta h)$, which was to be proved. If this remainder vanishes with h when n increases indefinitely, the finite series (2) can be identified with the infinite series (1).

Taylor's Theorem will fail when: (i) $f(x)$ or one of its derivatives becomes *infinite* between the values of the variable considered; (ii) $f(x)$ or one of its derivatives becomes *discontinuous* between the same values of the variable; (iii) the remainder $(h^n/n!)f^n(x+\theta h)$ cannot be made to vanish when $n\to\infty$, or the series is not convergent.

§ 33. Special Cases of Taylor's Theorem.

Some important series are special cases of Taylor's Theorem.

(1) *The Binomial Series.* Put y for x in (1), § 32, and let $f(y)=y^n$, so that $f(y+h)=(y+h)^n$. Then:

$$\frac{df(y)}{dx}=ny^{n-1},\quad \frac{d^2f(y)}{dx^2}=n(n-1)y^{n-2},\quad \frac{d^3f(y)}{dx^3}=n(n-1)(n-2)y^{n-3}, \text{ etc.}$$

The coefficients proceed according to a definite plan, and it is easily seen that after r differentiations:

$$\frac{d^rf(y)}{dx^r}=n(n-1)(n-2)\ \ldots\ (n-r+1)y^{n-r}.$$

Now put $h=x$ and $y=1$, then Taylor's Theorem gives:

$$(1+x)^n=1+nx+\frac{n(n-1)}{2!}x^2+\frac{n(n-1)(n-2)}{3!}x^3+\ \ldots$$
$$+\frac{n(n-1)(n-2)\ \ldots\ (n-r+1)}{r!}x^r+\ \ldots \qquad (1)$$

where the last term given is the $(r+1)$th. This is the *Binomial Series*, published by Newton in 1669.

If n is a positive integer the series will terminate at the $(n+1)$th term, which will contain the factor $(n-n)=0$, and since all the later coefficients also contain this factor, they also are all zero. But if n is not a positive integer, i.e. is negative or fractional, not one of the factors n, $(n-1)$, $(n-2)$, etc., can vanish, and the series will contain an infinite number of terms. In this case it is necessary to inquire whether it still has a finite sum, when it is said to be *convergent*, or whether this is not the case, when the series is said to be *divergent*. There are several *tests of convergency* of series:[1] the following (*D'Alembert's test*) is

[1] These are treated in works on algebra; the standard treatise is Bromwich, " An Introduction to the Theory of Infinite Series," 2nd edit., 1926; see also Knopp, " Theory and Application of Infinite Series," transl. Young, 1928 or 1944.

sufficient for our purpose: the infinite series $u_1+u_2+u_3+ \ldots +u_n+ \ldots$, where $u_1, u_2, \ldots$ are functions of x, is convergent if the limiting value of u_{r+1}/u_r is numerically less than unity, where u_{r+1} is the rth term of the series.

In the Binomial Series:

$$u_r=\frac{n(n-1)(n-2)\ldots(n-r+2)x^{r-1}}{(r-1)!}$$

$$u_{r+1}=\frac{n(n-1)(n-2)\ldots(n-r+2)(n-r+1)x^r}{r!}$$

$$\therefore\ u_{r+1}/u_r=(n-r+1)x/r=-x[1-(n+1)/r]$$

$$\therefore\ \lim_{r\to\infty}(u_{r+1}/u_r)=-x, \text{ since } \lim_{r\to\infty}[(n+1)/r]=0.$$

Thus, for convergence, x must be *numerically* less than 1. The numerical value of x is denoted by $|x|$, and the Binomial Series for a negative or fractional index n is convergent[1] when $-1<|x|<1$.

It may be noted that the so-called *binomial coefficients* are often represented by:

$$\binom{n}{k}=\binom{n}{n-k}=\frac{n!}{k!(n-k)!}$$

where $\binom{n}{k}$ is the number of combinations of n distinct things taken k at a time, which is also equal to the number of combinations when they are taken $n-k$ at a time:

$$(1+x)^n=\sum_r\binom{n}{r}x^{n-r}$$

Since $(a+x)^n=a^n(1+x/a)^n$, where a is a positive constant, there is no loss of generality in taking $(1+x)^n$ as the standard form of the Binomial Series, provided $|x/a|<1$, i.e. $x<a$. If $x>a$, the expansion of $x^n(1+a/x)^n$ is taken.

(2) *The Exponential Series.* Let $f(y)=e^y$, then $f(y+h)=e^{y+h}$. Then *all* the differential coefficients of e^y are equal to e^y, from the property of the exponential function (§ 13). Substitute in Taylor's Series, then:

$$e^{y+h}=f(y+h)=e^y(1+h+h^2/2!+h^3/3!+\ldots).$$

Put $h=x$ and $y=0$, then

$$e^x=1+x+x^2/2!+x^3/3!+\ldots \quad (2)$$

which is the exponential series (§ 13). It is evident from inspection that the rth term is $u_r=x^{r-1}/(r-1)!$, and $u_{r+1}=x^r/r!$ Therefore $u_{r+1}/u_r=x/r$, which vanishes for $r\to\infty$ for *all* finite values of x, for which the series is therefore convergent.

§ 34. Maclaurin's Theorem

In Taylor's Series (1), § 32, put $x=0$, then if all the differential coefficients of $f(x)$ remain finite:

$$f(h)=f(0)+h\frac{df(0)}{dx}+\frac{h^2}{2!}\frac{d^2f(0)}{dx^2}+\ldots\frac{h^n}{n!}\frac{d^nf(0)}{dx^n}+\ldots$$

$$=f(0)+hf'(0)+(h^2/2!)f''(0)+\ldots+(h^n/n!)f^n(0)+\ldots,$$

[1] The cases when $x=\pm1$ are unimportant and their consideration is difficult and tedious: see Chrystal, "Algebra," 1900, **2**, 186. They were first considered by Abel in 1826, who also considered imaginary exponents.

where, e.g. $d^2f(0)/dx^2$ or $f''(0)$, means that $f(x)$ is differentiated twice with respect to x, and then x put equal to zero *in the result after differentiation.* Now put $h=x$, then:

$$f(x)=f(0)+x\frac{df(0)}{dx}+\frac{x^2}{2!}\frac{d^2f(0)}{dx^2}+\ \ldots\ +\frac{x^n}{n!}\frac{d^nf(0)}{dx^n}+\ \ldots$$

$$=f(0)+xf'(0)+(x^2/2!)f''(0)+\ \ldots\ +(x^n/n!)f^n(0)+\ \ldots \qquad (1)$$

which is usually called *Maclaurin's Theorem.* It was noticed as a special case of Taylor's Theorem by Stirling in 1717, and was independently published by Maclaurin in 1742 without any claim to originality.[1]

Example. Let $f(x)=\ln(1+x)$, where $|x|<1$. Then $f(0)=\ln 1=0$, $f'(0)=1/(1+x)=1$, $f''(0)=-1/(1+x)^2=-1$, $f'''(0)=2/(1+x)^3=2$, and the general term is seen to be $(-1)^{n-1}(n-1)!/(1+x)^n$, or $f^n(0)=(-1)^{n-1}(n-1)!$. Hence by substitution in (1):

$$\ln(1+x)=x-x^2/2+x^3/3-x^4/4+\ \ldots\ +(-1)^{n-1}x^n/n+\ \ldots \qquad (2)$$

This series, first given by Mercator in 1668, can be found directly as follows:

$$\ln(1+x)=\int dx/(1+x)=\int(1+x)^{-1}dx=\int(1-x+x^2-x^3+\ \ldots)dx,$$

by division. The integral is $x-x^2/2+x^3/3-x^4/4+\ \ldots$, the constant vanishing when the lower limit of integration is $x=0$.

By putting $x=-x$ in (2) it is found that:

$$\ln(1-x)=-x-x^2/2-x^3/3-x^4/4-\ \ldots \qquad (3)$$

and by subtraction of (3) from (2):

$$\ln\frac{1+x}{1-x}=2\left(x+\frac{x^3}{3}+\frac{x^5}{5}+\ \ldots\right) \qquad (4)$$

If $x>0$, put $(1+x)/(1-x)=(y+1)/y$, therefore $x=1/(2y+1)<1$,

$$\therefore\ \ln(y+1)=\ln y+2\left[\frac{1}{(2y+1)}+\frac{1}{3}\left(\frac{1}{2y+1}\right)^3+\frac{1}{5}\left(\frac{1}{2y+1}\right)^5+\ \ldots\right].$$

By putting $y=1$, ln 2 is found by summing the series, which converges rapidly, and the natural logarithms of successive integers are so found; e.g. $\ln 4=2\ln 2$; ln 5 by putting $y=4$; $\ln 6=\ln 2+\ln 3$, etc.

It should be noted that $\ln x$ itself cannot be expanded, since $f(0)$, $f'(0)$, $f''(0)$, . . ., are all infinite, and the series fails.

§ 35. Symbolic Form of Taylor's Theorem

For a function of *two* (or more) variables the expansion takes the form (Fontana, 1788):

$$f(x+h,y+k)=f(x,y)+h\frac{\partial f}{\partial x}+k\frac{\partial f}{\partial y}+\frac{1}{2!}\left(h^2\frac{\partial^2 f}{\partial x^2}+2hk\frac{\partial^2 f}{\partial x\partial y}+k^2\frac{\partial^2 f}{\partial y^2}\right)+\ \ldots \qquad (1)$$

as can be shown for conditions in which Taylor's Theorem holds good. The demonstration will not be given. The expression in the brackets may be written in *symbolic form* as $(h\,.\,\partial/\partial x+k\,.\,\partial/\partial y)^2f$, the *operational symbols* $\partial/\partial x$ and $\partial/\partial y$ being treated like algebraic quantities. Further terms will be $(1/3!)(h\,.\,\partial/\partial x+k\,.\,\partial/\partial y)^3f$, etc. For three variables:

$$f(x+h,y+k,z+l)=f(x,y,z)+(h\,.\,\partial/\partial x+k\,.\,\partial/\partial y+l\,.\,\partial/\partial z)f$$
$$+(1/2)(h\,.\,\partial/\partial x+k\,.\,\partial/\partial y+l\,.\,\partial/\partial z)^2f+\ \ldots,\ \text{etc.} \qquad (2)$$

[1] The tendency in modern mathematical works is to omit any mention of Maclaurin in connexion with this series.

§ 36. Singularities of a Function

A function f(x) is *regular* (or *analytical*, or *holomorphic*) at a point $x=a$ if it can be expanded by Taylor's Theorem in a series of positive integral powers of $(x-a)$ in the neighbourhood of a. If the values of f(a), f'(a), f''(a) . . . are all zero, and $f^n(x)$ is the first derivative which is not zero, then:

$$f(x)=[(x-a)^n/n!]f^n[a+\theta(x-a)]$$

where $\theta<1$ (§ 32), is called a *zero* of the function, of order n.

A point $x=a$, where f(x) is not regular, is called a *singular point*, and Taylor's Theorem cannot be applied immediately at this point. But f(x) can now be expanded in the form:

$$f(x)=(x-a)^{-m}[A_0+A_1(x-a)+ \ . \ . \ .]$$

where m is an integer, and the point a where f(x) becomes infinite is called a *pole* of order m. The terms containing the negative powers form the *principal part* of the function relative to the pole a, the coefficient of $(x-a)^{-1}$ being called the *residue*, and $(x-a)^m f(x)$ is a regular function. But if m is not finite, the point a is called an *essential singularity*.

Any function which can be expanded in the form:

$$f(x)=(x-a)^p[A_0+A_1(x-a)+ \ . \ . \ .]$$

where p is a positive or negative integer, is called a *single valued* or *uniform* function. If p is fractional, the function is *many valued* or *multiform*. The simplest uniform function is the rational algebraic function (§ 2), the zeros of the function being the roots of the numerator, and the poles, where it becomes infinite, the roots of the denominator.[1]

§ 37. Leibniz's Theorem

Let y be a product of two functions of x: $y=f(x) \,.\, F(x)=uv$. It is required to find d^ny/dx^n. Denote

$$dy/dx,\ d^2y/dx^2,\ .\ .\ .\ d^ny/dx^n \text{ by } y',\ y'',\ .\ .\ .\ y^n$$
$$du/dx,\ d^2u/dx^2,\ .\ .\ .\ d^nu/dx^n \text{ by } u',\ u'',\ .\ .\ .\ u^n$$
$$dv/dx,\ d^2v/dx^2,\ .\ .\ .\ d^nv/dx^n \text{ by } v',\ v'',\ .\ .\ .\ v^n.$$

The rule for differentiation of a product (4), § 6, gives:

$$y'=uv'+vu'$$
$$y''=(uv''+u'v')+(vu''+u'v')=uv''+2u'v'+vu''$$
$$y'''=(uv'''+u'v'')+2(u'v''+v'u'')+(vu'''+u''v')$$
$$=uv'''+3u'v''+3u''v'+vu'''.$$

The coefficients are the same as those in the expansion of $(a+b)^2$ and $(a+b)^3$, and for the nth differentiation we infer that they will be the same as in the binomial expansion (§ 33) of $(a+b)^n$:

$$y^{(n)}=uv^{(n)}+nu'v^{(n-1)}+\frac{n(n-1)}{2!}u''v^{(n-2)}+ \ . \ . \ . \ +nu^{(n-1)}v'+u^{(n)}v \qquad (1)$$

[1] The study of singularities may be pursued in Forsythe's "Theory of Functions of a Complex Variable," Cambridge, 2nd edit., 1900, 3rd edit., 1918, or Harkness and Morley's "A Treatise on the Theory of Functions," 1893, but is not much required in physical chemistry. The most important part of the theory is Cauchy's Theorem of residues in complex integration.

which is Leibniz's Theorem. This can be written in full as:

$$\frac{d^n(uv)}{dx^n}=u\frac{d^n v}{dx^n}+n\frac{du}{dx}\frac{d^{n-1}v}{dx^{n-1}}+\frac{n(n-1)}{2!}\frac{d^2u}{dx^2}\frac{d^{n-2}v}{dx^{n-2}}+\ \ldots\ +v\frac{d^n u}{dx^n}.$$

If D_u denotes[1] differentiation of u with respect to x, and D_v differentiation of v with respect to x, the equation can be expressed in the compact symbolic form:

$$d^n(uv)/dx^n=(D_u+D_v)^n uv \quad . \quad . \quad . \quad . \quad . \quad . \quad . \quad . \quad (2)$$

where the operator sum is expanded by the Binomial Theorem.

Leibniz's Theorem is required in the study of spherical harmonics (considered later), and some other cases.

§ 38. Maximum and Minimum Values of a Function of Two Variables

Let

$$u=f(x, y) \quad . \quad . \quad . \quad . \quad . \quad . \quad . \quad . \quad . \quad . \quad (1)$$

be a continuous function of x and y which can be expanded in a power series. Equation (1) may be regarded as the equation of a surface, $u=z$ being the height of any point above the x, y plane. If x and y increase by small amounts h and k, respectively, the small increment of u is given by (1), § 35, as:

$$du=h\frac{\partial f}{\partial x}+k\frac{\partial f}{\partial y}+\frac{1}{2}\left(h^2\frac{\partial^2 f}{\partial x^2}+2hk\frac{\partial^2 f}{\partial x\partial y}+k^2\frac{\partial^2 f}{\partial y^2}\right)+\ \ldots \quad . \quad . \quad (2)$$

Since x and y are independent, either may be supposed to vary while the other is constant, and the condition for a maximum or minimum value of u is thus, by § 9:

$$\partial f/\partial x=0 \quad \text{and} \quad \partial f/\partial y=0 \quad . \quad . \quad . \quad . \quad . \quad . \quad . \quad . \quad (3)$$

If x_0, y_0 are values for which z has a maximum or minimum value, and A, B, C are the corresponding values of $\partial^2 f/\partial x^2$, $\partial^2 f/\partial x\partial y$, and $\partial^2 f/\partial y^2$:

$$f(x_0+h, y_0+k)-f(x_0, y_0)=\tfrac{1}{2}(Ah^2+2Bhk+Ck^2)+\ .\ .\ .\ .\ . \quad (4)$$

and when h and k are very small all terms except the one given may be neglected. Hence the *sign* of $f(x_0+h, y_0+k)-f(x_0, y_0)$ depends in general[2] on that of:

$$Ah^2+2Bhk+Ck^2=(1/A)[(Ah+Bk)^2+k^2(AC-B^2)] \quad . \quad . \quad (5)$$

If this is to be always positive, or always negative, for all small values of h and k, $(AC-B^2)$ must not be negative, since if it were the expression in the brackets [ ] would be positive when $k=0$, and negative when $Ah+Bk=0$. Hence, for a real maximum or minimum, *AC must not be less* than B^2, or (omitting the case of equality; see below):

$$\frac{\partial^2 f}{\partial x^2}\frac{\partial^2 f}{\partial y^2}>\left(\frac{\partial^2 f}{\partial x\partial y}\right)^2 \quad . \quad . \quad . \quad . \quad . \quad . \quad . \quad . \quad (6)$$

Since, for a *maximum value*, the left of (4) must be *negative*, and for a *minimum value* it must be *positive*, for all small values of h and k (see § 9), and since $(AC-B^2)$ is either positive or zero, the sign of the expression must, by (5), be determined by that of A, outside the brackets [ ], and hence, when (6) is satisfied, the function has a *maximum value* when $\partial^2 f/\partial x^2$ (or $\partial^2 f/\partial y^2$) is *negative*,

[1] The D notation is due to Arbogast, and is best postponed until differential equations are reached, when it becomes indispensable. The symbols d_u and d_v are sometimes used, but are very confusing.

[2] This condition is sometimes violated. but the results reached below are valid.

and a *minimum value* when it is *positive*. Equation (6) is called *Lagrange's criterion* for a maximum or minimum of f(x, y).

If A, B, and C all vanish, it is necessary to consider terms of the third and fourth degree in h and k in the expansion (2); for this, and the general case when f is a function of any number of variables, reference must be made to mathematical works.[1]

If, instead of $>$ in (6), the sign is $<$, then $\partial^2 f/\partial x^2$ and $\partial^2 f/\partial y^2$ have different signs (since the expression on the right is always positive), and the function has neither a maximum nor a minimum value; on a surface this would correspond, e g. with the top of a "pass" going in one direction but bounded by still higher "ground" on each side; or with the lowest part of a "ridge," sloping down to lower levels on each side, respectively. The case when the sign in (6) is $=$ is dealt with only in advanced mathematical works; [2] it may, but usually does not, correspond with a maximum or minimum.

Let $u=x^3+y^3-3axy$ (a=const.), then

$$\partial u/\partial x=3x^2-3ay=0 \quad \therefore\ y=x^2/a;\ \partial u/\partial y=3y^2-3ax=0,$$

$$\therefore\ y^2-ax=x^4/a^2-ax=0, \quad \therefore\ x^4-a^3x=0 \quad \text{or} \quad x(x^3-a^3)=0.$$

The real roots are $x=0$ and $x=a$, therefore $y=x^2/a=a$ or 0. Also:

$$\partial^2 u/\partial x^2=6x, \qquad \partial^2 u/\partial x\partial y=-3a, \qquad \partial^2 u/\partial y^2=6y;$$

hence (with the notation above) for the two roots:

$$x=0: \quad A=0,\ B=-3a,\ C=0,$$

$$x=a: \quad A=6a,\ B=-3a,\ C=6a$$

(since if $x=a$, $y=a$). Hence for $x=a$: $AC=36a^2$, $B^2=9a^2$, which satisfies the condition for a maximum or a minimum, and as A is positive, it is a minimum. The case $x=0$ makes $AC=0$, $B^2=9a^2$, and gives neither a maximum nor a minimum. The minimum value of u in the first case is $a^3+a^3-3a^3=-a^3$.

§ 39. Differentiation of a Definite Integral

Let the indefinite integral of a function f(x, c) involving a parameter (§ 26) c, be F(x, c). Then the definite integral between the limits a and b is:

$$J=\int_a^b \mathrm{f}(x, c)\mathrm{d}x=\mathrm{F}(b, c)-\mathrm{F}(a, c).$$

If a, b, and c are functions of some variable t:

$$\partial J/\partial a=-(\partial/\partial a)\mathrm{F}(a, c)=-\mathrm{f}(a, c),$$

$$\partial J/\partial b=(\partial/\partial b)\mathrm{F}(b, c)=\mathrm{f}(b, c),$$

$$\partial J/\partial c=(\partial/\partial c)\int_a^b \mathrm{f}(x, c)\mathrm{d}x=\int_a^b (\partial/\partial c)\mathrm{f}(x, c)\,.\,\mathrm{d}x,$$

$$\therefore\ \mathrm{d}J/\mathrm{d}t=(\partial J/\partial a)(\mathrm{d}a/\mathrm{d}t)+(\partial J/\partial b)(\mathrm{d}b/\mathrm{d}t)+(\partial J/\partial c)(\mathrm{d}c/\mathrm{d}t)$$

$$=\mathrm{f}(b, c)(\mathrm{d}b/\mathrm{d}t)-\mathrm{f}(a, c)(\mathrm{d}a/\mathrm{d}t)+\int_a^b [\partial \mathrm{f}(x, c)/\partial c]\mathrm{d}x \quad . \quad \mathbf{(1)}$$

[1] See e.g. Williamson, "Differential Calculus," 1887, 191 f.; Gibson, "Advanced Calculus," 1931, 216.

[2] Goursat, "Cours d'Analyse Mathématique," 4th edit., 1924, **1**, 107; Hobson, "Theory of Functions of a Real Variable," Cambridge, 1926, **2**, 214.

TRIGONOMETRIC FUNCTIONS

§ 40. Trigonometric Functions

Let ABC (Fig. 18.I) be a right-angled triangle. Then if the angle BAC (positive when described anti-clockwise) be denoted by α (θ is often used), the *primary trigonometric functions*, the *sine*, *cosine*, and *tangent* of α are defined by the ratios:

$$\sin \alpha = BC/AC, \qquad \cos \alpha = AB/AC, \qquad \tan \alpha = BC/AB = \sin \alpha/\cos \alpha.$$

What may be called *secondary functions* are:

$$\text{secant } \alpha = \sec \alpha = 1/\cos \alpha, \qquad \text{cosecant } \alpha = \text{cosec } \alpha = 1/\sin \alpha,$$
$$\text{cotangent } \alpha = \cot \alpha = 1/\tan \alpha.$$

The angle α is measured in *radians*, a radian (or unit of circular measure of an angle) being the angle subtended by two radii of a circle of unit radius when the part of the circumference between them is of unit length. Thus, as the total circumference is 2π, the right-angle 90° is $\frac{1}{4}(2\pi) = \pi/2$ radians, and $x° = (\pi/180)x$ radians. The values of the functions for zero angle are $\sin 0 = 0$, $\cos 0 = 1$, $\tan 0 = 0$. Since trigonometrical tables always give the functions in degrees, minutes, and seconds, a circular measure must be converted into these in order to find its function from the tables.

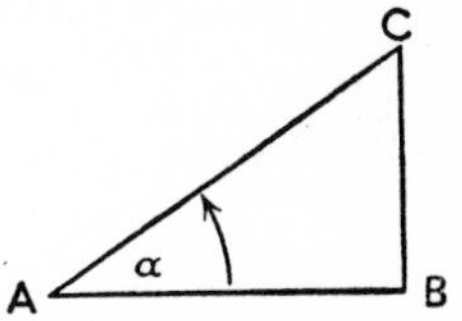

FIG. 18.I. Trigonometric Functions

The angle α may be regarded as generated by the line AC, the direction $\overrightarrow{AC}$ being always positive, rotating about A from the position $\overrightarrow{AB}$ taken as positive. If the region from $\alpha = 0$ to $\alpha = 90°$ or $\pi/2$ radians is called the *first quadrant*, the region $\pi/2$ to π the *second quadrant*, the region π to $3\pi/2$ the *third quadrant*, and the region $3\pi/2$ to 2π the *fourth quadrant*, then all possible values of the trigonometric functions are included in these, since after a complete revolution ($\alpha = 2\pi$) the sequence begins again. Thus the functions are *periodic*, the value for $\alpha = x + 2n\pi$, where n is any positive or negative integer, being the same as the value for $x = \alpha$; 2π is called the *period* of the function. The functions $\tan \alpha$ and $\cot \alpha$ have also the shorter period π. This is best appreciated by drawing the graphs of $\sin x$, $\cos x$, $\tan x$, and $\cot x$. When n is any positive or negative integer or zero:

$$\sin x = \sin[n\pi + (-1)^n x] \qquad \cos x = \cos(2n\pi \pm x).$$

The signs and limits of the trigonometric functions are tabulated below: e.g. if α is between 0 and $\pi/2$, $\sin \alpha$, $\cos \alpha$, and $\tan \alpha$ are obviously all positive, since AB and BC are both positive; but if α is between $\pi/2$ and π, AB is negative and BC positive, hence $\sin \alpha$ is positive, $\cos \alpha$ negative, and $\tan \alpha$ also negative, and so on.

Function	Quadrant I	Quadrant II	Quadrant III	Quadrant IV
sin	+ 0 to 1	+ 1 to 0	− 0 to 1	− 1 to 0
cos	+ 1 to 0	− 0 to 1	− 1 to 0	+ 0 to 1
tan	+ 0 to ∞	− ∞ to 0	+ 0 to ∞	− ∞ to 0
cot	+ ∞ to 0	− 0 to ∞	+ ∞ to 0	− 0 to ∞
sec	+ 1 to ∞	− ∞ to 1	− 1 to ∞	+ ∞ to 1
cosec	+ ∞ to 1	+ 1 to ∞	− ∞ to 1	− 1 to ∞

It is seen that $\sin(-\alpha) = -\sin \alpha$ and $\cos(-\alpha) = \cos \alpha$.

Important special values of the functions are:

	0°	30°	45°	60°	90°	180°	270°	360°
sin	0	$\frac{1}{2}$	$\sqrt{2}/2$	$\sqrt{3}/2$	1	0	-1	0
cos	1	$\sqrt{3}/2$	$\sqrt{2}/2$	$\frac{1}{2}$	0	-1	0	1
tan	0	$\sqrt{3}/3$	1	$\sqrt{3}$	∞	0	∞	0

In Fig. 19.I let the angle xOR=A. Draw TR at right-angles to OR, and on it take equal lengths PR and QR, such that $\widehat{POR}=\widehat{QOR}=B$. Draw perpen-

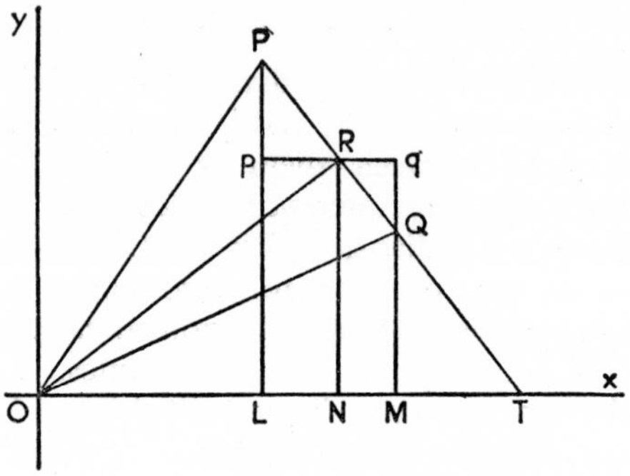

FIG. 19.I. Trigonometric Functions of Sum or Difference of Twc Angles

diculars PL, QM, RN, and draw pRq parallel to Ox. The triangles ONR, PpR, and RqQ are similar (since $Pp \perp ON$, etc.). The geometry of the figure shows that:

$$\sin(A\pm B)=\frac{LP}{OP} \quad\text{or}\quad \frac{MQ}{OQ}=\frac{NR\pm pP}{OP}=\frac{NR}{OR}\cdot\frac{OR}{OP}\pm\frac{pP}{RP}\cdot\frac{RP}{OP}$$

$$=\sin A\cos B\pm\cos A\sin B.$$

$$\cos(A\pm B)=\frac{OL}{OP} \quad\text{or}\quad \frac{OM}{OQ}=\frac{ON\mp Rq}{OQ}=\frac{ON}{OR}\cdot\frac{OR}{OQ}\mp\frac{Rq}{RQ}\cdot\frac{RQ}{OQ}$$

$$=\cos A\cos B\mp\sin A\sin B$$

The cases when A or B is greater than a right angle are easily found from appropriate figures. Thus, if A and B are *any* two angles:

$$\sin(A+B)=\sin A\cos B+\cos A\sin B \quad . \quad . \quad . \quad . \quad . \quad (1)$$

$$\sin(A-B)=\sin A\cos B-\cos A\sin B \quad . \quad . \quad . \quad . \quad . \quad (2)$$

$$\cos(A+B)=\cos A\cos B-\sin A\sin B \quad . \quad . \quad . \quad . \quad . \quad (3)$$

$$\cos(A-B)=\cos A\cos B+\sin A\sin B \quad . \quad . \quad . \quad . \quad . \quad (4)$$

From these, and the important formula

$$\sin^2 A+\cos^2 A=1 \quad . \quad . \quad . \quad . \quad . \quad . \quad . \quad . \quad (5)$$

(which is merely the trigonometrical equivalent of $OR^2=ON^2+NR^2$ in Fig. 19.I), a number of other equations are easily found.

Add (1) and (2), and (3) and (4), then:

$$\sin(A+B)+\sin(A-B)=2\sin A\cos B \quad . \quad . \quad . \quad (6)$$

$$\cos(A+B)+\cos(A-B)=2\cos A\cos B \quad . \quad . \quad . \quad . \quad (7)$$

In (1)–(4) put A=B and use (5), then:

$$\sin 2A=2\sin A\cos A \quad . \quad . \quad . \quad . \quad . \quad . \quad . \quad (8)$$

$$\cos 2A=\cos^2 A-\sin^2 A=2\cos^2 A-1=1-2\sin^2 A \quad . \quad . \quad (9)$$

$$\therefore \cos^2 \tfrac{1}{2}A=\tfrac{1}{2}(1+\cos A) \quad . \quad . \quad . \quad . \quad . \quad . \quad . \quad (10)$$

$$\sin^2 \tfrac{1}{2}A=\tfrac{1}{2}(1-\cos A) \quad . \quad . \quad . \quad . \quad . \quad . \quad . \quad (11)$$

by putting $A=\tfrac{1}{2}A$ in (8) and (9). By dividing (1) by (3):

$$\tan(A+B)=\frac{\sin A\cos B+\cos A\sin B}{\cos A\cos B-\sin A\sin B}=\frac{\tan A+\tan B}{1-\tan A\tan B} \quad . \quad (12)$$

by dividing top and bottom by cos A cos B, and similarly from (2) and (4):

$$\tan(A-B)=\frac{\tan A-\tan B}{1+\tan A\tan B} \quad . \quad . \quad . \quad . \quad . \quad . \quad . \quad (13)$$

(Equations (12) and (13) can also be found directly from Fig. 19.I.)

$$\begin{aligned}\sin(A+B)\sin(A-B) &= (\sin A\cos B+\cos A\sin B)(\sin A\cos B-\cos A\sin B)\\ &= \sin^2 A\cos^2 B-\cos^2 A\sin^2 B\\ &= \sin^2 A(1-\sin^2 B)-(1-\sin^2 B)\sin^2 B\\ &= \sin^2 A-\sin^2 B \quad . \quad . \quad . \quad . \quad . \quad . \quad . \quad . \quad . \quad . \quad . \quad . \quad (14)\end{aligned}$$

and similarly:

$$\cos(A+B)\cos(A-B)=\cos^2 A-\sin^2 B \quad . \quad . \quad . \quad . \quad . \quad (15)$$

Put A+B=C and A−B=D $\therefore A=\tfrac{1}{2}(C+D)$ and $B=\tfrac{1}{2}(C-D)$

$$\therefore \sin C+\sin D=2\sin\frac{C+D}{2}\cos\frac{C-D}{2}$$

$$\sin C-\sin D=2\cos\frac{C+D}{2}\sin\frac{C-D}{2}$$

$$\cos C+\cos D=2\cos\frac{C+D}{2}\cos\frac{C-D}{2}$$

$$\cos D-\cos C=2\sin\frac{C+D}{2}\sin\frac{C-D}{2}$$

(Note the reversal of order in the last formula.)

§ 41. Collected Trigonometric Formulae

A list of formulae is given below for reference, the angles being denoted by x and y. Those not proved above are easily found from preceding formulae.

$$1+\tan^2 x=\sec^2 x, \quad 1+\cot^2 x=\operatorname{cosec}^2 x \quad . \quad . \quad . \quad . \quad (1)$$

$$\tan x=\sqrt{(1-\sec^2 x)}, \quad \cot x=\sqrt{(1-\operatorname{cosec}^2 x)} \quad . \quad . \quad (2)$$

$$\sin(x+y)=\sin x\cos y+\cos x\sin y \quad . \quad . \quad . \quad . \quad . \quad . \quad . \quad (3)$$

$$\sin(x-y)=\sin x\cos y-\cos x\sin y \quad . \quad . \quad . \quad . \quad . \quad . \quad . \quad (4)$$

$$\cos(x+y)=\cos x\cos y-\sin x\sin y \quad . \quad . \quad . \quad . \quad . \quad . \quad . \quad (5)$$

$$\cos(x-y)=\cos x\cos y+\sin x\sin y \quad . \quad . \quad . \quad . \quad . \quad . \quad . \quad (6)$$

$$\tan(x+y)=(\tan x+\tan y)/(1-\tan x\tan y) \quad . \quad . \quad . \quad . \quad (7)$$

$$\tan(x-y)=(\tan x-\tan y)/(1+\tan x \tan y) \quad (8)$$

$$\sin 2x=2\sin x \cos x \quad (9)$$

$$\cos 2x=\cos^2 x-\sin^2 x=2\cos^2 x-1=1-2\sin^2 x \quad (10)$$

$$\sin 3x=3\sin x-4\sin^3 x \quad (11)$$

$$\cos 3x=4\cos^3 x-3\cos x \quad (12)$$

$$\tan 2x=2\tan x/(1-\tan^2 x) \quad (13)$$

$$\cot 2x=(\cot^2 x-1)/2\cot x \quad (14)$$

$$\sin \tfrac{1}{2}x=\pm\sqrt{[(1-\cos x)/2]} \quad (15)$$

$$\cos \tfrac{1}{2}x=\pm\sqrt{[(1+\cos x)/2]} \quad (16)$$

$$\tan \tfrac{1}{2}x=\pm\sqrt{(1-\cos x)}/\sqrt{(1+\cos x)}=(1-\cos x)/\sin x=\sin x/(1+\cos x) \quad (17)$$

$$\sin x\pm\sin y=2\sin \tfrac{1}{2}(x\pm y)\,.\,\cos \tfrac{1}{2}(x\mp y) \quad (18)$$

$$\cos x+\cos y=2\cos \tfrac{1}{2}(x+y)\,.\,\cos \tfrac{1}{2}(x-y) \quad (19)$$

$$\cos x-\cos y=-2\sin \tfrac{1}{2}(x+y)\,.\,\sin \tfrac{1}{2}(x-y) \quad (20)$$

$$\tan x\pm\tan y=\sin(x\pm y)/\cos x \cos y \quad (21)$$

$$\cot x\pm\cot y=\pm\sin(x\pm y)/\sin x \sin y \quad (22)$$

$$\sin^2 x+\cos^2 x=1 \quad (23)$$

$$\sin^2 x-\sin^2 y=\sin(x+y)\,.\,\sin(x-y) \quad (24)$$

$$\cos^2 x-\cos^2 y=-\sin(x+y)\,.\,\sin(x-y) \quad (25)$$

$$\cos^2 x-\sin^2 y=\cos(x+y)\,.\,\cos(x-y) \quad (26)$$

$$\sin(\tfrac{1}{2}\pi-x)=\cos x,\ \cos(\tfrac{1}{2}\pi-x)=\sin x \quad (27)$$

$$\tan(\tfrac{1}{2}\pi-x)=\cot x,\ \cot(\tfrac{1}{2}\pi-x)=\tan x \quad (28)$$

$$\sin(\pi-x)=\sin x,\ \cos(\pi-x)=-\cos x \quad (29)$$

$$\sin(\tfrac{1}{2}\pi+x)=\cos x,\ \cos(\tfrac{1}{2}\pi+x)=-\sin x \quad (30)$$

$$\sin(\pi+x)=-\sin x,\ \cos(\pi+x)=-\cos x \quad (31)$$

§ 42. Differentiation of Trigonometric Functions

In Fig. 20.I the angle POA$=x$ and the angle QOA$=x+\mathrm{d}x$, therefore QOP$=\mathrm{d}x$. The angles are in radians, hence $\mathrm{d}x=\mathrm{QP}/r$, where r=radius of circle.

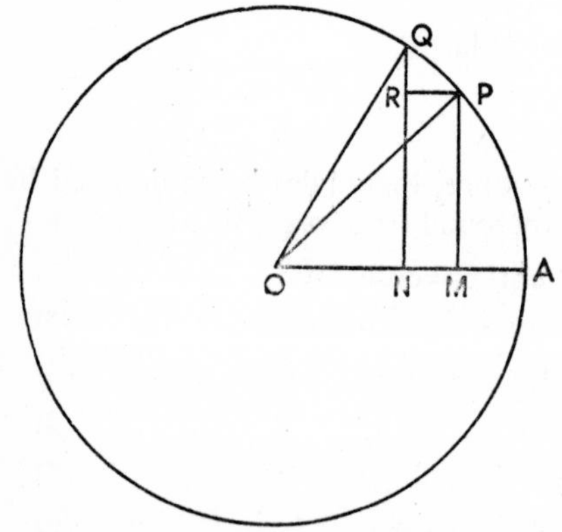

FIG. 20.I. Differentiation of Trigonometric Functions

$$\sin x=\mathrm{PM}/r \quad \text{and} \quad \sin(x+\mathrm{d}x)=\mathrm{QN}/r$$

$$\therefore\ \mathrm{d}\sin x=\sin(x+\mathrm{d}x)-\sin x=(\mathrm{QN}-\mathrm{PM})/r=\mathrm{QR}/r$$

$$=(\mathrm{QR/QP})(\mathrm{QP}/r)=(\mathrm{QR/QP})\mathrm{d}x$$

When $\mathrm{d}x$ is very small, the *arc* QP approaches the *hypotenuse* QP of the triangle PQR and QR/QP=cos QPR= cos NQP=cos AOP=cos x, since NQ is at right angles to OA and OP is at right angles to QP

$$\therefore\ \mathrm{d}\sin x=\cos x\,.\,\mathrm{d}x \quad (1)$$

Similarly, $d\cos x = (ON - OM)/r = -MN/r = -RP/r = -\frac{RP}{QP} \cdot \frac{QP}{r} = -\sin x \, . \, dx$

$$\therefore\ d\cos x = -\sin x \, . \, dx \quad \ldots \ldots \quad (2)$$

Also $d\tan x = d(\sin x/\cos x)$ and by the formula for differentiating a quotient, (5), § 6:

$$d\tan x = (\cos x \, d\sin x - \sin x \, d\cos x)/\cos^2 x$$
$$= (\cos^2 x \, . \, dx + \sin^2 x \, . \, dx)/\cos^2 x = dx/\cos^2 x = \sec^2 x \, . \, dx$$

$$\therefore\ d\tan x = \sec^2 x \, . \, dx \quad \ldots \ldots \quad (3)$$

Similarly, $d\cot x = d(\cos x/\sin x) = -dx/\sin^2 x = -\text{cosec}^2 x \, . \, dx$ . . (4)

§ 43. Integration of Trigonometric Functions

The integrals follow at once from the above results for differentiation:

$$\int \sin x dx = \int -d(\cos x) = -\cos x + C \quad \ldots \ldots \quad (1)$$
$$\int \cos x dx = \int d(\sin x) = \sin x + C \quad \ldots \ldots \quad (2)$$
$$\int dx/(\cos^2 x) = \int d(\tan x) = \tan x + C \quad \ldots \ldots \quad (3)$$

Many integrals are easily found by substitution of trigonometric functions. E.g. $\int \sqrt{(a^2 - x^2)} dx$, where a is a constant. Put $x = a \sin u \quad \therefore\ dx = a \cos u du$

$$\therefore\ \int \sqrt{(a^2 - x^2)} dx = a^2 \int \sqrt{(1 - \sin^2 u)} \, . \, \cos u du = a^2 \int \cos^2 u du, \text{ from (23), § 41,}$$
$$= \tfrac{1}{2} a^2 \int (1 + \cos 2u) du, \text{ from (10), § 41,}$$
$$= \tfrac{1}{2} a^2 (u + \tfrac{1}{2} \sin 2u) + C.$$

(Note that $\int \cos 2u du = \frac{1}{2} \sin 2u + C$, as is found by putting $2u = v \quad \therefore\ dv = 2du$ and the integral is $\frac{1}{2} \int \cos v dv = \frac{1}{2} \sin v + C = \frac{1}{2} \sin 2u + C$.)

But $\frac{1}{2} \sin 2u = \sin u \cos u$, from (9), § 41, and since

$$\sin u = x/a, \ \cos u = \sqrt{(1 - \sin^2 u)} = \sqrt{(a^2 - x^2)}/a \quad \therefore\ \sin u \cos u = x\sqrt{(a^2 - x^2)}$$

$$\therefore\ \int \sqrt{(a^2 - x^2)} dx = \tfrac{1}{2} a^2 \sin^{-1}(x/a) + \tfrac{1}{2} x \sqrt{(a^2 - x^2)}$$

where $\sin^{-1}(x/a)$ denotes an angle the sine of which is x/a.

The following integrals are sometimes required:

(1) $\int \sin mx \sin nx dx$. From (20), § 41, writing A and B for x and y:

$$\cos A - \cos B = -2 \sin \tfrac{1}{2}(A + B) \, . \, \sin \tfrac{1}{2}(A - B)$$
$$= 2 \sin \tfrac{1}{2}(A + B) \, . \, \sin \tfrac{1}{2}(B - A) \quad [\text{since } \sin(-x) = -\sin x]$$

Put $\frac{1}{2}(A + B) = mx$ and $\frac{1}{2}(B - A) = nx$

$$\therefore\ A = (m - n)x \quad \text{and} \quad B = (m + n)x$$
$$\therefore\ \cos(m - n)x - \cos(m + n)x = 2 \sin mx \sin nx$$
$$\therefore\ 2\int \sin mx \sin nx dx = \int \cos(m - n)x dx - \int \cos(m + n)x dx$$
$$= \frac{1}{m - n} \sin(m - n)x - \frac{1}{m + n} \sin(m + n)x + C$$

$$\therefore\ \int \sin mx \sin nx dx = -\frac{\sin(m + n)x}{2(m + n)} + \frac{\sin(m - n)x}{2(m - n)} + C.$$

(2) $\int \cos mx \cos nx dx$. From (19), § 41, writing A and B for x and y:

$$\cos A + \cos B = 2 \cos \tfrac{1}{2}(A + B) \, . \, \cos \tfrac{1}{2}(A - B)$$

Put $\frac{1}{2}(A+B)=mx$ and $\frac{1}{2}(A-B)=nx$

$$\therefore\ A=(m+n)x \quad\text{and}\quad B=(m-n)x$$

$$\therefore\ \cos(m+n)x+\cos(m-n)x=2\cos mx\cos nx$$

$$\therefore\ 2\int\cos mx\cos nx\,dx=\int\cos(m+n)x\,dx+\int\cos(m-n)x\,dx$$

$$=\frac{1}{m+n}\sin(m+n)x+\frac{1}{m-n}\sin(m-n)x+C$$

$$\therefore\ \int\cos mx\cos nx\,dx=\frac{\sin(m+n)x}{2(m+n)}+\frac{\sin(m-n)x}{2(m-n)}+C.$$

(3) $\int\sin mx\cos nx\,dx$. From (18), § 41, writing A and B for x and y:

$$\sin A-\sin B=2\sin\tfrac{1}{2}(A-B)\,.\,\cos\tfrac{1}{2}(A+B)$$

Put $\frac{1}{2}(A-B)=mx$ and $\frac{1}{2}(A+B)=nx$,

$$\therefore\ A=(m+n)x \quad\text{and}\quad -B=(m-n)x,$$

$$\therefore\ \sin(m+n)x+\sin(m-n)x=2\sin mx\cos nx$$

$$\therefore\ 2\int\sin mx\cos nx\,dx=\int\sin(m+n)x\,dx+\int\sin(m-n)x\,dx$$

$$\therefore\ \int\sin mx\cos nx\,dx=-\frac{\cos(m+n)x}{2(m+n)}-\frac{\cos(m-n)x}{2(m-n)}+C$$

By integration from 0 to 2π it is then easily seen that, since $\sin 0=\sin 2\pi=0$, and $\cos 0=\cos 2\pi=1$:

$$\int_0^{2\pi}\cos mx\cos nx\,dx=\int_0^{2\pi}\sin mx\sin nx\,dx=\int_0^{2\pi}\sin mx\cos nx\,dx=0$$

when $m\neq n$, a result used in deducing Fourier's series (§ 73).

Two functions $\psi_m(x)$ and $\psi_n(x)$, such that $\int\psi_m(x)\psi_n(x)dx=0$, when $m\neq n$, and the integration is taken between suitable limits, are said to be *orthogonal*, and $\cos mx$ and $\cos nx$, $\sin mx$ and $\sin nx$, are seen to be orthogonal.

Now suppose that $m=n$; the integrals (1)–(3) become:

(4) $$\int\sin^2 nx\,dx=\tfrac{1}{2}\int(1-\cos 2nx)dx \quad\text{(from (10), § 41)}$$

$$=x/2-(\sin 2nx)/4n+C,$$

$$\therefore\ \int_0^{2\pi}\sin^2 nx\,dx=\pi.$$

(5) Similarly

$$\int\cos^2 mx\,dx=\tfrac{1}{2}\int(1+\cos 2mx)dx \quad\text{(from (10), § 41))}$$

$$=x/2+(\sin 2mx)/4m+C,$$

$$\therefore\ \int_0^{2\pi}\cos^2 mx=\pi.$$

Since $$\int_0^{2\pi}(\sin mx/\sqrt{\pi})^2dx=\int_0^{2\pi}(\cos mx/\sqrt{\pi})^2dx=1$$

$1/\sqrt{\pi}$ is said to be a *normalising factor* for $\sin nx$ and $\cos mx$, these integrals being normalised to unity.

(6) $$\int\sin mx\cos mx\,dx=(1/m)\int\sin mx\,d(\sin mx)$$

$$=(\sin^2 mx)/2m+C,$$

$$\therefore\ \int_0^{2\pi}\sin mx\cos mx\,dx=0.$$

§ 44. Inverse Trigonometric Functions

The notation $\sin^{-1}x$, etc., is used to denote [1] an *angle* the sine of which is x, etc. The *inverse* functions $\sin^{-1}x$, etc., are much used in the calculus.

Let $y=\sin^{-1}x$, then $x=\sin y$, $\therefore\ dx/dy=\cos y=\sqrt{(1-\sin^2 y)}=\sqrt{(1-x^2)}$,

$$\therefore\ dy/dx=d(\sin^{-1}x)/dx=1/\sqrt{(1-x^2)}\quad\therefore\ \int\frac{dx}{\sqrt{(1-x^2)}}=\sin^{-1}x \quad . \quad (1)$$

If $y=\sin^{-1}(x/a)$, $\therefore\ x=a\sin y$, $\therefore\ dx/dy=a\cos y=a\sqrt{(1-\sin^2 y)}=a\sqrt{(1-x^2/a^2)}$,

$$\therefore\ d\left(\sin^{-1}\frac{x}{a}\right)/dx=1/\sqrt{(a^2-x^2)},\quad\therefore\ \int\frac{dx}{\sqrt{(a^2-x^2)}}=\sin^{-1}\frac{x}{a} \quad . \quad (2)$$

Let $y=\cos^{-1}x$ $\therefore\ x=\cos y$ $\therefore\ dx/dy=-\sin y=-\sqrt{(1-\cos^2 y)}=-\sqrt{(1-x^2)}$

$$\therefore\ d(\cos^{-1}x)/dx=-1/\sqrt{(1-x^2)}\quad\therefore\ \int\frac{dx}{\sqrt{(1-x^2)}}=-\cos^{-1}x\ . \quad . \quad (3)$$

and, similarly,

$$d\left(\cos^{-1}\frac{x}{a}\right)/dx=-1/\sqrt{(a^2-x^2)}\quad\therefore\ \int\frac{dx}{\sqrt{(a^2-x^2)}}=-\cos^{-1}\frac{x}{a} \quad . \quad (4)$$

(The signs apply to the first quadrant. It should be noted that (1) and (3) do not show that $\sin^{-1}x=-\cos^{-1}x$—which is not true—because the integration constants, here omitted, differ by $\pi/2$.)

Let $y=\tan^{-1}x$, $\therefore\ x=\tan y$, $\therefore\ dx/dy=\sec^2 y=1+\tan^2 y=1+x^2$,

$$\therefore\ d(\tan^{-1}x)/dx=1/(1+x^2),\quad\therefore\ \int\frac{dx}{1+x^2}=\tan^{-1}x \quad . \ . \ . \quad (5)$$

If $y=\tan^{-1}(x/a)$, $\therefore\ x=a\tan y$, $\therefore\ dx/dy=a\sec^2 y=a(1+\tan^2 y)$

$$\therefore\ d\left(\tan^{-1}\frac{x}{a}\right)/dx=a/(a^2+x^2),\quad\therefore\ \int\frac{dx}{a^2+x^2}=\frac{1}{a}\tan^{-1}\frac{x}{a}\ . \quad . \quad (6)$$

If $y=\cot^{-1}x$, $\therefore\ x=\cot y$, $\therefore\ dx/dy=-\mathrm{cosec}^2 x=-\cot^2 x-1=-x^2-1$,

$$\therefore\ d(\cot^{-1}x)/dx=-1/(x^2+1)\quad\therefore\ \int\frac{dx}{x^2+1}=-\cot^{-1}x \quad . \ . \quad (7)$$

and similarly

$$d\left(\cot^{-1}\frac{x}{a}\right)/dx=-a/(x^2+a^2),\quad\therefore\ \int\frac{dx}{x^2+a^2}=-\frac{1}{a}\cot^{-1}\frac{x}{a} \quad . \quad (8)$$

These results obviously allow of the integration of some common functions of x.

§ 45. Expansion of Trigonometric Functions

The functions $\sin x$ and $\cos x$ may be expanded in series of powers of x by Maclaurin's Theorem (1), § 34. Let $f(x)=\sin x$. Then:

$$df(x)/dx=\cos x,\quad d^2f(x)/dx^2=-\sin x,\quad d^3f(x)/dx^3=-\cos x,\ \text{etc.}$$

Also, $f(0)=0$, $df(0)/dx=1$, $d^2f(0)/dx^2=0$, $d^3f(0)/dx^3=-1$, $d^4f(0)/dx^4=0$, $d^5f(0)/dx^5=1$, etc.

$$\therefore\ \sin x=x-x^3/3!+x^5/5!-x^7/7!+\ .\ .\ .\ .\ .\ . \quad (1)$$

$$\text{Similarly, } \cos x=1-x^2/2!+x^4/4!-x^6/6!+\ .\ .\ .\ .\ .\ . \quad (2)$$

[1] Although $\sin^2 x=(\sin x)^2$, etc., $\sin^{-1}x$ does not mean $1/\sin x$, as might be expected. In older books, $\sin^{-1}x$, etc., are denoted by arc sin x, etc.

Note that $\sin x$ is an *odd* and $\cos x$ an *even* function of x. In (1) x may be written $x^1/1!$, and in (2) 1 may be written $x^0/0!$, since $x^0=1$ and $0!=1$. These series were published by Newton in 1669.

§ 46. De Moivre's Theorem

The square of every real number, positive or negative, is positive. Hence the square root of a negative quantity is *imaginary*. If $\sqrt{(-1)}=i$ (sometimes written ι; the symbol i is due to Euler, 1777), then every imaginary number can be written as a product of a real number and i; e.g. $\sqrt{(-25)}=\sqrt{(-1\times 25)}=5\sqrt{(-1)}=5i$. *Even* powers of i are real, e.g. $i^4=i^2 . i^2=(-1)\times(-1)=1$; *odd* powers of i are imaginary, e.g. $i^3=i(i^2)=-i$. The sum of a real and an imaginary number is called a *complex number*, e.g. $3+2i$. The expressions $(a+ib)$ and $(a-ib)$ are called *conjugate*, and their sum $(2a)$ and product (a^2+b^2) are real, whilst their difference $(-2ib$ or $+2ib)$ is imaginary. If x and y are real numbers, $z=x+iy$ is a complex number. If two complex numbers are equated to one another, the real and imaginary parts are *separately* equal in each; e.g. if $x_1+iy_1=x_2+iy_2$, then $x_1=x_2$, and $iy_1=iy_2$ or $y_1=y_2$.

If it is assumed that the exponential series (2), § 33, holds for an imaginary exponent ix, where x is real, then:

$$\begin{aligned} e^{ix} &= 1+ix+i^2x^2/2!+i^3x^3/3!+i^4x^4/4!+ \dots \\ &= 1+ix-x^2/2!-ix^3/3!+x^4/4!+ix^5/5!+ \dots \\ &= (1-x^2/2!+x^4/4!+ \dots)+i(x-x^3/3!+x^5/5!+ \dots) \quad (3) \end{aligned}$$

and hence, from (1) and (2), § 45:

$$e^{ix}=\cos x+i\sin x \quad (4)$$

The expression on the right (sometimes written as cis x) is a complex number. Similarly:

$$e^{-ix}=\cos x-i\sin x,$$

$$\therefore \sin x=(e^{ix}-e^{-ix})/2i \quad \text{and} \quad \cos x=(e^{ix}+e^{-ix})/2 \quad (5)$$

giving *exponential values for the sine and cosine*. It is readily found, by squaring and adding, that $\sin^2 x+\cos^2 x=1$. Also, $e^{inx}=(e^{ix})^n=(\cos x+i\sin x)^n$ for positive, negative, integral, or fractional values of n. Put $nx=z$, then:

$$e^{iz}=\cos z+i\sin z=\cos nx+i\sin nx \quad (6)$$

$$\therefore (\cos x+i\sin x)^n=\cos nx+i\sin nx \quad (7)$$

as may also be found by direct multiplication, and (3) and (5) of § 41. It should be noted that the expression on the right of (7) is only *one* value of that on the left, when n is not a positive integer. If $n=p/q$, where p and q are positive integers, there are q qth roots of any quantity, and hence there are q values of $(\cos x+i\sin x)^{1/q}$. The further discussion is given in books on trigonometry.[1]

Equations (6) and (7) are forms of *De Moivre's Theorem.*[2] In (5) put $x=n\pi$, where n is any positive or negative integer. Then:

$$\sin n\pi=0=(1/2i)(e^{in\pi}-e^{-in\pi}),$$

$$\therefore e^{in\pi}=e^{-in\pi},$$

and by dividing by $e^{-in\pi}$ an equation discovered by Euler [1] connecting i and π is found, viz.:

$$e^{2in\pi}=1 \quad (8)$$

[1] See Hobson, "A Treatise on Plane Trigonometry," 2nd edit., Cambridge, 1897, 280; Durell and Robson, "Advanced Trigonometry," 1920, 162.

[2] De Moivre, "Miscellanea Analytica de Seriebus et Quadraturis," London, 1730, 1.

§ 47. Hyperbolic Functions

The so-called *hyperbolic functions*, often met with, are defined as follows:

$$\cosh x = \cos ix = \tfrac{1}{2}(e^x + e^{-x}), \quad \sinh x = \frac{1}{i}\sin ix = \tfrac{1}{2}(e^x - e^{-x}),$$

$$\tanh x = \sinh x/\cosh x = (e^x - e^{-x})/(e^x + e^{-x}) \quad . \quad . \quad (1)$$

(The names are pronounced "cosh," "shin," and "tank.") They lead to equations similar to those holding for trigonometric functions, for example, $\cosh^2 x - \sinh^2 x = 1$ in place of $\cos^2 x + \sin^2 x = 1$; these equations are given in books on the calculus.[1] The hyperbolic functions can always be rewritten in terms of real exponential functions, and little use will be made of them. It is easily shown that: $d(\cosh x) = \sinh x \,.\, dx$, $d(\sinh x) = \cosh x \,.\, dx$, and $d \tanh x = (1/\cosh^2 x)dx = \operatorname{sech}^2 x \,.\, dx$.

The *inverse hyperbolic functions*, $\cosh^{-1}x$, etc., appear as alternative forms of some common integrals. If $\cosh y = x$, then $\sinh y = \sqrt{(x^2-1)}$, and:

$$e^y = \tfrac{1}{2}(e^y + e^{-y}) + \tfrac{1}{2}(e^y - e^{-y}) = \cosh y + \sinh y = x + \sqrt{(x^2-1)},$$

$$\therefore\ y = \cosh^{-1}x = \ln[x + \sqrt{(x^2-1)}].$$

Similarly: $y = \sinh^{-1}x = \ln[\sqrt{(1+x^2)} + x]$.

If $\tanh y = x$,

$$x = (e^y - e^{-y})/(e^y + e^{-y}) \quad \therefore\ e^{2y} = (1+x)/(1-x),$$

$$\therefore\ y = \tanh^{-1}x = \tfrac{1}{2}\ln[(1+x)/(1-x)] \quad (x<1).$$

Similarly: $$y = \coth^{-1}x = \tfrac{1}{2}\ln[(x+1)/(x-1)] \quad (x>1).$$

The values of the derived functions for x/a instead of x are easily found to be:

$$y = \cosh^{-1}(x/a) \quad \therefore\ x = a\cosh y, \quad \therefore\ dx = a\sinh y \,.\, dy = a\sqrt{(\cosh^2 y - 1)} \,.\, dy$$

$$\therefore\ \frac{d\cosh^{-1} x/a}{dx} = \frac{1}{\sqrt{(x^2-a^2)}}, \quad \therefore \int \frac{dx}{\sqrt{(x^2-a^2)}} = \cosh^{-1}\frac{x}{a} = \ln[x + \sqrt{(x^2-a^2)}].$$

Similarly:

$$\frac{d\sinh^{-1} x/a}{dx} = \frac{1}{\sqrt{(x^2+a^2)}}, \quad \therefore \int \frac{dx}{\sqrt{(x^2+a^2)}} = \sinh^{-1}\frac{x}{a} = \ln[\sqrt{(x^2+a^2)} + x],$$

$$\frac{d\tanh^{-1} x/a}{dx} = \frac{a}{a^2-x^2}\ (x<a), \quad \therefore \int \frac{dx}{a^2-x^2} = \frac{1}{a}\tanh^{-1}\frac{x}{a} = \frac{1}{2a}\ln\frac{a+x}{a-x},$$

$$\frac{d\coth^{-1} x/a}{dx} = \frac{a}{a^2-x^2} = -\frac{a}{x^2-a^2}(x>a), \quad \therefore \int \frac{dx}{x^2-a^2} = -\frac{1}{a}\coth^{-1}\frac{x}{a} = \frac{1}{2a}\ln\frac{x-a}{x+a}.$$

Since $\cosh x + \sinh x = e^x$, therefore $x = \ln e^x = \ln(\cosh x + \sinh x)$. If θ is an angle such that $\sinh x = \tan\theta$,

$$\cosh x = \sqrt{(1+\sinh^2 x)} = \sqrt{(1+\tan^2\theta)} = \sec\theta \text{ (from (1), § 41)},$$

$$\text{then } x = \ln(\sec\theta + \tan\theta) = \lambda(\theta)$$

is called the "lambda function of θ." The angle θ was called by Cayley the *gudermannian* of x (after Gudermann) and denoted by gd (x), when $x = \mathrm{gd}^{-1}(\theta)$ or $x = \mathrm{amh}^{-1}(\theta)$. The gudermannian is sometimes called the "hyperbolic

[1] For a good account of hyperbolic functions, see Greenhill, "Differential and Integral Calculus," 1896. The functions are sometimes denoted by ch, sh, th, which must be carefully distinguished from those of elliptic functions cn, sn. Some mathematicians, e.g. G. A. Gibson, "An Elementary Treatise on the Calculus," 1933, 140, are less enthusiastic about the use of hyperbolic functions than is Greenhill.

amplitude" of x. This function x was used by Edward Wright in 1599 in constructing Mercator's charts. No use will be made of these functions. The curve $y/a=\cosh(x/a)$ is called a *catenary*, the ordinate y/a being the arithmetic mean of the ordinates of the two exponential curves $y/a=e^{x/a}$ and $y/a=e^{-x/a}$. The catenary is the curve in which a uniform chain (Latin *catena*) hangs; or (of more interest to us), the vertical section of a soap-bubble film (*catenoid*) drawn up by a circular wire from a flat liquid surface.

§ 48. Curvature

Let P and P_1 be any two neighbouring points on a plane curve (Fig. 21.I). In passing along the small arc $PP_1=\delta s$, the tangent turns through the smal angle $\delta\phi$, which is called the *total curvature* of the arc δs. The *mean curvature* is the limiting value of $\delta\phi/\delta s$ when $\delta s\to 0$, i.e. $d\phi/ds$.

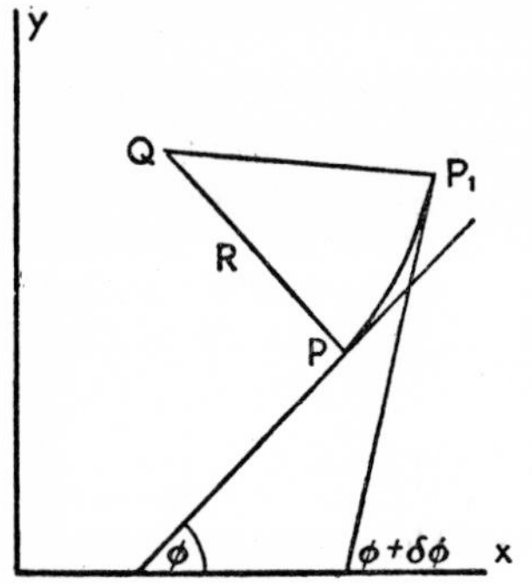

FIG. 21.I. Curvature of a Plane Curve

If QP and QP_1 are perpendiculars to the tangents at P and P_1, meeting at Q, the angle (in radians, § 40), $PQP_1=\delta\phi=\delta s/R$, where $QP=QP_1=R$, the arc PP_1 being very nearly circular. A circle in contact with a curve may be regarded as passing through *three* consecutive points infinitely close to one another, as a straight line (tangent) touching the curve passes through *two* such points, and this circle is called the *circle of curvature*, its radius being the *radius of curvature*.

For any given curve, $\tan\phi=dy/dx$,

$$\therefore\ d^2y/dx^2=d(\tan\phi)/dx=(1/\cos^2\phi)\,.\,d\phi/dx.$$

$$\text{Also}\quad d\phi/ds=(d\phi/dx)(dx/ds)=\cos\phi\,.\,(d\phi/dx)=\cos^3\phi(d^2y/dx^2),$$

since the projection of a very small arc ds on the x axis is $dx=ds\cos\phi$.

Hence: $$1/R=d\phi/ds=\cos^3\phi(d^2y/dx^2).$$

But $$\cos^2\phi+\sin^2\phi=1\ (\S\ 41)\ \therefore\ 1+\sin^2\phi/\cos^2\phi=1/\cos^2\phi,$$

$$\cos^2\phi=1/(1+\tan^2\phi)=1/[1+(dy/dx)^2],$$

$$\therefore\ \cos^3\phi=1/[1+(dy/dx)^2]^{3/2},$$

$$\therefore\ 1/R=[1+(dy/dx)^2]^{3/2}/(d^2y/dx^2)\quad\ldots\ldots\quad(1)$$

This is the standard formula for the radius of *curvature of a plane curve*. The consideration of the *curvature of a surface* is more difficult.[1]

If $Ax^2+By^2=1$ is a conic referred to its principal axes, r, r' the radii corresponding to the vectorial angles θ and $\theta+\pi/2$, so that the radii are at right angles, then $x=r\cos\theta$, $y=r\sin\theta$, hence:

$$Ar^2\cos^2\theta+Br^2\sin^2\theta=1\quad\therefore\ 1/r^2=A\cos^2\theta+B\sin^2\theta;$$

and similarly

$$1/r'^2=A\cos^2(\theta+\pi/2)+B\sin^2(\theta+\pi/2)=A\sin^2\theta+B\cos^2\theta$$

$$\therefore\ 1/r^2+1/r'^2=A(\cos^2\theta+\sin^2\theta)+B(\sin^2\theta+\cos^2\theta)=A+B=\text{const.}\quad(2)$$

[1] See e.g. Greenhill, "Differential and Integral Calculus," 1896, 266; Mach, "The Science of Mechanics," 1893, 388; C. Smith, "Solid Geometry," 1897, 213; Frost, "Solid Geometry," 1886, 278; Salmon and Rogers, "Analytical Geometry of Three Dimensions," 1914, **1**, 292; Bell, "Coordinate Geometry of Three Dimensions," 1920, 326; Serret, "Differential- und Integralrechnung," Leipzig, 1908, **1**, 490.

It may be assumed (and is proved below) that the section of *any* surface by a plane which is parallel to, and indefinitely near, the tangent plane to the surface at any point O on the surface, is a conic section, since powers of the variables higher than the square in the equation to the surface may be neglected. The centre of the conic is in the normal OV to the surface. Let any section of the surface by a plane containing OV cut the conic in the diameter QVQ′ (Fig. 22.I), and draw a circle of centre O′ which touches the curve at O and cuts it at an adjacent point (Fig. 23.I). Then:

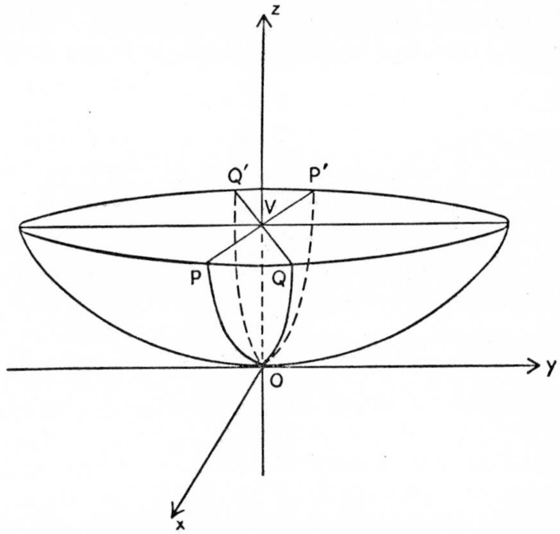

FIG. 22.I. Curvature of a Surface

$$QV^2=O'Q^2-O'V^2=O'Q^2-(O'O-OV)^2$$
$$=O'Q^2-O'O^2+2O'O \cdot OV-OV^2.$$

But $O'Q=O'O$, therefore $QV^2=OV\,(2O'O-OV)$. When Q moves up to and ultimately coincides with O, the circle becomes the circle of curvature at O, and $PQ=2O'O=2R$, where R is the radius of curvature, and $OV=0$. Hence:

$$QV^2=2R \cdot OV \quad . \quad . \quad . \quad . \quad . \quad . \quad . \quad . \quad . \quad (3)$$

This calculation was given by Newton. Hence for different normal sections through O, the radius of curvature R is proportional to the square of the semi-diameter QV of the conic through which the section passes.

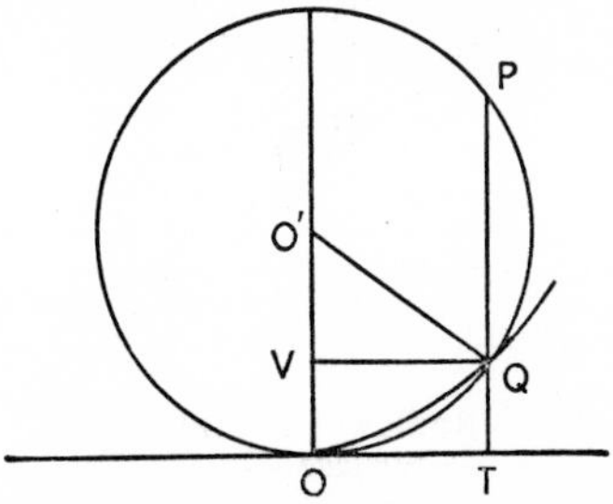

FIG. 23.I. Circle of Curvature

It is shown in (2) above that the sum of the squares of the reciprocals of *any* two perpendicular semi-diameters of a conic is constant, hence [1] the sum of the reciprocals of the radii of curvature of *any two* perpendicular normal sections through a given point on a surface is constant, and is equal to the sum of the reciprocals of the two principal radii of curvature, $1/R+1/R'$.

An important application of these results is to the curvature of a surface.[2] If the origin O is transferred to a point on the surface where $\partial f/\partial x=0$ and $\partial f/\partial y=0$, the equation to the surface being $z=f(x, y)$, then if z is small it replaces du in the notation of § 38; the notation may be further changed so that $h=x$, $k=y$ (where x, y, z are all very small),

[1] Young, in his memoir on capillarity, *Phil. Trans.*, 1805, **95**, i, 65, remarks obscurely that this is " easily shown by calculating the versed sines of two equal arcs taken at right-angles to the surface."

[2] For an elementary discussion, see Cayley, " On Contour and Slope Lines," *Phil. Mag.*, 1859, **18**, 264; and Maxwell, " Hills and Dales," *ibid.*, 1870, **40**, 421.

and r, s, and t denote (§ 26) $\partial^2 z/\partial x^2$, $\partial^2 z/\partial x \partial y$, and $\partial^2 z/\partial y^2$, respectively. The equation of the surface *in the immediate vicinity of* O thus becomes:

$$z=\tfrac{1}{2}(rx^2+2sxy+ty^2)+\text{higher powers of } x \text{ and } y \quad . \quad . \quad . \quad (4)$$

The tangent plane is the plane xOy itself, and the normal through O is the z axis. Equation (4) is the equation of a surface called an *osculating paraboloid*, and sections of it by planes $z=c$ (a constant) close to the tangent plane $z=0$, which approximate closely to sections of the surface, are similar conic sections:

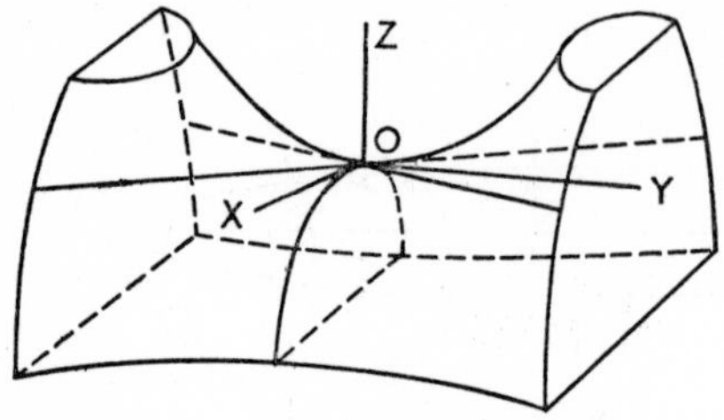

FIG. 24.I. The Hyperbolic Paraboloid

$$rx^2+2sxy+ty^2=2c.$$

In a plane infinitely near the tangent plane, the similar conic section obtained [1] by putting $2c=1$, viz.:

$$rx^2+2sxy+ty^2=1,$$

was called by Dupin (" Développment de Géométrie," 1813) the *indicatrix*. It is shown [2] that if $(rt-s^2)>0$, the indicatrix-conic is an *ellipse*, and a plane $z=c$ close to the tangent plane will, if it meets the surface, cut off a small cup. The point on the surface is then called a *synclastic* [3] (or *cup*) *point*, such as the top of a hill or the bottom of a depression, the contour lines being approximately similar ellipses. The osculating paraboloid is then an *elliptic paraboloid*.[4] If $(rt-s^2)<0$, the indicatrix conic is a *hyperbola*, and the tangent plane cuts the surface in two lines crossing at the point of contact, this point being called an *anticlastic* [3] (or *saddle*) *point*, such as a pass or bar, with contour lines approximately similar hyperbolas, and the osculating paraboloid is called a *hyperbolic paraboloid* [4] (Fig. 24.I).

Let [5] the surface OAP (Fig. 25.I) and the osculating paraboloid be cut by a plane OMP passing through the normal Oz, and inclined at an angle $MOK=\theta$ with the plane zx; and let OP be part of the section of this plane by the surface. If $OM=u$, the coordinates of the point P are $x=OG=u\cos\theta$, and $y=GM=u\sin\theta$. Substitute in (4), then:

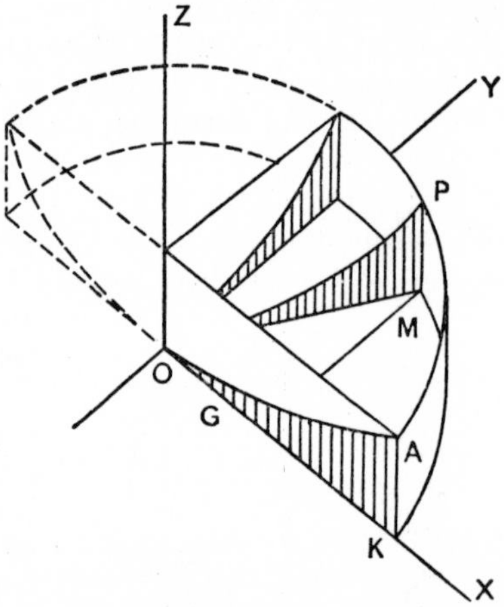

FIG. 25.I. Radius of Curvature of a Surface

$$z=\tfrac{1}{2}(u^2 r\cos^2\theta+2u^2 s\cos\theta\sin\theta+u^2 t\sin^2\theta)+\text{etc.},$$

and in the limit when $z=0$ (in the tangent plane):

$$2z/u^2=r\cos^2\theta+2s\cos\theta\sin\theta+t\sin^2\theta.$$

[1] The substitution $x=\sqrt{(2c)}x$ and $y=\sqrt{(2c)}y$ obviously alters merely the size of the curve and not its character.

[2] E.g. in F. G. W. Brown, " Higher Mathematics for Students of Engineering and Science," 1926, 221, 328.

[3] Greek συν with, κλάω to break, ἀντί against.

[4] See Frost, " Solid Geometry," 1886, 85.

[5] See de Morgan, " Differential and Integral Calculus," 1842, 429.

If OP is regarded as an infinitely small arc of a circle (the plane of which is perpendicular to the xy plane and makes an angle θ with the plane xOz) of radius a, (3) shows that the rectangle formed by $PM=z$ and the rest of the diameter is equal to $OM^2=u^2$, and in the limit the diameter is thus $2a=u^2/z$, therefore $2z/u^2=1/a=1/\rho$, where ρ is the *radius of curvature* of the normal section (i.e. the section plane passing through and parallel to Oz and perpendicular to the xy plane). Thus:

$$1/\rho=r^2\cos^2\theta+2s\cos\theta\sin\theta+t\sin^2\theta.$$

If another normal section inclined to the first at a right angle (still passing through Oz) is taken, this has an angle $(\theta+\pi/2)$ with the zx plane, and since $\sin(\pi/2+\theta)=\cos\theta$ and $\cos(\pi/2+\theta)=-\sin\theta$,

$$\therefore\ 1/\rho'=r\sin^2\theta-2s\sin\theta\cos\theta+t\cos^2\theta,$$

where ρ' is the radius of curvature of the section normal to the first. Hence:

$$1/\rho+1/\rho'=r(\cos^2\theta+\sin^2\theta)+t(\sin^2\theta+\cos^2\theta)=r+t=\text{const.},\quad .\quad (5)$$

since, by (23), § 41, $\sin^2\theta+\cos^2\theta=1$. This result, due to Euler, shows that the sum of the curvatures (reciprocals of the radii of curvature) of two normal sections perpendicular to one another is constant.

If the axes Ox and Oy are revolved around Oz, then xy may be made to vanish,[1] and equation (4) becomes:

$$z=\tfrac{1}{2}(rx^2+ty^2)+\ .\ .\ .\ =\tfrac{1}{2}x^2/R+\tfrac{1}{2}y^2/R'+\ .\ .\ .,$$

where R, R' are the principal radii of curvature, or the radii of curvature of the normal sections xOz, yOz; and for a normal section making an angle θ with Ox: $1/\rho=\cos^2\theta/R+\sin^2\theta/R'$. The quantity $(r+t)$ or $(1/\rho+1/\rho')$, or $(1/R+1/R')$ is called the *curvature of the surface*.[2]

If a normal plane to a sphere at any point is drawn, cutting the sphere in a great circle of radius R, and if an oblique plane, inclined to the first at an angle θ, is drawn through the same tangent line to the sphere, the radius of the small circle cut off by it from the sphere is $R\cos\theta$. If an oblique plane $z=x\tan\theta$ cuts the surface $z=\frac{1}{2}(rx^2+2sxy+ty^2)$, the curvature of the section of the surface is Lim $[(2z/\cos\theta)/x^2]$ with $y=0$, reducing to $r/\cos\theta$, so that the radius of curvature is $\cos\theta/r$. This is called *Meunier's Theorem*. The above equations are important in the theory of surface tension.

§ 49. Theory of Simple Harmonic Vibrations [3]

When a point P moves uniformly in a circular path (Fig. 26.I), its projection on *any* fixed diameter of the circle describes a *simple harmonic motion* in that line. The point returns to its original position once in every complete revolution on the circle, the *period* T being the time taken to describe the circle. If OP passes the x axis at a time τ reckoned from an arbitrary zero time, and if it is in the position OP at a time t, then (since the motion is uniform) the angle θ between OP and the x axis is:

$$\theta/2\pi=(t-\tau)/T\quad\text{or}\quad\theta=(2\pi/T)(t-\tau).$$

Whenever possible, it is simplest to make $\tau=0$, and for the present this will be

[1] This is shown in any work on conic sections; see e.g. C. Smith, "An Elementary Treatise on Conic Sections," 1914, 226.

[2] W. Thomson (Lord Kelvin), "Popular Lectures and Addresses," 1889, **1**, 17.

[3] E. H. and W. Weber, "Wellenlehre auf Experimente gegründet," Leipzig, 1825; Donkin, "Acoustics," Oxford, 1870, 30 f.; Lamb, "Dynamical Theory of Sound," 1910, 8; Coulson, "Waves," Edinburgh, 1941.

assumed, when $\theta=(2\pi/T)t$. If the *angular velocity* in the circle is ω radians per sec., $\theta=\omega t$.

Since the point makes a complete revolution in T secs., it makes $1/T$ revolutions in 1 sec., this being called the *frequency*, ν, hence $\nu=1/T$, therefore $\theta=2\pi\nu t$.

The projection ON$=s$ of OP on the x axis is:

$$\text{ON}=s=\text{OP}\cos\theta=A\cos\theta=A\cos(2\pi/T)t=A\cos 2\pi\nu t,$$

where A is the radius of the circle; and the projection ON$'$=NP of OP on the y axis is:

$$\text{ON}'=\text{OP}\cos(\pi/2-\theta)=\text{OP}\sin\theta=A\sin(2\pi/T)t=A\sin 2\pi\nu t.$$

If the length ON (or ON$'$) is plotted against t, a cosine (or sine) curve shown on the right in Fig. 26.I is obtained. The two curves are displaced with respect to each other by a time interval $(\frac{1}{2}\pi/2\pi)T=\frac{1}{4}\pi T$, called the *lead* or *lag* of one curve relative to the other, corresponding with a *phase angle* of $\frac{1}{2}\pi=90°$. As the point P moves uniformly in the circle, the point N moves non-uniformly along the

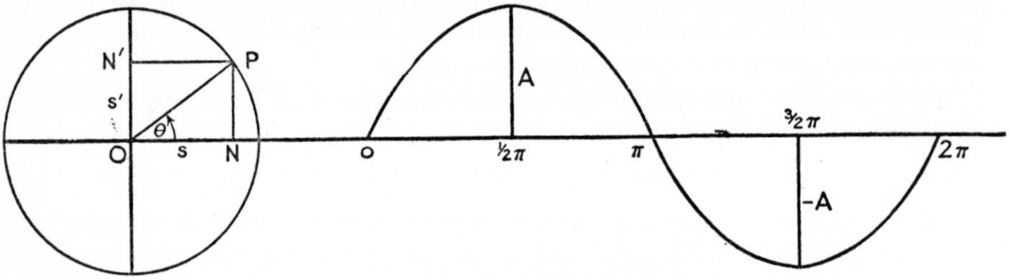

FIG. 26.I. Simple Harmonic Motion

x axis, oscillating between the extremes of the circle diameter in a time $\frac{1}{2}T$, or performing one *complete oscillation* from its initial position anywhere on the diameter back to this position again in a time T. The point N is said to execute a *simple harmonic motion* (S.H.M.). Let the distance of N from O, on either side, be denoted by s: this is called the *displacement*.

On the cosine or sine curve, the maximum displacement from the axis is $\pm A$, called the *amplitude*. On the cosine curve, this occurs when $\cos\theta=\pm 1$, i.e. $\theta=0$ or $n\pi$, where n is an integer, and $t=\theta/(2\pi/T)=n\pi/(2\pi/T)=\frac{1}{2}nT$. On the sine curve it occurs when $\sin\theta=\pm 1$, i.e. $\theta=n(\pi/2)$, where n is an odd integer, or $t=\frac{1}{4}nT$. The minimum displacement is 0, which occurs on the cosine curve when $\cos\theta=0$ or θ is an odd whole multiple of $\frac{1}{2}\pi$, or t is an odd whole multiple of $\frac{1}{4}T$, and on the sine curve when $\sin\theta=0$ or θ is a whole multiple of π and t a whole multiple of $\frac{1}{2}T$. Since N and N$'$ both execute linear simple harmonic motions of the same amplitude and period but differing in phase angle by $\frac{1}{2}\pi$, these two simultaneous linear harmonic motions are together equivalent to a uniform circular motion, and conversely.

Instead of considering the curve as giving successive values of the displacement from O at various times, it may be supposed that the horizontal axis is an x axis, and that the ordinates represent displacements at right angles of *fixed* points on it at different times, which are those of corresponding points on the t axis. The displacement then travels as a *wave*. The distance between two corresponding points is the *wave-length*, λ. The wave travels with a velocity u, and since the wave-length is described in the time of the period T, therefore $\lambda=Tu$. Since $1/T=\nu$, the frequency, $u=\nu\lambda$. The *wave number* μ, the number of waves per cm., is obviously $\mu=1/\lambda=\nu/u$.

The (variable) *velocity* of the point describing a simple harmonic motion on a circle diameter is found as follows. The displacement s is zero when the point is at O, and if the time is taken as zero for this position, the point N′ must be taken, for which:

$$s=A\sin(2\pi t/T) \quad \ldots \quad (1)$$

$$\therefore\ v=\mathrm{d}s/\mathrm{d}t=\dot{s}=(\mathrm{d}/\mathrm{d}t)A\sin(2\pi t/T)=(2\pi A/T)\cos(2\pi t/T) \quad . \quad (2)$$

and the (variable) *acceleration* is:

$$f=\mathrm{d}v/\mathrm{d}t=\mathrm{d}^2s/\mathrm{d}t^2=\ddot{s}=(\mathrm{d}/\mathrm{d}t)[(2\pi A/T)\cos(2\pi t/T)]=-(4\pi^2A/T^2)\sin(2\pi t/T)$$
$$=-(4\pi^2/T^2)s=-ks \quad . \quad (3)$$

if $4\pi^2/T^2=k$, a positive number. Thus, the acceleration is proportional to the displacement and is in the opposite direction to the displacement. When the point is leaving O it is retarded, when it is approaching O it is accelerated. The velocity has a maximum value when $t=0$, when the cosine is unity, i.e. when the point is passing O. As t increases the velocity decreases, reaching zero when $\cos(2\pi t/T)=0$, i.e. $t=\frac{1}{4}T$, when the point is at the upper extremity of the line of amplitude. With further increase of t, the velocity becomes negative, increasing till the point passes O again. From this point, the velocity, still negative, decreases in numerical value till the lowest extremity of the line of amplitude is reached (when the amplitude is $-A$), when it is zero. With further increase of t, v becomes positive and the point reaches O with its initial velocity.

If there are *two* points P_1 and P_2 moving uniformly on circles with the same period T, each describes the circle $1/T$ times per sec., or the *frequency*, ν, is $1/T$. The corresponding sine waves will be given by (1), but the position of each set of waves relative to the other obviously depends on the initial angles made by OP_1 and OP_2 with the t axis. Let these angles be ϕ_1, ϕ_2, then $\phi_1/2\pi$ and $\phi_2/2\pi$ are called the *phases* of the motion. The angles after a time t will now be $2\pi t/T+\phi_1$ and $2\pi t/T+\phi_2$, or $2\pi\nu t+\phi_1$ and $2\pi\nu t+\phi_2$. If OP reaches the x axis from its initial position (supposed *below* the axis) after a time τ, and if t is the total time from the initial position, $(t-\tau)$ is the time starting from the x axis, and the angle θ turned from the x axis is given by $\theta/2\pi=(t-\tau)/T$, or $\theta=(2\pi/T)(t-\tau)=\nu(t-\tau)$. The angle turned in time τ is given by $\phi/2\pi=\tau/T$, or $\phi=2\pi\tau/T$. Sometimes τ is called the *phase*; here this is τ/T. If the amplitudes of the two motions are different, say A_1 and A_2, then the displacements are:

$$s_1=A_1\sin(2\pi\nu t+\phi_1) \quad \text{and} \quad s_2=A_2\sin(2\pi\nu t+\phi_2) \quad . \quad . \quad (4)$$

The sum of the displacements may be regarded as the actual displacement of a single point in a medium through which the two sets of waves travel, the motion being in a plane [1]:

$$s=s_1+s_2=A_1\sin(2\pi\nu t+\phi_1)+A_2\sin(2\pi\nu t+\phi_2)$$
$$=A_1(\sin 2\pi\nu t\,.\,\cos\phi_1+\cos 2\pi\nu t\,.\,\sin\phi_1)$$
$$+A_2(\sin 2\pi\nu t\,.\,\cos\phi_2+\cos 2\pi\nu t\,.\,\sin\phi_2),$$

by (3), § 41. Let ϕ be an angle and A an amplitude such that:

$$s=A\sin(2\pi\nu t+\phi) \quad \ldots \quad (5)$$
$$=A(\sin 2\pi\nu t\,.\,\cos\phi+\cos 2\pi\nu t\,.\,\sin\phi),$$

[1] The case considered is for two vibrations in the same direction. When two simple harmonic motions are at *right angles*, their composition is easily effected graphically, and the so-called *Lissajous figures* result: Lissajous, *Ann. Chim.*, 1857, **51**, 147; Auerbach, in Winkelmann, "Handbuch der Physik," 1909, **2**, 42; Duncan and Starling, "Text-book of Physics," 1936, 673, the method being due to Perigal.

then
$$A\cos\phi=A_1\cos\phi_1+A_2\cos\phi_2,$$
$$A\sin\phi=A_1\sin\phi_1+A_2\sin\phi_2.$$

Square and add, remembering that $\sin^2\phi+\cos^2\phi=1$,

$$\therefore\ A^2=A_1^2+A_2^2+2A_1A_2(\cos\phi_1\cos\phi_2+\sin\phi_1\sin\phi_2)$$
$$=A_1^2+A_2^2+2A_1A_2\cos(\phi_1-\phi_2)\quad\ldots\ldots\quad(6)$$

by (6), § 41.

If $\phi_1-\phi_2=0$ or $2n\pi$, where n is an integer, i.e. $\phi_1-\phi_2$ is an *even* multiple of π, both vibrations are in the same phase, and $\cos(\phi_1-\phi_2)=\cos 0=1$, or $\cos 2n\pi=1$,

$$\therefore\ A^2=A_1^2+A_2^2+2A_1A_2=(A_1+A_2)^2,$$
$$\therefore\ A=A_1+A_2\quad\ldots\ldots\quad(7)$$

and if $A_1=A_2$, $A=2A_1$.

If $\phi_1-\phi_2=(2n+1)\pi$, an *odd* multiple of π, $\cos(\phi_1-\phi_2)=-1$

$$\therefore\ A^2=A_1^2+A_2^2-2A_1A_2=(A_1-A_2)^2$$
$$\therefore\ A=A_1-A_2\quad\ldots\ldots\quad(8)$$

and if $A_1=A_2$, $A=0$.

This is a case of *interference*; when the crest of one wave coincides with the trough of the other, the motion is annulled if the amplitudes are equal and differ in phase by an odd multiple of π.

If the displacement at the origin ($x=0$) along a y axis at a time t is $s=A\sin 2\pi(t/T)$, that in the y direction on an x axis will occur at a distance x from the origin at a time $t'=t-x/u$, since the wave-form moves along the x axis with a velocity u, and the displacement at x is the same as that at the origin at a time x/u before. Hence (since $uT=\lambda$, the wave-length):

$$y=A\sin 2\pi(t'/T)=A\sin[(t-x/u)/T]=A\sin(2\pi/\lambda)(ut-x)\quad.\quad(9)$$

This can also be written as:

$$y=A\sin 2\pi(ut/\lambda-x/\lambda)=A\sin 2\pi(t/T-x/\lambda)=A\sin 2\pi(\nu t-\mu x),$$

where $\nu=1/T$=frequency, and $\mu=1/\lambda$=wave number=number of waves per cm.

In these equations the amplitude A is supposed to be constant for all values of x. If $A(x)=f(x)$ is a variable amplitude, the variation of the displacement with x can be included in it, and the equations written:

$$y=A(x)\sin 2\pi(t/T)=A(x)\sin 2\pi\nu t\quad\ldots\quad(10)$$

Since the cosine function is identical with the sine except for a difference of phase, all the above equations can equally well be written with the cosine instead of the sine.

Let
$$f(x)=a\sin(bx+c)-b\cos(bx+c)\quad\ldots\ldots\quad(11)$$

where a, b, and c, are positive constants. Put $a=r\cos\phi$ and $b=r\sin\phi$, therefore $a^2+b^2=r^2$, and $\tan\phi=b/a$. Then:

$$f'(x)=r\cos\phi\,.\,\sin(bx+c)-r\sin\phi\,.\,\cos(bx+c)$$
$$=r\sin(bx+c-\phi)\ \text{(from (4), § 41).}$$

The differentiation of $y=f(x)=e^{ax}\sin(bx+c)$ is an important standard case. It gives:

$$f'(x)=ae^{ax}\sin(bx+c)+be^{ax}\cos(bx+c)\quad\ldots\quad(12)$$

Let $a=r\cos\phi$, and $b=r\sin\phi$, therefore $a^2+b^2=r^2$, and $\tan\phi=b/a$;

$$\therefore\ f'(x)=re^{ax}\cos\phi\sin(bx+c)+re^{ax}\sin\phi\cos(bx+c)$$
$$=re^{ax}\sin(bx+c+\phi)\ \text{(from (3), § 41)} \quad \text{(13)}$$

The operation of differentiation is thus equivalent to multiplication by r and adding ϕ to the angle. Hence for the nth derivative:

$$y^{(n)}=f^{(n)}(x)=r^n e^{ax}\sin(bx+c+n\phi).$$

Similarly, if $$y=f(x)=e^{ax}\cos(bx+c) \quad \text{(14)}$$
$$y^{(n)}=f^{(n)}(x)=r^n e^{ax}\cos(bx+c+n\phi) \quad \text{(15)}$$

If $$f(x)=e^{-ax}\sin(bx+c) \quad \text{(16)}$$
$$f''(x)=r^2e^{-ax}\sin(bx+c-2\phi) \quad \text{(17)}$$

f(x) has maximum or minimum values when $f'(x)=0$,

$$\therefore\ -re^{-ax}\sin(bx+c-\phi)=0,$$

and since e^{-ax} is not zero, $\sin(bx+c-\phi)=0$ therefore $(bx+c-\phi)=n\pi$, where $n=0, \pm1, \pm2, \pm3 \ldots$, the sine of 0 or any integral multiple of π being zero.

To distinguish maximum and minimum values, consider the sign of

$$f''(x)=r^2e^{-ax}\sin(bx+c-2\phi)=r^2e^{-ax}\sin(bx+c-\phi-\phi)$$
$$=r^2e^{-ax}\sin(n\pi-\phi)$$

when f(x) is a maximum or minimum. Since $\sin(n\pi-\phi)=-\cos n\pi\sin\phi$, by (4), § 41, and since r^2e^{-ax} and $\sin\phi$ are both positive, the sign of $f''(x)$ is the same as that of $-\cos n\pi$, i.e. (see the table in § 40) of $(-1)^{n+1}$. Hence $f''(x)$ is negative, or f(x) a maximum, when n is 0, 2, 4 . . . (an even number), and $f''(x)$ is positive, or f(x) a minimum, when n is 1, 3, 5 . . . (an odd number).

§ 50. Group Velocity and Phase Velocity

Actual waves in a medium are not propagated with an absolutely fixed frequency ν (which would be called a homogeneous wave) but are rather composed of " groups " of strictly homogeneous waves differing slightly in frequency within the limits ν and $\nu+\Delta\nu$. The displacement y is denoted (§ 49) by $A'=A\cos 2\pi(\nu t-\mu x)$, for an *infinite* wave train propagated in the direction of x with a velocity u. For another wave-train with the same A but slightly different frequency and wave number the displacement [1] is:

$$A''=A\cos 2\pi[(\nu+\Delta\nu)t-(\mu+\Delta\mu)x].$$

By superposing the two, the displacement of the resulting wave motion is found to be:

$$y=A'+A''=A\cos 2\pi(\nu t-\mu x)+A\cos 2\pi[(\nu+\Delta\nu)t-(\mu+\Delta\mu)x]$$
$$=2A\cos 2\pi(\nu t-\mu x)\,.\,\cos\pi(\Delta\nu\,.\,t-\Delta\mu\,.\,x) \quad \text{(1)}$$

when $\Delta\nu$ and $\Delta\mu$ are infinitesimal compared with ν and μ. This follows from (19), § 41:

$$\cos x+\cos y=2\cos\tfrac{1}{2}(x+y)\cos\tfrac{1}{2}(x-y).$$

Equation (1) represents a train of waves with a displacement varying between $2A$ and zero. There will be a series of regions of maximum displacement, the

[1] This is often called the " amplitude," but this is properly the quantity A.

crests travelling (as what may be called " wave packets ") with a *group velocity* v different from the *phase velocity*:

$$u=\nu/\mu=\nu\lambda \quad \ldots \ldots \ldots \quad (2)$$

in each wave train. Equation (1) shows that y has maximum values for $\Delta\nu\,.\,t=\Delta\mu\,.\,x$, hence the group velocity is, in the limit:

$$v=x/t=\Delta\nu/\Delta\mu=\mathrm{d}\nu/\mathrm{d}\mu=\mathrm{d}\nu/\mathrm{d}(1/\lambda)=-\lambda^2(\mathrm{d}\nu/\mathrm{d}\lambda) \quad \ldots \quad (3)$$

§ 51. Plane Wave

A *plane* may be defined as the locus of a straight line α which passes through a given point P (x_1, y_1, z_1), defined with reference to three perpendicular axes (Fig. 27.I), and is perpendicular to a given straight line β. For, by rotating the line α about the point P (x_1, y_1, z_1) so that it remains always perpendicular to the line β, the plane is obviously generated. The line β is the perpendicular OP from the origin to the plane: let its length be a. Project a on the axes, then x_1, y_1, z_1 will be its projections. The ratios $x_1/a=l$, $y_1/a=m$, and $z_1/a=n$, the cosines of the angles which the perpendicular to the plane makes with the three axes, define the direction of this line, and hence are called its *direction cosines*. Now take *any* point D (x, y, z) in the plane, and join PD. The line PD in the plane is perpendicular to OP. The projection of OD on OP is the sum of the projections of the coordinates of D on OP, i.e. $lx+my+nz$, and is also obviously equal to OP$=a$,

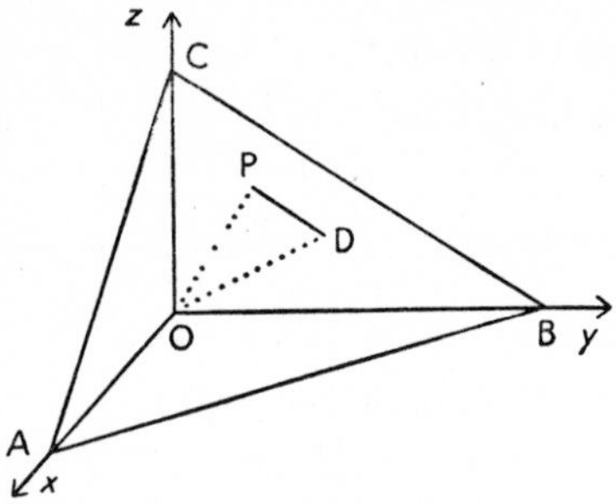

FIG. 27.I. Equation of a Plane

$$\therefore\ lx+my+nz=a \quad \ldots \ldots \ldots \quad (1)$$

is the *equation of the plane*. The expression:

$$\sin 2\pi\nu[t-(lx+my+nz)/u]$$

represents a *plane wave*. For, it is zero for a time $t=t'$ such that

$$2\pi\nu[t'-(lx+my+nz)/u]=k\pi,$$

where k is an integer (including zero). Thus:

$$-(ku/2\nu)+ut'=lx+my+nz.$$

But this is the equation of a plane with a perpendicular distance $lx+my+nz=a$ from the origin. Hence, the surfaces defined by various values of k form a series of equidistant parallel planes distant $\frac{1}{2}u/\nu$ apart, the distance from the origin increasing with the time proportionally with the velocity u. This corresponds with a wave of length $u/\nu=\lambda$, the places of zero displacement being half a wave-length apart.

§ 52. Energy of an Oscillator

Suppose that the point N′ in § 49 is a massive particle undergoing simple harmonic motion. A vibrating mass m has energy which is usually partly kinetic E_k, and partly potential, E_p. When at its maximum elongation the particle is momentarily at rest, before it moves in the opposite direction, and all its energy is potential; when it passes through the origin all its energy is kinetic, since the acceleration, and hence the force acting, is zero.

The *time average* of the kinetic energy is found by integrating $\frac{1}{2}mv^2$ over a period T and dividing by T:

$$\bar{E}_k=(1/T)\int_0^T \tfrac{1}{2}mv^2\mathrm{d}t=(m/2T)\int_0^T v^2\mathrm{d}t.$$

From (2), § 49, $v=(2\pi A/T)\cos(2\pi t/T)$, $\therefore\ v^2=(4\pi^2A^2/T^2)\cos^2(2\pi t/T)$.

From (10), § 41: $\cos^2(2\pi t/T)=\frac{1}{2}[1+\cos(4\pi t/T)]$

$$\therefore\ v^2=(2\pi^2A^2/T^2)[1+\cos(4\pi t/T)]$$

$$\therefore\ \bar{E}_k=(m/2T)(2\pi^2A^2/T^2)\int_0^T[1+\cos(4\pi t/T)]\mathrm{d}t$$

$$\therefore\ \bar{E}_k=(m/2T)(2\pi^2A^2/T^2)\times T=m\pi^2A^2/T^2 \quad . \quad . \quad . \quad . \quad . \quad (1)$$

since, from (2), § 43, $\int\cos nx\,.\,\mathrm{d}x=(1/n)\sin nx+C$,

$$\therefore\ \int_0^T\cos(4\pi t/T)\mathrm{d}t=\Big[(T/4\pi)\sin(4\pi t/T)\Big]_0^T=(T/4\pi)\sin 4\pi-0=0,$$

since $\sin 0=0$ and $\sin 4\pi=0$; hence the second part of the integral vanishes.

The kinetic energy on passing through the initial position (when the potential energy is zero) has a maximum value equal to the value for $\theta=2\pi\nu t=\pi/2$:

$$E_{k0}=\tfrac{1}{2}mv_0{}^2=\tfrac{1}{2}m\times(4\pi^2A^2/T^2)\sin^2(\pi/2)=2\pi^2A^2m/T^2=2\pi^2A^2m\nu^2 \quad . \quad (2)$$

since $\sin(\pi/2)=1$, and ν (frequency)$=1/T$. From (1) and (2):

$$\bar{E}_k=\tfrac{1}{2}E_{k0} \quad . \quad . \quad . \quad . \quad . \quad . \quad . \quad . \quad . \quad . \quad . \quad (3)$$

But the sum of the kinetic and potential energies is always equal to the maximum kinetic energy E_{k0} (when $E_p=0$):

$$\therefore\ \bar{E}_k+\bar{E}_p=\bar{E}_{k0} \quad . \quad . \quad . \quad . \quad . \quad . \quad . \quad . \quad . \quad (4)$$

$$\therefore\ \bar{E}_p=(E_{k0}-\bar{E}_k)=\tfrac{1}{2}E_{k0}=\bar{E}_k \quad . \quad . \quad . \quad . \quad . \quad . \quad . \quad (5)$$

i.e. *the time averages of the kinetic and potential energies in* (undamped) *simple* (linear) *harmonic motion are always equal.*

The *potential energy* of the oscillator for any displacement x from the equilibrium position is given by integrating the product of the force (=mass × acceleration) and displacement x, with the sign changed (since energy is gained when work is spent). The acceleration is, from (3), § 49, $-(4\pi^2/T^2)x=-4\pi^2\nu^2x$, hence:

$$E_p=4\pi^2\nu^2m\int_0^x x\mathrm{d}x=2\pi^2\nu^2mx^2 \quad . \quad . \quad . \quad (6)$$

When $x=A$, E_p is a maximum, $2\pi^2\nu^2mA^2$.

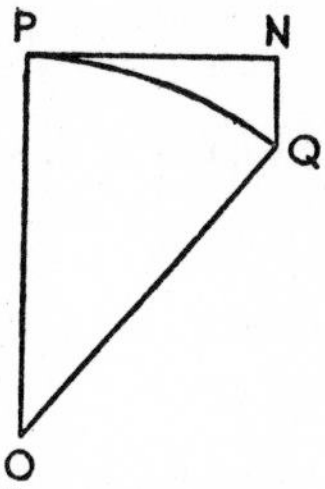

FIG. 28.I. Centripetal Force

§ 53. Centripetal Force

Consider a particle of mass m moving with uniform velocity v in a circle of radius r, and let P (Fig. 28.I) be its position at any instant. If the particle were not acted upon by any force, it would move along the tangent PN with the constant velocity v it had at P, and after a time dt it would reach N, where PN$=v\,.\,\mathrm{d}t$. Thus, NQ is the space moved in the time dt under the action of the force, which is directed towards the centre O of the circle, since the velocity in the circle is constant and there cannot be any force acting in the direction of the tangent. If f is the acceleration, the space described in time dt is $\frac{1}{2}f(dt)^2=QN$. In the limit, from (3), § 48:

$$PN^2=2QN \cdot OP, \quad \therefore (v \cdot dt)^2=2QN \cdot OP=f(dt)^2 r,$$

$$\therefore f=v^2/r \quad \ldots \quad (1)$$

If m is the mass of the particle, the *centripetal force* acting towards the centre of the circle is:

$$P=mv^2/r \quad \ldots \quad (2)$$

§ 54. Gamma Functions

Two important definite integrals are:

(I) the *first Eulerian integral*, or the *beta function*:

$$\int_0^1 x^{l-1}(1-x)^{m-1}dx=B(l, m) \quad \ldots \quad (1)$$

(II) the *second Eulerian integral*, or the *gamma function* [1]:

$$\int_0^\infty e^{-x}x^{n-1}dx=\Gamma(n) \quad \ldots \quad (2)$$

In (1) put $x=1-z$:

$$\therefore \int_0^1 x^{l-1}(1-x)^{m-1}dx=\int_0^1 z^{m-1}(1-z)^{l-1}dz, \quad \therefore B(m, l)=B(l, m).$$

Integration by parts (§ 19) gives:

$$\int e^{-x}x^n dx=-e^{-x}x^n+n\int e^{-x}x^{n-1}dx \quad \ldots \quad (3)$$

Since [2] $(e^{-x}x^n)=0$ for $x=0$ and $x\to\infty$, (2) and (3) give:

$$\Gamma(n+1)=n\Gamma(n) \quad \ldots \quad (4)$$

This is the fundamental equation defining the property of the gamma function.

Now $\int_0^\infty e^x x dx=\int_0^\infty e^{-x}dx=1$, by integration by parts,

$$\therefore \Gamma(1)=1, \quad \Gamma(2)=\Gamma(1)=1 \quad \ldots \quad (5)$$

from (4); hence if n is a positive *integer*, (4) shows that:

$$\Gamma(n+1)=n(n-1)(n-2)\ldots 1=n! \quad \ldots \quad (6)$$

$n!$ being factorial n.

It can now be shown that $\Gamma(\frac{1}{2})=\sqrt{\pi}$. Consider the integral:

$$\int_0^\infty e^{-kx}x^{n-1}dx.$$

Let $kx=z$, $\therefore dx=dz/k$; $x^{n-1}=z^{n-1}/k^{n-1}$

$$\therefore \int_0^\infty e^{-kx}x^{n-1}dx=\int_0^\infty e^{-z}(z^{n-1}/k^{n-1})(dz/k)$$

$$\therefore \int_0^\infty e^{-kx}x^{n-1}dx=(1/k^n)\int_0^\infty e^{-z}z^{n-1}dz=\Gamma(n)/k^n \quad \ldots \quad (7)$$

[1] The beta function was given by Wallis, Newton, and Stirling (1730), but both functions were first fully investigated by Euler (1731 f.). The name Eulerian integrals and the symbol $\Gamma(n)$ are due to Legendre (1811, 1839, respectively). The definition (2) is not the most general one of the gamma function, and holds only with some restrictions, but it is the only one required here.

[2] The proof is not difficult; cf. § 16.

Let
$$u=\int_0^\infty e^{-x^2}dx=\int_0^\infty e^{-y^2}dy,$$
$$\therefore\ u^2=\int_0^\infty e^{-x^2}dx\,.\int_0^\infty e^{-y^2}dy=\int_0^\infty\int_0^\infty e^{-(x^2+y^2)}dxdy.$$
Let
$$\int_{-\infty}^{+\infty} e^{-x^2}dx=\int_{-\infty}^{+\infty} e^{-y^2}dy=J,$$
$$\therefore\ \int_{-\infty}^{+\infty}\int_{-\infty}^{+\infty} e^{-(x^2+y^2)}dxdy=J^2.$$
Change to polar coordinates (Fig. 29.I) by writing $x^2+y^2=r^2$, and $dxdy=rdrd\phi$ (the small element $dxdy$ being equal in the limit to the small area $dr.rd\phi$). The value of r must be taken from 0 to ∞, and the angle ϕ from 0 to 2π (a complete circle),
$$\therefore\ \int_{-\infty}^{+\infty}\int_{-\infty}^{+\infty} e^{-(x^2+y^2)}dxdy=\int_0^\infty e^{-r^2}rdr\int_0^{2\pi}d\phi=2\pi\int_0^\infty e^{-r^2}rdr.$$
Since $d(e^{-r^2})=-2re^{-r^2}dr$, the integral is easily found:
$$2\int_0^\infty e^{-r^2}rdr=-\int_0^\infty d(e^{-r^2})=-\Big[e^{-r^2}\Big]_0^\infty=1,$$
since $e^{-\infty}=1/e^\infty=1/\infty=0$, and $e^0=1$. Hence $J^2=\pi$.

Since e^{-x^2} and e^{-y^2} are even functions (§ 21), each integral between the limits 0 and ∞ is one-half the value between the limits $-\infty$ and $+\infty$, hence:
$$u^2=\int_0^\infty\int_0^\infty e^{-x^2-y^2}dxdy=\pi/4,\quad \therefore\ u=\sqrt{(\pi)}/2.$$
By putting $n=\frac{1}{2}$ in (2) it follows that:
$$\Gamma(\tfrac{1}{2})=\int_0^\infty e^{-x}x^{-1/2}dx.$$
Put $x=y^2$, $\therefore\ dx=2ydy$, and $x^{-1/2}=1/y$,
$$\therefore\ \Gamma(\tfrac{1}{2})=2\int_0^\infty e^{-y^2}dy=2u=\sqrt{\pi}\quad\ldots\ldots\quad(8)$$

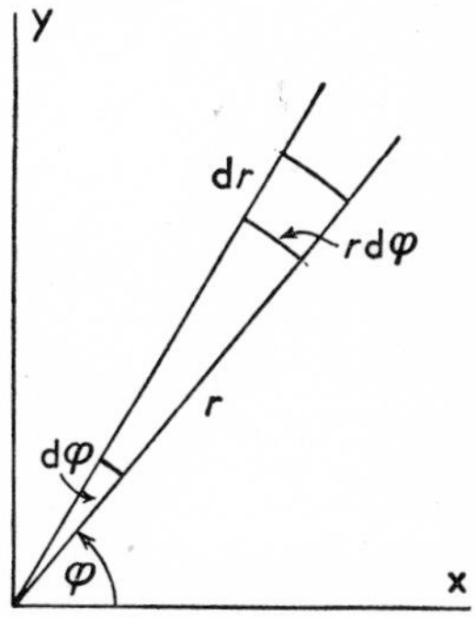

FIG. 29.I. Polar Surface Element

Several special integrals can be expressed in terms of gamma (or beta) functions.

(I) To find the value of the multiple integral: [1]
$$\iiint\ldots x^{l-1}y^{m-1}z^{n-1}\ldots dxdydz\ldots\quad\ldots\quad(9)$$
where the variables have all positive values consistent with the relation $x+y+z+\ldots\leqq 1$. Consider the case of three variables x, y, z. Integrate first with respect to z, the limits of integration being 0 and $1-x-y$. From (4):
$$\int z^{n-1}dz=\frac{(1-x-y)^n}{n}=\frac{\Gamma(n)}{\Gamma(n+1)}(1-x-y)^n\quad\ldots\quad(10)$$

Now integrate with respect to y. The limits of y are 0 and $1-x$, and the value of the integral:
$$\int_0^{1-x} y^{m-1}(1-x-y)^n dy\quad\ldots\ldots\quad(11)$$

[1] The notation means that the function is to be integrated in succession with respect to z, y, x, beginning with z. See § 22.

is to be found. Let:

$$J=\int_0^a x^{l-1}(a-x)^{m-1}\mathrm{d}x$$

and put $x=ay$, therefore $\mathrm{d}x=a\mathrm{d}y$, $(a-x)=a(1-y)$, and when x is a, y is 1,

$$\therefore\ J=a^{l+m-1}\int_0^1 y^{l-1}(1-y)^{m-1}\mathrm{d}y \quad . \quad . \quad . \quad . \quad . \quad (12)$$

Now consider the integral:

$$\int_0^\infty\int_0^\infty x^{l+m-1}y^{m-1}\mathrm{e}^{-(1+y)x}\mathrm{d}x\mathrm{d}y \quad . \quad . \quad . \quad . \quad . \quad . \quad (13)$$

Integrate (13) with respect to x, then from (7):

$$\int_0^\infty\int_0^\infty x^{l+m-1}y^{m-1}\mathrm{e}^{-(1+y)x}\mathrm{d}x\mathrm{d}y=\Gamma(l+m)\int_0^\infty \frac{y^{m-1}}{(1+y)^{l+m}}\mathrm{d}y \quad . \quad . \quad (14)$$

Integrate (13) with respect to y, then, from (7):

$$\int_0^\infty\int_0^\infty x^{l+m-1}y^{m-1}\mathrm{e}^{-(1+y)x}\mathrm{d}x\mathrm{d}y=\Gamma(m)\int_0^\infty \frac{\mathrm{e}^{-x}x^{l+m-1}}{x^m}\mathrm{d}x$$

$$=\Gamma(m)\int_0^\infty \mathrm{e}^{-x}x^{l-1}\mathrm{d}x=\Gamma(m)\Gamma(l) \quad . \quad (15)$$

from (3). Hence, from (14) and (15):

$$\Gamma(l+m)\int_0^\infty \frac{y^{m-1}\mathrm{d}y}{(1+y)^{l+m}}=\Gamma(l)\Gamma(m),$$

$$\therefore\ \int_0^\infty \frac{y^{m-1}\mathrm{d}y}{(1+y)^{l+m}}=\frac{\Gamma(l)\Gamma(m)}{\Gamma(l+m)} \quad . \quad . \quad . \quad . \quad . \quad . \quad (16)$$

Put $y/(1+y)=x$ in (1), then [since the limit of $y/(y+1)$ is 1 as $y\to\infty$]:

$$\int_0^1 x^{l-1}(1-x)^{m-1}\mathrm{d}x=\int_0^\infty \frac{y^{l-1}\mathrm{d}y}{(1+y)^{l+m}} \quad . \quad . \quad . \quad . \quad . \quad (17)$$

This is an important general equation from which, by special substitutions, various special results can be obtained. From (16) and (17):

$$\int_0^1 x^{l-1}(1-x)^{m-1}\mathrm{d}x=\int_0^1 y^{l-1}(1-y)^{m-1}\mathrm{d}y=\frac{\Gamma(l)\Gamma(m)}{\Gamma(l+m)} \quad . \quad . \quad (18)$$

since the value of the definite integral is the same for x or y. This integral is the *beta function* (1), the equation:

$$B(l, m)=\frac{\Gamma(l)\Gamma(m)}{\Gamma(l+m)} \quad . \quad . \quad . \quad . \quad . \quad . \quad . \quad . \quad . \quad (19)$$

giving a fundamental relation between the beta and gamma functions.

From (1) and (12):

$$J=a^{l+m-1}B(l, m) \quad . \quad . \quad . \quad . \quad . \quad . \quad . \quad . \quad (20)$$

In (17) put $y=ax/b$, then:

$$\int_0^\infty \frac{y^{l-1}dy}{(1+y)^{l+m}}=a^lb^m\int_0^\infty \frac{x^{l-1}dx}{(ax+b)^{l+m}},$$

$$\therefore \int_0^\infty \frac{x^{l-1}dx}{(ax+b)^{l+m}}=\frac{\Gamma(l)\Gamma(m)}{a^lb^m\Gamma(l+m)} \quad . \quad . \quad . \quad . \quad . \quad . \quad . \quad (21)$$

To find the value of (11), put $1-x=a$, and $n=l-1$, then

$$\int_0^{1-x} y^{m-1}(1-x-y)^n dy=\int_0^a y^{m-1}(a-x)^{l-1}dy$$

$$=a^{m+l-1}\int_0^1 y^{m-1}(1-y)^{l-1}dy, \text{ from (12)}$$

$$=a^{m+n}\int_0^1 y^{m-1}(1-y)^{l-1}dy$$

$$=(1-x)^{m+n}\frac{\Gamma(m)\Gamma(n+1)}{\Gamma(m+n+1)} \quad . \quad . \quad . \quad . \quad (22)$$

from (18). By replacing m in (18) by $(m+n)$, considered as a single constant:

$$\int_0^1 x^{l-1}(1-x)^{m+n}dx=\frac{\Gamma(l)\Gamma(m+n+1)}{\Gamma(l+m+n+1)} \quad . \quad . \quad . \quad . \quad (23)$$

Hence, from (9), (10), and (22):

$$\iiint \ldots x^{l-1}y^{m-1}z^{n-1} \ldots dxdydz \ldots$$

$$=\frac{\Gamma(n)}{\Gamma(n+1)}\cdot\frac{\Gamma(m)\Gamma(n+1)}{\Gamma(m+n+1)}\cdot\frac{\Gamma(l)\Gamma(m+n+1)}{\Gamma(l+m+n+1)}\ldots$$

$$=\frac{\Gamma(l)\Gamma(m)\Gamma(n)\ldots}{\Gamma(l+m+n+\ldots+1)} \quad . \quad . \quad . \quad . \quad . \quad . \quad . \quad . \quad . \quad . \quad . \quad (24)$$

which is the required result, for all values of $x, y, z \ldots$, such that $x+y+z+\ldots \leqq 1$.

(II) To find the value of:

$$\int_0^{\pi/2} \sin^n x dx=\int_0^{\pi/2} \cos^n x dx.$$

In (18), put $x=\sin^2\theta$, therefore $1-x=\cos^2\theta$, $dx=2\sin\theta\cos\theta d\theta$; when $x=0$, $\theta=0$, and when $x=1$, $\theta=\pi/2$; hence:

$$\int_0^1 x^{l-1}(1-x)^{m-1}dx=2\int_0^{\pi/2}(\sin^2\theta)^{l-1/2}(\cos^2\theta)^{m-1/2}d\theta.$$

Put $2l-1=p$ and $2m-1=q$, then the integral is:

$$2\int_0^{\pi/2}\sin^p\theta\cos^q\theta\, d\theta=2\int_0^{\pi/2}\sin^p x\cos^q x dx,$$

$$\therefore \text{ from (18): } \int_0^{\pi/2}\sin^p x\cos^q x dx=\frac{1}{2}\frac{\Gamma[\frac{1}{2}(p+1)]\Gamma[\frac{1}{2}(q+1)]}{\Gamma[\frac{1}{2}(p+q)+1]}.$$

Put $p=n$ and $q=0$, and then $q=n$ and $p=0$, when the same result is found,

$$\therefore \int_0^{\pi/2}\sin^n x dx=\int_0^{\pi/2}\cos^n x dx=\frac{1}{2}\frac{\Gamma[\frac{1}{2}(n+1)]\Gamma(\frac{1}{2})}{\Gamma(\frac{1}{2}n+2)} \quad . \quad . \quad (25)$$

(III) To find the value of:

$$\int_0^\infty x^n e^{-ax} dx.$$

Put $ax=z$, therefore $dx=dz/a$ and $x^n=z^n/a^n$, and the integral is

$$(1/a^{n+1})\int_0^\infty z^n e^{-z} dz.$$

Put $n=m-1$, when the integral becomes $\Gamma(m)=\Gamma(n+1)$, by (2),

$$\therefore \int_0^\infty x^n e^{-ax} dx = a^{-(n+1)}\Gamma(n+1) \quad . \quad . \quad . \quad . \quad . \quad . \quad (26)$$

Table of Gamma Functions

Values of log $\Gamma(n)$ when n lies between 1 and 2 are given to six decimal places by Legendre [1]; an abbreviated table to four places is given below.[2] Any other values may be obtained by using the fundamental equation (4) until a value of n between 1 and 2 is obtained in $\Gamma(n)$.

Example. Find $\Gamma(\frac{1}{4})$. This is given by $\frac{1}{4}\Gamma(\frac{1}{4})=\Gamma(1+\frac{1}{4})=\Gamma(1{\cdot}25)$ $\therefore$ $\Gamma(\frac{1}{4})=4\Gamma(1{\cdot}25)$. From the table, $\log \Gamma(1{\cdot}25)=\bar{1}{\cdot}9573$ $\therefore$ $\Gamma(1{\cdot}25)=0{\cdot}9064$ $\therefore$ $\Gamma(\frac{1}{4})=3{\cdot}6256$.

n	0·00	0·01	0·02	0·03	0·04	0·05	0·06	0·07	0·08	0·09
1·0	0·0000	$\bar{1}$·9975	$\bar{1}$·9951	$\bar{1}$·9928	$\bar{1}$·9905	$\bar{1}$·9883	$\bar{1}$·9862	$\bar{1}$·9841	$\bar{1}$·9821	$\bar{1}$·9802
1·1	$\bar{1}$·9783	$\bar{1}$·9765	$\bar{1}$·9748	$\bar{1}$·9731	$\bar{1}$·9715	$\bar{1}$·9699	$\bar{1}$·9684	$\bar{1}$·9669	$\bar{1}$·9655	$\bar{1}$·9642
1·2	$\bar{1}$·9629	$\bar{1}$·9617	$\bar{1}$·9605	$\bar{1}$·9594	$\bar{1}$·9583	$\bar{1}$·9573	$\bar{1}$·9564	$\bar{1}$·9554	$\bar{1}$·9546	$\bar{1}$·9538
1·3	$\bar{1}$·9530	$\bar{1}$·9523	$\bar{1}$·9516	$\bar{1}$·9510	$\bar{1}$·9505	$\bar{1}$·9500	$\bar{1}$·9495	$\bar{1}$·9491	$\bar{1}$·9487	$\bar{1}$·9483
1·4	$\bar{1}$·9481	$\bar{1}$·9478	$\bar{1}$·9476	$\bar{1}$·9475	$\bar{1}$·9473	$\bar{1}$·9473	$\bar{1}$·9472	$\bar{1}$·9473	$\bar{1}$·9473	$\bar{1}$·9474
1·5	$\bar{1}$·9475	$\bar{1}$·9477	$\bar{1}$·9479	$\bar{1}$·9482	$\bar{1}$·9485	$\bar{1}$·9488	$\bar{1}$·9492	$\bar{1}$·9496	$\bar{1}$·9501	$\bar{1}$·9506
1·6	$\bar{1}$·9511	$\bar{1}$·9517	$\bar{1}$·9523	$\bar{1}$·9529	$\bar{1}$·9536	$\bar{1}$·9543	$\bar{1}$·9550	$\bar{1}$·9558	$\bar{1}$·9566	$\bar{1}$·9575
1·7	$\bar{1}$·9584	$\bar{1}$·9593	$\bar{1}$·9603	$\bar{1}$·9613	$\bar{1}$·9623	$\bar{1}$·9633	$\bar{1}$·9644	$\bar{1}$·9656	$\bar{1}$·9667	$\bar{1}$·9679
1·8	$\bar{1}$·9691	$\bar{1}$·9704	$\bar{1}$·9717	$\bar{1}$·9730	$\bar{1}$·9743	$\bar{1}$·9757	$\bar{1}$·9771	$\bar{1}$·9786	$\bar{1}$·9800	$\bar{1}$·9815
1·9	$\bar{1}$·9831	$\bar{1}$·9846	$\bar{1}$·9862	$\bar{1}$·9878	$\bar{1}$·9895	$\bar{1}$·9912	$\bar{1}$·9929	$\bar{1}$·9946	$\bar{1}$·9964	$\bar{1}$·9982

§ 55. Dirichlet's Integral

This is the integral: [3]

$$J=\iiint \ldots \xi^{l-1}\eta^{m-1}\zeta^{n-1} \ldots d\xi d\eta d\zeta \quad \ldots \quad . \quad . \quad . \quad (1)$$

in which the variables . . . ξ, η, ζ . . . are given all *positive* values consistent with the condition that:

$$(\xi/\alpha)^p+(\eta/\beta)^q+(\zeta/\gamma)^r+ \ldots \text{ is not greater than 1.}$$

Let $(\xi/\alpha)^p=x$, $(\eta/\beta)^q=y$, $(\zeta/\gamma)^r=z$ . . .,

$$\therefore \ \xi=\alpha x^{1/p}, \qquad \eta=\beta y^{1/q}, \qquad \zeta=\gamma z^{1/r} \ldots,$$

$$d\xi=(\alpha/p)x^{1/p-1}dx, \quad d\eta=(\beta/q)y^{1/q-1}dy, \quad d\zeta=(\gamma/r)z^{1/r-1}dz.$$

[1] "Exercises de Calcul Intégral," Paris, 1817, 2, 85. The method of calculation is given in Lodge, "Integral Calculus for Beginners," 1905, 140.

[2] Adapted from the table in Williamson, "Integral Calculus," 1888, 169, where 10 has been added to all values, as in trigonometrical tables. See Nielsen, "Handbuch der Theorie der Gammafunktion," Leipzig, 1906.

[3] De Morgan, "Differential and Integral Calculus," 1842, 678 f.; Williamson, "Integral Calculus," 1888, 316.

Therefore (1) may be written:

$$J=(\alpha^l\beta^m\gamma^n\ \dots\ /pqr\ \dots)\int\int\int\ \dots\ x^{l/p-1}y^{m/q-1}z^{n/r-1}\ \dots\ \mathrm{d}x\mathrm{d}y\mathrm{d}z\ \dots,$$

with the condition that $x+y+z+\dots$ is not greater than 1. This integral has been found in (24), § 54:

$$\therefore\ J=(\alpha^l\beta^m\gamma^n\ \dots\ /pqr\ \dots)\frac{\Gamma(l/p)\Gamma(m/q)\Gamma(n/r)\ \dots}{\Gamma(l/p+m/q+n/r+\ \dots\ +1)}\quad . \quad (2)$$

Put $l=m=n=\dots=1$, then $\xi^{l-1}=\eta^{m-1}=\zeta^{n-1}=\dots=1$, and the value of (1) for all *positive* values of the N variables consistent with the condition that $\xi^2+\eta^2+\zeta^2+\dots$ is not greater than 1 is found from (2) by putting $\alpha=\beta=\gamma=\dots=1$ and $p=q=r=\dots=2$, to be:

$$J_1=\int\int\int\ \dots\ \mathrm{d}\xi\mathrm{d}\eta\mathrm{d}\zeta\ \dots\ =\frac{1}{2^N}\cdot\frac{[\Gamma(\frac{1}{2})]^N}{\Gamma(N/2+1)}=\frac{\pi^{N/2}}{2^N\Gamma(N/2+1)}\quad . \quad (3)$$

and the value of J_1 for *all positive and negative values* of the variables is found by multiplying (3) by 2^N, each positive term having a corresponding negative one.

The value of $\int\int\int\ \dots\ \mathrm{d}\xi\mathrm{d}\eta\mathrm{d}\zeta\ \dots$ for all *positive* values of the N variables such that $\xi^2+\eta^2+\zeta^2+\dots$ is not greater than r^2, i.e. $(\xi/r)^2+(\eta/r)^2+(\zeta/r)^2+\dots$ not greater than 1, is found by putting $\alpha=\beta=\gamma=\dots=r$, and $p=q=r=\dots=r$ in (2), and is:

$$(r^N/2^N)[\Gamma(1/2)]^N/\Gamma(N/2+1)\quad . \ . \ . \ . \ . \ . \quad (4)$$

and for *all positive and negative values* of the variables it is:

$$r^N[\Gamma(1/2)]^N/\Gamma(N/2+1)=r^N\pi^{N/2}/\Gamma(N/2+1)\quad . \ . \ . \ . \quad (5)$$

Now, from (4), § 54:

$$\Gamma(N/2+1)=(N/2)\Gamma(N/2)=\frac{N}{2}\Gamma\left(\frac{N-2}{2}+1\right)=\frac{N}{2}\cdot\frac{N-2}{2}\Gamma\left(\frac{N-4}{2}+1\right),\ \text{etc.}$$

If N is *odd*, the last factor is $\Gamma(1/2)=\sqrt{\pi}$, and it is seen that the number of factors besides this is $\frac{1}{2}(N+1)$. E.g. if $N=5$, its values are 5, 3, 1, i.e. three or $\frac{1}{2}(5+1)$; if $N=7$, it is 7, 5, 3, 1, or four values, i.e. $\frac{1}{2}(7+1)$. Hence the expression becomes:

$$r^N\frac{2^{(N+1)/2}\pi^{N/2}}{1\,.\,3\,.\,5\ \dots\ N\Gamma(\frac{1}{2})}=r^N\frac{2^{(N+1)/2}\pi^{(N-1)/2}}{1\,.\,3\,.\,5\ \dots\ N}\quad . \ . \ . \ . \quad (6)$$

If N is *even*, the last factor is $\Gamma(1)=1$, and the number of factors is $\frac{1}{2}N$; e.g. if $N=4$, its values are 4 and 2, or two, i.e. $\frac{1}{2}\times 4$; if 6, the values are 6, 4, 2, or three, i.e. $\frac{1}{2}\times 6$, etc. Hence the expression becomes:

$$r^N\frac{2^{N/2}\pi^{N/2}}{2\,.\,4\,.\,6\ \dots\ N}=r^N\frac{(2\pi)^{N/2}}{2\,.\,4\,.\,6\ \dots\ N}\quad . \ . \ . \ . \ . \quad (7)$$

If $N=3$, the expression becomes $(2^2\pi/1\times 3)r^3=\frac{4}{3}\pi r^3$, the volume of a sphere; hence (4) is the volume of a *hypersphere* of radius r in N-dimensional space.[1]

The volume of the *hyperellipsoid* with semi-axes a_1, b; a_2, b; ... a_N, b, bounded by the equation:

$$(x_1^2/a_1^2)+(x_2^2/a_2^2)+(x_3^2/a_3^2)+\ \dots\ =b^2,$$

is similarly shown to be:

$$\frac{\pi^{N/2}}{\Gamma(N/2+1)}b^N a_1 a_2 a_3\ \dots\ a_N\quad . \ . \ . \ . \ . \ . \ . \quad (8)$$

[1] See Berthoud, *J. Chim. Phys.*, 1919, **17**, 589, for simple deductions of the *surfaces* of hyperspheres of 4 and 5 dimensions; Lorentz, "Les Théories Statistiques en Thermodynamique," Leipzig and Berlin, 1916, 80.

DIFFERENTIAL EQUATIONS

§ 56. Differential Equations

An equation involving differential coefficients of any order is called a *differential equation*,[1] and these are of various types. The general methods used for their solution belong to advanced mathematics. The problem, in the simplest case, is to find a value (or values) of $y=f(x)$ which, when substituted in the differential equation involving y, dy/dx, d^2y/dx^2, . . . etc., satisfies the equation, with suitable values of constants. For example, if:

$$m(d^2x/dt^2)=-nx \quad . \quad . \quad . \quad . \quad . \quad . \quad . \quad . \quad (1)$$

this may represent a particle of mass m subject to a *restoring force*, i.e. *mass* × *acceleration*$=m(d^2x/dt^2)$, proportional to its displacement x from a position of equilibrium, n being a constant. The solution:

$$x=C\cos[\sqrt{(n/m)}\,.\,t+b] \quad . \quad . \quad . \quad . \quad . \quad . \quad . \quad (2)$$

where C and b are constants, satisfies (1). There must be *two* constants in the solution, because the second differential coefficient appears in (1) and a constant will have disappeared with each differentiation, which constants must be replaced in the integrations. Differentiate (2) twice with respect to t and substitute in (1):

$$dx/dt=-C\sqrt{(n/m)}\,.\,\sin[\sqrt{(n/m)}\,.\,t+b],$$

$$d^2x/dt^2=-C(n/m)\cos[\sqrt{(n/m)}\,.\,t+b]$$

$$\therefore\quad m(d^2x/dt^2)=-Cn\cos[\sqrt{(n/m)}\,.\,t+b]=-nx,$$

which is (1). This shows, from § 49, that the particle executes a simple harmonic motion.

A differential equation may (but need not) result from the differentiation of a function, sometimes called the *primitive*, and if this contains arbitrary constants, one of them disappears with each differentiation, so that the final differential equation contains no arbitrary constants. An *ordinary differential* equation involves one independent variable, say x, one dependent variable,

[1] Some treatises on differential equations which may be consulted are: Piaggio, " Differential Equations," 1942 (an excellent introductory treatise); Hitchcock and Robinson, "Differential Equations in Applied Chemistry," New York, 1923, 2nd edit., 1936 (elementary); Airy, "An Elementary Treatise on Partial Differential Equations," 1866, 2nd edit., 1873 (geometrical interpretations); Ince, "Ordinary Differential Equations," 1927; Murray, "Introductory Course in Differential Equations," New York, 1897, and many later editions (the one used being that of 1925); Green, " Introduction to Differential Equations," 1945; Johnson, " Treatise on Ordinary and Partial Differential Equations," 3rd edit., 1891; Forsyth, " A Treatise on Differential Equations," 4th edit., 1914; Webster, " Partial Differential Equations of Mathematical Physics," New York and Leipzig, 1927; Woods, " Advanced Calculus," Boston, 1934, 216 f.; a very good elementary account is given in Edwards, " Integral Calculus for Beginners," 1898, 211 f.; an advanced treatise is Riemann, " Partielle Differentialgleichungen und deren Anwendungen auf physikalische Fragen," 3rd edit., by K. Hattendorff, Brunswick, 1882 (reprinted 1938), which is better for most purposes than the elaborated later editions by Weber, e.g., " Die partielle Differentialgleichungen der mathematischen Physik," 5th edit., 2 vols., 1910–12; the latest edition by Franck and Mises, " Die Differential- und Integralgleichungen der Physik," 2 vols., Brunswick, 1925–27, is a pure mathematician's book; Boole's " Treatise on Differential Equations," 3rd final edit., 1872, with the (scarce) Supplementary Volume, 1877, is still useful for some purposes. The name " differential equation " (and also " derivative ") appears in a letter from Leibniz to Oldenburg of 21 June, 1677, intended for Newton: " Aequationem differentialem voco talem qua valor ipsius $d\bar{x}$ exprimitur, quaeque ex alia derivata est, qua valor ipsius x exprimibatur": " Leibnizens mathematische Schriften," edit. Gerhardt, Berlin, 1849, **1**, 156.

say y, and one or more differential coefficients of the latter. The example just given is an ordinary differential equation.

A *partial differential equation* involves two or more independent variables, one dependent variable, and partial differential coefficients of the latter; e.g. $(\partial z/\partial x)(\partial z/\partial y)=4xy$, where $z=\mathrm{f}(x, y)$.

If the highest differential coefficient present is the nth (e.g. $\mathrm{d}^n y/\mathrm{d}x^n$) the equation is said to be of the nth *order*; and if the highest differential coefficient is contained as the mth *power* when the equation is cleared of fractions, the equation is said to be of the mth *degree*. E.g. $x(\mathrm{d}y/\mathrm{d}x)^2-y(\mathrm{d}y/\mathrm{d}x)+a=0$, where a is a constant, is of the first order and second degree.

In the case of *partial* differential equations, *arbitrary functions* of the variables as well as constants may have been eliminated in the formation from the primitive. The elimination of an arbitrary *function* of x and y in forming a partial differential equation may be illustrated by taking $u=\mathrm{f}(at+x)$, where e.g. t denotes time and x distance. Then (with f′ denoting f differentiated with respect to $z=at+x$):

$$\partial u/\partial t=(\partial u/\partial z)(\partial z/\partial t)=\mathrm{f}'(at+x)\,.\,a,$$

$$\partial u/\partial x=(\partial u/\partial z)(\partial z/\partial x)=\mathrm{f}'(at+x)\,.\,1=\mathrm{f}'(at+x),$$

$$\partial^2 u/\partial t^2=\frac{\partial}{\partial t}\mathrm{f}'(at+x)\,.\,a=\frac{\partial}{\partial z}\mathrm{f}'(at+x)\,.\,a\frac{\partial z}{\partial t}=a\mathrm{f}''(at+x)a=a^2\mathrm{f}''(at+x),$$

$$\partial^2 u/\partial x^2=\frac{\partial}{\partial x}\mathrm{f}'(at+x)=\frac{\partial}{\partial z}\mathrm{f}'(at+x)\frac{\partial z}{\partial x}=\mathrm{f}''(at+x)\,.\,1=\mathrm{f}''(at+x),$$

whence $\partial^2 u/\partial t^2=a^2.\partial^2 u/\partial x^2$, an important equation (§ 72). This may be proved in detail for the special cases $u=at+x$, $u=\sin(at+x)$, etc.

The first part of the treatment (up to § 70) deals with ordinary differential equations.

§ 57. Linear Differential Equations of the First Order

A differential equation is called *linear* when the *dependent variable* and its *derivatives* (differential coefficients) occur only in the first degree. The most general form of a *linear differential equation of the first order* is:

$$\mathrm{d}y/\mathrm{d}x+Py=Q \quad \text{. . . . .} \quad (1)$$

where P and Q are either constants or functions of x.

(i) If P is a constant, say $P=-a$, then:

$$\mathrm{d}y/\mathrm{d}x-ay=Q \quad \text{. . . . .} \quad (2)$$

(*a*) If $Q=0$, $\mathrm{d}y/\mathrm{d}x-ay=0$, therefore $\mathrm{d}y/y-a\mathrm{d}x=0$, therefore $\ln y-ax=$ const. $=A$,

$$\therefore\ y=C\mathrm{e}^{ax} \quad \text{. . . . .} \quad (3)$$

where $C=\mathrm{e}^A$ is an arbitrary constant (see §13, Rule iv).

(*b*) If Q is not zero, multiply both sides of (2) by e^{-ax}:

$$\therefore\ \mathrm{e}^{-ax}(\mathrm{d}y/\mathrm{d}x)-ay\mathrm{e}^{-ax}=Q\mathrm{e}^{-ax} \quad \text{. . . . . .} \quad (4)$$

The expression on the left of (4) is equal to $(\mathrm{d}/\mathrm{d}x)(\mathrm{e}^{-ax}\,.\,y)$, as is easily found by differentiation. Hence:

$$(\mathrm{d}/\mathrm{d}x)(\mathrm{e}^{-ax}\,.\,y)=Q\mathrm{e}^{-ax},$$

and by integration:

$$\mathrm{e}^{-ax}y=\int Q\mathrm{e}^{-ax}\mathrm{d}x+C,$$

or (since $1/e^{-ax}=e^{ax}$):

$$y=e^{ax}\int Qe^{-ax}dx+Ce^{ax} \quad . \quad . \quad . \quad (5)$$

The solution (5) consists of two parts:

(i) $e^{ax}\int Qe^{-ax}dx$, which is called the *particular integral*;

(ii) Ce^{ax}, which is called the *complementary function.*

Special cases of solution arise according to the nature of the function $Q=f(x)$.

E.g. if $Q=He^{bx}$, where H and b are constants, $dy/dx-ay=He^{bx}$. Multiply both sides by e^{-ax},

$$\therefore\ e^{-ax}\,.\,dy/dx-aye^{-ax}=He^{(b-a)x},$$

$$\therefore\ (d/dx)(e^{-ax}y)=He^{(b-a)x},$$

$$\therefore\ e^{-ax}y=H\int e^{(b-a)x}dx=[H/(b-a)]e^{(b-a)x}+\text{const.},$$

$$\therefore\ y=[H/(b-a)]e^{bx}+Ce^{ax} \quad . \quad . \quad . \quad (6)$$

If $b=a$, (5) becomes:

$$y=e^{ax}\int Qe^{-ax}dx+Ce^{ax}$$

$$=e^{ax}\int He^{ax}e^{-ax}dx+Ce^{ax}$$

$$=Hxe^{ax}+Ce^{ax} \quad . \quad . \quad . \quad (7)$$

(ii) P is a function of x. In this case an *integrating factor* μ is introduced, this being a factor which converts the left-hand side of (1) into the differential of a function of x and y (see § 27). Thus, the expression:

$$\mu dy+\mu(Py-Q)dx=Ndy+Mdx \quad . \quad . \quad . \quad (8)$$

where M and N are functions of x and y, must be the differential of a function of x and y.

The Principle of Undetermined Coefficients (proved in books on Algebra) asserts that if two functions of a finite number of terms are equal for *all* values of any letter involved in them, the coefficients of like powers of this letter are equal in the two functions. Thence from (8), which is an identity:

$$\mu=N \quad \text{and} \quad \mu(Py-Q)=M.$$

By partial differentiation (§ 25):

$$\partial N/\partial x=\partial\mu/\partial x, \quad \text{and} \quad \partial M/\partial y=(Py-Q)\,.\,\partial\mu/\partial y+P\mu \quad . \quad . \quad (9)$$

Euler's criterion, (5), § 27, shows that the right-hand side of (8) is a perfect differential when $\partial N/\partial x=\partial M/\partial y$, therefore from (9):

$$\partial\mu/\partial x=(Py-Q)\,.\,\partial\mu/\partial y+P\mu,$$

$$\therefore\ (\partial\mu/\partial x)dx=(Py-Q)(\partial\mu/\partial y)dx+P\mu dx=-(\partial\mu/\partial y)dy+P\mu dx,$$

since $(Py-Q)(\partial\mu/\partial y)dx=-(dy/dx)(\partial\mu/\partial y)dx$, from (1) and $(dy/dx)dx=dy$,

$$(\partial\mu/\partial x)dx+(\partial\mu/\partial y)dy=P\mu dx \quad . \quad . \quad . \quad (10)$$

But the expression on the left is the perfect differential of μ, therefore $d\mu=P\mu dx$, therefore $P=(1/\mu)(d\mu/dx)$,

$$\therefore\ \int Pdx=\int d\mu/\mu=\int d\ln\mu=\ln\mu \quad . \quad . \quad . \quad (11)$$

the integration constant being supposed to be included in $\int Pdx$.

Since $\ln e=1$, the left-hand side can be multiplied by $\ln e$:

$$\therefore\ (\int Pdx)\ln e=\ln e^{\int Pdx}=\ln\mu \ (\text{since } n\ln x=\ln x^n),$$

$$\therefore\ \mu=e^{\int Pdx} \quad . \quad . \quad . \quad (12)$$

By substituting (12) in (8):

$$e^{\int P dx}(dy+Py dx)=d(ye^{\int P dx})=e^{\int P dx}Q dx \quad . \quad . \quad . \quad . \quad . \quad (13)$$

$$\therefore \; ye^{\int P dx}=\int e^{\int P dx}Q dx+C,$$

$$\text{or } y=e^{-\int P dx}\int e^{\int P dx}Q dx+Ce^{-\int P dx} \quad . \quad . \quad . \quad (14)$$

a solution first given by Leibniz.

The method of solution of (1) is seen from (13) to be given by the simple rule: *multiply both sides of* (1) *by* $e^{\int P dx}$ *and integrate.* This may well be remembered, instead of the formulae. Two examples will be given.

(1) $(1+x^2)(dy/dx)-xy+mx=0$,

$$\therefore \; dy/dx-[x/(1+x^2)]y=-mx/(1+x^2) \quad . \quad . \quad . \quad . \quad . \quad . \quad . \quad . \quad . \quad . \quad (15)$$

$$\int P dx=-\int x dx/(1+x^2)=-\tfrac{1}{2}\ln(1+x^2)=-\ln\sqrt{(1+x^2)},$$

$$e^{\int P dx}=e^{-\ln\sqrt{(1+x^2)}}=1/\sqrt{(1+x^2)}.$$

Multiply both sides of (15) by $\mu=1/\sqrt{(1+x^2)}$:

$$\frac{1}{\sqrt{(1+x^2)}}\frac{dy}{dx}-\frac{xy}{(1+x^2)^{3/2}}=-\frac{mx}{(1+x^2)^{3/2}}.$$

The expression on the left must be the differential coefficient of some function of x and y and the occurrence of dy/dx in one term and y in the other suggests that the function is of the form $yf(x)$. If $f(x)=1/\sqrt{(1+x^2)}$ then:

$$(d/dx)f(x)=-x/(1+x^2)^{3/2},$$

and the expression on the left is $(d/dx)[y/\sqrt{(1+x^2)}]$, its integral being $y/\sqrt{(1+x^2)}$. The integral of the expression on the right is

$$-m\int dx\,.\,x/(1+x^2)^{3/2}=m/\sqrt{(1+x^2)}+C,$$

hence $y/\sqrt{(1+x^2)}=m/\sqrt{(1+x^2)}+C$, or $y=m+C\sqrt{(1+x^2)}$. Since the equation is linear, there is only one integration constant.

The integrating factor has here been picked out by inspection: some rules for finding them are given in text-books.[1]

(2) An example of (1) is the equation of *motion of a particle in a viscous medium*, i.e. a massive particle subject to a resistance proportional to the velocity v, and to another force which is a given function of the time. Put m=mass of particle=1, for simplicity; the moving force is *mass* × *acceleration*= $1\times dv/dt$, and the equation of motion is:

$$dv/dt-kv=f(t).$$

This is of the form (1) when $P=-k$ (a constant) and $Q=f(t)$. The solution is given by (5) ($a=-k$):

$$v=e^{-kt}\int f(t)e^{kt}dt+Ce^{-kt}.$$

If $f(t)=g$=acceleration of gravity, the case is that of a particle of radius r falling in a viscous fluid, $k=6\pi\eta r$, η being the viscosity:

$$v=Ce^{-kt}+g/k.$$

As t increases, v asymptotically approaches the constant velocity g/k. The motion of ions in an electrolyte solution is also of this type.

The determination of the parameters k and n for the equation:

$$dx/dt=k(a-x)^n t^{p-1}$$

from experimental results is discussed by Barredo.[2]

1 Boole, "Differential Equations," 55; Murray, "Differential Equations." 23.
2 *An. Fis. Quim.*, 1935, 33, 844.

§ 58. Singular Solutions

The equation (Clairaut's equation, 1734):

$$y=x(\mathrm{d}y/\mathrm{d}x)+\mathrm{f}(\mathrm{d}y/\mathrm{d}x), \quad \text{or} \quad y=px+\mathrm{f}(p) \quad . \quad . \quad . \quad . \quad (1)$$

where $p=\mathrm{d}y/\mathrm{d}x$ (§ 26), is of the first order but of degree depending on the form of $\mathrm{f}(p)$. Differentiate with respect to x, putting $\mathrm{d}\mathrm{f}(p)/\mathrm{d}p=\mathrm{f}'(p)$:

$$p=p+x(\mathrm{d}p/\mathrm{d}x)+\mathrm{f}'(p)(\mathrm{d}p/\mathrm{d}x), \quad \therefore \quad [x+\mathrm{f}'(p)](\mathrm{d}p/\mathrm{d}x)=0,$$

$\therefore$ either $$x+\mathrm{f}'(p)=0 \quad . \quad . \quad . \quad . \quad . \quad . \quad . \quad . \quad . \quad . \quad (2)$$

or $$\mathrm{d}p/\mathrm{d}x=0 \quad . \quad . \quad . \quad . \quad . \quad . \quad . \quad . \quad . \quad . \quad (3)$$

Equation (3) gives $p=\mathrm{d}y/\mathrm{d}x=\text{const.}=c$, therefore from (1)

$$y=cx+\mathrm{f}(c) \quad . \quad . \quad . \quad . \quad . \quad . \quad . \quad . \quad . \quad . \quad (4)$$

E.g. if $y=px+a/p$, (1) gives $(x-a/p^2)\,.\,\mathrm{d}p/\mathrm{d}x=0$, therefore either $x-a/p^2=0$ (2), or $\mathrm{d}p/\mathrm{d}x=0$ (3), therefore $p=\text{const.}=c$, therefore $y=cx+a/c=cx+\mathrm{f}(c)$ (4). Equation (2) gives $p=\sqrt{(a/x)}$, and on substitution in (1) p is eliminated, giving $y=x\sqrt{(a/x)}+a\sqrt{(x/a)}$, therefore $y^2=4ax$ (5). This represents a parabola, and although it satisfies (1) it is not included in the *general solution* (4), which represents a system of straight lines differing in the value of the constant c. All these lines are tangents to various points of the parabola, the latter being called an *envelope* of the family of lines. In general, a family of curves may have more than one envelope. Equation (5) is called a *singular solution* of (1), and, in general, the singular solution of a differential equation is geometrically equivalent to the envelope of a family of curves representing the general solution, the equation of each of these curves being a *particular solution* of the differential equation (note that this has a different meaning from " particular integral " used in § 61). Each particular solution is contained, as a special case, in the general solution, but the singular solution is not.

From (1), $xp^2-yp+a=0$, which is a quadratic equation in p, the roots being $p=(1/2x)[y\pm\sqrt{(y^2-4ax)}]$. The condition for *equal roots* is $y^2=4ax$, which is called the *discriminant*, and as it represents the locus of all points for which two values of p (in this case the gradient of a line and the gradient of the parabola) become equal, it is called the *p-discriminant* of (1).

If c in the general solution (4) is regarded as variable (giving the various straight lines), $xc^2-yc+a=0$, and $c=(1/2x)[y\pm\sqrt{(y^2-4ax)}]$, the condition for equal roots being $y^2=4ax$, which is the equation of the locus of all points for which the value of c is the same, or the *c-discriminant*.

Various types of loci are encountered: [1]

(1) The *envelope locus* satisfies the differential equation, but is not included in the general solution (xx in Fig. 30.I).

(2) The *tac locus* passes through points where two non-consecutive members of a family of curves touch (pq in Fig. 30.I). Since these have two equal values of p, they appear in the p-discriminant, but as the touching curves are non-consecutive they have different c values, and the tac locus does not appear in the c-discriminant, neither does it satisfy the differential equation.

[1] See § 59; Hill, *Proc. Lond. Math. Soc.*, 1889, **19**, 561 (curves); *Phil. Trans.*, 1892, **183**, 141 (surfaces); Cayley, " Collected Mathematical Papers," Cambridge, 1889, **2**, 28; 1895, **8**, 529; Forsyth, " Treatise on Differential Equations," 1914, 35.

(3) The *node locus* passes through different points in which each curve of a given family crosses itself in a node (double, triple, etc.) (*rs* in Fig. 30.I), and it does not satisfy the differential equation. It appears in the *c*-discriminant, but not in the *p*-discriminant, since the gradients are different at the crossing point (hence the *p*'s are different), but changing *c* merely shifts the curve without changing its character.

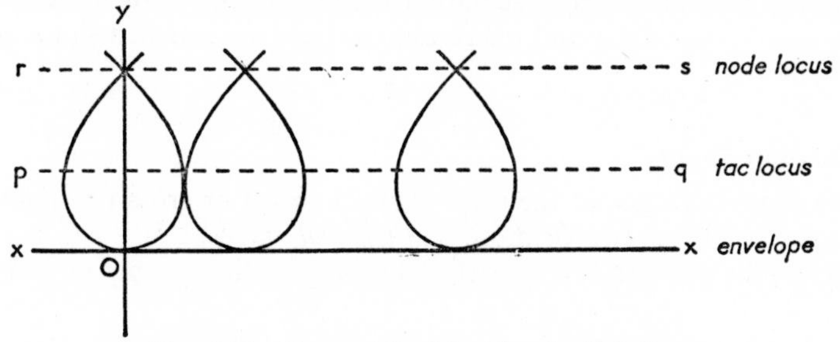

FIG. 30.I. Types of Loci for Singular Solutions

(4) The *cusp* (or *cuspidal*) *locus* passes through all the cusps (§ 59) of a family of curves (Fig. 31.I): it does not satisfy the differential equation, but it satisfies both the *p*-discriminant (since the *p*'s at cusps of consecutive curves are equal), and as the two curves are consecutive it also satisfies the *c*-discriminant.

If + denotes the satisfaction and − the non-satisfaction of an equation, the results may be summarised thus:

	Envelope locus	Tac locus	Node locus	Cusp locus
Differential equation ..	+	−	−	−
p-discriminant	+	+	−	+
c-discriminant	+	−	+	+

Only the envelope locus is a solution of the differential equation, and it is a singular solution: it can be derived from a consideration of the differential quation alone.

Example.

$4xp^2=(3x-a)^2$ . . . . (i)

$\therefore\ p=\pm(3x-a)/(2\sqrt{x})=$
$\pm(\frac{3}{2}x^{1/2}-\frac{1}{2}ax^{-1/2})$,

$\therefore\ dy=\pm(\frac{3}{2}x^{1/2}dx-\frac{1}{2}ax^{-1/2}dx)$.

By integration: $y+c=\pm x^{1/2}(x-a)$,

$\therefore\ (y+c)^2=x(x-a)^2$. (ii)

FIG. 31.I. Cusp Locus

This is the general solution. Equation (i) is a quadratic equation in *p* of the form $ax^2-c=0$ (the term bx being missing), and the condition for equal roots, $\sqrt{(b^2-4ac)}=0$, becomes $x(3x-a)^2=0$, which is the *p*-discriminant. The *c*-discriminant is found from (ii) written as:

$$c^2+2yc+y^2-x(x-a)^2=0,$$

$$\therefore\ c=-1/2y\pm\sqrt{[4y^2-4y^2+4x(x-a)^2]},$$

the condition for equal roots being $x(x-a)^2=0$, the *c*-discriminant. The condition $x=0$ is common to both discriminants, satisfies the original equation (with $p\to\infty$), and is a singular solution, the y axis being an envelope; $x=a$ satisfies the *c*-discriminant but not the *p*-discriminant or original equation, and hence represents the node locus; $x=\frac{1}{3}a$ satisfies the *p*-discriminant but not the *c*-discriminant or the original equation, and hence represents the tac locus. The resulting geometrical representation is like Fig. 30.I with the x and y axes interchanged. Since the p and c discriminants are not satisfied simultaneously, there are no cusps.

§ 59. Singular Points

Two or more branches of the same curve intersect or cross one another at a point where dy/dx has two or more real *unequal* values, and y has at least two *equal* values; the number of intersecting branches is the number of real roots of

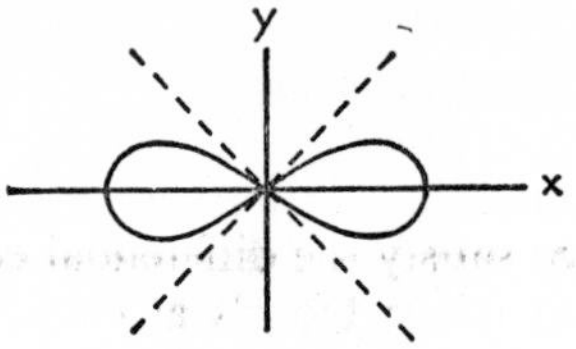

FIG. 32.I. Node

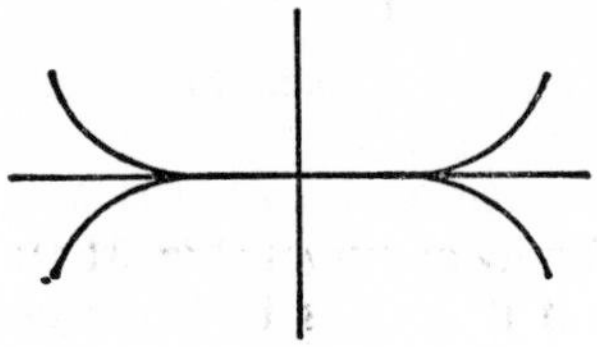

FIG. 33.I. Keratoid Cusp

the first differential coefficient dy/dx regarded as a function of x. The point of intersection is called a *multiple point* (with a *double point* as a special case).

If two branches of the curve *cross* each other (Fig. 32.I), as in the *lemniscate* (Latin, *lemniscus*, a loop), the point is called a *node* (Latin, *nodus*, a knot), or by Cayley [1] a *crunode* (Latin, *crux*, a cross).

A *cusp* (Latin, *cuspis*, a sharp point), or Cayley's *spinode* (Latin, *spina*, a thorn) occurs when the two branches of the curve have a common tangent at a point of contact and terminate at that point. There are several species:

A. Single Cusps

(1) a *cusp of the first species* or a *keratoid cusp* (Greek, κέρας, a horn), for which d^2y/dx^2 has two real equal values of opposite sign at the point of contact (Fig. 33.I);

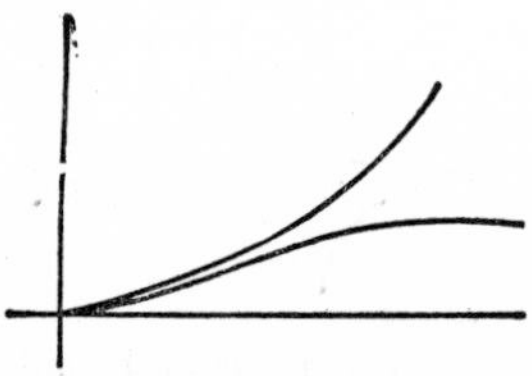

FIG. 34.I. Rhamphoid Cusp

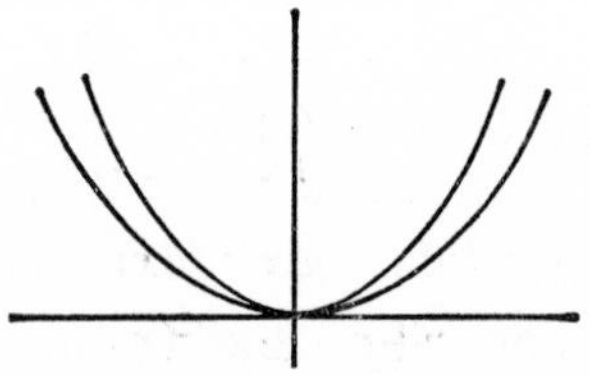

FIG. 35.I. Double Cusp. Type A

(2) a *cusp of the second order* or *rhamphoid cusp* (Greek, ῥάμφος, a beak), for which d^2y/dx^2 has two real unequal values of the same sign (Fig. 34.I).

[1] *Cambr. and Dublin Math. J.*, 1852, **7**, 166; " Mathematical Papers," Cambridge, 1889, **2**, 28; Salmon, " Analytical Geometry of Three Dimensions," 6th edit. (by Rogers), 1914, **1**, 268 f., called Cayley's *spinode* a *parabolic point*. See Frost, " An Elementary Treatise on Curve Tracing," 1872.

B. Double Cusps, or *points of osculation,* Cayley's *tacnodes* (Latin, *tango, tactum,* touch), for which dy/dx has two or more real equal roots, and y has at least two real and equal values on each side of the point (Figs. 35, 36.I).

A *conjugate point* or *acnode* (Latin, *acus,* a needle) has coordinates which satisfy the equation of the curve and yet is itself quite detached from the curve. E.g. $y^2=x^2(x-2)$ has a point at the origin ($x=0$, $y=0$) satisfying the equation, but the graph lies wholly to the right of the origin.

At a *terminal point* the curve stops abruptly. E.g. $y=x \ln x$ stops at the origin, when $x=0$, $y\rightarrow-\infty$, and y does not exist for negative values of x.

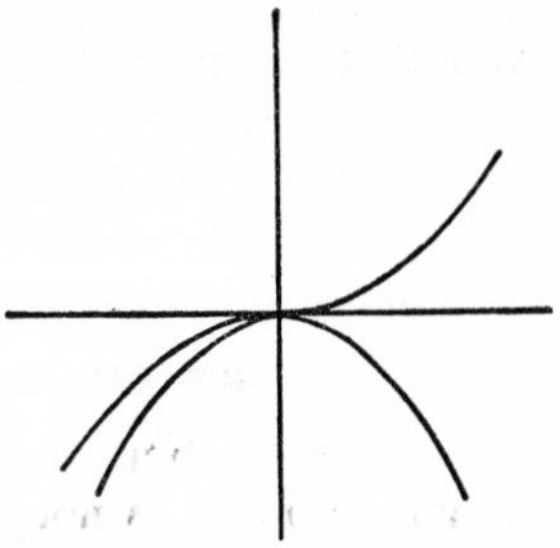

FIG. 36.I. Double Cusp. Type B

If $u=f(x, y)$, then the value of $(\partial^2u/\partial x^2)(\partial^2u/\partial y^2)-(\partial^2u/\partial x\partial y)^2$ is negative for a node, zero for a cusp, and positive for a conjugate point.[1]

§ 60. Exact Equations

The equation:

$$Mdx+Ndy=0 \qquad (1)$$

where M and N are functions of x and y (or of one of these) is said to be *exact* if Euler's criterion (§ 27) is satisfied, i.e. if:

$$\partial M/\partial y=\partial N/\partial x \qquad (2)$$

In this case, the equation has been formed by differentiating a function u of x and y: $u=f(x, y)$; $du=(\partial u/\partial x)dx+(\partial u/\partial y)dy$; and

$$\partial^2u/\partial x\partial y=\partial^2u/\partial y\partial x \qquad (3)$$

which is equivalent to (2), since $M=\partial u/\partial x$ and $N=\partial u/\partial y$. The most general form of a function, the x derivative of which is M, is obviously:

$$u=\int Mdx+Y \qquad (4)$$

where Y is independent of x, but may be a function of y or a constant, since (4) gives $\partial u/\partial x=M$. The only other condition to be satisfied by u is that $\partial u/\partial y=N$,

$$\therefore\ N=(\partial/\partial y)\int Mdx+\partial Y/\partial y,$$

$$\therefore\ \partial Y/\partial y=N-(\partial/\partial y)\int Mdx \qquad (5)$$

Since Y is a function of y alone, $\partial^2 Y/\partial y\partial x=0$ $\therefore$ $\partial N/\partial x=\partial M/\partial y$, as in (2). By integration of (5):

$$Y=\int Ndy-\int\left(\frac{\partial}{\partial y}\int Mdx\right)dy, \quad \text{or}$$

$$Y=\int\left(N-\frac{\partial}{\partial y}\int Mdx\right)dy \qquad (6)$$

Example 1.

$$x(x+2y)dx+(x^2-y^2)dy=0.$$

Since $\partial M/\partial y=\partial N/\partial x=2x$, condition (2) is satisfied, and the equation is exact.

$$\int Mdx=\int x(x+2y)dx=\tfrac{1}{3}x^3+2x^2y.$$

[1] See Williamson, "Differential Calculus," 1887, 261. See also Korteweg, *Wien Ber.*, 1889, **98**, II, 1154; *Arch. Néerl.*, 1891, **24**, 57, 295; Onnes and Keesom, "Enzykl. d. math. Wiss.," 1912, **5**, i, 653; Maxwell, "Theory of Heat," 1894, 200 f.

(Note that y is treated as constant in this integration.)

$$(\partial/\partial y)\int M\mathrm{d}x=2x^2.$$

(Note that x is treated as constant in this differentiation.) $N=x^2-y^2$,

$$\therefore \int\left(N-\frac{\partial}{\partial y}\int M\mathrm{d}x\right)\mathrm{d}y=\int(x^2-y^2-2x^2)\mathrm{d}y=\int(-y^2-x^2)\mathrm{d}y=-\tfrac{1}{3}y^3-x^2y.$$

(Note that x is treated as constant in this integration). Hence:

$$u=(\tfrac{1}{3}x^3+2x^2y)-(\tfrac{1}{3}y^3+x^2y)=\tfrac{1}{3}x^3-\tfrac{1}{3}y^3+x^2y+C,$$

where the integration constant is added to the final result.

If condition (2) is not satisfied, (1) is called a *non-exact* equation. In this case it is sometimes possible to convert it into an exact equation by multiplying by an *integrating factor*, μ (see § 57).

Example 2. $2xy\mathrm{d}x+(y^2-x^2)\mathrm{d}y=0$ is not exact, but if both sides are multiplied by $\mu=1/y^2$ it gives

$$2(x/y)\mathrm{d}x+(1-x^2/y^2)\mathrm{d}y=0,$$

which is exact ($\partial M/\partial y=\partial N/\partial x=-2x/y^2$), and may be solved as above, or by inspection, since the expression is obviously $\mathrm{d}(y+x^2/y)$,

$$\therefore\ y+x^2/y=C, \quad \text{or} \quad x^2+y^2=Cy.$$

General methods of finding integrating factors are given in books on differential equations,[1] where it is also shown that if one integrating factor exists, an infinite number can exist, the final solutions differing only in the integration constants. Thus, if $y\mathrm{d}x-x\mathrm{d}y=0$, three integrating factors are x^{-2}, $x^{-1}y^{-1}$, and y^{-2}, which give solutions $y=C'x$, $\ln(x/y)=C''$, and $x=C'''y$, respectively, which are all the same if $C'=1/C'''=e^{C''}$.

§ 61. Linear Differential Equation of the Second Order

The general *linear differential equation of the second order* is:

$$\mathrm{d}^2y/\mathrm{d}x^2+P(\mathrm{d}y/\mathrm{d}x)+Qy=R \quad \text{. . . . . . (1)}$$

where P, Q, and R are either constants or functions of x. Take first the case when P and Q are *constants*, and consider the equation:

$$\mathrm{d}^2y/\mathrm{d}x^2+P(\mathrm{d}y/\mathrm{d}x)+Qy=0 \quad \text{. . . . . . (2)}$$

The complete solution of (1) is:

$$y=u+w \quad \text{. . . . . (3)}$$

where w is *any* function which satisfies (1) as it stands, and u is the *general* solution of (2). For, if u is to be determined and w satisfies (1), substitution of (3) in (1) gives:

$$\mathrm{d}^2u/\mathrm{d}x^2+P(\mathrm{d}u/\mathrm{d}x)+Qu+d^2w/\mathrm{d}x^2+P(\mathrm{d}w/\mathrm{d}x)+Qw=\mathrm{R} \quad \text{. . (4)}$$

But, by hypothesis, since w satisfies (1):

$$\mathrm{d}^2w/\mathrm{d}x^2+P(\mathrm{d}w/\mathrm{d}x)+Qw=R,$$

hence, from (4): $$\mathrm{d}^2u/\mathrm{d}x^2+P(\mathrm{d}u/\mathrm{d}x)+Qu=0,$$

so that the function u must satisfy (2).

[1] E.g. Murray, "Differential Equations," 1925, 23; Boole, "Differential Equations," 1877, 55.

The function w is called the *particular integral* (P.I.), and the function u the *complementary function* (C.F.), of the general solution of (1). The particular integral is *any* solution of (1), the simplest being usually chosen; the complementary function is *any* solution of (2), which, since this function has been twice differentiated in forming (2), will involve *two* arbitrary constants (see § 56). Obviously, then, *the particular integral contains no arbitrary constants.* If u_1 and u_2 are two functions which satisfy (2), it is seen that equation (1) will be satisfied by:

$$y=C_1u_1+C_2u_2 \qquad (5)$$

where C_1 and C_2 are any two arbitrary constants. This result is verified by substitution, when a relation between the constants in (1) and (5) will result.[1]

§ 62. The Operator D

The operator $\mathrm{d}/\mathrm{d}x=\mathrm{D}$ corresponds to *differentiation*, and it has been shown in § 6 to have the following properties, u and v being any two functions of x, and a a constant:

$$\mathrm{D}(u+v)=\mathrm{D}u+\mathrm{D}v \qquad (1)$$

$$(\mathrm{D}+a)u=(a+\mathrm{D})u \qquad (2)$$

$$\mathrm{D}(au)=a\mathrm{D}u \qquad (3)$$

It must be carefully noted that $\mathbf{D}(xy)$ *is not equal to* $\mathbf{xDy}$, *and equation* (3) *is true only when* $\boldsymbol{a}$ *is a constant.* Further, as can be shown without difficulty:

$$\mathrm{D}^m\mathrm{D}^n u=\mathrm{D}^{m+n}u \qquad (4)$$

Thus, *the operator* **D** *alone or combined with constant multipliers obeys the laws of algebra.* This has been illustrated in § 37 in connection with Leibniz's Theorem, and is now assumed generally. Then, if $\mathrm{D}u=v$, $u=\mathrm{D}^{-1}v=(1/\mathrm{D})v$,

$$\therefore\ \mathrm{D}\mathrm{D}^{-1}=1 \qquad (5)$$

It follows that $1/\mathrm{D}$ or D^{-1} corresponds with the operation of *integration*; e.g. $\mathrm{D}^{-1}x^2=\frac{1}{3}x^3+\mathrm{C}$.

§ 63. Solution of the Linear Differential Equation of the Second Order

If λ_1, λ_2 are any two constants:

$$\begin{aligned}(\mathrm{D}-\lambda_1)(\mathrm{D}-\lambda_2)u&=(\mathrm{D}-\lambda_1)(\mathrm{d}u/\mathrm{d}x-\lambda_2u)\\ &=\frac{\mathrm{d}}{\mathrm{d}x}\left(\frac{\mathrm{d}u}{\mathrm{d}x}-\lambda_2u\right)-\lambda_1\left(\frac{\mathrm{d}u}{\mathrm{d}x}-\lambda_2u\right)\\ &=\mathrm{d}^2u/\mathrm{d}x^2-(\lambda_1+\lambda_2)(\mathrm{d}u/\mathrm{d}x)+\lambda_1\lambda_2u\\ &=[\mathrm{D}^2-(\lambda_1+\lambda_2)\mathrm{D}+\lambda_1\lambda_2]u.\end{aligned}$$

Hence, any equation of the form:

$$\mathrm{d}^2y/\mathrm{d}x^2-(\alpha+\beta)(\mathrm{d}y/\mathrm{d}x)+\alpha\beta y=0 \qquad (1)$$

where α and β are constants, can be written in the form:

$$(\mathrm{D}-\alpha)(\mathrm{D}-\beta)y=0.$$

[1] The full treatment pays more attention to independent *solutions* of the equation than to independent arbitrary constants; see Forsyth, "Treatise on Differential Equations," 1914, 10; Johnson, "Differential Equations," 1891, 74. For a valuable practical summary of methods of solution of differential equations of the second order, see Murray, "Differential Equations," 1925, 118.

Thus, equation (2), § 61, with $P=-(\lambda_1+\lambda_2)$, and $Q=\lambda_1\lambda_2$, may be written in the form: $D^2y-(\lambda_1+\lambda_2)Dy+\lambda_1\lambda_2 y=0$, or

$$[D^2-(\lambda_1+\lambda_2)D+\lambda_1\lambda_2]y=0 \quad . \quad . \quad . \quad . \quad (2)$$

The operator expression $D^2-(\lambda_1+\lambda_2)D+\lambda_1\lambda_2$, may be treated as a quadratic equation, and since its operation on y results in zero:

$$D^2-(\lambda_1+\lambda_2)D+\lambda_1\lambda_2=0, \quad \text{or}$$

$$D^2+PD+Q=0 \quad . \quad . \quad . \quad . \quad (3)$$

Equation (3) is called the *auxiliary equation* for the solution of (2), § 61.

The solution of (3) is:

$$D=\tfrac{1}{2}[-P\pm\sqrt{(P^2-4Q)}] \quad . \quad . \quad . \quad . \quad (4)$$

giving *two* values of D as the two roots of the equation. There are *three cases* to consider:

(*a*) If $P^2>4Q$, the root expression is real, and there will be *two unequal real roots*, so that equation (2) becomes:

$$(D-\lambda_1)(D-\lambda_2)y=0 \quad . \quad . \quad . \quad . \quad (5)$$

where λ_1 and λ_2 are the roots of (3), *i.e.*

$$\left.\begin{matrix}\lambda_1\\ \lambda_2\end{matrix}\right\}=-\tfrac{1}{2}P\pm\sqrt{(\tfrac{1}{4}P^2-Q)} \quad . \quad . \quad . \quad . \quad (6)$$

Let

$$(D-\lambda_2)y=z \quad . \quad . \quad . \quad . \quad (7)$$

then (5) becomes:

$$(D-\lambda_1)z=0 \quad . \quad . \quad . \quad . \quad (8)$$

which is a linear differential equation of the first order. A solution of (8) is:

$$z=Ae^{\lambda_1 x} \quad . \quad . \quad . \quad . \quad (9)$$

where A is a constant, since

$$(D-\lambda_1)z=(A\lambda_1 e^{\lambda_1 x}-\lambda_1 z)=\lambda_1(Ae^{\lambda_1 x}-z)=0,$$

which satisfies (8), since λ_1 is not zero. Substitution of (9) in (7) gives:

$$(D-\lambda_2)y=Ae^{\lambda_1 x} \quad . \quad . \quad . \quad . \quad (10)$$

This is linear and of the form $dy/dx-ay=Q$, where $Q=Ae^{\lambda_1 x}$, already discussed in § 57 under the form $Q=He^{bx}$, where H and b are constants. It was there shown in (6), § 57, that the solution is:

$$y=[H/(b-a)]e^{bx}+Ce^{ax},$$

where C=const. Substituting $a=\lambda_2$, $b=\lambda_1$, $H=A$, gives:

$$y=C_1e^{\lambda_1 x}+C_2e^{\lambda_2 x} \quad . \quad . \quad . \quad . \quad (11)$$

where $C_1=A/(\lambda_1-\lambda_2)$, and C_2 is an arbitrary constant. Since A is an arbitrary constant, both C_1 and C_2 are arbitrary, hence (11) is the most general solution of (3).

(*b*) If $P^2=4Q$ *the two roots of* (3) *are identical*: $D=-\tfrac{1}{2}P$, and (10) becomes:

$$(D-\lambda_1)y=Ae^{\lambda_1 x}, \quad \text{or} \quad dy/dx-\lambda_1 y=Ae^{\lambda_1 x}.$$

This is case (7) of § 57, where the solution was shown to be $y=Hxe^{ax}+Ce^{ax}$, which can be written in the form:

$$y=(Ax+B)e^{\lambda_1 x}=(C_1+C_2x)e^{\lambda_1 x} \quad . \quad . \quad . \quad . \quad (12)$$

where A and B, or C_1 and C_2, are arbitrary constants.

(*c*) If $P^2<4Q$, *the roots are imaginary*: $\sqrt{(P^2-4Q)}=i\sqrt{(4Q-P^2)}$, where $i=\sqrt{-1}$. This case leads to solutions in *periodic functions* and is considered below.

§ 64. Free Vibrations

Let the differential equation be (1), § 56, $m(d^2y/dx^2)=-ny$, and put $n/m=a^2$, a positive quantity. Then $d^2y/dx^2+a^2y=0$, or $(D^2+a^2)y=0$. The auxiliary equation is $\lambda^2+a^2=0$, or $(\lambda+ia)(\lambda-ia)=0$, where $i=\sqrt{-1}$. The solution is found as from (7), § 63, by putting $(D-ia)y=z$, when $z=Ae^{iax}$, where A is a constant. The final solution is found as for (11), § 63, and is:

$$y=C_1e^{iax}+C_2e^{-iax} \quad . \quad . \quad . \quad . \quad . \quad . \quad . \quad . \quad (1)$$

where C_1 and C_2 are arbitrary constants. From De Moivre's theorem (§ 46) with ax written for x:

$$e^{iax}=\cos ax+i\sin ax, \quad \text{and} \quad e^{-iax}=\cos ax-i\sin ax,$$

$$\therefore \ y=C_1(\cos ax+i\sin ax)+C_2(\cos ax-i\sin ax)$$

$$=(C_1+C_2)\cos ax+i(C_1-C_2)\sin ax.$$

Put
$$C_1+C_2=A, \quad \text{and} \quad i(C_1-C_2)=B,$$

$$\therefore \ y=A\cos ax+B\sin ax \quad . \quad . \quad . \quad . \quad . \quad . \quad (2)$$

Let $A=R\sin\epsilon$, and $B=R\cos\epsilon$ (as in § 49), where $R=\sqrt{(A^2+B^2)}$ and $A/B=\tan\epsilon$, or $\epsilon=\tan^{-1}(A/B)$. This substitution is always possible. Then:

$$y=R\cos ax\,.\,\sin\epsilon+R\sin ax\,.\,\cos\epsilon=R\sin(ax+\epsilon) \quad . \quad . \quad . \quad (3)$$

by (3), § 41. This result, however, is much more easily found as follows Multiply each side of $d^2y/dx^2+a^2y=0$, the differential equation, by $2(dy/dx)$:

$$\therefore \ 2(dy/dx)(d^2y/dx^2)+2a^2y(dy/dx)=0.$$

But the first term is $(d/dx)(dy/dx)^2$,

$$\therefore \ (d/dx)(dy/dx)^2+2a^2y(dy/dx)=0,$$

which is immediately integrable, giving $(dy/dx)^2+a^2y^2=\text{const.}$ Put the constant equal to R^2a^2, and separate the variables:

$$(dy/dx)^2=R^2a^2-a^2y^2=a^2(R^2-y^2),$$

$$\therefore \ (dy)^2/(R^2-y^2)=a^2(dx)^2,$$

$\therefore \ dy/\sqrt{(R^2-y^2)}=\pm a\,dx$. The integral of the left-hand term is (2), § 44, $\sin^{-1}(y/R)$, and the integral of the right-hand term is $\pm ax+\text{const.}$ Take the positive sign and put const.$=\epsilon$, then $y=R\sin(ax+\epsilon)$, as before.

§ 65. Damped Vibrations

The solution of $d^2y/dx^2+ay^2=0$, when t (time) is put for x, and x (distance) for y, corresponds with the free simple harmonic vibration of a mass-point. The amplitude is R, the phase-angle ϵ, and the frequency $T=2\pi/a=2\pi\sqrt{(k/m)}$. This equation is a simplified form of (1), § 61, since the linear term $P(dy/dx)$ is missing.

In the more general case, the two roots are (6), § 63:

$$\lambda_1=-\tfrac{1}{2}P+\sqrt{(\tfrac{1}{4}P^2-Q)}, \quad \text{and} \quad \lambda_2=-\tfrac{1}{2}P-\sqrt{(\tfrac{1}{4}P^2-Q)}.$$

This case applies to a particle vibrating in a viscous medium which sets up a frictional force proportional to the velocity (a *damped vibration*) (see § 57):

$$F=-f(\mathrm{d}x/\mathrm{d}t),$$

where f is a constant,

$$\therefore\ m(\mathrm{d}^2x/\mathrm{d}t^2)=-kx-f(\mathrm{d}x/\mathrm{d}t),\quad \text{or}$$

$$\mathrm{d}^2x/\mathrm{d}t^2+(f/m)(\mathrm{d}x/\mathrm{d}t)+(k/m)x=0 \quad . \quad . \quad . \quad . \quad . \quad (1)$$

This is of the general form (1), § 61, with $R=0$, which may be written:

$$\mathrm{d}^2y/\mathrm{d}x^2+a(\mathrm{d}y/\mathrm{d}x)+by=0 \quad . \quad . \quad . \quad . \quad . \quad . \quad (2)$$

where a and b are constants replacing P and Q. The auxiliary equation is:

$$(\mathrm{D}^2+a\mathrm{D}+b)y=0 \quad . \quad . \quad . \quad . \quad . \quad . \quad . \quad . \quad (3)$$

$$\therefore\ \lambda^2+a\lambda+b=0,\quad \therefore\ \left.\begin{matrix}\lambda_1\\ \lambda_2\end{matrix}\right\}=-\tfrac{1}{2}a\pm\sqrt{(\tfrac{1}{4}a^2-b)},$$

If $a^2>4b$ the roots are real, whilst if $a^2<4b$ the roots are imaginary. Consider the second case. Let [1] $y=ze^{-ax/2}$, where z is a new variable. Then, by differentiation:

$$\mathrm{D}y=\mathrm{e}^{-ax/2}(\mathrm{D}-\tfrac{1}{2}a)z,\quad \text{and}\quad \mathrm{D}^2y=\mathrm{e}^{-ax/2}(D^2-a\mathrm{D}+\tfrac{1}{4}a^2)z,$$

$\therefore$ from (3): $$\mathrm{d}^2z/\mathrm{d}x^2+(b-\tfrac{1}{4}a^2)z=0,$$

the solution of which is $z=A\cos\beta x+B\sin\beta x$, where $\beta=\sqrt{(b-\frac{1}{4}a^2)}$, hence:

$$y=\mathrm{e}^{-ax/2}(A\cos\beta x+B\sin\beta x)=R\mathrm{e}^{-ax/2}\sin(\beta x+\epsilon),$$

where A, B, R, and ϵ are arbitrary constants, the transformation being carried out as in § 64.

The solution of (1) is, therefore:

$$x=R\mathrm{e}^{-ft/2m}\sin(\beta t+\epsilon) \quad . \quad . \quad . \quad . \quad . \quad . \quad . \quad . \quad (4)$$

where $\beta=\sqrt{[k/m-\frac{1}{4}(f^2/m^2)]}$.

The period is $T=2\pi/\beta=2\pi/\sqrt{(k/m-f^2/4m^2)}$, which is obviously larger than $2\pi/\sqrt{(k/m)}$, shown above to be the period of the undamped vibration; hence the period of vibration is increased by damping. If t in (4) is replaced by $t+\frac{1}{2}T$, $t+T$, . . ., these correspond with successive vibrations on one side and then the other of the t axis (half complete vibrations). The difference between *any* two successive values of time is $\frac{1}{2}T$, and the corresponding displacements are of opposite sign:

$$\sin[\beta(t+\tfrac{1}{2}T)+\epsilon]=\sin[\beta(t+\pi/\beta)+\epsilon]=\sin[(\beta t+\pi)+\epsilon]=\sin(\beta t+\epsilon),$$

$$\therefore\ x_1=R\mathrm{e}^{-at_1/2}\sin(\beta t_1+\epsilon),\quad x_2=R\mathrm{e}^{-a(t_1+T/2)/2}\sin(\beta t_1+\epsilon)$$

$$\therefore\ x_1/x_2=\mathrm{e}^{aT/4} \quad . \quad . \quad . \quad . \quad . \quad . \quad . \quad . \quad . \quad (5)$$

The value of $\mathrm{e}^{aT/4}=K$ is Kohlrausch's *damping ratio*, and since it is a constant the ratio of the amplitude of any one half-vibration to the previous one is a constant, less than unity. The natural logarithm of K is Gauss's *logarithmic decrement*, $\lambda=\ln K=\frac{1}{4}aT=f\pi/2m\beta$.

Generally, if $x=A\sin(2\pi/T)t$ is an undamped vibration, and the corresponding uniformly damped vibration is:

$$x=A\mathrm{e}^{-2ft/T}\sin(2\pi/T)t \quad . \quad . \quad . \quad . \quad . \quad . \quad . \quad . \quad (6)$$

[1] Lamb, "Dynamical Theory of Sound," 1910, 24, 55.

where f is a constant, then the ratio of one swing (*half* a complete vibration) to the next (backward) swing is:

$$e^{-2ft/T} : e^{(-2f/T)(t+T/2)} = e^{f} = k \quad . \quad . \quad . \quad . \quad . \quad . \quad . \quad (7)$$

where k is the *damping ratio* and $\ln k = f$ is the *logarithmic decrement.*

If the roots λ_1, λ_2 of the auxiliary equation (3) are *real* and *unequal*, $a^2 > 4b$. In this case the solution is not periodic, but is:

$$x = C_1e^{-\lambda_1 t} + C_2e^{-\lambda_2 t},$$

and if the roots are *real* and *equal*, $\lambda_1 = \lambda_2 = \lambda$, say, the solution is:

$$x = (C_1 + C_2t)e^{-\lambda t},$$

both cases having previously been obtained. The motion is *aperiodic*, and the graph of x plotted against t shows that x first rises, reaches a maximum value, and then approaches its initial value asymptotically.[1] This corresponds with strong retarding forces.

§ 66. Forced Vibrations

If the particle, in addition to the two forces already considered, is subject to an *external periodic force* which prevents the vibrations dying away, the motion is called *forced vibration*, the preceding cases being called *free vibration.*[2] This leads to the complete form of (1), § 61, including the term R:

$$d^2x/dt^2 + a(dx/dt) + bx = f(t),$$

but a and b are still constants. This involves a *particular integral* (§ 61).

§ 67. Particular Integrals

The preceding discussion is limited to the discovery of the *complementary function* of equation (1), § 61, since the function R was put equal to zero. The *particular integral* in the general case, when R is not zero, remains to be considered. Since (1), § 61, can be written symbolically as $f(D)y = R$, where f denotes a function of D, the particular integral will be:

$$y = R/f(D) = f(D)^{-1}R \quad . \quad . \quad . \quad . \quad . \quad . \quad . \quad . \quad (1)$$

There are several special cases in which this equation can be solved. The general solution is always the sum of the particular integral and the complementary function. There are two general methods of solution:

(i) When $f(D)^{-1}$ *can be resolved into factors*; and (ii) when $f(D)^{-1}$ *can be expressed in partial fractions* (§ 23); both these cases are sometimes used at once, as in the example below.

Let $$d^2y/dx^2 - 7(dy/dx) + 12y = R,$$

$$\therefore \ (D^2 - 7D + 12)y = (D-4)(D-3)y = R.$$

If $R = 0$, the *complementary function* is (§ 63):

$$y_1 = C_1e^{4x} + C_2e^{3x}.$$

The *particular integral* is:

$$y = f(D)^{-1}R = \frac{1}{D-4} \cdot \frac{1}{D-3}R = \left(\frac{1}{D-4} - \frac{1}{D-3}\right)R.$$

[1] Interesting curves of all the cases dealt with, with special values of the constants, are given in Mellor's "Higher Mathematics," 1931, 406 f.

[2] This is not to be confused with simple harmonic motion under no damping forces, but is merely the antithesis of forced vibration.

Now $y=R/(\mathrm{D}-a)$ is equivalent to $\mathrm{D}y-ay=R$ or $dy/dx-ay=R$, the solution of which (5), § 57 is:[1]

$$y=e^{ax}\int e^{-ax}R\,dx,$$

which is, therefore, the result of operating on R with $1/(\mathrm{D}-a)$. *This result should be remembered:*

$$R/(\mathrm{D}-a)=e^{ax}\int e^{-ax}R\,dx \quad \ldots \ldots \quad (2)$$

Hence, in the present example:

$$y_2=e^{4x}\int e^{-4x}R\,dx-e^{3x}\int e^{-3x}R\,dx.$$

As a particular case, take $R=e^{5x}$, then:

$$e^{4x}\int e^{-4x}\,.\,e^{5x}\,.\,dx=e^{4x}\int e^{x}dx=e^{5x},$$

$$e^{3x}\int e^{-3x}\,.\,e^{5x}\,.\,dx=e^{3x}\int e^{2x}dx=\tfrac{1}{2}e^{5x},$$

$$\therefore\ y_2=e^{5x}-\tfrac{1}{2}e^{5x}=\tfrac{1}{2}e^{5x},$$

and the general solution is:

$$y=y_1+y_2=C_1e^{4x}+C_2e^{3x}+\tfrac{1}{2}e^{5x}.$$

If the factor form of $\mathrm{f(D)}^{-1}$:

$$\frac{1}{\mathrm{D}-a_1}\cdot\frac{1}{\mathrm{D}-a_2}\cdot\ldots\cdot\frac{1}{\mathrm{D}-a_n}$$

cannot be expressed as a sum of partial fractions, it is applied by operating in succession with the factors, beginning on the right:

$$\frac{1}{\mathrm{D}-a_1}\cdot\frac{1}{\mathrm{D}-a_2}\cdot\ldots\cdot\frac{1}{\mathrm{D}-a_{n-1}}\cdot e^{a_nx}\int e^{-a_nx}R\,dx.$$

Special forms of R, discussed in books on differential equations, include (i) $e^{ax}X$, where X is a constant or a function of x; (ii) x^n; (iii) xX; and (iv) $\sin(nx+a)$ or $\cos(nx+a)$.

(I). Let

$$R=e^{ax},$$

$$\therefore\ \frac{1}{\mathrm{f(D)}}R=\frac{1}{\mathrm{f(D)}}e^{ax}.$$

Now,

$$\mathrm{D}e^{ax}=ae^{ax},$$

$$\mathrm{D}^2e^{ax}=a^2e^{ax},$$

$$\ldots \qquad \ldots$$

$$\mathrm{D}^ne^{ax}=a^ne^{ax},$$

and if f(D) is supposed expanded in powers of D, every power D^r gives a term a^r, hence:

$$\mathrm{f(D)}e^{ax}=\mathrm{f}(a)e^{ax},$$

where f(a) is now an *algebraic multiplier*, not an operator. Operate on both sides with 1/f(D):

$$\frac{1}{\mathrm{f(D)}}\mathrm{f(D)}e^{ax}=e^{ax}=\frac{1}{\mathrm{f(D)}}\mathrm{f}(a)e^{ax}=\mathrm{f}(a)\frac{1}{\mathrm{f(D)}}e^{ax},$$

since the order of 1/f(D) and f(a) can be changed, because f(a) is a constant.[2]

[1] It should be remembered that the particular integral contains no arbitrary constant. See § 61.

[2] It must be carefully noted that the order of *operator* symbols *cannot* be so exchanged: see § 62.

Take the second and fourth terms and divide by the algebraic factor f(a):

$$\frac{1}{f(D)}e^{ax}=\frac{1}{f(a)}e^{ax}.$$

If a happens to be a root of the equation f(D)=0, then $1/f(a)\to\infty$. In this case, elementary algebra shows that $(D-a)$ is a factor of f(D), and if $\phi(D)$ is a function of D:

$$f(D)=(D-a)\phi(D),$$

hence,

$$\frac{1}{f(D)}e^{ax}=\frac{1}{D-a}\cdot\frac{1}{\phi(D)}e^{ax}=\frac{1}{D-a}\cdot\frac{1}{\phi(a)}e^{ax}=\frac{1}{\phi(a)}\cdot\frac{1}{D-a}e^{ax}$$

$$=\frac{1}{\phi(a)}e^{ax}\int e^{-ax}e^{ax}dx=\frac{xe^{ax}}{\phi(a)}.$$

(II). Let $R=e^{ax}X$, where X is a function of x. Then:

$$De^{ax}X=e^{ax}DX+ae^{ax}X=e^{ax}(D+a)X,$$

$$D^2e^{ax}X=D[e^{ax}(D+a)X]=ae^{ax}(D+a)X+e^{ax}D(D+a)X$$

$$=e^{ax}(aD+a^2+D^2+aD)X=e^{ax}(D+a)^2X$$

. . . . . .

$$D^ne^{ax}X=e^{ax}(D+a)^nX.$$

Thus, e^{ax} may be moved from the right to the left of the operator D^n if D is replaced by $(D+a)$.

(III). Let: $R=x^n$, where n is a positive integer. In evaluating $\frac{1}{f(D)}x^n$, (i) f(D) is raised to the power -1, the terms are arranged in ascending powers of D and powers beyond D^n are omitted (since they all give zero[1] on operating on x^n); (ii) the several terms in the expansion operate on x^n. As an example of (II) and (III) take:

$$d^2y/dx^2-2(dy/dx)+y=x^2e^{3x},$$

$$\therefore\ (D^2-2D+1)y=(D-1)(D-1)y=x^2e^{3x}.$$

The *particular integral* is:

$$y_1=\frac{1}{f(D)}x^2e^{3x}=\frac{1}{D-1}\cdot\frac{1}{D-1}x^2e^{3x}.$$

By rule II, move e^{3x} to the left of the operator, and put D+3 for D (a=3), hence D−1 becomes D+2:

$$y_1=e^{3x}\cdot\frac{1}{(D+2)^2}\cdot x^2=e^{3x}\cdot\frac{1}{D^2+4D+4}\cdot x^2$$

The case has now become (III):

$$\frac{1}{D^2+4D+4}=\frac{1}{4\left(1+D+\frac{D^2}{4}\right)}=\tfrac{1}{4}(1-D+\tfrac{3}{4}D^2+\ldots)$$

by division. Operate with this on x^2, giving:

$$\tfrac{1}{4}(x^2-2x+\tfrac{3}{2})=\tfrac{1}{4}x^2-\tfrac{1}{2}x+\tfrac{3}{8}.$$

Hence the particular integral is

$$e^{3x}(\tfrac{1}{4}x^2-\tfrac{1}{2}x+\tfrac{3}{8}).$$

[1] The result of operating on x^n with D^n will be a constant.

The *complementary function* is found by solving the equation with the right-hand member zero:

$$d^2y/dx^2-2dy/dx+y=0.$$

This is case (*b*), § 63, since $(D^2-2D+1)y=0$ or $(D-1)^2y=0$, with two equal roots. The solution is (12), § 63, i.e. $(C_1+C_2x)e^x$, and the complete solution is:

$$y=(C_1+C_2x)e^x+e^{3x}(\tfrac{1}{4}x^2-\tfrac{1}{2}x+\tfrac{3}{8}).$$

(IV). Let $R=\sin(ax+b)$, where a and b are constants. Then:

$$D\sin(ax+b)=a\cos(ax+b),$$

$$D^2\sin(ax+b)=-a^2\sin(ax+b),$$

$$D^3\sin(ax+b)=-a^3\cos(ax+b),$$

$$D^4\sin(ax+b)=a^4\sin(ax+b)=(-a^2)^2\sin(ax+b),$$

and, in general, as is easily seen [1]:

$$(D^2)^n\sin(ax+b)=(-a^2)^n\sin(ax+b).$$

If $f(D^2)$ is a rational integral function [2] of D^2:

$$f(D^2)\sin(ax+b)=f(-a^2)\sin(ax+b).$$

Since $f(-a^2)$ is only an algebraic multiplier:

$$\frac{f(D^2)}{f(-a^2)}\sin(ax+b)=\sin(ax+b)$$

$$\therefore\ \frac{1}{f(D^2)}\sin(ax+b)=\frac{1}{f(-a^2)}\sin(ax+b)$$

by dividing both sides by $f(D^2)$. In the same way it is proved that:

$$\frac{1}{f(D^2)}\cos(ax+b)=\frac{1}{f(-a^2)}\cos(ax+b).$$

The anomalous case when $D^2=a^2$ in D^2+a^2, which arises in solving $d^2y/dx^2+a^2y=\cos ax$, is shown [3] to give $x\sin ax/2a$.

The equation: [4]

$$d^2y/dx^2-2a\,dy/dx+by=ce^{px}\sin(qx+\alpha)$$

is important in many dynamical and electrical problems: some cases of it will be dealt with as they arise.

A simple case is [5] $d^2y/dx^2-k^2y=\sin mx$,

$$\therefore\ (D^2-k^2)y=(D-k)(D+k)y=\sin mx.$$

The complementary function is (putting $\sin mx=0$): $C_1e^{kx}+C_2e^{-kx}$. The particular integral is:

$$\frac{1}{D^2-k^2}\sin mx=\frac{1}{-m^2-k^2}\sin mx,$$

and the complete solution is:

$$y=C_1e^{kx}+C_2e^{-kx}-\sin mx/(m^2+k^2).$$

1 Note that $(D^2)^n$ is the operator, not D^n.
2 See § 2; note again that D^2, not D, is concerned.
3 Murray, "Differential Equations," 1925, 78.
4 See Forsyth, "Differential Equations," 1914, 77.
5 This is a simple case of *forced vibration* (§ 66) without damping.

Another example is:

$$d^2y/dx^2+mdy/dx+n^2y=a \sin nx,$$

$$(D^2+mD+n^2)y=a \sin nx.$$

If λ_1 and λ_2 are the roots of the auxiliary equation, the *complementary function* is $C_1e^{\lambda_1 x}+C_2e^{\lambda_2 x}$. The *particular integral* is:

$$\frac{1}{D^2+mD+n^2}a \sin nx.$$

Put $D^2=-n^2$ in accordance with the rule, and this becomes:

$$\frac{1}{mD}a \sin nx=\frac{-1}{mn}a \cos nx,$$

and the complete solution is:

$$y=C_1e^{\lambda_1 x}+C_2e^{\lambda_2 x}-(a \cos nx)/mn.$$

§ 68. Linear Differential Equations of Higher Orders

So far, linear differential equations of the first order (§ 57), and of the second order (§ 61), have been discussed. A homogeneous differential equation of the *third* order is:

$$x^3\frac{d^3y}{dx^3}+a_1x^2\frac{d^2y}{dx^2}+a_2x\frac{dy}{dx}+a_3y=X,$$

where a_1, a_2, are constants, and X is a function of x. Since y is a function of x containing x to the third power, all terms on the left are of the third order and the equation is homogeneous. This is obviously capable of extension to the nth order. If e^z is substituted for x, or $z=\ln x$, where z is a new variable, the equation transforms to one with constant coefficients, since $dz/dx=d(\ln x)/dx=1/x$:

$$\frac{dy}{dx}=\frac{dy}{dz}\frac{dz}{dx}=\frac{dy}{dz}\frac{1}{x}$$

$\therefore$ the term $x(dy/dx)$ becomes dy/dz;

$$\frac{d^2y}{dx^2}=\frac{d}{dx}\left(\frac{dy}{dx}\right)=\frac{d}{dx}\left(\frac{dy}{dz}\cdot\frac{1}{x}\right)=-\frac{1}{x^2}\frac{dy}{dz}+\frac{1}{x}\frac{d}{dz}\left(\frac{dy}{dz}\right)\frac{dz}{dx}=$$

$$\frac{1}{x^2}\frac{d^2y}{dz^2}-\frac{1}{x^2}\frac{dy}{dz}=\frac{1}{x^2}\left(\frac{d^2y}{dz^2}-\frac{dy}{dz}\right),$$

hence the term $x^2(d^2y/dx^2)$ becomes $d^2y/dz^2-dy/dz$;

$$\frac{d^3y}{dx^3}=\frac{d}{dx}\left(\frac{d^2y}{dx^2}\right)=\frac{d}{dx}\left[\frac{1}{x^2}\left(\frac{d^2y}{dz^2}-\frac{dy}{dz}\right)\right]=-2\frac{1}{x^3}\left(\frac{d^2y}{dz^2}-\frac{dy}{dz}\right)+\frac{1}{x^2}\frac{d}{dz}\left(\frac{d^2y}{dz^2}-\frac{dy}{dz}\right)\frac{dz}{dx}$$

$$=\frac{1}{x^3}\left(\frac{d^3y}{dz^3}-3\frac{d^2y}{dz^2}+2\frac{dy}{dz}\right);$$

and the term $x^3(d^3y/dx^3)$ becomes $d^3y/dz^3-3d^2y/dz^2+2dy/dz$.

§ 69. The Theta Operator

It is usual to denote the symbol xd/dx by ϑ (the theta operator) and (since $xdy/dx=dy/dz$), $xDy=\vartheta y$. Since the operator symbols are *not* interchangeable (§ 62), x^2D^2 is *not* equal to ϑ^2, but, as shown above:

$$x^2D^2y=\vartheta^2y-\vartheta y=\vartheta(\vartheta-1)y,$$

$$x^3D^3y=\vartheta^3y-3\vartheta^2y+2\vartheta y=\vartheta(\vartheta-1)(\vartheta-2)y, \text{ and so on.}$$

Let $x^3(d^3y/dx^3)+2x^2(d^2y/dx^2)+3x(dy/dx)-3y=x^2+x$,

$$\therefore\ \vartheta^3y+2\vartheta^2y+3\vartheta y-3y=\vartheta(\vartheta-1)(\vartheta-2)y+2\vartheta(\vartheta-1)y+3\vartheta y-3y$$
$$=(\vartheta-1)(\vartheta^2+3)y$$
$$=x^2+x=e^{2z}+e^z.$$

The *complementary function* is found from $(\vartheta-1)(\vartheta^2+3)y=0$, therefore $(\vartheta-1)(\vartheta+i\sqrt{3})(\vartheta-i\sqrt{3})=0$, which gives:

$$C_1e^z+C_2e^{i\sqrt{(3)}z}+C_3e^{-i\sqrt{(3)}z}.$$

The *particular integral is*:

$$\frac{x^2+x}{(\vartheta-1)(\vartheta^2+3)}=\frac{x^2}{\vartheta^3-\vartheta^2+3\vartheta-3}+\frac{x}{(\vartheta-1)(\vartheta^2+3)}\quad . \quad . \quad . \quad (1)$$

Now $$\vartheta x^m=x\frac{d}{dx}x^m=mx^m,\ \vartheta^2x^m=x^2\frac{d}{dx^2}x^m=m^2x^m,\text{ etc.},$$

and if $f(\vartheta)$ is a rational integral function of ϑ: $f(\vartheta)x^m=f(m)x^m$. Apply $1/f(\vartheta)$ to both members and transpose the algebraic factor $f(m)$:

$$\therefore\ \frac{1}{f(\vartheta)}x^m=\frac{1}{f(m)}x^m.$$

If m is a root of $f(\vartheta)=0$, then $f(m)=0$. In this case, put $f(\vartheta)=(\vartheta-m)\phi(\vartheta)$, when the particular integral is:

$$\frac{1}{\vartheta-m}\cdot\frac{1}{\phi(\vartheta)}\cdot x^m=\frac{1}{\phi(m)}\cdot\frac{1}{\vartheta-m}x^m=\frac{x^m\ln x}{\phi(m)}.$$

The first term on the right of (1) gives $x^2/(8-4+6-3)=x^2/7$, and the second gives $\frac{1}{4}[1/(\vartheta-1)]x=\frac{1}{4}x\ln x$. Hence the complete integral is:

$$y=C_1e^z+C_2e^{\sqrt{(3)}iz}+C_3e^{-\sqrt{(3)}iz}+\tfrac{1}{7}x^2+\tfrac{1}{4}x\ln x.$$

Replace z by $\ln x$ and use de Moivre's Theorem (§ 46) to find:

$$y=C_1x+C_2\cos(\sqrt{3}\ln x)+C_3\sin(\sqrt{3}\ln x)+\tfrac{1}{7}x^2+\tfrac{1}{4}x\ln x.$$

The operator $1/f(\vartheta)$ may be expressible in factors or partial fractions like $1/f(D)$ (§ 67), and the result of the operation of $1/(\vartheta-a)$ upon X may be noted. $[1/(\vartheta-a)]X$ is the particular integral of

$$x(dy/dx)-ay=X,\quad\text{or}\quad dy/dz-ay=X,\quad\text{where } z=\ln x.$$

By (5), § 57, the particular integral is:

$$e^{az}\int e^{-az}X\,dz,$$

or, by replacing z by $\ln x$ and dz by dx/x:

$$e^{a\ln x}\int e^{-a\ln x}X(dx/x)=x^a\int x^{-a-1}X\,dx.$$

Let $$x^2(d^2y/dx^2)-2x(dy/dx)-4y=x^4,$$
$$(x^2D^2-2xD-4)y=x^4,$$
$$[\vartheta(\vartheta-1)-2\vartheta-4]y=x^4,$$
$$(\vartheta-4)(\vartheta+1)y=x^4.$$

The *complementary function* is $C_1e^{4z}+C_2e^{-z}=C_1x^4+C_2/x$; the *particular integral* is (using partial fractions):

$$\frac{1}{(\vartheta-4)(\vartheta+1)}x^4=\frac{1}{5}\left(\frac{1}{\vartheta-4}x^4-\frac{1}{\vartheta+1}x^4\right)=\tfrac{1}{5}x^4\int x^{-4-1}\,.\,x^4dx-\tfrac{1}{5}x^{-1}\int x^{1-1}x^4dx$$
$$=(x^4/5)\ln x-x^4/25;$$

and the *complete integral* is:

$$y=C_1x^4+C_2/x+(x^4/5)\ln x,$$

the term $-x^4/25$ being included in the term C_1x^4 of the complementary function.

§ 70. Partial Differential Equations

Ordinary differential equations have two main classes of solutions: (i) the *complete integral* or *general solution* (including *particular integrals* as special cases), and (ii) the *singular solution*, a function of x and y satisfying the differential equation but not included in the general solution. The singular solution commonly represents (§§ 58, 59): (i) a locus of singular points such as nodes or cusps, or (ii) an *envelope* or locus of points of contact with the curve representing the general solution, such as the two parallel straight lines which are tangents to a family of circles of equal diameter with their centres on a given straight line.

Various types of *partial differential equations* are: [1]

I. $f(\partial z/\partial x, \partial z/\partial y)=0$, with the complete integral $z=ax+by+c$ with $b=f(a)$.

II. $f(z, \partial z/\partial x, \partial z/\partial y)=0$, which can be reduced to an ordinary differential equation $dz=\phi(z)dx+a\phi(z)dy$, therefore $x+ay=\int dz/\phi(z)+C$.

III. $f_1(x, \partial z/\partial x)=f_2(y, \partial z/\partial y)$, leading to $z=f_1(x, a)+f_2(y, a)+C$.

IV. $z=(\partial z/\partial x)x+(\partial z/\partial y)y+f(\partial z/\partial x, \partial z/\partial y)$, giving $z=ax+by+f(a, b)$.

Every ordinary differential equation with two variables is *analogous* to a partial differential equation in the same class, but, in the case of a common type of partial differential equation:

(i) the arbitrary constant in the solution of the ordinary equation is replaced by an *arbitrary function* in the solution of the partial equation; hence the latter has an infinite number of particular solutions; [2]

(ii) the solution Ce^{mx} of the ordinary equation, (3), § 57, becomes $e^{mx(\partial/\partial y)}\phi(y)$, where $\partial/\partial y$ is the operator, and this expression is called the *symbolic form of Taylor's Theorem* (§ 35). For:

$$f(y+mx)=f(y)+mx\frac{\partial f(y)}{\partial y}+\frac{m^2x^2}{2!}\frac{\partial^2 f(y)}{\partial y^2}+\ldots,$$

where x is regarded as constant, or:

$$f(y+mx)=\left(1+mx\frac{\partial}{\partial y}+\frac{m^2x^2}{2!}\frac{\partial^2}{\partial y^2}+\ldots\right)f(y),$$

where the bracket is an operator which operates on $f(y)$, and, as it is an exponential series (§ 33, No. 2), it may be represented by $e^{mx\partial/\partial y}$. *This is the central point of the whole treatment and must be kept constantly in mind.*

If $\partial/\partial y$ is represented by D′, the symbol D meaning $\partial/\partial x$:

$$f(y+mx)=e^{mxD'}f(y).$$

The general *linear partial differential equation* of two independent variables is:

$$A_0(\partial^2z/\partial x^2)+A_1(\partial^2z/\partial x\partial y)+A_2(\partial^2z/\partial y^2)+A_3(\partial z/\partial x)+A_4(\partial z/\partial y)+A_5z=A \quad . \quad . \quad (1)$$

[1] Wien, *Phys. Z.*, 1906, 7, 16; Forsyth, "A Treatise on Differential Equations," 1914, 408, 511.

[2] Riemann, "Particlle Differentialgleichungen," 1938, 107 f.

where $A_0, A_1, \ldots, A_5, A$ may be constants or functions of x and y. The complete solution is the sum of a *particular integral* and a *complementary function*, as in the case of an ordinary differential equation (§ 57). The complementary function is found by putting $A=0$ in (1), which becomes:

$$(A_0\mathrm{D}^2+A_1\mathrm{DD}'+A_2\mathrm{D}'^2+A_3\mathrm{D}+A_4\mathrm{D}'+A_5)z=\mathrm{F}(\mathrm{D}, \mathrm{D}')z=0.$$

Consider the case where $A_0, A_1, \ldots$ are *constants*. A *homogeneous equation* of this type, i.e. one in which the differential coefficients are of the same order ($\partial/\partial x$, etc., *or* $\partial^2/\partial x^2$, etc.) is, for the second order:

$$A_0(\partial^2 z/\partial x^2)+A_1(\partial^2 z/\partial x\partial y)+A_2(\partial^2 z/\partial y^2)=R \quad . \quad . \quad . \quad (2)$$

where R is a function of x and y. To find the complementary function put $R=0$. In the ordinary equation (§ 61), the solution $y=\mathrm{e}^{mx}$ was assumed; in the present case the solution will be a function of both x and y. Assume $z=\mathrm{f}(y+mx)$,

$$\therefore \ \partial z/\partial x=m\mathrm{f}'(y+mx), \quad \text{and} \quad \partial z/\partial y=\mathrm{f}'(y+mx),$$

and, as in § 56:

$$\partial^2 z/\partial x\partial y=m\mathrm{f}''(y+mx), \quad \partial^2 z/\partial x^2=m^2\mathrm{f}''(y+mx), \quad \text{and} \quad \partial^2 z/\partial y^2=\mathrm{f}''(y+mx).$$

If these are substituted in (2) with $R=0$, and the factor $\mathrm{f}''(y+mx)$ cancelled, the *auxiliary equation* (§ 63) is found to be:

$$A_0m^2+A_1m+A_2=0 \quad . \quad . \quad . \quad . \quad . \quad . \quad . \quad . \quad (3)$$

If m_1 and m_2 are the roots of this quadratic equation, then (2) may be written (with $R=0$), with m_1 and m_2 replacing λ_1 and λ_2 in § 63:

$$(A_0\mathrm{D}^2+A_1\mathrm{DD}'+A_2\mathrm{D}'^2)z=(\mathrm{D}-m_1\mathrm{D}')(\mathrm{D}-m_2\mathrm{D}')z=0.$$

Each factor will, as in (10), § 63, give a solution:

$$z=A\mathrm{e}^{m_1x\mathrm{D}'}=\mathrm{e}^{m_1x\mathrm{D}'}\phi_1(y),$$

where A is not now a constant but is an arbitrary function of y, say $\phi_1(y)$.

Hence:
$$z=\mathrm{e}^{m_1x\mathrm{D}'}\phi_1(y)+\mathrm{e}^{m_2x\mathrm{D}'}\phi_2(y)$$
$$=\phi_1(y+m_1x)+\phi_2(y+m_2x) \quad . \quad . \quad . \quad . \quad . \quad . \quad (4)$$

where ϕ_1 and ϕ_2 denote arbitrary functions, from the symbolic form of Taylor's Theorem.

If $m_1=m_2=m$, the solution of $(\mathrm{D}-m)^2z=0$ is:

$$z=\mathrm{e}^{mx}(Ax+B),$$

where A and B are independent of x, and as is seen by analogy with (12), § 63:

$$z=\mathrm{e}^{mx\mathrm{D}'}[\phi_1(y)+x\phi_2(y)]=x\phi_2(y+mx)+\phi_1(y+mx).$$

The equation:

$$(A_0\mathrm{D}^n+A_1\mathrm{D}^{n-1}\mathrm{D}'+\ \ldots\ +A_n\mathrm{D}'^n)z=\phi(x, y) \quad . \quad . \quad . \quad (5)$$

may be denoted symbolically by $\mathrm{F}(\mathrm{D}, \mathrm{D}')z=\phi(x, y)$, and the particular integral by $[1/\mathrm{F}(\mathrm{D}, \mathrm{D}')]\phi(x, y)$, this being a function which gives $\phi(x, y)$ when operated upon by $\mathrm{F}(\mathrm{D}, \mathrm{D}')$, so that:

$$\mathrm{F}(\mathrm{D}, \mathrm{D}')\cdot\frac{1}{\mathrm{F}(\mathrm{D}, \mathrm{D}')}=1.$$

Suppose that $1/\mathrm{F}(\mathrm{D}, \mathrm{D}')$ can be resolved into linear factors:

$$\frac{1}{\mathrm{F}(\mathrm{D}, \mathrm{D}')}\phi(x, y)=\frac{1}{\mathrm{D}-m_1\mathrm{D}'}\cdot\frac{1}{\mathrm{D}-m_2\mathrm{D}'}\cdot\ \ldots\ \frac{1}{\mathrm{D}-m_n\mathrm{D}'}\phi(x, y)$$

From (4): $$e^{-mxD'}\phi(x, y)=\phi(x, y-mx),$$

$$\therefore\ De^{-mxD'}\phi(x, y)=D\phi(x, y-mx) \quad \ldots\ldots (6)$$

Direct differentiation of $e^{-mxD'}\phi(x, y)$ gives:

$$De^{-mxD'}\phi(x, y)=-mD'e^{-mxD'}\phi(x, y)+e^{-mxD'}D\phi(x, y)$$

$$=e^{-mxD'}(D-mD')\phi(x, y) \quad \ldots\ldots (7)$$

and the right-hand members of (6) and (7) are, therefore, equal. Operate on each with $e^{mxD'}$, then:

$$e^{mxD'}D\phi(x, y-mx)=e^{mxD'}\,.\,e^{-mxD'}(D-mD')\phi(x, y),$$

$$\therefore\ (D-mD')\phi(x, y)=e^{mxD'}D\phi(x, y-mx) \quad \ldots\ldots (8)$$

The corresponding formula for the inverse operator:

$$\frac{1}{D-mD'}\phi(x, y)=e^{mxD'}\frac{1}{D}\phi(x, y-mx),$$

is verified by the application of $(D-mD')$ to both sides, when:

$$\phi(x, y)=(D-mD')e^{mxD'}\frac{1}{D}\phi(x, y-mx)$$

$$=(D-mD')e^{mxD'}\psi(x, y), \quad \text{say},$$

$$=(D-mD')\psi(x, y+mx), \quad \text{by (4)}.$$

The expression on the right would be obtained by putting $(y+mx)$ for y in $D\psi(x, y)$ *after* the differentiation had been performed, and this would be $\phi(x, y)$, from the definition of ψ:

$$\psi(x, y)=\frac{1}{D}\phi(x, y-mx),$$

$$\therefore\ D\psi(x, y)=\phi(x, y-mx).$$

Hence the value of $\frac{1}{D-mD'}\phi(x, y)$ is found by the following rule:

(i) subtract mx from y in $\phi(x, y)$, *paying attention to sign*; (ii) integrate the function so formed with respect to x; (iii) change y into $(y+mx)$ in the integral obtained. With several factors, this rule is applied to them in succession, beginning on the right.

Let $$\frac{\partial^2 z}{\partial x^2}-a^2\frac{\partial^2 z}{\partial y^2}=xy,$$

i.e. $$(D^2-a^2D'^2)z=xy, \quad (D-aD')(D+aD')z=xy.$$

The particular integral is: $$\frac{1}{D-aD'}\cdot\frac{1}{D+aD'}xy$$

$$=\frac{1}{D-aD'}e^{-axD'}\frac{1}{D}x(y-ax), \text{ by subtracting } ax \text{ from } y,$$

$$=\frac{1}{D-aD'}(\tfrac{1}{2}x^2y-\tfrac{1}{3}ax^3), \text{ by integration},$$

$$=e^{axD'}\frac{1}{D}(\tfrac{1}{2}x^2y+\tfrac{2}{3}ax^3), \text{ by subtracting } -ax \text{ from } y,$$

$=\frac{1}{6}x^3y+\frac{1}{6}ax^4$, by integration. Add $-ax$ to y, giving $\frac{1}{6}x^3y$, which is the answer.

There are several *special cases* [1] of:

$$F(D, D')z=\phi(x, y)=R$$

(where R is often used for the value of the function $\phi(x, y)$, as in (1), § 61 for $f(x)$):

(i). $R=f(ax+by)$; (ii) $R=\sin(ax+by)$ or $\cos(ax+by)$; (iii) $R=e^{ax+by}$; (iv) $R=x^r y^s$, where r and s are positive integers; (v) $R=e^{ax+by}X$, where X is a function of x. These all use devices explained in connection with ordinary differential equations, and do not call for detailed treatment.

§ 71. The Wave Equation

Consider a wave motion propagated in the x direction with a displacement at right angles to the direction of propagation (see § 49). If the frequency is ν, the generating point P performs ν revolutions per sec. and (if the phase angle is zero) the angle θ swept out per sec. is $2\pi\nu$. The angle for a time t is $2\pi\nu t=\theta$. In § 49 the amplitude (maximum displacement) was supposed to be constant and equal to the radius A of the circle. Now suppose that the amplitude is a function of the distance x travelled by the wave, and denote it by $a=f(x)$; and

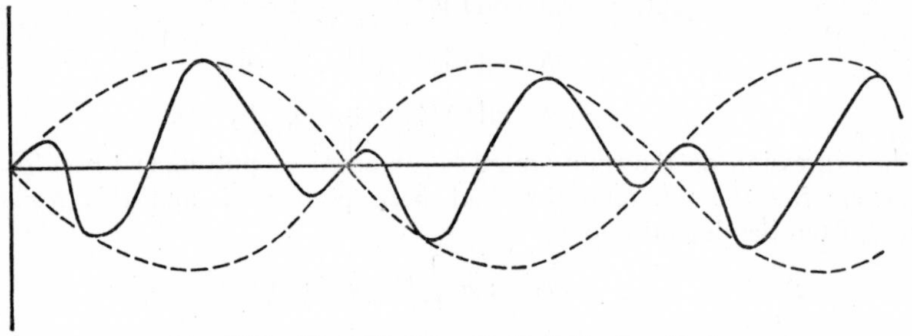

FIG. 37.I. Wave Motion with Variable Amplitude

let A now denote the displacement from the x axis, which depends on x and the time t, $A=F(x, t)$. In § 49 (1), the displacement was represented by $s=A\sin(2\pi t/T)=A\sin 2\pi\nu t$, where T is the period, and the values of $ds/dt=2\pi\nu A\cos(2\pi\nu t)$ and $d^2s/dt^2=-4\pi^2\nu^2 s$ were found. In the present case:

$$A=a\sin(2\pi\nu t) \quad \ldots \ldots \quad (1)$$

is assumed, a being variable (Fig. 37.I). Consider the general case

$$A=f(x, t) \quad \ldots \ldots \quad (2)$$

where A depends on x and t. From § 26:

$$\partial A/\partial t=(\partial A/\partial x)(dx/dt)$$

$$\partial^2 A/\partial t^2=(d/dt)[(\partial A/\partial x)(dx/dt)]$$

$$=\frac{\partial A}{\partial x}\frac{d^2x}{dt^2}+\frac{dx}{dt}\frac{\partial}{\partial x}\left(\frac{\partial A}{\partial x}\right)\cdot\frac{dx}{dt}$$

$$=(\partial A/\partial x)(d^2x/dt^2)+(dx/dt)^2(\partial^2 A/\partial x^2)=(dx/dt)^2(\partial^2 A/\partial x^2),$$

the first term containing the acceleration d^2x/dt^2 vanishing, as the wave velocity is supposed to be constant, $dx/dt=u$. Thus:

$$\partial^2 A/\partial t^2=u^2(\partial^2 A/\partial x^2) \quad \ldots \ldots \quad (3)$$

[1] See W. W. Johnson, "Differential Equations," 3rd edit., 1891, 355.

This equation represents a *plane wave*, travelling along the x axis in the x, y plane. If a *spherical wave* is considered, the corresponding equation is (see § 28):

$$\partial^2A/\partial t^2=u^2(\partial^2A/\partial x^2+\partial^2A/\partial y^2+\partial^2A/\partial z^2)=u^2\nabla^2A \quad . \; . \quad (4)$$

§ 72. D'Alembert's Equation

The partial differential equation: [1]

$$\partial^2u/\partial t^2=a^2(\partial^2u/\partial x^2) \quad . \; . \; . \; . \; . \; . \; . \; . \quad (1)$$

where [2] $u=f(x, t)$ and $a^2=$const. (first solved by D'Alembert in 1747—the first use of a partial differential equation) in the case when t denotes time and x a distance, is important in the theory of sound, where u may denote the transverse displacement of a particle in a vibrating string, or the longitudinal displacement of a particle in a vibrating column of gas. It is a particular case of the homogeneous partial differential equation already considered, but an alternative method of solution will be given.[3]

Let $\xi=x+at$, and $\eta=x-at$, be two new variables, then $d\xi/dt=a$ and $d\eta/dt=-a$, $d^2\xi/dt^2=d^2\eta/dt^2=0$. Also:

$$\left(\frac{du}{dt}\right)_x=\left(\frac{du}{d\xi}\right)_\eta\left(\frac{d\xi}{dt}\right)_x+\left(\frac{du}{d\eta}\right)_\xi\left(\frac{d\eta}{dt}\right)_x=\frac{du}{d\xi}a-\frac{du}{d\eta}a,$$

$$\left(\frac{d^2u}{dt^2}\right)_x=\frac{d}{dt}\left(\frac{du}{dt}\right)_x=\frac{\partial u}{\partial\xi}\cdot\frac{d^2\xi}{dt^2}+\frac{d\xi}{dt}\cdot\frac{d}{dt}\left(\frac{\partial u}{\partial\xi}\right)+\frac{\partial u}{\partial\xi}\cdot\frac{d^2\eta}{dt^2}+\frac{d\eta}{dt}\cdot\frac{d}{dt}\left(\frac{\partial u}{\partial\eta}\right) \quad (2)$$

But

$$\frac{d}{dt}\left(\frac{\partial u}{\partial\xi}\right)=\frac{\partial^2u}{\partial\xi^2}\cdot\frac{d\xi}{dt}+\frac{\partial^2u}{\partial\eta\partial\xi}\cdot\frac{d\eta}{dt},$$

$$\frac{d}{dt}\left(\frac{\partial u}{\partial\eta}\right)=\frac{\partial^2u}{d\xi\partial\eta}\cdot\frac{d\xi}{dt}+\frac{\partial^2u}{\partial\eta^2}\cdot\frac{d\eta}{dt}.$$

Substitute in (2) and put $\partial^2u/\partial\eta\partial\xi=\partial^2u/\partial\xi\partial\eta$ (§ 27), then:

$$\frac{\partial^2u}{\partial t^2}=\frac{\partial u}{\partial\xi}\cdot\frac{d^2\xi}{dt^2}+\frac{\partial u}{\partial\eta}\cdot\frac{d^2\eta}{dt^2}+\frac{\partial^2u}{\partial\xi^2}\left(\frac{d\xi}{dt}\right)^2+2\frac{\partial^2u}{\partial\xi\partial\eta}\cdot\frac{d\xi}{dt}\cdot\frac{d\eta}{dt}+\frac{\partial^2u}{\partial\eta^2}\left(\frac{d\eta}{dt}\right)^2.$$

Since $d^2\xi/dt^2=0$, $d^2\eta/dt^2=0$, $(d\xi/dt)^2=(d\eta/dt)^2=a^2$, and $(d\xi/dt)(d\eta/dt)=-a^2$;

therefore

$$\left(\frac{d^2u}{dt^2}\right)_x=a^2\frac{\partial^2u}{\partial\xi^2}-2a^2\frac{\partial^2u}{\partial\xi\partial\eta}+a^2\frac{\partial^2u}{\partial\eta^2} \quad . \; . \; . \; . \; . \quad (3)$$

and similarly:

$$\left(\frac{d^2u}{dx^2}\right)_t=\frac{\partial^2u}{\partial\xi^2}+2\frac{\partial^2u}{\partial\xi\partial\eta}+\frac{\partial^2u}{\partial\eta^2} \quad . \; . \; . \; . \; . \; . \; . \quad (4)$$

Substitute (3) and (4) in (1), then it follows that $\partial^2u/\partial\xi\partial\eta=0$, therefore $(d/d\xi)(du/d\eta)=(d/d\eta)(du/d\xi)=0$, hence $\partial u/\partial\xi$ depends only on ξ, and $\partial u/\partial\eta$ only on η. Thus u must be a function of ξ and η of the form $u=f_1(\xi)+f_2(\eta)$, where f_1 and f_2 are any two arbitrary functions. If ξ is replaced by $(x+at)$, and η by $(x-at)$:

$$u=f_1(x+at)+f_2(x-at) \quad . \; . \; . \; . \; . \; . \; . \quad (5)$$

An important result is that the independent variables appear in the functions only in the forms $(x+at)$ and $(x-at)$. The *forms* of the functions f_1 and f_2

[1] This must be distinguished from the equation of heat conduction: $\partial u/\partial t=a^2(\partial^2u/\partial x^2)$, considered later.

[2] Note that this is not the velocity u of § 71.

[3] Planck, " Mechanik deformierbarer Körper," Leipzig, 1919, 70; for another method, see Riemann, " Partielle Differentialgleichungen," 1938, 113.

cannot be deduced from the differential equation, but depend on the particular problem to which it is applied. A simple interpretation of (5) can, however, be given. If $f_2(x-at)=0$, then $u=f_1(x+at)$. Hence u is constant when $(x+at)$ is constant, i.e. when $d(x+at)=dx+adt=0$, or $dx/dt=-a$. Now dx/dt denotes a motion with a velocity $-a$ along the x axis, i.e. with a velocity a along the *negative* x axis, the " disturbance " u being propagated along this axis with a constant velocity. This corresponds with a *wave motion.* Similarly, $u=f_2(x-at)$ denotes a wave with a velocity a along the *positive* x axis.

In any particular problem, the forms of the arbitrary functions f_1 and f_2 (which, as usual, are eliminated in the partial differential equation) are determined by the conditions. If the case of a column of gas in longitudinal wave motion in a tube closed at one end, $x=0$, there is a node at this end and one at a distance l along the tube. The displacement u is zero for $x=0$ and $x=l$; hence:

$$u=0=f_1(at)+f_2(-at), \text{ for } x=0;$$

and
$$u=0=f_1(l+at)+f_2(l-at), \text{ for } x=l,$$

for all values of t. Put $x=at$, therefore $f_1(x)+f_2(-x)=0$, and $f_1(l+x)+f_2(l-x)=0$ are valid *for all values* of x. If $(l+x)$ is written for x in the second equation, $f_1(2l+x)+f_2(-x)=0$, and by comparison with the first, $f_1(2l+x)=f_1(x)$, and $f_2(2l+x)=f_2(x)$.

This shows that f_1 and f_2 have the same values for $(2l+x)$ as for x, i.e. their values *repeat* themselves when x increases by $2l$; hence they are both *periodic functions* of x with the period $2l$. Since:

$$u=f_1(x+at)+f_2(x-at),$$

the motion is also periodic with respect to time, the period being $2l/a$, since x has increased by $2l$ when t has increased by $2l/a$.

To find the most general form of a function $f(x)$ with the period $2l$, the equation $f(2l+x)=f(x)$ must be solved. The particular solution

$$f(x)=e^{\alpha x} \quad . \quad . \quad . \quad . \quad . \quad . \quad . \quad . \quad . \quad . \quad (6)$$

where α is a constant, satisfies the equation when $e^{2l\alpha}=1$, since:

$$f(2l+x)=e^{\alpha(2l+x)}=e^{\alpha x} \cdot e^{2l\alpha}=f(x) \cdot e^{2l\alpha}.$$

The only real solution of $e^{2l\alpha}=1$ is $2l\alpha=0$, which is not acceptable, since either $l=0$ or $\alpha=0$ (which makes $f(x)=1$). The exponent of e which suits the problem is *imaginary*, i.e. it is a multiple of $i=\sqrt{-1}$, and is given by Euler's equation, (8), § 46: $e^{2in\pi}=1$, therefore $2l\alpha=2n\pi i$, or $\alpha=n\pi i/l$. Substitute in (6), then:

$$f(x)=e^{n\pi ix/l} \quad . \quad . \quad . \quad . \quad . \quad . \quad . \quad . \quad . \quad (7)$$

From De Moivre's theorem, (6), § 46, when mx is written for x, m being any constant number, in this case $n\pi/l$:

$$f(x)=\cos(n\pi x/l)+i\sin(n\pi x/l).$$

By separating the real and imaginary parts of $f(x)$, *two* particular solutions, $\cos(n\pi x/l)$ and $\sin(n\pi x/l)$ are obtained. These can be multiplied by arbitrary constants, A_n and B_n for each value of n, from 1 to ∞, and the sum of all such values will also be a solution of $f(x+2l)=f(x)$,

$$\therefore \ f(x)=A_0+\sum_1^\infty A_n\cos(n\pi x/l)+\sum_1^\infty B_n\sin(n\pi x/l) \quad . \quad . \quad . \quad (8)$$

where A_0 is another constant. In (8) the *negative* values of n are omitted, since each term with $-n$ can be combined with the one for $+n$ to form a single term, and every term in the two sums $\sum\limits_1^\infty$ then really comprises two terms. The single term for $n=0$ ($\cos 0=1$, $\sin 0=0$) is denoted by A_0.

The series (8) is called a *Fourier's series*, and is dealt with in the next section. The constants A_0, A_n, and B_n are to be chosen to suit each particular problem. The series has the period $2l$ in x, since if x is replaced by $(x+2l)$, the angles increase by $n\pi(x+2l)/l-n\pi x/l=2n\pi$, and the sines and cosines are then the same as for x; and hence every periodic function with the period $2l$ can be represented by (8).

The solution of the equation $c^2 . \partial^2u/\partial x^2=\partial^2u/\partial t^2+2\beta . \partial u/\partial t+\gamma^2u$, where β and γ are constants, was investigated by Nagaoka.[1]

§ 73. Fourier's Series

Suppose that any periodic function of x may, by a suitable adjustment of the unit of x, be made to have a period of 2π and that it may be represented with sufficient approximation by a series containing both sines and cosines of multiples of the angle x:

$$\begin{aligned} f(x)=A_0+A_1\cos x+A_2\cos 2x+\ldots+A_r\cos rx+\ldots \\ +B_1\sin x+B_2\sin 2x+\ldots+B_r\sin rx+\ldots \quad . \quad . \quad (1)\end{aligned}$$

where r is an integer and the A's and B's are constants, which have such values that the series shall be valid for values of x lying within the period 2π. The series (1) can also be written in the form (8) of § 72:

$$f(x)=A_0+\sum_{r=1}^{r=n}A_r\cos rx+\sum_{r=1}^{r=n}B_r\sin rx \quad . \quad . \quad . \quad . \quad . \quad (2)$$

Multiply by $\cos rx\mathrm{d}x$, assume that the series can be integrated term by term, and integrate both sides from $-\pi$ to $+\pi$:

$$\int_{-\pi}^{\pi}f(x)\cos rx . \mathrm{d}x=\int_{-\pi}^{\pi}[(A_0+\sum_{r=1}^{r=n}A_r\cos rx+\sum_{r=1}^{r=n}B_r\sin rx)\cos rx]\mathrm{d}x \quad (3)$$

The separate integrals on the right are all of one or other of the three forms:

$$\int_{-\pi}^{\pi}A_0\cos rx\mathrm{d}x \quad . \quad . \quad . \quad . \quad . \quad . \quad . \quad . \quad (4)$$

$$\int_{-\pi}^{\pi}\sum_{r=1}^{r=n}A_r\cos^2 rx . \mathrm{d}x \quad . \quad . \quad . \quad . \quad . \quad . \quad . \quad (5)$$

and

$$\int_{-\pi}^{\pi}\sum_{r=1}^{r=n}B_r\sin rx\cos rx . \mathrm{d}x \quad . \quad . \quad . \quad . \quad . \quad . \quad (6)$$

Now

$$\int_{-\pi}^{\pi}\cos rx . \mathrm{d}x=(1/r)\Big[\sin rx\Big]_{-\pi}^{+\pi}=0 \quad . \quad . \quad . \quad . \quad . \quad (7)$$

since r is an integer and the values of $\sin(-\pi r)$ and $\sin(\pi r)$ are then both zero (§ 40). Also, from the trigonometrical formula (19), § 41, where sx and rx are written for the angles $\frac{1}{2}(x+y)$ and $\frac{1}{2}(x-y)$ and s and r are different integers:

$$\int_{-\pi}^{\pi}\cos(sx)\cos(rx) . \mathrm{d}x=\tfrac{1}{2}\int_{-\pi}^{\pi}[\cos(r+s)x+\cos(r-s)x]\mathrm{d}x \quad . \quad (8)$$

But

$$\tfrac{1}{2}\int_{-\pi}^{\pi}[\cos(r+s)x+\cos(r-s)x]\mathrm{d}x=\tfrac{1}{2}\left[\frac{\sin(r+s)x}{r+s}+\frac{\sin(r-s)x}{r-s}\right]_{-\pi}^{+\pi}=0 \quad (9)$$

[1] *Proc. Phys. Math. Soc. Tokyo*, 1906, 3, 17.

since $(r+s)x$ and $(r-s)x$ are integral multiples of π or $-\pi$, the sines being zero. When $s=r$ the integral (8) becomes, from (10), § 41:

$$\int_{-\pi}^{\pi}\cos^2 rx\,.\,dx=\tfrac{1}{2}\int_{-\pi}^{\pi}(1+\cos 2rx)\,.\,dx=\tfrac{1}{2}\Big[x+\sin(2rx)/2r\Big]_{-\pi}^{+\pi}=\pi \quad (10)$$

the sines again vanishing and only $\frac{1}{2}[\pi-(-\pi)]=\pi$ remaining.

Hence every term on the right of (3) vanishes except that which involves A_r $(s=r)$, which appears multiplied by π,

$$\therefore \int_{-\pi}^{\pi} f(x)\cos(rx)dx=\pi A_r, \quad \therefore A_r=(1/\pi)\int_{-\pi}^{\pi} f(x)\cos(rx)dx \quad (11)$$

In exactly the same way, by multiplying (2) by sin rx and integrating from $-\pi$ to π, it is found that:

$$B_r=(1/\pi)\int_{-\pi}^{\pi} f(x)\sin(rx)dx \quad . \; . \; . \; . \; . \; . \quad (12)$$

Integrating (2) from $-\pi$ to π gives:

$$\int_{-\pi}^{\pi} f(x)dx=\int_{-\pi}^{\pi} A_0 dx+\int_{-\pi}^{\pi}\sum_{r=1}^{r=n} A_r\cos(rx)dx+\int_{-\pi}^{\pi}\sum_{r=1}^{r=n} B_r\sin(rx)dx.$$

Equation (7) and the similar equation:

$$\int_{-\pi}^{\pi}\sin(rx)dx=-\Big[\cos(rx)\Big]_{-\pi}^{+\pi}=-(-1+1)=0 \quad . \; . \; . \quad (13)$$

show that:

$$\int_{-\pi}^{\pi} f(x)dx=\int_{-\pi}^{\pi} A_0 dx=2\pi A_0, \quad \therefore A_0=(1/2\pi)\int_{-\pi}^{\pi} f(x)dx \quad . \; . \quad (14)$$

(Note that the factor in (14) is $1/2\pi$, whilst in (11) and (12) it is $1/\pi$.) Equations (11), (12), and (14) give the required values of the coefficients A_0, A_r, and B_r in the series (1), and if the integrals can be evaluated, all these coefficients are explicitly determined for a given function f(x). It must be noted that the function is represented only in the range $-\pi$ to $+\pi$ of x.

If, instead of taking the range of integration from $-\pi$ to $+\pi$, it is taken as 0 to $+2\pi$, this simply means changing the origin for x from 0 to $(-\pi, 0)$, or putting $(x-\pi)$ in place of x, when the integrals and coefficients become:

$$A_0=(1/2\pi)\int_0^{2\pi} F(x)dx \quad . \; . \; . \; . \; . \; . \; . \; . \quad (15)$$

$$A_r=(1/\pi)\int_0^{2\pi} F(x)\cos(rx)dx \quad . \; . \; . \; . \; . \; . \quad (16)$$

and

$$B_r=(1/\pi)\int_0^{2\pi} F(x)\sin(rx)dx \quad . \; . \; . \; . \; . \; . \quad (17)$$

where f$(x-\pi)$ is represented by F(x). If the constant A_0 in (1) had been written $\frac{1}{2}A_0$, then (15) becomes a special case of (16) with $r=0$, since cos $0=1$, and many books use this convention.

The series (2), with the constants determined by (11), (12) and (14), or (alternatively) by (15), (16) and (17), is called a *Fourier Series*, after Jean Baptiste Joseph de Fourier (1768–1830), who in his famous book " Théorie Analytique de la Chaleur " (Paris, 1822), showed that an empirical function, not necessarily periodic, defined in the interval $-\pi$ to $+\pi$, or 0 to 2π, can be represented by such a series, and used it in the study of the conduction of heat. A " rigid proof " of the validity of the series was first given by Dirichlet in 1829, and the conditions which function must satisfy in order that they can be represented by such a series have occupied mathematicians ever since.[1] The general result is that if f(x) is single-valued and finite between $x=-\pi$ and $x=\pi$, and has only a finite number of discontinuities (§ 2), and of maxima and minima, in this range, then f(x) is representable by a Fourier's series (2) with the values of the constants given by (11), (12) and (14); and, further, this series alone is equal to f(x) for all values of x between $-\pi$ and π, except values of x corresponding to the discontinuities of f(x), and to the values $-\pi$ and π themselves if f(π) is not equal to f($-\pi$). It is said [2] that the announcement of Fourier was received by Lagrange "with astonishment and incredulity", and William Thomson (Lord Kelvin) in his first (anonymous) publication [3] defended Fourier's series against the criticism of Kelland [4] that they were "nearly all erroneous."

It is essential to test the series for the end values of the period, since it may be valid for all values of the variable within the period but not for just these boundary values themselves, as will be shown below. It must be carefully noted that the general derivative of a Fourier series cannot be found by differentiating it term by term, whilst its integral can be found by integrating it term by term. In many physical problems, however, when all the terms of the series are multiplied by an exponential factor, the series can be differentiated term by term.

When f(x) is given as a series of *numerical* values which can be represented graphically, the integrals cannot, of course, be evaluated analytically, but special methods have to be used. Generally, as in *Runge's method*, the interval between $x=0$ and $x=2\pi$ is divided into twelve equal parts on which ordinates y are drawn from the experimental values. Then if $\theta=2\pi n=\pi/6$, the coefficients are given [5] by:

$$A_0=\tfrac{1}{12}\sum_{s=0}^{s=11} y_s,\quad A_r=\tfrac{1}{6}\sum_{s=0}^{s=11} y_s\cos(rs\theta),\quad B_r=\tfrac{1}{6}\sum_{s=0}^{s=11} y_s\sin(rs\theta)\quad . \qquad (18)$$

and a scheme of tabulation due to Runge is used. Details of such methods must be sought in special works on Fourier's series and integrals.[6]

[1] See e.g. the dissertation of Harnack, in Serret and Scheffers, "Lehrbuch der Differential- und Integralrechnung," Leipzig and Berlin, 1911, **2**, 540.

[2] Hobson, "Theory of Functions of a Real Variable," Cambridge, 2nd edit., 1926, **2**, 476.

[3] *Cambr. Math. J.*, 1841, **2**, 258; "Math. and Phys. Papers," Cambridge, 1882, **1**, 1.

[4] "Theory of Heat," Cambridge, 1837, 64.

[5] See Gibson, "Introduction to the Calculus," 1906, 130; Grover, *Bur. Stand. Bull.*, 1913, **9**, 567.

[6] Fourier, "Théorie Analytique de la Chaleur," 1822; transl. by Freeman, "The Analytical Theory of Heat," Cambridge, 1878 [reprinted, New York, 1945], 137 f., 262 f.; Fourier, *Mém. de l'Inst.*, 1819–20 [1824], **4**, 185 (read 1811); *Mém. Acad. Sci.*, 1829, **8**, 581; "Oeuvres," 2 vols., 1888–9; Stokes, *Trans. Cambr. Phil. Soc.*, 1847, **8**, 533; "Math. and Phys. Papers," Cambridge, 1880, **1**, 236; Donkin, "Acoustics," Oxford, 1870, 51; Lord Kelvin, "Math. and Phys. Papers," Cambridge, 1884, **2**, 41; Byerly, "An Elementary Treatise on Fourier's Series and Spherical, Cylindrical, and Ellipsoidal Harmonics," Boston, 1893 (the standard treatise for the applications); Gibson, *Proc. Edin. Math. Soc.*, 1893, **11**, 137; Mellor, "Higher Mathematics," 1902, 360; Auerbach, in Winkelmann, "Handbuch der Physik," 1909, **2**, 23; Lamb, "Dynamical Theory of Sound," 1910, 87; Rosebrugh and Lash Miller, *J. Phys. Chem.*, 1910, **14**, 816; Hobson, "Theory of Functions of a Real Variable," 2nd edit., Cambridge, 1921–6, **2**, 476; Lederer, *Koll. Z.*, 1928, **44**, 108; Carslaw, "Fourier's Series and Integrals," 3rd edit., 1930; Campbell and Foster, *Bell Telephone Syst. Techn. Publ. Monogr.*, 1931, B **584**; Lash Miller and Gordon, *J. Phys. Chem.*, 1931, **35**, 2784; Titchmarsh, "Introduction to the Theory of Fourier Integrals," Oxford, 1937 (abstruse); Brill, Grimm, Hermann, and Peters, *Ann. Phys.*, 1939, **34**, 393; von Kármán and Biot, "Mathematical Functions in Engineering," New York, 1940; Danilson and Lanczos, *J. Franklin Inst.*, 1942, **233**, 365 (practical Fourier analysis); Carslaw and Jaeger, "Conduction of Heat in Solids," Oxford, 1947. For tables of functions, see McKay, *Proc. Phys. Soc.*, 1930, **42**, 547. An interesting elementary account of Fourier's work is given by Mach, "Principien der Wärmelehre," Leipzig, 1900, 78 f.

§ 74. Discontinuities

If the function f(x) has a *finite* discontinuity (i.e. does not run to $+\infty$ or $-\infty$) at a particular value of x, say $x=x_1$, it is proved in works on Fourier's series that the value of the *sum* S in the Fourier series is no longer equal to the value of the *function* (which really has *two* values, y_1 at B and y_2 at C) but to half of the sum of the two values of the function f(x)=y at the point of discontinuity: $S=\frac{1}{2}(y_1+y_2)$ (Fig. 38.I).

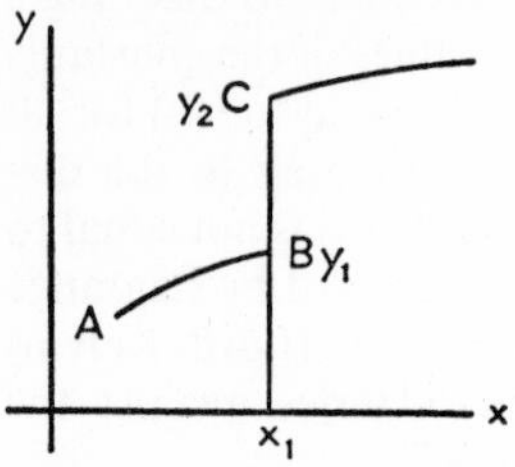

FIG. 38.I. Discontinuity of a Function

As an example, consider the function having the values f(x)=0 from $x=-\pi$ to $x=0$, and f(x)=1 from $x=0$ to $x=\pi$.

$$A_0=(1/2\pi)\int_{-\pi}^{\pi} f(x)dx=(1/2\pi)\int_{-\pi}^{0} 0\,.\,dx+(1/2\pi)\int_{0}^{\pi} 1\,.\,dx=\tfrac{1}{2},$$

$$A_r=(1/\pi)\int_{-\pi}^{\pi} f(x)\cos(rx)dx=(1/\pi)\int_{-\pi}^{0} 0\,.\,dx+(1/\pi)\int_{0}^{\pi} 1\,.\,\cos(rx)dx=0,$$

$$B_r=(1/\pi)\int_{0}^{\pi} 1\,.\,\sin(rx)dx=(1-\cos r\pi)/r\pi.$$

Hence $f(x)=\frac{1}{2}+(2/\pi)(\sin x+\sin 3x/3+\sin 5x/5+\ldots)$. When $x=0$, the *series* is equal to 1/2, and when $x=\pi$ the series is 1/2, but the *function* f(x) is 1; when $x=-\pi$, the series is 1/2, but the function is 0. The value at the discontinuity is $\frac{1}{2}(1+0)=\frac{1}{2}$.

§ 75. Fourier's Sine and Cosine Series

In some cases, the function may be represented by a series containing either sines or cosines only, instead of both, as in (2), § 73.

(i) Suppose that f(x) in (1), § 73, is an *odd function* of x (see § 21), so that $f(-x)=-f(x)$, e.g. $f(x)=x$, then:

$$\int_{-\pi}^{\pi} f(x)\cos(rx)dx=\int_{0}^{\pi} f(x)\cos(rx)dx+\int_{-\pi}^{0} f(x)\cos(rx)dx$$
$$=\int_{0}^{\pi} f(x)\cos(rx)dx-\int_{0}^{-\pi} f(x)\cos(rx)dx$$
$$=\int_{0}^{\pi} f(x)\cos(rx)dx+\int_{0}^{\pi} f(-x)\cos(rx)dx$$
$$=0 \quad (\text{since } \cos(-x)=\cos x).$$

Hence, from (11) and (14), § 73, $A_r=0$, and $A_0=0$ (the latter because the integral from $-\pi$ to 0 cancels that from 0 to $+\pi$). Thus, all the cosine terms disappear from (2), § 73, and, since, (12), § 73:

$$B_r=(1/\pi)\int_{-\pi}^{\pi} f(x)\sin(rx)dx=(1/\pi)\int_{0}^{\pi} f(x)\sin(rx)dx-(1/\pi)\int_{0}^{\pi} f(-x)\sin(rx)dx$$
$$=(2/\pi)\int_{0}^{\pi} f(x)\sin(rx)dx \quad (\text{since } \sin(-x)=-\sin x) \quad . \quad (1)$$

the series representing f(x) is a *sine series*:

$$f(x)=\sum_{r=1}^{r=\infty} B_r \sin(rx) \quad . \quad . \quad . \quad . \quad . \quad . \quad . \quad . \quad (2)$$

with the coefficients B_r given by (1). The *series* is zero both when $x=0$ and $x=\pi$, and does *not* represent the *function* at these limits unless $f(0)=0$ and $f(\pi)=0$. Note that this formula does not contain the constant term A_0.

(ii) If f(x) is an *even function* of x (see § 21), so that $f(x)=f(-x)$, e.g. $f(x)=x^2$, then:

$$B_n=(1/\pi)\int_0^\pi f(x)\sin(rx)dx-(1/\pi)\int_0^\pi f(-x)\sin(rx)dx=0,$$

$$\left.\begin{aligned} A_0&=(1/2\pi)\int_{-\pi}^{\pi} f(x)dx=(1/\pi)\int_0^\pi f(x)dx,\\ A_r&=(1/\pi)\int_{-\pi}^{\pi} f(x)\cos(rx)dx=(2/\pi)\int_0^\pi f(x)\cos(rx)dx \end{aligned}\right\} \quad . \quad . \quad (3)$$

and the function is represented by a *cosine series*:

$$f(x)=A_0+\sum_{r=1}^{r=\infty} A_r\cos(rx) \quad . \quad . \quad . \quad . \quad . \quad . \quad . \quad . \quad (4)$$

the coefficients being given by (3). This series represents the function both when $x=0$ and $x=\pi$. Note that this formula contains the constant term A_0. Since $\cos 0=1$, the equation for A_r will give A_0 also if $\frac{1}{2}A_0$ is used instead of A_0 in (1), §73.

As examples of sine and cosine series, three simple functions may be considered, viz. a constant, $f(x)=1$, an odd function, $f(x)=x$, and an even function, $f(x)=x^2$.

(i) Let $f(x)=1$. Since a period must be assigned, take this from 0 to π. Since $f(+1)=1$ and $f(-1)=-1$, the function is odd, and (2) applies; therefore from (1):

$$B_r=(2/\pi)\int_0^\pi \sin(rx)dx.$$

$$\int \sin(rx)dx=-(1/r)\cos(rx),$$

$$\therefore \int_0^\pi \sin(rx)dx=-(1/r)\Big[\cos(rx)\Big]_{x=0}^{x=\pi}=-(1/r)[\cos(r\pi)-1]=(1/r)[1-\cos(r\pi)].$$

When r is even, $\cos(r\pi)=1$; when r is odd $\cos(r\pi)=-1$; hence the integral is $2/r$ for odd values of r, and zero for even values, and hence:

$$f(x)=1=(4/\pi)(\sin x+\tfrac{1}{3}\sin 3x+\tfrac{1}{5}\sin 5x+\ .\ .\ .).$$

In Fig. 39.I the curves for $\sin x$, $\frac{1}{3}\sin 3x$, $\frac{1}{5}\sin 5x$, and $\frac{1}{7}\sin 7x$, each multiplied by $4/\pi$, are shown, and the sum of the ordinates is seen to approach the horizontal straight line $y=1$. For $x=0$ and $x=\pi$, the value of y is zero, so that the *function* does *not* represent the curve at the limits.

(ii) Let $f(x)=x$. Then $A_r=0$, $A_0=0$, $B_r=(1/\pi)\int_{-\pi}^{\pi} x\sin(rx)dx$. By integration by parts (§ 19):

$$\int x\sin(rx)dx=r^{-2}[\sin(rx)-rx\cos(rx)]$$

(put $rx=u$ and find $\int u\sin u du$). For $x=-\pi$ this is $r^{-1}\pi\cos(r\pi)$, and for $x=+\pi$ it is $-r^{-1}\pi\cos(r\pi)$ (since $\cos(-x)=\cos x$), therefore $B_r=-2\cos(r\pi)/r$. When r is even, $\cos(r\pi)$ is $+1$, and when r is odd $\cos(r\pi)=-1$. Hence:

$$f(x)=x=2(\sin x/1-\sin 2x/2+\sin 3x/3-\sin 4x/4+\ .\ .\ .)$$

The functions $y_1=2\sin x$, $y_2=\sin 2x$, $y_3=\frac{2}{3}\sin 3x$ are plotted as curves 1, 2, and 3 in Fig. 39.I, and by adding the ordinates the full curve 4 is found. This is an approximation to a straight line passing through $x=0$ and inclined at an angle of 45° to the x axis (i.e. $y=x$). It is seen that the series fails at $x=-\pi$ and $x=+\pi$, since it vanishes for both these values. By taking more sine curves a better approximation is found. The separate sine (or cosine) curves are often called *harmonics*, since they represent sines of multiples (or

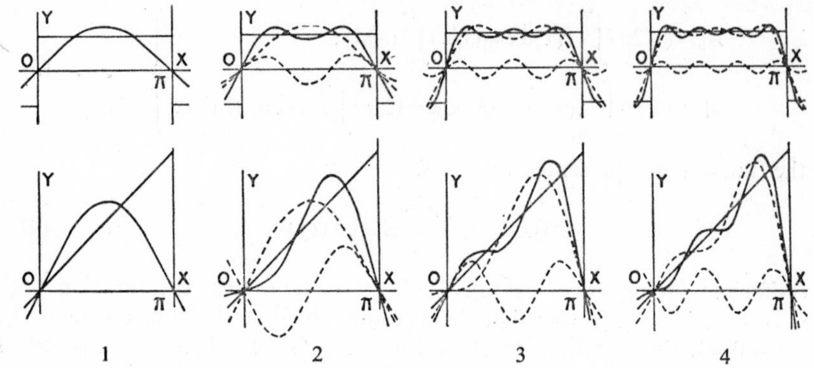

FIG. 39.I. Representations of f(x)=1 (upper figures) and f(x)=x (lower figures) by Fourier Series

" overtones ") of the angle x, and the problem of resolving a function (e.g. the height of a tide) into such components is called *harmonic analysis*.

(iii) Let $f(x)=x^2$. Then:

$$A_0=(1/2\pi)\int_{-\pi}^{\pi} x^2 dx=(1/6\pi)[\pi^3-(-\pi^3)]=\tfrac{1}{3}\pi^2;\ B_r=0;$$

$A_r=(1/\pi)\int_{-\pi}^{\pi} x^2\cos(rx)dx=\mp 4/r^2$, by integration by parts as before, the signs being $-$ or $+$ according as r is odd or even. Hence:

$$f(x)=x^2=\tfrac{1}{3}\pi^2-4(\cos x/1^2-\cos 2x/2^2+\cos 3x/3^2-\cos 4x/4^2+\ldots).$$

Both when $x=-\pi$ and $x=+\pi$, the value of the *series* is $\frac{1}{3}\pi^2-4(1/1^2+2/2^2+3/3^2+\ldots)$, which is known to be $\frac{1}{3}\pi^2+4(\pi^2/6)=\pi^2$, so that this time the series represents the function at the limits $\pm\pi$.

By plotting the first three cosine terms and adding the ordinates, a line which is an approximation to the curve $y=x^2$ is found.

§ 76. Fourier's Integral

In problems on vibrating strings or columns of gas, diffusion, etc. (some of which are considered later), the limits are given numbers a, e.g. lengths l, and in this case x is replaced by $x=az/\pi$, where z is a new variable, $z=\pi x/a$, so that when z changes from $-\pi$ to $+\pi$, x changes from $-a$ to $+a$. The function $f(x)=f(az/\pi)$ may be developed as a Fourier series (2), § 73, in terms of z:

$$f(az/\pi)=A_0+A_1\cos z+A_2\cos(2z)+\ldots+B_1\sin z$$
$$+B_2\sin(2z)+\ldots\ldots \quad (1)$$

where $A_r=(1/\pi)\int_{-\pi}^{\pi} f(az/\pi)\cos(rz)dz$, $B_r=(1/\pi)\int_{-\pi}^{\pi} f(az/\pi)\sin(rz)dz$,

$$\therefore\ f(x)=A_0+A_1\cos(\pi x/a)+A_2\cos(2\pi x/a)+\ldots+B_1\sin(\pi x/a)$$
$$+B_2\sin(2\pi x/a)+\ldots\ldots \quad (2)$$

the coefficients A and B being the same as in (1), hence (2) holds in the range $-a$ to $+a$, and (since $dz=\pi dx/a$):

$$A_r=(1/a)\int_{-a}^{a} f(x)\cos(r\pi x/a)dx, \quad B_r=(1/a)\int_{-a}^{a} f(x)\sin(r\pi x/a)dx \quad . \quad (3)$$

so that *any* arbitrary function f(x) can be represented for all values of x between $x=-a$ and $x=a$ by a series of *trigonometrical* functions with periods $2a$, a, $2a/3$, . . .

The formulae hold for *any* value of a, and in the limit for $a\to\infty$ should hold for *any* value of x. In order to indicate that equations (3) have been integrated it is conventional to replace x in them by λ (since the value of a *definite* integral does not depend on the independent variable, but only on the limits):

$$A_r=\frac{1}{a}\int_{-a}^{a} f(\lambda)\cos\frac{r\pi\lambda}{a}d\lambda, \quad B_r=\frac{1}{a}\int_{-a}^{a} f(\lambda)\sin\frac{r\pi\lambda}{a}d\lambda \quad . \quad . \quad . \quad (4)$$

On substituting these in (2), writing $\frac{1}{2}A_0$ instead of A_0 (see § 75), and using some of the trigonometrical formulae of § 41, it is found that:

$$f(x)=(1/a)\left\{\frac{1}{2}\int_{-a}^{a} f(\lambda)d\lambda+\int_{-a}^{a}\left[f(\lambda)\cos\frac{\pi\lambda}{a}\cos\frac{\pi x}{a}d\lambda+\ .\ .\ .\right]\right.$$
$$\left.+\int_{-a}^{a}\left[f(\lambda)\sin\frac{\pi\lambda}{a}\sin\frac{\pi x}{a}d\lambda+\ .\ .\ .\right]\right\}$$

$$=\frac{1}{a}\int_{-a}^{a} f(\lambda)d\lambda\left[\frac{1}{2}+\cos\frac{\pi}{a}(\lambda-x)+\cos\frac{2\pi}{a}(\lambda-x)+\ .\ .\ .\right]$$

(since $\cos(x-y)=\cos x\cos y+\sin x\sin y$ (6), § 41),

$$=\frac{1}{2a}\int_{-a}^{a} f(\lambda)d\lambda\left[1+2\cos\frac{\pi}{a}(\lambda-x)+2\cos\frac{2\pi}{a}(\lambda-x)+\ .\ .\ .\right]$$

$$=\frac{1}{2a}\int_{-a}^{a} f(\lambda)d\lambda\left\{1+\cos\left[\frac{\pi}{a}(\lambda-x)\right]+\cos\left[\left(\frac{-\pi}{a}\right)(\lambda-x)\right]+\ .\ .\ .\right\}$$

(by writing $2\cos(\pi/a)(\lambda-x)$ as $\cos(\pi/a)(\lambda-x)+\cos(\pi/a)(\lambda-x)$, and similarly $2\cos(2\pi/a)(\lambda-x)$, joining the second term of the first expression with the first term of the second, etc., and using (19), § 41):

$$=(1/2\pi)\int_{-a}^{a} f(\lambda)d\lambda\{(\pi/a)\cos[(0/a)(\lambda-x)]+(\pi/a)\cos[(\pi/a)(\lambda-x)]$$
$$+(\pi/a)\cos[(2\pi/a)(\lambda-x)]\ .\ .\ .+(\pi/a)\cos[(-\pi/a)(\lambda-x)]$$
$$+(\pi/a)\cos[(-2\pi/a)(\lambda-x)]+\ .\ .\ .\} \quad . \quad (5)$$

(by transferring $1/a$ after the integral sign, multiplying each term by π and dividing outside by π, and writing $\cos(0/a)(\lambda-x)=\cos 0$ for 1).

As a increases indefinitely to infinity, the limiting value of the expression in braces becomes a definite integral (§ 20):

$$\int_{-\infty}^{\infty}\cos[(r\pi/a)(\lambda-x)]d(r\pi/a),$$

and if $r\pi/a=\alpha$ (r being any positive or negative integer: see under (8), § 72), the expression for f(x) finally becomes:

$$f(x)=(1/2\pi)\int_{-\infty}^{\infty} f(\lambda)d\lambda\int_{-\infty}^{\infty}\cos[\alpha(\lambda-x)]d\alpha \quad . \quad . \quad . \quad . \quad (6)$$

for *all* values of x. The double integral (see § 22) in (6) is called *Fourier's Integral*, and equation (6), given originally in this form by him, is often called *Fourier's Theorem*.

§ 77. Alternative Forms of Fourier's Series

Several alternative forms of Fourier's series, (2), § 73, are derivable by suitable modifications. If f(x) is an *even* function, (4), § 75, is:

$$f(x)=A_0+\sum_1^\infty A_r \cos(rx)=(1/\pi)\int_0^\pi f(\lambda)d\lambda+(2/\pi)\sum_1^\infty \cos(rx)\int_0^\pi \cos(r\lambda)f(\lambda)d\lambda,$$

by changing x to λ to indicate that the integration has been effected. Suppose x has the range $-a$ to $+a$, change x to $\pi z/a$, or (keeping the symbol x) to $\pi x/a$, and change λ to $\pi\lambda/a$, then:

$$f(x)=\frac{1}{a}\int_0^a f(\lambda)d\lambda+\frac{2}{a}\sum_1^\infty \cos\frac{r\pi x}{a}\int_0^a \cos\frac{r\pi\lambda}{a}f(\lambda)d\lambda \quad . \quad . \quad . \quad (1)$$

Example. To find [1] an expression equal to v when x lies between 0 and c, inclusive,[2] and equal to zero when x lies between c and b. That is, $f(\lambda)=v$ from $\lambda=0$ to $\lambda=c$, and $f(\lambda)=0$ from $\lambda=c$ to $\lambda=b$. In (1) $a=b$,

$$\int \cos\frac{r\pi\lambda}{a}f(\lambda)d\lambda=v\int_0^c \cos\frac{r\pi\lambda}{b}d\lambda=\frac{vb}{r\pi}\sin\frac{r\pi c}{b},$$

$$\therefore\ f(x)=\frac{vc}{b}+\frac{2v}{\pi}\left(\sin\frac{\pi c}{b}\cos\frac{\pi x}{b}+\tfrac{1}{2}\sin\frac{2\pi b}{b}\cos\frac{2\pi x}{b}+\ .\ .\ .\right),$$

and when $x=c$ the series becomes $\frac{1}{2}v$, which is half the value of the function (see § 74).

Since (§ 21):

$$\int_{-\infty}^\infty \cos x dx=\int_{-\infty}^0 \cos x dx+\int_0^\infty \cos x dx$$

$$\int_{-\infty}^0 \cos x dx=\int_\infty^0 \cos(-x)d(-x)=-\int_\infty^0 \cos x dx=\int_0^\infty \cos x dx$$

(since $\cos(-x)=\cos x$), $\therefore\ \int_{-\infty}^\infty \cos x dx=2\int_0^\infty \cos x dx.$

Similarly: $$\int_{-\infty}^\infty \cos[\alpha(\lambda-x)]d\alpha=2\int_0^\infty \cos[\alpha(\lambda-x)]d\alpha,$$

and (6), § 76, can be written:

$$f(x)=(1/\pi)\int_{-\infty}^\infty f(\lambda)d\lambda\int_0^\infty \cos[\alpha(\lambda-x)]dx \quad . \quad . \quad . \quad . \quad (2)$$

The limits are independent of α and λ, and hence the order of integration of the double integral is optional,

$$\therefore\ \int_{-\infty}^\infty f(\lambda)d\lambda\int_0^\infty \cos[\alpha(\lambda-x)]d\alpha=\int_0^\infty d\alpha\int_{-\infty}^\infty f(\lambda)\cos[\alpha(\lambda-x)]d\lambda \ . \quad (3)$$

Now:

$$\int_{-\infty}^\infty f(\lambda)\cos[\alpha(\lambda-x)]d\lambda=\int_{-\infty}^0 f(\lambda)\cos[\alpha(\lambda-x)]d\lambda+\int_0^\infty f(\lambda)\cos[\alpha(\lambda-x)]d\lambda.$$

If f(x) is an *odd* function:

$$f(x)=-f(-x) \quad \text{or} \quad -f(x)=f(-x),$$

[1] Carslaw, "Fourier's Series and Integrals," 1930, 250.

[2] This is usually represented in mathematical books by $0\leqq x\leqq c$, which is not the same thing as $0<x<c$.

$$\therefore \int_{-\infty}^{0} f(\lambda)\cos[\alpha(\lambda-x)]d\lambda=\int_{\infty}^{0} f(-\lambda)\cos[\alpha(-\lambda-x)]d(-\lambda)$$

$$=-\int_{0}^{\infty} f(\lambda)\cos[\alpha(\lambda+x)]d\lambda.$$

Therefore from (2):

$$f(x)=(1/\pi)\int_0^\infty d\alpha\int_0^\infty f(\lambda)[\cos\alpha(\lambda-x)-\cos\alpha(\lambda+x)]d\lambda$$

$$=(2/\pi)\int_0^\infty d\alpha\int_0^\infty f(\lambda)\sin(\alpha\lambda)\sin(\alpha x)\,.\,d\lambda$$

$$=(2/\pi)\int_0^\infty f(\lambda)d\lambda\int_0^\infty \sin(\alpha\lambda)\sin(\alpha x)\,.\,d\alpha \quad . \; . \; . \; . \; . \quad (4)$$

from (20), § 41 (put $x=\alpha(\lambda-x)$, and $y=\alpha(\lambda+x)$, and use $\sin(-\theta)=-\sin\theta$).

Equation (4) holds for *all* odd functions f(x), and for all *positive* values of x in *any* function of x. If f(x) is an *even* function, $f(x)=f(-x)$, a similar process shows that (3) becomes:

$$f(x)=(2/\pi)\int_0^\infty f(\lambda)d\lambda\int_0^\infty \cos(\alpha\lambda)\cos(\alpha x)\,.\,d\alpha \quad . \; . \; . \; . \; . \quad (5)$$

which holds for *all* values of x if f(x) is an even function, and for all *positive* values of x in *any* function of x.

Finally, Fourier's series (2), § 73, may be written in the form:

$$f(x)=(1/2a)\int_{-a}^{a} f(\lambda)d\lambda+\sum_1^\infty\Big[(1/a)\cos(r\pi x/a)\int_{-a}^{a} f(\lambda)\cos(r\pi\lambda/a)\,.\,d\lambda$$

$$+(1/a)\sin(r\pi x/a)\int_{-a}^{a} f(\lambda)\sin(r\pi\lambda/a)\,.\,d\lambda\Big] \quad . \quad (6)$$

or, from (6), § 41:

$$f(x)=(1/2a)\int_{-a}^{a} f(\lambda)d\lambda+\sum_1^\infty(1/a)\int_{-a}^{a} f(\lambda)\cos[(r\pi/a)(x-\lambda)]d\lambda \quad . \quad (7)$$

where $\pi x/a$ can then be replaced by x, and, without loss of generality, the interval in which f(x) is defined taken as $-\pi$ to π, when:

$$f(x)=(1/2\pi)\int_{-\pi}^{\pi} f(\lambda)d\lambda+\sum_1^\infty(1/\pi)\int_{-\pi}^{\pi} f(\lambda)\cos[r(x-\lambda)]\,.\,d\lambda \quad . \; . \quad (8)$$

which is sometimes [1] taken as the " standard form " of Fourier's series. Such highly concentrated expressions are, however, less useful in the *practical* applications than the more intelligible series (2) of § 73.

§ 78. The Rayleigh-Jeans Equation

An equation giving the number of stationary waves or " proper vibrations " in unit volume of a medium, was found in connexion with the theory of radiation by Rayleigh [2] and Jeans,[3] and is also the basis of the theory of the atomic

[1] E.g. by Hobson, " Theory of Functions of a Real Variable," Cambridge, 1907, 645.

[2] *Phil. Mag.*, 1900, **49**, 539; *Nature*, 1905, **72**, 54, 243; " Scientific Papers," Cambridge, 1912, **5**, 253; Lodge, *Nature*, 1926, **118**, 81.

[3] *Phil. Mag.*, 1905, **10**, 91; " Dynamical Theory of Gases," 3rd edit., 1921, 349, 359; Rice, *Trans. Faraday Soc.*, 1915, **11**, 1; Rice, in Lewis " A System of Physical Chemistry," 1924, **3**, 313; Rice, " Introduction to Statistical Mechanics," 1930, 189, 209; Goldhammer, *Phys. Z.*, 1913, **14**, 1185, 1188; Brillouin, *Ann. de Phys.*, 1914, **1**, 433; *J. de Phys.*, 1914, **4**, 681; Flamm, *Phys. Z.*, 1918, **19**, 116; Preston, " Theory of Heat," 3rd edit., 1919, 284; Lorentz, " Theory of Electrons," 1923, 93; Planck, " Theorie der Wärmestrahlung," 1921, 197.

heat of a monatomic solid proposed by Debye.[1] Consider a cubical [2] cavity containing a medium (e.g. air) transmitting longitudinal waves, for which the directions of vibration are the same as the direction of wave propagation, the latter represented by a " ray " OS (Fig. 40.I).

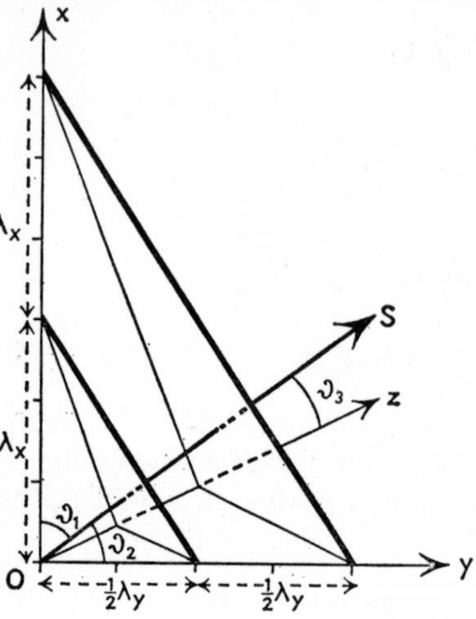

FIG. 40.I. Plane Waves in a Medium

The waves are reflected on the walls, and by interference set up a system of stationary waves which have nodes on the surfaces of the box and in parallel planes distant from one another by half a wave-length ($\lambda/2$) for each component, and such that a *whole number of nodal planes* are interposed between one wall and the opposite one. Since most of the rays strike the walls at oblique angles and the nodal planes are always perpendicular to the ray, it is necessary to consider rays traversing the box in all possible directions.

Take one corner of the box as the origin O of a right-handed coordinate system (Fig. 40.I) and let a ray OS make angles θ_1, θ_2, θ_3 with the x, y, and z axes. The components of the amplitude of vibration in the direction of the axes are given by the equations (which are not actually required in the present deduction):

$$\left.\begin{aligned} x \text{ axis:}\quad & \xi = A_{n_1, n_2, n_3} \cos 2\pi\nu t \sin\frac{n_1\pi x}{l} \cos\frac{n_2\pi y}{l} \cos\frac{n_3\pi z}{l} \\ y \text{ axis:}\quad & \eta = B_{n_1, n_2, n_3} \cos 2\pi\nu t \cos\frac{n_1\pi x}{l} \sin\frac{n_2\pi y}{l} \cos\frac{n_3\pi z}{l} \\ z \text{ axis:}\quad & \zeta = C_{n_1, n_2, n_3} \cos 2\pi\nu t \cos\frac{n_1\pi x}{l} \cos\frac{n_2\pi y}{l} \sin\frac{n_3\pi z}{l} \end{aligned}\right\} \quad . \quad (1)$$

Here n_1, n_2, n_3 are any three whole numbers, ν is the frequency, l is the side of the cube, A, B, and C are constants depending on n_1, n_2, n_3; t is the time, and x, y, z are the intercepts of the nodal plane on the axes.

Consider a point on the x axis which is also in a nodal plane; for this point $\xi=0$ and a plane through it perpendicular to the x axis and parallel to the yz plane is also a nodal plane for the component ξ. The next nodal plane parallel to it will be distant $\frac{1}{2}\lambda_x$, where $\frac{1}{2}\lambda_x$ is the part of the x axis cut off by two nodal planes distant $\frac{1}{2}\lambda$ apart perpendicular to OS. From the figure, it is seen that $\frac{1}{2}\lambda_x \cos\theta_1 = \frac{1}{2}\lambda$. Similar equations hold for the y and z axes, and hence:

$$\lambda_x \cos\theta_1 = \lambda, \quad \lambda_y \cos\theta_2 = \lambda, \quad \lambda_z \cos\theta_3 = \lambda \quad . \quad . \quad . \quad . \quad (2)$$

These sections, however, must satisfy the condition that the cube side l must contain a whole number of nodal planes:

$$\therefore\ n_1(\lambda_x/2) = n_2(\lambda_y/2) = n_3(\lambda_z/2) = l \quad . \quad . \quad . \quad . \quad . \quad (3)$$

[1] *Ann. Phys.*, 1912, **39**, 789. See Vol. II.

[2] A deduction for a cavity or body of any shape is given by Weyl, *Math. Ann.*, 1912, **71** 441; simplified by von Laue, *Ann. Phys.*, 1914, **44**, 1197; Kar and Mazumdar, *Z. Phys.*, 1929, **53**, 308.

where n_1, n_2, n_3 are positive whole numbers. From (2) and (3)

$$\left.\begin{aligned} n_1&=2l/\lambda_x=(2l/\lambda)\cos\theta_1\\ n_2&=2l/\lambda_y=(2l/\lambda)\cos\theta_2\\ n_3&=2l/\lambda_z=(2l/\lambda)\cos\theta_3\end{aligned}\right\} \quad . \; . \; . \; . \; . \; . \; . \; . \quad (4)$$

On squaring and adding the three equations (4) it is found that:

$$n_1^2+n_2^2+n_3^2=(2l/\lambda)^2(\cos^2\theta_1+\cos^2\theta_2+\cos^2\theta_3) \quad . \; . \; . \quad (5)$$

The values of $\cos\theta_1$, $\cos\theta_2$, and $\cos\theta_3$ are called the *direction cosines* of OS in the co-ordinate system, and it is a well-known result of analytical geometry that:

$$\cos^2\theta_1+\cos^2\theta_2+\cos^2\theta_3=1 \quad . \; . \quad (6)$$

This is easily seen from Fig. 41.I:

$$\begin{aligned} OS^2&=OY^2+YS^2=OY^2+(Y'Y^2+Y'S^2)\\ &=OY^2+OZ^2+OX^2\\ &=(OS\cos\theta_2)^2+(OS\cos\theta_3)^2+(OS\cos\theta_1)^2,\end{aligned}$$

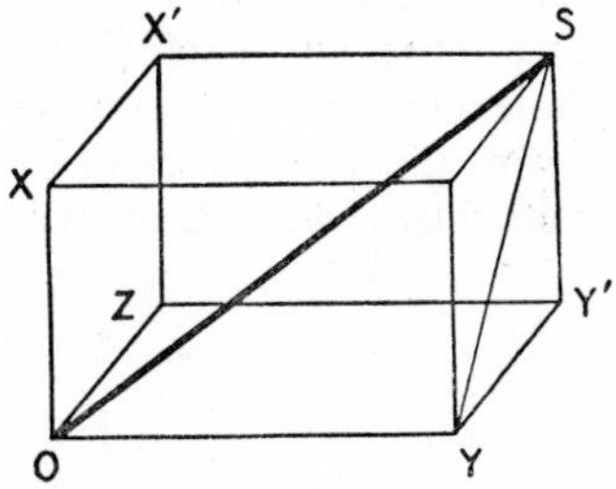

FIG. 41.I. Direction Cosines

from which (5) follows. From (5) and (6):

$$2l/\lambda=\pm\sqrt{(n_1^2+n_2^2+n_3^2)} \quad . \; . \; . \; . \; . \; . \; . \; . \quad (7)$$

and from (4):

$$\left.\begin{aligned} \cos\theta_1&=\pm n_1/\sqrt{(n_1^2+n_2^2+n_3^2)}\\ \cos\theta_2&=\pm n_2/\sqrt{(n_1^2+n_2^2+n_3^2)}\\ \cos\theta_3&=\pm n_3/\sqrt{(n_1^2+n_2^2+n_3^2)}\end{aligned}\right\} \quad . \; . \; . \; . \; . \quad (8)$$

Equations (8) show that only wave trains with definite directions and wave-lengths (given by (7) in terms of the n values) can be formed in the cavity; viz. those which satisfy (7) and (8) with given values of λ, θ_1, θ_2, and θ_3, and with whole number values of n_1, n_2, and n_3. The wave-length is related to the frequency ν and velocity c by (§ 49):

$$c=\nu\lambda \quad . \; . \; . \; . \; . \; . \; . \; . \; . \; . \; . \quad (9)$$

(in the case of cavity radiation $c=\mathbf{c}$, the velocity of light in vacuum). Equation (7) then becomes:

$$2l\nu/c=\sqrt{(n^2+n_2^2+n_3^2)} \quad . \; . \; . \; . \; . \; . \; . \; . \quad (10)$$

It is easily shown, although it is not required in the present deduction, that the equations (1) satisfy the conditions of the problem. At all times the amplitude at the origin ($x=0$, $y=0$, $z=0$) is zero, since the sine factors in all three equations (1) are then zero. There is, therefore, a permanent node at the origin. At any point on the x axis, $y=0$ and $z=0$, so that η and ζ vanish. The value of ξ is zero for $n_1x/l=$ a whole number (since $\sin n\pi=0$), i.e. from (3) for $x=\lambda_x/2, 2\lambda_x/2, 3\lambda_x/2 \ldots$.

Now consider a *plane* at right angles to the x axis at $x=\lambda_x/2$. For all points in this plane, $x=\lambda_x/2$, hence it is a nodal plane, since ξ is zero for all values of t, y, and z. If a plane is at right-angles to the x axis at $x=3\lambda_x/4$, then along a section of this plane with the xz plane ($y=0$), ξ varies periodically with z for a given value of t. For a plane with $x=3\lambda_x/4$ at right-angles to the x axis and cutting the xy plane, $z=0$ along the line of section, and at any instant ξ varies periodically with y. In a similar way it can be shown that in the nodal planes perpendicular to OS, the components ξ, η, and ζ are zero at all times.

It is now possible to find the number of wave trains with frequencies between ν_1 and ν_2 which can be formed in the cavity or in the block of medium, or (as it is usually expressed) the number of *proper vibrations* between these frequencies. Consider a cubic lattice of points which are the corners of elementary cubes of unit side; then the corners of *eight* such cubes meet at each lattice point. Since the numbers n_1, n_2, and n_3, which will be laid off along the x, y, and z axes, respectively, are all to be positive, only the positive octant in the coordinate system (Fig. 42.I) is to be considered. The coordinates give the values of n_1, n_2, and n_3, measured in multiples of the cube edge, and every point in the lattice space represents a set of three values n_1, n_2, n_3; conversely every set of three whole numbers represents a point in the lattice. (In Fig. 42.I four such cubes are shown; the other block of four will be laid on the shaded faces.) Every lattice point thus *represents* a wave train of fixed frequency and direction, given by

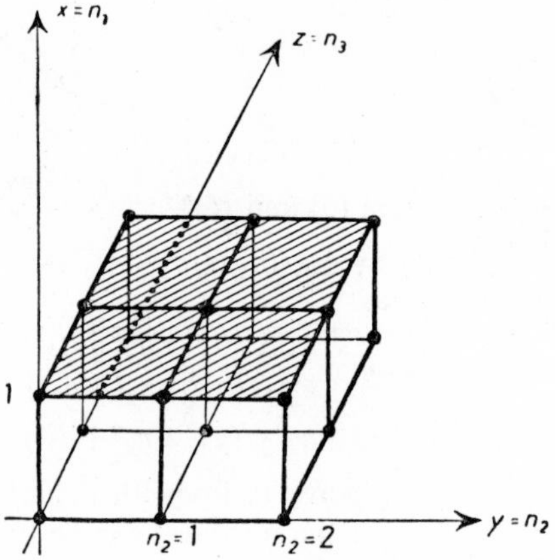

FIG. 42.I. Cubic Lattice of Points

(7) and (8), and conversely. All wave trains with frequency ν_1 correspond with points lying on the surface of a sphere of radius r_1 given by (10):

$$r_1=(2l/c)\nu_1=\sqrt{(n_1{}^2+n_2{}^2+n_3{}^2)} \quad . \quad . \quad . \quad . \quad . \quad (11)$$

and those with frequency ν_2 on the surface of a sphere of radius:

$$r_2=(2l/c)\nu_2=\sqrt{(n_1{}'^2+n_2{}'^2+n_3{}'^2)} \quad . \quad . \quad . \quad . \quad . \quad (12)$$

All wave trains with frequencies between ν_1 and ν_2 are represented by lattice points inside the spherical shell with radii r_1 and r_2. Since each unit cube represents *one* lattice point (the eight points at its corners being shared with eight other adjacent cubes), and the allowed values of n_1, n_2, n_3 must lie in the *positive* coordinate octant, the number of lattice points is one-eighth the volume of the shell: $(1/8)(4\pi/3)(r_2{}^3-r_1{}^3)$. From (11) and (12): $r_2{}^3-r_1{}^3=(2l/c)^3(\nu_2{}^3-\nu_1{}^3)$, and since $\nu_2-\nu_1=\Delta\nu$ is small,

$$(\nu_2{}^3-\nu_1{}^3)=[(\nu_1+\Delta\nu)^3-\nu_1{}^3]\simeq 3\nu_1{}^2\Delta\nu,$$

all higher powers of $\Delta\nu$ being negligible. Hence the volume is:

$$(1/8)(4/3)\pi\,.\,3\nu_1{}^2\Delta\nu(8l^3/c^3)=(4\pi l^3/c^3)\nu_1{}^2\Delta\nu;$$

or, by replacing ν_1 by ν and $\Delta\nu$ by $d\nu$, the number of proper vibrations in unit volume ($l^3=1$) is:

$$dZ=(4\pi/c^3)\nu^2 d\nu \quad . \quad . \quad . \quad . \quad . \quad . \quad . \quad . \quad . \quad (13)$$

This is the solution of the given problem.

SECTION II

THERMODYNAMICS

BIBLIOGRAPHY OF THERMODYNAMICS

Alexander, P. Treatise on Thermodynamics, 1892; Amagat, Notes sur la Physique et la Thermodynamique, 1912; Ariès, La Statique Chimique basée sur les deux Principes fundamentaux de la Thermodynamique, 1904.

Baynes, Lessons on Thermodynamics, Oxford, 1878; Berry, The Temperature-Entropy Diagram, New York and London, 1905; Berthelot, Essai de Mécanique Chimique, 2 vols., 1879, Thermochimie, données et lois numériques, 2 vols., 1897; Traité pratique de Calorimétrie chimique, 1893, 2nd edit., 1905; Bertrand, Thermodynamique, 1887; Bichowsky and Rossini, The Thermochemistry of Chemical Substances, New York, 1936; Birtwistle, The Principles of Thermodynamics, Cambridge, 1925; Blondlot, Introduction à l'Étude de la Thermodynamique, 1888, 2nd edit. 1909; *idem*, Einführung in die Thermodynamik, transl., with additions, by Schorr and Platschek, Dresden and Leipzig, 1913; Bošnjaković, Technische Thermodynamik, Dresden and Leipzig, 1937, **2**; Bouasse, Cours de Thermodynamique, pt. 2, Machines Thermique; Chimie Physique, 2nd edit., 1925; *idem*, Thermodynamique Générale: Gaz et Vapeurs, 1932; Boussinesq, Théorie Analytique de la Chaleur, 1901, **1**; Boutaric, Thermodynamique et Chimie, 1926; Bridgman, Condensed Collection of Thermodynamic Formulae, Cambridge (Mass.), 1925; The Nature of Thermodynamics, Cambridge (Mass.), 1941; Briot, Théorie mécanique de la Chaleur, 1869, 2nd edit., 1883; Bruhat, Cours de Thermodynamique, 2nd edit., 1933; Brunhes, La Dégradation de l'Énergie, 1908; Brunold, L'Entropie, 1930; Bryan, Thermodynamics, Leipzig, 1907; Buckingham, An Outline of the Theory of Thermodynamics, New York, 1900; Butler, The Fundamentals of Chemical Thermodynamics, 1946.

Clausius, Abhandlungen über die mechanische Wärmetheorie, Brunswick, 1864–7; The Mechanical Theory of Heat, transl. by Hirst, 1867; Die Mechanische Wärmetheorie, 3 vols., Brunswick, 1876–91; The Mechanical Theory of Heat, transl. by Browne, 1879.

De Donder, L'Affinité, 1927; new edit. by van Rysselberghe, 1936; transl. van Rysselberghe, Thermodynamic Theory of Affinity, Stanford (U.S.A.), 1936; De Haas, Thermodynamika, 2nd edit., Groningen, 1933; Dodge, Chemical Engineering Thermodynamics, New York, 1944; Doolittle and Zerban, Engineering Thermodynamics, New York, 1948; Draper, Heat and the Principles of Thermodynamics, 1893, 2nd edit., 1911; Duhem, Le Potentiel Thermodynamique, 1886, reprint 1895; *idem*, Traité élémentaire de la Mécanique Chimique, fondée sur la Thermodynamique, 4 vols, 1897–9; Thermodynamique et Chimie, 1902, 2nd edit., 1910; transl. Burgess, Thermodynamics and Chemistry, New York, 1903; *idem*, Traité d'Énergetique ou de Thermodynamique générale, 2 vols, 1911 f; Dupré, Théorie mécanique de la Chaleur, 1869.

Egli, *J. Appl. Mechan.*, 1937, **4**, 86; Emswiler and Schwartz, Thermodynamics, New York, 1943; Ennis, Applied Thermodynamics for Engineers, 1910; Epstein, Textbook of Thermodynamics, New York, 1937; Everett, Thermodynamics, 1939; Ewing, Thermodynamics for Engineers, Cambridge, 1920; *idem*, Thermodynamics, in Glazebrook, Dictionary of Applied Physics, 1922, **1**, 922.

Fabry, Éléments de Thermodynamique, 1928; Faires, Elementary Thermodynamics, New York, 1938, 2nd edit., 1948; *idem*, Applied Thermodynamics, 1938; Fermi, Thermodynamics, 1938; Fernald, Elements of Thermodynamics, 2nd edit., New York, 1938; Foster, Thermodynamics, in Watts, Dictionary of Chemistry, 1881, 3rd suppl., pt. ii, p. 1922.

Gibbs, Scientific Papers, 1906, **1**; reprinted 1928 as Collected Works, **1**; Thermodynamische Studien, transl. [unter Mitwirkung von] Ostwald, Leipzig, 1892; Équilibres des Systèmes Chimiques, trans. by Le Chatelier, 1899; A Commentary on the Scientific Writings of Gibbs, 2 vols., New Haven, 1936; Gillespie, Physical Chemistry, New York, 1931; Glasstone, Thermodynamics for Chemists, New York, 1946; Goransen, Thermodynamic Relations in Multicomponent Systems, Carnegie Inst. Publ. **408**, Washington, 1930; Guldberg, Thermodynamische Abhandlungen (1867–72), in Ostwald's *Klassiker*, 1903, **139**.

Haber, Thermodynamics of Technical Gas Reactions, transl. Lamb, 1908; Hawkins, Thermodynamics, New York, 1946; Helm, Die Lehre von der Energie historisch entwickelt, Leipzig, 1887; *idem*, Grundzüge der mathematischen Chemie, Leipzig, 1891, transl. Morgan, The Principles of Mathematical Chemistry: the Energetics of Chemical Changes, New York, 1897; *idem*, Die Energetik nach ihrer geschichtlichen Entwickelung, Leipzig, 1898; Helmholtz, Abhandlungen zur Thermodynamik chemischer Vorgänge, in Ostwald's *Klassiker*, 1902, **124**; *idem*, Vorlesungen über theoretische Physik, Leipzig, 1903, **6** (edit. Richarz); Henning, Die Grundlagen, Methoden und Ergebnisse der Temperaturmessung, Brunswick, 1915; Hercus, Elements of Thermodynamics, Melbourne, 1947; Hinshelwood, Thermodynamics for Students of Chemistry, 1926; Hirn, Recherches sur l'Équivalent Mécanique de la Chaleur, Colmar, 1858; Mémoire de la Thermodynamique, 1867; Théorie Mécanique de la Chaleur, 2 vols., 1868, 3rd [last] edit., 1875–6; Hoare, Thermodynamics, 2nd edit., 1938; Hollenweger, Thermodynamik, Bonn, 1939; Horstmann, Abhandlungen zur Thermodynamik chemischer Vorgänge (1869–81), in Ostwald's *Klassiker*, 1903, **137**; *idem*, Theoretische Chemie einschliesslich der Thermochemie, in Graham-Otto, Ausführliches Lehrbuch der Chemie, Brunswick, 1885, **1**, ii, 426; Hougen and Watson, Chemical Process Principles, Pt. II, Thermodynamics, New York, 1947; Hudleston, Chemical Affinity, 1928.

Jahn, Die Grundsätze der Thermochemie und ihre Bedeutung für die theoretische Chemie, Vienna, 1882; *idem*, Grundriss der Elektrochemie, 2nd edit., Vienna, 1905 [section on thermodynamics]; Jellinek, Lehrbuch der physikalischen Chemie, 2nd edit., 5 vols., Stuttgart, 1928–37; *idem*, Physikalische Chemie der Gasreaktionen, Leipzig, 1913; *idem*, Kurzes Lehrbuch der physikalischen Chemie, 2 vols., Deventer, 1938–9; Joule, Scientific Papers, 2 vols., 1884–7.

Keenan, Thermodynamics, New York, 1941; Kelvin, Lord [W. Thomson], Mathematical and Physical Papers, 6 vols., Cambridge, 1882–1911; Kirchhoff, Gesammelte Abhandlungen, Leipzig, 1882, and Nachtrag, edit. Boltzmann, Leipzig, 1891; *idem*, Vorlesungen über die Theorie der Wärme, edit. Planck, Leipzig, 1894; Kolossowsky, N. A., Recherches Thermodynamiques, 1934; Krause, Die Kältemaschinen und ihre thermodynamischen Grundlagen, Berlin and Leipzig, 1932; Krebs, Einleitung in die mechanische Wärmetheorie, Leipzig, 1874; Kuenen, Theorie der Verdampfung und Verflüssigung von Gemischen, Leipzig, 1906; Kuhn, Physikalische Chemie, Leipzig, 1938.

Laar, J. J. van, Die Thermodynamik in der Chemie, Amsterdam, 1893; *idem*, Lehrbuch der mathematischen Chemie, Leipzig, 1901; *idem*, Sechs Vorträge über das thermodynamische Potential, Brunswick, 1906; *idem*, Die Thermodynamik einheitlicher Stoffe und binärer Gemischen, mit Anwendungen auf verschiedene physikalisch-chemische Probleme, Groningen, 1936; Lamé, Leçons sur la Théorie analytique de la Chaleur, 1861; De Langen, Kinetische Afleiding van Thermodynamische Evenwichtsvoorwaarden, Groningen, 1907; Larmor, Energetics, in Encycl. Brit., 11th edit., 1910, **9**, 390; Lehmann, Energie und Entropie, Berlin 1921; Lewis and Randall, Thermodynamics and the Free Energy of Chemical Substances, New York, 1923, transl. (with additions) by Redlich, Thermodynamik und die freie Energie chemischer Substanzen, Vienna, 1937; Lippmann, Cours de Thermodynamique, 1889, 2nd edit., 1905; Lorentz, Technische Wärmelehre, Munich, 1904; Lucke, Engineering Thermodynamics, New York, 1912.

MacCulloch, Mechanical Theory of Heat, New York, 1876; MacDougall, Thermodynamics and Chemistry, New York, 1921, 3rd edit., 1939; Mach, Prinzipien der Wärmelehre, Leipzig, 1896; Mache, Einführung in die Theorie der Wärme, Berlin and Leipzig, 1921; Magnus, Lehrbuch der Thermodynamik, Leipzig, 1929; Marchis, Thermodynamique: Notions fondamentales, Paris and Grenoble, 1904; Martin, D. J., Thermodynamics for Chemists, 1933; Maxwell, Theory of Heat, 1871, new edit., 1897; Meyer, J., Einfürhrung in die Thermodynamik, Halle, 1906; Michaud, Énergetique Générale, 1921; Moutier, Éléments de la Thermodynamique, 1872; *idem*, La Thermodynamique et ses principales Applications, 1885; Müller-Pouillet, Lehrbuch der Physik, 1926, **3**, i; Murani, Lezioni di Termodinamica, 2nd edit., Milan, 1922.

Naumann, Grundriss der Thermochemie, Brunswick, 1869; *idem*, Lehrbuch und Handbuch der Thermochemie, Brunswick, 1882; Nernst, Theoretische Chemie, 11th–15th edit., Stuttgart, 1925; transl., Theoretical Chemistry, 1923; *idem*, Recent Applications of Thermodynamics to Chemistry, New York, 1907; *idem*, Grundlagen des neuen Wärmesatzes, Halle, 1918, 2nd edit., 1924; transl. Barr, The New Heat Theorem, 1926; Neumann, C., Vorlesungen über die mechanische Theorie der Wärme, Leipzig, 1875.

Obert, Thermodynamics, New York, 1948; Ostwald, Lehrbuch der allgemeinen Chemie, 2nd edit., vols. **1**, **2** i, ii, iii (in part), Leipzig, 1910–11; *idem*, Outlines of General Chemistry, 2nd edit., 1895, 3rd edit., 1912.

Parker, J., Elementary Thermodynamics, Cambridge, 1891; *idem*, Thermodynamics treated with Elementary Mathematics, 1894, and Supplementary Volume, 1896; Partington, A Text

Book of Thermodynamics, 1913; Chemical Thermodynamics, 1924, 1940; Thermodynamics, 1949; Perrin, Traité de Chimie Physique: les Principes, 1903, **1**; Planck, Das Prinzip der Erhaltung der Energie, Leipzig, 1887, 2nd edit., 1910; *idem*, Grundriss der allgemeinen Thermochemie, Breslau, 1893; *idem*, Vorlesungen über Thermodynamik, Leipzig, 1897, 3rd edit. 1911, 9th edit., 1930, transl., Thermodynamics, 1903, 3rd edit., 1927; *idem*, Theorie der Wärme, Leipzig, 1930, transl., Theory of Heat, 1932; *idem*, Vorlesungen über die Theorie der Wärmestrahlung, Leipzig, 1906, 5th edit., 1923, transl., Theory of Heat Radiation, Philadelphia, 1914; *idem*, Acht Vorlesungen über theoretische Physik, Leipzig, 1910; Poincaré, Thermodynamique (edit. by Blondin), 1892, 2nd edit., 1908, transl. Jäger and Grumlich, Berlin, 1893; Pollitzer, Berechnung chemischer Affinitäten nach dem Nernstschen Wärmetheorem, Stuttgart, 1912; Poynting and Thomson, Text Book of Physics, **3**, Heat, 5th edit., 1919; Preston, Theory of Heat, 1894, 4th edit., 1929.

Rankine, Scientific Papers, 1881; Raveau, Concrete Thermodynamics, *J. Phys. Chem.*, 1929, **26**, 1821; Robin, Thermodynamique Générale, in Oeuvres Scientifiques, 1901, **2**; Röntgen, Die Grundlehren der mechanischen Wärmetheorie, Jena, 1871; Roozeboom, Die heterogenen Gleichgewichte vom Standpunkte der Phasenlehre, 3 vols., Brunswick, 1901–13; Rothé, Cours de Physique, 1917, **2**; Rühlemann, Handbuch der mechanischen Wärmetheorie, Brunswick, 1876–85; De Rycker, L'Entropie et l'Affinité Chimique, Liège, 1945.

Sackur, Lehrbuch der Thermochemie und Thermodynamik, Berlin, 1912, 2nd edit. (with Simson), 1928; transl. A Text Book of Thermochemistry and Thermodynamics, 1917; de Saint-Robert, Principes de Thermodynamique, Turin, 1865, 2nd edit., 1870; Schmidt, E., Einführung in die techniche Thermodynamik, Berlin, 1936; Schottky, Ulich, and Wagner, Thermodynamik, Berlin, 1929; Schröter and Prandtl, Technische Thermodynamik, in Enzykl. d. math. Wiss., 1905, **5**, i, 231; Schüle, Technische Thermodynamik, 2 vols., Berlin, 1921–3; Steiner, Introduction to Chemical Thermodynamics, New York, 1941.

Tait, Sketch of Thermodynamics, Edinburgh, 1868, 2nd edit., 1877; French transl. de Moigno, 1870; *idem*, Recent Advances in Physical Science, 2nd edit., 1876; *idem*, Heat, 1895; *idem*, Scientific Papers, 2 vols., Cambridge, 1898–1900; Thomson, J. J., Applications of Dynamics to Physics and Chemistry, 1888; Tourpain, Éléments de Thermodynamique, 1927; Trevor, Thermodynamics, 1928; Tuckermann, Index of the Literature of Thermodynamics, Smithsonian Inst., Washington, 1890, **34**, ii; Tyndall, Heat a Mode of Motion, 1864, 7th edit., 1887.

Ubbelohde, An Introduction to Modern Thermodynamic Principles, Oxford, 1937; Ulich, Chemische Thermodynamik, Dresden, 1930; Urbain, Énergetique des Réactions Chimiques, 1925.

Van't Hoff, Lectures on Theoretical and Physical Chemistry, transl. Lehfeld, 3 vols., 1898–9; *idem*, Vorlesungen über theoretische und physikalische Chemie, 2nd edit., 3 vols., Brunswick, 1903; Verdet, Théorie Mécanique de la Chaleur, 1863; Verschaffelt, Thermostatica, Antwerp and Groningen, 1933; *idem*, Adnvullingen der Thermostatica, Antwerp, 1938; Voigt, Thermodynamik, 2 vols., Leipzig, 1903–4.

Waals, van der, and Kohnstamm, Lehrbuch der Thermodynamik, 2 vols., Amsterdam and Leipzig, 1908–12; *idem*, Lehrbuch der Thermostatik, 2 vols., Leipzig, 1927; Weber, Thermodynamics for Chemical Engineers, New York, 1939; Weinstein, Thermodynamik und Kinetik der Körper, 4 vols., Brunswick, 1901–11; Wenner, Thermochemical Calculations, New York, 1941; Weyrauch, Grundriss der Wärmetheorie, 2 vols., Stuttgart, 1905–7; Whetham, Theory of Solution, Cambridge, 1902; Williamson and Tarleton, An Elementary Treatise on Dynamics, containing Applications to Thermodynamics, 2nd edit., 1889; Winkelmann, Handbuch der Physik, Leipzig, 1906, **3**, ii; Winston, Thermodynamics, Chicago, 1939; Wormell, Thermodynamics, 1877; Wüllner, Lehrbuch der Experimentalphysik, 5th edit., Leipzig, 1896, **2** (Die Lehre von der Wärme), 6th edit., 1907.

Zemansky, Heat and Thermodynamics, New York, 1937, 2nd edit., 1943; Zernike, Thermodynamica en Statistiek en de Chemie, Deventer, 1942; Zeuner, Grundzüge der mechanischen Wärme-Theorie, Freiburg, 1860, 4th edit., Technische Thermodynamik, Leipzig, 1900, transl. from 5th edit., Technical Thermodynamics, 1907. [A complete French translation of the first edition is contained in Hirn's Exposition Analytique et Expérimentale de la Théorie Mécanique de la Chaleur, Paris and Colmar, 1862, **1**, 133–299; another French translation by Arnthal and Cazin was published in 1865.]

This list is not complete; see the bibliographies by Goransen and Tuckermann, referred to above. Articles in journals are referred to in appropriate places in the text.

THERMODYNAMIC SYMBOLS

Heat (entering a system)	q
Work (done by a system)	w
Temperature on any scale	θ, t
Temperature, absolute	T
Volume	v, V
Pressure	p, P
Energy	E
Heat Content (or enthalpy)	$H=E+PV$
Entropy	S
Free Energy	$F=E-TS$
Available Energy	$G=H-TS$
Specific Heat per unit mass:	
at constant volume	c_v
at constant pressure	c_p
Molecular Heat:	
at constant volume	C_v
at constant pressure	C_p
Ratio of Specific Heats (c_p/c_v)	γ
Latent Heat:	
per unit mass	l
per mol	L
Chemical Potential	μ
Activity	a
Density	ρ, d, D
Compressibility	κ
Elasticity	ϵ
Number of Mols	n
Mol Fraction	N (or x)
Concentration (n/V)	c or C
Equilibrium Constant:	
in terms of concentrations (or activities)	K
in terms of partial pressures	K'
Activity Coefficient:	
in terms of molarity [1]	f
in terms of molality [2]	γ

§ 1. True and Mean Specific Heats

The science of thermodynamics, as its name indicates (Greek θερμός, heat, δύναμις, power), is primarily concerned with the relations of transformation of *heat* into other forms of energy, which may, conveniently, be grouped under the name *work*, since they are all directly obtainable from, or convertible into, a quantity of mechanical potential energy represented by a raised weight. The measurement of quantities of heat and work will first be considered, then the ratio of their units (involving the First Law of Thermodynamics), then their reciprocal convertibility (involving the Second Law of Thermodynamics).

If a hot body is brought in conducting contact with a cold body, the temperature of the hot body falls and that of the cold body rises, and it is said that a *quantity of heat* has passed from the hot to the cold body.

[1] Mols/lit. solution. [2] Mols/kg. solvent.

Let a mass m of a given material be heated from the temperature θ_1 to the temperature θ_2, where θ denotes temperature measured on any scale. A quantity of heat q is absorbed, which is proportional to m and to the rise in temperature $(\theta_2-\theta_1)$, but varies with the material; hence:

$$q=\bar{c}m(\theta_2-\theta_1) \qquad (1)$$

where $\bar{c}$ is the *mean specific heat* of the material over the interval of temperature $\theta_2-\theta_1$; $m\bar{c}$ is the *mean heat capacity* of the body.[1] q is positive for heat absorbed by the body and negative for heat emitted.

It is found that $\bar{c}$ varies with temperature; if $\theta_2-\theta_1=\delta\theta$ is very small, then q is also small, δq, and:

$$\delta q=cm\delta\theta \qquad (2)$$

where, for unit mass ($m=1$) of material:

$$c=\lim_{\delta\theta\to 0}(\delta q/\delta\theta)=\mathrm{d}q/\mathrm{d}\theta \qquad (3)$$

is the *true specific heat* of the material at the temperature θ. It must be noted that c is also, in general, a function of temperature, $c=\mathrm{f}(\theta)=c_\theta$.

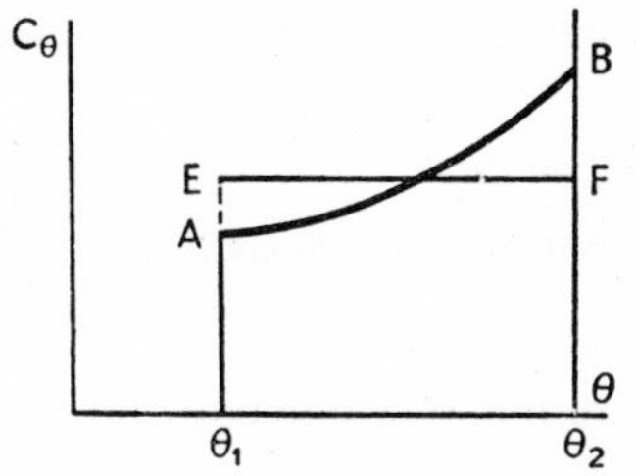

FIG. 1.II. True and Mean Specific Heats

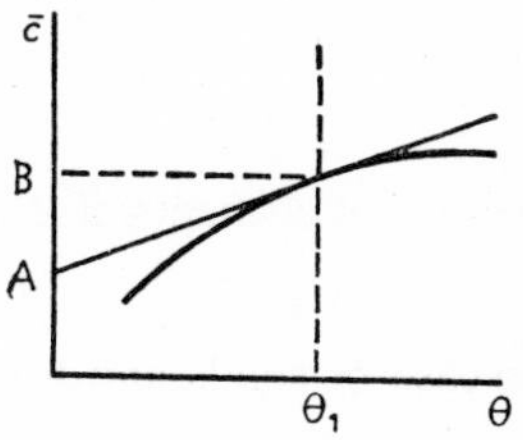

FIG. 2.II. Calculation of True from Mean Specific Heat

The heat absorbed during a finite rise in temperature is found by integration of (2):

$$q=m\int_{\theta_1}^{\theta_2} c_\theta \mathrm{d}\theta \qquad (4)$$

and by comparison of (1) and (4):

$$\bar{c}=\int_{\theta_1}^{\theta_2} c_\theta d\theta/(\theta_2-\theta_1) \qquad (5)$$

showing that $\bar{c}$ is the mean value of the function $c=\mathrm{f}(\theta)$ over the range $(\theta_2-\theta_1)$ of the argument θ. This is shown graphically in Fig. 1.II, in which the abscissa is θ and the ordinate is c_θ. The area $\mathrm{AB}\theta_2\theta_1$ represents $\int c_\theta \mathrm{d}\theta$, and if the horizontal EF is drawn so that area $\mathrm{EF}\theta_2\theta_1$=area $\mathrm{AB}\theta_2\theta_1$, then the ordinate of EF represents $\bar{c}$. To find the value of c (true sp. ht.), $\bar{c}$ (mean sp. ht.) may be plotted as a function of θ, and at a given value θ_1 a tangent drawn to the curve.[2] The intercept AB (Fig. 2.II) is then added to the ordinate giving $\bar{c}$ in order to obtain the value of c.

The form of the function:

$$c_\theta=\mathrm{f}(\theta) \qquad (6)$$

[1] Cf. Hansel, *Proc. Phys. Soc.*, 1942, **54**, 159; Duncanson, *ibid.*, 1942, **54**, 504, and discussion; *Phil. Mag.*, 1944, **35**, 81.

[2] White, *Amer. J. Sci.*, 1909, **28**, 334; 1919. **47**, 1, 44, Schübel, *Z. anorg. Chem.*, 1914, **87**, 81.

may sometimes be determined theoretically, e.g. from the kinetic theory of gases, or from the quantum theory (see Sections III and IV), but is often found experimentally by measurements of $\bar{c}$ or c_θ at different temperatures. Since c_θ is found to vary only slowly with temperature it may often be represented empirically by a power series:

$$c_\theta = c_0 + a\theta + b\theta^2 + \ldots \quad (7)$$

where c_0 is the value of c_θ for $\theta=0$, e.g. 0° C., and the terms after a certain power of θ may be neglected. It is obvious that if $\theta_1=0$ and $\theta_2=\theta$ in (5), then:

$$\bar{c} = (1/\theta)\int_0^\theta c_\theta \mathrm{d}\theta, \quad \therefore \; c_\theta = (\mathrm{d}/\mathrm{d}\theta)(\bar{c}\theta) \quad (8)$$

Hence the true specific heat is found by multiplying the mean specific heat over the temperature range 0 to θ by θ and differentiating the product with respect to θ.

The specific heat depends on the conditions under which heat is absorbed, and it is usual to distinguish the *specific heat at constant volume* c_v, and the *specific heat at constant pressure* c_p. If M is the molecular (molar) weight of a substance, the corresponding *molecular heats* (specific heats per g.mol. or mol, sometimes called *molar heat capacities*) are:

$$C_v = Mc_v \quad \text{and} \quad C_p = Mc_p \quad (9)$$

In the case of elements, if A is the atomic weight, the *atomic heats* are:

$$C_v = Ac_v \quad \text{and} \quad C_p = Ac_p \quad (9a)$$

In the case of solids and liquids, c_v and c_p are not very different; for gases see § 21.

The *unit of heat* is defined by making the true specific heat of water equal to unity when the temperature is 15° C., i.e. it is the amount of heat absorbed by 1 gram of water (the normal isotopic mixture), when its temperature rises from 14½° C. to 15½° C. This is called [1] the 15° *gram-calorie* (g.cal.). The *kilogram-calorie* (k.cal.) is 1000 times this value. In older literature the kilogram-calorie is written Cal. The *mean calorie* is 1/100 the heat absorbed by 1 g. of water on heating from 0° C. to 100° C., and is slightly larger than the 15° g.cal. The name *mayer* proposed by T. W. Richards [2] for the unit of capacity heated by 1° C. on absorption of 1 joule (§ 13) has not been adopted. The British Thermal Unit (B.Th.U.) is the heat required to raise the temperature of 1 lb. of water, at its temperature of maximum density, 39° F., by 1° F., and the Centigrade Heat Unit (C.H.U.) that required to raise the temperature of 1 lb. of water by 1° C.

Example. If the true molecular heat of hydrogen gas at constant pressure (1 atm.) is given by $C_p=6{\cdot}50+0{\cdot}0009T$, where T is the absolute temperature, t° C.+273, to find the heat absorbed when 50·4 g. of hydrogen are heated at 1 atm. pressure from 0° C. to 500° C.

[1] Warburg, *Phys. Z.*, 1900, **1**, 171; P. T. Reichsanstalt, *Z. Phys.*, 1924, **29**, 392; Auerbach, *Z. angew. Chem.*, 1925, **38**, 447. The German name " Kilocalorie " (kcal.) for the kilogram calorie is best avoided, as it does not fix the size of the calorie, of which it is the multiple by 1000. The Ostwald calorie, K=100 g.cal., is no longer used. Various other " calories " have been used. Regnault's calorie was the heat required to raise the temperature of 1 g. of water from 0° to 1° C.; for the British thermal unit (B.Th.U. or B.T.U.), 1 lb. of water through 1° F. at 60° F., see Powell, *Nature*, 1942, **149**, 525.

[2] *Z. phys. Chem.*, 1901, **36**, 358; Richards and Rowe, *J.A.C.S.*, 1921, **43**, 770.

50·4 g. H_2=25 g.mols. (mols). The heat absorbed is:

$$q=25\int_{273}^{773}(6{\cdot}50+0{\cdot}0009T)\mathrm{d}T$$
$$=25\times6{\cdot}50(773-273)+25\times\tfrac{1}{2}\times0{\cdot}0009(773^2-273^2)$$
$$=87{,}135 \text{ g.cal.}$$

Alternatively, the mean molecular heat C_p from 273° abs. to 773° abs., i.e. over a range of 500°, can be found:

$$\bar{C}_p=(1/500)\int_{273}^{773}(6{\cdot}50+0{\cdot}0009T)\mathrm{d}T=(1/500)\left[6{\cdot}50+\tfrac{1}{2}\times0{\cdot}0009T^2\right]_{273}^{773}$$
$$=(1/500)[6{\cdot}50(773-273)+0{\cdot}00045(773^2-273^2)]$$
$$=6{\cdot}97;\quad \therefore \text{heat absorbed}=500\times25\times6{\cdot}97$$
$$=87{,}135 \text{ g.cal.}$$

§ 2. Latent Heats

In some cases the definition of q by (1), § 1, fails, since q is finite whilst $\theta_2-\theta_1$ is zero. Heat absorbed by a body *at constant temperature* (e.g. in the fusion of ice or the boiling of water) is called *latent heat.* In such cases q is measured by the fall in temperature of another body (e.g. hot water) supplying heat, or by the energy equivalent of heat supplied by an electric current in a heating coil. Latent heat per gram is denoted by l (with an appropriate suffix) and per mol by L, where $L=Ml$.

§ 3. Thermal Coefficients

The *state* of unit mass of a homogeneous body of fixed chemical composition is definite when fixed values of any *two* of the variables [1] *pressure p, specific volume v* ($=1/\rho$, where ρ=density), and *temperature* θ are assigned. It is assumed that the pressure on a plane area is at right angles to the area, and that the pressure at a point is equal in all directions; the body is then a *fluid*, which may be a gas, a liquid, or an isotropic solid subjected to a uniform stress. These variables are connected by a *characteristic equation* or *equation of state* [2]:

$$\mathrm{f}(p, v, \theta)=0 \quad . \quad . \quad . \quad . \quad . \quad . \quad . \quad . \quad . \quad (1)$$

In all cases it is assumed, unless otherwise stated, that the effects of internal stress (other than pressure), surface tension, electrification, magnetisation and gravity, are either absent or negligible. All volume elements are " physically " small, i.e. include a large number of molecules. It should be noted that the characteristic equation, or equation of state, does not give *complete* information about the state, e.g. it does not specify its energy (although it says it has a definite value), so that the first name is preferable.

A small change of state may be defined in terms of *any two* of the differentials dv, dp and dθ, multiplied by *thermal coefficients*, which are usually functions of v, p and θ. The small amount of heat absorbed may be represented by any one of the three equations:

$$\delta q=c_v\mathrm{d}\theta+l_v\mathrm{d}v \quad . \quad . \quad . \quad . \quad . \quad . \quad . \quad . \quad . \quad (2a)$$
$$=c_p\mathrm{d}\theta+l_p\mathrm{d}p \quad . \quad . \quad . \quad . \quad . \quad . \quad . \quad . \quad . \quad (2b)$$
$$=\gamma_v\mathrm{d}v+\gamma_p\mathrm{d}p \quad . \quad . \quad . \quad . \quad . \quad . \quad . \quad . \quad . \quad (2c)$$

[1] Called by Rankine, *Edin. N. Phil. J.*, 1856, **2**, 120, " accidents."

[2] See Onnes and Keesom, " Enzykl. d. math. Wiss.," 1912, **5**, i (5), 636 f.; *Comm. Leiden*, 1912, Suppl., **23**, 22 f.; Neumann, " Vorlesungen über die mechanische Theorie der Wärme," Leipzig, 1875, 43.

The physical meanings of the thermal coefficients are found as usual from the differential coefficients: $(dq/d\theta)_v = c_v$, $(dq/dv)_\theta = l_v$, etc.; i.e. c_v and c_p are *specific heats* at constant volume and pressure, respectively; l_v and l_p are *latent heats* of volume and pressure change, respectively;[1] and γ_v and γ_p are coefficients which must not be confused with the *ratio of specific heats* at constant pressure and at constant volume, written without subscript:

$$\gamma = c_p/c_v \quad . \quad . \quad . \quad . \quad . \quad . \quad . \quad . \quad . \quad . \quad (3)$$

The equations (2) are definite and their legitimacy follows from the physical justification of the concept of "quantity of heat," which is based on experimental calorimetry in the way outlined above.[2] Although they rarely appear in the later books on Thermodynamics, their correctness admits of a formal proof,[3] which is not here regarded as necessary. The question of the interdependence of the variables is taken up in § 5. Clausius's use of $(dq/dv)_\theta$, etc., as definite and determinate quantities, although it has given rise to some misunderstanding, is perfectly correct,[4] and will be followed in the sequel.

§ 4. Reech's Theorem

Let unit mass of a fluid undergo two separate changes:

1. An *adiabatic change*, i.e. one in which no heat enters or leaves the system. Such an adiabatic change may be supposed to be carried out with the fluid (e.g. a gas) contained in a cylinder with a piston moving without friction, both the cylinder and piston being made of a perfect non-conductor of heat. By pressing down or raising the piston the fluid is made to undergo an adiabatic compression or expansion, respectively, since no heat can pass out of or into the system (the gas in the cylinder). This condition must be carefully distinguished from the absence of a generation of heat *in the system itself*, by compression, viscous motion, or chemical action. The temperature of a body usually rises in adiabatic compression, hence the body may be said to have heat generated in it, although $\delta q = 0$, as no heat crosses the bounding surface of the body. If the adiabatic conditions are maintained, the rapidity of the change is of no importance.

The name *adiabatic change* (Greek α, not; διαβαίνειν, to pass through) is due to Rankine;[5] Gibbs[6] called it an *isentropic change*, since in a *reversible* adiabatic change a quantity called the entropy of the system (§ 33) remains constant. The two cases are identical only when the change is reversible, and hence both names will be retained for use in appropriate cases.

In *practical* cases, an adiabatic change usually takes place very quickly, so that little time is allowed for sensible communication of heat with the surroundings by conduction (which is generally a slow process). Thus, if air is contained in a strong glass tube closed by a piston, and the piston is rapidly forced in, so much heat is generated that a piece of tinder attached to the bottom of the piston

[1] These must not be confused with latent heats of phase transition, which are heats absorbed for unit mass of phase change, not for unit volume or pressure change.

[2] See e.g. Mach., "Prinzipien der Wärmelehre," Leipzig, 1896, 153; Wiedeburg, *Ann. Phys.*, 1897, **61**, 705; Kuenen, *Arch. Néerl.*, 1901, **6**, 39; Bridgman, "The Logic of Modern Physics," New York, 1927, 108, 117.

[3] Blondlot, "Introduction à l'Étude de la Thermodynamique," Paris, 1888, 26; Tunell, *J. Phys. Chem.*, 1932, **36**, 1744; *J. Chem. Phys.*, 1941, **9**, 191.

[4] See the careful examination by Tunell, *J. Phys. Chem.*, 1932, **36**, 1744. In a different treatment by Buckingham, "Outline of the Theory of Thermodynamics," New York, 1900, 68, $(dE/dv)_\theta$ is denoted by λ, so that $dE = c_v d\theta + \lambda dv$, where E=energy.

[5] *Phil. Trans.*, 1870, **160**, 277: "Misc. Scient. Papers," 1881, 533.

[6] *Trans. Connecticut Acad.*, 1873, **2**, 309; "Scientific Papers," 1906, **1**, 3.

is inflamed (*fire syringe*). The rapid change of pressure in a sound wave is another example. The general condition for an adiabatic change is obviously:

$$\delta q = 0 \qquad (1)$$

Therefore from 2b and 2a, § 3:

$$0 = c_p d\theta + l_p dp \quad \therefore\ dp = -(c_p/l_p)d\theta \qquad (2a)$$

$$0 = c_v d\theta + l_v dv \quad \therefore\ dv = -(c_v/l_v)d\theta \qquad (2b)$$

Divide (2a) by (2b):

$$(dp/dv)_q = c_p l_v / c_v l_p \qquad (3)$$

where the differential coefficient refers to adiabatic conditions, hence the suffix q does not mean "q constant," but $\delta q = 0$.

2. An *isothermal change*, i.e. one occurring at a constant temperature. In this case the fluid (e.g. a gas) may be supposed to be contained in a cylinder closed by a movable piston, both of good conducting material, immersed in a large water bath, and the fluid compressed or expanded very slowly, so that any temperature changes are reduced to infinitesimal amount by the transmission of heat to or from the water bath through the walls of the cylinder. The general condition for an isothermal change is θ=constant,

$$\therefore\ d\theta = 0 \qquad (4)$$

Therefore from (2b) and (2a), § 3:

$$\delta q_\theta = l_p dp \qquad (5a)$$

and

$$\delta q_\theta = l_v dv \qquad (5b)$$

Divide (5a) by (5b):

$$(dp/dv)_\theta = l_v / l_p \qquad (6)$$

where the differential coefficient refers to an isothermal change, i.e. θ constant or $d\theta = 0$.

Divide (3) by (6):

$$(dp/dv)_q \div (dp/dv)_\theta = c_p/c_v = \gamma \qquad (7)$$

This equation expresses *Reech's theorem*,[1] and may be rewritten as follows.

The *bulk modulus of elasticity* of a fluid, ϵ, is the limiting value of the ratio: small increase in pressure/resulting relative decrease in volume, i.e.:

$$\epsilon = \lim_{\delta v \to 0} \delta p / -\delta v/v = -v(dp/dv) \qquad (8)$$

In all real cases ϵ is positive; it may refer to *adiabatic* conditions (ϵ_q) or *isothermal* conditions (ϵ_θ), and since v, the initial volume, is the same in both cases, (7) may be written:

$$\epsilon_q/\epsilon_\theta = c_p/c_v = \gamma \qquad (9)$$

Instead of the elasticity, its reciprocal the *compressibility*, κ, is often used:

$$\kappa = 1/\epsilon = -(1/v)(dv/dp) \qquad (10)$$

For an ideal gas, Boyle's law gives:

$$pv = \text{const.} = k_1 \text{ when } \theta \text{ is constant} \qquad (11)$$

Therefore $\epsilon_\theta = -v(dp/dv)_\theta = p$. Hence by (9): $\epsilon_q = \gamma p = -v(dp/dv)$, therefore for an adiabatic change:

$$-\gamma(dv/v) = dp/p \qquad (12)$$

[1] Reech, *J. de Math.* (Liouville), 1853, **18**, 357 (414); Moutier, "Thermodynamique," 1885, 61; for another deduction, see Burrows, *J. Phys. Chem.*, 1901, **5**, 233.

If γ *is constant* (which need not be the case even for an ideal gas),[1] (12) may be integrated:

$$-\gamma \ln v = \ln p + \text{const.}$$

$$\therefore\ pv^{\gamma} = \text{const.} = k_2 \quad \textbf{(13)}$$

This equation was given by Poisson.[2] Conversely, by differentiating (13), it is easily shown that $\epsilon_q = \gamma p$.

The *velocity of sound*, *u*, in a fluid is given by Newton's equation:

$$u^2 = \epsilon/\rho = -v^2(\mathrm{d}p/\mathrm{d}v) \quad \textbf{(14)}$$

where ϵ=elasticity=$-v(\mathrm{d}p/\mathrm{d}v)$, ρ=density=$1/v$. Since sound is propagated adiabatically in a gas, $\epsilon = \epsilon_q = \gamma p$,

$$\therefore\ u = \sqrt{(\gamma p/\rho)} = \sqrt{(\gamma p v)} \quad \textbf{(15)}$$

which provides a method of measuring γ. By substituting in (13) from the general gas equation:

$$pv = RT/M \quad \textbf{(16)}$$

where R is a constant for 1 g.mol. (mol), M, of gas, it is found that:

$$Tv^{\gamma-1} = \text{const.} \quad \textbf{(17)}$$

§ 5. Relations between Thermal Coefficients

In equations (2a)–(2c), § 3, δq is the same element of heat, hence the six thermal coefficients are not all independent. The rules of the calculus give:

$$\mathrm{d}\theta = (\mathrm{d}\theta/\mathrm{d}p)_v \mathrm{d}p + (\mathrm{d}\theta/\mathrm{d}v)_p \mathrm{d}v \quad \textbf{(1a)}$$

$$\mathrm{d}v = (\mathrm{d}v/\mathrm{d}\theta)_p \mathrm{d}\theta + (\mathrm{d}v/\mathrm{d}p)_\theta \mathrm{d}p \quad \textbf{(1b)}$$

$$\mathrm{d}p = (\mathrm{d}p/\mathrm{d}\theta)_v \mathrm{d}\theta + (\mathrm{d}p/\mathrm{d}v)_\theta \mathrm{d}v \quad \textbf{(1c)}$$

Put $\mathrm{d}\theta=0$ in (1a), $\mathrm{d}v=0$ in (1b), and $\mathrm{d}p=0$ in (1c), then:

$$(\mathrm{d}p/\mathrm{d}v)_\theta = -(\mathrm{d}\theta/\mathrm{d}v)_p/(\mathrm{d}\theta/\mathrm{d}p)_v \quad \textbf{(2a)}$$

$$(\mathrm{d}\theta/\mathrm{d}p)_v = -(\mathrm{d}v/\mathrm{d}p)_\theta/(\mathrm{d}v/\mathrm{d}\theta)_p \quad \textbf{(2b)}$$

$$(\mathrm{d}\theta/\mathrm{d}v)_p = -(\mathrm{d}p/\mathrm{d}v)_\theta/(\mathrm{d}p/\mathrm{d}\theta)_v \quad \textbf{(2c)}$$

Equation (2b), § 3, may be rewritten by substituting for dp from (1c):

$$\delta q = c_p \mathrm{d}\theta + l_p[(\mathrm{d}p/\mathrm{d}\theta)_v \mathrm{d}\theta + (\mathrm{d}p/\mathrm{d}v)_\theta \mathrm{d}v]$$

$$= [c_p + l_p(\mathrm{d}p/\mathrm{d}\theta)_v]\mathrm{d}\theta + l_p(\mathrm{d}p/\mathrm{d}v)_\theta \mathrm{d}v \quad \text{(3)}$$

By comparing coefficients in (3) and (2a), § 3, it follows that:

$$c_p = c_v - l_p(\mathrm{d}p/\mathrm{d}\theta)_v;\ l_v = l_p(\mathrm{d}p/\mathrm{d}v)_\theta \quad \therefore\ l_p = l_v(\mathrm{d}v/\mathrm{d}p)_\theta \quad \text{(4)}$$

Since l_p is usually negative (heat is *evolved* on compression) and $(\mathrm{d}p/\mathrm{d}v)_\theta$ is always negative for real changes, it follows that $c_p > c_v$ and $l_v > 0$.

In this way the following twelve equations, which are not all independent, can be found. They can all be obtained from the four in the column headed v, θ by making use of relations between the partial differential coefficients.[3] The independent variables are given at the head of each column.

[1] Cf. Moreau, *Compt. Rend.*, 1901, **133**, 732, for the case $pv = p_0 v_0(1 + \alpha t + \beta t^2)$.

[2] Poisson, "Traité de Mécanique," 2 edit., 1833, **2**, 637, 646; "A Treatise on Mechanics,' transl. Harte, 1842, **2**, 511, 593. This material is not in the first edition of 1811; for an alignment chart for adiabatic expansions, Cosens, *Proc. Cambr. Phil. Soc.*, 1922, **21**, 228.

[3] For other sets of equations see Baynes, "Thermodynamics," Oxford, 1878, 97; Burrows, *J. Phys. Chem.*, 1901, **5**, 233; Bridgman, "Condensed Collection of Thermodynamic Formulas," Cambridge (Mass.), 1925.

v, θ	p, θ	v, p
$c_v = c_p + l_p\,(\mathrm{d}p/\mathrm{d}\theta)_v$	$c_p = c_v + l_v\,(\mathrm{d}v/\mathrm{d}\theta)_p$	$\gamma_v = l_v + c_v\,(\mathrm{d}\theta/\mathrm{d}v)_p$
$l_v = l_p\,(\mathrm{d}p/\mathrm{d}v)_\theta$	$l_p = l_v\,(\mathrm{d}v/\mathrm{d}p)_\theta$	$\gamma_p = c_v\,(\mathrm{d}\theta/\mathrm{d}p)_v$
$c_v = \gamma_p\,(\mathrm{d}p/\mathrm{d}\theta)_v$	$c_p = \gamma_v(\mathrm{d}v/\mathrm{d}\theta)_p$	$\gamma_v = c_p(\mathrm{d}\theta/\mathrm{d}v)_p$
$l_v = \gamma_v + \gamma_p\,(\mathrm{d}p/\mathrm{d}v)_\theta$	$l_p = \gamma_p + \gamma_v\,(\mathrm{d}v/\mathrm{d}p)_\theta$	$\gamma_p = l_p + c_p\,(\mathrm{d}\theta/\mathrm{d}p)_v$

§ 6. Work of Expansion

Let a given volume of a fluid (e.g. a gas) be enclosed in a cylinder in which there is a weightless piston of area A moving without friction (Fig. 3.II), and let the force acting on the upper surface of the piston, e.g. by a weight P resting on it, be $P = pA$, where p is the *pressure*=force per unit area. If the fluid expands so that the piston moves upwards through a small distance dz, and the system remains always practically in the equilibrium state, the small amount of work done [1] is:

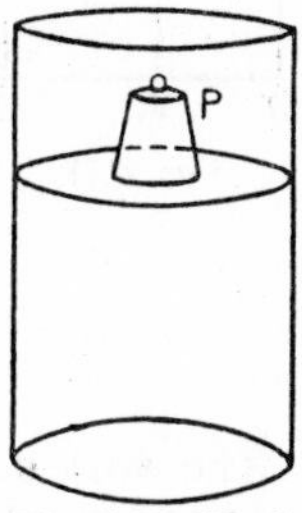

FIG. 3.II. Work of Expansion

$$\delta w = \text{force} \times \text{distance} = P\mathrm{d}z = pA\mathrm{d}z = p\mathrm{d}v \quad . \quad . \quad (1)$$

where $\mathrm{d}v = A\mathrm{d}z$ is the small volume increase. In all cases the work done by a system is taken as positive. For a finite expansion from an initial volume v_1 to a final volume v_2, the pressure p will usually change continuously, and the work done is given by the definite integral:

$$w = \int_{v_1}^{v_2} p\mathrm{d}v \quad . \quad . \quad . \quad . \quad . \quad . \quad . \quad . \quad . \quad . \quad (2)$$

The internal and external forces on the piston are assumed equal in the limit, since p is identified with the pressure of the gas; the expansion must, therefore, occur *reversibly* (see § 8).

Equations (1) and (2) apply to expansion with a bounding surface of *any* shape, since the space between the initial and final bounding surfaces of the fluid may be divided into a very large number of small cylinders, to each of which (1) applies, hence $\delta w = \Sigma p \delta v = p \Sigma \delta v$, as before.

Since $p > 0$, (2) shows that w is positive (work is done) when v_2 is greater than v_1 (expansion), but negative (work is spent) when v_2 is less than v_1 (compression). In *all cases* the work done by a fluid for which:

$$p = \mathrm{f}(v, \theta) \quad . \quad . \quad . \quad . \quad . \quad . \quad . \quad . \quad . \quad . \quad (3)$$

is given by (2), where v_1 is the initial and v_2 the final volume. The temperature may vary during the change of volume. If p is constant during changes of volume, e.g. for a saturated vapour in presence of liquid:

$$\int_{v_1}^{v_2} p\mathrm{d}v = p\int_{v_1}^{v_2} dv = p(v_2 - v_1) = p\Delta v \quad . \quad . \quad . \quad . \quad . \quad (4)$$

where Δv is the increase in volume=vol. of vapour−vol. of liquid.

[1] The effect of *rapid motion* of the piston on the work done, considered by Clausius, *Ann Phys.*, 1857, **100**, 353; Boltzmann, *ibid.*, 1870, **140**, 254; and Meissner and Meissner, *ibid.*, 1939, **36**, 303, does not come into physico-chemical applications.

The work of expansion can be represented on a *p, v-diagram*, or *indicator diagram*,[1] as an area. In Fig. 4.II the curve AB is traced out by a point moving as defined by (3). The small strip is $p\delta v$ and the integral in (2) is the area between the curve AB, the ordinates at v_1 and v_2, and the v axis. If the area is traced out from left to right, this corresponds with expansion and is positive; if it is traced out from right to left, this corresponds with compression and is negative. It should be noted that this is not a convention, but follows from the choice of the positive sign for work *done* by a system.

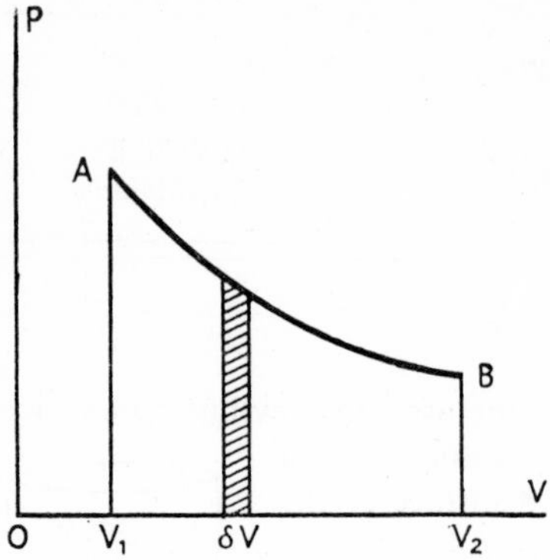

FIG. 4.II. Indicator Diagram

The work done in the *isothermal* expansion of an ideal gas is found by putting pv=const.$=k_1$ (Boyle's law):

$$w_\theta=\int_{v_1}^{v_2} p\mathrm{d}v=k_1\int_{v_1}^{v_2}\mathrm{d}v/v=k_1 \ln (v_2/v_1) \quad . \quad . \quad . \quad . \quad . \quad (5)$$

The work done in the *adiabatic* expansion of an ideal gas is found by putting pv^γ=const.$=k_2$:

$$w_q=\int_{v_1}^{v_2} p\mathrm{d}v=k_2\int_{v_1}^{v_2}\frac{\mathrm{d}v}{v^\gamma}=\frac{k_2}{1-\gamma}(v_2{}^{1-\gamma}-v_1{}^{1-\gamma}) \quad . \quad . \quad . \quad . \quad (6)$$

But $k_2v^{-\gamma}=p$, therefore $k_2v^{1-\gamma}=pv$, and $\gamma>1$,

$$\therefore\ w_q=(p_1v_1-p_2v_2)/(\gamma-1) \quad . \quad . \quad . \quad . \quad . \quad . \quad . \quad . \quad (7)$$

For 1 g.mol. (mol) of an ideal gas:

$$pv=\boldsymbol{R}T \quad . \quad . \quad . \quad . \quad . \quad . \quad . \quad . \quad . \quad . \quad . \quad (8)$$

where $\boldsymbol{R}$ is the general gas constant and T is the " absolute " gas temperature:

$$T=t^\circ\ \mathrm{C.}+1/\alpha=t^\circ\ \mathrm{C.}+273{\cdot}1 \quad . \quad . \quad . \quad . \quad . \quad . \quad (9)$$

where α is the coefficient of expansion of the gas:

$$\alpha=(v_t-v_0)/tv_0 \quad . \quad . \quad . \quad . \quad . \quad . \quad . \quad . \quad . \quad (10)$$

Hence in (5) $k_1=\boldsymbol{R}T$, and in (7) $pv=\boldsymbol{R}T$, therefore the isothermal and adiabatic works of expansion per mol are: [2]

$$w_\theta=\boldsymbol{R}T\ln (v_2/v_1) \quad . \quad . \quad . \quad . \quad . \quad . \quad . \quad . \quad . \quad (11)$$

$$w_q=\boldsymbol{R}(T_1-T_2)/(\gamma-1) \quad . \quad . \quad . \quad . \quad . \quad . \quad . \quad . \quad (12)$$

(Note that $T_1>T_2$ and $\gamma>1$, hence $w_q>0$.)

The work of expansion of a gas may be measured in any units of work, e.g. g.cm., ergs, etc., since the dimensions of pv in C.G.S. units are:

$$[(\mathrm{dyne})/(\mathrm{cm.}^2)]\times(\mathrm{cm.}^3)=(\mathrm{dyne})\times(\mathrm{cm.})=(\mathrm{erg}).$$

[1] The *indicator diagram* was used by James Watt in determining the performance of steam engines, for which purpose it is still employed. Its use in Thermodynamics is due to Clapeyron, *J. de l'École Polytechn.*, 1834, **14**, 153 (see § 41).

[2] These equations were given by Clapeyron with *C*, the " thermodynamic function," replacing *T*. The present form is due to Clausius, *Ann. Phys.*, 1850, **79**, 368. They also represent the isothermal heat absorption q_θ *for an ideal gas.*

A convenient unit called the *litre atmosphere* is obtained by measuring p in standard atmospheres ($76\times 13{\cdot}59545\times 980{\cdot}616=1{\cdot}013225\times 10^6$ dynes per cm.^{2} at sea-level and latitude 45°) and v in litres:

$$p=1 \text{ atm.}=1{\cdot}013225\times 10^6 \text{ dynes/cm.}^2$$
$$=1033{\cdot}2525 \text{ gm. wt./cm.}^2 \text{ at sea level and lat. } 45°$$
$$v=1 \text{ litre}=1000{\cdot}027 \text{ cm.}^3$$
$$\therefore\ 1 \text{ lit. atm.}=pv=1013225\times 1000{\cdot}027=1013{\cdot}25\times 10^6 \text{ ergs}$$
$$=1033{\cdot}2802\times 10^3 \text{ g.cm.}$$

It may be noted that, although p and v are independent variables for the definition of the *state* of a fluid, their absolute variations, from p_1, v_1 to p_2, v_2, do not define the *path* [1] joining the initial and final states; this may be regarded as defined by a parameter which is a function of p and v.[2]

§ 7. Cyclic Processes

The name *system* as used in Thermodynamics denotes, generally, any finite body or collection of bodies or any region possessing energy (even a perfect vacuum containing radiation), every part of which has a definite temperature and pressure,[3] and is the object of investigation. All things outside the system are spoken of as *external bodies.* An *isolated system* is one which cannot exchange matter or energy with external bodies; it may be regarded as enclosed in a perfectly rigid envelope impervious to heat, so that no work or heat can be exchanged with the surroundings. In all that follows, the system is supposed to be at rest, chemically stable, and appreciably free from the influence of directed forces, gravity, surface tension, electrification, and magnetisation.

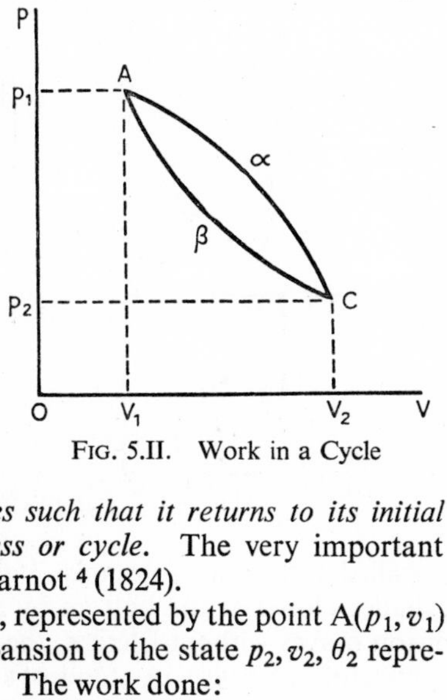

FIG. 5.II. Work in a Cycle

If a system undergoes any series of changes such that it returns to its initial state, these changes constitute a cyclic process or cycle. The very important conception of a cyclic process is due to Sadi Carnot [4] (1824).

Let a fixed mass of a gas in a state p_1, v_1, θ_1, represented by the point A(p_1, v_1) on the *p, v-diagram* in Fig. 5.II, change by expansion to the state p_2, v_2, θ_2 represented by the point C(p_2, v_2) along the path α. The work done:

$$\int_{a\ v_1}^{v_2} p dv = \text{area } A\alpha C v_2 v_1 > 0 \quad . \quad . \quad . \quad . \quad . \quad . \quad . \quad (1)$$

1 This name seems to have been introduced by Gibbs in 1873; " Collected Works," 1928, **1**, 3, from *Trans. Connecticut Acad.*, 1873, **2**, 309.

2 Tunell, *J. Phys. Chem.*, 1932, **36**, 1744.

3 Neumann, " Vorlesungen über die mechanische Theorie der Wärme," Leipzig, 1875, 43; Luder, *J. Chem. Educ.*, 1946, **23**, 54.

4 " Réflexions sur la Puissance Motrice du Feu et sur les Moyens propres à développer cette Puissance," Paris, 1824, 17, 33, 38 (first edit., exceedingly scarce; see § 22); facsimile reprint, 1903 (1912, 1924); another edit., Paris, 1878; Engl. transl. by Thurston, " Reflections on the Motive Power of Heat," 1890; Ostwald's *Klassiker*, 1892, **37**; criticism by Raveau, *Compt. Rend.*, 1929, **188**, 313.

is positive (area traced from left to right). Now let the gas be compressed from C along the path β so that it recovers its initial state A. The work done:

$$\int_{\beta\,v_2}^{v_1} p dv = \text{area } C\beta A v_1 v_2 < 0 \quad . \quad . \quad . \quad . \quad . \quad . \quad (2)$$

is negative (area traced from right to left). The expansion along α and the compression along β together constitute a cycle, and the net work, the algebraic sum of the amounts of work (1) and (2), is represented by:

$$\text{area } A\alpha C v_2 v_1 - \text{area } C\beta A v_1 v_2 = \text{area } A\alpha C\beta = \text{area of the loop.}$$

This is positive when the loop is traced out clockwise, since then area $A\alpha C v_2 v_1 >$ area $C\beta A v_1 v_2$, but if the loop is traced out counter-clockwise, the larger area is negative, corresponding with a compression, and the net work is negative. This is not a convention but follows from the positive sign of work done. If more than one loop is traced out, the net work is the algebraic sum of the areas. *The net work done in a cycle is represented by the area of the cycle on the p, v-diagram.*

§ 8. Carnot's Cycle

An important cyclic process, devised by Carnot (1824),[1] consists of four *reversible* operations, two of which are adiabatic and two isothermal. The

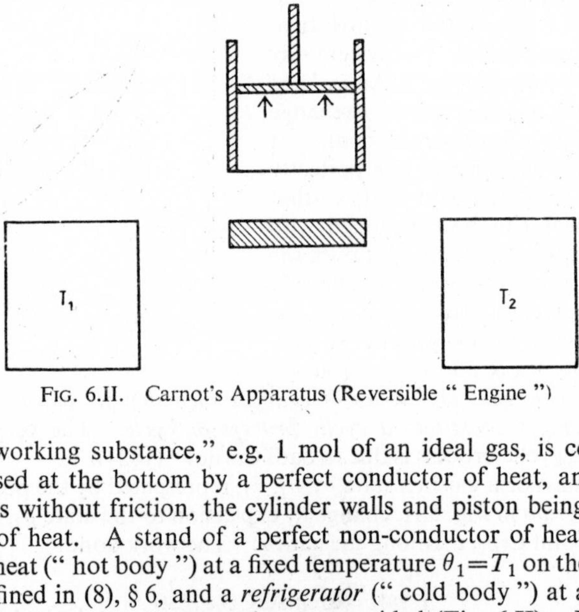

FIG. 6.II. Carnot's Apparatus (Reversible " Engine ")

so-called " working substance," e.g. 1 mol of an ideal gas, is contained in a cylinder closed at the bottom by a perfect conductor of heat, and in which a piston moves without friction, the cylinder walls and piston being perfect non-conductors of heat. A stand of a perfect non-conductor of heat is provided. A *source* of heat (" hot body ") at a fixed temperature $\theta_1 = T_1$ on the " absolute " gas scale defined in (8), § 6, and a *refrigerator* (" cold body ") at a temperature $\theta_2 = T_2$ on the " absolute " gas scale, are provided (Fig. 6.II). In order that T_1 and T_2 ($T_1 > T_2$) may remain constant when *finite* amounts of heat are taken from or added to the heat reservoirs, the source may contain steam and water at 100° C., and the refrigerator ice and water at 0° C.

The expansions and compressions of the gas in the cylinder become *reversible* when:

(i) the pressure p of the gas differs only infinitesimally from that above the piston, when a change $\pm\delta p$ will send the piston up or down through an in-

[1] " Réflexions sur la Puissance Motrice du Feu," 1824, 32; for a model of Carnot's cycle, see Shedd, *Phys. Rev.*, 1899, **8**, 174.

finitesimal distance; (ii) the temperature T of the gas differs only infinitesimally from that of the heat reservoir with which it is in thermal contact, when a change $\pm\delta T$ will change an absorption into an emission of heat and vice versa (Fig. 7.II).

It is obvious that as the given change approaches nearer and nearer to a reversible change it becomes slower and slower, since the changes of volume become smaller and smaller and more and more numerous, and *in the limit,* when $\delta p \to 0$ and $\delta T \to 0$, no change at all occurs, the system being then in equilibrium. In a *reversible change,* it is supposed that *the system can move continuously through a succession of such equilibrium states,* but of course this cannot actually occur, since an impulse which moves a system out of an equilibrium state is necessarily finite, although it may be very small. A reversible change is, therefore, *an ideal change,* which cannot actually occur, although an actual change may approach closer and closer to an ideal reversible change as the

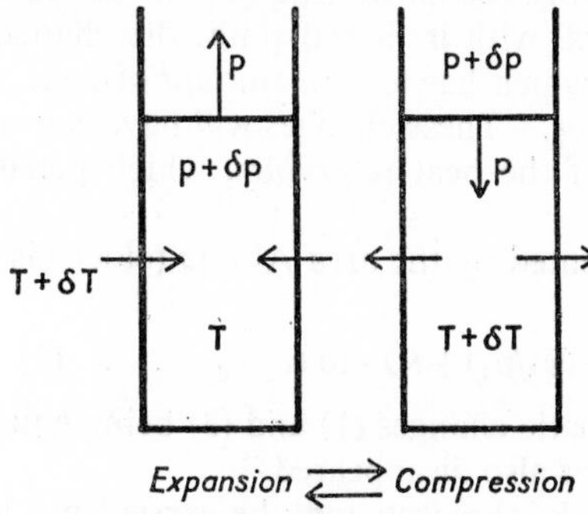

FIG. 7.II. Reversible Expansion and Compression

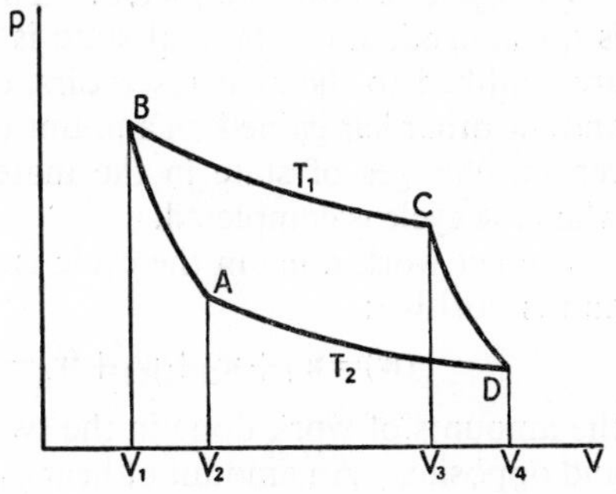

FIG. 8.II. Carnot's Cycle

pressure and temperature differences approach zero. *A reversible change may be defined as a continuous sequence of equilibrium states.*

The following *four reversible operations* are now performed in the order [1] stated:

(1) The cylinder containing gas in the state p_2, v_2, T_2 is placed on the stand and the gas compressed adiabatically till the temperature rises to T_1, and the state becomes p_1, v_1, T_1. This compression is represented on the indicator diagram (§ 7) by the curve AB (Fig. 8.II) connecting the point A(p_2, v_2, T_2) with the point B(p_1, v_1, T_1); the work done is negative and is given by (12), § 6:

$$w_1=[R/(\gamma-1)](T_2-T_1) \quad . \quad . \quad . \quad . \quad . \quad . \quad . \quad . \quad (1)$$

(2) The cylinder is placed on the hot body and the gas expanded isothermally to any *arbitrary* volume v_3, the state being then p_3, v_3, T_1, represented by C. The work done is positive and is given by (11), § 6:

$$w_2=RT_1 \ln (v_3/v_1) \quad . \quad . \quad . \quad . \quad . \quad . \quad . \quad . \quad (2)$$

[1] Carnot, Clapeyron, and Clausius all began with operation (2), in spite of some assertions to the contrary, e.g. in Preston, " Theory of Heat," 1894, 607, for Carnot. The present order is that of Maxwell, " Theory of Heat," 1875, 140, and removes the uncertainty in the fourth operation when the cycle is begun with the second. The cycle is performed without ambiguity if carried out as described for the direct and reverse cycles, being then completely defined by the isothermals BC and AD (Fig. 8.II), i.e. the only arbitrary element is the quantity of heat q_1 absorbed or rejected to the source. The diagram of the cycle is not given by Carnot, and is due to Clapeyron (1834; see § 6), who remarks that Carnot's treatment avoided mathematical analysis, and arrived at a result by " a series of delicate arguments difficult to comprehend," which result can be found without trouble from a general law; cf. Moss, *Phys. Rev.*, 1903, **16**, 28.

During this operation a quantity of heat q_1 is absorbed by the gas from the source.

(3) The cylinder is placed on the stand and the gas expanded adiabatically till the temperature falls to T_2. The state is p_4, v_4, T_2, represented by D. The work done is positive and is:

$$w_3=[R/(\gamma-1)](T_1-T_2) \quad . \quad . \quad . \quad . \quad . \quad . \quad . \quad (3)$$

(4) The cylinder is placed on the cold body and the gas compressed isothermally until the initial state p_2, v_2, T_2 is reached at A. The work done is negative and is:

$$w_4=RT_2 \ln (v_2/v_4) \quad . \quad . \quad . \quad . \quad . \quad . \quad . \quad . \quad (4)$$

During this operation a quantity of heat q_2 is rejected by the gas to the refrigerator.

The cycle is now completed. The working substance (the gas in this case) is unchanged, since its final state is identical with its initial state; the changes are confined to the heat reservoirs, one of which has lost an amount of heat q_1 and the other has gained an amount of heat q_2. These changes will have caused certain changes of state in the materials of the heat reservoirs, which persist when the cycle is completed.

The net work done in the cycle is represented by the area ABCD (clockwise) and is positive:

$$(w)=w_1+w_2+w_3+w_4=RT_1 \ln (v_3/v_1)+RT_2 \ln (v_2/v_4) \quad . \quad . \quad (5)$$

the amounts of work done in the two adiabatic changes (1) and (3) being equal and opposite. An amount of heat q_1-q_2 has also disappeared.

Since all the volume changes are reversible, the cycle may be carried out in the reverse sense, beginning at D, compressing adiabatically along DC till the temperature rises to T_1, then isothermally along CB with rejection of heat q_1 to the source, then expanding adiabatically along BA till the temperature falls to T_2, and finally expanding isothermally along AD till the original state is reached at D, the heat q_2 being absorbed from the refrigerator. The work done, represented by the area ADCB (counter-clockwise), is negative and is:

$$(w')=RT_1 \ln (v_1/v_3)+RT_2 \ln (v_4/v_2)=-(w) \quad . \quad . \quad . \quad . \quad (6)$$

An amount of heat q_1-q_2 has been produced.

From (17), § 4, for the two adiabatics DC and AB:

$$T_2v_4^{\gamma-1}=T_1v_3^{\gamma-1} \text{ and } T_2v_2^{\gamma-1}=T_1v_1^{\gamma-1} \quad . \quad . \quad . \quad . \quad . \quad (7)$$

hence by division:

$$\frac{T_1v_3^{\gamma-1}}{T_1v_1^{\gamma-1}}=\frac{T_2v_4^{\gamma-1}}{T_2v_2^{\gamma-1}} \quad \therefore \ v_3/v_1=v_4/v_2 \quad . \quad . \quad . \quad . \quad . \quad (8)$$

$$\therefore \ (w)=R(T_1-T_2) \ln (v_3/v_1)=-(w') \quad . \quad . \quad . \quad . \quad (9)$$

In the case of an ideal gas, here considered, the work done during isothermal expansion is equal to the heat absorbed (*Joule's Law*, § 54), therefore $q_1=w_2$' and $q_2=-w_4$ (the minus sign being taken because q_2 is heat given out by the working substance). Hence:

$$q_1=RT_1 \ln (v_3/v_1), \text{ and } q_2=RT_2 \ln (v_4/v_2)=RT_2 \ln (v_3/v_1)$$

$$\therefore \ R \ln (v_3/v_1)=q_1/T_1=q_2/T_2.$$

Therefore from (9):

$$w=q_1(T_1-T_2)/T_1=q_2(T_1-T_2)/T_2 \quad . \quad . \quad . \quad . \quad . \quad (10)$$

$$\text{or} \quad q_1/T_1=q_2/T_2 \quad . \quad . \quad . \quad . \quad . \quad . \quad . \quad . \quad (11)$$

It will be shown later (§ 32) that equations (10) and (11) are true generally for *any* Carnot's cycle, and are independent of the use of an ideal gas for the working substance.[1] Equation (10) shows that if $T_2=0$, $w=q_1$, i.e. all the heat absorbed from the hot body could be converted into work.

§ 9. The Reversible Conversion of Heat into Work

The conditions for the reversible conversion of heat into work follow from the previous discussion:

(1) The working substance must be left in the same state as at the beginning of the process, i.e. the operation must be cyclic.

(2) If transfer of heat occurs between bodies, their temperatures must differ only infinitesimally, i.e. the transfer must be isothermal in the limit.

(3) If a body is brought successively in contact with other bodies at different temperatures, the temperature of the body must first be brought to equality with these by reversible adiabatic processes before contact.

(4) All moving parts (e.g. pistons) must operate without friction (which would produce heat irreversibly from work), and in all compressions and expansions the internal and external pressures must differ only infinitesimally.

It is seen that all the conditions for reversible operation are satisfied in the reversible Carnot's cycle, and the description of this in § 8 formally demonstrates its reversibility.

The First Law of Thermodynamics

§ 10. The Nature of Heat

It was formerly supposed that heat was an imponderable fluid called *caloric*, existing between the ultimate particles of bodies, which passed from one body to another without loss. Thus, Dalton [2] says: " The most probable opinion concerning the nature of caloric, is, that of its being an elastic fluid of great subtilty, the particles of which repel one another, but are attracted by all other bodies." Many suggestions were made, however, from Lord Bacon's time,[3] that heat is really a " form of motion," i.e. the same in essence as the kinetic energy of the

[1] On Carnot's cycle for *any* fluid, see Morán, *An. Fis. Quim.*, 1941, **37**, 549.

[2] " A New System of Chemical Philosophy," Manchester, 1808, **1**, i, 1. For the earlier theories of heat see: Boerhaave, " Elementa Chemiae," Leyden, 1732, **1**, 126 f.; Black, " Lectures on the Elements of Chemistry," edit. by Robison, Edinburgh, 1803, **1**, 30 f., 117, 157; Scheele, " Chemical Observations and Experiments on Air and Fire," English transl. by Forster, 1780, 66, 109, 111; McKie and Heathcote, " The Discovery of Specific and Latent Heats," 1935; Partington and McKie, *Annals of Science*, 1938, **3**, 1, 337; 1939, **4**, 113; a long summary is given by Muncke, in Gehler's " Physikaliches Wörterbuch," 1841, **10**, 52 f.; the name *caloric* for the " imponderable matter of heat " is due to Lavoisier, " Elements of Chemistry," English transl., 1796, 53. Black favoured a modification of the caloric theory due to Cleghorn, which supposed the particles of caloric to be self-repellent but attracted with varying force by different kinds of matter.

[3] " Novum Organum," 1620; " Works," 1901, **4**, 154; more precisely, J. Hermann, " Phoronomia sive de Viribus et Motibus Corporum solidorum et fluidorum, libri duo," Amsterdam, 1716, 376 (Oehler, *Ann. Phys.*, 1880, **9**, 512), who says the heat of a body is proportional to its density multiplied by the square of the velocity of its particles: " calor, cæteris paribus, est in compositâ ratione ex densitate corporis calidi, & duplicatâ ratione agitationis particularum ejusdem." Lord Rayleigh, *Proc. Roy. Inst.*, 1894, **14**, 216, remarked that a large proportion of outstanding English scientists, including Newton, Cavendish, Rumford, Davy, and Young, always favoured the idea that heat is motion [Black and Dalton were notable exceptions], while the French school supported the caloric theory.

small particles of bodies. Experiments by Rumford [1] in 1798 and by Davy [2] in 1799 showed that unlimited amounts of heat can be generated by friction, and Hirn [3] in 1862 proved experimentally that in the operation of a steam engine heat disappears when work is done.

Newton [4] (1687) seems to have had an idea of the conservation of energy when mechanical work or kinetic energy is converted into heat by friction, since he says: " If the action of an agent be measured by the product of its force into its velocity [i.e. the work done per sec., or the *power*], and if similarly the reaction of the resistance be measured by the velocities of its several parts multiplied by their several forces, whether these arise from friction, cohesion, weight, or acceleration, action and reaction in all combinations of machines will be equal and opposite."

The statement of Leibniz [5] is more definite and striking: when two soft or inelastic bodies collide, part or all of their " force " [=kinetic energy; see § 11] " is received by the particles, they being agitated inwardly by the force of the collision. Thus the loss ensues only in appearance. The forces are not destroyed, but dissipated among the minute parts [mais dissipées parmi les parties menues]. This is not losing them, but is doing what those do who turn money into small change."

Lomonossov,[6] in a memoir written in 1744 and published in 1750, taught that heat is always a form of molecular motion: " calor consistit in motu gyratorio particularum corporis calidi." Cavendish [7] believed that heat consists in the " internal motion of the particles of bodies"; and although he calls this " Sir Isaac Newton's hypothesis," it is really Francis Bacon's.

Rumford's experiments were made as a result of his observation of the great amount of heat evolved in the boring of gunmetal cannon, when only a small quantity of chips or powder was removed from the metal, so that a mere change in the capacity for heat of such a small amount of metal could not account for the liberation of heat sufficient to boil a large mass of water. He made some special experiments on boring a hollow cylinder of gunmetal with a blunt steel borer, and arrived at the following conclusion:

" We have seen that a very considerable quantity of heat may be excited by the friction of two metallic surfaces, and given off in a constant stream or flux in all directions, without interruption or intermission, and without any signs of diminution or exhaustion. . . . In reasoning on this subject we must not forget that most remarkable circumstance, that the source of the heat generated by friction in these experiments appeared evidently to be inexhaustible. It is hardly necessary to add that anything which any insulated body or system of

1 *Phil. Trans.*, 1798, **88**, 80; " Works," Boston, 1870, **1**, 469.

2 " An Essay on Heat and Light," in *Contributions to Physical and Medical Knowledge*, edit. by T. Beddoes, Bristol, 1799; " Works," 1840, **2**, 11; " Elements of Chemical Philosophy," 1812, **1**, 94; " Works," 1840, **4**, 67; cf. Andrade, *Nature*, 1935, **135**, 359.

3 " Théorie mécanique de la Chaleur," 1865, **1**, 84. Preston, " Theory of Heat," 3rd edit., 1919, 46: the values 413 and 420·4 g.m. were found for the mechanical equivalent of heat.

4 Scholium to Third Law of Motion; " Principia," Geneva, 1739, **1**, 60; Tait, *Proc. Roy. Soc. Edin.*, 1863, **5**, 121; *Phil. Mag.*, 1864, **28**, 288; 1865, **29**, 55; " Recent Advances in Physical Science," 1876, 34; Thomson and Tait, " Treatise on Natural Philosophy," Cambridge, 1886, **1**, 247; Akin, *Phil. Mag.*, 1864, **28**, 470 (also other older hints of conservation of energy).

5 Letter to Clarke, q. by Stallo, " Concepts of Modern Physics," 2nd edit. 1882, 81; the idea, and name, of " dissipation of energy " are clearly expressed by Liebniz.

6 *Novi Comment. Acad. Imp. Petropol.* (1747–8), 1750, **1**, 206, 237; Ostwald's *Klassiker*, 1910, **178**, 19, 27, 53; A. Smith, *J.A.C.S.*, 1912, **34**, 111.

7 *Phil. Trans.*, 1783, **73**, 303; abdgd. edit., 1809, **15**, 424; Maxwell, " Theory of Heat," 1897, 73.

bodies can continue to furnish without limitation cannot possibly be a material substance; and it appears to me to be extremely difficult, if not quite impossible, to form any distinct idea of anything capable of being excited and communicated in the manner the heat was excited and communicated in these experiments except it be motion."

Some data given by Rumford lead [1] to the value of 940 ft.lb. to heat 1 lb. of water by 1° F.; the correct value is about 780 ft.lb.

Davy showed that two rods of ice are liquefied when rubbed together by clock-work under an exhausted receiver surrounded by ice, and concluded that:

"A motion or vibration of the corpuscles of bodies must be necessarily generated by friction and percussion. Therefore we may reasonably conclude that this motion or vibration is heat. . . . Heat . . . may be defined as a peculiar motion, probably a vibration of the corpuscles of bodies tending to separate them." In 1812 [2] he said: "The immediate cause of the phenomena of heat is motion, and the laws of its communication are precisely the same as the laws of communication of motion"; also that "it seems possible to account for all the phænomena of heat, if it be supposed that in solids the particles are in a constant state of vibratory motion, the particles of the hottest bodies moving with the greatest velocity and through the greatest space; that in fluids and elastic fluids [gases], besides the vibratory motion, which must be conceived greatest in the last, the particles have a motion round their own axes, with different velocities, the particles of elastic fluids moving with the greatest quickness; and that in etherial substances the particles move round their own axes, and separate from each other, penetrating in right-lines through space. Temperature may be conceived to depend upon the velocities of the vibrations; increase of capacity on the motion being performed in greater space; and the diminution of temperature during the conversion of solids into fluids or gasses, may be explained on the idea of the loss of vibratory motion, in consequence of the revolution of the particles round their axes, at the moment when the body becomes fluid or æriform, or from the loss of rapidity of vibration in consequence of the motion of the particles through greater space."

Roget [3] in 1829 gave what is essentially a partial statement of the law of conservation of energy. "All the powers and sources of motion, with the operation of which we are acquainted, when producing their peculiar effects, are expended in the same proportion as those effects are produced; and hence arises the impossibility of obtaining by their agency a perpetual effect; or, in other words, a perpetual motion." This passage was reproduced in 1840 by Faraday,[4] who himself never seemed to have distinguished clearly between

[1] Tait, "Recent Advances in Physical Science," 1876, 44; Preston, "Theory of Heat," 1894, 41, 3rd edit., 1919, 42, says Rumford estimated the thermal capacity of the water and apparatus as 26·58 lb. of water. One horse was sufficient to turn the machinery and raise the temperature from 33° F. to 212° F. in 2½ hours, from which Preston finds 847 ft.lb. as the mechanical equivalent, about 10 per cent. greater than Joule's value. Rumford actually used two horses, but says one would have been sufficient. Tait, "Sketch of Thermodynamics," Edinburgh, 1877, 11, calculated 940 ft.lb. from the same experiment.

[2] "Elements of Chemical Philosophy," 1812, 95; cf. *ibid.*, 213 f.; "Works," 1840, **4**, 67, 157 f. Rankine's "theory of vortices" (§ 3.IV), is a development of this hypothesis.

[3] "Galvanism," 1829, § 113, p. 32; see also Mrs. Somerville, "On the Connexion of the Physical Sciences," 1834, 250; 3rd edit., 1836, 237, 411.

[4] Note in "Experimental Researches," 29 March, 1840; 1842, **2**, 103; Everyman edit., 314. The statement by Roget is in general terms, and its importance has been exaggerated as a result of its quotation by Faraday.

" force " and " energy," or to have appreciated the work of Joule. It will be noted that Roget says nothing about heat.

Sadi Carnot, who died in 1832, left some notes which show that he was convinced that the caloric theory (used in his memoir of 1824) is incorrect. He says: [1] " Heat is simply motive power, or rather motion which has changed form. Whenever there is destruction of motive power, there is at the same time production of heat in quantity proportional to the quantity of motive power destroyed. Reciprocally, whenever there is destruction of heat, there is production of motive power . . . motive power is in quantity invariable in nature—that is, correctly speaking, never either produced or destroyed." He estimated that 1 g.cal. of heat is equivalent to 370 kg.cm. of work (see § 13).

Mohr [2] in 1837, after pointing out that radiant heat is regarded as an undulatory motion, goes on to say that: " heat is no longer a substance, but is rather an oscillatory motion of the smallest parts " [really Davy's theory]. He, like Mayer in 1842, used the name " Kraft " [force] for energy, and said heat is one form of it. He pointed out the relation of the difference of specific heats of air at constant volume and constant pressure to this nature of heat, but does not (as Mayer later did) calculate the mechanical equivalent of heat from this difference. Séguin [3] in 1839 gave data from which it follows that the mechanical equivalent of 1 g.cal. is 650 kg.m. Colding [4] in 1843 found from friction experiments similar to Rumford's the value of 350 kg.m. (Mayer gave 365; the correct figure is 427 kg.m.)

The hypothesis that *animal heat* is due to oxidation of material in the blood by atmospheric oxygen in the lungs was adopted by Crawford,[5] and had been supported by experiments similar to those made by Lavoisier and Laplace,[6] to which he refers. It was found that the heat of combustion of the carbon was insufficient to account for the heat; Crawford supposed this was due to a change of heat capacity of the blood; Lavoisier and Laplace later thought the balance was provided by the oxidation of hydrogen. Crawford (whose statements are not very clear) concluded from his experiments that " the quantity of heat produced when a given portion of pure air [oxygen] is altered by the respiration of an animal is nearly equal to that which is produced when the same quantity of air is altered by the combustion of wax or charcoal " (p. 352); and he supposed that the heat is given out in the lungs (p. 355). Others, e.g. Davies,[7] thought that animal heat was due to the friction of the blood in the veins and arteries, and this view, as a complete explanation of animal heat, had already

[1] " Réflexions sur la Puissance Motrice du Feu," 1878, 94; before his death in 1832, therefore, Carnot had arrived at *both* the fundamental laws of thermodynamics; Mach, " Die Prinzipien der Wärmelehre," Leipzig, 1896, 238, 242; Décombe, *Compt. Rend.*, 1918, **168**, 268.

[2] *Z. f. Phys. u. verwandte Wiss.* (ed. Baumgartner and Holger), 1837, **5**, 419; *Ann.*, 1837, **24**, 141; *Phil. Mag.*, 1876, **2**, 110 (transl. by Tait); " Allgemeine Theorie der Bewegung und Kraft als Grundlage der Physik und Chemie," 1869.

[3] " De l'Influence des Chemins de Fer, et de l'Art de les tracer et de les construire," Liège, 1839, 243 f., 385 f.; Tait, *Phil. Mag.*, 1864, **28**, 288; Tyndall, *ibid.*, 1864, **28**, 25; Joule, *ibid.*, 1862, **24**, 121; 1864, **28**, 150, claimed the priority of Séguin over Mayer.

[4] *Phil. Mag.*, 1864, **27**, 56, referring to communications of 1843 f., which I have been unable to trace.

[5] " Experiments and Observations on Animal Heat and the Inflammation of Combustible Bodies," 2nd edit., 1788, 310 f., 315, 346, 352, 354 f. In the first edition of his book, 1779, 17 f., 32, 53, 69, 80, Crawford followed the phlogiston theory and attributed animal heat to a change of heat capacity of air on phlogistication.

[6] *Mém. Acad. Sci.*, 1780 [1784], 355; Lavoisier, " Œuvres," 1862, **2**, 283; Ostwald', *Klassiker*, 1892, No. **40**.

[7] Quoted by Joule, *Phil. Mag.*, 1843, **23**, 435.

been proposed by Haller,[1] who expressly states that water can be heated by friction. In 1821 the Académie des Sciences in Paris offered a prize for an investigation of the problem, and Despretz and Dulong made experiments. Despretz received the prize in 1823, and published his results [2] in 1824. He concluded, from numerous experiments on animals, that the complete heat of oxidation of the carbon and hydrogen leaves unaccounted for about 20 per cent. of the animal heat, which he supposed was made up " by the motion of the blood and the friction of its different parts." Dulong read his paper in 1822, and the results were published in extract before Despretz' paper, but in full only in 1841.[3] He found results similar to Despretz', but suspected an error in the heats of combustion of carbon and hydrogen. He made fresh experiments on these, which were published posthumously,[4] and although these confirmed the previous value for carbon, they showed that the figure for hydrogen was much too low (24,000 units per g., whilst he found 34,444). The correction was much more than sufficient to remove the supposed discrepancy.

The physiological importance of animal heat, according to Epstein,[1] explains the interest aroused by it in Mayer and Helmholtz, both medical men.

J. R. Mayer [5] (who does not mention Mohr or others) arrived in 1842 by a semi-metaphysical argument at the idea that heat and work (*Kraft*) are two forms of an entity (which we now call *energy*): " Forces are causes and hence there is complete applicability to them of the fundamental law *causa aequat effectum*. If the cause c has the effect e, then $c=e$." He calculated the mechanical equivalent of heat as 365 kg.m. per g.cal. from the difference of the two specific heats of air, as explained in § 21, making an implicit assumption that all the heat absorbed in heating 1 g. of air through 1° at constant atmospheric pressure appears as external work. In spite of statements to the contrary,[6] Mayer in his publications

[1] " Elementa Physiologiae," Lausanne, 1760, **2**, 293, 339; cf. Burdach, " Die Physiologie als Erfahrungswissenschaft," Leipzig, 1840, **6**, 540; Winn, *Phil. Mag.*, 1839, **14**, 174; Epstein, " Textbook of Thermodynamics," New York, 1937, 30 f.

[2] *Ann. Chim.*, 1824, **26**, 337.

[3] *Ann. Chim.*, 1841, **1**, 440.

[4] *Ann. Chim.*, 1843, **8**, 180 (edit. by Cabart).

[5] *Ann.*, 1842, **42**, 233; reproduced in *Isis*, 1929, **13**, 18; Mayer, " Die Mechanik der Wärme," Stuttgart, 1867, 1 f., 26 (2nd edit., 1874; edit. by Weyrauch, Stuttgart, 1893); Ostwald's *Klassiker*, 1911, No. **180**; Weyrauch, " Robert Mayer, der Entdecker des Princips der Erhaltung der Energie," Stuttgart, 1890; cf. Partington, " Chemical Thermodynamics," 1924, 11, 26.

Mayer's papers were translated, at Tyndall's instigation, as follows:

I. [1842]. *Phil. Mag.*, 1862, **24**, 371 (by G. C. Foster); summary by Tyndall, *ibid.*, 1863, **25**, 378.

II [1845]. Summary by Tyndall, *Phil. Mag.*, 1864, **28**, 25.

III. [1848]. *Phil. Mag.*, 1863, **25**, 241, 387, 417 (by Debus).

IV [1851]. *Phil. Mag.*, 1863, **25**, 493 (by G. C. Foster).

Translations of Mayer's and Helmholtz's (1847: see below) publications, with reproductions of works by Grove and papers by Liebig and Carpenter, with biographical notices, are given by Youmans, " The Correlation and Conservation of Forces," New York, 1895. According to Ostwald, *Z. phys. Chem.*, 1910, **75**, 511, the letter of rejection of Mayer's second paper by the German Chemical Society was signed by A. W. Hofmann, the Secretary, and the paper was not accepted because of the large number of purely chemical papers in hand awaiting publication. See also Tyndall, *Phil. Mag.*, 1862, **24**, 57, 173, 308; Joule, *ibid.*, 1862, **24**, 121; 1864, **28**, 150; Tait, *ibid.*, 1864, **28**, 288; Lord Kelvin, " Math. and Phys. Papers," 1882, **1**, 174.

Views similar to Mayer's were put forward by W. R. Grove in January 1842: " A Lecture on the Progress of Natural Science . . . delivered on Wednesday, the 19th of January, 1842. Printed by order of the Managers of the London Institution," 1842 [privately issued], 27; " On the Correlation of Physical Forces: being the Substance of a Course of Lectures delivered in the London Institution in the year 1843," 1846, 21, 29, etc.

[6] Tyndall, *Phil. Mag.*, 1864, **28**, 25; Clausius, " Die mechanische Wärmetheorie," Brunswick, 1879, **2**, 324; Bertrand, " Thermodynamique," Paris, 1887, 66; Lippmann, " Abhandlungen und Vorträge," 1906, **1**, 551; *Chem. Ztg.*, 1923, **47**, 807.

did not justify this by reference to Gay-Lussac's experiment of 1807 (see § 23. VII A) until 1845, after the publication of Joule's first papers (which are not mentioned). Joule pointed out the assumption which had been made by Mayer, and justified it by experiment. Letters of Mayer to Baur,[1] however, show that he appreciated the significance of Gay-Lussac's experiment in 1841, and this is noteworthy.[2] In the early part of his paper,[3] sent to Poggendorff in June 1841, the calculation does not appear. The only experiment to which Mayer refers is the rise in temperature from 12° to 13° by shaking water in a medicine bottle, and he does not explain how the entry of heat from the hand was prevented.

The idea of the conservation of energy was again stated, in 1847, by Helmholtz,[4] who developed it in several directions. He refers to Joule's experiments, begun in 1840 (see below), which showed by various methods that there is a fixed relation between the measure of a quantity of work (or of electrical energy directly convertible into work) and that of the quantity of heat obtained from it by complete conversion. If these two measures are expressed in terms of the erg and the gram-calorie, respectively, there will also be a relation between the erg and the calorie, or in general between any two units used for the measurement of work and heat, respectively.

§ 11. Energy

The erg is the c.g.s. unit of work (or energy), and is the work done by a constant force of 1 dyne moving its point of application through 1 cm. in a straight line. The dyne is the c.g.s. unit of force, and is that force which imparts to a mass of 1 gram an acceleration of 1 cm. per sec. per sec. (i.e. when acting for 1 sec., imparts to it a velocity of 1 cm. per sec.). The dimensions [5] of force are $[mst^{-2}]$ and of work or energy $[ms^2t^{-2}]$, where m=mass, s=length, t=time.

If a constant force P is applied for a time t, during which the particle of mass m moves over a distance s in the direction of the force, the velocity of the particle changes from u_0 to u. Then: [6]

force=mass×acceleration,

$$\therefore\ P=m(\mathrm{d}^2s/\mathrm{d}t^2) \qquad (1)$$

[1] J. R. Mayer, "Kleinere Schriften und Briefe," edit. Weyrauch, Stuttgart, 1893, 131 (letter of 12 Sept., 1841), 152 (letter of 13 July, 1844), 262, 269, 281 (letters to Paris Acad. of Sci. of 1846–9); on the polemic between Mayer, *Compt. Rend.*, 1846, **23**, 544 [title only]; 1848, **27**, 385; 1849, **29**, 534; and Joule, *ibid.*, 1847, **25**, 309; 1849, **28**, 132; see Mayer, "Kleinere Schriften und Briefe," 1893, 258 f., and on Tyndall's part, *ibid.*, 322 f.; Sarton, *Isis*, 1929, **13**, 18 f.; on Mayer, see also E. Dühring, "Neue Grundgesetze zur rationellen Physik und Chemie," Leipzig, 1878, **1**, 99 f.

[2] Haber, "Thermodynamics of Technical Gas Reactions," 1908, 35; Hinshelwood, "Thermodynamics," 1926, 25.

[3] "Kleinere Schriften und Briefe," 1893, 100 f.

[4] Über die Erhaltung der Kraft, eine physikalische Abhandlung, vorgetragen in der Sitzung der physikalischen Gesellschaft zu Berlin am 23sten Juli 1847," Berlin, 1847 (72 pp.), mentioning Joule's publications on p. 25; "Wiss. Abhl.," Leipzig, 1882, **1**, 12; Ostwald's *Klassiker*, 1889, **1**; transl. in Taylor's "Scientific Memoirs," 1853, 114; Helmholtz, "Ueber die Wechselwirkungen der Naturkräfte," Königsberg, 1854; French transl. by Pérard, "Mémoire sur la Conservation de la Force," Paris, 1869.

[5] For a concise account of the subject of dimensions, see J. J. Thomson, "Elements of the Mathematical Theory of Electricity and Magnetism," Cambridge, 1904, 452; Maxwell, "Theory of Heat," 1897, 74; Maxwell and Jenkin, *B. A. Rep.*, 1863, 130; and the criticism of Planck, "Theorie der Elektrizität und des Magnetismus," Leipzig, 1928, 14. The study of dimensions goes back to Fourier, 1820; see § 73, I.

On the "relative" character of these definitions, see Newcomb, *Phil. Mag.*, 1889, **27**, 115.

Multiply both sides by the identity $ds=(ds/dt)dt$, and integrate, on the assumption (modified in the Theory of Relativity) that the mass is constant:

$$\int_0^s P ds = \int m(d^2s/dt^2)(ds/dt)dt = \tfrac{1}{2}m\int d(ds/dt)^2 = \tfrac{1}{2}m\int du^2$$

$$\therefore \; Ps = \tfrac{1}{2}mu^2 - \tfrac{1}{2}mu_0^2 \quad . \; . \; . \; . \; . \; . \; . \; . \; . \quad (2)$$

since ds/dt=velocity=u. The magnitude $\frac{1}{2}mu^2$ is called the *kinetic energy* of the particle, hence *the work done by a force is equal to the increase of kinetic energy of the mass moved by the force.*

The force exerted on a mass m by the gravitational attraction of the earth is mg, where g is the acceleration of gravity. In the c.g.s. system, g is approximately 981 cm. per sec. per sec., and the force exerted on a mass of m grams is $981m$ dynes. In the ft.-lb.-sec. system, g is approximately 32 ft. per sec. per sec., and the force exerted on a mass of m lb. is 32 m poundals. Very often the forces are given as m grams *weight* and m lb. *weight*. A mass of m g. or lb. raised through a height h cm. or ft. above the surface of the earth has a *potential energy* of mgh ergs or ft. poundals, or mh g.cm. or ft.lb.; it is, of course, the same energy in all these units. In falling freely the mass acquires this amount of kinetic energy just as it reaches the earth, and if allowed to fall slowly by a string over a pulley, the weight can do this amount of work on some other system. Equation (2) (in which $-Ps$ is the potential energy) shows that the *total mechanical energy* of a particle, i.e. the sum of the kinetic and potential energies, is constant, provided no work is spent by friction. If there is friction, however, some of the mechanical energy is converted into heat.

The name *energy* was given by Thomas Young [1] in 1807 to the product mv^2, which Leibniz [2] had called *vis viva* (i.e. twice the kinetic energy of a body); Rankine [3] called $\frac{1}{2}mv^2$ *actual* (or sensible) *energy*, and also used the name *potential* (or latent) *energy* (which Leibniz called *vis mortua*) [4] in its present sense. The name *kinetic energy* for half the *vis viva*, viz. $\frac{1}{2}mv^2$, was introduced by William Thomson (Lord Kelvin) and Tait.[5] The extension of the energy principle to optics is due mainly to Fresnel,[6] who was in close relation with Young, and the meaning of " energy " was extended to include its thermodynamic aspects by Thomson,[7] who at first called it the " mechanical energy " of a system, but later [8] used the name " intrinsic energy." The name " enérgie " in the sense used by Young seems to occur first in an article by D'Alembert in the French " Encyclopédie," [9] where it is said: " il y a dans un corps en mouvement un effort ou enérgie, qui n'est point dans un corps en repos."

[1] " A Course of Lectures on Natural Philosophy," 1807, **1**, 78; 2nd edit., 1845, **1**, 59.

[2] *Acta Erudit.*, Leipzig, 1695, 145 (149); cf. *ibid.*, 1686, 161 (where he uses mv^2); " Werke," edit. Gerhardt, 1860, iii Folge, **6**, 238.

[3] *Phil. Mag.*, 1853, **5**, 106; *Edin. N. Phil. J.*, 1855, **2**, 120; *Proc. Phil. Soc. Glasgow*, 1855, **3**, 381; *Ann. Chim.*, 1868, **13**, 73; " Misc. Sci. Papers," 1881, 203, 209, 229. He used the name " Energetics " (later popularised by Ostwald; see § 23) for the general science of energy, " whose subjects are material bodies and physical phenomena in general."

[4] Helmholtz, " Über die Erhaltung der Kraft," Berlin, 1847, 14, called it " Spannkraft."

[5] Thomson and Tait, *Good Words*, 1862, quoted by Tait, " Sketch of Thermodynamics," 1877, 64; Thomson and Tait, " A Treatise on Natural Philosophy," 1873, **1**, 53; Maxwell, " Theory of Heat," 1875, 91; A. Gray, " Lord Kelvin, an Account of his Scientific Life and Work," 1908, 99, 114; Thomson, in *B.A. Rep.*, 1854, II, 59, called it " actual " or " dynamical " energy.

[6] Fresnel, " Oeuvres Complètes," Paris, 1858, **2**, 44.

[7] *Trans. Roy. Soc. Edin.*, 1853, **20**, 261 (read 1851); *Phil. Mag.*, 1852, **4**, 8, 105, 168; 1855, **9**, 523.

[8] *Phil. Mag.*, 1878, **5**, 4; " Math. and Phys. Papers," 1882, **1**, 291.

[9] " Encyclopédie Méthodique," Sect. Mathématique, Paris, 1785, **2**, 82.

§ 12. The Mechanical Equivalent of Heat

The *mechanical equivalent of heat* **J** (after Joule) is the number of units of work which, if completely converted into heat, would give rise to one unit of heat. The work unit may be the ft.lb., g.cm., kg.cm., or erg; the unit of heat the lb.° F. (heat required to raise 1 lb. of water through 1° F.), lb.° C., g.cal., k.cal., etc. That such a mechanical equivalent exists is shown by (i) the fact that heat and work are interconvertible, (ii) the fact, first established by Joule, that the ratio is a fixed constant, depending only on the units of heat and work and independent of the process of conversion.

Osborne Reynolds, in his memoir on Joule,[1] points out that Joule's work was "received in complete silence," adding that "'the angels feared to tread,' and perhaps the most remarkable thing is that in this case there were no fools." Joule's researches may be summarised as follows; the details of the experiments will be found in the better type of works on physics.[2]

(*a*) In 1843 [3] the heat produced in a coil of wire by induction currents set up on rotation between the poles of an electromagnet was communicated to water in which the coil was placed, and was compared with the work done by falling weights in rotating the coil. This gave $J=459{\cdot}62$ g.m. per g.cal.

(*b*) In 1845–78 [4] the heat produced by stirring water, oil, and mercury was compared with the work done by falling weights which actuated the stirrer.

Joule's early water-stirring apparatus, which has great historical interest,[5] is shown in Fig. 9.II. The water was contained in the copper calorimeter AB with a lid carrying two tubes. Through one of these passed a thermometer and through the other the spindle of the brass paddle, consisting of eight sets of revolving arms working between four sets of stationary vanes fixed to the vessel. The spindle was interrupted by a boxwood cylinder, which minimised conduction of heat. The paddle was worked by the descent of lead weights *ee* suspended by string from the rollers *bb*, supported by steel axles *cc* on brass friction wheels *dd*, and the motion was communicated by fine twine from the pulleys *aa* to the central roller *f*, which could be detached, for the purpose of winding up the weights, by the pin *p*. The height of the weights (about $5\frac{1}{4}$ ft.) was read off on the scales *kk*. The weights were allowed to fall twenty times,

1 *Manch. Mem.*, 1892, 77; see also A. Wood, "Joule and the Study of Energy," 1925. James Prescott Joule, 1818–89, a pupil of Dalton and a brewer of Salford, near Manchester, must be regarded as the experimental founder of the law of conservation of energy. See his "Scientific Papers," 2 vols., 1884–7; Merz, "A History of European Thought in the Nineteenth Century," 1912, 2, 95.

2 Winkelmann, "Handbuch der Physik," 1906, **3**, 537 f.

3 *Phil. Mag.*, 1843, **23**, 263, 347, 435: "On the Calorific Effects of Magneto-Electricity and on the Mechanical Value of Heat."

4 *Phil. Mag.*, 1845, **27**, 205: "On the Existence of an Equivalent Relation between Heat and the ordinary forms of Mechanical Power"; *ibid.*, 1847, **31**, 173: "On the Mechanical Equivalent of Heat as determined by the Heat evolved by the Friction of Fluids"; *Compt. Rend.*, 1847, **25**, 309; *Phil. Trans.*, 1850, **140**, 61, read in June, 1849 (communicated by Faraday); *Ann. Phys.*, 1854, Ergzb. **4**, 601: "On the Mechanical Equivalent of Heat"; *Phil. Trans.*, 1878, **169**, 365: "New Determinations of the Mechanical Equivalent of Heat." Joule, "Scientific Papers," 1884, **1**, 123, 202, 277, 288, 298, 632. A German transl. of Joule's papers by Spengel is "Das mechanische Wärmeäquivalent. Ges. Abhl. von J. P. Joule," Brunswick, 1872. An excellent historical account of the determinations of the mechanical equivalent of heat, and a table of the values, is given by E. H. Griffiths, *Phil. Mag.*, 1895, **40**, 431; "Dictionary of Applied Physics," 1922, **1**, 477, dealing with work done to those dates. A table of all the values of the mechanical equivalent found to the time of publication is given by Miculescu, *Ann. Chim.* 1892, **27**, 202.

5 An illustration of part of the original apparatus, in the Science Museum, London, is given in Edser, "Heat for Advanced Students." 1899, 275.

taking in all 35 mins. A correction for cooling and one for the velocity of the weights on reaching the ground (i.e. having some kinetic energy) were applied, as well as minor corrections for friction. The method was also used with mercury (with an iron vessel), and in the third and fourth series two cast-iron rings were rubbed together under mercury. The water friction experiments gave 438·3, 428·9, and 423·9, the mercury 424·7, and the friction of iron 425·2, g.m. per cal. In 1878 Joule [1] used a method designed by Hirn,[2] afterwards used by Rowland [3] and others, in which the calorimeter was suspended by a bearing on the vertical axis of the paddle and prevented from rotating by an equal and opposite couple applied by a silk cord passing round a groove in the calorimeter, and attached, over pulleys, to scale pans containing weights. The result was 423·9 g.m.

In 1850 Joule chose as the best value of ***J***, 772 ft.lb. per lb. of water raised through 1° F., and in 1878 772·6 ft.lb. per lb. of water at 62° F. raised through

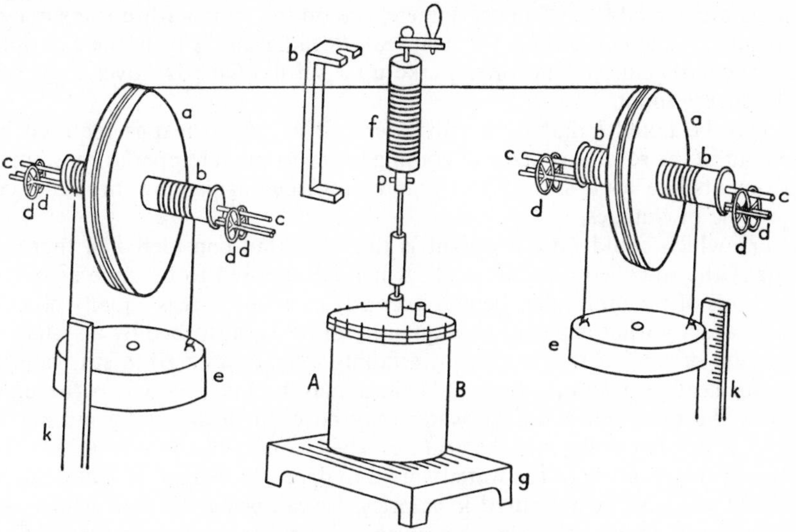

FIG. 9.II. Joule's Apparatus

1° F. The modern value is 778·57 ft.lb. per mean B.Th.U. A recalculation [4] of Joule's best experiments of this type, with modern temperature standards, etc., gave $J = 4{\cdot}1714 \times 10^7$ ergs per 15° g.cal.

(*c*) Some experiments [5] on the heat and cold produced by compressing and expanding air, made in 1844–5, gave 436·1 and 448·2 g.m., respectively, but these results were not considered accurate.

(*d*) In 1867 Joule [6] measured the heat produced by passing an electric current through a coil of wire immersed in a calorimeter, and compared it with the electrical energy spent by the current according to the law discovered by

[1] *Phil. Trans.*, 1878, **168**, 365.
[2] " Recherches sur l'Équivalent Mécanique de la Chaleur," Colmar, 1858, **1**, 85.
[3] *Proc. Amer. Acad.*, 1879–80, **7**, 75; " Physical Papers," Baltimore, 1902, 343, 469.
[4] Graetz, in Winkelmann, " Handbuch der Physik," 1906, **3**, 540 f.; cf. Griffiths, *Phil. Trans.*, 1893, **188**, 361.
[5] *Phil. Mag.*, 1845, **26**, 369: " On Changes of Temperature produced by the Rarefaction and Condensation of Air "; " Scientific Papers," 1884, **1**, 171.
[6] *B.A. Rep.*, 1867, I, 512.

Joule [1] in 1841, viz. that the energy is proportional to C^2Rt, where C=current, R=resistance, t=time. The result (recalculated [2] on the basis of modern electrical units) was $J=4{\cdot}1665\times10^7$ ergs per 15° g.cal.

The converse of Joule's experiments, viz. the conversion of a measured amount of heat into a measured amount of work, was made with a steam engine by Hirn,[3] who found J=415 g.m. per g.cal.

In a simple apparatus for determining the mechanical equivalent in the laboratory devised by Puluj,[4] the friction between two metal cones develops heat which is communicated to mercury in the inner cone, the rise in temperature being measured by a thermometer. A small apparatus with stirred water, similar to Joule's, is described by Christiansen.[5]

The validity of recalculation of older work has been disputed.[6] Very often, necessary experimental details are lacking, and there is doubt about the relations between units and standards of different periods, particularly in electrical measurements. In some cases the actual thermometers used by the experimenters are available, and hence some check on the temperature measurements is possible. The corrections for heat leak (" radiation ") from the calorimeter are particularly elusive, and often make up a substantial part (over 2 per cent.) of the energy input.

It may be noted [7] that to warm water just as much heat is required as is given out in the reverse process of cooling to the original temperature, so that in experiments like Joule's, the water may be regarded as passing through a complete cycle of changes.

Work which could raise a weight is the only kind considered in thermodynamics,[8] the so-called internal work, which is supposed to be done against the attractions of the molecules, being rigorously excluded. It is equally necessary to state exactly what is meant by a quantity of heat q absorbed by a system. If a quantity of work w is expended by a falling weight and used to stir water and generate heat by friction, the unit of heat may be taken equal to the unit of work. The same effect on the water may be brought about by putting it in contact with a hot body, and the heat absorbed from the body is w units. If the change of temperature of the water is used to define its change of state, the heat absorbed may also be measured in calories, 1 g.cal. being the heat which, when communicated to 1 g. of water in a given state, raises its temperature 1° C. It

[1] *Phil. Mag.*, 1841, **18**, 308 (abstract of a communication to the Royal Society, which was not published); 1841, **19**, 260; " Scientific Papers," 1884, **1**, 60.

[2] Graetz, in Winkelmann, "Handbuch der Physik," 1906, 3, 540 f.; cf. Griffiths, *Phil. Trans.*, 1893, **188**, 361.

[3] " Recherches sur l'Équivalent Mécanique de la Chaleur," Colmar, 1858, 20, 174; " Exposition Analytique et Expérimentale de la Théorie Mécanique de la Chaleur," Paris and Colmar, 1862, **1**, 84.

[4] *Ann. Phys.*, 1876. **157**, 437; Dorn, *ibid.*, 1885, **26**, 331; Sahulka, *ibid.*, 1890, **41**, 748, found $426\pm2{\cdot}5$ g.m. with an improved apparatus; Rubens, *Verhl. d. D. Phys. Ges.*, 1906, **8**, 77; *Phys. Z.*, 1906, **7**, 272 (revolving tube); Crémieu and Rispail, *Compt. Rend.*, 1908, **147**, 793; Rispail, *Ann. Chim.*, 1910, **20**, 417 (in an ice calorimeter: $J=4{\cdot}185\times10^7$); Kann, *Phys. Z.*, 1908, **9**, 263 (student's apparatus); Paschen and Wolff, *Phys. Z.*, 1911, **12**, 113; Waran, *Phil. Mag.*, 1920, **40**, 386 (Puluj type).

[5] *Ann. Phys.*, 1892, **47**, 374.

[6] Laby, *Proc. Phys. Soc.*, 1926, **38**, 169; discussion by F. E. Smith, G. M. Clark, E. Griffiths, and E. H. Griffiths, *ibid.*, 172 f.; Osborne, Stimson, and Ginnings, *Bur. Stand. J. Res.*, 1939, **23**, 197; see on dissolved air, Jessel, *Proc. Phys. Soc.*, 1934 .**46**, 747; Laby and Hercus, *ibid.*, **47**, 1003.

[7] Porter, " Thermodynamics," 1931, 10.

[8] The definition of "work" adopted here is that of Carnot, "Réflexions sur la Puissance Motrice du Feu," 1824 (1878), 4.

is important to notice, however, that the heat unit is defined primarily without reference to temperature. No other meaning will be given to heat absorbed than this.[1]

Later work by the water-stirring method indicated that Joule's result ($4{\cdot}1714 \times 10^7$) is probably about 0·3 per cent. too low: Rowland [2] (1879–80), found $4{\cdot}188 \times 10^7$ ($4{\cdot}187 \times 10^7$); Miculescu [3] (1892), $4{\cdot}181 \times 10^7$ ($4{\cdot}183 \times 10^7$); Reynolds and Moorby [4] (1898), $4{\cdot}1845 \times 10^7$ ($4{\cdot}183 \times 10^7$).

There were errors in Joule's thermometer (compared by Rowland with his own) and the specific heat values he used for water and the calorimetric apparatus also required correction. Most of the more recent workers used the electrical method. Some selected (recalculated) values (ergs/15° g.cal.) are:

E. H. Griffiths [5] (1893)	$4{\cdot}186 \times 10^7$ (*$4{\cdot}194 \times 10^7$)
Schuster and Gannon [6] (1894) ...	$4{\cdot}186 \times 10^7$ (*$4{\cdot}193 \times 10^7$)
Callendar and Barnes [7] (1902) ...	$4{\cdot}182 \times 10^7$ (*$4{\cdot}189 \times 10^7$)
Dieterici [8] (1905)	$4{\cdot}193 \times 10^7$ (*$4{\cdot}194 \times 10^7$)
W. R. and W. E. Bousfield [9] (1912)	$4{\cdot}181 \times 10^7$
Jaeger and von Steinwehr [10] (1915)	$4{\cdot}186 \times 10^7$
Laby and Hercus [11] (1927) ...	$4{\cdot}186 \times 10^7$ ($4{\cdot}184 \times 7$ at 16·7°)

Dieterici used a Bunsen's ice calorimeter, which can be very uncertain (see Vol. II); Callendar and Barnes used a " continuous flow calorimeter " (see Vol. II); the Bousfields used a glass spiral filled with mercury as the heating element (a device previously used by Pfaundler).[12] The value found by Bousfield and Bousfield is very low, and W. R. Bousfield [13] afterwards accepted the value of Callendar and Barnes as probably more accurate. The lack of accurate agreement among recent values of J is apparent, and becomes even more striking if the values of the specific heat of water at various temperatures are considered.

Laby and Hercus used an ingenious apparatus comprising an induction dynamometer and continuous-flow calorimetry. Their values near 20° seem to be affected by some error, and were withdrawn by the experimenters. A possible error due to dissolved air in the water was said by Laby and Hercus not to affect the results, and as a final value for both air-free and aerated water they gave $4{\cdot}1852 \times 10^7$ ergs per 15° g.cal.

[1] Cf. Bridgman, " The Nature of Thermodynamics," Cambridge (U.S.A.), 1941, 1.

[2] *Proc. Amer. Acad.*, 1879, **7**, 75–200; recalculated by Day, *Phil. Mag.*, 1897, **44**, 169; 1898, **46**, 1; the bracketed values are those recalculated by Scheel and Luther, *Z. Elektrochem.*, 1908, **17**, 743 (who adopted $4{\cdot}187 \times 10^7$), those starred also involve a recalculation of electrical units (difference of international and absolute ohms): Grüneisen and Giebe, *Ann. Phys.* 1920, **63**, 179, who give 4·1842 int. joule.

[3] *J. de Phys.*, 1892, **1**, 104; *Ann. Chim.*, 1892, **27**, 202; cf. Rispail, *ibid.*, 1910, **20**, 417; Roebuck, *Phys. Rev.*, 1913, **2**, 79 (porous plug experiment).

[4] *Phil. Trans.*, 1897, **190**, 301; *Proc. Roy. Soc.*, 1897, **61**, 293.

[5] *Proc. Roy. Soc.*, 1894, **55**, 23; *Phil. Trans.*, 1893, **184**, 361; *Phil. Mag.*, 1895, **40**, 431; " The Thermal Measurement of Energy," Cambridge, 1901 (popular).

[6] *Proc. Roy. Soc.*, 1894, **57**, 25; *Phil. Trans.*, 1895, **186**, 415.

[7] Callendar, *Phil Trans.*, 1902, **199**, 55, 149; Barnes, *ibid.*, 1912, **212**, 1; *Proc. Roy. Soc.*, 1909, **82**, 390; Callendar, *Proc. Phys. Soc.*, 1926, **38**, 174.

[8] *Ann. Phys.*, 1905, **16**, 593; earlier papers, *ibid.*, 1888, **33**, 417; 1896, **57**, 333; cf. Cotty, *Ann. Chim.*, 1911, **24**, 282.

[9] *Phil. Trans.*, 1912, **211**, 199.

[10] *Berlin Ber.*, 1915, 424; *Verhl. d. D. Phys. Ges.*, 1915, **17**, 362; 1919, **21**, 25; *Ann. Phys.*, 1919, **58**, 487; 1921, **64**, 305; cf. Sutton, *Phil. Mag.*, 1918, **35**, 27.

[11] *Phil. Trans.*, 1927, **227**, 63; Hercus, *Proc. Phys. Soc.*, 1936, **48**, 282.

[12] *Wien Ber.*, 1891, **100**, II A, 352; cf. von Steinwehr, *Z. phys. Chem.*, 1901, **38**, 185; Rümelin, *ibid.*, 1907, **58**, 449 (both used resistance lamps); Heydweiller, *Ann. Phys.*, 1915, **46**, 253 (Hg spiral.)

[13] *Proc. Roy. Soc.*, 1917, **93**, 587.

The work of Callendar and Barnes, described by Osborne, Stimson, and Ginnings [1] as " without doubt more pretentious and comprehensive than any of the other researches," has often been reviewed.[2] Callendar, who co-operated in the design and preparation of the apparatus, and Barnes, who carried out the experiments, differed in their interpretations of the heat-leak corrections.[3] There was also a correction for the standard cells. Barnes [4] in 1909 gave 4·1785 (4·1842 at 15°) abs. joules per g. per 1° C. as a definitive value, and Callendar [5] in 1925 gave 4·187, both for the 20° g.cal. (a peculiar unit used by Callendar, the mean value of the quantity of heat required per 1° per g. of water between 15° and 25°). Laby gave 4·1795 at 20°. Osborne, Stimson, and Ginnings [1] remarked that: " It is difficult to believe that Barnes' estimate in 1909 that the error of the measurements in any part of the range did not exceed 1 part in 10,000, or Callendar's estimate of 1 part in 4,000 for the absolute value of the mechanical equivalent, took into account all the possibilities for deviations from the true values."

The temperature scale and electrical units used by Jaeger and von Steinwehr were probably substantially the same as the present international standards: Jaeger [6] gave 4·1842 int. j./g. 1° C. cal. at 15°, but the individual results showed fairly large deviations from the smoothed values.[1]

The choice lies between 4·184 and 4·186, and it is difficult to decide which to adopt. The relation to other fundamental units is also involved. In 1924, the author [7] adopted the value $4·184 \times 10^7$ ergs/15° g.cal., from the Reichsanstalt " Wärmetabellen " [8]; many authors use the (older) value $4·186 \times 10^7$ ergs. In 1940 the author [9] adopted (with some reserve) the value $4·185 \times 10^7$ ergs, which is also the value found by Laby and Hercus (1927).

§ 13. Relation between Energy Units

ENERGY UNITS CONVERSION TABLE

Erg	Joule (abs.)	15° C. g.cal.	Lit.atm.	g.cm.
1	10^{-7}	$0·2389 \times 10^{-7}$	$9·869 \times 10^{-10}$	$1·0197 \times 10^{-3}$
10^7	1	0·2389	$9·869 \times 10^{-3}$	$1·0197 \times 10^4$
$4·185 \times 10^7$	4·185	1	$4·130 \times 10^{-2}$	$4·2675 \times 10^4$
$1·0133 \times 10^9$	$1·0133 \times 10^2$	24·21	1	$1·0333 \times 10^6$
$9·8066 \times 10^2$	$9·8066 \times 10^{-5}$	$2·343 \times 10^{-5}$	$9·678 \times 10^{-7}$	1

The modern calorimetric heat unit is essentially a unit of electrical energy. The *international joule* is defined as the product of the international volt by the

[1] *Bur. Stand. J. Res.*, 1939, **23**, 243.

[2] Ames, *Congrès Internat. Phys.*, 1900, **1**, 178; Laby, *Proc. Phys. Soc.*, 1926, **38**, 169; Fiock, *Bur. Stand. J. Res.*, 1930, **5**, 481; Roth, *Z. phys. Chem.*, 1938, **183**, 38; Osborne, Stimson, and Ginnings, see ref. [1].

[3] See the section on Specific Heats of Gases, § 5.VII G, for a disagreement between Callendar and other experimenters on a similar problem in gas calorimetry.

[4] *Proc. Roy. Soc.*, 1909, **82**, 390.

[5] *Proc. Phys. Soc.*, 1926, **38**, 174, discussion.

[6] In Geiger and Scheel, " Handbuch der Physik," 1926, **9**, 476.

[7] " Chemical Thermodynamics," 1924, 10; 4·184 is selected by de Groot, *Nederl. Tijdschr. Natuurkde.*, 1942, **9**, 497; *Amer. Chem. Abstr.*, 1944, **38**, 3884.

[8] " Wärmetabellen," P. T. Reichsanstalt, Berlin, 1919.

[9] " Chemical Thermodynamics," 1940, 214; see Mueller and Rossini, *Amer. J. Phys.*, 1944, **12**, 1 (1 " defined " g.cal.=4·1833 internat. joules); Birge, *Rep. Progr. Phys.*, 1942, **8**, 90, takes $4·1855 \times 10^7$.

international ampere by the second, whilst the *absolute joule* [1] is 10^7 ergs. The two are not quite the same.

The relation 1 internat. joule (or watt)$=1{\cdot}00020\pm0{\cdot}00005$ abs. joule (or watt) was given by Rossini,[2] who proposed to *define* the 15° g.cal. as 4·1833 internat. joules. The usual relation is 1 internat. joule=1·00032 abs. joule. The whole matter is in need of international unification, but is hardly one of convention, since temperature scales, specific heat of water, and other realities come in as well. The *therm* [3] is 100,000 B.Th.U (1 60° B.Th.U.=250 g.cal.).[4]

An energy unit used in spectroscopy is the *electron volt*, the energy acquired by an electron in falling through a potential difference of 1 volt. In electrostatic units 1 volt$=\frac{1}{300}$ e.s.u. and the electronic charge $\boldsymbol{e}=4{\cdot}80\times10^{-10}$ e.s.u., hence 1 electron volt$=4{\cdot}80\times10^{-10}/300=1{\cdot}60\times10^{-12}$ erg. This will be a suitable unit for a single molecule; for 1 mol in k.cal. it is

$$(1{\cdot}60\times10^{-12}\times6{\cdot}03\times10^{23})/(4{\cdot}185\times10^{7}\times10^{3})=23{\cdot}05 \text{ k.cal. per mol.}$$

(A value 23·053 is adopted by Birge.[5])

It is customary to speak of electron energies in " volts " when electron volts are meant, and a confusing nomenclature speaks of the " velocity " of a moving electron (say in cathode rays) as in " volts." In this case, the ratio *charge/mass* $=\boldsymbol{e}/m$ is measured in electromagnetic units per g. and for the electron $e/m=1{\cdot}76\times10^{7}$ e.m.u. per g. If V is the potential difference in e.m.u. and v the velocity of the electron in cm./sec. the energy is $\frac{1}{2}mv^2=V\boldsymbol{e}$,

$$\therefore\ v^2=2Ve/m=(e/m)\,.\,2V, \quad \therefore\ v=\sqrt{V}\,.\,\sqrt{(2\times1{\cdot}76\times10^{7})} \text{ cm./sec.}$$

Since 1 e.m.u. of potential$=10^{-8}$ volt, when V is in volts:

$$v=\sqrt{(V\,.\,10^{8})}\,.\,\sqrt{(2\times1{\cdot}76\times10^{7})}=5{\cdot}93\times10^{7}\sqrt{V} \text{ cm./sec.}$$

When the velocity is said to be " V volts " the actual velocity in cm./sec. is given by this equation.

Harkins [6] proposed the *micro-erg*, 10^{-6} erg, and *micri-erg*, 10^{-14} erg, as units. In Hartree [7] *atomic units*, unit energy is $\boldsymbol{e}^2/a_{\mathrm{H}}$, where $\boldsymbol{e}$=electronic charge and a_{H}=radius of smallest Bohr orbit in the hydrogen atom; it is $4{\cdot}307\times10^{-11}$ erg.

§ 14. The Specific Heat of Water

If the specific heat of water varies with temperature the value of $\boldsymbol{J}$ found by a method depending on the heating of water by a known amount of energy will vary with the temperature. By mixing known weights of water at different temperatures and finding the temperature of the mixture, Flaugergues [8] found a slight decrease in specific heat with rise of temperature, but Neumann [9] found that it increased slightly, the value at 100° being 1·0127 that at 27°. Regnault [10]

[1] Onnes and Keesom, *Comm. Leiden*, 1912, Suppl. **23**, 17, proposed to call these *electrojoule* and *thermojoule*, respectively. Griffiths, *Phil. Mag.*, 1895, **40**, 451, proposed to call 4·2 abs. joules a *rowland*. These names have not been adopted.

[2] *Bur. Stand. J. Res.*, 1931, **6**, 1; 1934, **12**, 735; *Chem. Rev.*, 1940, **27**, 1; Sturtevant, in Weissberger, " Physical Methods of Organic Chemistry," New York, 1945, **1**, 315.

[3] Couch, *Amer. J. Pharm.*, 1923, **95**, 150.

[4] The mean value 251·98 g.cal. is often taken, or 1054·6 abs. joules.

[5] *Rep. Progr. Phys.* (Phys. Soc. London), 1942, **8**, 90. A very useful set of interconversion tables for energies, wave-lengths, frequencies, etc., is given by Clark, *Phil. Mag.*, 1932, **14**, 291.

[6] *J.A.C.S.*, 1922, **44**, 653.

[7] *Proc. Cambr. Phil. Soc.*, 1928, **24**, 89, 111.

[8] *J. de Phys.*, 1813, **77**, 273.

[9] *Ann. Phys.*, 1831, **23**, 40.

[10] *Ann. Chim.*, 1840, **73**, 5(35); *Mém. Acad. Sci.*, 1847, **21**, 729; recalc. by Guillaume, *Compt. Rend.*, 1912, **154**, 1483.

found the mean specific heats in the regions 15°–100° and 0°–20° in the ratio 1·00709–1·0089 in two experiments, and in experiments at higher temperatures he deduced for the *true* specific heat at t° C. up to 230° the formula: $c=1+0{\cdot}00004t+0{\cdot}0_69t^2$. After correcting the temperatures from the mercury to the air thermometer scale, Bosscha [1] deduced the formula: $c=1+0{\cdot}00022(t-18)\simeq 1+0{\cdot}00022t$, and Velten [2] pointed out discrepancies in Regnault's results above 100° which make them doubtful. A large variation with temperature found by Pfaundler and Platter [3] was not confirmed.[4]

Rowland first definitely established the variation of specific heat with temperature. He observed the variation of J with the temperature of the water and found a minimum value at about 30° which he confirmed by the method of mixtures.[5]

The *mean* gram-calorie or " Bunsen calorie " $\bar{c}$ (0·01 × heat absorbed by 1 g. of water on heating from 0° to 100° C.) is somewhat larger than the 15° g.cal. (1 mean g.cal. = 1·0002 15° g.cal. according to Scheel and Luther [6]) but the difference is small.

The specific heats of water determined by Bartoli and Stracciati [7] between 0° and 35° were represented in 15° g.cal. by the formula

$$c_t=1{\cdot}006630-0{\cdot}0_3593962t+0{\cdot}0_54338650t^2+0{\cdot}0_6425520t^3-0{\cdot}0_82819t^4.$$

Callendar's [8] results are given in the table:

0°	1·0093	35°	0·9973	70°	1·0000
5°	1·0047	40°	0·9973	75°	1·0008
10°	1·0019	45°	0·9975	80°	1·0017
15°	**1·0000**	50°	0·9978	85°	1·0026
20°	0·9988	55°	0·9982	90°	1·0036
25°	0·9980	60°	0·9987	95°	1·0046
30°	0·9975	65°	0·9993	100°	1·0057

The values given by the Reichsanstalt [9] (which correspond with a value of J of 4·1842 internat. joules per 15° g.cal.) were:

0°	1·005	**15°**	**1·0000**	25°	0·9983
5°	1·030	18°	0·9994	29°	0·9980
10°	1·0013	20°	0·9990		

Dieterici [6] gave for the true sp. ht. at 35°–300° in 15° g.cal.:

$$c_t=0{\cdot}99827-0{\cdot}0_310368t+0{\cdot}0_520736t^2.$$

1 *Ann. Phys.*, *Pogg. Jubelband*, 1874, 549.
2 *Ann. Phys.*, 1844, **21**, 31.
3 *Ann. Phys.*, 1870, **140**, 574; 1870, **141**, 537.
4 Hirn, *Compt. Rend.*, 1870, **70**, 592, 831; Jamin and Amaury, *ibid.*, 1870, **70**, 661; Münchhausen (Wüllner), *Ann. Phys.*, 1877, **1**, 592; Stamo, *Dissert.*, Zürich, 1877; Henrichsen, *Ann. Phys.*, 1879, **8**, 83; Baumgartner (Pfaundler), *ibid.*, 1879, **8**, 648; Gerosa, *Atti R. Accad. Lincei*, 1881, **10**, 75; *Ann. Phys. Beibl.*, 1882, **6**, 222 (table).
5 See also Liebig, *Amer. J. Sci.*, 1883, **26**, 57; Lüdin, *Dissert.*, Zurich, 1895; abstr. and table in *Z. phys. Chem.*, 1896, **20**, 629; corrected by Pernet, *Arch. Sci. Phys. Nat.*, 1896, **2**, 531 (method of mixtures; $c=1$ at 0° C.); Barnes, *Phil. Trans.*, 1902, **199**, 149; *Trans. Roy. Soc. Canada*, 1902, **8**, iii, 141 (proposed 16° g.cal.); Griffiths, *Phil. Mag.*, 1895, **40**, 431 (on heat unit); Cotty, *Ann. Chim.*, 1911, **24**, 282 (minimum at 21°).
6 *Z. Elektrochem.*, 1908, **14**, 743; cf. Dieterici, *Ann. Phys.*, 1905, **16**, 653; Behn, *Berlin Ber.*, 1905, 72; Guillaume, *Compt. Rend.*, 1912, **154**, 1483.
7 *Gazz.*, 1894, **24**, II, 145; *Ann. Chim.*, 1893, **29**, 285; *Z. phys. Chem.*, 1893, **11**, 429.
8 *Phil. Trans.*, 1912, **212**, 1; *Proc. Phys. Soc.*, 1926, **38**, 174.
9 Scheel and Luther, *Z. Elektrochem.*, 1908, **14**, 743; Jaeger and von Steinwehr, *Ann Phys.*, 1921, **64**, 305; Landolt-Börnstein, " Tabellen," 5th edit., 1923, **2**, 1250; e.m.f. of Weston cell = 1·0183 volt.

The 20° g.cal. is very nearly 0·001 smaller than the 15° g.cal. The values for the specific heat of water, it will be seen, are in regrettably unsatisfactory agreement. There is, particularly, a divergence between the values of Callendar and Barnes on the one hand, and those of Jaeger and von Steinwehr on the other.[1] The former seemed to be supported by the measurements of Romberg.[2] Narbutt,[3] by combining all observations for water, found:

$$c_t\,(\text{true})=1{\cdot}0073-0{\cdot}0_3 7416t+0{\cdot}0_4 16845t^2-0{\cdot}0_7 9552t^3$$

$$\bar{c}\,(\text{mean})=1{\cdot}0073-0{\cdot}0_3 3708t+0{\cdot}0_5 5615t^2-0{\cdot}0_7 2388t^3,$$

taking $c_{15^\circ}=1$. This gives a minimum at 29°–30° and agrees best with Jaeger and von Steinwehr's results. The latest measurements,[4] calculated by Roth [5] for one 15° g.cal.=4·1833 int. joules, are (true sp. ht. at t° C.): $c=1{\cdot}0066-0{\cdot}0_3 5696t+0{\cdot}0_5 8742t^2$, which makes $c_0=c_{100^\circ}$.

Temp. ° C.	Callendar and Barnes	Jaeger and von Steinwehr	Temp. ° C.	Callendar and Barnes	Jaeger and von Steinwehr
5	1·0047	1·0029	40	0·9973	0·9981
10	1·0019	1·0013	45	0·9975	0·9987
15	1·0000	1·0000	50	0·9978	0·9996
20	0·9988	0·9990	60	0·9987	—
25	0·9980	0·9983	70	1·0000	—
30	0·9976	0·9979	80	1·0017	—
35	0·9973	0·9978	90	1·0036	—
			100	1·0057	—

Callendar and Barnes found a minimum sp. ht. at 37·5°, Bousfield at 25°, Jaeger and von Steinwehr at 33·5°, Jessel at 37° (lowered by dissolved air), Roth at 35° (0·9974).

The sp. hts. of heavy water (D_2O) were found [6] to be:

10° 1·0097   20° 1·0062   30° 1·0044   40° 1·0037   50° 1·0041

with a minimum at 41°.

The calorimeter used by Osborne, Stimson, and Ginnings,[7] shown diagrammatically in Fig. 10.II, consisted of a thin gold-plated copper sphere C, 5 in. diam., enclosing an electric resistance heater H of nichrome encased in a coiled metal tube filled with magnesia, two screw propellers P, and fixed guides for circulating the water. The energy input in the heater was measured by the potential drop and current. Platinum resistance thermometers and thermo-elements were used in temperature measurement and control; a resistance thermometer in a copper reference block R provided a reference datum, small differences from this in the calorimeter or other points being measured by chromel-constantan thermo-elements. The calorimeter globe was supported in an evacuated space surrounded by a controlled bath S of saturated water vapour shielding it against

1 Callendar, *Phil. Trans.*, 1912, **212**, 1; Jaeger and von Steinwehr, *Ann. Phys.*, 1921, **64**, 305; summary of older work in Winkelmann, " Handbuch der Physik," 1906, **3**, 165–177; cf. Kaye and Laby, " Tables of Physical and Chemical Constants," 9th edit., 1941, 66.

2 *Proc. Amer. Acad.*, 1922, **57**, 375; 73°/20°=1·0040.

3 *Phys. Z.*, 1918, **19**, 513.

4 Osborne, Stimson, and Ginnings, *Bur. Stand. J. Res.*, 1939, **23**, 197 (Res. Paper No. 1228); Jessel, *Proc. Phys. Soc.*, 1934, **46**, 747, who emphasised the error due to dissolved air in the continuous flow method; see the table by Awbery, " Internat. Crit. Tables," 1929, **5**, 113.

5 *Z. phys. Chem.*, 1939, **183**, 38.

6 Cockett and Ferguson, *Phil. Mag.*, 1940, **29**, 185.

7 *Bur. Stand. J. Res.*, 1939, **23**, 197.

heat exchange. The water sample was introduced from a container WC, and the saturated vapour could be withdrawn through a valve TV into a weighed glass receiver SR cooled in liquid air. The calorimeter and tubes were evacuated through VAC.

Two types of experiments were made: (i) heat capacity measurements in which the calorimeter and water sample were heated over a measured temperature range, in some cases with the calorimeter nearly full, and in others nearly empty, of liquid water; (ii) vaporisation experiments, practically isothermal, in which heat was supplied to evaporate water, the vapour being withdrawn at a controlled rate, collected in SR, and weighed:

In the first experiments the change of a quantity α is found:

$$\alpha=H-\beta=H-l_e v_l/(v_g-v_l)=H-Tv_l(\mathrm{d}p/\mathrm{d}T)$$

where H=enthalpy or heat content of saturated liquid [1] water, l_e=latent heat of evaporation, v_l=sp. vol. of saturated liquid, v_g=sp. vol. of saturated vapour,

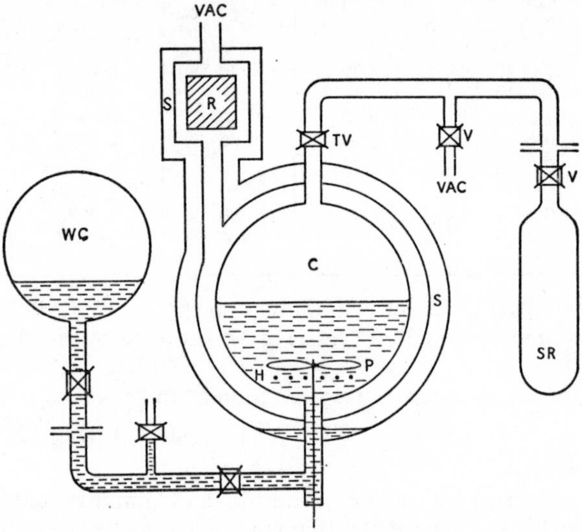

FIG. 10.II. Apparatus of Osborne, Stimson, and Ginnings

T=abs. temperature, and p=vapour pressure; $\mathrm{d}p/\mathrm{d}T$ was evaluated by an equation derived by Gerry [2] from Reichsanstalt measurements. In the second experiment a value γ is found: $\gamma=l_e+\beta$. The results in international joules per g. per 1° C. for air-free water at 1 atm. pressure were converted into absolute joules by multiplication by 1·00019, and the following equation found:

$$c_p=4{\cdot}169828+0{\cdot}0_3 364(t+100)^{5{\cdot}26}\times 10^{-10}+0{\cdot}046709(10)^{-0{\cdot}036t}.$$

In the table, the value of c_p in abs. joules, the heat content at 1 atm. (H at 0° C.=0), found by integration, $H=\int_0^t c_p \mathrm{d}t$, and the values in g.cal. per g. by the conversion factor, 1 abs. joule=0·238846 g.cal.,[3] are given.

[1] I.e. liquid under the pressure of its saturated vapour at a given temperature; this value requires correction to 1 atm. pressure before c_p=1 atm., as given in the table, is obtained. The terms are explained in § 8. viii. L, Vol. II.

[2] Osborne, Stimson, and Ginnings, *Bur. Stand. J. Res.*, 1939, **23**, 261.

[3] This is the so-called " international steam tables " (IT) value, defined as 1 g.cal.=1/860 internat. watt hour; cf. Mueller, *Mechan. Eng.* (N.Y.), 1930, **52**, 139.

t° C.	c_p	H abs. j.	H g.cal.	t° C.	c_p	H abs. j.	H g.cal.
0	4·2177	0·1026	0·0245	40	4·1786	167·5777	40·0253
5	4·2022	21·1498	5·0515	50	4·1807	209·3729	50·0079
10	4·1922	42·1341	10·0636	60	4·1844	251·1976	59·9975
15	4·1858	63·0779	15·0659	70	4·1896	293·0665	69·9977
20	4·1819	83·9963	20·0622	80	4·1964	334·9952	80·0123
25	4·1796	104·8994	25·0548	90	4·2051	377·0012	90·0452
30	4·1785	125·7943	30·0455	100	4·2160	419·1049	100·1015

There is a very flat minimum of c_p between 30° and 40°. The results agree better with those of Rowland, Laby and Hercus, and Jaeger and Steinwehr, than with those of Callendar and Barnes, and it seems as if the constant-flow calorimeter used by the latter was subject to some as yet untraced source of error both with gases and liquids. There is remarkable agreement with Rowland's values revised by Day.

In view of the disagreement among the older values of J and the fact that many energy determinations are made in terms of electrical units, Ostwald [1] proposed and used the *kilojoule* (kj.)$=10^{10}$ ergs as the thermal unit, and the *joule*$=10^7$ ergs is used in the thermochemistry section of the "International Critical Tables." In this case it is sometimes necessary to specify whether the absolute joule (10^7 ergs) or the international joule is used, the latter being [2] 1·0004 abs. joules. It is rarely that thermochemical values have a *real* accuracy affected by the difference between the two joules.

§ 15. Forms of Energy

Joule's results showed that the ratio of the work w completely spent in producing an amount of heat q is independent of the method by which the work is converted into heat, and depends only on the units of heat and work. This ratio:

$$J=w/q \qquad (1)$$

is called the *mechanical equivalent of heat*. If w is measured in ergs and q in 15° g.cals, then:

$$J=4{\cdot}185\times10^7 \text{ erg}/15^\circ \text{ g.cal.} \qquad (2)$$

It is convenient theoretically to have w and q measured in the same units, e.g. ergs, in which case $J=1$, and all equations in this book are based on this convention (first used by Rankine). It is important to notice that the equation:

$$w=q \qquad (3)$$

then obtained enables a quantity of heat to be measured in absolute units, independently of any temperature scale, or even of the conception of temperature, which is foreign to the First Law of Thermodynamics (§ 32).

The simplest explanation of Joule's results is to assume that *heat* and *work* are different forms of a physically real entity called *energy*, denoted by the symbol E. It is clear that the *potential energy* and *kinetic energy* of mechanics are other forms of this entity, and Joule's experiments show that *electrical energy* is another form. In magnetising iron or steel, energy, either in the form of mechanical work in magnetisation by contact with other magnets, or electrical energy in

[1] "Grundriss der allgemeinen Chemie," 1909, 290; "Outlines of General Chemistry," 1912, 249; the joule was proposed by Rogers, *Phys. Rev.*, 1900, **11**, 115.

[2] Bichowsky and Rossini, "Thermochemistry of Chemical Substances," New York, 1936, 9; Rossini, *Bur. Stand. J. Res.*, 1931, **6**, 1; 1934, **12**, 735; but see § 13.

electromagnets, must be supplied, and this is transformed into *magnetic energy* in the magnetised system. *Radiant energy* is familiar in the forms of light (including ultra-violet light), radiant heat, and the electromagnetic radiation used in wireless transmission. The heat (and sometimes electrical energy) set free in chemical processes leads to the assumption of the existence of *chemical energy*. To form surfaces of separation, e.g. in stretching soap films, work must be done, which is stored up as *surface energy*. Radioactive substances emit particles with large kinetic energies (α- and β-rays), or electromagnetic radiation (γ-rays), and this energy comes from changes in the interior of the atoms, or *atomic energy*. Thus, the following *forms of energy* may be recognised: [1]

(1) Kinetic energy of masses in motion.
(2) Potential energy of systems of forces.
(3) Heat.
(4) Radiant energy.
(5) Electrical energy.
(6) Magnetic energy.
(7) Chemical energy.
(8) Surface energy.
(9) Atomic energy.

These forms of energy are, in principle, interconvertible; as Rankine [2] said: " any kind of energy may be made the means of performance of any kind of work." It will be seen later (§ 29) that this interconvertibility is subject to certain restrictions. Bridgman [3] said: " No general meaning can be given to the energy concept, but only specific meanings in special cases." This rules out any validity in speculations about the energy of the " universe," and the applications of the energy principle to atomic nuclei, living organisms and the like are subject to checking of the consequences by experiment.

A good definition of energy is that due to Ostwald [4]: *energy is work or anything which can be produced from or converted into work*. All the forms of energy can thus be measured in work units. Rankine [5] defined energy as: " Every affection of substances which constitutes or is commensurable with a power of producing change in opposition to resistance," which is essentially the same definition. Although energy is sometimes defined [6] as the " capacity for doing work," it is much more than this; it has an objective existence, and is bought and sold in specified units.[7]

The modes of interconversion of forms of energy are, in general, familiar and need no description. One unusual case, in which heat energy is transformed into the mechanical energy of a sound wave, is that of the so-called " Trevelyan rocker " (really invented by Gilbert),[8] in which a hot bar of metal laid across a

[1] See the early table by J. R. Mayer (1845) in his " Mechanik der Wärme," Stuttgart, 1867, 49; practically the same in Ostwald, " Lehrbuch der allgemeinen Chemie," 1910, **2**, i, 11; the present table was given by Partington, " Thermodynamics," 1913, 27, including " Atomic energy," which is more important now than it was then.

[2] *Edin. N. Phil. J.*, 1855, **2**, 120; Buckingham, " Outline of the Theory of Thermodynamics," New York, 1900, 92.

[3] " The Logic of Modern Physics " New York, 1927, 127; Ostwald's standpoint, " Outlines of General Chemistry," 1912, 241, was that: " all we know of the outer world are energy relations, and it may well be described as a system in which different kinds of energy are arranged in a definite manner in time and space."

[4] *Z. phys. Chem.*, 1910, **68**, 757; " Outlines of General Chemistry," 1912, 16, 242.

[5] *Phil. Mag.*, 1853, **5**, 106.

[6] Maxwell, " Theory of Heat," 1875, 143.

[7] Tait, " Properties of Matter," 1899, 6, who remarked, *ibid.*, 13, that: " Titles, Family Secrets, and even Degrees, are occasionally sold," so that " to have its price " is not conclusive of objectivity; cf. Ostwald, " Lehrbuch der allgemeinen Chemie," 1910, **2**, i, 42.

[8] Gilbert, *Ann. Phys.*, 1806, **22**, 323; Trevelyan, *Phil. Mag.*, 1833, **2**, 321; *Trans. Roy. Soc. Edin.*, 1834, **12**, 137; Muncke, *Ann. Phys.*, 1832, **24**, 466; Poggendorff, *ibid.*, 1834, **33**, 553; Forbes, *Trans. Roy. Soc. Edin.*, 1834, **12**, 429; *Phil. Mag.*, 1834, **4**, 15, 182; Baden Powell,

ridge of cold metal (lead is best) emits a singing note, due to the vibration of the hot bar caused by the upward expansion of the cool support when heat passes to it, and its contraction when the heat passes into its interior by conduction.

§ 16. The First Law of Thermodynamics

As a result of the failure of actual attempts to construct a perpetual-motion machine the truth of the following statement be assumed:

A process which produces no other effects than the generation or destruction of mechanical work or of anything equivalent to mechanical work, i.e. of any form of energy, is impossible.

In order to ensure that no other changes occur, the process in which work is produced from heat or *vice versa* may be a cyclic process (§ 7). Let (q) units of heat be absorbed by a system in any cyclic process and (w) units of work be done. To denote that they refer to cyclic processes, these symbols are enclosed in brackets. Then if (q) and (w) are measured in the same units:

$$(w)=(q) \qquad \ldots \ldots \ldots \quad (1)$$

If (1) did not hold it would be possible to produce or destroy unlimited quantities of energy without producing any other change, which would contradict the First Law.

If a change is not cyclic (i.e. the initial and final states of the system are different) it is not necessary that $w=q$, since there may be a change in the energy of the system itself.

The energy content of a system is often called its *internal energy*, or *intrinsic energy*, or *total energy*, sometimes [1] denoted by U, but as it is a form of energy it may be spoken of simply as the *energy of the system*, and denoted by E. The *increase* in energy of a system in any change of state is denoted [2] by ΔE, and:

$$\Delta E \text{ (increase)} = q \text{ (absorbed)} - w \text{ (done)} \quad \ldots \ldots \quad (2)$$

This equation defines [3] ΔE, the increase of energy of the system as measured by the total amount of energy in the forms of heat (i.e. q) and work (i.e. $-w$) which passes into the system from outside during the given change of state. In the evaporation of 1 g. of water at 100° the heat $q=2251\times10^7$ ergs is absorbed, and the work 1662×10^7 ergs is done by the vapour expanding against the atmospheric pressure. The increase of energy is

$$\Delta E=(2251-1662)\times10^7=589\times10^7 \text{ ergs}=0{\cdot}589 \text{ kj.}$$

ΔE is zero *either* if q and w are separately zero, *or* if the difference $q-w$ is zero, i.e.

$$\Delta E=0 \quad \text{if} \quad q-w=0 \quad \text{or} \quad q=w \quad \ldots \ldots \quad (3)$$

This will obviously be true for *all* cyclic processes, for which ΔE is necessarily zero, and it may be true for some non-cyclic processes in which the energy of the system is constant, as in the isothermal expansion of an ideal gas (§ 8).

Suppose that a system in a given initial state (1) can pass into the final state (2) by two or more different paths (§ 7) α, β, etc., and let there be a reverse path ρ by which it can pass from the state (2) to the state (1).[4] Let the increase

Phil. Trans., 1834, **124**, 485; *Ann. Phys.*, 1835, **34**, 636; Tyndall, *Phil. Trans.*, 1854, **144**, 1; *Phil. Mag.*, 1854, **7**, 223; 1854, **8**, 1; Sondhauss, *Ann. Phys.*, 1862, **115**, 71, 177. On the conversion of vibrational energy into work, see Rayleigh, *Phil. Mag.*, 1902, **3**, 338.

1 By Clausius, *Ann. Phys.*, 1850, **79**, 368: the symbol E was used by Lord Kelvin and Maxwell.

2 The " operator " symbol Δ was used in this way by Trevor, *J. Phys. Chem.*, 1906, **10**, 392.

3 Cf. Trevor, *J. Phys. Chem.*, 1908, **12**, 297; 1909, **13**, 355; Tunell, *ibid.*, 1932, **36**, 1744.

4 This consciously excludes all vital and cosmic processes from the scope of the proof.

of energy of the system during changes along the paths α, β, and ρ be ΔE_α, ΔE_β, and $-\Delta E_\rho$ (the energy change along path ρ being of opposite sign to those along α and β, since the two together form a cycle, for which $\Delta E=0$). By combining each of the paths α and β separately with the path ρ, two different cyclic processes are obtained, for each of which the net energy change is zero:

$$\Delta E_\alpha - \Delta E_\rho = 0 \text{ and } \Delta E_\beta - \Delta E_\rho = 0$$

$$\therefore \Delta E_\alpha = \Delta E_\beta \quad \ldots\ldots\ldots \quad (3)$$

The increase of energy of a system undergoing any change of state depends only on the initial and final states of the system and is independent of the manner in which the change from one to the other is effected.

This statement has the following consequences:

(1) *The energy content of a system is a function only of the state of the system.*

(2) *When a system passes from one state* (1) *to another state* (2), *the energy change is the difference between the energies of the initial and final states*:

$$\Delta E = E_2 - E_1 \quad \ldots\ldots\ldots \quad (4)$$

(3) *The energy of an isolated system is constant*, since $q=0$ and $w=0$, therefore $E\Delta=0$, therefore $E_2=E_1$. This is sometimes called the *Principle of Conservation of Energy*.[1]

It should be carefully noted that ΔE in equation (2) cannot be written as E_2-E_1 without first proving equation (3); (2) can now be written:

$$E_2 - E_1 = q - w \quad \ldots\ldots\ldots \quad (5)$$

If the change is small $E_2-E_1=\mathrm{d}E$, $q=\delta q$, $w=\delta w$:

$$\therefore \mathrm{d}E = \delta q - \delta w \quad \ldots\ldots\ldots \quad (6)$$

It follows that $\mathrm{d}E$ is a perfect (or complete) differential (see § 27, I); since (5) and (6) show that it obeys the relation:

$$\int_1^2 \mathrm{d}E = E_2 - E_1 \quad \ldots\ldots\ldots \quad (7)$$

whereas δq and δw are not differentials of q and w but merely denote small values of q and w, the sums of which are denoted by $\int \delta q$ and $\int \delta w$. It has been proposed [2] to denote them by $\bar{\mathrm{d}}q$ and $\bar{\mathrm{d}}w$, or $đq$ and $đw$, but this is an inconvenient notation. The values of q and w for the change of state of the system depend on the path of change, whereas ΔE, equal to the difference $q-w$, is independent of the path of change.

This may be illustrated by considering the expansion of an ideal gas. If this is conducted isothermally and reversibly so that the state passes from (p_1, v_1, θ) to the state (p_2, v_2, θ), the work done is $w_\theta = k_1 \ln(v_2/v_1)$. The heat absorbed is q_θ. The energy of an ideal gas is independent of the volume if the temperature is constant (§ 8): $(\mathrm{d}E/\mathrm{d}v)_\theta=0$. Hence from (5): $w_\theta=q_\theta=k_1\ln(v_2/v_1)$ and $\Delta E=0$. This change may also be carried out irreversibly by allowing the

[1] Cf. Planck, "Das Prinzip der Erhaltung der Energie," Leipzig, 1887; 2nd edit., 1908; Bryan' "Thermodynamics," 1907, 39. Trevor, *J. Phys. Chem.*, 1909, **13**, 355, stated the first law in the form: " The algebraic sum of mechanical energy [work] and heat added to a body in any change of its thermodynamic state is equal to the concurrent change of the value of a quantity, determined it may be in different ways in different regions of state, but continuous and one-valued in any region, and containing an arbitrary additive constant." This is the energy E, and if its change is $[E_x+E_0]_a^b$ between the states a and b, E_x is the energy of the body and E_0 the arbitrary constant.

[2] By Neumann, " Vorlesungen über die mechanische Theorie der Wärme," Leipzig, 1875, pref., ix, where d is called a " differential " and $\bar{\mathrm{d}}$ a " diminutive "; see *Z. Elektrochem.*, 1912, **18**, 398; Trevor, *J. Phys. Chem.*, 1899, **3**, 389; 1900, **4**, 514, used d'W and d'Q.

volume v_1 of gas to expand into a vacuous vessel so that the total volume is v_2. In this case no external work is done, therefore $w=0$. It was found experimentally by Joule that $q=0$, hence, from $q=\Delta E+w$, it follows that again $\Delta E=0$.

§ 17. Heat Content

If the only work done in a change of state of a system is that due to expansion of volume V against an external pressure P, such as that of the atmosphere, (2), § 6 shows that:

$$w=\int_{V_1}^{V_2} P\mathrm{d}V \quad \ldots \quad (1)$$

If *the volume is constant*, $\mathrm{d}V=0$, therefore $w=0$, hence from (2), § 16:

$$\Delta E=q_v \quad \ldots \quad (2)$$

where q_v is the heat absorbed in the change at constant volume. This provides a method of measuring ΔE. *The heat absorbed by a system in any change at constant volume is equal to the increase in the energy of the system.*

If *the pressure is constant*, (1) becomes:

$$w=P(V_2-V_1) \quad \ldots \quad (3)$$

Therefore from (2), § 16:

$$\Delta E=q_p-P(V_2-V_1) \quad \ldots \quad (4)$$

where q_p is the heat absorbed in the change at constant pressure;

$$\therefore\ q_p=\Delta E+P(V_2-V_1)=\Delta E+P\Delta V$$
$$=E_2-E_1+P(V_2-V_1)$$
$$=(E_2+PV_2)-(E_1+PV_1).$$

Let

$$H=E+PV \quad \ldots \quad (5)$$

Then if P is constant:

$$q_p=(E_2+PV_2)-(E_1+PV_1)=H_2-H_1=\Delta H \quad \ldots \quad (6)$$

since E and V depend only on the actual state of the system, and hence ΔH can be equated to the difference of the values of H in the two states.

The function H sometimes symbolised by W, I, or (by Gibbs) χ, is now usually called the *heat content*. Kamerlingh Onnes [1] called it *enthalpy* (from θαλπος, heat). It is sometimes called [2] the *heat function for constant pressure.*

Equation (6) shows that *the heat absorbed by a system in changes at constant pressure is equal to the increase in the heat content of the system.* Hence *at constant pressure* the change of H depends only on the initial and final states of the system. This is not true when the pressure varies, since w is no longer given by (3) but by (1), which depends on the path of change.

From (6):

$$(\mathrm{d}q/\mathrm{d}\theta)_p=c_p=(\mathrm{d}H/\mathrm{d}\theta)_p \quad \ldots \quad (7)$$

so that *the specific heat at constant pressure is equal to the rate of increase of heat content with temperature at constant pressure.*

The energy and heat content, like the mass and volume, are proportional to the quantity of the system and are called *extensive properties*, whilst the pressure and temperature are independent of quantity and are called *intensive properties.*

[1] Dalton, *Proc. K. Akad. Wetens. Amsterdam*, 1909, **11**, 863; Porter, *Trans. Faraday Soc.*, 1922, **18**, 139; Tunell, *J. Phys. Chem.*, 1932, **36**, 1744, called it *enkaumy*, from καῦμα, burning (heat).

[2] Mollier, *Z. Verein D. Ingenieure*, 1904, **48**, 271 (for " *equal* pressures ").

If the system is composed of n_1 and n_2 mols of ideal gases before and after a chemical change, then, if the pressure and temperature remain unchanged:

$$PV_1=n_1RT \quad \text{and} \quad PV_2=n_2RT,$$

$$\therefore \; P\Delta V=P(V_2-V_1)=(n_2-n_1)RT=\Delta nRT$$

$$\therefore \; \Delta H=\Delta E+\Delta nRT \quad \text{or} \quad q_p=q_v+\Delta nRT \quad . \; . \; . \; . \quad (8)$$

§ 18. Hess's Law

The importance of the energy changes accompanying chemical reactions, although dimly perceived by the phlogistonists, was first clearly recognised by Lavoisier, who, in an investigation carried out jointly with Laplace,[1] stated as a self-evident truth that *as much heat is required to decompose a compound as is liberated when the compound is produced from its elements.* This is a special case of the First Law of Thermodynamics if the heat changes are those occurring at constant volume, when they are equal to the changes in the energy of the system, or at constant pressure, when they are equal to the changes of heat content.

In thermochemical calculations much use is made of a law discovered experimentally by Hess [2] in 1840, before Joule's experiments on the mechanical equivalent of heat:

If a chemical reaction occurs in stages, the algebraic sum of the amounts of heat evolved is equal to the total evolution of heat when the reaction occurs directly.

Equations (2) and (6), § 17, show that Hess's Law is strictly true [3] only when either (i) the volume or (ii) the pressure is constant, in which cases the heats of reaction evolved are $-\Delta E$ and $-\Delta H$. In reactions between liquids and solids the volume change ΔV is very small and the external work $P\Delta V$, where P is the atmospheric pressure, is negligible compared with ΔE. In such cases it is rarely necessary to specify whether the reaction has occurred at constant volume or pressure, or what the pressure was during the reaction. In modern work, heats of reaction are taken positive when absorbed, and are thus represented by ΔE and ΔH, the standard pressure for ΔH being 1 atm. The symbols *s*, *l*, *g* as affixes denote the solid, liquid, and gaseous states, and the absolute temperature as a suffix to ΔE or ΔH denotes the common temperature of the initial and final states, e.g.:

$$CH_3OH(l)+1\tfrac{1}{2}O_2(g)=CO_2(g)+2H_2O(l);\ \Delta H_{298}=-173{,}630 \text{ g.cal., or}$$

$$\Delta E_{298}=-173{,}330 \text{ g.cal.}$$

§ 19. Energy and Heat Content of a System

If the energy of a mass m of a homogeneous substance at some standard temperature T_0 (e.g. at 298·1° K.) is E^0, its energy at any other temperature T and the same volume is:

$$E=E^0+\int_{T_0}^{T} \mathrm{d}E \quad . \; . \; . \; . \; . \; . \; . \; . \quad (1)$$

[1] *Mém. Acad. Sci.*, 1780 [1784], 355 (359); Lavoisier, "Oeuvres," 1862, **2**, 283 (287); Ostwald's *Klassiker*, 1892, No. **40**.

[2] *Ann. Phys.*, 1840, **50**, 385; Ostwald's *Klassiker*, 1890, No. **9**; Ostwald, "Lehrbuch der allgemeinen Chemie," 1910, **2**, 54; Andrews, in 1840, mentioned Hess's "valuable memoir"; in 1849 he said Hess's law is "almost self-evident and scarcely required so elaborate a proof"; Andrews, "Scientific Papers," 1889, 89, 107, 205.

[3] Duhem, "Mécanique Chimique," 1897, **1**, 50.

From (2), § 17, and (2), § 1:

$$dE = \delta q_v = mc_v dT \quad \ldots \ldots \ldots \quad (2)$$

$$\therefore \; E = E^0 + \int_{T_0}^{T} mc_v dT \quad \ldots \ldots \ldots \quad (3)$$

Similarly if H^0 is the heat content at a temperature T_0 and given pressure, the heat content at a temperature T and the same pressure is:

$$H = H^0 + \int_{T_0}^{T} dH \quad \ldots \ldots \ldots \quad (4)$$

From (7), § 17:

$$dH = \delta q_p = mc_p dT \quad \ldots \ldots \ldots \quad (5)$$

$$\therefore \; H = H^0 + \int_{T_0}^{T} mc_p dT \quad \ldots \ldots \ldots \quad (6)$$

For 1 mol, $m = M$,

$$\therefore \; mc_v = C_v \text{ and } mc_p = C_p \quad \ldots \ldots \ldots \quad (7)$$

$$E = E^0 + \int_{T^0}^{T} C_v dT \quad \ldots \ldots \ldots \quad (8)$$

$$H = H^0 + \int_{T_0}^{T} C_p dT \quad \ldots \ldots \ldots \quad (9)$$

and for n mols the values are nE and nH. It should be noted that the specific and molecular heats in (2)–(9) are *true* specific and molecular heats (see § 1 (1)). They may, of course, be replaced by the *mean* specific and molecular heats by such relations as:

$$\int_{T_0}^{T} C_v dT = (T - T_0)\bar{C}_v$$

where $\bar{C}_v$ is the mean molecular heat in the interval of temperature $T - T_0$.

§ 20. Kirchhoff's Equation

One of the commonest problems in thermochemistry is to calculate a heat of reaction at any given temperature T, when its value at some standard temperature T_0 is given. In tables of thermochemical constants, the values of ΔE or ΔH generally refer to room temperature, 18° C. or 25° C.

Such problems are solved by an equation deduced by Person[1] and with greater generality by Kirchhoff.[2] The underlying principle is very simple. Consider first the process $aA + bB = cC$, which may denote a chemical reaction or a physical change, in which three substances are involved. Let the energies per mol of A, B, and C, at a standard temperature T_0 (abs.) be $E_A{}^0$, $E_B{}^0$, and $E_C{}^0$; then the heat of reaction (absorbed) at constant volume at T_0 is:

$$\Delta E^0 = cE_C{}^0 - (aE_A{}^0 + bE_B{}^0).$$

This will be found in tables, or can be calculated from these by Hess's law.

[1] *Ann. Chim.*, 1847, **21**, 295; 1849, **27**, 250; 1851, **33**, 437, 448; cf. Richards and Gucker, *J.A.C.S.*, 1929, **51**, 712.

[2] *Ann. Phys.*, 1858, **103**, 177; "Ges. Abhl.," 1882, 454; Ostwald's *Klassiker*, 1898, **101**; cf. Berthelot, *Ann. Chim.*, 1865, **6**, 290; "Mécanique Chimique," 1879, **1**, 102; Muir and Wilson, "The Elements of Thermal Chemistry," 1885, 49; Ostwald, "Lehrbuch der allgemeinen Chemie," 1910, **1**, 1010; **2**, 79.

Let the corresponding energies at the absolute temperature T be E_A, E_B, and E_C; then the heat of reaction at constant volume at T will be:

$$\Delta E = cE_C - (aE_A + bE_B),$$

and ΔE is to be calculated from ΔE^0.

Let C_{vA}, C_{vB}, and C_{vC} be the *true* molecular heats at constant volume of A, B, and C, which are supposed to be known as functions of temperature in the range T_0 to T, e.g. as expressed in power series (§ 1): $a+bT+cT^2+\ldots$, or given by theoretical equations, or tabulated at various temperatures in the range, when the integrals must be evaluated graphically. Then the energy per mol at the temperature T is:

$$E_T = E_{T_0} + \int_{T_0}^{T} C_v \mathrm{d}T = E^0 + \int_{T_0}^{T} C_v \mathrm{d}T, \quad \therefore\ aE_A = aE_A{}^0 + a\int_{T_0}^{T} C_{vA}\mathrm{d}T,$$

$$bE_B = bE_B{}^0 + b\int_{T_0}^{T} C_{vB}\mathrm{d}T, \quad cE_C = cE_C{}^0 + c\int_{T_0}^{T} C_{vC}\mathrm{d}T,$$

$$\Delta E = cE_C{}^0 - (aE_A{}^0 + bE_B{}^0) + c\int_{T_0}^{T} C_{vC}\mathrm{d}T - \left[a\int_{T_0}^{T} C_{vA}\mathrm{d}T + b\int_{T_0}^{T} C_{vB}\mathrm{d}T\right]$$

$$= \Delta E^0 + \int_{T_0}^{T} [cC_{vC} - (aC_{vA} + bC_{vB})]\mathrm{d}T \quad \ldots \quad (1)$$

where cC_{vC} is the total *heat capacity* at constant volume of the *final system*, and $(aC_{vA}+bC_{vB})$ is the total heat capacity at constant volume of the *initial system*. If the *algebraic sum* of the heat capacities is denoted by ΔC_v, taking those of the *products* as *positive*, and those of the initial substances as negative:

$$\Delta C_v = cC_{vC} - (aC_{vA} + bC_{vB})$$

$$\therefore\ \Delta E = \Delta E^0 + \int_{T_0}^{T} \Delta C_v \mathrm{d}T \quad \ldots \quad (2)$$

In exactly the same way, for *a reaction at constant pressure*, the equation:

$$\Delta H = \Delta H^0 + \int_{T_0}^{T} \Delta C_p \mathrm{d}T \quad \ldots \quad (3)$$

is found.

Evidently, (2) and (3) will hold for *any* reaction:

$$aA + bB + \ldots = cC + dD + \ldots$$

provided ΔC_v and ΔC_p include all the reacting substances, according to the rule stated:

$$\Delta C_v = (cC_{vC} + dC_{vD} + \ldots) - (aC_{vA} + bC_{vB} + \ldots)$$

$$\Delta C_p = (cC_{pC} + dC_{pD} + \ldots) - (aC_{pA} + bC_{pA} + \ldots)$$

It is also possible to use *mean* molecular heats, since from (5), § 1:

$$\int_{T_0}^{T} C_{vA}\mathrm{d}T = (T - T_0)\bar{C}_{vA}, \text{ etc.}$$

$$\therefore\ \Delta E = \Delta E^0 + (T - T_0)\Delta\bar{C}_v \quad \ldots \quad (4)$$

$$\Delta H = \Delta H^0 + (T - T_0)\Delta\bar{C}_p \quad \ldots \quad (5)$$

It is also possible to put $T_0 = 0$ (the absolute zero), when

$$\Delta E = \Delta E_0 + \int_0^T \Delta C_v \mathrm{d}T \quad \ldots \quad (6)$$

$$\Delta H = \Delta H_0 + \int_0^T \Delta C_p \mathrm{d}T \quad \ldots \quad (7)$$

where ΔE_0 and ΔH_0 are the heats of reaction at absolute zero. These are found from ΔE^0 and ΔH^0 (the values at $T=T_0$) by putting $T=0$ in (2) and (3), and will usually be fictitious values, since the known dependence of specific heats on temperature over the range $T-T_0$ may not hold below T_0; this does not lead to any error, provided that (6) and (7) are used for values of T in this range only, to which ΔE_0 and ΔH_0 apply. Differentiating (6) and (7) with respect to T (when ΔE_0 and ΔH_0 are constants) gives:

$$(\mathrm{d}\Delta E/\mathrm{d}T)_v=(\mathrm{d}q_v/\mathrm{d}T)=\Delta C_v \quad \text{. . . . . (8)}$$

$$(\mathrm{d}\Delta H/\mathrm{d}T)_p=(\mathrm{d}q_p/\mathrm{d}T)=\Delta C_p \quad \text{. . . . . . . (9)}$$

by the integration of which (6) and (7) are recovered, ΔE_0 and ΔH_0, or ΔE^0 and ΔH^0, being the constants of integration.

Particular care must be used in transforming specific heats given as power series involving *Centigrade* temperatures and those involving *absolute* temperatures to see that all terms are collected. Thus, a term $b(t+273)^2=bT^2$, will give $bt^2+2\times 273bt+b(273)^2$, i.e. it will contribute a term to the constant term, and one to the term involving t, in the series.

In thermochemical notation, the gaseous, liquid, and solid states may be denoted by (*g*), (*l*), and (*s*) placed after the symbols; an older notation used square brackets round the symbol for solids, e.g. [Cu], round brackets for gases, e.g. (O_2), and no brackets for liquids, e.g. H_2O; in another system, ordinary roman symbols were used for liquids, heavy type for solids, e.g. **NaCl**, and italic for gases, e.g. *Cl*₂.

As an example, consider the heat of formation of steam at constant volume:

$$H_2(g)+\tfrac{1}{2}O_2(g)=H_2O(g);\ \Delta E_{290}=-57{,}290 \text{ g.cal.}$$

For the initial system:

$$C_v(H_2)=4\cdot 650+0\cdot 75\times 10^{-3}T;\ C_v(O_2)=4\cdot 850+0\cdot 75\times 10^{-3}T$$

$$\therefore\ {}_i\Sigma C_v=7\cdot 075+1\cdot 125\times 10^{-3}T.$$

For the final system:

$$C_v(H_2O)=5\cdot 750+1\cdot 566\times 10^{-3}T-0\cdot 1878\times 10^{-5}T^2+0\cdot 1824\times 10^{-8}T^3 \\ -0\cdot 1308\times 10^{-15}T^5={}_f\Sigma C_v$$

$$\therefore\ \Delta C_v={}_f\Sigma C_v-{}_i\Sigma C_v=-1\cdot 325+0\cdot 441\times 10^{-3}T-0\cdot 1878\times 10^{-5}T^2 \\ +0\cdot 1824\times 10^{-8}T^3-0\cdot 1308\times 10^{-15}T^5.$$

From (6):

$$\Delta E_T=\Delta E_0+\int_0^T \Delta C_v \mathrm{d}T.$$

Substitute $\Delta E_T=\Delta E_{290}=-57{,}290$ and integrate from 0 to 290; then it is found that $\Delta E_0=-56{,}911$ g.cal.

$$\therefore\ \Delta E_T=-56{,}911-1\cdot 325T+0\cdot 2205\times 10^{-3}T^2-0\cdot 626\times 10^{-6}T^3 \\ +0\cdot 456\times 10^{-9}T^4-0\cdot 218\times 10^{-16}T^6.$$

§ 21. Difference of Specific Heats

Let unit mass of a fluid with the characteristic equation

$$p=\mathrm{f}(v, \theta) \quad \text{. . . . . (1)}$$

absorb a small amount of heat δq, and let a small amount of work $\delta w=p\mathrm{d}v$ be done by expansion. From (2), § 16:

$$\delta q=\mathrm{d}E+\delta w=\mathrm{d}E+p\mathrm{d}v \quad \text{. . . . . (2)}$$

The energy is a function of the state, and hence $\mathrm{d}E$ is a perfect differential:

$$\mathrm{d}E=(\mathrm{d}E/\mathrm{d}\theta)_v\mathrm{d}\theta+(\mathrm{d}E/\mathrm{d}v)_\theta\mathrm{d}v \quad . \quad . \quad . \quad . \quad . \quad . \quad . \quad (3)$$

from which, by substitution in (2):

$$\delta q=(\mathrm{d}E/\mathrm{d}\theta)_v\mathrm{d}\theta+[(\mathrm{d}E/\mathrm{d}v)_\theta+p]\mathrm{d}v \quad . \quad . \quad . \quad . \quad . \quad (4)$$

For a change at constant volume, $\mathrm{d}v=0$

$$\therefore\ \delta q_v=(\mathrm{d}E/\mathrm{d}\theta)_v\mathrm{d}\theta \quad \therefore\ (\mathrm{d}E/\mathrm{d}\theta)_v=(\mathrm{d}q/\mathrm{d}\theta)_v=c_v \quad . \quad . \quad . \quad (5)$$

from (3), § 1.

For a change at constant temperature, $\mathrm{d}\theta=0$:

$$\therefore\ \delta q_\theta=[(\mathrm{d}E/\mathrm{d}v)_\theta+p]\mathrm{d}v \quad \therefore\ (\mathrm{d}E/\mathrm{d}v)_\theta+p=(\mathrm{d}q/\mathrm{d}v)_\theta=l_v \quad . \quad . \quad (6)$$

Equation (6) is important, since it is a very common error to suppose that when the volume of a system changes at constant temperature by δv, leading to the performance of work $p\delta v$, this work is equal to the heat absorbed δq. The equation shows that this is true only when the energy of the system does not change, whereas it usually does. In (6), l_v is the *latent heat of expansion*, defined in § 3.

By substituting from (5) and (6) in (4), equation (2a), § 3 is found:

$$\delta q=c_v\mathrm{d}\theta+l_v\mathrm{d}v \quad . \quad . \quad . \quad . \quad . \quad . \quad . \quad . \quad . \quad (7)$$

and by dividing by $\mathrm{d}\theta$:

$$\mathrm{d}q/\mathrm{d}\theta=c_v+l_v(\mathrm{d}v/\mathrm{d}\theta) \quad . \quad . \quad . \quad . \quad . \quad . \quad . \quad . \quad . \quad (8)$$

Although δq is not a perfect differential (§ 27.I), $(\mathrm{d}q/\mathrm{d}\theta)_v$ and $(\mathrm{d}q/\mathrm{d}v)_\theta$ have definite values, since the state depends only on v and θ, and when either of these is kept constant the path of change is fixed, and hence $(\mathrm{d}\theta)_v$ and $(\mathrm{d}v)_\theta$ are definite changes.

In (8), $(\mathrm{d}q/\mathrm{d}\theta)$ is indefinite, since $(\mathrm{d}v/\mathrm{d}\theta)$ may have any number of values according to the conditions obtaining when θ is changed. If the pressure is constant, these two differential coefficients become definite and:

$$(\mathrm{d}q/\mathrm{d}\theta)_p=c_v+l_v(\mathrm{d}v/\mathrm{d}\theta)_p \quad . \quad . \quad . \quad . \quad . \quad . \quad . \quad . \quad (9)$$

But $(\mathrm{d}q/\mathrm{d}\theta)_p=c_p$, the specific heat at constant pressure, hence from (6) and (9):

$$c_p=c_v+l_v(\mathrm{d}v/\mathrm{d}\theta)_p=c_v+[(\mathrm{d}E/\mathrm{d}v)_\theta+p](\mathrm{d}v/\mathrm{d}\theta)_p \quad . \quad . \quad . \quad (10)$$

which [1] gives the difference of specific heats c_p-c_v.

In the case of an ideal gas [2] $(\mathrm{d}E/\mathrm{d}v)_\theta=0$ (§ 8) and $pv=\boldsymbol{R}T$ per mol

$$\therefore\ C_p=C_v+p(\mathrm{d}v/\mathrm{d}T)_p=C_v+\boldsymbol{R} \quad . \quad . \quad . \quad . \quad . \quad . \quad (11)$$

The term $p(\mathrm{d}v/\mathrm{d}T)_p$ is the external work of expansion per 1° rise in temperature. Equation (6) shows that for an ideal gas

$$l_v=p \quad . \quad . \quad . \quad . \quad . \quad . \quad . \quad . \quad . \quad . \quad . \quad (12)$$

J. R. Mayer [3] made the first calculation of the mechanical equivalent of heat by using (11), the term $p(\mathrm{d}v/\mathrm{d}T)_p$, the external work of expansion against the atmospheric pressure, being expressed in mechanical (work) units, and c_p-c_v (in g. cal. per g.) in thermal units, in the case of air. With modern values, $c_p=0{\cdot}2389$, $c_v=0{\cdot}1702$ (calculated from c_p by using the experimental value of $c_p/c_v=1{\cdot}4034$) g.cal., therefore $c_p-c_v=0{\cdot}0687$ g.cal. One g. of air at 0° expands by 2·83 cm.³ on heating to 1° C., and 1 atm. pressure=1033 g./cm.², therefore work done in expansion=1033×2·83=2923·4 g.cm., therefore $J=2923{\cdot}4/0{\cdot}0686=42{,}615$ g.cm. per g.cal. The value found directly is 42,670. Mayer, with less accurate data, calculated 36,500.

[1] Clausius, *Ann. Phys.*, 1856, **98**, 173. [2] *Ibid.*, 1850, **79**, 368. [3] *Ann.*, 1842, **42**, 233.

Equation (10) has only a very limited application, since l_v is not usually known, but the Second Law of Thermodynamics (§ 47) transforms it into an equation of wide applicability.

THE SECOND LAW OF THERMODYNAMICS

§ 22. History of the Second Law of Thermodynamics

Whereas the First Law of Thermodynamics seems easy to understand, since the idea of energy is familiar even in elementary teaching, this is not the case with the Second Law. Most students of chemistry find difficulty in appreciating its meaning and content.

The underlying principle of the Second Law of Thermodynamics was discovered by Sadi Carnot [1] in 1824 in a theoretical consideration of the method of obtaining work (" motive power ") from heat by heat engines, such as the steam engine. In comparing the efficiencies of heat engines, i.e. the work they can produce from a given quantity of heat, he was led to consider an ideal engine which converts the maximum fraction of the heat supplied into work, and this is the reversible engine described in § 8. He proved that such a reversible engine is the most efficient one, and that all reversible engines, working between the same two temperatures of hot body and cold body, are equally efficient. At that time Carnot (with all professional physicists and most chemists) regarded heat as an imponderable fluid, *caloric*, which cannot be created or destroyed, and can " flow " from a hotter body to a cooler one, and he supposed that the work done was derived from a quantity of caloric " falling " from a high to a low temperature, the work being proportional to the difference of temperatures, just as the work done by a quantity of falling water is proportional to the difference in level. This superficial analogy is, of course, incorrect, since some of the heat is converted into work, and if heat " falls " reversibly from one temperature to a lower one, it is the *entropy* (§ 33) transferred which, when multiplied by the difference of temperature, gives the work done, so that entropy has been identifiable with Carnot's caloric.[2] This purely formal analogy is of little significance or importance.[3]

The Second Law of Thermodynamics was first satisfactorily stated by Clausius in a paper read on 18 February, 1850, to the Berlin Academy of Science, and published in March and April of that year.[4] William Thomson (Lord

[1] " Réflexions sur la Puissance Motrice du Feu et sur les Machines propres à développer cette Puissance," Paris, 1824; collation on Cambridge University Library copy (Syn. 6. 82. 24[1]): i *r* title, i *v* Imprimerie de Guiraudet, Rue Saint Honoré N° 315; ii *r* title page, ii *v* blank; pp. 118, plate; facsimilé reprint, 1903 (1912, 1924); reprint in *Ann. de l'École Norm.*, 1872, **1**, 393, and in book form, with additions of unpublished notes by Carnot, Paris, 1878; transl. by Thurston, " Reflections on the Motive Power of Heat," London, 1890; Ostwald's *Klassiker*, 1892, **37**; Harper's " Scientific Memoirs," New York, 1899, **6**. The book of 1824 was extremely scarce even as early as about 1845, and Carnot's ideas were mostly known only from Clapeyron's memoir of 1834 (§ 41). " Sadi Carnot. Biographie et Manuscrit publiées sur le haut patronage de l'Académie des Sciences avec une Introduction de M. Émile Picard," Paris, 1927, with two portraits of Carnot, the usual one (aged 17) and one later in life.

[2] See § 34; Callendar, *Phil. Mag.*, 1913, **26**, 787; Larmor, *Proc. Roy. Soc.*, 1918, **94**, 326; " Math. and Phys. Papers," Cambridge, 1929, **2**, 590.

[3] See § 23.

[4] Ueber die bewegende Kraft der Wärme and die Gesetze welche sich daraus für die Wärmelehre selbst ableiten lassen, *Ann. Phys.*, 1850, **79**, 368, 500; *Jahresb.*, 1850, 37; *Ann. Chim.*, 1852, **35**, 482; *Phil. Mag.*, 1851, **2**, 1, 102; " Die mechanische Wärmetheorie," Brunswick, 1876, 72, 355; " The Mechanical Theory of Heat," transl. Browne, 1879, 69; Harper's " Scientific Memoirs," New York, 1899, **6**.

Kelvin),[1] who says he had independently arrived at his statement of Carnot's principle in terms of the efficiency of a reversible engine at the commencement of 1851, without knowledge of Clausius's paper of 1850, states unequivocally that " the merit of first establishing the proposition upon correct principles is entirely due to Clausius," and as Clausius and Thomson are the only possible claimants for the honour of founding the science of thermodynamics, the question of priority may be regarded as closed. The " conciliation " of Carnot's and Mayer's principles, which was discovered by Clausius and Thomson, was also discussed (apparently independently) by Hirn.[2]

§ 23. Energetics

Since *work=force×distance*, it seems possible that other forms of energy might be represented as the product of two factors. Rankine [3] interpreted Carnot's cycle as involving the " fall of heat " down a temperature difference; he later [4] introduced the name " science of energetics " as meaning a generalised thermodynamics, and supposed that " every kind of energy may be made the means of performing any kind of work," so that it may be represented as a product of two factors, x a " passive accident " and X an " effort " or " active accident." J. Thomson [5] had similar ideas. Gibbs [6] represented small changes of various forms of energy by expressions of the general form $X\mathrm{d}x$, where X may be called a *generalised force* and x a *generalised coordinate*, but these names are not used by Gibbs. Maxwell,[7] in discussing the work of Gibbs (which he was practically the first to notice), remarked that the existence of a system depends on the *quantities* or *magnitudes* of the system, which are the quantities of the components, the volumes, and the entropies, as well as on the *intensities* of the system, viz. the temperature and the chemical potentials of the components. He says [8] the variables defining the state of a system may be separated into two sets, one of which includes intensities (pressure, temperature, etc.) and the other magnitudes (volume, entropy, etc.). The first are sometimes called the *intensive properties*, and the second the *extensive properties*, of a system. The intensive properties are independent of the quantity (e.g. mass) of the system, whilst the extensive properties of a homogeneous system in a given state are proportional to its quantity. Trevor [9] said that " work " terms are of the form *force×space change* and other energy terms of the form *potential×quantity change*, so that he distinguished between " work " and " work equivalent."

1 *Trans. Roy. Soc. Edin.*, 1853, **20**, 261 (read 1851); *Phil. Mag.*, 1852, **4**, 8, 105, 168; *Ann. Chim.*, 1852, **36**, 118; *Jahresb.*, 1851, 32; " Math. and Phys. Papers," 1882, **1**, 174; see Larmor, *Proc. Roy. Soc.*, 1908, **81**, Appendix, iii; *ibid.*, 1918, **94**, 326; " Math. and Phys. Papers," Cambridge, 1929, **2**, 281, 590; Clausius, " Die mechanische Wärmetheorie," 1879, **2**, 321 f.; Harper's " Scientific Memoirs," New York, 1899, **6**.

2 " Recherches sur l'Équivalent Mécanique de la Chaleur," Colmar, 1858, 200. Hirn's work has generally received little attention.

3 *Phil. Mag.*, 1853, **5**, 106; " Misc. Sci. Papers," 1881, 203.

4 *Proc. Phil. Soc. Glasgow*, 1855, **3**, 381; *Edin. N. Phil. J.*, 1855, **2**, 120; " Misc. Sci. Papers," 1881, 209.

5 *Proc. Roy. Soc.*, 1861, **11**, 473; cf. Mach, " Geschichte und Wurzel des Satzes von der Erhaltung der Arbeit," Prague, 1872, 54; q. by Ostwald, " Lehrbuch der allgemeinen Chemie," 1910, **2**, 45.

6 *Trans. Connect. Acad.*, 1875–8, **3**, 108, 343; " Scientific Papers," 1906, **1**, 55.

7 " Conferences. Special Loan Collection of Scientific Apparatus " [South Kensington Museum], 1876, 145; *Proc. Cambr. Phil. Soc.*, 1876, **2**, 427; *Phil. Mag.*, 1908, **16**, 818; " Scientific Papers," 1890, **2**, 498; Larmor, " Math. and Phys. Papers," Cambridge, 1929, **2**, 705.

8 " Theory of Heat," 1875, 194.

9 *J. Phys. Chem.*, 1899, **3**, 339.

The use of intensity and capacity factors of energy was extended by Popper,[1] Le Chatelier,[2] Helm,[3] and Ostwald.[4] Such factors are usually given as follows, and the idea has often been used:[5]

Intensity factors	*Capacity factors*
force	distance
velocity	momentum
pressure	volume
temperature	entropy
electromotive force	quantity of electricity
surface tension	surface
chemical potential	quantity of substance

In some cases, e.g. with radiation,[6] this scheme is less obvious. Clausius had emphasised[7] that the Second Law is quite different in nature from the First Law, and the whole basis of " Energetics " was criticised by Boltzmann[8] and by Planck.[9] Its revival[10] seems to serve no useful purpose, and no use will be made of it here.

§ 24. Perpetual Motion of the Second Kind

The First Law of Thermodynamics is equivalent to the negation of a *perpetual motion of the first kind*, in which work or energy would be derived from nothing, and in particular work could appear without heat disappearing, and *vice versa.* The Second Law of Thermodynamics corresponds with the negation of a *perpetual motion of the second kind*,[11] in which work (or any form of energy which is directly and completely convertible into work, such as electrical energy)

[1] " Die physikalische Grundsätze der elektr. Kraftübertragung," Vienna, 1884, 9 f.; q. by Ostwald, " Lehrbuch der allgemeinen Chemie," 1910, **2**, 45.

[2] *Compt. Rend.*, 1887, **104**, 356; *J. de Phys.*, 1894, **3**, 289, 352; *Z. phys. Chem.*, 1895, **15**, 700.

[3] " Die Lehre von der Energie," Leipzig, 1897, 59; " Die Energetik nach ihrer geschichtlichen Entwickelung," Leipzig, 1898, 253, 299; " Grundzüge der mathematischen Chemie," Leipzig, 1894, 24; transl. Morgan, " Principles of Mathematical Chemistry," New York, 1897, 43; *Ann. Phys.*, 1896, **57**, 647; *Verhl. d. D. Phys. Ges.*, 1907, **9**, 442; *Phys. Z.*, 1907, **8**, 836.

[4] *Z. phys. Chem.*, 1892, **9**, 563; 1892, **10**, 363; 1894, **15**, 399 (the " chemometer "); 1895, **18**, 305; *Ann. Phys.*, 1897, **58**, 154; " Lehrbuch der allgemeinen Chemie," 1910, **2**, 44; " Outlines of General Chemistry," 1912, 243; Ostwald, " Lebenslinien," 1927, **2**, 176, afterwards admitted that the treatment of " heat factors " was erroneous, and had led to later mistakes; Donnan, *J.C.S.*, 1933, 346, says Ostwald in his lectures tried to deduce the Second Law from the First.

[5] Glennie, *Phil. Mag.*, 1861, **21**, 24, 274, 350 (on " energetics "); Nichols, *ibid.*, 1876, **1**, 22, 369; Meyerhoffer, *Z. phys. Chem.*, 1891, **7**, 544; Peddie, *Proc. Roy. Soc. Edin.*, 1892, **19**, 253; *Z. phys. Chem.*, 1894, **13**, 128; Volkmann, *Ann. Phys.*, 1897, **61**, 196; Wiedeburg, *ibid.*, 1897, **61**, 705; Gruner, *Z. phys. Chem.*, 1897, **23**, 636; Hastelet, *Rev. Gén. Sci.*, 1907, **18**, 483.

[6] Joffé, *Ann. Phys.*, 1911, **36**, 534 (capacity factor unknown).

[7] Quoted by Szily, *Phil. Mag.*, 1876, **1**, 1.

[8] *Ann. Phys.*, 1896, **57**, 39, 773; 1896, **58**, 595; 1897, **60**, 231, 392; 1897, **61**, 790; " Wiss. Abhl.," 1909, **3**, 558, 567, 579, 638; " Populäre Schriften," Leipzig, 1905, 25, 113, 137; Lorentz, *J. de Phys.*, 1905, **4**, 533.

[9] *Ann. Phys.*, 1896, **57**, 72; " Acht Vorlesungen über theoretische Physik," Leipzig, 1910, 11.

[10] Garver, *J. Phys. Chem.*, 1911, **15**, 20, 613; Michaud, " Enérgetique Générale," Paris, 1921; *J. Chim. Phys.*, 1942, **39**, 11; Hazlehurst, *J. Phys. Chem.*, 1939, **43**, 759; Brönsted, " Physical Chemistry," 1937; *J. Phys. Chem.*, 1940, **44**, 699; *Kgl. Danske Vidensk. Selskab., Mat. fys.*, 1939, **16**, No. 10; 1941, **19**, No. 8; and criticism, Anon., *Nature*, 1939, **142**, 273; MacDougall, *J. Phys. Chem.*, 1940, **44**, 713; Rosenberg, *Fysik. Tidsskr.*, 1943, **41**, 1. See also Damianovich, *An. Soc. Cient. Argentina*, 1917, **84**, 105; 1928, **105**, 225; Denina, *Gazz.*, 1925, **55**, 638; 1927, **57**, 3, 415.

[11] This name is due to Balfour Stewart, " An Elementary Treatise on Heat," Oxford, 1888, 380; and Ostwald, *Z. phys. Chem.*, 1892, **10**, 362; " Lehrbuch der allgemeinen Chemie," 1910, **2**, 474.

is derivable from heat taken from a body at a uniform temperature without any other permanent change or changes occurring anywhere else during the process.

This seems sufficiently obvious. A steamship might be supposed to draw on the immense store of heat in the ocean, convert it into work, and return it again as heat by the friction of the propeller and of the ship itself. Such a method of propelling a ship, which does not contradict the First Law, involves a perpetual motion of the second kind and is obviously impossible. Ostwald [1] suggested that the negation of a perpetual motion of the second kind is a special case of a more general principle, that " what is in equilibrium in one way is in equilibrium in all ways, and what is not in equilibrium in one way is not in equilibrium in any way."

It might be supposed, on the basis of the impossibility of a perpetual motion of the second kind, that heat taken from a body of uniform temperature cannot be converted into work, but this conclusion is false.[2] Suppose that a quantity of a gas, e.g. air, is contained in a thermally conducting cylinder A (Fig. 11.II) closed by a frictionless piston *a* maintained in equilibrium by suitable weights placed upon it, and let A be immersed in a large bath of water B. Now allow the gas to expand *reversibly* by removing successively very small weights from the piston, which rises to *b*. The expanding gas does work *w*. The energy *E* of the ideal gas is unchanged (this is very nearly the case with air), and the whole of the energy *w* must be derived from an equal quantity of heat, *q*, absorbed isothermally by the gas from the water bath. Hence work *w* has been done at the expense of heat *q* taken from a body at a uniform temperature.

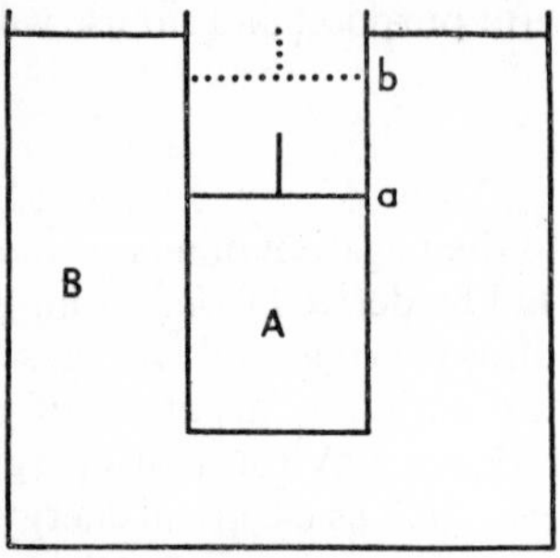

FIG. 11.II. Isothermal Expansion of a Gas

This is not a perpetual motion of the second kind, since there is a permanent change in the gas: it now occupies a larger volume. To restore the original volume, the work *w* must be spent on compressing the gas and the equal amount of heat *q* is given out by the gas to the water bath. On the whole, therefore, no work is done and no heat is taken from the water bath, when the gas is first expanded reversibly, and then compressed reversibly so as to recover its initial state, and no changes are left in other bodies.

This seems obvious, but now consider the following case. The cylinder is closed by a thin glass diaphragm at *a*, and at *b* is another strong diaphragm, the space *ab* being vacuous. If the diaphragm *a* is broken (say by rolling against it a marble in the space *ab*), the gas expands by rushing into *ab* without doing external work, and Joule's experiment (§ 23.VII C) showed that its temperature remained the same as before expansion, hence no heat is taken from the water bath. To recover the original state of the gas, i.e. occupying the initial volume, the work *w* must be spent in compressing the gas isothermally and the equal amount of heat *q* passes into the water bath. This result is quite different from the first, in which the work *w* was first obtained and then spent, and the heat *q* was first absorbed and then emitted. Here a permanent change has occurred, not in the gas, which is restored to its initial state, but in the water bath, which

[1] *Z. phys. Chem.*, 1894, **15**, 399; " Principles of Inorganic Chemistry," 1904, 135; in " Outlines of General Chemistry," 1912, 34, he says this is due to Lord Kelvin, but gives no reference; cf. Bridgman, " The Nature of Thermodynamics," Cambridge (U.S.A.), 1941, 116 f.

[2] Clausius, *Phil. Mag.*, 1868, **35**, 405.

has gained an amount of heat q. At the same time a weight, the descent of which furnished the work of compression, is left at a lower level and has so lost an amount of potential energy, which could have been obtained in the form of work but is now converted into an equivalent amount of heat given to a body of constant temperature. In order to make the whole change completely reversible, i.e. to leave *everything*, gas and surroundings, in exactly the same state as at the start, this heat would have to be taken from the water bath and converted into potential energy by raising the weight to its original height. This process, however, would be a perpetual motion of the second kind. The essential difference between the two cases is that, in the first case the volume changes of the gas are *reversible* (in the thermodynamic sense), whilst in the second case they are *irreversible*, and the importance of reversibility in connection with a perpetual motion of the second kind, and hence with the Second Law, thus becomes obvious.

§ 25. Equilibrium and Thermodynamic Reversibility

The following are stated by way of definitions: (i) *An equilibrium state is one which is independent of time.* In practice systems are encountered which are only apparently in equilibrium, e.g. a mixture of hydrogen and oxygen gases at room temperature in the absence of a catalyst, when liquid water would be the stable system. Such systems are in states of " false " equilibrium. In all cases only " true " equilibrium states are contemplated, and are more formally defined in (4) below.

(ii) *A reversible process is a continuous sequence of equilibrium states.* The following consequences are immediately deducible.

(1) Any equation specifying a reversible change is a condition of equilibrium of a system.

(2) Any change which occurs spontaneously is an irreversible change, and reversible changes are only ideal limiting cases of real changes.

(3) A system σ in an equilibrium state a can pass into another system σ' in a state a' only by the action of external influences, X. If the system σ' in the second state a' is also an equilibrium state, the change from σ to σ' is *in the limit* a reversible change, and this is the case only when all states intermediate between a and a' are also equilibrium states.

(4) In a true equilibrium state, the smallest change of any external condition which influences the state will produce a small change of state in one direction or the opposite ($\pm\delta a$) according to the sense of the change of the influence ($\pm\delta X$).

(5) All irreversible changes proceed in one sense only, since if the change could proceed spontaneously equally well in the reverse sense, the change would be reversible. Hence irreversible changes correspond with the passage of a system in a given state to a system in a state of greater *probability*, or if W_1 and W_2 are the probabilities of the initial and final states, then $W_2 > W_1$ for all irreversible changes. In reversible changes $W_2 = W_1$, the case $W_2 < W_1$ being excluded by reason of the reversibility, since for the reverse change $W_2 > W_1$, corresponding with an irreversible change. For this reason, the properties of irreversible changes and the Second Law of Thermodynamics have a statistical validity only (see Section IV).

(6) Certain functions of state of a system must change in the same sense in an irreversible change, i.e. functions of one class (A) always decrease, and functions of another class (B) always increase. A function of class B must be at the same time a function of the probability of the system. It will be shown later than the

free energy F is a function of class A, and the entropy S a function of class B, such that $S=k \ln W$, where k is a universal constant.[1]

§ 26. Free Energy

The reversible or irreversible expansion of a gas at constant temperature can be considered from another point of view. It has been seen that when the expansion is carried out reversibly the maximum amount of work can be obtained. It seems simple to *postulate* that this *maximum work* [2] of an *isothermal* change is equal to the *diminution* of the *free energy*,[3] F, of the system:

$$w_T = -\Delta F \quad . \quad . \quad . \quad . \quad . \quad . \quad . \quad . \quad . \quad (1)$$

where ΔF is the *increase* of free energy in the given change.

For an ideal gas (1 mol), from § 6:

$$w_T = RT \ln (V_2/V_1) = -\Delta F.$$

The apparent simplicity of the idea of free energy is belied by a consideration of the two cases of expansion of a gas considered in § 24. In the first, *reversible*, expansion, the free energy of the gas decreases by $RT \ln (V_2/V_1)$, but in actual fact the *energy* of the gas remains constant, so that the whole of the diminution of free energy of the gas has come from the energy of the water bath, drawn upon to provide the work of expansion.[4] In the second, *irreversible*, expansion, the energy of the gas and that of the water bath are both unchanged and no work is done, yet the free energy of the gas still diminishes by $RT \ln (V_2/V_1)$, since the gas by its irreversible expansion has lost the capacity it had, in its unexpanded state, of making use of the energy of the water bath by doing this amount of work when expanded *reversibly* from the initial volume V_1 to the final volume V_2.

[1] On the concepts underlying this section, see Duhem, *J. Math.* (Liouville), 1892, **8**, 269; 1893, **9**, 293; 1894, **10**, 207; " Traité Élémentaire de la Mécanique Chimique fondée sur la Thermodynamique," Paris, 1897, **1**, 32, 56 f.; Poincaré, " Thermodynamique," in " Cours de Phys. Math.," Paris, 1892, **3**; Wald, *Z. phys. Chem.*, 1887, **1**, 408; Wesendonck, *Ann. Phys.*, 1899, **69**, 809; Guye, *J. Chim. Phys.*, 1917, **15**, 215; Berthoud, *ibid.*, 1919, **17**, 589; Kimball, *J. Phys. Chem.*, 1931, **35**, 611; Partington, " Chemical Thermodynamics," 3rd edit., 1940, 25; Wilson, *Phil. Mag.*, 1942, **33**, 831; Scatchard, *Science*, 1942, **95**, 27.

[2] The name " maximum work " for the work obtained in a *reversible* change is due to Clausius, *Ann. Phys.*, 1850, **79**, 500. It was more particularly used for an *isothermal* change by Nernst, " Theoretical Chemistry," 1904, 17 (where it is denoted by *A*).

[3] The name " free energy " is due to H. von Helmholtz, *Berlin Ber.*, 1882, I, 22; " Vorlesungen über thoretische Physik, Theorie der Wärme," 1903, 109 f.; Ostwald's *Klassiker*, 1902, **124**, 18; R. von Helmholtz, *Ann. Phys.*, 1887, **30**, 401; *Z. phys. Chem.*, 1887, **1**, 203. Other names are " puissance motrice " (Carnot, 1824; Le Chatelier, *J. de Phys.*, 1894, **3**, 289), " action maximum " (Clapeyron, 1834), " force " (Kraft) (Mayer, 1842; Helmholtz, 1847; Saint-Robert, " Principes de Thermodynamique," Turin, 1865), " motivity " (W. Thomson, *Phil. Mag.*, 1879, **7**, 348; " Math. and Phys. Papers," 1882, **1**, 456; 1911, **5**, 6), " power of working " or " work-producing power " (Tait, " Sketch of Thermodynamics," Edinburgh, 1877, 62), " available energy " (Maxwell, 1871), and " work function " (Fowler, " Statistical Mechanics," Cambridge, 1929, 96, 570). The name " free energy " is, unfortunately, used for a different function ($F+PV$) by G. N. Lewis, *J.A.C.S.*, 1913, **35**, 1, and Lewis and Randall, " Thermodynamics," New York, 1923, 158, and other authors, e.g. Butler, " Chemical Thermodynamics," 1946, 259; see § 44. This function, $G=E-TS+PV$ (S=entropy), is called the " available energy " in the present book. The name " free energy " for it does not seem correct, since if $F=E-TS$ is the free energy, $G=E-TS+PV=(E+PV)-TS=H-TS$, should be called the " free heat content " or " free enthalpy." See the interesting discussion by Larmor, *Phil. Trans.*, 1897, **190**, 205; " Math. and Phys. Papers," Cambridge, 1929, **2**, 82 f.

[4] It may, of course, be said that the work comes *initially* from the energy of the gas, the loss of which is continually and exactly replenished by energy drawn in from the water bath by absorption of heat, but no obvious purpose is served by this complication in the *thermodynamic* argument. In the *kinetic* description, the energy of the gas necessarily intervenes.

§ 27. Dissipation of Energy

The idea of free energy is closely related to a general principle of *dissipation of energy* introduced by Lord Kelvin [1] (1852). In this, potential energy, electrical energy, and, in general, all forms of free energy, are regarded as useful forms of energy, available for direct conversion into work; heat in a body of uniform temperature is completely unavailable energy, since it cannot be converted into work unless some other changes, which render energy unavailable, occur as well. All irreversible changes tend to produce unavailable energy. The conversion of free energy into unavailable energy is called *dissipation* (or degradation) of energy, and all irreversible processes lead to dissipation of energy; the final result of all these will, if the principle holds good, be the reduction of the whole stock of energy in any system into heat at a uniform temperature, when all change will cease.

The various aspects of the principle of dissipation of energy were clearly stated in a Royal Institution lecture by Lord Rayleigh,[2] in which its implications for chemistry were pointed out, and in a later paper, discussed in the next paragraph, he gave an excellent quantitative illustration of it in connection with the mixing of chemically different gases.

§ 28. Mixing of Gases

If a light gas such as hydrogen is carefully stratified over a heavy gas such as carbon dioxide in a cylinder, it is found that the two gases slowly mix by *diffusion*. This is an irreversible process, taking place spontaneously, and no external work is obtained. It is, however, possible to mix the gases reversibly and so obtain work, by making use of a *semi-permeable diaphragm* (first used in thermodynamics by Gibbs [3]) which permits only one gas to pass through it. The energy dissipated in the spontaneous mixing of gases was first calculated by Lord Rayleigh [4] and by Boltzmann.[5]

Call the two gases (1) and (2). Let n_1 mols of gas (1) occupying a volume V_1 be separated from n_2 mols of gas (2) occupying a volume V_2 in a cylinder (Fig. 12.II) by two selectively permeable (" semi-permeable ") pistons A (freely permeated by gas (1) but impervious to gas (2)), and R (freely permeated by gas (2) but impervious to gas (1)). The pistons tend to separate, A by the pressure exerted by gas (2) and R by the pressure exerted by gas (1). If the expansive forces are balanced by thrusts applied to the piston rods, and the whole

1 *Proc. Roy. Soc. Edin.*, 1857, **3**, 139 (read 1852); *Phil. Mag.*, 1852, **4**, 304; 1853, **5**, 102; " Math. and Phys. Papers," 1882, **1**, 511; 1884, **2**, 182; 1911, **5**, 1, 6, 11; Liveing, " Chemical Equilibrium," Cambridge, 1885, 7; Arrhenius, " Das Werden der Welten," Leipzig, 1907, iv, 58, 85, 199; transl. Borns, " Worlds in the Making," New York, 1908, xiii, 94, 209; Brunhes, " La Dégradation de l'Enérgie," Paris, 1908; Franklin, *Phys. Rev.*, 1910, **30**, 766.

2 *Nature*, 1875, **11**, 454; " Scientific Papers," 1899, **1**, 238. The dissipation of energy is equivalent to the principle of *compensating transformations* stated by Clausius in *Ann. Phys.*, 1854, **93**, 481, and especially to Clausius's concept of *disgregation*, *Ann. Phys.*, 1862, **116**, 73; 1863, **120**, 426; *Phil. Mag.*, 1868, **35**, 405. It is noteworthy that Thomson restricted the unquestioned validity of the principle to " inanimate material processes," but said that its application to vegetable or animal life is also " probable "; cf. Bridgman, " The Nature of Thermodynamics," Cambridge (U.S.A.), 1941, 208.

3 *Trans. Connect. Acad.*, 1876, **3**, 108; " Sci. Papers," 1906, **1**, 83.

4 *Phil. Mag.*, 1875, **49**, 311; " Sci. Papers," 1899, **1**, 242. A curious inability to understand Rayleigh's calculation by Burbury, *Nature*, 1907, **76**, 290, 638; *Phil. Mag.*, 1907, **14**, 122, 422; 1908, **15**, 768, was criticised by Bryan, *Nature*, 1907, **76**, 637; and Orr, *Phil. Mag.*, 1908, **15**, 297.

5 *Wien Ber.*, 1878, **78**, II, 733. The result was stated in terms of entropy (§ 51) bv Maxwell, " Ency. Brit.," 9th edit., 1877, **7**, 220; " Sci. Papers," 1890, **2**, 644.

apparatus is immersed in a large water bath of temperature T, the mixing can be carried out isothermally and reversibly, and work w_T is obtained. By pressing in the pistons, the gas mixture is separated isothermally and reversibly into its constituents and work w_T is spent. If it is assumed that the pressure exerted by each gas is independent of the presence of the other gas, then:

$$-\Delta F = w_T = n_1 RT \ln \frac{V_1+V_2}{V_1} + n_2 RT \ln \frac{V_1+V_2}{V_2} \quad . \quad . \quad . \quad (1)$$

The first expression on the right is the maximum work of isothermal expansion of n_1 mols of gas (1) from the volume V_1 into the volume (V_1+V_2), and the second the maximum work of expansion of n_2 mols of gas (2) from the volume V_2 to the volume (V_1+V_2). It is obvious that the whole process depends on the condition that the two gases must be different; no work could be obtained from two portions of the same gas. The equation, however, does not contain any

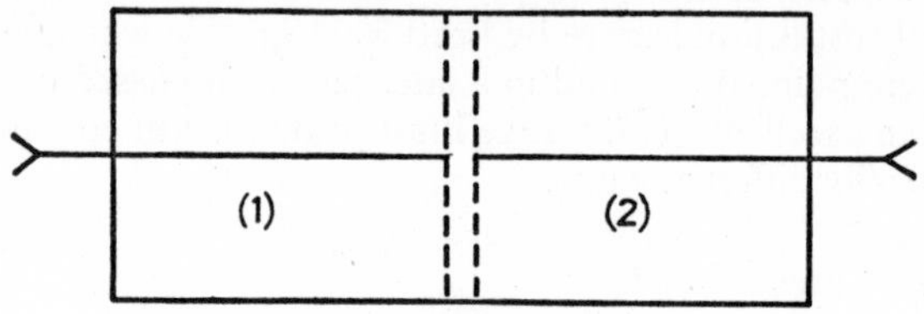

FIG. 12.II. Reversible Mixing of Gases

reference to the chemical character of the gas.[1] This result, on which a great amount of argument has been misdirected, is called *Gibbs's paradox*.[2] An experimental verification of the work obtainable by mixing gases was given by Woodward.[3] Since (as will be shown) the total energy of the gases is unchanged by mixture, the work in (1) must have been derived from an equal amount of heat $q_T = w_T$ absorbed from the water bath. To reverse the process work w_T is spent and heat $q_T = w_T$ is given to the water bath. Hence, if the gases were first allowed to mix by diffusion, for which irreversible process $w=0$, this process can be reversed only by expending work w_T and *completely* converting it into heat in a constant temperature reservoir, when it is completely unavailable energy.

New light was thrown on the irreversible mixing of gases and allied spontaneous changes by an idea of Maxwell's.[4] Let the cylinder containing the mixed gas be supposed to be divided into the spaces (1) and (2) by a partition with a very small aperture which can be opened and closed without performance of work by sliding horizontally an ideal frictionless shutter. Now let a micro-

[1] Larmor, " Math. and Phys. Papers," Cambridge, 1929, **2**, 99: the chemical difference of the gases cannot change *continuously* to zero.

[2] See e.g. Wiedeburg, *Ann. Phys.*, 1894, **53**, 684; Guillaume, *Arch. Sci. Phys. Nat.*, 1916, **41**, 445; Ehrenfest-Afanassjewa, *Proc. K. Akad. Wetens. Amsterdam*, 1918, **20**, 1049; 1918, **21**, 53; Szilard, *Z. Phys.*, 1925, **32**, 753; 1929, **53**, 40; van Laar, *ibid.*, 1927, **45**, 635; von Neumann, " Mathematische Grundlagen der Quantentheorie," Berlin, 1932, 179.

[3] *Proc. Phys. Soc.*, 1883, **5**, 318.

[4] " Theory of Heat," 1871, 308 (a " being "; the name " sorting demon " was used by Lord Kelvin in 1874: *Proc. Roy. Soc. Edin.*, 1875, **8**, 325; *Phil. Mag.*, 1892, **33**, 291; " Math. and Phys. Papers," 1911, **5**, 11; " Popular Lectures and Addresses," 1889, **1**, 137); Lippmann, *Congrès Internat. Phys.*, 1901, **1**, 346; Smoluchowski, *Ann. Phys.*, 1906, **21**, 756; *Gött. Nachr.*, 1913, 146; Guye, *J. Chim. Phys.*, 1917, **15**, 215; Boutaric, *ibid.*, 1919, **17**, 589; Pratolongo, *Gazz.*, 1918, **48**, i, 121; Szilard, *Z. Phys.*, 1929, **53**, 840; Baas Becking, *Proc. K. Akad. Wetens. Amsterdam*, 1942, **45**, 895; Demers, *Canad. J. Res.*, 1944, **22** A, 27.

scopic being (" demon ")[1] be stationed at the aperture. All molecules of gas (1) in the mixture which (by heat motion in the gas) approach the aperture from right to left are permitted by the demon to pass through, and similarly all molecules of gas (2) approaching from left to right, but all molecules approaching in the opposite directions are refused passage by sliding the shutter, from which they rebound as perfectly elastic bodies. In course of time the gas mixture spontaneously separates into gases (1) and (2) in the left and right compartments *without the expenditure of work*. The gases could then be mixed reversibly by the semipermeable pistons, and work obtained by drawing on heat from the constant temperature reservoir, and the two processes repeated indefinitely—a result which contradicts the Second Law. An irreversible process (diffusion) would have been completely reversed without leaving any other changes anywhere, and the distinction between reversible and irreversible processes would disappear.

If the cylinder is filled with a single gas, this could be sorted into a hotter portion consisting of molecules with greater speeds and a cooler portion consisting of slower molecules, since the individual molecules in a gas at a uniform temperature have different speeds and kinetic energies. A gas which had undergone irreversible expansion could be restored to its initial state by controlling the passage of molecules in a particular direction.

The Second Law holds only for matter in the aggregate, and is not necessarily true if individual molecules could be the object of control. This could be achieved only by an imaginary " demon." Unlike the First Law, the Second Law has only a *statistical* meaning; it has only a very large *probability*, not an absolute validity. This aspect receives further consideration in § 14.IV, where it is shown that the microscopic technique of the imaginary demon is illusory, and hence the basis of the Second Law is firmer than Maxwell supposed.

The Second Law of Thermodynamics, as is seen from these merely preliminary considerations, is of a subtle character, and presents various aspects of meaning. It is, perhaps, the most extraordinary natural law with which science is yet acquainted, and its understanding demands much thought. The equations which follow from it are some of the simplest and most easily understood of any in physical chemistry.

The statistical basis of the Second Law was developed quantitatively by Lord Kelvin[2] in 1874; he showed, e.g. that in a vessel of air containing 10^{13} molecules, the chance of their separating so that all the oxygen is in one-fifth of the volume and all the nitrogen in four-fifths, is of the order of the ratio of 1 to 2×10^{12}. This separation could be effected by a plane array of Maxwell's demons armed with " molecular cricket bats." The full meaning of the quantitative connection between probability and entropy (§ 33), however, was first made clear by Boltzmann,[3] who calculated[4] that the spontaneous separation of 100 c.c. of a mixture of equal volumes of two gases would not be expected to occur in a period of time less than $10^{10^{10}}$ years.

Modern experimental technique now reaches in some degree to the control of single atoms and molecules, so that G. N. Lewis,[5] in an interesting paper on

1 The concept is that of a micro-robot.

2 *Proc. Roy. Soc. Edin.*, 1874, **8**, 325; *Nature*, 1874, **9**, 441; *Phil. Mag.*, 1892, **33**, 291; " Math. and Phys. Papers," 1911, **5**, 11; cf. Helmholtz, *Nature*, 1885, **32**, 25; " Wiss. Abhl.," 1895, **3**, 587.

3 *Wien Ber.*, 1877, **76**, II, 373; 1878, **78**, II, 7; " Wiss. Abhl.," 1909, **2**, 164, 250.

4 " Vorlesungen über Gastheorie," 1898, **2**, 254.

5 *Science*, 1930, **71**, 569; cf. Bridgman, " The Nature of Thermodynamics," Cambridge (U.S.A.), 1941, 133 f.

the subject of irreversibility and Maxwell's demons, said: " In recent years, if I may say so without offence, physicists have become demons." The Brownian movement is a phenomenon in which the limit of applicability of the Second Law has almost been reached in visible systems.[1]

§ 29. The Second Law of Thermodynamics

The postulate that a perpetual motion of the second kind is impossible is one form of the Second Law of Thermodynamics, and as such it may be stated as follows: [2]

The operation of a finite cyclic process which produces no other effects than the abstraction of heat from a reservoir and the raising of a weight is impossible.

Since every other form of energy except *heat* may be converted *completely* into the potential energy of a raised weight by suitable ideal reversible processes, e.g. electrical energy by an ideal motor in which there is no production of heat by friction or by finite currents flowing through resistances, all these forms of energy may be included in the group of " work," and it may be asserted that:

(1) All forms of energy, including heat, are quantitatively interconvertible.

(2) A quantity of any other form of energy is completely convertible into heat.

Statements (1) and (2) are consequences of the definition and the measurement of energy according to the First Law.

(3) The conversion of heat into work is, in general, either impossible or only partly possible, unless other changes (" compensating changes ") occur as well. This is implied in the Second Law.

The conversion of heat into work is thus limited by certain restrictions, due to some essential difference in quality between heat and the other forms of energy (Gibbs; Boltzmann).[3] Putilov [4] regarded heat and work not so much as *quantities* of energy, as *forms* in which it is transmitted, work then appearing as the macro-form, and heat as the micro-form.

§ 30. Moutier's Theorem

The work done in any isothermal reversible cyclic process is zero (J. Moutier, 1875): [5]

$$(w)_T = 0 \quad \quad (1)$$

For if $(w)_T > 0$, this contradicts the Second Law. If $(w)_T < 0$, this is possible if the cycle is irreversible, since work can always be wasted by conversion into heat by friction. But if the cycle is reversible it can be carried out in the opposite sense, and then $(w)_T > 0$, which is impossible. Hence $(w)_T = 0$.

Since for a cyclic process $(w) = \Sigma q$, it follows also that *the algebraic sum of the quantities of heat absorbed and emitted in an isothermal reversible cyclic process is zero*:

$$(q)_T = 0 \quad \quad (2)$$

which is a second form of Moutier's Theorem.

1 Lorentz, " Les Théories Statistique en Thermodynamique," Leipzig and Berlin, 1916, 47.

2 Planck, " Thermodynamik," 1911, 86; cf. Demers, *Canad. J. Res.*, 1944, **22** A, 27.

3 Gibbs, " Scientific Papers," 1906, I, 406: " I use the term ' equivalent ' *strictly* to denote reciprocal convertibility, and not in the loose and often misleading sense in which we speak of heat and work as equivalent when there is only a one-sided convertibility." The same idea is expressed by Boltzmann, *Wien Ber.*, 1883, **88**, II, 861; *Ann. Phys.*, 1884, **22**, 39; " Wiss. Abhl.," 1909, **3**, 66.

4 *Bull. Acad. Sci. U.R.S.S.*, 1937, 701, 713 (Chim.).

5 *Bull. Soc. Philomath.*, 1875, **12**, 38; " La Thermodynamique et ses principales Applications," 1885, 344. The theorem does not follow from the *First* Law, as erroneously stated by Taylor, " Treatise on Physical Chemistry," 1924, **1**, 57.

§ 31. Alternative Forms of the Second Law of Thermodynamics

Clausius [1] stated the Second Law in the form: " Heat cannot, of itself, pass from a colder to a hotter body," adding that: " We may replace the words ' of itself ' by ' without compensation,' and then enunciate the principle as follows: ' A passage of heat from a colder to a hotter body cannot take place without compensation.' "

Thomson [2] expressed the law in the form: " It is impossible, by means of inanimate material agency, to derive mechanical effect from any portion of matter by cooling it below the temperature of the coldest of surrounding objects," adding that: " If this axiom be denied for all temperatures, it would have to be admitted that a self-acting machine might be set to work and produce mechanical work by cooling the sea or earth, with no limit but the total loss of heat from the earth and sea, or, in reality, from the whole material world."

Schidlof [3] thought it should read: " It is impossible to obtain work by a reversible cyclic process without at the same time passing a *finite* amount of heat from the hot to the cold body."

Maxwell [4] stated the law in the form: " It is impossible, by the unaided action of natural processes, to transform any part of the heat of a body into mechanical work, except by allowing heat to pass from that body into another at a lower temperature," and he very truly adds, with reference to the statements by Clausius, Thomson, and himself: " By comparing together these statements, the student will be able to make himself master of the fact which they embody, an acquisition which will be of much greater importance to him than any form of words on which a demonstration may be more or less compactly constructed."

The equivalence of the various forms of the Second Law is most easily demonstrated by remembering that it is possible to transfer heat from one body to another at a *higher* temperature by means of a *reversed* Carnot's cyclic process (§ 8). In this, a quantity of work is spent, and the equivalent amount of heat is given up to a reservoir at the higher temperature. To restore everything to its initial state, these two changes would have to be reversed, which would contradict the form of the Second Law which denies the possibility of a perpetual motion of the second kind.[5]

In 1854 Clausius [6] modified his statement of the Second Law to: " Heat can never pass from a colder to a warmer body unless simultaneously some other connected [zusammenhängende] change occurs"; in 1863 he said [7] that this could not be regarded as " self-evident," but is a postulate which can be tested

[1] *Ann. Phys.*, 1850, **79**, 368; " The Mechanical Theory of Heat," 1879, 78.

[2] *Trans. Roy. Soc. Edin.*, 1853, **20**, 261 (read 1851); *Phil. Mag.*, 1852, **4**, 8; " Mathematical and Physical Papers," 1882, **1**, 174; cf. Schiller, *Ann. Phys.*, 1901, **5**, 313; Bryan, *ibid.*, *Boltzmann Festschr.*, 1904, 123; Guye, " Physico-Chemical Evolution," 1925, 172.

[3] *J. Chim. Phys.*, 1926, **23**, 814; Lewis, *J.A.C.S.*, 1931, **53**, 2578, thought " no valid statement of the second law of thermodynamics has yet been formulated," and proceeds to give one (see § 5.IV).

[4] " Theory of Heat," 1875, 153; cf. Wilson, *Phil. Mag.*, 1943, **34**, 828; Guye, *J. Chim. Phys.*, 1917, **15**, 215, compared the different statements of the law; in a rather formal treatment, Ehrenfest-Afanassjewa, *Z. Phys.*, 1925, **33**, 933; 1925, **34**, 638, maintained that the statements of Clausius and Thomson are not quite equivalent. Jellinek, " Lehrbuch der physikalischen Chemie," 1928, **1**, 81, 87, said that a consideration of the result of a Carnot's cycle with the cold body at the absolute zero (§ 8) shows that the form of the impossibility of a perpetual motion of the second kind (§ 24) " does not quite reach the heart [Kern] of the second law," and Cantelo, *J. Phys. Chem.*, 1928, **32**, 982, amplified this point.

[5] Detailed proofs, see Partington, " Chemical Thermodynamics," 1940, 28.

[6] *Ann. Phys.*, 1854, **93**, 481.

[7] *Ann. Phys.*, 1863, **120**, 426; cf. Wesendonck, *ibid.*, 1899, **67**, 444.

by comparing the inferences from it with experience. In 1854 he introduced the " absolute temperature " T, and called $q(1/T_2-1/T_1)$ the " equivalence value " of the quantity of heat q. He showed that the integral $\int(dq/T)$ round a reversible cycle is zero; round an irreversible cycle it is greater than zero. In 1856, in a paper [1] on the application to the steam engine, Clausius (taking $T=t°$ C.+273) used the equation: $\int(dq/T)=-N$, where N is called the *equivalence value* of all *uncompensated* changes, the work obtainable from q being $w=q-T_0\int(dq/T)$, where T_0 is the lowest available temperature. In 1863 he [2] introduced the concept of *disgregation*, which is the sum of the internal and external work divided by the absolute temperature, and pointed out the implications of the Second Law in chemical processes; $\int(dq/T)$ is here called the " transformation value " (Verwandlungswerth). In 1865, finally, the name *entropy* and the symbol S for it, were introduced.[3]

From the time of its enunciation, various objections to the Second Law were raised: these depended on misunderstandings, and some of the more sensible earlier ones were refuted by Clausius.[4] Since its statement in the form involving the impossibility of a perpetual motion of the second kind, these objections to the law have abated. The Second Law is an example of what Whitehead [5] called " postulates of impotence," which assert " the impossibility of achieving something, even though there may be an infinite number of ways of trying to achieve it." Many of the most fundamental laws (e.g. the quantum theory) have this character, limiting some possibility to a narrow region of actuality, whilst the surrounding regions are empty.

§ 32. Carnot's Theorem

The Second Law shows that *reversible* transformation of heat into work by a cyclic process can occur only if at least two bodies at different temperatures are available, from one of which, at the higher temperature, a quantity of heat q_1 is taken, and to the other, at the lower temperature, the balance of this heat, q_2, is rejected. Such a process is the Carnot's cycle described in § 8. If w is the work done in the cycle, the ratio $w/q_1=\eta$ is called the *efficiency* of the cycle; Carnot [6] (1824) showed that it is independent of the nature of the cyclic process and depends only on the temperatures θ_1 and θ_2 of the hot and cold bodies: $\eta=f(\theta_1, \theta_2)$. This is known as *Carnot's Theorem* and is a consequence of the Second Law.

Let two cyclic processes [α] and [β], [α] reversible, be carried out with the same hot and cold bodies (the source and refrigerator, respectively), and if possible let [β] be more efficient than [α]. Let each process be arranged to absorb heat q_1 from the source per cycle. Since [α] is reversible, let [β] be

[1] *Ann. Phys.*, 1856, **97**, 441, 513.

[2] *Ann. Phys.*, 1863, **116**, 73; 1863, **120**, 426: here, the expression $\int(dq/T)\geqq 0$ is used; *Phil Mag.*, 1868, **35**, 405 (from a lecture).

[3] *Ann. Phys.*, 1865, **125**, 353: alternatively, the name " Verwandlungswerth " is used for the entropy. On the history of the development of thermodynamics, see Rosenfeld, *Bull. Soc. Roy. Sci. Liége*, 1941, **10**, 199.

[4] *Ann. Phys.*, 1851, **83**, 118 (against Holtzmann); 1863, **120**, 426 (against Hirn, etc.); " Mechanical Theory of Heat," 1879, 332 f.; an objection by Fairbourne, *Phil. Mag.*, 1922, **43**, 1047, was removed by Witmer, *ibid.*, 1924, **47**, 152; and Fisher, *ibid.*, 1924, **47**, 779.

[5] *Phil. Mag.*, 1942, **33**, 353.

[6] " Réflexions sur la Puissance Motrice du Feu," 1824, 14, 22, 38; see Helm, " Principles of Mathematical Chemistry," transl. Morgan, New York, 1897, 56 f. On an apparent objection, see Ruark, *Phil. Mag.*, 1925, **49**, 584; Lewis and Randall, " Thermodynamics," New York, 1923, 129, prefer to call w/q_1 the " conversion factor."

coupled so as to work [α] backwards. Then in a cycle the components of the coupled processes perform the following operations:

[β]	[α]
(i) takes heat q_1 from the source;	(i) gives up heat q_1 to the source;
(ii) does work w';	(ii) absorbs work w;
(iii) gives up heat q'_2 to the refrigerator	(iii) takes heat q_2 from the refrigerator.

By the First Law: $w+q_2=w'+q_2'=q_1$. By assumption:

$$w'/q_1>w/q_1 \quad \therefore\ w'>w,$$

Therefore

$$q_2>q_2'.$$

Thus, in the cycle, the heat $(q_2-q_2')>0$ is taken from the cold body, at a single temperature, and the work $(w'-w)>0$ is done, say by raising a weight, two operations which contradict the Second Law. Hence [β] cannot be more efficient than [α].

If [β] is also a reversible cyclic process, it can be arranged that [α] works [β] backwards, and proved as above that [α] cannot be more efficient than [β]. Hence, as [β] can neither be more nor less efficient than [α], [α] and [β] must be equally efficient, which proves Carnot's Theorem.

If [β] is not reversible, it must be less efficient than [α], since otherwise it would satisfy the definition of a reversible cyclic process, as is proved above.[1]

Carnot calculated the efficiency $\eta=w/q_1$ for a cycle between the temperatures 78·7° and 77·7° for water vapour and alcohol vapour, finding approximately the same values; W. Thomson (Lord Kelvin) [2] extended the calculation to water, air, ether, alcohol, and turpentine, using, among others, some results found by Reguault. The deviations from the calculated values were of the order of the errors in the experimental data. Since only w and q_1 (not q_2) are involved, the results are independent of the First Law, and both Carnot and Thomson, in fact, assumed the caloric theory of heat (§ 10).

§ 33. Entropy

When a system undergoes a reversible isothermal non-cyclic change and does an amount of work w_T, it is said to have lost an amount of *free energy*, the change of free energy, ΔF, being *defined* by the equation:

$$-\Delta F=w_T \qquad (1)$$

It is explained in § 26 that the system itself (e.g. an expanding gas) may not lose any energy at all, although it has suffered a loss of free energy. Consider [3] the equation:

$$F=E-TS \qquad (2)$$

where E is the energy and F the free energy, and T and S are functions the properties of which are to be investigated. These functions are assumed to be real, finite, and continuous, and to have the following properties. T is a function of temperature θ, which increases as the temperature increases, and $T=f(\theta)$ is called the *absolute temperature*. S is a function called the *entropy*.

[1] Boltzmann, *Ann. Phys.*, 1905, **18**, 642: " there is no finite cyclic process different from Carnot's which is so efficient as this."

[2] *Phil. Mag.*, 1848, **33**, 313; " Math. and Phys. Papers," 1882, **1**, 100.

[3] Partington, *Scientia*, 1947, **41**, 85; *Phil. Mag.*, 1947, **38**, 672; cf. Schiller, *Ann. Phys.*, 1901, **5**, 313; Putilov, *Bull. Acad. Sci. U.R.S.S.*, 1937 (Chim.), 715, 733.

For a reversible change at constant temperature (T=const.):

$$\Delta F = \Delta E - T\Delta S \quad \dots \quad (3)$$

Hence, from (1):

$$-w_T = \Delta E - T\Delta S \quad \text{or} \quad T\Delta S = \Delta E + w_T.$$

The First Law, § 16 (2), shows that $q_T = \Delta E + w_T$, hence:

$$q_T = T\Delta S, \quad \text{or} \quad \Delta S = q_T/T \quad \dots \quad (4)$$

The *increase of entropy* in a reversible isothermal change is thus *measured* by dividing the heat absorbed in the change by the absolute temperature at which it is absorbed. If the change is very small, (4) can be written:

$$\delta S = dS = \delta q/T \quad \dots \quad (5)$$

It is necessary to show that $\delta S = dS$, the differential of S, i.e. that the change of S is independent of the path of change, provided this is reversible and isothermal. This is shown by considering (3). The First Law shows (§ 16) that ΔE is independent of the path, and the Second Law (§ 30) that this is true for ΔF (i.e. $-w_T$). Hence, if T is constant, this is true for ΔS, and hence for δS, i.e. $\delta S = dS$.

Since ΔF for a reversible isothermal change is independent of the path, the free energy in a given state does not depend on how the system has been brought into that state, and hence the change of free energy *of the system itself* is the same, for a given change of state, whether this change is reversible or irreversible. If the change is irreversible, however, there will have been a decrease of free energy outside the system (§ 27). It follows that F is a *function of the state* of the system, and is definite for a given state, and hence that:

$$\Delta F = F_2 - F_1 \quad \dots \quad (6)$$

where F_1 and F_2 are the free energies in the initial and final states.

It can next be shown that ΔS is independent of the path in *all* changes, whether isothermal or not. For, *any* change of state may be assumed to be brought about by a succession of very small isothermal changes, each pair being separated by a very small adiabatic change, i.e. (§ 4) one for which $\delta q = 0$, this adiabatic change producing the very small temperature change between the two isothermals, e.g. a small rise of temperature in adiabatic compression. This assumption, in some form or other, is made in all deductions of the properties of the entropy function.[1] All these small changes are assumed to be reversible. For all the adiabatic changes $\Sigma\delta q/T = 0$, and hence for them, from (5), $\Sigma dS = 0$. Hence the entropy change is due entirely to the isothermal changes:

$$\Delta S = \Sigma\delta q/T = \Sigma dS(\text{isothermal}) \quad \dots \quad (7)$$

and since for each of them dS depends only on the initial and final states, this is true for the whole change, which was to be proved. Hence it follows that:

$$\Delta S = S_2 - S_1 \quad \dots \quad (8)$$

This is true, *for the system itself*, also for irreversible changes, and in all cases $\Delta S = 0$ for a cycle. In irreversible changes, however, since F decreases, S must increase, and somewhere outside the system there must be an increase of entropy.

In continuous changes of state, where the isothermal and adiabatic changes become infinitesimally small, the sums in the above equations are to be replaced by integrals.

[1] Cf. Bridgman, " The Nature of Thermodynamics," 1941, 116.

In another aspect of the above argument, it may be assumed that, in the immediate vicinity of any given state, there will be an infinite number of neighbouring states which cannot be reached from the given state by adiabatic changes alone (§ 37). For, a given adiabatic change can bring the system into one state only, in which it has a definite temperature, and to attain any other state it will, in general, be necessary to add or withdraw heat from the system by an isothermal change.

Equation (4) in quite a different notation was first given by William Thomson [1] in a paper of December, 1851. The standard form, $\Sigma(q/T)=0$, for a number of absolute temperatures (not merely two), which may form a continuous sequence and thus correspond with the integration round a cycle, $\oint\delta q/T=0$, was given by Thomson [2] in a most fundamental paper read in May 1854. It was only a step, but it was a highly significant step, and one which led to the full development of thermodynamics, to recognise that $\delta q/T$ is the differential of a function of state, and to give a name (entropy), and symbol S, to this function, and this step was first taken by Clausius [3] in 1864. He gives no derivation of the word "entropy," which may be from the Greek ἡ τροπή, "change," or ἐντρέπομαι, "to turn inside" (with reference to its one-sided tendency of change). It is the same as the "thermodynamic function" (F) used by Rankine [4] in 1854 (an adiabatic being then called a "curve of no transformation"). As Wesendonck [5] remarked, the function "appears almost automatically" in the thermodynamic method of Clausius.

The above discussion is intended to justify Larmor's statement [6] that "the available [free] energy is thus a single characteristic function which includes and determines completely the circumstances, mechanical, thermal, and constitutive, of the steady states of an inanimate material system."

In a Carnot's cycle, consisting of two adiabatics, and two isothermals at absolute temperatures T_1 and T_2 ($T_1>T_2$), along which quantities of heat q_1 and q_2 are absorbed and emitted, respectively, by the substance (or system) undergoing the cycle, equation (7), with $\Delta S=0$, becomes:

$$q_1/T_1-q_2/T_2=0 \quad \text{or} \quad T_1/T_2=q_1/q_2 \qquad (9)$$

i.e. the absolute temperatures of two bodies are in the ratio of the quantities of heat taken from and rejected to the bodies in a reversible Carnot's cycle operating with the two bodies as source and refrigerator (hot and cold bodies), respectively. Equation (9) may also be written in the form

$$(q_1-q_2)/q_1=(T_1-T_2)/T_1 \qquad (10)$$

or, since $q_1-q_2=w$, the work done in the cycle:

$$w/q_1=(T_1-T_2)/T_1 \qquad (11)$$

If $T_1-T_2=\delta T$, a very small difference of absolute temperature, $w=\delta w$ is a small amount of work done in the cycle, and if $q_1=q=$heat absorbed from the hot body at the absolute temperature $T_1=T$, then:

$$\delta w=q\delta T/T \qquad (12)$$

1 *Proc. Roy. Soc. Edin.*, 1857, **3**, 91 (read 1851); *Phil. Mag.*, 1879, **7**, 346; "Math. and Phys. Papers," 1882, **1**, 316; 1911, **5**, 4; if Carnot's function is expressed as $\mu=1/T$, equation (b) there becomes of the standard form.

2 *Trans. Roy. Soc. Edin.*, 1854, **21**, 123; "Math. and Phys. Papers," 1882, **1**, 232.

3 *Ann. Phys.*, 1865, **125**, 353.

4 *Phil. Trans.*, 1854, **144**, 115; "Misc. Scient. Papers," 1881, 352.

5 *Ann. Phys.*, 1899, **69**, 809.

6 *Phil. Trans.*, 1897, **190**, 205; "Math. and Phys. Papers," Cambridge, 1929, **2**, 88.

Equation (11) may be written as $w=(q_1/T_1)(T_1-T_2)$, and since $q_1/T_1=q_2/T_2=\Delta S$, the work done in the cycle may be said to be that done by a quantity of entropy passing from an absolute temperature T_1 to an absolute temperature T_2, multiplied by the absolute temperature difference.[1] If entropy is identified with Carnot's "caloric," the original deduction of Carnot then holds good.

§ 34. Alternative Treatment of the Entropy

The extension of the result for a simple cycle (two isotherms and two adiabatics) to any reversible cycle, given in § 33, is essentially that first used by Clausius.[2] He later [3] adopted a method due to Zeuner,[4] which is exactly the same in principle, but since it has points of interest it will be given here.[5]

The absolute temperatures are *defined* as in the ratio of the heat absorbed to the heat emitted in the cycle, or if heat absorbed by the working substance is taken as positive and that emitted as negative ($-q_2$ is written for q_2):

$$T_1/T_2=-q_1/q_2, \quad \text{or} \quad q_1/T_1+q_2/T_2=0 \quad \ldots \quad (1)$$

In Carnot's cycle there are reversible exchanges of heat at only two temperatures. In general, reversible exchanges of heat will occur at a large number of temperatures. Any reversible cycle may, however, be decomposed into a very large number of infinitesimal Carnot's cycles (Fig. 13.II), to each of which (1) applies. The adiabatic parts of these cycles which lie inside the loop of the given cycle cancel out in the limit, since each is traversed twice in opposite directions, except the vanishingly small adiabatics at the left- and right-hand extremities, but the upper and lower isothermals are traversed only once, and in the limit these constitute the contour of the given cycle. Hence for the latter, in the limit:

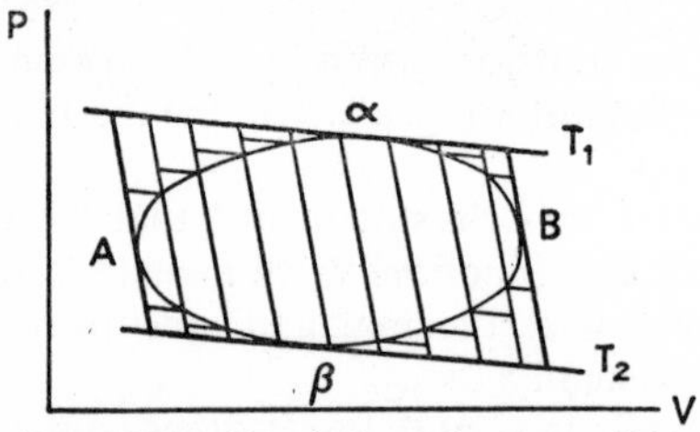

FIG. 13.II. Resolution of a Reversible Cycle into Elementary Carnot's Cycles

$$\Sigma(\delta q_1/T_1+\delta q_2/T_2)=\Sigma\delta q/T=\oint\delta q/T=0$$

$$\therefore \oint\delta q/T=0 \quad \ldots\ldots\ldots\ldots \quad (2)$$

If the cycle is divided into two parts (Fig. 5.II) and is integrated from A to C along α and from C to A along β:

$$\oint\delta q/T={}_\alpha\int_A^C \delta q/T+{}_\beta\int_C^A \delta q/T=0,$$

$$\therefore {}_\alpha\int_A^C \delta q/T={}_\beta\int_A^C \delta q/T,$$

which proves that $\delta q/T=\mathrm{d}S$ is a perfect differential (§ 27.I) of a function S of the state of the system, S being the *entropy* of the system. In *reversible* adiabatic

[1] Lippmann, "Cours de Thermodynamique," Paris, 1889, 78, long anticipating Callendar, *Phil. Mag.*, 1913, **26**, 787; and Brönsted, "Physical Chemistry," 1937, 11; *J. Phys. Chem.* 1940, **44**, 699; Finck, *J. Franklin Inst.*, 1948, **245**, 301, 365.

[2] *Ann. Phys.*, 1854, **93**, 481; "Mechanical Theory of Heat," transl. Browne, 1879, 88.

[3] "Mechanical Theory of Heat," transl. Browne, 1879, 89.

[4] "Mechanische Wärmelehre," 2nd edit., Leipzig, 1866; 3rd edit., Leipzig, 1887, 42.

[5] Cf. Buckingham, *Phys. Rev.*, 1896, **4**, 39; Durand, *J. Phys. Chem.*, 1896, **1**, 10; Trevor *ibid.*, 1899, **3**, 389; 1900, **4**, 514; Bryan, "Thermodynamics," 1907, 64; Jazyna, *Phys. Z.*, 1925, **26**, 622.

changes $\delta q=0$, therefore $dS=0$ and such changes are *isentropic*. (It must be carefully noted that this applies only to *reversible* changes.)

Formerly, the entropy, although freely used by engineers, was for some reason regarded by English chemical students as mysterious and difficult, and even eminent physical chemists [1] fought shy of it. After Lewis and Gibson [2] had calculated the numerical values of the entropies of elements, however, students mastered their fear of entropy, and now no longer find any difficulty in using it. It has many of the properties of the old caloric (§ 33) [3]. No teacher need be discouraged by the inability of students to grasp even the elementary parts of thermodynamics; the present writer's experience agrees with that of Johnston [4]: " I fear that it is nearly impossible to write a good brief exposition of thermodynamics . . . which will appeal with any degree of success to the *average* student of chemistry." The interpretation of entropy as " heat weight " [5] does not seem very helpful.

It is probable that the " average student " gains some idea as to what thermodynamics is about only by a *varied* method of treatment.[6] He wearies of long stretches of neat mathematical formulae, and too rigid formalism of " partial molal quantities " not only leads the unsophisticated into error,[7] but also " gives the student facility in manipulating equations whose full meaning escapes him," [8] a habit which all theoretical physicists of eminence have heartily condemned. As he makes progress, the student finds the elementary mathematics more and more interesting, and he should in the end realise that it can convey in a very small compass what would otherwise be less completely said in very many words. But unless he knows these words, the symbols are useless.

A long discussion [9] on entropy in 1903 brought out some interesting features, but is perhaps more noteworthy in showing how the concept may be misunderstood by those who can use, competently and correctly, equations which involve entropy changes in the practical applications of thermodynamics. Bryan,[10] who *defined* the entropy increase as the loss of available energy divided by the lowest available absolute temperature, $\Delta S=(\Delta E-\Delta F)/T$, approached the position taken in the present work, viz. that the concept of entropy is much wider than that which regards it as one factor of heat, absolute temperature being the other (§ 23), that it is most suitably connected with the free energy, and that the equation $dS=\delta q/T$, which applies only to a reversible change, is one more concerned with *measuring* entropy than *defining* it.

1 See e.g. Nernst, " Theoretical Chemistry," 1911, 28; cf. the remarks in the preface of my " Text-book of Thermodynamics," 1913, where the " modern " point of view (held generally since about 1925) is expressed.

2 *J.A.C.S.*, 1917, **39**, 2554; Lewis, Gibson, and Latimer, *ibid.*, 1922, **44**, 1008.

3 Wiedeburg, *Ann. Phys.*, 1898, **64**, 519; 1898, **65**, 921; 1899, **69**, 66; *Z. phys. Chem.*, 1899, **29**, 27; Callendar, *B.A. Rep.*, 1912, 387; *Phil. Mag.*, 1913, **26**, 787.

4 *J.A.C.S.*, 1929, **51**, 1955.

5 Zeuner, " Mechanische Wärmetheorie," 2nd edit., Leipzig, 1866; 3rd edit., 1887, 41; Trevor, *J. Phys. Chem.*, 1899, **3**, 389; 1900, **4**, 514, 529; " Thermodynamics," 1928.

6 Partington, *J. Phys. Chem.*, 1926, **30**, 288.

7 See Onsager, *J. Phys. Chem.*, 1928, **32**, 146.

8 Edsall, *J.A.C.S.*, 1935, **57**, 967.

9 Swinburne, Perry, Evershed, Robinson, Lodge, Heaviside, Planck, Swan, and Poincaré, *Electrician*, 1903, **50**, 315, 398, 477, 478, 560, 656, 688, 694, 695, 735, 821; Swinburne, " What is Entropy?," 1904; Morley, *Engineer*, 1912, **113**, 457; Wainwright, *ibid.*, 1912, **113**, 658; 1912, **114**, 90; Neumann, *Stahl u. Eisen*, 1942, **62**, 89; Allen, *Nature*, 1943, **151**, 225; Campbell, *ibid.*, 1943, **151**, 138; Swinburne, *ibid.*, 1943, **151**, 335; Thwing, *ibid.*, 1943, **151**, 672; Darrow, *Amer. J. Phys.*, 1944, **12**, 183. The popular articles contributed by Rankine to *The Engineer* in 1867–70, and reprinted in " Misc. Scient. Papers," 1881, 432 f., are also noteworthy.

10 *Ann. Phys.*, *Boltzmann Festschr.*, 1904, 123; " Thermodynamics," 1907, 56.

§ 35. Calculation of Entropy Changes

The increase of entropy of a system in passing from a state A to a state B is, from (7), § 33:

$$\int_A^B \delta q/T = \int_A^B dS = S_B - S_A = \Delta S.$$

Since the entropy depends only on the state, the change of entropy, whether the change is carried out reversibly or irreversibly, is always $S_B - S_A$. It is only in reversible changes, however, that this is measured by $\int_A^B \delta q/T$. In irreversible cycles the equation applies to the system in the form $\oint dS = 0$ but not in the form $\oint \delta q/T = 0$.

If a system σ undergoes a change in which the entropy increases by ΔS, then two identical σ systems undergoing the same change will gain entropy $2\Delta S$. Hence entropy, like energy, is an extensive property, and the entropy content S is proportional to the total mass (or quantity) of the system. The only case in which entropy is not additive is when a pencil of radiation is divided into reflected and refracted parts by partial reflection. The sum of their entropies is not equal to the entropy of the incident pencil and the absolute temperatures of the three pencils are generally different.[1]

If q is in g.cal. and T is the absolute Centigrade temperature (§ 36), the entropy unit is called the *clausius*.[2] For unit mass of a homogeneous substance heated reversibly at constant volume ($\delta q = dE$):

$$dS = \delta q/T = c_v dT/T = c_v d \ln T = dE/T \quad . \quad . \quad . \quad . \quad . \quad (1)$$

$$\therefore \; (dS/dE)_v = 1/T \quad . \quad . \quad . \quad . \quad . \quad . \quad . \quad . \quad . \quad (2)$$

$$\text{and } (dS/dT)_v = c_v/T \quad . \quad . \quad . \quad . \quad . \quad . \quad . \quad . \quad (3)$$

and if heated reversibly at constant pressure ($\delta q = dH$):

$$dS = \delta q/T = c_p dT/T = c_p d \ln T = dH/T \quad . \quad . \quad . \quad . \quad (4)$$

$$\therefore \; (dS/dH)_p = 1/T \quad . \quad . \quad . \quad . \quad . \quad . \quad . \quad . \quad . \quad (5)$$

$$\text{and } (dS/dT)_p = c_p/T \quad . \quad . \quad . \quad . \quad . \quad . \quad . \quad . \quad (6)$$

The increase of entropy on heating unit mass of a system at constant volume is therefore given by (3) as:

$$\Delta S_v = \int_{T_0}^{T} (c_v/T) dT = \int_{T_0}^{T} c_v d \ln T \quad . \quad . \quad . \quad . \quad . \quad . \quad (7)$$

and at constant pressure by (6) as:

$$\Delta S_p = \int_{T_0}^{T} (c_p/T) dT = \int_{T_0}^{T} c_p d \ln T \quad . \quad . \quad . \quad . \quad . \quad . \quad (8)$$

If c_v and c_p are constant over the range of temperature considered:

$$\Delta S_v = c_v \ln (T/T_0) \quad . \quad . \quad . \quad . \quad . \quad . \quad . \quad . \quad . \quad (9)$$

$$\Delta S_p = c_p \ln (T/T_0) \quad . \quad . \quad . \quad . \quad . \quad . \quad . \quad . \quad . \quad (10)$$

[1] Von Laue, *Ann. Phys.*, 1906, **20**, 365; 1907, **23**, 1, 795; Epstein, *Phys. Z.*, 1914, **15**, 673; von Hirsch, *Ann. Phys.*, 1935, **22**, 609. On entropy in moving media, see Meissner, *Ann. Phys.*, 1938, **32**, 115. On the relation between heat capacity and entropy, Trevor, *J. Phys. Chem.*, 1900, **4**, 529, and between temperature and entropy, Karapetoff, *Gen. Elec. Rev.*, 1913, **16**, 7.

[2] Onnes and Keesom, "Enzykl. d. math. Wiss.," 1912, **5**, i, 631; *Comm. Leiden*, 1912, Suppl. **23**, 17, use this name for the unit 1 joule/1° K. The distinction drawn by Neumann, *Leipzig Ber.*, 1891, **43**, 75, and Smith, *Phil. Mag.*, 1942, **33**, 775, between *entropy* and *specific entropy* (entropy per unit mass) is unnecessary.

If c_v or c_p is not constant, the calculation may be made graphically by plotting c_v or c_p against ln T and finding the area under the curve.[1] Generally, $\log_{10} T$ is used, when the result must be multiplied by 2·3026.

§ 36. Absolute Temperature

The proper understanding of the Second Law is closely related to the definition of *absolute temperature*.[2] Temperature is naïvely associated with the degree of " hotness " or " coldness " of a body, and has obviously no relation to the energy content (loosely expressed as " the amount of heat in a body "), since this is much greater in a ton of ice than in a pound of boiling water. Further, if bodies at different temperatures, which do not react chemically, are put in contact, they gradually equalise their temperatures, and there is thermal equilibrium only when the temperature, as measured by a thermometer, has the same value throughout the system of bodies.

Maxwell [3] defined the temperature of a body as: " its thermal state considered with reference to its power of communicating heat to other bodies," and stated the fundamental law of temperature equilibrium in the form that: " bodies whose temperatures are equal to that of the same body have themselves equal temperatures." If the bodies A and B, and A and C, are separately in thermal equilibrium, then B and C will be found to be in thermal equilibrium on contact. This must be regarded as a result of experiment.[4]

Temperature is usually measured by thermometers, in which the changes of volume of a liquid or a gas are related to changes of temperature. If the temperature interval between the freezing- and boiling-points of water is taken as 100° C., this scale may be extended above and below the two fixed points, but if equal volume changes are again supposed to correspond with equal temperature changes, the temperatures as measured by mercury, air, and hydrogen thermometers are not equal, and some " standard " scale has to be adopted. What this scale is and how it is related to the actual thermometer scales are questions which can only be answered by the Second Law of Thermodynamics.

Carnot's Theorem (§ 32) leads to a definition [5] of temperature which, unlike the ordinary scales depending on the expansion of mercury, air, etc., is quite independent of any particular substance used in a thermometer. William Thomson (afterwards Lord Kelvin) was the first to see that from Carnot's ideas an absolute scale of temperature could be derived, and he gave [6] the foundation of one such scale in 1848. This was still based on Carnot's assumption that heat is indestructible (§ 10) and did not mention Joule's work.

[1] Examples, see Partington and Tweedy, " Calculations in Physical Chemistry," 1928, 32.

[2] See e.g. Day and Sosman, in Glazebrook, " Dict. of Applied Physics," 1922, **1**, 836, for the thermodynamic definition of temperature and the practical realisation of the absolute scale. On several aspects of the matter, see Burton, *Phil. Mag.*, 1887, **24**, 96; Rücker, *ibid.*, 1889, **27**, 104; Blakesley, *ibid.*, 1889, **27**, 178; Larmor, *Phil. Trans.*, 1897, **109**, 205; " Math. and Phys. Papers," Cambridge, 1929, **2**, 85, 590, 724; Tunell, *J. Phys. Chem.*, 1932, **36**, 1744; Benham, *Proc. Phys. Soc.*, 1942, **54**, 121; O'Leary, *Amer. J. Phys.*, 1946, **14**, 364.

[3] " Theory of Heat," 1871, 32; Mach, " Principien der Wärmelehre," 2nd edit., Leipzig, 1900, 42; Wertheimer, *Verhl. d. D. Phys. Ges.*, 1919, **21**, 435; Wensel, in " Temperature. Its Measurement and Control in Science and Industry," New York, 1941, 3; Worthing, *ibid.*, 41.

[4] Fowler and Guggenheim, " Statistical Thermodynamics," Cambridge, 1939, 56, would regard this as a " zeroth law of thermodynamics." See § 37

[5] For a deduction from Carnot's principle alone, see Raveau, *Compt. Rend.*, 1918, **167**, 20, 329.

[6] *Proc. Cambr. Phil. Soc.*, 1848, **1**, 66; *Phil. Mag.*, 1848, **33**, 313; " Math. and Phys. Papers," 1882, **1**, 100; *Ann. Chim.*, 1850, **30**, 118 (abstr.); Larmor, *Proc. Roy. Soc.*, 1908, **81**, Appendix. The symbol ° K. (=Kelvin) for absolute temperature was proposed by Onnes and Keesom, *Comm. Leiden*, 1912, Suppl. **23**, 16.

The good agreement between his measurement of the effect of pressure on the melting-point of ice and the value calculated by James Thomson from Carnot's principle in its original form, made William Thomson reluctant to accept Joule's theory until he had, with much difficulty, reconciled it with Carnot's principle. Clausius [1] first showed how Carnot's reasoning must be modified to agree with Joule's results, but he did not develop the idea of absolute temperature. Thomson [2] then gave the correct argument.

In fixing his first absolute scale, Thomson [3] assumed with Carnot that the work done when the heat unit "falls" (§ 22) from the temperature ϑ to $\vartheta-1$ depends only on ϑ, and he chose the scale so that this work is the same for all values of ϑ. His second absolute scale [4] is identical with that developed here. In principle, *any* thermodynamic equation involving temperature could be used to measure temperature absolutely, e.g. a vapour-pressure equation.[5] In practice, the method followed is to link up the absolute thermodynamic temperature $T=f(\theta)$ with the temperature reading of an *ideal gas* thermometer (§ 8).[6]

It has been shown in § 33 (9), that the ratio of the absolute temperatures of two bodies participating as heat reservoirs in a direct reversible Carnot's cycle is equal to the ratio of the quantity of heat q_1 withdrawn from the body at the higher absolute temperature T_1 to the quantity of heat q_2 rejected to the body at the lower absolute temperature T_2:

$$q_1/q_2=T_1/T_2.$$

This result does not depend on the particular system undergoing the cycle of changes, and hence it will be true for an ideal gas. In this case, T_1 and T_2 are defined by the equation (§ 8): $q_1/q_2=T_1'/T_2'$, where T' is now written for the *ideal gas temperature*, defined by $T'=t°$ C.$+1/\alpha_0$, where α_0 is the coefficient of expansion of the ideal gas (§ 6). It has been shown by experiment that $1/\alpha_0=$ 273·16. But $q_1/q_2=T_1/T_2$, hence $T_1/T_2=T_1'/T_2'$, or $T=kT'$, where k is some arbitrary numerical constant which fixes the absolute temperature scale. If $k=1$, $T=T'$. The thermodynamic absolute temperature scale is thus identical with the temperature on the ideal gas scale.

The *size of the degree* is fixed by the number chosen in the interval between the boiling- and freezing-points of water: if this is 100°, the degree is the Centigrade degree; if 180°, it is the Fahrenheit degree. The *zero of absolute temperature* (usually called "absolute zero") is determined by (10), § 33, since if q_1 and T_1 are finite, $T_2=0$ when $q_2=0$, i.e. if all the heat taken from the hot body is converted into work, the temperature of the cold body is zero. T_2 cannot be negative, since then q_2 is negative, or work is being obtained by taking heat from

[1] *Ann. Phys.*, 1850, **79**, 368.

[2] *Trans. Roy. Soc. Edin.*, 1853, **20**, 261 (read 1851); "Math. and Phys. Papers," 1882, **1**, 174; Larmor, *Proc. Roy. Soc.*, 1908, **81**, Appendix.

[3] *Phil. Mag.*, 1848, **33**, 313; cf. Schreber, *Ann. Phys.*, 1898, **64**, 163; 1898, **65**, 648; 1898, **66**, 1186; *Z. phys. Chem.*, 1898, **26**, 751; Auerbach, *Ann. Phys.*, 1898, **64**, 754; *Z. phys. Chem.*, 1898, **26**, 751.

[4] Thomson, *Trans. Roy. Soc. Edin.*, 1853, **20**, 261 (read 1851); *Phil. Mag.*, 1852, **4**, 8; "Math. and Phys. Papers," 1882, **1**, 174. Although Thomson says the suggestion that Carnot's function *C* should be equated to *JT*, where *J* is the mechanical equivalent of heat, was made to him by Joule in December 1848, Clausius, *Phil. Mag.*, 1856, **11**, 388, pointed out that it had been proposed by Holtzmann in 1845; cf. Thomson, *Phil. Mag.*, 1856, **11**, 447; "Math. and Phys. Papers," 1911, **5**, 45. An interesting sketch of the development of thermodynamics is given by Maxwell, "Scientific Papers," 1890, **2**, 660.

[5] W. Thomson, "Math. and Phys. Papers, " Cambridge, 1890, **3**, 152; Buckingham, *Bur. Stand. Bull.*, 1910, **6**, 409; Cotter, *Phil. Mag.*, 1928, **6**, 318.

[6] Cf. Verschaffelt, *Bull. Acad. Roy. Belg.*, 1927, **13**, 180.

each of *two* bodies at temperatures T_1 and T_2, without any other changes resulting, which contradicts the Second Law twice. (Since the cold body when $T_2=0$ takes no part in the cycle, it looks as if it could be stealthily removed, when the cycle will continue to work without it and apparently contradict the Second Law. The reader may like to perceive the fallacy in this argument for himself.)

The existence of a *lower* limit of temperature (0° K.) suggests that there might also be an *upper* limit; thermodynamics predicts no such upper limit, but other considerations [1] (e.g. of the energy of the neutron) suggest an upper limit of $1{\cdot}08\times10^{13}$ ° K. Lehmann [2] argued that absolute temperature is proportional to the average kinetic energy of molecules, and the molecular velocity cannot exceed the velocity of light. (For this velocity, however, the *mass* would seem to become infinite.) The characteristic equation of matter at excessively high temperature and pressure, discussed by Hund,[3] is of some interest in astrophysics (interior of hot stars) and in the explosion of the atomic bomb, but will not concern us here. It is possible that some entirely new principle, as yet unknown, is involved.[4]

§ 37. Temperature as an Integrating Factor

Zeuner [5] first defined the absolute temperature as *the* integrating divisor of the element of heat, i.e. $1/T$ as the factor which makes δq a perfect differential. Boltzmann, and later Budde,[6] pointed out that there must be an infinite number of such divisors, and every integrating divisor of an imperfect differential $M\mathrm{d}x+N\mathrm{d}y$ can be obtained from every other by multiplication by a function of x and y. If there is *one* which is a function of x only, it is the *only* one with such a property and the condition for this is $(\partial N/\partial x-\partial M/\partial y)/N=\mathrm{f}(x)$. This agrees with Clausius's [7] formulation of Carnot's principle:

$$\left[\frac{\partial}{\partial t}(\partial q/\partial v)-\frac{\partial}{\partial v}(\partial q/\partial t)\right]\bigg/(\partial q/\partial v)=\mathrm{f}(t) \quad . \quad . \quad . \quad . \quad . \quad (1)$$

where $\mathrm{f}(t)$ is measured on an arbitrary (e.g. air) thermometric scale, and v is an independent variable of state. Thus, the absolute temperature is *the* one integrating divisor which is a function *only* of the thermometric scale, and a

1 Pláček, *Amer. Chem. Abstr.*, 1939, **33**, 8067; 1944, **38**, 3172; Laska, *ibid.*, 1944, **38**, 3173; Rosenblum, *J. Chem. Educ.*, 1940, **17**, 438; Jankowsky, *Z. Elektrochem.*, 1919, **25**, 1, 325, suggested that the upper limit corresponds with the case when change of heat into potential energy is impossible (converse of 0° K., when the change is completely possible); Pokrowski, *Z. Phys.*, 1928, **51**, 730, calculated an upper limit of 3×10^{12} deg. On the supposed temperature of space, 0·75° K., see Nernst, *Z. Phys.*, 1937, **106**, 633; *Ann. Phys.*, 1938, **32**, 44.

2 *Phys. Z.*, 1908, **9**, 251.

3 *Ergebn. exakt. Naturwiss*, 1936, **15**, 189 (46 refs.).

4 Mott, *Endeavour*, 1946, **5**, 107.

5 " Technische Thermodynamik," 3rd edit., Leipzig, 1887, 30.

6 Boltzmann, *Ann. Phys.*, 1870, **140**, 635; " Wiss. Abhl.," 1909, **1**, 139; Budde, *Ann. Phys.*, 1892, **45**, 751; see also Fliegner, *Ann. Phys. Beibl.*, 1896, **20**, 255; Farkas, *ibid.*, 1896, **20**, 256; Durand, *Phys. Rev.*, 1897, **4**, 343; Schiller, *J. Russ. Phys. Chem. Soc.*, 1898, **30**, 31 (P); *Ann. Phys.*, 1901, **5**, 313; Denizot, *ibid.*, 1902, **7**, 358; 1902, **8**, 927; Voigt, *ibid.*, 1902, **8**, 472; Hasenöhrl, *Wien Ber.*, 1906, **115**, II A, 1005; Press, *Phil. Mag.*, 1927, **4**, 1245; *Z. Phys.*, 1928, **49**, 306; *Sow. Phys. Z.*, 1933, **3**, 487; Hausen, *Forscharb. Gebiet Ingenieurw.*, 1932, **3**, 203; Odone, *Atti. R. Accad. Lincei*, 1936, **23**, 865; *Nuov. Cim.*, 1936, **13**, 310; A. Daniel, " Note on Equations of State and the First and Second Laws of Thermodynamics," Edinburgh, 1940 (privately printed); Ehrenberg, *Phil. Mag.*, 1943, **34**, 396; 1945, **36**, 250; Wilson, *ibid.*, 1943, **34**, 828.

7 " Mechanical Theory of Heat," transl. Browne, 1879, 116 (equation 13), 122 (equations 32–40).

thermodynamic definition of absolute temperature T can be given as follows:

$$T = T_0 e^{\int t X dt} \qquad \qquad (2)$$

where $X=f(t)$, from (1), and T_0 defines the size of the degree, an equation given by Lippmann.[1]

The temperature concept is regarded as given; no interpretation of it is attempted in thermodynamics, which only gives a possibility of setting up a *scale*. " Classical thermodynamics begins with the assumption, not only that unambiguous temperature symbols exist [defining the position of a body in a temperature series], but also that these symbols are quantitative." The justification is found in the agreement of the results with experiment.[2]

The laws of thermodynamics have been derived in a purely formal mathematical way by Carathéodory [3] from a consideration of the integrating factor of Pfaff's [4] expression $du = \Sigma X_i dx_i$ (becoming *Pfaff's equation* when $du=0$; the case for two variables has been dealt with in § 27, I: $du = Xdx + Ydy$), where X_i is in general a function of all the independent variables x_i. The method is too abstract to appeal to many students of physical chemistry, and no more than an indication of its existence can be given here. The fundamental principle is that if a system is in a given state, then there are many other states near the initial state which cannot be reached by an adiabatic change; e.g. for a gas, if p_1, v_1 are the initial pressure and volume, the values after an adiabatic change are definite, p_2, v_2, other values being excluded. An interesting derivation of the general principles of thermodynamics was given by G. N. Lewis,[5] who said that: " There are endless ways of making contact between our theoretical principles and experiment, and the choice of a particular method of making such contact will be largely a matter of taste."

§ 38. Entropy Diagrams

If the entropy S is plotted against the absolute temperature T, the area of this entropy-temperature diagram will give the heat absorbed in a *reversible* change, since $q = \int TdS$, just as the area of a p, v diagram (§ 6) gives the work done, $w = \int pdv$. An entropy-temperature diagram was, apparently, first mentioned by Belpaire [6]; its characteristics were fully worked out by Gibbs,[7] and the diagram was first used for steam by MacFarlane Gray [8]: it is now applied

1 " Cours de Thermodynamique," 1889, 80 f., 93.

2 Barnett, *J. Phys. Chem.*, 1942, **46**, 715, who also considers more fully the meaning of the " bodies in contact," used in imaginary experiments in the working out of the idea of temperature, but, in general, gets little further than Maxwell, " Theory of Heat," 1871, 32.

3 *Math. Ann.*, 1909, **67**, 355; *Berlin Ber.*, 1925, 39; Epstein, *Ann. Phys.*, 1917, **53**, 76; criticism by Ehrenfest-Afanassjewa, *Z. Phys.*, 1925, **33**, 933; 1925, **34**, 638; for less abstract expositions, see Born, *Phys. Z.*, 1921, **22**, 218, 249, 282; Planck, *Berlin Ber.*, 1926, 453; " Thermodynamik," 8th edit., 1927, 88; " Theorie der Wärme," 1930, 45; *Physica*, 1935, **2**, 1029; Landé, in Geiger and Scheel, " Handbuch der Physik," 1926, **9**, 281; Larmor, " Math. and Phys. Papers," Cambridge, 1929, **2**, 590; Mimura, *J. Sci. Hiroshima Univ.*, 1930, **1** A, 43; Yamaoka, *Proc. Phys. Math. Soc. Japan*, 1937, **19**, 246; Putilov, *Bull. Acad. Sci. U.R.S.S.*, 1937 (*Chim.*), 715, 733; Margenau and Murphy, " The Mathematics of Physics and Chemistry," New York, 1943, 26. The accounts by Planck and Yamaoka are intelligible.

4 Pfaff, *Abhl. K. Akad. Berlin*, 1814–15, 76; Forsyth, " Theory of Differential Equations," Cambridge, 1890, **1**.

5 *J.A.C.S.*, 1931, **53**, 2578.

6 *Bull. Acad. Roy. Belg.*, 1872, **34**, 509; Boulvin, " The Entropy Diagram and its Application," transl. Donkin, 1898, 2; de Saussure, *Arch. Sci. Phys. Nat.*, 1894, **31**, 421; Thurston, *J. Franklin Inst.*, 1896, **141**, 27; Fox, *ibid.*, 1898, **145**, 214.

7 *Trans. Connecticut Acad.*, 1873, **2**, 309, 382; " Scientific Papers," 1906, **1**, 1, 33.

8 *Proc. Inst. Mech. Eng.*, 1889, 379, 399; Ewing, *Phil. Mag.*, 1920, **39**, 633.

generally in steam engineering. The so-called *Mollier chart* [1] is a plot of heat content H against entropy S, when the gradient of the curve of constant pressure is $(dH/dS)_p = T$ (§ 35).

Since $dE = TdS - pdv$ for a reversible change, for a cycle:

$$\oint dE = 0 = \oint TdS - \oint pdv, \quad \therefore \oint TdS = \oint pdv,$$

so that the areas of the p, v and T, S diagrams are equal if the units are suitably chosen.[2] Entropy and Mollier charts for helium, hydrogen, nitrogen, methane, and acetylene were given by Keesom and Houthoff,[3] and Keesom, Bijl, and Monté [4] modified the diagram (for nitrogen) by plotting H against $\log p$.

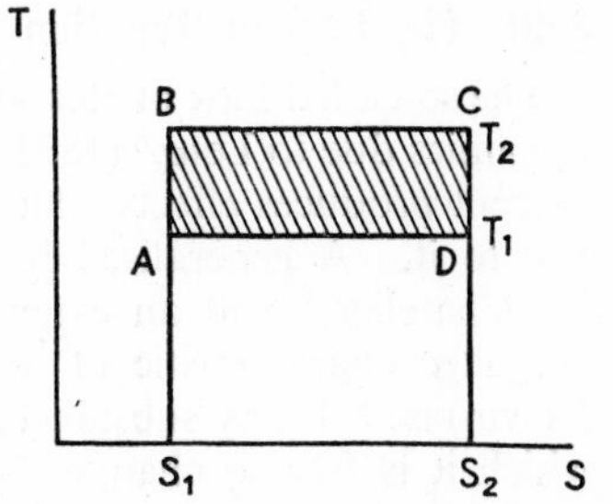

FIG. 14.II. Entropy-Temperature Diagram

In a reversible Carnot's cycle, since

$$dE = \delta q - \delta w = TdS - pdv = 0,$$

it follows that $\oint TdS = \oint pdv$. If S and T are used as axes instead of v and p, respectively, a rectangular area (Fig. 14.II) $ABCD = (T_2 - T_1)(S_2 - S_1)$ is obtained, giving the net heat absorbed in the cycle, and equal (in the same work units) to the area in the p, v diagram. In some cases, a simplification of representation in thermodynamic diagrams is achieved by using cylindrical instead of Cartesian coordinates.[5]

§ 39. Methods in Thermodynamics

The use of ideal processes for imaginary reversible changes in thermodynamic reasoning is perfectly legitimate; a truly reversible process, in any case, could never be carried out, and the ideas underlying such imaginary processes are, of course, much nearer natural reality than the pictures of pre-quantum dynamics.[6] The *calculation* of an entropy change (§ 35) requires at least one reversible path between the initial and final states to be known.[7] Since no method of reversing life-processes is known, careful thinkers [8] have always hesitated in applying the two laws of thermodynamics to them (see § 31).

The use of cyclic processes in thermodynamics has characterised most of the original contributions, and they are of considerable value in preventing errors which can slip into symbolic treatments.[9] The interesting and instructive

[1] Mollier, *Verhl. d. Vereins z. Beförd. d. Gewerbfl.*, 1893, **72**, 160; Roberts, "Heat and Thermodynamics," 1940, 284, 302; Ellenwood and Mackey, "Thermodynamic Charts," New York, 1944.

[2] Saurel, *J. Phys. Chem.*, 1901, **5**, 179.

[3] *Comm. Leiden*, 1928, Suppl. **65**.

[4] *Bull. Inst. Internat. Froid.*, 1942, **23**, D4; *Amer. Chem. Abstr.*, 1944, **38**, 4845.

[5] Lartigue, *Compt. Rend.*, 1924, **178**, 2169; 1924, **179**, 30.

[6] Planck, *Z. phys. Chem.*, 1891, **8**, 647; *Ann. Phys.*, 1903, **10**, 436; cf. Cantor, *ibid.*, 1903, **10**, 205; G. N. Lewis, *J.A.C.S.*, 1931, **53**, 2578.

[7] Kohl, *Ann. Phys.*, 1908, **25**, 155.

[8] W. Thomson, *Proc. Roy. Soc. Edin.*, 1875, **8**, 325 (read 1874); *Phil. Mag.*, 1892, **33**, 291; "Math. and Phys. Papers," 1911, **5**, 11; q. in Partington, "Thermodynamics," 1913, 87; Planck, *Ann. Phys.*, 1900, **1**, 621; Lewis and Randall, "Thermodynamics," New York, 1923, 121.

[9] Orr, *Phil. Mag.*, 1904, **8**, 509 (appreciation of van't Hoff); Nernst, "Theoretical Chemistry," 1904, 22.

method of this type used by Washburn [1] called out a typical over-zealous denunciation of cyclic processes in general from van Laar,[2] who had rendered notable services by the use of the thermodynamic potential ($G=E-TS+PV$). Although Lewis and Randall [3] spoke rather slightingly of cyclic processes, it is noteworthy that many of the original contributions described in their book were actually derived by the senior author by such cyclic processes.[4] Over-systematised schemes of thermodynamic relations [5] are more confusing than illuminating to some students.

§ 40. The Law of Reaction

The so-called Law of Reaction is based historically on the principle of electrodynamics due to Lenz[6] (1833), that the direction of a secondary induced electric current produces effects which oppose the action of the primary current giving rise to it. A generalised form of it was proposed by J. Thomson [7] and by Le Chatelier,[8] and an extended form by Braun.[9] Thomson's statement (in language characteristic of himself and his brother William, afterwards Lord Kelvin) is: " If any substance, or any system of substances, be in a condition in which it is free to change its state (whether of molecular arrangement, or of mechanical relative position and connexion of its parts, or of rest or motion), and if mechanical work be applied to it (or put into it) as potential energy, in such a way as that the occurrence of the change of state will make it lose (or enable it to lose) (or be accompanied by its losing) that mechanical work from the condition of potential energy, without receiving other potential energy as an equivalent; *then the substance or system will pass into the changed state.*" He considered many special cases and apparent exceptions. Le Chatelier's form, as phrased by Ostwald, reads:

If a system in equilibrium is subjected to a constraint, whereby the equilibrium is modified, a change takes place, if possible, which partially annuls the constraint.

The essentially vague character of this rule was later emphasised,[10] and attempts were made to give it greater precision.[11] For our purposes, however, it will

[1] *J.A.C.S.*, 1910, **32**, 467, 653, 1636; *J. Chim. Phys.*, 1910, **8**, 358; *Z. phys. Chem.*, 1910, **74**, 385; " Principles of Physical Chemistry," 2nd edit., New York, 1921, 475.

[2] *Z. phys. Chem.*, 1911, **76**, 67; see his valuable book, " Sechs Vorträge über das thermodynamische Potential," Brunswick, 1906.

[3] " Thermodynamics," New York, 1923, 2: " limping cycles."

[4] G. N. Lewis, *Proc. Amer. Acad.*, 1900, **36**, 145; 1901, **37**, 49; 1907, **43**, 259 (cycle); *Z. phys. Chem.*, 1900, **32**, 364; 1900, **35**, 343; 1901, **38**, 205; 1907, **61**, 129; *Z. Elektrochem.*, 1904, **10**, 633.

[5] Lange, *Z. Elektrochem.*, 1937, **43**, 158.

[6] *Mém. Acad. St. Petersb.*, 1833, **2**, 427; *Ann. Phys.*, 1834, **31**, 483.

[7] *Proc. Roy. Soc.*, 1861, **11**, 473; cf. Maxwell, " Theory of Heat," 1875, 131. Traces of the idea are seen in Aristotle's theory of *antiperistasis*, or the resistance of a substance to change of substantial form, and the *horror vacui* of the later schools: see Boyle, " New Experiments and Observations Touching Cold . . . To which are added An Examen of Antiperistasis," 1665, 697; " Works," 1744, **2**, 355; van Deventer, *Z. phys. Chem.*, 1888, **2**, 92; 1927, **130**, 33.

[8] *Compt. Rend.*, 1884, **99**, 786; *Z. phys. Chem.*, 1887, **1**, 565; " Les Équilibres Chimiques," 1888, 210; Gouy, *Compt. Rend.*, 1889, **108**, 341; Ostwald, " Principles of Inorganic Chemistry," 1904, 133.

[9] *Ann. Phys.*, 1887, **30**, 250; 1888, **33**, 336; 1889, **36**, 591; 1910, **32**, 1102; *Z. phys. Chem.*, 1887, **1**, 259, 269; Berthelot, " Thermochimie," 1897, **1**, 13.

[10] Raveau, *Compt. Rend.*, 1909, **148**, 767, 1093; *J. de Phys.*, 1909, **8**, 572; Ariès, *Compt. Rend.*, 1914, **158**, 492.

[11] Rayleigh, *Phil. Mag.*, 1875, **49**, 218; *J.C.S.*, 1917, **111**, 250; Wiedeburg, *Ann. Phys.*, 1899, **69**, 66; Ehrenfest, *J. Russ. Phys. Chem. Soc.*, 1909, **41**, 341, 365 (P.); *Z. phys. Chem.*, 1911, **77**, 227; Volkhorsky, *J. Russ. Phys. Chem. Soc.*, 1912, **44**, 310 (C.); 1916, **48**, 272 (C.); Bursian, *ibid.*, 1918, **49**, 87 (P.); Benedicks, *Z. phys. Chem.*, 1922, **100**, 42; Schottky, Ulich, and Wagner,

remain a useful *qualitative* guide,[1] which, in the great majority of cases, leads to correct results. Its mathematical formulation is hampered by the difficulty of making a satisfactory choice of the independent variables, and the equations derived have no advantages over the ordinary thermodynamic formulae.

§ 41. Clapeyron's Equation

Carnot's fundamental ideas were first put into a symbolic form by Clapeyron[2] in 1834. Let unit mass of a system defined by the characteristic equation $f(p, v, T)=0$, be taken round a very small reversible Carnot's cycle between the absolute temperatures T (isothermal BC) and $T-\delta T$ (isothermal AD), the volume change along the upper isothermal, $PQ=\delta v$, being also very small (Fig. 15.II). The cycle $ABCD$ may be regarded as a parallelogram, quantities of the third order being neglected in comparison with those of the second.

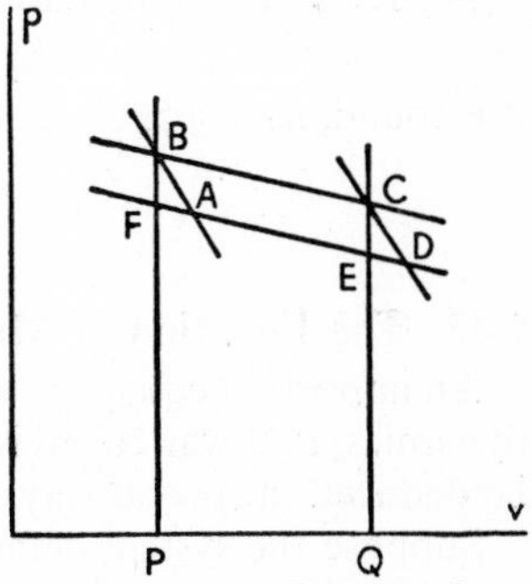

FIG. 15.II. Clapeyron's Diagram

The work done in the cycle is (from § 7), equal to the area of the cycle: $(\delta w)=$area $ABCD=$area $FBCE=FB\times PQ=FB\times\delta v$. FB is the pressure rise at constant volume for an increase in temperature δT, therefore $FB=(\mathrm{d}p/\mathrm{d}T)_v\delta T$,

$$\therefore\ (\delta w)=(\mathrm{d}p/\mathrm{d}T)_v\delta T\delta v \quad \ldots \ldots \quad (1)$$

Since the change along BC is isothermal, the heat absorbed is, from (2a), § 3:

$$\delta q=l_v\delta v \quad \ldots \ldots \quad (2)$$

hence by substitution of (2) in (1):

$$(\delta w)=(\mathrm{d}p/\mathrm{d}T)_v\delta T\delta q/l_v \quad \ldots \ldots \quad (3)$$

But, from § 33 (11), the work done in the cycle is equal to the heat absorbed at the higher temperature divided by this temperature and multiplied by the difference of temperatures:

$$(\delta w)=\delta q\delta T/T \quad \ldots \ldots \quad (4)$$

hence from (3) and (4) Clapeyron's equation is found:

$$l_v=T(\mathrm{d}p/\mathrm{d}T)_v \quad \ldots \ldots \quad (5)$$

Since (l_v/T) is the entropy change per unit increase in volume at constant temperature, viz. $(\mathrm{d}S/\mathrm{d}v)_T$, hence:

$$(\mathrm{d}S/\mathrm{d}v)_T=(\mathrm{d}p/\mathrm{d}T)_v, \quad \text{or} \quad (\mathrm{d}v/\mathrm{d}S)_T=(\mathrm{d}T/\mathrm{d}p)_v \quad \ldots \quad (6)$$

"Thermodynamik," Berlin, 1929; Frank, *Lignan Sci. J.*, 1930, **9**, 81; Bijvoet, *Chem. Weekbl.*, 1933, **30**, 742; Posthumus, *Rec. Trav. Chim.*, 1933, **52**, 25; 1934, **53**, 308 (crit.); reply by Le Chatelier, *Compt. Rend.*, 1934, **198**, 1329; Verschaffelt, *ibid.*, 1933, **197**, 753; Planck, *Berlin Ber.*, 1934, 79; *Ann. Phys.*, 1934, **19**, 759; 1934, **20**, 196; Epstein, "Textbook of Thermodynamics," New York, 1937, 374; Renaud and Baumgardt, *Compt. Rend.*, 1935, **201**, 1129; Prigogine, *Bull. Acad. Roy. Belg.*, 1946, **31**, 600.

[1] Chwolson, "Lehrbuch der Physik," Brunswick, 1905, **3**, 474; Bancroft, *J.A.C.S.*, 1910, **36**, 91; "The Phase Rule," Ithaca (N.Y.), 1897, 4.

[2] *J. de l'École Polytechnique*, 1834, **14**, 153; *Ann. Phys.*, 1843, **59**, 446, 556 (a poor translation); Ostwald's *Klassiker*, 1926, **216**; Taylor's *Scientific Memoirs*, 1837, **1**, 347; Wilson, *Phil. Mag.*, 1943, **34**, 828; Clapeyron assumed (which is not necessary for the deduction) that the heat given out along DA=the heat absorbed along BC; Clausius, *Ann. Phys.*, 1850, **79**, 368, made what he calls " a small change " by putting the difference equal to the work done in the cycle.

which is one of Maxwell's equations (§ 48). Conversely, equation (5) may be deduced [1] from the first equation (6) by multiplying both sides by T.

If the work done in a small reversible change is given by $\delta w = X\mathrm{d}x$, instead of by $p\mathrm{d}v$, where X is called a *generalised force* and x a *generalised coordinate*, X and x can be used in the diagram instead of p and v, giving:

$$l_x = T(\mathrm{d}X/\mathrm{d}T)_x \quad . \quad . \quad . \quad . \quad . \quad . \quad . \quad (7)$$

where l_x is a latent heat corresponding with unit change of x at constant T (see § 42).[2]

Again, if equations (2a) and (2b), § 3, are written in the form:

$$\delta q = c_x \mathrm{d}T + l_x \mathrm{d}x = c_X \mathrm{d}T + l_X \mathrm{d}X,$$

it is found, as in § 5, that:

$$c_X = c_x - l_X(dX/\mathrm{d}T)_x \quad . \quad . \quad . \quad . \quad . \quad . \quad . \quad . \quad . \quad (8)$$

$$l_x = l_X(\mathrm{d}X/\mathrm{d}x)_T \quad . \quad . \quad . \quad . \quad . \quad . \quad . \quad . \quad . \quad (9)$$

§ 42. The Equation of Maximum Work

An important equation, which includes the First and Second Laws of Thermodynamics, and was called by the author [3] the *Equation of Maximum Work*, may be deduced in several ways.

Suppose the system defined by the absolute temperature T and a set of other variables $x_1, x_2, \ldots x_n$ so chosen that in a change of temperature with constant x's no work is done; these are called *normal variables*. Let the system pass reversibly and isothermally from an initial state $T, (x_1)_0, (x_2)_0, \ldots (x_n)_0$ to a final state $T, x_1, x_2, \ldots x_n$. Then, from (3), § 33, $\Delta F = \Delta E - T\Delta S$,

$$\therefore \; (\mathrm{d}\Delta F/\mathrm{d}T)_{\Delta x} = (\mathrm{d}\Delta E/\mathrm{d}T)_{\Delta x} - T(\mathrm{d}\Delta S/\mathrm{d}T)_{\Delta x} - \Delta S \quad . \quad . \quad (1)$$

the subscript showing that in the finite change at $T+\mathrm{d}T$ instead of T the values of $x_1-(x_1)_0$, $x_2-(x_2)_0$, etc., remain constant, with the same values as they had at the temperatures T. By analogy with (5), § 21, and (3), § 35:

$$(\mathrm{d}E/\mathrm{d}T)_x = T(\mathrm{d}S/\mathrm{d}T)_x,$$

hence the first two terms on the right in (1) vanish,

$$\therefore \; (\mathrm{d}\Delta F/\mathrm{d}T)_{\Delta x} = -\Delta S = (\Delta F - \Delta E)/T$$

$$\text{or } \Delta F - \Delta E = T(\mathrm{d}\Delta F/\mathrm{d}T)_{\Delta x} \quad . \quad . \quad . \quad . \quad . \quad . \quad . \quad (2)$$

The equation (2) is nearly always called the " Gibbs-Helmholtz equation," although, as Bancroft [4] said, it is one which " Gibbs could have, and perhaps should have, deduced, but did not." Larmor [5] very properly suggested that it should be called the *Thomson equation*, since it was deduced in 1855 by W. Thomson [6] (Lord Kelvin) by the following very elegant method.[7]

[1] Saurel, *J. Phys. Chem.*, 1901, **5**, 256.

[2] Saurel, *J. Phys. Chem.*, 1900, **4**, 193; 1901, **5**, 393; who says Clapeyron's deduction " is as general as it is simple."

[3] " Thermodynamics," 1913, 112; Szarvassi, *Ann. Phys.*, 1905, **17**, 248.

[4] *J. Phys. Chem.*, 1927, **31**, 638: he is in error in saying that Helmholtz did not deduce it, since it is equn. 1*h*, p. 31, in his paper, Die Thermodynamik chemischer Vorgänge, in *Berlin Ber.*, 1882, I, 22 f.; Ostwald's *Klassiker*, 1902, **124**, 17; " Wiss. Abhl.," 1883, **2**, 958; 1895, **3**, 92; Scarpa, *Atti Accad. Ital., fis. mat.*, 1941, **2**, 1057.

[5] *Proc. Roy. Soc.*, 1908, **81**, Appendix, xlv; " Math. and Phys. Papers," Cambridge, 1929, **2**, 102, 724.

[6] *Quart. J. Math.*, 1857, **1**, 57 (dated 1855); *Phil. Mag.*, 1878, **5**, 4; " Math. and Phys. Papers," 1882, **1**, 297; Tait, " Thermodynamics," 1877, 141; another deduction, without the use of entropy, was given by Lord Kelvin in 1898: *Proc. Roy. Soc. Edin.*, 1898, **22**, 126; " Math. and Phys. Papers," 1911, **5**, 24; Gruner, *Verhl. d. D. Phys. Ges.*, 1912, **14**, 655, 727; Boutaric, *J. Chim. Phys.*, 1913, **11**, 638; *Compt. Rend.*, 1919, **168**, 939; 1919, **169**, 432; *Le Radium*, 1919, **11**, 257, 298, 348.

[7] Buckingham, " An Outline of the Theory of Thermodynamics," New York, 1900, 170 f.

Consider any definite change of state at the absolute temperature T, and reversed at the temperature $T+\delta T$, so that the cycle consists of these two isothermals and two other parts in which no work is done during the temperature changes (e.g. at constant volume). Let heat q be absorbed at T and heat $q+\delta q$ be given out at $T+\delta T$; there will be heat $(\mathrm{d}E/\mathrm{d}T)_x\delta T$ taken in at the upper transition and $(\mathrm{d}E_0/\mathrm{d}T)_x\delta T$ at the lower, where $\Delta E=E-E_0$, and $T+\frac{1}{2}\delta T$ is the average temperature for these changes. Then (§ 33):

$$\sum\frac{q}{T}=\frac{q}{T}-\frac{q+\delta q}{T+\delta T}+\left(\frac{\mathrm{d}\Delta E}{\mathrm{d}T}\right)_{\Delta x}\frac{\delta T}{T+\frac{1}{2}\delta T}=\Delta S=0$$

$$\therefore\ \left(\frac{\mathrm{d}\Delta E}{\mathrm{d}T}\right)_{\Delta x}=-\frac{T+\frac{1}{2}\delta T}{\delta T}\cdot\frac{q}{T}+\frac{(T+\frac{1}{2}\delta T)}{\delta T}\cdot\frac{q+\delta q}{T+\delta T}.$$

Multiply out and neglect a term with δT^2, then:

$$(\mathrm{d}\Delta E/\mathrm{d}T)_{\Delta x}=-q/T+(\mathrm{d}q/\mathrm{d}T)_{\Delta x}.$$

Put $q=\Delta E+w$,

$$\therefore\ (\mathrm{d}q/\mathrm{d}T)_{\Delta x}=(\mathrm{d}\Delta E/\mathrm{d}T)_{\Delta x}+(\mathrm{d}w/\mathrm{d}T)_{\Delta x},$$

$$\therefore\ \Delta E+w=T(\mathrm{d}w/\mathrm{d}T)_{\Delta x} \quad . \quad . \quad . \quad . \quad . \quad . \quad . \quad . \quad . \quad (3)$$

or, since $w=-\Delta F$, equation (2) is found. ΔE may be replaced by q_v.

Helmholtz gave the following deduction. The system is defined by T and the normal variables x_1, x_2, . . ., as before. If X_1 is the generalised force (§§ 41, 50) corresponding with x_1, the work done during a change of x_1, x_2, . . . at constant temperature is:

$$\delta w=\Sigma X_1\mathrm{d}x_1 \quad . \quad . \quad . \quad . \quad . \quad . \quad . \quad . \quad . \quad . \quad (4)$$

and the energy increase due to a change of all the variables is:

$$\mathrm{d}E=(\mathrm{d}E/\mathrm{d}T)_x\mathrm{d}T+\Sigma(\mathrm{d}E/\mathrm{d}x_1)_T\mathrm{d}x_1.$$

Hence the heat absorption is:

$$\delta q=\mathrm{d}E+\delta w$$

$$=(\mathrm{d}E/\mathrm{d}T)_x\mathrm{d}T+\Sigma[(\mathrm{d}E/\mathrm{d}x_1)_T+X_1]\mathrm{d}x_1 \quad . \quad . \quad . \quad . \quad . \quad (5)$$

$$\therefore\ \delta q/T=(1/T)(\mathrm{d}E/\mathrm{d}T)_x\mathrm{d}T+(1/T)\Sigma[(\mathrm{d}E/\mathrm{d}x_1)_T+X_1]\mathrm{d}x_1 \quad . \quad . \quad (6)$$

where the suffix x indicates that *all* the values of x_1, x_2, . . . are held constant during the change of temperature (cf. (5) and (4), § 21). But:

$$\delta q/T=\mathrm{d}S=(\mathrm{d}S/\mathrm{d}T)_x\mathrm{d}T+\Sigma(\mathrm{d}S/\mathrm{d}x_1)_T\mathrm{d}x_1 \quad . \quad . \quad . \quad . \quad (7)$$

giving, on comparison of (6) and (7):

$$(\mathrm{d}S/\mathrm{d}T)_x=(1/T)(\mathrm{d}E/\mathrm{d}T)_x \quad . \quad . \quad . \quad . \quad . \quad . \quad . \quad (8)$$

$$\text{and}\ (\mathrm{d}S/\mathrm{d}x_1)_T=(1/T)[(\mathrm{d}E/\mathrm{d}x_1)_T+X_1] \quad . \quad . \quad . \quad . \quad (9)$$

Put $F=E-TS$, then

$$(\mathrm{d}F/\mathrm{d}T)_x=(\mathrm{d}E/\mathrm{d}T)_x-T(\mathrm{d}S/\mathrm{d}T)_x-S.$$

who gives this deduction, found it " less easy to analyse and less clear " than the alternative one given below:

$$F=E-TS;\quad \mathrm{d}E=T\mathrm{d}S-\Sigma X\mathrm{d}x;\quad \mathrm{d}F=-S\mathrm{d}T-\Sigma X\mathrm{d}x$$

$$S=-(\partial F/\partial T)_x \quad \therefore\ F=E+T\,.\,\partial F/\partial T.$$

This is not really equation (2), and the meaning of " $\partial F/\partial T$ " is obscure.

The cycle here described was, apparently, first used by Rankine, *Trans. Roy. Soc. Edin.*, 1853, **20**, 147 (read 1850); " Misc. Scient. Papers," 1881, 251, and hence might be called a " Rankine cycle ": Partington, " Text-Book of Thermodynamics," 1913, 113; Rankine calls the curves representing changes without performance of work, *adynamics*.

From (8), the first two terms on the right hand vanish,

$$\therefore\ (\mathrm{d}F/\mathrm{d}T)_x = -S = (F-E)/T \quad . \quad . \quad . \quad (10)$$

If there is only one normal variable, say volume, $x_1 = V$, then:

$$(\mathrm{d}F/\mathrm{d}T)_V = (F-E)/T$$

and for two states, V_1 and V_2, at the same temperature:

$$(\mathrm{d}F/\mathrm{d}T)_{V_2} - (\mathrm{d}F/\mathrm{d}T)_{V_1} = (\Delta F - \Delta E)/T \quad . \quad . \quad . \quad (11)$$

which may be written in the shorter form: [1]

$$(\mathrm{d}\Delta F/\mathrm{d}T)_{\Delta V} = (\Delta F - \Delta E)/T \quad . \quad . \quad . \quad (12)$$

or in the general case:

$$(\mathrm{d}\Delta F/\mathrm{d}T)_{\Delta x} = (\Delta F - \Delta E)/T \quad . \quad . \quad . \quad (13)$$

An early use of the Maximum Work Equation in chemistry is that of Horstmann,[2] in 1872. Jüptner [3] by dividing each side of the equation $\mathrm{d}w = q\mathrm{d}T/T$ by w found $\mathrm{d}w/w = (\mathrm{d}T/T) \cdot q/w$, or $\mathrm{d} \ln w/\mathrm{d} \ln T = q/w$.

§ 43. Relation between Energy and Free Energy

If E_0 and S_0 are the energy and entropy in the standard state, the free energy defined by $F=E-TS$ contains an arbitrary linear function of temperature $E_0 - TS_0$. Since E and S are extensive properties (§ 23), and T is an intensive property, it follows that F is also an extensive property and proportional to the total mass (or quantity) of the system.

For an infinitesimal change in which there is a change in temperature:

$$\mathrm{d}F = \mathrm{d}E - T\mathrm{d}S - S\mathrm{d}T \quad . \quad . \quad . \quad (1)$$

From the First Law:

$$\mathrm{d}E = \delta q - \delta w \quad . \quad . \quad . \quad (2)$$

For a *reversible* process (only), (5), § 33 gives $\delta q = T\mathrm{d}S$, and if the only external work is due to volume change, $\delta w = P\mathrm{d}V$, then:

$$\mathrm{d}E = T\mathrm{d}S - P\mathrm{d}V \quad . \quad . \quad . \quad (3)$$

Hence, from (1) and (3), $\mathrm{d}F = -S\mathrm{d}T - P\mathrm{d}V$

$$\therefore\ (\mathrm{d}F/\mathrm{d}V)_T = -P \quad . \quad . \quad . \quad (4)$$

and

$$(\mathrm{d}F/\mathrm{d}T)_V = -S \quad . \quad . \quad . \quad (5)$$

$$\therefore\ F - E = -TS = T(\mathrm{d}F/\mathrm{d}T)_V \quad . \quad . \quad . \quad (6)$$

From (5), and § 35 (3):

$$(\mathrm{d}^2F/\mathrm{d}T^2)_V = -(\mathrm{d}S/\mathrm{d}T)_V = -c_v/T \quad . \quad . \quad . \quad (7)$$

and from (4):

$$(\mathrm{d}^2F/\mathrm{d}V^2)_T = -(\mathrm{d}P/\mathrm{d}V)_T \quad . \quad . \quad . \quad (8)$$

[1] The commonly used symbol $(\mathrm{d}\Delta F/\mathrm{d}T)_V$ may be misleading, since it could suggest that ΔF is a free energy change at constant volume, whereas ΔF often involves a volume change, as in the isothermal expansion of 1 mol of ideal gas, when $\Delta F = RT \ln (V_2/V_1)$ and $(\mathrm{d}\Delta F/\mathrm{d}T)_{\Delta V} = R \ln (V_2/V_1)$. The volumes in the two terms F_1 and F_2 of ΔF may be different, and in differentiating with respect to T, *each* must be held constant. In some cases, as in dealing with the temperature variation of electromotive force, the volume itself may be held constant whilst the temperature changes.

[2] *Ann.*, 1872, Supplbd. **8**, 112; Ostwald's *Klassiker*, 1903, **137**, 8.

[3] *Z. phys. Chem.*, 1907, **60**, 114; 1908, **64**, 709; " Das chemische Gleichgewicht auf Grund mechanischer Vorstellungen," Leipzig and Berlin, 1911; von Lang, *Wien Ber.*, 1890, **99**, II, 899 (applications).

Rearrange (6) and divide by T^2:

$$\therefore\ -\frac{1}{T}\left(\frac{\mathrm{d}F}{\mathrm{d}T}\right)_V+\frac{F}{T^2}=-\frac{\mathrm{d}}{\mathrm{d}T}\left(\frac{F}{T}\right)_V=\frac{E}{T^2}$$

$$\therefore\ -F/T=\int(E/T^2)\mathrm{d}T+C \quad (9)$$

where C is the integration constant, giving a relation between the free energy F and the energy E.

For finite changes in state of a system:

$$-\frac{\mathrm{d}}{\mathrm{d}T}\left(\frac{\Delta F}{T}\right)=\frac{\Delta E}{T^2}\quad\therefore\ -\frac{\Delta F}{T}=\int\frac{\Delta E}{T^2}\mathrm{d}T+C. \quad (10)$$

§ 44. Available Energy

A function of state here called [1] the *available energy* is defined by:

$$G=F+PV=E-TS+PV \quad (1)$$

In isothermal changes at constant pressure:

$$\Delta G=\Delta F+P\Delta V \quad (2)$$

But in reversible isothermal changes, $\Delta F=-w_T$, and $P\Delta V=w_V$, the external work due to volume change, hence:

$$-\Delta G=w_T-w_V=w'_T \quad (3)$$

where w'_T is the *available* (or net) *work*, i.e. the maximum work w_T of the reversible change at constant temperature and pressure *less* the external work done by expansion under a constant pressure, e.g. the pressure of the atmosphere.

For an infinitesimal change (1) gives:

$$\begin{aligned}\mathrm{d}G&=\mathrm{d}F+P\mathrm{d}V+V\mathrm{d}P\\&=(\mathrm{d}E-T\mathrm{d}S-S\mathrm{d}T)+P\mathrm{d}V+V\mathrm{d}P\\&=(\mathrm{d}E-T\mathrm{d}S+P\mathrm{d}V)-S\mathrm{d}T+V\mathrm{d}P.\end{aligned}$$

If the only external work is due to volume change:

$$\mathrm{d}E+P\mathrm{d}V=\delta q,$$

and since, for a reversible change, $\delta q=T\mathrm{d}S$, the expression in brackets is zero; hence:

$$\mathrm{d}G=-S\mathrm{d}T+V\mathrm{d}P$$

$$\therefore\ (\mathrm{d}G/\mathrm{d}T)_P=-S \quad (4)$$

and

$$(\mathrm{d}G/\mathrm{d}P)_T=V \quad (5)$$

The heat content is:

$$H=E+PV \quad (6)$$

$\therefore$ from (1) and (6):

$$H=F+TS+PV=G+TS \quad (7)$$

$\therefore$ from (4):

$$H=G-T(\mathrm{d}G/\mathrm{d}T)_P \quad (8)$$

or

$$\Delta H=\Delta G+T\Delta S=\Delta G-T(\mathrm{d}\Delta G/\mathrm{d}T)_P \quad (9)$$

Hence [2] from (9) and (3), and § 17 (6):

$$w'_T+q_P=T(\mathrm{d}w'_T/\mathrm{d}T)_P \quad (10)$$

[1] Other names are "thermodynamic potential" (Duhem), "free energy" (G. N. Lewis). Strictly, it should perhaps be called "free-heat function" or "free enthalpy" (Martin, *Amer. Chem. Abstr.*, 1943, **37**, 2250).

[2] On equation (10), see Lorenz and Katayama, *Z. phys. Chem.*, 1908, **62**, 119; Gruner, *Verhl. d. D. Phys. Ges.*, 1912, **14**, 655; Wesendonck, *ibid.*, 1913, **15**, 839; Nernst, *Berlin Ber.*, 1913, 972; Wegscheider, *Z. phys. Chem.*, 1912, **79**, 223; 1920, **94**, 746; Lorenz, *ibid.*, 1924, **110**, 40; Partington, "Thermodynamics," 1913, 107.

In (9) the pressures in the two terms of $\Delta G=G_2-G_1$ need not be the same, but may be P_2 and P_1, respectively. In this case each pressure must be held constant during differentiation by T. The case is similar to that of (11), § 42, for ΔF. This would apply, for example, to a gas cell having the same gas at pressures P_1 and P_2 at the two electrodes. Since E (or H) and S are functions of state, having definite values for a system in a given state, this is also true of G.

Differentiate (1) with respect to T at constant pressure,

$$(\mathrm{d}G/\mathrm{d}T)_P=(\mathrm{d}F/\mathrm{d}T)_P+P(\mathrm{d}V/\mathrm{d}T)_P,$$

$$\therefore\ G=H+T(\mathrm{d}F/\mathrm{d}T)_P+PT(\mathrm{d}V/\mathrm{d}T)_P,$$

$$\therefore\ F=H+T(\mathrm{d}F/\mathrm{d}T)_P+P[T(\mathrm{d}V/\mathrm{d}T)_P-V/T] \quad . \quad . \quad \textbf{(11)}$$

The maximum work at constant pressure is still $-\Delta F$, not $-\Delta G$ (there has been some confusion on this point), hence the equation $w+\Delta H=T(\mathrm{d}w/\mathrm{d}T)$, is *not* correct unless $(\mathrm{d}V/\mathrm{d}T)_P=V/T$, i.e. for an ideal gas.

Natanson [1] called G (which he symbolised K) the " inner potential energy," $-pv$ the " inner mechanical energy," and TS the " inner thermal energy "; $-S\mathrm{d}T$ is the " transformed heat," equal to $\mathrm{d}F+\mathrm{d}w$.

From (4), and § 35 (6):

$$(\mathrm{d}^2G/\mathrm{d}T^2)_P=-(\mathrm{d}S/\mathrm{d}T)_P=-c_p/T \quad . \quad . \quad . \quad . \quad . \quad \textbf{(12)}$$

Since $\mathrm{d}H=\mathrm{d}(E+PV)=\mathrm{d}E+P\mathrm{d}V+V\mathrm{d}P$, and $\mathrm{d}E+P\mathrm{d}V=\delta q=T\mathrm{d}S$; therefore $\mathrm{d}H=T\mathrm{d}S+V\mathrm{d}P$

$$\therefore\ (\mathrm{d}H/\mathrm{d}S)_P=T \quad . \quad . \quad . \quad . \quad . \quad . \quad . \quad . \quad \textbf{(13)}$$

and

$$(\mathrm{d}H/\mathrm{d}P)_S=V \quad . \quad . \quad . \quad . \quad . \quad . \quad . \quad . \quad \textbf{(14)}$$

From (6) it is found, as in the deduction of (9) and (10), § 43, that:

$$[\mathrm{d}(G/T)/\mathrm{d}T]_P=-H/T^2 \quad . \quad . \quad . \quad . \quad . \quad . \quad . \quad \textbf{(15)}$$

and

$$[\mathrm{d}(\Delta G/T)/\mathrm{d}T]_P=-\Delta H/T^2 \quad . \quad . \quad . \quad . \quad . \quad . \quad \textbf{(16)}$$

These equations give a relation between the available energy G and heat content H.

§ 45. Note on Thermodynamic Functions

Massieu [2] in 1869 showed that *all* characteristic properties of fluids can be expressed in terms of one or other of two functions or their differential coefficients:

$$H=-(E-TS)/T; \quad H'=-(E-TS+PV)/T$$

which he called *characteristic functions*; in 1876, following a suggestion by Bertrand, he used the functions $H=-(E-TS)$ and $H'=-(E-TS+PV)$. Planck [3] later used $-(E-TS+PV)/T$, which he called Φ or Ψ, as a *potential function*; it has the same properties in a system at constant temperature and pressure as the entropy at constant energy and volume.

Maxwell [4] observed that the maximum work in an isothermal process is the decrease of a function $E-TS$, for which he used the name *available energy*.

[1] *Ann. Phys.*, 1891, **42**, 178; *Z. phys. Chem.*, 1892, **10**, 733; 1897, **24**, 302; see Trevor, *J. Phys. Chem.*, 1899, **3**, 389; 1900, **4**, 514, on the interpretation of these terms.

[2] *Compt. Rend.*, 1869, **69**, 858, 1057; *J. de Phys.*, 1877, **6**, 216; *Mém. div. Sav.* [Étrangère] *Acad. Sci.*, 1876, **22**, No. 2, 9, 26; Bertrand, " Thermodynamique," 1887, 121.

[3] *Ann. Phys.*, 1887, **32**, 462; " Thermodynamik," 1911, 116.

[4] " Theory of Heat," 1871, 185.

He confused it with the entropy, but later corrected the mistake.[1] Gibbs [2] in 1873 used the function $E-TS+PV$, which Duhem [3] called the *thermodynamic potential*. Gibbs [4] in 1876 used the three functions (in his notation):

$$\psi=\epsilon-t\eta\ [=E-TS=F]$$
$$\zeta=\epsilon-t\eta+pv\ [=E-TS+PV=G]$$
$$\chi=\epsilon+pv\ [=E+PV=H],$$

calling $-\psi$ the *force function for constant temperature*, $+\chi$ the *heat function at constant pressure*, but not naming ζ.

Lord Kelvin [5] (1879) used the name *motivity* for " the possession, the waste of which is called dissipation," and at constant temperature this is the free energy F. Helmholtz [6] (1882) generalised the potential energy function of mechanics so as to obtain a function the decrease of which at a given constant temperature represents the maximum work obtainable for a given change of configuration. This function could be transferred to other temperatures by an application of the Second Law; he called it the *free energy* and denoted it by F.

In the earlier editions of his " Theory of Heat," Maxwell used the name " entropy " for what was really the free energy,[7] but in the edition of 1875 this was corrected, and the name " available energy " substituted. The 1875 edition (p. 195 f.) also contains a clear account of Gibbs's method [8] of representation of the properties of a substance by means of a surface, and a diagram (p. 207) of a volume, entropy, and energy surface from a model made by Maxwell. The " thermodynamic function " introduced by Rankine [9] in 1854 is the same as the entropy.

The fact that the energy E and heat content H are also " potential " functions for constant entropy and volume, or constant entropy and pressure, respectively, which follows from the equations $\mathrm{d}E=T\mathrm{d}S-p\mathrm{d}v$, $\mathrm{d}H=T\mathrm{d}S+v\mathrm{d}p$; and similar equations with generalised coordinates and forces (§ 42), has, of course, long been recognised,[10] with the other obvious result that the entropy is a potential function for constant energy and volume (or generalised coordinates). The names " Helmholtz free energy " and " Gibbs free energy " for F and G, respectively, are historically incorrect.

§ 46. Calculation of Free and Available Energies

In order to integrate equation (10), § 43:

$$-\Delta F/T=\int(\Delta E/T^2)\mathrm{d}T \quad . \quad . \quad . \quad . \quad . \quad . \quad . \quad (1)$$

and equation (16), § 44:

$$-\Delta G/T=\int(\Delta H/T^2)\mathrm{d}T \quad . \quad . \quad . \quad . \quad . \quad . \quad . \quad (2)$$

1 " Theory of Heat," 1875, 187.
2 " Scientific Papers," 1906, **1**, 50; he says $E-TS$ " had been called the *available energy*."
3 " Le Potentiel Thermodynamique et ses Applications," Paris, 1886, vii.
4 " Scientific Papers," 1906, **1**, 87–92; from *Trans. Connecticut Acad.*, 1875–6, **3**, 108 f.; Nutting, *Science*, 1946, **104**, 317.
5 *Phil. Mag.*, 1879, **7**, 348; " Math. and Phys. Papers," 1911, **5**, 4.
6 *Berlin Ber.*, 1882, i, 22; Ostwald's *Klassiker*, 1902, **124**, 27.
7 See Gibbs, " Scientific Papers," 1906, **1**, 52.
8 Gibbs, " Scientific Papers," 1906, **1**, 1 f.
9 *Phil. Trans.*, 1854, **144**, 126; " Misc. Scient. Papers," 1881, 352.
10 See e.g. Buckingham, " An Outline of the Theory of Thermodynamics," New York, 1900, 167 f; on Gibbs's methods, see Lash Miller, *Chem. Rev.*, 1924, **1**, 293; Nutting, *Science*, 1946, **104**, 317; Coffin, *J. Chem. Educ.*, 1946, **23**, 584.

ΔE and ΔH must be known as functions of temperature. Kirchhoff's equations (§ 20) give:

$$\Delta E = \Delta E^0 + \int \Delta C_v \mathrm{d}T \quad . \quad . \quad . \quad . \quad . \quad . \quad . \quad (3)$$

$$\Delta H = \Delta H^0 + \int \Delta C_p \mathrm{d}T \quad . \quad . \quad . \quad . \quad . \quad . \quad . \quad (4)$$

Substitution of (3) in (1) and (4) in (2) gives:

$$-\Delta F = T\int \frac{(\Delta E^0 + \int \Delta C_v \mathrm{d}T)}{T^2}\mathrm{d}T$$

$$\therefore \quad -\Delta F = -\Delta E_0 + T\int \frac{\mathrm{d}T}{T^2}\int \Delta C_v \mathrm{d}T \quad . \quad . \quad . \quad . \quad . \quad . \quad (5)$$

and

$$-\Delta G = -\Delta H_0 + T\int \frac{\mathrm{d}T}{T^2}\int \Delta C_p \mathrm{d}T \quad . \quad . \quad . \quad . \quad . \quad . \quad (6)$$

If the true molecular heats are of the form: [1]

$$C_v = a + bT + cT^2 + \ldots$$

$$C_p = a' + b'T + c'T^2 + \ldots$$

then (3) and (4) give:

$$\Delta E = \Delta E_0 + \Sigma a \,.\, T + 1/2 \,.\, \Sigma b \,.\, T^2 + 1/3 \,.\, \Sigma c \,.\, T^3 + \ldots \quad . \quad . \quad (7)$$

$$\Delta H = \Delta H_0 + \Sigma a' \,.\, T + 1/2 \,.\, \Sigma b' \,.\, T^2 + 1/3 \,.\, \Sigma c' \,.\, T^3 + \ldots \quad . \quad (8)$$

and (5) and (6):

$$\Delta F = \Delta E_0 - \Sigma a \,.\, T \ln T - 1/2 \,.\, \Sigma b \,.\, T^2 - 1/6 \,.\, \Sigma c \,.\, T^3 + \ldots + IT \quad . \quad . \quad (9)$$

$$\Delta G = \Delta H_0 - \Sigma a' \,.\, T \ln T - 1/2 \,.\, \Sigma b' \,.\, T^2 - 1/6 \,.\, \Sigma c' \,.\, T^3 + \ldots + I'T \quad . \quad (10)$$

The integration constants I and I' may be eliminated if ΔF and ΔG are known for *one* temperature.

The molecular heats may be calculated from theoretical functions (such as the Einstein and Debye functions for solids, or spectroscopic data for gases), and the values of ΔC_v and ΔC_p can then be obtained from tables. Since *absolute* values of S can be calculated from Nernst's Heat Theorem (§ 69), standard values of F and G may also be tabulated.

§ 47. Difference of Specific Heats

From (10), § 21:

$$c_p - c_v = l_v(\mathrm{d}v/\mathrm{d}T)_p = [(\mathrm{d}E/\mathrm{d}v)_T + p](\mathrm{d}v/\mathrm{d}T)_p \quad . \quad . \quad . \quad . \quad (1)$$

The value of $l_v = T(\mathrm{d}p/\mathrm{d}T)_v$ may be substituted from Clapeyron's equation, (5), § 41, and the product of the partial differential coefficients transformed according to (11), § 25.I. This gives:

$$c_p - c_v = T(\mathrm{d}p/\mathrm{d}T)_v(\mathrm{d}v/\mathrm{d}T)_p$$

$$= -T(\mathrm{d}v/\mathrm{d}T)_p^2/(\mathrm{d}v/\mathrm{d}p)_T$$

$$= -T(\mathrm{d}v/\mathrm{d}T)_p^2(\mathrm{d}p/\mathrm{d}v)_T \quad . \quad . \quad . \quad . \quad . \quad . \quad (2)$$

The important difference $c_p - c_v$ is now expressed in terms of experimentally available magnitudes such as the coefficient of expansion[2] $\alpha = (\mathrm{d}v/\mathrm{d}T)_p/v_0$, the coefficient of tension $\beta = (\mathrm{d}p/\mathrm{d}T)_v/p_0$, the isothermal elasticity $\epsilon_T = -v_0(\mathrm{d}p/\mathrm{d}v)_T$, and the isothermal compressibility $\kappa_T = -(\mathrm{d}v/\mathrm{d}p)_T/v_0$.

[1] See Nernst, *Gött. Nachr.*, 1906, 1; " Experimental and Theoretical Applications of Thermodynamics to Chemistry," New York, 1907; Jellinek, " Physikalische Chemie der Gasreaktionen," Leipzig, 1913, 55, 88; Bozza and Devoto, *Atti R. Accad. Lincei*, 1927, **5**, 180, 287.

[2] See Peczalski, *Compt. Rend.*, 1913, **157**, 770.

§ 48. Maxwell's Equations

Four very useful differential equations, first deduced by Maxwell [1] by a geometrical method which is not very easy to follow,[2] are obtained as follows. The deduction depends on the principle that the energy E, heat content H, free energy F, and available energy G are all functions of state (§§ 16, 17, 33, 34, 44), having definite values when the system is in a given state; for any system the state of which is defined by *two* independent variables x and y, Euler's criterion (§ 27.I) gives (where X may be E, H, F, or G):

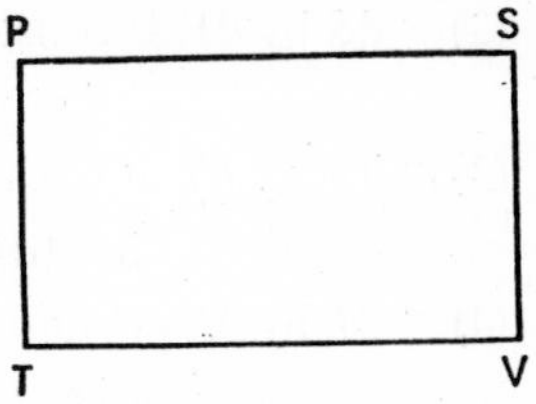

FIG. 16.II. Maxwell's Equations

$$\frac{d}{dx}\left(\frac{dX}{dy}\right)_y=\frac{d}{dy}\left(\frac{dX}{dx}\right)_x:$$

I. $$dE=TdS-PdV \text{ from (3), § 43,}$$

$$\therefore\ (dE/dV)_S=-P, \quad \text{and} \quad (dE/dS)_V=T,$$

$$\therefore\ \left(\frac{dP}{dS}\right)_V\left[=-\frac{d}{dS}\left(\frac{dE}{dV}\right)_S=-\frac{d}{dV}\left(\frac{dE}{dS}\right)_V\right]=-\left(\frac{dT}{dV}\right)_S \quad . \quad . \quad (1)$$

II. $$d(E+PV)=dH=dE+PdV+VdP$$

$$=TdS+VdP, \text{ from the above equation for } dE,$$

$$\therefore\ (dH/dS)_P=T, \quad \text{and} \quad (dH/dP)_S=V,$$

$$\therefore\ \left(\frac{dT}{dP}\right)_S\left[=\frac{d}{dP}\left(\frac{dH}{dS}\right)_P=\frac{d}{dS}\left(\frac{dH}{dP}\right)_S\right]=\left(\frac{dV}{dS}\right)_P \quad . \quad . \quad . \quad (2)$$

III. $$d(E-TS)=dF=dE-TdS-SdT$$

$$=-SdT-PdV \text{ from the equation for } dE,$$

$$\therefore\ (dF/dT)_V=-S, \quad \text{and} \quad (dF/dV)_T=-P$$

$$\therefore\ \left(\frac{dP}{dT}\right)_V\left[=-\frac{d}{dT}\left(\frac{dF}{dV}\right)_T=-\frac{d}{dV}\left(\frac{dF}{dT}\right)_V\right]=\left(\frac{dS}{dV}\right)_T \quad . \quad . \quad (3)$$

IV. $$d(E-TS+PV)=dG=dE-TdS-SdT+PdV+VdP$$

$$=(dE-TdS+PdV)-SdT+VdP$$

$$=-SdT+VdP, \text{ from the equation for } dE,$$

$$\therefore\ (dG/dT)_P=-S, \quad \text{and} \quad (dG/dP)_T=V,$$

$$\therefore\ \left(\frac{dS}{dP}\right)_T\left[=-\frac{d}{dP}\left(\frac{dG}{dT}\right)_P=-\frac{d}{dT}\left(\frac{dG}{dP}\right)_T\right]=-\left(\frac{dV}{dT}\right)_P \quad . \quad . \quad (4)$$

The four equations are easily written down by the following rule (which is not, of course, a deduction). Write down the letters *PSTV* in this (alphabetical) order in two parallel lines as shown in Fig. 16.II and complete a rectangle. Starting at P, read round two sides clockwise, and then round the two parallel sides

[1] Maxwell, "Theory of Heat," 1871, 163; 1897, 165. Maxwell's numbering of the equations is 1, 2, 3, and 4 for equations 4, 2, 3, and 1 above; Natanson, *Ann. Phys.*, 1891, **42**, 178, observed that Maxwell's equations are conditions establishing the existence of the functions E, H, F, and G.

[2] Tait, "Heat," 1895, 322. It may be noted that the replacement of ydx by $-xdy$ by subtraction of $d(xy)$ is called a *Legendre transformation*: see Trevor, *J. Phys. Chem.*, 1899, **3**, 339, 523; 1900, **4**, 570; Runge, *Ann. Phys.*, *Boltzmann Festschr.*, 1904, 260.

anti-clockwise. Then start at S, V, and T, in succession and repeat the operation. The *sign* order is $- + - +$, in accordance with the second rule below:

(1) " dP by dS at constant V equals *minus* dT by dV at constant S,"

i.e. $(\mathrm{d}P/\mathrm{d}S)_V=-(\mathrm{d}T/\mathrm{d}V)_S$, equation (1).

(2) " dS by dV at constant T equals dP by dT at constant V,"

i.e. $(\mathrm{d}S/\mathrm{d}V)_T=(\mathrm{d}P/\mathrm{d}T)_V$, equation (3).

(3) " dV by dT at constant P equals *minus* dS by dP at constant T,"

i.e. $(\mathrm{d}V/\mathrm{d}T)_P=-(\mathrm{d}S/\mathrm{d}P)_T$, equation (4).

(4) " dT by dP at constant S equals dV by dS at constant P,"

i.e. $(\mathrm{d}T/\mathrm{d}P)_S=(\mathrm{d}V/\mathrm{d}S)_P$, equation (2).

If the three letters in the second half of the equality, or these letters reversed, are in alphabetical order (P, T, V; V, S, P reversed) the *sign* is $+$; if they (as written or reversed) are not in alphabetical order the sign is $-$ (T, V, S; S, P, T).

Maxwell's equations lead very directly to a large number of important thermodynamic equations and deserve to be more widely used in physical chemistry.

A generalisation of this type of equation is obviously possible, and several resulting sets of equations are available.[1] For most purposes, a knowledge of the fundamental equations and the exercise of a little ingenuity provide a more interesting route to such special equations. It should be noticed that all the equations (1)–(4) can *at once* be deduced from the expressions for dE, dH, dF, and dG, expressed in the general form $\mathrm{d}u=X\mathrm{d}x+Y\mathrm{d}y$, by using the result (§ 27.I) for a perfect differential, $\partial Y/\partial x=\partial X/\partial y$.

Some general thermodynamic formulae are of frequent use, and the following (all of which have been deduced) are particularly important:

$$(\mathrm{d}T/\mathrm{d}V)_S=-(\mathrm{d}P/\mathrm{d}S)_V, \qquad (\mathrm{d}T/\mathrm{d}P)_S=(\mathrm{d}V/\mathrm{d}S)_P,$$
$$(\mathrm{d}V/\mathrm{d}T)_P=-(\mathrm{d}S/\mathrm{d}P)_T, \qquad (\mathrm{d}P/\mathrm{d}T)_V=(\mathrm{d}S/\mathrm{d}V)_T,$$
$$(\mathrm{d}H/\mathrm{d}S)_P=T=(\mathrm{d}E/\mathrm{d}S)_V, \qquad (\mathrm{d}F/\mathrm{d}V)_T=-P=(\mathrm{d}E/\mathrm{d}V)_S,$$
$$(\mathrm{d}H/\mathrm{d}P)_S=V=(\mathrm{d}G/\mathrm{d}P)_T, \qquad (\mathrm{d}F/\mathrm{d}T)_V=-S=(\mathrm{d}G/\mathrm{d}T)_P.$$

§ 49. Effect of Pressure on Specific Heats

From (3) and (6), § 35:

$\mathrm{d}S=c_v\mathrm{d}T/T$ at constant volume, therefore $(\mathrm{d}S/\mathrm{d}T)_V=c_v/T$;

$\mathrm{d}S=c_p\mathrm{d}T/T$ at constant pressure, therefore $(\mathrm{d}S/\mathrm{d}T)_P=c_p/T$. Hence

$$\left(\frac{\mathrm{d}c_v}{\mathrm{d}V}\right)_T=T\frac{\mathrm{d}}{\mathrm{d}V}\left(\frac{\mathrm{d}S}{\mathrm{d}T}\right)_V=T\frac{\mathrm{d}}{\mathrm{d}T}\left(\frac{\mathrm{d}S}{\mathrm{d}V}\right)_T=T\frac{\mathrm{d}}{\mathrm{d}T}\left(\frac{\mathrm{d}P}{\mathrm{d}T}\right)_V=T\left(\frac{\mathrm{d}^2P}{\mathrm{d}T^2}\right)_V \quad . \quad (1)$$

from Maxwell's equation (3), § 48, $(\mathrm{d}S/\mathrm{d}V)_T=(\mathrm{d}P/\mathrm{d}T)_V$. Also,

$$\left(\frac{\mathrm{d}c_p}{\mathrm{d}P}\right)_T=T\frac{\mathrm{d}}{\mathrm{d}P}\left(\frac{\mathrm{d}S}{\mathrm{d}T}\right)_P=T\frac{\mathrm{d}}{\mathrm{d}T}\left(\frac{\mathrm{d}S}{\mathrm{d}P}\right)_T=-T\frac{\mathrm{d}}{\mathrm{d}T}\left(\frac{\mathrm{d}V}{\mathrm{d}T}\right)_P=-T\left(\frac{\mathrm{d}^2V}{\mathrm{d}T^2}\right)_P \quad . \quad (2)$$

from Maxwell's equation (4), § 48, $(\mathrm{d}S/\mathrm{d}P)_T=-(\mathrm{d}V/\mathrm{d}T)_P$.

[1] Natanson, *Ann. Phys.*, 1891, **42**, 178; *Z. phys. Chem.*, 1892, **10**, 733; Trevor, *J. Phys. Chem.*, 1896–7, **1**, 205; 1899, **3**, 339, 523, 573; 1900, **4**, 570; Burrows, *ibid.*, 1901, **5**, 233; Bridgman, *Phys. Rev.*, 1914, **3**, 273; " A Condensed Collection of Thermodynamic Formulas," Cambridge (U.S.A.), 1925; Lunn, *Phys. Rev.*, 1920, **15**, 299; Koenig, *J. Chem. Phys.*, 1935, **3**, 29; McKay, *ibid.*, 1935, **3**, 715; Lerman, *ibid.*, 1937, **5**, 792, 994; Slater, " Introduction to Chemical Physics," 1939, 24; Morán, *An. Fis. Quim.*, 1941, **37**, 405; Tobolsky, *J. Chem. Phys.*, 1942, **10**, 644; Creely, Le Compte, and Lucasse, *J. Franklin Inst.*, 1943, **235**, 617.

Equations (1) and (2) are useful in correcting measured specific heats of actual gases to the values in the ideal state, but they are quite general and apply also to liquids and solids. For an *ideal gas*, $(dP/dT)_V$ and $(dV/dT)_P$ are both independent of temperature (§ 54), and hence its specific heats are independent of pressure, although they may depend on temperature.

§ 50. Generalised Coordinates and Forces

A system is *normally defined* when its state is specified in terms of the temperature T and the least number of other so-called *normal variables* $x_1, x_2, \ldots, x_n$, so chosen that no work is done provided all the x's remain constant. E.g. with a gas, the independent variables are any *two* of the group p, v, T, and clearly v and not p is a normal variable. With each x a so-called *generalised force* X may be associated so that the element of work done *at constant temperature* is:

$$\delta w_T = \Sigma X_1 dx_1 \quad \ldots \ldots \ldots \quad (1)$$

and a *generalised latent heat* l_1, so that the element of heat absorbed is:

$$\delta q_T = \Sigma l_1 dx_1 \quad \ldots \ldots \ldots \quad (2)$$

It should be noted that δw_T in (1) should be such that it may ultimately, by suitable apparatus, be realised as the potential energy of a raised weight.

For each pair of variables x_1 and X_1 an equation similar to the Clapeyron equation (7), § 41 has been deduced by taking x_1 instead of v and X_1 instead of p in the diagram:

$$l_1 = T(dX_1/dT)_{x_1} \quad \ldots \ldots \ldots \quad (3)$$

The latent heat due to a change of one normal variable at constant temperature is, from (2) and (3):

$$q_T = \int_1^2 l_1 dx_1 = T\int_{x_1'}^{x_1''} (dX_1/dT)_{x_1} dx_1 \quad \ldots \ldots \quad (4)$$

in which all the other normal variables are constant. In the general equation (since the x's are supposed to remain constant when the temperature alters):

$$\frac{d}{dT}\int_{x'}^{x''} X dx = \int_{x'}^{x''} (dX/dT)_x dx + X''(dx''/dT) - X'(dx'/dT) \quad \ldots \quad (5)$$

the second and third terms on the right vanish; hence (4) may be written:

$$q_T = T\frac{d}{dT}\int_{x'}^{x''} X dx = T\frac{d}{dT}\int \delta w_T = T(dw_T/dT)_{\Delta x} \quad \ldots \quad (6)$$

from (1). This is the equation of maximum work (§ 42).

The following equations follow from the fundamental definitions[1]:

$$\delta q = dE + \delta w = (dE/dT)_x dT + \Sigma[(dE/dx_1)_T + X_1]dx_1 \quad \ldots \quad (7)$$

$$= T(dS/dT)_x dT + T\Sigma(dS/dx_1)_T dx_1 \quad \ldots \ldots \quad (8)$$

$$[d(E-TS)/dT]_x = (dF/dT)_x = -S \quad \ldots \ldots \quad (9)$$

$$[d(E-TS)/dx_1]_T = (dF/dx_1)_T = -X_1 \quad \ldots \ldots \quad (10)$$

[1] Von Lang, *Wien Ber.*, 1890, **99**, II, 899; Boltzmann, *Ann. Phys.*, 1896, **57**, 39; Trevor, *J. Phys. Chem.*, 1896–7, **1**, 205; Duhem, "Traité de Mécanique Chimique," 1897, **1**, 90, 138; Pellat, *Compt. Rend.*, 1897, **125**, 699; Buckingham, "Outline of the Theory of Thermodynamics," New York, 1900, 89, 117 f., 158 f.; Whetham, "Theory of Solution," Cambridge 1902, 23; Partington, "A Text-Book of Thermodynamics," 1913, 107; Koenig, *J. Chem. Phys.*, 1935, **3**, 29; *J. Phys. Chem.*, 1937, **41**, 597; McKay, *J. Chem. Phys.*, 1935, **3**, 715; Lerman, *ibid.*, 1937, **5**, 792, 994. It should be noted that δw in (14) involves the temperature, as X is not a normal variable.

$$E = F - T(dF/dT)_x \quad \ldots \quad (11)$$

$$\delta q = T[(dS/dT)_X dT + \Sigma(dS/dX_1)_T dX_1] \quad \ldots \quad (12)$$

$$dE = (dE/dT)_X dT + \Sigma(dE/dX_1)_T dX_1 \quad \ldots \quad (13)$$

$$\delta w = \Sigma X_1[(dx_1/dX_1)_T dX_1 + (dx_1/dT)_X dT] \quad \ldots \quad (14)$$

$$\text{If } G = E - TS + \Sigma X_1 x_1 \quad \ldots \quad (15)$$

$$(dG/dT)_X = -S; \; (dG/dX_1)_T = x_1 \quad \ldots \quad (16)$$

$$E = G - T(dG/dT)_X - \Sigma X_1 x_1$$
$$= G - T(dG/dT)_X - \Sigma X_1 (dG/dX_1)_T \quad \ldots \quad (17)$$

It is often more convenient to proceed rather differently. For example,[1] in discussing the change with temperature of the electromotive force of a cell, the electrical work is $\delta w_e = e\delta Q$, where e is the potential difference $V_1 - V_2$ between the poles, i.e. the electromotive force, and δQ is a small quantity of positive electricity flowing inside the cell from pole 2 to pole 1, and the external work against the atmospheric pressure is $\delta w_v = p dv$, where dv is the total change in volume. If heat δq_T is absorbed at constant temperature:

$$dE = \delta q_T - \delta w_e - \delta w_v = \delta q_T - e dQ - p dv$$
$$= T dS - e dQ - p dv \quad \ldots \quad (18)$$

Subtract d(TS) from both sides of (18):

$$d(E - TS) = dF = -S dT - e dQ - p dv$$

$$\therefore (dF/dQ)_{T,v} = -e \quad \text{and} \quad (dF/dT)_{Q,v} = -S \quad \ldots \quad (19)$$

Alternatively, subtract d($TS - pv$) from both sides of (18):

$$d(E - TS + pv) = dG = -S dT - e dQ + v dp$$

$$\therefore (dG/dQ)_{T,p} = -e \quad \text{and} \quad (dG/dT)_{Q,p} = -S \quad \ldots \quad (20)$$

§ 51. Entropy Changes in Irreversible Processes

In a reversible cycle (§ 32), $(w) = q_1 - q_2$ is a maximum, and hence the only way in which an irreversible cycle can differ from a reversible Carnot's cycle is that $(q_1 - q_2)_i < (q_1 - q_2)_r$; or if $q_{1r} = q_{1i}$, then $q_{2i} > q_{2r}$, i.e. more heat is given to the cold body. Hence (taking q_2 as negative for heat given out by the working substance):

$$(q_1/T_1 + q_2/T_2)_i < (q_1/T_1 + q_2/T_2)_r < 0,$$

and for the general case:

$$\oint \delta q/T \leqq 0 \quad \ldots \quad (1)$$

in which the equality refers to reversible and the inequality to irreversible *cycles*. In (1) T was taken by Wesendonck [2] as the temperature of the *working substance* or *system* undergoing change, whilst Neumann [3] maintained that it is the temperature of the *reservoir* from which heat is taken; in irreversible changes these two temperatures need not be (within an infinitesimal amount) the same, as must be the case in reversible changes (§ 8), and it is a disputed point as to which attribution is correct.

[1] Partington, "Text-Book of Thermodynamics," 1913, 462; "Chemical Thermodynamics," 1940, 71.

[2] *Ann. Phys.*, 1899, **67**, 444.

[3] *Leipzig Ber.*, 1891, **43**, 75 (89); Voigt, "Thermodynamik," Leipzig, 1903, **1**, 251.

An irreversible *process* can be coupled with a reversible process to form an irreversible *cycle*:

$$\int_{i\,A}^{B}\delta q/T+\int_{r\,B}^{A}\delta q/T={}_{i}\oint\delta q/T<0=-\delta^2 \quad . \quad . \quad . \quad . \quad . \quad (2)$$

where δ^2 is some positive number,

$$\therefore \int_{i\,A}^{B}\delta q/T-(S_B-S_A)=-\delta^2, \quad \therefore S_B-S_A-\delta^2=\int_{i\,A}^{B}\delta q/T.$$

For a thermally isolated system ($\delta q=0$):

$$S_B-S_A=\delta^2>0 \quad . \quad . \quad . \quad . \quad . \quad . \quad . \quad . \quad . \quad (3)$$

i.e. the entropy of such a system tends to increase and will be a maximum in equilibrium.

Equation (2) is usually called the *inequality of Clausius.* In 1868 Clausius [1] announced the Second Law in the form that: " the entropy of the universe tends towards a maximum," and, from time to time, philosophical or semi-philosophical speculations have centred about this. It has been suggested,[2] for example, that a direction in *time* is somehow connected with increasing entropy. It should be emphasised, as was done by G. N. Lewis,[3] that the Second Law of Thermodynamics has nothing to do with time, and that its extension to the " universe " is meaningless,[4] unless the universe is defined so as to constitute a thermodynamic system. That the laws of thermodynamics apply both to the " universe " and also inside the atom,[5] seems doubtful. Kolosovsky [6] calculated the *energy* of the universe as $8{\cdot}1\times10^{67}$ g.cal., and the *entropy* of the universe as approaching a maximum of $4{\cdot}8\times10^{66}$ g.cal./1° C.

The thermodynamics of irreversible processes is entirely qualitative and of little interest in physical chemistry. A selection from the very extensive literature on the subject is given: [7] some of it contains material interesting from other

[1] *Phil. Mag.*, 1868, **35**, 405; cf. Bridgman, " The Nature of Thermodynamics," Cambridge (U.S.A.), 1941, 133.

[2] Eddington, " Nature of the Physical World," Cambridge, 1928, 98 f.; Ubbelohde, " Time and Thermodynamics," Oxford, 1947; Milne, *Astrophys. J.*, 1940, **91**, 129; de Donder, *Bull. Acad. Roy. Belg.*, 1946, **31**, 560.

[3] *Science*, 1930, **71**, 569; Dingle, *Proc. Phys. Soc.*, 1948, **60**, 402.

[4] See also Steinmetz, *Gen. Electric Rev.*, 1912, **15**, 419; *Mech. Eng.*, 1912, **30**, 123; *Engineer*, 1912, **114**, 103.

[5] Schack, *Phys. Z.*, 1921, **22**, 73.

[6] *J. Gen. Chem. U.S.S.R.*, 1931, **1**, 393; cf. Zwicky, *Proc. Nat. Acad.*, 1928, **14**, 592.

[7] Clausius, *Ann. Phys.*, 1863, **120**, 426; " Die mechanische Wärmetheorie," 1879, **2**, 319; Allard, *Arch. Sci. Phys. Nat.*, 1868, **32**, 89; Parker, *Phil. Mag.*, 1888, **25**, 512; " Elementary Thermodynamics," 1891, 138; " Thermodynamics with Elementary Mathematics," 1894, 102; Neumann, *Leipzig Ber.*, 1891, **43**, 75; Gros, *Ann. Phys.*, 1892, **46**, 339, 517; 1892, **47**, 213; Duhem, on the thermodynamic theory of viscosity, friction, and false chemical equilibrium, *Mém. Soc. Sci. Phys. Nat. Bordeaux*, 1896, **2**, 1 (207 pp.; summary by Trevor, *J. Phys. Chem.*, 1896–7, **1**, 369); " Théorie Thermodynamique de la Viscosité, du Frottement, et des faux Équilibres Chimiques," Paris, 1896; *Z. phys. Chem.*, 1897, **22**, 545; 1897, **23**, 193, 496; 1897, **24**, 666; 1898, **28**, 577; 1900, **33**, 641; 1900, **34**, 312, 683; 1901, **37**, 91; 1903, **43**, 695; Natanson, *Z. phys. Chem.*, 1894, **13**, 437; 1895, **16**, 289; 1896, **21**, 193; 1897, **24**, 302; 1898, **26**, 285; 1899, **30**, 681; 1903, **43**, 179; *Phil. Mag.*, 1896, **41**, 383; *J. Phys. Chem.*, 1896–7, **1**, 374; who used Hamilton's principle of varying action and Rayleigh's dissipation function (Rayleigh, *Proc. London Math. Soc.*, 1873, **4**, 357; " Scientific Papers," 1899, **1**, 176; " Theory of Sound," 2nd edit., 1926, **1**, 103); Wassmuth, *Ann. Phys.*, 1897, **62**, 522; Wiedeburg, *Ann. Phys.*, 1897, **61**, 705; 1897, **62**, 652; 1897, **63**, 154; 1898, **64**, 519; 1899, **69**, 66; 1900, **7**, 758; 1901, **5**, 514; *Z. phys. Chem.*, 1897, **24**, 563; 1898, **25**, 180; 1898, **26**, 741; 1899, **28**, 369; 1899, **29**, 27; 1900, **32**, 406; Carvallo, *J. de Phys.*, 1899, **8**, 161; Wesendonck, *Ann. Phys.*, 1899, **67**, 444; 1899, **69**, 809; 1900, **2**, 746; 1902, **7**, 576; 1902, **9**, 1133; 1903, **10**, 456; 1905, **16**, 588; Liebenow, *Ann. Phys.*, 1900, **2**, 636; Planck, *Ann. Phys.*, 1900, **1**, 621; Trevor, *J. Phys. Chem.*, 1900, **4**, 514; Weinstein,

aspects. The validity of the deduction of the inequality of Clausius has been questioned,[1] and has also been defended: [2] with the approach from the general conception of reversibility and irreversibility given in § 25, the conclusion that irreversible processes involve a net increase of entropy follows almost automatically.[3]

The principle that there is a *net* increase of entropy in all irreversible changes is so general that a *formal* proof which does not depend on the principle of dissipation of energy (§ 27), or some other very general assertion, can hardly be given.[4] An example of a special case is given in § 52.

Discussions [5] of supposed cases (thermocouples; thermal diffusion of gases) in which an overall *decrease* of entropy occurs, and the proposal to limit the statement to: " an *isolable* reversible process never changes the entropy of the universe," seem to be based on misunderstandings, and in any case " isolable " is already implied in the definition of a "process." In thermal diffusion, e.g. a gas is contained in two vessels at different temperatures, which cannot be in thermodynamic equilibrium. A supposed case in crystallisation is only apparent.[6]

§ 52. Transfer of Heat

Let a large mass of copper at 100° C. be put in contact for a short time with another at 0° C. The hot copper becomes slightly cooler and the cold copper slightly warmer, so that a quantity of heat q passes from the hot to the cold copper. This is an irreversible change. The masses are supposed so large that only an infinitesimal change of temperature occurs in each. The entropy lost by the hot copper is $q/373$ and the entropy gained by the cold copper is $q/273$. There has, therefore, been an increase of entropy, since

$$\Delta S = q(1/273 - 1/373) > 0.$$

The aspect of the Second Law which applies directly to this case is that stated by Clausius: *heat cannot of itself pass from one body to another body at a higher temperature*. It is easily shown that this is exactly equivalent to the form stated in § 24. Let the heat q which passed to the cold body be removed by a *reversed*

" Thermodynamik und Kinetik der Körper," 1903, **2**, 351; Orr, *Phil. Mag.*, 1904, **8**, 509; Ponsot, *J. de Phys.*, 1907, **6**, 505; Amagat, *Compt. Rend.*, 1908, **146**, 555; " Notes sur la Physique," 1912, 140; Duhem, *Compt. Rend.*, 1913, **156**, 284, 421; Kolosovsky, *J. Russ. Phys. Chem. Soc.*, 1928, **60**, 1079; Enskog, *Z. Phys.*, 1929, **54**, 498 (entropy of gases in irrev. changes); Klein, *Z. Phys.*, 1931, **72**, 767; Defaye, *Bull. Acad. Roy. Belg.*, 1938, **24**, 474, 534; Eckart, *Phys. Rev.*, 1940, **58**, 267, 269, 919; Bridgman, *Phys. Rev.*, 1940, **58**, 845; Meixner, *Ann. Phys.*, 1941, **39**, 333; 1943, **43**, 244; *Z. phys. Chem.*, 1943, **53** B, 235; Verschaffelt, *Bull. Acad. Roy. Belg.*, 1942, **28**, 490; Ehrenberg, *Phil. Mag.*, 1943, **34**, 396; 1946, **36**, 250; Prigogine, *Compt. Rend.*, 1946, **222**, 278; Prigogine and Defay, *Bull. Acad. Roy. Belg.*, 1946, **32**, 694; Prigogine, Defay, and de Donder, *ibid.*, 1947, **33**, 48.

[1] Bertrand, " Thermodynamique," 1887, 265; Buckingham, *Phys. Rev.*, 1896, **4**, 39; *Phil. Mag.*, 1904, **9**, 208; " An Outline of the Theory of Thermodynamics," 1900, 99, 104, 109, 113, 126, 151 f., 153; Chwolson, " Lehrbuch der Physik," 1923, **3**, ii, 88.

[2] Lippmann, " Cours de Thermodynamique," 1889, 228 f.; Poincaré, " Thermodynamique," 1892, xv, 140 f., 209.

[3] Partington, *J. Phys. Chem.*, 1928, **32**, 1439.

[4] Chwolson, " Lehrbuch der Physik," 1923, **3**, ii, 88; Partington, " Thermodynamics," 1940, 26, 28; Tolman and Fine, *Rev. Mod. Phys.*, 1948, **20**, 51.

[5] Bridgman, *Proc. Nat. Acad.*, 1929, **15**, 765; 1932, **18**, 242 (where the correct explanations are given); Kennard, *ibid.*, 1932, **18**, 237 (an interesting and instructive discussion); Urbach, *Wien Ber.*, 1930, **139**, II A, 473 (fluorescence); Sugita, *Proc. Phys. Math. Soc. Japan*, 1932, **14**, 577, 636; 1933, **15**, 12; Gogate, *Phil. Mag.*, 1944, **35**, 760.

[6] Sommerfeld, *Centr. Min.*, 1932, A, 189, 321.

Carnot's cycle. An amount of work w must be spent in the cycle and an amount of heat $(q+w)$ will be given up at the temperature of the hot body. Of this, q passes into the hot body, and the amount of heat w can be given to another body at the same temperature as the hot body. The heat exchange q has been reversed, but another, compensating, change has occurred, viz. work w has been converted into heat in a body at a constant temperature. This last change cannot be completely reversed (when everything would be restored to its original state), since this would contradict the first statement of the Second Law. Hence the heat q cannot pass from the cold body to the hot body " of itself," i.e. without a compensating change, in this case the passage of a quantity of heat w into a body.

The maximum work obtainable by a Carnot's cycle from two heat reservoirs initially at the absolute temperatures T_1 and T_2, and with finite heat capacities c_1 and c_2, assumed independent of temperature, is:[1]

$$c_1T_1+c_2T_2-(c_1+c_2)T_1^{c_1/(c_1+c_2)}T_2^{c_2/(c_1+c_2)}.$$

Trevor[2] related heat capacity C and entropy S by the equation:

$$\mathrm{d}(TS)/\mathrm{d}T=T(\mathrm{d}S/\mathrm{d}T)+S=\mathrm{d}q/\mathrm{d}T+S=C+S,$$

where the term on the left is called the total increase of heat stored per 1°, the term $\mathrm{d}q/\mathrm{d}T$ or C, the heat capacity per 1°, and S or $S(\mathrm{d}T/\mathrm{d}T)$ the work stored as heat per 1°.

§ 53. Conditions of Equilibrium

Equation (3), § 51, for a small change may be written $(\mathrm{d}S)_q\geqq 0$, reversible changes being included with the sign of equality. If, therefore, in any small change for which $\delta q=0$ the corresponding (virtual) entropy change δS is *negative*, the change is impossible, while if $\delta S=0$ the change is reversible. In both cases the system is in equilibrium (since reversible changes are possible only in that case; § 25), and Clausius's *criterion of equilibrium* is:

$$(\delta S)_q\leqq 0 \quad . \quad . \quad . \quad . \quad . \quad . \quad . \quad . \quad . \quad . \quad (1)$$

Gibbs[3] stated the condition in a slightly different form: " For the equilibrium of any isolated system it is necessary and sufficient that in all possible variations in the state of the system which do not alter its energy, the variation of its entropy shall either vanish or be negative ":

$$(\delta S)_E\leqq 0 \quad . \quad . \quad . \quad . \quad . \quad . \quad . \quad . \quad . \quad . \quad (2)$$

He did not show the exact relation between (1) and (2), but this is clear[4] when an *isolated system* is understood as one in which no work (e.g. by volume changes) can be done, in which case $\delta w=0$ in $\delta q=\mathrm{d}E+\delta w$, therefore $\delta q=\mathrm{d}E$, and if $\mathrm{d}E=0$, then $\delta q=0$, which is equivalent to case (1).

[1] Tait, *Proc. Roy. Soc. Edin.*, 1867–8, **6**, 309 (another case); " Sketch of Thermodynamics," 1877, 123; Luther, *Z. Elektrochem.*, 1935, **41**, 20, 884; Skrabal, *ibid.*, 147, 883; Emden, *ibid.*, 622; the case for $c_1=c_2$ was given by Tait as a simplification of a general equation derived by W. Thomson (Lord Kelvin), *Phil. Mag.*, 1853, **5**, 102; " Mathematical and Physical Papers," 1882, **1**, 554.

[2] *J. Phys. Chem.*, 1900, **4**, 529.

[3] *Trans. Connecticut Acad.*, 1875, **3**, 108; " Scientific Papers," 1906, **1**, 56; Wilson, in " A Commentary on the Scientific Writings of J. W. Gibbs," New Haven, 1936, **1**, 22, 32; Duhem *J. de Math.* (Liouville), 1893, **9**, 293; " Traité de Mécanique Chimique," 1897, **1**, 136.

[4] A formal proof is given by Helm, " Grundzüge der mathematischen Chemie," Leipzig, 1894, 46; " Die Energetik," Leipzig, 1898, 146; Saurel, *J. Phys. Chem.*, 1899, **1**, 334; 1904, **8**, 325, 436, 488; Buckingham, " An Outline of the Theory of Thermodynamics," New York, 1900, 149; Bloch, *J. de Phys.*, 1911, **1**, 912, 988; Tammann, *Ann. Phys.*, 1913, **40**, 297; Gorbachev, *J. Phys. Chem. U.S.S.R.*, 1931, **2**, 823; Wereide, *Z. Phys.*, 1934, **88**, 469.

As an antithesis to (2), Gibbs formulated the second condition: " For the equilibrium of any isolated system it is necessary and sufficient that in all possible variations in the state of the system which do not alter its entropy, the variation of the energy shall either vanish or be positive ":

$$(\delta E)_S \geqq 0 \quad . \quad . \quad . \quad . \quad . \quad . \quad . \quad . \quad . \quad (3)$$

He justified (3) by remarking that it is always possible to increase or decrease both the entropy and energy of the system together, by adding or taking away heat, since $\delta q = \mathrm{d}E$. If (2) is not satisfied, a variation for which $\delta S > 0$ and $\delta E = 0$ is possible, and hence by decreasing both the entropy and energy in the varied state, a state will be obtained for which, considered as a variation of the original state, $\delta S = 0$ and $\delta E < 0$, and (3) is not satisfied. Conversely, if (3) is not satisfied, there must be a variation for which $\delta E < 0$ and $\delta S = 0$, and hence one for which $\delta E = 0$ and $\delta S > 0$, and hence (2) is not satisfied. Hence, the truth of (2) necessarily implies that of (3).

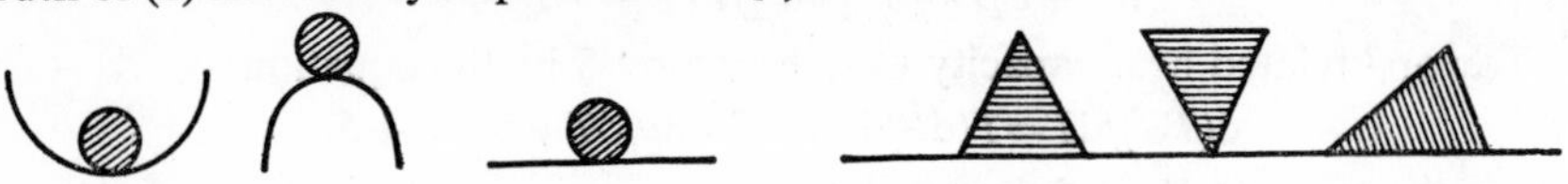

FIG. 17.II. Kinds of Equilibrium

The conditions of equilibrium at *constant temperature* are more conveniently expressed in terms of the free energy F at constant volume, and the available energy G at constant pressure. For any very small reversible isothermal change, (1), § 33 gives $\delta w_T = -\mathrm{d}F$, therefore $(\delta w + \mathrm{d}F)_T = 0$. If the only external work is due to a volume change, $\delta w = P\mathrm{d}V$, therefore:

$$(P\mathrm{d}V + \mathrm{d}F)_T = 0 \quad . \quad . \quad . \quad . \quad . \quad . \quad . \quad . \quad . \quad (4)$$

Since a reversible change is possible only if the system is in equilibrium (§ 25), it follows (since $P\mathrm{d}V = 0$ when $\mathrm{d}V = 0$, or V is constant) that (4) gives the condition for *equilibrium at constant temperature and volume* as:

$$(\mathrm{d}F)_{V,T} = 0 \quad . \quad . \quad . \quad . \quad . \quad . \quad . \quad . \quad . \quad (5)$$

From the Principle of Dissipation of Energy (§ 27) it can be inferred that (5) is the condition that the free energy is a *minimum* when stable equilibrium is reached. From (1), § 44:

$$G = F + PV \quad . \quad . \quad . \quad . \quad . \quad . \quad . \quad . \quad . \quad (6)$$

$$\therefore \mathrm{d}G = \mathrm{d}(F + PV) = \mathrm{d}F + P\mathrm{d}V + V\mathrm{d}P \quad . \quad . \quad . \quad . \quad . \quad (7)$$

But if T is constant (4) gives, for equilibrium:

$$(\mathrm{d}G - V\mathrm{d}P)_T = 0 \quad . \quad . \quad . \quad . \quad . \quad . \quad . \quad . \quad (8)$$

and hence if P is also constant:

$$(\mathrm{d}G)_{P,T} = 0 \quad . \quad . \quad . \quad . \quad . \quad . \quad . \quad . \quad . \quad (9)$$

and again it is inferred that (9) is the condition that the available energy is a *minimum* when stable equilibrium is reached at constant temperature and pressure.

In dynamics, states of equilibrium are classified as (i) *stable*, (ii) *unstable*, and (iii) *neutral*, according as the system, when slightly displaced from its position of equilibrium by some external force, tends (i) to return to its initial state, (ii) to move further away from this state, or (iii) to remain in the displaced state, respectively, when the displacing force is removed. Examples are afforded by a sphere resting at the bottom of a bowl, on the top of the inverted bowl, and on a smooth table, respectively; or a cone resting on its base, on its point, or on its side, respectively (Fig. 17.II).

It is shown (and is obvious from the examples quoted) that the condition for stable, unstable, and neutral equilibrium of a *mechanical* system is that, for any *possible* small displacement, the resulting change of *potential energy* shall vanish to the first order, and be positive, negative, and zero, respectively, to the second order; that is to say, the potential energy of the system is a minimum, a maximum, or stationary (§§ 9–11.I) respectively (*Dirichlet's Theorem*). Thus, the work done in any infinitesimal displacement is zero to the first order, and negative, positive, or zero to the second order. The values of the second order changes are to be calculated by Taylor's theorem (§ 32.I).

In Thermodynamics the corresponding criteria are seen on a little consideration [1] to be:

(1) $(\mathrm{d}S)_E=0$; $(\mathrm{d}^2S)_E<0$ *stable*, $(\mathrm{d}^2S)_E>0$ *unstable*, $(\mathrm{d}^2S)_E=0$ *neutral.*

(2) $(\mathrm{d}E)_S=0$; $(\mathrm{d}^2E)_S>0$ *stable*, $(\mathrm{d}^2E)_S<0$ *unstable*, $(\mathrm{d}^2E)_S=0$ *neutral.*

(3) $(\mathrm{d}F)_{T,V}=0$; $(\mathrm{d}^2F)_{T,V}>0$ *stable*, $(\mathrm{d}^2F)_{T,V}<0$ *unstable*, $(\mathrm{d}^2F)_{T,V}=0$ *neutral.*

(4) $(\mathrm{d}G)_{T,P}=0$; $(\mathrm{d}^2G)_{T,P}>0$ *stable*, $(\mathrm{d}^2G)_{T,P}<0$ *unstable*, $(\mathrm{d}^2G)_{T,P}=0$ *neutral.*

Thermodynamics of Special Systems

§ 54. The Ideal Gas

An ideal gas may be defined by the equation:

$$pv=\boldsymbol{R}T \quad . \quad . \quad . \quad . \quad . \quad . \quad . \quad . \quad . \quad (1)$$

where p is the pressure, v the volume of 1 g.mol. (mol), T the absolute temperature $t°$ C.+273·1, and $\boldsymbol{R}$ the *general gas constant*, which Avogadro's hypothesis shows must have the same value for a mol (molecular weight in grams) of any ideal gas.

In an experiment made by Joule in 1845 (§ 23.VII A), air was allowed to rush from one copper globe into another vacuous copper globe until the pressures were equalised: in this process, no *external* work is done, therefore $w=0$. The globes were in a water bath, and it was found after stirring that there was no change in temperature of the water; hence no heat was absorbed or emitted by the gas, therefore $q=0$. From the First Law, $q=\Delta E+w$, it follows that $\Delta E=0$, or the energy of a gas is unchanged in a volume change at constant temperature i.e. the energy at constant temperature is independent of the volume, and hence it is a function of temperature only.

From (6), § 21, $l_v=(\mathrm{d}E/\mathrm{d}v)_T+p$, i.e. during an expansion $\mathrm{d}v$ at constant temperature, the heat absorbed is the sum of the *external work* done, viz. $p\mathrm{d}v$, and the increase of energy due to volume increase, viz. $(\mathrm{d}E/\mathrm{d}v)_T\mathrm{d}v$. (The second term is sometimes called the *internal work.*)

Clapeyron's equation, (5), § 41, shows that:

$$l_v=T(\mathrm{d}p/\mathrm{d}T)_v$$

$$\therefore\ (\mathrm{d}E/\mathrm{d}v)_T+p=T(\mathrm{d}p/\mathrm{d}T)_v \quad . \quad . \quad . \quad . \quad . \quad . \quad (2)$$

This equation is general. For an ideal gas (1) gives:

$$(\mathrm{d}p/\mathrm{d}T)_v=\boldsymbol{R}/v \quad . \quad . \quad . \quad . \quad . \quad . \quad . \quad . \quad . \quad (3)$$

$$\therefore\ T(\mathrm{d}p/\mathrm{d}T)_v=\boldsymbol{R}T/v=p \quad . \quad . \quad . \quad . \quad . \quad . \quad . \quad (4)$$

[1] For details, see van der Waals and Kohnstamm, "Lehrbuch der Thermodynamik," Leipzig, 1908, **1**, 125; Partington, "Thermodynamics," 1913, 90 f.; the concept of *metastable* equilibrium was introduced by Ostwald, "Lehrbuch der allgemeinen Chemie," 1910, **2**, i, 517. On stability in small isothermal-adiabatic changes, see Verschaffelt, *Bull. Acad. Roy. Belg.*, 1945, **31**, 252, 304; Bijvoet and Wiebenga, *Rec. Trav. Chim.*, 1946, **65**, 518 (change of type of equilibrium).

∴ from (2):

$$l_v = p \quad . \quad . \quad . \quad . \quad . \quad . \quad . \quad . \quad (5)$$

$$\therefore (\mathrm{d}E/\mathrm{d}v)_T = 0 \quad . \quad . \quad . \quad . \quad . \quad . \quad . \quad . \quad (6)$$

or *the energy of an ideal gas is independent of the volume.* This is the result found in Joule's experiment.[1]

From (3),

$$(\mathrm{d}^2p/\mathrm{d}T^2)_v = 0 \quad . \quad . \quad . \quad . \quad . \quad . \quad . \quad . \quad (7)$$

and from (1),

$$(\mathrm{d}v/\mathrm{d}T)_p = R/p \quad . \quad . \quad . \quad . \quad . \quad . \quad . \quad . \quad (8)$$

$$\therefore (\mathrm{d}^2v/\mathrm{d}T^2)_p = 0 \quad . \quad . \quad . \quad . \quad . \quad . \quad . \quad . \quad (9)$$

From (1) and (2), § 49:

$$(\mathrm{d}c_v/\mathrm{d}v)_T = T(\mathrm{d}^2p/\mathrm{d}T^2)_v \text{ and } (\mathrm{d}c_p/\mathrm{d}p)_T = -T(\mathrm{d}^2v/\mathrm{d}T^2)_p,$$

and (7) and (9) above, it follows that, for an ideal gas:

$$(\mathrm{d}c_v/\mathrm{d}v)_T = 0 \quad . \quad . \quad . \quad . \quad . \quad . \quad . \quad . \quad (10)$$

$$(\mathrm{d}c_p/\mathrm{d}p)_T = 0 \quad . \quad . \quad . \quad . \quad . \quad . \quad . \quad . \quad (11)$$

i.e. the specific heat is independent of volume or pressure. It should be noted, however, that nothing can be said about $(\mathrm{d}c_v/\mathrm{d}T)_v$ and $(\mathrm{d}c_p/\mathrm{d}T)_p$, except that if $(\mathrm{d}c_v/\mathrm{d}T)_v$ is zero, $(\mathrm{d}c_p/\mathrm{d}T)_p$ must also be zero.

It has been proved in (11), § 21, that for one mol of an ideal gas:

$$C_p = C_v + R \quad . \quad . \quad . \quad . \quad . \quad . \quad . \quad . \quad (12)$$

For a small change of volume and temperature, the heat absorbed is in general (§ 3), $\delta q = c_v \mathrm{d}T + l_v \mathrm{d}v$. But for an ideal gas, $l_v = p$, from (5),

$$\therefore \delta q = c_v \mathrm{d}T + p\mathrm{d}v \quad . \quad . \quad . \quad . \quad . \quad . \quad . \quad . \quad (13)$$

Equation (13) holds only for an ideal gas, since it assumes that no energy change results from a change of volume only. For an *isothermal change* ($\mathrm{d}T = 0$):

$$q_T = \int p\mathrm{d}v = w_T \quad . \quad . \quad . \quad . \quad . \quad . \quad . \quad . \quad (14)$$

and for an expansion of 1 mol from a volume v_1 to a volume v_2:

$$q_T = w_T = \int_{v_1}^{v_2} (RT/v)\mathrm{d}v = RT \ln (v_2/v_1) = RT \ln (p_1/p_2) \quad . \quad . \quad (15)$$

In *adiabatic changes* of an ideal gas, $\delta q = 0$, therefore (13) gives:

$$c_v \mathrm{d}T + p\mathrm{d}v = 0,$$

or per mol ($C_v = Mc_v$; $V = Mv$):

$$p\mathrm{d}V = -C_v\mathrm{d}T = -R\mathrm{d}T/(\gamma - 1)$$

from (12) and $\gamma = C_p/C_v$. If γ is assumed constant (i.e. c_v independent of temperature):

$$w_q = \int p\mathrm{d}V = -RT/(\gamma-1) + \text{const.} = R(T_1 - T_2)/(\gamma - 1) \quad . \quad . \quad (16)$$

as found in (12), § 6.

[1] For a different treatment, see Buckingham, "Theory of Thermodynamics," 1900, 68. It is obvious that any *two* of the laws of Boyle, Charles, and Joule, are sufficient to define an ideal gas, since from these the third can be deduced by thermodynamics; Stuart, *Ann. Phys.*, 1863, **119**, 327; Bryan, "Thermodynamics," 1907, 117; Partington, "A Text Book of Thermodynamics," 1913, 139. See the unnecessary discussion between Bakker, *Z. phys. Chem.*, 1894, **14**, 671; 1895, **17**, 171; 1896, **20**, 461; 678; 1897, **22**, 543; *J. de Phys.*, 1899, **8**, 214; and Baynes, *Z. phys. Chem.*, 1895, **18**, 335; 1896, **21**, 556; also Carré, *J. de Phys.*, 1898, **7**, 718; Webster and Rosanoff, *Phys. Rev.*, 1909, **29**, 304; Buckingham, *Bur. Stand. Bull.*, 1910, **6**, 409; Farnau, *Phys. Rev.*, 1912, **35**, 47; Clark, *Trans. Roy. Soc. Canada*, 1924, **18**, III, 293; Koltschin, *Z. anorg. Chem.*, 1925, **146**, 312; Foz, *An. Fis. Quim.*, 1941, **37**, 25.

If n mols of gas occupy a volume V at the pressure p and temperature T, the *concentration* is $c=n/V$, and since the volume occupied by 1 mol is V/n, equation (1) may be written:

$$p(V/n)=RT \quad \therefore \; p=(n/V)RT=cRT \quad . \; . \; . \; . \; . \; (17)$$

§ 55. Thermodynamic Functions for an Ideal Gas

For 1 mol of an ideal gas (13), § 54, and (5), § 21, give:

$$\delta q=C_v\mathrm{d}T+p\mathrm{d}V=\mathrm{d}E+p\mathrm{d}V \quad . \; . \; . \; . \; . \; . \; (1)$$

Hence the *energy* per mol is:

$$E=E_0+\int C_v\mathrm{d}T \quad . \; . \; . \; . \; . \; . \; . \; . \; . \; (2)$$

The *heat content* per mol is:

$$H=H_0+\int C_p\mathrm{d}T \quad . \; . \; . \; . \; . \; . \; . \; . \; . \; . \; (3)$$

and the *entropy* per mol is, from (13), § 54: [1]

$$S=\int\delta q/T=S_0+\int C_v\mathrm{d}T/T+\int p\mathrm{d}V/T$$
$$=S_0+\int C_v\mathrm{d}T/T+\int R\mathrm{d}V/V \text{ (since } p=RT/V)$$
$$=S_0+\int C_v\mathrm{d}T/T+R\ln V \quad . \; . \; . \; . \; . \; . \; . \; . \; (4)$$

If C_v is independent of temperature:

$$E=E_0+TC_v \quad . \; . \; . \; . \; . \; . \; . \; . \; . \; . \; . \; (2a)$$
$$H=H_0+TC_p \quad . \; . \; . \; . \; . \; . \; . \; . \; . \; . \; . \; (3a)$$
$$S=S_0+C_v\ln T+R\ln V \quad . \; . \; . \; . \; . \; . \; (4a)$$

The *free energy* per mol is:

$$F=E-TS=E_0-TS_0+\int C_v\mathrm{d}T-T\int C_v\mathrm{d}T/T-RT\ln V \quad . \; . \; (5)$$

and the *available energy* per mol is:

$$G=F+PV=F+RT$$
$$=E_0-TS_0+\int C_v\mathrm{d}T-T\int C_v\mathrm{d}T/T-RT(\ln V-1) \quad . \; . \; . \; (6)$$

The first four terms on the right of (5) are functions of temperature only. Put

$$E_0-TS_0+\int C_v\mathrm{d}T-T\int C_v\mathrm{d}T/T=\mathrm{g}(T) \quad . \; . \; . \; . \; . \; . \; (7)$$
$$\text{and} \quad \bar{\mathrm{g}}(T)=\mathrm{g}(T)+RT \quad . \; . \; . \; . \; . \; . \; . \; . \; (8)$$

where $\mathrm{g}(T)$ and $\bar{\mathrm{g}}(T)$ are functions of temperature, and if $c=1/V=$concentration in mol/lit.

$$F=\mathrm{g}(T)-RT\ln V=\mathrm{g}(T)+RT\ln c \quad . \; . \; . \; . \; . \; . \; (9)$$

and

$$G=F+RT=\mathrm{g}(T)+RT+RT\ln c=\bar{\mathrm{g}}(T)+RT\ln c \quad . \; (10)$$

If C_v is constant, (5) can be written:

$$F=E_0-TS_0+TC_v-TC_v\ln T-RT\ln V \quad . \; . \; . \; . \; (5a)$$

Since $pV=RT$, equation (4) can be written:

$$S=S_0+\int C_v\mathrm{d}T/T+R\ln(RT/p)$$
$$=(S_0+R\ln R)+\int(C_v+R)\mathrm{d}T/T-R\ln p$$
$$=S_0'+\int C_p\mathrm{d}T/T-R\ln p \quad . \; . \; . \; . \; . \; . \; . \; . \; . \; . \; (4b)$$

[1] For the entropy of a gas obeying van der Waals's equation:

$$S=S_0+C_v\ln T+R\ln(v-b)+a/Tv,$$

see Njegovan, *Z. Elektrochem.*, 1922, **28**, 259, 313; 1924, **30**, 291; 1925, **31**, 5, 631. On general equations for the energy and entropy of gases, see Huang, *Phys. Rev.*, 1931, **37**, 1171; 1931, **38**, 1385; Michaud, *J. Chim. Phys.*, 1937, **34**, 333.

where $$S_0'=S_0+R\ln R \quad \ldots \quad (4c)$$

If C_p is constant:

$$S=S_0'+C_p\ln T-R\ln p \quad \ldots \quad (4d)$$

From (3) and (4b):

$$G=H-TS$$
$$=H_0-TS_0'+\int C_p\mathrm{d}T-T\int C_p\mathrm{d}T/T+RT\ln p \quad \ldots \quad (6a)$$

and if C_p is constant:

$$G=H_0-TS_0'+TC_p-TC_p\ln T+RT\ln p \quad \ldots \quad (6b)$$

The decrease of free energy per mol for isothermal expansion from a volume V_1 to a volume V_2 is, from (5):

$$-\Delta F=RT\ln(V_2/V_1)=RT\ln(p_1/p_2) \quad \ldots \quad (11)$$

and the increase of entropy is, from (4):

$$\Delta S=R\ln(V_2/V_1)=R\ln(p_1/p_2) \quad \ldots \quad (12)$$

which also follows from (11), § 6 (since $w_T=q_T$) by dividing the heat absorbed by the absolute temperature.

§ 56. Ideal Gas Mixture

If $n_1, n_2, n_3 \ldots$ mols of different gases occupying volumes $V_1, V_2, V_3 \ldots$ at the same temperature T and at the same or different pressures are put in communication so that the total volume is V (which need not be the sum of the separate volumes), then it is found by experiment that, after the gases have mixed by diffusion and the temperature has its original value, the pressure of the mixture is:

$$p=(RT/V)\Sigma n_1=\Sigma p_1 \quad \ldots \quad (1)$$

where p_1 is the pressure the first gas would exert if it alone occupied the total volume of the mixture; p_1 is called the *partial* pressure of the first gas and (1) is Dalton's *law of partial pressures.* This cannot be deduced by thermodynamics from the general gas equation, $pV=RT$ alone; some additional assumption is necessary, and an *ideal gas mixture* [1] may be defined as one for which *the free energy is the sum of the free energies of the separate gases, each occupying the total volume of the mixture, V*:

$$F=\Sigma F_{1,V} \quad \ldots \quad (2)$$

Therefore from (9), § 55, in which V is the volume of 1 mol:

$$F=\Sigma n_1 g_1(T)-RT\Sigma n_1\ln(V/n_1) \quad \ldots \quad (3)$$

where V is the total volume of the mixture. Hence:

$$(\mathrm{d}F/\mathrm{d}V)_T=-(RT/V)\,.\,\Sigma n_1=-\Sigma p_1 \quad \ldots \quad (4)$$

where p_1 is the partial pressure of the first gas. But from (4), § 43:

$$(\mathrm{d}F/\mathrm{d}V)_T=-p \quad \ldots \quad (5)$$
$$\therefore\ p=\Sigma p_1 \quad \ldots \quad (6)$$

which is Dalton's Law of Partial Pressures.[2] From (5), § 43:

$$(dF/\mathrm{d}T)_V=-S \quad \ldots \quad (7)$$

[1] Not to be confused with "a mixture of ideal gases," which need not possess the required property (2).

[2] See Partington, *Annals of Science*, 1939, **4**, 245. The experimental results are considered in § 22.VII A. For non-ideal (van der Waals) gases, see Carrara, *Nuov. Cim.*, 1928, **5**, 225.

Therefore from (3), and (4) and (7), § 55:

$$S=-\Sigma n_1(-S_0-\int C_v\mathrm{d}T/T-R\ln V)=\Sigma n_1 S_1 \quad . \quad . \quad . \quad (8)$$

where S_1 is the entropy of the first gas occupying the total volume of the mixture. Hence, *the entropy of an ideal gas mixture is the sum of the entropies of the separate gases at the same temperature and each occupying the total volume of the mixture.*

Since

$$E=F+TS \quad . \quad . \quad . \quad . \quad . \quad . \quad . \quad . \quad . \quad (9)$$

therefore from (3) and (8), and (7), § 55:

$$E=\Sigma n_1(E_0+\int C_v\mathrm{d}T)=\Sigma n_1 E_1 \quad . \quad . \quad . \quad . \quad . \quad . \quad (10)$$

i.e. *the energy of an ideal gas mixture is the sum of the energies of the separate gases at the same temperature.* This is independent of the volume, from (6), § 54. Hence, if E^0 and E are the sums of the energies of the separate and mixed gases, respectively:

$$q_v=\Delta E=E-E^0=0 \quad . \quad . \quad . \quad . \quad . \quad . \quad . \quad . \quad (11)$$

i.e. *no heat is evolved on mixing ideal gases at constant volume*, which may be regarded as an extension of Joule's law (6), § 54. At constant pressure, $q_p=\Delta H=\Delta E+p\Delta V$. But $pV_1=n_1RT$, and $pV=\Sigma n_1RT$, therefore $V=\Sigma V_1$, therefore $\Delta V=0$,

$$\therefore\ q_p=\Delta H=0 \quad . \quad . \quad . \quad . \quad . \quad . \quad . \quad . \quad . \quad (12)$$

i.e. *no heat is evolved on mixing ideal gases at constant pressure.* Equations (11) and (12) show that no change of temperature occurs when ideal gases are mixed at constant volume or at constant pressure.

§ 57. Mixing of Ideal Gases

In § 28 an equation for the decrease of free energy on mixing ideal gases was obtained by a method which assumed that the free energy of the mixture is the sum of the free energies of the components, each occupying the total volume of the mixture. The same equation follows from the expressions for the free energies given in § 55. Let there be given n_1, n_2, n_3, . . . mols of different gases (1), (2), (3), . . ., at the same temperature T and occupying volumes V_1, V_2, V_3, . . . in separate containers. The total free energy of the initial system consisting of the unmixed gases is from (3), § 56:

$$F^0=\Sigma n_1 g_1(T)-RT\Sigma n_1\ln(V_1/n_1) \quad . \quad . \quad . \quad . \quad . \quad . \quad (1)$$

Now let the gases be allowed to mix by putting the separate vessels in communication so that the total volume is

$$V=\Sigma V_1 \quad . \quad . \quad . \quad . \quad . \quad . \quad . \quad . \quad . \quad . \quad (2)$$

Since (11) and (12), § 56, show that the temperature remains constant, the total free energy of the gas mixture is, by (3), § 56:

$$F=\Sigma n_1 g_1(T)-RT\Sigma n_1\ln(V/n_1) \quad . \quad . \quad . \quad . \quad . \quad . \quad (3)$$

Hence the *diminution of free energy* on mixing is

$$F^0-F=-\Delta F=RT\Sigma n_1\ln(V/V_1) \quad . \quad . \quad . \quad . \quad . \quad (4)$$

which is the value found in § 28, and is obviously positive. Hence the free energy decreases on mixing, although from (11), § 56, the energy is unchanged. The process is attended by a dissipation of energy, and hence will occur spontaneously. The *increase of entropy*:

$$\Delta S=-\mathrm{d}\Delta F/\mathrm{d}T=R\Sigma n_1\ln(V/V_1) \quad . \quad . \quad . \quad . \quad . \quad (5)$$

is obviously positive.

No assumption as to the nature of the gases has been made; if they are separate portions of the same gas, then obviously no change of free energy occurs, although if the separate molecules could be marked they would also mix by diffusion owing to molecular motions. This result is known as *Gibbs's paradox* (cf. § 28).[1] The molecular aspect of the process throws no light on the matter, since there is an entropy change on mixing, say, nitrous oxide and carbon dioxide, with physically almost identical molecules, but not on mixing either gas with itself.

An alternative form may be given in terms of the *mol fractions*, N, of the components of the mixture. For two gases:

$$N_1=n_1/(n_1+n_2),\quad N_2=n_2/(n_1+n_2) \quad . \; . \; . \; . \; . \quad (7)$$

where $N_1+N_2=1$. Then the work *per mol of mixture* is:

$$-\Delta F/(n_1+n_2)=-RT(N_1 \ln N_1+N_2 \ln N_2) \quad . \; . \; . \quad (8)$$

if the pressures of the separate gases and the pressure of the mixture are equal, since, from Avogadro's hypothesis, $V_1/(V_1+V_2)=n_1/(n_1+n_2)=N_1$, etc. Hence, *per mol of mixture*, for any number of gases:

$$\Delta F=RT\Sigma N_1 \ln N_1 \quad . \; . \; . \; . \; . \; . \; . \; . \; . \quad (9)$$

For two gases, since $N_2=1-N_1$, (8) may be written:

$$\Delta F=RT[N_1 \ln N_1+(1-N_1) \ln (1-N_1)] \quad . \; . \; . \; . \quad (10)$$

and (5) may be written:

$$\Delta S=-R[N_1 \ln N_1 +(1-N_1) \ln (1-N_1)] \quad . \; . \; . \; . \quad (11)$$

or for any number of gases:

$$\Delta S=-R\Sigma N_1 \ln N_1 \quad . \; . \; . \; . \; . \; . \; . \; . \quad (12)$$

§ 58. Chemical Potentials

Consider a solution, gaseous or liquid, composed of the masses, m_1, m_2, . . . m_n of n different substances, with a total volume V, a total energy E, and a total entropy S. The energy may be expressed as a function of S, V, and the n masses:

$$E=f(S, V, m_1, m_2, \ldots, m_n) \quad . \; . \; . \; . \; . \; . \; . \quad (1)$$

Hence for a small change of entropy, volume, and composition, the change of energy is:

$$dE=(dE/dS)_{V, m_1, m_2 \ldots}\, dS+(dE/dV)_{S, m_1, m_2 \ldots}\, dV + \Sigma(dE/dm_1)_{S, V, m_2 \ldots}\, dm_1 \quad . \quad (2)$$

In differentiating E with respect to m_1, it is supposed that S, V, and all the masses except the first are constant. When *all* the masses are constant ($dm_1=0$, $dm_2=0$, etc.) the system is a simple one of unvarying composition, for which, from (3), § 43:

$$dE=TdS-PdV \quad . \; . \; . \; . \; . \; . \; . \; . \quad (3)$$

where P is the total pressure. Hence, by comparing coefficients of dS and dV in (2) and (3):

$$(dE/dS)_{V, m_1, m_2 \ldots}=T \quad . \; . \; . \; . \; . \; . \; . \; . \quad (3a)$$

and

$$(dE/dV)_{S, m_1, m_2 \ldots}=-P \quad . \; . \; . \; . \; . \; . \; . \; . \quad (3b)$$

[1] See Bridgman, " The Nature of Thermodynamics," Cambridge (U.S.A.), 1941, 168.

Therefore (2) can be written:

$$dE = TdS - PdV + \Sigma\mu_1'dm_1 \quad \ldots \ldots \quad (4)$$

where [1]

$$\mu_1' = (dE/dm_1)_{S, V, m_2 \ldots} \quad \ldots \ldots \quad (5)$$

is called the *chemical potential* of the first component in the solution (equations similar to (5) will hold for the other components). Convenient alternative definitions of the chemical potential are found as follows. From (1), § 43:

$$dF = d(E - TS) = dE - TdS - SdT \quad \ldots \ldots \quad (6)$$

Therefore from (4) and (6):

$$dF = -SdT - PdV + \Sigma\mu_1'dm_1 \quad \ldots \ldots \quad (6a)$$

$$\therefore \mu_1' = (dF/dm_1)_{T, V, m_2 \ldots} \quad \ldots \ldots \quad (7)$$

From (1), § 44, and (4) and (3) above:

$$dG = d(E - TS + PV) = dE - TdS - SdT + PdV + VdP$$

$$= (dE - TdS + PdV) - SdT + VdP + \Sigma\mu_1'dm_1$$

$$= -SdT + VdP + \Sigma\mu_1'dm_1 \quad \ldots \ldots \quad (8)$$

$$\therefore \mu_1' = (dG/dm_1)_{T, P, m_2 \ldots} \quad \ldots \ldots \quad (9)$$

For a single pure substance, $m_2 = 0$, etc., hence:

$$\mu_1' = (dG/dm_1)_{T, P} = G_1 \quad \ldots \ldots \quad (10)$$

i.e. *the chemical potential of a pure substance is equal to its available energy per unit mass.* The meaning of the differential coefficient in (10) is that unit mass of the pure substance is added to any mass of the same pure substance *at constant temperature and pressure*, when the increase of G of the system is obviously equal to the value of G for unit mass, viz. G_1. (It should be noted that a similar argument does not apply to (7), since then the *volume* must remain constant.) Instead of referring chemical potentials to unit mass, it is more convenient to refer them to molar quantities. If M_1 is the molecular weight of the first substance:

$$dm_1 = M_1 dn_1 \quad \ldots \ldots \quad (11)$$

where n_1 denotes the number of mols. Let:

$$M_1\mu_1' = \mu_1 \quad \ldots \ldots \quad (12)$$

be the *chemical potential per mol*, then (5), (7), and (10) may be written:

$$\mu_1 = (dE/dn_1)_{S, V, n_2 \ldots} = (dF/dn_1)_{T, V, n_2 \ldots} = (dG/dn_1)_{T, P, n_2 \ldots} \quad . \quad (13)$$

In the applications to systems in equilibrium, the effects of gravitational [2] and electric [3] fields, and surface tension,[4] are neglected; the first two are nearly always unimportant, but the third is important in special cases, which will be considered later.

1 μ' is written instead of μ for a reason explained in equation (12).

The publications on the chemical potential are overwhelmingly numerous; for a few, see e.g. Riecke, *Ann. Phys.*, 1891, **42**, 483; 1894, **53**, 378; *Z. phys. Chem.*, 1891, **7**, 97, 115; van Laar, " Sechs Vorträge über das thermodynamische Potential," Brunswick, 1906; Gruner, *Verhl. d. D. Phys. Ges.*, 1912, **14**, 655, 727; Bródy, *Ann. Phys.*, 1914, **44**, 585; Wegscheider, *Z. phys. Chem.*, 1920, **94**, 739; 1923, **106**, 18; Plank, *ibid.*, 1922, **100**, 372; Frenzel, *ibid.*, 1924, **110**, 547; Donnan, " The Influence of J. Willard Gibbs on the Science of Physical Chemistry," *Franklin Inst. Centenary Celebration*, 1924.

2 Gibbs, *Trans. Connecticut Acad.*, 1876, **3**, 108 f.; " Scientific Papers," 1906, **1**, 144; Shorter, *Phil. Mag.*, 1913, **25**, 31; Koenig, *J. Phys. Chem.*, 1936, **40**, 373.

3 Koenig, *J. Phys. Chem.*, 1936, **40**, 597.

4 Gibbs, *Trans. Connecticut Acad.*, 1877–8, **3**, 343 f.; " Scientific Papers," 1906, **1**, 219.

§ 59. Conditions of Chemical Equilibrium

Consider a chemical reaction:

$$\nu_1 A_1 + \nu_2 A_2 + \ldots = \nu_1' A_1' + \nu_2' A_2' + \ldots,$$

where ν represents the number of mols of the substance A undergoing change, and suppose that a small change of mass dm_1 of A_1 occurs; the changes of mass of all the other substances are completely determined by dm_1 and the *stoichiometric coefficients* $\nu_1, \ldots \nu_1', \ldots$. Let:

$$dm_1 = \nu_1 M_1 d\lambda = m_1 d\lambda \quad \ldots \ldots \quad (1)$$

where $d\lambda$ is a small arbitrary positive number which determines the *extent* of the chemical reaction. It may happen that some components of the system do not undergo chemical change (e.g. solvents), and these indifferent substances may be denoted by the suffixes i to n, the reacting substances having the suffixes 1 to h. Then (6a), § 58, gives:

$$dF = -SdT - PdV + \sum_1^h \mu_1' dm_1 + \mu_i' dm_i + \ldots + \mu_n' dm_n \quad . \quad . \quad (2)$$

From (1), and (12), § 58, (2) can be written:

$$dF = -SdT - PdV + d\lambda \sum_1^h \nu_1 \mu_1 + \mu_i' dm_i + \ldots + \mu_n' dm_n \quad . \quad . \quad (3)$$

For equilibrium at constant temperature and volume, $dF=0$, from (5), § 53, hence (3) shows that for equilibrium at given temperature and volume and given quantities of indifferent components, i.e. $dT=0$, $dV=0$, $dm_i=0 \ldots$, $dm_n=0$, it is necessary and sufficient that:

$$\Sigma \nu_1 \mu_1 = 0 \quad \ldots \ldots \quad (4)$$

the sum being taken for all the reacting substances, the products of reaction being counted positive, and the initial (disappearing) substances negative.

In exactly the same way, by starting with (8), § 58, and using (9), § 53, it can be shown that (4) also gives the condition of equilibrium of the system at constant temperature, pressure, and quantities of indifferent components. The condition of equilibrium in a system undergoing a reversible reaction is, from (4), specified by substituting for each chemical symbol in the reaction equation the symbol for the chemical potential.[1]

§ 60. Equilibrium in Gaseous Systems

Equation (4), § 59, is very general, but of no actual use unless μ can be related to the pressure (or volume), temperature, and composition of the system by some equation. This is possible in the case of an ideal gas mixture, for which (3), § 56, gives:

$$F = \Sigma n_1 g_1(T) - \boldsymbol{R} T \Sigma n_1 \ln (V/n_1) \quad \ldots \ldots \quad (1)$$

[1] Gibbs, "Scientific Papers," 1906, **1**, 92; Van Laar, "Sechs Vorträge über das thermodynamische Potential," Brunswick, 1906, 45; Larmor, "Math. and Phys. Papers," Cambridge, 1929, **2**, 377, 715. The inert phases could just as well be left out, since "they are of no greater importance than the beaker containing the system"; Partington, *J. Phys. Chem.*, 1925, **29**, 494. See also Saurel, *J. Phys. Chem.*, 1901, **5**, 21; Ariès, *Compt. Rend.*, 1903, **137**, 46, 253, 738, 1239; Wereide, *Z. Phys.*, 1934, **88**, 469; Finck, *J. Franklin Inst.*, 1938, **225**, 411; 1940, **229**, 201; 1942, **233**, 51; 1947, **243**, 1, 116; Van Dantzig, *Proc. K. Akad. Wetens. Amsterdam*, 1940, **43**, 387, 609; Fuchs, *Proc. Roy. Soc.*, 1942, **179**, 340, 408, 433; Prigogine and Defay, "Thermodynamique Chimique," 2 vols., Liége, 1944–6; Brinkley, *J. Chem. Phys.*, 1946, **14**, 563, 686; 1947, **15**, 107; Schulz, *Z. Naturforsch.*, 1947, **2**, 27; Gurney, *Proc. Phys. Soc.*, 1947, **59**, 629 (generalised stress); Dubrissy, *Bull. Soc. Chim.*, 1947, 8.

Since n_1 mols of the first gas are present in a total volume V, its volumetric molar concentration (mols/lit.) is:

$$c_1 = n_1/V \quad \text{. . . . . (2)}$$

$$\therefore \; F = \Sigma n_1 g_1(T) + RT\Sigma n_1 \ln c_1 \quad \text{. . . . . . . (3)}$$

Differentiate (1) with respect to n_1, keeping T, V and all the other n's constant, and use (2):

$$\therefore \; (dF/dn_1)_{T, V, n_2 \ldots} = \mu_1 = g_1(T) + RT + RT \ln c_1 \quad \text{. . . (4)}$$

or if, as in (8), § 55, $\bar{g}_1(T) = g_1(T) + RT$,

$$\mu_1 = \bar{g}_1(T) + RT \ln c_1 \quad \text{. . . . . (5)}$$

A comparison of (5) with (10), § 55, shows that μ_1 is equal to the available energy G_1 of 1 mol of the first gas, when it alone occupies the total volume of the mixture. The function $\bar{g}_1(T)$ is, however, known explicitly for an ideal gas from (7), § 55; it is, per mol:

$$\bar{g}(T) = E_0 - TS_0 + \int C_v dT - T\int (C_v/T) dT + RT \quad \text{. . . (6)}$$

From (5), and (4), § 59, the condition of equilibrium in an ideal gas mixture is found to be:

$$\Sigma \nu_1 [\bar{g}_1(T) + RT \ln c_1] = 0 \quad \text{. . . . . (7)}$$

$$\therefore \; \Sigma \nu_1 \ln c_1 = -\Sigma \nu_1 \bar{g}_1(T)/RT = f(T) \quad \text{. . . . . (8)}$$

which is the equation for the *law of mass action*, with the *equilibrium constant K* given by: [1]

$$\ln K = -\Sigma \nu_1 \bar{g}_1(T)/RT \quad \text{. . . . . (9)}$$

From (9) and (6):

$$\frac{d \ln K}{dT} = -\frac{1}{R}\frac{d}{dT}\frac{\Sigma \nu_1 \bar{g}_1(T)}{T} \quad \text{. . . . . . . (10)}$$

where:

$$\bar{g}(T)/T = E_0/T - S_0 + (1/T)\int C_v dT - \int (C_v/T) dT + R,$$

$$\therefore \; (d/dT)[\bar{g}(T)/T] = -E_0/T^2 + C_v/T - (1/T^2)\int C_v dT - C_v/T$$

$$= -(E_0 + \int C_v dT)/T^2 = -E/T^2 \quad \text{. . . . (11)}$$

from (8), § 19; hence from (10) and (11):

$$d \ln K/dT = \Sigma \nu_1 E_1/RT^2 = \Delta E/RT^2 = q_v/RT^2 \quad \text{. . . . (12)}$$

This is the so-called *Reaction Isochore* equation, deduced by van't Hoff in 1885: [2] a full account of it will be given later.

If p_1 and N_1 are the partial pressure and mol fraction corresponding with the concentration c_1, then, since $p_1 = n_1 RT/V$ and $p = \Sigma p_1 = \Sigma n_1 \,.\, RT/V$:

$$p_1 = N_1 p \quad \text{. . . . . (13)}$$

Hence (5) may be written in the alternative forms:

$$\mu_1 = \mu_1^0(T) + RT \ln p_1 \quad \text{. . . . . (14)}$$

$$= \mu_1^{0\prime}(p, T) + RT \ln N_1 \quad \text{. . . . . . . (15)}$$

where:

$$\mu_1^0(T) = \bar{g}_1(T) - RT \ln (RT) \quad \text{. . . . . . . (16)}$$

$$\mu_1^{0\prime}(p, T) = \bar{g}_1(T) - RT \ln (RT/p) \quad \text{. . . . . . (17)}$$

[1] This holds also for $p(v-b) = RT$; Robertson, *J. Phys. Chem.*, 1906, **10**, 520; for another deduction, see Larmor, *Phil. Trans.*, 1897, **190**, 205 (276); Boutaric, *Le Radium*, 1919, **11**, 298.

[2] *Arch. Néerl.*, 1885, **20**, 302; *K. Svensk. Akad. Handl.*, 1885, **21**, No. 17; *Z. phys. Chem.*, 1887, **1**, 481; *Phil. Mag.*, 1888, **26**, 81; *Alembic Club Reprints*, 1929, **19**, 5. The name is derived from ἴση, equal; χώρα, space [volume].

It should be noted that $\mu_1^{0\prime}$ in (17) is a function of the total pressure as well as of the temperature, which is not the case with μ_1^0 in (16).

§ 61. Remarks on Chemical Potential

The chemical potential was first used (and named) by Gibbs,[1] and later (sometimes in somewhat modified forms) by many later authors.[2] Essentially the same theory is hinted at for a simple case by Maxwell in two letters to Andrews [3] in 1874 and 1876, and especially in a letter to Stokes [4] in August, 1875, in which, as Larmor [5] says, " he spelled out the whole abstract theory of the co-existence of two phases in a mixture of substances, exactly in the manner of Gibbs and, moreover, looked forward to getting clearer ideas regarding the functions afterwards named by Gibbs the 'potentials' of the constituents." As G. N. Lewis [6] said, Gibbs's treatment practically completed classical chemical thermodynamics: " nothing has to be subtracted, and remarkably little has to be added to satisfy all the demands of modern thermodynamics." Essentially, Gibbs's method is developed in a very practical and attractive form by Lewis and Randall,[7] whose writings have popularised it in chemical circles, although the earlier efforts of Ostwald [8] should not be forgotten, since they made Gibbs's methods known to physical chemists.

§ 62. Activity

The chemical potential per mol of a substance present in an ideal gas mixture, from (15), § 60, is:

$$\mu=\mu^{0\prime}(p, T)+RT \ln N \quad . \quad . \quad . \quad . \quad . \quad . \quad . \quad (1)$$

where N is the mol fraction and $\mu^{0\prime}(p, T)$ is a function of pressure and temperature. Thus:

$$\mu-\mu^{0\prime}=RT \ln N \quad . \quad . \quad . \quad . \quad . \quad . \quad . \quad . \quad (2)$$

by (13), § 58, is the increase in available energy, ΔG, when 1 mol of the substance is isothermally and reversibly transferred, at constant pressure, from a standard

[1] *Trans. Connecticut Acad.*, 1875, **3**, 108,; " Scientific Papers," 1906, **1**, 65; " potential."

[2] Duhem, " Le Potentiel Thermodynamique et ses Applications," Paris, 1886, 31; " Traité Élémentaire de Mécanique Chimique," Paris, 1898, **3**, 1; Planck, *Ann. Phys.*, 1887, **30**, 562; 1887, **31**, 189; 1887, **32**, 462; 1888, **34**, 139; *Z. phys. Chem.*, 1887, **1**, 577; Riecke, *Z. phys. Chem.*, 1891, **7**, 97; *Ann. Phys.*, 1891, **42**, 483; Trevor, *J. Phys. Chem.*, 1896–7, **1**, 204; Ariès, " La Statique Chimique, basée sur les deux Principes Fondamentaux de la Thermodynamique," 1904; van Laar, " Sechs Vorträge über das thermodynamische Potential," Brunswick, 1906, 43; Shorter, *Phil. Mag.*, 1911, **22**, 933; 1912, **23**, 483; 1913, **25**, 31; Bródy, *Ann. Phys.*, 1914, **44**, 585; Lash Miller, *Chem. Rev.*, 1925, **1**, 293; Kleeman, *Phys. Rev.*, 1925, **25**, 250; Larmor, " Math. and Phys. Papers," Cambridge, 1929, **2**, 715; Goranson, *Carnegie Inst. Publ.*, 1930, **408** (multi-component systems); Gibson and Adams, *J.A.C.S.*, 1933, **55**, 2679; Scatchard and Hamer, *ibid.*, 1935, **57**, 1805, 1809; Shaw, *Phil. Trans.*, 1935, **234**, 299; Lerman, *J. Chem. Phys.*, 1937, **5**, 792; Sherwood and Reed, " Applied Mathematics in Chemical Engineering," New York, 1939; Wagner, *Z. phys. Chem.*, 1940, **46** B, 379; Gehlen, *Z. Elektrochem.*, 1942, **48**, 110. It is the same as Lewis and Randall's " partial molal free energy " (see ref. 7).

[3] Andrews, " Scientific Papers," 1889, liv.

[4] " Memoir and Scientific Correspondence of Sir G. G. Stokes," edit. Larmor, Cambridge, 1907, **2**, 34, where he calls the chemical potential (our μ') the " reaction," $r_1=dE/dq_1$ (q=mass, m).

[5] *Proc. Roy. Soc.*, 1908, **81**, Appendix, 1; cf. " Math. and Phys. Papers," Cambridge, 1929, **2**, 377, 705, 715.

[6] *J.A.C.S.*, 1937, **59**, 2750.

[7] " Thermodynamics," New York, 1923, 203, 254.

[8] " Lehrbuch der allgemeinen Chemie," 1902, **2**, ii, 114, based on his translation of Gibbs, " Thermodynamische Studien," Leipzig, 1892; Whetham, " Theory of Solution," Cambridge, 1902.

phase in which $N=1$ (in this case the pure substance) to a large mass of a phase in which the mol fraction is N. Since $N<1$ this ΔG will be negative, i.e. work could be gained in the process. It is assumed here that the same equations apply to very dilute (or *ideal*) liquid solutions.

For *non-ideal* gases or solutions, put:

$$\mu-\mu^{0\prime}(p, T)=RT \ln a \quad . \quad . \quad . \quad . \quad . \quad . \quad . \quad . \quad (3)$$

where $\mu-\mu^{0\prime}$ has the same significance as in (2), and a is one form of what was called by G. N. Lewis [1] the *activity* of the substance. If N is the mol fraction of a substance in the solution, the ratio:

$$\gamma=a/N \quad . \quad . \quad . \quad . \quad . \quad . \quad . \quad . \quad . \quad . \quad . \quad (4)$$

is one definition of the *activity coefficient*. Since (2) is assumed to hold in very dilute solution, γ takes the limiting value [2] 1 for the solution when the mol fraction of the *solvent* approaches unity. Thus, from (3):

$$\mu-\mu^{0\prime}(p, T)=RT \ln N+RT \ln \gamma \quad . \quad . \quad . \quad . \quad . \quad . \quad (5)$$

Differentiation of (3) at constant temperature and pressure gives:

$$(\mathrm{d} \ln a/\mathrm{d}\mu)_{p,T}=1/RT \quad . \quad . \quad . \quad . \quad . \quad . \quad . \quad . \quad (6)$$

or

$$\mathrm{d}\mu=RT\, \mathrm{d} \ln a \quad . \quad . \quad . \quad . \quad . \quad . \quad . \quad . \quad . \quad (7)$$

which may be regarded as alternative definitions of activity. For any reversible isothermal change:

$$\mu''-\mu'=\Delta\mu=RT \ln (a''/a') \quad . \quad . \quad . \quad . \quad . \quad . \quad . \quad (8)$$

Each activity is referred to a *standard state* (specified by $\mu^{0\prime}$) and the correct choice of this is important. For gases, the standard state is the gas in the *ideal* state at 1 atm. pressure and a given temperature. In the case of a liquid solution, the standard state for the *solvent* is the pure liquid solvent at 1 atm. pressure [3] and the given temperature, and for the *solute* the standard state is that in an infinitely dilute solution at the given temperature and 1 atm. pressure.

Instead of the mol fraction, it is often more convenient to use the *volumetric molar concentration c* (sometimes called the *molarity*, when the volume unit is the litre, i.e. mols per litre), or else the *molality m* mols per 1000 g. of *solvent*, for which appropriate definitions of activity can be given. Thus, with the concentration,[4] (4) is replaced by:

$$f=a/c \quad . \quad . \quad . \quad . \quad . \quad . \quad . \quad . \quad . \quad . \quad . \quad (9)$$

where f is an appropriate activity coefficient, and (3) becomes:

$$\mu-\mu^{0\prime\prime}(p, T)=RT \ln a=RT \ln c+RT \ln f \quad . \quad . \quad . \quad . \quad (10)$$

Let a solution of density ρ contain $n_1, n_2, n_3 \ldots$ mols of the various components in a volume V. If n_1 denotes the solvent, the solution is dilute if $n_2, n_3 \ldots$ are small compared with n_1. The *mol fractions* are:

$$N_1=n_1/\Sigma n_1 \quad N_2=n_2/\Sigma n_1 \ldots, \text{ where } \Sigma N_1=1 \quad . \quad . \quad . \quad (11)$$

[1] *Proc. Amer. Acad.*, 1900, **36**, 145 (" escaping tendency "); 1901, **37**, 49 (fugacity); 1907, **43**, 259 (activity); *Z. phys. Chem.*, 1900, **35**, 343; 1901, **38**, 205; 1907, **61**, 129; Lewis and Randall, " Thermodynamics," New York, 1923, 254. For a criticism see e.g. van Laar, *Z. phys. Chem.*, 1911, **76**, 67. See also van Rysselberghe, *Bull. Acad. Roy. Belg.*, 1934, **20**, 234; De Donder, " L'Affinité," edit. by van Rysselberghe, Paris, 1936; Mund, Fripiat, and Sallets, *Bull. Soc. Chim. Belg.*, 1946, **55**, 245.

[2] It should be noted that γ may be either smaller *or larger* than unity.

[3] In the case of liquids, the effect of moderate pressure changes is small, and the specification of the pressure is usually omitted.

[4] In differentiating with respect to T, it should be remembered that c is really variable, owing to the volume change; see Harned and Owen, " The Electrochemistry of Solutions," New York, 1943, 11.

and in dilute solutions $\Sigma n_1 \simeq n_1$; the *volumetric molar concentrations* (*molarities*) are:

$$c_1 = n_1/V, \quad c_2 = n_2/V \quad \ldots \quad (12)$$

the *molalities* (mols per 1000 g. solvent, denoted by subscript 1) are:

$$m_1 = 1000/M_1, \quad m_2 = 1000n_2/n_1M_1 \ldots \quad (13)$$

where M is a molecular weight. If V is in litres:

$$1000\rho V = \Sigma n_i M_i \quad (14)$$

$$n_i/n_1 = m_i M_1/1000 \quad (15)$$

$$\simeq N_i \text{ in dilute solutions} \quad (16)$$

$$c_i/N_i = \Sigma n_i/V = 1000\rho \Sigma n_i/\Sigma n_i M_i$$
$$= 1000\rho(1 + n_2/n_1 + \ldots)/(M_1 + (n_2/n_1)M_2 + \ldots) \quad (17)$$

$$\therefore \; c_i/N_i \simeq 1000\rho_0/M_1 \quad (18)$$

in very dilute solutions, where ρ_0 is the density of the pure solvent. Also:

$$m_i/N_i = 1000\Sigma n_i/n_1 M_1 = 1000/N_1 M_1 \quad (19)$$

$$= (1000/M_1)(1 + m_2M_1/1000 + m_3M_1/1000 + \ldots) \quad (20)$$

$$\simeq 1000/M_1 \text{ in very dilute solutions} \quad (21)$$

From (17)–(18) and (5) it follows that:

$$\mu = \mu^{0\prime}(p, T) + RT \ln (M_1/1000\rho_0) + RT \ln c + RT \ln \frac{\rho_0 \Sigma n_i M_i}{\rho M_1 \Sigma n_i} \gamma$$

hence in (10):

$$\mu^{0\prime\prime}(p, T) = \mu^{0\prime}(p, T) + RT \ln (M_1/1000\rho_0) \quad (22)$$

$$f = (\rho_0 \Sigma n_i M_i/\rho M_1 \Sigma n_i)\gamma \quad (23)$$

and the corresponding activity is defined by (9). Again, from (19)–(21) and (5) it follows that:

$$\mu = \mu^{0\prime}(p, T) + RT \ln (M_1/1000) + RT \ln m + RT \ln \gamma/(1 + m_2M_1/1000 + \ldots),$$

hence if the activity is defined in terms of the molality:

$$a = \gamma_m m \quad (24)$$

$$\mu - \mu^{0\prime\prime\prime}(p, T) = RT \ln m + RT \ln \gamma_m \quad (25)$$

$$\mu^{0\prime\prime\prime}(p, T) = \mu^{0\prime}(p, T) + RT \ln (M_1/1000) \quad (26)$$

$$\gamma_m = \gamma/(1 + m_2M_1/1000 + m_3M_1/1000 + \ldots) \quad (27)$$

In an infinitely dilute solution ($N_1 = 1$) it follows from (23) that $\gamma = f = 1$, since the factor multiplying γ may be written:

$$\rho_0 \Sigma n_i M_i/\rho M_1 \Sigma n_i = \frac{\rho_0(1 + m_2M_2/1000 + m_3M_3/1000 + \ldots)}{\rho(1 + m_2M_1/1000 + m_3M_1/1000 + \ldots)} \quad (28)$$

Also it follows from (27) that, in an infinitely dilute solution, $\gamma = \gamma_m = 1$. In an *ideal* solution which is not infinitely dilute, $\gamma = 1$, but f and γ_m are not in general equal to unity; γ_m is then equal to N_1, the mol fraction of the solvent.[1]

For equilibrium, (4), § 59, and (3) or (10) give:

$$K = a_1'^{\nu_1'} a_2'^{\nu_2'} \ldots / a_1^{\nu_1} a_2^{\nu_2} \ldots \quad (29)$$

where K is a constant at a given temperature and pressure, and (29) may be regarded as a generalised law of mass action, since unlike K in (9), § 60, K in (29) is independent of concentration in non-ideal systems. K is sometimes called the *thermodynamic equilibrium constant.*

[1] Young and Vogel, *J.A.C.S.*, 1932, **54**, 3025.

From (13), § 58, (3) or (10), and (29), the available energy decrease in a reversible isothermal reaction is:

$$-\Delta G = w_T' = RT \ln K - RT\Sigma\nu_1 \ln a_1 \quad . \quad . \quad . \quad . \quad . \quad (30)$$

where a_1 is the activity of a substance in its initial or final state. If K in (9), § 60, is denoted [1] by K_0:

$$K = K_0(f_{A_1'}^{\nu_1'} f_{A_2'}^{\nu_2'} \ldots / f_{A_1}^{\nu_1} f_{A_2}^{\nu_2} \ldots) \quad . \quad . \quad . \quad . \quad . \quad . \quad . \quad (31)$$

From (16), § 44, $d(\Delta G/T)/dT = -\Delta H/T^2$, the differentiation being at constant pressure and initial and final states.[2] If the normal states for the activities are in the region of ideal solutions, then:

$$d(\Delta G^0/dT) = -\Delta H^*/T^2 \quad . \quad . \quad . \quad . \quad . \quad . \quad . \quad . \quad (32)$$

where ΔG^0 refers to the standard states, and ΔH^* is the heat of reaction in the ideal (infinitely dilute) state. But from (30), $\Delta G^0 = -RT \ln K$, therefore $d(\Delta G^0/T)/dT = -R d \ln K/dT$.

$$\therefore \ d \ln K/dT = \Delta H^*/RT^2 \quad . \quad . \quad . \quad . \quad . \quad . \quad . \quad . \quad (33)$$

§ 63. Partial Molar (or Molal) Quantities

An *extensive property* (volume, energy, heat content, heat capacity, entropy, free energy, available energy) of a system, which is proportional to the total mass, may be denoted by the general symbol:

$$X = f(p, T, n_1, n_2, n_3, \ldots) \quad . \quad . \quad . \quad . \quad . \quad . \quad . \quad . \quad (1)$$

where p=pressure, T=temperature, and $n_1, n_2, n_3, \ldots$ are the numbers of mols of the components. The *partial molar* (or *molal*) *values* [3] of X are then defined as:

$$\left.\begin{aligned} \bar{X}_1 &\equiv (dX/dn_1)_{p,\,T,\,n_2,\,n_3\ldots} = \partial X/\partial n_1 \\ \bar{X}_2 &\equiv \partial X/\partial n_2;\ \bar{X}_3 = \partial X/\partial n_3 \ldots \end{aligned}\right\} \quad . \quad . \quad . \quad . \quad . \quad . \quad (2)$$

where p, T, and all values of n except the one varied are kept constant in the differentiation. At constant pressure and temperature:

$$dX = (\partial X/\partial n_1)dn_1 + (\partial X/\partial n_2)dn_2 + \ldots = \bar{X}_1 dn_1 + \bar{X}_2 dn_2 + \ldots \quad . \quad (3)$$

The values of $\bar{X}_1, \bar{X}_2, \ldots$ depend on p, T, and the composition of the solution, but not on the total mass, and they are thus *intense properties* (§ 23). If dX is the increase in X for the addition of $dn_1, dn_2, \ldots$ mols of the components to a solution containing $n_1, n_2, n_3 \ldots$ mols, the value of X for a finite mass of this solution is found by supposing all the quantities of the components increased by finite amounts so that their ratios remain constant, and at constant temperature and pressure:

$$X = \int dX = \int_0^{n_1} \bar{X}_1 dn_1 + \int_0^{n_2} \bar{X}_2 dn_2 + \ldots = \bar{X}_1 \int_0^{n_1} dn_1 + \bar{X}_2 \int_0^{n_2} dn_2 + \ldots$$

$$\therefore \ X = \bar{X}_1 n_1 + \bar{X}_2 n_2 + \ldots \quad . \quad . \quad . \quad . \quad . \quad . \quad . \quad (4)$$

$$X_m = X/(n_1 + n_2 + \ldots) = \bar{X}_1 N_1 + \bar{X}_2 N_2 + \ldots \quad . \quad . \quad . \quad (5)$$

[1] To distinguish K in (29) from K for ideal systems, the first is sometimes written K_a and the second K_c, but it is usual to denote both by K, the distinction being clear from the context.

[2] The small change of concentration c with temperature is usually negligible. If the molality m is used, this does not arise.

[3] Lewis and Randall, *J.A.C.S.*, 1921, **43**, 233; "Thermodynamics," 1923, 41; Partington and Tweedy, "Calculations in Physical Chemistry," 1928, 4, 62; Adams, *J.A.C.S.*, 1931, **53**, 3769; Gucker, *J. Phys. Chem.*, 1934, **38**, 307; Fredenhagen, *Z. Elektrochem.*, 1942, **48**, 136; 1943, **49**, 61; on the possibility of error from the bar notation, see Onsager, *J. Phys. Chem.*, 1928, **32**, 1461.

where X_m is the value of X for 1 mol of solution, and $N_i = n_i/\Sigma n_i$ is a mol fraction. By differentiation of (4) at constant temperature and pressure:

$$dX = \bar{X}_1 dn_1 + n_1 d\bar{X}_1 + \bar{X}_2 dn_2 + n_2 d\bar{X}_2 + \dots,$$

and by comparison with (3), which is true in general:

$$n_1 d\bar{X}_1 + n_2 d\bar{X}_2 + \dots = 0 \quad . \quad . \quad . \quad . \quad . \quad . \quad . \quad (6)$$

or

$$N_1 d\bar{X}_1 + N_2 d\bar{X}_2 + \dots = 0 \quad . \quad . \quad . \quad . \quad . \quad . \quad . \quad . \quad (7)$$

which is called the *Gibbs-Duhem equation.*[1] For the special case of a two-component system:

$$N_1 d\bar{X}_1 + N_2 d\bar{X}_2 = 0, \quad \text{or} \quad N_1(dX/dn_1)_{n_2} + N_2(dX/dn_2)_{n_1} = 0,$$

$$\therefore (dX/dn_1)_{n_2} = -(N_2/N_1)(dX/dn_2)_{n_1} \quad \therefore \bar{X}_1 = -(N_2/N_1)\bar{X}_2 \quad . \quad (8)$$

If $X = G$, the available energy, then from (13), § 58:

$$\bar{X}_1 = dX/dn_1 = dG/dn_1 = \mu_1; \quad \bar{X}_2 = dX/dn_2 = dG/dn_2 = \mu_2, \dots,$$

are the chemical potentials. Hence an alternative form of the Gibbs-Duhem equation is:

$$N_1 d\mu_1 + N_2 d\mu_2 + \dots = 0 \quad . \quad . \quad . \quad . \quad . \quad . \quad . \quad . \quad (9)$$

or, for a binary mixture, from (7), § 62:

$$d\mu_1 = -(N_2/N_1) d\mu_2 \quad . \quad . \quad . \quad . \quad . \quad . \quad . \quad . \quad . \quad (10)$$

$$d \ln a_1 = -(N_2/N_1) d \ln a_2 \quad . \quad . \quad . \quad . \quad . \quad . \quad . \quad . \quad (11)$$

Since $N_1 + N_2 = 1$, therefore $dN_1 = -dN_2$, therefore from (10):

$$(d\mu_1/d \ln N_1)_{T,p} = (d\mu_2/d \ln N_2)_{T,p} \quad . \quad . \quad . \quad . \quad . \quad (12)$$

$$\therefore N_1(d \ln a_1/dN_1)_{T,p} = N_2(d \ln a_2/dN_2)T,p \quad . \quad . \quad . \quad . \quad (13)$$

Equations (12) and (13) are alternative forms of the Gibbs-Duhem equation for a binary mixture. The treatment of partial molal quantities at infinite dilution given by Lewis and Randall has been extended and made more precise by Krichevsky and Kasarnovsky.[2]

Example. The density of 39·19 per cent. sulphuric acid at 15° is 1·300. The solution contains 39·19 gm. H_2SO_4 $= 39{\cdot}19/98 = 0{\cdot}40$ mol $H_2SO_4 = n_1$, and $60{\cdot}81/18 = 3{\cdot}38$ mols $H_2O = n_2$. The mol fractions are: H_2O $3{\cdot}38/3{\cdot}78 = 0{\cdot}89$; H_2SO_4 $1 - 0{\cdot}89 = 0{\cdot}11$. The *mol ratio* of acid is $0{\cdot}11/0{\cdot}89 = 0{\cdot}124$. For 100 gm. solution $100/1{\cdot}3 = 77$ ml., therefore molal volume=vol. for $n_1 + n_2 = 1$, is $77/3{\cdot}78 = 20{\cdot}37$ ml.

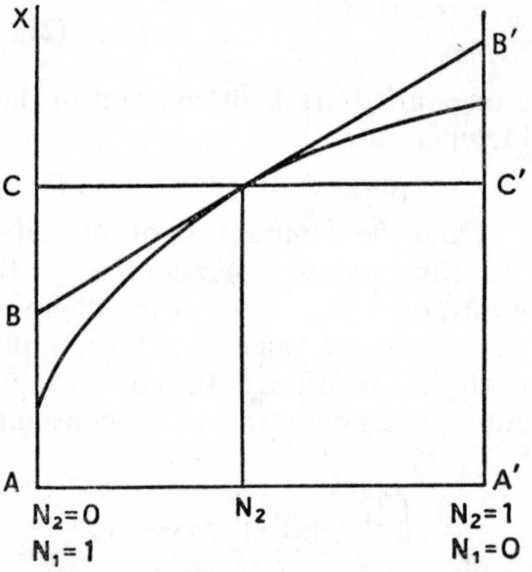

FIG. 18.II. Graphical Calculation of Partial Molal Quantities

The values of $\bar{X}_1$ and $\bar{X}_2$ for a binary solution may be found graphically by plotting X against n_1 for a fixed value of n_2, and then against n_2 for a fixed value of n_1, and finding the slopes of the tangents, dX/dn_1 and dX/dn_2, for particular

[1] The deduction here given is essentially that of Gibbs, *Trans. Connecticut Acad.*, 1875, **3**, 143; Duhem, "Le Potentiel Thermodynamique," 1886, 33, used Euler's Theorem (§ 30.I); Kireev, *Acta Physicochim. U.R.S.S.*, 1941, **15**, 293.

[2] *J.A.C.S.*, 1935, **57**, 2171: Lewis and Randall found $\partial\bar{G}_1/\partial N_2 \div \partial\bar{G}_2/\partial N_1 = -N_2/N_1$, where $\bar{G}_1$ and $\bar{G}_2$ are our μ_1 and μ_2, and assumed that when $N_2/N_1 = 0$, $\partial\bar{G}_1/\partial N_2 = 0$ or $\partial\bar{G}_2/\partial N_1 = \infty$. but there are three other cases.

values of n_1 and n_2. In a more convenient method, due to Roozeboom,[1] $X_M = x = X/(n_1+n_2)$ is plotted against the mol fraction N_2 (Fig. 18.II), a tangent to the curve is drawn for any value of N_2, and the intercepts of the tangent on the axes $N_1=1$ and $N_2=1$, give $\bar{X}_1$ and $\bar{X}_2$, respectively. This is proved as follows:

$$AB = AC - BC,$$
$$AC = X_M = x \text{ for } N_2 = X/(n_1+n_2),$$
$$BC = N_2(dx/dN_2) = N_2 \times (\text{slope of } BB').$$
$$(dx/dn_1)_{n_2} = [1/(n_1+n_2)](dX/dn_1) - X/(n_1+n_2)^2,$$
$$(dN_2/dn_1)_{n_2} = (d/dn_1)[n_2/(n_1+n_2)] = -n_2/(n_1+n_2)^2,$$
$$\therefore (dx/dN_2) = (dx/dn_1)(dn_1/dN_2) = -[(n_1+n_2)/n_2](dX/dn_1) + X/n_2,$$
$$\therefore N_2(dx/dN_2) = -(dX/dn_1) + X/(n_1+n_2) = -\bar{X}_1 + X_m,$$
$$\therefore AB = \bar{X}_1; \text{ and similarly } A'B' = \bar{X}_2.$$

Example.—The heat absorbed, ΔH g.cal., in the formation of a mol of aqueous solution containing the mol fraction N_2 of sulphuric acid (=heat absorbed per mol of acid $\times N_2$) is:

N_2	0·95	·85	·75	·65	·55	·45	·40	·35	·25	·15
$-\Delta H$	427	1207	1950	2639	3195	3456	3452	3378	2969	2125

ΔH is the *total* or *integral heat of solution.* If a small amount of solute (or solvent) dn is added to a given solution, $\bar{H} = d\Delta H/dn$ is the *partial* or *differential heat of solution* (or *dilution*). ΔH is plotted against N_2 and the tangent is drawn at, say, $N_2=0·5$. The intercept of the tangent on the $N_1=1$ axis is -4820, which is the differential heat of dilution, $d\Delta H/dn_1 = \bar{H}_1$, in acid of mol fraction 0·5. The intercept on the $N_2=1$ axis is -1900, which is the differential heat of solution, $d\Delta H/dn_2 = \bar{H}_2$, of acid in the solution. The partial heat of solution of a solution of mol fraction $N_2=0·1$ in a solution of mol fraction $N_2=0·5$ is -2940, the intercept on the ordinate at $N_2=0·1$ between the tangent at $N_2=0·5$ and the curve.

The *differential heat of solution* $\bar{H}_2$ of sulphuric acid in solution of mol fraction N_2 of sulphuric acid is:

$-\bar{H}_2$	12970	7520	4040	2960	1890	670	460	173	102	47
N_2	0·1	·25	·40	·45	·50	·60	·65	·75	·80	·90

From (8): $\int d\bar{H}_1 = -\int (N_2/N_1) d\bar{H}_2$. Plot N_2/N_1 as ordinate against $\bar{H}_2$ as abscissa and find the area under the curve from $N_1=0$ to $N_1=0·4$ (therefore $N_2=0·6$). Its negative value, $+2010$, is the difference between the values of $\bar{H}_1$ for $N_1=0·4$ and $N_1=0$. From the previous graph $\bar{H}_1$ for $N_1=0$ is found to be -8300, therefore $\bar{H}_1 = 2010 - 8300 = -6290$ g.cal. for a solution containing $N_2=0·60$ of acid.

§ 64. Heterogeneous Systems

Consider a pure solid in contact with a saturated solution, the total available energies of the solid and solution being G' and G''. Let δn mols of solid be supposed to pass into solution at constant temperature and pressure. Then

[1] Cf. Partington, "Thermodynamics," 1913, 311; Sosnick, *J.A.C.S.*, 1927, **49**, 2255; Randall and Rossini, *ibid.*, 1929, **51**, 323; Young and Vogel, *ibid.*, 1932, **54**, 3024 (with useful tables for change of variable); Koenig, *ibid.*, 1936, **58**, 317.

G' decreases by $(dG'/dn)\delta n$ and G'' increases by $(dG''/dn)\delta n$. The total change of available energy is:

$$dG = dG'' + dG' = (dG''/dn)\delta n - (dG'/dn)\delta n,$$

which, by (9), § 53, is zero when the system is in equilibrium:

$$\therefore\ (dG'/dn) = (dG''/dn) \quad . \quad . \quad . \quad . \quad . \quad . \quad . \quad . \quad (1)$$

Hence from (13), § 58:

$$\mu' = \mu'' \quad . \quad . \quad . \quad . \quad . \quad . \quad . \quad . \quad . \quad . \quad . \quad (2)$$

i.e. there is equilibrium when the chemical potential is the same in both phases.

This result is obviously true for each of any number of components in any number of phases, and such a system is in equilibrium when the chemical potential of *each* component is equal in all the phases.

This general condition leads to the formula known as the *Phase Rule*, as was shown by Gibbs,[1] who says: "If a homogeneous body has n independently variable components, the phase of the body is evidently capable of $n+1$ independent variations. A system of r coexistent phases, each of which has the same n independently variable components, is capable of $n+2-r$ variations of phase. For the temperature, the pressure, and the potentials for the actual components have the same values in the different phases, and the variations of these quantities are . . . subject to as many conditions as there are different phases. Therefore, the number of independent variations in the values of these quantities, i.e. the number of independent variations of phase of the system [the number of degrees of freedom], will be $n+2-r$."

Gibbs's statement may be slightly expanded as follows. In (4), § 58, there are $2n+5$ variables (the n values of m, the n values of μ, and the values of E, T, S, P, and V), but of these $n+2$, viz. the n values of μ, T, and P, can be found by differentiation, as in (3a), (3b), and (5), § 58, and to these (4) is an additional relation, making $n+3$ in all. Thus, the number of *independent* variables is $(2n+5)-(n+3)=n+2$. But if all the m's, S, and V are varied *in the same ratio*, only the amount of the system and not its state is varied, and there are $n+1$ independent ratios of these $n+2$ quantities (e.g. m_1/V, m_2/V, . . ., S/V), so that the number of independent variations of state and composition of a homogeneous body is $n+1$.

The total number of independent variations of the r separate phases is $r(n+1)$, but if the phases co-exist, the temperature, pressure, and the chemical potential of each of the n components in each phase must be equal, giving $(n+2)(r-1)$ conditions (any *one* phase may be taken out as a "test phase" and it must be in equilibrium with the remaining $r-1$). Hence the number of independent variables for all the phases is $r(n+1)-(n+2)(r-1)=n+2-r$.

The Nernst Heat Theorem

§ 65. The Principle of Maximum Work

From an early period[2] the cause of chemical change was identified with a semi-occult "force" called *affinity*, which brought about the union and separation of substances. According to Bergman (1775)[3] the reaction A+BC=

[1] *Trans. Connecticut Acad.*, 1876, **3**, 108 f.; "Scientific Papers," 1906, **1**, 96; Butler, in "A Commentary on the Scientific Writings of J. W. Gibbs," New Haven, 1936, **1**, 105.

[2] Ostwald, "Lehrbuch der allgemeinen Chemie," 1911, **2**, ii, 1 f.; Partington, "A Short History of Chemistry," 1948, 322 f.

[3] De attractionibus electivis, in *Nova Acta Upsal.*, 1775, **2**, 159–248; "Opuscula," Uppsala, 1783, **3**, 291; "A Dissertation on Elective Attractions," transl. Beddoes, London, 1785.

AB+C takes place *completely* if the affinity of A for B is greater than the affinity of B for C. Berthollet [1] clearly recognised the importance of secondary factors (temperature, volatility, insolubility, mass) in determining the course of a reaction, and he emphasised the *reversibility* of reactions, so that the reaction A+BC=AB+C is not usually complete, but a state of *equilibrium* is reached in which B divides itself between A and C in proportion to their affinities and " masses " (i.e. concentrations): $A+BC \rightleftharpoons AB+C$. Attempts were made to determine the relative affinities from the ratio of partition of one substance between two others competing for it. This will be fully dealt with in a later volume.

A new point of view was introduced when Julius Thomsen in 1853 proposed [2] to measure affinity by the amount of heat evolved in a reaction. He started with the correct fundamental principle that the energy of a body is constant under the same conditions, and showed that Hess's law (§ 18) is in agreement with this. In order to bring the heat of reaction into relation with chemical energy, he assumed that the heat evolved in a reaction is equal to the difference between the energies of the substances before and after the reaction, a proposition which is strictly correct only if no external work is done, or any other forms of energy except heat are produced. This is usually the case when the change occurs at constant volume, and is approximately true for *all* reactions between liquids and solids. To this consequence of the First Law, Thomsen in 1854 added a new " principle " which he developed from views on chemical affinity then in vogue. He assumed that *the heat evolved in a chemical reaction is a measure of the work done by the chemical forces*, and so is *a measure of the chemical affinity*.

In the decomposition of an exothermic compound (one formed with evolution of heat), a great expenditure of energy is necessary, and only such processes can bring it about which themselves develop more heat than is absorbed in the decomposition. Metals such as zinc, iron, and magnesium, the oxides of which are formed with the evolution of more heat than is developed in the formation of water vapour from the same amount of oxygen, decompose steam, but if the heat of formation of the oxide is less than the heat of formation of steam, the metal (e.g. copper, silver, gold) is not oxidised by steam.

From such considerations, Thomsen arrived at the general conclusion: " Every simple or complex action of a purely chemical nature is accompanied by an evolution of heat." The criterion of the possibility of a reaction was, on this hypothesis, $\Sigma Q_f - \Sigma Q_i = a$, where ΣQ_f and ΣQ_i are the algebraic sums of the heats of formation (evolved) of the final products and of the initial substances, respectively, and a is a *positive* magnitude.

Similar ideas were advanced by Marcellin Berthelot [3] in his *principle of maximum work* (" principe de travail maximum "), which he regarded as somewhat different from Thomsen's principle, and stated as follows: " Every chemical change, accomplished without the intervention of a foreign energy [énergie étrangère] tends to the production of the body or system of bodies which

[1] " Recherches sur les Lois de l'Affinité," 1801; " Essai de Statique Chimique," 2 vols., 1803.

[2] *Ann. Phys.*, 1853, **88**, 349; 1853, **90**, 261; 1854, **91**, 83; 1854, **92**, 34; " Thermochemische Untersuchungen," 4 vols., Leipzig, 1882–6, **1**, 15.

[3] " Leçons sur les Méthodes générales de Synthèse en Chimie Organique," 1864, 399; *Compt. Rend.*, 1867, **64**, 413; 1870, **71**, 303; *Ann. Chim.*, 1869, **18**, 5 (103); 1875, **4**, 5; " Essai de Mécanique Chimique fondée sur la Thermochimie," 2 vols, 1879, **1**, xxix; Henry, *Compt. Rend.*, 1924, **178**, 2248.

evolves the most heat. . . . Every chemical reaction susceptible of accomplishment without the intervention of preliminary work, and apart from the intervention of energy foreign to the bodies present in the system, is necessarily produced if it evolves heat."

It is noteworthy that Berthelot called this the principle of maximum work, not of maximum heat (although he used heat evolution as a criterion of chemical work), and he later [1] restricted it to reactions between solids (in which case it is approximately true). He pointed out that it would be more exact at low temperatures, and defined chemical heat, to which the principle applies, as that transformable into work, i.e. really *free energy* (see § 26).

At the time when Thomsen and Berthelot put forward their " principles " they seemed to be logical consequences of the First Law, and eminent physicists, such as William Thomson [2] (Lord Kelvin) and Helmholtz,[3] had made an exactly similar mistake in another field, viz. the relation between the electromotive force of a cell and the heat of reaction of the chemical process occurring in it, as will be explained later.

The following, among other, objections were brought against the principle of maximum work: [4]

(1) It implies that a reaction should proceed in one direction only, in which heat is evolved, and thus reversible reactions should be impossible. In this sense it is a retreat to the old theory of Bergman.

(2) There are many reactions which occur spontaneously with absorption of heat, whereas such endothermic reactions should be impossible.

The second objection was got over by assuming that some physical change (e.g. solution, conversion of a solid into a gas, etc.) accompanied by absorption of heat occurred as well as a chemical change, and the reactions were not " of a purely chemical nature." This is not altogether without significance.

§ 66. Applications of the Second Law of Thermodynamics to Chemistry

The first applications of the second law of thermodynamics to chemistry were made by Horstmann,[5] who used the entropy and extended the method of Clausius; his first paper (1869) was merely an application of the Clapeyron-Clausius equation to dissociation.[6] The first application of the free energy to chemical problems was made in a Royal Institution lecture in 1875 by Lord Rayleigh,[7] in the form of Lord Kelvin's principle of dissipation of energy (§ 27), when he pointed out that " a chemical transformation is impossible, if its occurrence would involve the opposite of dissipation (for which there is no convenient word) "; he gave as an example the lowering of vapour pressure of a solvent by a dissolved substance, the argument being identical with that later used by Helmholtz.

[1] *Compt. Rend.*, 1894, **118**, 1378; " Thermochimie," 2 vols., Paris, 1897, **1**, 10 f.; Tantzov, *J. Russ. Phys. Chem. Soc.*, 1928, **60**, 361.

[2] *Phil. Mag.*, 1851, **2**, 429; " Math. and Phys. Papers," Cambridge, 1882, **1**, 472, 490, 503.

[3] " Über die Erhaltung der Kraft," Berlin, 1847, 45 f.

[4] Ostwald, " Lehrbuch der allgemeinen Chemie," 1910, **2**, i, 64 f.; 1911, **2**, ii, 83 f.; in Watts' " Dictionary of Chemistry," edit. Morley and Muir, 1890, **1**, 86, where the criticism is too sweeping, and not closely enough related to numerical data.

[5] *Ber.*, 1868, **1**, 210 (kinetic); 1869, **2**, 137; 1871, **4**, 635; 1881, **14**, 1242; *Ann.*, 1872, Supplbd. **8**, 112; 1873, **170**, 192; *Verhl. Naturhist.-Med. Vereins Heidelberg*, 1877, **1**, 177; Ostwald's *Klassiker*, 1903, **137**.

[6] Independently applied also by Peslin, *Ann. Chim.*, 1871, **24**, 208 (dissoc. $CaCO_3$); Moutier, *Compt. Rend.*, 1871, **72**, 759 (dissoc. $CaCO_3$, salt hydrates, etc.).

[7] " Scientific Papers," 1899, **1**, 238.

Gibbs [1] in 1874–8 gave a complete thermodynamic treatment of chemical equilibrium (see § 59), but his memoir was published in a journal of limited circulation, and was composed in a very abstract and dry mathematical form, which did not appeal to chemists. Helmholtz [2] in 1882 showed (§ 42) that the heat evolved in a chemical reaction is not generally a true measure of the work done by the chemical forces (" Arbeitswerth der chemischen Verwandtschaftkräfte "), and in some cases the two can be opposite in sign. The true measure is the maximum work, or diminution of free energy, $-\Delta F$, in the reaction. The applications of thermodynamics in the measurement of affinity were clearly realised and stated by van't Hoff,[3] who emphasised that free energy changes could be treated like heats of reaction by Hess's law (§ 18).

In spite of its incorrectness on general theoretical grounds, the Thomsen-Berthelot principle often gave results surprisingly near the truth. In practical sciences, a zealously critical symbolic-algebraic method of approach can be grossly misleading, and can easily blunder over a large bulk of important truth concealed under a thin crust of apparent error.

§ 67. The Nernst Heat Theorem

Nernst,[4] in a searching criticism of Berthelot's principle, after pointing out that it cannot be regarded as a general law, added that: " a rule which holds good in many cases, but which fails in a few cases, contains a genuine kernel of truth, a kernel which has not as yet been shelled from its enclosing hull. . . . A law of nature lies hidden in this ' principle of maximum work,' the further development of which is very important." This law was revealed in 1906 by Nernst's discovery [5] of a new principle in thermodynamics, which is usually

1 *Trans. Connecticut Acad.*, 1874–8, **3**, 108, 342; " Thermodynamische Studien," transl. Ostwald, Leipzig, 1892; Gibbs, " Scientific Papers," 1906, **1**, 55; " Collected Works," 1928, **1**, 55; a long summary is given in Ostwald, " Lehrbuch der allgemeinen Chemie," 1902, **2**, i, 114–48.

2 *Berlin Ber.*, 1882, I, 22; "Wiss. Abhl.," 1883, **2**, 958; 1895, **3**, 92; Ostwald's *Klassiker*, 1902, **124**; summary by R. von Helmholtz, *Ann. Phys.*, 1887, **30**, 401; *Z. phys. Chem.*, 1887, **1**, 203.

3 " L'Étude de Dynamique Chimique," Amsterdam, 1884, 177; *Z. anorg. Chem.*, 1898, **18**, 1.

4 "Theoretical Chemistry," 1904, 689.

5 *Gött. Nachr.*, 1906, 1; long abstr. in *Z. Elektrochem.*, 1906, **12**, 738; *J. Chim. Phys.*, 1910, **8**, 228; *Berlin Ber.*, 1906, 933; 1911, 65; 1912, 134; *Phys. Z.*, 1911, **12**, 976; *Proc. K. Akad. Wetens. Amsterdam*, 1911, **14**, 201; *Ber.*, 1914, **47**, 608; " Experimental and Theoretical Applications of Thermodynamics to Chemistry," New York, 1907; " Die theoretischen und experimentellen Grundlagen des neuen Wärmesatzes," Halle, 1919, 2nd edit., 1924; transl. as " The New Heat Theorem," 1926; Haber, " Thermodynamics of Technical Gas Reactions," transl. Lamb, 1908, 83; Pollitzer, Die Berechnung chemischer Affinitäten nach dem Nernstschen Wärmetheorem, *Samml. chem.- und chem.-techn. Vorträge*, Stuttgart, 1912, **17**; Partington, " A Text-Book of Thermodynamics," 1913, 483; Jellinek, " Physikalische Chemie der Gasreaktionen," Leipzig, 1913, 57; Schüle, " Technische Thermodynamik," 1923, **2**, 216; Herzfeld, in Wien-Harms, " Handbuch der Experimentalphysik," 1928, **8**, ii, 723; Simon, *Ergebn. d. exakt. Naturwiss.*, 1930, **9**, 222 (review of 25 years of progress). For some general publications on the Nernst heat theorem, see: Kohnstamm and Ornstein, *Proc. K. Akad. Wetens. Amsterdam*, 1912, **14**, 802 (critical); Kohl, *Monatsh. Math. Phys.*, 1912, **23**, 81; Gruner, *Verhl. d. D. Phys. Ges.*, 1912, **14**, 655, 727; Campetti, *Nuov. Cim.*, 1913, **5**, 302; Lorentz, *Chem. Weekbl.*, 1913, **10**, 621 (strict derivation); Schames, *Verhl. d. D. Phys. Ges.*, 1914, **16**, 518; van Laar, *Chem. Weekbl.*, 1918, **15**, 1124; 1927, **24**, 302 (critical); Boutaric, *Le Radium*, 1919, **11**, 348; Carrelli, *Nuov. Cim.*, 1928, **5**, 341 (criticism); Schmolke, *Z. ges. Kälte-Ind.*, 1929, **36**, 154; Bijvoet and Verweel, *Chem. Weekbl.*, 1932, **29**, 210; Bernini, *Nuov. Cim.*, 1932, **9**, lxv; Kohnstamm, *Rec. Trav. Chim.*, 1932, **51**, 538 (critical); Schmolke, *Berlin Ber.*, 1932, 780; di Jorio, *Nuov. Cim.*, 1937, **14**, 480; Denina, *Ricerca Sci.*, 1939, **10**, 1044; Ulich, *Die Chemie*, 1942, **55**, 211.

called the *Nernst heat theorem*; Nernst himself,[1] and most American authors (following Lewis and Gibson),[2] called it " the third law of thermodynamics."

Approaches, to varying distances, towards the Nernst heat theorem had been made, after Berthelot, by several scientists, including van't Hoff [3] and T. W. Richards,[4] whose contributions were fairly stated by Nernst. Richards gave $-q$ and w curves meeting both tangentially and at a sharp angle, and said the calculation, although fundamental, is quite impossible. A nearer miss than his may be found in a paper by Ponsot,[5] where it is said that: " at absolute zero, two systems of solids containing the same elements have the same specific heat," that the specific heats of a solid and its saturated vapour approach equality and vanish at the absolute zero, and that the specific heat of the saturated vapour is less than that of the solid.

A statistical deduction of Nernst's heat theorem, based on the quantum theory, was first given by Sackur [6] in 1911; this aspect is considered in Section IV.

In view of its historical interest, a sketch of Nernst's own treatment will first be given. Equations (3), § 42, and (10), § 44:

$$w_T+q_v=T(\mathrm{d}w_T/\mathrm{d}T) \quad . \quad . \quad . \quad . \quad . \quad . \quad . \quad . \quad (1)$$

$$w_T'+q_p=T(\mathrm{d}w'/\mathrm{d}T) \quad . \quad . \quad . \quad . \quad . \quad . \quad . \quad . \quad (2)$$

are of the same form and may be combined in the single equation: [7]

$$w+q=T(\mathrm{d}w/\mathrm{d}T) \quad . \quad . \quad . \quad . \quad . \quad . \quad . \quad . \quad (3)$$

in which w is the maximum work (or w' the nett work, respectively), and q is the heat of reaction (absorbed) at constant volume (or pressure, respectively). Equation (3) may be integrated by writing:

$$q=q_0+(q-q_0) \quad . \quad . \quad . \quad . \quad . \quad . \quad . \quad . \quad . \quad (4)$$

where q_0 is the value for $T=0$ (absolute zero), and then:

$$\left[w/T\right]_0^T=\int_0^T(q_0/T^2)\mathrm{d}T+\int_0^T[(q-q_0)/T^2]\mathrm{d}T$$

$$w/T-(w/T)_0=-q_0/T+(q/T)_0+\int_0^T[(q-q_0)/T^2]\mathrm{d}T$$

$$\therefore\ w=-q_0+T\int_0^T[(q-q_0)/T^2]\mathrm{d}T+T[(w+q]/T]_0 \quad . \quad . \quad (5)$$

The integration constant is, from (3):

$$[(w+q)/T]_0=(\mathrm{d}w/\mathrm{d}T)_0 \quad . \quad . \quad . \quad . \quad . \quad . \quad . \quad . \quad (6)$$

The Thomsen-Berthelot principle (§ 65):

$$w=-q, \quad \text{or} \quad w+q=0 \quad . \quad . \quad . \quad . \quad . \quad . \quad . \quad . \quad (7)$$

1 " Theoretische Chemie," 7 Aufl., 1913, 753.

2 *J.A.C.S.*, 1917, **39**, 2554.

3 *Ann. Phys., Boltzmann Festschr.*, 1904, 233.

4 *Z. phys. Chem.*, 1902, **42**, 129; *Z. Elektrochem.*, 1904, **10**, 637; *J.A.C.S.*, 1914, **36**, 2417; crit. by Trevor, *J. Phys. Chem.*, 1905, **9**, 299; Bell, *ibid.*, 1905, **9**, 381; see also Brønsted, *K. Danske Videns. Selskab. Skrift.*, 1906, **9**, 103, 297; Nernst, " The New Heat Theorem," 1926, 227.

5 *Compt. Rend.*, 1902, **134**, 651, 703; full abstr. in *J. Phys. Chem.*, 1902, **6**, 429.

6 *Ann. Phys.*, 1911, **34**, 455; 1911, **36**, 958.

7 Nernst, " The New Heat Theorem," 1926, 213.

although untrue generally, is approximately valid in many reactions between condensed phases (especially solids), and more nearly true at lower temperatures. If it is assumed for condensed systems that:

$$w_0+q_0=0 \quad \ldots \ldots \ldots \quad (8)$$

then (6) shows that $(dw/dT)_0$ must be finite (including zero) or infinite to a smaller order than $1/T$. Equations (6) and (8) give:

$$(dw/dT)_0=[(w+q)/T]_0=0/0 \quad \ldots \ldots \quad (9)$$

but the indeterminate value is found (§ 16.I) by differentiating the numerator and denominator of the second term of (9) with respect to T and then putting $T=0$:

$$(dw/dT)_0=[(dw/dT)+(dq/dT)/(dT/dT)]_0=(dw/dT)_0+(dq/dT)_0 \quad . \quad (10)$$

With the sign system adopted, w is work done and q is heat absorbed, or $-q$ is heat evolved. Nernst's fundamental assumption was that, in view of the approximate validity of (8) at finite temperatures for reactions between pure solid or liquid substances (not gases or solutions), the curves of w and $-q$ plotted against T not only meet at the absolute zero but do so tangentially [1] (Fig. 19.II, where $Q=-q$). Hence:

$$-(dq/dT)_0=(dQ/dT)_0=(dw/dT)_0 \quad . \quad . \quad (11)$$

and from (10):

$$(dw/dT)_0=0 \quad . \quad . \quad . \quad . \quad (12)$$

$$(dq/dT)_0=0 \quad . \quad . \quad . \quad . \quad (13)$$

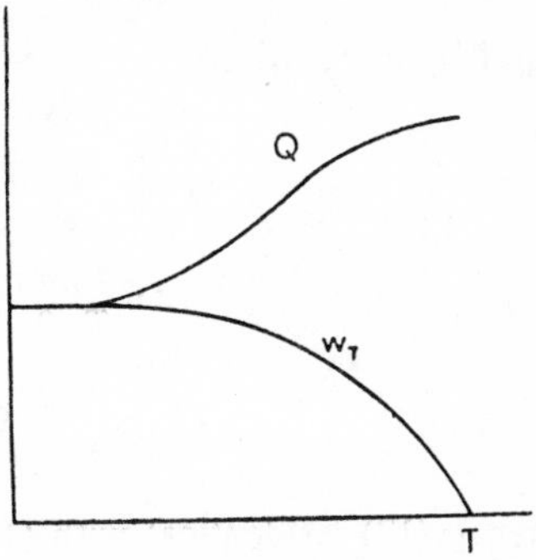

FIG. 19.II. Maximum Work and Heat of Reaction for Condensed system near the Absolute Zero

Hence (6) shows that w may be calculated from (5) for such reactions from purely thermal data, since q, the heat of reaction, may be expressed in terms of q_0 and heat capacities by Kirchhoff's equation (§ 20). Kistiakowski [2] stated Berthelot's principle in the form that, for every transformation, a temperature can be found for which $w=-q$. Nernst's heat theorem makes this always true for $T=0$.

The integral of (1) is (see § 43):

$$w_T=T\int(q_v/T^2)dT+aT,$$

where a is an integration constant. Equation (12) gives:

$$w_T=T\int^T(q_v/T^2)dT,$$

with the meaning that an indefinite integral (§ 17.I) is to be found, and then the upper limit T inserted in the result.[3] Byk [4] used a complex variable, and in some cases took as the lower limit of the integral an imaginary quantity.

Nernst at first gave both (7) and (11) as the necessary and sufficient statement

[1] This enables the w curve to be drawn when the $Q=-q$ curve is known: see Ganz and Miguez, *Phys. Z.*, 1915, **16**, 247 (mechanical pantograph type integrator); Drägert, *ibid.*, 1915, **16**, 295, 451. Richards, *Z. phys. Chem.*, 1902, **42**, 129; *J.A.C.S.*, 1914, **36**, 2417 (2433), supposed that $dw/dT=-M \,.\, dQ/dT$, the average value of M being 2.

[2] *J. Russ. Phys. Chem. Soc.*, 1921, **53**, I, 247 (C).

[3] Nernst, "Grundlagen des neuen Wärmesatzes," Halle, 1918, 68; "The New Heat Theorem," 1926, 81; Schmolke, *Z. Phys.*, 1934, **88**, 139.

[4] *Phys. Z.*, 1919, **20**, 505.

of his theorem, but both are included in (12), which is the kernel of the theorem.[1] The assumption that (10) leads to (13) is true only when $(\mathrm{d}w/\mathrm{d}T)$ is zero or finite, otherwise $(\mathrm{d}q/\mathrm{d}T)_0$ could be $\infty-\infty$, i.e. indeterminate, in proceeding to the limit in (10). Equation (8) can be replaced by the alternative statements that: (i) w_0 is finite (including zero), or (ii) q_0 is finite (including zero). The theorem may also be expressed in another form. Let

$$\lim_{T\to 0}\left(\frac{\mathrm{d}w}{\mathrm{d}T}\right)=\frac{1}{b}\lim_{T\to 0}\left(\frac{\mathrm{d}q}{\mathrm{d}T}\right) \quad . \quad . \quad . \quad . \quad . \quad . \quad . \quad \textbf{(11a)}$$

where b is an unknown positive constant; then (11a) applies in the immediate neighbourhood of the absolute zero, which need not be the case with (11). By differentiation of (3):

$$\mathrm{d}q/\mathrm{d}T=T.\mathrm{d}^2w/\mathrm{d}T^2 \quad . \quad . \quad . \quad . \quad . \quad . \quad . \quad . \quad \textbf{(3a)}$$

In the neighbourhood of the absolute zero (3a) can be substituted in (11a):

$$\therefore \lim_{T\to 0}\left(\frac{\mathrm{d}w}{\mathrm{d}T}\right)=\lim_{T\to 0}\frac{T}{b}\frac{\mathrm{d}^2w}{\mathrm{d}T^2}$$

and by integration:

$$\lim_{T\to 0}\frac{\mathrm{d}^2w/\mathrm{d}T^2}{\mathrm{d}w/\mathrm{d}T}=\lim_{T\to 0}\frac{\mathrm{d}[\ln(\mathrm{d}w/\mathrm{d}T)]}{\mathrm{d}T}=b/T$$

by § 14, I,

$$\therefore \lim_{T\to 0}\ln(\mathrm{d}w/\mathrm{d}T)=b\ln T+\text{const.},$$

$$\therefore \lim_{T\to 0}(\mathrm{d}w/\mathrm{d}T)=\text{const. }T^b,$$

$$\therefore (\mathrm{d}w/\mathrm{d}T)_0=0;$$

hence (12) is identical with (11a). If a negative sign had been used in (11a), the result would have been $(\mathrm{d}w/\mathrm{d}T)=(\text{const.}/T^b)_0\to\infty$; hence Nernst's theorem requires that the curves for w and $-q$ must separate from $T=0$ on opposite sides of the horizontal (Fig. 19.II). The other assumption had been made by van't Hoff.[2] Nernst's theorem in its original form may thus be stated in a number of alternative ways:

I. $w_0=-q_0$; w_0 is finite; q_0 is finite.

II. $(\mathrm{d}q/\mathrm{d}T)_0=0$; $(\mathrm{d}w/\mathrm{d}T)_0$ is finite (including zero).

III. $(\mathrm{d}w/\mathrm{d}T)_0=-(\mathrm{d}q/\mathrm{d}T)_0$.

IV. $(\mathrm{d}w/\mathrm{d}T)_0=0$; $[(w+q)/T]_0=0$; $\lim_{T\to 0}\left(\frac{\mathrm{d}w}{\mathrm{d}T}\right)=\frac{1}{b}\lim_{T\to 0}\left(\frac{\mathrm{d}q}{\mathrm{d}T}\right)$, where b is a positive undetermined constant.

Equations (5), (6), and (12) give:

$$w=-q_0+T\int_0^T[(q-q_0)/T^2]\mathrm{d}T \quad . \quad . \quad . \quad . \quad . \quad . \quad . \quad . \quad \textbf{(14)}$$

which, with Kirchhoff's equation (§ 20):

$$q-q_0=\int_0^T\Delta C\mathrm{d}T \quad . \quad . \quad . \quad . \quad . \quad . \quad . \quad . \quad \textbf{(15)}$$

[1] Jüptner, *Z. phys. Chem.*, 1907, **60**, 114; 1908, **64**, 709; Bennewitz, in Geiger and Scheel, "Handbuch der Physik," 1926, **9**, 154; Brunner, *Z. Phys.*, 1936, **100**, 584; di Jario, *Nuov. Cim.*, 1937, **14**, 480; Schottky, *Naturwiss.*, 1943, **31**, 400.

[2] *Ann. Phys. Boltzmann Festschr.*, 1904, 233.

(where C is C_v or C_p according as q is q_v or q_p, and hence w is w_T or w'_T) provides a complete solution of the problem of calculating a free energy change w from a heat of reaction q. From (14) and (15), integration by parts (§ 19.I) gives:

$$w=-q_0+T\int_0^T\frac{\mathrm{d}T}{T^2}\int_0^T\Delta C\mathrm{d}T$$

$$=-q_0-\int_0^T\Delta C\mathrm{d}T+T\int_0^T(\Delta C/T)\mathrm{d}T$$

$$=-q+T\int_0^T(\Delta C/T)\mathrm{d}T \quad . \quad . \quad . \quad . \quad . \quad . \quad . \quad . \quad (16)$$

The substitutions $w=-\Delta F$ or $-\Delta G$, $q=\Delta E$ or ΔH, give:

$$\Delta F=\Delta E_0+\int_0^T\Delta C_v\mathrm{d}T-T\int_0^T(\Delta C_v/T)\mathrm{d}T$$

$$=\Delta E-T\int_0^T(\Delta C_v/T)\mathrm{d}T \quad . \quad . \quad . \quad . \quad . \quad . \quad . \quad . \quad (17)$$

and

$$\Delta G=\Delta H_0+\int_0^T\Delta C_p\mathrm{d}T-T\int_0^T(\Delta C_p/T)\mathrm{d}T$$

$$=\Delta H-T\int_0^T(\Delta C_p/T)\mathrm{d}T \quad . \quad . \quad . \quad . \quad . \quad . \quad . \quad . \quad (18)$$

Nernst assumed as an approximation that $-\Delta E$ can be expressed in a series of powers of T:

$$-\Delta E=-\Delta E_0+\alpha T+\beta T^2 \quad . \quad . \quad . \quad . \quad . \quad (19)$$

$$\therefore\ -\mathrm{d}\Delta E/\mathrm{d}T=-\mathrm{d}q/\mathrm{d}T=\alpha+2\beta T.$$

But from (11), $\alpha=0$,

$$\therefore\ -\Delta E=-\Delta E_0+\beta T^2 \quad . \quad . \quad . \quad . \quad . \quad . \quad . \quad . \quad (20)$$

Therefore from (1) $-\mathrm{d}(\Delta F/T)/\mathrm{d}T=\Delta E/T^2=(-\Delta E_0+\beta T^2)/T^2$, therefore by integration $-\Delta F=-\Delta E_0-\beta T^2+\text{const.}\times T$. By differentiation and comparison with (12) when $T=0$ it is found that " const."$=0$,

$$\therefore\ -\Delta F=-\Delta E_0-\beta T^2 \quad . \quad . \quad . \quad . \quad . \quad . \quad . \quad . \quad (21)$$

All these equations apply only to pure substances in condensed systems, not to gases or solutions, but Nernst showed that the Heat Theorem can be extended to apply to gas reactions, as will be explained in a later volume.

§ 68. Alternative Statement of the Nernst Heat Theorem

From (12), §42, and (3), § 33:

$$\mathrm{d}w/\mathrm{d}T=-\mathrm{d}\Delta F/\mathrm{d}T=\Delta S \quad . \quad . \quad . \quad . \quad . \quad . \quad . \quad . \quad (1)$$

an alternative form of Nernst's heat theorem is found, viz.:

$$(\Delta S)_{T=0}\equiv\Delta S_0=0 \quad . \quad . \quad . \quad . \quad . \quad . \quad . \quad . \quad . \quad . \quad (2)$$

In reactions between pure condensed phases at the absolute zero there is no change of entropy.

Fowler and Sterne,[1] after concluding that " it is not true in general that $\Delta S_0=0$," surmised that the Nernst heat theorem " is always irrelevant and

[1] *Rev. Mod. Phys.*, 1932, **4**, 635 (707).

useless . . . and should now be eliminated." It is, of course, equally correct to say that Newton's laws of motion " are not true in general," but both they and the Nernst heat theorem play their part in the practical applications of Science and are unlikely to be eliminated. Result (2) has been held [1] to suggest that the velocity of an irreversible process vanishes at the absolute zero, but Thermodynamics is not really concerned with velocities or time.

Nernst [2] expressed the heat theorem in the form that: *it is impossible by a thermodynamic process to cool a finite condensed system to the absolute zero.*

In an *adiabatic* process in which dn mols react, let the temperature decrease by dT. Then if C is the total heat capacity [3] and q the heat absorbed per mol:

$$\mathrm{d}T = q\,\mathrm{d}n/C \qquad (3)$$

If the process were carried out *isothermally*:

$$q = T\Delta S = T\Delta S_0 + T\int_0^T (\Delta C/T)\mathrm{d}T \qquad (4)$$

Assume that the temperature is so low that the specific heats obey a law:

$$C = aT^b, \quad \text{or} \quad \Delta C = a'T^b, \quad \text{where } b > 1 \qquad (5)$$

(as will be shown later to follow from the quantum theory), then:

$$\Delta S = \Delta S_0 + \int_0^T (a'T^b/T)\mathrm{d}T = \Delta S_0 + a''T^b$$

and

$$q = T(\Delta S_0 + a''T^b) \qquad (6)$$

From (3)–(6):

$$\mathrm{d}T = \mathrm{d}n(\Delta S_0 + a''T^b)/aT^{b-1} \qquad (7)$$

As T approaches zero, the numerator approaches d$n\Delta S_0$ and the denominator zero, hence dT becomes large and the cooling effect will reach absolute zero. If this result is to be excluded, then:

$$\Delta S_0 = 0 \qquad (8)$$

when the fraction becomes $a''T/a$, which vanishes as T approaches zero. Equation (8), however, is identical with (2).

Although this deduction was criticised by Einstein,[4] it is upheld by Epstein.[5] According to the Nernst heat theorem, the isothermal $T=0$ coincides with an adiabatic and intersects no other adiabatics, so that any cycle in which the isotherm $T=0$ forms a part would seem impossible.

[1] Ubbelohde, *Trans. Faraday Soc.*, 1937, **33**, 599, 1198, 1203; *Phil. Mag.*, 1938, **26**, 260; Gorter, *Physica*, 1938, **5**, 483.

[2] *Berlin Ber.*, 1912, 134; " The New Heat Theorem," 1926, 87; Czukor, *Verhl. d. D. Phys. Ges.*, 1914, **16**, 486; Simon, *Z. Phys.*, 1927, **41**, 806; *Physica*, 1937, **4**, 1089 (suggests that the Nernst heat theorem applies to changes between states in internal thermodynamic equilibrium, and can be stated in the form: *entropy differences between states of a system between which a reversible transition is possible in principle even at the lowest temperature, vanish at the absolute zero*); Ehrenfest-Afanassjewa, *Z. Phys.*, 1925, **33**, 933; Schidlof, *J. Chim. Phys.*, 1926, **23**, 814; Ptáček, *Chem. Obzor.*, 1943, **18**, 13.

[3] The heat capacity is clearly that of the *final* system.

[4] In " Structure de la Matière," 2e Solvay Congress (1913), 1921, 293; Schmolke, *Z. Phys.*, 1938, **108**, 183 ($T=0$ can be reached if sp. heats remain finite).

[5] " Textbook of Thermodynamics," New York, 1937, 245; cf. Fowler and Guggenheim, "Statistical Thermodynamics," Cambridge, 1939, 224; Cross and Eckstrom, *J. Chem. Phys.*, 1942, **10**, 287.

§ 69. Planck's Form of the Nernst Heat Theorem.

Equation (2), § 68, $\Delta S_0=0$ (due to Planck), is obviously satisfied if the entropy of each pure condensed phase is separately zero at the absolute zero, and this was assumed by Planck: [1]

$$(S)_{T=0}=S_0=0 \quad . \quad . \quad . \quad . \quad . \quad . \quad . \quad . \quad . \quad (1)$$

Quantum statistics (Section IV) show that this is true only when the multiplicity at $T=0$ is 1, and when this is not the case, or when transitions to this state of lowest multiplicity do not occur in the range of temperature used in the specific heat measurements, (1) will not be true. Since in the majority of cases (1) is true, it seems preferable to refer to the exceptions separately rather than to attempt a wide general statement which excludes them. The case is analogous to the retention of Taylor's Theorem by mathematicians.

Equation (1), with (7) or (8), § 35, will give finite entropy values:

$$S=\int_0^T (C_v/T)\mathrm{d}T \quad \text{or} \quad S=\int_0^T (C_p/T)\mathrm{d}T \quad . \quad . \quad . \quad . \quad (2)$$

The necessary and sufficient condition that the entropy shall remain finite as T approaches zero is that C_v or C_p shall decrease faster than T, which is the case for specific heats based on the quantum theory (§ 68), and that C_v and C_p shall be zero at $T=0$, which is in agreement both with the quantum theory and with experiment.

If the solid undergoes allotropic change, or changes into a liquid or gas, at a certain temperature T_0, the increase of entropy is:

$$\Delta S_t=l_t/T_0 \quad . \quad . \quad . \quad . \quad . \quad . \quad . \quad . \quad . \quad (3)$$

where l_t is the latent heat of transition per g. or mol, and the addition of (2) and (3) gives the entropy of the new solid, the liquid, or the gas, the integration (2) being continued with the appropriate specific heat. The complete equations (apart from allotropic or other changes or transitions of a single phase) for the *standard entropy* $S°$ at the temperature T, when corrected for deviations from the ideal gas state are:

(i) When the boiling-point at 1 atm. is below T:

$$S_T°=S_0+\int_0^{T_M} C_p\text{ (solid) d ln }T+\Delta H\text{ (fusion)}/T_M$$

$$+\int_{T_M}^{T_B} C_p\text{ (liquid) d ln }T+\Delta H\text{ (evaporation)}/T_B$$

$$+\int_{T_B}^{T} C_p\text{ (gas at 1 atm.) d ln }T+\frac{27}{32}R\frac{p}{p_c}\frac{T_c^3}{T^3} \quad . \quad . \quad . \quad (4)$$

where T_M, T_B are the melting- and boiling-points in °K. and the last term is the correction to the ideal gas state given by Berthelot's equation (§ 15.VII E).

(ii) When the boiling-point at 1 atm. is above T:

$$S_T°=S_0+\int_0^{T_M} C_p\text{ (solid) d ln }T+\Delta H\text{ (fusion)}/T_M$$

$$+\int_{T_M}^{T} C_p\text{ (liquid) d ln }T+R\ln p_T+\frac{27}{32}R\frac{p_T}{p_c}\frac{T_c^3}{T^3} \quad . \quad . \quad (5)$$

[1] "Thermodynamik," 3rd edit., 1911, 266; *Phys. Z.*, 1911, **12**, 681; 1912, **13**, 165; *Ber.*, 1912, **45**, 5.

where p_T is the vapour pressure at $T°$ K. The Berthelot correction term is usually only about 0·1 unit per mol. The Nernst-Planck heat theorem requires that $S_0=0$ in these equations.

The pioneer experiments of Nernst and his school [1] showed that the heat theorem was verified, but some examples are unsuitable and some calculations are not clear; a more striking demonstration of the validity of the "third law" was provided by experiments and critical treatment of data by G. N. Lewis and collaborators,[2] and it is now part of everyday Physical Chemistry. The link between the heat theorem and quantum statistics is also very firm (see Section IV).

§ 70. Standard Free and Available Energies

In the modern applications of the Nernst heat theorem, it is usual to calculate and tabulate the values of the free energies F and available energies G, or their changes, for the substances concerned. The *available energy change* is:

$$\Delta G_T=\Delta H_T-T\Delta S_T$$

$$=\left(\Delta H_{298}+\int_{298}^{T}\Delta C_p\,\mathrm{d}T\right)-T\left(\Delta S_{298}+\int_{298}^{T}\Delta C_p\,\mathrm{d}\ln T\right) \quad . \quad (1)$$

Alternatively, the free energy may be found [3] from (9), § 43:

$$F=-T\int_0^T(E/T^2)\mathrm{d}T \quad . \quad . \quad . \quad . \quad . \quad . \quad . \quad . \quad (2)$$

Hence E/T^2 is plotted against T (E being found by plotting C_v against T and graphical integration, or from formulae for C_v) and the area under the curve evaluated. This area multiplied by T gives F. The entropy S is then given by $(E-F)/T$. In a similar way the available energy is found from (15), § 44:

$$G=-T\int_0^T(H/T^2)\mathrm{d}T \quad . \quad . \quad . \quad . \quad . \quad . \quad . \quad . \quad (3)$$

and the entropy is

$$S=(H-G)/T \quad . \quad . \quad . \quad . \quad . \quad . \quad . \quad . \quad . \quad . \quad (4)$$

More used, however, are the so-called *standard values*, giving the excess of F or (usually) G at 1 atm. and 25° C. (298·1° K.) of given substances as compared with standard states, e.g. hydrogen gas, oxygen gas, rhombic sulphur, graphite, etc. The standard entropy changes [4] at 298·1° K. can be calculated from the equation $\Delta S°=(\Delta H^0-\Delta G^0)/298{\cdot}1$, and are usually given in g.cal./1° C. units (1 clausius).

The entropy of 1 mol of nitrogen gas at 25° C. and 1 atm. pressure in the ideal

[1] Summarised in Nernst, "The New Heat Theorem," 1926; for a criticism, see van de Sande Bakhuyzen, *Z. phys. Chem.*, 1924, **111**, 39, 57.

[2] Lewis and Gibson, *J. A. C. S.*, 1917, **39**, 2554; 1920, **42**, 1529; Lewis, Gibson, and Latimer, *ibid.*, 1922, **44**, 1008; Gibson and Giauque, *ibid.*, 1923, **45**, 93; and many later papers; see Sect. IV. Parks and Kelley, *J. Phys. Chem.*, 1928, **32**, 734; Eastman, *Chem. Rev.*, 1936, **18**, 257. In 1876, Massieu, *Mém. div. Savants Acad. Sci.*, 1876, **22**, No. 2, 43, had pointed out that: " on devra avant tout rechercher, pour chaque substance que l'on voudra étudier, sa fonction caractéristique [F or G] . . . une fois ce but atteint, le reste ne sera qu'une affaire de calcul, puisque tout s'exprimera au moyen de la fonction caractéristique et de ses derivées partielles."

[3] Miething, "Tabellen zur Berechnung des gesamten und freien Wärmeinhalt fester Körper," Halle, 1920.

[4] It should be noted in calculating $\Delta S°$ that the S values for all standard states of elements are assumed to be zero.

state (S°) is calculated as follows,[1] the initial state ($S=0$) being crystalline solid at zero absolute:

0° K. to 10° K. from Debye's equation ...	0·458
10° K. to 35·61° K. by graphical integration ...	6·034
Transition 54·71 g.cal./35·61° ...	1·536
35·61° K. to 61·14° K. (m.p.) by graphical integration ...	5·589
Fusion 172·3 g.cal./63·14° ...	2·729
63·14° K. to 77·32° K. (b.p.) by graphical integration ...	2·728
Evaporation 1332·9 g.cal./77·32° ...	17·239
Total entropy of gas at b.p. ...	36·31±0·1
Correction to ideal gas state (Berthelot's equation) ...	0·22
	36·53
77·32° K. to 298·1° K. by spectroscopic data ...	9·36
Hence the final result is $S^\circ_{298\cdot 1}$ ...	45·89

The following table [2] contains material for a test of Nernst's heat theorem, the values of the calorimetric entropy of the vapour at the boiling-point (1 atm. pressure), corrected to the ideal state by Berthelot's equation, as found by an application of the Nernst heat theorem ($S=0$ at $T=0$ for the solid) being compared with the values of the entropy in g.cal./1° C. per mol calculated by statistical methods from spectroscopic data (see Section IV). The agreement is excellent, many supposed anomalies found by Eucken and his pupils having been eliminated by later accurate experiments.

Gas	*S* N.H.T.	*S* spectr.	Gas	*S* N.H.T.	*S* spectr.
A [3] ...	30·85	30·87	HBr [10] ...	44·9	44·92
Kr [4] ...	34·63	34·65	HI [11] ...	47·8	47·8
O_2 [5] ...	40·70	40·68	NH_3 [12] ...	44·13	44·10
N_2 [6] ...	36·53	36·42	S_2 (298°) [13] ...	—	53·85
Cl_2 [7] ...	51·56	51·55	H_2S [14] ...	46·38	46·44
F_2 [8] ...	37·29	—	C_2N_2 [15] ...	55·43	55·67
HCl [9] ...	41·3	41·45	HCN [16] ...	47·94	48·25

[1] Giauque and Clayton, *J.A.C.S.*, 1933, **55**, 4875.

[2] For other data see Aston *et al.*, *J.A.C.S.*, 1944, **60**, 1171 (trimethylamine); Yost and Felt, *ibid.*, 1934, **56**, 68 (chlorine monoxide, $S=67\cdot 9$ at 25°); Clusius and Frank, *Z. phys. Chem.*, 1936, **34 B**, 405 (phosphine); Jones and Giauque, *J.A.C.S.*, 1947, **69**, 983 (nitromethane).

[3] Clusius and Frank, *Z. Elektrochem.*, 1943, **49**, 308.

[4] Clusius, Kruis, and Konnertz, *Ann. Phys.*, 1938, **33**, 642 (34·65 calc. by Tetrode's formula, § 14, IV).

[5] Giauque and Johnston, *J.A.C.S.*, 1929, **51**, 2300.

[6] Giauque and Clayton, *J.A.C.S.*, 1933, **55**, 4875.

[7] Giauque and Powell, *J.A.C.S.*, 1939, **61**, 1970 (N.H.T.); Giauque and Overstreet, *ibid.*, 1932, **54**, 1731 (spectr.).

[8] Kanda, *Bull. Chem. Soc. Japan*, 1937, **12**, 511.

[9] Giauque and Wiebe, *J.A.C.S.*, 1928, **50**, 101.

[10] Giauque and Wiebe, *J.A.C.S.*, 1928, **50**, 2193.

[11] Giauque and Wiebe, *J.A.C.S.*, 1929, **51**, 1441.

[12] Overstreet and Giauque, *J.A.C.S.*, 1937, **59**, 254; cf. Bryant, *ibid.*, 1931, **53**, 3014; Stephenson and McMahon, *ibid.*, 1939, **61**, 437.

[13] Godnew and Sswerdlin, *Z. Phys.*, 1935, **97**, 124.

[14] Giauque and Blue, *J.A.C.S.*, 1936, **58**, 831; Clusius and Frank, *Z. phys. Chem.*, 1936, **34 B**, 420.

[15] Ruhrwein and Giauque, *J.A.C.S.*, 1939, **61**, 2940; McMorris and Badger, *ibid.*, 1933, **55**, 1952, find *S* spectr.$=57\cdot 8$ at 25° C.

[16] Giauque and Ruhrwein, *J.A.C.S.*, 1939, **61**, 2626 (an anomalous sp. ht. curve, and a complicated calculation, of doubtful validity, assuming double and triple polymers in the vapour).

Gas		S N.H.T.	S spectr.	Gas		S N.H.T.	S spectr.
COS [1]	... ...	52·56	52·66	CH_3Cl [7]	...	54·27	54·31
CS_2 [2]	... ...	57·48	57·60	CH_3Br [8]	...	57·86	57·99
CCl_4 (25° C.) [3]	...	74·35	74·05	C_2H_6 (25° C.) [9]	...	54·85	54·62
SO_2 [4]	... ...	58·07	58·23	C_3H_6 [10] ...	...	59·93	61·0
AsF_3 [5]	... ...	72·09	72·12	CH_4 (25° C.) [11]	...	43·39	—
C_2H_4 [6]	... ...	47·36	47·35	$COCl_2$ [12]	...	66·63	68·26

The case of hydrogen is fully considered in § 24.IV. The following substances show an anomaly between the two entropy values (at the boiling-point):

		S N.H.T.	S spectr.
CO [13]	...	37·2	38·32
NO [14]	...	43·03	43·75
N_2O [15]	...	47·36	48·50

The cases of CO and N_2O are discussed in § 26.IV. Nitric oxide shows a deviation of 0·72, approximately $\frac{1}{2}\boldsymbol{R} \ln 2=0{\cdot}69$, which could be explained by assuming the presence of two isomers of N_2O_2 with an entropy of mixing. Oxygen, a paramagnetic gas, shows no anomaly.

The entropy of a binary compound is not, in general, half-way between those of its components, as is seen for the following [16] (gaseous state):

Br_2 ... 55·4   IBr ... 60·6 I_2 ... 62·29

Entropies calculated by Kelley [17] (in g.cal./deg. mol at 25° C. for the actual physical states at 25°) are:

[1] Kemp and Giauque, *J.A.C.S.*, 1937, **59**, 79; cf. Wagner, *Z. phys. Chem.*, 1941, **48** B, 309; Eucken and Schäfer, *ibid.*, 1942, **51** B, 126 (correcting *ibid.*, 1941, **51** B, 60).

[2] Brown and Manov, *J.A.C.S.*, 1937, **59**, 500.

[3] Lord and Blanchard, *J. Chem. Phys.*, 1936, **4**, 707; correcting Yost and Blair, *J.A.C.S.*, 1933, **55**, 2610.

[4] Giauque and Stephenson, *J.A.C.S.*, 1938, **60**, 1389.

[5] Russell, Rundle, and Yost, *J.A.C.S.*, 1941, **63**, 2825.

[6] Egan and Kemp, *J.A.C.S.*, 1937, **59**, 1267; York and White, *Trans. Amer. Inst. Chem. Eng.*, 1944, **40**, 227.

[7] Messerly and Aston, *J.A.C.S.*, 1940, **62**, 886, 3529.

[8] Egan and Kemp, *J.A.C.S.*, 1938, **60**, 2097.

[9] De Witt and Kemp, *J.A.C.S.*, 1937, **59**, 273; Kemp and Pitzer, *ibid.*, 1937, **59**, 276; Hunsmann, *Z. phys. Chem.*, 1938, **39** B, 23; Kistiakowski and Nazmi, *J. Chem. Phys.*, 1938, **6**, 18 (correcting Eucken and Weigert, *Z. phys. Chem.*, 1933, **23** B, 265).

[10] Powell and Giauque, *J.A.C.S.*, 1939, **61**, 2366, who regard it as anomalous; cf. Kistiakowsky *et al.*, *ibid.*, 1939, **61**, 2980.

[11] Storch, *J.A.C.S.*, 1931, **53**, 1266.

[12] Giauque and Jones, *J.A.C.S.*, 1948, **70**, 120; the discrepancy of 1·63 units is interpreted as due to random orientation of triangular $COCl_2$ molecules in the solid, the maximum effect for which would be $\boldsymbol{R} \ln 3=2{\cdot}18$.

[13] Clusius and Teske, *Z. phys. Chem.*, 1929, **6** B, 134; Clayton and Giauque, *J.A.C.S.*, 1932, **54**, 2610; 1933, **55**, 5071.

[14] Johnston and Giauque, *J.A.C.S.*, 1929, **51**, 3194; for NOCl (S=64·04 at 298°) see Jahn, *J. Chem. Phys.*, 1938, **6**, 335.

[15] Clusius, Hiller, and Vaughen, *Z. phys. Chem.*, 1930, **7** B, 427; Blue and Giauque, *J.A.C.S.*, 1935, **57**, 911.

[16] McMorris and Yost, *J.A.C.S.*, 1931, **53**, 2625.

[17] *Bur. Mines Bull.*, 1940, **434**; for earlier values (including methods of calculation), *ibid.*, 1932, **350**; 1934, **371**; 1936, **394**; for earlier calculations of $\Delta G°$ (later revised in their book, "Thermodynamics and the Free Energy of Chemical Substances," New York, 1923) see Lewis and Randall, *J.A.C.S.*, 1914, **36**, 1968 (H and O), 2259 (I), 2468 (S); 1915, **37**, 458 (C), 2308 (N); 1916, **38**, 2348 (Br); for H_2O at 25° (16·9), Giauque and Ashley, *Phys. Rev.*, 1933, **43**, 81; values of $(G_0-E_0°)/T$ from spectroscopic data, Murphy, *J. Chem. Phys.*, 1937, **5**, 637; for light hydrocarbons, Holcomb and Brown, *Ind. Eng. Chem.*, 1942, **34**, 590; Thompson,

Al	6·75	O_2	49·0	CS_2	36·2	Ag_2O	29·1
Sb	10·5	K	15·2	CCl_4	74·2	AgCl	23·5
A	36·99	Se	10·0	CH_4	44·5	NaCl	17·3
Be	2·28	Si	4·5	C_2N_2	57·9	$NaNO_3$	27·8
Bi	13·6	Ag	10·20	CuO	10·4	SO_2	59·2
Br_2	36·7	Na	12·2	H_2O	16·75	SnO	13·5
C (diamond)	0·59	S-α	7·62	H_2S	49·2	SnO_2	12·5
		S-β	7·78	FeO	13·5	$SnCl_4$	62·1
C (graphite)	1·36	Sn	12·3	Fe_2O_3	21·5	TiO_2	12·4
		W	8·0	Fe_3O_4	35·0	V_2O_3	23·5
Cl_2	53·3	V	7·0	PbO	16·6	V_2O_4	24·5
Cu	7·97	Zn	9·95	HgO	16·6	V_2O_5	31·3
*H_2	31·2	$BiCl_3$	45·8	HgCl	23·5	ZnO	10·4
I_2	27·9	BCl_3	68·6	N_2O	52·58	ZnS	13·8
Fe	6·47	CaO	9·5	NO	50·3	$ZnCl_2$	25·9
Pb	15·49	†$CaCO_3$	22·2	NH_3	46·0	ZnI_2	38·5
Hg	18·5	$CaSO_4$	25·5	KCl	19·76	$ZnCO_3$	19·7
Ni	7·1	CO	47·3	KNO_3	31·8		
N_2	45·79	CO_2	51·1	‡SiO_2	10·1		

* Excluding nuclear spin. † Calcite. ‡ Quartz.

The following table gives the values of $-\Delta H^\circ$ and $-\Delta G^\circ$ in kg.cal. per mol at 1 atm. and 25° C. (A positive sign denotes energy *evolved*.) The standard state for gases is ideal.

	$-\Delta H^\circ$	$-\Delta G^\circ$		$-\Delta H^\circ$	$-\Delta G^\circ$
H_2 (*g*)	0	0	Cl_2 (*g*)	0	0
O_2 (*g*)	0	0	HCl (*g*)	22·00	22·67
H_2O (*g*)	57·836	54·508	HCl (*aq*)	39·55	31·35
H_2O (*l*)	68·330	56·560	N_2 (*g*)	0	0
H_2O (*s*)	69·991	56·419	NH_3 (*g*)	10·98	3·910
S_2 (*g*)	−29·69	−18·28	NH_3 (*aq*)	19·35	6·3
S_β	−0·082	−0·018	NO (g)	−21·60	−20·85
S_α	0	0	NO_2 (*g*)	−6·84	−11·92
H_2S (*g*)	4·76	7·84	HNO_3 (*g*)	34·40	18·21
H_2S (*aq*)	9·32	6·40	HNO_3 (*aq*)	49·79	26·50
SO_2 (*g*)	69·30	69·66	Br_2 (*g*)	−7·59	−0·755
SO_3 (*g*)	91·60	85·89	Br_2 (*l*)	0	0
H_2SO_4 (*l*)	212·40	176·50	NaCl	97·80	91·79
HBr (*g*)	8·30	12·54	KCl	105·60	98·43
HBr (*aq*)	28·59	24·60	AgCl	30·1	26·22
I_2 (*g*)	−15·10	−4·63	Ag_2O	6·94	2·395
I_2 (*s*)	0	0	HgCl	31·84	25·14
HI (*g*)	−6·20	−0·315	Hg_2SO_4	175·0	147·80
HI (*aq*)	13·32	12·36	HgO	21·60	13·81
C (graphite)	0	0	$PbCl_2$	85·60	75·04
C (diamond)	−0·204	−0·390	PbO (red)	52·36	45·05
CH_4 (*g*)	18·24	12·20	MnO_2	125·30	112·60
CS_2 (*g*)	−26·01	−17·60	CaO	151·7	154·5
C_6H_6 (*l*)	−19·73	−30·64	Al_2O_3	393·3	389·6
CO (*g*)	26·45	33·01	SiO_2 *	208·3	195·3
CO_2 (*g*)	94·40	94·45	FeO	64·25	60·0
CH_3OH (*l*)	57·28	39·96	Fe_2O_3	195·2	189·8
C_2H_5OH (*l*)	67·14	42·63			

* α-quartz.

" The Total and Free Energies of Formation of the Oxides of Thirty-two Metals," New York, 1943; Rossini *et al.*, " Tables of Selected Values of Chemical Thermodynamic Properties," *U.S. Bur. Stand.*, 1947 (3 series, loose-leaf); for ions in crystals, Gapon, *J. Phys. Chem. U.S.S.R.*, 1946, **20**, 941; for free energies and entropies of formation from atomic values, see Kireev, *Acta Physicochim. U.R.S.S.*, 1945, **20**, 905; 1946, **21**, 159; *J. Phys. Chem. U.S.S.R.*, 1946, **20**, 339; *J. Gen. Chem. U.S.S.R.*, 1946, **16**, 1199, 1391, 1569.

The entropies of some ions in aqueous solution have been calculated:[1] the following table gives also some values of ΔH° and ΔG° at 25° for 1 molal concentration in the ideal state.

	$-\Delta H^{\circ}$	$-\Delta G^{\circ}$	S°
$H^{\cdot}$ ...	0	0	—
$Na^{\cdot}$ ...	57·53	62·59	14·0
$K^{\cdot}$ ...	60·31	67·43	24·2
$NH_4^{\cdot}$ ...	31·46	18·93	26·4
$Ag^{\cdot}$ ...	−24·90	−18·45	17·5
$Cu^{\cdot\cdot}$ ...	−16·50	−15·91	−26·5
$Zn^{\cdot\cdot}$ ...	36·60	34·98	−25·7
$Cd^{\cdot\cdot}$ ...	17·40	18·35	−16·4
$Hg^{\cdot\cdot}$ ...	−40·20	−36·85	—
$Ca^{\cdot\cdot}$ ...	129·5	133·70	−11·4
$Sn^{\cdot\cdot}$ ...	−2·40	6·28	−4·9
$Pb^{\cdot\cdot}$ ...	0·50	5·55	3·9
$Fe^{\cdot\cdot}$ ...	20·80	20·35	—
$Fe^{\cdot\cdot\cdot}$ ...	9·60	3·12	−61
OH' ...	54·53	37·46	−2·49

	$-\Delta H^{\circ}$	$-\Delta G^{\circ}$	S°
Cl' ...	39·55	31·36	13·5
Br' ...	28·95	24·58	19·7
I' ...	13·32	12·36	25·3
IO_3' ...	54·20	31·58	28·0
HS' ...	3·40	−2·98	−14·9
S'' ...	−10·00	−23·45	—
HSO_3'	147·5	123·92	32·6
SO_3'' ...	146·9	116·68	3·0
SO_4'' ...	215·8	176·50	4·4
NO_2' ...	25·60	8·50	29·9
NO_3' ...	49·79	26·50	35·0
HCO_3'	164·6	140·00	22·2
CO_3'' ...	161·1	125·76	−13·0
HSO_4'...	—	—	30·6

The following table gives the entropies and the standard available energies $-\Delta G^{\circ}$, at 25° C., for a number of organic compounds. Other values have been collected.[45] The substances are all in the state in which they normally exist at 25° C. and 1 atm. pressure. Heats of combustion of hydrocarbons [21] provide data for calculations of $-\Delta G$. According to Huffman, Parks, and Barmore,[18] the entropy of normal paraffins is a linear function of the number n of carbon atoms in the molecule, and that of substituted hydrocarbons at 25° C. is given by $S=25{\cdot}0+7{\cdot}7n-4{\cdot}5r+19{\cdot}5p$, where r=no. of CH_3 branches in main aliphatic chain, and p=no. of phenyl groups. (In the table, the small numerals after the names of the substances belong to the literature references.

	S	$-\Delta G$
propane [32]	64·7	
n-butane [18]	54·9	6·2
n-pentane [17] ...	62·0	11·9
n-hexane [18] ...	70·6	7·0
n-heptane [14, 15] ...	78·9	73·0
n-octane [18]	86·0	3·0
n-nonane [18] ...	93·9	—
n-decane [18] ...	102·5	2·9
n-undecane [18] ...	110·9	—
n-dodecane [18] ...	118·1	—
n-tetradecane $C_{14}H_{30}$ [22] ...	134·4	—
2-methylhexane [14, 15]	75·3	72·0
3-methylhexane [14, 15]	74·0	68·0
3-ethylpentane [14, 15]	74·6	60·0

	S	$-\Delta G$
2, 2-dimethylpentane [14, 15] ...	68·1	61·0
2, 3-dimethylpentane [14, 15] ...	73·2	67·0
2, 4-dimethylpentane [14, 15] ...	69·7	56·0
3, 3-dimethylpentane [14, 15] ...	70·1	67·0
2, 2, 3-trimethylbutane [14, 15] ...	64·8	51·0
methylnonanes [37] ...	*c.* 100	—
cis-2-butene [26] ...	73·0	−14·86
trans-2-butene [26] ...	71·2	−14·45
*iso*butene [26] ...	69·0	−14·20
butene [26]	72·5	−16·78

For notes to this table, see page 228

[1] Latimer and Kasper, *J.A.C.S.*, 1929, **51**, 2293; Latimer and Ahlberg, *ibid.*, 1930, **52**, 549; Latimer, Schutz, and Hicks, *ibid.*, 1934, **56**, 88; *J. Chem. Phys.*, 1934, **2**, 82; Ahlberg and Latimer, *J.A.C.S.*, 1934, **56**, 856; Brown, Smith, and Latimer, *ibid.*, 1936, **58**, 2144; 1937, **59**, 921; Pitzer, *ibid.*, 1937, **59**, 2365; 1938, **60**, 1828; Smith, Pitzer, and Latimer, *ibid.*, 1937, **59**, 2640, 2642; Pitzer and Smith, *ibid.*, 1937, **59**, 2633; Smith, Brown, and Pitzer, *ibid.*, 1937, **59**, 1213; Pitzer, Smith, and Latimer, *ibid.*, 1938, **60**, 1826; Latimer, Pitzer, and Smith, *ibid.*, 1938, **60**, 1829 (summary and table); Latimer and Slansky, *ibid.*, 1940, **62**, 2019; Coulter and Latimer, *ibid.*, 1940, **62**, 2557; Coulter, Pitzer, and Latimer, *ibid.*, 1940, **62**, 2845; Kapustinsky, *Compt. Rend. U.R.S.S.*, 1941, **30**, 799, 802; 1946, **53**, 719; *J. Phys. Chem. U.S.S.R.*, 1941, **15**, 1055; Latimer, " Oxidation Potentials," New York, 1938; for *absolute* entropies, see F. H. Lee and Y. K. Tai, *J. Chinese Chem. Soc.*, 1941, **8**, 60 ($H^{\cdot}=-5{\cdot}4$); Eley, *Trans. Faraday Soc.*, 1944, **40**, 184; Yatsimirsky, *J. Gen. Chem. U.S.S.R.*, 1947, **17**, 169; *Bull. Acad. Sci. U.R.S.S.*, Chim., 1947, 453; Gapon, *J. Phys. Chem. U.S.S.R.*, 1947, **21**, 759, 1057.

	S	$-\Delta G$
n-heptene [28] ...	78·6	−19·05
1, 4-pentadiene [28] ...	58·2	−39·97
ethylene dichloride [33]	49·8	—
ethylene dibromide [33]	53·4	—
butylethylene [31] ...	61·3	—
di-*iso*butylethylene [17]	71·4	−3·60
propylene [18] ...	63·1	−14·8
trimethylethylene [17]	59·5	−11·0
dimethylacetylene (*l*) [40]	46·6	—
cyclopentane [23, 48]	49·4	−4·4
cyclohexene [17, 48] ...	51·8	−15·4
methylcyclohexane [17, 48] ...	59·3	0
methylcyclopentane [18] ...	59·2	2·7
1, 2-dimethylcyclopentane [18] ...	64·5	1·0
isoprene [46]	54·8	—
benzene [16]	41·9	−27·6
toluene [13]	52·4	−24·3
ethylbenzene [16, 47] ...	61·2	−23·6
n-butylbenzene [18] ...	76·8	−27·5
tert-butylbenzene [16]	66·6	−25·1
o-xylene [16]	59·3	−24·5
m-xylene [16]	60·3	−24·2
p-xylene [16]	60·5	−20·4
pentamethylbenzene [18]	70·3	−28·1
hexamethylbenzene [16]	74·0	−27·1
diphenyl [16] ...	49·2	−54·5
diphenylmethane [16]	57·2	−60·1
triphenylmethane [16]	74·6	−101·4
dibenzyl [16]	64·6	−60·1
triphenylbenzene [27]	87·8	−115·10
naphthalene [16] ...	39·9	−42·9
β-methylnaphthalene [18]	48·7	—
anthracene [18] ...	49·6	−69·4
phenanthrene [18] ...	50·6	−68·2
stilbene [17]	60·0	−75·3
ψ-cumene [18] ...	67·7	−21·0
p-cymene [18] ...	73·3	−28·4
durene [18]	58·7	−24·0
iso-durene [18] ...	74·1	—
pyrene [23]	51·4	0
prehnitene [18] ...	69·5	—
methyl alcohol [3, 8, 12]	31·0	44·2
ethyl alcohol [2, 3, 8, 12]	38·4	43·2
n-propyl alcohol [6, 12]	46·1	43·3
*iso*propyl alcohol [4, 6, 7, 10, 12]	43·1	48·1
n-butyl alcohol [3, 12]	54·5	43·2
tert-butyl alcohol [5, 12]	45·3	50·1
n-amyl alcohol [20] ...	60·9	39·1
tert-amyl alcohol [20]	54·8	47·7
hexyl alcohol [9] ...	68·6	41·7
cyclohexanol [11] ...	47·6	37·5
glycol [4, 12, 47] ...	39·9	81·8
glycerol [4, 12, 47] ...	49·7	115·7
erythritol [5, 12, 47] ...	39·8	152·0
dulcitol [6, 12, 47] ...	56·0	226·8
mannitol [5, 12, 47] ...	57·0	226·1
glucose [4, 12] ...	50·5	219·0
α-*d*-glucose [30] ...	50·7	218·72
β-*d*-glucose [30] ...	54·4	218·32
α-*d*-glucose hydrate [30] ...	60·4	275·76
sucrose [20]	86·1	371·6
α-lactose monohydrate [38] ...	99·1	418·2
β-lactose [38] ...	92·3	373·7
β-maltose monohydrate [38] ...	99·8	412·6
l-sorbose [39] ...	52·8	217·1
α-*d*-galactose [39] ...	49·1	219·6
ethyl ether [6, 12] ...	60·4	32·3
*iso*propyl ether [20] ...	70·4	—
acetone [7, 10, 12] ...	47·8	36·6
formic acid [1, 12] ...	30·7	85·2
acetic acid [4, 12] ...	38·2	95·4
n-butyric acid [5, 12]	54·1	95·1
palmitic acid [4, 12] ...	113·7	94·0
lactic acid [25] ...	45·9	124·3
d(*l*+) lactic acid [34]	34·3	—
l(*d*−) lactic acid [34] ...	34·0	—
oxalic acid [4, 12] ...	28·7	166·5
maleic acid [17, 30] ...	38·1	151·3
fumaric acid [17, 30] ...	39·7	157·2
succinic acid [17, 30] ...	42·0	180·4
ethyl acetate [20] ...	62·0	77·3
glycine [20]	26·1	87·8
urea [1, 20, 35] ...	25·0	47·2
dl-alanine [29] ...	31·6	89·44
d-alanine [19] ...	31·6	88·8
l-asparagine [19] ...	41·7	125·2
l-asparagine hydrate [19] ...	51·0	183·3
l-aspartic acid [19] ...	41·5	173·5
d-glutamic acid [19] ...	45·7	170·2
creatine [19] ...	45·3	64·1
creatinine [19] ...	40·0	2·9
dl-leucine [29] ...	49·5	83·83
d-arginine [29] ...	59·9	58·49
l-tyrosine [29] ...	53·0	97·75
adenine [24]	36·1	−70·42
hypoxanthine [24] ...	34·8	−17·25
guanine [24]	38·3	−10·22
xanthine [24]	38·5	40·73
uric acid [24]	41·4	91·46
allantoin [24] ...	46·6	107·47
alloxan [24]	44·6	182·88
phenol [20]	34·1	11·0
benzyl alcohol [27] ...	51·8	8·1
benzoic acid [20] ...	40·8	60·1
o-hydroxybenzoic acid [22]	42·6	101·8
m-hydroxybenzoic acid [22]	42·3	101·6
p-hydroxybenzoic acid [22]	42·0	102·4
phthalic acid [27] ...	49·7	143·6
phthalic anhydride [27]	42·9	79·8
dibenzoylethylene [17]	76·3	−18·0
dibenzoylethane [17] ...	77·6	6·5
1, 4-dioxane [23] ...	47·0	56·3
thiophene [23] ...	42·2	−26·3
nitrobenzene [27] ...	53·6	−33·9
aniline [20]	45·8	−35·4
thiophenol [27] ...	52·6	—
pyridine [27]	42·8	−37·3
quinoline [27] ...	51·9	−63·2

For notes to this table, see page 228

[1] Gibson, Latimer, and Parks, *J.A.C.S.*, 1920, **42**, 1533.
[2] Gibson, Parks, and Latimer, *J.A.C.S.*, 1920, **42**, 1542.
[3] Parks, *J.A.C.S.*, 1925, **47**, 338.
[4] Parks and Kelley, *J.A.C.S.*, 1925, **47**, 2089; Hünig, *Z. Electrochem.*, 1945, **51**, 41 (simple sugars).
[5] Parks and Anderson, *J.A.C.S.*, 1926, **48**, 1506.
[6] Parks and Huffman, *J.A.C.S.*, 1926, **48**, 2788.
[7] Parks and Kelley, *J. Phys. Chem.*, 1928, **32**, 734.
[8] Kelley, *J.A.C.S.*, 1929, **51**, 180.
[9] Kelley, *J.A.C.S.*, 1929, **51**, 779.
[10] Kelley, *J.A.C.S.*, 1929, **51**, 1145.
[11] Kelley, *J.A.C.S.*, 1929, **51**, 1400.
[12] Parks, Kelley, and Huffman, *J.A.C.S.*, 1929, **51**, 1969; for acetaldehyde, Smith, *Trans. Amer. Inst. Chem. Eng.*, 1946, **42**, 983.
[13] Kelley, *J.A.C.S.*, 1929, **51**, 2738.
[14] Parks, Huffman, and Thomas, *J.A.C.S.*, 1930, **52**, 1032; for free energies of 40 paraffin hydrocarbons, see Prosen, Pitzer, and Rossini, *Bur. Stand. J. Res.*, 1945, **34**, 403; for entropy of 11-*n*-decylheneicosane, Fischl, Naylor, Ziemer, Parks, and Aston, *J.A.C.S.*, 1945, **67**, 2075; for hydrocarbons, see Hamai, *Bull. Chem. Soc. Japan*, 1943, **18**, 376.
[15] Huffman, Parks, and Thomas, *J.A.C.S.*, 1930, **52**, 3241.
[16] Huffman, Parks, and Daniels, *J.A.C.S.*, 1930, **52**, 1547.
[17] Parks and Huffman, *J.A.C.S.*, 1930, **52**, 4381; Douslin and Huffman, *ibid.*, 1946, **68**, 173.
[18] Huffman, Parks, and Barmore, *J.A.C.S.*, 1931, **53**, 3876; cf. Parks, Shomate, Kennedy, and Crawford, *J. Chem. Phys.*, 1937, **5**, 359; Douslin and Huffman, *J.A.C.S.*, 1946, **68**, 1704 (five isomeric hexanes), 2753 (correction); Hachmuth, Hanson, and Smith, *Trans. Amer. Inst. Chem. Eng.*, 1946, **42**, 959, 975, 983.
[19] Huffman and Borsook, *J.A.C.S.*, 1932, **54**, 4297.
[20] Parks, Huffman, and Barmore, *J.A.C.S.*, 1933, **55**, 2733.
[21] Banse and Parks, *J.A.C.S.*, 1933, **55**, 3223.
[22] Parks and Light, *J.A.C.S.*, 1934, **56**, 1511.
[23] Jacobs and Parks, *J.A.C.S.*, 1934, **56**, 1513; Douslin and Huffman, *J.A.C.S.*, 1946, **68**, 173.
[24] Stiehler and Huffman, *J.A.C.S.*, 1935, **57**, 1741.
[25] Parks, Thomas, and Light, *J. Chem. Phys.*, 1936, **4**, 64; Scott, Ferguson, and Brickwedde, *Bur. Stand. J. Res.*, 1944, **33**, 1.
[26] Todd and Parks, *J.A.C.S.*, 1936, **58**, 134; for pentenes, Todd, Oliver, and Huffman, *ibid.*, 1947, **69**, 1519.
[27] Parks, Todd, and Moore, *J.A.C.S.*, 1936, **58**, 398; Pearce and Bakke, *Proc. Iowa Acad.*, 1938, **43**, 171.
[28] Parks, Todd, and Shomate, *J.A.C.S.*, 1936, **58**, 2505.
[29] Huffman and Ellis, *J.A.C.S.*, 1937, **59**, 2150.
[30] Huffman and Fox, *J.A.C.S.*, 1938, **60**, 1400.
[31] Kennedy, Shomate, and Parks, *J.A.C.S.*, 1938, **60**, 1507.
[32] Kemp and Egan, *J.A.C.S.*, 1938, **60**, 1521.
[33] Pitzer, *J.A.C.S.*, 1940, **62**, 331.
[34] Huffman, Ellis, and Borsook, *J.A.C.S.*, 1940, **62**, 297.
[35] Huffman, *J.A.C.S.*, 1940, **62**, 1009; Ruhrwein and Huffman, *ibid.*, 1946, **68**, 1759.
[36] Huffman, *J.A.C.S.*, 1941, **63**, 688.
[37] Parks, West, and Moore, *J.A.C.S.*, 1941, **63**, 1133.
[38] Anderson and Stegeman, *J.A.C.S.*, 1941, **63**, 2119.
[39] Jack and Stegeman, *J.A.C.S.*, 1941, **63**, 2121.
[40] Yost, Osborne, and Garner, *J.A.C.S.*, 1941, **63**, 3492.
[41] Osborne, Garner, Doescher, and Yost, *J.A.C.S.*, 1941, **63**, 3496.
[42] Russell, Osborne, and Yost, *J.A.C.S.*, 1942, **64**, 165.
[43] Osborne, Doescher, and Yost, *J.A.C.S.*, 1942, **64**, 169.
[44] Guthrie and Huffman, *J.A.C.S.*, 1943, **65**, 1139, 2481.
[45] Parks and Huffman, "The Free Energies of Some Organic Compounds," New York, 1932; cf. "Chemischer Taschenbuch," Berlin, 1937, III, 237 f.; Uhlich, "Kurzes Lehrbuch der physikalischen Chemie," 1938, 303 (inorganic only); Rossini, Pitzer, Taylor, Ebert, Kilpatrick, Beckett, Williams, and Werner, Selected Values of Properties of Hydrocarbons, *Bur. Stand. Circ.*, 1947, **461**.
[46] Bekkedahl and Wood, *Bur. Stand. J. Res.*, 1937, **19**, 551.
[47] Parks, West, Naylor, Fujii, and McClaine, *J.A.C.S.*, 1946, **68**, **2524**.
[48] Spitzer and Pitzer, *J.A.C.S.*, 1946, **68**. 2537.

Since many organic compounds should, in principle, pass spontaneously into simpler substances, their preparation has been said,[1] from the standpoint of thermodynamics, to be " skating over thin ice." Standard entropies of inorganic and organic compounds were calculated by Meissner [2] with empirical formulae.

§ 71. Remarks on the Nernst Heat Theorem

Eastman's [3] assumption that a pure perfect crystal may have a positive if small entropy at absolute zero if the unit cell contains many atoms, was shown by Pauling and Tolman [4] to be unsound. The very cautious statement of the " third law " by Lewis and Randall: [5] " every substance has a finite positive entropy, but at the absolute zero of temperature the entropy may become zero, and does so become in the case of perfect crystalline substances," does not cover all cases, as will be seen below, and is over-sophisticated. Fowler [6] consistently, if with diminishing assurance, rejected the " third law " in the form $S_0=0$, preferring the older form $\Delta S_0=0$ (but see § 68). This means, in practice, that an additive constant is first added and then subtracted regularly and monotonously in all calculations, which consumes time to no obvious purpose.

Kleeman's treatment of an " absolute zero of entropy " [7] divides the energy and entropy of a substance into " controllable " and " uncontrollable " parts, the latter being assumed independent of temperature and volume, and the controllable energy and entropy to have minimum values for certain values of v and T. The value of C_v is never negative, and $(\mathrm{d}p/\mathrm{d}T)_v$ and $(\mathrm{d}^2p/\mathrm{d}T^2)_v$ are always finite. A substance or mixture in the condensed state in contact with its vapour at 0° K. corresponds to a state on the adiabatic of zero entropy, and zero entropy is the same as zero energy, the zero being called the " absolute zero of control." At this zero, $C_v=0$, even for a gas at infinite volume. Some of Kleeman's conclusions seem to be incorrect. The postulation of a thermodynamic " potential energy," affected only by change of heat capacity and not by temperature,[8] is also rather obscure. Kolossowsky [9] and Njegovan [10] supposed that the entropy of a gas at 0° K. is zero.

1 Partington, *J. Phys. Chem.*, 1925, **29**, 494.
2 *Ind. Eng. Chem.*, 1948, **40**, 904.
3 *J.A.C.S.*, 1924, **46**, 39.
4 *J.A.C.S.*, 1925, **47**, 2148.
5 " Thermodynamics," New York, 1923, 448.
6 " Statistical Mechanics," Cambridge, 1929, 141, 149; 2nd edit., 1936, 204, 228, 231; " Statistical Thermodynamics," Cambridge, 1939, 192. It seems as if Fowler did not quite appreciate the significance of " order-disorder " effects in connection with the law (clearly hinted by Partington, " A Textbook of Thermodynamics," 1913, 531), as his calculation in *Proc. Roy. Soc.*, 1928, **118**, 52, shows; see Rodebush, *Proc. Nat. Acad.*, 1927, **13**, 185; Giauque and Johnston, *J.A.C.S.*, 1928, **50**, 3221 (see § 70). Fowler and Sterne, *Rev. Mod. Phys.*, 1932, **4**, 635 (707) felt that the idea of absolute entropy " has caused much confusion and has been of little assistance in the development of the subject," an opinion with which no one else agrees.
7 *Science*, 1927, **65**, 210, 426; 1927, **66**, 216; *Phil. Mag.*, 1927, **3**, 883; 1927, **4**, 257; 1928, **5**, 668; *J. Phys. Chem.*, 1927, **31**, 747, 937, 1559, 1669; 1928, **32**, 1396, 1840; Verschaffelt, *Phil. Mag.*, 1927, **4**, 335; *Z. Phys.*, 1927, **43**, 152; Jazyna, *Z. Phys.*, 1924, **30**, 372, 376; 1926, **37**, 304; 1927, **41**, 211; *Phys. Z.*, 1925, **26**, 622; 1927, **28**, 908. Cf. Simon, *Ergebn. d. exakt. Naturwiss.*, 1930, **9**, 222; Schmolke, *Z. Elektrochem.*, 1935, **41**, 654.
8 Njegovan, *Acta Physicochim. U.R.S.S.*, 1940, **13**, 829.
9 *Phys. Z.*, 1927, **28**, 476; *Z. Phys.*, 1927, **43**, 509; 1927, **44**, 756.
10 *Coll. Czech Chem.*, 1933, **5**, 415, 424; *Acta Phys. Polon.*, 1933, **2**, 425; 1934, **3**, 213; 1937, **6**, 109; *Z. Phys.*, 1935, **94**, 377; 1935, **97**, 390; 1935, **98**, 415; Baborovsky, *Chem. Listy*, 1937, **31**, 187.

Lewis and Gibson [1] stated the Nernst heat theorem in the form: "if the entropy of each element in some crystalline form be taken as zero at the absolute zero, the entropy of any pure crystal at the absolute zero is zero, and the entropy of any other substance is greater than zero." Eastman's statement: [2] "at the absolute zero entropy changes in reactions of the same type are equal, and in reactions in which the system does not change in type the entropy changes are zero," if it has any meaning at all, seems to have an erroneous one, and his idea that entropy depends on crystal structure is also wrong.[5] Gibson, Parkes, and Latimer [3] concluded, from some rather indefinite results, that the entropy of a solid solution of ethyl and propyl alcohols is not zero at the absolute zero. The experiments of Gibson and Giauque,[4] usually quoted as showing a finite entropy for a glassy solid (glycerol) at absolute zero, are indecisive: what was actually found was a difference of 5·6 g.cal./1° per mol at the high temperature of 70° K., and it was *assumed* that this difference would, approximately, persist down to zero absolute. Pauling and Tolman [5] concluded, from theory, that the entropies of a perfect crystal and a supercooled glass differ by $\boldsymbol{R} \ln a$, where a is a small number given by $\phi(N')=Ca^{N'}$, where $\phi(N')$ is the number of ways in which the mean positions of the N' molecules in the glass can be arranged when the degrees of freedom corresponding to the positional coordinates are excited to the first quantum state, arrangements due to permutations of atoms being excluded.

The *very* slow adjustments of glassy solids or very viscous liquids to equilibrium even at moderate temperatures should have suggested that specific heat measurements made rapidly in an ordinary vacuum calorimeter would be of doubtful value in testing Nernst's theorem, and Simon [6] predicted that this disturbing effect had vitiated some experiments. This was proved experimentally by Obald and Newton,[7] who used the calorimetric method of mixtures, and allowed several hours for supercooled liquid glycerol to reach statistical equilibrium at 167°–293° K. The results at low temperatures were decidedly lower than those found by Gibson and Giauque, and no relevant conclusion can be drawn from the latter results. In the case of stiff glasses, weeks would probably be required to reach equilibrium, and there is no valid evidence that the entropy of a glass differs from zero at 0° K. A similar effect probably vitiated the results of Anderson [8] with glassy selenium, for which a higher entropy was found than for the stable crystals.

Kelley [9] disproved a consequence of Eastman's statement (see ref. [2]), that the entropies of two different crystalline forms of the same substance must differ at 0° K., by showing that this is not true for two forms of cyclohexane. Later experimental and theoretical research has been unkind to some of the more zealous critics of the Nernst heat theorem, whose errors were in no way mitigated by the intemperate language in which they were sometimes expressed. G. N. Lewis was a notable exception among many workers in his careful and appreciative, although critical, attitude.

[1] *J.A.C.S.*, 1920, **42**, 1529.
[2] *J.A.C.S.*, 1924, **46**, 39.
[3] *J.A.C.S.*, 1920, **42**, 1542.
[4] *J.A.C.S.*, 1923, **45**, 93.
[5] *J.A.C.S.*, 1925, **47**, 2148.
[6] *Z. anorg. Chem.*, 1931, **203**, 219; Schmolke, *Z. Phys.*, 1931, **64**, 714.
[7] *J.A.C.S.*, 1937, **59**, 2495; Parks, Thomas, and Light, *J. Chem. Phys.*, 1936, **4**, 64; Parks, West, and Moore, *J.A.C.S.*, 1941, **63**, 1133; Nelson and Newton, *ibid.*, 1941, **63**, 2178.
[8] *J.A.C.S.*, 1937, **59**, 1036.
[9] *J.A.C.S.*, 1929, **51**, 1400.

§ 72. Empirical Formulae

Latimer [1] proposed the formula:

$$S=\tfrac{3}{2}R\ln A-0{\cdot}94 \quad . \quad . \quad . \quad . \quad . \quad . \quad . \quad . \quad (1)$$

for the entropy of 1 mol of a solid element at 25° C., where A=atomic weight; and for compounds the entropy is the sum of the atomic entropies, provided the atomic heats are all approximately equal to 6 (the Dulong and Petit value, hence the rule does not, e.g. apply to oxides). This useful but crude rule implies, among other things,[2] that the molecular diameter d is given by $d^2=\text{const.}\,(A_1+A_2)/\sqrt{(A_1A_2)}$ for a binary compound. Herz [3] found the empirical rule:

$$S\sqrt[3]{c}=\text{const.} \quad . \quad . \quad . \quad . \quad . \quad . \quad . \quad . \quad . \quad (2)$$

where S=entropy at 25° C. and c=specific heat. For elements, the constant is 9, for salts $9n$, where n=number of atoms in the molecule. Although the theoretical interpretation of such formulae is not always clear, this does not impair their usefulness.[4] For binary salts: [5]

$$S/\sqrt[3]{V_i}\simeq 6 \quad . \quad . \quad . \quad . \quad . \quad . \quad . \quad . \quad . \quad (3)$$

where V_i is the molar volume calculated from the ionic radii. According to Bruzs,[6] the entropy is a periodic function of the atomic number, and the entropy at the melting-point T_m° K., calculated from Lewis, Gibson, and Latimer's [7] values at 25° C. by the equation:

$$S_m=S_{298}+2{\cdot}303C_p\log(T_m/298) \quad . \quad . \quad . \quad . \quad . \quad (4)$$

assuming C_p (atomic heat) constant above 0° C., has an approximately constant value of 20 units (S, Br_2, and I_2 are abnormal). The few data available suggest that entropies would be equal at the critical temperature, which would be a " corresponding state " for entropies,[6] when $S_{T_c}=49$.

Kelley, Parks, and Huffman [8] expressed the specific heat of a solid in the form:

$$c_p=c_p{}^{\circ}(A+BT) \quad . \quad . \quad . \quad . \quad . \quad . \quad . \quad . \quad (5)$$

where $c_p{}^{\circ}$ is that of a standard substance and A and B are constants. Then the molar entropy of a substance at a fairly low temperature, say 90° K., is:

$$S_{90}=AS^{\circ}{}_{90}+B\int_0^{90}C_p{}^{\circ}\mathrm{d}T \quad . \quad . \quad . \quad . \quad . \quad . \quad . \quad (6)$$

where $S_{90}{}^{\circ}$ and the temperature dependence of $C_p{}^{\circ}$ are assumed known.

In calculating the free and available energy changes in gas reactions, the following approximation formulae may be used.[9] The various cases depend on the values of ΔC_v and ΔC_p.

Case 1. $\Delta C_v=0$, $\Delta C_p=0$. Then:

$$\Delta F_T-\Delta F_{T_0}=\Delta G_T-\Delta G_{T_0}=-\int_{T_0}^{T}\Delta S\mathrm{d}T=-\Delta S_{T_0}(T-T_0)$$

[1] *J.A.C.S.*, 1921, **43**, 818; Herz, *Z. anorg. Chem.*, 1928, **175**, 245.
[2] Jellinek and Rudat, *Z. anorg. Chem.*, 1928, **175**, 281.
[3] *Z. anorg. Chem.*, 1929, **182**, 189.
[4] Cf. Herz, *Z. anorg. Chem.*, 1929, **181**, 281.
[5] Herz, *Z. anorg. Chem.*, 1930, **186**, 251.
[6] *J. Phys. Chem.*, 1927, **31**, 681.
[7] *J.A.C.S.*, 1922, **44**, 1008.
[8] *J. Phys. Chem.*, 1929, **33**, 1802.
[9] Ulich, " Kurzes Lehrbuch der physikalischen Chemie," 1938, 94; Partington, " Chemical Thermodynamics," 1940. 40.

also $\Delta E_0 = \Delta F_0 + T_0 \Delta S_0, \quad \Delta H_0 = \Delta G_0 + T\Delta S_0,$

$$\therefore \Delta F_T = \Delta E_0 - T\Delta S_0 \text{ and } \Delta G_T = \Delta H_0 - T\Delta S_0.$$

Case 2. $\Delta C_v = \text{const.} = a$ and $\Delta C_p = \text{const.} = a'$. Then:

$$\Delta S_T - \Delta S_{T_0} = \int_{T_0}^{T} dT(\Delta C_v/T) \text{ or } \int_{T_0}^{T} dT(\Delta C_p/T) = a \ln (T/T_0) \text{ or } a' \ln (T/T_0)$$

$$\Delta F_T = \Delta F_{T_0} - \Delta S_0(T - T_0) - aT[\ln (T/T_0) + T_0/T - 1]$$

$$\Delta G_T = \Delta G_{T_0} - \Delta S_0(T - T_0) - a'T[\ln (T/T_0) + T_0/T - 1]$$

$$\Delta F_T = \Delta E_0 - T\Delta S_0 - aT[\ln (T/T_0) + T_0/T - 1]$$

$$\Delta G_T = \Delta H_0 - T\Delta S_0 - a'T[\ln (T/T_0) + T_0/T - 1]$$

If $T_0 = 298°$, the expression in brackets can be replaced up to $T = 1600°$ by $0{\cdot}0007T - 0{\cdot}20$ with an error of only a few per cent.

Case 3. ΔC_v and ΔC_p vary appreciably with temperature. The values of a and a' in case (2) are then modified as follows:

(i) $T < 500$: $a = \Delta C_v$ and $a' = \Delta C_p$ at 300° K.

(ii) T 500—1000 : a and a' are mean values of ΔC_v and ΔC_p between 300° K. and 600° K.

(iii) T 1000—2000 : a and $a' = \frac{1}{2}$ (mean value of $\Delta C_{v,p}$ between 300° and 600° + mean value between 600° and 1200°).

(iv) T 2000—3500 : a and $a' = \frac{1}{3}$ (mean value of $\Delta C_{v,p}$ between 300° and 600° + mean value between 600° and 1200° + mean value between 1200° and 2400°).

§ 73. Properties of Substances at Very Low Temperatures

From Maxwell's equation (3), § 48: $(dp/dT)_v = (dS/dv)_T$, and since $dS = c_v dT/T$, it follows that:

$$(dp/dT)_v = \int_0^T \frac{1}{T}\left(\frac{dc_v}{dv}\right)_T dT.$$

But, from (1), § 49: $(dc_v/dv)_T = T(d^2p/dT^2)_v$, it follows that:

$$(dp/dT)_v = \int_0^T (d^2p/dT^2)_v dT = (dp/dT)_v - (dp/dT)_{v_0},$$

where the zero subscript denotes $T = 0$. Hence:

$$(dp/dT)_{v_0} = 0 \quad . \quad . \quad . \quad . \quad . \quad . \quad . \quad . \quad . \quad (1)$$

Similarly, from Maxwell's equation (4), § 48: $(dv/dT)_p = -(dS/dp)_T$, and since $dS = c_p dT/T$, it follows that:

$$(dv/dT)_p = -\int_0^T \frac{1}{T}\left(\frac{dc_p}{dp}\right)_T dT.$$

From (2), § 49: $(dc_p/dp)_T = -T(d^2v/dT^2)_p$, it follows that:

$$(dv/dT)_p = \int_0^T (d^2v/dT^2)_p dT = (dv/dT)_p - (dv/dT)_{p_0},$$

$$\therefore (dv/dT)_{p_0} = 0 \quad . \quad . \quad . \quad . \quad . \quad . \quad . \quad . \quad . \quad (2)$$

These results [1] are in agreement with experiment, as will be described later in Vol. II.

Although van Laar [2] maintained that Planck's deduction (given above) of the equation $(dv/dT)_{p_0}=0$ is incorrect, since it does not agree with a formula proposed by van Laar, Keesom [3] in experiments on the melting-point curve of helium at very low temperatures found evidence in support of Planck's equation, and the prediction of van Laar that $(dp/dT)_{p_0}=\infty$ was disproved: the curve of d^2p/dT^2 had a maximum at 1·8° K. In a similar way it can be shown [4] that the temperature coefficients of surface tension, thermoelectric force, and magnetic susceptibility vanish at the absolute zero.

Equations such as (1) and (2) may be generalised.[5] If the system is defined by the absolute temperature T and generalised coordinates (§ 50), $x_1, x_2, \ldots$, corresponding with the generalised forces $X_1, X_2, \ldots$, then in changes in which only one of these alters and the rest remain constant:

$$dS=(dS/dx_1)_{T, x_2, x_3, \ldots} dx_1,$$

and $$dS=(dS/dX_1)_{T, X_2, X_3, \ldots} dX_1+(dS/dT)_{X_1, X_2, \ldots} dT.$$

For $T=0$, dS must vanish, by Nernst's theorem, hence:

$$(dS/dx_1)_{T=0, x_2, x_3, \ldots}=0, \quad \text{and} \quad (dS/dX_1)_{T=0, X_2, X_3, \ldots}=0 \quad . \quad (3)$$

The analogues of Maxwell's relations (§ 48) then show that:

$$(dx_1/dT)_{T=0}=0, \quad \text{and} \quad (dX_1/dT)_{T=0}=0 \quad . \quad . \quad . \quad (4)$$

§ 74. Solid Solutions

Planck [6] suggested that solid solutions at $T=0$ had a finite entropy of mixing: $S=-R\Sigma N_1 \ln N_1$ (§ 57), and this seemed to be confirmed for mixtures of water and glycerol,[7] and mixed crystals of silver bromide and iodide.[8] The first example is unsuitable, in view of the anomalous behaviour of water and the error due to time-lag with glassy solids (§ 71). In the second case, the experimental accuracy was not very high. Stern [9] (who assumed a zero-point energy) concluded that the entropy of a solid solution at $T=0$ will be zero if one state at this temperature has a smaller entropy than the others. Keesom [10] concluded from theory that the entropy of mixing of gases (§ 57) should vanish at $T=0$.

[1] Planck, " Thermodynamik," 1911, 271; cf. Slotte, *Öfv. Finska Vet. Soc. Förhl.*, 1904, **47**, No. 8.

[2] *Proc. K. Akad. Wetens. Amsterdam*, 1924, **27**, 897.

[3] *Proc. K. Akad. Wetens. Amsterdam*, 1927, **30**, 952 (*Comm. Leiden* Suppl., **61b**). Objections to Planck's deduction raised by Weinstein, *Ann. Phys.*, 1917, **52**, 218; 1917, **53**, 47; 1917, **54**, 79, were answered by Epstein, *ibid.*, 1917, **53**, 176.

[4] Nernst, *Berlin Ber.*, 1913, 972; " The New Heat Theorem," 1926, 211; cf. Keesom, *Phys. Z.*, 1913, **14**, 670 (Peltier effect).

[5] Epstein, " Textbook of Thermodynamics," 1937, 229.

[6] " Thermodynamik," 1911, 279.

[7] Simon, in Geiger and Scheel, " Handbuch der Physik," 1926, **10**, 393; Simon and Lange, *Z. Phys.*, 1926, **38**, 227.

[8] Eastman and Milner, *J. Chem. Phys.*, 1933, **1**, 444 (bibl.).

[9] *Ann. Phys.*, 1916, **49**, 823; 1916, **51**, 236.

[10] *Proc. K. Akad. Wetens. Amsterdam*, 1913, **16**, 227; 1914, **16**, 669 (*Comm. Leiden* Suppls. **30a**, **33**); *Phys. Z.*, 1913, **14**, 665; 1914, **15**, 217, 368.

SECTION III

THE KINETIC THEORY OF GASES

BIBLIOGRAPHY OF THE KINETIC THEORY OF GASES

Arrhenius, Theories of Chemistry, 1907, 109 (elementary); Bloch, The Kinetic Theory of Gases, 1924 (simple and useful); Boltzmann, Vorlesungen über Gastheorie, 2 vols., Leipzig, 1896–8 (mathematical); Boynton, Applications of the Kinetic Theory, New York, 1904; Burbury, A Treatise on the Kinetic Theory of Gases, Cambridge, 1899 (mathematical); Byk, Einführung in die kinetische Theorie der Gase. I. Die idealen Gase [all published], Leipzig and Berlin, 1910; Clausius, Die kinetische Theorie der Gase, in Die mechanische Wärmetheorie, vol. 3, edit. by Planck and Pulfrich, Brunswick, 1889–91; Dushman, *Gen. Elec. Rev.*, 1915, **18**, 93, 952, 1042, 1159; Herzfeld, in Müller-Pouillet, Lehrbuch der Physik, 11th edit., **3**, ii, Brunswick, 1925, and (re-written) in Taylor, Treatise on Physical Chemistry, 2nd edit., 1931, **1**, 72 (clarifying many difficult points); Jäger, Die Fortschritte der kinetischen Gastheorie, Brunswick, 1906, and later editions (clear and excellent); *idem*, articles in Winkelmann, Handbuch der Physik, Leipzig, 1906, **3**, 68, and Geiger and Scheel, Handbuch der Physik, Berlin, 1926, **9**, 341; Jeans, The Dynamical Theory of Gases, Cambridge, 1904, 3rd edit., 1921, 4th edit., 1925 (mathematical; a standard work); *idem*, Introduction to The Kinetic Theory of Gases, Cambridge, 1940 (excellent mathematical introduction); Kennard, Kinetic Theory of Gases, New York, 1938 (modern, mathematical, but clear and informative); Kirchhoff, Vorlesungen über die Theorie der Wärme, edit. Planck, Leipzig, 1894; Kleeman, A Kinetic Theory of Gases and Liquids, New York, 1920; Knudsen, The Kinetic Theory of Gases, 1934 (parts only of subject, especially Knudsen's own researches); Loeb, Kinetic Theory of Gases, New York, 1927, 2nd edit., 1934 (straightforward and intelligible); O. E. Meyer, Die kinetische Theorie der Gase, Breslau, 1877, 2nd edit., 1899, transl. [with additions] by Baynes, The Kinetic Theory of Gases, 1899 (intelligible); Risteen, Molecules and the Molecular Theory of Matter, Boston, 1895 (elementary); Tolman, Statistical Mechanics, New York, 1927 (some aspects); Watson, H. W., A Treatise on the Kinetic Theory of Gases, Oxford, 1876, 2nd edit., 1893; Weinstein, Thermodynamik und Kinetik der Körper, 4 vols. (I–III i and ii), Brunswick, 1901–8.

§ 1. History of the Kinetic Theory of Gases

The earliest form of the Greek atomic theory, due to Leukippos and Demokritos about 450 B.C., postulated that the smallest particles (atoms) of matter are in ceaseless motion, this being a natural property and not due to an external cause.[1] The theory was used by Gassendi [2] to explain the three states (solid, liquid, and gaseous) of matter, and changes of state. Boyle [3] and Newton,[4] however, explained gaseous pressure by a statical theory, although Huygens [5] and Hooke [6] accepted the older view of moving particles, and the latter attempted to explain Boyle's law by the assumption that air consists of small particles set in swift motion by the ether and separated by

[1] Lindsay and Smith, *B.A. Rep.*, 1871, 30; Giua, *Gazz.*, 1919, **49**, ii, 1; Polvani, *Nuov. Cim.*, 1924, **1**, 1 (115 refs.); Partington, The Origins of the Atomic Theory, in *Annals of Science*, 1939, **4**, 245.

[2] "Syntagma Philosophicum," 1658; see Lasswitz, *Ann. Phys.*, 1874, **153**, 373.

[3] "New Experiments Physico-Mechanicall," 1660; Works, 1744, **1**, 8.

[4] "Principia," Amsterdam, 1723, 270.

[5] "Traité de la Lvmière," 1690 (written in 1678), ch. 1; Larmor, "Aether and Matter," Cambridge, 1900, 311.

[6] "De Potentia Restitutiva," 1678, 16; Tait, "Properties of Matter," 4th edit., 1899, 295.

large spaces. Hooke says: "If therefore a quantity of this body [air] be inclosed by a solid body, and that be so contrived as to compress it into less room, the motion thereof (supposing the heat the same) will continue the same, and consequently the Vibrations and Occursions will be increased in reciprocal proportion." Newton [1] proved mathematically that if an elastic fluid consists of particles at rest, between which are repulsive forces inversely proportional to the distance between contiguous particles, the density would be proportional to the pressure, a result which, in his characteristic way, he did not identify with Boyle's law. A deduction of Boyle's law for a gas composed of particles (*corpuscula*) in ceaseless motion, between which no forces act, and which give rise to the pressure on a container by bombarding its walls and lid and being reflected from them, was given in 1738 by Daniel Bernoulli,[2] who gave a figure illustrating his idea. Lomonossov in his treatise [3] on the "Theory of the Elastic Force of Air" also made use of a kinetic theory. But the great authority of Newton long prevented these early applications of the kinetic theory from receiving the attention they deserved.[4] It was not until 1845, when Joule [5] showed that there is no change of temperature when a gas rushes from a rigid vessel into another rigid evacuated vessel, so that no external work is done, that it was clear that there could be no repulsive forces between the molecules, and Newton's static theory was perforce abandoned.

The real development of the kinetic theory of gases, as we now understand it, must be said to date from the memoir of Clausius,[6] published in 1857, i.e. in the opening years of the second half of the nineteenth century, and its further amplification was mainly due to Maxwell and Boltzmann, the former giving the very important law of the distribution of molecular velocities (§ 10).

The revival of the kinetic theory of gases (Greek *kinesis*, motion) early in the nineteenth century by Herapath [7] passed unnoticed, and the long and interesting memoir by J. J. Waterston, of Bombay, sent to the Royal Society in December 1845, and read in March 1846, was not published until Lord Rayleigh found the paper in the Archives of the Society in 1892 and had it printed, with interesting annotations.[8] A paper by Joule [9] passed without notice, and it was the one by

[1] "Principia," lib. II, sect. V, prop. xviii, Amsterdam edit., 1723, p. 270; Partington, *Annals of Science*, 1939, **4**, 245.

[2] "Hydrodynamica," Strasburg, 1738, 200, Fig. 56; reproduced in Guareschi, *Atti Accad. Torino*, 1910, **45**, 641; Du Bois Reymond, *Ann. Phys.*, 1859, **107**, 490, reproduced Bernoulli's account. See also J. Hermann, "Phoronomia sive de Viribus et Motibus Corporum solidorum et fluidorum, libri duo," Amsterdam, 1716, 376 (de Motu intestino fluidorum); see § 10.II.

[3] *Novi Comment. Acad. Petropol.*, 1747–8, **1**, 230, 307 (published in 1750); Ostwald's *Klassiker*, 1910, **178**, 28, 34, 54, 55; Smith, *J.A.C.S.*, 1912, **34**, 109.

[4] O. E. Meyer, "Kinetic Theory of Gases," 1899, 11.

[5] *Phil. Mag.*, 1845, **26**, 369; "Scientific Papers," 1884, **1**, 172.

[6] *Ann. Phys.*, 1857, **100**, 353; *Phil. Mag.*, 1857, **14**, 108 ("On the Nature of the Motion which we call Heat"); Bouty, *Scientia*, 1916, **19**, 182, 260.

[7] *Ann. Phil.*, 1816, **8**, 56; 1821, **1**, 273, 340, 401; *Phil. Mag.*, 1823, **62**, 61, 328.

[8] "On the Physics of Media that are composed of Free and Perfectly Elastic Molecules in a State of Motion," in *Phil. Trans.*, 1892, **183**, 1; a perplexed Referee reported that: "The paper is nothing but nonsense, unfit even for reading before the Society," and the chemical part is also notably modern for its time, as Rayleigh pointed out. Some obvious algebraic inaccuracies in the paper are not destructive of its general conclusions. See Nernst, "Theoretical Chemistry," 1911, 198; "Collected Scientific Papers" of Waterston, edit. Haldane, 1928.

[9] *Manch. Mem.*, 1848, **9**, 107; reprinted in *Phil. Mag.*, 1857, **14**, 211; "Scientific Papers," 1884, **1**, 288, 290. Joule had shown that the *vis viva* (mv^2) was proportional to the absolute temperature, and calculated the velocity of hydrogen molecules as 6225 ft./sec. at 0° C.

Krönig [1] which drew the attention of Clausius,[2] who gave the main lines of the theory in a satisfactory form. Maxwell [3] and Boltzmann [4] extended the theory. The name *dynamical* theory of gases was used by Maxwell,[3] and signifies that the laws of dynamics are assumed to hold for the motion of the gas molecules; the name *kinetic* theory, first used by Lord Kelvin,[5] was afterwards adopted by Maxwell,[6] and is now commonly used.

By introducing various simplifying assumptions it is possible to develop *quantitatively* the main features of the theory in a very elementary manner.[7] The more elaborate mathematical treatment gives more information on many points of detail, and covers properties not amenable to the simpler theory; some of the equations then found are of fundamental importance in Physical Chemistry.

§ 2. Elementary Kinetic Theory

It is assumed [8] that a gas consists of a very large number of perfectly elastic molecules, the volume occupied by which is negligible compared with the whole space occupied by the gas; that the duration of each molecular collision is infinitesimal compared with the interval between two such molecular collisions; and that the influence of any forces between the molecules is vanishingly small. The particles, not being acted upon by any forces, describe straight-line paths with a constant velocity between collisions, and as they are perfectly elastic they rebound from the walls with unchanged kinetic energy. Since the temperature is assumed to be determined by the kinetic energy, it remains constant.

The pressure exerted by a gas on its container is due to the bombardment by the gas molecules. The velocities remain constant at a given temperature, and obviously when the volume of a given quantity of gas is reduced to $1/n$ of its initial value, the number of molecules per cm.^{3} is increased n-fold, the number of collisions per second is also increased n-fold, and so also is the pressure. Thus the pressure is inversely proportional to the volume. This deduction of Boyle's law was given by Bernoulli in 1738 (see § 1).

The increase in pressure when a gas is heated in a container at constant

[1] " Grundzüge einer Theorie der Gase," Berlin, 1856; reprinted in *Ann. Phys.*, 1856, **99**, 315.

[2] *Ann. Phys.*, 1857, **100**, 353; *Phil. Mag.*, 1857, **14**, 108, mentioning Joule (whose paper he had not seen) and Krönig; reissued in Die kinetische Theorie der Gase in " Die mechanische Wärmetheorie," Brunswick, 1889–91, **3**, 1.

[3] *Phil. Mag.*, 1860, **19**, 19; 1860, **20**, 21; *Phil. Trans.*, 1867, **157**, 49; " Scientific Papers," 1890, **1**, 377; " Theory of Heat," 1897, 308 f.

[4] Numerous papers in *Wien Ber.*, 1866 f.; " Wissenschaftliche Abhandlungen," 3 vols., edit. Hasenöhrl, Leipzig, 1909; " Vorlesungen über Gastheorie," 2 vols., Leipzig, 1896–8; "Populäre Schriften," Leipzig, 1905; Boltzmann and Nabl, art. Kinetische Theorie der Materie, in " Encykl. d. math. Wiss.," 1907, **5**, i, Heft 4, 493.

[5] *B.A. Report*, 1871, p. xciii (Presidential Address).

[6] *Nature*, 1873, **8**, 298; " Scientific Papers," 1890, **2**, 343. Jeans still used Maxwell's name in his " Dynamical Theory of Gases," Cambridge, 1904, 4th edit., 1925, but his new book is called " The Kinetic Theory of Gases," Cambridge, 1940.

[7] The *simple* deducations (§ 2) of the gas laws from the kinetic theory given in most elementary books are due to Naumann, *Ann.*, 1870, Supplbd. **7**, 339, and Zöppritz, *ibid.*, 348; see the criticism by Pfaundler, *Wien Ber.*, 1871, **63**, II, 159, who gives a simple deduction similar to that in Jeans, "The Kinetic Theory of Gases," 1940, 17. The device of imagining one third of the molecules in a cube moving along directions parallel to the edges goes back to Joule (1848), but he assumed all the molecules combined in three masses.

[8] Clausius, *Phil. Mag.*, 1857, **14**, 108; cf. O. E. Meyer, " Kinetic Theory of Gases," transl. Baynes, 1899; Edser, "Heat for Advanced Students," 1899, 287; Partington, " College Course of Inorganic Chemistry," 1945, 96.

volume is supposed to be due to an increase in the velocity of the molecules: this causes an increase in the number of collisions per second and also an increase in the violence of each collision. The heat absorbed by the gas, as a form of energy, is supposed to increase the kinetic energy of its molecules. This consists partly of the kinetic energy of the molecules due to their motion in straight lines (*translatory motion*), and this is the only effect when the gas is monatomic (mercury vapour, argon, etc.). The pressure of the gas is in *all* cases due only to this translatory motion, whether the molecules are monatomic or not. If the molecules are not monatomic, part of the energy supplied goes to increase the *rotation* of the molecules about their centres of gravity; e.g. a diatomic molecule (O_2, H_2, etc.) may be pictured as a minute rotating rigid dumb-bell: O——O. In some cases the atoms *vibrate* along the lines joining their centres, e.g. in the Cl_2 molecule the two chlorine atoms are vibrating along the line of centres: Cl〰Cl. The total energy of the gas is composed of the translational, rotational, and vibrational energies [1] (the last being partly kinetic and partly potential): $E=E_T+E_R+E_V$. The translatory velocity depends, at a given temperature, on the mass of the molecules, and since the average translational kinetic energy is supposed to be the same for all molecules at the same temperature, heavier molecules move more slowly than lighter. This appears in the greater diffusibility of light as compared with heavier gases. In air at the ordinary temperature, the molecules move with speeds of the order of a quarter of a mile a second.

The average distance through which a molecule moves between successive collisions with another molecule is called the *mean free path*. It depends on the pressure, and is smaller at higher pressures. In air at atmospheric pressure, the mean free path is about a ten-thousandth of a millimetre (10^{-5} cm.). If all the free paths of an air molecule are joined to make up the distance traversed per second, 4000 million (4×10^9) are required, and this gives the *number of collisions per second*.

The gas laws may be deduced as follows. Suppose n molecules each of mass m of a gas are contained in a box in the form of a centimetre cube. The results are obviously independent of the shape and size of the container. Collisions of molecules with one another are neglected. A single molecule moving to and fro between opposite faces of the box with a velocity u will traverse 2 cm. between successive collisions with *one* face (from this face to the opposite face and back), and (if the duration of the collision is neglected) the interval between collisions with this face is $2/u$ sec., or the number of collisions per second with any *one* face is $u/2$. The *momentum* (mass × velocity) of a molecule relative to the face changes from mu before collision to $m(-u)=-mu$ after collision, i.e. by $mu-(-mu)=2mu$, and the change of momentum per second is $(u/2)\times 2mu=mu^2$. If *all* the molecules were moving similarly in parallel lines the total change of momentum per second on a face would be nmu^2 and this would be equal to the pressure on the face of unit area. As a first approximation, Joule (1848) assumed that *one third* of the molecules are moving at right angles to each pair of opposite faces. Hence the pressure on the walls is $(n/3)mu^2$, or $p=\frac{1}{3}nmu^2=\frac{1}{3}\rho u^2$, where ρ=mass per cm.^{3}=density. This may be called the *primary equation* of the Kinetic Theory of Gases.[2]

The molecules are actually moving in all directions at random, but the velocity V of each can be resolved into three components u, v, and w parallel to three cube edges meeting in a point, and taken as the x, y, and z axes, respectively. Also $V^2=u^2+v^2+w^2$ (§ 78.I). At any face, it is only the velocity

[1] Clausius, *loc. cit.*

[2] See del Lungo, *Nuov. Cim.*, 1916, **12**, 166.

component at right angles which is reversed on collision, say u, and the interval between impacts is determined by this component. For three perpendicular faces:

$$p_x = m(n_1u_1^2 + n_2u_2^2 + n_3u_3^2 + \ldots),$$
$$p_y = m(n_1v_1^2 + n_2v_2^2 + n_3v_3^2 + \ldots),$$
$$p_z = m(n_1w_1^2 + n_2w_2^2 + n_3w_3^2 + \ldots),$$

where n_1 molecules have component velocities u_1, v_1, w_1, and so on. The expressions in brackets can be replaced by averages, $n\overline{u^2}$, $n\overline{v^2}$, $n\overline{w^2}$, and since $p_x = p_y = p_z = p$, it follows that $n\overline{u^2} = n\overline{v^2} = n\overline{w^2}$, and $p = \frac{1}{3}nm\overline{c^2}$, where $\overline{c^2} = \overline{u^2} + \overline{v^2} + \overline{w^2}$ is the *mean square velocity*. Since nm=mass of all the molecules in 1 cm.^{3}=density ρ of the gas,

$$p = \tfrac{1}{3}\rho\overline{c^2} \quad \ldots \ldots \ldots \ldots \quad (1)$$

Since the molecular velocity is constant at a given temperature, by assumption, (1) shows that the pressure is then proportional to the density, which is *Boyle's law*. (It should be noted that the average is over the *squares* of the velocities, viz. $\overline{u^2}$, etc., not $(\overline{u})^2$, etc., which would be the squares of average velocities.) Since $\rho = M/v$ = mass/volume:

$$p = \tfrac{1}{3}\rho\overline{c^2} = \tfrac{1}{3}(M/v)\overline{c^2}, \quad \text{therefore} \quad pv = \tfrac{2}{3}(\tfrac{1}{2}M\overline{c^2}) = \tfrac{2}{3}E_k,$$

where E_k is the kinetic energy of translation of all the molecules. Although it has been stated [1] that the relation $pv = \frac{2}{3}$(*kinetic energy*) is true only for a gas obeying Maxwell-Boltzmann statistics, it is, apparently,[2] true also for Bose-Einstein and Fermi-Dirac statistics (§§ 31, 33, 36.IV).

It is assumed that the absolute *temperature* of a gas is proportional to the *average translatory kinetic energy* of the molecules [3] (energy of rotation or vibration not entering into consideration). Hence:

$$pv = \tfrac{2}{3}E_k = kT \quad \ldots \ldots \ldots \ldots \quad (2)$$

where E_k is the kinetic energy of translation, and k is a constant. This is equivalent to *Charles's law*.

If two gases contain n_1 and n_2 molecules per cm.^{3} at the same pressure and temperature, then, if the masses of the molecules are m_1 and m_2:

$$p = \tfrac{1}{3}n_1m_1\overline{c_1^2} = \tfrac{1}{3}n_2m_2\overline{c_2^2} \text{ (pressures equal)}$$
$$\tfrac{1}{2}m_1\overline{c_1^2} = \tfrac{1}{2}m_2\overline{c_2^2} \text{ (temperatures equal)}$$
$$\therefore\ n_1 = n_2 \quad \ldots \ldots \ldots \ldots \quad (3)$$

which is *Avogadro's hypothesis*.[4]

The relation $\frac{1}{2}m_1\overline{c_1^2} = \frac{1}{2}m_2\overline{c_2^2}$ at the same temperature gives $\overline{c_1^2}/\overline{c_2^2} = m_2/m_1$, and if the molecular velocities are taken *approximately* as the square roots of the mean square velocities (see § 8):

$$V_1/V_2 = \sqrt{(m_2/m_1)} \quad \ldots \ldots \ldots \quad (4)$$

or the molecular velocities are inversely proportional to the square roots of the molecular weights, which is related to *Graham's law of diffusion*.

[1] Suzuki, *Proc. Phys. Math. Soc. Japan*, 1933, **15**, 257.
[2] Mayer and Mayer, "Statistical Mechanics," New York, 1940, 377, 425.
[3] See Brillouin, *Ann. Chim.*, 1909, **18**, 387.
[4] Clausius, *Phil. Mag.*, 1857, **14**, 108; Maxwell, *Phil. Mag.*, 1860, **19**, 19; Boltzmann, *Wien Ber.*, 1871, **63**, 397; Waterston (1845), *Phil. Trans.*, 1892, **183**, 1; but see Maxwell, *Trans. Cambr. Phil. Soc.*, 1878, **13**, 547.

From equation (1), as Joule showed, the average translatory velocity of the molecules of a gas at a given temperature may be calculated. Assume for simplicity a constant molecular velocity u. For oxygen at 0° and 1 atm. pressure, $p=1$ atm.$=76\times 13\cdot595\times 980\cdot6=1{,}013{,}225$ dynes/cm.^{2}, $\rho=0\cdot001429$ g./cm.^{3}

$$\therefore\ pv=1{,}013{,}225=\tfrac{1}{3}\times 0\cdot001429\times u^2, \qquad \therefore\ u=46{,}000 \text{ cm./sec.}$$

Some values of the translatory velocities (really $\sqrt{(\overline{c^2})}$ so calculated are given below:

Molecular Velocities at 0° *C. in m./sec.*

Hydrogen, 1,693 (1,286)	Oxygen, 425 (317)
Helium, 1,202	Carbon dioxide, 362 (257)
Steam, 565 (401)	Chlorine, 285 (206)
Nitrogen, 455 (337)	Mercury vapour, 170

The velocity of a projectile fired from a high-muzzle-velocity gun may be about 1700 m. per second; if fired vertically into vacuum with a speed of 11,000 m. per second it would escape into space from the earth's attraction. The velocities of sound in the gases, calculated by equation (3), § 3, are given in brackets.

If M is the total mass of gas in a volume V, then $\rho=M/V$, therefore from (1):

$$pV=\tfrac{1}{3}M\overline{c^2}=\tfrac{2}{3}(\tfrac{1}{2}M\overline{c^2}) \quad . \quad . \quad . \quad . \quad . \quad . \quad . \quad (5)$$

so that *the product of pressure and volume is two-thirds the kinetic energy of translation of the molecules.* If M is the molar weight, Avogadro's hypothesis and Boyle's law show that pV has the same constant value at a given temperature for all gases (since V is the same for all, and pV is constant), so that *the kinetic energy of translation of the molecules is the same for a mol of any gas at a given temperature and is equal to* $\tfrac{3}{2}pV$. For any gas at S.T.P.,

$$V=22\cdot415 \text{ lit.}=22\cdot415\times 1000\cdot028 \text{ cm.}^3$$

$$\therefore\ \tfrac{3}{2}pV=\tfrac{3}{2}\times 1{,}013{,}225\times 22\cdot415\times 1000\cdot028=3\cdot407\times 10^{10} \text{ ergs},$$

which is large enough to raise a weight of about a ton through 1 foot.

Since the experimental gas law is $pV=\boldsymbol{R}T$, equation (5) shows that *the molecular translational velocity is proportional to the square-root of the absolute temperature* for any one gas. The assumption of this result, which is equivalent to the assumption that the absolute temperature is proportional to the translational kinetic energy, will, conversely lead to a deduction of Avogadro's hypothesis, as is shown above.[1]

If several gases are separately contained in a volume V for each, and if $n_1, n_2, \ldots$ are the numbers of molecules of masses $m_1, m_2, \ldots$ in this volume, (5) gives (since $m_1n_1=M_1$, etc.):

$$p_1=\tfrac{1}{3}m_1n_1\overline{c_1^2};\quad p_2=\tfrac{1}{3}m_2n_2\overline{c_2^2};\ \ldots,$$

$$\text{or}\quad p_1=\tfrac{2}{3}E_1;\quad p_2=\tfrac{2}{3}E_2;\ \ldots,$$

where $E_1, E_2, \ldots$ are the kinetic energies of the gases. If, now, all the gases are mixed in the volume V, the kinetic energy E is the sum of those of the separate gases, since it is found by experiment that no heat is evolved or absorbed on mixing. Hence:

$$E=E_1+E_2+\ldots \quad . \quad . \quad . \quad . \quad . \quad . \quad . \quad (6)$$

[1] See del Lungo, *Atti R. Accad. Lincei*, 1916, **25**, II, 322; *Nuov. Cim.*, 1917, **14**. 262.

From (5), $p=\frac{1}{3}\Sigma m_1 n_1 \overline{c_1^2}_m$, where $\overline{c_1^2}_m$, etc., are the root-mean-square velocities *in the mixture*. Since (6) shows that $\Sigma m_1\overline{c_1^2}_m=\Sigma m_1\overline{c_1^2}$, it follows that:

$$p=\Sigma p_1 \quad \ldots\ldots\ldots\ldots \quad (7)$$

which is Dalton's law of partial pressures (§ 56.II).

The heating of gases by *adiabatic compression* is explained [1] by assuming that the molecules rebounding from a piston moving so as to reduce the volume of the gas acquire additional kinetic energy, since they are thrown back with higher velocity. This, however, corresponds with a higher temperature.

§ 3. Specific Heats

For a *monatomic gas* the heat absorbed at constant volume goes entirely to increase the translational kinetic energy of the molecules. For 1 mol of gas and 1° rise in temperature this heat absorbed is the *molecular heat at constant volume*, C_v. From (5), § 2, $\frac{1}{2}Mu^2=\frac{3}{2}pV=\frac{3}{2}RT$, per mol, where M=mol. wt. Hence per 1° rise in temperature the increase of kinetic energy is $\frac{3}{2}R(T+1)-\frac{3}{2}RT=\frac{3}{2}R$, and this is equal to C_v. The gas constant is:

$$R=pV/T=\tfrac{2}{3}\times 3{\cdot}407\times 10^{10}/273{\cdot}116=8{\cdot}315\times 10^7 \text{ ergs}/1°=$$
$$8{\cdot}315\times 10^7/4{\cdot}185\times 10^7=1{\cdot}987 \text{ g.cal.}/1°,$$

so that for a monatomic gas $C_v=\frac{3}{2}R=3$ g.cal., very nearly. This is found to be the value for mercury vapour, argon, etc.

The *molecular heat at constant pressure* is found as follows. Since it is assumed that no forces exist between the molecules of an ideal gas, the energy of the gas is not changed by an increase of volume at constant temperature, and the difference C_p-C_v for *any* gas must be equal to the *external* work done during heating at constant pressure (usually atmospheric), i.e. *pressure × increase in volume* (§ 6.II):

$$\therefore\ C_p-C_v=p(V'-V)=pV[(T+1)/T-1]=pV/T=R \quad . \quad . \quad (1)$$

Hence for a *monatomic* gas $C_p(=C_v+R)\simeq 3+2=5$ g.cal., and the *ratio of specific heats* is $\gamma=c_p/c_v=C_p/C_v=5/3=1{\cdot}666\ldots$ (since $C_v=Mc_v$ and $C_p=Mc_p$), which is the value found for mercury vapour, argon, etc.

For *polyatomic* molecules, the heat supplied at constant volume will increase the translational, rotational, and (sometimes) vibrational energies,[2] the first being due to the movement of the molecule as a whole, the second to its rotation, and the third to the vibration of its atoms. If E is the part due to rotation and vibration per 1° rise in temperature:

$$C_p/C_v=\frac{\frac{3}{2}R+R+E}{\frac{3}{2}R+E}<\frac{\frac{3}{2}R+R}{\frac{3}{2}R}<1{\cdot}666\ldots \quad \ldots\ldots \quad (2)$$

This is found to be the case; for many diatomic gases C_p/C_v is 1·400; for more complex molecules, with greater possibilities of rotation and vibration, the value is less than 1·400; e.g. for CO_2 it is 1·30, and for ethylene ($CH_2{=}CH_2$) it is 1·25.

The *velocity of sound* U in a gas is given (§ 4.II) by:

$$U=\sqrt{(\gamma p/\rho)}=\sqrt{(\gamma pv)}=\sqrt{(\gamma RT/M)} \quad \ldots\ldots \quad (3)$$

1 Krönig, *Ann. Phys.*, 1856, **99**, 315; Clausius, *ibid.*, 1857, **100**, 353; Voigt, *Gött. Nachr.*, 1885, 228; Natanson, *Ann. Phys.*, 1889, **37**, 341; Clausius, Die kinetische Theorie der Gase, in "Die mechanische Wärmetheorie," 1889–91, **3**, 29; O. E. Meyer, "Kinetic Theory of Gases," 1899, 34; Paul, *Ann. Phys.*, 1937, **29**, 179; Jeans, "Kinetic Theory of Gases," 1940, 27.

2 Waterston (1845), *Phil. Trans.*, 1892, **183**, 1; Clausius, *Phil. Mag.*, 1857, **14**, 108.

hence if $\overline{c^2}$ is the mean-square molecular velocity (see (1), § 2):

$$\sqrt{\overline{c^2}}=\sqrt{(3p/\rho)},$$

$$\therefore\ U=\sqrt{\overline{c^2}}\ .\ \sqrt{(\gamma/3)} \quad . \quad . \quad . \quad . \quad . \quad . \quad . \quad . \quad (4)$$

and hence the velocity of sound is something under three-quarters of the root-mean-square velocity (for diatomic gases with $\gamma=1{\cdot}4$, such as air, the factor is 0·683).[1]

§ 4. Mean Free Path

The molecules in a gas move with quite high speeds, in air of the order of a quarter of a mile per second. If a little ammonia gas is released at one end of a room, however, an appreciable time elapses before the smell is noticed at the opposite end, so that the rate of diffusion is quite slow. The apparent difficulty [2] here was explained by Clausius.[3] The reason for the slowness of diffusion is that the molecules are constantly entering into *collisions*, so that the long path which a single molecule would describe if it were unimpeded is broken up into a very large number of zig-zags in all directions. The average length of one of these zig-zag paths is called the *mean free path*. In the same way, gnats in a swarm move about with considerable speeds, but the swarm itself may be nearly stationary. The possibility of collision must depend on the finite size of the molecules; if they were mere points occupying no space they would not impede the motion of other molecules. From the rate of diffusion and other results depending on the length of the mean free path, the diameters of molecules may be calculated. The *diameter* of an oxygen molecule, assumed spherical, is about 3×10^{-8} cm.=3 A. (A.=Ångström unit=10^{-8} cm.=10^{-10} m.) and all ordinary molecular diameters are of the order of a few A. An approach to molecular dimensions can be made by finite objects. Platinum wires can be drawn to 10^{-4} cm. in diameter, ordinary gold leaf is 10^{-5} cm. thick, the black parts of soap films are 6×10^{-7} cm. thick, and oil films on water are only 10^{-7} cm. thick, or even less, and are often unimolecular.

The *mean free path* l is most conveniently calculated, as will be shown later, from the *viscosity* η of a gas by the formula $l=1{\cdot}25\eta/\sqrt{(p\rho)}$, where ρ=density, p=pressure, in suitable units. It increases when the pressure is lowered, because the molecules are then less crowded together. In oxygen at S.T.P. the mean free path l is about 10^{-5} cm., the same as the thickness of the thinnest gold leaf; it is nearly double this in hydrogen. At 1 mm. pressure the mean free path is about 1/10 mm. in hydrogen. At low pressures, such as exist between the walls of " thermos " flasks, the free path is several centimetres, and a molecule rebounds from opposite walls of such a flask many times without encountering another. In hydrogen at 1 millionth of an atmosphere the free path is 18 cm. The free paths in the atmosphere at high altitudes are large: at 100 km. the free path is only a few centimetres, but at 300 km. it may range from 200 km. (125 miles) on a summer day up to a maximum of perhaps 15,000 km. (over 9000 miles). Observations of heights of the aurora show that the upper

[1] Stefan, *Ann. Phys.*, 1863, **118**, 494; S. Tolver Preston, *Phil. Mag.*, 1877, **3**, 441, who says Maxwell told him the velocity of sound was $\sqrt{(5)/3}=0{\cdot}745$ times the velocity of the molecules. Waterston (1845), *Phil. Trans.*, 1892, **183**, 1, had tried to connect velocity of sound and molecular velocity, but his result is incorrect.

[2] Buijs-Ballot, *Ann. Phys.*, 1858, **103**, 240; Holm, *ibid.*, 1858, **104**, 279; Jochmann, *ibid.*, 1859, **108**, 153.

[3] *Ann. Phys.*, 1858, **105**, 239; *Phil. Mag.*, 1859, **17**, 81.

atmosphere (stratosphere) extends at least 300 km. (200 miles) and to a slight extent even to 1000 km. (600 miles). At 100 km. the density on a summer day is only 6×10^{-6} of that at 1 standard atm. pressure; at 300 km. it is only 10^{-7} of that at 100 km., but even so there are still [1] about a million molecules per cm.^{3}.

The number of collisions per second between the molecules of a gas is called the *collision frequency*, and is calculated as follows. The sum of the free paths described by a molecule per second is the mean velocity $\bar{c}$ (§ 10). The *number of impacts* per second is [2] thus $\bar{c}/l$, but as *two* molecules collide at each impact, the collision frequency referred to *one selected molecule* is half this. The number of impacts per second in oxygen at S.T.P. is $\bar{c}/l = 4{\cdot}25 \times 10^4/10^{-5} = 4{\cdot}25 \times 10^9$. At very low pressures, when the mean free path is 1 cm., there are still 10^5 or 100,000 impacts per second.

An *approximate* formula for the mean free path is easily found. Select any molecule (A) in the gas and consider its collisions with other molecules (B, C, D . . .). Let σ be the *diameter* of each molecule; then a collision will occur when the centre of A and that of any other molecule approach within a distance σ. The result is the same if we consider A to have a *radius* σ and all the other molecules to be points. If B, C, D . . . are supposed to be at rest, A moves among them, and for each centimetre of motion it sweeps out [3] a *volume* $\pi\sigma^2$. If there are N molecules per cm.^{3}, the chance that the centre of any of the molecules B, C, D . . . falls inside this volume is $N\pi\sigma^2$, and hence the average distance A would travel without making a collision is $1/N\pi\sigma^2$, which is the length of the mean free path. The detailed calculation (§ 22) shows that the correct value is $1/\sqrt{(2)}N\pi\sigma^2 = 1/1{\cdot}414N\pi\sigma^2 = 0{\cdot}707/N\pi\sigma^2$.

Although the molecules are very small and the total *volume* in 1 cm.^{3} occupied by the actual molecules is only a very small fraction of the total volume, being $\frac{4}{3}\pi N(\sigma/2)^3$, the *area of surface* exposed by the molecules is very large. The surface of all the molecules (assumed spherical) in 1 cm.^{3} of oxygen at S.T.P., $4\pi N(\sigma/2)^2$, is about 7 m.^{2}.

§ 5. Liquids and Solids

Since liquids and solids are only slightly compressible, even by very large forces, it is assumed that their molecules are relatively closely packed with only a small amount of free space, and exert large repulsive forces on one another when an attempt is made to bring them closer together. A liquefied gas occupies only a small fraction of the volume of the gas. Since the molecules of liquids and solids, unlike those of gases, do not tend to separate and to spread through a space available to them, they are supposed to be held together by an attractive force of *cohesion* when an attempt is made to separate them. In the normal state, the repulsive and cohesive forces are in equilibrium in a system of forces which also involves a tendency to spread owing to the heat-motion of the molecules, and the external pressure. In the case of gases the cohesive force is very small compared with the external pressure, but in liquids and solids the opposite is the case. When the gas is strongly compressed, however, the cohesive forces increase as the distances between the molecules

[1] Kennard, " Kinetic Theory of Gases," 1938, 80.

[2] Actually $\bar{c}/l$ = number of impacts per second -1, since the first path has only one collision at the end, but 1 is quite negligible compared with the number of impacts per second.

[3] The volume is $\pi\sigma^2 + \frac{2}{3}\pi\sigma^3 - \frac{2}{3}\pi\sigma^3 = \pi\sigma^2$, if the hemispherical caps at each end are taken into account.

become small, and (especially if the gas is cooled, so that the heat-motion is reduced) the gas may ultimately pass into a liquid.

The general molecular morphology of the liquid and solid states was also sketched by Clausius: [1] a good summary of his views is given by J. J. Thomson: [2] " In the solid state the molecules oscillate about a position of equilibrium and never get far from their original position in the body; in the liquid state the molecules are supposed not to oscillate about positions of equilibrium, but to be comparatively free to move in any direction; they cannot, however, move far without coming under the influence of other molecules, so that their courses are constantly being changed and do not bear any approximation to straight lines; in the gaseous state the molecules are so far apart that for the greater part of the time they are describing straight lines, the time during which they are under the influence of other molecules being an exceedingly small fraction of the whole time."

§ 6. Sizes of Molecules

Leslie,[3] from the fact that a single grain of musk would perfume a large room for twenty years, computed (by a method he does not explain) that it contained 320×10^{24} particles; he assumed that the " seeds of contagion " [bacteria] were even smaller. Attempts to find an upper limit for the divisibility of matter by the dilution of coloured solutions are quite old.[4]

The first attempt to calculate the sizes of molecules was made by Loschmidt,[5] and the number N_L of molecules per cm.³ at S.T.P. is sometimes called *Loschmidt's number*. He calculated the density of liquid air by taking atomic volumes of oxygen and nitrogen from the molecular volumes of liquids after the manner of Kopp (see Vol. II) as 11 and 12, respectively, and hence the liquid densities $16/11 = 1{\cdot}4545$ and $14/12 = 1{\cdot}1666$, whence the density of liquid air was 1·224. If the molecules are close-packed spheres, the volume they occupy is 1·17 times the sum of their volumes and the " true " density is $1{\cdot}224 \times 1{\cdot}17 = 1{\cdot}5$. The ratio of the volume of the molecules to the volume of the gas, which Loschmidt called the " condensation coefficient," is $v = 0{\cdot}001293/1{\cdot}5 = 0{\cdot}00086$. The Maxwell formula for the mean free path (18), § 21, is $l = 1/\sqrt{(2)}N\pi\sigma^2$. For 1 cm.³ of gas $v = \frac{4}{3}N_L\pi(\sigma/2)^3 = \frac{1}{6}\pi N_L\sigma^3$ $\therefore$ $N_L = 6v/\pi\sigma^3$, $\therefore$ $l = \sigma/6\sqrt{(2)}v$. By taking $l = 140$ mμ from viscosity measurements, Loschmidt thus found $\sigma = 1$ mμ $= 10^{-6}$ mm. The value $l = 95$ mμ, adopted by O. E. Meyer, gives $\sigma = 0{\cdot}68$ mμ.

1 *Phil. Mag.*, 1857, **14**, 108.

2 Watts, " Dictionary of Chemistry," edit. Morley and Muir, 1890, **1**, 83.

3 " Elements of Natural Philosophy," Edinburgh, 1823, **1**, 14 f., 2nd edit., 1829, **1**, 15 f.; Tait, " Properties of Matter," 4th edit., 1899, 90; Aitken, *Proc. Roy. Soc. Edin.*, 1904–5, **25**, 894; the tenuity of odorous exhalations is an old argument for the existence of atoms and molecules; Partington, *Annals of Science*, 1939, **4**, 245. For a good survey of various methods of finding molecular sizes see Rutherford, *Engineering*, 1925, **119**, 296, 326, 358, 410.

4 Muncke, in Gehler's " Physikalisches Wörterbuch," 1838, **9**, 709 (" Theilbarkeit "), and Karsten, " Allgemeine Encyclopaedie der Physik," Leipzig, 1869, **1**, 820, 877, summarised these experiments, dating back to Musschenbroek, " Introductio ad Philosophiam Naturalem," Leiden, 1762, **1**, 27. For earlier views and experiments, see Partington, *Annals of Science*, 1939, **4**, 245 (267); for methods of determining atomic dimensions, see Lunnon, *Proc. Phys. Soc.*, 1926, **38**, 93 (64 refs.); Virgo, *Sci. Progr.*, 1933, **27**, 634. Annaheim, *Ber.*, 1876, **9**, 1151, and Bürki, *Helv. Chim. Acta*, 1919, **2**, 703, detected fluorescence in solutions of fluorescein containing 2×10^{-8} g./lit. A survey of the methods for finding the sizes of atoms, molecules, and ions is given by Herzfeld, *Jahrb. Radioakt. Elektronik*, 1922, **19**, 259 (bibl.).

5 *Wien Ber.*, 1865, **52**, II, 395; *Z. Math. Phys.* (Schlömilch), 1865, **10**, 511; Wallot, *Phys. Z.*, 1942, **43**, 530.

Lothar Meyer [1] showed that the ratios of the volumes of the molecules in two gases is very nearly equal to the ratio of the specific volumes of the liquids, and calculations of molecular diameters were also made by A. Naumann,[2] Lord Kelvin,[3] and Maxwell.[4] A full consideration of the molecular diameters as calculated from the volume in the liquid state, deviations from Boyle's law, dielectric constant, mean free path, and various other methods, was given by O. E. Meyer [5] in 1899. A few values for the "condensation coefficients" v calculated by Meyer are (at S.T.P.):

	H_2	O_2	N_2	NO	NH_3	HCl	H_2S	SO_2	C_2N_2
$v\times10^6$.	0·98	2·30	2·54	2·66	3·93	3·98	5·01	7·36	9·20

Dorn [6] and Exner [7] calculated the "condensation coefficient" v from the Clausius and Mossotti formula, based on the assumption that unit volume of a dielectric, of dielectric constant K, consists of conducting spheres occupying a volume v surrounded by a non-conducting medium: $v=(K-1)/(K+2)$. According to Maxwell's electromagnetic theory of light, $K=n^2$, where n=refractive index for waves of infinite length, therefore $v=(n^2-1)/(n^2+2)$. If ρ is the density of the gas, v/ρ gives the volume of the molecules in unit mass. The following values of v were calculated: [8]

	Air	CO_2	N_2O	CH_4	C_2H_4	NH_3	NO	H_2S	HCl	C_2N_2	SO_2
$v\times10^6$.	2·0	3·1	3·3	3·1	4·4	2·6	2·0	4·3	3·0	5·6	4·4

An interesting collection of the older results of various methods for obtaining an approximate value of molecular dimensions is given by Rücker: [9] the values are in mμ (10^{-6} mm.):

Liquid films, upper limit (Plateau, Maxwell, Quincke) [10]	118–50
Range of unstable thickness of film (Reinold and Rücker) [11] ..	96–12
Limiting thickness of film of silver on glass which alters the phase of reflected light (Wiener) [12]	12
Thickness of permanent gas or water film on glass at 23° (Bunsen) [13]	10·5

1 *Ann.*, 1867, Supplbd. **5**, 129.
2 *Ann.*, 1867, Supplbd. **5**, 252.
3 *Amer. J. Sci.*, 1870, **50**, 38, 258; *Ann.*, 1871, **157**, 54; *Nature*, 1870, **1**, 551; 1883, **28**, 203, 250, 274; "Popular Lectures and Addresses," 1889, **1**, 147.
4 *Phil. Mag.*, 1873, **46**, 453, "Ency. Brit.," 9th edit., 1875, **3**, 36, art. Atom; "Scientific Papers," 1890, **2**, 361, 445.
5 "Kinetic Theory of Gases," 1899, 299 f.; cf. also Nernst, "Theoretical Chemistry," 1904, 416 f.; Jeans, *Phil. Mag.*, 1904, **8**, 692; Sirk, *Ann. Phys.*, 1908, **25**, 894; crit. by Reinganum, *ibid.*, 1908, **28**, 142.
6 *Ann. Phys.*, 1881, **13**, 378.
7 *Repert. Physik*, 1885, **21**, 446.
8 Rücker, *J.C.S.*, 1888, **53**, 222.
9 *J.C.S.*, 1888, **53**, 222 (references given); *Z. phys. Chem.*, 1888, **2**, 973.
10 Drude, *Ann. Phys.*, 1891, **43**, 158, calculated the thickness of the black spots on soap films as $1{\cdot}7\times10^{-6}$ cm. or 17 mμ; Röntgen, *ibid.*, 1890, **41**, 321, found $5{\cdot}6\times10^{-8}$ cm. for an oil film on water, and Rayleigh, *Nature*, 1890, **42**, 43, found 1·6 mμ; letter to Lord Rayleigh, Miss Pockels, *Nature*, 1891, **43**, 437 (film trough); on Miss Pockels, see Ostwald, *Koll. Z.*, 1932, **58**, 1; films on mercury, $<5\times10^{-7}$ cm., Fischer, *Ann. Phys.*, 1899, **68**, 414; Weber, *ibid.*, 1901, **4**, 706 (oil film $<$115 mμ); Chamberlain, *Phys. Rev.*, 1910, **31**, 170 ($1{\cdot}5\times10^{-7}$ cm.).
11 *Phil. Trans.*, 1886, **177**, 627.
12 *Ann. Phys.*, 1887, **31**, 629.
13 Faraday, *Phil. Trans.*, 1830, **120**, 1 (49); Magnus, *Ann. Phys.*, 1853, **90**, 601; Quincke, *ibid.*, 1859, **108**, 326; 1900, **2**, 414; Wüllner and Grotrian, *ibid.*, 1880, **11**, 545; Kayser, *ibid.*, 1881, **14**, 450; 1884, **23**, 416; Bunsen, *ibid.*, 1883, **20**, 545; 1885, **24**, 321; 1886, **29**, 161; Pfeiffer, *Ann. Phys. Beibl.*, 1884, **8**, 630; Bottomley, *Chem. News*, 1885, **51**, 85; Müller-Erzbach, *Ann. Phys. Beibl.*, 1885, **9**, 699; Warburg and Ihmori, *Ann. Phys.*, 1886, **27**, 481; Schumann, *ibid.*, 1886, **27**, 91; Ihmori, *ibid.*, 1887, **31**, 1006; Krause, *ibid.*, 1889, **36**, 923; Mühlfarth, *Dissert.*

Mean distance between centres of neighbouring gas molecules at S.T.P. (O. E. Meyer)	3–4
Smallest thickness of metal films showing their e.m.f. on platinum (Oberbeck) [1]	3–1
Thickness of electrical double layer (Lippmann, Oberbeck) [2]	1–0·02
Diameter of hydrogen molecule (O. E. Meyer, van der Waals, Exner)	0·14–0·11
Mean distance between centres of nearest liquid molecules (W. Thomson)	0·07–0·02
Inferior limit to diameter of gas molecules (W. Thomson)	0·02

Thus, in 1888, the approximate minimum value of the molecular diameter had been calculated as about 10^{-8} cm., a surprising achievement in view of the crude nature of the methods then available.

§ 7. Molecular Magnitudes

Important constants in the kinetic theory are N_L=number of molecules per cm.^{3} at S.T.P., called *Loschmidt's number*, and N=number of molecules in a g.mol. or mol, called *Avogadro's constant* [3] or *Avogadro's number*. The following table [4] contains some representative molecular magnitudes.

TABLE OF MOLECULAR MAGNITUDES.

Number of molecules per cm.^{3} of gas at S.T.P.$=N_L=2{\cdot}69\times10^{19}$
Number of molecules per mol (22·415 lit. at S.T.P.)$=N=6{\cdot}03\times10^{23}$
Mass of hydrogen atom$=1{\cdot}69\times10^{-24}$ g.
Mean velocity of hydrogen molecule at 0° C. $\bar{c}=16{\cdot}93\times10^4$ cm./sec.
Translational kinetic energy of a molecule at 0° C.$=5{\cdot}66\times10^{-14}$ erg.
Rate of change of translational kinetic energy per 1°$=5{\cdot}66\times10^{-14}/273=2{\cdot}07\times10^{-16}$ erg/1°

Bonn, 1900; *Ann. Phys.*, 1900, **3**, 328 (long bibl.); *Phys. Z.*, 1901, **2**, 239; Parks, *Phil. Mag.*, 1903, **5**, 517; Briggs, *J. Phys. Chem.*, 1905, **9**, 617; Guye and Ter-Gazarian, *Compt. Rend.*, 1906, **143**, 1233; Mylius and Groschuff, *Z. anorg. Chem.*, 1907, **55**, 101; Mylius, *ibid.*, 1907, **55**, 233; Scheel and Heuse, *Verhl. d. D. Phys. Ges.*, 1908, **10**, 785; Gray and Burt, *J.C.S.*, 1909, **95**, 1633; Drucker and Ullmann, *Z. phys. Chem.*, 1910, **74**, 567; Guichard, *Compt. Rend.*, 1911, **152**, 876; Cohnstaedt, *Ann. Phys.*, 1912, **38**, 223; Drucker, Jiméno, and Kangro, *Z. phys. Chem.*, 1915, **90**, 541; Langmuir, *J.A.C.S.*, 1916, **38**, 2221; Pettijohn, *ibid.*, 1919, **41**, 477 ($0{\cdot}0_5166$ cm.); Sherwood, *Phys. Rev.*, 1918, **12**, 448; Pirani, *Z. Phys.*, 1922, **9**, 327 (removal of water film by electron bombardment and rinsing with mercury vapour); McHaffie and Lenher, *J.C.S.*, 1925, **127**, 1559; Lenher, *ibid.*, 1926, 1785 (H_2O on fused quartz); Bangham and Burt, *J. Phys. Chem.*, 1925, **29**, 113, 540, 1594; *Proc. Roy. Soc.*, 1924, **105**, 481; Frazer, Patrick, and Smith, *J. Phys. Chem.*, 1927, **31**, 897 (unimolecular film on fire-polished glass, but 50 molecules thick on acid-treated glass); Shishakov, *J. Appl. Phys.* (Moscow), 1927, **4**, 37 (H_2O on glass); Biltz and Müller, *Z. anorg. Chem.*, 1927, **163**, 297 (fused silica apparatus slowly evolves gas, probably CO, on strong heating in vacuum); Francis and Burt, *Proc. Roy. Soc.*, 1927, **116**, 586 (NH_3 on glass); Latham, *J.A.C.S.*, 1928, **50**, 2987 (unimolecular water film on amalgamated silver, but 30 molecules thick on amalgamated platinum); Burt, *Trans. Faraday Soc.*, 1932, **28**, 179 (NH_3); Michaud, *J. Chim. Phys.*, 1939, **36**, 23 (most probable thickness of water film on glass$=4\times10^{-6}$ cm.); Keesom and Schweers, *Physica*, 1941, **8**, 1007, 1020; Van Itterbeek and Vereycken, *Medel. Kon. Vlaam. Akad.*, 1940, No. 9, 3; *Amer. Chem. Abstr.*, 1943, **37**, 3989; Veith, *Z. phys. Chem.*, 1944, **193**, 378 (water films on various glasses 5 to 800 A. thick); Kistemaker, *Physica*, 1947, **13**, 81 (He on glass); Razouk and Satem, *J. Phys. Chem.*, 1948, **52**, 1208 (H_2O on glass); see also Ostwald, "Lehrbuch der allgemeinen Chemie," 1911, 3, i, 217; Landolt-Börnstein, "Tabellen," 5th edit., 1923, 124 (bibl.). For films on twenty-year-old flint glass, see Sissingh, *Physica*, 1925, **5**, 77.

[1] *Ann. Phys.*, 1887, **31**, 337; 1891, **42**, 193.

[2] Lorenz, *Ann. Phys.*, 1870, **140**, 644; Lippmann, *Ann. Chim.*, 1875, **5**, 494; *Compt. Rend.*, 1882, **95**, 686 (0·03 mμ); Oberbeck, *Ann. Phys.*, 1884, **21**, 139 (157) (0·02 mμ).

[3] Apparently first by Perrin, *Ann. Chim.*, 1909, **18**, 5; *Compt. Rend.*, 1911, **152**, 1380; "Les Atomes," 1914, 37; cf. Heydweiller, *Ann. Phys.*, 1913, **42**, 1273.

[4] From Partington, "General and Inorganic Chemistry," 1948, 32.

Diameter of hydrogen molecule $=2{\cdot}40\times10^{-8}$ cm.
Mean free path of hydrogen molecules at S.T.P. $=1{\cdot}22\times10^{-5}$ cm.
Average distance apart of centres of gas molecules at S.T.P. $=3\times10^{-7}$ cm.
Number of collisions per second per cm.^{3} of oxygen molecules at S.T.P. $=5{\cdot}85\times10^{28}$
Time of describing free path of oxygen molecules at S.T.P. $=2{\cdot}3\times10^{-10}$ sec.

This completes the elementary treatment of the Kinetic Theory. In the following sections the subject is dealt with in greater mathematical detail. In this way many finer features come to light and some phenomena beyond the reach of elementary treatment come within the scope of discussion.[1] The modifications introduced by the more exact treatment are usually only in numerical coefficients in the equations, and even now these are sometimes in doubt.

§ 8. The Pressure of a Gas

An expression for the pressure of a gas is found as follows.[2] Consider a sphere of radius a and let θ and ϕ be angles measured as shown in Fig. 1.III, θ between the z axis and a, and ϕ in the x, y plane between the x axis and the

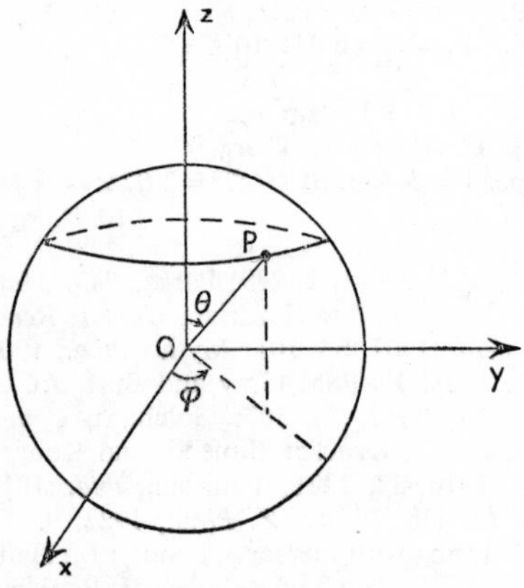

FIG. 1.III. Spherical Polar Coordinate System

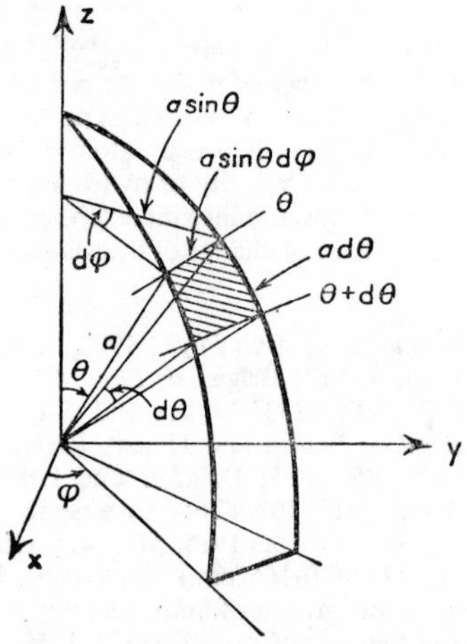

FIG. 2.III. Solid Angle measured on Sphere

projection of a, the origin being the centre of the sphere. Consider a small element of surface $d\sigma$ bounded on the sphere between four radii as shown in Fig. 2.III. The length of the element on the longitude is $a d\theta$, and that on the latitude is $(a \sin\theta)d\phi$, hence:

$$d\sigma = a d\theta \times (a \sin\theta) d\phi = a^2 \sin\theta \, d\theta d\phi \quad . \quad . \quad . \quad . \quad . \quad . \quad (1)$$

[1] Cf. Planck, *Z. phys. Chem.*, 1891, **8**, 647, who pointed out that the difficulties increase greatly in an attempt to attain greater strictness, a general result in most branches of Physics.

[2] Joule, Krönig, and Clausius, see § 1; Maxwell, *Phil. Mag.*, 1860, **19**, 19; 1868, **35**, 129, 185; Stefan, *Wien Ber.*, 1863, **47**, II, 81; 1872, **65**, II, 323; Pfaundler, *ibid.*, 1871, **63**, II, 159; von Lang, *ibid.*, 1871, **64**, II, 485; *Ann. Phys.*, 1872, **145**, 290. The present treatment follows Jäger, " Fortschritte der kinetischen Gastheorie," 1906, 4f., and in Winkelmann, " Handbuch der Physik," 1906, **3**, 703. For a different treatment, see O. E. Meyer, " Kinetic Theory of Gases," 1899, 22, 355; Kennard, " Kinetic Theory of Gases," New York, 1938, 7; Jeans, " Kinetic Theory of Gases," 1940, 17; Glasstone, " Textbook of Physical Chemistry," 1940, 244.

If $a=1$, this becomes the *solid angle* $d\omega$, subtended by the area with the centre of the sphere: [1]

$$d\omega=\sin\theta d\theta d\phi \quad . \quad . \quad . \quad . \quad . \quad . \quad . \quad . \quad (2)$$

The small *volume element* $d\tau$ cut off between two such surfaces a distance da apart is $d\sigma \times da$, i.e.:

$$d\tau=a^2 \sin\theta d\theta d\phi da \quad . \quad . \quad . \quad . \quad . \quad . \quad . \quad (3)$$

a is always positive, θ can vary from 0 to π, and ϕ can vary from 0 to 2π, these variations of the angles comprising the whole space about the centre of the sphere.

Consider N gas molecules in a volume V. Let their *velocities* be represented in magnitude and direction by radii of the sphere, each specified by particular values of a, θ, ϕ. There will be N of these radii, and they will cut the surface of the sphere in N points. They also cut the surface of the sphere of unit radius, i.e. of area 4π, in N points. Assume that N is very large, when the points can

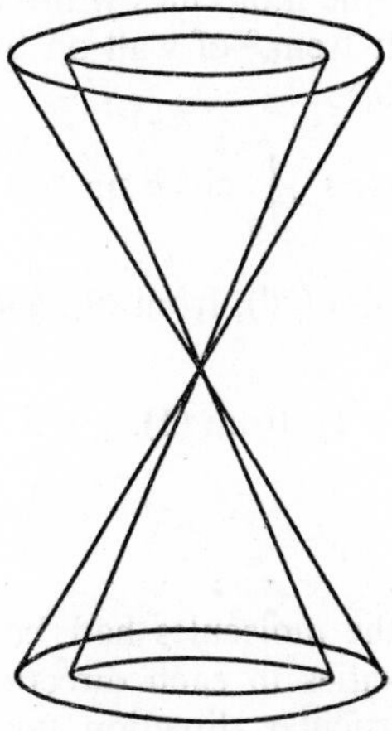

FIG. 3.III. Spherical Zones between Double Cones

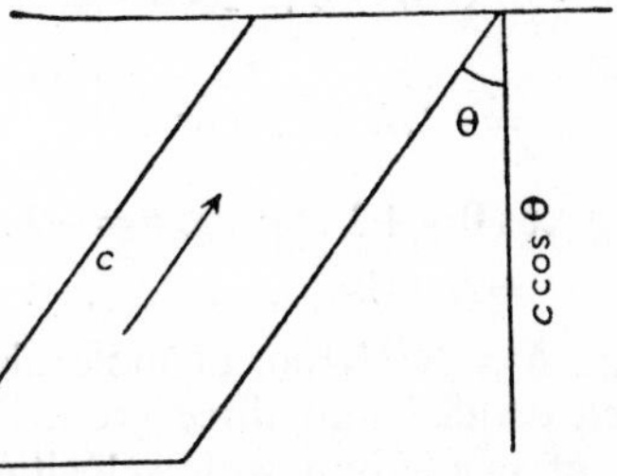

FIG. 4.III. Collisions with Wall

be regarded as *uniformly* distributed over the surface, with a density of distribution given by the number of points on unit surface, i.e. $N/4\pi$.

The number of molecules having velocities in the directions θ to $\theta+d\theta$ and ϕ to $\phi+d\phi$ will be represented by the number of radii in a small cone of solid angle $d\omega$, i.e. $Nd\omega/4\pi$, hence the number having velocities in the direction θ to $\theta+d\theta$ for all values of ϕ, i.e. in the thin *double* cone bounded by θ and $\theta+d\theta$ (Fig. 3.III) will be, from (2):

$$(N/4\pi)\int d\omega=(N/4\pi)\int_0^{2\pi} \sin\theta d\theta d\phi=(N/2)\sin\theta d\theta \quad . \quad . \quad . \quad (4)$$

the integration being with respect to ϕ.

To find the *number of collisions* per second made on unit area of the wall by all the molecules represented by radii in the cone of solid angle $d\omega=\sin\theta d\theta d\phi$, it is first assumed that all the molecules in the gas have the same velocity c along the various directions of motion. The number of molecules per cm.^{3}

[1] A *solid angle* is measured by the area cut off on a sphere of unit radius (" unit sphere ") by a cone, not necessarily circular, with its vertex at the centre of the sphere, and subtending (or enclosing) the given solid angle. Clearly, the total solid angle surrounding a point is 4π, this being the total area of the surface of the unit sphere ($4\pi a^2$, where a=radius=1).

having velocities in the directions enclosed by the solid angle $d\omega$ is $(N/V)(d\omega/4\pi)$. All the molecules contained in a cylinder of length c and 1 cm.^{2} cross-section will just collide with 1 cm.^{2} of the wall in 1 sec. (Fig. 4.III). The volume of the cylinder is $c \cos \theta$, hence the number of molecules in the cylinder is:

$$(N/V)(d\omega/4\pi)c \cos \theta = (Nc/4\pi V) \cos \theta \sin \theta d\theta d\phi \quad . \quad . \quad . \quad (5)$$

This expression involves two differentials $d\theta$ and $d\phi$, so that two integrations will be necessary: first integrate with respect to ϕ, keeping θ constant, and then integrate the result with respect to θ, keeping ϕ constant (since θ and ϕ are independent variables). This is represented by a double integral, as explained in § 22.I.

The total number of collisions per second on 1 cm.^{2} by *all the molecules* in the volume V will be:

$$(Nc/4\pi V)\int_0^{\pi/2}\int_0^{2\pi} \cos \theta \sin \theta d\theta d\phi \quad . \quad . \quad . \quad . \quad . \quad (6)$$

in which θ is taken from 0 to $\pi/2$ only, since only the molecules with velocities in the direction of one *hemisphere* can collide with 1 cm.^{2} of wall on that side. The integration with respect to ϕ will give simply 2π.

$$\text{Now } (Nc/4\pi V)\int_0^{\pi/2}\int_0^{2\pi} \cos \theta \sin \theta d\theta d\phi = (Nc\,.\,2\pi/4\pi V)\int_0^{\pi/2} \cos \theta \sin \theta d\theta$$

$$= (Nc/2V)\int_0^{\pi/2} \tfrac{1}{2} \sin 2\theta d\theta = (Nc/2V)\int_0^{\pi/2} \tfrac{1}{4} \sin 2\theta d(2\theta), \text{ from (9), § 41.I}$$

$$= -(Nc/8V)\Big[\cos 2\theta\Big]_{\theta=0}^{\theta=\pi/2} = -(Nc/8V)[-1-1], \text{ from (1), § 43.I}$$

(since $\cos 0 = +1$ and $\cos \pi = -1$; see § 40.I).

$$= Nc/4V \quad . \quad . \quad . \quad . \quad . \quad . \quad . \quad . \quad (7) \qquad = N_L c/4 \quad . \quad . \quad . \quad . \quad . \quad . \quad . \quad (8)$$

where $N_L = N/V =$ no. of molecules per cm.^{3} If the molecules had been supposed divided into three groups with equal velocities in each direction, and half of one group with velocities towards a particular direction taken, the incorrect result $N_L c/6$ would have been found. The simple calculation of § 2 gives the correct formula for the pressure, but an incorrect value for the number of molecules colliding with the wall.

Only the component $c \cos \theta$ of the velocity c is effective in producing a *pressure* on the wall, and hence the change of momentum per collision of each molecule of mass m with the wall is $mc \cos \theta - (-mc \cos \theta) = 2mc \cos \theta$. The total change of momentum per second is found by multiplying this by the number of collisions per second in the (θ, ϕ) direction, and then integrating over all possible values of θ and ϕ:

$$\therefore p = \frac{Nc}{4\pi V}\int_0^{\pi/2}\int_0^{2\pi} \cos \theta \sin \theta d\theta d\phi \,.\, 2mc \cos \theta$$

$$= \frac{2Nc^2m}{4\pi V}\int_0^{\pi/2}\int_0^{2\pi} \cos^2 \theta \sin \theta d\theta d\phi = \frac{2Nc^2m\,.\,2\pi}{4\pi V}\int_0^{\pi/2} \cos^2 \theta \sin \theta d\theta$$

$$= \frac{Nmc^2}{V}\int_0^{\pi/2} \cos^2 \theta \sin \theta \, d\theta = -\frac{Nmc^2}{3V}\int_0^{\pi/2} d\,(\cos^3 \theta),$$

since $d\,(\cos^3 \theta) = -3 \cos^2 \theta \sin \theta d\theta$ (see §§ 8 and 42.I), and since $\cos (\pi/2) = 0$ and $\cos 0 = 1$ (see § 40.I):

$$\therefore p = -\tfrac{1}{3}(Nmc^2/V)\Big[\cos^3 \theta\Big]_0^{\pi/2} = -\tfrac{1}{3}(Nmc^2/V)(0-1) = Nmc^2/3V \quad . \quad (9)$$

Since Nm/V is the total mass of all the molecules in the volume V divided by this volume, it is equal to the density ρ (mass per cm.³) of the gas. Hence:

$$p=\tfrac{1}{3}\rho c^2 \quad . \quad . \quad . \quad . \quad . \quad . \quad . \quad . \quad . \quad . \quad (10)$$

Now suppose the molecules have *different velocities* instead of a constant velocity c. The contribution to the pressure of a group of N_1 molecules having a velocity c_1 is, from (9): $p_1=N_1mc_1^2/3V$, and the total pressure, found by summing over all the velocities $c_1, c_2, \ldots$, is:

$$p=\Sigma N_1mc_1^2/3V=(m/3V)\Sigma N_1c_1^2.$$

Put $$\Sigma N_1c_1^2=N\overline{c^2} \quad . \quad . \quad . \quad . \quad . \quad . \quad . \quad . \quad (11)$$

where $N=\Sigma N_1$ is the total number of molecules in the volume V, and $\overline{c^2}$ is the *mean square velocity*, i.e. the average of the squares of the velocities (which is different from $(\bar{c})^2$, the square of the mean velocity), defined by:

$$\overline{c^2}=(N_1c_1^2+N_2c_2^2+\ldots)/(N_1+N_2+\ldots)=\Sigma N_1c_1^2/\Sigma N_1=\Sigma N_1c_1^2/N \quad (12)$$

If all the molecules had the same velocity $\sqrt{(\overline{c^2})}$ the pressure would be that observed, hence:

$$p=\tfrac{1}{3}Nm\overline{c^2}/V=\tfrac{1}{3}N_Lm\overline{c^2}=\tfrac{1}{3}\rho\overline{c^2} \quad . \quad . \quad . \quad . \quad . \quad . \quad (13)$$

which is the same result as that found in § 2 (where u replaced c).

Let V_m=molar volume (containing 1 g.mol. wt. or 1 mol, M). Then $\rho=N_Lm=M/V_m$,

$$\therefore\ p=(M/3V_m)\overline{c^2} \quad . \quad . \quad . \quad . \quad . \quad . \quad . \quad . \quad (14)$$

The *absolute temperature*, T, of the gas, which is identical with that defined by the general gas law (§ 6.II), $pV_m=\boldsymbol{R}T$, may now be introduced into (14): $pV_m=\tfrac{1}{3}M\overline{c^2}=\boldsymbol{R}T$,

$$\therefore\ \overline{c^2}=3\boldsymbol{R}T/M=3\boldsymbol{k}T/m \quad . \quad . \quad . \quad . \quad . \quad . \quad . \quad (15)$$

where $\boldsymbol{k}=\boldsymbol{R}/N$ is the gas constant per *molecule*, called *Boltzmann's constant*, N being N_LV_m, Avogadro's number (§ 7), or the number of molecules in a mol, and $m=M/N$ is the mass of a molecule. Hence:

$$T=\tfrac{2}{3}\cdot\tfrac{1}{2}M\overline{c^2}/\boldsymbol{R}=\tfrac{2}{3}E/\boldsymbol{R}=\tfrac{2}{3}\bar{\epsilon}/\boldsymbol{k},$$

where E is the translational kinetic energy of a mol of gas, and $\bar{\epsilon}$ is the mean translational kinetic energy of a molecule, $\bar{\epsilon}=E/N$. Hence:

$$\bar{\epsilon}=\tfrac{3}{2}\boldsymbol{R}T/N=\tfrac{3}{2}\boldsymbol{k}T \quad . \quad . \quad . \quad . \quad . \quad . \quad . \quad (16)$$

The value of $\boldsymbol{k}$ is $1{\cdot}38\times10^{-16}$ erg/degree per molecule. An alternative procedure is to *define* T by (15), when the discussion rests wholly on the kinetic theory (see § 2). Brillouin [1] attempted to extend the kinetic definition of temperature to liquids and solids by taking the equation: $1+b\bar{E}=aT$, where $\bar{E}$ is the mean kinetic energy of the molecules, a is a constant, and b is a function of the coordinates.

From (16), the part of the heat capacity per mol (*molecular heat*) at constant volume of a gas due to the translational kinetic energy only is found to be:

$$C_v=(\mathrm{d}E/\mathrm{d}T)_V=\tfrac{3}{2}\boldsymbol{R}\simeq3\ \text{g.cal./mol} \quad . \quad . \quad . \quad . \quad . \quad (17)$$

For an ideal gas (§ 3, (1)), $C_p=C_v+\boldsymbol{R}$, and hence for a monatomic gas, for which (17) gives the *total* heat capacity per mol at constant volume, $C_p/C_v=\gamma=5/3=1{\cdot}666\ldots$

[1] *Ann. Chim.*, 1909, **18**, 387

If u, v, w are the components of the molecular velocity c in the directions of the x, y, z axes:

$$c^2=u^2+v^2+w^2,$$

$$\therefore\ \tfrac{1}{2}m\overline{c^2}=\tfrac{1}{2}m\overline{u^2}+\tfrac{1}{2}m\overline{v^2}+\tfrac{1}{2}m\overline{w^2}.$$

Boltzmann [1] assumed a state of *molecular chaos*, viz. that on the average there is no correlation between the positions and velocities of the molecules. In that case, the molecular velocities have no preferred directions in space, and the mean values of u^2, v^2, and w^2 must all be equal; hence, from (15):

$$\tfrac{1}{2}m\overline{u^2}=\tfrac{1}{2}m\overline{v^2}=\tfrac{1}{2}m\overline{w^2}=\tfrac{1}{2}(\tfrac{1}{3}m\overline{c^2})=\tfrac{1}{2}kT \quad . \quad . \quad . \quad . \quad . \quad (18)$$

This is a special case of the *principle of equipartition of energy*, further considered in § 9.

For a *mixture of different kinds of molecules*, the same reasoning which led to (9) gives:

$$p=N_1m_1\overline{c_1^2}/3V+N_2m_2\overline{c_2^2}/3V+\ldots \quad . \quad . \quad . \quad . \quad . \quad (19)$$

The assumption that the average translational kinetic energy of each kind of molecule is the same at the same temperature (see § 2) [2] (another form of the principle of equipartition of energy):

$$\tfrac{1}{2}m_1\overline{c_1^2}=\tfrac{1}{2}m_2\overline{c_2^2}=\ldots \quad . \quad . \quad . \quad . \quad . \quad . \quad . \quad (20)$$

then gives: $p=(m_1\overline{c_1^2}/3V)(N_1+N_2+\ldots)=(3kT/3V)(N_1+N_2+\ldots)$

$$=(RT/NV)(N_1+N_2+\ldots)=(RT/V)(n_1+n_2+\ldots) \quad . \quad . \quad . \quad (21)$$

where n_1, n_2, . . . are the numbers of *mols* of the gases in the volume V. Equation (21) is *Dalton's Law of Partial Pressures* (§ 2). If this is assumed as an experimental result, the validity of (20) follows.

§ 9. Equipartition of Energy

The theorem of *equipartition of energy* was first stated by Waterston in a paper presented in 1845, read in 1846, and first published in 1892.[3] It was again stated by Maxwell, in 1859,[4] and a few years later it was brought into prominence by Boltzmann.[5] It was treated from a different point of view by Maxwell in 1879,[6] who regarded it as doubtful, saying that: " The theorem that the average kinetic energy of a single molecule is the same for different gases is not sufficient to establish the condition of equilibrium of temperature between

[1] " Gastheorie," 1896, **1**, 20; this assumption was criticised by Burbury, " A Treatise on the Kinetic Theory of Gases," Cambridge, 1899, 10, 24 f.; Holm, *Ann. Phys.*, 1915, **48**, 481; see § 10.

[2] For two kinds of smooth hard elastic spheres this may be proved directly from the laws of collision: see Jeans, " Kinetic Theory of Gases," 1940, 21; cf. Maxwell, *Phil. Mag.*, 1860, **20**, 21; Holm, *loc. cit.*

[3] *Phil. Trans.*, 1892, **183**, 1 (16); published by Lord Rayleigh. Waterston says: " In mixed media, the mean square molecular velocity is inversely proportional to the specific weight of the molecule. This is the law of the equilibrium of *vis-viva*." Lord Rayleigh, who found the paper in the archives of the Royal Society, and had it printed, remarks in a footnote: " This is the first statement of a very important theorem," but adds that Waterston's proof of it " can hardly be defended." See Haldane, " Gases and Liquids," 1928, 4 f.

[4] *Phil. Mag.*, 1860, **19**, 19; 1860, **20**, 21; " Scientific Papers," Cambridge, 1890, **1**, 377.

[5] Boltzmann, *Wien Ber.*, 1866, **53**, II, 195; 1867, **56**, II, 682; 1868, **58**, II, 517; 1871, **63**, II, 397, 679, 712; 1876, **74**, II, 553; 1881, **84**, II, 136; 1887, **94**, II, 613; 1887, **95**, II, 153; 1888, **96**, II, 891; 1894, **103**, II, 1125; *Phil. Mag.*, 1882, **14**, 299; 1887, **23**, 305; 1888, **25**, 81; 1893, **35**, 153; *Berlin Ber.*, 1888, 1395; *Z. phys. Chem.*, 1893, **11**, 751; " Wiss. Abhl.," 1909, **1**, 9, 34, 49, 237, 288; **2**, 103, 572, 582; **3**, 225, 272, 293, 366, 428, 500, 510, 598, 645.

[6] *Trans. Cambr. Phil. Soc.*, 1879, **12**, 547; " Scientific Papers," Cambridge, 1890, **2**, 713; " Theory of Heat," edit. Rayleigh, 1897, 326; his treatment was improved by Jeans, " Dynamical Theory of Gases," 3rd edit., 1921, 97; Rayleigh, *Phil. Mag.*, 1892, **33**, 356; **1900**, **49**, 98; " Scientific Papers," 1902, **3**, 554; 1903, **4**, 433.

gases of different kinds, such as oxygen and nitrogen, because when the gases are mixed we have no means of ascertaining the temperature of the oxygen and of the nitrogen separately. We can only ascertain the temperature of the mixture by putting a thermometer into it."

The theorem of equipartition of energy was regarded with peculiar animosity by most British physicists, Lord Kelvin,[1] e.g., saying that it is: "not only unproved but untrue." It is now a standard theorem in regions in which it applies, i.e. where the quantum theory goes over into it in the limiting case, and a general proof, due essentially to Boltzmann, will be given later (§ 20.IV).

§ 10. Maxwell's Distribution Law

Even if all the molecules of a gas had initially the same velocity c (without regard to direction), this would be upset by collisions, as is seen from the simple case shown in Fig. 5.III, in which a collision of two molecules moving with equal velocities at right angles is depicted. Molecule A is then brought to rest and molecule B moves off with a velocity $\sqrt{2}$ times its initial velocity, in a direction inclined at 45° to its original motion. The problem of the distribution of molecular velocities in a gas in a steady state (p and T constant) was solved by Maxwell[2] in 1859 by the following method.[3] He probably arrived at the result intuitively, and then constructed a demonstration.[4]

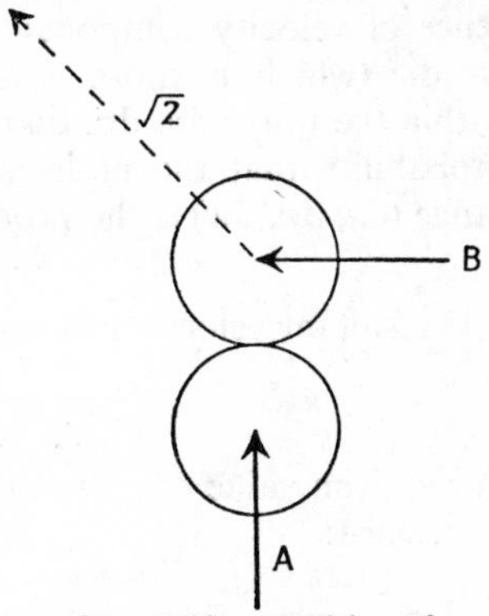

FIG. 5.III. Collision of Molecules

Maxwell considered a large number of gas molecules having component velocities u, v, w, and assumed that the *probability* for the occurrence of a given velocity component, say u, is independent of the values of the

[1] *Proc. Roy. Soc.*, 1891, **50**, 79; 1892, **51**, 397; *Phil. Mag.*, 1892, **33**, 466; *Nature*, 1901, **63**, 387; "Math. and Phys. Papers," 1910, **4**, 484, 495; in his "Baltimore Lectures," 1904, 504, he admitted the force of Rayleigh's criticisms. See Larmor, *Proc. Roy. Soc.*, 1909, **83**, 82.

[2] *B.A. Rep.*, 1859, ii, 9; *Phil. Mag.*, 1860, **19**, 19; "Scientific Papers," 1890, **1**, 377; an essentially similar deduction is given by Kirchhoff, "Theorie der Wärme," 1894, 134, 142; and Weinstein, "Thermodynamik and Kinetik der Körper," 1901, **1**, 134; Hodges, *Phys. Rev.*, 1900, **10**, 253; Wassmuth, *Wien Ber.*, 1921, **130**, IIA, 159.

[3] Since the deduction does not introduce the consideration of molecular collisions, it cannot be regarded as *dynamically* satisfactory, and there is a very large literature giving, and criticising, other proofs. A proof by O. E. Meyer, "Kinetische Theorie der Gase," 1877, 259, was criticised by Boltzmann, *Wien Ber.*, 1877, **76**, II, 373; "Wiss. Abhl.," 1909, **2**, 164, and a second proof by O. E. Meyer, *Ann. Phys.*, 1880, **10**, 296, was again criticised by Boltzmann, *Ann. Phys.*, 1880, **11**, 529; "Wiss. Abhl.," 1909, **2**, 354. Boltzmann's own proof, *Wien Ber.*, 1871, **63**, II, 397; "Wiss. Abhl.," 1909, **1**, 237 (see H. W. Watson, "Kinetic Theory of Gases," 1876, 1f.) was criticised by Burbury, "A Treatise on the Kinetic Theory of Gases," Cambridge, 1899, 10, 24f.; Kirchhoff's deduction (see [2]) was criticised by Boltzmann, *Munich Ber.*, 1894, **24**, 207; *Ann. Phys.*, 1894, **53**, 955; "Wiss. Abhl.," 1909, **3**, 528. Planck, *Ann. Phys.*, 1895, **55**, 220, attempted to improve Kirchhoff's deduction, but the improvement was not admitted by Boltzmann, *Munich Ber.*, 1895, **25**, 25; *Ann. Phys.*, 1895, **55**, 223; "Wiss. Abhl.," 1909, **3**, 532. A discussion between Zemplén Győző, *Ann. Phys.*, 1900, **2**, 404; 1900, **3**, 761, and Burbury, *ibid.*, 1900, **3**, 355; 1901, **4**, 646, may be mentioned. Jeans, *Phil. Mag.*, 1903, **5**, 597; "Dynamical Theory of Gases," 3rd edit., 1921, 39, was criticised by Burbury, *Phil. Mag.*, 1903, **6**, 529; 1904, **7**, 467, but his views were not accepted by Jeans, *ibid.*, 1903, **6**, 720; 1904, **7**, 468; see also Lenz, *Phys. Z.*, 1910, **11**, 1175, 1260; Borel, *Rev. Gén. Sci.*, 1912, **23**, 842; del Lungo, *Nuov. Cim.*, 1916, **12**, 215; a simple strict deduction is given by von Mises, *Phys. Z.*, 1918, **19**, 81.

[4] Polvani, *Nuov. Cim.*, 1924, **1**, 1.

other two velocity components, say v and w. This assumption (which is one form of what has been called the principle of *molecular chaos*; § 8) is one of the largest bones of contention over which the opposing schools have quarrelled. The assumption was rejected by Burbury,[1] and by Poincaré [2]; the first claimed that molecular chaos had never been properly defined, and the second stated that it is an unjustifiable application of the laws of probability. In the presence of so much stir, one can only wonder at the genius of Maxwell, which produced such a fundamental and accurate law by a method which gave so little satisfaction to the mathematical purists. Maxwell's deduction proceeds as follows.

The probability that a velocity component of a selected molecule lies between u and $u+du$ is assumed to be a function $f(u)du$ of u alone, and independent of v and w; and similarly for $f(v)dv$ and $f(w)dw$. The probabilities for the occurrence of velocity components in the ranges u to $u+du$, v to $v+dv$, and w to $w+dw$ (which is more concisely stated by saying that the components lie within the range du, dv, dw) are, therefore, $f(u)du$, $f(v)dv$, and $f(w)dw$, and the probability that the molecule has *simultaneously* velocity components in the range (du, dv, dw) is the product of the separate probabilities:

$$f(u)f(v)f(w)du dv dw \quad . \quad . \quad . \quad . \quad . \quad . \quad . \quad . \quad (1)$$

The resultant velocity c is supposed to be constant, and since:

$$c^2=u^2+v^2+w^2 \quad . \quad . \quad . \quad . \quad . \quad . \quad . \quad . \quad (2)$$

$$\therefore \quad d(c^2)=udu+vdv+wdw=0 \quad . \quad . \quad . \quad . \quad . \quad . \quad (3)$$

For a given value of c the value of $f(u)f(v)f(w)$ is constant, hence by differentiation, since:

$$df(u)=f'(u)du, \text{ etc.} \quad . \quad . \quad . \quad . \quad . \quad . \quad . \quad (4)$$

$$\therefore \quad f'(u)f(v)f(w)du+f(u)f'(v)f(w)dv+f(u)f(v)f'(w)dw=0 \quad . \quad . \quad (5)$$

Divide by $f(u)f(v)f(w)$:

$$\therefore \quad \frac{f'(u)}{f(u)}du+\frac{f'(v)}{f(v)}dv+\frac{f'(w)}{f(w)}dw=0 \quad . \quad . \quad . \quad . \quad . \quad (6)$$

Now multiply (3) by an arbitrary constant λ and add to (6):

$$\therefore \quad \left(\frac{f'(u)}{f(u)}+\lambda u\right)du+\left(\frac{f'(v)}{f(v)}+\lambda v\right)dv+\left(\frac{f'(w)}{f(w)}+\lambda w\right)dw=0 \quad . \quad . \quad (7)$$

Since the values of du, dv, and dw, are now perfectly arbitrary, it follows [3] that their multipliers are *separately* zero:

$$\frac{f'(u)}{f(u)}+\lambda u=0 \qquad \therefore \quad \frac{f'(u)}{f(u)}du=-\lambda udu,$$

$$\frac{f'(v)}{f(v)}+\lambda v=0 \qquad \therefore \quad \frac{f'(v)}{f(v)}dv=-\lambda vdv,$$

$$\frac{f'(w)}{f(w)}+\lambda w=0 \qquad \therefore \quad \frac{f'(w)}{f(w)}dw=-\lambda wdw.$$

[1] " A Treatise on the Kinetic Theory of Gases," Cambridge, 1899, 10, 24 f.; see his polemics with Zemplén Győző, and Jeans, in ref. [3], p. 251; also the polemic between Bertrand, *Compt. Rend.*, 1896, **122**, 963, 1083, 1174, 1314, and Boltzmann, *ibid.*, 1896, **122**, 1173, 1314; also Rayleigh, *Phil. Mag.*, 1891, **32**, 424; " Scientific Papers," 1902, **3**, 473 (on collisions); Edgeworth, *Phil. Mag.*, 1920, **40**, 248; 1922, **43**, 241 (on probabilities); Holm, *Ann. Phys.* 1915, **48**, 481.

[2] " Calcul des Probabilités," Paris, 1896, 21. Oseen, *Arkiv Mat. Astron. Fys.*, 1921, **16**, No. 3, said it will not hold if the particles have potential energy.

[3] On this point, see Moelwyn-Hughes, " Physical Chemistry," Cambridge, **1940**, 59; Hinshelwood, " The Kinetics of Chemical Change," Oxford, 1945, 21.

Integration (§ 18.I) gives:

$$\ln f(u) = -\lambda u^2/2 + \ln A,$$
$$\ln f(v) = -\lambda v^2/2 + \ln A,$$
$$\ln f(w) = -\lambda w^2/2 + \ln A,$$

where $\ln A$ is written for the constant of integration. Thus (§ 13.I), if α is a constant given by $\lambda/2 = 1/\alpha^2$:

$$f(u) = Ae^{-\lambda u^2/2} = Ae^{-u^2/\alpha^2}$$
$$f(v) = Ae^{-\lambda v^2/2} = Ae^{-v^2/\alpha^2}$$
$$f(w) = Ae^{-\lambda w^2/2} = Ae^{-w^2/\alpha^2}$$

Thus: $$f(u) = Ae^{-u^2/\alpha^2}, \text{ etc.} \qquad (8)$$

$$\therefore f(u)du = Ae^{-u^2/\alpha^2}du, \text{ etc.} \qquad (9)$$

If the total number of molecules in the gas is N, the *number of molecules* having a velocity component between u and $u+du$ will be the product of N and the probability for this range:

$$dN_u = NAe^{-u^2/\alpha^2}du \qquad (10)$$

and the number with velocity components *simultaneously* between u and $u+du$, v and $v+dv$, and w and $w+dw$ i.e. in the range (du, dv, dw) will be:

$$dN_{uvw} = (NAe^{-u^2/\alpha^2}du)(Ae^{-v^2/\alpha^2}dv)(Ae^{-w^2/\alpha^2}dw)$$
$$= NA^3e^{-(u^2+v^2+w^2)/\alpha^2}dudvdw = NA^3e^{-c^2/\alpha^2}dudvdw \qquad (11)$$

The values of the constants A and α are found as follows. *Each* velocity *component*, u, v, and w, has all possible values between $-\infty$ and $+\infty$, and hence the integration [1] of (10) between these limits gives the total number of molecules, N:

$$\therefore \int dN_u = N = NA\int_{-\infty}^{+\infty} e^{-u^2/\alpha^2}du$$

$$\therefore A\int_{-\infty}^{+\infty} e^{-u^2/\alpha^2}du = 1 \qquad (12)$$

and similarly

$$A\int_{-\infty}^{+\infty} e^{-v^2/\alpha^2}dv = 1 \qquad (13)$$

$$\therefore \left(A\int_{-\infty}^{+\infty} e^{-u^2/\alpha^2}du\right)\left(A\int_{-\infty}^{+\infty} e^{-v^2/\alpha^2}dv\right) = A^2\int_{-\infty}^{+\infty}\int_{-\infty}^{+\infty} e^{-(u^2+v^2)/\alpha^2}dudv = 1.$$

Put $u/\alpha = x$, $v/\alpha = y$, $\therefore du = \alpha dx$, $dv = \alpha dy$,

$$\therefore A^2\alpha^2\int_{-\infty}^{+\infty}\int_{-\infty}^{+\infty} e^{-(x^2+y^2)}dxdy = 1 \qquad (14)$$

The double integral was evaluated in § 54.I, and is equal to π, hence $\pi A^2\alpha^2 = 1$ from (14),

$$\therefore A = 1/\alpha\sqrt{\pi} \qquad (15)$$

$$\int_{-\infty}^{+\infty}\int_{-\infty}^{+\infty} e^{-(x^2+y^2)}dxdy = \pi. \qquad (16)$$

From (8) and (15):

$$f(u) = (1/\alpha\sqrt{\pi})e^{-u^2/\alpha^2}, \quad f(v) = (1/\alpha\sqrt{\pi})e^{-v^2/\alpha^2}, \quad f(w) = (1/\alpha\sqrt{\pi})e^{-w^2/\alpha^2} \qquad (17)$$

The constant α remains to be determined, and this is taken up below.

[1] The integral $\int_{-\infty}^{+\infty} e^{-x^2}dx$ was evaluated by Laplace, 1778.

The distribution of velocities given by Maxwell's law is of the same type as the distribution of shots on a target made by a practised marksman,[1] both being subject to the same law as the distribution of errors given by the method of least squares.[2] Equations (17) show, as Maxwell pointed out, that a zero value for *one* of the three components of velocity is more probable than any other, since e^{-u^2/α^2}, etc., have the maximum value 1 when u, etc., $=0$. This does not mean that the *resultant* velocity is zero, since the other two components can have all possible values. With the analogy of the target, if a series of parallel lines are drawn across it (parallel to the x or y axis), the one of each set which passes through the origin has most points on it; points equidistant from the centre lie on a circle described about the centre, and the *circle* passing through most shot-marks is not one of the inner circles, which are too small to contain many marks, but a circle of medium size.

The probability for a given velocity c *in a definite direction* is:

$$f(u)f(v)f(w)dudvdw=(1/\alpha^3\pi^{3/2})e^{-c^2/\alpha^2}dudvdw \quad . \quad . \quad . \quad . \quad (18)$$

or, since $dudvdw=d\tau=c^2 \sin\theta d\theta d\phi dc$, as shown in § 8, where c is taken as a, this probability is also:

$$(1/\alpha^3\pi^{3/2})e^{-c^2/\alpha^2}c^2 \sin\theta d\theta d\phi dc \quad . \quad . \quad . \quad . \quad . \quad . \quad (19)$$

The probability for a given velocity between c and $c+dc$ *without regard to a particular direction* is found by integrating (19) over all directions in space, i.e. taking θ from 0 to π and ϕ from 0 to 2π, which gives a complete sphere:

$$(1/\alpha^3\pi^{3/2})c^2e^{-c^2/\alpha^2}dc\int_0^{\pi}\int_0^{2\pi}\sin\theta d\theta d\phi$$

$$=(2\pi c^2/\alpha^3\pi^{3/2})e^{-c^2/\alpha^2}dc\int_0^{\pi}\sin\theta d\theta=-(2c^2/\alpha^3\sqrt{\pi})e^{-c^2/\alpha^2}dc\int_0^{\pi}d(\cos\theta)$$

$$=-(2c^2/\alpha^3\sqrt{\pi})e^{-c^2/\alpha^2}\Big[\cos\theta\Big]_0^{\pi}dc=(4/\alpha^3\sqrt{\pi})c^2e^{-c^2/\alpha^2}dc \quad . \quad . \quad . \quad (20)$$

since $\cos\pi=-1$ and $\cos 0=1$.

Hence the number of molecules in a total number N having velocities between c and $c+dc$ *in any direction* is

$$dN_c=(4N/\alpha^3\sqrt{\pi})c^2e^{-c^2/\alpha^2}dc \quad . \quad . \quad . \quad . \quad . \quad . \quad (21)$$

The value of the constant α is next found as follows. The *most probable velocity* is found from the condition that (21) is a maximum, i.e. (§ 9.I):

$$(d/dc)c^2e^{-c^2/\alpha^2}=0.$$

The differentiation (§ 13.I) gives:

$$2ce^{-c^2/\alpha^2}+c^2(d/dc)e^{-c^2/\alpha^2}=2ce^{-c^2/\alpha^2}+c^2e^{-c^2/\alpha^2}(d/dc)(-c^2/\alpha^2)$$

$$=2ce^{-c^2/\alpha^2}-(2c/\alpha^2)c^2e^{-c^2/\alpha^2}=2e^{-c^2/\alpha^2}(1-c^2/\alpha^2)=0,$$

and since e^{-c^2/α^2} is not zero:

$$\therefore\ 1-c^2/\alpha^2=0, \quad \therefore\ c^2=\alpha^2 \quad . \quad . \quad . \quad . \quad . \quad . \quad . \quad . \quad (22)$$

or α is *the most probable velocity*; hence α can be retained in the equations with this meaning. (It should be noted that c in (22) is a special value of the velocity, viz. α, and is not the general symbol of previous, and later, equations.)

[1] Maxwell, *J.C.S.*, 1875, **13**, 493; Mellor, "Higher Mathematics for Students of Chemistry and Physics," 1919, 511, 534.

[2] Gauss, "Theoria Combinationis Observationum," Göttingen, 1823; "Werke," Göttingen, 1873, **4**, 1; Poincaré, "Calcul des Probabilités," Paris, 1896, 147; Czuber, "Wahrscheinlichkeitsrechnung," Leipzig and Berlin, 4th edit., 1924, **1**, 291.

To find the *mean* (or average) *velocity*, $\bar{c}$, the sum of all the velocities of the molecules must be divided by N, the total number of molecules. Thus, (21) is multiplied by c and integrated [1] from $c=0$ to $c=\infty$, and then the result divided by N:

$$c=\frac{1}{N}\cdot\frac{4N}{\alpha^3\sqrt{\pi}}\int_0^\infty c^2e^{-c^2/\alpha^2}\,.\,c\,.\,dc=(4/\alpha^3\sqrt{\pi})\int_0^\infty c^3e^{-c^2/\alpha^2}dc.$$

Put $c/\alpha=x$, $\therefore\ c^3=x^3\alpha^3$; $c^2/\alpha^2=x^2$; $dc=\alpha dx$,

$$\therefore\ \bar{c}=(4\alpha/\sqrt{\pi})\int_0^\infty x^3e^{-x^2}dx=(4\alpha/\sqrt{\pi})J_1,$$

where J_1 is the value of the integral. The value of J_1 can be found by integration by parts (§ 19, I): $\int u dv=uv-\int v du$. Put $u=x^2$, $\therefore\ du=2xdx$, and $dv=xe^{-x^2}dx$, $\therefore\ udv=x^3e^{-x^2}dx$, and $v=\int xe^{-x^2}dx=-\frac{1}{2}\int d(e^{-x^2})=-\frac{1}{2}e^{-x^2}$. Hence:

$$\int_0^\infty x^3e^{-x^2}dx=\left[-\tfrac{1}{2}x^2e^{-x^2}+\int xe^{-x^2}dx\right]_0^\infty=\left[\tfrac{1}{2}x^2e^{-x^2}-\tfrac{1}{2}e^{-x^2}\right]_0^\infty.$$

The first term vanishes at both limits (0 and ∞); the second vanishes at the limit ∞, but becomes $\frac{1}{2}$ at the limit 0; hence:

$$J_1=\int_0^\infty x^3e^{-x^2}dx=\tfrac{1}{2}. \quad . \quad . \quad . \quad . \quad . \quad . \quad . \quad (23)$$

and $$\bar{c}=\tfrac{1}{2}(4\alpha/\sqrt{\pi})=2\alpha/\sqrt{\pi} \quad . \quad . \quad . \quad . \quad . \quad . \quad (24)$$

i.e. *mean velocity*$=(2/\sqrt{\pi})(=1{\cdot}1284)\times$*most probable velocity*.

The *mean square velocity* $\overline{c^2}$ is, similarly, found by multiplying (21) by c^2, the result being integrated from 0 to ∞, and divided by N (the division by N, a constant, is performed first):

$$\overline{c^2}=(4/\alpha^3\sqrt{\pi})\int_0^\infty c^2\,.\,c^2e^{-c^2/\alpha^2}dc=(4/\alpha^3\sqrt{\pi})\int_0^\infty c^4e^{-c^2/\alpha^2}dc \quad . \quad . \quad (25)$$

Put $c/\alpha=x$, and integrate by parts twice:

$$\overline{c^2}=(4\alpha^2/\sqrt{\pi})\int_0^\infty x^4e^{-x^2}dx=(4\alpha^2/\sqrt{\pi})J_2,$$

where J_2 denotes the integral.

(i) Put $u=x^3$, $\therefore\ du=3x^2dx$; and $dv=xe^{-x^2}$, $\therefore\ v=-e^{-x^2}/2$. Hence:

$$J_2=\int_0^\infty x^4e^{-x^2}dx=\left[-\tfrac{1}{2}x^3e^{-x^2}+\tfrac{3}{2}\int x^2e^{-x^2}dx\right]_0^\infty \quad . \quad . \quad . \quad (25a)$$

The first term in the brackets vanishes at both limits; to find the second, integrate by parts.

(ii) Put $u=x$, $\therefore\ du=dx$; and $dv=xe^{-x^2}dx$, $\therefore\ v=-\frac{1}{2}e^{-x^2}$,

$$\therefore\ \int_0^\infty x^2e^{-x^2}dx=\left[-\tfrac{1}{2}xe^{-x^2}+\tfrac{1}{2}\int e^{-x^2}dx\right]_0^\infty \quad . \quad . \quad . \quad (25b)$$

The first term in the brackets vanishes at both limits; to find the second the formula (16) is used:

$$\pi=\int_{-\infty}^{+\infty}\int_{-\infty}^{+\infty}e^{-(x^2+y^2)}dxdy=\left[\int_{-\infty}^{+\infty}e^{-x^2}dx\right]^2.$$

Since e^{-x^2} is an even function of x (§ 21.I), i.e. has the same value and sign for equal positive and negative real values of x (since $(-x)^2=x^2$), it follows

[1] Note that c is never negative; it is the velocity along the path of the molecule.

that the integral from $-\infty$ to 0 is the same as the integral from 0 to $+\infty$, hence from (3), § 21.I:

$$\pi = \left[2\int_0^\infty e^{-x^2}dx\right]^2,$$

$$\therefore \int_0^\infty e^{-x^2}dx = \frac{\sqrt{\pi}}{2}, \quad \text{and} \quad \int_0^\infty x^2 e^{-x^2}dx = \frac{\sqrt{\pi}}{4} \quad . \quad . \quad . \quad (26)$$

Hence from (25), (25a), and (25b):

$$\overline{c^2} = \frac{4\alpha^2}{\sqrt{\pi}}\int_0^\infty x^4 e^{-x^2}dx = \frac{4\alpha^2}{\sqrt{\pi}} \cdot \tfrac{3}{2} \cdot \tfrac{1}{2}\frac{\sqrt{\pi}}{2} = \tfrac{3}{2}\alpha^2 \quad . \quad . \quad . \quad (27)$$

$$\therefore \sqrt{(\overline{c^2})} = \sqrt{(3/2)}\alpha = 1{\cdot}2248\alpha,$$

$$\text{or } \alpha = 0{\cdot}8165\sqrt{(\overline{c^2})} \quad . \quad . \quad . \quad (27a)$$

This most important result allows the constant α in Maxwell's equation to be replaced by an expression involving the absolute temperature, since, from (15), § 8, $\overline{c^2} = 3\boldsymbol{k}T/m$, where $\boldsymbol{k}$ is Boltzmann's constant,

$$\therefore \alpha^2 = \tfrac{2}{3}\overline{c^2} = 2\boldsymbol{k}T/m \quad . \quad . \quad . \quad (28)$$

On substituting $\alpha = \sqrt{(2\boldsymbol{k}T/m)}$ in (21), this becomes:

$$dN_c = (4N/\alpha^3\sqrt{\pi})c^2 e^{-c^2/\alpha^2}dc$$

$$= [N\sqrt{(2/\pi)}](m/\boldsymbol{k}T)^{3/2}c^2 e^{-mc^2/2\boldsymbol{k}T}dc \quad . \quad . \quad . \quad (29)$$

$$= [N\sqrt{(2/\pi)}](M/RT)^{3/2}c^2 e^{-Mc^2/2RT}dc \quad . \quad . \quad . \quad (30)$$

since $m/\boldsymbol{k} = M/R$, where M=molecular weight. Put $\tfrac{1}{2}mc^2 = \epsilon$, the energy of a single molecule, then $m = 2\epsilon/c^2$, $c^2 = 2\epsilon/m$, $dc = d\epsilon/mc$,

$$\therefore dN_c = [N\sqrt{(2/\pi)}](m/\boldsymbol{k}T)^{3/2}c^2 e^{-mc^2/2\boldsymbol{k}T}dc \quad . \quad . \quad . \quad (31)$$

$$\text{and} \quad dN_\epsilon = N[2/\sqrt{\pi}(\boldsymbol{k}T)^{3/2}]e^{-\epsilon/\boldsymbol{k}T}\sqrt{(\epsilon)}d\epsilon \quad . \quad . \quad . \quad (32)$$

Boltzmann, and Jeans,[1] put:

$$1/2\boldsymbol{k}T = h \quad . \quad . \quad . \quad (33)$$

$$\therefore dN_c = 4\pi N(hm/\pi)^{3/2}e^{-hmc^2}c^2dc \quad . \quad . \quad . \quad (34)$$

Equations (24) and (28) give for the *mean* or *average velocity*:

$$\bar{c} = 2\alpha/\sqrt{\pi} = 2\sqrt{(2\boldsymbol{k}T/\pi m)} = 2\sqrt{(2RT/\pi M)} \quad . \quad . \quad . \quad (35)$$

It should be noted that $\bar{c}$ (sometimes denoted by Ω) is not the same as $\sqrt{(\overline{c^2})}$ (sometimes denoted by G):[2]

$$\bar{c} = 2\sqrt{(2\boldsymbol{k}T/\pi m)}, \quad \sqrt{(\overline{c^2})} = \sqrt{(3\boldsymbol{k}T/m)}$$

$$\therefore \bar{c} = [4/\sqrt{(6\pi)}]\sqrt{(\overline{c^2})} = 0{\cdot}9213\sqrt{(\overline{c^2})} \quad . \quad . \quad . \quad (36)$$

To find the *distribution of velocities in a given direction*, (11) can be used in the form:

$$dN_{uvw} = (N/\alpha^3\pi^{3/2})e^{-(u^2+v^2+w^2)/\alpha^2}du\,dv\,dw$$

$$= N(m/2\pi\boldsymbol{k}T)^{3/2}e^{-m(u^2+v^2+w^2)/2\boldsymbol{k}T}du\,dv\,dw \quad . \quad . \quad . \quad (37)$$

The *mean kinetic energy component in a given direction* is:

$$\tfrac{1}{2}m\overline{u^2} = (1/N)\int\frac{mu^2}{2}dN = \frac{\int_{-\infty}^{+\infty}(mu^2/2)\,.\,e^{-mu^2/2\boldsymbol{k}T}du}{\int_{-\infty}^{+\infty}e^{-mu^2/2\boldsymbol{k}T}du} = \frac{J_1}{J_2}.$$

[1] Fowler, *Phil. Mag.*, 1922, **43**, 785, proposed j instead of h, to avoid confusion with Planck's constant $\boldsymbol{h}$, but the "Continental" notation used above is almost universally adopted.

[2] Cf. Weinstein, "Thermodynamik und Kinetik der Körper," 1901, **1**, 142.

To find the integrals J_1 and J_2, put $u^2=2kTx^2/m$, therefore $\frac{1}{2}mu^2=kTx^2$,

$$\therefore\ J_1=kT\int_{-\infty}^{+\infty}x^2e^{-x^2}dx,\quad\text{and}\quad J_2=\int_{-\infty}^{+\infty}e^{-x^2}dx.$$

It has been shown (25b) that:

$$\int_0^\infty x^2e^{-x^2}dx=\frac{1}{2}\int_0^\infty e^{-x^2}dx,\quad\therefore\ J_1/J_2=\frac{1}{2},$$

$$\text{and}\quad \frac{1}{2}m\overline{u^2}=\frac{1}{2}kT \quad . \quad . \quad . \quad . \quad . \quad . \quad . \quad . \quad (38)$$

Similarly $\frac{1}{2}m\overline{v^2}=\frac{1}{2}kT$ and $\frac{1}{2}m\overline{w^2}=\frac{1}{2}kT$, and since $c^2=u^2+v^2+w^2$, therefore $\frac{1}{2}m\overline{c^2}=\frac{3}{2}kT$, a result already found in (15), § 8.

The number of molecules with a *kinetic energy component greater than some assigned value* [1] $\frac{1}{2}mu_1^2$ will be:

$$N'=N\frac{\int_{u_1}^\infty e^{-mu^2/2kT}du}{\int_0^\infty e^{-mu^2/2kT}du}$$

$$\therefore\ (N'/N)=(2/\sqrt{\pi})\int_{x_1}^\infty e^{-x^2}dx=J \quad . \quad . \quad . \quad . \quad . \quad (39)$$

where $x_1=\sqrt{(mu_1^2/2kT)}$. The integral cannot be evaluated by elementary mathematics, but:

$$\frac{2}{\sqrt{\pi}}\int_{x_1}^\infty e^{-x^2}dx=\frac{e^{-x_1^2}}{x_1\sqrt{\pi}}\sum_{s=0}^{s=s}\frac{(-1)^s(2s)!}{s!(2x_1)^{2s}} \quad . \quad . \quad . \quad . \quad . \quad (40)$$

in which as many terms are to be taken as are given by the next whole number s' less than x_1. The error is then $(\sqrt{2}/x_1)e^{-x_1^2-s'}$.

Values of J (39) are: [2]

x	0·1	0·2	0·3	0·4	0·5	0·6	0·8	1·0	1·5	2·0	3·0
J	0·89	0·78	0·67	0·57	0·48	0·40	0·26	0·16	0·034	$4{\cdot}7\times10^{-3}$	$2{\cdot}2\times10^{-5}$

The percentages of molecules having velocities in excess of stated values of $u/\bar{u}$ ($\bar{u}$=mean velocity) are: [3]

$u/\bar{u}$	0·5	1·0	1·5	2·0	2·5	3·0
Per cent.	88·80	46·70	12·55	1·70	0·12	0·01

If the motion of the molecules is restricted to a *plane*, the number having component velocities between u and $u+du$ and v and $v+dv$ is, from (10):

$$dN_{uv}=NA^2e^{-(u^2+v^2)/\alpha^2}dudv=NA^2e^{-c^2/\alpha^2}dudv=(1/\pi\alpha^2)e^{-c^2/\alpha^2}dudv,$$

from (15), where $c^2=u^2+v^2$. This equation is exactly the same in form as the Gauss formula for the distribution of shots fired by a marksman aiming at the centre of a plane target if u and v stand for x and y, the coordinates of the shots measured from the centre of the target as the origin. The chance that the x coordinate shall be between x and $x+dx$, and the y coordinate between y and $y+dy$, is then $(\kappa/\pi)e^{-(x^2+y^2)}dxdy$, where κ is a constant which measures the skill of the marksman.[4]

1 Alexejev, *J. Chim. Phys.*, 1926, **23**, 415.

2 Fuller table in Jeans, "Kinetic Theory of Gases," 1940, 305; Edquist, *Phys. Z.*, 1930, **31**, 1032; cf. Herzfeld in H. S. Taylor, "Physical Chemistry," 1931, **1**, 100.

3 Kennard, "Kinetic Theory of Gases," 1938, 51; cf. Järvinen, *Z. phys. Chem.*, 1919, **93**, 743.

4 Maxwell, *J.C.S.*, 1875, **13**, 493; "Scientific Papers," 1890, **2**, 418.

In polar coordinates (§ 54.I): $\mathrm{d}u\mathrm{d}v=c\mathrm{d}c\mathrm{d}\phi$,

$$\therefore\ \mathrm{d}N_{uv}/N=(1/\pi\alpha^2)\mathrm{e}^{-c^2/\alpha^2}\,c\mathrm{d}c\mathrm{d}\phi.$$

Integration from $\phi=0$ to $\phi=2\pi$ (i.e. over all directions in the plane) gives:

$$\mathrm{d}N_{uv}/N=(2/\alpha^2)\mathrm{e}^{-c^2/\alpha^2}c\mathrm{d}c.$$

But $\alpha^2=2kT/m=2RT/M$, from (28), and $E=\frac{1}{2}Nmc^2=\frac{1}{2}Mc^2$, therefore $\mathrm{d}E=Mc\mathrm{d}c$,

$$\therefore\ \mathrm{d}N_{uv}/N=(1/RT)\mathrm{e}^{-E/RT}\mathrm{d}E \quad . \ . \ . \ . \ . \ . \ \mathbf{(41)}$$

Since $RT=\frac{1}{2}M\alpha^2=$most probable energy per mol$=E_0$, this can also be written as:

$$\mathrm{d}N_{uv}=(N/E_0)\mathrm{e}^{-E/E_0}\mathrm{d}E \ . \ . \ . \ . \ . \ . \ . \ \mathbf{(41a)}$$

By integration, the number of molecules having energy [1] E is

$$N_E=(N/E_0)\int_0^E \mathrm{e}^{-E/E_0}\mathrm{d}E=-N\left[\mathrm{e}^{-E/E_0}\right]_0^E=N(1-\mathrm{e}^{-E/E_0}),$$

$$\therefore\ N_E-N=-N\mathrm{e}^{-E/E_0},$$

$$\text{or}\quad N/(N-N_E)=\mathrm{e}^{E/E_0} \quad . \ . \ . \ . \ . \ . \ . \ \mathbf{(42)}$$

The fraction of the total number of molecules in a plane having energy *in excess* of a given value E is given by:

$$N_E/N=(1/RT)\int_E^\infty \mathrm{e}^{-E/RT}\mathrm{d}E=\mathrm{e}^{-E/RT}$$

$$\therefore\ N_E=N\mathrm{e}^{-E/RT} \ . \ . \ . \ . \ . \ . \ . \ . \ . \ . \ . \ . \ \mathbf{(43)}$$

This equation applies whenever the energy can be expressed as the sum of two so-called " square terms ": $E=\frac{1}{2}ax^2+\frac{1}{2}by^2$, where a and b are constants. In this case $a=b=m$, $x=u$, $y=v$. Equation (43) finds extensive application in the theory of reaction velocities.[2]

The deduction of Maxwell's distribution law given in this section cannot be regarded as rigorous from the point of view of classical dynamics, since it takes no explicit account of molecular collisions, which are nevertheless considered as giving rise to the distribution of velocities. A more rigorous proof, in which the effect of collisions on the distribution was considered in detail, was given by Maxwell,[3] and Boltzmann,[4] but as the derivation on the basis of Statistical Mechanics (§ 33.IV) is much more direct, the rather long deduction on the basis of collision processes will not be given. Attempts to extend it to liquids have been made.[5]

[1] See Kotournitzky, *J. Russ. Phys. Chem. Soc.*, 1912, **44**, i, 151 (P); Sutton, *Phil. Mag.*, 1914, **28**, 798.

[2] See Hinshelwood, " The Kinetics of Chemical Change," Oxford, 1945, 11, 39, 81.

[3] *Phil. Trans.*, 1867, **157**, 49; 1879, **170**, 231; *Phil. Mag.*, 1868, **35**. 129, 185; *Trans. Cambr. Phil. Soc.*, 1878–9, **12**, 547; " Scientific Papers," 1890, **2**, 26, 681.

[4] *Wien Ber.*, 1868, **58**, II, 517; 1872, **66**, 275; " Wiss. Abhl.," 1909, **1**, 49, 316; objection by Lorentz, *Wien Ber.*, 1887, **95**, II, 115; new proof by Boltzmann, *ibid.*, 1887, **95**, II, 153; 1887, **96**, II, 891; " Wiss. Abhl.," 1909, **3**, 272, 292; " Gastheorie," 1896, **1**, 15; see also O. E. Meyer, " Kinetic Theory of Gases," 1899, 45, 368 (including summary of older proofs); Berthoud, *J. Chim. Phys.*, 1911, **9**, 352; 1913, **11**, 577; 1914, **12**, 565; Jeans, " Kinetic Theory of Gases," 1940, 102.

[5] Buchanan, *Phil. Mag.*, 1888, **25**, 165; correction for molecular attraction in gases, Shiba, *Proc. Phys. Math. Soc. Japan*, 1927, **9**, 157; *Bull. Inst. Phys. Chem. Res. Tokyo*, 1928, **7**, 740.

DISTRIBUTION LAW

§ 11. Summary of Formulae

The equations deduced in § 10 are of such fundamental importance that a summary [1] of the main results (in some cases slightly modified by inserting values found later in the paragraph than the main equation, numbered below as in § 10), is appended for convenience of reference.

(1) Number of molecules having velocity components in the range du, dv, dw:

$$\mathrm{d}N=N(m/2\pi kT)^{3/2}\mathrm{e}^{-m(u^2+v^2+w^2)/2kT} \quad . \; . \; . \; . \; . \; (37)$$

(2) Number of molecules having a velocity c in the direction of motion given by angles θ and ϕ in the range dc, dθ, dϕ:

$$\mathrm{d}N=N(m/2\pi kT)^{3/2}\mathrm{e}^{-mc^2/2kT}c^2 \sin\theta \mathrm{d}\theta \mathrm{d}\phi \mathrm{d}c \quad . \; . \; . \; . \; (19)$$

(3) Number of molecules having a velocity c in the range dc without reference to direction:

$$\mathrm{d}N=4\pi N(m/2\pi kT)^{3/2}\mathrm{e}^{-mc^2/2kT}c^2\mathrm{d}c. \quad . \; . \; . \; . \; . \; (21)$$

(4) Number of molecules each having a kinetic energy in the range ϵ to $\epsilon+\mathrm{d}\epsilon$:

$$\mathrm{d}N=2\pi N(1/\pi kT)^{3/2}\mathrm{e}^{-\epsilon/kT}\epsilon^{1/2}\mathrm{d}\epsilon \quad . \; . \; . \; . \; . \; . \; (32)$$

(5) Mean velocity of molecules:

$$\bar{c}=\sqrt{(8kT/\pi m)}=14500\sqrt{(T/M)} \text{ cm./sec., where } M=\text{mol. wt.} \quad . \; (35)$$

(6) Root mean square velocity:

$$\sqrt{(\overline{c^2})}=\sqrt{(3kT/m)}=15800\sqrt{(T/M)} \text{ cm./sec.} \quad . \; . \; . \; (27)\text{–}(28)$$

(7) Most probable velocity:

$$\alpha=\sqrt{(2kT/m)}=12900\sqrt{(T/M)} \text{ cm./sec.} \quad . \; . \; . \; . \; . \; (28)$$

The various types of molecular velocities are given by O. E. Meyer,[2] in a book still frequently consulted, as follows:

(i) The *Joule-Clausius velocity*, G, defined by $p=\frac{1}{3}DG^2$, where D=density in g./cm.^{3}, which is our $\sqrt{(\overline{c^2})}$;

(ii) The *arithmetic mean velocity*, $\Omega=\sqrt{(8/3\pi)}\,G=0{\cdot}9213G$, which is our $\bar{c}$;

(iii) The *most probable velocity* $W=\frac{1}{2}\sqrt{(\pi)}\Omega=\sqrt{(2/3)}G$, which is our α;

(iv) The *mean probable velocity* $O=1{\cdot}09W=0{\cdot}96\Omega$, meaning that there are as many molecules with velocities less than O as there are with velocities greater than O: this is not much used. The substitution [3] of the translational kinetic energy by $TC_v=3T$ g.cal./mol, seems unnecessary.

§ 12. Some Useful Integrals

In the Kinetic Theory of Gases integrals of the type:

$$\int x^n \mathrm{e}^{-\beta x^2}\mathrm{d}x$$

[1] Tolman, "Statistical Mechanics," Oxford, 1938, 90, 92; cf. Webb, "Elementary Principles in Physical Chemistry," New York, 1936; Moelwyn-Hughes, "Physical Chemistry," Cambridge, 1940, 63 f.

[2] "Kinetic Theory of Gases," 1899, 54, 388.

[3] Berthoud, *J. Chim. Phys.*, 1911, **9**, 352; 1913, **11**, 577; 1914, **12**, 565 (deduction of Maxwell's equation); Tolman, *J. Franklin Inst.*, 1927, **203**, 661, 811.

(n is an integer) are frequently met with, and some of these have been evaluated by integration by parts in § 10. They can be evaluated in finite terms when n is odd, and when n is even they can all be related to the integral:

$$\int_0^x e^{-\beta x^2}dx = J.$$

A general formula for cases when n is even ($n=2k$) is:

$$\int_0^\infty x^{2k}e^{-\beta x^2}dx = \{[1.3\ .\ .\ .\ (2k-1)]/2^{k+1}\}\sqrt{(\pi/\beta^{2k+1})},$$

and one for cases when n is odd ($n=2k+1$) is:

$$\int_0^\infty x^{2k+1}e^{-\beta x^2}dx = k!/2\beta^{k+1}.$$

Special cases [1] (each of which may be obtained from the one immediately above it by differentiation with respect to β under the integral sign) [2] are:

n	n even (including $n=0$):	n odd:	n
0	$\int_0^\infty e^{-\beta x^2}dx = \frac{1}{2}\sqrt{(\pi/\beta)}$	$\int_0^\infty xe^{-\beta x^2}dx = 1/2\beta$	1
2	$\int_0^\infty x^2e^{-\beta x^2}dx = \frac{1}{4}\sqrt{(\pi/\beta^3)}$	$\int_0^\infty x^3e^{-\beta x^2}dx = 1/2\beta^2$	3
4	$\int_0^\infty x^4e^{-\beta x^2}dx = \frac{3}{8}\sqrt{(\pi/\beta^5)}$	$\int_0^\infty x^5e^{-\beta x^2}dx = 1/\beta^3$	5
6	$\int_0^\infty x^6e^{-\beta x^2}dx = \frac{15}{16}\sqrt{(\pi/\beta^7)}$	$\int_0^\infty x^7e^{-\beta x^2}dx = 3/\beta^4$	7
n	$\int_0^\infty x^ne^{-\beta x^2}dx = 1.3.5\ldots(n-1)(\pi\beta)^{\frac{1}{2}}/[(2\beta)^{\frac{1}{2}n+1}]$	$\int_0^\infty x^ne^{-\beta x^2}dx = [\frac{1}{2}(n-1)]!/2\beta^{\frac{1}{2}(n+1)}$	n

The integral $(2/\sqrt{\pi})\int_0^x e^{-x^2}dx = (2/\sqrt{\pi})J$, called by Glaisher [3] the error function, erf$x$, cannot be evaluated in finite form, but must be expanded in a power series and integrated term by term.

§ 13. Numerical Values and Graphical Representations based on Maxwell's Distribution Law

Some values of the root mean square velocities and average velocities [4] at 20° C. in cm./sec., are:

	H_2	N_2	O_2	Hg
$\bar{c}\times10^{-5}$ ..	1·755	0·4703	0·4401	0·1842
$\sqrt{\bar{c^2}}\times10^{-5}$ ..	1·904	0·5106	0·4778	0·1908

Of 1000 molecules of oxygen at 0° C. (mean speed 425 m. per sec.): [5]

13 to 14	have a speed below 100 m. per sec.	i.e. $\frac{1}{100}$
81 „ 82	„ „ from 100 to 200 „ ..	$\frac{1}{4}$
166 „ 167	„ „ „ 200 „ 300 „ ..	
214 „ 215	„ „ „ 300 „ 400 „ ..	$\frac{1}{2}$
202 „ 203	„ „ „ 400 „ 500 „ ..	
151 „ 152	„ „ „ 500 „ 600 „ ..	
91 „ 92	„ „ „ 600 „ 700 „ ..	$\frac{1}{5}$
76 „ 77	„ „ greater than 700 „ ..	

1 Moelwyn-Hughes, " Physical Chemistry," Cambridge, 1940, 622; Jeans, " Kinetic Theory of Gases, " Cambridge, 1940, 306.

2 Riemann, " Partielle Differentialgleichungen," edit. Hattendorff, Brunswick, 1938, 37.

3 *Phil. Mag.*, 1871, **42**, 294, 421; Pendlebury, *ibid.*, 1871, **42**, 437; Burgess, *Trans. Roy. Soc. Edin.*, 1897–8, **39**, 257 (tables).

4 Dushman, " Production and Measurement of High Vacuum," Schenectady, 1922, 9.

5 J. J. Thomson, in Watts, " Dictionary of Chemistry," edit. Morley and Muir, 1890, **1**, 87; O. E. Meyer, " Kinetic Theory of Gases," 1899, 57.

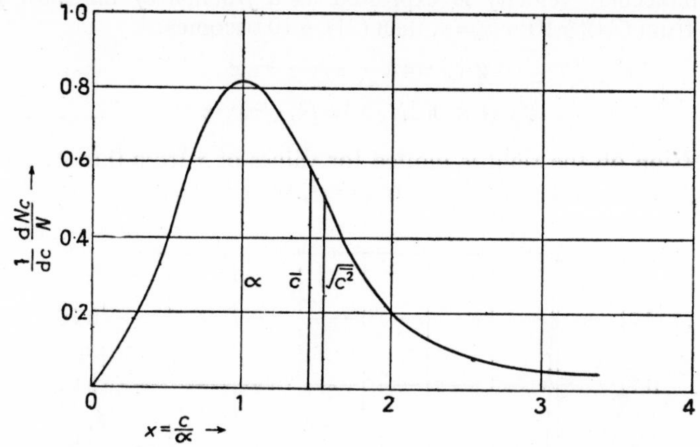

FIG. 6.III. Graph of $(4/\sqrt{\pi})x^2e^{-x^2}$ against x for Maxwell's Distribution Law

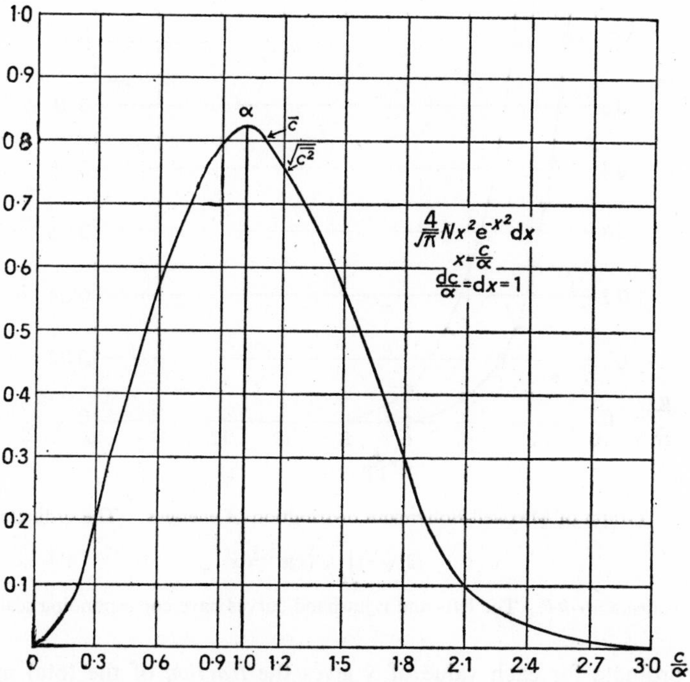

FIG. 7.III. Maxwell-Boltzmann distribution of velocities irrespective of direction. Ordinates represent the fraction dN_c/N of the molecules having velocities c/α, where α=most probable velocity, in an interval $dc/\alpha=1$ about the value of α/c.

$$\bar{c}=2\alpha/\sqrt{\pi}=1{\cdot}128\alpha$$

$$\sqrt{\overline{c^2}}=\sqrt{(3/2)}\alpha=1{\cdot}224\alpha$$

$$\bar{c}=\sqrt{(8/3\pi)}\sqrt{\overline{c^2}}=0{\cdot}921\sqrt{\overline{c^2}}$$

Plot of $dN_c=(4/\sqrt{\pi})N(c^2/\alpha^2)e^{-c^2/\alpha^2}(dc/\alpha)$

$$=(4/\sqrt{\pi})Nx^2e^{-x^2}dx$$

$$x=c/\alpha$$

If the molecular velocity is expressed as *a fraction of the most probable velocity* α from (24), § 10: $c/\alpha = x$, then (21), § 10 becomes: [1]

$$dN_c = (4N/\sqrt{\pi})x^2 e^{-x^2} dx,$$

$$\therefore\ (1/dx)(dN_c/N) = (4/\sqrt{\pi})x^2 e^{-x^2} \quad . \quad . \quad . \quad . \quad . \quad (1)$$

The expression on the right is plotted for values of x from 0 to 4 in Fig. 6.III (on finding values of $e^{-x^2} = e^{-y}$, where $y = x^2$, see § 13.I).

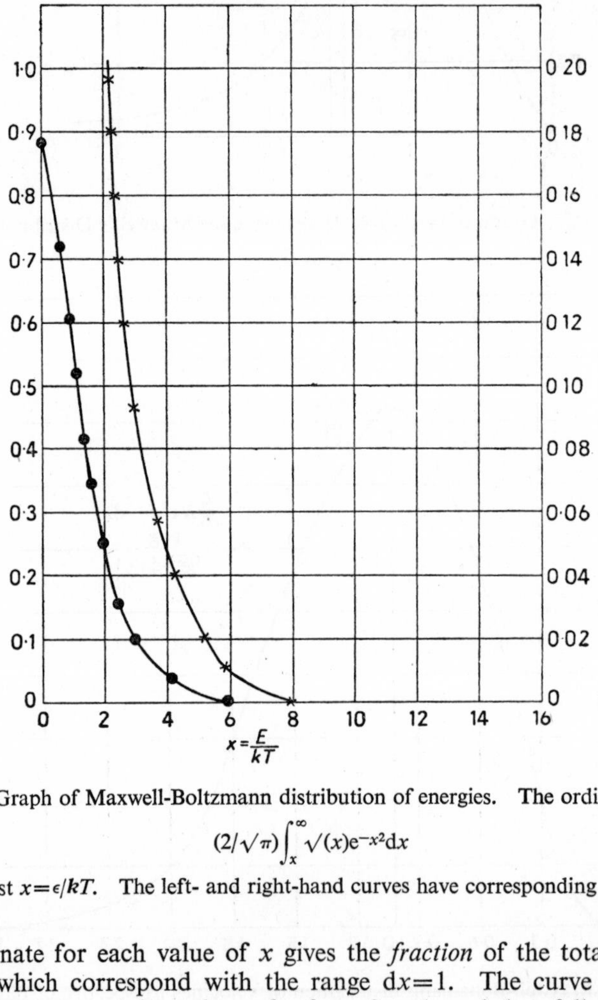

FIG. 8.III. Graph of Maxwell-Boltzmann distribution of energies. The ordinates represent

$$(2/\sqrt{\pi})\int_x^\infty \sqrt{(x)}e^{-x^2}dx$$

plotted against $x = \epsilon/kT$. The left- and right-hand curves have corresponding scales.

The ordinate for each value of x gives the *fraction* of the total number of molecules which correspond with the range $dx = 1$. The curve rises steeply to a maximum at $x = 1$ for values of x from 0 to 1, and then falls more slowly for larger values of x, the ordinate at $x = 3$ being already quite small. The ordinate approaches the limit zero only when x approaches the limit infinity, but it is clear that the values are quite negligible for values of x greater than about 4.

If a small rectangle is erected on the base dx, its area is $dx(1/dx)(dN_c/N) = dN_c/N$, hence it gives the fraction of the number of molecules having velocities

[1] Natanson, *Ann. Phys.*, 1888, **34**, 970; *Z. phys. Chem.*, 1894, **14**, 151; O. E. Meyer, " Kinetic Theory of Gases," 1899, 51; Järvinen, *Z. phys. Chem.*, 1919, **93**, 743.

between x and $x+dx$. This depends on the position of dx, and is given in the following table:

dx	dN_c/N	dx	dN_c/N
0–0·1	0·001	1·3–1·5	0·112
0·1–0·3	0·021	1·5–1·7	0·078
0·3–0·5	0·063	1·7–1·9	0·058
0·5–0.7	0.112	1·9–2·1	0·034
0·7–0·9	0·149	2·1–2·5	0·030
0·9–1·1	0·161	2·5–3·0	0·008
1·1–1·3	0·150		

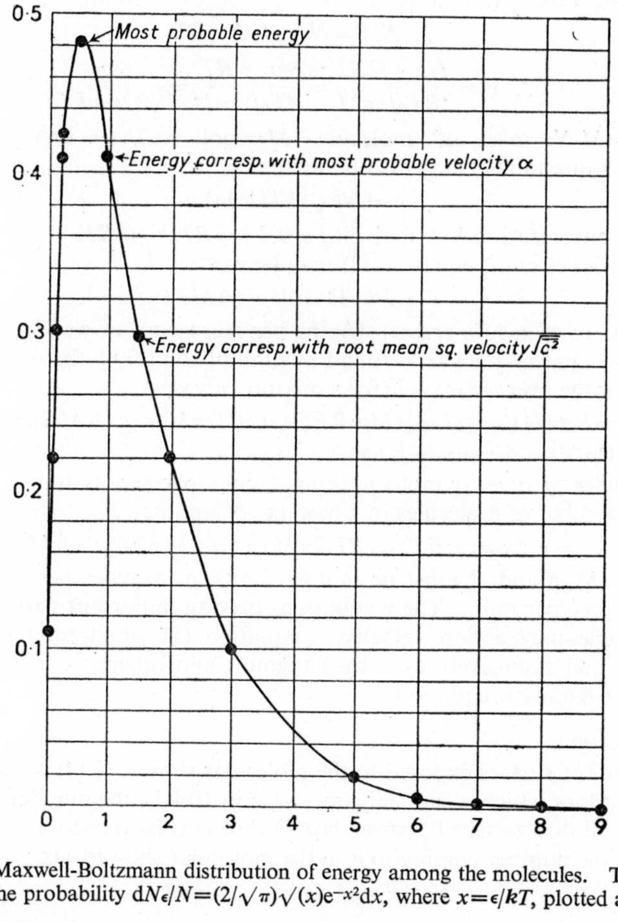

FIG. 9.III. Maxwell-Boltzmann distribution of energy among the molecules. The ordinates represent the probability $dN_\epsilon/N=(2/\sqrt{\pi})\sqrt{(x)}e^{-x^2}dx$, where $x=\epsilon/\boldsymbol{k}T$, plotted against x.

The total area under the curve is $(1/N)\int_0^\infty dN_c=1$. The table shows that the fraction is greatest in the neighbourhood of $x=1$, i.e. when the molecular velocity is the most probable velocity α. The curve is not symmetrical as regards $c=\alpha$ or $x=1$, the area on the right being somewhat larger, hence the *average* velocity $\bar{c}$ is somewhat greater than α, as shown. From (24), § 10, $\bar{c}=1{\cdot}128\alpha$. The value of the *root-mean-square* velocity, $\sqrt{(\overline{c^2})}=1{\cdot}2248\alpha$, is also shown.

§ 14. Molecular Shower Formulae

The kinetic-molecular interpretation of the pressure exerted by a gas on a containing vessel is that a continuous hail or " shower " of molecules, pictured as excessively small elastic hailstones, beats constantly against all parts of the surface and is reflected from it. The number ν of collisions per second on unit area is given by (7), § 8, in which, to include all types of molecules moving in a direction normal to the wall, c is replaced by $\bar{c}$, the mean velocity, given by (35), § 10:

$$\nu = N\bar{c}/4V = (N/2V)\sqrt{(2RT/\pi M)} \quad . \quad . \quad . \quad . \quad . \quad . \quad (1)$$

which gives the *number of molecules* striking 1 cm.^{2} per sec. For 1 g.mol. (mol) of gas, $V=V_m$ (molar vol.), $N=N$ (Avogadro's number),

$$\therefore\ N/V = N/V_m = Np/RT,$$

$$\therefore\ \nu' = \frac{Np}{2RT}\sqrt{\frac{2RT}{\pi M}} = \frac{Np}{RT}\sqrt{\frac{RT}{2\pi M}} = \frac{p}{\sqrt{(2\pi mkT)}} \quad . \quad . \quad . \quad (2)$$

where $m=M/N$=mass of molecule (M=mol. wt.), $k=R/N$=Boltzmann's constant. Equation (2) may also be written as:

$$\nu' = N\xi\sqrt{(kT/2\pi m)} \quad . \quad . \quad . \quad . \quad . \quad . \quad . \quad . \quad (3)$$

where ξ=concentration [1] in mols/lit., since $p=RT/V=\xi RT$.

If p is in dynes/cm.^{2}, equation (2) may be written: [2]

$$\nu' = 2{\cdot}653 \times 10^{19} p/\sqrt{(MT)} \quad . \quad . \quad . \quad . \quad . \quad . \quad . \quad (2a)$$

The *mass*, μ, of gas (*in grams*) striking per sec. 1 cm.^{2} of wall (or other solid), exposed to 1 cm.^{3} of the gas, is found by multiplying (1) by the mass m of a gas molecule (or the average mass $\overline{m}$ for a mixture of gases):

$$\mu = \nu m = Nm\bar{c}/4V = \tfrac{1}{4}\rho\bar{c} = \tfrac{1}{4}(Mp/RT)2\sqrt{(2RT/\pi M)} = p\sqrt{(M/2\pi RT)} \quad . \quad (4)$$

where $\rho=Mp/RT$=density in g./cm.^{3}.

The *number of mols* (g.mol.) striking 1 cm.^{2} per sec. is found by dividing (2) by the number of molecules in a mol, i.e. N, and is:

$$\nu'' = \nu'/N = (p/RT)\sqrt{(RT/2\pi M)} = [1/\sqrt{(2\pi R)}][p/\sqrt{(MT)}] \quad . \quad . \quad (5)$$

In (4) and (5), p and R must be in c.g.s. units, p in dynes per cm.^{2} and R in ergs per degree per mol. These equations play an important part in the theory of heterogeneous reaction velocity. Equation (2), apparently first deduced by Hertz,[3] and extensively used by Langmuir and others, is sometimes called the " Hertz-Knudsen equation."

§ 15. Effusion

If the cm.^{2} of surface exposed to the molecular shower (§ 14) is supposed to be a small trapdoor which is suddenly opened (Fig. 10.III), the number of molecules rushing in all directions [4] (" cosine law ") through the trapdoor into a vacuum is equal to the number coming to it in the molecular shower, viz.:

$$N\bar{c}/4V = \rho\bar{c}/4m = p/\sqrt{(2\pi mkT)} \quad . \quad . \quad . \quad . \quad . \quad . \quad (1)$$

[1] Since the symbol c is here reserved for the molecular velocity, an alternative symbol for concentration is taken as the Greek letter ξ, this being the symbol used by Guldberg and Waage in their classical memoir on mass action and so having an historical sanction. (An alternative would be [c], or some other symbol.)

[2] Dushman, " Production and Measurement of High Vacuum," Schenectady, 1922, 11.

[3] H. Hertz, *Ann. Phys.*, 1882, **17**, 177; O. E. Meyer, " Kinetic Theory of Gases," 1899, 80; Knudsen, *Ann. Phys.*, 1909, **29**, 179; Marcelin, *J. Chim. Phys.*, 1912, **10**, 680; Langmuir, *Phys. Z.*, 1913, **14**, 1273; *J.A.C.S.*, 1913, **35**, 105, 931; 1915, **47**, 417, 1139; Volmer and Estermann, *Z. phys. Chem.*, 1921, **99**, 383.

[4] The uniform distribution of velocities in space was experimentally proved by Mayer, *Z. Phys.*, 1928, **52**, 235, with a torsion balance and molecular rays.

where ρ=density, from (4), § 14. Equation (1) applies only to a gas streaming into a vacuum. The rate of efflux (or *effusion*) is the same as if the gas of density ρ streamed through the aperture with a uniform linear velocity $\frac{1}{4}\bar{c}$. The dependence on m shows that *the rates of effusion of different gases at the same temperature and pressure are inversely as the square roots of the molecular weights or the densities.* This is *Graham's law of effusion* (§ 5.VII D).

Graham [1] in 1846 tested this by measuring the rates of passage of various gases streaming through a fine perforation in a brass plate into air, with the following results:

Gas	√density (air=1)	Rate of Effusion (air=1)
Hydrogen	0·263	0·276
Methane	0·745	0·753
Ethylene	0·985	0·987
Nitrogen	0·986	0·986
Air	1·000	1·000
Oxygen	1·051	1·053
Carbon Dioxide ..	1·237	1·203

The numbers in the second and third columns should be equal; the divergences probably exceed the experimental errors. The reason was discovered by Knudsen [2] in 1909. The molecules, which are of finite size, enter into collisions with one another in passing through the aperture, and this interferes with the molecular streaming. Knudsen used a very small hole in a thin platinum sheet sealed on the end of a glass tube. In one case the sheet was 0·0025 mm. thick and the hole had an area 5×10^{-6} cm.^{2}; in another the sheet was 0·005 mm. thick and the hole 66×10^{-6} cm.^{2}. The results agreed with the theory at very low pressures (down to 0·01 mm. Hg), when collisions were very infrequent.

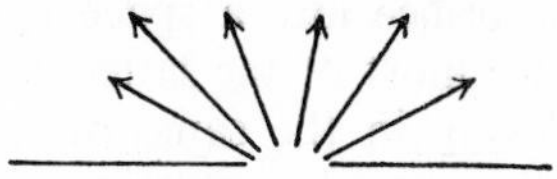

FIG. 10.III. Effusion

The agreement was good when the mean free path (§ 4) in the issuing gas was not less than ten times the diameter of the hole. For smaller free paths, the amount of gas effusing was somewhat greater than that given by (1), and as the pressure increased the molecular flow passed over into a mass flow, as predicted by the hydrodynamical formula for the flow of a continuous fluid. This can readily be deduced for the simple case of the *Bunsen effusion apparatus* (described in § 5.VII D), in which apertures of 0·01–0·1 mm. are used, as follows.[3]

The amount of work spent in forcing each of two different gases through the aperture is represented by the rise in level of the liquid between fixed marks on the effusion tube, and is the same in each case, so that the kinetic energy imparted to each gas is the same. If u_1 and u_2 are the velocities of *bulk* motion of the gases, i.e. the speeds at which the liquid level rises, $\frac{1}{2}m_1u_1^2=\frac{1}{2}m_2u_2^2$, where m_1 and m_2 are the total masses of gases expelled. These occupy equal volumes, therefore $m_1/m_2=\rho_1/\rho_2=M_1/M_2$, where ρ=density, M=mol.wt. But $u_1/u_2=t_2/t_1$, where t_1 and t_2 are the effusion times for equal volumes. Hence:

$$t_2^2/t_1^2=\rho_1/\rho_2=M_1/M_2 \quad . \quad . \quad . \quad . \quad . \quad . \quad . \quad (2)$$

1 *Phil. Trans.*, 1846, **136**, 573; " Researches," 1876, 88.
2 *Ann. Phys.*, 1909, **28**, 75; 1911, **35**, 389; Smoluchowski, *ibid.*, 1910, **33**, 1559.
3 Ostwald, " Lehrbuch der allgemeinen Chemie," 1910, **1**, 176.

This applies only to isothermal effusion. For adiabatic effusion the ratio of specific heats $\gamma = c_p/c_v$ is involved.[1]

Consider a small aperture of area A in a thin plate dividing two portions of gas at pressures p_1 and p_2. The numbers of molecules reaching the two sides of A will be, from (1):

$$\nu_1 A = p_1 A/\sqrt{(2\pi mkT)}, \text{ and } \nu_2 A = p_2 A/\sqrt{(2\pi mkT)},$$

hence the number passing through per second will be $(p_2 > p_1)$:

$$A(\nu_2 - \nu_1) = (p_2 - p_1)[A/\sqrt{(2\pi mkT)}] \quad . \quad . \quad . \quad . \quad . \quad (3)$$

or the volume in cm.³ measured at unit pressure (1 dyne/cm.²) is:

$$V = A(\nu_2 - \nu_1)kT = (p_2 - p_1)A\sqrt{(kT/2\pi m)} = A\Delta p\sqrt{(RT/2\pi M)} \quad . \quad (4)$$

For a circular opening of diameter d cm.:

$$V = \Delta p(\pi d^2/4)\sqrt{(RT/2\pi M)} = 2864 d^2 \Delta p \sqrt{(T/M)} \text{ cm.}^3 \quad . \quad . \quad (5)$$

The case when the gas issues into another gas (e.g. the atmosphere, as in Graham's and Bunsen's experiments) instead of into a vacuum requires special consideration. Saint-Venant and Wantzel[2] found by experiment that the rate of efflux is about the same as that into a vacuum, provided the gas is driven through the orifice by a pressure not less than twice that in the gas into which it passes, and this result is easily explained.[3] The gas molecules passing through the orifice into a space less densely filled with gas rarely collide with others, since most of the latter have also only just emerged from the orifice, and are moving in the same direction, with nearly the same speed, as those which follow, and hence are rarely overtaken by them. If the exterior pressure is not much less than that within, the distribution of pressure in the orifice, and in its immediate neighbourhood, is quite different from that when flow occurs into a vacuum. But with two different gases, with the same values of the pressure within and without, the pressures in the orifice will be the same in the two cases, and the speed of efflux is still proportional to the molecular speed.

The amount Q of gas passing in a given time by effusion through a capillary of diameter d with a pressure difference Δp, is approximately given[4] by $Q = Kd^2\sqrt{\Delta p}$ for $\Delta p = 0{\cdot}1$–$1{\cdot}1$ atm., and $Q = Kd^2\sqrt[3]{\Delta p}$ for $\Delta p = 1{\cdot}1$–$2{\cdot}0$ atm., K being a constant depending on the gas.

An interesting application of low pressure effusion, to which (1) applies, is the determination of the degree of dissociation of a gas or vapour at various temperatures. A small constant flow of gas at a small pressure ($\simeq 0{\cdot}1$ mm. Hg) escapes through a small hole of area A into a high vacuum. For a substance $X_2 \rightleftharpoons 2X$, if there were no dissociation: $N' = Ap'/\sqrt{(2\pi m_2 kT)}$, but if there is dissociation: $N_2 = Ap_2/\sqrt{(2\pi m_2 kT)}$, and $N_1 = Ap_1/\sqrt{(2\pi m_1 kT)}$, where the suffixes 1 and 2 refer to X and X_2. But $N' = N_2 + \frac{1}{2}N_1$, and $p = p_1 + p_2$, where p is the pressure at the small hole. Thence it can be shown that $p_1 = [\sqrt{2}/(\sqrt{2}-1)](p - p')$, and as p is measured and p' can be calculated, p_1 and hence the degree of dissociation, can be found.[5]

[1] Bunsen, "Gasometry," 1857, 121; O. E. Meyer, *Ann. Phys.*, 1866, **127**, 253; Donnan, *Phil. Mag.*, 1900, **49**, 423 (bibl.); Voss, *Ann. de Phys.*, 1923, **20**, 66.

[2] *J. de l'École Polytechn.*, 1839, **16**, xxvii, 85.

[3] O. E. Meyer, "Kinetic Theory of Gases," 1899, 85.

[4] Kulisky, Schevchenko, and Goronovsky, *Amer. Chem. Abstr.*, 1943, **37**, 3647.

[5] Weide and Bichowsky, *J.A.C.S.*, 1926, **48**, 2529 (I_2); De Vries and Rodebush, *ibid.*, 1927, **49**, 656 (Br_2 and I_2); Bichowsky and Copeland, *ibid.*, 1928, **50**, 1315 (H); Eyring, *ibid.*, 1928, **50**, 2398; Wrede, *Z. Phys.*, 1929, **54**, 53 (H, N, O).

§ 16. Thermal Diffusion (or Thermal Transpiration)

If a gas is contained in a vessel divided into two parts A and B (Fig. 11.III) by a porous plug, molecules of gas pass from A to B and from B to A through the plug. At low pressures, the rates of transpiration are given *approximately* by (1), § 15. If the pressures are equal, the rates of transpiration are equal, for the same gas, at a given temperature. Further, if the pressures are unequal they will gradually reach equality by transpiration. If, however, the temperatures of A and B are different, the rates of transpiration will differ, the gas tending to pass from the cooler to the warmer region, and a steady state is reached with different pressures in A and B. This phenomenon was predicted by Neumann,[1] and was experimentally discovered by Feddersen[2] and by Reynolds,[3] independently, the latter calling it *thermal transpiration.* A theory of it was given by Maxwell,[4] who called it *thermal effusion.*

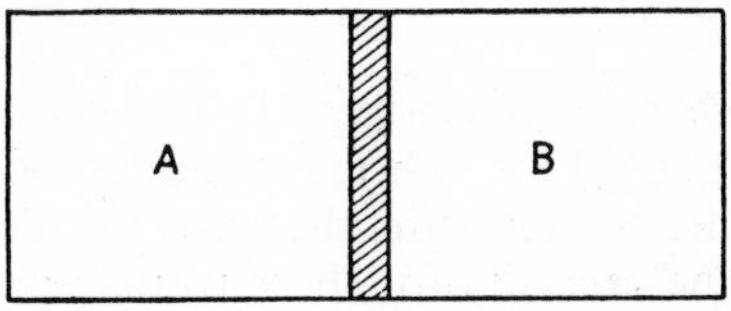

FIG. 11.III. Thermal Diffusion

If p_A, ρ_A, T_A and p_B, ρ_B, T_B are the corresponding pressures, densities and absolute temperatures in A and B, the temperature difference being permanently maintained, the flow of gas ultimately becomes equal in both directions and a steady state is reached. Equation (1), § 15, shows that $\rho_A\sqrt{T_A}=\rho_B\sqrt{T_B}$, and hence the ratio of the pressures is:

$$p_A/p_B=\rho_A T_A/\rho_B T_B=\sqrt{(T_A/T_B)} \quad . \quad . \quad . \quad . \quad . \quad . \quad (1)$$

Reynolds, who used temperatures of 8° C. and 100° C., found good agreement with (1) at sufficiently low pressures. At higher pressures the agreement broke down.

The phenomenon of thermal transpiration is of considerable importance when pieces of apparatus at different temperatures are connected by narrow tubes. Not only will the total pressures in these parts of the apparatus be different, so that considerable errors may be made when the pressure is measured only in one part, but also in the case when a mixture of gases is used there may be differences in *composition* in different parts of the apparatus,[5] which is of importance in determining equilibrium compositions.[6]

[1] *Leipzig Ber.*, 1872, **24**, 49.

[2] *Ann. Phys.*, 1873, **148**, 302; Dufour, *Arch. Sci. Phys. Nat.*, 1872, **45**, 9; 1874, **49**, 103; 1875, **53**, 177.

[3] *Phil. Trans.*, 1879, **170**, 727; " Sci. Papers," Cambridge, 1900, **1**, 257.

[4] *Phil. Trans.*, 1879, **170**, 231; " Sci. Papers," Cambridge, 1890, **2**, 681 (711); Knudsen, *Ann. Phys.*, 1909–10, **31**, 205, 633; 1910, **33**, 1435; West, *Proc. Phys. Soc.*, 1919, **31**, 278; Schreiner, *Z. phys. Chem.*, 1924, **112**, 1 (63); Weber, *Z. Phys.*, 1924, **24**, 267; Van Itterbeek and de Grande, *Physica*, 1947, **13**, 289, 422.

[5] Enskog, *Phys. Z.*, 1911, **12**, 56, 533; *Arkiv Mat. Astron. Fys.*, 1922, **16**, No. 16; Chapman *Phil. Mag.*, 1917, **34**, 146; 1919, **38**, 182; 1928, **5**, 630; 1929, **7**, 1 (errors); Chapman and Dootson, *Phil. Mag.*, 1917, **33**, 248; Ibbs, *Proc. Roy. Soc.*, 1921, **99**, 385; 1925, **107**, 470; *Physica*, 1937, **4**, 1133; Elliott and Masson, *Proc. Roy. Soc.*, 1925, **108**, 378; Eastman, *JA.C.S.*, 1926, **48**, 1482; 1927, **49**, 794; Eastman and Rubin, *ibid.*, 1935, **57**, 97; Rodebush, *ibid.*, 1927, **49**, 792 (correcting Eastman); Lugg, *Phil. Mag.*, 1929, **8**, 1019; Weber, *Comm. Leiden*, 1932, Suppl. **71***b*; Weber and Keesom, *ibid.*, 1932, **223***b* (low temperatures); Blüh, Blich, and Puschner, *Phil. Mag.*, 1937, **24**, 1103; Wall and Holley, *J. Chem. Phys.*, 1940, **8**, 949; Leaf and Wall, *J. Phys. Chem.*, 1942, **46**, 820.

[6] Förster and Geib, *Ann. Phys.*, 1934, **20**, 250; Schmall and Knepper, *Z. Elektrochem.*, 1936, **42**, 681; Emmett and Shultz, *J.A.C.S.*, 1932, **54**, 3780; 1933, **55**, 1376; Chipman and Fontana, *ibid.*, 1934, **56**, 2011; Tompkins and Wheeler, *Trans. Faraday Soc.*, 1933, **29**, 1248; Towndrow, *Thesis*, London, 1937; Damköhler, *Z. Elektrochem.*, 1936, **42**, 846; 1937, **43**, **1**, 8; Darken and Smith, *J.A.C.S.*, 1945, **67**, 1411.

The correction for the pressure read on a manometer which is at a different temperature from the vessel is possible only in two extreme cases: (i) when the diameter of the connecting tube is small compared with the mean free path (1) can be used; (ii) when the diameter is large compared with the mean free path the correction is more complicated and is based on a formula deduced by Maxwell:

$$\frac{\Delta p}{\Delta T}=\frac{6\eta^2\boldsymbol{R}}{Mp}\bigg/\left(\frac{d^2}{4}+4\zeta\frac{d}{2}\right) \quad . \; . \; . \; . \; . \; . \; . \quad (2)$$

where η=viscosity, M=mol. wt., d=diameter of tube, ζ=coefficient of slip (§ 12.VII F). Owing to the dependence of η on temperature and of ζ on temperature and pressure, the exact calculation is difficult and is best made graphically.[1] The necessity for these troublesome corrections is not always appreciated and large errors may enter at low pressures. The factor 6·1 has been used by Knudsen[2] in place of 4 in $4\zeta d/2$. For higher pressures ζ may be neglected and (2) integrated to give:

$$p_1^2-p_2^2=6\eta_0\boldsymbol{R}(T_1^2-T_2^2)/(d^2T_0/4)M \quad . \; . \; . \; . \quad (3)$$

in which Knudsen replaced 6 by 7·4. Knudsen's formula is:

$$p_1^2-p_2^2=c(T_1^2-T_2^2)/273^2\ (\text{dyne/cm.}^2)^2,$$

where c varies only slightly with temperature but depends on the tube radius R, viscosity η_0 of the gas at 0° C., density ρ_0 at 0° C. and 1 dyne/cm.^{2} pressure, and Sutherland's constant C (see § 5.VII F):

$$c=\frac{k}{0{\cdot}30967}\left(\frac{1+C/273}{1+C/T}\right)\frac{\eta_0^2}{\rho_0 R^2}.$$

The constant k from elementary kinetic theory is 1, but experiments gave k=2·3.

The separation effect in thermal diffusion has been largely used in the separation of isotopes,[3] an application suggested by Chapman[4] in 1919.

1 Bichowsky and Wilson, *Phys. Rev.*, 1929, **33**, 851; Herzfeld, in H. S. Taylor, "Physical Chemistry," 1931, **1**, 196; Kennard, "Kinetic Theory of Gases," 1938, 330.

2 *Ann. Phys.*, 1910, **33**, 1435; 1927, **83**, 797; Weber, *Comm. Leiden*, 1937, **246*b***; Weber, Keesom, and Schmidt, *ibid.*, 1937, **246*a***.

3 Clusius and Dickel, *Naturwiss.*, 1938, **26**, 546; 1939, **27**, 110, 148; 1940, **28**, 461, 711; 1941, **29**, 560; *Z. phys. Chem.*, 1939, **44** B, 397, 451; Welch, *Ann. Rep. C.S.*, 1940, **37**, 153 (review); Cacciapuoti, *Nuov. Cim.*, 1941, **18**, 114 (review). A selection from the exuberant literature on thermal transpiration and gas and isotope separation is given below: Ibbs and Underwood, *Proc. Phys. Soc.*, 1927, **39**, 227 (CO, N_2; CO_2, N_2O); Blüh and Blüh, *Z. Phys.*, 1934, **90**, 12; Shibata and Kitawaga, *J. Chem. Soc. Japan*, 1936, **57**, 1300; Blüh, Blüh, and Puschner, *Phil. Mag.*, 1937, **24**, 1103; Ibbs, *Physica*, 1937, **4**, 1133; Puschner, *Z. Phys.*, 1937, **106**, 597; Eucken, *Österr. Chem. Ztg.*, 1938, **41**, 137; Korsching and Wirtz, *Naturwiss.*, 1939, **27**, 110, 367; *Ber.*, 1940, **73**, 249; Blumenthal, *Phil. Mag.*, 1939, **27**, 341; Gillespie, *J. Chem. Phys.*, 1939, **7**, 530; Atkins, Bastick, and Ibbs, *Proc. Roy. Soc.*, 1939, **172**, 142; Nier, *Phys. Rev.*, 1939, **56**, 1009; 1940, **57**, 30, 338; Furry, Jones, and Onsager, *ibid.*, 1939, **55**, 1083 (bibl.); Brewer and Bromley, *ibid.*, 1939, **55**, 590; Watson, *ibid.*, 1939, **56**, 703; 1940, **57**, 899; Bramley and Brewer, *J. Chem. Phys.*, 1939, **7**, 553, 972; Maier, *ibid.*, 1939, **7**, 854; Taylor and Glockler, *ibid.*, 1939, **7**, 851; 1940, **8**, 843; Taylor, *Nature*, 1939, **144**, 8; van der Grinten, *Naturwiss.*, 1939, **27**, 317; Waldmann, *ibid.*, 1939, **27**, 230; 1943, **31**, 204; 1944, **32**, 222, 223; *Z. Phys.*, 1939, **114**, 53; 1943, **121**, 501; Groth, *Naturwiss.*, 1939, **27**, 260; Frankel, *Phys. Rev.*, 1940, **57**, 661; Bardeen, *ibid.*, 1940, **57**, 35; 1940, **58**, 94; Brown, *ibid.*, 1940, **57**, 242; 1940, **58**, 661; Jones and Furry, *ibid.*, 1940, **57**, 547; Jones, *ibid.*, 1940, **58**, 111 (summary of theory); Fleischmann, *Phys. Z.*, 1940, **41**, 14; Groth and Harteck, *Naturwiss.*, 1940, **28**, 47; Srivastava, *Proc. Roy. Soc.*, 1940, **175**, 474; *Proc. Nat. Inst. Sci. India*, 1941, **7**, 289; Westhaver and Brewer, *J. Chem. Phys.*, 1940, **8**, 314; Seaborg, Wahl, and Kennedy, *ibid.*, 1940, **8**, 639; Wall and Holley, *ibid.*, 1940, **8**, 348; Chapman, *Nature*, 1940, **146**, 431, 607; *Proc. Roy. Soc.*, 1940, **177**, 38; Krasny-Ergen, *Phys. Rev.*,

4 See note 5 on page 267.

Enskog's[1] theory predicts a tendency of heavier molecules to diffuse towards the lower temperature region until the thermal diffusion is balanced by ordinary diffusion tending to produce a uniform composition; lighter molecules tend to pass into the higher temperature region.

If a mixture of two gases of molecular weights M_1, M_2, in mol fractions (§ 57.II) N_1, N_2, is contained in two connected vessels at absolute temperatures T_1, T_2, the difference in mol fraction of either constituent is $\Delta N = k_T \ln (T_2/T_1)$, where k_T is the thermal separation coefficient, equal to $D_T/D_{12} = \alpha N_1 N_2$, where D_T, D_{12} are the thermal and ordinary diffusivities and α is the thermal diffusion constant. If the molecules are perfect elastic spheres, $\alpha = 105(M_2 - M_1)/118(M_2 + M_1)$, but the imperfect behaviour of real gas molecules reduces the value of α to about half the theoretical. The equation for ΔN also applies to a gas mixture between horizontal parallel plates at temperatures T_1, T_2, with a concentration difference on the plate surfaces. If this apparatus is turned so that the plates are vertical, a convection current in the direction shown by arrows in Fig. 12.III is set up. This carries upwards the gas enriched in lighter constituent at A, and the gas descending at B contains more of the heavier constituent. A second concentration gradient develops in the direction CD, which may be considerable even if the changes due to thermal diffusion along AB are very small. If the apparatus is very tall, the opposing effects of convection currents are relatively unimportant, and considerable enrichments of the components are produced at the top and bottom. In Clusius and Dickel's apparatus, a long vertical glass tube, cooled externally by running water, had an electrically heated axial platinum or nichrome wire;

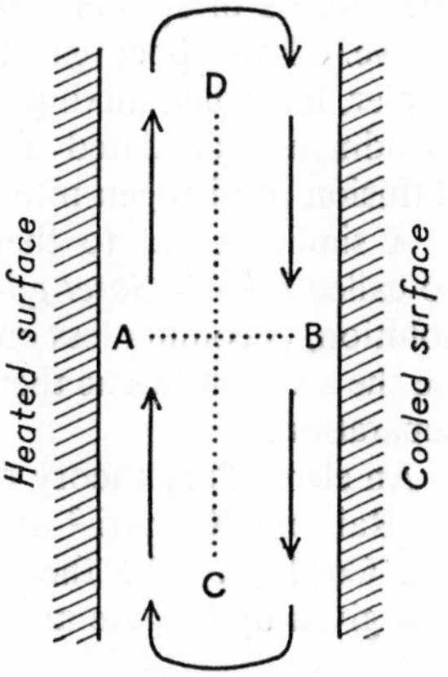

FIG. 12.III. Separation of Gases by Convection and Thermal Diffusion

1940, **58**, 1078; *Nature*, 1940, **145**, 742; Grew, *Proc. Roy. Soc.*, 1941, **178**, 390; *Nature*, 1942, **150**, 320; 1945, **156**, 267; Schmal and Schewe, *Z. Elektrochem.*, 1940, **46**, 203; Heath, Ibbs, and Wild, *Proc. Roy. Soc.*, 1941, **178**, 380; Nier and Bardeen, *J. Chem. Phys.*, 1941, **9**, 690; Hirota, *Bull. Chem. Soc. Japan*, 1941, **16**, 274; Clusius and Kowalski, *Z. Elektrochem.*, 1941, **47**, 819; Meixner, *Ann. Phys.*, 1941, **39**, 333; Akabori *et al.*, *Proc. Phys. Math. Soc. Japan*, 1941, **23**, 568, 599; Stier, *Phys. Rev.*, 1942, **62**, 548; Kendall, *Nature*, 1942, **150**, 136 (review); Verschaffelt, *Bull. Acad. Roy. Belg.*, 1942, **28**, 455, 476; de Groot, Hoogstraten, and Gorter, *Physica*, 1942, **9**, 923; Steinwald, *Die Chemie*, 1942, **55**, 152; Stetter, *Österr. Chem. Ztg.*, 1942, **45**, 130; *Amer. Chem. Abstr.*, 1944, **38**, 4846; Clusius and Dickel, *Z. phys. Chem.*, 1942, **52B**, 348; 1943, **53B**, 178; 1944, **193**, 274 (see also above); Harrison, *Proc. Roy. Soc.*, 1942, **181**, 93; Watson and Woernley, *Phys. Rev.*, 1943, **63**, 181; Hirota and Kimura, *J. Chem. Soc. Japan*, 1943, **64**, 756; Hirota and Oguro, *ibid.*, 1943, **64**, 450; Kihara and Kotani, *Proc. Phys. Math. Soc. Japan*, 1943, **25**, 602; Fournier, *J. de Phys.*, 1945, **6**, 104; Furry and James, *Phys. Rev.*, 1946, **69**, 459; Schrader, *ibid.*, 1946, **69**, 439; Klemm, *Z. Naturforsch.*, 1946, **1**, 252; Hogerton, *Chem. Met. Eng.*, 1946, **52**, No. 12, 98 (large scale separation of ^{235}U); Kitagawa, *J. Chem. Soc. Japan*, 1946, **67**, 1; Waldmann, *Z. Naturforsch.*, 1946, **1**, 10, 12; 1947, **2** A, 358; *Z. Phys.*, 1948, **124**, 175; Grew, *Proc. Roy. Soc.*, 1947, **189**, 402; Murphy, *Phys. Rev.*, 1947, **72**, 834; Schäfer, *Naturwiss.*, 1947, **34**, 166; *Angew. Chem.*, 1947, **59** A, 83; Van Itterbeek, Van Paemel, and Van Lierde, *Physica*, 1947, **13**, 231; Prigogine, *Physica*, 1947, **13**, 319; Becker, *Z. Naturforsch.*, 1947, **2** A, 297, 441, 447; Niini, *Suomen Kemist.*, 1947, **20** B, 49; *Amer. Chem. Abstr.*, 1948, **42**, 2822; Lauder, *Trans. Faraday Soc.*, 1947, **43**, 620; Clusius and Becker, *Z. Naturforsch.*, 1947, **2** A, 154; Ney and Armistead, *Phys. Rev.*, 1947, **71**, 14; Watson, Buchanan, and Elder, *ibid.*, 1947, **71**, 887 (^{10}B and ^{11}B by diffusion of BF_3); Mann, *Phys. Rev.*, 1948, **73**, 412; Drickamer, O'Brien, Bresee, and Ockert, *J. Chem. Phys.*, 1948, **16**, 122; Chipman and Dastur, *ibid.*, 1948, **16**, 636; Bernstein and Taylor, *ibid.*, 1948, **16**, 903.

[1] See note 5 on page 267.

the parallel surfaces were thus in the form of concentric cylinders. In other forms a rigid internally heated inner tube replaced the axial wire. The chlorine isotopes ^{35}Cl and ^{37}Cl were separated in a nearly pure state as $H^{35}Cl$ and $H^{37}Cl$ by using hydrogen chloride, and $^{13}CH_4$ from methane. In some cases, chemical exchange methods lead to better isotopic separation than thermal diffusion.

A supposed inversion of the thermal diffusion effect is said [1] to occur during the process of spontaneous mixing of two gases stratified with the lighter gas above. The upper gas becomes slightly warmer and the lower gas slightly cooler, but when mixing is complete the temperature has again its initial value. Waldmann calculated a possible maximum change of temperature of 7° on diffusion of nitrogen into hydrogen.

A similar effect to thermal diffusion in gases is found in liquids, and the so-called *Ludwig-Soret effect*, a change of concentration of an unequally heated solution, becoming less concentrated in the warmer part, is supposed to depend on the same causes as thermal transpiration.[2] It has also been used for isotope separation.

An elementary theory of thermal transpiration and gas separation was given by Rai and Kothari [3] and by Fournier,[4] an advanced treatment by Chapman and Cowling; [5] the theory for Bose-Einstein and Fermi-Dirac gases (§ 36.IV) was given by Gogate and Kothari.[6]

[1] Clusius, *Naturwiss.*, 1942, **30**, 711; Waldmann, *Z. Naturforsch.*, 1947, **2** A, 358; *Z. Phys.*, 1947, **124**, 1; cf. Dufour, *Arch. Sci. Phys. Nat.*, 1872, **45**, 9; 1874, **49**, 103; 1875, **53**, 177.

[2] Ludwig, *Wien Ber.*, 1856, **20**, 539 (note of fact only); Soret, *Arch. Sci. Phys. Nat.*, 1879, **2**, 48; 1880, **4**, 209 (many experiments and theory); *Ann. Chim.*, 1881, **22**, 293; van't Hoff, *Z. phys. Chem.*, 1887, **1**, 487; van Berchem, *Compt. Rend.*, 1890, **110**, 82 (ment. Ludwig); Des Coudres, *Ann. Phys.*, 1894, **52**, 191 (bibl.); Arrhenius, *Öfversigt af K. Vetensk. Akad. Förhandl.*, 1894, No. **2**, 61; *Z. phys. Chem.*, 1898, **26**, 187; Abegg, *ibid.*, 1898, **26**, 161; Duane, *Ann. Phys.*, 1898, **65**, 374; *Z. phys. Chem.*, 1898, **27**, 674 (abstr.); Liebenow, *Ann. Phys.*, 1899, **68**, 316; 1900, **2**, 636; Voigt, *ibid.*, 1899, **69**, 706; Wessels, *Z. phys. Chem.*, 1914, **87**, 215 (bibl.); Eilert, *Z. anorg. Chem.*, 1914, **88**, 1; Chipman, *J.A.C.S.*, 1926, **48**, 2577; Porter, *Trans. Faraday Soc.*, 1927, **23**, 314; Bruins, *Z. phys. Chem.*, 1927, **130**, 601; Eastman, *J.A.C.S.*, 1928, **50**, 283; Bružs, *Z. phys. Chem.*, 1931, **157**, 422 (bibl.); Clusius and Dickel, *Naturwiss.*, 1938, **26**, 546; 1939, **27**, 148; *Z. phys. Chem.*, 1944, **193**, 274; Korsching and Wirtz, *Naturwiss.*, 1939, **27**, 110, 367; *Z. Elektrochem.*, 1939, **45**, 662; *Ber.*, 1940, **73**, 249; Wirtz, *Naturwiss.*, 1939, **27**, 369; *Ann. Phys.*, 1939, **36**, 295; Debye, *Ann. Phys.*, 1939, **36**, 284; Hiby and Wirtz, *Phys. Z.*, 1940, **41**, 77; Taylor and Ritchie, *Nature*, 1940, **145**, 670; Gillespie and Breck, *J. Chem. Phys.*, 1941, **9**, 370; Carr, *Phys. Rev.*, 1942, **61**, 726; *J. Chem. Phys.*, 1944, **12**, 349; Hirota, *Bull. Chem. Soc. Japan*, 1941, **16**, 475; 1942, **17**, 286; *J. Chem. Soc. Japan*, 1942, **63**, 105, 292, 999, 1061; 1943, **64**, 16, 112, 756; Hirota, Matsunaga, and Tanaka, *ibid.*, 1943, **64**, 811 (fused salts); Hirota and Kimura, *Bull. Chem. Soc. Japan*, 1942, **17**, 42; 1943, **18**, 111; Fournier, *Compt. Rend.*, 1942, **215**, 529; Korsching, *Naturwiss.*, 1943, **31**, 348; 1944, **32**, 220; Wirtz, *ibid.*, 1943, **31**, 349, 416; Alkhazov, Murin, and Ratner, *Bull. Acad. Sci. U.R.S.S.*, 1943, 3; for Soret effect in *solid* mixed crystals: Reinhold, *Z. phys. Chem.*, 1929, **141**, 137; *Z. Elektrochem.*, 1929, **35**, 627; Reinhold and Schulz, *Z. phys. Chem.*, 1933, **164**, 241; for isotope of Ag separation by conduction of ion transport in solid AgI, Klemm, *Z. Naturforsch.*, 1947, **2**A, 9; Van Dranen and Bergsma, *Physica*, 1947, **13**, 558; de Groot, " L'Effet Soret," Amsterdam, 1945; *Compt. Rend.*, 1947, **225**, 377; *J. de Phys.*, 1947, **8**, 129, 193; Ninii, *Suomen Kemist.*, 1947, **20** B, 49; *Amer. Chem. Abstr.*, 1948, **42**, 2822.

[3] *Indian J. Phys.*, 1943, **17**, 103; Cacciapuoti, *Nuov. Cim.*, 1943, **1**, 126.

[4] *J. de Phys.*, 1944, **5**, 1 (including effects of molecular diameter).

[5] " Mathematical Theory of Non-Uniform Gases," Cambridge, 1939, 252; Powell, *Rep. Progr. Phys.*, 1939, **5**, 164; Fürth, *Proc. Roy. Soc.*, 1941–2, **179**, 461; Jensen and Waldmann, *Naturwiss.*, 1941, **29**, 467; Jensen, *Angew. Chem.*, 1941, **54**, 405 (the complicated equations are given in full in *Amer. Chem. Abstr.*, 1942, **36**, 4411); Gurevich, *J. Phys. U.S.S.R.*, 1945, **9**, 312.

[6] *Phys. Rev.*, 1942, **61**, 349.

§ 17. Evaporation

The equilibrium between a liquid or solid and its saturated vapour is kinetic, i.e. as many molecules leave the liquid or solid in unit time as pass back to it from the vapour.[1] The rate of evaporation from the condensed phase is constant at a given temperature, so that if the pressure of the vapour is lowered the rate of evaporation exceeds the rate of condensation, since the latter is proportional to the number of vapour molecules impinging on the condensed phase per second, and this is shown by (2), § 14 to be proportional to the pressure. If the pressure of the vapour is increased above the saturation value the rate of condensation exceeds the rate of evaporation. In both cases, when the equilibrium has been upset, it is ultimately restored by evaporation or condensation (see § 40.II).

Since the rates of evaporation and condensation are equal when the vapour is saturated, it might seem that the rate of evaporation could be found by equating it to the rate at which vapour molecules impinge on the condensed phase, as given by (1), § 14. A difficulty arises from the fact that it is by no means certain that all the vapour molecules striking a solid are condensed; a fraction may be reflected from it without condensing. A factor α, called the *coefficient of evaporation*, giving the fraction of the impinging molecules which condense, must be introduced, and unless α is known or can be shown to be unity, the rate of evaporation cannot be found. The amount of material evaporated in g. per cm.[2] per sec., and also returned to the condensed phase by the vapour, is then given by (4), § 14, multiplied by α:

$$w = \nu m\alpha = \alpha p\sqrt{(M/2\pi RT)} \quad . \quad . \quad . \quad . \quad . \quad . \quad . \quad (1)$$

Information on the value of α in the evaporation of mercury is given by direct experiments [2] in which the mercury was contained in a very high vacuum between the walls of a thermos vessel, the inner wall being cooled by liquid air, and the mercury was kept at a given temperature by immersing the vessel in a thermostat. The evaporating molecules passed across the space practically in free paths without collisions, and condensed on the glass at liquid-air temperature. The deposit was melted off and weighed, and thence the rate of evaporation determined. The value of α was found to be approximately 1 for liquid mercury and for solid mercury below −140° C., whilst for solid mercury above −100 °C. it was about 8 to 10 per cent. less than 1. Since the formula (1) contains the molecular weight, and the vapour pressures of isotopes are probably nearly equal,[3] the rates of evaporation of the isotopes of mercury should be slightly different; this was shown to be the case by measuring the density of the liquid condensed mercury and of the residual mercury. If α is known or is assumed=1, equation (1) gives a means of measuring vapour pressures (see § 12.VIII J, Vol. II).

[1] Clausius, *Ann. Phys.*, 1857, **100**, 353; Die mechanische Theorie der Gase, in "Die mechanische Wärmetheorie," Brunswick, 1889–91, **3**, 12.

[2] Knudsen, *Ann. Phys.*, 1915, **47**, 697; Brönsted and Hevesy, *Nature*, 1920, **106**, 144 (Hg); 1921, **107**, 619 (Cl_2); *Z. phys. Chem.*, 1921, **99**, 189; *Phil. Mag.*, 1922, **43**, 31 (Hg); Volmer and Estermann, *Z. Phys.*, 1921, **7**, 1; Mulliken and Harkins, *J.A.C.S.*, 1922, **44**, 37, 1033; Egerton and Lee, *Proc. Roy. Soc.*, 1923, **103**, 499 (Zn).

[3] For theory of small differences, see Lindemann and Aston, *Phil. Mag.*, 1919, **37**, 523; Lindemann, *ibid.*, 1919, **38**, 173; Grimm, *Z. phys. Chem.*, 1929, **2** B, 180; Grimm and Braun, *ibid.*, 1929, **2** B, 200, failed to separate CCl_4 or Cl_2 by fractionation; with H and D compounds, the differences are quite large. See § 10.VIII L, Vol. II.

§ 18. Experimental Tests of Maxwell's Distribution Law

Several experimental tests of Maxwell's law of the distribution of molecular velocities have been made.

(i) The wavelength of light emitted by a moving atom will be modified by a Doppler effect, and the broadening of the spectrum lines of monatomic gases agrees [1] with Maxwell's law applied to a large number of radiating atoms.

(ii) If a copper plate is covered on one side with glass and suspended from a fibre as a vane in chlorine gas, the copper side experiences a smaller pressure than the glass side because some chlorine molecules combine with the copper and do not rebound elastically; the momentum imparted is then mu and not $2mu$, where u is the velocity normal to the plate. If it is assumed that combination occurs only with a minimum velocity, the variation with temperature of the pressure difference and the increase in weight of the plate were found by Cantor [2] to agree with the distribution law. A similar method used by Kappler [2] depended on the condensation of molecules from a vapour at low pressure on a vane of a miniature torsion balance.

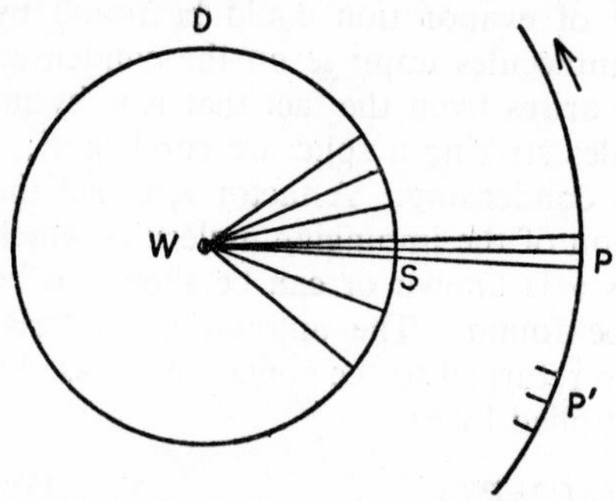

FIG. 13.III. Stern's Experiment

(iii) A model in which steel balls moving on a glass plate by sliding a wood containing-frame gave results corresponding with a Maxwellian distribution.[3]

(iv) The first direct measurement of molecular velocities was made by Stern.[4] The principle is the same as that used in the aberration method for determining the velocity of light. A platinum wire W (Fig. 13.III) heavily plated with silver was surrounded by a cylindrical drum D with a narrow slit S, this being in turn enclosed in a larger concentric drum PP′. The whole could be rotated as a rigid body about W and was contained in a vacuous enclosure. The wire W was heated electrically to such a temperature that silver atoms were thrown off, and as the pressure was very low these had long free paths and many passed through the slit S. With the apparatus at rest these condensed at P on the outer drum, but if it was rapidly rotating the outer drum moved an appreciable distance before the beam of silver atoms struck it, and the atoms were deposited at P′. Atoms moving at different speeds deposited at different places, and the position and intensities of the deposits would indicate the distribution of velocities of the atoms. By rotating the drum first in one and then in the other direction, two lines each displaced from the central position P by equal amounts were obtained. The average velocity of the silver atoms was found

[1] Rayleigh, *Phil. Mag.*, 1889, **27**, 298; Michelson, *ibid.*, 1892, **34**, 280; Fabry and Buisson, *Compt. Rend.*, 1912, **154**, 1224; *J. de Phys.*, 1912, **2**, 442; Ornstein and van Wyk, *Z. Phys.*, 1932, **78**, 734.

[2] Cantor, *Ann. Phys.*, 1897, **62**, 482; *Z. phys. Chem.*, 1898, **26**, 568; Predwoditelew, *Z. Phys.*, 1927, **46**, 406; Frommer and Polanyi, *Z. phys. Chem.*, 1928, **137**, 201; Bennewitz and Neumann, *ibid.*, 1930, **7B**, 246; 1932, **17B**, 457; Kappler, *Ann. Phys.*, 1938, **31**, 377 (torsion balance).

[3] Minnaert, *Z. phys. chem. Unterr.*, 1919, **32**, 69; Wulf, *ibid.*, 1921, **34**, 5.

[4] *Z. Phys.*, 1920, **2**, 49; 1920, **3**, 417; *Phys. Z.*, 1920, **21**, 582; on molecular rays (or beams), see Fraser, "Molecular Rays," Cambridge, 1931; Rodebush, *Rev. Mod. Phys.*, 1931, **3**, 392; Bessey and Simpson, *Chem. Rev.*, 1942, **30**, 239; Estermann, Simpson, and Stern, *Phys. Rev.*, 1947, **71**, 238; Estermann and Foner, *ibid.*, 1947, **71**, 250.

to be 643–675 m. per sec., as compared with the theoretical value 672 m. per sec. for the given temperature.

A more sensitive apparatus on this principle, in which a beam of bismuth molecules emitted from a stationary oven passed through a fixed slit, and then into a rapidly rotating drum with a slit coming opposite the fixed slit, was used by Zartman [1] and Cheng Chuan Ko.[2] The number of molecules with velocities between c and $c+dc$ passing through the slits is proportional to $c\mathrm{d}N$, where $\mathrm{d}N$ is given by (19), § 11, i.e. to $c^3e^{-\beta c^2}\mathrm{d}c$, where $\beta=m/2kT$. The point of impact with the drum is displaced from the point at which they aim on entry by a distance $s=(D/c).\pi Dn$, where D=diameter of drum, n=frequency of rotation. The molecules in the range $\mathrm{d}c$ thus spread over a distance $\mathrm{d}s=-\pi nD^2\mathrm{d}c/c^2$ and if λ is the number depositing per unit length:

$$\lambda\mathrm{d}s=-Cc^3e^{-\beta c^2}\mathrm{d}c,$$

$$\therefore\ \lambda=(C/\pi nD^2)c^5e^{-\beta c^2}=(C'/s^5)e^{-\mu},$$

where $\mu=\pi^2n^2D^4\beta/s^2$, and C and C' are constants.

Ko found that the velocity spectrum was not in complete agreement with Maxwell's law. This was explained by assuming the presence of three kinds of molecules in the vapour, Bi, Bi_2 and Bi_3, and if these are assumed to be present at 827° C. in the ratios Bi : Bi_2 : Bi_3=44 : 54 : 2, the molecules of each kind obeying Maxwell's law, the relative intensity plotted against the displacement s gave a curve which resembled the Maxwell distribution curve in general shape, and could be obtained by superimposing three curves for the separate kinds of molecules. By calculating the ratios of Bi to Bi_2 at different temperatures, the heat of dissociation of Bi_2 was calculated by the van't Hoff Isochore Equation (12), § 60.II.

Experiments with a similar apparatus by Cohen and Ellett [3] with alkali metals gave a very good confirmation of Maxwell's law. They also studied the velocity distribution in a beam of potassium atoms which had been scattered by a magnesium oxide crystal, and found agreement with Maxwell's law, the absolute velocities depending only on the temperature of the scattering crystal and being independent of the origin of the beam. This indicates that the atoms were not specularly reflected, but were first adsorbed on the crystal surface and then emitted diffusely at a temperature corresponding with this (" cosine law "). This agrees with experiments of Knudsen,[4] Langmuir,[5] and others, who found that the directions of molecules after impact were not in any way related to the directions of the molecules impinging on a surface. Cohen and Ellett passed the charged atoms through a magnetic field, which produced curved tracks, the radius of curvature being proportional to the velocity. This magnetic method was also used for lithium and potassium by Scheffers and Meissner,[6] who found excellent agreement with Maxwell's law.

(v) A method proposed by Stern,[7] similar to the toothed-wheel method used by Fizeau to measure the velocity of light, was applied to the determination of

[1] *Phys. Rev.*, 1931, **37**, 383.
[2] *J. Franklin Inst.*, 1934, **217**, 173; Loeb, " Kinetic Theory of Gases," New York, 1934, 132; Kennard, " Kinetic Theory of Gases," New York, 1938, 71.
[3] *Phys. Rev.*, 1937, **52**, 502, 509.
[4] *Ann. Phys.*, 1915, **48**, 1113; " Kinetic Theory of Gases," 1934, 26 f.; Wood, *Phil. Mag.*, 1915, **30**, 300; 1916, **32**, 364.
[5] *Phys. Rev.*, 1916, **8**, 149; *J.A.C.S.*, 1918, **40**, 1361; *Trans. Faraday Soc.*, 1921, **17**, 607; Loeb, " Kinetic Theory of Gases," 1934, 338 f.
[6] *Phys. Z.*, 1933, **34**, 48, 245.
[7] *Z. Phys.*, 1926, **39**, 751.

molecular velocities by Costa, Smyth, and Compton,[1] by Eldridge,[2] and by Lammert.[3] A beam of atoms or molecules from an oven O (Fig. 14.III) passed through a slit S and then in succession through two wheels W_1 and W_2 with slits, rapidly turning on the same shaft. The widths of the three slits were equal but the slit in W_2 was set at an angle of 2° behind that in W_1. Thus, those molecules which travel exactly the distance between W_1 and W_2 whilst the wheels turn through 2° pass through both slits, the slower and faster molecules being stopped by W_2. By rotating the wheels at different speeds, molecules travelling with any assigned speed in a given range were transmitted and formed a deposit on a transparent screen, from the density of which the number of molecules could be calculated (Lammert); or the molecular beam was allowed to fall on a small radiometer vane behind W_2, from the deflection of which the number of mole-

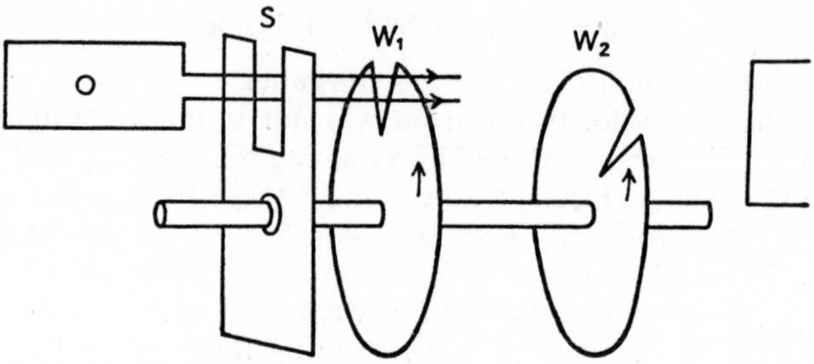

FIG. 14.III. Apparatus for Determination of Molecular Velocities

cules in the beam was calculated (Costa, Smyth, and Compton). The slits separated the molecules into a velocity spectrum, and Maxwell's law was verified with considerable accuracy.

(vi) Some miscellaneous methods depend on the structure of rotational band spectra,[4] and on the velocities of electrons and positive ions emitted by hot bodies [5] (see " Thermionics," § 11.VIII K, Vol. II).

These quite different lines of experimental evidence leave no doubt of the validity of Maxwell's Distribution Law. The theoretical deduction given in § 10 is, as stated, not regarded as satisfactory, and others have been given. Boltzmann in 1872 established what is generally called the *H-theorem*; by a detailed analysis of the effects of molecular collisions he showed [6] that the Maxwellian distribution is actually the *only* steady state possible in a gas, and that any other distribution will almost certainly alter by collisions so as to approach the Maxwellian form. The details of such investigations will be omitted here, since the law is more easily and directly obtained from the general principles of Statistical Mechanics (§ 33.IV).

[1] *Phys. Rev.*, 1927, **30**, 349.
[2] *Phys. Rev.*, 1927, **30**, 931; cf. Tykocinski-Tykosiner, *J. Opt. Soc. Amer.*, 1927, **14**, 423.
[3] *Z. Phys.*, 1929, **56**, 244.
[4] Eva von Bahr, *Verhl. d. D. Phys. Ges.*, 1913, **15**, 710.
[5] Richardson, " The Emission of Electricity from Hot Bodies," 1921, 154 f., 206 f.; Langmuir, *Z. Phys.*, 1927, **46**, 271; Loeb, " Kinetic Theory of Gases," 1934, 114; T. J. Jones, " Thermionic Emission," 1936.
[6] " Gastheorie," 1896, **1**, 32; Jäger, *Ann. Phys.*, 1905, **16**, 46; Holm, *ibid.*, 1915, **48**, 481; Jeans, " Dynamical Theory of Gases," 3rd edit., 1921, 22, 64; " Kinetic Theory of Gases," 1940, 297; Kennard, " Kinetic Theory of Gases," 1938, 52.

§ 19. Boltzmann's Equation

A very important general equation deduced by Maxwell [1] and Boltzmann [2] concerns the distribution of molecules (or ions) in a static field of force. The consideration of Boltzmann's equation may be approached by way of the very simple formula for the decrease in atmospheric pressure with height (*Barometer Formula*). Consider a gas in a tall vertical cylinder of 1 cm.^{2} cross-section, and height z (Fig.15.III). Let the number of molecules per cm.^{3} at heights $z=z_0=0$ ("ground level") and $z=z$ be N_0 and N respectively, the temperature T being constant throughout the column (see below). If m is the mass of a molecule, the masses of gas in g. per cm.^{3} (densities) at heights $z=z_0$ and $z=z$ will be $N_0m=\rho_0$ and $Nm=\rho$, respectively, and the *weights* per cm.^{3} are N_0mg and Nmg, where g is the acceleration of gravity, supposed constant in the column. Let p and $p-dp$ be the pressures in the planes of height z and $z+\mathrm{d}z$, respectively; then, as the mass of gas in the slice of the thickness dz is $\rho \mathrm{d}z=(M/V)\mathrm{d}z$, where M=molecular weight, V=molar volume, the pressure difference (in absolute units) is:

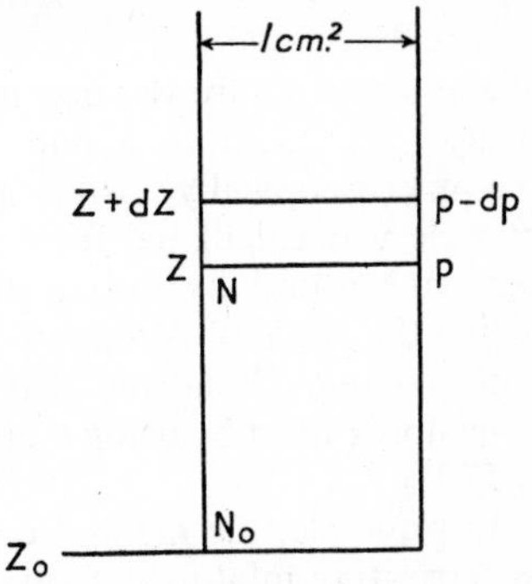

FIG. 15.III. Gas in Gravitational Field

$$-\mathrm{d}p=g(M/V)\mathrm{d}z=(Mg/RT)p\mathrm{d}z,$$

the minus sign being taken because p decreases as z increases. Hence,

$$\mathrm{d}p/p=\mathrm{d}\ln p=-(Mg/RT)\mathrm{d}z,$$

$$\therefore \ln p=(-Mg/RT)z+\text{const.}$$

Put $z=0$, therefore $\ln p_0$=const., where p_0=pressure at the base of the column,

$$\therefore \ln(p/p_0)=-(Mg/RT)z=-(mg/kT)z \quad . \quad . \quad . \quad . \quad (1)$$

where $m=M/N$ and $k=R/N$, N being Avogadro's number and k Boltzmann's constant. Equation (1) is the barometer formula. Boyle's law gives $p/p_0=\rho/\rho_0$, and $\rho/\rho_0=Nm/N_0m=N/N_0$, where N, N_0 are the numbers of *molecules* per cm.^{3},

$$\therefore \ln(N/N_0)=-mgz/kT \quad . \quad . \quad . \quad . \quad . \quad . \quad . \quad . \quad (2)$$

$$\text{and } N=N_0e^{-mgz/kT} \quad . \quad . \quad . \quad . \quad . \quad . \quad . \quad . \quad (3)$$

Now $mgz=\epsilon_p$, the *potential energy* of the molecule at the height z referred to that at the heighi z_0 as zero,

$$\therefore N=N_0e^{-\epsilon_p/kT} \quad . \quad . \quad . \quad . \quad . \quad . \quad . \quad . \quad . \quad . \quad (4)$$

Since the pressures are proportional to the numbers of molecules per cm.^{3}, it follows from (4) that:

$$p=p_0e^{-\epsilon_p/kT} \quad . \quad . \quad . \quad . \quad . \quad . \quad . \quad . \quad . \quad . \quad (5)$$

1 *B.A. Report*, 1873, II, 29.

2 *Wien Ber.*, 1875, **72**, II, 427; 1876, **74**, II, 503; 1879, **78**, II, 7 (gas under gravity); "Gastheorie," 1896, **1**, 134; "Wiss. Abhl.," 1909, **2**, 1, 55, 250; H. W. Watson, "Kinetic Theory of Gases," Oxford, 1876, 12 f.; Ferrini, *R.R. Inst. Lombardo*, 1885, **18**, 319; Jäger, "Fortschritte der kinetischen Gastheorie," 1906, 68; Onnes and Keesom, "Enzykl. d. math. Wiss.," 1912, **5**, i, 769; Herzfeld, in H. S. Taylor, "Physical Chemistry," 1931, **1**, 116; the criticism of Loschmidt, *Wien Ber.*, 1876, 73, II, 128, 366, is mentioned below.

Equation (2) was used by Perrin [1] in the study of the distribution of uniform gamboge particles in a vertical column of suspension. In this case, the gravitational force on the particle is reduced by the upward thrust due to the buoyancy of the liquid, which can be calculated by Archimedes' principle, and the resulting equation is:

$$\ln (N/N_0) = -(Mgz/RT)(1-d/D) \quad . \quad . \quad . \quad . \quad . \quad (6)$$

where d and D are the densities of the liquid and of the solid particle, respectively. By counting N and N_0, the value of M, the " molecular weight " of the microscopically visible particle, was calculated. The mass m of each particle was calculated from the counted number per cm.^{3} and the total mass per cm.^{3} found by evaporation and weighing. From M and m, $N = M/m$, giving the value of Avogadro's number as $6{\cdot}8 \times 10^{23}$.

Schrödinger [2] showed that two isotopic gases of different masses could be reversibly mixed by using a gravitational field, giving the usual entropy equation (§ 57.II).

In principle, the method could be used, especially if assisted by a centrifuge, in separating mixtures of gases of different density.[3]

The above calculation, although it gives the correct result for the distribution in molecular density (N) with height, throws no light on the way in which this is brought about. A consideration of the matter from the point of view of the kinetic theory shows that the gradation of density in the gas must be due to the motion of the molecules. A molecule having a velocity component w in the direction of the vertical z axis will behave like a stone projected vertically upwards in a gravitational field,[4] i.e. it will rise to a height z such that it acquires a potential energy mgz equal to its *initial* kinetic energy $\frac{1}{2}mw^2$, and will come to rest with zero kinetic energy. It then falls back, and the potential energy is converted into kinetic. Since the temperature is proportional to the mean kinetic energy, it might seem that the temperature of the gas should fall off with increasing height,[5] but it must be remembered that it is just those molecules having higher kinetic energies than the average which will reach the upper layers of the gas and leave the lower layers; there is thus a compensation, and the average kinetic energy, and hence the temperature, remains the same throughout the column.[6]

A vertical column of gas under gravitational action might be supposed to have a somewhat higher " temperature " in the lowest levels, because of the fall of the molecules (so acquiring kinetic energy) by gravity, although this does not lead to heat flow, and is in *apparent* contradiction to the Second Law of Thermodynamics.[7] This has been called [8] the *sama effect*; attempts to detect it [9] failed (it should be 3×10^{-6} degree per cm. at 10^{-4} mm. pressure),

[1] " Les Atomes," 1914, 129 f.

[2] *Z. Phys.*, 1921, **5**, 163; cf. Gouy, *Compt. Rend.*, 1914, **158**, 664.

[3] See e.g. Mazza, Brit. Pat. 423,003/1935; Rabu, *L'Industrie Chim.*, 1935, **22**, 896.

[4] Cf. Löw, *Z. phys. Chem.*, 1912, **80**, 192.

[5] This was supposed to be the case by Loschmidt, *Wien Ber.*, 1876, **73**, II, 128, 366.

[6] Ehrenfest, *Z. Phys.*, 1923, **17**, 421 (already emphasised by Boltzmann); see also de Boer, *Arch. Néerl.*, 1901, **6**, 641; Exner, *Ann. Phys.*, 1902, **7**, 683. For the action of gravity on a *gas mixture*, see Gouy, *Compt. Rend.*, 1914, **158**, 664.

[7] Loschmidt, *Wien Ber.*, 1876, **73**, II, 128, 366; 1877, **75**, II, 287; 1878, **76**, II, 209; cf. Polvani, *Nuov. Cim.*, 1920, **19**, 225.

[8] Von Dallwitz-Wegner, *Z. Phys.*, 1923, **15**, 280; see criticism by Ehrenfest, *ibid.*, 1923, **17**, 421, as " an old deceptive delusion."

[9] Holm, *Arkiv Mat. Astron. Fys.*, 1927, **19** A, No. 34; 1928, **20** A, No. 1; **21** A, No. 12; *Compt. Rend.*, 1928, **187**, 531.

but a flow of gas detectable by a light vane (*gravimolecular pressure*) was claimed.

It must now be shown that the Maxwellian distribution will hold in the different parts of the force field, and in the first place it will be supposed that the molecules moving vertically do not enter into collisions. Consider the levels z and $z+\mathrm{d}z$. Then, if Maxwell's law holds in the region of the plane z, the number of molecules leaving 1 cm.[2] of this plane in an upward direction which have velocities in the range w to $w+\mathrm{d}w$ will be, from (37), § 10:

$$N(m/2\pi kT)^{1/2}w\mathrm{e}^{-mw^2/2kT}\mathrm{d}w \quad . \quad . \quad . \quad . \quad . \quad . \quad . \quad (7)$$

since the cube-root of the expression in (37), § 10, giving the number of molecules of specified type per cm.[3], is multiplied by w to give the number crossing the plane per second. Each molecule reaching the upper plane $z+\mathrm{d}z$ will have lost kinetic energy $mg\mathrm{d}z$, hence if primed symbols are used for the $z+\mathrm{d}z$ plane:

$$\tfrac{1}{2}mw'^2+mg\mathrm{d}z=\tfrac{1}{2}mw^2, \quad \therefore \; w'\mathrm{d}w'=w\mathrm{d}w.$$

$$\text{But} \quad c^2=u^2+v^2+w^2, \quad c'^2=u'^2+v'^2+w'^2,$$

and $u'=u$, $v'=v$; hence (7) can be written:

$$N\mathrm{e}^{-mg\mathrm{d}z} \, . \, (m/2\pi kT)^{1/2}w'\mathrm{e}^{-mw'^2/2kT}\mathrm{d}w' \quad . \quad . \quad . \quad . \quad (8)$$

Since $N\mathrm{e}^{-mg\mathrm{d}z}=N'$, by (4), it is seen that (7) and (8) are the same expressions for the conditions which apply to the heights z and $z+\mathrm{d}z$, respectively, and hence Maxwell's law applies to $z+\mathrm{d}z$. This shows that it must apply throughout the gravitational field.

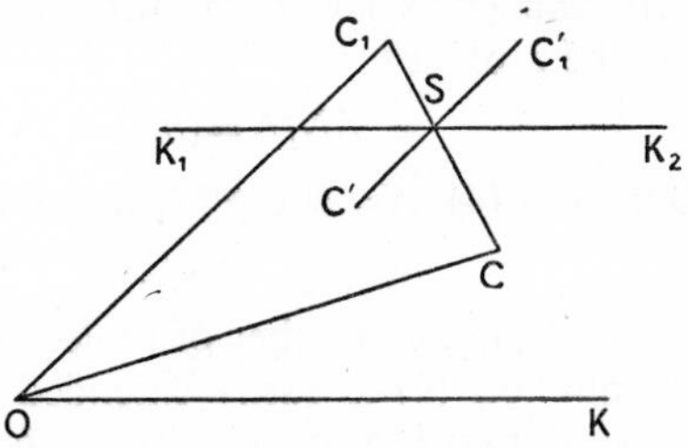

FIG. 16.III. Boltzmann's Construction for Molecular Collisions

Next consider the effects of collisions. These will change the group of velocities to which a molecule belongs, but if a Maxwellian distribution holds at any point, collisions will add as many molecules to a group moving in any given direction as are removed from it, so that the final effect of collisions is to leave things as they would be without collisions. If two molecules collide, they merely exchange velocities along the axis of collision, and the other two velocity components at right angles are unchanged. Thus, the product $\mathrm{d}u\mathrm{d}v\mathrm{d}w\mathrm{d}u'\mathrm{d}v'\mathrm{d}w'$ before collision becomes $\mathrm{d}u'\mathrm{d}v\mathrm{d}w\mathrm{d}u\mathrm{d}v'\mathrm{d}w'$ after collision and the two products remain equal.

A mathematical proof of this was given by Boltzmann.[1] Although Rothe [2] maintained that Boltzmann's proof was unsound, and gave one in which a functional determinant is shown to be equal to -1, Jeans [3] pointed out that the result is almost obvious. It is a special case of Liouville's equation (§ 13.IV).

Boltzmann's argument, which applies to two kinds of molecules, is as follows.[4] Through the centres of two molecules of masses m and m_1 at the moment of collision draw a line OK, and from O draw OC and OC_1 representing in magnitude and direction the velocities of the molecules (Fig. 16.III). Then CC_1 represents the relative velocity of one molecule with respect to the other. Divide

[1] *Wien Ber.*, 1868, **58**, II, 517; 1872, **66**, II, 275; 1875, **72**, II, 427; 1886, **94**, II, 613; " Gastheorie," 1896, **1**, 19, 27; " Wiss. Abhl.," 1909, **1**, 49, 316; **2**, 1; 1909, **3**, 225; Stankevitsch, *Ann. Phys.*, 1886, **29**, 153.

[2] *Ann. Phys.*, 1917, **53**, 151.

[3] " Dynamical Theory of Gases," 3rd edit., 1921, 21.

[4] See Watson, " Kinetic Theory of Gases," 2nd edit., Oxford, 1893, 9, 21

CC_1 at S such that $m_1 . C_1S = m . CS$, then OS represents the velocity of the centre of gravity of m and m_1. OK can be taken as the axis of the velocity component u. The two components of the relative velocity perpendicular to OK will be unchanged on collision, so that v and w remain the same. If the components parallel to OK are u and u_1 before collision, and u' and u_1' after collision, the principle of conservation of momentum gives $mu+m_1u_1=mu'+m_1u_1'$, and the principle of conservation of energy gives $\frac{1}{2}mu^2+\frac{1}{2}m_1u_1^2=\frac{1}{2}mu'^2+\frac{1}{2}m_1u_1'^2$; hence either $u'=u$ and $u_1'=u_1$, or $u'=-u$ and $u_1'=-u_1$. Since the molecules fly apart after collision, only the second solution is possible. Hence the two components of the relative velocity which fall in the direction of K_1K_2 parallel to OK are simply reversed on collision. In the plane of K_1K_2 and CC_1 draw SC′ and SC_1' equal to SC and SC_1 with the same inclinations to K_1K_2 as these but reversed, i.e. $\angle K_1SC_1=\angle K_2SC_1'$. Then C′ and C_1' are the ends of the velocity vectors OC′ and OC_1' after collision, and $C'C_1'$ represents the relative velocity of m and m_1 after collision.

If now, with C fixed, the point C_1 describes a small parallelepiped volume element $du_1dv_1dw_1=d\omega_1$, then the complete symmetry of the figure shows that C′ must describe a congruent parallelepiped $du_1'dv_1'dw_1'=d\omega_1'$, which is the mirror image of $d\omega_1$. With C_1 fixed, C will describe a parallelepiped $dudvdw=d\omega$, and again the complete symmetry of the figure shows that C′ will describe a parallelepiped $du'dv'dw'=d\omega'$, which is the mirror image of $d\omega$. Hence $d\omega'd\omega_1'=d\omega d\omega_1$.

If Maxwell's law holds for all parts of the gas (thermal equilibrium) then for the z plane:

$$dN/N=(m/2\pi kT)^{3/2}e^{-(mu^2+mv^2+mw^2)/2kT}dudvdw.$$

But from (4), $N=N_0e^{-\epsilon_p/kT}$, where N_0 refers to the plane $z=0$; hence:

$$dN/N_0=(m/2\pi kT)^{3/2}e^{-(mu^2+mv^2+mw^2+2\epsilon_p)/2kT}dudvdw. \quad . \quad . \quad (9)$$

where N_0 is the number of molecules in a given volume in the plane $z=0$.

Equation (4) is easily extended to other kinds of potential energy, e.g. of charged particles in an electric field. If an element of volume $d\tau$ contains mass points which exert no attractive or repulsive forces, and if N_0 is the number of particles per cm.^{3}, then the number of particles in $d\tau$ is $N_0d\tau$. But if the particles exert forces on one another and are free to move, this number will be less (repulsion) or greater (attraction) than $N_0d\tau$, say $Nd\tau$. Let the force originate from a central point (e.g. a charged ion), and consider a small volume at a distance r from it. Let the average electric potential be V. In equilibrium, the same numbers of particles pass across *any* section, but the number will be smaller (attraction) or greater (repulsion) than in the absence of the central charge. Now take N_0 in the vicinity of this. Formula (4) may be applied if the gravitational force mgz is replaced by the electrical force of attraction Vev, where e is the (positive) electronic charge and ν is the valency of the ion. Thus, $\ln (N/N_0)=-Vev/kT$, or:

$$N=N_0e^{-Vev/kT} \quad . \quad . \quad . \quad . \quad . \quad . \quad . \quad . \quad (10)$$

This is the equation used in the theory of strong electrolytes of Debye and Hückel.[1]

Boltzmann's principle is stated by Noyes [2] as follows: " When a large number of molecules possessing an average kinetic energy $\frac{3}{2}kT$ are distributed throughout

[1] *Phys. Z.*, 1923, **24**, 185, 334; Debye, *ibid.*, 1924, **25**, 97; Partington, " Chemical Thermodynamics," 1940, 129.

[2] *J.A.C.S.*, 1924, **46**, 1080.

a region where there prevail at different points different fields of force, whereby any kind of molecule A in any given volume element dv acquires a potential energy ϵ, the number of such molecules will be equal to the number n_A per unit volume in a place where this energy is zero, multiplied by the factor $e^{-\epsilon/kT}$ and by the volume dv." A correction of the equation is necessary for small mean free paths.[1]

§ 20. Mean Free Path

A single molecule moves in a straight line with the average velocity $\bar{c}$ until it collides with another molecule, when its path is deflected but its average speed remains the same. The molecules will first be regarded as hard elastic spheres exerting no forces on one another except at the moment of impact. The total path will then be an irregular zig-zag, with a collision at each corner, and a straight-line free path between each pair of collisions. The individual lengths of these free paths will vary considerably, but for a very large number the *average* length will approach a definite value called the *mean free path* and denoted by l. This was first calculated by Clausius,[2] whose method is essentially followed here.

The collisions will occur at irregular intervals, but over a sufficiently long time, the *average* number of collisions per second approaches a definite number called a *collision frequency* and denoted by Z (German, " Stosszahl "). Since the distance traversed per second, $\bar{c}$, is broken up by Z collisions into free paths of *average* [3] length l:

$$c=Zl \quad \ldots\ldots\ldots\ldots \quad (1)$$

Z and l may also be referred to a *group* of molecules instead of to a single molecule. The average of the free paths described by *all* the molecules in a given volume of gas in any given interval of time is [4] the mean free path l. A large number N of molecules per cm.^{3} make NZ collisions per second; the total number of molecular impacts made by N molecules per cm.^{3} is NZ, but if the molecules are of the same kind the total number of complete collisions per second, each involving *two* impacts, is $\frac{1}{2}NZ$. Otherwise expressed, the number of times an A molecule collides with another, B, molecule per second is NZ, but if the other molecule is also an A molecule, then two A molecules collide at each impact and the number of complete collisions of each A molecule is $\frac{1}{2}NZ$.

The probability of collision of a molecule obviously increases with its speed, and it has a greater probability of striking another molecule when this is moving than if it is at rest. Thus, l and Z depend on the velocity. The probability that a molecule moving with a velocity $\bar{c}$ collides with another molecule during a short interval of time dt is proportional to dt, since if molecular chaos is assumed (§ 10), the position of one molecule has no correlation with the positions and velocities of any of the others. If the molecules are distributed at random, however, the chance of one molecule meeting another is also, obviously, proportional to their mean density.

[1] Holm, *Ann. Phys.*, 1915, **48**, 481; *Meddel. Nobelinst.*, 1919, **5**, No. 27.
[2] *Ann. Phys.*, 1858, **105**, 239; *Phil. Mag.*, 1859, **17**, 81; Die kinetische Theorie der Gase, in " Die mechanische Wärmetheorie," Brunswick, 1889–91, **3**, 46, 204; O. E. Meyer, " Kinetic Theory of Gases," 1899, 153.
[3] The *mean* free path should, strictly, be written $\bar{l}$, but this is rarely done.
[4] A " strict " proof of this need hardly be given.

Two general conclusions follow from first principles:

(i) If the temperature is raised, the average velocity $\bar{c}$ increases proportionally to $\sqrt{T}$ (see (35) § 10,). Increase in temperature is equivalent to multiplying all the velocities by a uniform factor $\sqrt{(T_2/T_1)}$, the relative distribution of velocities being the same at all temperatures. The collision frequency is thus proportional to $\sqrt{T}$ as well as to the density.

(ii) The mean free path varies only with the density and is inversely proportional to it, and thus at a given temperature it is inversely proportional to the pressure. This follows from (1), $l=\bar{c}/Z$, which shows that l is independent of temperature if both $\bar{c}$ and Z are proportional to $\sqrt{T}$.

§ 21. Molecular Collisions

The *collision* of two molecules is simply defined for two hard elastic spheres; if r is the radius there is a collision when the two centres come within a distance $2r=\sigma$, where σ is the *diameter* of a molecule ($r=\sigma/2$), as is seen from Fig. 17.III. If, however, the molecules are not spheres, or if they are supposed to exert repulsive forces increasing rapidly with decreasing distance, the definition of a collision becomes more difficult. Maxwell [1] showed that the calculations are fairly simple for the cases of (i) hard perfectly elastic spheres with the Maxwellian distribution of velocities, and (ii) spherical molecules which repel one another with a force inversely proportional to the fifth power of the distance, $F=kr^{-5}$, when the results are very like those for hard elastic spheres. More recently, the very difficult calculations for general force laws have been carried through, but the results are very complicated (see § 3.VII F).

It is simplest to begin with the case [2] of hard elastic spheres of *diameter* σ. Obviously if $\sigma=0$, the molecules never collide, and the probability of collision increases with σ, and is proportional to σ^2, i.e. to the target-area offered by a molecule. First assume that all the molecules have the same velocity c, that there are N molecules per cm.^{3}, and that all are at rest in fixed positions except one, which threads its way among the fixed molecules with a velocity c. There is a collision when the distance between the centre of the moving sphere and that of any fixed sphere becomes equal to σ (it cannot be less than σ). Hence if a *point* (the centre of the moving molecule) moved with a velocity c among fixed spheres of *radius* σ, the number of collisions would be just the same as in the case considered. This point may be taken as the centre of molecule B and the fixed sphere is C (Fig. 17.III).

Let the probability that the point moves a distance x *without* collision be $W_x=\mathrm{f}(x)$, and the probability that it moves a distance $x+\mathrm{d}x$ without collision be $W_{x+\mathrm{d}x}=\mathrm{f}(x+\mathrm{d}x)$. The probability $\mathrm{f}(x+\mathrm{d}x)$ is composed of two probabilities: (i) the probability that there is no collision in a path x, and (ii) the probability that there is still no collision in a further path $\mathrm{d}x$. The probability that there *is* a collision in the path $\mathrm{d}x$ is obviously proportional to $\mathrm{d}x$, say $a\mathrm{d}x$, where a is a constant, and hence the probability that there is *no* collision in the path $\mathrm{d}x$ is:

$$1-a\mathrm{d}x \quad . \quad . \quad . \quad . \quad . \quad . \quad . \quad . \quad . \quad . \quad (1)$$

[1] *Phil. Mag.*, 1860, **19**, 19; *Phil. Trans.*, 1868, **157**, 49; "Scientific Papers," 1890, **1**, 377; 1890, **2**, 26.

[2] Clausius, *Ann. Phys.*, 1858, **105**, 239; 1862, **115**, 239; *Phil. Mag.*, 1859, **17**, 81.

The function $f(x+dx)$ may be expanded by Taylor's Theorem (§ 32.I):

$$f(x+dx)=f(x)+f'(x)dx=f(x)(1-a dx) \quad . \quad . \quad . \quad . \quad (2)$$

$$\therefore \ f'(x)=-af(x), \quad \therefore \ f'(x)/f(x)=-a \quad \text{or} \quad f(x)=be^{-ax}$$

where b is a constant. The probability that there is no collision in the path $x=0$ is obviously certainty, i.e. 1, therefore $b=1$,

$$\therefore \ f(x)=e^{-ax} \quad . \quad . \quad . \quad . \quad . \quad . \quad . \quad . \quad . \quad (3)$$

This case would presumably apply to the motion of a very fast and very small electron moving among gas molecules which, for all practical purposes, are at rest in comparison with the moving electron (see below).

Now return to equation (2) to calculate the probability of *no* collision in a distance dx, i.e. $f'(x)dx$. Draw two parallel planes dx apart, cut at right angles by a cylinder of cross-section 1 cm.^{2} (The arrangement is shown in section at right angles to the planes in Fig. 18.III). The volume cut out of the cylinder is

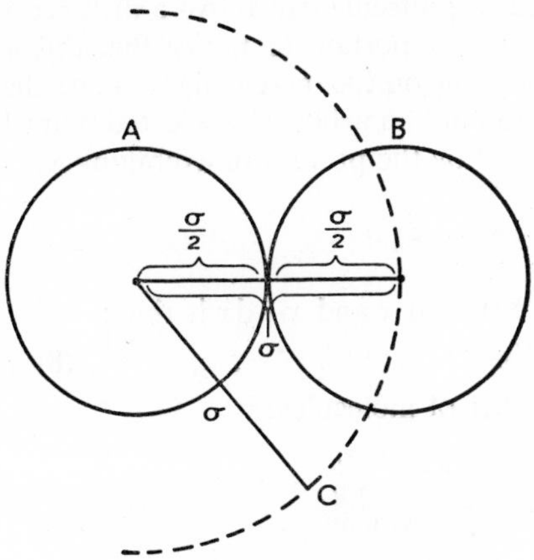

FIG. 17.III. Collision of Spheres

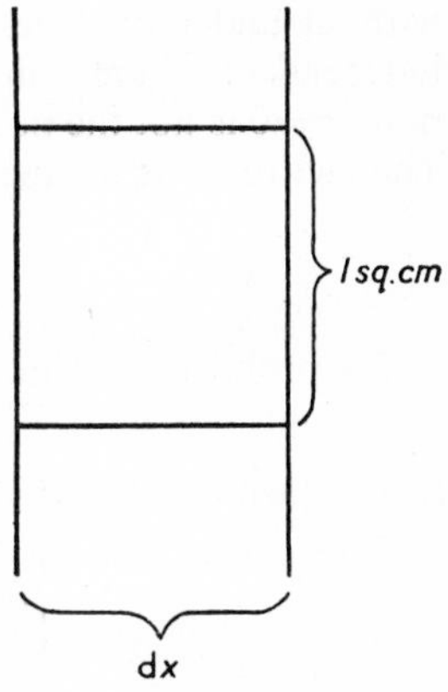

FIG. 18.III

(1 cm.^{2})$\times dx=dx$ cm.^{3}, therefore the number of molecules contained in it is $N dx$. Each exposes a target area of $\pi\sigma^2$ cm.^{2}, hence the total target area exposed in the cylinder is $N\pi\sigma^2 dx$. The *free area* for the moving molecule in the cylinder is thus $(1-N\pi\sigma^2 dx)$, and the probability of there being no collision is given by the ratio:

$$(\text{free area}/\text{total area})=(1-N\pi\sigma^2 dx)/1=(1-a dx),$$

$$\therefore \ a=N\pi\sigma^2, \quad \therefore \ f(x)=e^{-N\pi\sigma^2 x} \quad . \quad . \quad . \quad . \quad . \quad . \quad . \quad (4)$$

Now consider a very large number n of *possible* paths for the molecule between two successive collisions. The number of these paths which are less than x, i.e. which lie between 0 and x, is $n'=n\times$(probability that the molecule goes a distance x without collision)$=ne^{-N\pi\sigma^2 x}$.

The *number of paths* with lengths between 0 and $x+dx$ is similarly:

$$n''=ne^{-N\pi\sigma^2(x+dx)}=ne^{-N\pi\sigma^2 x}\times e^{-N\pi\sigma^2 dx}$$

Expand the exponential function $e^{-N\pi\sigma^2 dx}$, and, as dx is small, retain only the first term (see § 13, I): $e^{-N\pi\sigma^2 dx}=1-N\pi\sigma^2 dx$. Hence $n''=n'(1-N\pi\sigma^2 dx)<n'$. The number of paths with lengths between x and $x+dx$ is $n'-n''=n'.N\pi\sigma^2 dx$ $=ne^{-N\pi\sigma^2 x}.N\pi\sigma^2 dx$

$$=nae^{-ax}dx, \quad . \quad . \quad . \quad . \quad . \quad . \quad . \quad . \quad . \quad (5)$$

where $a=N\pi\sigma^2$

The length of each of these paths will be x, hence the total length of such paths is $nae^{-ax}x\mathrm{d}x$, and the total length of all the molecular paths is:

$$na\int_0^\infty e^{-ax}x\mathrm{d}x,$$

and this divided by the total number of paths n gives the *mean free path, l*:

$$\therefore\ l=a\int_0^\infty e^{-ax}x\mathrm{d}x=a\Big[-xe^{-ax}/a\Big]_0^\infty+\int_0^\infty e^{-ax}\mathrm{d}x=$$

$$-(1/a)\Big[e^{-ax}\Big]_0^\infty \text{(see § 16, I)}=1/a=1/N\pi\sigma^2,$$

$$\therefore\ l=1/N\pi\sigma^2 \quad . \quad . \quad . \quad . \quad . \quad . \quad . \quad . \quad (6)$$

Substitute $a=N\pi\sigma^2=1/l$ in (3),

$$\therefore\ f(x)=e^{-x/l} \quad . \quad . \quad . \quad . \quad . \quad . \quad . \quad . \quad (7)$$

Equation (7) shows that the probability that a molecule can move a distance x without undergoing collision is $e^{-x/l}$, and it is important to notice that this is independent of the point at which the last collision has taken place, since the point $x=0$ is not the point of the last collision but an arbitrarily selected point.[1] The fact that l is the mean free path is proved by the process of averaging x:

$$\int_0^\infty xe^{-x/l}\mathrm{d}x\Big/\int_0^\infty e^{-x/l}\mathrm{d}x=l.$$

The proportion of molecules with paths between x and $x+\mathrm{d}x$ is thus:

$$\mathrm{d}f(x)=(\mathrm{d}x/l)e^{-x/l} \quad . \quad . \quad . \quad . \quad . \quad . \quad . \quad . \quad (8)$$

from which it is found that, of a given number of molecules:

1/148	have free paths greater than	$5l$
1/22027	,, ,, ,,	$10l$
$1/2{\cdot}7\times10^{43}$	,, ,, ,,	$100l$

According to a calculation by O. E. Meyer,[2] out of 100 molecules:

99 traverse the path	$0{\cdot}01l$	78 traverse the path	$0{\cdot}25l$	14 traverse the path	$2l$
98 ,, ,,	$0{\cdot}02l$	72 ,, ,,	$0{\cdot}333l$	5 ,, ,,	$3l$
90 ,, ,,	$0{\cdot}1l$	61 ,, ,,	$0{\cdot}5l$	2 ,, ,,	$4l$
82 ,, ,,	$0{\cdot}2l$	37 ,, ,,	$1l$	1 ,, ,,	$4{\cdot}6l$

in all cases without making a collision.

Equation (7) has been tested in the case of a beam of electrons entering a gas with velocities comparable with the molecular speeds, when the diminution of the current i should follow the equation $i=i_0e^{-\alpha x}$, where α is a coefficient of extinction, corresponding with $1/l$. The experiments [3] show that there is

[1] Clausius, *Ann. Phys.*, 1880, **10**, 92; Korteweg, *ibid.*, 1881, **12**, 136; Holm, *ibid.*, 1916, **51**, 768 (bibl.).

[2] "Kinetic Theory of Gases," 1899, 160.

[3] Lenard, *Ann. Phys.*, 1903, **12**, 714; Ramsauer, *Phys. Z.*, 1920, **21**, 576; *Ann. Phys.*, 1921, **64**, 513; 1921, **66**, 546; 1927, **83**, 1129; Mayer, *ibid.*, 1921, **64**, 451; Brode, *Phys. Rev.*, 1925, **25**, 636; Rusch, *Ann. Phys.*, 1926, **80**, 707; Brüche, *ibid.*, 1927, **82**, 25; 1927, **83**, 1065; 1927, **84**, 279; 1929, **1**, 93; 1929, **2**, 909; 1930, **4**, 387; 1930, **5**, 281; 1930, **7**, 579; Kollath, *Phys. Z.*, 1928, **29**, 834; 1930, **31**, 985 (49 refs.); 1931, **32**, 80; *Ann. Phys.*, 1932, **15**, 485; Holtsmark, *Z. Phys.*, 1929, **55**, 437; Bailey and Duncanson, *Phil. Mag.*, 1930, **10**, 145; Brose and Keyston, *Nature*, 1930, **126**, 806; *Phil. Mag.*, 1935, **20**, 902; McMillen, *Phil. Mag.*, 1930, **36**, 1034; Löhner, *Ann. Phys.*, 1930, **6**, 50; 1935, **24**, 349; Ramsauer and Kollath, *ibid.*, 1930, **7**, 176; 1931, **9**, 756; 1931, **10**, 143; 1932, **12**, 529; 1933, **16**, 560, 570; 1933, **17**, 755; Ramsauer, Kollath, and Lilienthal, *ibid.*, 1931, **8**, 709; Holst and Holtsmark, *Kgl. Norsk. Vidensk. Selsk*

good agreement, except for very slow electrons moving through monatomic gases, when a curious sharp decrease in apparent atomic diameter or collision area sets in, known as the *Ramsauer effect*. This cannot be explained on the basis of the kinetic theory but is covered by a consideration of the phenomenon from the point of view of wave-mechanics.[1] In this, a massive particle is replaced by a train of probability waves and the intensity of the scattered waves corresponds with the number of molecules scattered by collisions. If the molecular wave-length is small compared with the distances within which the scattering potential varies appreciably, the scattering approximately follows the classical laws, but if the wave-length exceeds this limit the phenomenon of diffraction comes in, and the classical picture fades out, just as geometrical optics fails for very long waves of electromagnetic radiation.

Equation (7) has also been applied to the scattering of atoms or molecules (e.g. beams of *molecular rays*, such as silver atoms) by gases, and with satisfactory results.[2] In such experiments a beam of silver atoms from a small aperture in a heated vessel passed through a vessel first vacuous and then containing inert gas at low pressure, and the density D of the deposit of silver on glass plates at varying distances x was measured. From the relation $D=D_0 e^{-x/l}$, where D_0 is the density for a vacuum, l can be calculated.

If c is the velocity of the molecules in a gas, the *duration of a free path* is:

$$\tau = l/c \qquad (9)$$

The *number of collisions* per sec., Z, made by the selected moving molecule with the other fixed molecules per cm.³ is equal to the number of free paths described per second, since each free path is terminated by a collision:

$$Z = 1/\tau = c/l \qquad (10)$$

Let $f(t)$ be the probability of *no* collisions occurring in a time interval t, then this is found from (7) by putting $x=ct$, and $1/l=Z/c$ (c is a constant),

$$\therefore f(t) = e^{-Zt} \qquad (11)$$

a result easily found directly by a method similar to that used in deducing (7). The probability that a selected molecule will collide with a fixed molecule in the time interval t is $(1-e^{-Zt})$, and the probability that it will collide in the time interval $t+dt$ is $[1-e^{-Z(t+dt)}]$. Hence, the probability of a collision in the interval dt after an interval t without collision is:

$$[1-e^{-Z(t+dt)}]-(1-e^{-Zt}) = e^{-Zt}-e^{-Z(t+dt)} = Ze^{-Zt}dt \qquad (12)$$

Forhl., 1931, **4**, 89; Townsend, *Proc. Roy. Soc.*, 1931, **134**, 352; Gaertner, *Ann. Phys.*, 1931, **8**, 135; Arnot, *Proc. Roy. Soc.*, 1931, **133**, 615; Bullard and Massey, *ibid.*, 1931, **133**, 637; Klemperer, *Ann. Phys.*, 1932, **15**, 361; Rosenberg, *ibid.*, 1932, **15**, 757; Hughes and McMillen, *Phys. Rev.*, 1932, **39**, 585; 1932, **40**, 469; Bailey, *Phil. Mag.*, 1932, **13**, 993; Bailey and Rudd, *ibid.*, 1932, **14**, 1033; Bailey and Somerville, *ibid.*, 1934, **17**, 1169; Voss, *Z. Phys.*, 1933, **83**, 581; Siegert, *Ann. Phys.*, 1934, **21**, 503; Wolf, *ibid.*, 1935, **23**, 285, 627; Rostagni, *ibid.*, 1935, **24**, 543; Goodrich, *Phys. Rev.*, 1937, **52**, 259; Fisk, *ibid.*, 1937, **51**, 25; Davydov, *Sow. Phys. Z.*, 1937, **12**, 269; Roscoe, *Phil. Mag.*, 1938, **26**, 32; Bracewell, *Phys. Rev.*, 1938, **54**, 639; Amdur and Pearlman, *J. Chem. Phys.*, 1941, **9**, 503; for positive rays, see Wien, *Ann. Phys.*, 1912, **39**, 519; 1923, **70**, 1; for neutrons, von Halban and Kowarski, *Nature*, 1938, **142**, 392, and many later papers by various authors.

[1] Fraser, "Molecular Rays," Cambridge, 1931; summary in Mohr and Massey, "The Theory of Atomic Collisions," Oxford, 1933, 133 f.; Kennard, "Kinetic Theory of Gases," 1938, 124; Rice, *J.A.C.S.*, 1932, **54**, 4559; Schmidt, *Z. Elektrochem.*, 1936, **42**, 8; Champion, *Rep. Progr. Physics,* 1938, **5**, 348.

[2] Born, *Phys. Z.*, 1920, **21**, 578; Bielz, *Z. Phys.*, 1925, **32**, 81; Stern, *Z. Phys.*, 1926, **39**, 751; Knauer and Stern, *ibid.*, 1926, **39**, 764; Ochiai, *Proc. Phys. Math. Soc. Japan*, 1928, **10**, 120; Johnson, *Phys. Rev.*, 1928, **31**, 103; Knauer, *Z. Phys.*, 1933, **80**, 80; 1934, **90**, 559; Massey and Mohr, *Proc. Roy. Soc.*, 1933, **141**, 434; 1934, **144**, 188 (theoretical); Schmidt, *Z. Elektrochem.*, 1934, **40**, 498; Hirota, *Bull. Chem. Soc. Japan*, 1944, **19**, 102, 109.

as is found by expanding the second exponential function:

$$e^{-Z(t+dt)}=e^{-Zt} \cdot e^{-Zdt}=e^{-Zt}(1-Zdt).$$

Suppose that a selected molecule can exist in some special (e.g. excited or activated) state and that τ is its *average life* in this state; the probability that it will remain in this state after a time t is defined as $e^{-t/\tau}$, and the probability that it will make a collision whilst it is in its special state in the interval between t and $t+dt$ is:

$$e^{-t/\tau} \cdot Ze^{-Zt}dt \quad \ldots \ldots \ldots \quad (13)$$

$$=Ze^{-t(1+Z\tau)/\tau}dt \quad \ldots \ldots \ldots \quad (14)$$

The probability that any selected molecule will make a collision whilst it is in its special state is:

$$Z\int_0^\infty e^{-t(1+Z\tau)/\tau}dt=Z\tau/(1+Z\tau) \quad \ldots \ldots \quad (15)$$

and if there are N molecules in the special state, the probability that *one* of them will make a collision with other molecules during its active life is:

$$NZ\tau/(1+Z\tau) \quad \ldots \ldots \ldots \quad (16)$$

The simple formula (6) was deduced by Clausius.[1] It is based on two assumptions: (i) the actual state of affairs can be simplified by assuming that only one molecule moves and the others are all at rest, and (ii) the speed of the moving molecule c is constant. Both obviously require correction. Clausius in 1858 also showed that the assumption (i) when corrected for the motion of *all* the molecules gave a factor $\frac{3}{4}=0{\cdot}750$ to equation (6), and a better value for l would thus be given by:

$$l=0{\cdot}750/N\pi\sigma^2 \quad \ldots \ldots \ldots \quad (17)$$

This still assumes that all the molecules have the same velocity. This second assumption is corrected [2] by replacing the constant velocity c by the mean (or average) velocity $\bar{c}$ calculated by Maxwell's equation (35), § 10. This gives a still better value:

$$l=1/\sqrt{(2)}N\pi\sigma^2=0{\cdot}7071/N\pi\sigma^2 \quad \ldots \ldots \quad (18)$$

as is proved in § 22, and equation (18) is the one used in later calculations.

If λ is the mean distance apart of two neighbouring molecules in a gas, then λ^3 is the volume of a cube containing a molecule,[3]

$$\therefore \lambda^3=1/N \quad \text{or} \quad N\lambda^3=1, \quad \therefore l=\lambda^3/\sqrt{(2)}\pi\sigma^2,$$

$$\text{or} \quad \lambda=\sqrt[3]{[\sqrt{(2)}\pi\sigma^2 l]} \quad \ldots \ldots \quad (19)$$

The *collision frequency* is given from (18) as before by:

$$Z=\bar{c}/l=\sqrt{(2)}N\pi\bar{c}\sigma^2 \quad \ldots \ldots \ldots \quad (20)$$

and the *time of describing a free path by*:

$$\tau=1/\sqrt{(2)}N\pi\bar{c}\sigma^2 \quad \ldots \ldots \ldots \quad (21)$$

Ray [4] suggested for the mean free path $l=\sqrt[3]{(N/3)}-\sigma$ in place of (18), the latter giving $l=\infty$ when $\sigma=0$.

[1] *Ann. Phys.*, 1858, **105**, 239.
[2] Maxwell, *Phil. Mag.*, 1860, **19**, 19; "Scientific Papers," 1890, **1**, 377.
[3] Clausius, *Ann. Phys.*, 1858, **105**, 239; Holm, *ibid.*, 1916, **51**, 768; Gans, *Phys. Z.*, 1922, **23**, 108.
[4] *Proc. XV Indian Sci. Congr.*, 1928, 141.

§ 22. Collision Frequency by Maxwell's Equation

The calculation of the mean free path may readily be generalised by taking account of the Maxwellian distribution of velocities.[1] The assumptions of colliding elastic spheres still holds; the modern quantum-mechanical theory of the exchange of energy on collision of molecules will receive treatment later. Although Maxwell's result was criticised by Clausius,[2] this was based on a misunderstanding, and the formula is perfectly correct.[3] For greater generality, a mixture of two gases is considered.

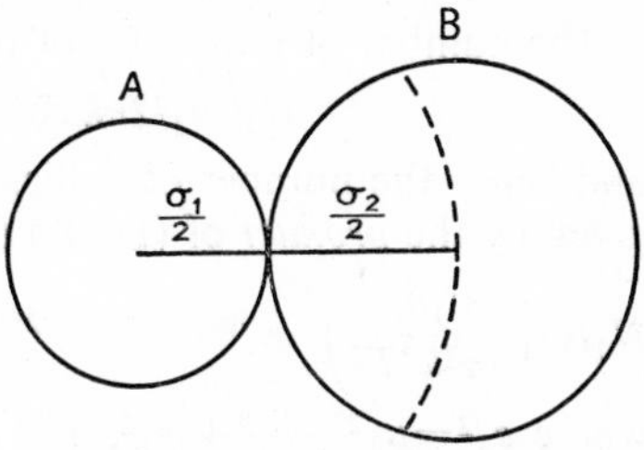

FIG. 19.III. Condition for a Molecular Collision

Consider 1 cm.³ of gas containing N_1 and N_2 molecules of two kinds of gases, A and B, with masses m_1 and m_2, and *diameters* σ_1 and σ_2, respectively. At the instant of contact, the centres of the two molecules are $\frac{1}{2}(\sigma_1+\sigma_2)$ cm. apart (Fig. 19.III), hence if one molecule is chosen, the centre of the second molecule must, at the instant of collision, lie on a sphere of *radius* $\frac{1}{2}(\sigma_1+\sigma_2)=\sigma_{12}$ drawn about the centre of the first molecule. Let two selected molecules, (A) and (B), one of each kind of gas, have velocity components in the ranges:

for (A): u_1 and u_1+du_1 v_1 and v_1+dv_1 w_1 and w_1+dw_1,

for (B): u_2 and u_2+du_2 v_2 and v_2+dv_2 w_2 and w_2+dw_2,

and consider such a type of collision that the line of centres at the moment of collision lies inside a small solid angle $d\omega$, where $d\omega=\sin\theta d\theta d\phi$ (see § 8), θ being the angle between the *relative velocity*, V, of the two molecules and the

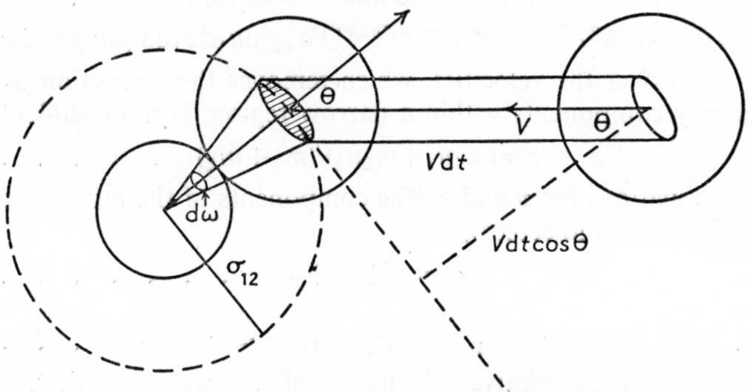

FIG. 20.III. Collision Frequency

line of centres at the moment of collision, and ϕ the angle between the line of centres and any definite plane through the relative velocity (Fig. 20.III). In order that this collision shall occur, the centre of the second molecule must, at an instant dt *before* the instant of collision, lie inside a small cylinder of base

[1] Maxwell, *Phil. Mag.*, 1860, **19**, 19; " Scientific Papers," 1890, **1**, 377; H. W. Watson, " Kinetic Theory of Gases," Oxford, 1876, 9, 2nd edit., 1893, 11; Boltzmann, " Gastheorie," 1896, **1**, 61; O. E. Meyer, " Kinetic Theory of Gases," 1899, 162, 413; Jeans, " Dynamical Theory of Gases," 1921, 18 f.; Loeb, " Kinetic Theory of Gases," 1927, 35, 56 f., 90, 250; Jaffé, *Ann. Phys.*, 1930, **6**, 195.

[2] *Phil. Mag.*, 1860, **19**, 434.

[3] Niven's note in Maxwell, " Scientific Papers," 1890, **1**, 387.

$\sigma_{12}^2 d\omega$ and height $V dt \cos\theta$, i.e. of volume $V\sigma_{12}^2 \cos\theta dt d\omega$. The number of B molecules per cm.³ is given by Maxwell's law (37), § 10, as:

$$N_2(m_2/2\pi kT)^{3/2} e^{-m_2(u_2^2+v_2^2+w_2^2)/2kT} du_2 dv_2 dw_2,$$

hence the number with centres inside the cylinder is:

$$N_2(m_2/2\pi kT)^{3/2} e^{-m_2(u_2^2+v_2^2+w_2^2)/2kT} du_2 dv_2 dw_2 V dt \cos\theta \sigma_{12}^2 d\omega \quad . \quad (1)$$

where N_2 is the total number of molecules of the second type per cm.³

The number of molecules of type (A) per cm.³ is:

$$N_1(m_1/2\pi kT)^{3/2} e^{-m_1(u_1^2+v_1^2+w_1^2)/2kT} du_1 dv_1 dw_1 \quad . \quad . \quad . \quad . \quad (2)$$

and hence the number of collisions of the selected type per cm.³ in a time dt is given by the *product* of (1) and (2) as:

$$N_1 N_2 \left(\frac{m_1 m_2}{4\pi^2 k^2 T^2}\right)^{3/2} e^{-(m_1c_1^2+m_2c_2^2)/2kT} V\sigma_{12}^2 dt \cos\theta d\omega du_1 dv_1 dw_1 du_2 dv_2 dw_2 . \quad (3)$$

where $c_1^2 = u_1^2 + v_1^2 + w_1^2$, and $c_2^2 = u_2^2 + v_2^2 + w_2^2$.

To find the total number of collisions per cm.³, the restrictions put on the type of collision must be successively removed. First remove the restriction that the direction of the line of centres shall lie in the solid angle $d\omega$ by integrating over $d\omega = \sin\theta d\theta d\phi$, i.e. over the limits [1] of θ from 0 to $\pi/2$ and over the limits of ϕ from 0 to 2π. Taking $\cos\theta\, d\omega$ from the expression (3) this gives (as in (6) and (7), § 8):

$$\int_0^{\pi/2}\int_0^{2\pi} \cos\theta \sin\theta d\theta d\phi = \pi,$$

and by dividing (3) by dt to give the number of collisions per cm.³ *per second* between molecules having velocities between the specified limits, but now without regard to the direction of the line of centres, this gives:

$$\pi N_1 N_2 (m_1 m_2/4\pi^2 k^2 T^2)^{3/2} e^{-(m_1c_1^2+m_2c_2^2)/2kT} V\sigma_{12}^2 du_1 dv_1 dw_1 du_2 dv_2 dw_2 \quad . \quad (4)$$

The integration over the velocities, which removes the restriction to molecules having velocity components within a narrow region, is more difficult. Put:

$$u = (m_1 u_1 + m_2 u_2)/(m_1 + m_2) \quad . \quad . \quad . \quad . \quad . \quad . \quad (5)$$

with similar equations for v and w (the components of the motion of the centre of gravity of the two molecules),

$$c^2 = u^2 + v^2 + w^2 \quad . \quad . \quad . \quad . \quad . \quad . \quad . \quad . \quad (6)$$

and

$$\alpha = u_2 - u_1, \quad \beta = v_2 - v_1, \quad \gamma = w_2 - w_1 \quad . \quad . \quad . \quad . \quad (7)$$

(the components of the relative velocity, V, of the two molecules). Then:

$$V^2 = \alpha^2 + \beta^2 + \gamma^2 \quad . \quad . \quad . \quad . \quad . \quad . \quad . \quad . \quad (8)$$

It is then easy to show that:

$$m_1 c_1^2 + m_2 c_2^2 = (m_1 + m_2)c^2 + V^2[m_1 m_2/(m_1 + m_2)] \quad . \quad . \quad . \quad (9)$$

The transformation of the differential product $du_1 dv_1 dw_1 du_2 dv_2 dw_2$ is done in three steps, since u_1 and u_2 are functions only of u and α, and so on. From (5), $du = du_1 . m_1/(m_1+m_2) + du_2 . m_2/(m_1+m_2)$, and from (7), $d\alpha = -du_1 + du_2$, and the solution of the simultaneous equations gives $du_1 du_2 = du d\alpha$; and similarly $dv_1 dv_2 = dv d\beta$, and $dw_1 dw_2 = dw d\gamma$. Hence:

$$du_1 dv_1 dw_1 du_2 dv_2 dw_2 = du dv dw d\alpha d\beta d\gamma \quad . \quad . \quad . \quad . \quad (10)$$

[1] Since collision occurs only on *approach*, only a hemisphere is considered, i.e. θ varies from 0 to $\pi/2$.

The number of collisions per cm.^{3} per sec. between molecules with restricted velocity components is then, from (4):

$$\pi N_1N_2(m_1m_2/4\pi^2k^2T^2)^{3/2}e^{-[(m_1+m_2)c^2+V^2m_1m_2/(m_1+m_2)]/2kT}V\sigma_{12}{}^2d\tau \quad . \ (11)$$

where $d\tau = dudvdwd\alpha d\beta d\gamma$, and, from (8), $V=\sqrt{(\alpha^2+\beta^2+\gamma^2)}$. To integrate (11) it is first transformed to polar coordinates by putting, from (3), § 8:

$$dudvdw = c^2 \sin\theta' d\theta' d\phi' dc,$$

and the integration is the same as that in § 8 except that c replaces a in (3) there; hence:

$$\int_0^\pi\int_0^{2\pi} c^2 \sin\theta' d\theta' d\phi' dc = 4\pi c^2 dc \quad . \ . \ . \ . \ . \ (12)$$

Similarly, it is found that:

$$d\alpha d\beta d\gamma = V^2 \sin\theta'' d\theta'' d\phi'' dV,$$

$$\int_0^\pi\int_0^{2\pi} V^2 \sin\theta'' d\theta'' d\phi'' dV = 4\pi V^2 dV \quad . \ . \ . \ . \ . \ (13)$$

The number of collisions per cm.^{3} per sec. for which c and V lie within the ranges c and $c+dc$, and V and $V+dV$, without regard to direction, is thus:

$$16\pi^3N_1N_2(m_1m_2/4\pi^2k^2T^2)^{3/2}\sigma_{12}{}^2e^{-[(m_1+m_2)c^2+V^2m_1m_2/(m_1+m_2)]/2kT}c^2V^3dcdV \ . \ (14)$$

Integration from $c=0$ to $c=\infty$ gives the number of collisions in which V lies between V and $V+dV$. The integral:

$$\int_0^\infty e^{-(m_1+m_2)c^2/2kT}c^2dc$$

is evaluated by putting:

$$(m_1+m_2)c^2/2kT = x^2, \quad c^2=[2kT/(m_1+m_2)]x^2, \quad x/c=\sqrt{[(m_1+m_2)/2kT]},$$

$$\therefore \ 2cdc = 2xdx[2kT/(m_1+m_2)]$$

$$\therefore \ dc=(x/c)[2kT/(m_1+m_2)]dx=[2kT/(m_1+m_2)]^{1/2}dx$$

$$\therefore \ e^{-(m_1+m_2)c^2/2kT}c^2dc=[2kT/(m_1+m_2)]^{3/2}e^{-x^2}x^2dx.$$

From (26), § 10:

$$\int_0^\infty e^{-x^2}x^2dx=\sqrt{\pi}/4,$$

$$\therefore \ \int_0^\infty e^{-(m_1+m_2)c^2/2kT}c^2dc=(\sqrt{\pi}/4)[2kT/(m_1+m_2)]^{3/2}.$$

The final integration between $V=0$ and $V=\infty$ then gives the *total* number of collisions of the two kinds of molecules per cm.^{3} per sec. as:

$$4N_1N_2\sqrt{\pi}\left[\frac{2kT}{(m_1+m_2)}\right]^{3/2}\left(\frac{m_1m_2}{4k^2T^2}\right)^{3/2}\sigma_{12}{}^2\int_0^\infty e^{-m_1m_2V^2/2kT(m_1+m_2)}V^3dV \quad . \ (15)$$

Put $[m_1m_2/2kT(m_1+m_2)]V^2=x^2, \quad \therefore \ x^2/V^2=m_1m_2/2kT(m_1+m_2)$

$$\therefore \ V=[(m_1+m_2)2kT/m_1m_2]^{1/2}x$$

$$\therefore \ V^3=[(m_1+m_2)2kT/m_1m_2]^{3/2}x^3$$

$$\therefore \ dV=[(m_1+m_2)2kT/m_1m_2]^{1/2}dx$$

$$\therefore \ \int_0^\infty e^{-m_1m_2V^2/2kT(m_1+m_2)}V^3dV=[(m_1+m_2)2kT/m_1m_2]^2\int_0^\infty e^{-x^2}x^3dx$$

$$=2[kT(m_1+m_2)/m_1m_2]^2,$$

since from (23), § 10: $\displaystyle\int_0^\infty e^{-x^2}x^3dx=\tfrac{1}{2}.$

The total number of collisions is, therefore:

$$Z_{12}=4N_1N_2\sqrt{(\pi)}\sigma_{12}^2\left[\frac{2kT}{(m_1+m_2)}\right]^{3/2}\cdot\left(\frac{m_1m_2}{4k^2T^2}\right)^{3/2}\cdot 2\left[\frac{kT(m_1+m_2)}{m_1m_2}\right]^2$$

$$=2\sqrt{(2\pi)}N_1N_2\sigma_{12}^2\sqrt{[(m_1+m_2)kT/m_1m_2]} \quad . \quad . \quad . \quad . \quad . \quad . \quad . \quad (16)$$

$$=2N_1N_2\sigma_{12}^2\sqrt{[(\pi/h)(1/m_1+1/m_2)]} \quad . \quad . \quad . \quad . \quad . \quad . \quad . \quad . \quad . \quad (17)$$

where $h=1/2kT$. It will be remembered that $\sigma_{12}=\frac{1}{2}(\sigma_1+\sigma_2)$.

If N_1, N_2 molecules are each present in a volume v cm.[3] (not to be confused with the velocity v above), the expressions above must be divided by v^2 to find the number of collisions per cm.[3] per sec., since N_1/v and N_2/v replace N_1 and N_2 above.

If $\overline{c_1}$ and $\overline{c_2}$ are the *average* (*mean*) *velocities* of the two kinds of molecules, (16) can be written in the form:

$$Z_{12}=2N_1N_2\sigma_{12}^2[2\pi kT(m_1+m_2)/m_1m_2]^{1/2} \quad . \quad . \quad . \quad . \quad (18)$$

and the substitution from (35), § 10, then gives:

$$\overline{c_1}=2(2kT/\pi m_1)^{1/2},\quad \overline{c_2}=2(2kT/\pi m_2)^{1/2},$$

$$\therefore (\overline{c_1}^2+\overline{c_2}^2)^{1/2}=(4\,.\,2kT/\pi m_1+4\,.\,2kT/\pi m_2)^{1/2}$$

$$=[8kT(m_1+m_2)/\pi m_1m_2]^{1/2}$$

$$=2[2kT(m_1+m_2)/\pi m_1m_2]^{1/2} \quad . \quad . \quad . \quad . \quad (19)$$

Thus, an alternative expression [1] is:

$$Z_{12}=\pi N_1N_2\sigma_{12}^2(\overline{c_1}^2+\overline{c_2}^2)^{1/2} \quad . \quad . \quad . \quad . \quad . \quad . \quad (20)$$

An expression for the *mean relative velocity* $\overline{V}$ was found by Maxwell.[2] It is found by taking V from (8) or (9), multiplying by the exponential factor and differential element from (3), and integrating over the surface of a sphere. The actual result is also obtained by intuition by considering that, since the mean velocities $\overline{c_1}$ and $\overline{c_2}$ may be inclined at all angles from 0° to 180°, the *average* angle will be 90°, and the resultant relative velocity will be represented by the hypotenuse of a right-angled triangle having the component mean velocities as sides:

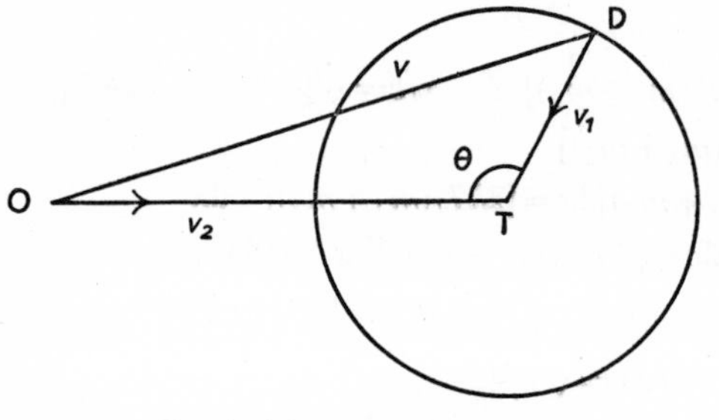

FIG. 21.III. Mean Velocity

$$\therefore \overline{V}^2=\overline{c_1}^2+\overline{c_2}^2,\quad \therefore \overline{V}=\sqrt{(\overline{c_1}^2+\overline{c_2}^2)} \quad . \quad . \quad . \quad . \quad (21)$$

For identical molecules ($\overline{c_1}=\overline{c_2}=\overline{c}$):

$$\overline{V}=\sqrt{2}\,.\,\overline{c} \quad . \quad . \quad . \quad . \quad . \quad . \quad . \quad . \quad . \quad . \quad (22)$$

Hence (20) can be written:

$$Z_{12}=\pi N_1N_2\sigma_{12}^2\overline{V} \quad . \quad . \quad . \quad . \quad . \quad . \quad . \quad . \quad . \quad (23)$$

By starting with (21), a very simple deduction of the collision formula (17) can be obtained.[3]

[1] Note that $\overline{c_1}^2$ and $\overline{c_2}^2$ are the squares of the average velocities $\overline{c_1}$ and $\overline{c_2}$, not the mean square velocities $\overline{c_1^2}$ and $\overline{c_2^2}$.

[2] *Phil. Mag.*, 1860, **19**, 19; " Scientific Papers," 1890, **1**, 377; Clausius, *Phil. Mag.*, 1860, **19**, 434; *Ann. Phys.*, 1862, **115**, 239; see Weinstein, " Thermodynamik und Kinetik der Körper," 1901, **1**, 172; Rothe, *Ann. Phys.*, 1917, **53**, 151; Ishida, *Phil. Mag.*, 1917, **10**, 305.

[3] See Glasstone, " Text Book of Physical Chemistry," 1940, 267 f.

If the velocities of two molecules are c_1 and c_2, and are represented in magnitude and direction by DT$=c_1$ and OT$=c_2$ (Fig. 21.III; in the figure c_1 and c_2 are denoted by v_1 and v_2), meeting at an angle θ, the relative velocity is represented by:

$$\mathrm{OD}=V=\sqrt{(c_1^2+c^2-2c_1c_2\cos\theta)}.$$

The mean relative velocity $\bar{V}$ is found by integrating over the surface of a sphere with centre O, and is:[1]

$$\bar{V}=(c_2+\tfrac{1}{3}c_1^2/c_2) \text{ when } c_2>c_1 \quad . \quad . \quad . \quad . \quad . \quad (24)$$

$$\text{and} \quad \bar{V}=(c_1+\tfrac{1}{3}c_2^2/c_1) \text{ when } c_1>c_2 \quad . \quad . \quad . \quad . \quad . \quad (25)$$

Equation (16) gives the number of free paths of the N_1 molecules of kind A per cm.³ which terminate by collisions with B molecules. If both molecules are of the same type, it might be supposed that the number of collisions per cm.³ per sec. would be found by putting $m_1=m_2=m$ in (16)–(18), viz.:

$$2\sqrt{(2\pi)}N^2\sigma^2\sqrt{(2mkT/m^2)}=2N^2\sigma^2\sqrt{(4\pi kT/m)}=4N^2\sigma^2\sqrt{(\pi kT/m)}.$$

But in this case each collision has been counted twice, once when the molecule is a colliding molecule (B type molecule) and once when it is a struck molecule (A type molecule); hence to find the actual number of collisions per cm.³ per sec. the above expression must be halved, giving:

$$Z_{11}=2N^2\sigma^2\sqrt{(\pi kT/m)} \quad . \quad . \quad . \quad . \quad . \quad . \quad . \quad (26)$$

and, by substituting from (35), § 10, $\bar{c}=2\sqrt{(2kT/\pi m)}$, it is found that:

$$Z_{11}=(\pi/\sqrt{2})N^2\sigma^2\bar{c} \quad . \quad . \quad . \quad . \quad . \quad . \quad . \quad (27)$$

Since each collision terminates *two* free paths, one from each molecule, the number of free paths described per cm.³ per sec. by all the molecules is:

$$(2\pi/\sqrt{2})N^2\sigma^2\bar{c}=\sqrt{(2)}\pi N^2\sigma^2\bar{c}=4N^2\sqrt{(\pi)}\sigma^2\sqrt{(kT/m)} \quad . \quad . \quad (28)$$

which is equal to the total distance $N\bar{c}$ moved in 1 sec. by all the molecules. Thus, the mean length of a free path will be:

$$l=N\bar{c}/\sqrt{(2)}\pi N^2\sigma^2\bar{c}=1/\sqrt{(2)}\pi\sigma^2N=0{\cdot}7071/\pi\sigma^2N \quad . \quad . \quad . \quad (29)$$

which is Maxwell's expression given in (18), § 21.

The equations deduced in this section are of fundamental importance in the theory of bimolecular gas reactions. It is noteworthy that, although they have been known for many years from the time of their deduction by Maxwell[2] and Boltzmann,[3] it is only fairly recently that they have been systematically applied in the study of such reactions. Some readers may not follow the rather elementary mathematics used in the deduction; in that case they may rest content with a knowledge of the results, which are of great simplicity and wide practical utility.

The equations appear in various forms in the literature, and the relations between these are usually matters of elementary algebra or arithmetic. Thus, if the factor 2 is put inside the square-root sign in (18), and $\boldsymbol{k}=\boldsymbol{R}/N$ and $m=M/N$ (where M=molecular weight, N=Avogadro's number) substituted, a useful variant:

$$Z_{12}=N_1N_2\sigma_{12}^2\sqrt{[8\pi \boldsymbol{R}T(M_1+M_2)/M_1M_2]} \quad . \quad . \quad . \quad (30)$$

[1] Boltzmann, "Gastheorie," 1896, **1**, 62; Langmuir, *J.A.C.S.*, 1919, **41**, 167; Kuenen, "Die Eigenschaften der Gase" (Ostwald-Drucker, "Handbuch der allgemeinen Chemie," **3**), Leipzig, 1919, 29; Kennard, "Kinetic Theory of Gases," New York, 1938, 105 f. (detailed proof); Preissmann, *Arch. Sci. Phys. Nat.*, 1946, **28**, 61.

[2] *Phil. Mag.*, 1860, **19**, 19; "Scientific Papers," 1890, **1**, 377.

[3] *Wien Ber.*, 1868, **58**, II, 517; "Wiss. Abhl.," 1909, **1**, 49; "Gastheorie," 1896, **1**, 61 f. On the mean free path and the width of spectrum lines, see Schönrock, *Ann. Phys.*, 1907, **22**, 209.

is found. By collecting the numerical constants, and using instead of N_1 and N_2 the molar concentrations, ξ_1 and ξ_2 (mols/cm.^{3}), the equations: [1]

$$Z_{12}/N = 10^{28 \cdot 4427}\xi_1\xi_2\sigma_{12}^2\sqrt{[T(M_1+M_2)/M_1M_2]} \quad . \quad . \quad . \quad (31)$$

$$Z_{11}/N = 10^{28 \cdot 2922}\xi^2\sigma^2\sqrt{(T/M)} \quad . \quad . \quad . \quad . \quad . \quad . \quad (32)$$

are found, in which Z/N is the number of *mols* (g.mols.) colliding per cm.^{3} per sec.

Now consider a *single molecule* of kind A moving in a mixture of A and B molecules. The total number of collisions it makes per cm.^{3} per sec. will be the sum of its collisions (Z_1) with A molecules and of its collisions (Z_2) with B molecules:

$$Z_1 = \sqrt{(2)}\pi\sigma_1^2N_1\bar{c}_1 + \pi\sigma_{12}^2N_2\sqrt{(\bar{c}_1^2+\bar{c}_2^2)} \quad . \quad . \quad . \quad . \quad (33)$$

and similarly for a B molecule colliding with A and B molecules:

$$Z_2 = \sqrt{(2)}\pi\sigma_2^2N_2\bar{c}_2 + \pi\sigma_{12}^2N_1\sqrt{(\bar{c}_1^2+\bar{c}_2^2)} \quad . \quad . \quad . \quad . \quad (34)$$

The substitutions $\bar{c}_1 = 2\sqrt{(2kT/\pi m_1)}$ and $\bar{c}_2 = 2\sqrt{(2kT/\pi m_2)}$ give:

$$Z_1 = 4\sqrt{(\pi)}N_1\sigma_1^2\sqrt{(kT/m_1)} + 2\sqrt{(2\pi)}N_2\sigma_{12}^2[(m_1+m_2)kT/m_1m_2]^{1/2} \quad (35)$$

$$Z_2 = 4\sqrt{(\pi)}N_2\sigma_2^2\sqrt{(kT/m_1)} + 2\sqrt{(2\pi)}N_2\sigma_{12}^2[(m_1+m_2)kT/m_1m_2]^{1/2} \quad (36)$$

The reciprocals of the mean free paths for each type of molecule are found by dividing Z by the value of $\bar{c}_1$ in (33) and of $\bar{c}_2$ in (34):

$$1/l_1 = \sqrt{2} \, . \, \pi\sigma_1^2N_1 + \pi\sigma_{12}^2N_2\sqrt{[(m_1+m_2)/m_2]} \quad . \quad . \quad . \quad (37)$$

$$1/l_2 = \sqrt{2} \, . \, \pi\sigma_2^2N_2 + \pi\sigma_{12}^2N_1\sqrt{[(m_1+m_2)/m_1]} \quad . \quad . \quad . \quad (38)$$

equations also deduced by Maxwell.[2]

The number of collisions per cm.^{3} per sec. between molecules with a *relative velocity* greater than an assigned value V_0 is found [3] by integrating (15) between the limits V_0 and ∞:

$$4N_1N_2\sigma_{12}^2\sqrt{\pi}\left[\frac{m_1m_2}{2kT(m_1+m_2)}\right]^{3/2}\int_{V_0}^{\infty} e^{-m_1m_2V^2/2(m_1+m_2)kT}V^3\mathrm{d}V \quad . \quad (39)$$

$$= Z\left[1+\frac{m_1m_2}{m_1+m_2}\cdot\frac{V_0^2}{2kT}\right]e^{-m_1m_2V_0^2/2(m_1+m_2)kT} \quad . \quad . \quad . \quad . \quad (40)$$

where Z is the total number of collisions.

The number of collisions per cm.^{3} per sec. in which the component of the relative velocity parallel to the line of centres of the molecules, $R = V\cos\theta$, is greater than an assigned value R_0 is found by integrating (3) first over all values of c from (6), and then over all values of ϕ:

$$\left[2\pi\times4\pi\times\frac{\sqrt{\pi}}{4}\left(\frac{2kT}{m_1+m_2}\right)^{3/2}\times4\pi\right]$$

$$\times N_1N_2\left(\frac{m_1m_2}{4\pi^2k^2T^2}\right)^{3/2}\sigma_{12}^2e^{-m_1m_2V^2/2(m_1+m_2)kT}V^3\sin\theta\cos\theta\mathrm{d}\theta\mathrm{d}V$$

$$= 8\left[\frac{\pi m_1^3m_2^3}{(m_1+m_2)^38k^3T^3}\right]^{1/2}N_1N_2\sigma_{12}^2e^{-m_1m_2V^2/2(m_1+m_2)kT}V^3\sin\theta\cos\theta\mathrm{d}\theta\mathrm{d}V,$$

[1] Dushman, *J.A.C.S.*, 1921, **43**, 397.

[2] *Phil. Mag.*, 1860, **19**, 19; "Scientific Papers," 1890, **1**, 377; O. E. Meyer, "Kinetic Theory of Gases," 1899, 415.

[3] For equations (39)–(42), see Tolman, "Statistical Mechanics," 1927, 67; Herzfeld, in H. S. Taylor, "Physical Chemistry," 1931, **1**, 124; cf. Langevin and Rey, *Le Radium*, 1913, **10**, 142.

and then integrating over all values of V from R_0 to ∞ and of $\cos\theta$ between 1 and R_0/V:

$$\int_{R_0}^{\infty}\int_{1}^{R_0/V} 8N_1N_2\sigma_{12}^2\left[\frac{\pi m_1^3m_2^3}{8k^3T^3(m_1+m_2)^3}\right]^{1/2} e^{-m_1m_2V^2/2(m_1+m_2)kT}V^3\sin\theta\cos\theta d\theta dV$$

$$=Ze^{-m_1m_2R_0^2/(m_1+m_2)2kT} \quad . \quad . \quad . \quad . \quad . \quad . \quad . \quad (41)$$

where Z is the total number of collisions. The fraction in a given range is found by differentiation:

$$dZ=Z\frac{m_1m_2}{m_1+m_2}\cdot\frac{1}{kT}\cdot e^{-m_1m_2R^2/2(m_1+m_2)kT}RdR \quad . \quad . \quad . \quad . \quad (42)$$

It should be noted that the mean free path as defined and calculated by Maxwell's method, which may be called *Maxwell's mean free path*, is not the only one which can be obtained, although it is the one most commonly used. It is obtained by finding the average value of the collision frequency Z for molecules moving with velocities distributed according to Maxwell's law, and dividing the average velocity $\bar{c}$ by this frequency.

Another free path was calculated by Tait.[1] At a given instant the number of molecules per cm.^{3} with speeds between c and $c+dc$ is dN_c, given by (21), § 10. Suppose all these molecules describe an *average* path, λ, from the given instant until their next collision; then if N is the *total* number of molecules in 1 cm.^{3}, Tait's free path is defined as:

$$l'=(1/N)\int\lambda dN_c \quad . \quad . \quad . \quad . \quad . \quad . \quad . \quad . \quad . \quad (43)$$

and it can be shown that this is given by:

$$l'=\frac{1}{\pi N\sigma^2}\int_0^{\infty}\frac{4x^4e^{-x^2}dx}{\psi(x)}=\frac{0{\cdot}677}{\pi N\sigma^2} \quad . \quad . \quad . \quad . \quad . \quad . \quad (44)$$

where $\psi(x)=xe^{-x^2}+(2x^2+1)\int_0^x e^{-y^2}dy$, and the integral in this cannot be expressed in simpler terms and must be found by quadrature. Tait's free path is about 4 per cent. less than Maxwell's, in which the numerical factor is $1/\sqrt{2}=0{\cdot}7071$. Jeans [2] found the factor to be $1{\cdot}255/\sqrt{2}=0{\cdot}7079$.

Natanson [3] worked out the case in which 2, 3, ..., molecules after collision may remain together as a complex; he showed that the velocity of the centre of gravity of the complex follows Maxwell's distribution law, and the average kinetic energies of the single and complex particles are equal. Gibbs's dissociation formula was deduced. He also pointed out [4] that Tait had calculated that 99 per cent. of the Maxwellian distribution is set up in a gas in 5×10^{-10} sec., but the remaining 1 per cent. would, theoretically, require an *infinite* time.

Let δ be the short distance between the surfaces of two colliding molecules, small compared with the diameters. Before collision the molecules are in this

[1] *Trans. Roy. Soc. Edin.*, 1886, **33**, 65 (the tables are incorrectly copied into some books); Boltzmann, "Gastheorie," 1896, **1**, 73; Bouty, *J. de Phys.*, 1914, **4**, 450; Dushman, "Production and Measurement of High Vacuum," Schenectady, 1922, 24; Jaffé, *Ann. Phys.*, 1930, **6**, 195; Rosenberg, *Phys. Rev.*, 1942, **61**, 528.

[2] *Phil. Mag.*, 1904, **8**, 692.

[3] *Ann. Phys.*, 1888, **33**, 683.

[4] *Ann. Phys.*, 1888, **34**, 970; Drude, *ibid.*, 1897, **62**, 693.

region δ for a time δ/R, and for an equal time after collision; hence the mean duration of a collision is $2\delta/R$, and the mean duration for all collisions is:

$$\tau=\int_0^\infty \frac{2\delta}{R}\cdot\frac{m_1m_2}{(m_1+m_2)kT}\cdot e^{-R^2m_1m_2/2kT(m_1+m_2)}\,.\,RdR$$

$$=\delta\sqrt{[2\pi m_1m_2/kT(m_1+m_2)]} \quad . \quad . \quad . \quad . \quad . \quad . \quad . \quad . \quad . \quad (45)$$

or, if $m_1=m_2=m$:

$$\tau=\delta\sqrt{(\pi m/kT)} \quad . \quad . \quad . \quad . \quad . \quad . \quad . \quad . \quad (46)$$

and $1/\tau$ is the probability per unit time that a pair of molecules at a distance δ will break apart.

The probability of a *triple collision*, in which *three* molecules collide, is much smaller than that of a binary collision; [1] it has been calculated in different ways. Herzfeld [2] defined it in terms of a collision time equal to the interval in which the distance between two colliding molecules afterwards struck by a third like molecule is less than the molecular diameter; it may then be shown that the ratio of the probability of a triple collision to that of a binary collision (between two molecules) is approximately equal to the ratio of the molecular diameter to the mean free path; and hence if Z_2, Z_3 are the binary and triple collision frequencies:

$$Z_3/Z_2\simeq\sigma/l \quad . \quad . \quad . \quad . \quad . \quad . \quad . \quad . \quad . \quad (47)$$

Therefore from (29) and (27):

$$Z_3=2\sqrt{(2)}\pi N^3\sigma^5\sqrt{(\pi kT/m)} \quad . \quad . \quad . \quad . \quad . \quad . \quad (48)$$

Since $l\simeq10^{-5}$ cm. at 1 atm. presure, and $\sigma\simeq10^{-8}$ cm., it follows that Z_3 is of the order of 10^{-3} times Z_2; at lower pressures (l increases) the ratio is larger.

This completes the discussion of the fundamental equations of the Kinetic Theory of Gases. The applications of the theory to the specific heats, viscosity, thermal conductivity, and diffusion of gases, and the properties of gases at very low pressures, are dealt with in Section VII.

[1] Larmor, *Manch. Mem.*, 1908, **52**, No. 10.

[2] *Z. Phys.*, 1922, **8**, 132; Syrkin, *Phys. Z.*, 1923, **24**, 236; Tolman, "Statistical Mechanics," 1927, 247.

SECTION IV

STATISTICAL MECHANICS AND QUANTUM THEORY

BIBLIOGRAPHY OF STATISTICAL MECHANICS

Aston, in H. S. Taylor and Glasstone, " Treatise on Physical Chemistry," New York, 1942, **1**, 511; Boltzmann, " Vorlesungen über Gastheorie," Leipzig, 1895, **1**, 38, 58; 1898, **2**, 62 f.; Darrow, *Rev. Mod. Phys.*, 1929, **1**, 90; Fowler, " Statistical Mechanics," Cambridge, 1929, 2nd edit., 1936; Fowler and Guggenheim, " Statistical Thermodynamics," Cambridge, 1939; Gibbs, " Elementary Principles in Statistical Mechanics," 1902; " Principes Élémentaires de Mécanique Statistique," Paris, 1926; " Collected Works," 1928, **2**, 1 f.; Glasstone, " Recent Advances in General Chemistry " 1936, 53; *idem*, " Theoretical Chemistry," New York, 1944; Herzfeld, in Müller-Pouillet, " Lehrbuch der Physik," 11th edit., Brunswick, 1925, **3**, ii; Hinshelwood, " The Kinetics of Chemical Change," Oxford, 1945; Jeans, " Dynamical Theory of Gases," 3rd edit., Cambridge, 1921, 349; Kennard, " Kinetic Theory of Gases," New York, 1938, 338; Landau and Lifshitz, " Statistical Physics," transl. Schönberg, Oxford, 1938; Lindsay and Margenau, " Foundations of Physics," New York, 1936, 218; Lorentz, " Les Théories Statistique en Thermodynamique," Leipzig and Berlin, 1916; Mayer and Mayer, " Statistical Mechanics," New York, 1940; Moelwyn-Hughes, " Physical Chemistry," Cambridge, 1940; *idem*, " Kinetics of Reactions in Solution," Oxford, 1947; Orr, in Butler, " Chemical Thermodynamics," 1946, 537 f.; Planck, " Theorie der Wärmestrahlung," 4th edit., Leipzig, 1921, 111 f.; *idem*, " Theorie der Wärme," 1930, 183 f.; Rice, " Introduction to Statistical Mechanics for Students of Physics and Physical Chemistry," 1930; Rodebush and Webb, in H. S. Taylor, " Treatise on Physical Chemistry," New York, 1931, **2**, 1417; Schrödinger, " Statistical Thermodynamics," Cambridge, 1946; Tolman, " Statistical Mechanics," New York, 1927; *idem*, Oxford, 1938; Zeise, " Thermodynamik auf den Gründen der Quantentheorie, Quantenstatistik, und Spektroscopie," Leipzig, 1944.

§ 1. Thermodynamic- and Micro-States

The kernel of Statistical Mechanics is the concept of *state*, and the most general formal definition of state is that it is represented by a function of certain variables, the choice of which sets up a description of the state which, when treated according to specified rules (which may vary with the nature of the system considered), leads to significant results. It is usually possible to give alternative descriptions of a state and, as far as possible, these should be equivalent.

The *thermodynamic states* of systems, defined in terms of such variables as volume, pressure, and temperature, are what Francis Bacon would have called " Idols of the Market Place." The pressure is not a continuous distribution of force over an area, but an average of countless blows delivered by separate molecules. The temperature is not a continuously distributed property; the readings of an exceedingly minute and very rapidly acting thermometer in a gas would fluctuate from that when no molecule was colliding with it to a very high temperature when one of the fastest molecules hit it. The temperature is only an average value of the kinetic energy of translatory motion of the molecules, and comes into being only when the thermometer is large enough to smooth out the very different indications delivered over various parts of its surface by colliding molecules of varying kinetic energies.

The kinetic theory of gases gives (§ 2.III) $pv=\frac{1}{3}nm\overline{c^2}$ for n molecules, each of mass m, in a volume v and with the mean-square velocity $\overline{c^2}$. Hence, if $\frac{1}{2}m\overline{c^2}=\bar{\epsilon}_t$=average translational kinetic energy of a molecule, and $n=N$, the number of molecules in a mol (Avogadro's number), $pv=\frac{2}{3}N(\frac{1}{2}m\overline{c^2})=\frac{2}{3}N\bar{\epsilon}_t$. But $pv=RT$, therefore $\bar{\epsilon}_t=\frac{3}{2}(R/N)T=\frac{3}{2}kT$, where k is the gas constant per molecule, or *Boltzmann's constant.* Obviously, $\bar{\epsilon}_t$ has no definite value for a *single* molecule, but only for a molecule forming part of an assembly, and the same must, therefore, hold for the temperature T of the gas.

From the molecular standpoint, the state of a gas is defined by such things as numbers of molecules per cm.^{3} instead of density, and energies of molecules instead of temperature. These may be called the *micro-states.* A system, then, has an immense number of micro-states, e.g. varieties of molecular energies, at a given instant. The problem now is to connect the micro-states with the single thermodynamic state, which is something which can be measured. It is not too much to say that modern thermodynamic theory, including statistical mechanics, is almost wholly preoccupied with the correct definition of states. The problem is largely one of statistics.

Any object or event, when sufficiently closely scrutinised by the eye of the mind, becomes discontinuous, and the supposedly continuous processes described by Newtonian physics are illusions. The only " truly " continuous entity which could be imagined was the nineteenth-century " ether " (or " aether," in more refined terminology, Greek *αἰθήρ*) and, as far as can be seen now, the ether is non-existent. The continuous functions of mathematics are also merely convenient approximations when applied to actual systems.

§ 2. Types of Statistics

In daily life, fairly accurate predictions can be made about events happening in large collections of individuals. In a large enough population, the birth and death rates are known to a certain degree of accuracy, although it is impossible to say anything definite about individuals as such. The precision increases with the number of individuals. In the same way, statistical mechanics obtains *average values* over immense numbers of micro-states, and these averages specify the thermodynamic states. Just as in life statistics, something must be known of the character of the population, as the birth rate in London, for example, may be different from that in Southampton, so in statistical mechanics use is made of appropriate rules of calculation. The one which applies to the great majority of cases is *Maxwell-Boltzmann statistics.* Two other kinds, based on the quantum theory, are *Bose-Einstein statistics* and *Fermi-Dirac statistics.*

Statistics deals with probabilities rather than certainties, and it is first necessary to define the *probability* of a state. Any given thermodynamic state may be realised in a great number of different ways by taking different sets of micro-states, and its probability is *defined* as equal to the number of sets of micro-states. This is denoted by W (German, *Wahrscheinlichkeit*), and will be a very large number. If every molecule in 1 cm.^{3} of a gas has a different energy from the rest, and if it were possible to read out the energies of the molecules at the rate of a million a second, it would take just a million years to specify this single set of micro-states. The molecules, however, are constantly exchanging energies by collisions, and in a very short space of time the gas has assumed another set of micro-states.

The relation of all this to the second law of thermodynamics was first pointed out by Maxwell (§ 28.II). In the expansion of a gas into a vacuum there is an increase of entropy. Now suppose the vessel divided by a partition half way up the cylinder, with a microscopic hole fitted with a sliding shutter, and suppose a " demon " or " micro-robot " stationed at the aperture. When a molecule coming down approaches the aperture, it is let through; but when a molecule coming up approaches, the shutter is slid and the molecule is reflected back. In time, all the molecules will get back to the lower half and the gas is as it was. No heat or work changes are involved (since the ideal sliding shutter absorbs no work), yet after a time the entropy change has been compensated. But after what a time! This would take millions of years, even if a micro-robot could be found. The second law is *statistically* true to a very high degree of probability, even if not ideally true in the sense of " absolute " truth—if there is such a thing.

It is outside the province or power of thermodynamics to link changes of state with time changes. That the second law of thermodynamics and entropy are connected with time, and that the uniform increase of entropy in physico-chemical changes can be regarded as providing a " pointer " from past to future, as has been asserted,[1] seem incorrect.[2] Neither has thermodynamics any legitimate business in an undefined " universe," since this does not constitute a thermodynamic system (§ 7.II); nor can its results be applied with confidence to living organisms, except in so far as their states can be defined in terms of the variables of thermodynamic states alone. That the states of living organisms can be completely so defined cannot be asserted with any confidence. The results of thermodynamics are entirely in place in the biochemical laboratory, but not in philosophical speculations about universes or living beings.

Since the probability that two independent events having the separate probabilities W_1 and W_2 shall occur together is $W=W_1\times W_2$, probabilities are multiplicative. Entropies, however, are additive, $S=S_1+S_2$. This suggests that entropy and probability are connected by the equation $S=\boldsymbol{k}\ln W$, where $\boldsymbol{k}$ is a constant. The absence of an additive constant (S_0) follows from the Nernst Heat Theorem, since at absolute zero all the molecules are in the same state, i.e. there is only one micro-state, $W=1$, $\ln 1=0$, and since $S=0$, it follows that $S_0=0$. Suppose the system consists of a very large number N of " parts " [3] with different energies, N_1 with energy E_1, N_2 with energy E_2, and so on, the total energy being $E=\Sigma N_1E_1$. The problem is to find how the energies are distributed over the parts, i.e. to find N_1, N_2, etc., where $\Sigma N_1=N$.

Suppose the parts sorted into " boxes," each labelled with an energy value, then N_1, N_2, etc., are the numbers in the boxes. There are three main kinds of statistics to consider [4] (the new Gentile statistics is mentioned in § 37):

(1) In *Maxwell-Boltzmann statistics*, the parts, e.g. gas molecules, are supposed to have individuality, so that if there are three molecules A, B, and C,

[1] Franklin, *Phys. Rev.*, 1910, **30**, 766; Bohr, *J.C.S.*, 1932, 349; Bronstein and Landau, *Sow. Phys. Z.*, 1933, **4**, 114; Eddington, "Nature of the Physical World," Cambridge, 1938, 98 f.; Weizsäcker, *Ann. Phys.*, 1939, **36**, 275; Gruenewold, *Physica*, 1946, **12**, 405–60; Ubbelohde, " Time and Thermodynamics," Oxford, 1947.

[2] G. N. Lewis, *Science*, 1930, **71**, 569; Dingle, *Proc. Phys. Soc.*, 1948, **60**, 402.

[3] These may be, but need not be, *molecules*; they may be modes of electromagnetic vibration in a vacuum, or energy quanta, etc.

[4] Lennard-Jones, *Proc. Phys. Soc.*, 1928, **40**, 320.

and two boxes, corresponding with the energies E_1 and E_2, the three arrangements in Fig. 1.IV are all different:

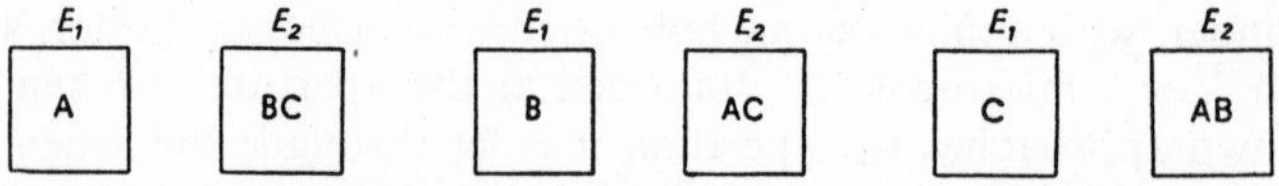

FIG. 1.IV. Maxwell-Boltzmann Arrangements of Three Parts in Two Boxes

The arrangement *inside* each box, however, is regarded as unspecifiable, e.g. BC is the same as CB, since, if it could be given, everything would be known in the minutest detail and there would be no field for statistics and no thermodynamic states. Thus, the arrangements in Fig. 2.IV,

FIG. 2.IV. Identical Maxwell-Boltzmann Arrangements

must, in Maxwell-Boltzmann statistics, be regarded as identical.

If the energies of the various parts in the group E_1 were not identically E_1, but differed by infinitesimal amounts, dE_1 as a maximum, from E_1, the box E_1 would still be regarded as containing them all, and no specification of the actual energies of the parts within this range dE_1 would be regarded as possible. In classical kinetic theory, the value of dE_1 is regarded as *continuously* variable, with zero as the lower limit and the maximum value dE_1 as the upper limit. In quantum statistics, however, the parts are regarded as having only discrete multiples of a quantum, the parts with each different multiple going into a separate box.

(2) In *Bose-Einstein statistics* the " parts " lack individuality and are identifiable only if they have different energies, or are in different boxes, so that the three arrangements in Fig. 1.IV are identical. If the parts are light quanta or photons, the condition $\Sigma N_1 = N$ drops out, since the total number may vary owing to absorption or emission. The result leads to Planck's radiation formula. In Bose-Einstein statistics, N may have any value up to infinity; in Gentile statistics (§ 37) N is supposed to be finite.

(3) In *Fermi-Dirac statistics* any box can contain either no part or only one. This applies to electrons, but since there can be two electrons with the same energy but with different spins, two electrons can go into one box, but only two (*Pauli's principle*).

The idea of these kinds of statistics may be illustrated by supposing there are two parts and two boxes, when the following arrangements are possible:

(i) *Maxwell-Boltzmann* (Fig. 3.IV)—four arrangements of parts regarded as identifiable:

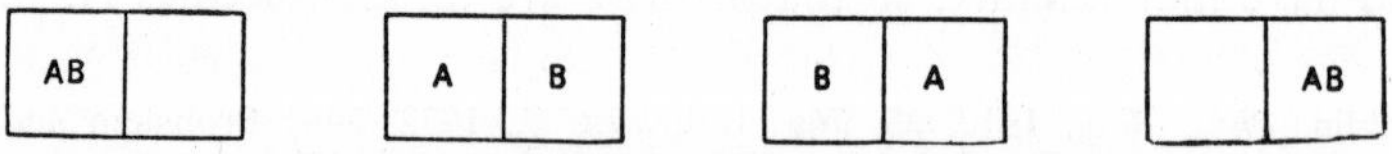

FIG. 3.IV. Maxwell-Boltzmann Arrangements

(ii) *Bose-Einstein* (Fig. 4.IV)—three arrangements of identical parts:

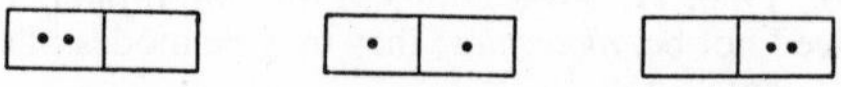

FIG. 4.IV. Bose-Einstein Arrangements

(iii) *Fermi-Dirac* (Fig. 5.IV)—one arrangement only of identical parts:

FIG. 5.IV. Fermi-Dirac Arrangement

The formulae for Bose-Einstein and Fermi-Dirac statistics are very much alike, and it will be shown that both go over into the Maxwell-Boltzmann formula as a limiting case in conditions fulfilled for systems consisting of molecules at not too low temperatures. At very low temperatures, however, a gas should obey Bose-Einstein statistics, and it seems as if liquid helium at very low temperatures behaves as a Bose-Einstein gas. The electrons in a metal, even at moderately high temperatures, obey Fermi-Dirac statistics, and are in a degenerate state, which explains why they contribute practically nothing to the thermal energy of the metal. The modern quantum theory shows that the Maxwell-Boltzmann statistics never applies strictly to any system, but is only an approximation.

Although it has been rather maliciously said [1] that Statistical Mechanics is " a subject which however and by whomever belabored has never refused to yield at least what was already well known," and although many publications on it could well be spared, its great utility and interest emerge from more detailed treatment.[2]

§ 3. Mechanical Interpretations of Thermodynamics

The first attempt to relate the laws of thermodynamics to *mechanical* principles was Rankine's [3] hypothesis of *molecular vortices*, which is not unlike the theory proposed by Davy (§ 10.II).[4] His exposition is not very comprehensible, and Maxwell's [5] quotation from Milton, that he " through the palpable obscure finds out his uncouth way," is not unjustified. The " explanation " of the laws of thermodynamics by molecular vortices is now quite lacking in cogency. Vibrating " ethers " and rotating " ether particles " have also been invoked in attempts to " explain " the quantum theory.[6] Clausius,[7] starting from his virial theorem (§ 40.VII C), gave an explanation of the laws of thermodynamics in terms of quasi-periodic motions. Similar attempts by Boltzmann,[8] Szily,[9] Burbury,[10] Nichols,[11] Watson,[12] etc.,[13] did not lead much further.

[1] Keyes, *J.A.C.S.*, 1928, **50**, 931.

[2] Tolman, *J. Franklin Inst.*, 1927, **203**, 661, 811.

[3] *Trans. Roy. Soc. Edin.*, 1850, **20**, 147; 1851, **20**, 425; 1853, **20**, 565; 1869, **25**, 557; *Phil Mag.*, 1851, **2**, 61, 509; 1855, **10**, 354, 411; 1865, **30**, 241; *Jahresb.*, 1851, 39; *Phil. Trans.*, 1854, **144**, 115; " Miscell. Scientific Papers," 1881, 16, 49, 234, 307, 375, 427.

[4] As Rankine himself says, *Trans. Roy. Soc. Edin.*, 1853, **20**, 565.

[5] " Scientific Papers," 1890, **2**, 660.

[6] Zehnder, *Verhl. d. D. Phys. Ges.*, 1912, **14**, 438; 1916, **18**, 181; Umow, *Phys. Z.*, 1914, **15**, 380; Nernst, *Verhl. d. D. Phys. Ges.*, 1916, **18**, 83; for collisions of gas and " ether " atoms, Edwards, *Chem. News*, 1919, **118**, 270; a large mass of worthless literature is passed over unnoticed.

[7] *Ann. Phys.*, 1870, **141**, 124; 1871, **142**, 433; 1872, **144**, 265; *Berlin Ber.*, 1884, 663.

[8] *Wien Ber.*, 1866, **53**, II, 195; 1871, 63, II, 712 ; *Ann. Phys.*, 1871, **143**, 211; 1896, **57**, 771; 1897, **60**, 392; " Wiss. Abhl.," 1909, **1**, 9, 228, 288; 1909, **3**, 578.

[9] *Ann. Phys.*, 1872, **145**, 295; 1873, **149**, 74; *Phil. Mag.*, 1876, **1**, 22.

[10] *Phil. Mag.*, 1876, **1**, 61; 1882, **13**, 417; 1902, **3**, 225; " A Treatise on the Kinetic Theory of Gases," Cambridge, 1899, 122, 130.

[11] *Phil. Mag.*, 1876, **1**, 22, 369.

[12] " A Treatise on the Kinetic Theory of Gases," Oxford, 1876, 46.

[13] See e.g. J. J. Thomson, *Phil. Trans.*, 1885, **176**, 307; 1887, **178**, 471; " Applications of Dynamics to Physics and Chemistry," 1888, 91.

The elaborate purely dynamical theory of monocyclic systems, proposed by Helmholtz,[1] and extended by Boltzmann,[2] Poincaré,[3] Bryan and Boltzmann,[4] Larmor and Bryan,[5] Zermelo,[6] Schiller,[7] and Einstein,[8] gave only formal analogies, mostly useful in driving home the conviction that in thermodynamics, dynamics cannot be regarded as *the* fundamental physical science. Ostwald's " energetic " view (§ 23.II), that dynamics is merely a branch of a science of energy, was, in fact, true and helpful in this sense. A very refined discussion, introducing Pauli's principle, was given by Kimball and Berry.[9]

The recognition that an explanation of the second law of thermodynamics must be sought in statistics is due to Maxwell, Lord Kelvin, and Boltzmann. Maxwell [10] said: " The state of the system at any instant is ascertained by distributing the molecules in groups, the definition of each group being founded on some variable property of the molecules. Each individual molecule is sometimes in one of these groups and sometimes in another, but we make no attempt to follow it: we simply take account of the number of molecules which at a given instant belong to each group. . . . We thus meet with a new kind of regularity, the regularity of averages, a regularity which, when we are dealing with millions of millions of individuals, is so unvarying that we are almost in danger of confounding it with absolute uniformity." Whether " statistics is a method of arrangement rather than of demonstration," [11] depends on what is understood by " demonstration." The difficulty of adapting dynamical systems to explain thermodynamics may be appreciated from the experiments of Horzelski,[12] who used a mechanically operated lever for tossing a coin into the air so that it revolved several times. With a new sixpence, he found 98 heads in 100 throws, and with a slight readjustment of the lever, 99 tails in 100 throws. The laws of probability do not operate with a machine.

The relation between probability and entropy, which is fundamental to the whole development of statistical mechanics, is due to Lord Kelvin [13] and Boltzmann.[14] It is much more subtle than Newtonian dynamics, and proved capable of comprehending the development of quantum mechanics, intro-

[1] *Berlin Ber.*, 1884, 159, 311, 755; " Wiss. Abhl.," 1895, **3**, 119, 142, 163, 173, 179, 203; see Bryan, " Thermodynamics," Leipzig, 1907, 188; Décombe, *Compt. Rend.*, 1910, **151**, 1044; Boguslawski, *J. Russ. Phys. Chem. Soc.*, 1918, **49**, 138 (P); *Phys. Z.*, 1922, **23**, 209; Mimura, *J. Sci. Hiroshima Univ.*, 1931, **1** A, 43, 117; Schimank, *Naturwiss.*, 1947, **34**, 2.

[2] *J. f. Math.* [Crelle], 1884–5, **98**, 68; 1887, **100**, 201; " Wiss. Abhl.," 1909, **3**, 122, 258; *Wien Ber.*, 1885, **92**, II, 853; *Gött. Nachr.*, 1886, 209; " Wiss. Abhl.," 1909, **3**, 153, 176.

[3] *Compt. Rend.*, 1889, **108**, 550.

[4] *Wien Ber.*, 1894, **103**, IIA, 1125; *Proc. Phys. Soc.*, 1895, **13**, 485; Boltzmann, " Wiss.. Abhl.," 1909, **3**, 510.

[5] *B.A. Rep.*, 1891, 85, where it is clearly stated that thermodynamics cannot be " deduced " from dynamics.

[6] *Ann. Phys.*, 1896, **57**, 485; 1896, **59**, 793.

[7] *Ann. Phys.*, 1907, **22**, 593.

[8] *Ann. Phys.*, 1902, **9**, 417; 1903, **11**, 170; 1904, **14**, 354; Witte, *Phys. Z.*, 1910, **11**, 347.

[9] *Phil. Mag.*, 1932, **13**, 1131.

[10] Quoted from MS. notes by H. W. Watson, " A Treatise on the Kinetic Theory of Gases," Oxford, 1876, vii, where Laplace is mentioned as an originator; Pelseneer, " L'Évolution de la Notion de Phénomène Physique des Primitifs à Bohr et Louis de Broglie," Brussels, n.d. [1947], 77.

[11] Larmor, " Math. and Phys. Papers," Cambridge, 1929, **2**, 215.

[12] *Nature*, 1945, **155**, 111.

[13] *Nature*, 1874, **9**, 441; *Proc. Roy. Soc. Edin.*, 1875, **8**, 325; " Popular Lectures and Addresses," 1889, **1**, 137; *Phil. Mag.*, 1892, **33**, 291; " Math. and Phys. Papers," 1911, **5**, 11.

[14] *Wien Ber.*, 1877, **76**, II, 373; 1878, **78**, II, 7; " Wiss. Abhl.," 1909, **2**, 164, 250; Fredey, *Compt. Rend.*, 1906, **142**, 513; Herzfeld, *Wien Ber.*, 1913, **122**, IIA, 1553; Ehrenfest, *Phys. Z.*, 1914, **15**, 657.

duced by Planck in 1900 (§ 15); it is not so much an "explanation" as an instrument, and as G. N. Lewis [1] said, "gain of entropy means loss of information," a remark which will be more fully appreciated later.

§ 4. Probability and Thermodynamic States

One mol of a monatomic gas occupying a volume V at a temperature T is in a definite *thermodynamic state*, or constitutes a "thermodynamic system," the pressure p having a definite value corresponding with V and T according to the equation $pV=RT$. The gas is composed of a very large number ($N=6{\cdot}03\times10^{23}$) of molecules, and the positions and velocities (and hence energies) of these are constantly changing, owing to motions and collisions. The gas in an adiabatic enclosure can assume an immense number of *dynamical states* or *micro-states* (defined by the positions and energies of all the individual molecules) consistent with the total energy of the gas being E, and with the molecules distributed so that an average pressure p is exerted over the surface of the vessel. The temperature does not come into the dynamical picture at all. If the gas is contained in a vessel permeable to heat and placed in a bath at constant temperature T, the exchanges of energy between the gas and the bath, consequent on deviations from the average value of the energies of translation of molecules colliding with the walls, will be so small that the energy E of the gas at any instant will still be practically the same as it would have been in an adiabatic enclosure at the same temperature, and hence E is practically constant.[2] Thus, every thermodynamic state may be realised by an assembly of a very large number of micro-states, having the same total volume and total energy as the given system.

The probability W of any thermodynamic state may be *defined* as equal to the number of micro-states which belong to the thermodynamic state. In classical dynamics, these micro-states form a continuum, their number is infinite, and no progress can be made in defining the probability of the thermodynamic state. In quantum theory, however, their number is finite (but usually very large), i.e. the totality of micro-states forms a discrete manifold, and the finite number of these states defines the *thermodynamic probability*, W, of the thermodynamic state, W being equal to the number of ways in which the thermodynamic state may be realised from suitable assemblies of micro-states.

§ 5. Entropy and Probability

A system in a given thermodynamic state which undergoes a spontaneous change passes from a state of less to a state of greater probability, and in stable equilibrium the probability is a maximum. The probability changes in the same sense as the entropy, S. The result of identifying this probability of state with W as defined in § 4 may be examined. Entropies are additive, but probabilities multiplicative, and a relation $S=\mathrm{f}(W)$ satisfying this condition is:

$$S=k\ln W \qquad (1)$$

where k is a universal constant, later (§ 14) shown to be the Boltzmann constant, or the gas constant per molecule,[3] R/N, where R is the general gas constant, and N is Avogadro's number ($6{\cdot}03\times10^{23}$), the number of molecules

[1] *Science*, 1930, **71**, 569; cf. Décombe, *Compt. Rend.*, 1924, **178**, 694; von Laue, *Forschungen und Fortschritte*, 1944, **20**, 46; Groenewold, *Physica*, 1946, **12**, 405–60.
[2] Schrödinger, "Statistical Thermodynamics," Cambridge, 1946, 3, 7, etc.
[3] Kimball, *J. Phys. Chem.*, 1929, **33**, 1558.

in a mol. Equation (1) is a modification by Planck [1] of one due to Boltzmann [2]; it contains no arbitrary additive constant S_0, nor can it contain such a constant if W is to have the definite value postulated in § 4. Since W cannot be less than 1, S has the minimum value zero.

According to the Nernst-Planck theorem (§ 69.II), the entropy of a solid at the absolute zero is zero:

$$S_0=0 \quad \ldots\ldots\ldots\ldots \quad (2)$$

hence (1) shows that in this case $W=1$, i.e. the entropy vanishes when the state of the system can be realised in only one way. The absence of an additive constant in (1) is characteristic of Planck's form of the Nernst heat theorem.

Since discussions of probability are foreign to classical dynamics, all dynamical or micro-states would have equal probability, and in course of time a thermodynamic system could be supposed to assume all the possible dynamical states, e.g. for a system confined in a rigid adiabatic enclosure, all those consistent with the volume and energy (one of these states, e.g., will be that in which all the energy is possessed by a single molecule). This statement (usually called the *ergodic hypothesis*) seems at first sight to be incompatible with the existence of a thermodynamic equilibrium state of maximum entropy, and hence incompatible with the second law of thermodynamics, since the micro-states are not confined to those belonging to the equilibrium state.[3] This objection is only apparent.

The probability of the thermodynamic equilibrium state is the ratio of its thermodynamic probability W_m, which is the maximum for all possible thermodynamic states, to the sum of the thermodynamic probabilities for *all* the thermodynamic states (including all non-equilibrium states) possible in the given conditions. Since the entropy is a maximum in the thermodynamic state ($S=S_m$), corresponding with a maximum probability ($W=W_m$), equation (1) gives:

$$W/W_m=e^{(S-S_m)/k}=e^{-\Delta S/k} \quad \ldots\ldots\ldots \quad (3)$$

Since $\Delta S=S_m-S>0$, $e^{-\Delta S/k}$ is a proper fraction. W is very large, whilst S has a moderate value in the usual units, hence k (in the same units) must be very small (it is later, in § 14, shown to be $1{\cdot}38\times10^{-16}$ erg/1° C.). For a moderate value of ΔS, W/W_m must, therefore, be extremely small, and hence any appreciable spontaneous deviation from the equilibrium state must be excessively rare. In consequence, the second law of thermodynamics retains its full validity in the statistical sense, in which it deals with average values, for which there are quantitative laws to any desired degree of approximation. The statistical character of the second law is, in fact, experimentally verifiable in experiments on the Brownian movement and similar " fluctuation " phenomena

[1] "Theorie der Wärmestrahlung," 4th ed., Leipzig, 1921, 111; "Theorie der Wärme," Leipzig, 1930, 183.

[2] "Gastheorie," 1896, **1**, 38; Fortrat, *Rev. Gén. Sci.*, 1919, **30**, 135. Boltzmann had proved on classical grounds that a magnitude H always increases in spontaneous changes in a gas, and that it can be related to the entropy; Boltzmann, " Gastheorie," 1896, **1**, 124; 1898, **2**, 217; Cohen, *Phys. Z.*, 1909, **10**, 138, 196; Planck, *ibid.*, 1909, **10**, 195; Tolman, "Statistical Mechanics," Oxford, 1938, 99; on the H-theorem for a van der Waals gas, see Happel, *Ann. Phys.*, 1910, **33**, 275. The H-theorem is considered in works on the kinetic theory of gases; see Section III, Bibliography; for a criticism, see, e.g., Postma, *Proc. K. Akad. Wetens. Amsterdam*, 1906, **8**, 630; 1907, **9**, 492; and a reply by Ehrenfest and Ehrenfest, *Phys. Z.*, 1907, **8**, 311, referring to seven letters of criticism in *Nature*, 1894–5. The matter is considered further in § 6. For thermodynamics and probability, see Reboul, *Compt. Rend.*, 1939, **209**, 792; 1941, **212**, 149, 222; 1946, **222**, 1063; 1947, **224**, 314.

[3] Davydov, *J. Phys. U.S.S.R.*, 1947, **11**, 33; Born, *Research*, 1948, **1**, 165.

with sufficiently coarse micro-states.[1] Another way of expressing these ideas is to say that there are so many more ways of realising disordered as compared with ordered states, that disorder (leading to large entropy) is always much more probable than order.

The following very simple case was considered by Einstein.[2] Suppose that a gas contains n molecules, which exert no forces on one another, in a volume v_0, the entropy being S_0. Now imagine a volume $v(v<v_0)$ in the gas, and suppose the entropy for the n molecules in a volume v is S (the temperature remaining constant). The probability that at a given moment all the n molecules will be in the volume v (owing to their motion in the volume v_0) is $W=(v/v_0)^n$. Boltzmann's equation, $\Delta S=k \ln W=(\boldsymbol{R}/N) \ln W$, then gives $\Delta S=(\boldsymbol{R}/N)n \ln (v/v_0)=\boldsymbol{R} \ln (v/v_0)$, when $n=N$, which is the correct expression for the entropy change per mol (§ 55, II). From this, since $\mathrm{d}E=0$ when T=const. (dilute gas with no forces between the molecules), it follows that $-\mathrm{d}(E-TS)=p\mathrm{d}v=T\mathrm{d}S=\boldsymbol{R}T(\mathrm{d}v/v)$, therefore $p=\boldsymbol{R}T/v$, the general gas law. Nernst [3] considered the limiting case for the isothermal work done by an expanding gas consisting of a single molecule, and concluded that an infinite time would be required to furnish a finite amount of work.

Einstein [4] then considered the case where the state is defined by a parameter λ, which undergoes a small reversible change from λ_0 to $\lambda=\lambda_0+\delta$, at constant energy. Then, from thermodynamics, $w=\int \mathrm{d}E-\int T\mathrm{d}S$, and if the change is very small (since $\mathrm{d}E=0$), $w=-T(S-S_0)$.

Since $$S=(\boldsymbol{R}/N) \ln W,$$

$$\therefore\ S-S_0=(\boldsymbol{R}/N) \ln (W/W_0) \qquad \therefore\ w=-(\boldsymbol{R}T/N) \ln (W/W_0),$$

$$\text{or} \quad W=W_0 e^{-Nw/\boldsymbol{R}T}=W_0 e^{-w/kT}.$$

Actually, it is more correct to speak of the probability of a *region* [Gebiet] of states rather than of a state, and to write:

$$\mathrm{d}W=\text{const.}\ e^{-w/kT}\,.\,\mathrm{d}\lambda$$

putting $\mathrm{d}\lambda$ instead of $\mathrm{d}f(\lambda)$ without loss of generality.

§ 6. The Ergodic Hypothesis

The ergodic hypothesis,[5] mentioned in § 5, has been the object of much discussion, and its meaning is not very obvious. As G. N. Lewis [6] said, the student is introduced to: " the various forms of the ergodic hypothesis, according to

1 On the theory of fluctuations see e.g. Perrin, " Les Atomes," 1914, 190; Tolman, " The Principles of Statistical Mechanics," Oxford, 1938, 636; Kennard, " Kinetic Theory of Gases," New York, 1938, 267.

2 *Ann. Phys.*, 1905, **17**, 132.

3 *Berlin Ber.*, 1933, 467; for the consideration of a single molecule in a sphere or parallelepiped, see Planck, *ibid.*, 1916, 653.

4 *Ann. Phys.*, 1907, **22**, 569; Hertz, *Gött. Nachr.*, 1912, 566; Ornstein, *Proc. K. Akad. Wetens. Amsterdam*, 1912, **14**, 840; see the interesting extension of Einstein's idea by G. N. Lewis, *J.A.C.S.*, 1931, **53**, 2578, dealing with earlier papers on the statistical basis of the Second Law by Einstein, *Ann. Phys.*, 1902, **9**, 417; 1903, **11**, 170; 1904, **14**, 354; Smoluchowski, *Ann. Phys. Beibl.*, 1916, **40**, 494; Fürth, *Phys. Z.*, 1917, **18**, 395; Schottky, *Ann. Phys.*, 1922, **68**, 481; Herzfeld, *ibid.*, 1922, **69**, 54; de Waard, *Physica*, 1927, **7**, 109; Lewis and Mayer, *Proc. Nat. Acad.*, 1928, **14**, 569, 575; Mayer, *J. Chem. Phys.*, 1942, **10**, 629. On the statistics of particles occupying sites in two and three dimensions, see Miller, *Proc. Cambr. Phil. Soc.*, 1942, **38**, 109. On dilute solutions, Larmor, *Proc. Cambr. Phil. Soc.*, 1897, **9**, 240; *Phil. Trans.*, 1897, **190**, 205 (275); " Aether and Matter," Cambridge, 1900, 286.

5 Greek, ἔργον, work, ὁδός, a way.

6 *J.A.C.S.*, 1937, **59**, 2750.

which every system returns over and over to something like its original state, so that on the average no property, such as the entropy, has even the probability of changing in one direction rather than in another. Finally, to complete his mystification, the student learns that the entropy is determined completely by such variables as the energy, the volume, and the masses of the various constituents, so that when these are fixed, the entropy cannot be considered to change at all, even in thought." C. E. Guye [1] quotes Herodotos (5th century B.C.) as saying: " qu'on prodigue le temps tout possible s' arrive "; yet Herodotos says: [2] " in a life of seventy years there is not one day but will produce events unlike the rest." The ergodic hypothesis was introduced by Boltzmann,[3] and adopted (as the " principle of continuity of path ") by Maxwell.[4] It was criticised by Lord Rayleigh [5] and others,[6] and has been shown [7] by a mathematical argument depending on the assumption of orders of infinity, not to be possible for a gas, so that it may be said to fail for classical statistics. It is doubtful if the mathematics has any physical meaning. If all the possible states of a system could be represented by a surface, the ergodic hypothesis is equivalent to the statement that the path representing the succession of states is a Peano curve, passing through every point of the surface. In quantum statistics, a system may be truly ergodic, since the number of arrangements for a given energy is finite.

The so-called *quasi-ergodic hypothesis*, proposed by P. and T. Ehrenfest,[8] states that the simple undisturbed motion of a system, when indefinitely prolonged, will bring the state of the system indefinitely near every physically possible point on the surface representing the total energy, and (unlike the ergodic hypothesis) this can be applied to a gas.[9] Krylov [10] argued that the phase spaces retain their size in the motion of the system, but the parts are distributed with a steadily decreasing degree of uniformity, and with a relaxation time.

§ 7. Most Probable and Average Distribution

For a system composed of a very large number N of parts [11] (e.g. of molecules), having a total energy E, the classical kinetic theory calculates for the thermodynamic equilibrium state the number n_r of molecules each having an energy lying between ϵ_r and $\epsilon_r + d\epsilon_r$, where $d\epsilon_r$ may be as small as is wished ; i.e. ϵ_r is regarded as *continuously* variable, with a lower limit of zero. In the quantum theory, on the contrary, the energy of a part cannot vary continuously, but will

1 *J. Chim. Phys.*, 1917, **15**, 215; " Physico-Chemical Evolution," 1925, 30, 60; I have not found the remark in Herodotos.

2 " History," i, 32.

3 *Wien Ber.*, 1868, **58**, II, 517; " Wiss. Abhl.," 1909, **1**, 49; Kennard, " Kinetic Theory of Gases," 1938, 341, calls it the " ergodic surmise."

4 *Trans. Cambr. Phil. Soc.*, 1879, **12**, 547; " Scient. Papers," Cambridge, 1890, **2**, 713.

5 *Phil. Mag.*, 1900, **49**, 98; " Scient. Papers," Cambridge, 1903, **4**, 433 (bibl.).

6 Cf. Zermelo, *Ann. Phys.*, 1896, **57**, 485; Jeans, "Dynamical Theory of Gases," 3rd edit., Cambridge, 1921, 101, and references.

7 Rosenthal, *Ann. Phys.*, 1913, **42**, 769; Plancherel, *ibid.*, 1913, **42**, 1061; Brillouin, " Die Quantenstatistik," Berlin, 1931, 90; for the statistics of non-ergodic systems, see Jaffé, *Ann. Phys.*, 1924, **74**, 628; 1925, **76**, 680.

8 Begriffliche Grundlagen der statistischen Auffassung der Mechanik, " Enzykl. d. math. Wiss.," 1911, **4**, 2, II (32), 31 (sep. pagination).

9 Rosenthal, *Ann. Phys.*, 1914, **43**, 894.

10 *Nature*, 1944, **153**, 709.

11 These may, for example, be modes of electromagnetic vibration in a perfect vacuum.

assume a finite number of discrete values, so that a specification would give the number n_r of molecules *each* having the energy ϵ_r.

Before temperature or entropy can be assigned to such a system, the restriction that the N parts are completely isolated must be removed, since the statistical basis of the second law of thermodynamics requires a sequence of changes of micro-states into one another in course of time, so as to give rise to an average or thermodynamic state. This restriction may be removed by imagining the system, e.g. a gas, immersed in a constant-temperature bath, since exchanges of energy between the system and the bath, consequent upon fluctuations of molecular energies, are always vanishingly small, and cancel one another in course of time. Such a system is practically equivalent to an isolated portion of the gas.

When the *average* numbers of molecules (or parts) in specified energy states are known, the thermodynamic functions of the system can be calculated, e.g. the energy E and entropy S. The *most probable* distribution is more easily calculated than the average distribution, but the two are not the same unless the most probable distribution is rigidly maintained. This is not the case if, in course of time, some molecules assume less probable states owing to fluctuations. As is indicated in § 5, however, such departures from the most probable distribution (W a maximum) are quite negligible if N is very large, which is always the case in a thermodynamic system, and hence the most probable distribution may always be substituted for the average distribution without sensible error.[1]

§ 8. Maxwell-Boltzmann Statistics

In the great majority of cases the method of calculating most probable distributions used by Maxwell and by Boltzmann [2] applies with sufficient approximation. Consider a system composed of a very large number N of parts (e.g. particles, or molecules), completely independent and having states characterised by the *discrete* energies $\epsilon_1, \epsilon_2, \epsilon_3, \ldots \epsilon_r$, the total energy being E; let the numbers of parts in each of these energy groups (" box " or " cell ") [3] be $n_1, n_2, n_3, \ldots n_r$, where:

$$n_1+n_2+n_3+\ldots+n_r=\Sigma n_r=N \quad \ldots \ldots \quad (1)$$

$$\text{and} \quad n_1\epsilon_1+n_2\epsilon_2+n_3\epsilon_3+\ldots+n_r\epsilon_r=\Sigma n_r\epsilon_r=E \quad \ldots \quad (2)$$

[1] Mayer and Mayer, " Statistical Mechanics," 1940, 80.

[2] Maxwell, *B.A. Rep.*, 1873, II, 29; Boltzmann, *Wien Ber.*, 1877, **76**, II, 373; 1878, **78**, II, 7; " Wiss. Abhl.," 1909, **2**, 164, 250; Lorentz, *Verhl. d. D. Phys. Ges.*, 1907, **9**, 206; " Les Théories statistiques en Thermodynamique," Leipzig and Berlin, 1916; van der Waals, junr., *Phys. Z.*, 1911, **12**, 547; Onnes and Keesom, " Enzykl. d. math. Wiss.," 1912, **5**, i, 768; Guillaume, *Arch. Sci. Phys. Nat.*, 1914, **38**, 375; 1915, **39**, 205, 301; 1916, **41**, 445; Schidlof, *ibid.*, 1915, **39**, 25; 1924, **6**, 281, Suppl., 61; Flamm, *Phys. Z.*, 1918, **19**, 116, 166; Herzfeld, *Z. phys. Chem.*, 1920, **95**, 139; Jeans, " Dynamical Theory of Gases," 3rd edit., Cambridge, 1921, 76; Tolman, *J.A.C.S.*, 1922, **44**, 75; de Waard, *Physica*, 1927, **7**, 109; Lennard-Jones, *Proc. Phys. Soc.*, 1928, **40**, 320; Larmor, " Math. and Phys. Papers," Cambridge, 1929, **2**, 396; Lewis and Mayer, *Proc. Nat. Acad.*, 1929, **15**, 208; Giauque, *J.A.C.S.*, 1930, **52**, 4808; Planck, " Theorie der Wärme," 1930, 195; Lewis, *J.A.C.S.*, 1931, **53**, 2578; Klein, *Z. Phys.*, 1931, **72**, 767; Zeise, *Z. Elektrochem.*, 1933, **39**, 758, 895, 904; 1934, **40**, 662, 885; 1935, **41**, 267; 1940, **46**, 38, 293; 1941, **47**, 380, 595, 644; 1942, **48**, 425, 476, 693; 1944, **50**, 113; *idem*, " Thermodynamik auf den Grunden der Quantentheorie, Quantenstatistik, und Spektroskopie," Leipzig, 1944; Gebelin, *Ann. Phys.*, 1934, **19**, 533; Moelwyn-Hughes, " Physical Chemistry," Cambridge, 1940, 51; Margenau and Murphy, " The Mathematics of Physics and Chemistry," New York, 1943, 415; Staverman, *Chem. Weekbl.*, 1947, **43**, 199.

On Ludwig Boltzmann (1844–1906), see Schäfer, *Naturwiss.*, 1946, **33**, 33.

[3] The " boxes " must not themselves be permutable: Ehrenfest-Afanassjewa, *Proc. K. Akad. Wetens. Amsterdam*, 1918, **21**, 53.

Now consider the number of ways in which the N parts can be distributed among the r energy values. If the N parts were arranged in a line there would be $N!$ ways of arranging them, if each is assumed to have the possibility of having all energy values between ϵ_1 and ϵ_r. If n_1 of them have the same energy value ϵ_1, however, the possible number of arrangements is less, since there would have been $n_1!$ further ways of arranging these n_1 parts if they were all different. If the number of arrangements is now W_1, then $N!=W_1 \times n_1!$, therefore $W_1=N!/n_1!$.

In this arrangement account is taken of the individuality of the parts, but it is assumed that the actual arrangement *inside* the " cell " ϵ_1 is not known. If n_2 parts are now supposed to be in the cell ϵ_2, the number of arrangements is further reduced, and becomes $W_2=N!/n_1!n_2!$, and so on.

In the general case, the total number of ways in which the energies can be distributed among the parts if (as is assumed in Maxwell-Boltzmann statistics) there are no special restrictions, is:

$$W=N!/(n_1!n_2!n_3! \ldots n_r!) \quad \ldots \ldots \quad (3)$$

and this will be the *thermodynamic probability* in accordance with § 4. Equation (3) thus *defines* the Maxwell-Boltzmann statistics. A special case of (3) is explained in detail in § 30.

The *most probable* distribution is that which makes W a maximum: [1]

$$\delta W=0 \quad \ldots \ldots \ldots \quad (4)$$

subject to the conditions that (i) the total number of parts, and (ii) the total energy, are constant, i.e. from (1) and (2):

$$\Sigma \delta n_r=0 \quad \ldots \ldots \ldots \quad (5)$$

$$\text{and} \quad \Sigma \epsilon_r \delta n_r=0 \quad \ldots \ldots \ldots \quad (6)$$

Take logarithms of (3) and use (4), then:

$$\delta \ln W=\delta \ln N!-\Sigma \delta \ln n_r!=0 \quad \ldots \ldots \quad (7)$$

When n_r is large, which is true when the states contribute effectively to the whole assembly, the factorials in (7) can be transformed by using a simplified form of Stirling's theorem:

$$N!=(N/e)^N \quad \ldots \ldots \ldots \quad (8)$$

$$\therefore \ln n_r!=n_r \ln n_r-n_r \ln e=n_r \ln n_r-n_r \quad \ldots \ldots \quad (9)$$

A simple deduction of (8) is the following.[2] For $\Delta N=1$ the equation:

$$\Delta \ln N!/\Delta N=[\ln N!-\ln (N-1)!]/1=\ln [N.(N-1)!/(N-1)!]=\ln N$$

is an identity, since $N!=N.(N-1)!$. Now write the equation in differential form: $d \ln N!/dN=\ln N$, therefore $d \ln N!=\ln N dN$, therefore $\ln N!=\int \ln N dN$. By integration by parts (§ 19.I):

$$\int \ln N dN=N \ln N-\int dN=N \ln N-N,$$

$$\therefore \ln N!=N \ln N-N,$$

$$\text{or} \quad N!=(N/e)^N, \text{ which is equation (8).}$$

[1] It is assumed, without investigation, that (4) is, as is the case, the condition for a maximum value of W, and not a minimum value.

[2] Satterly, *Nature*, 1923, **111**, 220. A more complete form is $N!=\sqrt{(2\pi N)}(N/e)^N$, the deduction of which is given, e.g., by Poincaré, "Calcul des Probabilités," Paris, 1896, 62; Hack, " Wahrscheinlichkeitsrechnung," Leipzig, 1911, 46; Czuber, " Wahrscheinlichkeitsrechnung," 4th edit., Leipzig, 1924, 1, 24; Planck, "Theorie der Wärme," Leipzig, 1930, 197. The form $N!=\sqrt{(2\pi N)}(N/e)^N$ is sufficiently accurate for $N>10$; for very large values of N, the large quantity $\sqrt{(2\pi N)}$ can be taken as of the order of unity in comparison with the very much larger quantity $(N/e)^N$, and (8) is then very nearly true. The method used by Fowler, " Statistical Mechanics," Cambridge, 1936, does not involve Stirling's theorem.

Equations (5), (7), and (9) give:

$$\delta \ln W = -\Sigma \delta n_r \ln n_r = 0 \quad . \quad . \quad . \quad . \quad . \quad . \quad . \quad . \quad (10)$$

Multiply (5) by λ and (6) by μ, where λ and μ are arbitrary constants, called undetermined multipliers, and subtract from (10):

$$\therefore \ \Sigma \delta n_r(\ln n_r + \lambda + \mu\epsilon_r) = 0 \quad . \quad . \quad . \quad . \quad . \quad . \quad . \quad . \quad (11)$$

Since δn_r is now arbitrary, apart from the restriction implied in (5), it follows (the full argument will be found in textbooks of algebra) [1] that (11) is satisfied only when the expression in the brackets vanishes:

$$\ln n_r + \lambda + \mu\epsilon_r = 0 \quad . \quad . \quad . \quad . \quad . \quad . \quad . \quad . \quad . \quad (12)$$

$$\therefore \ n_r = (1/C)e^{-\mu\epsilon_r} \quad . \quad . \quad . \quad . \quad . \quad . \quad . \quad . \quad (13)$$

where

$$C = e^{\lambda} \quad . \quad . \quad . \quad . \quad . \quad . \quad . \quad . \quad . \quad . \quad . \quad (14)$$

Equation (13) is the fundamental equation of Maxwell-Boltzmann statistics. It follows that:

$$N = \Sigma n_r = (1/C)\Sigma e^{-\mu\epsilon_r} = Z/C \quad . \quad . \quad . \quad . \quad . \quad . \quad (15)$$

where

$$Z = \Sigma e^{-\mu\epsilon_r} \quad . \quad . \quad . \quad . \quad . \quad . \quad . \quad . \quad . \quad . \quad (16)$$

is called by Planck the *state sum* (" Zustandssumme "), and this name is the best one,[2] since it expresses clearly what the symbol denotes.

Also, from (2) and (13):

$$E = \Sigma n_r\epsilon_r = (1/C)\Sigma\epsilon_r e^{-\mu\epsilon_r} \quad . \quad . \quad . \quad . \quad . \quad . \quad . \quad (17)$$

The *average energy* of a part (e.g. a molecule) is thus:

$$\bar{\epsilon} = E/N = \frac{(1/C)\Sigma\epsilon_r e^{-\mu\epsilon_r}}{(1/C)\Sigma e^{-\mu\epsilon_r}} = \frac{\Sigma\epsilon_r e^{-\mu\epsilon_r}}{\Sigma e^{-\mu\epsilon_r}} \quad . \quad . \quad . \quad . \quad . \quad (17a)$$

Put $\Sigma e^{-\mu\epsilon_r} = x$, then $(d/d\mu) \ln x = (1/x)(dx/d\mu)$. But

$$dx/d\mu = (d/d\mu)\Sigma e^{-\mu\epsilon_r} = -\Sigma\epsilon_r e^{-\mu\epsilon_r},$$

$$\therefore \ (d/d\mu) \ln \Sigma e^{-\mu\epsilon_r} = -(1/\Sigma e^{-\mu\epsilon_r})\Sigma\epsilon_r e^{-\mu\epsilon_r}.$$

Hence

$$\bar{\epsilon} = -(d/d\mu) \ln \Sigma e^{-\mu\epsilon_r} = -d \ln Z/d\mu \quad . \quad . \quad . \quad . \quad . \quad (18)$$

$$\therefore \ E = N\bar{\epsilon} = -N(d \ln Z/d\mu) \quad . \quad . \quad . \quad . \quad . \quad . \quad (19)$$

If $N = \mathbf{N}$ (Avogadro's number), (19) is the energy per mol. From (1), § 5 and (3), the entropy is $S = \boldsymbol{k} \ln W = \boldsymbol{k} (\ln N! - \Sigma \ln n_r!)$, and from (9):

$$S = \boldsymbol{k}[N \ln N - N - \Sigma(n_r \ln n_r - n_r)] = \boldsymbol{k}(N \ln N - N - \Sigma n_r \ln n_r + N)$$
$$= \boldsymbol{k}(N \ln N - \Sigma n_r \ln n_r) = \boldsymbol{k}[N \ln N - N\Sigma(n_r/N) \ln n_r],$$

$$\therefore \ S = -\boldsymbol{k}N\Sigma(n_r/N) \ln (n_r/N) \quad . \quad . \quad . \quad . \quad . \quad . \quad (20)$$

From (13) and (15):

$$n_r/N = e^{-\mu\epsilon_r}/Z, \quad \therefore \ \ln (n_r/N) = \ln e^{-\mu\epsilon_r} - \ln Z = -\mu\epsilon_r - \ln Z,$$

$$\therefore \ S = -\boldsymbol{k}N\Sigma(n_r/N)(-\mu\epsilon_r - \ln Z) = \boldsymbol{k}\mu\Sigma n_r\epsilon_r + \boldsymbol{k}N \ln Z$$

$$\therefore \ S = \boldsymbol{k}N \ln Z + \boldsymbol{k}\mu E \quad . \quad . \quad . \quad . \quad . \quad . \quad . \quad (21)$$

[1] See e.g. C. Smith, " A Treatise on Algebra," 1892, 151.

[2] See e.g. Margenau and Murphy, " The Mathematics of Physics and Chemistry," New York, 1943, 449, who also use the symbol Z. " Sum over states," used by Tolman, seems an incorrect translation of " Zustandssumme." The name " partition function," and symbol f, introduced by Fowler (whose treatment does not introduce the sum explicitly, and hence cannot use the name) seem rather misleading, because Z is not in itself a " partition " function in the same sense as Maxwell's distribution law (§ 10.III), but only half of one. The symbol f given in the " Report of a Joint Committee of the Chemical Society, the Faraday Society, and the Physical Society on Symbols for Thermodynamical and Physico-Chemical Quantities," London, 1937, was introduced after the Committee had presented its report, and was never approved.

from (2). By denoting $e^{-\mu\epsilon_r}$ by Z_r, (20) can be written in the alternative form:

$$S=-kN\Sigma Z_r \ln Z_r \quad \text{(20a)}$$

The value of the multiplier μ may be found from the general thermodynamic equation (2), § 35.II:

$$(dS/dE)_V=1/T \quad \text{(22)}$$

Differentiate (21) with respect to μ at constant volume:[1]

$$(dS/d\mu)=kN(d \ln Z/d\mu)+kE+k\mu(dE/d\mu)$$
$$=-kE+kE+k\mu(dE/d\mu), \text{ from (19)},$$
$$\therefore (dS/dE)=(dS/d\mu)/(dE/d\mu)=k\mu=1/T,$$
$$\therefore \mu=1/kT \quad \text{(23)}$$

This gives a definition of temperature, which so far has not entered the formulae. This value of μ may now be inserted in equation (13), giving:

$$n_r=(1/C)e^{-\epsilon_r/kT} \quad \text{(24)}$$

which may be regarded as the fundamental equation of Maxwell-Boltzmann statistics. The insertion of the value of μ in (19), with $d\mu=-(1/kT^2)dT$, and in (21) gives the values of the energy E and entropy S, and hence also the free energy F:

$$E=kNT^2(d \ln Z/dT) \quad \text{(25)}$$
$$S=kN \ln Z+E/T \quad \text{(26)}$$
$$F=E-TS=-kNT \ln Z \quad \text{(27)}$$

An alternative formula for the entropy is:

$$S=(E-F)/T$$
$$=kN[\ln Z+T(d \ln Z/dT)] \quad \text{(28)}$$

The molecular heat at constant volume (with $N=\boldsymbol{N}$, Avogadro's number, and $\boldsymbol{R}=\boldsymbol{N}k$) is, from (19), (23), and (25):

$$C_v=(dE/dT)=(dE/d\mu)(d\mu/dT)=(dE/d\mu)(-1/kT^2)$$
$$=-k\mu^2(dE/d\mu)=kN\mu^2(d^2 \ln Z/d\mu^2)$$
$$=(\boldsymbol{R}/T^2)\frac{d^2 \ln Z}{d(1/T)^2} \quad \text{(29)}$$

From (27):

$$Z=e^{-F/\boldsymbol{R}T} \quad \text{(30)}$$

From (13), (15), and (23):

$$C=Z/N \quad \text{and} \quad n_r=(N/Z)e^{-\epsilon_r/kT} \quad \text{(30a)}$$

From (30), by dividing numerator and denominator of the index by $\boldsymbol{N}$ (which may be $=N$, Avogadro's number), $Z=e^{-f_r/kT}$, where f_r is the free energy per *molecule*. Hence

$$C/N=e^{-f_r/kT} \quad \text{and} \quad n_r=Ne^{(f_r-\epsilon_r)/kT} \quad \text{(31)}$$

All the fundamental formulae of Maxwell-Boltzmann statistics have now been obtained. The use of Stirling's theorem by Boltzmann,[2] and Planck [3]

[1] The state sum for the *translational* kinetic energy depends on the volume, as is shown in § 33.

[2] " Gastheorie," 1896, 1, 41.

[3] " Theorie der Wärmestrahlung," 1921, 124.

has been criticised.[1] An alternative method,[2] using Cauchy's contour-integration for a complex variable, and a "method of steepest descents," a purely mathematical device for evaluating certain coefficients in power series, is unsuitable for elementary exposition; Kistiakowski [3] was "still to be convinced that the . . . method has any advantages, except some mathematical elegance, over the much more instructive Boltzmann procedure," and considered that "statistical mechanics could be adequately presented with a greater economy of mathematical symbols." The involved mathematics, in fact, led one of its originators into error in one application.[4]

Another procedure, used by Gibbs,[5] assumes in effect that the integral:

$$\int e^{-(\alpha+\epsilon)/kT} d\tau = 1 \quad . \quad . \quad . \quad . \quad . \quad . \quad . \quad . \quad (32)$$

is unity when taken over all the coordinates, $d\tau$ being an element of generalised space (§ 13), ϵ the energy, and α a parameter to be determined. Bichowski [6] generalised this to:

$$\int f(\epsilon/kT) e^{-(\alpha+\epsilon)/kT} d\tau = 1 \quad . \quad . \quad . \quad . \quad . \quad . \quad . \quad (33)$$

where $f(\epsilon/kT)$ is a function of the argument ϵ/kT; the Nernst heat theorem requires that $f(\epsilon/kT)=0$ when $T=0$. Brillouin [7] showed that (32) is applicable to quantum statistics.

§ 9. Statistical Weights

In some cases a group of g energy states occurs in which the values ϵ_r, ϵ_{r+1}, ϵ_{r+2}, . . ., are such that the difference $(\epsilon_{r+g}-\epsilon_r)$ is *very* small compared with the difference between the average energy of the group, and the energy of the next state or group of states. In such cases, the group of g states are taken together as one state in the state sum, g being called the *statistical weight* (sometimes, oddly, "quantum weight") of the state. Thus equation (13), § 8 $(\mu=1/kT)$ for this group is replaced by:

$$n_r = (1/C) g_r e^{-\epsilon_r/kT} \quad . \quad . \quad . \quad . \quad . \quad . \quad . \quad . \quad (1)$$

which is equivalent to the sum of the separate terms all having (practically) the same energy ϵ_r. The complete state sum will then be:

$$Z = g_0 e^{-\epsilon_0/kT} + g_1 e^{-\epsilon_1/kT} + \ldots + g_r e^{-\epsilon_r/kT} + \ldots = \Sigma g_r e^{-\epsilon_r/kT} \quad . \quad (2)$$

[1] See e.g. Flamm, *Phys. Z.*, 1918, **19**, 116, 166; Lichtenecker, *ibid.*, 1919, **20**, 12; 1922, **23**, 43; *Verhl. d. D. Phys. Ges.*, 1919, **21**, 236; *Leipzig Ber.*, 1925, **77**, 189; Schrödinger, *Phys. Z.*, 1924, **25**, 41; *Berlin Ber.*, 1925, 434; and the reply by Planck, *Berlin Ber.*, 1925, 49, 442; Széll, *Z. Phys.*, 1933, **84**, 112; 1934, **86**, 810.

[2] Darwin and Fowler, *Proc. Cambr. Phil. Soc.*, 1922, **21**, 262, 391, 730; *Phil. Mag.*, 1922, **44**, 450, 823; Fowler, *ibid.*, 1923, **45**, 497; "Statistical Mechanics," Cambridge, 1936, 32; Schottky, *Ann. Phys.*, 1925, **78**, 434; Rice, "Introduction to Statistical Mechanics," 1930, 282; Lindsay and Margenau, "Foundations of Physics," New York, 1936, 252; Fowler and Guggenheim, "Statistical Thermodynamics," Cambridge, 1939, 34; Margenau and Murphy, "The Mathematics of Physics and Chemistry," New York, 1943, 436; Schrödinger, "Statistical Thermodynamics," Cambridge, 1946, 27 (who says the method "appeals to some scholars").

[3] *J.A.C.S.*, 1940, **62**, 2889.

[4] Fowler and Sterne, *Rev. Mod. Phys.*, 1932, **4**, 649: "really incorrect."

[5] "Elementary Principles in Statistical Mechanics," 1902, 32; "Collected Works," New York, 1928, **2**, 32; Postma, *Proc. K. Akad. Wetens. Amsterdam*, 1907–8, **10**, 390; 1908–9, **11**, 303, 781; Ratnowsky, *Verhl. d. D. Phys. Ges.*, 1916, **18**, 263; *Phys. Rev.*, 1918, **11**, 62; on the limitations of Gibbs's procedure, see Eucken, *Naturwiss.*, 1938, **26**, 230; Nernst, *ibid.*, 1939, **27**, 393.

[6] *Phys. Rev.*, 1928, **32**, 494.

[7] *J. de Phys.*, 1921, **2**, 65; cf. von Neumann, *Gött. Nachr.*, 1927, 245, 273; Wigner, *Phys. Rev.*, 1932, **40**, 749; Mayer and Band, *J. Chem. Phys.*, 1947, **15**, 141.

All the g states are assumed to have equal statistical weights, i.e. given equal opportunities to possess the energies necessary for their separate existences, all these states are equally probable.[1] A state said to have an *a priori* weight g is really a group of g states which have so nearly equal energies that they are nearly equally affected by temperature change, and for simplicity in calculations they are grouped together as one state of weight g.

Equations (17a) and (18), § 8, must now be re-written in the form: [2]

$$\bar{\epsilon}=\frac{E}{N}=\frac{(1/C)\Sigma g_r\epsilon_r e^{-\epsilon_r/kT}}{(1/C)\Sigma g_r e^{-\epsilon_r/kT}}=-\frac{1}{Z}\cdot\frac{dZ}{d\mu}=-\frac{d\ln Z}{d\mu} \quad . \quad . \quad . \quad (3)$$

If the energies in each of the group of g states become *identical*, the group of states is said to become *degenerate*, each energy ϵ_r then corresponding with g_r micro-states. In certain circumstances, e.g. in a magnetic field, these states may unfold into different states, with slightly different energies, and they must therefore be counted separately in *all* cases.

In Wave Mechanics (see § 10.V) the *multiplicity* g of a state with an energy E is the result of the existence of g distinct proper functions (ψ) satisfying the wave equation, and the proper function of the system is a linear combination of these functions with g arbitrary constants. The physical significance may be illustrated by considering an atom with a magnetic moment $m\mu$. In a magnetic field **H**, the magnetic axis will set itself so that its projections in the direction of the field will have only the discrete values:

$$m=j,\ j-1,\ \ldots,\ 1,\ \ldots\ -j \quad . \quad . \quad . \quad . \quad . \quad (4)$$

where j is the so-called inner quantum number. The energy in the field is $-m\mu\mathbf{H}$, and the state sum has $g=(2j+1)$ terms, corresponding with the values of m:

$$Z=\sum_m e^{m\mu\mathbf{H}/kT} \quad . \quad . \quad . \quad . \quad . \quad . \quad . \quad . \quad . \quad . \quad (5)$$

When $\mathbf{H}=0$, the system is degenerate and:

$$Z=2j+1 \quad . \quad . \quad . \quad . \quad . \quad . \quad . \quad . \quad . \quad . \quad (6)$$

§ 10. Canonical Assembly

An assembly of systems all having exactly the same energy and all in the state of maximum entropy was called by Gibbs [3] a *micro-canonical ensemble* (or assembly); [4] this corresponds with isolated systems ($dE=0$).

An assembly in which the *average* energy, set up by exchange of energy with a constant temperature bath, has reached an almost constant value, corresponding

[1] Giauque, *J.A.C.S.*, 1930, **52**, 4808; on phase space with degenerate or coherent degrees of freedom, Epstein, *Berlin Ber.*, 1918, 435. The *assumption* of equal statistical weights for the g states is made into a " fundamental hypothesis " by Tolman, " Statistical Mechanics," Oxford, 1938, 59, and Fowler and Guggenheim, " Statistical Thermodynamics," Cambridge, 1939, 7 (" no short or simple discussion is of any value ").

[2] Ehrenberg, *Nature*, 1946, **158**, 308.

[3] " Elementary Principles in Statistical Mechanics," 1902, 115; " Collected Works," 1928, **2**, 115.

[4] The name " assembly " is used by Slater, " Introduction to Chemical Physics," New York, 1939, 32, 46, and other modern authors, as equivalent to Gibbs's " ensemble." In German, " Gesamtheit " is sometimes used. See Herz, *Ann. Phys.*, 1910, **33**, 225; Einstein, *ibid.*, 1910, **34**, 175; Tolman, *J.A.C.S.*, 1920, **42**, 2506; 1921, **43**, 126; 1922, **44**, 75; Adams, *ibid.*, 1921, **43**, 1251. As van der Waals, jnr., *Ann. Phys.*, 1911, **35**, 185, pointed out, Boltzmann considered systems in which the *energy* is regarded as constant, but did not really define his distribution of states before reaching the account in the second volume of his " Gastheorie " (1898, **2**, 68 f.), whilst Gibbs's treatment is essentially one in which the *temperature* is regarded as constant. The treatment adopted here follows Planck, *Berlin Ber.*, 1925, 442.

with the maximum entropy, was called by Gibbs [1] a *canonical ensemble* (or assembly). For all but a negligible fraction of the states, the two assemblies, as has been indicated (§ 7), may be regarded as identical, and hence the name " micro-canonical " is rather misleading.

The probability that any arbitrarily selected or sample elementary configuration in the assembly shall have the energy ϵ_r is given by (13) and (15), § 8, as:

$$n_r/N = e^{-\epsilon_r/kT}/\Sigma e^{-\epsilon_r/kT}.$$

Since the elementary configurations are all of the same kind, they undergo the same changes in lapse of time, these changes giving rise to the various micro-states. The above probability, therefore, also gives the probability that a single elementary configuration, undergoing changes with lapse of time, shall have the energy ϵ_r at any selected moment, the energy changes in this case being due to the constant temperature bath, as a kind of Brownian movement. The equation then gives the definite energy fluctuations of a single elementary configuration immersed in a bath of temperature T, these depending only on the temperature.

If $\bar{\epsilon}$ is the average energy, it is easily shown [2] that

$$\Delta = \overline{(\epsilon_r - \bar{\epsilon})^2}/\bar{\epsilon}^2 = -kT^2(d/dT)(1/\bar{\epsilon}).$$

In a degenerate group of g_r states, each having the energy ϵ_r, in a constant temperature bath, the energy fluctuations of a single elementary configuration will be specified by (13) and (15), § 8, and (2), § 9:

$$n_r/N = g_r e^{-\epsilon_r/kT}/\Sigma g_r e^{-\epsilon_r/kT} \quad . \quad . \quad . \quad . \quad . \quad . \quad . \quad . \quad (1)$$

When $g_r = 1$, the smallest energy ϵ_0 will occur most frequently, the exponential in the numerator then having its largest value, but in a degenerate system ($g_r > 1$), g_r increases with r,s ince a larger energy may be distributed in many more ways over the different coordinates (degrees of freedom) than a smaller. Thus, the numerator of (1) will first increase rapidly with r, but later with sufficiently large values of ϵ_r, it will become vanishingly small, on account of the increasing effect of the exponential function. The maximum value of (1) then no longer occurs for ϵ_0 (as when $g = 1$), but nearer the average energy $\bar{\epsilon}$; i.e. the energy fluctuations are smaller than in a non-degenerate system, and (1) has a small and steep maximum. The *most probable* energy is thus very nearly equal to the *average* energy, and hence such an elementary configuration with many degrees of freedom has, for every temperature, a definite average energy. Conversely, each energy corresponds with a definite temperature of the configuration, which temperature exists independently of a constant temperature bath in which the system may be supposed to be immersed.

Since, in the state sum, all terms in which the energy differs *appreciably* from the average energy, $\bar{E} = E$, are negligible, any body of finite dimensions may be treated as a single elementary configuration with many degrees of freedom.[3] Then: [4]

$$Z = \mathrm{G} \, . \, e^{-E/kT} \quad . \quad . \quad . \quad . \quad . \quad . \quad . \quad . \quad (2)$$

where $\mathrm{G} = \Sigma g_r$ is the sum of the statistical weights of all the states in which the energy is very close to E. The steep maximum at $E_r = E$ is conditioned by: (i) the factor G for values $E_r < E$, and (ii) the exponential function for values $E_r > E$; and hence on both sides of E, the contributions to (2) are negligible.

[1] " Elementary Principles in Statistical Mechanics," 1902, 34, 48, 68; " Collected Works," New York, 1928, **2**, 34, 46, 68.

[2] Planck, " Theorie der Warme," 1930, 205.

[3] Planck, *Z. Phys.*, 1925, **35**, 155; *Berlin Ber.*, 1925, 442.

[4] G is here printed in roman type to distinguish it from the symbol of available energy *G*.

Since $\ln Z = \ln G - E/kT$, equation (27), § 8 (since all the N states are now counted separately) gives:

$$F = -kT \ln Z = -kT \ln G + E \quad . \quad . \quad . \quad . \quad . \quad . \quad (3)$$

$$\therefore \quad S = (E - F)/T = k \ln G \quad . \quad . \quad . \quad . \quad . \quad . \quad (4)$$

The comparison of (4) with (1), § 5, shows that the statistical weight G which must be substituted in (1), § 5, to give the entropy of a system of given energy is practically equal to the total number of micro-states of the system the energy of which does not exceed E.

It is often more convenient to use an expression in which the micro-states having a common energy E_r are written separately:

$$Z = \sum_r G_r e^{-E_r/kT} = \sum_z e^{-E_r/kT} \quad . \quad . \quad . \quad . \quad . \quad . \quad (5)$$

in which z denotes summation over the separate states having this energy; [1] equation (5) comprises all the micro-states of the assembly, from the smallest to the largest energies, to infinity, and any arbitrary grouping of the terms can be used in finding the sum.

In the case where the state at absolute zero, $T=0$, has a statistical weight g_0 not equal to unity, i.e. consists of g_0 states with practically equal energies, it is easily seen that (28), § 8, must be written:

$$S_i = S_0 + \boldsymbol{R}[\ln Z_i - \ln g_0 + T(\mathrm{d} \ln Z_i/\mathrm{d}T)] \quad . \quad . \quad . \quad . \quad (6)$$

where $\boldsymbol{R} \ln g_0 = \boldsymbol{R} \ln Z_{i0}$ is the entropy (if any) at the absolute zero. Planck's form of Nernst's theorem, $S_0 = 0$, is therefore strictly true only when $g_0 = 1$, which, in the majority of cases, is true.

The values of S referring to a crystalline solid at $T=0$ as zero have been called the " virtual " or Nernst theorem (NT) values; the values of S calculated from the complete state sums (including nuclear spins: see § 21) have been called the " absolute " or nuclear spin (NS) values.[2] The NT energy is all the energy liberated on cooling from the given temperature to $T=0$ at constant volume, whilst the NS energy includes in addition the zero-point energy of the molecules, which is not thermodynamically observable. The effect of nuclear spin multiplicity cancels out in thermodynamic calculations, since it is not affected by temperature and concentration, and for such calculations nuclear spin effects may be subtracted from the NS functions. At present it cannot be decided experimentally if Nernst's theorem, $S=0$ at $T=0$, applies only to NT entropy, or whether, at temperatures very near $T=0$, the effects of nuclear spin multiplicity also vanish.

The entropy of a *mixture of isotopes* [3] in mol fractions x and $(1-x)$ would be:

$$S = xS_1 + (1-x)S_2 - \boldsymbol{R}[x \ln x + (1-x) \ln (1-x)] \quad . \quad . \quad . \quad (7)$$

[1] Planck, " Theorie der Wärme," 1930, 211; " Hier soll der Index z bedeuten, dass die Summation nicht über die Ordnungszahlen r der Energie, sondern über die einzelnen Zustände zu erstrecken ist, so dass jede Energie E_r so oft gezählt wird, als es Zustände gibt, welche diese Energie zukommt."

[2] On the distinction, see Nernst, *Berlin Ber.*, 1913, 972; Keesom, *Phys. Z.*, 1913, **14**, 665; Stern, *Ann. Phys.*, 1916, **49**, 823; Epstein, " Textbook of Thermodynamics," New York, 1937, 243; Ubbelohde, " Introduction to Modern Thermodynamical Principles," Oxford, 1937, 55; and the papers by Giauque *et al.* given in § 29.

[3] Maxwell, " Ency. Brit.," 9th edit., 1877, **7**, 220; " Scientific Papers," Cambridge, 1890, 2, 644, in discussing Gibbs's paradox (§ 28.II), said: " It is not probable, but it is possible, that two gases derived from different sources, but hitherto supposed to be the same, may hereafter be found to be different, and that a method may be discovered of separating them by a reversible process. If this should happen, the process of interdiffusion which we had formerly supposed not to be an instance of the dissipation of energy would now be recognised as such an instance," and he gave an equation equivalent to (7).

where the last two terms specify the entropy change due to the mixture effect (§ 57.II), but since no ordinary process affects x they usually cancel in the calculations. If there is a specific heat anomaly at a given temperature involving an entropy change S_a, then S(NT) is reckoned from an apparent NT zero, $S(NT)+S_a$ from a true NT zero, and $S(\text{NS})=S(\text{NT})+S_a+S_i$, where S_i is the nuclear spin part, from the statistical (NS) zero.

A highly mathematical justification of Gibbs's [1] postulate that a statistical ensemble of mechanical systems generally converges in course of time to a state of statistical equilibrium, if it is not already in that state, is given by Kroò,[2] and the treatment of Gibbs's statistical mechanics on the basis of polydimensional geometry by Herz [3] may also be mentioned. The statistical foundation of the quantum theory is considered by Wereide [4] to imply that the element of generalised space $d\tau$ (§§ 13–14) is chosen so large that the state at absolute zero is always included in it. These mathematical considerations are outside our province. As Born [5] says, the laws of probability can be regarded as having the same validity as other physical laws, i.e. as " demonstrated " by the agreement of their consequences with experience. Each type of statistics depends on the choice of equally probably cases, or, more generally, on the assignment of suitable statistical weights, and the result from classical mechanics that the statistical weight is proportional to the extension in phase-space can be justified only by the agreement of the consequences with observations. The description of statistical weights is even simpler for quantised systems, each state of given energy which cannot be split into several states by physical means having the same statistical weight.

§ 11. Zero-point Energy

The value of ϵ_0 in (2), § 9, in the application to molecular systems, is the spectroscopically determined zero-point energy in the ground state of the molecule (see § 17). If the free atoms are used as zero states for the energy-levels of the molecule, these levels differ from those in the above convention by ϵ_D, the energy of dissociation of the molecule in its ground state into normal atoms, and the state sum is then

$$Z'=Ze^{-\epsilon_D/kT} \quad \ldots\ldots\ldots\ldots \quad (1)$$

In this case the zero-point energy factor is automatically included in the factor for vibrational energies (§ 16). In other cases,[6] the state sum is defined as:

$$Z''=g_0+g_1e^{-\epsilon_1/kT}+g_2e^{-\epsilon_2/kT}+\ldots \quad \ldots\ldots \quad (2)$$

$$\therefore \quad Z=Z''e^{-\epsilon_0/kT} \quad \ldots\ldots\ldots\ldots \quad (3)$$

If the energy of a molecule can be separated into translational (ϵ_t), rotational [7] (ϵ_r), vibrational (ϵ_v), and electronic (ϵ_e), parts, as is usual in spectroscopy:

$$\epsilon=\epsilon_t+\epsilon_r+\epsilon_v+\epsilon_e \quad \ldots\ldots\ldots\ldots \quad (4)$$

[1] " Elementary Principles of Statistical Mechanics," 1902, 142.

[2] *Ann. Phys.*, 1911, **34**, 907; crit. by Silberstein, *ibid.*, 1912, **37**, 386; reply by Kroò, *ibid.*, 1912, **38**, 885.

[3] *Ann. Phys.*, 1910, **33**, 225, 537; cf. also T. and P. Ehrenfest, *Wien Ber.*, 1906, **115**, IIA, 89; Epstein, *Ann. Phys.*, 1916, **51**, 168.

[4] *Ann. Phys.*, 1916, **49**, 966; cf. Blokhintsev, *J. Phys. U.S.S.R.*, 1940, **2**, 71; Blokhintsev and Nemirovsky, *ibid.*, 1940, **3**, 191.

[5] " Experiment and Theory in Physics," Cambridge, 1943, 26.

[6] Giauque, *J.A.C.S.*, 1930, **52**, 4808; see Glasstone, *Ann. Rep. Chem., Soc.*, 1935, 67; Riewe, *Z. Phys.*, 1938, **109**, 753; Clusius, *Die Chemie*, 1943, **56**, 241.

[7] Not to be confused with the general symbol ϵ_r used in § 8.

the state sum will be equal to the product[1] of the state sums for these separate parts:

$$Z=\Sigma e^{-\epsilon/kT}=\Sigma e^{-(\epsilon_t+\epsilon_r+\epsilon_v+\epsilon_e)/kT}=Z_t \,.\, Z_r \,.\, Z_v \,.\, Z_e \quad . \; . \; . \quad (5)$$

The last three factors may be grouped as an *internal* state sum:

$$Z_i=Z_r \,.\, Z_v \,.\, Z_e \quad . \; . \; . \; . \; . \; . \; . \; . \quad (6)$$

This is only an approximation, since changes in vibrational energy affect the spacing of the rotational levels, and both the vibrational and rotational levels are influenced by the electronic energy state of the molecule.

§ 12. Some Equations of General Dynamics

Some equations of dynamics[2] will be required later. The fundamental equation for a mass m considered as a particle is Newton's second law:[3]

$$\textit{force}=\textit{time rate of change of momentum}, \text{ or } P=\mathrm{d}(mv)/\mathrm{d}t \quad . \quad (1)$$

and when the mass is constant (non-relativistic dynamics), force=mass × acceleration:

$$P=m(\mathrm{d}v/\mathrm{d}t)=m(\mathrm{d}^2s/\mathrm{d}t^2)=mf \quad . \; . \; . \; . \; . \; . \quad (2)$$

If the force is resolved into components X, Y, Z, parallel to the coordinate axes of x, y, z:

$$X=m\ddot{x}; \quad Y=m\ddot{y}; \quad Z=m\ddot{z} \quad . \; . \; . \; . \; . \; . \quad (3)$$

where $x=\mathrm{d}^2x/\mathrm{d}t^2$, etc. (§ 6.I).

If a system of forces acts on any number of particles and if i denotes any selected particle, equations (3) become:

$$m_i\ddot{x}_i-X_i=0; \quad m_i\ddot{y}_i-Y_i=0; \quad m_i\ddot{z}_i-Z_i=0 \quad . \; . \; . \; . \quad (4)$$

Multiply these equations by the arbitrary (" virtual ") displacements δx_i, δy_i, δz_i, and form the sum for all the particles; then the resulting equation:

$$\sum_i[(m_i\ddot{x}_i-X_i)\delta x_i+(m_i\ddot{y}_i-Y_i)\delta y_i+(m_i\ddot{z}_i-Z_i)\delta z_i]=0 \quad . \; . \quad (5)$$

is called *D'Alembert's principle*.[4] The virtual displacements must be consistent with any conditions of constraint imposed on the system; e.g. if any two particles are rigidly connected no displacement is possible in the line joining them.

[1] Since the energies in the *exponential* are additive.

[2] See e.g. Thomson and Tait, " Treatise on Natural Philosophy," Cambridge, 1886, **1**, 301; J. J. Thomson, " Applications of Dynamics to Physics and Chemistry," 1888, 8; Boltzmann, " Prinzipien der Mechanik," 2 vols., Leipzig, 1892–1904; Webster, " The Dynamics of Particles, and of Rigid, Elastic, and Fluid Bodies," Leipzig, 1904; Riemann and Weber, " Partielle Differentialgleichungen der mathematischen Physik," 1910, **1**, 295; Routh, " Elementary Rigid Dynamics," 1913, 45, 317; Schaefer, " Die Prinzipien der Dynamik," Leipzig, 1919; Planck, " Einführung in die allgemeine Mechanik," Leipzig, 1920, 167; Phillips, *J. Opt. Soc. Amer.*, 1922, **6**, 229; Whittaker, " Analytical Dynamics," 3rd edit., Cambridge, 1927, 34; Sommerfeld, " Atomic Structure and Spectral Lines," 3rd edit., 1934, **1**, 96; Margenau and Murphy, " The Mathematics of Physics and Chemistry," New York, 1943, 268 (vector notation). For the history of dynamics, see Whewell, " History of the Inductive Sciences," 1857, **2**, 1 f.; Mach, " The Science of Mechanics," 1893, 269 f., 331 f., 466 f.

[3] As de Morgan, " Differential and Integral Calculus," 1842, 504, said: " the word force, when used to signify both the pressure which produces acceleration, and the acceleration itself, has always been a stumbling-block to beginners." A force is " something " which, acting on a mass m, can give it an acceleration f, and is *measured* by the product mf, the unit of force being derived from those of mass and acceleration (i.e. of length and time) so that this equation is true without a constant. In statics, forces act without producing accelerations. The dynamical symbol of force, P (" potentia "), must not be confused with the same symbol for pressure (=force/area).

[4] Jean le Rond D'Alembert (1717–83), " Traité de Dynamique," 1743.

Now introduce, instead of the space-coordinates x, y, z, a system of *generalised coordinates* (which may e.g. include angles), denoted by $q_1, q_2, q_3, \ldots, q_k, \ldots$, and suppose the space-coordinates expressed as functions of these:

$$x_i = x_i(q_1, q_2, \ldots q_k, \ldots), \text{ etc.}$$

$$\delta x_i = (\partial x_i/\partial q_1)\delta q_1 + (\partial x_i/\partial q_2)\delta q_2 + \ldots + (\partial x_i/\partial q_k)\delta q_k + \ldots$$
$$= \sum_k (\partial x_i/\partial q_k)\delta q_k \quad \ldots \quad (6)$$

In (6), $\partial x_i/\partial q_k$ is an abbreviated form of $\partial x_i(q_1, q_2, \ldots)/\partial q_k$, whilst in general δx_i is a variation of the coordinate x_i. Since $\delta x_i/\delta t = \dot{x}_i$, and $\delta q_k/\delta t = \dot{q}_k$, the velocity components follow from (6) as:

$$\dot{x}_i = (\partial x_i/\partial q_1)\dot{q}_1 + (\partial x_i/\partial q_2)\dot{q}_2 + \ldots = \sum_k (\partial x_i/\partial q_k)\dot{q}_k \quad \ldots \quad (7)$$

and similarly for $\dot{y}_i$ and $\dot{z}_i$.

Now replace δx_i by (6), and δy_i and δz_i by similar equations, in (5), then:

$$\sum_i [(m_i\ddot{x}_i - X_i)\sum_k (\partial x_i/\partial q_k)\delta q_k] = 0,$$

the terms involving y_i and z_i being supposed included. Now:

$$\ddot{x}_i\frac{\partial x_i}{\partial q_k} = \frac{d}{dt}\left[\dot{x}_i\frac{\partial x_i}{\partial q_k}\right] - \dot{x}_i\frac{d}{dt}\frac{\partial x_i}{\partial q_k} \quad \ldots \quad (8)$$

and from (7) by partial differentiation:

$$\partial\dot{x}_i/\partial\dot{q}_k = (\partial x_i/\partial q_k)(\partial\dot{q}_k/\partial\dot{q}_k) = \partial x_i/\partial q_k$$

$$\therefore \quad \frac{d}{dt}\left[\dot{x}_i\frac{\partial x_i}{\partial q_k}\right] = \frac{d}{dt}\left[\dot{x}_i\frac{\partial\dot{x}_i}{\partial\dot{q}_k}\right] = \frac{1}{2}\frac{d}{dt}\left[\frac{\partial(\dot{x}_i^2)}{\partial\dot{q}_k}\right] \quad \ldots \quad (9)$$

$$\text{and} \quad \frac{d}{dt}\frac{\partial x_i}{\partial q_k} = \frac{\partial^2 x_i}{\partial q_1\partial q_k}\dot{q}_1 + \frac{\partial^2 x_i}{\partial q_2\partial q_k}\dot{q}_2 + \ldots$$
$$= (\partial/\partial q_k)[(\partial x_i/\partial q_1)\dot{q}_1 + (\partial x_i/\partial q_2)\dot{q}_2 + \ldots]$$
$$= \partial\dot{x}_i/\partial q_k, \quad \text{from (7).}$$

Hence:

$$\dot{x}_i\frac{d}{dt}\frac{\partial x_i}{\partial q_k} = \dot{x}_i\frac{\partial\dot{x}_i}{\partial q_k} = \frac{\partial}{\partial q_k}(\tfrac{1}{2}\dot{x}_i^2) \quad \ldots \quad (10)$$

Substitute from (9) and (10) in (8), then:

$$\ddot{x}_i\frac{\partial x_i}{\partial q_k} = \frac{d}{dt}\left[\frac{1}{2}\frac{\partial(\dot{x}_i^2)}{\partial\dot{q}_k}\right] - \frac{\partial}{\partial q_k}(\tfrac{1}{2}\dot{x}_i^2).$$

Hence in (5):

$$m_i\ddot{x}_i\delta x_i = \sum_k\left[\frac{d}{dt}\frac{\partial}{\partial\dot{q}_k}(\tfrac{1}{2}m_i\dot{x}_i^2) - \frac{\partial}{\partial q_k}(\tfrac{1}{2}m_i\dot{x}_i^2)\right]\delta q_k \quad \ldots \quad (11)$$

since $m_i(d/dt)(\frac{1}{2} . \partial\dot{x}_i^2/\partial\dot{q}_k) = (d/dt)(\partial/\partial\dot{q}_k)(\frac{1}{2}m_i\dot{x}_i^2)$, and δx_i is given by (6). Since $\frac{1}{2}m_i\dot{x}_i^2$ is the kinetic energy of the ith particle along the x axis, and there are similar equations to (11) for $m_i\ddot{y}_i\delta y_i$ and $m_i\ddot{z}_i\delta z_i$, the sum of the right-hand sides of these three equations will give in place of the first term in (11):

$$\sum\frac{d}{dt}\frac{\partial}{\partial\dot{q}_k}(\tfrac{1}{2}m_i\dot{x}_i^2 + \tfrac{1}{2}m_i\dot{y}_i^2 + \tfrac{1}{2}m_i\dot{z}_i^2)\delta q_k = \sum\frac{d}{dt}\frac{\partial}{\partial\dot{q}_k}(\tfrac{1}{2}m_i v_i^2)\delta q_k$$

where $v_i^2 = \dot{x}_i^2 + \dot{y}_i^2 + \dot{z}_i^2$, v_i being the resultant velocity. Since $\sum_i \frac{1}{2}m_i v_i^2 = T$, the total *kinetic energy*, the first term will be $\Sigma(d/dt)(\partial T/\partial\dot{q}_k)\delta q_k$. A similar summation gives $\Sigma(\partial T/\partial q_k)\delta q_k$ for the second term in (11).

Suppose the forces can be derived from a function V of the coordinates $x_1, y_1, z_1, x_2, y_2, z_2, \ldots$, by the equations:

$$X_i = -\partial V/\partial x_i;\quad Y_i = -\partial V/\partial y_i;\quad Z_i = -\partial V/\partial z_i.$$

In this case the system is said to be conservative and V is the total *potential energy*. Thus:

$$\sum_i (X_i\delta x_i + Y_i\delta y_i + Z_i\delta z_i) = -\mathrm{d}V = -\sum_k (\partial V/\partial q_k)\delta q_k \quad . \quad . \quad . \quad (12)$$

Then (5) can be written, by using (12) and results just found, as:

$$\sum_k \left[\frac{\mathrm{d}}{\mathrm{d}t}\left(\frac{\partial T}{\partial \dot{q}_k}\right) - \frac{\partial T}{\partial q_k} + \frac{\partial V}{\partial q_k}\right]\delta q_k = 0 \quad . \quad . \quad . \quad . \quad . \quad . \quad (13)$$

Let

$$L = T - V \quad . \quad . \quad . \quad . \quad . \quad . \quad . \quad . \quad . \quad . \quad (14)$$

be the *Lagrangian function* or *kinetic potential.* Since V is supposed to be a function only of the coordinates q_k and not of the velocities $\dot{q}_k$, $\partial V/\partial \dot{q}_k = 0$, and (13) can be written:

$$\sum_k \left[\frac{\mathrm{d}}{\mathrm{d}t}\left(\frac{\partial L}{\partial \dot{q}_k}\right) - \frac{\partial L}{\partial q_k}\right]\delta q_k = 0 \quad . \quad . \quad . \quad . \quad . \quad . \quad . \quad (15)$$

The variations $\delta q_1, \delta q_2, \ldots$ are arbitrary, hence (15) can be true only if each of the coefficients of δq_k is zero:

$$(\mathrm{d}/\mathrm{d}t)(\partial L/\partial \dot{q}_k) - \partial L/\partial q_k = 0 \quad . \quad . \quad . \quad . \quad . \quad . \quad . \quad (16)$$

This is called *Lagrange's equation of motion.*[1] If the configuration of the system is represented by a minimum number k of generalised coordinates, the system is said to have k *degrees of freedom*, and the deduction shows that the Lagrangian equations of motion are true for any system of coordinates, provided that the number of coordinates is equal to the number of degrees of freedom. There will be k equations of type (16) expressing the motion of the system, and each is a differential equation of the second order (§ 56.I). It will now be shown that these k equations may be replaced by $2k$ differential equations of the first order by using generalised momenta and including differentiation with respect to time.

Corresponding with each generalised coordinate is a *generalised momentum* p_k defined by

$$p_k = \partial L/\partial \dot{q}_k = \partial T/\partial \dot{q}_k \quad . \quad . \quad . \quad . \quad . \quad . \quad . \quad . \quad (17)$$

For the simplest case where $T = \frac{1}{2}mv^2$, $\dot{q}_k = v$, and $\partial T/\partial \dot{q}_k = (\mathrm{d}/\mathrm{d}v)(\frac{1}{2}mv^2) = mv$. It should be noted that V is not a function of $\dot{q}_k$, but $L = T - V$ is a function of $q_1, q_2, \ldots, \dot{q}_1, \dot{q}_2, \ldots$, and in the most general case also of the time t:

$$L = L(q_k, \dot{q}_k, t) \quad . \quad . \quad . \quad . \quad . \quad . \quad . \quad . \quad . \quad (18)$$

From (16) and (17), since $(\mathrm{d}/\mathrm{d}t)p_k = \dot{p}_k$:

$$\dot{p}_k = \partial L/\partial q_k \quad . \quad . \quad . \quad . \quad . \quad . \quad . \quad . \quad . \quad . \quad (19)$$

which is a simple form of Lagrange's equation.

Now introduce the *Hamiltonian function*:

$$H = p_1\dot{q}_1 + p_2\dot{q}_2 + \ldots + p_k\dot{q}_k - L = \sum_k p_k\dot{q}_k - L \quad . \quad . \quad . \quad . \quad (20)$$

and write down its total differential, supposing for generality that L may depend explicitly on the time t:

$$\mathrm{d}H = \Sigma p_k\mathrm{d}\dot{q}_k + \Sigma\dot{q}_k\mathrm{d}p_k - \Sigma(\partial L/\partial q_k)\mathrm{d}q_k - \Sigma(\partial L/\partial \dot{q}_k)\mathrm{d}\dot{q}_k - (\partial L/\partial t)\mathrm{d}t$$
$$= \Sigma\dot{q}_k\mathrm{d}p_k - \Sigma(\partial L/\partial q_k)\mathrm{d}q_k - (\partial L/\partial t)\mathrm{d}t \quad . \quad . \quad . \quad . \quad . \quad . \quad . \quad . \quad (21)$$

[1] Joseph Louis, Compte Lagrange (1736–1813), "Mécanique Analytique," 1788.

by (17). If H is supposed to be expressed as a function of the q_k's, p_k's, and t, then (21) can be resolved into the partial differential equations:

$$\dot{q}_k = \partial H/\partial p_k \quad \text{and} \quad \partial L/\partial q_k = -\partial H/\partial q_k,$$

and from (19):

$$\dot{q}_k = \partial H/\partial p_k \quad \text{and} \quad \dot{p}_k = -\partial H/\partial q_k \quad (k=1, 2, \ldots k) \quad . \quad . \quad (22)$$

which form a system of $2k$ differential equations of the first order, replacing the k Lagrangian equations (16) of the second order. Equations (22) are called the *canonical equations* of Hamilton.[1] In the particular case where the conditions defining the motion are independent of time, and the kinetic energy T is a homogeneous quadratic (second degree) function of the $\dot{q}_k$'s, Euler's theorem of homogeneous functions (§ 30.I) gives, with (17) and (20):

$$2T = \sum_k (\partial T/\partial \dot{q}_k)\dot{q}_k = \sum_k p_k \dot{q}_k = H + L = H + T - V,$$

$$\therefore \; H = T + V = E \quad . \quad . \quad . \quad . \quad . \quad . \quad . \quad . \quad . \quad (23)$$

the total energy, here expressed as a function of the q's and p's. Hence the canonical equations for this case can be written in the form:

$$\dot{q}_k = \partial E/\partial p_k \quad \text{and} \quad \dot{p}_k = -\partial E/\partial q_k \quad . \quad . \quad . \quad . \quad . \quad (24)$$

§ 13. Liouville's Theorem

An important equation of general dynamics is equivalent to one deduced by Liouville.[2] A dynamical system is assumed to be defined as to configuration or " position " by k generalised coordinates, $q_1, q_2, \ldots q_k$, and as to " velocity " by their time rates $\dot{q}_1, \dot{q}_2, \ldots, \dot{q}_k$. For a mass point m, the generalised velocity $\dot{q}_k$ can be replaced by the generalised momentum, $p_k = m\dot{q}_k$. Now suppose the mass points to move so that after a small interval of time $\mathrm{d}t$ the coordinates have changed by:

$$\mathrm{d}q_k = (\partial q_k/\partial t)\mathrm{d}t = \dot{q}_k \mathrm{d}t,$$

and the momenta by:

$$\mathrm{d}p_k = (\partial p_k/\partial t)\mathrm{d}t = \dot{p}_k \mathrm{d}t.$$

[1] Sir William Rowan Hamilton (1805–65), *Phil. Trans.*, 1834, **124**, 247; 1835, **125**, 195. Hamilton is also famous as the inventor of quaternions (1843), a quaternion being the sum of a scalar and a vector, and involving four independent numbers, such as the scalar and three coefficients of the vector. The general equations of dynamics may also be deduced by methods involving the calculus of variations, depending on the so-called principle of least action, in which the integral $\int_{t_0}^{t_1} L\mathrm{d}t$ shall have a minimum value (*Hamilton's principle*). For the Calculus of Variations, see de Morgan, " Differential and Integral Calculus," 1842, 446; Jellett, " Elementary Treatise on the Calculus of Variations," Dublin, 1850 (less strict and more intelligible and practical); Todhunter, " History of the Progress of the Calculus of Variations," 1861; *idem*, " Treatise on the Integral Calculus," 1891, 388; Williamson, " Integral Calculus," 1906, 425; Bolza, " Vorlesungen über Variationsrechnung," Leipzig and Berlin, 1909; Bliss, " Calculus of Variations," Chicago, 1925; Kneser, " Lehrbuch der Variationsrechnung," Brunswick, 1925; Forsyth, " Calculus of Variations," Cambridge, 1927; Koschmeider, " Variationsrechnung," I, Berlin, 1933; Morse, " The Calculus of Variations in the Large," New York, 1934; Margenau and Murphy, " The Mathematics of Physics and Chemistry," New York, 1943, 193.

[2] *J. de Math.* [Liouville], 1838, **3**, 342. See H. W. Watson, " Kinetic Theory of Gases," Oxford, 1876, 12; Boltzmann, " Gastheorie," 1898, **2**, 66, 77; Planck, " Theorie der Wärmestrahlung," 1921, 129; Jeans, " Dynamical Theory of Gases," 3rd edit., Cambridge, 1921, 70; Tolman, " Statistical Mechanics," Oxford, 1938, 48. The theorem is called by Gibbs, " Elementary Principles in Statistical Mechanics," 1902, 10 (with a deduction), the " principle of conservation of density in phase "; on the quantum aspect, see von Neumann, *Gött. Nachr.*, 1927, 245, 273; Wigner, *Phys. Rev.*, 1932, **40**, 749; Mayer and Band, *J. Chem. Phys.*, 1947, **15**, 141.

The element of "phase volume," or the small region of generalised space defined (by analogy with $dv=dx\,dy\,dz$) by:

$$d\tau=dq_1dq_2\ldots dq_kdp_1dp_2\ldots dp_k,$$

may be regarded as an infinitesimal parallelepiped of $2k$ dimensions with its edges parallel to the axes of the q's and p's. After the time dt the volume $d\tau$ becomes $d\tau'$, which is approximately again a "right-angled" parallelepiped, if terms of higher order are neglected:

$$d\tau'=d(q_1+\dot{q}_1dt)d(q_2+\dot{q}_2dt)\ldots d(p_1+\dot{p}_1dt)d(p_2+\dot{p}_2dt)\ldots$$

Now $d\dot{q}_1=(\partial\dot{q}_1/\partial q_1)dq_1, \ldots, d\dot{p}_1=(\partial\dot{p}_1/\partial p_1)dp_1, \ldots,$

$$\therefore\ d\tau'-d\tau=d\tau(\partial\dot{q}_1/\partial q_1+\ldots+\partial\dot{p}_1/\partial p_1+\ldots)dt=0 \quad . \quad . \quad (1)$$

the expression vanishing because, from (24), § 12:

$$\partial\dot{q}_1/\partial q_1=\partial^2E/\partial p_1\partial q_1, \quad \text{and} \quad \partial\dot{p}_1/\partial p_1=-\partial^2E/\partial q_1\partial p_1,$$

and the two expressions are equal, since dE is a perfect differential (§ 27.I). Thus, *Liouville's theorem* is proved for the given coordinates $q_1, q_2, \ldots,$ since $d\tau$ is independent of time.

To show that it is independent of the choice of coordinates, let the k coordinates $q_1, \ldots, q_k$ be replaced by k new coordinates $x_1, \ldots, x_k$, which are functions of $q_1, \ldots, q_k$. Now compare the values of $d\tau_q$ and $d\tau_x$, the phase volume elements expressed in terms of the q's and the x's, respectively, and the corresponding momenta p's and ξ's, say. After a finite time, let $d\tau_q$ and $d\tau_x$ have moved in the generalised space far from their original positions, when their values have become $d\tau_q'=d\tau_q$ and $d\tau_x'=d\tau_x$. Now take a third set of coordinates $z_1, \ldots, z_k$, which shall very closely coincide with $q_1, \ldots, q_k$ at the beginning of the motion and with $x_1, \ldots, x_k$ at the end: this is allowable, since no functional relations among the coordinates have been laid down. Since the momentum coordinates are completely determined by the configuration coordinates, the set $\zeta_1, \ldots \zeta_k$ corresponding with $z_1, \ldots z_k$ will closely coincide with the set $\xi_1, \ldots \xi_k$ corresponding with $x_1, \ldots x_k$. Hence $d\tau_z=d\tau_q$ and $d\tau_z'=d\tau_x'$. Liouville's theorem shows that $d\tau_z'=d\tau_z$, hence $d\tau_q=d\tau_x$, and this proves that the value of $d\tau$ is independent of the choice of coordinates.

§ 14. Ideal Gas

The general equation for the energy per mol of any system is (25), § 8:

$$E=kNT^2(d\ln Z/dT)=RT^2(d\ln Z/dT) \quad . \quad . \quad . \quad . \quad (1)$$

Since $\mu=1/kT$, from (23), § 8, therefore $1/\mu=d\ln\mu/d\mu$ (from § 14.I) $=kT=RT/N$; hence $RT=N(d\ln\mu/d\mu)$, and $d\mu/dT=-1/kT^2$, and the heat content is:

$$\begin{aligned}H=E+PV=E+RT&=RT^2(d\ln Z/dT)+RT\\&=RT^2(-1/kT^2)(d\ln Z/d\mu)+N(d\ln\mu/d\mu)\\&=-N(d\ln Z/d\mu-d\ln\mu/d\mu)\\&=-N[d\ln(Z/\mu)/d\mu] \quad . \quad . \quad . \quad . \quad . \quad . \quad . \quad . \quad (2)\end{aligned}$$

The molecular heat at constant pressure is (since $N/kT^2=Nk/k^2T^2=R\mu^2$):

$$\begin{aligned}C_p=dH/dT&=(dH/d\mu)(d\mu/dT)\\&=-N[d^2\ln(Z/\mu)/d\mu^2](-1/kT^2)\\&=R\mu^2[d^2\ln(Z/\mu)/d\mu^2] \quad . \quad . \quad . \quad . \quad . \quad . \quad . \quad . \quad (3)\end{aligned}$$

A molecule of an ideal[1] monatomic gas is dynamically specified by its position coordinates x, y, z, and its velocity coordinates $\dot{x}=\mathrm{d}x/\mathrm{d}t$, $\dot{y}=\mathrm{d}y/\mathrm{d}t$, and $\dot{z}=\mathrm{d}z/\mathrm{d}t$. Instead of the velocity components, the corresponding momenta $m\dot{x}$, $m\dot{y}$, $m\dot{z}$ (where m=mass of molecule) may be used. The coordinates are then (i) generalised position coordinates ($q_1=x$, $q_2=y$, $q_3=z$), and (ii) generalised momentum coordinates ($p_1=m\dot{x}$, $p_2=m\dot{y}$, $p_3=m\dot{z}$), satisfying Hamilton's canonical equations of motion, (24), § 12 :

$$\dot{q}_1=\partial E/\partial p_1, \ldots; \quad \dot{p}_1=-\partial E/\partial q_1, \ldots \quad \ldots \quad (4)$$

where E is the total energy (kinetic+potential), expressed as a function of the p's and q's, and supposed to be constant; the p's and q's are called canonical coordinates.

Let the micro-state of a system be defined by $2f$ canonical coordinates $q_1, q_2, q_3, \ldots, q_f, p_1, p_2, p_3, \ldots, p_f$, which may be regarded as rectangular coordinates of a point in generalised space of $2f$ dimensions. The changes of the micro-state in time are then represented by the trajectory of the point in this generalised space. In the classical theory the phase points fill the phase space continuously. Any finite element of phase space will in course of time undergo displacement and deformation, every phase point in it moving along a definite curve according to the equations of dynamics.

In classical theory, the element:

$$\mathrm{d}\tau=\mathrm{d}q_1\mathrm{d}q_2 \ldots \mathrm{d}q_f\mathrm{d}p_1\mathrm{d}p_2 \ldots \mathrm{d}p_f$$

can be infinitesimally small, but the quantum theory shows that it has a minimum size, and since the product $\mathrm{d}q\mathrm{d}p$ has the dimensions [energy]×[time]=[action], the same as the dimensions of Planck's constant $\boldsymbol{h}$, Planck suggested that the finite minimum volume will be $\mathrm{d}\tau=\boldsymbol{h}^f$. The number of micro-states in a given system is proportional to the statistical weight W (§ 4), and the quantum theory shows that this is finite.[2]

Liouville's theorem (§ 13) shows that:

$$\mathrm{d}\tau=\mathrm{d}q_1\mathrm{d}q_2\mathrm{d}q_3 \ldots \mathrm{d}q_f\mathrm{d}p_1\mathrm{d}p_2\mathrm{d}p_3 \ldots \mathrm{d}p_f \quad \ldots \quad (5)$$

is independent of time and of the choice of coordinates, provided these satisfy (4). (The finite extension is sometimes emphasised by using Δ instead of d.) Thus, the same probability may be assigned to a representative point in an element of given volume situated anywhere in the generalised space, i.e. this probability is proportional to $\mathrm{d}\tau$.

According to Heisenberg's[3] *uncertainty principle*, it is impossible to specify *exactly* simultaneously both the position and the momentum of a particle; if a molecule has coordinates lying between q_1 and $q_1+\mathrm{d}q_1$, and momenta lying between p_1 and $p_1+\mathrm{d}p_1$, the product $\mathrm{d}q_1\mathrm{d}p_1$ has a minimum size $\boldsymbol{h}/4\pi$, or with sufficient accuracy, $\boldsymbol{h}$, where $\boldsymbol{h}$ is Planck's constant$=6{\cdot}6\times10^{-27}$ erg sec. Hence in (5):

$$\mathrm{d}\tau=\boldsymbol{h}^f \quad \ldots \quad (6)$$

One mol of an ideal monatomic gas can be regarded as a single system (" molecule ") having a large number f of degrees of freedom, in temperature equilibrium in a heat bath.

[1] For the statistics of a van der Waals gas, see Waldmann, *Physica*, 1937, **4**, 1117.

[2] Sommerfeld, *Phys. Z.*, 1911, **12**, 1057; Planck, *Berlin Ber.*, 1916, 653.

[3] *Z. Phys.*, 1927, **43**, 1; Bohr, *Nature*, 1928, **121**, 580; Lewis and Mayer, *Proc. Nat. Acad.*, 1929, **15**, 127; Darwin, *Science*, 1931, **73**, 653; Kothari, *Phil. Mag.*, 1939, **27**, 65; Margenau and Murphy, "The Mathematics of Physics and Chemistry," New York, 1943, 332; Paniker, *An. Fis. Quim.*, 1945, **41**, 573; Bopp, *Z. Naturforsch.*, 1947, **2** A, 202. For another treatment, depending on the " free volume " of a molecule, see Svenson, *Ann. Phys.*, 1928, **87**, 424.

For a system of N identical parts, each with f degrees of freedom, the phase-space of the individuals, of dimensions $2f$, is sometimes called [1] the *mu-space* or μ-space (" molecular space "), and the configuration of the whole system is represented by N points in μ-space. But it is also possible to represent the state of the whole system by *one* point in a space of $2Nf$ dimensions, called the *gamma-space* or γ-space (" gas space "). The present discussion refers to a γ-space.

Since each monatomic molecule has 3 degrees of freedom, $f=3N$ and:

$$d\tau=(dq_1dp_1)(dq_2dp_2)\ldots(dq_{3N}dp_{3N}) \quad . \quad . \quad . \quad . \quad (7)$$

The energy of a molecule is:

$$\epsilon=\tfrac{1}{2}m(\dot{x}^2+\dot{y}^2+\dot{z}^2)+\epsilon_0=(1/2m)(p_1{}^2+p_2{}^2+p_3{}^2)+\epsilon_0 \quad . \quad . \quad (8)$$

since $p_1=m\dot{x}$, $p_2=m\dot{y}$, $p_3=m\dot{z}$; ϵ_0 is the zero-point energy. The total energy of the gas (if $N\epsilon_0=E_0$) is:

$$E=E_0+(p_1{}^2+p_2{}^2+\ldots+p_{3N}{}^2)/2m \quad . \quad . \quad . \quad . \quad . \quad (9)$$

The state sum in the appropriate form is (5), § 10, and can, for an ideal gas, be replaced by an integral extending over the whole phase space of $6N$ dimensions, since the differences of translational energies are very small. But as this includes all the micro-states derived by permutations of the N identical molecules, viz. $N!$, this integral must be divided by $N!$ in order to represent the thermodynamic state, in which each micro-state is counted only once.[2] The interchange of any two identical molecules, in fact, leads to no change of state. Each term in the state sum is multiplied by $d\tau/h^f=1$, from (6), and the integral taken over all points for the position coordinates, and all momenta from $-\infty$ to $+\infty$:

$$Z=\frac{1}{h^fN!}\int e^{-E/kT}dq_1dp_1\ldots dq_{3N}dp_{3N} \quad . \quad . \quad . \quad . \quad . \quad (10)$$

E being substituted from (9), and $N!$ replaced by $(N/e)^N$ by Stirling's theorem (8), § 8. Integration over the $3N$ position coordinates gives:

$$Z=e^{-E_0/kT}\left[\frac{eV}{h^3N}\iiint_{-\infty}^{+\infty}dp_1dp_2dp_3e^{-(p_1{}^2+p_2{}^2+p_3{}^2)/2mkT}\right]^N$$

where V is the volume of the gas. Since $\int_{-\infty}^{+\infty}e^{-x^2}dx=\sqrt{\pi}$ (from (16), § 10.III):

$$\therefore\ Z=e^{-E_0/kT}[(eV/h^3N)(2\pi mkT)^{3/2}]^N \quad . \quad . \quad . \quad . \quad (11)$$

Thus, from (3), § 10, the free energy is:

$$F=-kT\ln Z=-kNT\ln[(eV/h^3N)(2\pi mkT)^{3/2}]+E_0 \quad . \quad . \quad (12)$$

1 P. and T. Ehrenfest, " Enzykl. d. math. Wiss.," **4**, II, ii, Heft 6.

2 Planck, *Berlin Ber.*, 1916, 653; *Ann. Phys.*, 1921, **66**, 365; see the criticisms by Lichtenecker, *Verhl. d. D. Phys. Ges.*, 1919, **21**, 236; *Phys. Z.*, 1919, **20**, 12; 1922, **23**, 43; *Leipzig Ber.*, 1925, **77**, 189; Nordheim, *Z. Phys.*, 1924, **27**, 65; Schrödinger, *Phys. Z.*, 1924, **25**, 41; *Berlin Ber.*, 1925, 434; and the reply by Planck, *Berlin Ber.*, 1925, 49, 442. A deduction is given by Bose-Einstein or Fermi-Dirac statistics (§ 33), but the assumptions and the result are identical. Schrödinger, " Statistical Thermodynamics," Cambridge, 1946, 56, said that " the classical theory gives pure nonsense," which is an exaggeration. The division by $N!$ really applies only to such a dilute gas that it is improbable that any appreciable number of micro-states will have more than a single molecule in any given small element of generalised space. Each n in the denominator of (3), § 8, is then either 1 or 0, its factorial ($n_r!$) in either case being 1, and the expression reduces to $N!$.

From (4), § 43.II, and (12):

$$-(dF/dV)_T = p = kNT/V \quad . \quad . \quad . \quad . \quad . \quad . \quad . \quad (13)$$

But

$$p = RT/V \quad . \quad . \quad . \quad . \quad . \quad . \quad . \quad . \quad (14)$$

hence, as stated in § 5:

$$k = R/N \quad . \quad . \quad . \quad . \quad . \quad . \quad . \quad . \quad . \quad (15)$$

From (12) with $V = RT/p = kNT/p$, the entropy follows from (5), § 43.II:

$$S = -(dF/dT)_V = R\{\tfrac{5}{2} \ln T - \ln p + \tfrac{5}{2} + \ln [(2\pi mk)^{3/2} k/h^3]\} \quad . \quad (16)$$

$$= R \ln (T^{5/2} A/p) \quad . \quad . \quad . \quad . \quad . \quad . \quad . \quad . \quad . \quad (17)$$

where

$$A = (2\pi mk)^{3/2} k e^{5/2}/h^3 \quad . \quad . \quad . \quad . \quad . \quad . \quad (18)$$

The values of the constants in (18) are $k = 1{\cdot}38 \times 10^{-16}$ erg/1° C., $h = 6{\cdot}61 \times 10^{-27}$ erg sec. Also $R = Nk$, where $N = 6{\cdot}03 \times 10^{23}$, and $m = M/N$, where M = molar weight. Hence:

$$\ln [(2\pi m)^{3/2} k^{5/2}/h^3] = \ln [(2\pi/N)^{3/2}(k^{5/2}/h^3)] + \tfrac{3}{2} \ln M. \quad . \quad . \quad (19)$$

The entropy of 1 mol of a monatomic gas ($C_v = \tfrac{3}{2}R$) is given by (4a), § 55.II:

$$S = S_0 + \tfrac{3}{2} R \ln T + R \ln V,$$

and since $pV = RT$ this may be written as:

$$S = S_0 + \tfrac{5}{2} R \ln T - R \ln p + R \ln R.$$

By comparison with (16) it follows that the entropy constant is:

$$S_0 = \tfrac{5}{2} R - R \ln R + R \ln [(2\pi mk)^{3/2} k/h^3]$$

$$= \tfrac{5}{2} R - R \ln R + R \ln [(2\pi/N)^{3/2}(k^{5/2}/h^3)] + \tfrac{3}{2} R \ln M \quad . \quad . \quad (20)$$

from (19), and this also represents the constant for the translational entropy per mol of *any* gas. The translational entropy per mol is thus:

$$S_{tr} = R\{\ln [(2\pi mkT)^{3/2} V/h^3 N] + \tfrac{5}{2}\} \quad . \quad . \quad . \quad . \quad . \quad (21)$$

If p is in atm. (1 atm. = $1{\cdot}0132 \times 10^6$ dynes/cm.²) and $m = M/N$ in (16):

$$S_{tr} = \tfrac{3}{2} R \ln M + \tfrac{5}{2} R \ln T - R \ln p + R \ln [(2\pi k/h^2 N)^{3/2} k/1{\cdot}0132 \times 10^6] + \tfrac{5}{2} R$$

$$= \tfrac{3}{2} R \ln M + \tfrac{5}{2} R \ln T - R \ln p - 7{\cdot}262 + 4{\cdot}965 \quad . \quad . \quad . \quad . \quad . \quad . \quad . \quad (22)$$

where R is put equal to 1·986 g.cal. per 1° C. per mol.

In the standard state (ideal gas at 1 atm.) $p = 1$, the entropy is:

$$S_{tr}{}^0 = \tfrac{3}{2} R \ln M + \tfrac{5}{2} R \ln T - 2{\cdot}297 \quad . \quad . \quad . \quad . \quad . \quad (23)$$

The available energy per mol of ideal monatomic gas is, from (16), and $E = E_0 + C_v T = E_0 + \tfrac{3}{2} RT$:

$$G = E - TS + RT$$

$$= E_0 - \tfrac{5}{2} RT \ln T + RT \ln p - RT \ln [(2\pi m)^{3/2}(k^{5/2}/h^3)] \quad . \quad . \quad . \quad (24)$$

From (21) and $E = E_0 + \tfrac{3}{2} RT$ it follows that:

$$G = -RT \ln \frac{(2\pi mkT)^{3/2} V}{Nh^3} + E_0 \quad . \quad . \quad . \quad . \quad . \quad . \quad (25)$$

The entropy constant equation for a monatomic gas was deduced in various ways,[1] the forms sometimes differing slightly, the present one being found by

[1] Sackur, *Ann. Phys.*, 1911, **36**, 958; 1913, **40**, 67, 87; *Nernst Festschr.*, 1912, 405; *Ber.*, 1914, **47**, 1318; Tetrode, *Ann. Phys.*, 1912, **38**, 434; 1912, **39**, 255; *Proc. K. Akad. Wetens. Amsterdam*, 1915, **17**, 1167; Keesom, *Proc. K. Akad. Wetens. Amsterdam*, 1913, **16**, 227; 1914, **17**, 20; *Phys. Z.*, 1913, **14**. 665; 1914, **15**, 217, 695; *Verslag. K. Akad. Wetens. Amsterdam*, 1914, **22**, 1215; Planck, *Gött. Nachr.*, 1913, 137; del Lungo, *Nuov. Cim.*, 1918, **16**, 68; Schames, *Phys. Z.*, 1920, **21**,

Tetrode. A different deduction, in which quantisation is confined to a solid phase in equilibrium with the gas, was given by Stern.[1]

The so-called " ultimate rational units " system of G. N. Lewis[2] and Tolman's[3] " principle of similitude " can only be mentioned. Lewis,[4] from his theory, deduced for the entropy constant ln $[k^{3/2}c^3/N^{5/2}(4\pi e)^6]$, where e=electronic charge, c=velocity of light, but direct comparisons with experiment[5] favour Tetrode's form.

§ 15. The Quantum Theory

The quantum theory was introduced into science on 14 December 1900 by Max Planck,[6] to explain a serious difficulty, or " cloud ",[7] which had arisen in the theory of radiation. By an application of the classical theory of equipartition of energy (§ 20) to black-body radiation, Lord Rayleigh,[8] whose calculation was later overhauled and confirmed by Jeans,[9] deduced an equation:

$$\rho_\nu = 8\pi k\nu^2 T/c^3 \quad . \quad . \quad . \quad . \quad . \quad . \quad . \quad . \quad (1)$$

for the energy density ρ_ν in ergs/cm.^{3} of radiation of frequency ν in equilibrium with a black body of temperature T, where k is Boltzmann's constant $=R/N$, and c is the velocity of light. Although (1) gave good results for long waves (small ν), it failed for shorter waves, and for no apparent reason.

38, 39; Tolman, *J.A.C.S.*, 1920, **42**, 1185; 1921, **43**, 1592; Ehrenfest and Trkal, *Proc. K. Akad. Wetens. Amsterdam*, 1920, **23**, 162; *Ann. Phys.*, 1921, **65**, 609; Planck, *Ann. Phys.*, 1921, **66**, 365; Byk, *ibid.*, 1922, **69**, 161; Tolman and Badger, *J.A.C.S.*, 1923, **45**, 2277; Urey, *ibid.*, 1923, **45**, 1445; Enskog, *Ann. Phys.*, 1923, **72**, 321; Schidlof, *Arch. Sci. Phys. Nat.*, 1924, **6**, 281, Suppl. 61; Syrkin, *Z. Phys.*, 1924, **24**, 355; Becker, *ibid.*, 1924, **28**, 256; Rasetti, *Nuov. Cim.*, 1926, **3**, 67; Saha and Sur, *Phil. Mag.*, 1926, **1**, 279; Wertheimer, *Phys. Z.*, 1926, **27**, 771; Gibson and Heitler, *Z. Phys.*, 1928, **49**, 465; Sackur and Simson, " Thermodynamik und Thermochemie," 1928, 308. Although Fowler and Guggenheim, " Statistical Thermodynamics," Cambridge, 1939, 156, did not regard any earlier discussion than that of Ehrenfest and Trkal (a pupil of Fowler's) as " logically convincing," the formula was known and had been used nearly ten years before this.

[1] *Phys. Z.*, 1913, **14**, 629; *Ann. Phys.*, 1914, **44**, 497; *Z. Elektrochem.*, 1919, **25**, 66; Born, " Atomtheorie des festen Zustandes," 1923, 705; Nernst, " The New Heat Theorem," 1926, 170.

[2] Lewis and Adams, *Phys. Rev.*, 1914, **3**, 92; 1914, **4**, 331; Lewis, Gibson, and Latimer, *J.A.C.S.*, 1922, **44**, 1008; Lewis, *Phil. Mag.*, 1923, **45**, 266; 1925, **49**, 739; Lewis and Randall, " Thermodynamics," 1923, 456; Van Vleck, *Phys. Rev.*, 1926, **28**, 980; criticised by Lodge, *Phil. Mag.*, 1923, **45**, 275; 1925, **49**, 751; Campbell, *ibid.*, 1924, **47**, 159. Witmer, *Proc. Nat. Acad.*, 1946, **32**, 283, found $hc/e^2 = 861 = \frac{1}{2}(42\times 41)$.

[3] *Phys. Rev.*, 1914, **4**, 244; *J.A.C.S.*, 1921, **43**, 866; Bridgman, " Dimensional Analysis," New Haven, 1922; *J. Phys. Chem.*, 1924, **28**, 410.

[4] Lewis and Adams, *Phys. Rev.*, 1914, **3**, 92; Lewis, *ibid.*, 1921, **18**, 121; Lewis, Gibson, and Latimer, *J.A.C.S.*, 1922, **44**, 1008.

[5] Giauque and Wiebe, *J.A.C.S.*, 1928, **50**, 2193.

[6] *Verhl. d. D. Phys. Ges.*, 1900, **2**, 202 (formula), 237 (deduction); *Ann. Phys.*, 1901, **4**, 553, 564; 1901, **9**, 629; " Theorie der Wärmestrahlung," 1906, 148; on the origin of the theory, see Planck's Nobel Prize lecture, " Die Entstehung und bisherige Entwicklung der Quantentheorie," Leipzig, 1920, and *Naturwiss.*, 1943, **31**, 153; Rosenfeld, *Osiris.*, 1936, **2**, 149; Jordan, *Forschungen u. Fortschritte*, 1943, **19**, 321. On Max Planck, b. Kiel, 23 April, 1858, d. Göttingen, 4 October, 1947, see Flint, *Nature*, 1948, **161**, 13; Partington, *ibid.*, 1948, **161**, 47.

[7] Lord Kelvin, Royal Institution lecture, April, 1900; *Phil. Mag.*, 1901, **2**, 1.

[8] *Phil. Mag.*, 1900, **49**, 539; *Nature*, 1905, **72**, 54, 243; McLaren, *Phil. Mag.*, 1912, **23**, 513, later proved that the energy distribution in black-body radiation cannot be deduced on a classical basis.

[9] *Phil. Mag.*, 1905, **10**, 91; *Phys. Z.*, 1908, **9**, 853; Planck, *Ann. Phys.*, 1910, **31**, 758; " Theorie der Wärmestrahlung," Leipzig, 1921, 197; Swan, *Phys. Rev.*, 1916, **7**, 154; see, however, Carwile, *Phil. Mag.*, 1938, **25**, 926.

Planck considered the emission and absorption of radiation by a linear Hertzian oscillator consisting of two equal and opposite electric charges oscillating in a fixed straight line. He considered a number of such oscillators in a closed space, assuming them free from damping and at large distances apart, and subject to the action of monochromatic radiation. Observable radiation cannot be regarded as *strictly* monochromatic;[1] its frequency covers a small but finite range from ν to $\nu+d\nu$, and it would appear in a spectroscope as a very narrow band and not as a mathematical line (cf. § 50.I).

Kirchhoff's law that in a closed space or cavity ("Hohlraum"), containing bodies of any character whatever, the distribution of the radiant energy over the frequencies ultimately acquires a steady or equilibrium state, was interpreted by Planck as indicating that in such an enclosure a magnitude, which he called the *electromagnetic entropy*, exists, which increases to a maximum value in thermodynamic equilibrium. He assumed that, in natural radiation, the deviations of single rapidly varying magnitudes from their average values is random, and the theory of probabilities was carried over from the kinetic theory of gases to radiation.

Planck, from classical theory, found for the mean energy $\bar{E}$ of a Herzian oscillator of frequency ν:

$$\nu^2\bar{E}=k\rho_\nu \quad . \quad . \quad . \quad . \quad . \quad . \quad . \quad . \quad . \quad . \quad (1)$$

where k is a universal constant, and from Wien's displacement law,[2] that $\lambda_m T_m$=const., where λ_m is the wave-length of the maximum-intensity radiation in the black-body spectrum at the absolute temperature T_m, which is also deduced on classical grounds, it was shown that:

$$\nu/T=\mathrm{f}(\rho_\nu/\nu^3) \quad . \quad . \quad . \quad . \quad . \quad . \quad . \quad . \quad . \quad (2)$$

where f denotes a function of the argument ρ_ν/ν^3. Equation (2), § 35.II: $1/T=dS/dE$, then gave:

$$S=\mathrm{F}(\bar{E}/\nu) \quad . \quad . \quad . \quad . \quad . \quad . \quad . \quad . \quad . \quad . \quad (3)$$

If there are N identical oscillators in the cavity, so far apart that they exert no mutual actions, the state at a given moment is assumed to be the same as that of a single oscillator in N consecutive states. If the total energy $N\bar{E}$ is divided into P equal "energy elements," ϵ, distributed at random among the oscillators, then:

$$N\bar{E}=P\epsilon \quad . \quad . \quad . \quad . \quad . \quad . \quad . \quad . \quad . \quad . \quad . \quad (4)$$

The number of possible ways in which the P identical energy elements can be distributed among the N oscillators is given by the theory of "combination with repetition," when the things permuted are not all different, and the general formula[3] is:

$$W=(N+P-1)!/(N-1)!P! \quad . \quad . \quad . \quad . \quad . \quad . \quad (5)$$

The number of "complexions" W was defined by Planck as the probability of a state, this increasing in proportion to the number of ways in which the state can be realised in the given conditions. The general equation connecting probability and entropy (1), § 5:

$$S=k \ln W \quad . \quad . \quad . \quad . \quad . \quad . \quad . \quad . \quad . \quad . \quad (6)$$

if 1 is neglected in comparison with N and $(N+P)$ in (5), and the factorial transformed by Stirling's theorem (8), § 8, $\ln N!=N(\ln N-1)$, gives:

$$S=k[(N+P)\ln(N+P)-N\ln N-P\ln P].$$

[1] Schuster, "Theory of Optics," 1920, 35.

[2] See § 10.VI B.

[3] C. Smith, "A Treatise on Algebra," 3rd edit., 1892, 352; Ehrenfest and Onnes, *Ann. Phys.*, 1915, **46**, 1021; for a deduction without using entropy, see Weinstein, *ibid.*, 1916, **49**, 363.

Substitution of $P=N\bar{E}/\epsilon$ from (4), and simplification, gives:

$$S=kN[(1+\bar{E}/\epsilon)\ln(1+\bar{E}/\epsilon)-(\bar{E}/\epsilon)\ln(\bar{E}/\epsilon)] \quad . \quad . \quad . \quad . \quad (7)$$

Since S is a function of a single argument $\bar{E}/\epsilon$, it follows from (3) that this must be proportional to $\bar{E}/\nu$, and hence:

$$\epsilon=\boldsymbol{h}\nu \quad . \quad . \quad . \quad . \quad . \quad . \quad . \quad . \quad . \quad . \quad . \quad (8)$$

where $\boldsymbol{h}$ is a universal constant, since F in (3) is a universal function, i.e. the same for every system involving radiation and oscillators.

Assumption (4) is the kernel of the deduction: as Planck [1] said: " it is necessary to regard $\bar{E}$, not as a continuous magnitude divisible without restriction, but rather as a discrete quantity composed of a finite number of equal parts. If we call such a part an *energy element* [2] ϵ, it is thus necessary to put $\bar{E}=P\epsilon$, where P is a whole number, usually large, whilst the value of ϵ we leave, for the present, undetermined."

The entropy of a single oscillator, S', is found by dividing (7) by N, and if $\bar{E}/\boldsymbol{h}\nu=x$:

$$S'=\boldsymbol{k}[\ln(1+x)+x\ln(1+x)-x\ln x] \quad . \quad . \quad . \quad . \quad (9)$$

Again, $\mathrm{d}S/\mathrm{d}E=1/T$. But $\mathrm{d}S/\mathrm{d}E=(\mathrm{d}S/\mathrm{d}x)(\mathrm{d}x/\mathrm{d}E)$. If $\bar{E}$ now denotes the mean energy of a single oscillator, then $\bar{E}=(1/\boldsymbol{h}\nu)(\mathrm{d}S'/\mathrm{d}x)$. Differentiate (9) with respect to x, multiply by $1/\boldsymbol{h}\nu$, and equate the result to $1/T$:

$$(\boldsymbol{k}/\boldsymbol{h}\nu)\ln[(1+x)/x]=(\boldsymbol{k}/\boldsymbol{h}\nu)\ln[(\boldsymbol{h}\nu/\bar{E})+1]=1/T$$

$$\therefore\ \ln(\boldsymbol{h}\nu/\bar{E}+1)=\boldsymbol{h}\nu/\boldsymbol{k}T, \quad \text{or } e^{\boldsymbol{h}\nu/\boldsymbol{k}T}=\boldsymbol{h}\nu/\bar{E}+1$$

$$\therefore\ \bar{E}=\boldsymbol{h}\nu/(e^{\boldsymbol{h}\nu/\boldsymbol{k}T}-1)=\boldsymbol{h}\nu(e^{\boldsymbol{h}\nu/\boldsymbol{k}T}-1)^{-1} \quad . \quad . \quad . \quad . \quad (10)$$

The quantum theory presented a strange contrast to the nineteenth-century idea of the essential continuity of physical change. It asserted [3] that there are physical systems which exist only in definite discrete states, and never occupy intermediate states, without solving the problem as to how such systems pass from one of these states to another. Planck [4] said: " The continuity of all

[1] *Ann. Phys.*, 1901, **4**, 553; Planck used U_N for $\bar{E}$, and calculated $\boldsymbol{h}=6{\cdot}55\times10^{-27}$ erg sec. In *Ann. Phys.*, 1901, **4**, 564, he calculated the mass of the hydrogen atom as $1{\cdot}64\times10^{-24}$ g., and in *ibid.*, 1902, **9**, 629, as $1{\cdot}62\times10^{-24}$ g., and the electronic charge as $\boldsymbol{e}=4{\cdot}69\times10^{-10}$ e.s.u., from radiation data. The present value is $\boldsymbol{h}=6{\cdot}62\times10^{-27}$ erg sec.; see Millikan, *Ann. Phys.*, 1938, **32**, 34, 520; Dunnington, *Rev. Mod. Phys.*, 1939, **11**, 55; Birge, *Phys. Rev.*, 1940, **58**, 658; *Rep. Progr. Phys.*, 1942, **8**, 90 (who takes $6{\cdot}624\times10^{-27}$).

[2] The name *quantum*, apparently first used (as " Lichtquant ") by Einstein, *Ann. Phys.*, 1906, **20**, 199, is now very generally used for " energy quantum," although there are other quanta (e.g. of electricity, i.e. the electron) besides this. The name *ergon*, proposed by the writer, " Text Book of Thermodynamics," 1913, 521, did not find favour. This name " ergon " was used by the translator of a paper by Clausius, *Phil. Mag.*, 1868, **35**, 405, as the equivalent of " Werk," i.e. " action," and the dimensions of $\boldsymbol{h}$ are (energy × time), or " action," as understood in dynamics. The ergon has not a constant value, but depends on the frequency ν, as does the " photon."

[3] Poincaré, *J. de Phys.*, 1912, **2**, 5; " Dernières Pensées," Paris, 1913, 163; Gibson, *Engineering*, 1912, **94**, 515; Millikan, *Science*, 1913, **119** (historical); Jeans, *B.A. Rep.*, 1913, 376; " Report on Radiation and the Quantum Theory " (Physical Society), 1914, 66, 2nd edit., 1924, 51; *idem*, " Dynamical Theory of Gases," 3rd edit., 1921, 373, 404; Lorentz, *Naturwiss.*, 1925, **13**, 1077; Debye, *Z. techn. Phys.*, 1938, **19**, 121 (with portrait of Planck, aged 80).

[4] *Phil. Mag.*, 1914, **28**, 60. For connected earlier accounts of the quantum theory, see e.g. Jeans, *opp. cit.*; " La Théorie du Rayonnement et les Quanta," Solvay Congress (Brussels, 1911), 1912; various authors, in *Abhl. d. D. Bunsen Ges.*, 1914, **7** (edited and transl. from Solvay Congress, 1911, by Eucken); Ladenburg, " Plancks elementares Wirkungsquantum und die Methoden zu seiner Messung," Leipzig, 1921; Valentiner, " Anwendungen der Quantenhypothese in der kinetischen Theorie der festen Körper und des Gases," 2nd edit., Brunswick, 1921; Gerlach, " Die experimentellen Grundlagen der Quantentheorie," Brunswick, 1921; Tolman, *J. Opt. Soc. Amer.*. 1922, **6**, 211; Bligh, " The Evolution and Development of the

dynamical effects . . . was formerly taken for granted as the basis of all physical theories, and, in close correspondence with Aristotle, was condensed in the well-known dogma: *Natura non facit saltus* [" Nature makes no leaps "]. But even in this venerable stronghold of Physical Science present-day investigation has made a considerable breach. This time it is the principles of thermodynamics with which that theorem has been brought into collision by new facts, and unless all signs are misleading, the days of its validity are numbered. Nature does indeed seem to make jumps—and very extraordinary ones."

At a time when it was thought that some " explanation " of the discontinuous energy exchange might be given in classical terms, several " interpretations " of Planck's hypothesis were forthcoming.[1] All these must now be regarded as fundamentally unsound. One difficulty seemed especially serious. The quantum $h\nu$ corresponding with an oscillator of very high frequency is relatively large, whilst in all radiation at realisable temperatures the intensity corresponding with high frequencies is relatively very small; hence it would seem that a high-frequency quantum would only very rarely be available, and the oscillator would not be able to absorb energy from the radiation. The same difficulty occurs for all frequencies at very low temperatures.

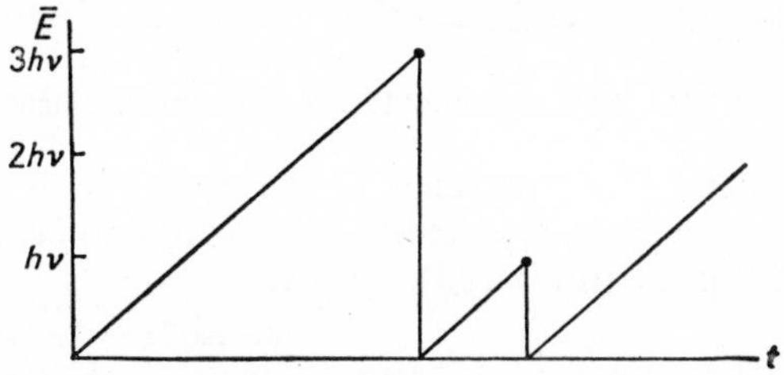

FIG. 6.IV. Continuous Absorption and Discontinuous Emission by an Oscillator

Planck, therefore, modified the theory by assuming a continuous absorption but a discontinuous emission of energy by oscillators, at first [2] on the assumption that the oscillator emits a single quantum, but later [3] on the assumption that absorption occurs continuously until a whole number of quanta are taken up, and then emission occurs by loss of the whole of the absorbed energy (Fig. 6.IV). This gives the same formula for the energy density of black-body radiation as the early quantum theory, but the energy of the oscillator is now:

$$\bar{E}=h\nu(e^{h\nu/kT}-1)^{-1}+\tfrac{1}{2}h\nu \quad . \; . \; . \; . \; . \; . \; . \; (11)$$

instead of (10). The first term on the right vanishes for $T=0$ (see below), and whereas (10) gives zero energy for the oscillator at absolute zero, (11) leaves it with a *zero-point energy* [4] of half a quantum. Although Planck's " second quantum theory " (continuous absorption but discontinuous emission) is now given up, the idea of zero-point energy plays an important part in modern quantum theory.

When T is very small, the exponential function in (10) or (11) is very large compared with unity, and $(e^{h\nu/kT}-1)^{-1}\simeq e^{-h\nu/kT}$, and for $T\to 0$ this approaches $e^{-\infty}=1/e^{\infty}=0$.

Quantum Theory," 1926; Persico, *Scientia*, 1928, **44**, 373; Reiche, " The Quantum Theory," 3rd edit., 1930.

[1] Haas, *Jahrb. Radioakt. Elektronik*, 1910, **7**, 261; J. J. Thomson, *Phil. Mag.*, 1910, **20**, 238; Wertheimer, *Phys. Z.*, 1911, **12**, 408; Schidlof, *Ann. Phys.*, 1911, **35**, 90; Gibson, *Verhl. d. D. Phys. Ges.*, 1912, **14**, 104; Goldhammer, *Phys. Z.*, 1912, **13**, 535; Planck, *Ber.*, 1912, **45**, 5; Houstoun, *Phil. Mag.*, 1947, **38**, 479.

[2] *Ann. Phys.*, 1910, **31**, 758; *Verhl. d. D. Phys. Ges.*, 1911, **13**, 138.

[3] *Berlin Ber.*, 1911, 723; *Ann. Phys.*, 1912, **37**, 642. For other deductions of (10) see Einstein, *Ann. Phys.*, 1905, **17**, 132; 1906, **20**, 199; 1907, **22**, 180, 800; Hasenöhrl, *Phys. Z.*, 1911, **12**, 931; Frank, *ibid.*, 1912, **13**, 506; Bichowsky, *Phys. Rev.*, 1918, **11**, 58.

[4] Cf. Einstein and Stern, *Ann. Phys.*, 1913, **40**, 551.

The expression (11) is closely related [1] in form to the function:

$$x/(e^x-1)+\tfrac{1}{2}x=\tfrac{1}{2}x(e^x+1)/(e^x-1)=\tfrac{1}{2}x\coth\tfrac{1}{2}x,$$

the expansion of which gives the so-called *Bernoulli numbers* as coefficients of even powers of x.

§ 16. Energy of Oscillator

Many formulae of the quantum theory are easily, but not strictly, found by dividing up the generalised (p, q) space into " cells " of equal volume, associating each cell with a quantum state, and using the Heisenberg uncertainty principle, (6), § 14. If there is only one q and a related p, the space will be two-dimensional, and the relation between p and q will be represented by a plane curve.

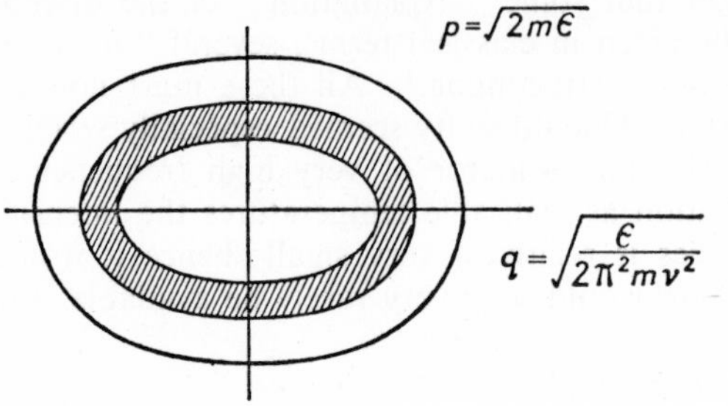

FIG. 7.IV. Energy Cells of Linear Harmonic Oscillator

For a single harmonic oscillator [2] of frequency ν the energy ϵ is the sum of the kinetic energy $\tfrac{1}{2}m\dot{q}^2=p^2/2m$ ($\dot{q}=dq/dt=$velocity; $p=$momentum$=\dot{q}m$) and the potential energy $2\pi^2m\nu^2q^2$ ((6), § 52.I). Thus:

$$\epsilon=p^2/2m+2\pi^2m\nu^2q^2 \quad . \quad . \quad . \quad . \quad . \quad . \quad . \quad (1)$$

$$\therefore\ p^2/[\sqrt{(2m\epsilon)}]^2+q^2/[\sqrt{(\epsilon/2\pi^2m\nu^2)}]^2=1 \quad . \quad . \quad . \quad . \quad (2)$$

which is the equation of an ellipse [3] of semi-axes $\sqrt{(2m\epsilon)}$ and $\sqrt{(\epsilon/2\pi^2m\nu^2)}$. The plane " cells " are then bounded by ellipses of constant energy (Fig. 7.IV), and, as the area between the curves is $\boldsymbol{h}$ (since $f=1$ in (6), § 14), the area of the nth ellipse is $n\boldsymbol{h}$. This area is also given by the formula of analytical geometry [3] as πab, where a and b are the semi-axes of the ellipse, hence:

$$\pi\sqrt{(2m\epsilon)}\,.\,\sqrt{(\epsilon/2\pi^2m\nu^2)}=\epsilon/\nu=n\boldsymbol{h},\quad \therefore\ \epsilon=n\boldsymbol{h}\nu \quad . \quad . \quad . \quad (3)$$

The oscillator energy is thus a whole multiple of the quantum $\boldsymbol{h}\nu$.

In the old quantum theory, the only permitted energy levels lie on the ellipses themselves, and in transitions from one energy state to a neighbouring one, the phase point must jump abruptly from one ellipse to the next. Heisenberg's uncertainty principle (§ 14), however, suggests that an energy level will be blurred into a band such as the shaded area, which represents the " cell " of phase space, and the naïve assumption that the *average* energy of the oscillator is that of the middle point of the " cell " between the nth and $(n+1)$th levels leads to:

$$\epsilon=\tfrac{1}{2}[(n+1)+n]\boldsymbol{h}\nu=(n+\tfrac{1}{2})\boldsymbol{h}\nu \quad . \quad . \quad . \quad . \quad . \quad . \quad (4)$$

This result is shown later (§ 7, V) to follow strictly from wave mechanics.

The state sum for a set of simple harmonic oscillators is (§ 9):

$$Z_v=\Sigma g_r e^{-\epsilon_r/kT} \quad . \quad . \quad . \quad . \quad . \quad . \quad . \quad . \quad . \quad (5)$$

$$\therefore\ Z_v=e^{-\epsilon_0/kt}+e^{-(\epsilon_0+h\nu)/kT}+e^{-(\epsilon_0+2h\nu)/kT}+\ldots+e^{-(\epsilon_0+nh\nu)/kT}+\ldots \quad (6)$$

[1] O. Lodge, *Nature*, 1925, **115**, 798; A. Lodge, *ibid.*, 1925, **115**, 838; Greenhill, " Differentia and Integral Calculus," 1896, 235.

[2] Planck, " Theorie der Wärmestrahlung," 4th edit., 1921, 138; Sommerfeld, " Atomic Structure and Spectrum Lines," 1923, 195.

[3] Gibson, " Elementary Treatise on the Calculus," 1933, 50, 310.

where ϵ_0 is the zero point energy, and all the statistical weights g_r are unity. This can be written as:

$$Z_v = e^{-\epsilon_0/kT}(1 + e^{-h\nu/kT} + e^{-2h\nu/kT} + \ldots + e^{-nh\nu/kT} + \ldots) \quad . \quad . \quad (7)$$

If $h\nu/kT = x$, the expression in brackets is an infinite geometrical series with the common ratio e^{-x}, and its sum is $1/(1-e^{-x}) = (1-e^{-x})^{-1} = (1-e^{-h\nu/kT})^{-1}$,

$$\therefore\ Z_v = e^{-\epsilon_0/kT}(1-e^{-h\nu/kT})^{-1} \quad . \quad . \quad . \quad . \quad . \quad . \quad . \quad (8)$$

It follows from (18), § 8, that the average energy of an oscillator is,[1] since $\mu = 1/kT$:

$$\bar{\epsilon} = -\mathrm{d}\ln Z_v/\mathrm{d}\mu = h\nu(e^{h\nu/kT}-1)^{-1} + \epsilon_0 \quad . \quad . \quad . \quad . \quad . \quad . \quad (9)$$

For,

$$\ln Z_v = \ln e^{-\epsilon_0/kT} - \ln(1-e^{-h\nu/kT}) \quad . \quad . \quad . \quad . \quad . \quad (10)$$

$$= -\epsilon_0\mu - \ln(1-e^{-h\nu\mu}),$$

$$\therefore\ -\ln Z_v = \epsilon_0\mu + \ln(1-e^{-h\nu\mu}),$$

$$\therefore\ -\mathrm{d}\ln Z_v/\mathrm{d}\mu = \epsilon_0 + \frac{1}{1-e^{-h\nu\mu}} \cdot \frac{\mathrm{d}}{\mathrm{d}\mu}(-e^{-h\nu\mu})$$

$$= \epsilon_0 + \frac{1}{1-e^{-h\nu\mu}} \cdot (-e^{-h\nu\mu})(-h\nu)$$

$$= \epsilon_0 + \frac{h\nu\,.\,e^{-h\nu\mu}}{1-e^{-h\nu\mu}} = \epsilon_0 + \frac{h\nu}{e^{h\nu\mu}-1}$$

$$= \epsilon_0 + h\nu(e^{h\nu/kT}-1)^{-1} \quad . \quad . \quad . \quad . \quad . \quad . \quad . \quad (11)$$

The vibrational entropy per mol is given by (28), § 8:

$$S_v = kN[\ln Z_v + T(\mathrm{d}\ln Z_v/\mathrm{d}T)].$$

From (10):

$$\ln Z_v = -\epsilon_0/kT - \ln(1-e^{-h\nu/kT}) \quad . \quad . \quad . \quad . \quad . \quad . \quad . \quad (12)$$

$$\therefore\ kT^2(\mathrm{d}\ln Z_v/\mathrm{d}T) = \epsilon_0 + h\nu(e^{h\nu/kT}-1)^{-1}$$

$$\therefore\ T(\mathrm{d}\ln Z_v/\mathrm{d}T) = (1/kT)[\epsilon_0 + h\nu(e^{h\nu/kT}-1)^{-1}] \quad . \quad . \quad . \quad . \quad (13)$$

The sum of (12) and (13) multiplied by $kN = R$ gives:

$$S_v = R[(h\nu/kT)(e^{h\nu/kT}-1)^{-1} - \ln(1-e^{-h\nu/kT})] \quad . \quad . \quad . \quad (14)$$

which is seen to be independent of ϵ_0, the zero-point energy.

§ 17. The Morse Equation

A system of n free mass points has $3n$ degrees of freedom (§ 14). If the mass points, which may be considered as atoms, are combined into a molecule, this will have 3 degrees of freedom of translational motion of its own centre of mass, and 3 degrees of freedom of rotation about this. Hence there are $3n-6$ degrees of freedom of *vibration* possible for the atoms. For a linear molecule (rotation about the axis being excluded; see § 23) there will be $3n-5$ degrees of freedom of vibration; if the molecule is diatomic ($n=2$) there is only one degree of vibrational freedom, that in the line joining the atomic nuclei.

The forces binding the atoms are essentially electrical, and may be simplified into an attractive force varying as $1/r^7$, and a repulsive force which increases more rapidly than the attractive at small distances and is of the order of $1/r^n$ where n is 9 to 14. Generally, the resultant force between the nuclei is:

$$F = -a/r^m + b/r^n \quad . \quad . \quad . \quad . \quad . \quad . \quad . \quad . \quad . \quad (1)$$

[1] For another deduction, see Tolman. "Statistical Mechanics," Oxford, 1938, 379. The above deduction is strict.

where m is the exponent of the attractive force and n that of the repulsive force. For a certain value of $r=r_e$, $F=0$, and this corresponds with the equilibrium position.

It is usual to plot the potential energies rather than the forces against the nuclear separation r, the potential energy of the molecule being:

$$V=\int_{\infty}^{r} F\mathrm{d}r=\int_{\infty}^{r}(-ar^{-m}+br^{-n})\mathrm{d}r=mar^{-(m-1)}-nbr^{-(n-1)} \quad . \quad . \quad (2)$$

In constructing a so-called *potential energy curve*, the curves $V_m=ma/r^{m-1}$ and $V_n=-nb/r^{n-1}$ are plotted separately for given values of m and n, and the sum of the ordinates at each value of r gives the resultant potential energy curve. This has a minimum at $r=r_e$, corresponding with the equilibrium position. This corresponds with $F=0$ on the force diagram.

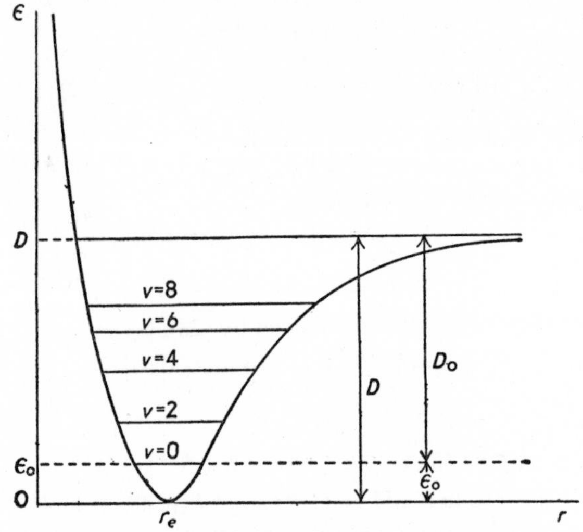

FIG. 8.IV. Morse Curve for Diatomic Molecule

The potential energy of a diatomic molecule is a function of the distance r between the nuclei and has a minimum for the distance r_e. For other values of r, the energy may be expressed as a function of r in a Taylor's series (§ 32.I):

$$\epsilon=a_0+a_1\mathrm{f}+(a_2/2!)\mathrm{f}^2+(a_3/3!)\mathrm{f}^3+ \ldots,$$

where f is a function of r which is zero for $r=r_e$, when $\epsilon=a_0$, so that $a_0=-D$, i.e. minus the bond energy, since by convention (cf. § 13.V) the potential energy is zero for $r\to\infty$ (separated atoms), and as energy D is absorbed in separating the nuclei *at rest* in the position $r=r_e$ to infinite distance, the energy at r_e must be $-D$ if $-D+D=0$. Again, as ϵ has a minimum at $r=r_e$, $\mathrm{d}\epsilon/\mathrm{d}r$ must be zero when $r=r_e$ (§ 9, I), therefore $\mathrm{d}\epsilon/\mathrm{df}=a_1+a_2\mathrm{f}+\ldots=0$ when $\mathrm{f}=0$, therefore $a_1=0$, therefore $\epsilon=-D+(a_2/2!)\mathrm{f}^2+(a_3/3!)\mathrm{f}^3+\ldots$

It is usually sufficient to retain only the term in f^2, giving $\epsilon=-D+\frac{1}{2}a_2\mathrm{f}^2$. The arbitrarily chosen function $\mathrm{f}=(\mathrm{e}^{-a(r-r_e)}-1)$ satisfies the condition that $\mathrm{f}=0$ when $r=r_e$ (a is a constant),

$$\therefore\ \epsilon=-D+\tfrac{1}{2}a_2[\mathrm{e}^{-a(r-r_e)}-1]^2,$$

and as $\epsilon=0$ when $r\to\infty$, i.e. $\mathrm{e}^{-a(r-r_e)}\to 0$,

$$\therefore\ 0=-D+a_2/2 \quad \therefore\ a_2/2=D,$$

$$\therefore\ \epsilon=-D+D[\mathrm{e}^{-a(r-r_e)}-1]^2$$

$$\therefore\ \epsilon=D[\mathrm{e}^{-2a(r-r_e)}-2\mathrm{e}^{-a(r-r_e)}] \quad . \quad . \quad . \quad . \quad . \quad . \quad (3)$$

Equation (3), which is semi-empirical, was proposed by Morse,[1] and has been overworked in many branches of investigation. The value of D in (3) includes the zero-point energy (in D_0, Fig. 8.IV this is omitted). Differentiation of $-\epsilon$ with respect to r gives the force F between the nuclei:

$$F=-\mathrm{d}\epsilon/\mathrm{d}r=2aD[\mathrm{e}^{-2a(r-r_e)}-\mathrm{e}^{-a(r-r_e)}] \quad . \quad . \quad . \quad . \quad (4)$$

For $r=r_e$, F vanishes, as it should according to the previous discussion.

The first term in (4) refers to the repulsion, important at small distances, and the second (negative) term to the attraction, significant at larger distances. Fig. 8.IV shows a Morse curve for the energy of a diatomic molecule, the quantum numbers v being marked for various vibrational levels. Some values of the constants (from which Morse curves can be drawn) are given for diatomic molecules and radicals in the table (distances are in A$=10^{-8}$ cm.).[2]

	D in k.cal./mol	D in electron volts/molecule	r_e in A	a in A^{-1}	$\Theta_v{}^\circ$ abs.
H_2	103	4·454	0·75	1·94	6140
CH	81	3·5	1·12	1·99	4100
NH	97	4·2	1·08	1·96	4400
OH	102	4·4	0·96	2·34	5360
HCl	102	4·40	1·27	1·91	4300
NO	123	5·3	1·15	3·06	2740
O_2	117	5·09	1·20	2·68	2260
N_2	170	7·35	1·09	3·11	3380
CO	223	9·6	1·13	2·48	3120
C_2	128	5·6	1·31	2·32	2370
Cl_2	57	2·47	1·98	2·05	810
Br_2	46	1·96	2·28	1·97	470
I_2	36	1·53	2·66	1·86	310
Li_2	26	1·14	2·67	0·83	500
Na_2	18	0·76	3·07	0·84	230
K_2	12	0·51	3·91	0·78	140

The Morse equation can also be used to calculate the frequency of vibration $\tilde{\omega}$ of a diatomic molecule. Suppose the atoms displaced by a small amount from the equilibrium distance r_e, and expand the exponentials, taking as a first approximation only the first terms:

$$F=2aD[1-2a(r-r_e)-1+a(r-r_e)]=-2a^2D(r-r_e) \quad . \quad . \quad (5)$$

For two particles of masses m_1 and m_2 at distances r_1 and r_2 from the centre of mass, where $(r_1+r_2)=r$, the forces are:

$$m_1(\mathrm{d}^2r_1/\mathrm{d}t^2)=-2a^2D(r_1+r_2-r_e),$$

and

$$m_2(\mathrm{d}^2r_2/\mathrm{d}t^2)=-2a^2D(r_1+r_2-r_e).$$

[1] *Phys. Rev.*, 1929, **34**, 57; Bates and Andrews, *Proc. Nat. Acad.*, 1928, **14**, 124; Huggins, *J. Chem. Phys.*, 1936, **4**, 308; Chakravorti, *Z. Phys.*, 1938, **109**, 25; Schmidt and Gerö, *Ann. Phys.*, 1938, **33**, 70; Alyea, *J. Chem. Educ.*, 1942, **19**, 337; Coulson and Bell, *Trans. Faraday Soc.*, 1945, **41**, 141; Valatin, *J. Chem. Phys.*, 1946, **14**, 568; 1947, **15**, 336; *Proc. Phys. Soc.*, 1946, **58**, 695; ter Haar, *Phys. Rev.*, 1946, **70**, 222; Rees, *ibid.*, 1947, **59**, 998.

[2] Bichowsky and Rossini, "Thermochemistry of the Chemical Substances," New York, 1938; Slater, "Introduction to Chemical Physics," New York, 1938, 132; Herzberg, "Molecular Spectra and Molecular Structure. Diatomic Molecules," New York, 1939; *Phys. Rev.*, 1946, **69**, 362; Moelwyn-Hughes, "Physical Chemistry," Cambridge, 1940, 403; A. G. Gaydon, "Dissociation Energies and Spectra of Diatomic Molecules," London, 1947; Glockler, *J. Chem. Phys.*, 1948, **16**, 602, 604; Hagstrum, *ibid.*, 1948, **16**, 848. Very discordant values are given in the literature.

Divide the first equation by m_1 and the second by m_2 and add:

$$d^2(r_1+r_2)/dt^2=-2a^2D(r_1+r_2-r_e)(1/m_1+1/m_2).$$

Put $1/m_1+1/m_2=1/\mu$, where μ is called the *reduced mass* (not to be confused with μ in (12), § 8), then:

$$\mu(d^2r/dt^2)=-2a^2D(r-r_e) \quad . \quad . \quad . \quad . \quad . \quad . \quad (6)$$

This equation is of the same form as that for a simple harmonic motion (§ 49.I): $m(d^2x/dt^2)=-kx$, with $\mu=m$ and $2a^2D=k$, when the frequency is given by $\tilde{\omega}=(1/2\pi)\sqrt{(k/m)}$. Hence in the present case:

$$\tilde{\omega}=(1/2\pi)\sqrt{(2a^2D/\mu)} \quad . \quad . \quad . \quad . \quad . \quad . \quad . \quad . \quad (7)$$

The so-called *characteristic temperature* is:

$$\Theta_v=h\tilde{\omega}/k=(h/2\pi k)\sqrt{(2a^2D/\mu)} \quad . \quad . \quad . \quad . \quad . \quad . \quad (8)$$

The values of Θ_v are given in the table. They show that the vibrational energy is insignificant for all molecules standing above Cl_2 in the table, except at very high temperatures, which agrees with the measured specific heat values.

The bond energy D in (3) and (4) is not what is commonly called the *heat of dissociation*, D_0, of the molecule, since this refers to the energy of separation of the nuclei in the *ground state* to infinite distance. In the ground state ($v=0$), however, the molecule has still the *zero-point energy* ϵ_0, hence the heat of dissociation (per molecule) is $D_0=D-\epsilon_0$.

Since $\tilde{\omega}$ may vary with the amplitude, the value for very small amplitudes, or $\tilde{\omega}_e$ (" equilibrium value "), is often used, and instead of the frequency, the wave-number $\omega=\tilde{\omega}/c$ (c=velocity of light) is used.

Many modifications of the Morse equation have been proposed. Birge [1] and Mecke [2] suggested $\omega_e r_e^2$=const., but Morse [3] found considerable deviations and proposed $\omega_e r_e^3$=const.$=3\times10^{-21}$ (ω_e in cm.$^{-1}$, r_e in cm.). Clark [4] suggested a relation to the rows in the periodic table of the elements to which the two atoms of a diatomic molecule belong, using a so-called molecular period constant k and a group number N; CO, for example, has a group number 10, since it has 4 and 6 electrons contributed by the C and O atoms, respectively, to form a shared group (these two atoms belonging to Groups IV and VI in the periodic system), and a symmetrical completed non-bonding (KK) pair of electrons, giving the period number $k=2$. A constant k' is a correction for ionised molecules (for neutral molecules $k'=1$), and the equation as given [5] is $\omega_e r_e^3\sqrt{N}=k-k'$. The best known equation in this group was proposed by Badger [6] in the form $k_0(r_e-d_{ij})^3$=const., where k_0 is a force constant for the bond, in dynes cm.$^{-1}$, d_{ij} is a constant depending on the rows (i and j) of the two atoms in the periodic table, and the constant is $1{\cdot}86=10^5$ with r_e in A. units. Badger's equation is given by other authors as $r_e=(C/K_e)^{1/3}-D$, where C, K_e, and D are constants for a given molecular period (in the sense explained above). Allen and Longair [7] gave an equation $\omega_e r_e^3\sqrt{\mu}$=const.,

[1] The reference given by Morse, Clark, etc., is *Phys. Rev.*, 1925, **25**, 240, but in this abstract the equation is not given in any form.

[2] *Z. Phys.*, 1925, **32**, 823 (no equation given).

[3] *Phys. Rev.*, 1929, **34**, 57.

[4] *Proc. Leeds Phil. Soc.*, 1934, **2**, 502; *Phil. Mag.*, 1934, **18**, 459; 1935, **19**, 476; *Phys. Rev.*, 1935, **47**, 238; *Trans. Faraday Soc.*, 1935, **31**, 1017; Clark and Stoves, *Phil. Mag.*, 1936, **22**, 1137; Sutherland, *J. Chem. Phys.*, 1940, **8**, 161 (correction).

[5] In almost every case, authors in this group quote each other's equations in different forms, according to no ascertainable plan.

[6] *J. Chem. Phys.*, 1934, **2**, 128; 1935, **3**, 710; Huggins, *ibid.*, 1935, **3**, 473; 1936, **4**, 308; Glockler and Evans, *ibid.*, 1942, **10**, 606.

[7] *Phil. Mag.*, 1935, **19**, 1032; Newing, *ibid.*, 1935, **19**, 759.

where $\mu = m_1 m_2/(m_1+m_2)$ is the reduced mass of the two atoms, and this is quoted by other authors as $r_e = (K/K_e)^{1/6}$. Sutherland [1] showed that a plausible derivation of such equations results from a potential function of the type (2): $V = -a/r^m + b/r^n$; and Wu and Chang-Tsing Yang [2] derived another equation from the Born-Mayer potential function, $V = be^{-r/p} - a/r^m$. Crespin and Désirant [3] proposed $\mu x_e \omega_e r_e^2 = 230$ (420 for halogens), where μ=reduced mass in 10^{-24} g. units, x_e=anharmonicity constant (§ 25), ω_e is in cm.$^{-1}$, r_e in A. This does not hold for hydrides. Puppi [4] found $\omega_e r_e^{3/2} = \beta 220/\sqrt{\mu}$ sec.$^{-1}$ cm.$^{3/2}$, where the molecule is assumed to be an electric quadrupole, β being a constant depending on the position of the atoms in the periodic table.

Lennard-Jones,[5] with the potential energy function $\epsilon_p = \lambda r^{-n} - \mu r^{-m}$, found the rule that the ratio of the total depth of the potential energy trough to the critical temperature T_c is a constant for gases, and with $n=12$, $m=6$:

$$(L_0+E_0)/RT_c \simeq 6{\cdot}45,$$

where L_0=latent heat of evaporation at $T=0$ and E_0=zero-point energy, per mol. This was confirmed for xenon.[6] Walsh,[7] who postulated a relation between bond-order and ionisation potential, found a linear relation between bond-order and force constant.

§ 18. Rigid Diatomic Rotor

For a diatomic gas with rigid molecules the state sum will, from § 11, include a factor Z_r for the rotational energy. Let the molecule consist of two different atoms of masses m_1 and m_2, situated at fixed distances r_1 and r_2 from a fixed axis of rotation passing through a point O in the axis of the molecule, and at right angles to it (Fig. 9.IV). If θ is the angle between the axis and any straight line at right angles to the axis of rotation (the axis of rotation is shown by the dotted line in the plane of the paper in Fig. 9.IV), then if $d\theta/dt$ is constant it is the *angular velocity*,[8] ω. Since each mass m_1 and m_2 moves in a circle, the velocities v are $r_1\omega$ and $r_2\omega$, respectively (see § 40.I), the kinetic energies $\frac{1}{2}mv^2$ are $\frac{1}{2}m_1 r_1^2\omega^2$ and $\frac{1}{2}m_2 r_2^2\omega^2$, and the total kinetic energy is $\frac{1}{2}\omega^2 \Sigma m_1 r_1^2 = \frac{1}{2}\omega^2 I$, where I is the moment of inertia about the axis of rotation. The moment of momentum (sometimes called the angular momentum) of a particle is $mv.r = m\omega r^2$, and the total moment of momentum is $\Sigma m\omega r^2 = \omega I = p_\theta$, say. Hence, the kinetic energy is $p_\theta^2/2I$.

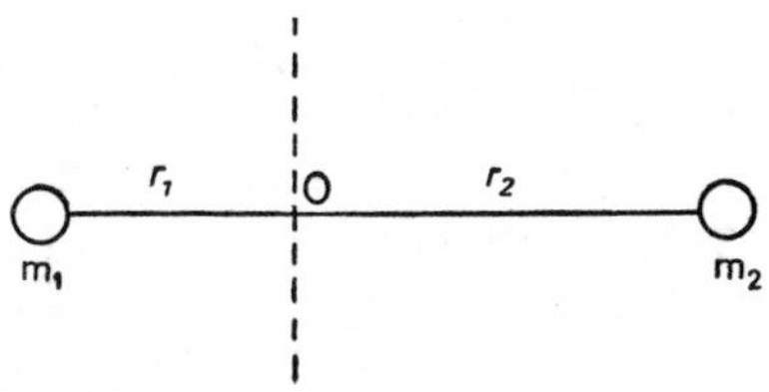

FIG. 9.IV. Model of Rigid Diatomic Rotor

1 *Proc. Indian Acad. Sci.*, 1938, **8**, 341; *J. Chem. Phys.*, 1940, **8**, 161; *Ann. Rep. Chem. Soc.*, 1938, **35**, 46; Skinner, *Trans. Faraday Soc.*, 1945, **41**, 645.

2 *J. Phys. Chem.*, 1944, **48**, 295; Thompson and Linnett, *J.C.S.*, 1937, 1396; Linnett, *Trans. Faraday Soc.*, 1940, **36**, 1123; 1942, **38**, 1; Gordy, *J. Chem. Phys.*, 1946, **14**, 305; Puppi, *Nuov. Cim.*, 1946, **3**, 338; Cook, *J. Phys. Chem.*, 1947, **51**, 407; Wu and Chao, *Phys. Rev.*, 1947, **71**, 118.

3 *Bull. Acad. Roy. Belg.*, 1937, **23**, 308 (with long table of values of r_e).

4 *Nuov. Cim.*, 1946, **3**, 198.

5 *Physica*, 1937, **4**, 941; Lennard-Jones and Devonshire, *Proc. Roy. Soc.*, 1938, **165**, 1.

6 Clusius and Weigand, *Z. phys. Chem.*, 1939, **42** B, 111.

7 *Trans. Faraday Soc.*, 1946, **42**, 779; 1947, **43**, 60; see also Kavanau, *J. Chem. Phys.*, 1944 **12**, 467; Lagemann, *ibid.*, 1946, **14**, 743.

8 The conventional symbol ω for angular velocity (radians per sec.) used here must not be confused with ω for wave number.

For rotation about an axis through O perpendicular to the first (in the plane of the paper) with an angle ϕ, the kinetic energy is, similarly, $p_\phi^2/2I$, and the total kinetic energy of rotation of the molecule is thus $\epsilon_k = p_\theta^2/2I + p_\phi^2/2I$.

The phase space is two-dimensional, the q-coordinates being the angles θ and ϕ, and by comparison with (10), § 14, the state sum for rotation can (since the energy levels are closely spaced) be taken as an integral:

$$Z_r = (1/h^2)\int_{-\infty}^{+\infty} e^{-p_\theta^2/2kIT} dp_\theta \int_{-\infty}^{+\infty} e^{-p_\phi^2/2kIT} dp_\phi \int_0^\pi \int_0^{2\pi} \sin\theta d\theta d\phi \quad . \quad . \quad (1)$$

in which the solid angle $\sin\theta d\theta d\phi$ is integrated over a unit sphere (see § 8.III) by varying θ from 0 to π, and ϕ from 0 to 2π. The integrations are easily carried out (see § 8.III), and the result is:

$$Z_r = 8\pi^2 IkT/h^2 \quad . \quad . \quad . \quad . \quad . \quad . \quad . \quad . \quad (2)$$

If the two atoms are identical, the two ends of the molecule are identical (as in O_2, N_2, as distinguished from NO), and the position after rotation through an angle π about an axis at right angles to the molecular axis is identical with the initial position, so that all distinguishable positions of the molecule can be included by integrating over 0 to π, instead of 0 to 2π, with respect to ϕ; the state sum (2) must now be divided [1] by a *symmetry factor*, s (sometimes denoted by σ)=2. Corresponding with Z_r there will be a rotational entropy, which may be calculated by (28), § 8, or from the rotational free energy F calculated by (27), § 8. The rotational free energy per mol is, from (27), § 8:

$$F_r = -kNT \ln Z_r = -RT \ln Z_r$$
$$= -RT \ln(8\pi^2 Ik/h^2 s) - RT \ln T \quad . \quad . \quad . \quad . \quad . \quad . \quad (3)$$

and the rotational entropy is, from (5), § 43.II:

$$S_r = -dF_r/dT = R \ln(8\pi^2 Ik/h^2 s) + R \ln T + R \quad . \quad . \quad . \quad . \quad (4)$$

The complete values for a rigid diatomic molecule are found by adding the translational parts (12) and (16), § 14, the sums being:

$$F = -RT \ln[(eV/h^3 N)(2\pi mkT)^{3/2}] + E_0 - RT \ln(8\pi^2 Ik/h^2 s) - RT \ln T \quad . \quad . \quad (5)$$

$$S = R\{\tfrac{5}{2}\ln T - \ln p + \tfrac{5}{2} + \ln[(2\pi m)^{3/2}(k^{5/2}/h^3)]\} + R\ln(8\pi^2 Ik/h^2 s) + R + R\ln T$$
$$= R\{\tfrac{7}{2}\ln T - \ln p + \tfrac{7}{2} + \ln[(2\pi m)^{3/2}(k^{5/2}/h^3)(8\pi^2 Ik/h^2 s)]\} \quad . \quad . \quad . \quad . \quad . \quad (6)$$

The available energy per mol is $G = E - TS + RT$, and since the classical energy per mol of a molecule with 5 degrees of freedom (rigid diatomic molecule) is $E = E_0 + \tfrac{5}{2}RT$:

$$G = (E_0 + \tfrac{5}{2}RT) + RT - RT\{\tfrac{7}{2}\ln T - \ln p + \tfrac{7}{2} + \ln[(2\pi m)^{3/2}(k^{5/2}/h^3)(8\pi^2 Ik/h^2 s)]\}$$
$$= E_0 - \tfrac{7}{2}RT\ln T + RT\ln p - RT\ln[(2\pi m)^{3/2}(k^{5/2}/h^3)(8\pi^2 Ik/h^2 s)] \quad . \quad . \quad . \quad (7)$$

These equations do not take account of nuclear spins or electronic multiplicity (§ 21).

§ 19 Rotational Energy

The expression for the energy of a rigid rotor composed of two mass particles at a fixed distance apart, and with the axis free in space, will be found from wave mechanics (§ 12.V) to be:

$$\epsilon_{rJ} = J(J+1)h^2/8\pi^2 I \quad . \quad . \quad . \quad . \quad . \quad . \quad . \quad . \quad (1)$$

[1] Sackur, *Ann. Phys.*, 1913, **40**, 87; Tetrode, *Proc. K. Akad. Wetens. Amsterdam*, 1915, **17**, 1167; Planck, *Verhl. d. D. Phys. Ges.*, 1915, **17**, 40, 418; Lorentz, *Proc. K. Akad. Wetens. Amsterdam*, 1917, **19**, 737; Ehrenfest and Trkal, *ibid.*, 1920, **23**, 162; *Ann. Phys.*, 1921, **65**, 609; Schames, *Phys. Z.*, 1920, **21**, 38, 39; Partington, *Phil. Mag.*, 1922, **44**, 988; Cox, *Proc. Cambr. Phil. Soc.*, 1923, **21**, 541; Van Vleck, *Phys. Rev.*, 1926, **28**, 980; Saha and Sur, *Phil. Mag.*, 1926, **1**, 279; Mayer, Brunauer, and Mayer, *J.A.C.S.*, 1933, **55**, 37.

where I is the moment of inertia, and J is the rotational quantum number, $J=0, 1, 2, \ldots$. A simple, but not strict, deduction[1] of (1) is based on the method of p, q-space described in § 16 for the oscillator. Consider a freely rotating wheel of moment of inertia I and put $q=\theta$, the angular displacement. In this case ϕ is supposed constant (i.e. rotation about a fixed axis is first considered). Then p=moment of momentum$=I\omega$, where $\omega=\mathrm{d}\theta/\mathrm{d}t$=angular velocity. The energy is wholly kinetic, $E_r=\frac{1}{2}I\omega^2=p^2/2I$, and lines of constant energy are straight lines, p=const. (Fig. 10.IV). Since θ has a period 2π, only values from 0 to 2π need be considered and the diagram may be taken as Fig. 10.IV wrapped round a cylinder. As the area of each " cell " is $\boldsymbol{h}$, it must be bounded by lines $p=n\boldsymbol{h}/2\pi$, where n is an integer, since the area $n\boldsymbol{h}$ is $2\pi p$, and the energy associated with the nth line is:

$$\epsilon_r=p^2/2I=n^2\boldsymbol{h}^2/8\pi^2I \quad . \quad . \quad . \quad (2)$$

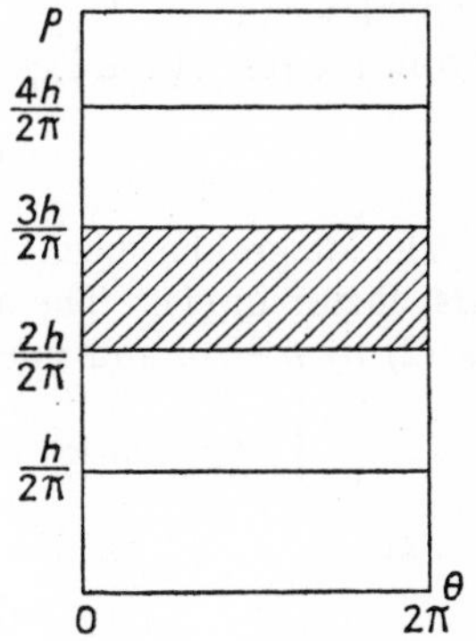

FIG. 10.IV. Phase Space Diagram for Rigid Rotor

This equation differs from (1) only in the factor n^2 instead of $J(J+1)$. Equation (2) refers to a different case, viz. a rotor with an axis *fixed* in space, and for this exactly the same result (2) is found by wave-mechanics. As in the case of the oscillator (§ 16), a naïve assumption is now made that the energy levels are spread into bands, and in this case n^2 is replaced by the square of the geometric mean of successive quantum numbers n and $(n+1)$, i.e. by $n(n+1)$, giving:

$$\bar{\epsilon}_r=n(n+1)\boldsymbol{h}^2/8\pi^2I \quad . \quad . \quad . \quad . \quad . \quad . \quad . \quad . \quad (3)$$

which is the same as (1) with $J=n$. A zero-point energy of *rotation* was suggested, on the basis of magnetic properties at low temperatures, by Oosterhuis.[2]

Before the advent of wave mechanics, quantisation was carried out by the so-called *Wilson-Sommerfeld rule*: [3]

$$\oint p\mathrm{d}q=n\boldsymbol{h} \quad . \quad . \quad . \quad . \quad . \quad . \quad . \quad . \quad . \quad . \quad (4)$$

where q is a generalised coordinate, p the corresponding generalised momentum, n a whole number (quantum number), the integration being taken over a complete period.

§ 20. Equipartition of Energy

On the assumption that the energy can vary *continuously*, the mean translational kinetic energy of a molecule per degree of freedom is:

$$\bar{\epsilon}_x=(2\pi mkT)^{-1/2}\int_{-\infty}^{+\infty}(p_x^2/2m)e^{-p_x^2/2mkT}\mathrm{d}p_x=\tfrac{1}{2}kT \quad . \quad . \quad . \quad (1)$$

This is proved as follows. The energy component for the x-direction is $\frac{1}{2}m\dot{x}^2=\frac{1}{2}m(m\dot{x})^2/m=\frac{1}{2}p_x^2/m$, where p_x is the momentum component (§ 14),

[1] Modified from Planck, " Theorie der Wärmestrahlung," 1921, 139; Ehrenfest, *Verhl. d. D. Phys. Ges.*, 1913, **15**, 451.

[2] *Phys. Z.*, 1913, **14**, 862.

[3] W. Wilson, *Phil. Mag.*, 1915, **29**, 795; 1916, **31**, 156; Sommerfeld, *Munich Ber.*, 1915, 425, 459; *Ann. Phys.*, 1916, **51**, 1, 125; *Rapport Cons. Phys. Solvay* (1930), 1932, 1; " Atomic Structure and Spectral Lines," 1923, 198, 233; Ishiwara, *Proc. Math. Phys. Soc. Japan*, 1915, **8**, 106; Husimi, *ibid.*, 1938, **20**, 757; Schwarzschild, *Berlin Ber.*, 1916, 548; Swann, *J. Franklin Inst.*, 1928, **205**, 323; for treatment of restricted rotor by this method, see Halford, *J. Chem. Phys.*, 1947, **15**, 645; 1948, **16**, 410, 560; King, *ibid.*, 1947, **15**, 820.

i.e. $\epsilon_x = p_x^2/2m$. The energy of the molecule can be expressed as $p_x^2/2m + \epsilon'$, where ϵ' depends on all the p's and q's (§ 12) except p_x. The mean value of $p_x^2/2m$ is:

$$\bar{\epsilon}_x = \frac{\iint \ldots (p_x^2/2m) e^{-p_x^2/2mkT} e^{-\epsilon'/kT} dp_x \ldots dq_x \ldots}{\iint \ldots e^{-p_x^2/2mkT} e^{-\epsilon'/kT} dp_x \ldots dq_x \ldots}.$$

The first two factors in the integral in the numerator, and the first in the denominator, are the only ones which depend on p_x alone, and the remaining variables can be integrated first (see § 22.I) to yield factors which cancel. From the rest of the expression take out:

$$e^{-p_x^2/2mkT} dp_x \Big/ \int_{-\infty}^{+\infty} e^{-p_x^2/2mkT} dp_x \quad . \quad . \quad . \quad . \quad . \quad . \quad (2)$$

The integral has been shown in (11), § 14, to be equal to $(2\pi mkT)^{1/2}$, giving the first factor in (1). The average energy is found by multiplying the numerator of (2) by $p_x^2/2m$ and integrating as shown in (1).

$$\int_{-\infty}^{+\infty} (p_x^2/2m) e^{-p_x^2/2mkT} dp_x = kT \int_{-\infty}^{+\infty} (p_x^2/2mkT) e^{-p_x^2/2mkT} dp_x = J.$$

Put $$p_x^2/2mkT = x^2, \quad \therefore (2p_x/2mkT) dp_x = 2x dx$$

$$\therefore dp_x = 2mkT(x/p_x) dx = 2mkT[1/\sqrt{(2mkT)}] dx,$$

$$\therefore J = kT\sqrt{(2mkT)} \int_{-\infty}^{+\infty} x^2 e^{-x^2} dx = (\sqrt{\pi}/2)\sqrt{(2m)}(kT)^{3/2}.$$

The integral $\int x^2 e^{-x^2} dx$ is found in (26), § 10.III, for the limits 0 and ∞ as $\sqrt{\pi}/4$, and as both x^2 and e^{-x^2} are even functions (§ 21.I), the value between $-\infty$ and $+\infty$ is $\sqrt{\pi}/2$.

Hence $$\bar{\epsilon}_x = (\sqrt{\pi}/2)\sqrt{(2m)}(kT)^{3/2}(2\pi mkT)^{-1/2} = \tfrac{1}{2}kT.$$

Any momentum or coordinate expressible as a square term (p_x^2) in (1) will obviously give $\frac{1}{2}kT$ for the mean energy,[1] e.g. a rotational energy $p^2/2I$, where I is a moment of inertia, and a potential energy of an oscillator $Kx^2/2$. In all these cases, however, a *continuous* variation of energy is assumed and the resulting *equipartition of energy* of $\frac{1}{2}kT$ per degree of freedom holds only for this assumption. It should be noted that all the above expressions, and also (11), § 14, when referring to *translational* energy, are not restricted to monatomic molecules, and that when both kinetic and potential energy are involved (harmonic oscillator), the *average energy* is twice this amount, viz. kT, or $\boldsymbol{R}T$ per mol, and the corresponding heat capacity is $C_v = 3\boldsymbol{R} \simeq 6$ g.cal. Tolman [2] found that the equipartition of energy cannot hold exactly for relativistic mechanics, but it is approximately correct.

§ 21. State Sums for Atoms

The calculations made so far take no account of the contributions of the electrons and nuclei of the atoms to the state sum (cf. § 11). This will now be considered, the necessary results from theory being merely stated and a more detailed discussion being deferred.[3] The *nuclear* state sum Z_n of an atomic nucleus specifies the finite number of possible orientations of the nuclear

[1] Jeans, "Dynamical Theory of Gases," 3rd edit., Cambridge, 1921, 80; Hinshelwood, "Kinetics of Chemical Change in Gaseous Systems," Oxford, 1933, 22, etc.

[2] *Phil. Mag.*, 1914, **28**, 583.

[3] For an elementary account, see Glasstone, "Recent Advances in General Chemistry," 1936, 62 f.; "Theoretical Chemistry," New York, 1945, 368 f.

spin in a perturbing field, but as the energy of orientation is small compared with kT, each exponential term in Z_n is practically unity (since $e^0=1$), and Z_n is practically the statistical weight:[1]

$$Z_n=g_n e^{-\epsilon_n/kT} \simeq g_n=2i_s+1 \quad . \quad . \quad . \quad . \quad . \quad . \quad . \quad . \quad (1)$$

where i_s is the number of units of nuclear spin. For any *electronic* level, the statistical weight is:

$$g_e=2j_s+1 \quad . \quad . \quad . \quad . \quad . \quad . \quad . \quad . \quad . \quad . \quad (2)$$

where $j_s=l\pm s$ has only positive values, l being the orbital and s the spin quantum number:

$$\therefore\ Z_e=\Sigma(2j_s+1)e^{-\epsilon_{js}/kT} \quad . \quad . \quad . \quad . \quad . \quad . \quad . \quad . \quad (3)$$

the sum being taken over all electronic energy levels, ϵ_{js}. Usually only the ground state contributes appreciably, except (i) when successive levels are very close together, or (ii) at high temperatures, when T exceeds $\epsilon_{js}/k=h\nu_e/4k$, where ν_e is the frequency separation of the given level above the ground state.

For the hydrogen atom $i_s=\frac{1}{2}$ therefore $Z_n=2$. The ground state ($\epsilon_{js}=0$) has the quantum number 1 and $j_s=\frac{1}{2}$ therefore $Z_e=2$, therefore $Z=Z_n\,.\,Z_e=2\times2=4$.

For the chlorine atom, $i_s=5/2$ therefore $Z_n=6$. The electronic ground state is an inverted doublet, ^2P, with $j_s=3/2$ for the lower component and $j_s=1/2$ for the higher component, and the frequency (wave number) separation $\Delta\nu'=881$ cm.$^{-1}$. For these two components, $2j_s+1$ is 4 and 2, respectively, hence:

$$Z_e=4+2e^{-881hc/kT}$$

and

$$Z=Z_n\,.\,Z_e=6(4+2e^{-881hc/kT}).$$

For the oxygen atom, the ground state is an inverted triplet, ^3P, the j_s values being 2, 1, 0, respectively, with $\Delta\nu'$ 157·4 cm.$^{-1}$ and 226·1 cm.$^{-1}$ above the lowest level for $^3P_1$ and $^3P_0$. The statistical weights $2j_s+1$ are 5, 3, and 1. The two higher metastable levels are $^1D_2$ ($\Delta\nu'=15807$ cm.$^{-1}$) and $^1S_0$ ($\Delta\nu'=33662$ cm.$^{-1}$), with $j_s=2$ and 0, respectively, and weights 5 and 1, but they do not contribute appreciably except at high temperatures. The value of Z_e is found by summing the three or five $ge^{-hc\nu'/kT}$ terms, and as the nuclear spin is zero ($i_s=0$), $Z_n=1$, therefore $Z=Z_e$.

The complete expression for the available energy of one mol of an ideal monatomic gas in the ground state is found from (24), § 14, to be:

$$G=E_0-\tfrac{5}{2}RT\ln T+RT\ln p-RT\ln\left[(2\pi m)^{3/2}k^{5/2}g_e g_n/h^3\right] \quad . \quad . \quad (4)$$

This has been verified[2] for alkali metal and thallium vapours, which have a ground state $^2P_{1/2}$ and $g_e=2$. (It is clear that (4) will not apply in that form if excited atomic states are included.)

In calculating entropy it is usual to omit the nuclear spin factor; for the chlorine atom, e.g.:

$$Z_e=4+2e^{-881hc/kT}.$$

The factor hc/k, frequently required in spectroscopic calculations, is numerically $6{\cdot}61\times10^{-27}\times2{\cdot}998\times10^{10}/1{\cdot}38\times10^{-16}=1{\cdot}436$ (the value 1·438 is often

[1] Unsöld, *Ann. Phys.*, 1926, **82**, 355; Pauling and Goudsmid, "The Structure of Line Spectra," New York, 1930; Bacher and Goudsmid, "Atomic Energy States," New York, 1932; Condon and Shortley, "The Theory of Atomic Spectra," Cambridge, 1935.

[2] Rodebush, *Proc. Nat. Acad.*, 1927, **13**, 185; Harteck, *Z. phys. Chem.*, 1928, **134**, 1, 21 (Cu, Ag, Au, Ga, Sn, Pb); Ladenburg and Thiele, *ibid.*, 1930, **7 B**, 161 (Na); Coleman and Egerton, *Phil. Trans.*, 1935, **234**, 177 (Tl).

used). Hence $Z_e=4+2e^{-1265/T}$. For $T=298{\cdot}1°$ K., $Z_e=4{\cdot}028$ (on the evaluation of e^{-x} see § 12.I) and $\log_{10} Z_e=0{\cdot}605$.

To find the entropy, use (28), § 8:

$$S_e=\boldsymbol{R}[\ln Z_e+T(\mathrm{d}\ln Z_e/\mathrm{d}T)]$$

and add the result to the entropy calculated by (23), § 14:

$$S_{tr}{}^0=\tfrac{3}{2}\boldsymbol{R}\ln M+\tfrac{5}{2}\boldsymbol{R}\ln T-2{\cdot}297.$$

The term $T(\mathrm{d}\ln Z_e/\mathrm{d}T)$ is found as follows:

$$Z_e=4+2e^{-1265/T}$$

$$\mathrm{d}Z_e/\mathrm{d}T=2(\mathrm{d}/\mathrm{d}T)e^{-1265/T}=(2530/T^2)e^{-1265/T}$$

$$\therefore\ T(\mathrm{d}\ln Z_e/\mathrm{d}T)=(T/Z_e)(\mathrm{d}Z_e/\mathrm{d}T)=(T/Z_e)(2530/T^2)e^{-1265/T}$$

$$=(2530/TZ_e)e^{-1265/T}.$$

For $T=298{\cdot}1$, $Z_e=4{\cdot}028$, $e^{-1265/T}=e^{-4.446}=1/86{\cdot}9$,

$$\therefore\ T(\mathrm{d}\ln Z_e/\mathrm{d}T)=2530/(4{\cdot}028\times298{\cdot}1\times86{\cdot}9),$$

$$T(\mathrm{d}\log_{10}Z_e/\mathrm{d}T)=2530/(4{\cdot}028\times298{\cdot}1\times86{\cdot}9\times2{\cdot}3026)=0{\cdot}0133.$$

Hence $\quad S_e{}^0=2{\cdot}3026\times1{\cdot}988(0{\cdot}605+0{\cdot}0133)=2{\cdot}828$ g.cal./1° C.

The translational entropy at $T=298{\cdot}1$ with $M=35{\cdot}457$ is:

$$S_{tr}{}^0=2{\cdot}3026\times1{\cdot}988(\tfrac{3}{2}\log_{10}35{\cdot}457+\tfrac{5}{2}\log_{10}298{\cdot}1]-2{\cdot}297=36{\cdot}65\text{ g.cal./1° C.}$$

Hence $S^0=36{\cdot}65+2{\cdot}83=39{\cdot}48$ g.cal./1° C. mol. The electronic part is about 7 per cent. of the total.

§ 22. State Sums for Diatomic Molecules

The *rotational* statistical weight of a diatomic molecule is shown in § 11.V to be:

$$g_r=2J+1 \quad \text{. . . . .} \quad (1)$$

where J is the rotational quantum number (§ 19).

The complete statistical weight for any rotational state (which may, for simplicity, be denoted also by g_r, different from that in (2), § 9) is the product of the nuclear spin multiplicity and the rotational statistical weight. For diatomic molecules composed of *different* atoms the nuclear spin multiplicity is [1] $(2i_s+1)(2i_s'+1)$, where i_s, i_s' are the nuclear spins of the two atoms in $\boldsymbol{h}/2\pi$ units.

For diatomic molecules consisting of *identical* atoms, the nuclear spin multiplicity depends on whether the nuclei have an even or odd number of units of spin. If they have an *even* number, the nuclear spin multiplicity is $(i_s+1)(2i_s+1)$ for even values (including zero) of J, and $i_s(2i_s+1)$ for odd values of J. If the nuclei have an *odd* number of units of nuclear spin, the relation of the two factors to the values of J is just reversed, i.e. $i_s(2i_s+1)$ for even values, and $(i_s+1)(2i_s+1)$ for odd values of J. The reasons for all these rules cannot be explained here.[2]

For hydrogen $i_s=1$ unit$=\frac{1}{2}$, and the nuclear spin multiplicity is $i_s(2i_s+1)$ when J is even, and $(i_s+1)(2i_s+1)$ when J is odd; for deuterium $i_s=2$ units$=1$, and the factors are reversed. The nuclear spin state sum Z_n is essentially equal to the nuclear spin multiplicity factor only.

1 See Mayer and Mayer, " Statistical Mechanics," New York, 1940, 135.
2 For the deduction, see Mayer and Mayer, *op. cit.*, 174 f.

For most diatomic molecules (common exceptions are O_2, NO, OH, and CN) the ground state is a $^1\Sigma$ term and the rotational state sum (omitting nuclear spin) is:

$$Z_r = \Sigma g_r e^{-\epsilon_r/kT}$$

where $g_r = 2J+1$, and $\epsilon_r = J(J+1)h^2/8\pi^2 I$, from (1), § 19,

$$\therefore\ Z_r = \Sigma(2J+1)e^{-\sigma J(J+1)} \quad . \quad . \quad . \quad . \quad . \quad . \quad . \quad . \quad (2)$$

where

$$\sigma = h^2/8\pi^2 IkT = 4{\cdot}10\times10^{-39}/IT \quad . \quad . \quad . \quad . \quad . \quad . \quad (3)$$

When σ is small (i.e. T is large and I, which is usually of the order of 10^{-40}, is not too small) the sum in (3) can be replaced by an integral:

$$Z_r = \sum_{J=0}^{\infty}(2J+1)e^{-\sigma J(J+1)} \simeq \int_0^{\infty}(2J+1)dJ e^{-\sigma J(J+1)} = \int_0^{\infty} e^{-\sigma x}dx = 1/\sigma \quad . \quad . \quad (4)$$

where $x = J(J+1)$. If nuclear spin is included, the value of Z_r is multiplied by Z_n.

The calculation of the state sum (2) in cases where the simple approximation (4) is not made is tedious, and is usually followed by an equally laborious summation over vibrational states (see § 25). The difference between the results and those found by the approximate method is nearly always (hydrogen and deuterium, with small values of I are important exceptions) within the limits of experimental error. For HCl the values of Z_r found by summation and by integration are:

Temperature T° K.	1000°	2000°
Z_r summation ...	67·618	135·85
Z_r integral	67·618	135·84

The correction when the diatomic molecule is assumed *non-rigid*, i.e. when stretching occurs, leading to a slight modification of the moment of inertia I, is usually negligible except at high temperatures (see § 25).[1]

For *unsymmetrical* diatomic molecules (composed of unlike atoms), both the odd and even levels have the statistical weight $2J+1$ and the complete rotational state sum, including nuclear spin multiplicity, is found by multiplying Z_r by $Z_n = (2i_s+1)(2i_s'+1)$. For *symmetrical* diatomic molecules (composed of identical atoms), the even terms are multiplied by $(i_s+1)(2i_s+1)$ and the odd terms by $i_s(2i_s+1)$. In the summation of the $(2J+1)e^{-\sigma J(J+1)}$ terms over all values of J from 0 to ∞, the sum of the terms for even J is found to be equal to the sum for odd J, provided σ is small:[2]

$$\sum_{J=0,2,4,\ldots}^{\infty}(2J+1)e^{-\sigma J(J+1)} = \sum_{J=1,3,5,\ldots}(2J+1)e^{-\sigma J(J+1)} \simeq 1/2\sigma$$

$$\therefore\ Z_r = i_s(2i_s+1)/2\sigma + (i_s+1)(2i_s+1)/2\sigma = (2i_s+1)^2/2\sigma \quad . \quad . \quad (5)$$

1 Gibson and Heitler, *Z. Phys.*, 1928, **49**, 465; Mulholland, *Proc. Cambr. Phil. Soc.*, 1928, **24**, 280; Giauque and Wiebe, *J.A.C.S.*, 1928, **50**, 101, 2193; Giauque and Overstreet, *ibid.*, 1932, **54**, 1731; Urey and Rittenberg, *J. Chem. Phys.*, 1933, **1**, 137; Gordon and Barnes, *ibid.*, 1933, **1**, 297; Gordon, *ibid.*, 1934, **2**, 65, 549; 1935, **3**, 259; Kassel, *ibid.*, 1933, **1**, 576; *J.A.C.S.*, 1934, **56**, 1838; *Chem. Rev.*, 1936, **18**, 277; Johnston and Davis, *J.A.C.S.*, 1934, **56**, 271; Johnston and Weimer, *ibid.*, 1934, **56**, 625; Wilson, *J. Chem. Phys.*, 1939, **7**, 948; *Chem. Rev.*, 1940, **27**, 17 (bibl.). A method of summation using the Euler-Maclaurin formula (see Margenau and Murphy, "The Mathematics of Physics and Chemistry," New York, 1943, 457) is explained by Mayer and Mayer, " Statistical Mechanics," New York, 1940, 150, 431. For a rotating vibrator, see Dunham, *Phys. Rev.*, 1932, **41**, 721.

2 For a proof of this, depending on summation by an Euler-Maclaurin series, see Mayer and Mayer, " Statistical Mechanics," New York, 1940, 153.

For H_2 ($i_s=\frac{1}{2}$) the factor $(2i_s+1)^2/2$ is 2; for deuterium D_2 ($i_s=1$), it is 9/2; for oxygen O_2 ($i_s=0$) it is 1/2; for molecules of the last type, in which the alternate rotational levels are missing and the others show no nuclear spin degeneracy, Z_r is approximately $1/2\sigma$.

Equation (5) gives a satisfactory result for hydrogen at 25° C., when practically only rotations contribute to the internal state sum Z_i. From (5), $d \ln Z_r/dT=1/T$ $\therefore$ $T\, d \ln Z_r/dT=1$, $\therefore$ from (28), § 8:

$$S_r^0=R(\ln Z_r+1) \quad . \quad . \quad . \quad . \quad . \quad . \quad . \quad . \quad (6)$$

Inserting (5) for Z_r, with $\sigma=h^2/8\pi^2IkT$ gives:

$$S_r^0=R \ln IT+178{\cdot}00+R \ln [(2i_s+1)^2/2] \quad . \quad . \quad . \quad . \quad (7)$$

With $I=0{\cdot}47\times10^{-40}$, $T=298{\cdot}1°$ K., $i_s=\frac{1}{2}$, for H_2, S_r^0 is found to be 6·27. On adding the translational entropy 28·05 from (23), § 14:

$$S_{tr}^0=\tfrac{3}{2}R \ln M+\tfrac{5}{2}R \ln T-2{\cdot}297 \quad . \quad . \quad . \quad . \quad . \quad (8)$$

the final value for the total entropy (including nuclear spin contribution) is 34·32, in good agreement with the actual value of 34·00.

In calculations of chemical equilibria the nuclear spin contribution to the entropy is usually omitted (it cancels out in any case) and the so-called *virtual entropy* is then, from (7):

$$S_r^*=R \ln IT+178{\cdot}00-R \ln 2 \quad . \quad . \quad . \quad . \quad . \quad . \quad . \quad (9)$$

since the symmetry factor (in this case $s=2$) must be retained.

The orbital angular momentum of the electrons in a diatomic molecule is space-quantised, and the quantum number Λ has zero or integral values along the inter-nuclear axis, its $L+1$ possible values being $\Lambda=L, L-1, L-2, \ldots 2, 1, 0$, where L is the quantum number for the resultant orbital angular momentum for all the electrons in the molecule. (Only positive values of Λ are significant.) In the electric field of the two nuclei, the energy of the electron is the same, irrespective of the direction of the angular motion, $\Lambda=+L$ and $\Lambda=-L$ corresponding with identical energies, and, except when $\Lambda=0$ (Σ states) the $L+1$ states are thus doubly degenerate. Interaction between electronic and rotational motions, however, separates the degenerate levels, and each rotational line in Π ($\Lambda=1$) and Δ($\Lambda=2$) states is split into two components. This so-called Λ-type doubling [1] is never very appreciable.

In the case of nitric oxide, NO, $i_s=0$ for ^{16}O and $i_s=1$ for ^{14}N, therefore $Z_n=1\times3=3$, and, as there is Λ-type doubling, the complete rotational state sum is:

$$Z_rZ_n=2\times3 \sum_{J=\frac{1}{2},\frac{3}{2},\frac{5}{2},\ldots} (2J+1)e^{-\epsilon/kT}+2\times3 \sum_{J'=\frac{3}{2},\frac{5}{2},\ldots} (2J'+1)e^{-\epsilon'/kT} \quad . \quad (10)$$

where ϵ and ϵ' are the lower and upper rotational energies of the two main parts of the doublet. It will be noted that the lowest value of J for the lower level is $\frac{1}{2}$, while that for the upper level is $\frac{3}{2}$.

For the triplet state of the oxygen molecule $^{16}O^{16}O$, for which $\Lambda=0$ (and there is no Λ-type doubling) the total angular momentum (apart from spin) is represented by a quantum number K, having values Λ, $\Lambda+1$, $\Lambda+2$, . . ., and hence for $\Lambda=0$ the values 0, 1, 2 . . . . The total spin quantum number S

[1] See Mulliken, *Phys. Rev.*, 1928, **32**, 880; Giauque and Johnston, *J.A.C.S.*, 1929, **51**, 2300; Johnston and Dawson, *ibid.*, 1933, **55**, 2744; Herzberg, *Rev. Mod. Phys.*, 1942, **14**, 219; Nielsen and Schaffer, *J. Chem. Phys.*, 1943, **11**, 140; and for an elementary account, Glasstone, "Recent Advances in General Chemistry," 1936, 67 f.; *idem*, "Theoretical Chemistry," New York, 1944, 171.

is the algebraic sum of the spins of the electrons in the atoms; as these normally form pairs with opposite spins in molecules with an even number of electrons, S is zero, but for oxygen, which has two unpaired electron spins in the molecule, $S=1$.

The quantum numbers K and S combine to a quantum number J according to the rule:

$$J=K+S,\ K+S-1,\ K+S-2,\ldots,\ |K-S| \quad . \quad . \quad . \quad (11)$$

where $|K-S|$ denotes a positive value, each level (except when $K<S$) having a multiplicity of $2S+1$. In the present case, the values of J are $K+1$, K, and $K-1$, the three corresponding levels being denoted by F_1, F_2, and F_3, and the corresponding energies by ϵ_1, ϵ_2 and ϵ_3. The molecule is homonuclear and the nuclear spin is zero, and it is known from wave mechanics that alternate rotational levels are then missing, and the only values of K are 1, 3, 5, ... The nuclear spin multiplicity is $(i_s+1)(2i_s+1)=1$ $(i_s=0)$. The values of $(2J+1)$ are $(2K+3)$, $(2K+1)$, and $(2K-1)$ and the complete rotational state sum for oxygen is, therefore:

$$Z_rZ_n=\sum_{K=1,3,5,\ldots}(2K+3)e^{-\epsilon_1/kT}+\sum_{K=1,3,5,\ldots}(2K+1)e^{-\epsilon_2/kT}+\sum_{K=1,3,5,\ldots}(2K-1)e^{-\epsilon_3/kT} \quad (12)$$

If the molecule is not rigid, the state sum will include a factor for the vibrational energy for each mode of vibration, and if (as is usual) the vibrational energy is reckoned from the lowest energy level (i.e. does *not* include the zero-point energy $\epsilon_0=0$, § 11):

$$Z_v=(1-e^{-h\nu/kT})^{-1} \quad . \quad . \quad . \quad . \quad . \quad . \quad . \quad . \quad . \quad (13)$$

according to (8), § 16; the corresponding entropy contribution is, from (14). § 16:

$$S_v=R[(h\nu/kT)(e^{h\nu/kT}-1)^{-1}-\ln(1-e^{-h\nu/kT})] \quad . \quad . \quad . \quad . \quad (14)$$

The complete expression for the available energy of 1 mol of a diatomic gas with rigid molecules in the ground state is seen from (7), § 18, to be:

$$G=E_0-\tfrac{7}{2}RT\ln T+RT\ln p-RT\ln\frac{(2\pi m)^{3/2}k^{5/2}}{h^3}\cdot\frac{8\pi^2Ik}{h^2s}g_eg_n^{(1)}g_n^{(2)} \quad . \quad (15)$$

in which the last term of (7), § 18, is completed by multiplication by the electronic statistical weight g_e, and the statistical weights $g_n^{(1)}$ and $g_n^{(2)}$ of the nuclear spins of the two atoms. If the molecule is non-rigid, the last term also includes a factor $(1-e^{-h\nu/kT})^{-1}$, from (13), for each vibrational frequency.

§ 23. The Specific Heat of Hydrogen

The energy of rotation of a molecule according to the classical equipartition theory (§ 20) is $\frac{1}{2}RT$ per mol per degree of freedom of rotation, and hence for a rigid polyatomic molecule with three axes of rotation at right angles, the energy of rotation is $\frac{3}{2}RT$, and the contribution to the specific heat is $\frac{3}{2}R\simeq3$ g.cal. per mol, independent of temperature. For rigid diatomic ("dumb-bell") molecules, the classical energy due to rotation about the molecular axis is supposed to be constant, hence the contribution is $\frac{2}{2}R\simeq2$ g.cal. Since the energy of translation is $\frac{3}{2}RT$ (3 degrees of freedom), the molecular heat should be $C_v=3+2=5$ g.cal. This is approximately true for oxygen, nitrogen, carbon monoxide, nitric oxide, and hydrogen chloride, but the value for hydrogen is appreciably lower at room temperature and decreases with temperature, until at about 60° K. it is only 3 g.cal., the value for a monatomic gas, so that the rotational part of the specific heat has disappeared.[1] A similar result is found for D_2 and HD. This behaviour is quite inexplicable on the classical theory.[2]

The specific heats of other diatomic gases, corrected to the ideal state, show no appreciable fall at low temperatures. Scheel and Heuse [3] found for oxygen, carbon monoxide, and nitrogen (the value of C_p being reduced to the ideal gas state, C_p^0):

N_2...	... −181°	+20°	O_2	... −181°	+20°	CO	... −180°	+18°
C_p^0	... 6·718	6·969	C_p^0	... 6·90	6·97	C_p^0	... 6·74	6·99

Heuse [4] found for nitric oxide ($\gamma = C_p/C_v$):

t° C.	C_p	C_v	C_p^0	C_v^0	γ	γ_0
+15	7·25	5·25	7·23	5·25	1·38	1·38
−45	7·17	5·16	7·14	5·15	1·39	1·39
−55	7·26	5·25	7·22	5·24	1·38	1·38
−80	7·33	5·31	7·28	5·29	1·38	1·38

The differences are due to experimental errors in the continuous flow method used, since the values of C_p^0 for argon were also found to vary with temperature, being 4·85 at −180° and 5·05 at +15°. Bartels and Eucken [5] found almost the classical value ($C_p^0=6{\cdot}873$) for N_2 at 92° K. The rather large decrease in C_v for gases at 60–100° K. found by Shreiner [6] are almost certainly due to experimental errors.

The equation for the rotational energy is (§ 19):

$$\epsilon_{rJ} = J(J+1)h^2/8\pi^2 I \qquad (1)$$

For all diatomic molecules the moment of inertia I about the axis of the molecule is very small, hence the corresponding quantum ϵ_r, from (1), is very large, and hence this degree of freedom makes no appreciable contribution except at very high temperatures, since $e^{-\epsilon_{rJ}/kT}$ is practically unity, $e^0=1$.

For molecules such as O_2, N_2, CO and HCl, the value of I at right angles to the axis of rotation is about 10^{-39}, hence $h^2/8\pi^2 I$ is so small that equipartition is practically followed. In the case of H_2, however, the value is distinctly smaller, $0{\cdot}47 \times 10^{-40}$, and the size of the rotational quantum is large enough to cause appreciable departure from equipartition even at room temperature, and at 60° K. the rotational specific heat has disappeared.

It was obvious that the peculiar behaviour of hydrogen was due to the quantisation of its rotational energy, but all earlier attempts [7] to reproduce the

[1] Eucken, *Berlin Ber.*, 1912, 141; Clusius and Bartholomé, *Z. Elektrochem.*, 1934, **40**, 524.
[2] Ewing, *Engineering*, 1920, **109**, 842.
[3] *Ann. Phys.*, 1913, **40**, 473.
[4] *Ann. Phys.*, 1919, **59**, 86.
[5] *Z. phys. Chem.*, 1921, **98**, 70.
[6] *Archiv Math. Naturvidenskab*, Christiania, 1916, **34**, No. 9.
[7] Eucken, *Berlin Ber.*, 1912, 141; Bjerrum, *Nernst Festschr.*, 1912, 90; Sackur, *Ann. Phys.*, 1913, **40**, 87; Holm, *ibid.*, 1913, **42**, 1311; Einstein and Stern, *ibid.*, 1913, **40**, 551 (zero-point energy); Ehrenfest, *Verhl. d. D. Phys. Ges.*, 1913, **15**, 451; Fokker, *Ann. Phys.*, 1914, **43**, 810; Keesom, *Phys. Z.*, 1914, **15**, 8; Planck, *Verhl. d. D. Phys. Ges.*, 1915, **17**, 407, 438; Nernst, *ibid.*, 1916, **18**, 83; Krüger, *Ann. Phys.*, 1916, **50**, 346; 1916, **51**, 450 (precessional motion); van Weyssenhoff, *ibid.*, 1916, **51**, 285; Rotszajn, *ibid.*, 1918, **57**, 81; Kemble, *Phys. Rev.*, 1918. **11**, 156; Széll, *Verhl. d. D. Phys. Ges.*, 1918, **20**, 75; Reiche, *Ann. Phys.*, 1919, **58**, 657; *idem.*, "The Quantum Theory," 1930, 68 f. (summary); Macdougall, *J.A.C.S.*, 1921, **43**, 23; Ingold and Usherwood, *J.C.S.*, 1922, **121**, 2286; Born and Heisenberg, *Ann. Phys.*, 1924, **74**, 1; Van Vleck, *Phys. Rev.*, 1926, **28**, 980; Hund, *Z. Phys.*, 1927, **42**, 93; Eucken, in Wien-Harms, "Handbuch der Experimentalphysik," 1929, **8**, i, 459 (12 equations, all incorrect). For attempts to calculate specific heats from the Bohr-Sommerfeld theory of the structure of the molecule, see Krüger, *Ann. Phys.*, 1916, **50**, 346; 1916, **51**, 450; Laski, *Phys. Z.*, 1919,

experimental curve theoretically failed. The problem was first solved after the recognition that ordinary hydrogen is a mixture of *ortho*-H_2 and *para*-H_2 molecules, in which the nuclear spins are in the same and opposite senses, respectively, and if it is assumed that the mixture contains 3 parts of *ortho*- to 1 of *para*-, the observed specific heat curves are closely reproduced.[1] In Fig. 11.IV the theoretical curves for the rotational specific heat for mixtures from 0 per cent to 100 per cent of *para*-H_2 are shown dotted; the full curves include some measured values. The maximum on the curve for *para*-H_2 is noteworthy. Since *ortho*-H_2 has antisymmetrical wave-functions, corresponding with odd rotational states only (J=1, 3, 5, . . .), and *para*-H_2 has symmetrical wave-functions, corresponding with even rotational states (J=0, 2, 4, . . .) only,

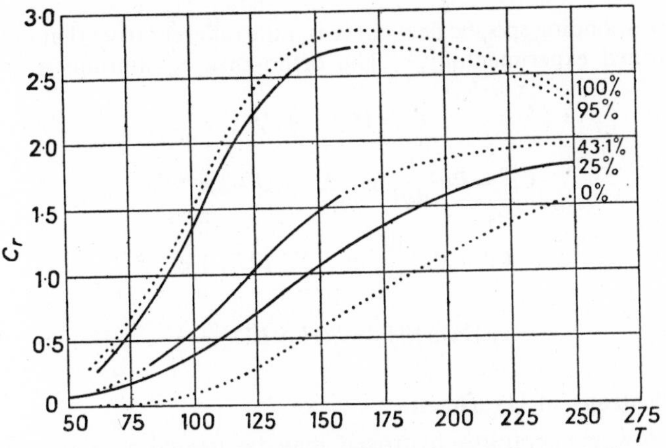

FIG. 11.IV. Curves showing the Rotational Specific Heat per mol of Mixtures of o-H_2 and p-H_2. (The percentages are those of p-H_2.)

and since the two forms are practically non-convertible, the rotational state sum for the mixture is ($\sigma = h^2/8\pi^2IkT$):

$$Z_r = 3 \sum_{1,3,5,\ldots} (2J+1)e^{-\sigma J(J+1)} + \sum_{0,2,4,\ldots} (2J+1)e^{-\sigma J(J+1)} \quad . \quad . \quad . \quad (2)$$

The rotational molecular heat is the sum of two parts, one for ortho-states and one for para-states:

$$C_r = \tfrac{1}{4}(3C_r^{\mathrm{O}} + C_r^{\mathrm{P}}) \quad . \quad . \quad . \quad . \quad . \quad . \quad . \quad . \quad . \quad . \quad (3)$$

The values of C_r^{O} and C_r^{P} are most conveniently found by differentiating (2) twice with respect to σ and using equation (29), § 8 ($\sigma = h^2/8\pi^2IkT$):

$$C_r = \frac{R}{T^2} \cdot \frac{d^2 \ln Z_r}{d(1/T)^2} = \frac{R}{T^2} \cdot \frac{d^2 \ln Z_r}{(8\pi^2Ik/h^2)^2 d\sigma^2}$$

$$= R(h^2/8\pi^2IkT)^2(d^2 \ln Z_r/d\sigma^2) = R\sigma^2(d^2 \ln Z_r/d\sigma^2) \quad . \quad . \quad . \quad (4)$$

$$\therefore \; C_r^{\mathrm{O}} \text{ (ortho)} = R\sigma^2(d^2/d\sigma^2) \ln (1 + 5e^{-6\sigma} + 9e^{-20\sigma} + \ldots) \quad . \quad . \quad (5)$$

$$C_r^{\mathrm{P}} \text{ (para)} = R\sigma^2(d^2/d\sigma^2) \ln (3e^{-2\sigma} + 7e^{-12\sigma} + \ldots) \quad . \quad . \quad . \quad (6)$$

20, 269; Macdougall, *J.A.C.S.*, 1921, **43**, 23. The correct suggestion that the theory was at fault, not the experiments, was made by Partington and Shilling, " The Specific Heats of Gases," 1924, 6, 238.

[1] Giauque and Johnston, *J.A.C.S.*, 1928, **50**, 3221; Josephy, *Angew. Chem.*, 1933, **46**, 256 (32 refs.); Motz and Patat, *Monatsh.*, 1934, **64**, 17; Clusius and Bartholomé, *Z. Elektrochem.*, 1934, **40**, 524; Farkas, " Orthohydrogen, Parahydrogen, and Heavy Hydrogen," Cambridge, 1935.

where 1, 5, 9, . . ., etc., are $(2J+1)$ for $J=0, 2, 4, \ldots$, etc.; 3, 7, . . ., etc., are $(2J+1)$ for $J=1, 3, \ldots$, etc.; and the indices of e are the values of $-\epsilon_J/kT$ given by (1) and $\sigma=h^2/8\pi^2IkT$, for values of $J(J+1)$, when $J=0, 1, 2, 3, 4, \ldots$. These series converge fairly rapidly, and are easily calculated.[1]

The values of C_r for hydrogen given [2] by (4) for temperatures below room temperature agree quite well with experiment, and equations (5) and (6) have been confirmed with synthetic mixtures enriched in p-H_2 (which, unlike o-H_2, can be obtained nearly pure). C_r for p-H_2, from (6), shows a maximum well above the equipartition value $R\simeq 2$ g.cal./1°. In the case of deuterium the state sum for D_2 is:

$$Z_r=3\sum_{1,3,5,\ldots}(2J+1)e^{-\sigma J(J+1)}+6\sum_{0,2,4,\ldots}(2J+1)e^{-\sigma J(J+1)} \quad . . \quad (7)$$

and the corresponding specific heat curve is quite different from that of hydrogen, as is confirmed experimentally.[3] The ortho-para equilibrium ratio is 2 : 1, hence:

$$C_r=\tfrac{2}{3}C_r^{\mathrm{O}}+\tfrac{1}{3}C_r^{\mathrm{P}} \quad . . . . \quad (8)$$

$$C_r^{\mathrm{O}}=R\sigma^2\frac{d^2}{d\sigma^2}\ln\sum_{0,2,4,\ldots}(2J+1)e^{-\epsilon_J/kT} \quad . . . . . \quad (9)$$

$$C_r^{\mathrm{P}}=R\sigma^2\frac{d^2}{d\sigma^2}\ln\sum_{1,3,5,\ldots}(2J+1)e^{-\epsilon_J/kT} \quad . . . . \quad (10)$$

where

$$\epsilon_J(D_2)/\epsilon_J(H_2)=I(H_2)/I(D_2)=\tfrac{1}{2} \quad . . . . . . \quad (11)$$

§ 24. The Entropy of Hydrogen

At very low temperatures hydrogen may be treated as a monatomic gas ($C_v=\tfrac{3}{2}R\simeq 3$ g.cal./1°); at higher temperatures, the rotational specific heat contributes to the entropy by $\int C_r d\ln T$. This is easily calculated for pure o-H_2 and p-H_2 by (5) and (6), § 23, and if the 3 : 1 o-p mixture which constitutes ordinary hydrogen at room temperature persists unchanged at low temperatures (actually, slow change of o into p occurs), C_r can be calculated for this by (3), § 23. At low temperatures, however, this is not a true equilibrium mixture. In calculating the virtual or HT entropy from the latent heat of sublimation of solid hydrogen there is also a transition in the solid (§ 69.II), which makes the calculated HT entropy (i.e. less nuclear spin entropy) at 298° K. 31·23 units, instead of 29·65 units when it is not taken into account. The total entropy including nuclear spin at 298° K. is calculated as 33·98 units.[4]

At temperatures between 50° K. and 300° K. the entropy (excluding nuclear spin) is given by:

$$S=\tfrac{1}{4}S^{\mathrm{P}}+\tfrac{3}{4}S^{\mathrm{O}}-R[\tfrac{3}{4}\ln\tfrac{3}{4}+\tfrac{1}{4}\ln\tfrac{1}{4}] \quad . . . . . \quad (1)$$

where

$$S^{\mathrm{P}}=\int C^{\mathrm{P}}d\ln T \quad . . . . \quad (2)$$

$$S^{\mathrm{O}}=\int C^{\mathrm{O}}d\ln T \quad . . . . \quad (3)$$

[1] See Partington, "Thermodynamics," 1940, 224.
[2] Dieke, *Physica*, 1925, **5**, 412.
[3] Clusius and Bartholomé, *Z. Elektrochem.*, 1934, **40**, 524; *Z. phys. Chem.*, 1935, **30** B, 258.
[4] Giauque and Johnston, *J.A.C.S.*, 1928, **50**, 3221; Giauque, *ibid.*, 1930, **52**, 4808, 4816; for deuterium (D_2) see Clusius and Bartholomé, *Z. phys. Chem.*, 1935, **30** B, 258, who find at 298° K. the statistical entropy 38·98 (correcting Johnston and Long, *J. Chem. Phys.*, 1934, **2**, 389) and the HT entropy 33·91.

C^P and C^O being given by (5) and (6), § 23. The last two terms on the right of (1) give the entropy of mixing [1] from § 57.II; they may be omitted, and cancel out in all applications of the equation when the mixture retains the same ortho-para ratio.

At temperatures above 300° K., but not so high that vibrational energies are involved, hydrogen behaves as a normal diatomic gas, for which (4), § 22, gives:

$$Z_r = \sum_{J=0}^{\infty} (2J+1)e^{-\sigma J(J+1)} \simeq 1/\sigma = 8\pi^2 IkT/h^2 \quad . \quad . \quad . \quad . \quad (4)$$

$$\therefore \; S = R[\ln A + \ln (8\pi^2 Ik/sh^2)] \quad . \quad . \quad . \quad . \quad . \quad . \quad (5)$$

(omitting nuclear spin and entropy of isotope mixture), where the symmetry factor (§ 18) is $s=2$, and A is given by (18), § 14. At ordinary temperatures $1/\sigma$ is of the order of 10–100 for most diatomic gases.

§ 25. Vibrational Levels in Molecules

At higher temperatures the vibrational contribution must be included. For simple diatomic molecules there is only one mode of vibration ($g_v=1$), and if the temperature is not too high the vibration may be assumed to be a simple harmonic motion and the state sum (omitting zero point energy) is given by (8), § 16 ($\epsilon_0=0$):

$$Z_v = \Sigma(1-e^{-h\nu/kT})^{-1} \quad . \quad . \quad . \quad . \quad . \quad . \quad . \quad . \quad (1)$$

the sum being taken over all the vibration frequencies ν. Actually, as the vibrational quanta are fairly large, the vibrations cease to be harmonic when only a few quanta have been taken up, and the actual values for the individual energy levels as found from spectroscopic data must then be used in the state sum.

The notation used in spectroscopy differs from that employed in § 16 (which is standard in quantum theory). Instead of (4), § 16, for the vibrational energy of the simple harmonic oscillator: $\epsilon=(n+\frac{1}{2})h\nu$, the vibrational quantum number is v instead of n, and the frequency is $\tilde{\omega}_e$ instead of ν, the suffix e denoting the "equilibrium," or simple-harmonic, value for zero amplitude. Hence:

$$\epsilon_v = h\tilde{\omega}_e(v+\tfrac{1}{2}) \quad . \quad . \quad . \quad . \quad . \quad . \quad . \quad . \quad . \quad (2)$$

For finite amplitudes, (2) is replaced by:

$$\epsilon_v = h\tilde{\omega}_e(v+\tfrac{1}{2}) - h\tilde{\omega}_e x(v+\tfrac{1}{2})^2 \quad . \quad . \quad . \quad . \quad . \quad . \quad (3)$$

where x is the *anharmonicity constant*. The zero-point energy ($v=0$) [2] is then:

$$\epsilon_{v0} = \tfrac{1}{2}h\tilde{\omega}_e - \tfrac{1}{4}h\tilde{\omega}_e x \quad . \quad . \quad . \quad . \quad . \quad . \quad . \quad . \quad (4)$$

In spectroscopy, the frequency is replaced by the *wave-number* $\omega=\tilde{\omega}/c=\tilde{\omega}/2{\cdot}998\times10^{10}$ (c=velocity of light in vacuum), giving the number of waves per cm. (dimensions cm.$^{-1}$), and the results of band-spectrum analysis are expressed by an empirical wave-number formula: [3]

$$\nu = \nu_0 + \omega_e(v+\tfrac{1}{2}) - x\omega_e(v+\tfrac{1}{2})^2 + \ldots$$
$$+ B_v J(J+1) + D_v J^2(J+1)^2 + F_v J^3(J+1)^3 + \ldots \quad . \quad (5)$$

[1] See Kelley, *J.A.C.S.*, 1929, **51**, 353; Giauque, *ibid.*, 1930, **52**, 4808, 4816; in Fowler's calculation, *Proc. Roy. Soc.*, 1928, **118**, 52, for *o*- and *p*-H_2, the entropy of mixing was, perhaps inadvertently, omitted. Keesom, *Proc. K. Akad. Wetens. Amsterdam*, 1914, **16**, 669 (*Comm. Leiden* Suppl. 33); *Phys. Z.*, 1914, **15**, 217, 368, concluded that the entropy of mixing is zero at 0° K.

[2] See § 11. It should be noted that the zero point energy still depends on x.

[3] The notation varies: see Mulliken, *Rev. Mod. Phys.*, 1930, **2**, 60; 1932, **4**, 1; Jevons, "Report on Band Spectra," 1932; Glasstone, "Theoretical Chemistry," New York, 1944, 156.

where:

ν_0=electronic wave number separation ($\nu_0=0$ for the ground state);

ω_e=fundamental vibration (" equilibrium ") wave-number in any electronic state;

x=anharmonicity constant for vibration;

v=vibrational quantum number;

J=rotational quantum number (sometimes K is used);

$B_v=B_e-\alpha(v+\frac{1}{2})+\gamma(v+\frac{1}{2})^2- \ldots$;

$D_v=D_e+\beta(v+\frac{1}{2})+ \ldots$;

In these equations the small dependence of F_v on v is neglected, and the half quantum of zero-point energy is added to v. Allowance is made for changes of moment of inertia in the rotational levels due to the stretching of the molecule under centrifugal force, and for the interaction of the vibrational and rotational quanta, as the average size of the molecule increases with v. In practice, simplification is usually possible,[1] e.g. for rigid molecules $D_v=F_v=0$, and $B_v=h^2/8\pi^2Ic$ (constant).

Z is calculated at a given temperature by summation over all rotational levels with $v=0$, and repeating for $v=1, 2, 3, \ldots$, as long as the contributions are significant. The process is repeated for any electronic levels which are near enough to the ground state to give appreciable contributions. The complete internal state sum is then given by (6), § 11, as the product of the vibrational, rotational, and electronic functions. The summations must be repeated for various temperatures, as the thermodynamic functions involve Z as a function of temperature. Various approximation methods, integration, etc., often replace this laborious procedure.

The series (3) can be extended if necessary by further terms:

$$\epsilon_v=h\tilde{\omega}_e[(v+\tfrac{1}{2})-x_e(v+\tfrac{1}{2})^2+k_3(v+\tfrac{1}{2})^3-k_4(v+\tfrac{1}{2})^4 \ldots] \quad . \quad . \quad (6)$$

The difference between two energy levels for *successive* quantum numbers v' and v'', where $v'=v''+1$, is, if terms beyond the second are neglected:

$$\Delta\epsilon_v=h\tilde{\omega}_e\{[(v'+\tfrac{1}{2})-x_e(v'+\tfrac{1}{2})^2]-[(v''+\tfrac{1}{2})-x_e(v''+\tfrac{1}{2})^2]\}$$

$$=h\tilde{\omega}_e(1-2x_ev''-2x_e)=h\tilde{\omega}_e-2h\tilde{\omega}_ex_e(v''+1)=h\tilde{\omega}_e-2h\tilde{\omega}_ex_ev' \quad . \quad (7)$$

As the successive vibrational levels rise with increasing v, they crowd closer together, and when they approach the line $\epsilon=D$ (D=dissociation energy) the separation $\Delta\epsilon$ is zero, or the lines form a continuum.[2] When $\Delta\epsilon=0$, the vibrational quantum number is given by $h\tilde{\omega}_e-2h\tilde{\omega}_ex_ev'=0$, therefore $v'=1/2x_e$. Substitute this for v in (6):

$$\therefore\ \epsilon_v=h\tilde{\omega}_e[(1/2x_e+\tfrac{1}{2})-x_e(1/2x_e+\tfrac{1}{2})^2]=h\tilde{\omega}_e/4x_e-hx_e\tilde{\omega}_e/4.$$

[1] Smith, Boord, Adams, and Pease, *J.A.C.S.*, 1927, **49**, 1335; Kassel, *Chem. Rev.*, 1936, **18**, 277; Jeunehomme, " Calcul des Équilibres Physico-Chimiques," Paris, 1937; Gordon and Barnes, *J. Chem. Phys.*, 1933, **1**, 297, 308; Gordon, *ibid.*, 1934, **2**, 65; corrected by Wilson, *ibid.*, 1936, **4**, 526; and by Giauque, *J.A.C.S.*, 1937, **59**, 1158. For the wave mechanics of the anharmonic vibrator, see Sokolov, *J. Exptl. Theor. Phys. U.S.S.R.*, 1932, **2**, 154.

[2] Franck, *Trans. Faraday Soc.*, 1925, **21**, 536; Birge and Sponer, *Phys. Rev.*, 1926, **28**, 259; Franck, Kuhn, and Rollefson, *Z. Phys.*, 1927, **43**, 155; Winans and Stueckelberg, *Proc. Nat. Acad.*, 1928, **14**, 867; Finkelnburg, *Phys. Z.*, 1930, **31**, 1; 1933, **34**, 529; Beutler and Mie, *Naturwiss.*, 1934, **22**, 418; Mie, *Z. Phys.*, 1934, **91**, 475; Beutler, *Z. phys. Chem.*, 1934, **27 B**, 287 ($D_{HI}=103{\cdot}50$, $D_{D_2}=104{\cdot}48$, $D_{HCl}=101{\cdot}63$); Clusius, *Die Chemie*, 1943, **56**, 241.

The value of D, the energy of dissociation, is:

$$D=\epsilon_v-\epsilon_{v0}=h\tilde{\omega}_e/4x_e-hx_e\tilde{\omega}_e/4-(h\tilde{\omega}_e/2-hx_e\tilde{\omega}_e/4)$$
$$=h\tilde{\omega}_e/4x_e-h\tilde{\omega}_e/2,$$

and with reference to zero energy this is:

$$D=h\tilde{\omega}_e/4x_e, \quad \text{or } x_e=h\tilde{\omega}_e/4D \quad . \quad . \quad . \quad . \quad . \quad . \quad . \quad (8)$$

Equation (6) is usually applied in spectroscopy in the form:

$$\epsilon_v'=\epsilon_v-\epsilon_{v0}=hc\omega_0(v-x_0v^2+yv^3+\ldots) \quad . \quad . \quad . \quad . \quad (9)$$

where ϵ_{v0} is the zero point energy and ω_0 is a wave number ($\tilde{\omega}/c$), so that, from (4):

$$\epsilon_{v0}=hc\omega_e(\tfrac{1}{2}-x_e/4).$$

By equating coefficients of v, v^2 and v^3 in (6) and (9), it is found that:

$$\omega_0=\omega_e-x_e\omega_e+\tfrac{3}{4}k_3\omega_e+\ldots,$$
$$x_0\omega_0=x_e\omega_e+\tfrac{3}{2}k_3\omega_e+\ldots,$$
$$y\omega_0=k_3\omega_e+\ldots.$$

For H_2, the spectroscopic values[1] are: $\omega_0=4276$ cm.$^{-1}$, $x_0\omega_0=114$, $y\simeq k_4\simeq k_3\simeq 0$, $\omega_e=4390$ cm.$^{-1}$, $x_e=0{\cdot}026$. Morse's equation (§ 17) with $D=4{\cdot}725$ electron volts gives $x_e=0{\cdot}0286$. Rosen[2] calculated theoretically $\omega_e=4260$ cm.$^{-1}$, and James and Coolidge[3] $D=4{\cdot}722\pm0{\cdot}013$ electron volts. From the wave-length of the beginning of the continuous spectrum (see above) D is calculated as $4{\cdot}725\pm0{\cdot}005$ electron volts.

Giauque and Overstreet[4] used the following method. The rotational levels for a non-rigid diatomic molecule were represented (energies in wave-number units) by:

$$\epsilon_r=Bm^2+Dm^4+Fm^6+\ldots \quad . \quad . \quad . \quad . \quad . \quad . \quad (10)$$

where $m=J+\tfrac{1}{2}$; B, D, F, . . . are constants; $g_r=2J+1=2m$. Hence:

$$Z_r=\Sigma 2m \exp\{[-hc(Bm^2+Dm^4+Fm^6+\ldots)]/kT\}$$
$$=\Sigma 2m[\exp(-Bhcm^2/kT)][\exp(-Dhcm^4/kT)][\exp(-Fhcm^6/kT)]\ldots$$
$$=\Sigma 2m\exp(-Bhcm^2/kT)[1-Dhcm^4/kT+\tfrac{1}{2}(Dhcm^4/kT)^2\ldots]\times$$
$$[1-Fhcm^6/kT+\tfrac{1}{2}(Fhcm^6/kT)^2+\ldots]$$
$$=\Sigma 2m\exp(-Bhcm^2/kT)[1-Dhcm^4/kT-Fhcm^6/kT$$
$$+\tfrac{1}{2}(Dhcm^4/kT)^2+(Dhcm^4/kT)(Fhcm^6/kT)+\tfrac{1}{2}(Fhcm^6/kT)^2+\ldots]$$

where $\exp(-x)=e^{-x}$. As a first approximation sums are replaced by integrals:

$$Z_re^{-\epsilon_0hc/kT}=\int_0^\infty 2me^{-z}dm-\int_0^\infty(2Dhc/kT)m^5e^{-z}dm-\int_0^\infty(2Fhc/kT)m^7e^{-z}dm$$
$$+\int_0^\infty(Dhc/kT)^2m^9e^{-z}dm+\int_0^\infty(2DFhc/kT)^2m^{11}e^{-z}dm+\ldots$$

where $z=Bhcm^2/kT$, and the factor of Z_r is due to the fact that the zero of energy in the integrals is for $m=0$, whilst the zero used is for $m=\tfrac{1}{2}$. Integration gives:

$$Z_re^{-\epsilon_0hc/kT}=(kT/Bhc)[1-2!(D/B^2)\beta-3!(F/B^3)\beta^2+(4!/2!)(D^2/B^4)\beta^2$$
$$+5!(DF/B^5)\beta^3+\ldots] \quad . \quad . \quad (11)$$

[1] Hyman and Birge, *Nature*, 1930, **123**, 277; Hyman, *Phys. Rev.*, 1930, **36**, 187.
[2] *Phys. Rev.*, 1931, **38**, 2099.
[3] *J. Chem. Phys.*, 1933, **1**, 825; 1935, **3**, 129.
[4] *J.A.C.S.*, 1932, **54**, 1731; Gordon and Barnes, *J. Chem. Phys.*, 1933, **1**, 297.

where $\beta = kT/hc$. The correction necessary when integration is used instead of summation was investigated by Mulholland [1] and Sutherland [2] for rigid diatomic molecules; they found:

$$\Sigma 2me^{-z} = (kT/Bhc)(1 + Bhc/12kT + \ldots) \quad \ldots \quad (12)$$

The other integrals did not require correction. In (11), therefore, the term $(B/12)\beta$ is added to the series in square brackets, giving:

$$Z_r e^{-\epsilon_0 hc/kT} = (kT/Bhc)[1 + (B/12)\beta - 2!(D/B^2)\beta - 3!(F/B^3)\beta^2 + (4!D^2/2!B^4)\beta^2 + 5!(DF/B^5)\beta^3 + \ldots] \quad . \quad . \quad (13)$$

Giauque and Overstreet showed that equation (13) gave values for HCl differing only inappreciably from those found by actual summation, at $T = 1000°$ and 2000°. In the case of molecules containing isotopes (e.g. HCl containing Cl=35 and Cl=37), Mulliken [3] found that the constants B, D, and F are inversely proportional to μ, μ^2, and μ^3, respectively, where μ is the reduced mass $(1/\mu = 1/M_1 + 1/M_2)$ of the molecule. In the case of vibrational levels, where (in wave-number units):

$$\epsilon_v = \omega_e(v + \tfrac{1}{2}) + x_e\omega_e(v + \tfrac{1}{2})^2 + y_e\omega_e(v + \tfrac{1}{2})^3$$

$\mu^{-1/2}$ occurs in each term to the same power as $(v + \frac{1}{2})$.

In calculating the entropy of nitrogen gas Giauque and Clayton [4] used the spectroscopic equations (ϵ in wave-number units):

$$\epsilon_r = [B_e + \alpha(v + \tfrac{1}{2})]m^2 + [D_e + \gamma(v + \tfrac{1}{2})]m^4$$

$$\epsilon_v = \omega_e(v + \tfrac{1}{2}) + x_e\omega_e(v + \tfrac{1}{2})^2$$

with [5] $B_e = 2{\cdot}003$, $\alpha = -0{\cdot}023$, $D_e = -5{\cdot}773 \times 10^{-6}$, $\gamma = 8{\cdot}61 \times 10^{-8}$, $\omega_e = 2359{\cdot}61$, $x_e\omega_e = -14{\cdot}445$, all referred to the hypothetical state of zero vibration. Equation (13) then gives for the internal state sum (rotation and vibration):

$$Z_i = \exp\,[(B/4 + D/16)/\beta]\,.\,\beta[1 + \beta/12 - (2D/B^2)\beta + (12D^2/B^4)\beta^2 + \ldots]$$

this value being reduced to one-half because of the molecular symmetry of N_2 ($s=2$) and nuclear spin omitted.

From Z_i the internal entropy was calculated from (28), § 8, as

$$S_i = R \ln Z_i + RT(\mathrm{d} \ln Z_i/\mathrm{d}T)$$

and added to the translational entropy, as usual. The final result gave $S_{298} = 45{\cdot}788$, to be compared with the calorimetric (Nernst heat theorem) value 45·89 calculated as in § 70.II.

In the summation over the vibrational states an empirical relation between Z_v's for adjacent vibrational states [6] enables the calculation to be curtailed. Alternative methods of calculating the state sums for diatomic molecules were also used by Gordon and Barnes [7] and by Kassel.[8]

[1] *Proc. Cambr. Phil. Soc.*, 1928, **24**, 280.
[2] *Proc. Cambr. Phil. Soc.*, 1930, **26**, 402 (arithmetical error in calculation for NO).
[3] *Phys. Rev.*, 1925, **25**, 119 (isotope effect on specific heats).
[4] *J.A.C.S.*, 1933, **55**, 4875.
[5] Rasetti, *Phys. Rev.*, 1929, **34**, 367 (rotational constants); Birge and Hopfield, *ibid.*, 1927, **29**, 356 (vibrational constants).
[6] Johnston and Davis, *J.A.C.S.*, 1934, **56**, 271.
[7] *J. Chem. Phys.*, 1933, **1**, 297.
[8] *J. Chem. Phys.*, 1933, **1**, 576; *Chem. Rev.*, 1936, **18**, 277.

§ 26. Statistical Calculation of Entropies

In calculating gas equilibria from free energies the nuclear spin contribution to the state sum may be omitted, since it cancels,[1] except in the case of hydrogen. The case of iodine (I_2) seems to be peculiar,[2] since the *ortho-* and *para*-forms carry their spin multiplicities, but not their rotational multiplicities, into the solid state. The spectroscopic entropy of the gas is $S_{298\cdot1}=62\cdot29$ (not including the nuclear spin contribution). Giauque found the NT entropy of the solid $S_{298\cdot1}=27\cdot9$. The calculated latent heat of sublimation at 298·1° K. is 14,877 g.cal./mol., which would seem to give $\Delta S=14877/298\cdot1=49\cdot91$, hence for the gas the NT entropy is $27\cdot9+49\cdot91=77\cdot81$. Giauque (who does not calculate the NT value) gives no explanation of the enormous difference between 62·29 and 77·81. In the case of bromine (Br_2) at 265·8° K. the discrepancy is also serious [3]: S (NT)=62·1, S (spectr.)=58·63 (61·69 less $\frac{1}{2}\boldsymbol{R}\ln 2$).

The values for carbon monoxide (CO) are anomalous.[4] At the b.p. S (NT)= 37·2 (ideal gas) and S (spectr.)=38·32. The difference is about $\boldsymbol{R}\ln 2$, which suggests a lack of discrimination in the lattice of the crystal for the O and C ends of the CO molecules (see § 18). The entropy of water vapour calculated from spectroscopic data is about 1 g.cal./1° per mol discrepant [5]: S (NT) at 25°=44·28,[6] S (spectr.) at 25°=45·10; [7] the difference of 0·82 is near the value $0\cdot806=\boldsymbol{R}\ln(6/4)$ calculated by Pauling [8] on the assumption of non-ordered orientation of H_2O molecules in the ice lattice. It is noteworthy that [9] ice has no measurable heat capacity at 0·2°–4° K. The entropy of H_2O vapour at 25° calculated indirectly [10] from those of $Mg(OH)_2$ and MgO, and the thermal and equilibrium constants of the reaction $Mg(OH)_2 \rightleftharpoons MgO+H_2O$, is 45·10, in excellent agreement with the spectroscopic value 45·13. The discrepancy found [11] for crystal water in $Na_2SO_4,10H_2O$ probably arises from the same cause as that for ice. For tetramethylmethane,[12] $C(CH_3)_4$, S (NT)= 71·71 and S (spectr.)=78·89, at the b.p. The difference 7·18 is nearly equal to $5\,\boldsymbol{R}\ln 2=6\cdot89$, and the case may be analogous to the above. The rather large discrepancy with methylamine: [13] S (NT)=56·42, S (spectr.)=58·06, at the b.p., is probably due to some error in the spectroscopic assignment, e.g. neglect of the potential associated with the rotation of the methyl group.

§ 27. Polyatomic Molecules

The calculations of state sums [14] for polyatomic molecules are usually only possible with approximations, e.g. the vibrational state sum is often small (for N_2O at 298° K., $Z_r=496$, $Z_v=1\cdot1$), and sums may often be replaced by integrals,

1 Gibson and Heitler, *Z. Phys.*, 1928, **49**, 465; see Zeise, *Z. Elektrochem.*, 1934, **40**, 665.
2 Giauque, *J.A.C.S.*, 1931, **53**, 507.
3 Brown, *J.A.C.S.*, 1932, **54**, 2394.
4 Clayton and Giauque, *J.A.C.S.*, 1932, **54**, 2610.
5 Ashley, *Phys. Rev.*, 1933, **43**, 81.
6 Gordon, *J. Chem. Phys.*, 1934, **2**, 65.
7 Giauque and Stout, *J.A.C.S.*, 1936, **58**, 1144.
8 *J.A.C.S.*, 1935, **57**, 2680.
9 MacDougall and Giauque, *J.A.C.S.*, 1936, **58**, 1032.
10 Giauque and Archibald, *J.A.C.S.*, 1937, **59**, 561.
11 Pitzer and Coulter, *J.A.C.S.*, 1938, **60**, 1310.
12 Aston and Messerly, *J.A.C.S.*, 1936, **58**, 2354.
13 Aston, Siller, and Messerly, *J.A.C.S.*, **59**, 1743.
14 The calculations are purely routine and very tedious, and seem ripe for the punched-card or " electronic brain " technique; see King, *J. Chem. Phys.*, 1946, **15**, 85; Hamer and King *ibid.*, 1946, **15**, 89.

especially when the moment of inertia is large. Some results are merely stated here ($\sigma = h^2/8\pi^2 IkT$; s=symmetry number)[1]:

1. *Linear molecules* (N_2O, CO_2, C_2H_2, HCN) are treated as diatomic: $Z_r = 1/s\sigma$. For HCN and N_2O, $s=1$, for the other molecules it is 2. Entropies per mol at 25° calculated by Badger and Woo[2] are:

	CO_2	N_2O	HCN	C_2H_2
S including nuclear spin	51·07	56·94	51·79	50·57
S excluding nuclear spin	51·07	52·58	48·23	48·00

2. *Spherical rotors* (CH_4, CCl_4, but not $C(CH_3)_4$ with rotating groups), with $I_A = I_B = I_C$, $s=12$: $Z_r = \sqrt{\pi}/s\sigma^{3/2}$.

3. *Spherical tops* (NH_3, $CHCl_3$), with $I_A = I_B \neq I_C$, $Z_r = \sqrt{\pi}/s\sigma_A\sigma_C^{1/2}$; C_2H_6 is a double top, with $Z_r = \pi/s\sigma_A\sigma_C$.

4. *Asymmetrical tops* with I_A, I_B, I_C all different, with the approximation $I = (I_A I_B I_C)^{1/2}$, $Z_r = (1/s)(\pi/\sigma_A\sigma_B\sigma_C)^{1/2}$. For H_2O, $s=2$; for C_6H_6, $s=12$.

5. *More complex molecules* (n degrees of freedom of rotation):

$$Z_r = (1/s\pi)[8\pi^3(I_A I_B I_C \ldots)^{1/n}(kT/h^2)]^{n/2}$$

The complete expression for the available energy per mol of an ideal gas with polyatomic linear molecules is:

$$G = E_0 - \tfrac{7}{2}RT\ln T + RT\ln p + RT\Sigma\ln(1 - e^{-h\nu/kT}) - RT\ln\frac{(2\pi m)^{3/2}k^{5/2}}{h^3}\cdot\frac{8\pi^2 Ik}{h^2 s}g_e\Pi(g_n) \quad \ldots\ldots (1)$$

where $\Pi(g_n)$ is the product of the nuclear spin weights; and for an ideal gas with polyatomic non-linear molecules:

$$G = E_0 - 4RT\ln T + RT\ln p + RT\Sigma\ln(1 - e^{-h\nu/kT}) - RT\ln\frac{(2\pi m)^{3/2}k^{5/2}}{h^3}\cdot\frac{8\pi^2(2\pi k)^{3/2}(I_A I_B I_C)^{1/2}}{h^3 s}g_e\Pi(g_n) \quad \ldots (2)$$

In the case of rigid molecules $\Sigma\ln(1 - e^{-h\nu/kT}) = 0$.

Syrkin[3] calculated for a polyatomic gas:

$$S = kN\ln(2\pi mkT)^{n/2}a^{n-3}Ve^{1+n/2}/Nh^n \quad \ldots\ldots (3)$$

where n=number of degrees of freedom, a=diameter of molecule, V=volume.

The entropies calculated from spectroscopic data for polyatomic gases must be used with caution, since it is always possible that the ascertained energy levels are either incomplete or not sufficiently accurate. As an example of the disagreement with the Nernst heat theorem value (which the physical chemist will prefer if it is known) the case of CCl_4 at 25° C. may be mentioned[4]: *S* (NT)=71·2, *S* (spectr.)=74·3. Kistiakowski and Wilson[5] pointed out the arbitrary and sometimes erroneous results found for entropies when hypothetical " potential barriers " (§ 28) are assumed, but the protagonists of this

[1] Mayer, Brunauer, and Mayer, *J.A.C.S.*, 1933, **55**, 37 (who consider the case of optical isomers also) define the *symmetry number* as the number of permutations of identical particles in the molecule which can be carried out by changes in the coordinates of rotation and spin alone. Cf. Witmer, *Proc. Nat. Acad.*, 1927, **13**, 60. For a sketch of the calculations, see Glasstone, " Theoretical Chemistry," New York, 1944, 386 f.

[2] *J.A.C.S.*, 1932, **54**, 3523.

[3] *Z. Phys.*, 1924, **24**, 355.

[4] Yost and Blair, *J.A.C.S.*, 1933, **55**, 2610; Fink and Bonilla, *J. Phys. Chem.*, 1933, **37**, 1135; the fact that some values have been improved by later manipulation does not affect the general principle stated.

[5] *J.A.C.S.*, 1938, **60**, 494, where the results are said to be " rather meaningless."

method [1] have given considered arguments in support of the calculations. The exaggerated claims to high precision urged in this field, and the affected contempt of mere experiments, are in themselves suspicious. In other calculations,[2] the difference is about 20 per cent (propylene). Eucken and Schäffer's [3] calculation of the " potential barrier " of ethane is erroneous, but even this simple case is not satisfactorily disposed of.

Eucken [4] at first imagined that the moments of inertia of some di- and triatomic molecules as calculated from thermal and spectroscopic data were different, but the discrepancies were due to experimental errors in both parts, and newer work (§ 29) has given closer agreement with increasing accuracy, so that Eucken [5] abandoned his former opinion.

In tabulated values a mean moment of inertia for polyatomic gases, $\bar{I}=(I_A I_B I_C)^{1/3}$, is often given, and in this case $\frac{1}{2}\ln(I_A I_B I_C)$ in (2) is replaced by $\frac{3}{2}\ln\bar{I}$. (Sometimes I_A, I_B, and I_C are denoted by A, B, and C). Some values of various quantities connected with gases are given in the tables below.[6]

I. Monatomic Gases

Gas	Symbol of Energy level	Statistical weight, g_e	Entropy (less nuclear spin contribution). $S°$ g.cal./1° C. mol, at 25° C.
Inert gases	$^1S_0$	1	A 36·99
H, alkali metals, Cu, Ag, Au	$^2S_{1/2}$	2	H 27·40
Zn, Cd, Hg alkaline earth metals	$^1S_0$	1	Zn 38·46 Cd 40·07
C	$^3P_0$, $^3P_1$, $^3P_2$	$1+3e^{-22\cdot7/T}+5e^{-60\cdot8/T}$ $\simeq 9$ above room temperature	37·77
N, P, As, Sb, Bi ...	$^4S_{3/2}$	4	N 36·62 P 38·99
O	$^3P_2$, $^3P_1$, $^3P_0$	$5+3e^{-229/T}+e^{-325/T}$	38·48
F	$^2P_{3/2}$, $^2P_{1/2}$	$4+2e^{-582/T}$	37·93
Cl		$4+2e^{-1265/T}$	39·46
Br		$4+2e^{-5270/T}\simeq 4$	41·81
I		$4+2e^{-10900/T}\simeq 4$	43·19

For di- and polyatomic gases the values of the chemical constant j' (see § 10.VIII L, Vol. II), the characteristic temperatures ((18), § 17), $\Theta=h\nu/k$, for

1 See e.g. Pitzer and Kemp, *J.A.C.S.*, 1938, **60**, 1515.
2 Pitzer, *J. Chem. Phys.*, 1937, **5**, 469, 473; Kistiakowsky *et al.*, *J.A.C.S.*, 1939, **61**, 2980.
3 *Naturwiss.*, 1939, **27**, 122.
4 *Jahrb. Radioakt. Elektronik*, 1920, **16**, 361; *Z. Elektrochem.*, 1920, **26**, 377; *Phys. Z.*, 1929, **30**, 818; " Lehrbuch der chemischen Physik," 1930, 235, 248; Eucken, Karwat, and Fried, *Z. Phys.*, 1924, **29**, 34.
5 Eucken, Clusius, and Woitinek, *Z. anorg. Chem.*, 1931, **203**, 39.
6 Wohl and Zeise, in Landolt-Börnstein, " Tabellen," 5th edit., 1936, Ergzbd. **3**, 2345 f.; Kelley, *U.S. Bur. Mines Bull.*, 1936, **394**; Epstein, " Textbook of Thermodynamics," 1937, 298; Latimer, " Oxidation Potentials," New York, 1938, Appendix V; Macdougall, " Thermodynamics and Chemistry," 3rd edit., New York, 1939, 469. See also the publications of Zeise quoted in § 29.

the vibrational quantum, and for polyatomic gases the values of I_A, I_B, and I_C and the mean moment of inertia $\bar{I}$ are given:

for diatomic gases: $j'=(S_0'-\frac{7}{2}R)/2{\cdot}3026R$ . . . . (4)

for polyatomic gases: $j'=(S_0'-\frac{8}{2}R)/2{\cdot}3026R$ . . . . (5)

II. Diatomic Gases

Gas	Θ_v	$g_0=g_e$ in lowest level	Symmetry number s	Moment of inertia, $I\times10^{40}$ g.cm.^{2}	Chemical constant, j'	Entropy S° g.cal/1° mol, gas at 25° C.
H_2	6130	1	2	0·46637	−3·369	31·23
N_2	3350	1	2	13·84	−0·183	45·79
O_2	2224	3	2	19·23	+0·524	49·03
F_2	1533	1	2	27·76	+0·318	48·00
Cl_2	801	1	2*	113·9	+1·448	53·31
Br_2	461	1	2*	342·5	+2·496	58·63
I_2	305	1	2	741·5	+2·982	62·29
HCl ...	4200	1	1	2·6494	−0·428	44·66
HBr ...	3787	1	1	3·2634	+0·182	47·48
HI	3245	1	1	4·308	+0·601	49·40
CO	3085	1	1	14·43	+0·137	47·32

* The values 1·57 (Cl_2) and 1·42 (Br_2), usually given, represent mean values for isotopes.

III. Polyatomic Gases

Gas	Θ_v	s	$I_A\times10^{40}$	$I_B\times10^{40}$	$I_C\times10^{40}$	$\bar{I}\times10^{40}$	j'
N_2O	847 (2), 1850 (1) 3200 (1)	1				66·0	1·091
CO_2	960 (2), 1900 (1), 3400 (1)	2				70·4	0·818
C_2H_2	889 (2), 1048 (2), 2840 (1), 4730 (1), 4850 (1)	2				23·502	0·000
H_2O	2294, 5180, 5400	2	0·996	1·908	2·981	1·784	−1·787
NH_3	1366 (1), 2340 (2), 4790 (1), 4990 (2)	3	2·78	2·78	4·33	3·22	−1·616
CH_4	1875 (3), 2185 (2), 4190 (1), 4340 (3)	12	5·267	5·267	5·267	5·267	−1·936

§ 28. Molecules with Restricted Rotation

The case where some or all of the groups in a polyatomic molecule are capable of free or restricted rotation is a difficult one, and some of the theoretical results seem worthless.[1] The group may also be capable of rotation within itself (e.g. CH_3CH_2—in butane). The calculation of the entropy on the assumption of particular rotating groups and its comparison with the entropy found from the Nernst heat theorem has been used in surmising the structure of organic molecules assumed to contain free rotating groups, and also groups with restricted rotation. The following cases are briefly considered.

[1] See e.g. Kassel, *J.A.C.S.*, 1937, **59**, 2746, on the disagreement with butanes; Thompson, *Ann. Rep. Chem. Soc.*, 1941, **39**, 46. The literature in § 29 contains many examples of this type of calculation; see the summary by Aston, in Taylor and Glasstone, " Physical Chemistry," 1942, **1**, 590 f., and Glasstone, " Theoretical Chemistry," 1945, 415.

(i) For a molecule having f free internal rotations, the theory of equipartition of energy (§ 20) gives $E_r = \frac{1}{2}fRT$ per mol, and the detailed calculation gives exactly the same result.

(ii) For a molecule with restricted internal rotation consider the case of ethane, $H_3C.CH_3$. Suppose that if one CH_3 group rotates relative to the other, a repulsive force between the hydrogens causes three equally spaced maxima of potential energy, V (" potential barriers "), and three equally spaced minima, in a complete rotation (Fig. 12.IV). The two parts of the molecule normally execute to-and-fro twisting movements, and only when the energy is sufficiently large will one part rotate past a potential barrier relative to the other. The motion has been described as " rather drunken." An arbitrary

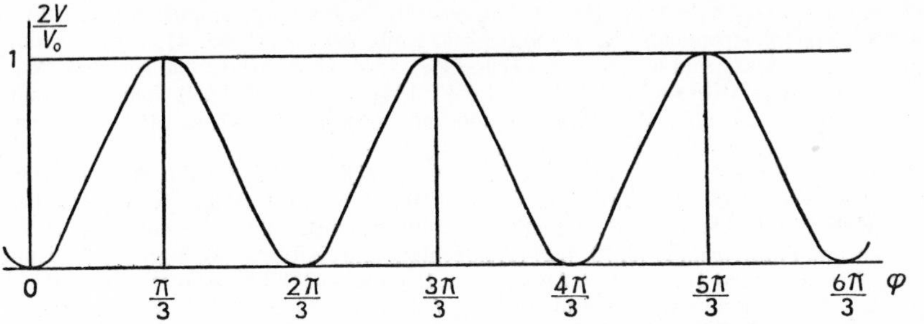

FIG. 12.IV. Potential Energy Barriers for Restricted Rotation

function which represents this type of motion is [1] $V = A - k \sin^2 \frac{1}{2}\theta$, but one which has been more used [2] is:

$$V = \tfrac{1}{2}V_0(1 - \cos 3\phi) \quad \ldots \ldots \quad (1)$$

which has minima at $\phi = 0$, $2\pi/3$, and $4\pi/3$, and maxima at $\phi = \pi/3$, π, and $5\pi/3$. A general case has n instead of 3. The energy levels are given by the wave equation (§ 2.V):

$$\mathrm{d}^2\psi/\mathrm{d}\phi^2 + (8\pi^2 I/h^2)[E_r - \tfrac{1}{2}V_0(1 - \cos n\phi)]\psi = 0.$$

Put $\phi = 2x/n$, $8\pi^2 I V_0/n^2 h^2 = \theta$, $\psi(\phi) = \mathrm{M}(x)$; then:

$$\mathrm{d}^2\mathrm{M}(x)/\mathrm{d}x^2 + (a_r + 2\theta \cos 2x)\mathrm{M}(x) = 0 \quad \ldots \quad (2)$$

where

$$a_r = (32\pi^2 I/n^2 h^2)(E_r - \tfrac{1}{2}V_0) \quad \ldots \ldots \quad (3)$$

Equation (2) is a Mathieu's equation,[3] and is known to give physically significant solutions for $\mathrm{M}(x)$ only if a_r has proper values $a_1, a_2, \ldots$, from which the energy levels $\epsilon_1, \epsilon_2, \ldots$ can be calculated by (3), and the state sum is then $Z_r = \Sigma e^{-\epsilon_r/kT}$.

1 Olson, *Trans. Faraday Soc.*, 1931, **27**, 6, 69; Olson and Hudson, *J.A.C.S.*, 1933, **55**, 1410; Smyth, Dornte, and Wilson, *J.A.C.S.*, 1931, **53**, 4242; Mizushima and Higasi, *Proc. Imp. Acad. Tokyo*, 1932, **8**, 482.

2 Eyring, *J.A.C.S.*, 1932, **54**, 3191; Nielsen, *Phys. Rev.*, 1932, **40**, 445; 1941, **60**, 794; Teller and Topley, *J.C.S.*, 1935, 885; Kemp and Pitzer, *J.A.C.S.*, 1937, **59**, 276; Pitzer, *J. Chem. Phys.*, 1937, **5**, 469; Kistiakowski, Lacher, and Ranson, *ibid*,, 1938, **6**, 900; Kistiakowski, Lacher, and Stitt, *ibid.*, 1938, **6**, 407; 1939, **7**, 289; Wilson, *ibid.*, 1938, **6**, 408; Gorin, Walter, and Eyring, *J.A.C.S.*, 1939, **61**, 1876; Crawford, *J. Chem. Phys.*, 1940, **8**, 273; 1941, **9**, 323; Wilson, *Chem. Rev.*, 1940, **27**, 17; Charlesby, *Proc. Phys. Soc.*, 1942, **54**, 471; Aston, Isserow, Szasz, and Kennedy, *J. Chem. Phys.*, 1944, **12**, 336; Halford, *ibid.*, 1947, **15**, 645; Lassettre and Dean, *ibid.*, 1948, **16**, 151, 553.

3 Whittaker and Watson, " A Course of Modern Analysis," 3rd edit., Cambridge, 1920, 404; Condon, *Phys. Rev.*, 1928, **31**, 891; see also Ince, *Proc. Cambr. Phil. Soc.*, 1922, **21**, 117; *Proc. Roy. Soc. Edin.*, 1925–6, **46**, 20, 316; 1926–7, **47**, 294; 1931–2, **52**, 355 (tables); Goldstein, *Trans. Cambr. Phil. Soc.*, 1927, **23**, 303 (tables); Stratton, Morse, Chu, and Hunter, " Elliptic. Cylinder, and Spheroidal Wave Functions," New York. 1941.

§ 29. Bibliography of Statistical Calculations of Entropy

From an exuberant literature on the statistical calculation of thermodynamic quantities, mostly from spectroscopic data or assumed molecular models, the following selection is offered. Some valuable papers have, without doubt, suffered inadvertent omission.

Aston and Messerly, *J.A.C.S.*, 1936, **58**, 2354 (tetramethylmethane); 1940, **62**, 1917 (*n*-butane); Aston, Siller, and Messerly, *ibid.*, 1937, **59**, 1743 (methylamine); Aston, Eidinoff, and Forster, *ibid.*, 1939, **61**, 1539 (dimethylamine); Aston, Kennedy, and Schumann, *ibid.*, 1940, **62**, 2059 (*iso*butane); Aston and Kennedy, *ibid.*, 1940, **62**, 2567 (tetramethylsilane); Aston, Kennedy, and Messerly, *ibid.*, 1941, **63**, 2343 (tetramethylsilane); Aston *et al.*, *ibid.*, 1942. **64**, 1034, 1039 (*iso*pentane; corrected by Guthrie and Huffman, *ibid.*, 1943, **65**, 1139, and Aston *et al.*, *ibid.*, 1948, **70**, 3525); *idem*, in H. S. Taylor and Glasstone, " A Treatise on Physical Chemistry," New York, 1942, **1**, 590 (general); Aston, Fink, and Schumann, *J.A.C.S.*, 1943, **65**, 341 (cyclopentane); Aston, Szasz, and Fink, *ibid.*, 1943, **65**, 1135 (cyclohexane); Aston, Isserow, Szasz, and Kennedy, *J. Chem. Phys.*, 1944, **12**, 336 (potential barriers); Aston, Sagenkahn, Szasz, Moessen, and Zuhr, *J.A.C.S.*, 1944, **66**, 1171 (trimethylamine, paraffins, alcohols, ether, mercaptan, thio-ethers); Aston and Szasz, *ibid.*, 1947, **69**, 3108 (butadiene); Austin, *ibid.*, 1932, **54**, 3459 (HCl, HBr, HI).

Badger and Woo, *J.A.C.S.*, 1932, **54**, 3523 (CO_2, N_2O, HCN, C_2H_2); Bak, *K. Dansk. Vidensk. Selskab.*, 1946, **22**, No. 16 (CH_4, C_2H_6); 1948, **24**, Nos. 1 (C_2H_6), 9, 10 (CH_3Br); Beach and Turkevich, *J.A.C.S.*, 1939, **61**, 303 (ethylene chlorobromide, ethylene dibromide); Beckett, Freeman, and Pitzer, *ibid.*, 1948, **70**, 4227 (cyclopentane and cyclohexane); Bigeleisen, Goeppert Mayer, Stevenson, and Turkevich, *J. Chem. Phys.*, 1948, **16**, 442 (UF_6); Bijvoet, *Chem. Weekbl.*, 1931, **28**, 26 (gas equilibria); Blue and Giauque, *J.A.C.S.*, 1935, **57**, 991 (N_2O); Bonino, *Boll. Sci. Fac. Chim. Ind. Bologna*, 1942, **3**, 1911 (paraffins).

Charlesby, *Proc. Phys. Soc.*, 1942, **54**, 471 (C_2H_6); Clayton and Giauque, *J.A.C.S.*, 1932, **54**, 2610 (CO); 1933, **55**, 5071 (CO); Crawford and Rice, *J. Chem. Phys.*, 1939, **7**, 437 (dimethylacetylene); Crawford, Kistiakowsky, Rice, Wells, and Wilson, *J.A.C.S.*, 1939, **61**, 2980 (propylene); Crawford, *J. Chem. Phys.*, 1940, **8**, 273 (propylene); 1941, **9**, 323 (nitromethane, ethane, tetramethylmethane); Crawford and Parr, *ibid.*, 1948, **16**, 233 (various); Cross, *ibid.*, 1935, **3**, 825 (COS, SO_2, CS_2).

Davis and Johnston, *J.A.C.S.*, 1934, **56**, 1045 (H_2); De Vries and Collins, *ibid.*, 1942, **64**, 1224 (nitromethane); Dietz and Andrews, *J. Chem. Phys.*, 1933, **1**, 62 (C_6H_6); Dobratz, *Ind. Eng. Chem.*, 1941, **33**, 759 (organic vapours).

Egan and Kemp, *J.A.C.S.*, 1937, **59**, 1264 (ethylene); 1938, **60**, 2097 (methyl bromide); Eidinoff and Aston, *J. Chem. Phys.*, 1935, **3**, 379 (tetramethylmethane); Elert, *Z. Phys.*, 1928, **51**, 6 (CH_4; incorrect); Eucken and Berger, *Z. techn. Phys.*, 1934, **15**, 369 (CH_4); Eyring, *J.A.C.S.*, 1932, **54**, 3191 (C_2H_6).

Fink and Bonilla, *J. Phys. Chem.*, 1933, **37**, 1135 (CCl_4); Frank and Clusius, *Z. phys. Chem.*, 1937, **36** B, 290 (CH_4); Fuchs, *Proc. Roy. Soc.*, 1941–2, **179**, 194, 340, 408, 433 (assorted subjects).

Giauque and Wiebe, *J.A.C.S.*, 1928, **50**, 101 (HCl), 2193 (HBr); 1929, **51**, 1441 (HI); Giauque and Johnston, *ibid.*, 1929, **51**, 2300 (O_2); Giauque, *ibid.*, 1930, **52**, 4808 (general theory), 4816 (H_2); 1931, **53**, 507 (I_2); Giauque, Blue, and Overstreet, *Phys. Rev.*, 1931, **38**, 196 (CH_4, NH_3); Giauque and Overstreet, *J.A.C.S.*, 1932, **54**, 1731 (HCl, Cl); Giauque and Clayton, *ibid.*, 1933, **55**, 4875 (N_2); Giauque and Blue, *ibid.*, 1936, **58**, 831 (H_2S); Giauque and Stout, *ibid.*, 1936, **58**, 1144 (H_2O); Giauque, *ibid.*, 1937, **59**, 1157 (H_2O); Giauque and Egan, *J. Chem. Phys.*, 1937, **5**, 45 (CO_2); Giauque and Stephenson, *J.A.C.S.*, 1938, **60**, 1389 (SO_2); Giauque and Ruhrwein, *ibid.*, 1939, **61**, 2626 (HCN); Gibson and Heitler, *Z. Phys.*, 1928, **49**, 465 (I_2); Glasstone, *Ann. Rep. Chem. Soc.*, 1935, 66; " Recent Advances in General Chemistry," 1936, 53; " Theoretical Chemistry," New York, 1944, 203; Godnev, Payukhina, and Sverdlin, *J. Phys. Chem. U.S.S.R.*, 1940, **14**, 374; Godnev and Filatova, *Compt. Rend. U.R.S.S.*, 1946, **52**, 43 (hydrocarbons); Golden, *J. Chem. Phys.*, 1948, **16**, 78 (asymmetric rotor); Gordon and Barnes, *J. Phys. Chem.*, 1932, **36**, 1143 (H_2O), 2293 (Cl_2), 2601 (CH_4: see corrections by Wilson, *J. Chem. Phys.*, 1936, **4**, 526, and Giauque, *J.A.C.S.*, 1937, **59**, 1158); *J. Chem. Phys.*, 1933, **1**, 297 (Cl_2, HCl, CO, Br_2, O_2, NO), 308 (H_2O, CO_2); Gordon, *ibid.*, 1934, **2**, 65 (H_2O); 1938, **6**, 219 (C_2H_2); Gordon and Giauque, *J.A.C.S.*, 1948, **70**, 1506 (ethyl chloride); Gorin, Walter, and Eyring, *J.A.C.S.*, 1939, **61**, 1876 (hydrocarbons); Goubeau and Karweil, *Z. phys. Chem.*, 1938, **40** B, 376 (C_2H_6; correcting Eucken and Schäfer, *Naturwiss.*, 1939, **27**, 122); Gregory, *Z. Phys.*, 1932, **78**, 791 (diatomic gases); Guillemin, *Ann. Phys.*, 1926, **81**, 173 (CH_4); Guttman, Westrum, and Pitzer, *J.A.C.S.*, 1943, **65**, 1246 (styrene).

Halford, *J. Chem. Phys.*, 1934, **2**, 694 (alcohols, ether, hydrocarbons); 1941, **9**, 859 (acetic acid); Herzberg, "Infra-Red and Raman Spectra of Polyatomic Molecules," New York, 1945; Hicks and Mitchell, *J.A.C.S.*, 1926, **48**, 1520 (HCl); Hutchisson, *ibid.*, 1928, **50**, 1895 (HCl).

Jahn, *Ann. Phys.*, 1935, **23**, 529 (CH_4); *J. Chem. Phys.*, 1938, **6**, 335 (NOCl); Johnston and Giauque, *J.A.C.S.*, 1929, **51**, 3194 (NO); Johnston and Chapman, *ibid.*, 1933, **55**, 153, 5073 (NO); Johnston and Walker, *ibid.*, 1933, **55**, 172, 5075 (O_2), 187 (O); Johnston and Dawson, *ibid.*, 1933, **55**, 2744 (OH); Johnston and Davis, *ibid.*, 1934, **56**, 271 (CO, N_2); Johnston and Walker, *ibid.*, 1935, **57**, 682 (O_2); Justi and Langer, *Z. techn. Phys.*, 1940, **21**, 189 (CH_2Cl_2, CF_2Cl_2); 1941, **22**, 124 (CF_3Cl, CCl_3F).

Karweil and Schäfer, *Z. phys. Chem.*, 1938, **40** B, 382 (C_2H_6); Kassel, *J.A.C.S.*, 1933, **55**, 1351 (rigid symm. top); 1934, **56**, 1838 (N_2O, CO_2, CO); 1937, **59**, 2746; *J. Chem. Phys.*, 1933, **1**, 576 (CO); 1935, **3**, 115 (tetramethylmethane); 1936, **4**, 276 (benzene and methyl derivatives), 493 (methanol); *Chem. Rev.*, 1936, **18**, 277 (general); Kazarnovsky, *J. Phys. Chem. U.S.S.R.*, 1945, **19**, 392 (N_2, H_2 and mixts.; NH_3); Kelley, *U.S. Bur. Mines Bull.*, 1936, **394** (general, on entropies from spectra); Kemble, *J. Opt. Soc. Amer.*, 1926, **12**, 1 (HCl); Kemp and Pitzer, *J.A.C.S.*, 1937, **59**, 276 (C_2H_6); Kemp and Giauque, *ibid.*, 1937, **59**, 79 (COS); Kemp and Egan, *ibid.*, 1938, **60**, 1521 (propane); Kennedy, Sagenkahn, and Aston, *ibid.*, 1941, **63**, 2267 (ether); Kienitz, *Z. Elektrochem.*, 1944, **50**, 216 (C_3 hydrocarbons); Kilpatrick and Pitzer, *J.A.C.S.*, 1946, **68**, 1066 (dimethylbutane); *Bur. Stand. J. Res.*, 1947, **38**, 191 (ethylene, etc.); Kilpatrick, Pitzer, and Spitzer, *J.A.C.S.*, 1947, **69**, 2483 (cyclopentane), 2488 (cyclohexane and derivatives); King, Hainer, and Cross, *J. Chem. Phys.*, 1943, **11**, 27; 1944, **12**, 210 (asymm. rotor); Kistiakowski, Lacher, and Ranson, *J. Chem. Phys.*, 1938, **6**, 900 (potential barriers); Kistiakowski, Lacher, and Stitt, *ibid.*, 1938, **6**, 407 (ethane); 1939, **7**, 289 (ethane).

Langseth and Bak, *K. Dansk. Vidensk. Selskab.*, 1948, **24**, No. 3 (CH_3Br); Lord, Ahlberg, and Andrews, *J. Chem. Phys.*, 1937, **5**, 649 (solids); Lord, *ibid.*, 1941, **9**, 693, 700 (solids); Ludolph, *Phys. Rev.*, 1931, **37**, 830 (CH_4); Lütgemeier, *Z. Phys.*, 1926, **38**, 251 (di- and poly-atomic molecules; old quantum theory).

McCrea, *Proc. Cambr. Phil. Soc.*, 1927, **23**, 890, 942; 1928, **24**, 290 (CO_2, H_2O); Macdougall, *Phys. Rev.*, 1931, **38**, 2074 (CH_4, NH_3); Manning, *J. Chem. Phys.*, 1935, **3**, 136 (NH_3); Maue, *Ann. Phys.*, 1937, **30**, 555 (CH_4); Mayer, Brunauer, and Mayer, *J.A.C.S.*, 1933, **55**, 37 (C_2H_6, C_2H_2); Meyer and Buell, *J. Chem. Phys.*, 1948, **16**, 744 (SF_6); Messerly and Aston, *J.A.C.S.*, 1940, **62**, 886 (methyl chloride); Michels, de Groot, and Geldermans, *Appl. Sci. Res.*, 1947, **1** A, 55 (C_2H_4); Mizushima and Higasi, *Proc. Imp. Acad. Tokyo*, 1932, **8**, 482 (theory of restricted rotation).

Nielsen, *Phys. Rev.*, 1932, **40**, 445; 1941, **60**, 794 (torsional oscillator).

Oliver, Eaton, and Huffman, *J.A.C.S.*, 1948, **70**, 1502 (C_6H_6); Olson and Hudson, *J.A.C.S.*, 1933, **55**, 1410 (restricted rotation); Osborne, Garner, and Yost, *J. Chem. Phys.*, 1940, **8**, 131 (dimethylacetylene); Osborne, Doescher, and Yost, *J.A.C.S.*, 1942, **64**, 169 ($(CH_3)_2S$); Overstreet and Giauque, *ibid.*, 1937, **59**, 254 (NH_3).

Pace and Aston, *J.A.C.S.*, 1948, **70**, 567 (C_2F_6); Pitzer, *J. Chem. Phys.*, 1937, **5**, 469, 473 (C_2H_6); 1940, **8**, 711 (long chain hydrocarbons); 1942, **10**, 605 (hydrocarbons); 1944, **12**, 310 (propane); 1946, **14**, 239 (tops on frame); *Chem. Rev.*, 1940, **27**, 39; *J.A.C.S.*, 1940, **62**, 331 ($C_2H_4Cl_2$; $C_2H_4Br_2$); 1947, **69**, 184 (B_2H_6); *Ind. Eng. Chem.*, 1944, **36**, 829 (paraffins); Pitzer and Scott, *J.A.C.S.*, 1941, **63**, 2419 (trimethylpentane); 1943, **65**, 803 (benzene, toluene, xylenes); Pitzer and Gwinn, *ibid.*, 1941, **63**, 3313 (nitromethane); *J. Chem. Phys.*, 1941, **9**, 485 (internal rotation); 1942, **10**, 428 (internal rotation); Pitzer and Kilpatrick, *Chem. Rev.*, 1946, **39**, 435; Price, *J. Chem. Phys.*, 1941, **9**, 807; 1942, **10**, 80 (errors corrected).

Renner, *Phys. Z.*, 1934, **35**, 811 (CH_4); Riewe, *Z. Phys.*, 1938, **109**, 753; Rodebush, *Chem. Rev.*, 1931, **9**, 319; *Phys. Rev.*, 1932, **40**, 113 (N_2O, CO_2); Rolla, *Boll. Sci. Fac. Chim. Ind. Bologna*, 1941, 65 (C_6H_6); Ruhrwein and Giauque, *J.A.C.S.*, 1939, **61**, 2940 (C_2N_2); Ruhrwein and Powell, *ibid.*, 1946, **68**, 1063 (cyclopropane); Russell, Osborne, and Yost, *ibid.*, 1942, **64**, 165 (CH_3SH).

Schäfer, *Z. phys. Chem.*, 1938, **40** B, 375 (C_2H_6); Schaffer and Nielsen, *J. Chem. Phys.*, 1941, **9**, 847 (linear Y_2X_2 molecules); Schumann and Aston, *J.A.C.S.*, 1938, **60**, 985 (ethyl and *iso*propyl alcohols; acetone); *J. Chem. Phys.*, 1938, **6**, 480 (ethyl alcohol), 485 (*iso*propyl alcohol; acetone); Schumann, Aston, and Sagenkahn, *J.A.C.S.*, 1942, **64**, 1039 (*iso*pentane); Silver, *J. Chem. Phys.*, 1942, **17**, 565 (planar ZXY_2 molecules); Silver and Ebers, *ibid.*, 1942, **10**, 559 (planar ZXY_2 molecules); Sirkar and Gupta, *Nature*, 1938, **141**, 915 (CO_2); Skinner, *J. Chem. Phys.*, 1948, **16**, 553 (CH_3X); Spencer, *J. Chem. Phys.*, 1946, **14**, 729 (B compds.); Stephenson and Giauque, *ibid.*, 1937, **5**, 149 (PH_3); Stephenson and McMahon, *J.A.C.S.*, 1939, **61**, 437 (ammonia); Sterne, *Phys. Rev.*, 1932, **39**, 993 (ammonia); Stuart, *ibid.*, 1931, **38**, 1372; Stevenson, *J. Chem. Phys.*, 1939, **7**, 171 (C_2N_2 and halides).

Taylor and Pitzer, *Bur. Stand. J. Res.*, 1947, **38**, 1 (hydrocarbons); Teller and Topley, *J.C.S.*, 1935, 885; Thompson, *Ann. Rep. Chem. Soc.*, 1941, **38**, 46; Tolman and Badger, *J.A.C.S.*, 1923, **45**, 2277 (diatomic gases); Trautz and Ader, *Z. Phys.*, 1934, **89**, 1 (air, O_2, N_2), 12 (H_2O vap.), 15 (Cl_2 and Cl).

Villars, *Phys. Rev.*, 1931, **38**, 1552 (ammonia, ethane); *J.A.C.S.*, 1931, **53**, 2006 (polyatomic molecules); Villars and Schultze, *Phys. Rev.*, 1931, **38**, 998 (methane); Viney, *Proc. Cambr. Phil. Soc.*, 1933, **29**, 142 (symmetrical top); Vold, *J.A.C.S.*, 1935, **57**, 1192 (CH_4 and halogen derivs.).

Wilson, *J. Chem. Phys.*, 1938, **6**, 408 (ethane); *Chem. Rev.*, 1940, **27**, 17 (bibl.); Witmer, *Proc. Nat. Acad.*, 1927, **13**, 60; *J.A.C.S.*, 1934, **56**, 2229 (NO); Wooley, *Bur. Stand. J. Res.*, 1948, **40**, 163 (O_2).

Zeise, *Z. Elektrochem.*, 1933, **39**, 758, 895, 904; 1934, **40**, 662, 885; 1935, **41**, 267; 1936, **42**, 785; 1937, **43**, 704; 1940, **46**, 38, 293; 1941, **47**, 380, 595, 644; 1942, **48**, 425, 476, 693; 1944, **50**, 53, 113 (summaries); "Thermodynamik auf den Gründen der Quantentheorie, Quantenstatistik, und Spektroskopie," Leipzig, 1944.

§ 30. The New Statistics

So far, the discussion has been based on the classical or Maxwell-Boltzmann statistics (§§ 2, 8). In 1924, two new statistics were introduced, one by Bose and the other by Fermi, and the first was extended by Einstein and the second by Dirac; a modification of the first was introduced by Gentile in 1940.

The distinction between Maxwell-Boltzmann, Bose-Einstein, and Fermi-Dirac statistics is illustrated by the following simple example.[1] Suppose there are three "parts"[2] *a, b, c* (which may e.g. be molecules, light-quanta or photons, or electrons), which are to be distributed among four "cells"[3] in phase space, corresponding with given energies, which are numbered I, II, III, IV. The number of parts in each cell may be 0, 1, 2, or 3, and the possible arrangements are:

	1	2	3	4	1	2	3	4	5	6	7	8	9	10	11	12	1	2	3	4
Cell I	3	0	0	0	2	2	2	1	0	0	1	0	0	1	0	0	1	0	1	1
" II	0	3	0	0	1	0	0	2	2	2	0	1	0	0	1	0	1	1	0	1
" III	0	0	3	0	0	1	0	0	1	0	2	2	2	0	0	1	1	1	1	0
" IV	0	0	0	3	0	0	1	0	0	1	0	0	1	2	2	2	0	1	1	1
	4				12												4			

If all three parts are in one cell there are four possible arrangements, shown in the second column between heavy vertical lines, the horizontal rows corresponding with the cases when the three parts are in the cells I, II, III, IV, respectively, in each case three cells being empty. If there are two parts in one cell, one in another, and two cells are empty, there are twelve possible arrangements, shown between the second and third heavy vertical lines. In the first vertical column between these lines, two parts are in cell I, one part in cell II, and none in cells III and IV; in the second vertical column, two parts are in cell I, one in cell III, and none in cells II and IV; and so on. If there cannot be more than

[1] Lennard-Jones, *Proc. Phys. Soc.*, 1928, **40**, 320; Bligh, *Sci. Progr.*, 1929, **23**, 619; Bloch, "L'ancienne et la nouvelle Théorie des Quanta," Paris, 1930, 390; Epstein, "Textbook of Thermodynamics," New York, 1937, 252 f.; De Donder, *Bull. Acad. Roy. Belg.*, 1944, **30**, 327.

[2] What is here called a "part" is sometimes called an "element"; it may be a material particle (electron, proton, neutron, atom, or molecule), or an energy particle (quantum or photon), or a vibrational mode in vacuum; a "parton" would be a convenient name.

[3] The "cells" are sometimes called "energy-levels," sometimes "complexions in phase space."

one part in any cell, the four cases shown after the third heavy vertical line are possible, and in this case one cell is always empty. The total number of arrangements of the three types considered is thus 4+12+4=20.

This case corresponds with Bose-Einstein statistics,[1] in which no distinction is made between identical parts (e.g. light quanta). Thus, in the group of 12 arrangements, the two parts in the cells may be *a b*, *b c*, or *c a*, and the single part may be *c*, *a*, or *b*; no distinction is made between $ab+c$, $bc+a$, and $ca+b$. In the general case of Bose-Einstein statistics, if the cells are numbered 1, 2, 3, . . ., *a*, and the parts 1, 2, 3, . . ., *n*, the numbers 1, 2, 3, . . ., *a* are to be distributed among the parts 1, 2, 3, . . ., *n* in all possible ways, each number being capable of being repeated *n* times (all the parts in one cell), but no distinction is to be made between the order of the numbers, i.e. between the individuality of the parts. The required number of arrangements is the same as the number of combinations of *a* things taken *n* at a time when each thing may be repeated any number of times, up to *n*.

Let the *a* things be denoted by letters A, B, C, ... Write down all the combinations required and add the *a* letters A, B, C, . . . to each of them. This leaves the number of combinations unchanged, but each letter will occur at least once in every combination, the number of letters of which is now $n+a$. Hence the number of combinations of *a* things taken *n* at a time, repetitions being allowed, is the same as the number of combinations of *a* things taken $(a+n)$ at a time, repetitions being allowed, but with the restriction that each thing appears at least once in every combination.

To find this, take $(n+a)$ units in a line, having $(n+a-1)$ intervals between them, and divide the units into *a* groups by putting $(a-1)$ partition marks between them in any way; e.g.

1 1 1 | 1 1 | 1 | 1 1 1 1 1 | 1 | 1 1 . . .

Then if the units in the first group are replaced by letters A, those in the second group by letters B, and so on, a selection of $(n+a)$ letters is obtained in which each letter occurs at least once:

A A A | B B | C | D D D D D | E | F F

Since the different positions of the partition marks give different combinations, the required number of combinations is equal to the number of ways of selecting $(a-1)$ intervals for the partition marks. This is the number of combinations of $(n+a-1)$ things taken $(a-1)$ at a time, viz. ${}_{(n+a-1)}C_{(a-1)}$. But ${}_nC_r={}_nC_{(n-r)}$, since every selection of *r* from *n* things leaves $(n-r)$ behind, and any change in the first selection gives a corresponding change in the second. Hence:

$$
\begin{aligned}
{}_{(n+a-1)}C_{(a-1)} &= {}_{(n+a-1)}C_n \\
&= \frac{(n+a-1)(n+a-2)\ .\ .\ .\ (a+2)(a+1)a}{n!} \\
&= \frac{(n+a-1)(n+a-2)\ .\ .\ .\ (a+2)(a+1)a\times(a-1)(a-2)\ .\ .\ .\ 2.1}{n!(a-1)!} \\
&= \frac{(n+a-1)!}{n!(a-1)!}.
\end{aligned}
$$

[1] S. N. Bose, *Z. Phys.*, 1924, **26**, 178; 1924, **27**, 384 (light quanta); Schidlof, *Arch. Sci. Phys. Nat.*, 1924, **6**, 381; Einstein, *Berlin Ber.*, 1924, 261; 1925, 3, 18 (gas molecules); Planck, *ibid.*, 1925, 49; Kofink, *Ann. Phys.*, 1937, **28**, 264. This case, with the correct formula, had been worked out for quanta by Planck in 1900; see § 15.

Hence, the required number of arrangements in the particular example is:

$$\frac{(3+4-1)!}{3!(4-1)!}=\frac{6!}{3!3!}=\frac{6\times5\times4\times3\times2\times1}{(3\times2\times1)\times(3\times2\times1)}=20.$$

In Maxwell-Boltzmann statistics (§ 8), account is taken of the individuality of the parts, and the number of possible arrangements is much larger than the above. The arrangement *inside* each cell, however, is still indifferent, so that the first four cases (when all the parts are in one cell) remain the same. In the second group each arrangement must be divided into three, since the single part may be *a*, *b*, or *c*, regarded as different, so that instead of twelve arrangements there are $12\times3=36$ *complexions*, a complexion being an arrangement taking account of the individuality of the parts. In the fourth group, each arrangement corresponds with six complexions, since the three parts in three cells may be changed by permutations in $3!=3\times2\times1=6$ ways, viz. *a b c*, *b c a*, *c a b*, *a c b*, *b a c*, and *c b a*. Thus the number of complexions in Maxwell-Boltzmann statistics is $4+36+24=64$. This is 4^3, and is the number of arrangements with repetition of three parts among four cells; it is in general $n_r!/n_1!n_2!\ldots$, where n_1, n_2, . . . are the numbers of parts in the *separate* cells, the permutations of which are not to be taken into account.

In *Fermi-Dirac statistics*,[1] the basis is Pauli's exclusion principle, which states that no two electrons in an atom can have identical sets of the four quantum numbers (§§ 14–16.V) defining the energy of an electron. The sets of four quantum numbers representing the energy levels of different electrons must be distinct, and if each set corresponds with a point in generalised space, this space can be divided into cells, each of which can contain only one electron or none. (If the spin quantum number is left out, each cell can contain a maximum of *two* electrons with opposite spins.)

Fermi extended Pauli's principle to energy states of certain gas molecules, including the translational energy, and if the internal energies are all the same, e.g. if all the molecules are in the normal state, the differences in quantum states relate only to translational energy, and there cannot be two molecules having translational energies defined by the same quantum numbers.

In the case considered, only the four distributions in the last column are possible, since all the others take account of more than one part in a cell, and the four distributions are supposed to have equal probabilities. It is seen that the number of arrangements (36) is greatest for Maxwell-Boltzmann statistics, and least (4) for Fermi-Dirac statistics, that for Bose-Einstein statistics (20) being intermediate. In Bose-Einstein statistics, the number of parts in a cell may vary from zero to infinity; in Gentile statistics it is supposed always to remain finite.

In Fermi-Dirac statistics, the number of arrangements of n parts in a cells, with the restriction that each cell can contain either one part or none, is equal to the number of combinations of a things taken n at a time ($a\geqq n$), or (what is the same thing; see above) taken $(a-n)$ at a time:

$$\begin{aligned}{}_aC_n&=\frac{a(a-1)(a-2)\ldots(a-n+1)}{n!}\\&=\frac{a(a-1)\ldots(a-n+1)\times(a-n)(a-n-1)\ldots3.2.1}{n!(a-n)!}\\&=\frac{a!}{n!(a-n)!}.\end{aligned}$$

[1] Fermi, *Nuov. Cim.*, 1924, **1**, 145; *Atti R. Accad. Lincei*, 1926, **3**, 145; *Z. Phys.*, 1926, **36**, 902; Pauli, *Z. Phys.*, 1925, **31**, 765; Dirac, *Proc. Roy. Soc.*, 1926, **112**, 661; Lindemann, "The Physical Significance of the Quantum Theory," Oxford, 1932, 58; Kofink, *Ann. Phys.*, 1937, **28**, 264; Stoner, *Phil. Mag.*, 1939, **28**, 257.

§ 31. Bose-Einstein Statistics

In this,[1] identical parts (e.g. light quanta, or identical molecules, but not electrons) are supposed to be distinguishable only if they have different energies, i.e. are in different cells in the phase space. If there are n_r parts, and a_r cells corresponding with energies lying between ϵ_r and $\epsilon_r+\delta\epsilon_r$, then if the cells are numbered from 1 to a_r, these numbers are to be distributed among the n_r parts in all possible ways, each number being repeated n_r times but without distinction of the order of the numbers, i.e. of the individuality of the parts.

The elements n_r and a_r are first written down in any arbitrary order; e.g.

$$a_1\ n_1\ n_2\ a_2\ n_3\ a_3\ n_4\ n_5\ n_6\ a_4\ a_5\ n_7\ \ldots$$

means that parts n_1, n_2 are in cell a_1, part n_3 in cell a_2, parts n_4, n_5, n_6 in cell a_3, no part in cell a_4, etc. The first letter must denote a cell, i.e. be an a, and can be chosen in a_r ways; the remaining (a_r-1+n_r) letters may be arranged in $(a_r-1+n_r)!$ ways, so that the total number of arrangements is $a_r(a_r-1+n_r)!$. Of these, permutations of cells or of parts among themselves do not represent different states, and as the number of these permutations is $a_r!n_r!$ the number of distinguishable arrangements is:

$$w_r=\frac{a_r(a_r-1+n_r)!}{a_r!n_r!}=\frac{(n_r+a_r-1)!}{n_r!(a_r-1)!} \quad \ldots\ldots \quad (1)$$

Thus, a set $(n_1, n_2, \ldots, n_r)$ of n's is given, subject to the condition that $\Sigma n_r=N$, the total number of parts, and *any* set of n's then represents a possible arrangement.

The total probability of an arrangement having n_1 parts with energies between ϵ_1 and $\epsilon_1+\delta\epsilon_1$, n_2 parts with energies between ϵ_2 and $\epsilon_2+\delta\epsilon_2$, etc., is the continued product (Π) of (1) for all values of r:

$$W_{n,r}=\prod_r w_r \quad \ldots\ldots\ldots\ldots \quad (2)$$

and the maximum value of W, or ln W, gives the most probable distribution. In (1), unity may be neglected in comparison with a_r and Stirling's theorem (9), § 8, gives:

$$\delta \ln W_{n,r}=\Sigma\delta[(n_r+a_r)\ln(n_r+a_r)-n_r\ln n_r-a_r\ln a_r]=0 \quad \ldots \quad (3)$$

with the subsidiary conditions

$$\delta\Sigma n_r=0 \quad \text{and} \quad \delta\Sigma n_r\epsilon_r=0 \quad \ldots\ldots\ldots \quad (4)$$

By introducing two undetermined multipliers, λ and μ, as in (11), § 8, (3) and (4) give:

$$\ln(n_r+a_r)-\ln n_r=\lambda+\mu\epsilon_r,$$

$$n_r=a_r/(Ce^{\mu\epsilon_r}-1) \quad \ldots\ldots\ldots \quad (5)$$

where $C=e^\lambda$ and $\mu=1/kT$.

Bose-Einstein statistics should apply to photons (light quanta), and to hydrogen and helium molecules (heavier gases *practically* follow Maxwell-Boltzmann statistics even at very low temperatures, " gas degeneration " setting in at temperatures so low that the gases practically cease to exist). In the first case, the subsidiary condition $\delta\Sigma n_r=0$ in (4) drops out, since photons may be absorbed or emitted, and their number is variable. Hence $\lambda=0$, and $C=1$ in (5), and in this case Planck's formula, (10), § 15, results.

[1] See reference, § 30; Smekal, *Z. Phys.*, 1925, **33**, 613; Lennard-Jones, *Proc. Phys. Soc.* 1928, **40**, 320; Brillouin, " Die Quantenstatistik," Berlin, 1931, 128; Born, " Atomic Physics, 1937, 203, 211; Pauli, *Phys. Rev.*, 1940, **58**, 716; Band, *Proc. Phys. Soc.*, 1946, **58**, 302.

It is of interest to follow the process [1] which led Bose to the formulation of his statistics. The number of frequencies per cm.^{3} between ν and $\nu+d\nu$ is found from (13), § 78.I as:

$$a_r=8\pi\nu^2 d\nu/c^3 \quad . \quad . \quad . \quad . \quad . \quad . \quad . \quad . \quad (6)$$

the number being doubled because radiation consists of transverse vibrations at right angles to the direction of propagation of the ray, and each ray having transverse vibrations in a plane at right angles to its direction may be compounded from two rays polarised at right angles and with independent phases.

The number of photons which may be distributed among these frequencies is limited by the fact that they all have the same energy $h\nu$, and this is a case of degeneracy (§ 9) with the statistical weight given by (6). In Maxwell-Boltzmann statistics, the number of photons is given by (13), § 8 ($\mu=1/kT$, and $\epsilon_r=h\nu$) multiplied by the statistical weight:

$$n_r=(1/C)(8\pi\nu^2 d\nu/c^3)e^{-h\nu/kT}$$

Multiplying the number of photons by the energy $h\nu$ of each gives the energy density ρ_ν:

$$\rho_\nu d\nu=(1/C)(8\pi h\nu^3/c^3)d\nu e^{-h\nu/kT}$$

which (since $C=1$) is Wien's law (§ 11.VI B), which law holds only at high frequencies. Bose then found equation (5) above and showed that $C=1$, and by multiplying by (6) he obtained Planck's radiation formula:

$$\rho_\nu d\nu=(8\pi h\nu^3/c^3)d\nu(e^{-h\nu/kT}-1)^{-1}.$$

§ 32. Fermi-Dirac Statistics

In Fermi-Dirac statistics [2] (which should, perhaps, be called Pauli-Fermi-Dirac statistics) the arrangement of n_r parts among a_r cells is further restricted by the condition that each cell can contain either one part or none, instead of the very large number (up to n_r) permitted by Bose-Einstein statistics; the number of arrangements of n_r parts among a_r cells, subject to this condition, is equal to the number of combinations of a_r things taken n_r at a time:

$$w_r=\frac{a_r!}{n_r!(a_r-n_r)!} \quad . \quad . \quad . \quad . \quad . \quad . \quad (1)$$

and the total probability is:

$$W_{n,r}=\prod_r w_r \quad . \quad . \quad . \quad . \quad . \quad . \quad . \quad . \quad . \quad . \quad (2)$$

The distribution with $\ln W_{n,r}$ a maximum, with the subsidiary conditions $\delta\Sigma n_r=0$, and $\delta\Sigma n_r\epsilon_r=0$, gives:

$$n_r=a_r/(Ce^{\mu\epsilon_r}+1) \quad . \quad . \quad . \quad . \quad . \quad . \quad . \quad . \quad (3)$$

($C=e^\lambda$; $\mu=1/kT$), which differs from (5), § 31, for Bose-Einstein statistics in having $+1$ instead of -1 in the denominator.

[1] See Schidlof, *Arch. Sci. Phys. Nat.*, 1924, **6**, 381; equation (1) had been applied to photons by Planck, *Verhl. d. D. Phys. Ges.*, 1900, **2**, 237; *Ann. Phys.*, 1901, **4**, 553, 564; Wolfke, *Phys. Z.*, 1914, **15**, 308; Krutow, *ibid.*, 1914, **15**, 133, 363.

[2] See reference, § 30; Ornstein and Kramers, *Z. Phys.*, 1927, **42**, 481; Hall, *Proc. Nat. Acad.*, 1928, **14**, 366; Lennard-Jones, *Proc. Phys. Soc.*, 1928, **40**, 320; Brillouin, "Die Quantenstatistik," Berlin, 1931, 132, 503; Born, "Atomic Physics," 1937, 214; Loeb, "Atomic Structure," New York, 1938, 371; Slater, "Introduction to Chemical Physics," New York, 1939, 65; Hellmann and Jost, *Z. Elektrochem.*, 1934, **40**, 807; Stoner, *Phil. Mag.*, 1938, **25**, 899; 1939, **28**, 257; Pauli, *Phys. Rev.*, 1940, **58**, 716; on Fermi-Dirac functions, Auluck, *Phil. Mag.*, 1942, **33**, 159; on relatavistic Fermi-Dirac statistics, Kothari and Singh, *Proc. Roy. Soc.*, 1942, **180**, 414; tables of Fermi-Dirac functions, McDougall and Stoner, *Phil. Trans.*, 1938, **237**, 67; law of mass action with Fermi-Dirac gases, Bothe, *Z. Phys.*, 1928, **46**, 327.

The equations of Maxwell-Boltzmann, (13), § 8, Bose-Einstein, (5), § 31, and Fermi-Dirac, (3), statistics, become identical when $Ce^{\mu\epsilon_r}$ is very large compared with unity, $Ce^{\mu\epsilon_r} \gg 1$, when unity may be neglected in the denominators of the Bose-Einstein and Fermi-Dirac formulae, both of which then reduce to $(1/C)e^{-\mu\epsilon_r}$, the Maxwell-Boltzmann formula. This condition is fulfilled for gases, except at very low temperatures, when " degeneracy " sets in (§ 36). The Maxwell-Boltzmann statistics is a limiting case of both the Bose-Einstein and Fermi-Dirac statistics, because it applies to such dilute systems that so few molecules are distributed among the many cells that the chance of finding more than one molecule in a cell is negligible in any case.[1] In modern quantum theory, no actual system ever obeys Maxwell-Boltzmann statistics *exactly*.

Molecules the nuclei of which contain an even number of protons and neutrons together, i.e. have an equal number of units of nuclear spin (§ 21), obey Bose-Einstein statistics; while those with an odd number of protons and neutrons, having an odd number of units of nuclear spin, obey Fermi-Dirac statistics,[2] as is also the case with electrons.

If $n_r'=n_r/a_r$=average number of parts in a cell, and C is put equal to $e^{-\mu\epsilon_0}$ $(\mu=1/kT)$, then (3) can be written $n_r'=1/[e^{(\epsilon_r-\epsilon_0)/kT}+1]$. The constant ϵ_0 is determined by the condition that the total number of parts per cell is:

$$n=\Sigma n_r'=\Sigma[1/(e^{(\epsilon_r-\epsilon_0)/kT}+1)] \quad . \quad . \quad . \quad . \quad . \quad . \quad (4)$$

This equation cannot be solved directly for ϵ_0, which must be obtained by approximation. When $\epsilon_r<\epsilon_0$, the exponential decreases rapidly as T increases, and hence n_r' is only slightly less than 1. When $\epsilon_r>\epsilon_0$ the exponential increases rapidly as T increases, and as unity in the denominator may then be neglected, this corresponds with Maxwell-Boltzmann statistics (24), § 8, $n_r'=e^{(\epsilon_0-\epsilon_r)/kT}$.

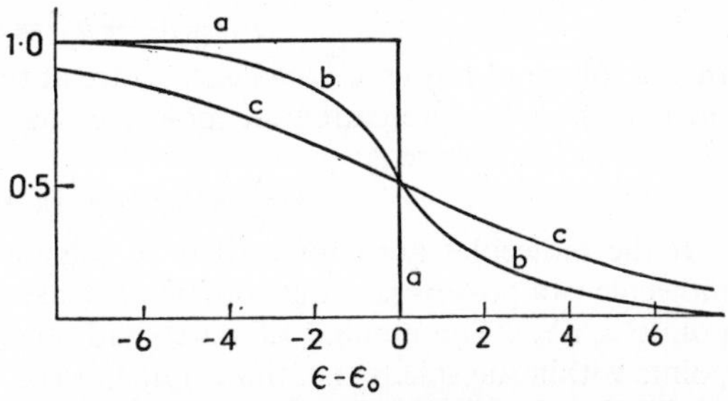

FIG. 13.IV. Fermi-Dirac Distributions for Three Temperatures

Fig. 13.IV shows

$$1/[e^{(\epsilon-\epsilon_0)/kT}+1]$$

for various values of $(\epsilon-\epsilon_0)$ at three temperatures, (*a*) $kT=0$, (*b*) $kT=1$, (*c*) $kT=2{\cdot}5$. At $T=0$, the function drops sharply from 1 to 0 when $\epsilon=\epsilon_0$; at higher temperatures it falls smoothly, and for large values of ϵ approaches the Maxwell-Boltzmann exponential function. Since:

$$1-n_r'=[e^{(\epsilon_r-\epsilon_0)/kT}+1-1]/[e^{(\epsilon_r-\epsilon_0)/kT}+1]=1/[e^{-(\epsilon_r-\epsilon_0)/kT}+1] \quad . \quad (5)$$

the value of the function in Fig. 13.IV at any point to the right of ϵ_0 is equal to 1 minus the function at the same distance to the left of ϵ_0; hence the curve is symmetrical about $\epsilon=\epsilon_0$ and the ordinate $\frac{1}{2}$, and this implies that ϵ_0 is nearly constant at low temperatures. Since the function changes most rapidly with temperature in the neighbourhood of ϵ_0, a determination of the distribution of energy levels there, assuming that they are approximately continuous, will be sufficient for all practical purposes.

1 Schrödinger, *Berlin Ber.*, 1925, 434.
2 Wigner and Witmer, *Z. Phys.*, 1928, **51**, 859; Heitler and Herzberg, *Naturwiss.*, 1929, **17**, 673.

§ 33. Monatomic Gas

The entropy of a monatomic gas was calculated in § 14 by Maxwell-Boltzmann statistics by a method which involved a division of the classical state sum by $N!$, where N is the number of identical molecules. This procedure is quite obvious and legitimate; a deduction using Bose-Einstein or Fermi-Dirac statistics [1] circumvents it, because the assumption that no distinction should be made between identical molecules is already contained in the formulae. It will be shown that equation (16), § 14 is found for the case in which $Ce^{\mu\epsilon_r} \gg 1$, which, as is explained in § 32, is formally equivalent to the assumption of Maxwell-Boltzmann statistics, the value of C being somewhat different from that previously assumed.

The gas molecules have positions defined by x_1, x_2, x_3 along three axes at right angles, and momenta defined by p_1, p_2, p_3. The representative point of a molecule with coordinates between x_1 and $x_1+\Delta x_1 \ldots, p_1$ and $p_1+\Delta p_1 \ldots$, lies in a cell of phase space of minimum volume (7), § 14:

$$\Delta x_1 \Delta x_2 \Delta x_3 \Delta p_1 \Delta p_2 \Delta p_3 = \boldsymbol{h}^3 \quad \ldots \ldots \quad (1)$$

Every molecule must lie within the physical volume:

$$v = \iiint \mathrm{d}x_1 \mathrm{d}x_2 \mathrm{d}x_3 \quad \ldots \ldots \quad (2)$$

A point in the momentum space with coordinates p_1, p_2, p_3 represents a molecule of energy ϵ defined by:

$$2m\epsilon = p_1^2 + p_2^2 + p_3^2 \quad \ldots \ldots \quad (3)$$

and if

$$p_1^2 + p_2^2 + p_3^2 = R^2 \quad \ldots \ldots \quad (4)$$

then a sphere of radius $\sqrt{(2m\epsilon)}$ and centre at the origin of the momentum space includes points representing all molecules having an energy less than ϵ. The volume of this sphere is:

$$V = \tfrac{4}{3}\pi R^3 = (4\pi/3)(2m\epsilon)^{3/2} \quad \ldots \ldots \quad (5)$$

If the molecules are contained in a volume v, and if the greatest energy a molecule can possess is ϵ, the volume of phase space occupied by representative points is vV. The number of states with energy less than ϵ is the number of points within the sphere, i.e. the volume of the sphere multiplied by the number of points per unit volume:

$$(4\pi/3)(2m\epsilon)^{3/2} v/\boldsymbol{h}^3 \quad \ldots \ldots \quad (6)$$

The number of states with energies between ϵ and $\epsilon + \mathrm{d}\epsilon$ is found by differentiation of (6) to be:

$$2\pi v(2m)^{3/2} \epsilon^{1/2} \mathrm{d}\epsilon / \boldsymbol{h}^3 \quad \ldots \ldots \quad (7)$$

The average energy difference between successive states is, from the reciprocal of (7), $\boldsymbol{h}^3/2\pi(2m)^{3/2} v\epsilon^{1/2}$. For a helium atom, $m = 6{\cdot}6 \times 10^{-24}$ g., in a volume $v = 1$ cm.^{3}, and with an energy $\epsilon = \boldsymbol{k} \times 1° = 1{\cdot}38 \times 10^{-16}$ erg, the energy difference is 8×10^{-38} erg, which is negligible. Hence, the *translational* energy levels of a gas are so closely spaced as to be practically continuous.

From (7), the maximum number of cells lying between ϵ_r and $\epsilon_r + \mathrm{d}\epsilon_r$ among which molecules having energies within this range can be distributed is:

$$a_r = 2\pi v(2m/\boldsymbol{h}^2)^{3/2} \epsilon^{1/2} \mathrm{d}\epsilon = A\epsilon^{1/2} \mathrm{d}\epsilon \quad \ldots \ldots \quad (8)$$

where $A = 2\pi v(2m/\boldsymbol{h}^2)^{3/2}$.

[1] Lewis and Mayer, *Proc. Nat. Acad.*, 1929, **15**, 208; Condon, *Phys. Rev.*, 1938, **54**, 937; Mayer and Mayer, "Statistical Mechanics," 1940, 109, 363; Glasstone, "Theoretical Chemistry," 1945, 321 f. For a non-ideal Fermi-Dirac gas, see Uhlenbeek and Gnopper, *Phys. Rev.*, 1932, **41**, 79; Nath and Auluck, *Proc. Nat. Inst. Sci. India*, 1943, **9**, 257; Dutta, *ibid.*, 1947, **13**, 247.

The energy and entropy per mol may be calculated from the equations:

$$N=\Sigma n_r,\quad E=\Sigma n_r\epsilon_r,\quad S=k\ln W \qquad (9)$$

and, since the energy levels are very closely spaced, the sums may be replaced by integrals. The values of n_r from (5), § 31, and (3), § 32, are expressed in terms of a_r by (8), and S is found from (2), § 31, and (2), § 32.

I. *For Bose-Einstein Statistics.*—In this case, from (5), § 31:

$$n_r=a_r/(Ce^{\mu\epsilon_r}-1)=A\epsilon^{1/2}d\epsilon/(Ce^{\mu\epsilon}-1),$$

$$\therefore\ N=\Sigma n_r=A\int_0^\infty \epsilon^{1/2}d\epsilon/(Ce^{\mu\epsilon}-1) \qquad (10)$$

$$E=\Sigma n_r\epsilon_r=A\int_0^\infty \epsilon^{3/2}d\epsilon/(Ce^{\mu\epsilon}-1) \qquad (11)$$

Equation (10) will give the value of C, since $\mu=1/kT$, as in Maxwell-Boltzmann statistics, because the latter is a special case when $Ce^{\mu\epsilon}\gg 1$.

II. *For Fermi-Dirac Statistics.*—In this case, similarly:

$$N=A\int_0^\infty \epsilon^{1/2}d\epsilon/(Ce^{\mu\epsilon}+1) \qquad (12)$$

$$E=A\int_0^\infty \epsilon^{3/2}d\epsilon/(Ce^{\mu\epsilon}+1) \qquad (13)$$

These two cases do not differ appreciably from the values found by Maxwell-Boltzmann statistics except when $Ce^{\mu\epsilon}$ becomes of the same order as ± 1, i.e. at very low temperatures. At other temperatures $Ce^{\mu\epsilon}\gg 1$, and ± 1 in the brackets may be neglected, when the Maxwell-Boltzmann formula results. In this case

$$N=(A/C)\int_0^\infty \epsilon^{1/2}e^{-\mu\epsilon}d\epsilon \qquad (13a)$$

$$\therefore\ C=(A/N)\int_0^\infty \epsilon^{1/2}e^{-\mu\epsilon}d\epsilon$$

$$=[2\pi v(2m/h^2)^{3/2}/N]\int_0^\infty \epsilon^{1/2}e^{-\mu\epsilon}d\epsilon$$

$$=(v/Nh^3)(2\pi mkT)^{3/2}=3{\cdot}074\times 10^{-4}M^{3/2}T^{3/2}/\xi \qquad (14)$$

where ξ=concentration in mol/lit. and M=molecular weight. This follows by putting $Nm=M$, $\xi=1/v$, $\mu=1/kT$, and evaluating the integral. For the latter, put $\epsilon=x$, and $x=t^2$, therefore $dx=2tdt$,

$$\therefore\ \int_0^\infty x^{1/2}e^{-\mu x}dx=2\int_0^\infty t^2e^{-\mu t^2}dt=2\,.\,\tfrac{1}{4}\sqrt{(\pi/\mu^3)}\quad \text{(by (2), § 12, III)}$$

$$=\tfrac{1}{2}\sqrt{\pi}(kT)^{3/2}, \text{ giving the result in (14).}$$

The calculation of the entropy is not quite so simple. For Bose-Einstein statistics, from (1) and (2), § 31:

$$S=k\ln W=k\Sigma\ln[(n_r+a_r-1)!/n_r!(a_r-1)!].$$

By neglecting 1 in comparison with a_r, and using Stirling's theorem, (9), § 8, this is easily transformed into:

$$S=k\Sigma[(n_r+a_r)\ln(n_r+a_r)-n_r\ln n_r-a_r\ln a_r]$$

$$=k\Sigma[a_r\ln(1+n_r/a_r)+n_r\ln(a_r/n_r+1)] \qquad (15)$$

In the same way, for Fermi-Dirac statistics, (1) and (2), § 32, give:

$$S=k\Sigma[-a_r\ln(1-n_r/a_r)+n_r\ln(a_r/n_r-1)] \qquad (15a)$$

so that both types are given by the formula:

$$S=k\Sigma[\pm a_r \ln (1\pm n_r/a_r)+n_r \ln (a_r/n_r\pm 1)] \quad . \quad . \quad . \quad . \quad (16)$$

the upper sign in $\pm$ referring to Bose-Einstein statistics, and the lower sign to Fermi-Dirac statistics. Also:

$$a_r/n_r=Ce^{\mu\epsilon_r}\mp 1,$$

with the same rule for the sign.

For Bose-Einstein statistics, $a_r/n_r=Ce^{\mu\epsilon_r}-1$, therefore $a_r/n_r+1=Ce^{\mu\epsilon_r}$, therefore $\ln (a_r/n_r+1)=\ln C+\mu\epsilon_r$,

$$\therefore\ k\Sigma n_r \ln (a_r/n_r+1)=k\Sigma n_r \ln C+k\Sigma n_r\mu\epsilon_r=R \ln C+E/T.$$

Also:

$$\begin{aligned}1+n_r/a_r&=1+1/(Ce^{\mu\epsilon_r}-1)\\ &=Ce^{\mu\epsilon_r}/(Ce^{\mu\epsilon_r}-1)\\ &=Ce^{\mu\epsilon_r}C^{-1}e^{-\mu\epsilon_r}/(1-1/Ce^{\mu\epsilon_r})=1/(1-e^{-\mu\epsilon_r}/C)\end{aligned}$$

$$\therefore\ a_r \ln (1+n_r/a_r)=-a_r \ln (1-e^{-\mu\epsilon_r}/C).$$

By substituting a_r from (8) and replacing the sum by an integral, it is found from (16) that:

$$S=R \ln C+E/T-Ak\int_0^\infty \epsilon^{1/2}d\epsilon \ln (1-e^{-\mu\epsilon}/C) \quad . \quad . \quad . \quad . \quad (17)$$

The calculation for Fermi-Dirac statistics follows the same lines, using $a_r/n_r=Ce^{\mu\epsilon}+1$, and gives:

$$S=R \ln C+E/T+Ak\int_0^\infty \epsilon^{1/2}d\epsilon \ln (1+e^{-\mu\epsilon}/C) \quad . \quad . \quad . \quad . \quad (18)$$

The entropy equations may be found by an alternative method.[1]

From (2), § 34.I, $\ln (1+1/Ce^{\mu\epsilon})\simeq e^{-\mu\epsilon}/C$,

$$\begin{aligned}\therefore\ S&=R \ln C+E/T+(A/C)k\int_0^\infty \epsilon^{1/2}e^{-\mu\epsilon}d\epsilon\\ &=R \ln C+E/T+R=R(5/2+\ln C) \quad . \quad . \quad . \quad . \quad (19)\end{aligned}$$

from (13a), since $E=(3/2)RT$ and $Nk=R$. Substitute for C from (14), and put $pv=RT$, then:

$$S=R\{(5/2) \ln T-\ln p+5/2+\ln [(2\pi mk)^{3/2}(k/h^3)]\} \quad . \quad . \quad (20)$$

giving for the entropy constant:

$$S_0{}^G/R=\ln [(2\pi mk)^{3/2}(k/h^3)]+5/2 \quad . \quad . \quad . \quad . \quad . \quad (21)$$

When $Ce^{\mu\epsilon}$ becomes comparable with 1, deviations from classical properties set in, and C is no longer given by (14). The state of *gas degeneracy* would then be reached, but calculations show that this would be appreciable for actual gases only at unattainably low temperatures or high pressures, except possibly for helium (see § 36).

If $C=(v/Nh^3)(2\pi mkT)^{3/2}$ from (14), and $a_r=(2\pi v)(2m/h^3)^{3/2}\epsilon^{1/2}d\epsilon$ from (8), are substituted in the approximate (Maxwell-Boltzmann) form of (5), § 31, or (3), § 32:

$$n_r=a_r/Ce^{\mu\epsilon},$$

μ replaced by $1/kT$, and n_r, the number of molecules having kinetic energies of translation in the range ϵ to $\epsilon+d\epsilon$, replaced by dN, then (since N can be replaced by N, *any* given number of molecules):

$$dN=[2N/\sqrt{\pi}(kT)^{3/2}]e^{-\epsilon/kT}\epsilon^{1/2}d\epsilon \quad . \quad . \quad . \quad . \quad . \quad . \quad (22)$$

which is one form of Maxwell's distribution law, (32), § 10.III.

[1] Mayer and Mayer, "Statistical Mechanics," New York, 1940, 424.

If c is the velocity of the molecule without regard to direction, the momentum is $p=mc=\sqrt{(p_x^2+p_y^2+p_z^2)}$, and the kinetic energy of translation is $\epsilon=\frac{1}{2}mc^2=p^2/2m$; hence the fraction of the molecules having velocities in the range c to $c+\mathrm{d}c$ is found by substituting ϵ, $\epsilon^{1/2}=p/\sqrt{(2m)}$, and $\mathrm{d}\epsilon=p\mathrm{d}p/m$, in (21), as:

$$\mathrm{d}N/N=4\pi(m/2\pi \boldsymbol{k}T)^{3/2}c^2e^{-mc^2/2\boldsymbol{k}T}\mathrm{d}c \quad . \quad . \quad . \quad . \quad . \quad (23)$$

which is equation (31), § 10.III.

§ 34. The Electron Theory of Metals

Perhaps the most useful application of Fermi-Dirac statistics is in the electron theory of metals,[1] where the pure mathematics is beyond the scope of this book. As Slater [2] said: "The theory of metals is based on wave mechanics, and unfortunately on the more difficult and involved wave mechanics; and there seems to be no short cut in understanding it."

In Fermi-Dirac statistics, no more than one particle (or *two* electrons, with opposite spins) can occupy one energy level, and hence at the absolute zero it is impossible for more than one particle to have zero energy. The remainder will have finite and different zero-point energies up to a *maximum* value, usually called the *Fermi energy*, and variously symbolised as ϵ_{00}, W_i, or ϵ^*. If all the energy levels are filled, (6), § 33, gives the number of particles in a volume v. The number of states or energy levels with energies up to ϵ_{00} is thus:

$$N=(4/3)\pi(2m\epsilon_{00})^{3/2}v/\boldsymbol{h}^3,$$

$$\therefore \epsilon_{00}=(1/2m)(3N\boldsymbol{h}^3/4\pi v)^{2/3} \quad . \quad . \quad . \quad . \quad . \quad . \quad . \quad . \quad (1)$$

If the particles are electrons, $2N$ must be written for N, when:

$$\epsilon_{00}=(1/2m)(6N\boldsymbol{h}^3/4\pi v)^{2/3} \quad . \quad . \quad . \quad . \quad . \quad . \quad . \quad . \quad (2)$$

Even in the case of electrons, (1) is generally used, the difference being only conventional, although important.

The value of ϵ_{00} for free electron gas is first calculated. The density of the electron gas can be taken as of the order of the density of free electrons in the metal, one electron per atom of metal, taking N as the number of atoms per cm.^{3} ($v=1$), say one electron in a cube of side 3×10^{-8} cm., or $N=(1/27)\times10^{24}$ particles per cm.^{3}. With 1 k.cal.$=4{\cdot}184\times10^{10}$ ergs, 1 mol$=6{\cdot}03\times10^{23}$

[1] Sommerfeld, *Z. Phys.*, 1928, **47**, 1, 43; *Naturwiss.*, 1928, **16**, 374; *Congrès Internat. Électricité*, 1932, **1**, No. 9; *Ann. Phys.*, 1937, **28**, 1; Sommerfeld and Bethe, in Geiger and Scheel, "Handbuch der Physik," 1932, **24**, II, 333; Lennard-Jones, *Proc. Phys. Soc.*, 1928, **40**, 320; Hall, *Proc. Nat. Acad.*, 1928, **14**, 370, 377; Bloch, *Z. Phys.*, 1928, **52**, 555; Frenkel, *Z. Phys.*, 1924, **29**, 214; 1928, **49**, 31; *Sow. Phys. Z.*, 1932, **2**, 247; Houston, *Z. Phys.*, 1928, **48**, 449; Darrow, *Rev. Mod. Phys.*, 1929, **1**, 90; Nordheim, *Ann. Phys.*, 1931, **9**, 607; Becker, *Z. Elektrochem.*, 1931, **37**, 403; Peierls, *Ergebn. exakt. Naturwiss.*, 1932, **11**, 264; Slater, *Rev. Mod. Phys.*, 1934, **6**, 209; *idem*, "Introduction to Chemical Physics," New York, 1939, 72, 472; Frenkel, "Wave Mechanics. Elementary Theory," Oxford, 1932; Bethe, Brillouin, Nordheim, Peierls, Sommerfeld, *et al.*, "La Théorie des Électrons dans les Métaux," Confer. Intern. Sci. Math., Geneva, 1934, issued as Supplement to *Helv. Phys. Acta*, 1934, **7**; Brillouin, *Rev. Gén. Electr.*, 1935, **38**, 491; Fröhlich, "Elektronentheorie der Metalle," Berlin, 1936; Konobejewski, *Ann. Phys.*, 1936, **26**, 97; Mott, *Sci. Progr.*, 1937, **31**, 414; Borelius, *Ann. Phys.*, 1937, **29**, 251; Davisson, *J. Appl. Phys.*, 1937, **8**, 391; Slater, *ibid.*, 1937, **8**, 385; Anderson, *J.S.C.I.*, 1937, **56**, 677 (elementary); Loeb, "Atomic Structure," New York, 1938, 380; Seitz, "The Theory of Metals," New York, 1943, 246; Raynor, "Introduction to the Electron Theory of Metals," 1947, 36; Hume-Rothery, "Atomic Theory for Students of Metallurgy," 1947, 151; Koppe, *Z. Naturforsch.*, 1947, **2** A, 429 (correction for resonance).

[2] *J.A.C.S.*, 1937, **59**, 427.

particles, and $m=M\times 1{\cdot}66\times 10^{-24}$ g. for a substance of atomic weight M, the Fermi energy in k.cal. per mol is:

$$N\epsilon_{00}=\frac{6{\cdot}03\times 10^{23}}{4{\cdot}184\times 10^{10}\times 2M\times 1{\cdot}66\times 10^{-24}}\left[\frac{3\times(6{\cdot}6\times 10^{-27})^3}{4\times 3{\cdot}1416\times 27\times 10^{-24}}\right]=0{\cdot}081/M.$$

For electrons $1/M=1813$, therefore $\epsilon_{00}=148$ k.cal./mol$=6{\cdot}4$ electron-volts/ molecule. This is a large value as compared with the thermal energies of molecules at the ordinary temperature, and hence electron gas at high density, as in metals, even at the absolute zero, has a large energy, corresponding with a high velocity.

This is, of course, a consequence of the fact that ϵ_{00} is the *highest* occupied level at the absolute zero, and must have an appreciable value because there are very many occupied levels between this and the single state of zero energy.

The zero-point energy, or the *mean* energy of a particle at $T=0$, is easily shown to be $\frac{3}{5}\epsilon_{00}$. For, from (7), § 33, the number of energy levels between ϵ and $\epsilon+d\epsilon$ is ($v=1$):

$$dN=2\pi(2m)^{3/2}\epsilon^{1/2}d\epsilon/\boldsymbol{h}^3$$

$$\therefore\ \bar{\epsilon}=(1/N)\int_0^{\epsilon_{00}}\epsilon dN=(1/N)[2\pi(2m)^{3/2}/\boldsymbol{h}^3]\int_0^{\epsilon_{00}}\epsilon^{3/2}d\epsilon$$

$$=[(2\pi/N\boldsymbol{h}^3)(2m)^{3/2}\epsilon_{00}{}^{5/2}]\div\tfrac{5}{2}=\tfrac{3}{5}\epsilon_{00},$$

from (1), and the mean energy per mol at $T=0$ is $\frac{3}{5}N\epsilon_{00}$.

The calculation of the mean energy at other temperatures involves wave mechanics; the final result per mol is:

$$E=N[\tfrac{3}{5}\epsilon_{00}+(\pi^2/4)(\boldsymbol{k}T)^2/\epsilon_{00}] \quad . \quad . \quad . \quad . \quad . \quad . \quad (3)$$

$$\therefore\ C_v=dE/dT=N\boldsymbol{k}(\pi^2/2)(\boldsymbol{k}T/\epsilon_{00})=\boldsymbol{R}(\pi^2/2)(\boldsymbol{k}T/\epsilon_{00}) \quad . \quad . \quad . \quad (4)$$

For ordinary gases, with relatively large M values, ϵ_{00} is of the order of $\boldsymbol{k}T$, as is seen from the above calculation, and the T^2 term in (3) is large even at low temperatures. With electron gas, ϵ_{00} is much larger than $\boldsymbol{k}T$, and is $(\pi^2/3)$ $(\boldsymbol{k}T/\epsilon_{00})$ times the value $\frac{3}{2}\boldsymbol{k}T$ for a monatomic gas obeying Maxwell-Boltzmann statistics. At ordinary temperatures, therefore, the heat capacity of electron gas in metals is quite small. Even at 1000° K., where $N\boldsymbol{k}T$ is 2 k.cal., C_v for electron gas in a metal is only about 4 per cent that for an ideal gas obeying Maxwell-Boltzmann statistics, whilst at room temperature it is only about 1 per cent.

This result solved the puzzle that, if a metal consists of positive ions and free electrons, its atomic heat should be 9 for a normal monatomic metal, i.e. 3 for the kinetic energy of the electrons and 6 for the kinetic and potential energies of the positive metal ions, whereas the actual value is about 6. The calculation shows, in fact, that the electrons contribute practically nothing to the heat capacity, as they are extremely " degenerate." For silver at room temperature, the heat capacity of the electrons is only about 0·05 g.cal. per g. atom. Since (4) shows that C_v for electrons is proportional to T, whilst for atoms the Debye equation for atomic heats at low temperatures shows that it is proportional to T^3, the contribution of the electrons becomes of the same order as that of the atoms at very low temperatures, and this, and equation (4), have been experimentally verified for silver.[1]

[1] Keesom and Kok, *Proc. K. Akad. Wetens. Amsterdam*, 1934, **37**, 377; *Physica*, 1934, **1**, 770; *Comm. Leiden*, 1934, **232***d*; Keesom and Clark, *Proc. K. Akad. Wetens. Amsterdam*, 1935, **38**, 569; *Physica*, 1935, **2**, 698; for calculation of Fermi energy of metals, see Bardeen, *J. Chem. Phys.*, 1938, **6**, 367. This subject will be taken up in § 16.IX L, Vol. II.

§ 35. Gibbs's Grand Canonical Assembly

The equations for Maxwell-Boltzmann, Bose-Einstein, and Fermi-Dirac statistics may be very concisely deduced [1] by a method based on what Gibbs [2] called the "grand canonical ensemble," in which a given system with a fixed number of particles N is replaced by a very large number of similar systems differing in N-values, in such a way that the relative number of systems with N particles and *a definite energy* E is proportional to $e^{-\lambda N}$, where λ is a constant, and the relative number with a given energy E is proportional to $e^{-\mu E}$, as in § 8. Thus, the probability for a given number of particles N and given energy E, is proportional to $e^{-\lambda N-\mu E}$, where $\mu=1/kT$. A formal proof is not attempted here.[3] It may be noted that the canonical assembly (§ 10) is defined by the probability $e^{-\lambda-\mu E}$, where λ is a constant defined by the *fixed* number N of particles in the system. If, as in (2), § 9:

$$Z=\sum_N\sum_E e^{-\lambda N-\mu E} \quad . \; . \; . \; . \; . \; . \; . \; . \; . \quad (1)$$

is the state sum (the weight factor g being explicitly dropped, on the assumption that only *allowed* distributions for various types of statistics are to be included), the average values of N and E are given, from (15) and (19), § 8, by:

$$\bar{N}=-(\partial/\partial\lambda)\ln Z, \quad \text{and} \quad \bar{E}=-(\partial/\partial\mu)\ln Z \quad . \; . \; . \; . \quad (2)$$

In *Bose-Einstein statistics* (§ 31) the statistical weight is $g=1$ for all values of the distribution numbers $N_1, N_2, \ldots, N_k$, and k refers to different quantised states of a single particle:

$$\therefore \; N=\sum_k N_k, \quad E=\sum_k N_k E_k \quad . \; . \; . \; . \; . \; . \; . \; . \quad (3)$$

$$Z=\sum_N e^{-\sum_k(\lambda+\mu E_k)N_k} \quad . \; . \; . \; . \; . \; . \; . \; . \; . \quad (4)$$

where $\sum_N$ denotes summation over all values of N_k from 0 to ∞, regardless of the total number of particles $N=\sum_k N_k$. The restriction $\sum_k N_k=\text{const.}$ is thus dropped (cf. § 31), as must be the case with photons. Thus, Z reduces to the product of the sums referring to each individual state taken separately, i.e. the product of the sums:

$$\sum_{N_k=0}^{\infty} e^{-(\lambda+\mu E_k)N_k}=1/(1-e^{-(\lambda+\mu E_k)}).$$

The expression on the left is the binomial expansion of that on the right. For, let $e^{-(\lambda+\mu E_k)}=x_k$, then:

$$Z=\sum_N x_1^{N_1}x_2^{N_2}\ldots=\sum_{N_1} x_1^{N_1}\sum x_2^{N_2}\ldots \text{ (an identity)}=\prod_k\sum_0^{\infty} x_k^{N_k},$$

the summation being over the values of N_k. But the continued product is equal to $\prod_k[1/(1-x_k)]$, the sum in it being the binomial expansion of $1/(1-x_k)$. Hence, by taking logarithms (when the product becomes a sum), and restoring the value of x_k, it follows that:

$$\ln Z=-\sum_k \ln\left[1-e^{-(\lambda+\mu E_k)}\right] \quad . \; . \; . \; . \; . \; . \; . \quad (5)$$

[1] Frenkel, "Wave Mechanics. Elementary Theory," Oxford, 1932, 201; Tolman, "Statistical Mechanics," Oxford, 1938, 511.

[2] "Elementary Principles in Statistical Mechanics," 1902, 189; "Collected Works," 1928, **2**, 189; Lorentz, "Les Théories Statistique en Thermodynamique," Leipzig and Berlin, 1916, 30; Haas, "Commentary on the Writings of J. W. Gibbs," New Haven, 1936, **2**, 449; McMillan and Mayer, *J. Chem. Phys.*, 1945, **13**, 276.

[3] The classical deduction follows the lines of §§ 8 and 10.

Hence, from (2):

$$\bar{N}=\sum_k[1/(e^{\lambda+\mu E_k}-1)] \quad . \quad . \quad . \quad (6)$$

$$\bar{E}=\sum_k[E_k/(e^{\lambda+\mu E_k}-1)] \quad . \quad . \quad . \quad (7)$$

which show that the *average* number of parts in the different (individual) states is given by the distribution law found in § 31 (with $a=1$):

$$\bar{N}_k=1/(e^{\lambda+\mu E_k}-1) \quad . \quad . \quad . \quad (8)$$

In *Fermi-Dirac Statistics*, $g=1$ for $N_k=0$ or 1, but $g=0$ for all other values of N_k. The state sum has only two terms, that for $N_k=0$ being unity:

$$Z=\prod_k\sum_0^1 e^{-(\lambda+\mu E_k)N_k}=\prod_k[1+e^{-(\lambda+\mu E_k)}],$$

$$\therefore \ln Z=\sum_k \ln[1+e^{-(\lambda+\mu E_k)}] \quad . \quad . \quad . \quad (9)$$

$$\text{and} \quad \bar{N}_k=1/(e^{\lambda+\mu E_k}+1) \quad . \quad . \quad . \quad (10)$$

as in § 32 ($a=1$).

In *Maxwell-Boltzmann statistics*, $g=N!/N_1!N_2! \ldots$, and (with N now fixed), equation (1), with $x_k=e^{-\lambda-\mu E_k}$, becomes:

$$Z=\Sigma \ln \frac{N!}{N_1!N_2!\ldots} e^{-\lambda N-\mu E}=\sum_N \ln \frac{N!}{N_1!N_2!\ldots} x_1^{N_1}x_2^{N_2}\ldots$$

$$=\sum_N(x_1+x_2+\ldots)^N \quad . \quad . \quad . \quad (11)$$

If $\sum_k x_k=e^{-\lambda}\sum_k e^{-\mu E_k}=z$, equation (11) becomes:

$$Z=1/(1-z) \quad . \quad . \quad . \quad (12)$$

where z must be less than unity if Z is to be significant.

Hence from (3), $\bar{N}=z/(1-z)$, and $\bar{E}=\sum_k E_k x_k/(1-z)$,

$$\therefore \bar{N}_k=x_k/(1-z)=\text{const. } e^{-\mu E_k} \quad . \quad . \quad . \quad (13)$$

which is the Maxwell-Boltzmann distribution law.

The three types of statistics may be summarised [1] by writing down the conditions for maximum probability:

$$-\delta \ln W=0=\begin{cases}\sum_k(\ln n_k-\ln a_k+1)\delta n_k & \text{Maxwell-Boltzmann}\\ \sum_k[\ln n_k-\ln(a_k+n_k)]\delta n_k & \text{Bose-Einstein}\\ \sum_k[\ln n_k-\ln(a_k-n_k)]\delta n_k & \text{Fermi-Dirac}\end{cases}$$

with the subsidiary conditions (*a*) $\delta n=\sum_k\delta n_k=0$, and (*b*) $\delta E=\sum_k\epsilon_k\delta n_k=0$. By multiplying (*a*) by λ and (*b*) by μ, and adding to the expressions for $-\delta \ln W=0$, the assignment of elements n_k to different groups of a_k states is expressed by keeping the total number of elements constant (except in the case of photons, when condition (*a*) drops out), and the total energy constant, and in the manner explained in § 8 it is found that:

$$n_k=\frac{a_k}{e^{\lambda+\mu\epsilon_k}\pm 1(0)} \quad \begin{cases}0 \text{ for Maxwell-Boltzmann}\\ -1 \text{ for Bose-Einstein}\\ +1 \text{ for Fermi-Dirac}\end{cases}$$

with the special values of $\pm 1(0)$ in the denominator, as shown on the right.

[1] Tolman, "Statistical Mechanics," Oxford, 1938, 372.

§ 36. Gas Degeneracy

The problem of the entropy and specific heat of a gas at the absolute zero has led to some fruitless discussion.[1] If Maxwell-Boltzmann statistics apply, the term $C_v \ln T$ in the expression for the entropy in (4a), § 55.II, would make this $-\infty$ at the absolute zero.[2] Nernst [3] worked out a theory of " gas degeneration " in which the equation $p=RT/V$ is replaced by:

$$p=(R/V)\beta\nu/(1-e^{-\beta\nu/T})\simeq(RT/V)(1+\beta\nu/2T),$$

($\beta=h/k$), but Bennewitz [4] detected a slip in the calculation (later admitted by Nernst), and the correct equation should be:

$$p=(RT/V)[1+\tfrac{1}{12}(\beta\nu/T)^2],$$

leading to a deviation from the gas law so small as to be experimentally undetectable.

Széll [5] showed that the deviations introduced by Bose-Einstein or Fermi-Dirac statistics for diatomic or polyatomic gases are entirely negligible in experimentally attainable conditions. Schrödinger [6] found that degeneration sets in at a temperature $\Theta=h^2/8ml^2k$, where l is a characteristic length; if this is taken as the mean free path, Θ is about 1/10,000° K.

Bose-Einstein statistics points to a real gas degeneracy at very low temperature, but this is so small that it could not be detected experimentally, the alleged drop in C_v for helium to 2·90 g.cal. at low temperature, reported by Eucken,[7] being certainly due to experimental error. The peculiar " condensation " effect which should appear at very low temperatures has been investigated theoretically, and it is suggested that liquid helium-II behaves as a degenerate Bose-Einstein gas.[8] London showed that the sp. ht. should be proportional to $(T/T_c)^{3/2}$. The rate of effusion should depend only on the temperature, and not on the concentration.[9]

[1] Njegovan, *Z. Elektrochem.*, 1925, **31**, 6; *J. Chim. Phys.*, 1928, **25**, 65; Kolossowsky, *ibid.*, 1925, **22**, 77; 1926, **23**, 728; 1927, **24**, 621, 723; *Z. phys. Chem.*, 1928, **136**, 314; Verschaffelt, *J. Chim. Phys.*, 1926, **23**, 238; van Laar, *Z. phys. Chem.*, 1928, **134**, 311.

[2] Planck, " Thermodynamik," 3rd edit., 1911, 274.

[3] *Z. Elektrochem.*, 1914, **20**, 357; 1916, **22**, 185; *Berlin Ber.*, 1919, 118; " The New Heat Theorem," 1926, 193, 268; Sackur, *Z. Elektrochem.*, 1914, **20**, 563; Meissner, *Z. Phys.*, 1926, **36**, 325.

[4] *Z. phys. Chem.*, 1924, **110**, 725.

[5] *Z. Phys.*, 1933, **84**, 810; 1933, **86**, 810.

[6] *Phys. Z.*, 1924, **25**, 41.

[7] *Verhl. d. D. Phys. Ges.*, 1916, **18**, 4; Scheel and Heuse, *Ann. Phys.*, 1912, **37**, 79; 1913, **40**, 473; *Z. Elektrochem.*, 1913, **19**, 593, also reported a small decrease at −180° C., which, if not due to error, was certainly not due to degeneracy; Fowler and Guggenheim, " Statistical Thermodynamics," 1939, 125.

[8] Uehling and Uhlenbeek, *Phys. Rev.*, 1933, **43**, 552; Uehling, *ibid.*, 1934, **45**, 766; 1934, **46**, 917; Kahn and Uhlenbeek, *Physica*, 1937, **4**, 1155; 1938, **5**, 399; Born, *ibid.*, 1937, **4**, 1034; London, *Phys. Rev.*, 1938, **54**, 947; *J. Chem. Phys.*, 1943, **11**, 203; Condon, *Phys. Rev.*, 1938, **54**, 937; Tisza, *Compt. Rend.*, 1938, **207**, 1035; Fowler and Jones, *Proc. Cambr. Phil. Soc.*, 1938, **34**, 573; Wergeland, *K. Norske Vidensk. Selsk. Forhl.*, 1940, **13**, 127; Schiff, *Phys. Rev.*, 1941, **59**, 751, 758; Gogate and Kathavate, *Phil. Mag.*, 1942, **33**, 310; de Boer and Michels, *Physica*, 1940, **7**, 368; de Boer, *Physica*, 1943, **10**, 348; Goldstein, *J. Chem. Phys.*, 1946, **14**, 276; Einbinder, *Phys. Rev.*, 1948, **74**, 805; for summary, see Mayer and Mayer, " Statistical Mechanics," New York, 1940, 363 f.; for " condensation " of a Fermi-Dirac gas, see Sen, *Proc. Nat. Inst. Sci. India*, 1941, **7**, 405; Singh and Chowdri, *ibid.*, 1942, **8**, 89; Nath and Bhatnagar, *ibid.*, 1942, **8**, 361; Kothari and Nath, *Nature*, 1943, **151**, 420. The properties of He-II will be discussed in § 8.VIII F, Vol. II.

[9] Gogate and Kathavate, *Phil. Mag.*, 1942, **33**, 310.

The pressure of a Bose-Einstein or a Fermi-Dirac gas may be calculated from equation (2), § 2.III, $pV=\frac{2}{3}E$, which holds generally for all types of statistics, although the energy E is very different for the Maxwell-Boltzmann and Fermi-Dirac cases. Since E in Fermi-Dirac statistics (§ 34) is very large at $T=0$, but increases only slowly with rising temperature, with a term proportional to T^2, and also depends on the volume, the term pV behaves similarly.[1] For a metal at absolute zero, the calculated electron gas pressure is 149,000 atm. The dependence of energy on volume is not due to intermolecular forces but to the dependence of kinetic energy (through ϵ_{00}) on the volume.

In Bose-Einstein statistics, the molecules are concentrated in the *lower* energy states, in contrast to Fermi-Dirac statistics, which crowds them into the *higher* energy states, and Maxwell-Boltzmann statistics, which spreads them more evenly over the energy states in a way which is, in a sense, intermediate between the other two cases. Instead of the large zero-point pressure at low temperatures predicted by Fermi-Dirac statistics, Bose-Einstein statistics leads to a kind of " condensation," corresponding with that which would be produced by attractive forces leading to the liquefaction of a real gas.[2] There are indications that departure from Maxwell-Boltzmann statistics with hydrogen and helium may occur at very low temperatures (these gases obeying Bose-Einstein statistics), but such deviations are swamped by approach to liquefaction.

A mere sketch of the treatment of ideal monatomic gases[3] is all that can be attempted here; the upper signs in the equations refer to Bose-Einstein statistics, and the lower to Fermi-Dirac statistics. If two functions:

$$\mathrm{F}(A)=\frac{2}{\sqrt{\pi}}\int_0^\infty \frac{Ax^{1/2}e^{-x}dx}{1\mp Ae^{-x}} \quad . \quad . \quad . \quad . \quad . \quad . \quad . \quad (1)$$

$$\mathrm{G}(A)=\frac{4}{3\sqrt{\pi}}\int_0^\infty \frac{Ax^{3/2}e^{-x}dx}{1\mp Ae^{-x}} \quad . \quad . \quad . \quad . \quad . \quad . \quad . \quad (2)$$

are defined, the following relation exists between them:

$$A\,.\,\mathrm{dG}(A)/\mathrm{d}A=\mathrm{F}(A) \quad . \quad . \quad . \quad . \quad . \quad . \quad . \quad . \quad (3)$$

Put $\mathrm{F}(A)=\Theta^{-3/2}$ and regard $\mathrm{G}(A)$ as a function of $\mathrm{F}(A)$ or of Θ, the expression:

$$\mathrm{P}(\Theta)=\Theta^{5/2}\mathrm{G}(A) \quad . \quad . \quad . \quad . \quad . \quad . \quad . \quad . \quad . \quad (4)$$

being a function of Θ. For two extreme cases, when Θ is very large or very small compared with unity, the expansions of $\mathrm{P}(\Theta)$ may be obtained:

(i) Θ very large:

$$\mathrm{P}(\Theta)=\Theta\left(1\mp\frac{1}{2^{5/2}\Theta^{3/2}}+\ldots\right) \quad . \quad . \quad . \quad . \quad . \quad . \quad (5)$$

(ii) Θ very small (Fermi-Dirac case only):

$$\mathrm{P}(\Theta)=\frac{3^{2/3}\pi^{1/3}}{5\,.\,2^{1/3}}\left(1+\frac{5\,.\,2^{2/3}\pi^{4/3}}{3^{7/3}}\Theta^2+\ldots\right) \quad . \quad . \quad . \quad . \quad (6)$$

[1] Jensen, *Z. Phys.*, 1937, **106**, 620.

[2] See Mayer and Mayer, " Statistical Mechanics," 1940, 416; Glasstone, " Theoretical Chemistry," New York, 1944, 321. This part of the theory has been amended in Gentile statistics, § 37.

[3] Rodebush, in H. S. Taylor, " Treatise on Physical Chemistry," New York, 1931, **2**, 1444; Epstein, " A Commentary on the Scientific Writings of J. Willard Gibbs," New Haven. 1936, **2**, 83; Tolman, " Statistical Mechanics," Oxford, 1938, 381, 388; Mayer and Mayer, " Statistical Mechanics," New York, 1940, 374, 385, 416; Leibfried, *Z. Naturforsch.*, 1947, **2** A, 305.

The ideal gas equation is then (m=mass of gas atom):

$$pv=\frac{h^2N^{5/3}}{2\pi mv^{2/3}}\mathrm{P}\left(\frac{2\pi mkv^{2/3}T}{h^2N^{2/3}}\right) \quad . \quad . \quad . \quad . \quad . \quad . \quad (7)$$

P being the function of the argument in brackets. If the argument of P is very large, i.e. T or v very large, $\mathrm{P}(\Theta)$ can be replaced by Θ, and the equation becomes $pv=NkT=RT$. If the argument is very small, gas degeneration results The thermodynamic equation (2), § 54.II:

$$T(\mathrm{d}p/\mathrm{d}T)_v-p=(\mathrm{d}E/\mathrm{d}v)_T \quad . \quad . \quad . \quad . \quad . \quad . \quad . \quad . \quad (8)$$

gives on integration:

$$E=\int[T(\mathrm{d}p/\mathrm{d}T)_v-p]\mathrm{d}v+\mathrm{f}(T) \quad . \quad . \quad . \quad . \quad . \quad . \quad . \quad (9)$$

the function $\mathrm{f}(T)$ being determined so as to give (E_0=zero-point energy):

$$E=3RT/2+E_0 \quad . \quad . \quad . \quad . \quad . \quad . \quad . \quad . \quad . \quad (10)$$

at high temperatures, without making E infinite for T=0. The integration gives:

$$E=\tfrac{3}{2}\frac{h^2N^{5/3}}{2\pi mv^{2/3}}\mathrm{P}\left(\frac{2\pi mkv^{2/3}T}{h^2N^{2/3}}\right)+E_0 \quad . \quad . \quad . \quad . \quad . \quad . \quad (11)$$

Equations (5) and (6), for large values of T and v give:

$$p=\frac{RT}{v}\left(1\mp\tfrac{1}{16}\frac{h^3N}{(\pi mkT)^{3/2}}\frac{1}{v}+\ldots\right) \quad . \quad . \quad . \quad . \quad . \quad (12)$$

$$E-E_0=\tfrac{3}{2}RT\left(1\mp\tfrac{1}{16}\frac{h^3N}{(\pi mkT)^{3/2}}\frac{1}{v}+\ldots\right) \quad . \quad . \quad . \quad . \quad (13)$$

while for small values of T and v (Fermi-Dirac case only):

$$p=\tfrac{1}{20}\left(\frac{6}{\pi}\right)^{2/3}\frac{h^2N^{5/3}}{mv^{5/3}}+\frac{2^{4/3}\pi^{8/3}}{3^{5/3}}\frac{mN^{1/3}k^2T^2}{h^2v^{1/3}}-\ldots \quad . \quad . \quad (14)$$

$$E-E_0=\tfrac{3}{40}\left(\frac{6}{\pi}\right)^{2/3}\frac{h^2N^{5/3}}{mv^{2/3}}+\frac{2^{1/3}\pi^{8/3}}{3^{2/3}}\frac{mN^{1/3}v^{2/3}k^2T^2}{h^2} \quad . \quad . \quad . \quad (15)$$

The first term in (14) gives the zero-point pressure (p_0 for T=0). It is easily seen that for the Fermi-Dirac gas the coefficient of expansion,

$$-(1/v)(\mathrm{d}p/\mathrm{d}T)_v/(\mathrm{d}p/\mathrm{d}v)_T,$$

and the specific heat at constant volume, $(\mathrm{d}E/\mathrm{d}T)_v$, are proportional to $v^{10/3}T$ and $v^{2/3}T$, respectively, both vanishing at T=0, in accordance with the Nernst heat theorem. The entropy is found from (7) and (11), the thermodynamic equation (1), § 55.II giving:

$$\mathrm{d}S=\delta q/T=(\mathrm{d}E+p\mathrm{d}v)/T=\mathrm{dP}(\Theta)/\Theta \quad . \quad . \quad . \quad . \quad (16)$$

$$\text{with} \quad \Theta=2\pi mv^{2/3}kT/h^2N^{2/3} \quad . \quad . \quad . \quad . \quad . \quad . \quad . \quad (17)$$

$$\therefore \; S=\tfrac{3}{2}R\int_0^{\Theta}\mathrm{dP}(\Theta)/\Theta \quad . \quad . \quad . \quad . \quad . \quad . \quad . \quad (18)$$

giving, with (4) and (3):

$$S=R\left[\tfrac{5}{2}\frac{\mathrm{G}(A)}{\mathrm{F}(A)}-\ln A\right] \quad . \quad . \quad . \quad . \quad . \quad . \quad . \quad (19)$$

For large values of T and v, the classical ideal gas state is approached; Θ is then large and $\mathrm{F}(A)$ very small, and (1) shows that this is true only when A is very small, when $\mathrm{F}(A)\simeq\mathrm{G}(A)\simeq A$, and (18) becomes:

$$S=R(5+3\ln\Theta)/2=\tfrac{5}{2}R\ln T-R\ln p+\tfrac{5}{2}R+R\ln\frac{(2\pi m)^{3/2}R^{5/2}}{N^{5/2}h^3}$$

which is the classical Tetrode equation, (20), § 14.

The Bose-Einstein case is less simple, since the parameter A, which for the Fermi-Dirac case can have any real and positive value, is now restricted to the values $0 \leqq A \leqq 1$, the integrals (1) and (2) with the upper sign becoming divergent when $A>1$. This restriction gives upper limits $F(1)=2{\cdot}612$ and $G(1)=1{\cdot}341$ for the functions, and a lower limit $\Theta_{min}=0{\cdot}527$, i.e. a lower limit for $v^{2/3}T$. The gas volume cannot be decreased below a lower limiting value at a given temperature, although the atoms are supposed to occupy no volume. Einstein suggested that, when v is reduced below this limiting value, some of gas atoms " condense " (like molecules of a saturated vapour) to the lowest quantum state of zero kinetic energy, forming a " condensed phase " (though probably still mixed with the remaining atoms), having only the zero-point energy, no specific volume, and zero entropy, the available energy being $G=E_0$. The remaining atoms form a " saturated phase " of the ideal gas (corresponding with a saturated vapour), the pressure being independent of the volume at a given temperature. The pressure equation (7) may be transformed into:

$$p=[(2\pi m)^{3/2}(kT)^{5/2}/h^3]G(A) \quad . \quad . \quad . \quad . \quad . \quad . \quad (20)$$

giving, with (3) and (17):

$$(\mathrm{d}p/\mathrm{d}v)_T=-\frac{NkT}{v^2}\frac{1}{\Theta^{3/2}A}\frac{\mathrm{d}A}{\mathrm{dF}} \quad . \quad . \quad . \quad . \quad . \quad . \quad (21)$$

From (1), $\mathrm{d}F/\mathrm{d}A\rightarrow\infty$ when $A=1$ (saturated state), hence $\mathrm{d}A/\mathrm{dF}=0$, and $(\mathrm{d}p/\mathrm{d}v)_T=0$, the p-v isotherm having a horizontal tangent. This corresponds with the separation of the single phase, then unstable, into two phases in the theory of van der Waals's equation, at points for which $(\mathrm{d}p/\mathrm{d}v)_T=0$ (see § 7.VII C).

Helium, with the smallest m and atomic weight M, and smallest Θ of all monatomic gases, should show degeneration at a higher temperature than any other such gas. Since $\Theta_{min}=0{\cdot}527$, the minimum atomic volume is given by:

$$v_{min}/N=(h^2N^2\Theta_{min}/2\pi MRT)^{3/2}=(2{\cdot}01/M^{3/2}T^{3/2})\times 10^{-21}.$$

Therefore $v_{min}=0{\cdot}25T^{-3/2}\times 10^{-21}$, so that the phenomenon of spontaneous condensation could not be observed at a temperature sufficiently removed from the critical state while the gas still remains ideal. In the saturated state $(A=1)$, $pv=0{\cdot}513RT$. The adiabatic equation is found from (18), $\mathrm{d}S=0$, therefore S=constant when Θ is constant, and from (17), $Tv^{2/3}$=const., or, with (7), $pv^{5/3}$=const., the same as for a classical monatomic gas. The velocity of sound, in measurable conditions, will be practically that in a classical gas.

Although the Bose-Einstein " condensation " has been related to critical phenomena,[1] this part of the theory is unattractive, and an alternative is provided by Gentile statistics, considered in the next paragraph.

§ 37. Gentile Statistics

A statistics intermediate between Bose-Einstein statistics and Fermi-Dirac statistics, in which the maximum occupation of any cell of phase space is assumed to be finite, was proposed by Gentile.[2] In Bose-Einstein statistics the

[1] Mayer, *J. Chem. Phys.*, 1937, **5**, 67; Mayer and Ackermann, *ibid.*, 1937, **5**, 74; Mayer and Harrison, *ibid.*, 1938, **6**, 87; Harrison and Mayer, *ibid.*, 1938, **6**, 101; Kahn and Uhlenbeek, *Physica*, 1938, **5**, 399; see ref. 8, p. 365.

[2] *Nuov. Cim.*, 1940, **17**, 493; 1942, **19**, 109 (liq. He); *Ricerca Sci.*, 1941, **12**, 341; Tisza, *J. de Phys.*, 1940, **1**, 164; Caldirola, *Ricerca Sci.*, 1941, **12**, 1020; *Nuov. Cim.*, 1943, **1**, 205 (liq. He-II); Salvetti, *Ricerca Sci.*, 1941, **12**, 894; *Atti. Accad. Ital. Mem. Fis. Mat. Nat.*, 1942, **13**, 651 (thermal cond. and visc. gas); Einbinder, *Phys. Rev.*, 1948, **74**, 805; Giovanni Gentile.

maximum occupation of an energy state may be infinite, and in Fermi-Dirac statistics it is unity.

Let the number of quantum states corresponding with an energy ϵ_s be a_s, and let $n_{0s}, n_{1s}, \ldots, n_{ds}$ be the numbers of states occupied by 0, 1, . . ., d parts, where d is finite. Then:

$$\sum_{r=0}^{=d} n_{rs}=a_s \quad \ldots \ldots \ldots \quad (1)$$

and

$$\sum_{r=0}^{r=d} rn_{rs}=n_s \quad \ldots \ldots \ldots \quad (2)$$

where n_s is the number of parts with energy ϵ_s. The number of ways of distributing the n_s parts over the a_s states is:

$$W=\Pi a_s!/n_{0s}!n_{1s}!n_{2s}! \ldots n_{ds}! \quad \ldots \ldots \ldots \quad (3)$$

Stirling's theorem, (9), § 8, gives:

$$\ln W=\Sigma a_s \ln a_s-\sum_s\sum_r n_{rs} \ln n_{rs} \quad \ldots \ldots \quad (4)$$

and ln W is to be a maximum, with the conditions:

$$E=\sum_s n_s\epsilon_s=\sum_s\sum_r n_{rs} \,.\, r\epsilon_s \quad \ldots \ldots \ldots \quad (5)$$

$$N=\sum_s n_s=\sum_s\sum_r rn_{rs} \quad \ldots \ldots \ldots \quad (6)$$

With the undetermined multipliers λ and μ (§ 8) this gives:

$$\sum_s\sum_r(1+\ln n_{rs}+\lambda r+\mu r\epsilon_s)\delta n_{rs}=0$$

$$\therefore\; n_{rs}=C_s\mathrm{e}^{-(\lambda+\mu\epsilon_s)r} \quad \ldots \ldots \ldots \quad (7)$$

and the general equations $\mathrm{d}S/\mathrm{d}E=1/T$, $S=k \ln W$ show (as in § 8) that $\mu=1/kT$. Equation (1) shows that:

$$C_s=n_s(1-\mathrm{e}^{-\gamma_s})/(1-\mathrm{e}^{-(d+1)\gamma_s}) \quad \ldots \ldots \quad (8)$$

where $\gamma_s=\lambda+\mu\epsilon_s$, and (2) shows that

$$n_s=a_s\mathrm{f}(\gamma_s)=a_s\frac{\mathrm{e}^{-\gamma_s}+d\mathrm{e}^{-(d+2)\gamma_s}-(d+1)\mathrm{e}^{-(d+1)\gamma_s}}{(1-\mathrm{e}^{-\gamma_s})(1-\mathrm{e}^{-(d+1)\gamma_s})} \quad \ldots \quad (9)$$

which is the fundamental equation of Gentile statistics. When $d\to\infty$ it passes over into Bose-Einstein statistics, and with $d=1$ into Fermi-Dirac statistics.

In the application to an ideal monatomic gas, the usual procedure (§ 33) is followed, and if $\epsilon/kT=x$, (6) becomes:

$$n=N/V=[(2\pi mkT)^{3/2}/h^3]\mathrm{F}(\lambda) \quad \ldots \ldots \quad (10)$$

$$\mathrm{F}(\lambda)=(2/\sqrt{\pi})\int_0^\infty x^{1/2}\mathrm{f}(x)\mathrm{d}x \quad \ldots \ldots \quad (11)$$

$$\mathrm{f}(x)=1/(\mathrm{e}^{\lambda+x}-1)-(d+1)/[\mathrm{e}^{(\lambda+x)(d+1)}-1] \quad \ldots \quad (12)$$

as defined by (8). Equation (10) determines λ. The mean energy (assumed wholly kinetic) of a particle is given by:

$$\bar{\epsilon}=E/N=\tfrac{3}{2}kT\mathrm{G}(\lambda)/\mathrm{F}(\lambda) \quad \ldots \ldots \quad (13)$$

$$\mathrm{G}(\lambda)=(4/3\sqrt{\pi})\int_0^\infty x^{3/2}\mathrm{f}(x)\mathrm{d}x \quad \ldots \ldots \quad (14)$$

junr., professor in Milan, died 1942: see portrait in *Nuov. Cim.*, 1943, **1**, pt. 3, and notices by Sommerfeld, *ibid.*, 1943, **1**, 151, and Polvani, *ibid.*, 1943, **1**, 155. The calculations (particularly the use of Stirling's theorem) have been criticised by Sommerfeld, *Ber.*, 1942, **75**, 1988; *Z. Naturforsch.*, 1946, **1**, 120; Schubert, *Z. Naturforsch.*, 1946, **1**, 113; 1947, **2** A, 250; Leibfried, *ibid.*, 1947, **2** A, 305; Leibfried and Kaempfer, *Z. Phys.*, 1948, **124**, 441; they suppose there is no real difference from Bose-Einstein statistics, but the results of the latter are still unsatisfactory.

Equations (8) and (13) show that λ may be negative, since f(x) for $\lambda+x=0$ tends to a finite limit $d/2$. This corresponds with gas degeneration, as is shown in detail by Gentile. The functions F(λ) and G(λ) are related by the equation:

$$(\mathrm{d}/\mathrm{d}\lambda)\mathrm{G}(\lambda)=-\mathrm{F}(\lambda) \quad \ldots \ldots \ldots \quad (15)$$

and F(λ) has different values for $\lambda>0$ and $\lambda<0$.

The pressure is given by the general equation (§ 36):

$$p=\tfrac{2}{3}(E/V) \quad \ldots \ldots \ldots \quad (16)$$

Equation (9) for the ideal monatomic gas becomes:

$$n_s=a_s[1/(\mathrm{e}^{x+\lambda}-1)-(d+1)/(\mathrm{e}^{(d+1)(x+\lambda)}-1)] \quad \ldots \quad (17)$$

giving the particular cases:

(i) $d=1$, Fermi-Dirac statistics: $n_s=a_s/(\mathrm{e}^{x+\lambda}+1)$,

(ii) $d\to\infty$, Bose-Einstein statistics: $n_s=a_s/(\mathrm{e}^{x+\lambda}-1)$.

Case (i) corresponds with low temperatures; case (ii) with high temperatures. The characteristic equations corresponding with the two cases are:

$$\lambda>0: \quad pV=NkT\left[1-\frac{1}{2^{5/2}}\frac{N}{V}\frac{h^3}{(2\pi mkT)^{3/2}}+\ldots+\frac{d}{(d+1)^{3/2}}\frac{Nh^3/V}{(2\pi mkT)^{(3/2)d}}\right] \quad (18)$$

$$\lambda<0: \quad p=\tfrac{1}{20}(6/\pi)^{2/3}(h^2/m)(N/V)^{5/3}(1/d^{3/2})+\ldots \quad (19)$$

The entropy of the gas is zero at 0° K., and has the Sackur-Tetrode value (13), § 14, at high temperatures.

The particular value of Gentile statistics is in dealing with gas degeneration in the region where Bose-Einstein "condensation" (§ 36) sets in, and in particular with liquid helium-II, considered as a degenerate Bose-Einstein gas. In this region, λ has a very small negative value and:

$$N/V=[(2\pi mkT)^{3/2}/h^3][(4/3\sqrt{\pi})N(-\lambda)^{3/2}+2{\cdot}612] \quad \ldots \quad (20)$$

the first term corresponding with an Einstein liquid and the second with the gas. The pressure is now proportional to $T^{5/2}$ and is independent of the volume (as for a saturated vapour). The specific heat has a pronounced maximum at the so-called λ-point, and below this is proportional to $T^{3/2}$, as is found experimentally.

The extension of Einstein's equation below the "condensation" point is mathematically impossible, but Gentile's function is holomorphic from $T=0$ to $T=\infty$, and gives zero entropy at $T=0$, as required by the Nernst heat theorem. The calculated transition point of liquid helium at 3·13° K. is not a critical temperature but a fairly sudden continuous change, or λ-point between He-I and He-II. The observed point is at 2·19° K., and the difference between this and 3·13° K. is assumed to be due to van der Waals forces. Gentile assumed the helium gaseous, Sommerfeld liquid, and Salvetti assumed that the van der Waals forces produce two different liquids above and below 2·19°, the transition between liquid I and liquid II being discontinuous, whilst the change from gas to liquid is continuous.

§ 38. Specification of Zero-point Energy

The energy zero has been taken for each substance as its own zero-point energy (with the vibrational quantum number $v=0$, and the rotational quantum number $J=0$), but for the energy change in a chemical reaction some arbitrary zero level must be taken for all the substances.[1] If $E_{0\mathrm{A}}$, $E_{0\mathrm{B}}$ are the energy

[1] Murphy, *J. Chem. Phys.*, 1937, **5**, 637.

differences from this for two substances A and B (Fig. 14.IV), then for 1 mol of each:

$$Z'' = e^{-E_0/RT} Z \quad . \quad . \quad . \quad . \quad . \quad . \quad . \quad . \quad (1)$$

where Z'' is the state sum with the zero-point energy of the substance as the zero standard, by (3), § 11.

If the superscript zero denotes a standard state (see § 70.II), 1 atm. pressure and 25° C. for gases, this choice of standard state affects only the translational state sum in (11), § 14:

$$Z_t = [(2\pi mkT)^{3/2}/h^3](RT/p) = (2\pi mkT/h^3)RT \quad . \quad . \quad . \quad . \quad (2)$$

if $p=1$. If $\Delta E_0°$ is the reaction energy change with standard states at 0° K. ($v=0$, $J=0$), then:

$$-\Delta(G° - E_0°)/T = -\Delta G°/T + \Delta E_0°/T \quad . \quad . \quad . \quad . \quad . \quad (3)$$

the values of $\Delta G°$ being as tabulated in § 70.II. The values:

$$G° = (G° - E_0°) + \Delta E_0° \quad . \quad . \quad . \quad . \quad . \quad . \quad . \quad . \quad (4)$$

$$H° = (H° - E_0°) + \Delta E_0° \quad . \quad . \quad . \quad . \quad . \quad . \quad . \quad . \quad (5)$$

may be defined for compounds if the values $E_0°$ for the elements are taken as zero. (Note that $\Delta H_0° = \Delta E_0°$ for gases ($H=E+RT$), and for solids HvE when $T=0$.) $\Delta E_0°$ is the reaction energy (heat of formation) at absolute zero. The quantities (4) and (5) refer to the reaction between the elements in standard states at $T=0$ to form a compound in the standard state at $T°$ K., and have been tabulated.[1]

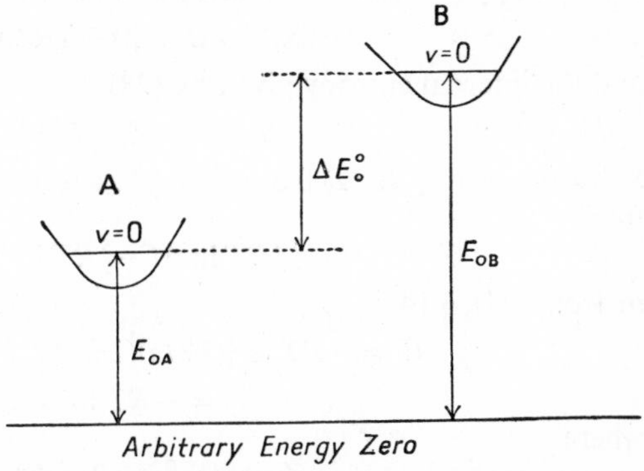

FIG. 14.IV. Reaction Energy at Absolute Zero

In using statistical methods it is necessary to know not only Z but also the value of $\Delta E_0°$, since the tabulated values of $\Delta E°$ and $\Delta H°$ always refer to an *arbitrary* zero for *each* element. The values of $\Delta E_0°$ may be found from spectroscopic values for heats of dissociation (§ 25), since these refer to the lowest (zero) energy levels. Another method is to calculate the zero-point energy $E_0 = N\epsilon_{v0}$ for each element by (4), § 25, and thence find $\Delta E_0°$. Still another method is to use the statistical equations. For the *internal* energy $E_i°$, (25), § 8, gives $E_i° = RT^2(\mathrm{d}\ln Z_i/\mathrm{d}T)$, Z_i being the internal state sum (§ 11). The total energy $E°$ is the sum of $E_i°$, the zero-point energy $E_0°$, and the translational energy $E_t = \frac{3}{2}RT$. Hence:

$$H° = E° + RT = E_i° + E_0° + \tfrac{5}{2}RT = E_0° + \tfrac{5}{2}RT + RT^2(\mathrm{d}\ln Z_i/\mathrm{d}T),$$

$$\therefore\ \Delta E_0° = \Delta H° - \Delta[\tfrac{5}{2}RT + RT^2(\mathrm{d}\ln Z_i/\mathrm{d}T)] \quad . \quad . \quad . \quad (6)$$

so that $\Delta E_0°$ can be calculated if $\mathrm{d}\ln Z_i/\mathrm{d}T$ is known.[2]

[1] Rodebush and Rodebush, in " Internat. Crit. Tables," 1929, **5**, 87 f.

[2] Glasstone, " Recent Advances in General Chemistry," 1936, 60; Aston, in Taylor and Glasstone, " Treatise on Physical Chemistry," 1942, **1**, 606.

Some values of $-(G_0-E_0°)/T$ are given below [1] (ideal gas state):

T°K.	298·1	300	400	600	800	1000	1200	1500
H_2	24·44	24·48	26·44	29·22	31·20	32·75	34·03	35·61
O_2	42·08	42·13	44·13	46·98	49·06	50·72	52·10	53·83
N_2	38·83	38·88	40·88	43·71	45·73	47·32	48·65	50·30
Cl_2	45·95	46·00	48·15	51·30	53·61	55·45	56·98	58·88
CO	40·36	40·41	42·41	45·24	47·27	48·88	50·21	51·88
NO	42·99	43·03	45·14	48·10	50·31	51·88	53·26	54·98
H_2O	37·18	37·23	39·51	42·77	45·12	47·00	48·58	50·59
CO_2	—	43·62	45·85	49·26	51·92	54·14	56·05	58·51

§ 39. Calculation of Chemical Equilibria

The standard available energy (p=1 atm.) per mol of ideal gas is:

$$G°=E°+RT-TS° \quad \dots\dots\dots \quad (1)$$

The energy $E°$ includes the zero-point energy $E_0°$ and the translational and internal energies:

$$E°=E_0°+E_{tr}°+E_i° \quad \dots\dots\dots \quad (2)$$

The entropy $S°$ includes the translational entropy given by (25), § 14:

$$S_{tr}°=\tfrac{3}{2}R \ln M+\tfrac{5}{2}R \ln T-2{\cdot}297 \quad \dots\dots \quad (3)$$

and the internal entropy given by (28), § 8:

$$S_i=R[\ln Z_i+T(\mathrm{d} \ln Z_i/\mathrm{d}T)] \quad \dots\dots \quad (4)$$

Substitute for $E_i°$ in (2) from (25), § 8, and substitute from (2), (3) and (4) in (1), then:

$$G°-E_0°=-\tfrac{3}{2}RT \ln M-\tfrac{5}{2}RT \ln T-RT \ln Z_i+7{\cdot}262T \quad .\ . \quad (5)$$

or from (24), § 14:

$$G°=-RT \ln [(kT/a)(2\pi mkT/h^2)^{3/2} . Z_i . e^{-E_0°/RT}] \quad .\ .\ . \quad (6)$$

$$=-RT \ln (ZkT/a) \quad \dots\dots\dots \quad (7)$$

where

$$Z=e^{-E_0°/RT} . (2\pi mkT/h^2)^{3/2} . Z_i \quad \dots\dots \quad (8)$$

is the state sum including the factors $e^{-E_0°/RT}$ for zero-point energy, $(2\pi mkT/h^2)^{3/2}$ for three degrees of freedom of translational energy or $(2\pi mkT/h^2)^{1/2}$ per degree of freedom, and Z_i for internal energy (rotation and vibration).

Consider a reaction between gases. Let an initial system consist of 2 mols of hydrogen gas at concentration C_{H_2} and 1 mol of oxygen gas at concentration C_{O_2}, both at the temperature T. Let these be converted reversibly and isothermally into 2 mols of steam at concentration C_{H_2O} and temperature T. The change may be carried out as follows.

The gases $2H_2$ and O_2 are contained in separate vessels at concentrations C_{H_2} and C_{O_2} (Fig. 15.IV). An arbitrary amount of the gas mixture in equilibrium:

$$2H_2+O_2 \rightleftharpoons 2H_2O$$

is contained in a box (" equilibrium box ") fitted with semipermeable diaphragms (shown dotted) which can be closed by impervious plates except

[1] In these, the nuclear spin contribution is omitted; values are given by Aston, ref. 2, p. 371, to three decimal places, but the second place is uncertain. For calculations of gas equilibria, see Bijvoet, *Chem. Weekbl.*, 1931, **28**, 26; Partington, " Chemical Thermodynamics." 1940, 208; Wasserman, *Proc. Roy. Soc.*, 1941, **178**, 370.

when the appropriate gases are passing through them. Let c_{H_2}, c_{O_2}, c_{H_2O} be the equilibrium concentrations in the box.

(1) By means of impervious pistons the concentrations of the hydrogen and oxygen in the cylinders are isothermally and reversibly changed from C_{H_2} and C_{O_2} to the concentrations c_{H_2} and c_{O_2} in which they exist in the equilibrium box. The two amounts of work done are, from (11), § 6.II (since $V_2/V_1=C_1/C_2$):

$$2RT \ln (C_{H_2}/c_{H_2}) \quad \text{and} \quad RT \ln (C_{O_2}/c_{O_2}).$$

(2) The gases are admitted through the semipermeable diaphragms into the box, the pistons being pressed in. Since the pressures are constant, the amounts of work done are $-2RT$ and $-RT$.

(3) In order that the equilibrium shall not be disturbed, the $2H_2O$ formed in the box is simultaneously removed through the semipermeable diaphragm into the cylinder on the right at the concentration c_{H_2O}. The work done is $+2RT$.

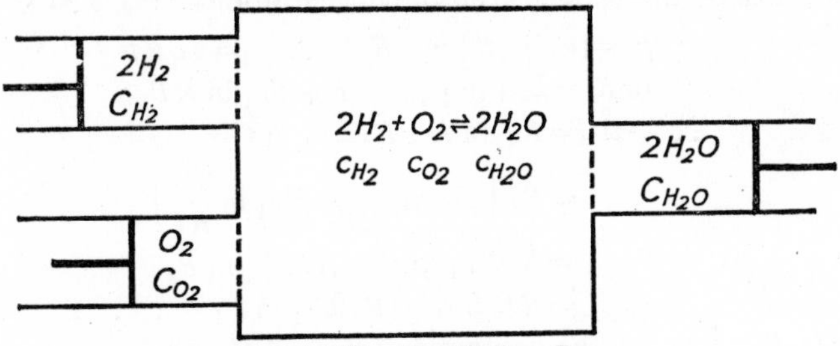

FIG. 15.IV. Equilibrium Box

(4) The water vapour is now brought from concentration c_{H_2O} to concentration C_{H_2O}. The work done is $2RT \ln (c_{H_2O}/C_{H_2O})$.

The process is now complete and the total work done is:

$$w_T = -\Delta F = -2RT - RT + 2RT \ln (C_{H_2}/c_{H_2}) + RT \ln (C_{O_2}/c_{O_2}) + 2RT + 2RT \ln (c_{H_2O}/C_{H_2O})$$

$$= RT \ln \frac{c^2_{H_2O}}{c^2_{H_2} \times c_{O_2}} - RT \ln \frac{C^2_{H_2O}}{C^2_{H_2} \times C_{O_2}} - RT \quad . \quad . \quad . \quad . \quad (9)$$

Since, from (6), § 33.II, this depends only on the initial and final states, it cannot depend on the individual concentrations c in the equilibrium box, hence the first term on the right in (9) must be constant at a given temperature, $c^2_{H_2O}/(c^2_{H_2} \cdot c_{O_2}) = K$, where K is the *equilibrium constant* (§ 60.II).

Equation (9) is easily generalised for any reversible gas reaction:

$$\nu_1 A_1 + \nu_2 A_2 + \ldots = \nu_1' A_1' + \nu_2' A_2' + \ldots$$

$$-\Delta F = RT \ln K - RT \Sigma \nu_1 \ln C_1 + RT \Sigma \nu_1 \quad . \quad . \quad . \quad . \quad (10)$$

$$\ln K = (\nu_1' \ln c_1' + \nu_2' \ln c_2' + \ldots) - (\nu_1 \ln c_1 + \nu_2 \ln c_2 + \ldots)$$

$$\Sigma \nu_1 \ln C_1 = (\nu_1' \ln C_1' + \nu_2' \ln C_2' + \ldots) - (\nu_1 \ln C_1 + \nu_2 \ln C_2 + \ldots)$$

$$\Sigma \nu_1 = (\nu_1' + \nu_2' + \ldots) - (\nu_1 + \nu_2 + \ldots)$$

$$c_1'^{\nu_1'} c_2'^{\nu_2'} \ldots / c_1^{\nu_1} c_2^{\nu_2} \ldots = K \quad . \quad . \quad . \quad . \quad . \quad (11)$$

In the sums the terms corresponding with the products of the reaction (right-hand side of the chemical equation) are taken as positive.[1]

[1] This convention (Union Internationale de Chimie, 1928) is now general.

Equation (10), due to van't Hoff,[1] is sometimes called the *Reaction Isotherm* equation, and the value of $-\Delta F$ the *affinity* of the reaction. The term $RT\Sigma\nu_1$ disappears only when the numbers of mols of products and reacting substances are equal (e.g. $H_2+Cl_2=2HCl$).

The *available* (*net*) *work* or diminution of *available energy*, $-\Delta G$, is the maximum work minus the external work $RT\Sigma\nu_1$ at constant pressure:

$$\Delta G=\Delta F+P\Delta V=\Delta F+\Sigma\nu_1 RT$$

$$\therefore\ -\Delta G=-\Delta F-RT\Sigma\nu_1=RT\ln K-RT\Sigma\nu_1\ln C_1 \quad . \ . \ (12)$$

$-\Delta G$ is sometimes called the *affinity* of the reaction, instead of $-\Delta F$. If all the concentrations C_1, etc., are unity, then:

$$-\Delta F=RT\ln K+RT\Sigma\nu_1$$

$$-\Delta G=RT\ln K$$

giving the *standard* free energy and available energy changes.

If *partial pressures* are used instead of concentrations, (17), § 54.II, gives:

$$p_1=(\nu_1/V)RT=c_1RT \quad \therefore\ c_1=p_1/RT$$

$$\ln K'=\Sigma\nu_1\ln p_1=\ln K+\Sigma\nu_1\ln RT$$

$$\therefore\ -\Delta G=RT\ln K-RT\Sigma\nu_1\ln C_1$$

$$=RT\left(\Sigma\nu_1\ln\frac{p_1}{RT}-\Sigma\nu_1\ln\frac{P_1}{RT}\right)$$

$$=RT\Sigma\nu_1\ln p_1-RT\Sigma\nu_1\ln P_1$$

$$=RT\ln K'-RT\Sigma\nu_1\ln P_1 \quad . \ . \ . \ . \ (12a)$$

where $P_1=C_1RT$, etc., are the pressures of the initial and final substances, and $p_1=c_1RT$ the equilibrium partial pressures. If all the free pressures are unity (e.g. 1 atm.)

$$-\Delta G^\circ=RT\ln K' \quad . \ . \ . \ . \ . \ . \ . \ . \ (13)$$

giving an expression for the standard available energy change (since the free pressures are all 1 atm., ΔG is ΔG°, the standard value). Equation (13) may be written in the form:

$$-\Delta(G^\circ-E_0^\circ)/RT-\Delta E_0^\circ/RT=\ln K' \quad . \ . \ . \ . \ . \ (14)$$

$$\therefore\ -\ln K'=\Delta E_0^\circ/RT-(3/2)\Sigma\nu_1\ln M_1-(5/2)\Delta\nu\ln T$$
$$-\Sigma\nu_1\ln Z_{i,1}+7{\cdot}262\Delta\nu/R \quad . \ . \ . \ . \ . \ . \ . \ (15)$$

from (5), where $\Delta\nu=(\nu_1'+\nu_2'+\ldots)-(\nu_1+\nu_2+\ldots)$.

The value of ΔE_0°, the change of zero-point energy in the reaction, may be found from spectroscopic data for heats of dissociation, as explained in § 38, or from the oscillator formula (4), § 25:

$$E_0^\circ=Nh\tilde{\omega}_e(\tfrac{1}{2}-\tfrac{1}{4}x_e)$$

the value of E_0° for a polyatomic molecule with n vibrational degrees of freedom being ΣE_0°. If ΔH° is the heat of reaction at constant pressure:

$$\Delta E^\circ=\Delta H^\circ-RT\Delta\nu$$

and from (1), and (25), § 8:

$$\Delta E_0^\circ=\Delta H^\circ-\Delta\left(\tfrac{5}{2}RT+RT^2\frac{d\ln Z_i}{dT}\right) \quad . \ . \ . \ . \ . \ (16)$$

From (7) and (8):

$$K'=\frac{Z_1'^{\nu_1'}\,.\,Z_2'^{\nu_2'}\ldots}{Z_1^{\nu_1}\,.\,Z_2^{\nu_2}\ldots}\left(\frac{kT}{a}\right)^{\Delta\nu} \quad . \ . \ . \ . \ . \ . \ (17)$$

[1] *K. Svensk. Vet. Akad. Handl.*, 1886, **21**, No. 17, pp. 1–58 (presented 14 October, 1885); *Arch. Néerl.*, 1885, **20**, 239–302; *Z. phys. Chem.*, 1887, **1**, 481; *Phil. Mag.*, 1888, **26**, 81; *Alembic Club Reprint*, Edinburgh, 1929, **19**.

in which pressures are in atm., and $a=1{\cdot}0132\times 10^6$ is the conversion factor for pressures in dyne/cm.^{2} from atm. If $a^{-\Delta\nu}$ is omitted, pressures are in dyne/cm.^{2}. If the factor $(kT/a)^{\Delta\nu}$ is omitted:

$$K=\frac{Z_1'^{\nu_1'}\,.\,Z_2'^{\nu_2'}\ldots}{Z_1^{\nu_1}\,.\,Z_2^{\nu_2}\ldots} \quad \text{(18)}$$

where K is the equilibrium constant in terms of molecules per ml.

For diatomic molecules, the state sum for rotation and vibration, excluding nuclear spin but including the symmetry factor s (§ 18) may be written:

$$Z_i=(8\pi^2 IkT/h^2 s)(1-e^{-h\tilde{\omega}_e/kT})^{-1} \quad \text{(19)}$$

If free atoms are involved, the corresponding state sum (excluding nuclear spin) is (§ 21), $Z_e\simeq 2j_s+1$. If $\Delta\nu=0$, (15) becomes (since $K=K'$):

$$-\ln K=\Delta E_0^\circ/RT-(3/2)\Sigma\nu_1 \ln M_1-\Sigma\nu_1 \ln Z_{i,1} \quad \text{(20)}$$

or for a reaction of the type:

$$AB+CD=AC+BD$$

$$-\ln K=\Delta E_0^\circ/RT-\tfrac{3}{2}\ln\frac{M_{AC}\,.\,M_{BD}}{M_{AB}\,.\,M_{CD}}-\ln\frac{Z_{iAC}\,.\,Z_{iBD}}{Z_{iAB}\,.\,Z_{iCD}} \quad \text{(21)}$$

From (19), on the assumption that the vibrational factors ($\simeq 1$) cancel out:

$$-\ln K=\Delta E_0^\circ/RT-\tfrac{3}{2}\ln\frac{M_{AC}\,.\,M_{BD}}{M_{AB}\,.\,M_{CD}}-\ln\frac{I_{AC}\,.\,I_{BD}}{I_{AC}\,.\,I_{CD}}+\ln\frac{s_{AC}\,.\,s_{BD}}{s_{AB}\,.\,s_{CD}} \quad \text{(22)}$$

Some equilibria calculated by statistical methods are:

1. *Dissociation of hydrogen*: $H_2\rightleftharpoons 2H$; $K'=p_H^2/p_{H_2}$.

The state sums for H_2 at various temperatures (cf. § 23) are NT values, the nuclear spin effect $R \ln 4$ having been subtracted. The state sum for H is that for the ground level, viz. 2, neglecting nuclear spin (cf. § 21). In calculating ΔE_0°, the zero-point energy of H_2 in its lowest state is taken as zero (cf. § 11), and E_0° for the two hydrogen atoms is taken as the spectroscopic heat of dissociation of H_2, 102·80 k.cal. per mol.

Temperature °K.	Z		K′	
	H_2	2 H	Calc.	Obs.
1000	6·262	4·00	—	—
2000	13·274	”	3×10^{-6}	10^{-7}
2500	17·424	”	7×10^{-4}	10^{-3}
3000	22·648	”	$2{\cdot}7\times10^{-2}$	2×10^{-2}
3500	28·262	”	$3{\cdot}7\times10^{-1}$	2×10^{-1}

2. *Nitric oxide synthesis*: $\tfrac{1}{2}N_2+\tfrac{1}{2}O_2\rightleftharpoons NO$; $K'=p_{NO}/p_{O_2}^{1/2}p_{N_2}^{1/2}$.

In this case (14) was used, the value of ΔE_0° being taken as 21·40 k.cal.

Temperature ° K.	$(G^\circ-E_0^\circ)/T$			$-\Delta[(G^\circ-E_0^\circ)/T]$ $NO-\tfrac{1}{2}N_2-\tfrac{1}{2}O_2$	K′	
	NO	N_2	O_2		Calc.	Obs.
1000	51·878	47·322	50·715	2·859	$8{\cdot}8\times10^{-5}$	—
1500	54·979	50·301	53·826	2·915	$3{\cdot}3\times10^{-3}$	$2{\cdot}4\times10^{-3}$
2000	57·255	52·497	56·122	2·945	$2{\cdot}0\times10^{-2}$	$1{\cdot}5\times10^{-2}$
2500	59·063	54·246	57·955	2·962	$6{\cdot}0\times10^{-2}$	$4{\cdot}5\times10^{-2}$
3000	60·567	55·706	59·489	2·970	$1{\cdot}2\times10^{-1}$	$0{\cdot}9\times10^{-1}$

3. *Dissociation of iodine* [1]: $I_2 \rightleftharpoons 2I$; $K' = p_I^2/p_{I_2}$.

For the iodine atom $Z_e = 2j_s + 1 = 4$, the only value of j_s involved being for the ground state, $\frac{3}{2}$. For the diatomic I_2 molecule $Z_i = Z_r \cdot Z_v = (8\pi^2 IkT/h^2)(1 - e^{-h\nu/kT})^{-1}s^{-1}$, where $I = 742 \cdot 6 \times 10^{-40}$, $\nu/c = 213 \cdot 67$ cm.$^{-1}$; $\Delta E_0^\circ = 35 \cdot 59$ k.cal.

$\theta°$ C.	800	900	1000	1100	1200
K' calc. ...	$1 \cdot 13 \times 10^{-2}$	$4 \cdot 79 \times 10^{-2}$	$1 \cdot 65 \times 10^{-1}$	$4 \cdot 94 \times 10^{-1}$	1·22
K' obs.	$1 \cdot 14 \times 10^{-2}$	$4 \cdot 74 \times 10^{-2}$	$1 \cdot 65 \times 10^{-1}$	$4 \cdot 92 \times 10^{-1}$	1·23

4. *Hydrogen-deuterium equilibrium*: $H_2 + D_2 \rightleftharpoons 2HD$; $K = c^2_{HD}/c_{H_2}c_{D_2}$.

At temperatures for which the rotations are fully excited but the vibrations not excited, (22) gives [2]:

$$\ln K = -(2E_0{}^\circ{}_{HD} - E_0{}^\circ{}_{H_2} - E_0{}^\circ{}_{D_2})/RT + \tfrac{3}{2}\ln\frac{M^2_{HD}}{M_{H_2}M_{D_2}} + \ln\frac{I^2_{HD}}{I_{H_2}I_{D_2}} + \ln 4.$$

From spectroscopic data, $2E_0{}^\circ{}_{HD} - E_0{}^\circ{}_{H_2} - E_0{}^\circ{}_{D_2} = \Delta E_0^\circ = 157$ g.cal. The moments of inertia may be calculated from the values of $B_v = h^2/8\pi^2 Ic$ (§ 25): H_2 60·848 cm.$^{-1}$, D_2 30·46 cm.$^{-1}$, HD 45·655 cm.$^{-1}$. The observed and calculated values of K are:

$\theta°$ C.	−190	0	25	110	397	468
K calc.	2·2	3·19	3·27	3·46	3·78	3·82
K obs.	2·3	3·16	3·28	3·56	3·77	3·75

[1] From Gibson and Heitler, *Z. Phys.*, 1928, **49**, 465; for a recalculation with modern data, see Zeise, *Z. Elektrochem.*, 1934, **40**, 665.

[2] The term ln 4 appears because two unsymmetrical (HD; $s=1$) molecules are formed from two symmetrical ones (H_2, D_2; $s=2$).

SECTION V

WAVE MECHANICS

BIBLIOGRAPHY OF WAVE MECHANICS

H. S. Allen, Electrons and Waves, 1932; Bauer, Introduction à la Théorie des Groupes et à ses Applications à la Physique Quantique, 1933; *idem*, Grundlagen der Atomphysik, Vienna, 1938; Bethe, in Geiger and Scheel, Handbuch der Physik, 1933, **24**, i, 273; Biggs, Wave Mechanics, Oxford, 1927; Birtwistle, The New Quantum Mechanics, Cambridge, 1928; Born, Atomic Physics, 4th edit., 1946; *idem*, Experiment and Theory in Physics, Cambridge, 1943; Born and Jordan, Elementare Quantenmechanik, Berlin, 1930; Brillouin, Les Statistiques Quantiques et leurs Applications, 2 vols., Paris, 1930; *idem*, Die Quantenstatistik und ihre Anwendung auf die Elektronentheorie der Metalle, Berlin, 1931; *idem*, *J. de Phys.*, 1926, **7**, 135, 320, 353; Condon and Morse, Quantum Mechanics, New York, 1929; Condon and Shortley, The Theory of Atomic Spectra, New York, 1935; Dänzer, Grundlagen der Quantenmechanik, Dresden and Leipzig, 1935; Darrow, Elementare Einführung in die Quantenmechanik, Leipzig, 1933; *idem*, *Rev. Mod. Phys.*, 1934, **6**, 23; Darrow and Rabinowitsch, Elementare Einführung in die Wellenmechanik, Leipzig, 1932; Darwin, The New Conception of Matter, 1931, 78; Dirac, The Principles of Quantum Mechanics, Oxford, 1930, 2nd edit., 1935, 3rd edit., 1947; Dushman, The Elements of Quantum Mechanics, New York, 1938; *idem*, in Taylor and Glasstone, Treatise on Physical Chemistry, 1942, **1**, 119; Eyring, Walter, and Kimball, Quantum Chemistry, New York, 1944; Flamm, *Phys. Z.*, 1926, **27**, 600; Flint, *Sci. Progr.*, 1926, **25**, 48; *idem*, Wave Mechanics, 3rd edit., 1938; Flügge and Krebs, Experimentelle Grundlagen der Wellenmechanik, Dresden and Leipzig, 1936; *idem*, Einführung in die Wellenmechanik, Berlin, 1929; Frenkel, Wave Mechanics. Elementary Theory, Oxford, 1932; *idem*, Wave Mechanics. Advanced General Theory, Oxford, 1934; Fues, Einführung in die Quantemechanik, Berlin, 1929, Leipzig, 1935; *idem*, Einführung in die Quantenmechanik, Bezugsversuche mit Materiewellen, Leipzig, 1935; Gerthsen, Atomphysik, 2 vols., Berlin, 1938; Groenewold, *Physica*, 1946, **12**, 405–60; Gurney, Elementary Quantum Mechanics, Cambridge, 1934; Gurney and Condon, *Phys. Rev.*, 1929, **33**, 127; Haas, Materiewellen und Quantenmechanik, 2nd edit., Leipzig, 1929; *idem*, Wave Mechanics and the New Quantum Theory, 1928; Haïssinsky, L'Atomistique Moderne et la Chimie, Paris, 1932; Halpern and Thirring, The Elements of the New Quantum Mechanics, 1932; Heisenberg, Die physikalische Prinzipien der Quantentheorie, Leipzig, 1930; *idem*, The Physical Principles of the Quantum Theory, Chicago, 1930; *idem*, Wandlungen in den Grundlagen der Naturwissenschaft, Leipzig, 1935; Hellmann, Einführung in die Quantenchemie, Leipzig and Vienna, 1937; Herzberg, Atomic Spectra and Atomic Structure, 1937, 2nd edit., 1944; *idem*, Molekülspektren und Molekülstruktur, Dresden and Leipzig, 1939; *idem*, Molecular Spectra and Molecular Structure. Diatomic Molecules, New York, 1939; *idem*, Infra-red and Raman Spectra of Polyatomic Molecules, New York, 1945; Hoffmann, The Strange Story of the Quantum, New York, 1947; Hopf, Materie und Strahlung, Berlin, 1936; Houtermans, Neuere Arbeiten über Quantentheorie des Atomkerns, in *Ergebn. d. exakt. Naturwiss*, 1930, **9**; Hume-Rothery, Atomic Theory for Students of Metallurgy, 1947; Hund, in Geiger and Scheel, Handbuch der Physik, 1933, **24**, i, 561; Hylleraas, Die Grundlagen der Quantenmechanik, Oslo, 1932 (Skrift. Norsk. Vidensk. Akad., Mat. Nat., No. **6**); Jordan, Anschauliche Quantentheorie, Berlin, 1936; Juvet, Mécanique Analytique et Théorie des Quantas, Paris, 1926; Kemble, The Fundamental Principles of Quantum Mechanics, New York, 1937; *idem*, *Phys. Rev. Suppl.*, 1929, **1**, 157; Kemble and Hill, *Rev. Mod. Phys.*, 1930, **2**, 1; Kramers, Die Grundlagen der Quantentheorie, in *Hand und Jahrb. der chem. Physik*, 1938, **1**, i, ii; Landé, Fortschritte der Quantentheorie, Dresden and Leipzig, 1922; *idem*, Principles of Quantum Mechanics, Cambridge, 1937; von Laue, in Marx, Hand buch der Radiologie, 1933, **6**, i, 1; Lindemann, The Physical Significance of the Quantum Theory, Oxford, 1932; Madelung, Die mathematische Hilfsmittel des Physikers, 3rd edit., Berlin, 1936; Mott, An Outline of Wave Mechanics, Cambridge, 1930; Mott and Sneddon, Wave Mechanics and its Applications, Oxford, 1948; von Neumann,

Mathematische Grundlagen der Quantenmechanik, Berlin, 1932, New York, 1943; Pauling and Wilson, Introduction to Quantum Mechanics, New York, 1935; Pelseneer, L'Évolution de la Notion de Phénomène Physique des Primitifs à Bohr et Louis de Broglie, Brussels, [1947]; Persico, Fundamenti dello Meccanica Atomica, Bologna, 1936; Planck, Wege zur physikalischen Erkenntnis, Leipzig, 1933; Rabinowitsch, *Z. Elektrochem.*, 1932, **38**, 370; Reichenbach, Philosophical Foundations of Quantum Theory, Berkeley and Los Angeles, 1946; Rojansky, Introduction to Quantum Mechanics, New York, 1938; Ruark and Urey, Atoms, Molecules, Quanta, New York, 1930; Schiff, Quantum Mechanics, New York, 1949; Shu, *Canad. J. Res.*, 1947, **25** A, 96; Smekal, Allgemeine Grundlagen der Quantenstatistik und Quantentheorie, Leipzig and Berlin, 1926; Sommerfeld, Wave Mechanics, 1930; *idem, Z. angew. Chem.*, 1928, **41**, 1; *idem*, Atombau und Spektrallinien, **2**, Brunswick, 1944; Teichmann, Einführung in die Quantenphysik, Leipzig and Berlin, 1935; Temple, An Introduction to Quantum Theory, 1934; J. Thomson, Introduction to Atomic Physics, 1935; Tolansky, Introduction to Atomic Physics, 1947; Van der Waerden, Die Gruppentheoretische Methode in der Quantenmechanik, Berlin, 1932 (unintelligible, according to C. G. Darwin, *J. Phys. Chem.*, 1932, **36**, 2845); Van Vleck, *J. Opt. Soc. Amer.*, 1927, **14**, 108; 1928, **16**, 301; Webb, Elementary Principles in Physical Chemistry, New York, 1936; Weitzel, in Wien-Harms, Handbuch der Experimentalphysik, 1931, Ergzb. **1**; Weyl, Gruppentheorie und Quantenmechanik, 1931; *idem*, The Theory of Groups and Quantum Mechanics, 1931; Wigner, Gruppentheorie und ihre Auwendung auf die Quantenmechanik der Atomspektren, Brunswick, 1931; Zimmer, Umsturz im Weltbild der Physik, 6th edit., Munich. 1942; *idem*, Revolution in Physics, 1936.

§ 1. De Broglie's Equation

The modern quantum theory is based on *the wave nature of the electron.* Electrons in motion *behave* as if they were associated with characteristic waves, the lengths of which are given by a formula due to Louis de Broglie: [1]

$$\lambda = \boldsymbol{h}/mv \qquad (1)$$

where $\boldsymbol{h}$ is Planck's constant and m and v are the mass and velocity of the electron. Since $mv = p =$ momentum, this can be written:

$$\lambda = \boldsymbol{h}/p \qquad (2)$$

Beams of electrons are diffracted by matter, e.g. by reflection from a crystal or in passing through a thin metal foil, in the same way as X-rays.[2] This dual aspect of an electron, particle or wave, is analogous to the dual character of light, which sometimes *behaves* as if it consisted of corpuscles or photons (e.g. in the photo-electric effect, when electrons are expelled from a metal by ultraviolet light), and sometimes as if it consisted of waves, which give rise to interference and diffraction.

§ 2. Schrödinger's Wave Equation

The basic equation of wave mechanics was found by Schrödinger.[3] Although the equation and the interpretation may be " conveniently taken as fundamental postulates, with no derivation from other principles necessary," [4] a more

[1] *Phil. Mag.*, 1924, **47**, 446; *Ann. de Phys.*, 1925, **3**, 22; *J. de Phys.*, 1926, **1**, 321; " Ondes et Mouvement," 1926; " Introduction à l'Étude de la Mécanique Ondulatoire," 1930; " Théorie de Quantisation dans la nouvelle Mécanique," 1932; " Matter and Light," transl. Johnston, 1939; de Broglie and Brillouin, " Selected Papers on Wave Mechanics," 1928.

[2] Davisson and Germer, *Phys. Rev.*, 1927, **30**, 705; *J. Franklin Inst.*, 1928, **205**, 597; G. P. Thomson, *Proc. Roy. Soc.*, 1928, **117**, 600; 1928, **119**, 651; " The Wave Mechanics of Free Electrons," New York, 1930; Germer, *J. Chem. Educ.*, 1928, **5**, 1041, 1255; Lindemann, " Physical Significance of the Quantum Theory," Oxford, 1932, 24; Jüttner, *Z. Phys.*, 1938, **109**, 139.

[3] *Ann. Phys.*, 1926, **79**, 361, 489, 734; 1926, **80**, 437; 1926, **81**, 109; 1927, **82**, 265; 1927, **83**, 956; collected and reprinted as " Abhandlungen zur Wellenmechanik," Leipzig, 1927; " Collected Papers on Wave Mechanics," 1929; *Bull. Soc. Philomath.*, 1941, **123**, 26; Heisenberg, *Naturwiss.*, 1926, **14**, 989; Bohr, *Nature*, 1928, **121**, 580; Lorentz, *J. Franklin Inst.*, 1928, **205**, 449; Swann, *ibid.*, 1928, **205**, 323; Slater, *ibid.*, 1929, **207**, 449; Press, *Phil. Mag.*, 1928, **6**, 33.

[4] Pauling and Wilson, " Introduction to Quantum Mechanics," New York, 1935, 52.

gradual approach through a simple analogous type of equation is not without value. For this purpose, consider the case of a vibrating string, the motion of which is defined by equation (3), § 71.I:

$$\partial^2 A/\partial t^2 = u^2(\partial^2 A/\partial x^2) \quad . \quad . \quad . \quad . \quad . \quad . \quad . \quad . \quad . \quad (1)$$

A being the amplitude. Assume a solution:

$$A = \mathrm{g}(t) \,.\, \mathrm{f}(x) \quad . \quad . \quad . \quad . \quad . \quad . \quad . \quad . \quad . \quad . \quad (2)$$

where g and f are functions of t and x. Differentiate twice with respect to t and x, divide by u^2fg, and compare with (1):

$$\therefore\ (1/\mathrm{f})(\partial^2\mathrm{f}/\partial x^2) = (1/u^2\mathrm{g})(\partial^2\mathrm{g}/\partial t^2).$$

Since the left side is a function of x and independent of t and the right side is a function of t and independent of x, it follows that each is equal to a constant, say $-m^2$:

$$\therefore\ \partial^2\mathrm{f}/\partial x^2 + m^2\mathrm{f} = 0 \quad . \quad . \quad . \quad . \quad . \quad . \quad . \quad . \quad . \quad (3)$$

$$\partial^2\mathrm{g}/\partial t^2 + m^2u^2\mathrm{g} = 0 \quad . \quad . \quad . \quad . \quad . \quad . \quad . \quad . \quad . \quad (4)$$

These may be regarded as two ordinary differential equations, and particular solutions (see (2), § 64.I) are:

$$\mathrm{f} = C\cos(mx) + D\sin(mx),$$

$$\mathrm{g} = C'\cos(mut) + D'\sin(mut),$$

as is found by differentiation and substitution in (3) and (4). The constants C, D, C', and D' depend on the conditions of the particular problem. For a string of length l fixed at both ends, $A=0$ both for $x=0$ and $x=l$, and for all values of t. In this case, for $x=0$, f(0)=0, therefore f(x)=f(0)=C, therefore $C=0$, therefore f$=D\sin mx$. But $\sin mx=0$ only for $mx=0$, or $mx=n\pi$, where n is an integer, hence $m=n\pi/l$ are the *proper values* corresponding with the nodal points ($A=0$), and the corresponding values of f(x) are the *proper functions*.[1] If g=0 for $t=0$, then g(0)=C', therefore $C'=0$, therefore g=$D'\sin(mut)$. But $\sin(mut)=0$ only for $mut=0$ or $mut=n\pi$, where n is an integer, therefore $m=n\pi/ut=n\pi/l$, as before.

If λ is the wavelength, f(x) is zero when x is an integral multiple of $\lambda/2$ (nodes), therefore $l=n\lambda_n/2$, therefore f$=D\sin(n\pi x/l)=D\sin(2\pi x/\lambda_n)$, which is zero for $x=0$ or $x=n\lambda_n/2$. Since $u=\nu\lambda$, where ν is the frequency (§ 49.I), it follows that $g=D'\sin(2\pi\nu_n t)$. The particular solution of (1) is thus:

$$A = \mathrm{f}(x)\mathrm{g}(t) = DD'\sin(2\pi x/\lambda_n)\sin(2\pi\nu_n t).$$

In the general case where the function ψ replaces the amplitude A, the places where ψ vanishes are nodes, and may be points, lines, or surfaces. If ψ is separable, as $A=\mathrm{g}(t)\,.\,\mathrm{f}(x)$ above each factor has its own nodes, which must obviously also be those of ψ itself, since if any factor vanishes, ψ also vanishes. If $\psi=\mathrm{R}(r)\Theta(\theta)\Phi(\phi)$, where r, θ, and ϕ are spherical polar coordinates (§ 28.I), and R, Θ and Φ denote functions of r, θ, and ϕ, respectively, such that $\psi(r,\theta,\phi)=\mathrm{R}(r)\Theta(\theta)\Phi(\phi)$, then the nodes of R($r$) are concentric spheres (values of r for which R(r) vanishes), the nodes of $\Theta(\theta)$ are cones through the origin (θ=const.), the nodes of $\Phi(\phi)$ are half planes containing the θ axis (ϕ=const.). (See Fig. 1.V.)

Consider the function $\Phi(\phi)=\cos(n\phi)$. For each value of the integer n, the period is 2π and the number of nodal half-planes is $2n$, which combine to form

[1] Coulson, "Waves," Edinburgh, 1941, 21. In wave mechanics the half-German names *eigenvalues* and *eigenfunctions* are commonly (but unnecessarily) used.

n whole planes, dividing space into double wedges, and cutting the sphere into double " pieces of an orange."

The values of Φ and Φ^2 are graphed in Fig. 2.V for various values of ϕ for the three cases where $n=0$, $n=1$, and $n=2$; and the values of Φ^2 are shown in three figures by the varying thickness of the circumference of a circle round which the values of ϕ are marked. The four wedges for $n=2$ are clear.

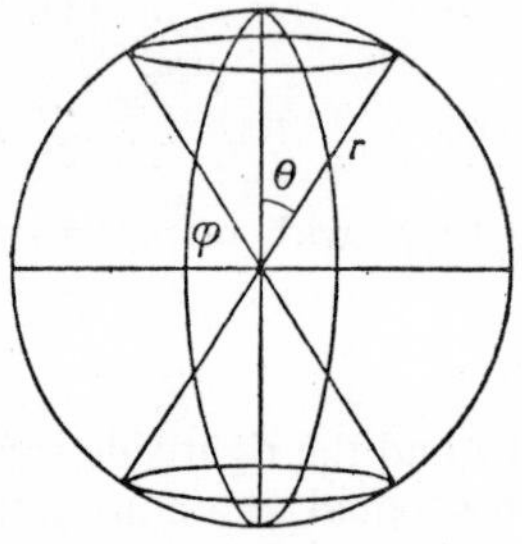

FIG. 1.V. Spherical Polar Coordinate System

In passing a node, $\Phi=\cos(n\phi)$ changes sign, and when ϕ increases by π it has the same numerical value but the same or opposite sign, according as in the increase of ϕ by π an even or odd number of nodal planes has been crossed. In general, by a reflection in the origin (i.e. a change of ϕ by π), the function may have the same absolute value and either the same sign (when it is an *even* or g [gerade] function) or the opposite sign (when it is an *odd* or u [ungerade] function).

By putting $n=1$, $m=n\pi/l$, $l=n\lambda/2$, in (3), this becomes:

$$\frac{\partial^2 f}{\partial x^2}+\frac{4\pi^2}{\lambda^2}f=0.$$

In passing to the wave-mechanical case, the part of the amplitude f which is independent of time is replaced by an amplitude ψ of the de Broglie " matter wave," the interpretation of which is left open [1]:

$$\frac{\partial^2\psi}{\partial x^2}+\frac{4\pi^2}{\lambda^2}\psi=0.$$

If the fundamental equation, (1), § 1, $1/\lambda=mv/h$, is introduced, this gives:

$$\frac{\partial^2\psi}{\partial x^2}+\frac{4\pi^2m^2v^2}{h^2}\psi=0.$$

The kinetic energy of the particle is $T=\frac{1}{2}mv^2$, therefore $m^2v^2=2Tm=2(E-V)m$, where E is the total energy and V the potential energy (§ 12.IV): $E=T+V$, hence:

$$\frac{\partial^2\psi}{\partial x^2}+\frac{8\pi^2m}{h^2}(E-V)\psi=0 \quad . \; . \; . \; . \; . \; . \; . \; . \quad (5)$$

which is Schrödinger's wave equation for one dimension. For three dimensions:

$$\frac{\partial^2\psi}{\partial x^2}+\frac{\partial^2\psi}{\partial y^2}+\frac{\partial^2\psi}{\partial z^2}+\frac{8\pi^2m}{h^2}(E-V)\psi=0 \quad . \; . \; . \; . \; . \quad (6)$$

$$\text{or } \nabla^2\psi+\frac{8\pi^2m}{h^2}(E-V)\psi=0 \quad . \; . \; . \; . \; . \; . \; . \; . \quad (6a)$$

which is the general form of Schrodinger's equation.[2] The value [3] of $8\pi^2m/h^2$ is $1{\cdot}63881\times10^{27}$ erg^{-1}.

The reader may now perhaps wish to know the " meaning " of equation (6), and it should be clearly said at the outset that this cannot be given in an " intelligible " form, if this is understood to mean something in terms of ordinary

[1] Cf. Möglich, *Naturwiss.*, 1938, **26**, 409; Ertel, *ibid.*, 1938, **26**, 463.
[2] For an attempted interpretation, see Madelung, *Naturwiss.*, 1926, **14**, 1004.
[3] Du Mond and Cohen, *Rev. Mod. Phys.*, 1948, **20**, 82.

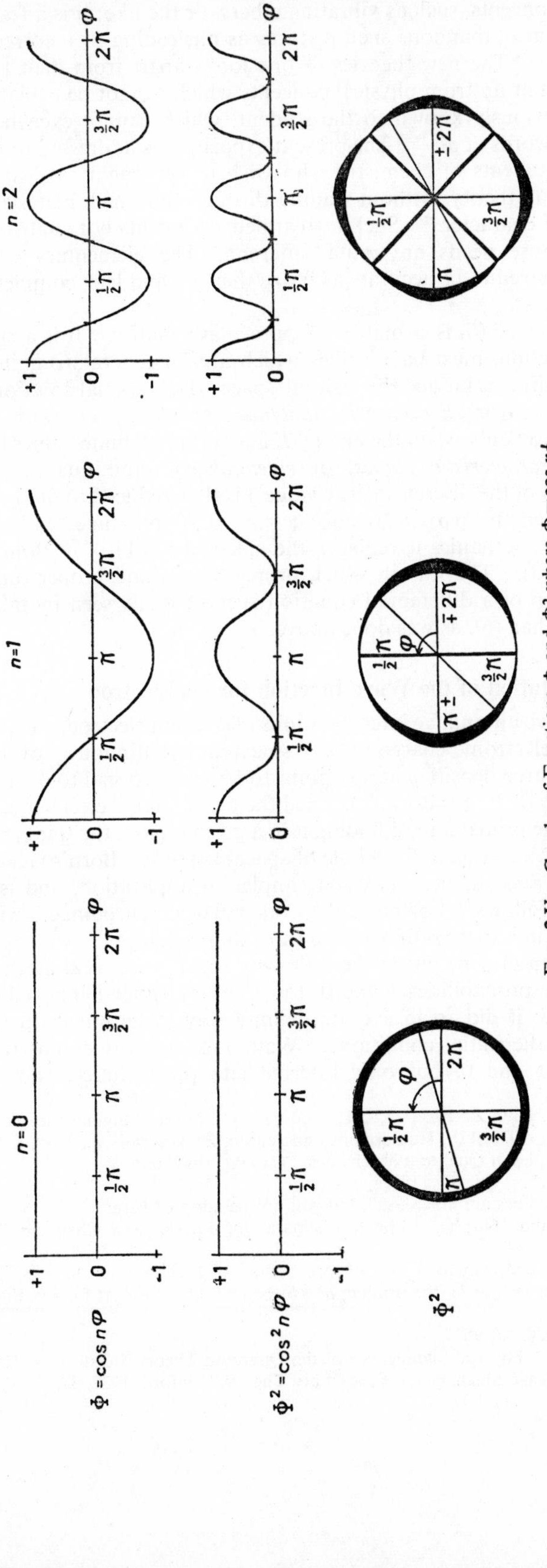

FIG. 2.V. Graphs of Functions Φ and Φ² where Φ = cos nφ

mechanical concepts, such as vibrating ethers, or the like; it is a feature of wave mechanics that it abandons such pictures as misleading or incorrect.[1] Dirac[2] has said that: " The new theories, if one looks apart from their mathematical setting, are built up from physical concepts which cannot be explained in terms of things previously known to the student, which cannot even be adequately explained in words at all." The present exposition is addressed to those called[3] " advanced students of chemistry who wish to (or ought to) learn something about quantum theory, without wading through too much material of a highly mathematical character." Such a treatment is not likely to satisfy the mathematician, whose needs are quite different. The elementary considerations below are believed to be accurate as far as they go, and lack completeness rather than correctness.

The solution of (6) is a matter of pure mathematics. It is assumed that ψ, the wave function, must have values which are, in general, (i) finite, (ii) single-valued, and (iii) continuous throughout space; these special solutions are called *proper functions* (or *characteristic functions*, or *eigenfunctions*).[4] It is found that they appear only when the energy E has certain definite values called *proper values* (or *characteristic values*, or *eigenvalues*),[4] and quantisation (or the determination of the discrete energy values) is thus reduced to finding the proper values.[5] When the particle is an electron, ψ is sometimes called an *orbital*, since in wave mechanics it replaces the electron " orbit " in Bohr's theory of the atom (§ 13). The way in which proper values and proper functions arise in the solution of a differential equation is most easily seen by taking a much simpler case than (6), as was done above.

§ 3. Interpretation of the Wave-function for an Electron

There are two alternative interpretations of ψ for an electron. (1) Schrödinger assumed the electronic charge to be " smeared " continuously over space, and the electric charge density ρ at any point to be proportional to ψ^2, the square of the wave function.[6] (2) Born[7] retained the point-charge electron, and regarded ψ^2 as giving the probability of finding it in a given region, the total probability of finding it anywhere (i.e. in the whole of space) being 1. Born's view is generally adopted, but Schrödinger's is often simpler in application, and is sometimes used in what follows. For more than one particle Schrödinger's view requires a distribution in a space of more than three dimensions.[8]

The situation may be put in the following way.[9] Classical mechanics recognised only the probabilities 1 and 0, for an event either happened or did not; if it happened, it did so in a quite definite way, determined (in the sense of causality) by the initial conditions. Wave mechanics does not recognise the probabilities 1 and 0, but only intermediate probabilities, and it does not

[1] Sommerfeld, *Phys. Z.*, 1927, **28**, 231; Lindemann, " Physical Significance of the Quantum Theory," Oxford, 1932, 128; Houtermans and Jensen, *Z. Naturforsch.*, 1947, **2** A, 146.

[2] " The Principles of Quantum Mechanics," Oxford, 1930, pref. v.

[3] Rice., *J.A.C.S.*, 1931, **53**, 1187.

[4] The hybrid names are much used, but will not be adopted here.

[5] Margenau and Murphy, " The Mathematics of Physics and Chemistry," New York, 1943, 240 f.

[6] Actually, to $\psi\psi^*$, where ψ and ψ^* are conjugate functions of the type $\psi=a+bi$ and $\psi^*=a-bi$ (where $i=\sqrt{-1}$), the product a^2+b^2 being real. In what follows the form ψ^2 will mostly be used.

[7] *Z. Phys.*, 1926, **37**, 863.

[8] Lindemann, " Physical Significance of the Quantum Theory," Oxford, 1932, 10.

[9] Frenkel, " Wave Mechanics. Elementary Theory," Oxford, 1932, 37.

recognise exact initial conditions; in place of determining certain single events, it finds the probabilities of all possible events. When the probability function has a sharp maximum, the corresponding event (or rather, the group of very similar events) is extremely probable, and is usually, but not certainly, observed. This is closely connected with Heisenberg's uncertainty principle (§ 14.IV).

§ 4. Formal Derivation of the Wave Equation

The wave equation (6), § 2, may be derived in a purely formal but interesting way as follows.[1] For one coordinate, the *energy*$=E=\frac{1}{2}mv^2+V=\frac{1}{2}m\dot{x}^2+V$, and the *momentum*$=p_x=m\dot{x}$,

$$\therefore\ E=(1/2m)p_x{}^2+V \quad \text{. . . . . (1)}$$

Now use the rule: replace p_x by an *operator* $(h/2\pi i)(\partial/\partial x)$, where $i=\sqrt{-1}$, and regard the left- and right-hand sides of the equation (1) as operating on a function ψ:

$$E\psi=\left[\frac{1}{2m}\left(\frac{h}{2\pi i}\cdot\frac{\partial}{\partial x}\right)^2+V\right]\psi,$$

$$\therefore\ E\psi=\left(-\frac{h^2}{8\pi^2 m}\frac{\partial^2}{\partial x^2}+V\right)\psi,$$

$$\therefore\ \partial^2\psi/\partial x^2+(8\pi^2 m/h^2)(E-V)\psi=0.$$

Extend to y and z, and the wave equation (6), § 2, results.

This method is related to Born and Jordan's equation:

$$pq-qp=h/2\pi i \quad \text{. . . . . (2)}$$

in which q and p are the corresponding generalised coordinate and momentum (§ 12.IV).[2] For, if the momentum is represented, as above, by the differential operator $(h/2\pi i)(\mathrm{d}/\mathrm{d}q)$, equation (2) reduces to the trivial statement that, for any function $\mathrm{f}(q)$:

$$\frac{\mathrm{d}}{\mathrm{d}q}q\mathrm{f}(q)-q\frac{\mathrm{d}}{\mathrm{d}q}\mathrm{f}(q)=\mathrm{f}(q).$$

§ 5 Normalising Factor and Orthogonality

The value of ψ^2 for an electron must agree with the condition that the total charge over all space is one electron; or, alternatively, that the probability P of finding the electron in all space is unity. This implies the equation:

$$\int_0^\infty P\mathrm{d}v=\int_0^\infty \psi^2\mathrm{d}v=1 \quad \text{. . . . . (1)}$$

where $\mathrm{d}v=\mathrm{d}x\mathrm{d}y\mathrm{d}z$; sometimes a *normalising factor* (§ 43.I) for ψ, such as $1/\sqrt{2}$, must be introduced to make (1) true. This is permissible, because (6), § 2, is still true when ψ is multiplied by any constant. Consider the integral $\int\psi_m\psi_n\mathrm{d}v$, where $\mathrm{d}v$ is an element of volume, and suppose that:

$$\int\psi_m\psi_n\mathrm{d}v=0 \quad \text{if } m\neq n, \quad \text{and } \int\psi_m\psi_n\mathrm{d}v=1 \quad \text{if } m=n \quad \text{. . (2)}$$

In this case ψ_m and ψ_n are called *orthogonal functions* (§ 43.I).[3]

[1] See Frenkel, "Wave Mechanics. Advanced Theory," Oxford, 1934, 47.

[2] Born and Jordan, *Z. Phys.*, 1925, **34**, 858; Born, "Experiment and Theory in Physics," Cambridge, 1943, 22; see § 22.

[3] The relations (2) were established for spherical harmonics (§ 12), P_m and P_n, by Legendre in 1784–9; Whittaker and Watson, "A Course of Modern Analysis," 3rd edit., Cambridge, 1920, 305.

§ 6. Translational Energy of an Ideal Gas

Although the state sum for the translational energy of an ideal gas was calculated in § 14.IV by a classical method, it is easily shown that wave mechanics gives the same result.[1] The case is sometimes called the " particle in a box."

Consider a molecule of a monatomic gas in a rectangular box of sides l_1, l_2, l_3, and volume $v=l_1l_2l_3$, and take axes x_1, x_2, x_3, parallel to the sides. If m is the mass of the particle and ϵ a possible value of its energy, the Schrödinger wave equation (6), § 2 (for this case the potential energy V is zero, and $x=x_1$, $y=x_2$, $z=x_3$) is:

$$\partial^2\psi/\partial x_1^2+\partial^2\psi/\partial x_2^2+\partial^2\psi/\partial x_3^2+(8\pi^2m\epsilon/h^2)\psi=0.$$

Put $\epsilon=\epsilon_1+\epsilon_2+\epsilon_3$, and $\psi=\psi_1(x_1)\psi_2(x_2)\psi_3(x_3)$, then the equation separates into three ordinary differential equations of the form:

$$\partial^2\psi_1/\partial x_1^2+(8\pi^2m\epsilon_1/h^2)\psi_1=0,$$

the solution of which is (§ 64.I):

$$\psi_1=A\sin[(8\pi^2m\epsilon_1/h^2)^{1/2}x_1+B].$$

Since ψ_1 vanishes for $x_1=0$, and $x_1=l$ (the walls of the box),[2] it is found by the appropriate substitutions (cf. § 2) that $B=0$, and $(8\pi^2m\epsilon_1/h^2)^{1/2}l_1=n_1\pi$, where n_1 is any integer, including zero. Hence the energy components are:

$$\epsilon_1=n_1^2h^2/8ml_1^2,\quad \epsilon_2=n_2^2h^2/8ml_2^2,\quad \text{and } \epsilon_3=n_3^2h^2/8ml_3^2.$$

The state sums are of the form (§ 8.IV) $Z_1=\Sigma e^{-\epsilon_1/kT}$, and, as $h^2/8ml_1^2kT$ is very small, the sum may be replaced by an integral:

$$Z_1=\int_0^\infty e^{-h^2n_1^2/8ml_1^2kT}dn_1=(2\pi mkT)^{1/2}l_1/h,$$

$$\therefore\ Z=Z_1Z_2Z_3=(2\pi mkT)^{3/2}l_1l_2l_3/h^3=(2\pi mkT)^{3/2}v/h^3.$$

For N particles, take Z^N instead of Z, and divide [3] by $N!$ as in § 14.IV, thus finding for the whole gas:

$$Z=[(ev/h^3N)(2\pi mkT)^{3/2}]^N$$

which is the same as the value found in § 14.IV, if the zero-point energy is omitted.

The same result is found from de Broglie's equation (1), § 1, for the length of the mass wave $\lambda=h/mv$, where v is now the velocity. The translational energy is $\epsilon_t=\frac{1}{2}mv^2$, hence the wave number (no. of waves per cm.) is $\omega=1/\lambda=\sqrt{(2m\epsilon_t)}/h$. The Rayleigh-Jeans formula for the number of waves in a volume V (§ 78.I) is:

$$dn=4\pi V\nu^2d\nu/v^3=4\pi V\omega^2d\omega,$$

where $\omega=\nu/v$ (§ 49.I). Since:

$$d\omega=d\sqrt{(2m\epsilon_t)}/h=(1/2h)\sqrt{(2m/\epsilon_t)}d\epsilon_t,$$

$$\therefore\ dn=(4\pi V/2h^3)(2m)^{3/2}\epsilon_t^{1/2}d\epsilon_t,$$

which replaces a statistical weight g_t in the state sum (§ 9.IV). Since the energy levels are closely spaced, the sum can be replaced by an integral, and as

[1] Pauling and Wilson, " Introduction to Quantum Mechanics," New York, 1935, 95; Macdougall, " Thermodynamics and Chemistry," 3rd edit., New York, 1939, 453.

[2] In the case of an *electron*, of course, there is a finite probability that it will extend beyond the walls of the " box." See Dushman, " Elements of Quantum Mechanics," 1938, 55.

[3] The objections to this procedure have been mentioned in § 14.IV. A suitable modification of procedure gives the same result directly.

the upper limit (E_t) is very large compared with the molecular energy ϵ_t it can be replaced by infinity:

$$\therefore\ Z_t=(2\pi/h^3)(2m)^{3/2}V\int_0^\infty \epsilon_t^{1/2}e^{-\epsilon_t/kT}d\epsilon=[(2\pi mkT)^{3/2}/h^3]V,$$

the integral being evaluated in § 33.IV.

The further consideration of the proper functions for such a "potential barrier," or "particle in a box," problem [1] would lead too far from general principles at this stage. The results are of no interest in relation to the properties of real gases, which do not leak through jars or containers.

In what follows the systems studied and the types of mathematical functions which are involved in their treatment are:

(1) *Linear harmonic oscillator:* the proper values are $E=(n+\frac{1}{2})h\tilde{\omega}_e$; the proper functions are Hermite polynomials.

(2) *Rigid rotor with fixed axis:* the proper values are $E=m^2h^2/8\pi^2I$; the proper functions are $Ce^{\pm im\phi}$.

(3) *Rigid rotor with free axis*: the proper values are $E=m(m+1)h^2/8\pi^2I$; the proper functions are spherical harmonics.

(4) *Hydrogen-like atom:* the proper values are $E=-2\pi^2\mu Z^2e^4/n^2h^2$; the proper functions are Laguerre polynomials.

§ 7. Linear harmonic oscillator

The wave theory of the linear harmonic oscillator (§ 16.IV) may be developed [2] from the wave equation (5), § 2:

$$d^2\psi/dx^2+(8\pi^2m/h^2)(E-V)\psi=0.$$

The classical theory (§ 52.I) gives the potential energy $V=\frac{1}{2}\alpha x^2(\alpha>0)$, and the kinetic energy $T=\frac{1}{2}mv^2$, hence the total energy $E=T+V=\frac{1}{2}mv^2+\frac{1}{2}\alpha x^2$. If x_0 is the maximum displacement, $v=0$ and $E=\frac{1}{2}\alpha x_0^2$. The "equilibrium" frequency is:

$$\tilde{\omega}_e=(1/2\pi)\sqrt{(\alpha/m)} \quad . \quad . \quad . \quad . \quad (1)$$

and the wave equation becomes:

$$d^2\psi/dx^2+(8\pi^2m/h^2)(E-\tfrac{1}{2}\alpha x^2)\psi=0.$$

Put:

$$8\pi^2mE/h^2=A,\quad 4\pi^2m\alpha/h^2=B \quad . \quad . \quad . \quad (2)$$

$$\therefore\ d^2\psi/dx^2+(A-Bx^2)\psi=0 \quad . \quad . \quad . \quad (3)$$

The solution is obtained by the so-called asymptotic method. First consider very large values of x, i.e. very large negative values of the kinetic energy $(E-\frac{1}{2}\alpha x^2)$. Then $A \ll Bx^2$ (the symbol $\ll$ meaning "much smaller than"),

$$\therefore\ d^2\psi/dx^2 \simeq Bx^2\psi \quad . \quad . \quad . \quad . \quad (4)$$

with the solution (c an arbitrary constant) found by the method of § 63.I:

$$\psi=ce^{-\frac{1}{2}\sqrt{(B)}x^2} \quad . \quad . \quad . \quad . \quad (5)$$

[1] See e.g. Eyring, Walter, and Kimball, "Quantum Chemistry," 1944, 68.

[2] Schrödinger, *Ann. Phys.*, 1926, **79**, 489; Fues, *ibid.*, 1926, **80**, 367; Born and Oppenheimer, *ibid.*, 1927, **84**, 457; Sommerfeld, "Wave Mechanics," 1930, 14; Frenkel, "Wave Mechanics. Elementary Theory," Oxford, 1932, 77; Pauling and Wilson, "Introduction to Quantum Mechanics," New York, 1935, 67; Dushman, "The Elements of Quantum Mechanics," New York, 1938, 111; Margenau and Murphy, "The Mathematics of Physics and Chemistry," New York, 1943, 76.

The part of the solution with the exponent $+\frac{1}{2}\sqrt{(B)}x^2$ is not admissible, since it makes $\psi\rightarrow\infty$. Equation (5), in fact, gives:

$$d^2\psi/dx^2=c(Bx^2-\sqrt{B})e^{-\frac{1}{2}\sqrt{(B)}x^2}=(Bx^2-\sqrt{B})\psi,$$

which is (3) with $A=\sqrt{B}$, equivalent to (4) when x is very large.

From this asymptotic value of ψ (when x is very large) the exact value is found by replacing the constant c in (5) by a function of x, $f(x)=c(x)$, which can be found by substituting (5) in (3). Let $B=\beta^2$, then:

$$d^2\psi/dx^2=c(\beta^2x^2-\beta)e^{-\frac{1}{2}\beta x^2}-2(dc/dx)\beta x e^{-\frac{1}{2}\beta x^2}+(d^2c/dx^2)e^{-\frac{1}{2}\beta x^2}$$

$$\therefore\ d^2\psi/dx^2+(A-\beta^2x^2)\psi=e^{-\frac{1}{2}\beta x^2}[c(A-\beta)-2\beta x(dc/dx)+d^2c/dx^2]=0$$

$$\therefore\ d^2c/dx^2-2\beta x(dc/dx)+(A-\beta)c=0 \quad . \quad . \quad . \quad . \quad (6)$$

which is the required equation for $c=f(x)$.

In considering the proper functions it is convenient to use a variable $z=\sqrt{(\beta)}x$, so that the function $c(x)$ becomes $H(z)$ by substituting $x=z/\sqrt{\beta}$, therefore $dx=dz/\sqrt{\beta}$, $dx^2=dz^2/\beta$, and (6) becomes (after dividing by β, and putting $\lambda=A/\beta$):

$$d^2H/dz^2-2z(dH/dz)+(\lambda-1)H=0 \quad . \quad . \quad . \quad . \quad . \quad (7)$$

The solution uses the so-called *polynomial method.* Assume that $H(z)$ can be expressed as a power series:

$$H(z)=a_0+a_1z+a_2z^2+a_3z^3+a_4z^4+\ldots+a_nz^n,$$

then [1] this cannot be infinite, but must terminate at the nth power, since otherwise:

$$\psi=H(z)e^{-\frac{1}{2}z^2} \quad . \quad . \quad . \quad . \quad . \quad . \quad . \quad . \quad . \quad . \quad (8)$$

will not vanish for $z\rightarrow\infty$, i.e. $x\rightarrow\infty$, as it is required to do (see § 2). Thus:

$$dH/dz=a_1+2a_2z+3a_3z^2+4a_4z^3+\ldots$$

$$d^2H/dz^2=2a_2+2\,.\,3a_3z+3\,.\,4a_4z^2+\ldots$$

$$-2z\,.\,dH/dz=-2a_1z-4a_2z^2-6a_3z^3-8a_4z^4$$

$$(\lambda-1)H=(\lambda-1)a_0+(\lambda-1)a_1z+(\lambda-1)a_2z^2+\ldots$$

The sum of the last three lines must, by (7), vanish for all values of z, and hence the coefficients of powers of z must be separately zero:

$$1\,.\,2a_2+(\lambda-1)a_0=0 \text{ for } z^0=1$$

$$2\,.\,3a_3+(\lambda-1-2)a_1=0 \text{ for } z$$

$$3\,.\,4a_4+(\lambda-1-2\,.\,2)a_2=0 \text{ for } z^2$$

from which it is easily seen that for z^n:

$$(n+1)(n+2)a_{n+2}+(\lambda-1-2n)a_n=0,$$

$$\text{or } a_{n+2}=-\frac{(\lambda-1-2n)}{(n+1)(n+2)}a_n \quad . \quad . \quad . \quad . \quad . \quad . \quad . \quad . \quad (9)$$

If the series stops at the nth term, a_{n+2} and all higher values of a must be zero, hence, from (9):

$$\lambda=2n+1, \quad \text{or } A=(2n+1)\beta=(2n+1)\sqrt{B} \quad . \quad . \quad . \quad (10)$$

From (2) and (10), $E=(2n+1)h\sqrt{(\alpha/m)}/4\pi$, or, from (1):

$$E=(n+\tfrac{1}{2})\boldsymbol{h}\tilde{\omega}_e \quad . \quad . \quad . \quad . \quad . \quad . \quad . \quad . \quad . \quad (11)$$

[1] For proof, see Pauling and Wilson, "Introduction to Quantum Mechanics," New York, 1935, 71.

which shows that the linear harmonic oscillator has discrete quantised energies, which are whole multiples of $h\tilde{\omega}_e$ added to a zero-point energy $\frac{1}{2}h\tilde{\omega}_e$ for $n=0$. The quantum number n (usually denoted by v) enters merely as the degree of the polynomial H(z), without any special assumptions.

§ 8. Hermite Polynomials

Since the coefficients of the polynomial considered in § 7 are known except for either a_0 or a_1, which are arbitrary, the values of the un-normalised wave function (8), § 7, can be calculated. From (9) and (10), § 7:

$$a_n=-\frac{\lambda-1-2(n-2)}{n(n-1)}a_{n-2}=\frac{-2\,.\,2}{n(n-1)}a_{n-2},$$

$$a_{n-2}=\frac{2\,.\,2^2}{(n-2)(n-3)}a_{n-4},$$

etc. Hence:

$$\mathrm{H}_n(z)=a_n\left[z^n-\frac{n(n-1)z^{n-2}}{1\,.\,2^2}+\frac{n(n-1)(n-2)(n-3)z^{n-4}}{1\,.\,2\,.\,2^4}\ldots\right],$$

where a_n is an arbitrary constant, and if this is taken as $a_n=2^n$ the function is called a *Hermite polynomial* of degree n: [1]

$$H_n(z)=(2z)^n-\frac{n(n-1)}{1!}(2z)^{n-2}+\frac{n(n-1)(n-2)(n-3)}{2!}(2z)^{n-4}-\ldots$$

The first five are easily calculated:

$$\mathrm{H}_0(z)=2^0\,.\,z^0=1 \qquad \mathrm{H}_2(z)=2^2(z^2-\tfrac{1}{2}z^0)=4z^2-2$$

$$\mathrm{H}_1(z)=2z \qquad \mathrm{H}_3(z)=2^3\left(z^3-\frac{3\,.\,2z}{4}\right)=8z^3-12z$$

$$\mathrm{H}_4(z)=2^4(z^4-\frac{4\,.\,3z^2}{4}+\frac{4\,.\,3\,.\,2\,.\,1}{32}z^0)=16z^4-48z^2+12.$$

It was proved by Hermite that these functions are all given by the formula:

$$\mathrm{H}_n(z)=(-1)^n\mathrm{e}^{z^2}[\mathrm{d}^n(\mathrm{e}^{-z^2})/\mathrm{d}z^n],$$

and this is easily confirmed for simple cases, e.g.:

$$\mathrm{H}_2(z)=(-1)^2\,.\,\mathrm{e}^{z^2}\frac{\mathrm{d}^2(\mathrm{e}^{-z^2})}{\mathrm{d}z^2}=\mathrm{e}^{z^2}(4z^2\mathrm{e}^{-z^2}-2\mathrm{e}^{-z^2})=4z^2-2.$$

The Hermitian function (8), § 7:

$$y=\mathrm{e}^{-\frac{1}{2}x^2}\mathrm{H}_n(x)$$

satisfies the differential equation:

$$\mathrm{d}^2y/\mathrm{d}x^2+(2n+1-x^2)y=0$$

and the functions in the domain $-\infty$ to $+\infty$ form an orthogonal system (§ 5), since if m and n are two different integers:

$$\int_{-\infty}^{+\infty}\mathrm{H}_m(x)\mathrm{H}_n(x)\mathrm{e}^{-x^2}\mathrm{d}x=0.$$

[1] Nielsen, *K. Danske Vidensk. Selsk.* (*Mat. fys.*), 1918, I, 6; Margenau and Murphy, "The Mathematics of Physics and Chemistry," New York, 1943, 76, 117.

§ 9. Proper Functions for the Linear Harmonic Oscillator

Equation (8), § 7, still needs the normalising factor, N_n, defined (§ 5) by:

$$(1/N_n^2)\int_{-\infty}^{\infty}\psi_n^2 dx=1.$$

The calculation [1] (which is tedious, and is omitted here) gives for the normalised proper functions:

$$\psi_n(z)=[\sqrt{\beta}/2^n n!\sqrt{\pi}]^{1/2}H_n(z)e^{-z^2/2}.$$

These, for $n=0, 1, 2, 3$ and 4 are graphed in Fig. 3.V ($x=z$). Each has two nodes at $\pm\infty$, and n other nodes for finite values of z. The curves for $n=0, 2, 4$, are

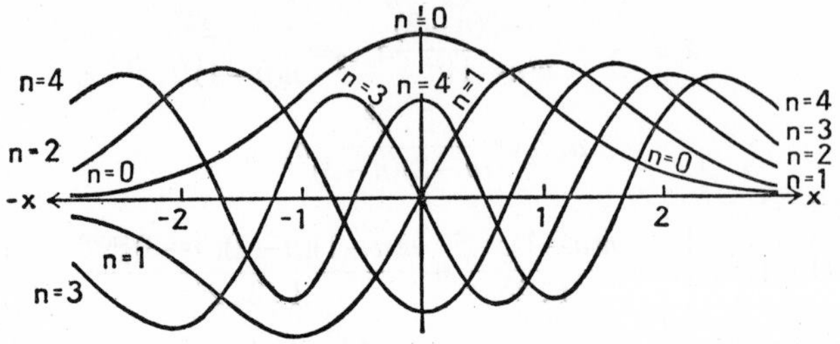

FIG. 3.V. Normalised Proper Functions: $\psi_n(z)=[1/(2^n n!\sqrt{\pi})^{1/2}]H_n(z)e^{-\frac{1}{2}z^2}$ for $n=0, 1, 2, 3$, and 4.

symmetrical for positive and negative values of z (even functions); those for $n=1, 3$, are antisymmetrical.

If the vibrating particle is an electron, the charge distribution, on Schrödinger's view (§ 3), is found by plotting $\psi_n^2(z)$ against z, and is shown in the curves marked A in Fig. 4.V. Normalisation makes the area under each curve $\frac{1}{2}$, since symmetry about the ψ_n^2 axis makes the contributions for negative values of z (not shown) equal to those for positive, and the total area is 1, this representing the charge of one electron. The curves marked B represent the charge distribution according to classical theory, in which there is no charge beyond the two maximum amplitudes of the vibrating electron (shown, for the positive side of the displacement, by dotted verticals), whereas the wave equation makes the charge (or the probability of its occurrence) extend to infinity. It is seen, however, that the contributions beyond the classical amplitudes are relatively small in this case.

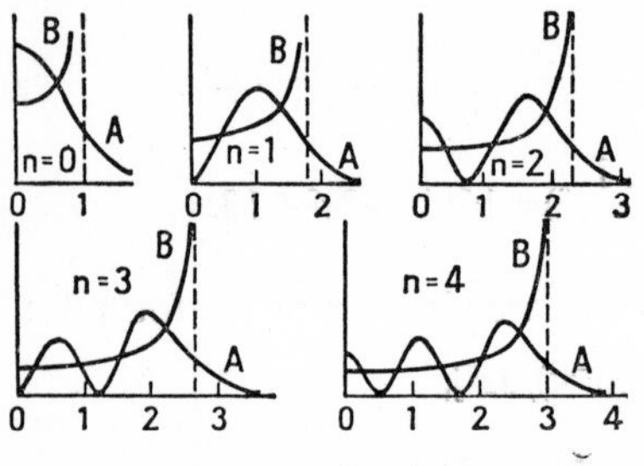

FIG. 4.V. Charge Distribution for Linear Harmonic Oscillator

A further mathematical deduction [2] is that energy transitions are possible only when n changes by unity, i.e. when the harmonic oscillator energy increases or decreases by one quantum at a time. On the old quantum theory, the energy of such an oscillator could increase or decrease by any number of quanta in one act (see § 15.IV), and this is still the case if the oscillator is anharmonic.

[1] Dushman, "Quantum Mechanics," New York, 1938, 117; Pauling and Wilson, "Introduction to Quantum Mechanics," New York, 1935, 80; Eyring, Walter, and Kimball, "Quantum Chemistry," New York 1944, 62, 77.

[2] Dushman, "Quantum Mechanics," 1938, 131; Eyring, Walter, and Kimball, "Quantum Chemistry," 1944, 117.

§ 10. Rigid Rotor with Fixed Axis

Consider two massive points m_1 and m_2 at a fixed distance r apart (typifying a rigid diatomic molecule, § 18.IV) and the pair capable of rotation like a dumb-bell. This rotation may be regarded as occurring about an axis passing through the centre of gravity in the line joining m_1 and m_2 and distant r_1 and r_2 from them and at right angles to this line. (Rotation *about* the line of centres is not considered.) If this axis of rotation is fixed in space (i.e. points in a constant direction) the system is said to have a *fixed axis*; if it has also a precessional motion (i.e. the axis moves so that each end sweeps out a spherical surface), the rotor is said to have a *free axis*. These two cases will be considered in order, the fixed axis here and the free axis in § 11.

In this case there is no potential energy, hence $E=T=\frac{1}{2}mv^2$, the kinetic energy. This will first be expressed in terms of polar coordinates (§ 28.I). The velocity square is given by $v^2=\dot{x}^2+\dot{y}^2+\dot{z}^2$, where the point denotes differentiation with respect to time, $\dot{x}=\mathrm{d}x/\mathrm{d}t$, etc. In spherical coordinates (r, θ, ϕ):

$$x=r\sin\theta\cos\phi,\quad y=r\sin\theta\sin\phi,\quad z=r\cos\theta,$$

$$\dot{x}=r\cos\theta\,.\,\dot{\theta}\,.\cos\phi-r\sin\theta\,.\sin\phi\,.\,\dot{\phi}+\dot{r}\,.\sin\theta\,.\cos\phi$$

$$\dot{y}=r\cos\theta\,.\,\dot{\theta}\,.\sin\phi+r\sin\theta\,.\cos\phi\,.\,\dot{\phi}+\dot{r}\sin\theta\,.\sin\phi$$

$$\dot{z}=-r\sin\theta\,.\,\dot{\theta}+\dot{r}\cos\theta.$$

By squaring, adding, and putting $\cos^2 x+\sin^2 x=1$ from (23), § 41.I, the complicated expression ultimately reduces to:

$$v^2=\dot{r}^2+r^2\dot{\theta}^2+r^2\sin^2\theta\,.\,\dot{\phi}^2,$$

and the kinetic energy of a mass m with a position defined in polar coordinates is:

$$T=\tfrac{1}{2}mv^2=\tfrac{1}{2}m\dot{r}^2+\tfrac{1}{2}mr^2\dot{\theta}^2+\tfrac{1}{2}mr^2\sin^2\theta\,.\,\dot{\phi}^2 \quad . \; . \; . \quad (1)$$

In the case of a rigid rotor, the origin may be taken at the centre of gravity of the line joining the two particles, the rotation being about an axis at right angles to this. There will be two expressions of the form (1), one for each particle, but as the line joining the points is of fixed [1] length, $\dot{r}_1^2$ and $\dot{r}_2^2$ are zero, hence:

$$T=E=\tfrac{1}{2}(m_1r_1^2+m_2r_2^2)(\dot{\theta}^2+\sin^2\theta\,.\,\dot{\phi}^2) \quad . \; . \; . \; . \quad (2)$$

The equation for the centre of gravity gives $m_1r_1=m_2r_2$, and since $r_1+r_2=r$, the length of the axis of the rotor:

$$r_1=m_2r/(m_1+m_2),\quad r_2=m_1r/(m_1+m_2),$$

$$\therefore\; m_1r_1^2+m_2r_2^2=m_1m_2r^2/(m_1+m_2)=\mu r^2=I \quad . \; . \; . \quad (3)$$

where μ is called the *reduced mass*, and I is the moment of inertia (§ 18.IV) about an axis passing through the centre of gravity,

$$\therefore\; E=\tfrac{1}{2}I(\dot{\theta}^2+\sin^2\theta\,.\,\dot{\phi}^2) \quad . \; . \; . \; . \; . \; . \; . \; . \quad (4)$$

The wave equation (6a), § 2, becomes:

$$\nabla^2\psi+(8\pi^2mE/\boldsymbol{h}^2)\psi=0,$$

since $V=0$. The operator ∇^2 in polar coordinates is given in (8), § 28.I, the first two terms being zero since $r=$constant:

$$\frac{1}{r^2\sin\theta}\frac{\partial}{\partial\theta}\left(\sin\theta\frac{\partial\psi}{\partial\theta}\right)+\frac{1}{r^2\sin^2\theta}\frac{\partial^2\psi}{\partial\phi^2}+\frac{8\pi^2IE}{r^2\boldsymbol{h}^2}\psi=0 \quad . \; . \; . \; . \quad (5)$$

[1] The case where "stretching" occurs is more complicated, and is not considered here.

in which, in the last term, the reduced mass μ has been substituted for m and, from $I=\mu r^2$, μ replaced by I/r^2. For a fixed axis, the precessional angle θ is constant, and the equation, after multiplication by r^2, reduces to:

$$d^2\psi/d\phi^2+(8\pi^2EI/h^2)\psi=0 \quad . \quad . \quad . \quad . \quad . \quad . \quad . \quad . \quad (6)$$

since θ (which is arbitrary) may be taken as $\pi/2$, therefore $\sin\theta=1$. To indicate that the multiplier of ψ is positive, write [1]:

$$8\pi^2EI/h^2=m^2 \quad . \quad . \quad . \quad . \quad . \quad . \quad . \quad . \quad . \quad . \quad (7)$$

then the equation to be solved is $d^2\psi/d\phi^2+m^2\phi=0$. As in § 64.I, a solution is:

$$\psi=Ce^{im\phi}=C(\cos m\phi+i\sin m\phi) \quad . \quad . \quad . \quad . \quad . \quad (8)$$

by de Moivre's theorem (§ 46.I), where C is a constant. Since ψ must be real, the value $C\cos m\phi$ may be taken, and, since it is a cosine function, for any given value of m, the wave function ψ will not be single-valued for $\phi=0$ and $\phi=2\pi$, which correspond with identical positions, unless m is zero or a positive or negative integer. Since $Ce^{-im\phi}$ is a solution as well as $Ce^{im\phi}$, the positive values of m may be chosen, the sign of m merely depending on the direction of rotation. Thus, $m=0, 1, 2, \ldots$, are the proper values, and, from (7):

$$E_m=m^2h^2/8\pi^2I \quad . \quad . \quad . \quad . \quad . \quad . \quad . \quad . \quad . \quad (9)$$

which is the same as the value found in § 19.IV from the old quantum theory. Here, m is evidently a *rotational quantum number*, having integral values: it is usually denoted by J (§ 19.IV) in the case of diatomic molecules.

It should be noted that, although the energy (involving m^2) is the same for either direction of rotation, this will no longer be true if the rotor has an electric moment and is in an electric field of fixed direction, or has a magnetic moment and is in a magnetic field of fixed direction. For each single proper value there are two proper functions, $Ce^{im\phi}$ and $Ce^{-im\phi}$, and the function is said to be *degenerate*. The values of J must now include negative as well as positive values of m, i.e. there are $2m+1$ values (including the value 0) in all. It is only when the rotor is in a directed field which acts upon it that the two functions are significant, the energies being then slightly less or slightly greater than without the field, depending on the direction of rotation.

§ 11. Rigid Rotor with Free Axis

The case of the rigid rotor with a free axis is more difficult than that with a fixed axis, since ψ now depends on θ as well as ϕ, and in equation (5), § 10, after multiplication by r^2 (r=const.):

$$\frac{1}{\sin\theta}\frac{\partial}{\partial\theta}\left(\sin\theta\frac{\partial\psi}{\partial\phi}\right)+\frac{1}{\sin^2\theta}\frac{\partial^2\psi}{\partial\phi^2}+\frac{8\pi^2EI}{h^2}\psi=0 \quad . \quad . \quad . \quad . \quad (1)$$

the variables ϕ and θ represent the rotation around, and the precession of, the free axis, respectively.

Assume that $\psi(\theta, \phi)=\Theta(\theta)\Phi(\phi)$, where Θ and Φ are functions of θ and ϕ, respectively. Then:

$$\partial\psi/\partial\theta=\Phi(\partial\Theta/\partial\theta); \quad \partial^2\psi/\partial\theta^2=\Phi(\partial^2\Theta/\partial\theta^2); \quad \text{and} \quad \partial^2\psi/\partial\phi^2=\Theta(\partial^2\Phi/\partial\phi^2);$$

where $\Theta(\theta)\equiv\Theta$ and $\Phi(\phi)\equiv\Phi$. Hence, on substitution in (1), and with:

$$8\pi^2EI/h^2=\lambda^2 \quad . \quad . \quad . \quad . \quad . \quad . \quad . \quad . \quad . \quad . \quad (2)$$

[1] This is the conventional symbol; it must not be confused with m, standing for the mass of a particle, in the previous equations.

a positive constant, it is found that:

$$\frac{\Phi}{\sin\theta}\frac{\partial}{\partial\theta}\left(\sin\theta\frac{\partial\Theta}{\partial\theta}\right)+\frac{\Theta}{\sin^2\theta}\frac{\partial\Phi^2}{\partial\phi^2}+\lambda^2\Theta\Phi=0.$$

Since $\sin^2\theta/\Theta\Phi$ is never infinite, multiply by this:

$$\therefore\quad \frac{\sin\theta}{\Theta}\frac{\partial}{\partial\theta}\left(\sin\theta\frac{\partial\Theta}{\partial\theta}\right)+\lambda^2\sin^2\theta=-\frac{1}{\Phi}\frac{\partial^2\Phi}{\partial\phi^2}\quad . \quad . \quad . \quad . \quad (3)$$

The left side depends only on θ, and the right only on ϕ, and (as θ and ϕ are independent variables) each side must be equal to a constant, say m^2, and hence (3) breaks up into two ordinary differential equations:

$$d^2\Phi/d\phi^2+m^2\Phi=0 \quad . \quad . \quad . \quad . \quad . \quad . \quad . \quad . \quad (4)$$

$$\sin\theta\frac{d}{d\theta}\left(\sin\theta\frac{d\Theta}{d\theta}\right)+(\lambda^2\sin^2\theta-m^2)\Theta=0 \quad . \quad . \quad . \quad . \quad (5)$$

which will be solved in this order.

Equation (4) is the same as (6), § 10, and has the solutions:

$$\Phi_m=Ce^{\pm im\phi} \quad . \quad . \quad . \quad . \quad . \quad . \quad . \quad . \quad . \quad . \quad (6)$$

where m has the positive values, $m=0, 1, 2, \ldots$, and C is a constant which corresponds with the normalising factor. This is found from (1), § 5, by using the conjugate functions: [1]

$$C^2\int_0^{2\pi} e^{im\phi}\,.\,e^{-im\phi}d\phi=1$$

$$\therefore\ C^2=1/2\pi \quad \text{or} \quad C=1/\sqrt{(2\pi)}.$$

The normalised wave functions corresponding with (8), § 10, and (6) are, therefore:

$$\Phi_m=[1/\sqrt{(2\pi)}]e^{im\phi} \quad . \quad . \quad . \quad . \quad . \quad . \quad . \quad . \quad (7)$$

where m now has the values 0, 1, 2, 3, . . . -1, -2, -3, . . ., or (as they are usually arranged) . . . 3, 2, 1, 0, -1, -2, -3, ... For $m=0$ there is only one wave function:

$$\Phi_0=1/\sqrt{(2\pi)} \quad . \quad . \quad . \quad . \quad . \quad . \quad . \quad . \quad . \quad . \quad (8)$$

but for every other absolute value $|m|$ (i.e. value taken without regard to sign) there are two, one for $+m$ and one for $-m$; hence there are $2|m|+1$ values in all.

For every value of $|m|$, the two functions $\Phi_{|m|}$ and $\Phi_{-|m|}$ satisfy (4), and hence their sum or difference, multiplied by any constant, will do so. Since, by de Moivre's theorem (§ 46.I), $\frac{1}{2}(e^{im\phi}+e^{-im\phi})=\cos m\phi$ and $(1/2i)(e^{im\phi}-e^{-im\phi})=\sin m\phi$, the real functions $\cos m\phi$ and $\sin m\phi$ may be used, and:

$$\Phi_{|m|}=[1/\sqrt{(2\pi)}]\cos|m|\phi \quad \text{or} \quad [1/\sqrt{(2\pi)}]\sin|m|\phi \quad . \quad . \quad . \quad (9)$$

For each value of $|m|$ there are $2|m|+1$ wave functions $\Phi_{|m|}$, so that (§ 9.IV) $\Phi_{|m|}$ is $(2m+1)$-fold degenerate. In the case of a diatomic molecule, m is usually denoted by J, the rotational quantum number, and the degeneracy is $(2J+1)$.

The solution of (5) is next to be considered. The solutions ψ of the wave equation (6), § 2, represent, in the most general case, the amplitudes of de Broglie waves (§ 1) in three dimensions, and cannot be visualised. When r is constant (as in the present case), ψ represents the amplitude of vibration of a spherical surface, and the functions representing ψ are called *surface spherical harmonics*, " harmonics " because they have nodes along meridian circles and

[1] See the footnote to § 3. Note the simplicity resulting from their use in this case.

zonal circles (parallel to the equatorial plane) of the sphere. They are quite complicated expressions, and a digression will first be made for their consideration.

§ 12. Spherical Harmonics [1]

Equation (5), § 11, is a form of a well-known differential equation of the second order known as *Legendre's equation.* First put $\cos\theta=\mu$ (not to be confused with the reduced mass),[2] then:

$$\sin^2\theta=1-\mu^2, \text{ and } d\mu=-\sin\theta d\theta \quad . \quad . \quad . \quad . \quad . \quad (1)$$

Divide (5), § 11, by $\sin^2\theta$:

$$\therefore \frac{1}{\sin\theta}\frac{d}{d\theta}\left(\sin\theta\frac{d\Theta}{d\theta}\right)+\left(\lambda^2-\frac{m^2}{\sin^2\theta}\right)\Theta=0.$$

Substitute from (1):

$$\therefore \frac{d}{d\mu}\left[(1-\mu^2)\frac{d\Theta}{d\mu}\right]+\left(\lambda^2-\frac{m^2}{1-\mu^2}\right)\Theta=0 \quad . \quad . \quad . \quad . \quad . \quad (2)$$

Obviously, μ can vary only from -1 to $+1$, and for ±1 themselves, $1-\mu^2=0$; as this occurs in the denominator in the second term, these will be singular points (§ 36.I). Equation (2) is Legendre's equation of order m in μ. The equation of zero order ($m=0$) is:

$$(d/d\mu)(1-\mu^2)(d\Theta/d\mu)+\lambda^2\Theta=0,$$

$$\text{or } (1-\mu^2)(d^2\Theta/d\mu^2)-2\mu(d\Theta/d\mu)+\lambda^2\Theta=0 \quad . \quad . \quad . \quad (3)$$

Assume that Θ can be represented by a polynomial of degree k, where $k=$ 0, 1, 2, . . .:

$$\Theta=\Sigma a_k\mu^k \quad . \quad . \quad . \quad . \quad . \quad . \quad . \quad . \quad . \quad . \quad (4)$$

$$\therefore d\Theta/d\mu=\Sigma a_k k\mu^{k-1}, \quad -2\mu(d\Theta/d\mu)=-\Sigma 2a_k k\mu^k,$$

$$d^2\Theta/d\mu^2=\Sigma a_{k+2}(k+2)(k+1)\mu^k \text{ (by differentiating } \mu^{k+2}),$$

$$\therefore -\mu^2(d^2\Theta/d\mu^2)=-\Sigma a_{k+2}(k+2)(k+1)\mu^{k+2},$$

or, by lowering the degree by 2:

$$-\mu^2(d^2\Theta/d\mu^2)=-\Sigma a_k k(k-1)\mu^k.$$

[1] Ferrers, "An Elementary Treatise on Spherical Harmonics," 1877; Byerly, "An Elementary Treatise on Fourier's Series and Spherical, Cylindrical, and Ellipsoidal Harmonics," Boston, 1893, 144 f., 195 f., 277 f.; Macrobert, "Spherical Harmonics," 1927, are standard works. Other treatises are: Todhunter, "Elementary Treatise on Laplace's Functions, Lamé's Functions, and Bessel's Functions," 1875; Heine, "Kugelfunktionen," 2nd edit., Berlin, 1878; Tallqvist, *Acta Soc. Sci. Fenn.*, 1899, **26**, No. 4,; Hill, *Arkiv Mat. Astron. Fys.*, 1918, **13**, No. 17; Hobson, "Theory of Spherical and Ellipsoidal Harmonics," Cambridge, 1931. See also the sections on spherical harmonics in Maxwell, "A Treatise on Electricity and Magnetism," Oxford, 1873, **1**, 151–180 (ch. ix; abridged in the later editions); Thomson and Tait, "A Treatise on Natural Philosophy," Cambridge, 1886, **1**, 171; Jeans, "Mathematical Theory of Electricity and Magnetism," Cambridge, 1909, 203 f.; Riemann and Weber, "Partielle Differentialgleichungen," 1910, **1**, 278; Forsyth, "Treatise on Differential Equations," 1914, 159; Ford, "Differential Equations," New York, 1933, 190; Bethe, in Geiger and Scheel, "Handbuch der Physik," 1933, **24**, i, 551; Dushman, "The Elements of Quantum Mechanics," New York, 1938, 149 f.; Margenau and Murphy, "The Mathematics of Physics and Chemistry," New York, 1943, 212 f., 223 f.; "Tables of Associated Legendre Functions," Math. Tables Project, Columbia Univ. Press, New York, 1945. For a compact and intelligible introductory treatment, see Williamson, "Differential Calculus," 6th edit., 1887, 416; *idem*, "Integral Calculus," 7th edit., 1896, 332. The mathematics goes back to Laplace, *Mém. Acad. Sci.*, 1782 (1785), 113, which Byerly, *op. cit.*, 267, calls "one of the most remarkable memoirs ever written."

[2] In this section the recognised symbols in spherical harmonics are used.

The coefficient of μ^k in (3) is thus:

$$a_{k+2}(k+2)(k+1)-a_k[k(k-1)+2k-\lambda^2],$$

and as each coefficient must vanish identically:

$$a_{k+2}=\frac{a_k[k(k+1)-\lambda^2]}{(k+2)(k+1)} \quad . \quad . \quad . \quad . \quad . \quad . \quad . \quad . \quad (5)$$

$$\therefore \; a_{k+2}/a_k=k/(k+2)-\lambda^2/(k+1)(k+2).$$

If k can increase without limit, $a_{k+2}/a_k=1$ for very large values of k, and if the series (4) is to converge for $\mu=\pm 1$, it must have a finite number of terms, breaking off at μ^k; hence $a_{k+2}=0$, and from (5):

$$k(k+1)=\lambda^2, \quad . \quad . \quad . \quad . \quad . \quad . \quad . \quad . \quad . \quad . \quad (5a)$$

therefore from (2), § 11:

$$8\pi^2EI/\boldsymbol{h}^2=k(k+1),$$

$$\therefore \; E_k=k(k+1)\boldsymbol{h}^2/8\pi^2I \quad . \quad . \quad . \quad . \quad . \quad . \quad . \quad . \quad (6)$$

where $k=0, 1, 2, \ldots$, giving the energy of the rotor with free axis. This differs from the formula (9), § 10, for a fixed axis in having $k(k+1)$ instead of k^2 (k is denoted in (9), § 10, by m), and is in better agreement with experiment. For diatomic molecules, as stated in § 19.IV, the rotational quantum number is denoted by J instead of k in (6).

In (3), λ^2 can now be put equal to $k(k+1)$, giving the standard form of Legendre's equation:

$$(1-\mu^2)(d^2\Theta_k/d\mu^2)-2\mu(d\Theta_k/d\mu)+k(k+1)\Theta_k=0 \quad . \quad . \quad . \quad (7)$$

as the differential equation for Θ_k, which is the proper function corresponding with the proper value E_k. From (5), by putting a_k and a_{k-2} for a_{k+2} and a_k, and $\lambda^2=k(k+1)$:

$$a_k=\frac{(k-2)(k-1)-k(k+1)}{k(k-1)}a_{k-2}=-\frac{2(2k-1)}{k(k-1)}a_{k-2},$$

$$\text{or } a_{k-2}=-\frac{k(k-1)}{2(2k-1)}a_k \quad . \quad . \quad . \quad . \quad . \quad . \quad . \quad . \quad (8)$$

Similarly:

$$a_{k-4}=-\frac{(k-2)(k-3)}{4(2k-3)}a_{k-2}=\frac{k(k-1)(k-2)(k-3)}{2.4.(2k-1)(2k-3)}a_k \quad . \quad . \quad . \quad (9)$$

$$a_{k-6}=\frac{k(k-1)(k-2)(k-3)(k-4)(k-5)}{2.4.6.(2k-1)(2k-3)(2k-5)}a_k \quad . \quad . \quad . \quad . \quad (10)$$

and so on. If k is even, the power series beginning with μ^k will end with a_0, and if k is odd with $a_1\mu$. Equations (8)–(10) are often called recursion formulae.

The series for Θ_k thus becomes:

$$\Theta_k=a_k[\mu^k+(a_{k-2}/a_k)\mu^{k-2}+(a_{k-4}/a_k)\mu^{k-4}+\ldots],$$

where the coefficients are given by (8), (9), (10), etc., and the single value a_k is arbitrary. If the special value for a_k:

$$a_k=(2k-1)(2k-3)(2k-5)\ldots 1/k! \quad . \quad . \quad . \quad . \quad . \quad . \quad (11)$$

is chosen, the function Θ_k is then called a *Legendre function* of order zero and degree k, or a *surface zonal harmonic*, and is generally denoted by $P_m(\mu)$, k being replaced [1] by m. Thus:

$$P_m(\mu)=\frac{(2m-1)(2m-3)\ldots 1}{m!}\times$$

$$\left[\mu^m-\frac{m(m-1)}{2(2m-1)}\mu^{m-2}+\frac{m(m-1)(m-2)(m-3)}{2.4.(2m-1)(2m-3)}\mu^{m-4}\ldots\right] \quad . \quad (12)$$

[1] This is standard notation; m must not be confused with previous uses.

Values of $P_m(\mu)$ for m from 0 to 5 are given below, and it is seen that the value (11) for a_k was chosen so as to make $P_0(\mu)=1$. (Note that μ means $\cos\theta$.)

$$P_0(\mu)=1 \qquad P_3(\mu)=\tfrac{1}{2}(5\mu^3-3\mu)$$
$$P_1(\mu)=\mu \qquad P_4(\mu)=\tfrac{1}{8}(35\mu^4-30\mu^2+3)$$
$$P_2(\mu)=\tfrac{1}{2}(3\mu^2-1) \qquad P_5(\mu)=\tfrac{1}{8}(63\mu^5-70\mu^3+15\mu).$$

For $\theta=0$, $\mu=1$, for $\theta=\pi$, $\mu=-1$, and for $\theta=\pi/2$, $\mu=0$. The functions can be plotted against θ or $\cos\theta=\mu$; in the first case the extreme values are 0 and π, in the second 1 and -1. From the graphs (Figs. 5.V–6.V) it is seen that, at the

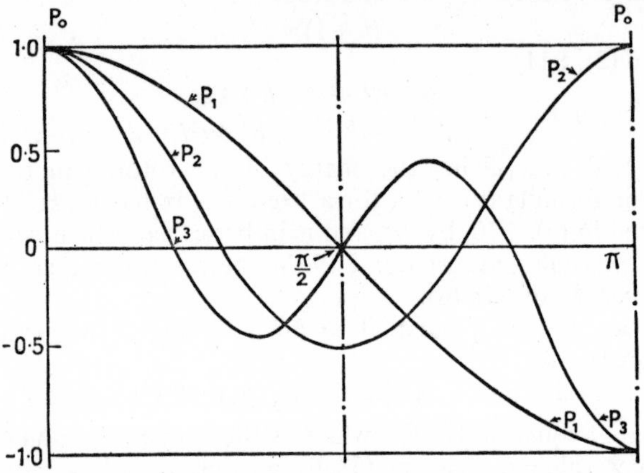

FIG. 5.V. Values of $P_m(\mu)$

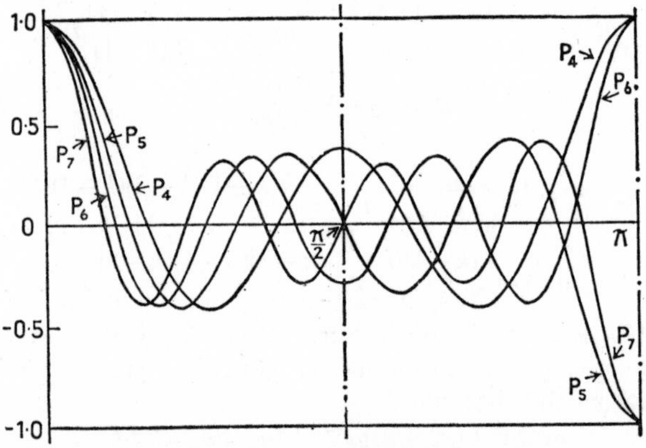

FIG. 6.V. Values of $P_m(\mu)$

extreme values, all the functions have the value 1 or -1, and that each curve crosses the θ or μ axis m times if the degree of the function is m; these are the *nodes* of the function.

The surface zonal harmonics are also given by *Rodrigues' equation*: [1]

$$P_m(\mu)=\frac{1}{2^m m!}\frac{d^m(\mu^2-1)^m}{d\mu^m} \quad . \quad . \quad . \quad . \quad . \quad . \quad . \quad \textbf{(12a)}$$

From this (or otherwise) it can also be shown [1] that the Legendre polynomials form an orthogonal system, and that the normalising factor for $P_m(\mu)$ is $\sqrt{[(2m+1)/2]}$.

[1] For proofs, see Dushman, " Quantum Mechanics," 1938, 153.

A short table of values of $P_m(\mu)$ is given below for values of θ in $\cos\theta=\mu$ from 0° to 90° in steps of 10° from a longer table drawn up by Perry,[1] and the functions ($P_1=P_2=P_3=P_4=1$ for $\theta=0°$) are plotted in Figs. 5.V–6.V.

$$P_0=1,\quad P_1=\mu,\quad P_2=\tfrac{1}{2}(3\mu^2-1),\quad P_3=\tfrac{1}{2}(5\mu^3-3\mu),\quad P_4=\tfrac{1}{8}(35\mu^4-30\mu^2+3).$$

$\theta=$	10°	20°	30°	40°	50°	60°	70°	80°	90°
P_1	0·9848	0·9397	0·8660	0·7660	0·6428	0·5000	0·3420	0·1736	0·0000
P_2	0·9548	0·8245	0·6250	0·3802	0·1198	−0·1250	−0·3245	−0·4548	−0·5000
P_3	0·9106	0·6649	0·3248	−0·0252	−0·3002	−0·4375	−0·4130	−0·2474	0·0000
P_4	0·8532	0·4750	0·0234	−0·3190	−0·4275	−0·2891	0·0038	0·2659	0·3750

Return now to equation (2), and to prevent confusion with m in (12) replace it by n for the order of the function; also put $\lambda^2=m(m+1)$ in place of (5a), since k is replaced by m:

$$\frac{d}{d\mu}\left[(1-\mu^2)\frac{d\Theta}{d\mu}\right]+\left[m(m+1)-\frac{n^2}{1-\mu^2}\right]\Theta=0 \quad . \; . \; . \; (13)$$

Put

$$\Theta=(1-\mu^2)^{n/2}X(\mu) \quad . \; . \; . \; . \; . \; . \; . \; . \; . \; (14)$$

where $X(\mu)$ is a new function of $\mu=\cos\theta$,

$$\therefore\ (1-\mu^2)(d\Theta/d\mu)=-n\mu(1-\mu^2)^{n/2}X+(1-\mu^2)^{n/2+1}(dX/d\mu)$$

$$\therefore\ \frac{d}{d\mu}\left[(1-\mu^2)\frac{d\Theta}{d\mu}\right]=\left[-n(1-\mu^2)^{n/2}+\frac{n^2\mu^2(1-\mu^2)^{n/2}}{(1-\mu^2)}\right]X$$

$$-[n\mu(1-\mu^2)^{n/2}+2\mu(n/2+1)(1-\mu^2)^{n/2}]\frac{dX}{d\mu}+(1-\mu^2)^{n/2+1}\frac{d^2X}{d\mu^2}.$$

Substitute in (13) and divide by $(1-\mu^2)^{n/2}$, which is not zero except at the limits $\mu=\pm1$; then:

$$(1-\mu^2)(d^2X/d\mu^2)-2(n+1)\mu(dX/d\mu)+(m-n)(m+n+1)X=0 \quad . \; (15)$$

Substitute $\lambda^2=m(m+1)$ from (5a) in (3),

$$\therefore\ (1-\mu^2)(d^2\Theta/d\mu^2)-2\mu(d\Theta/d\mu)+m(m+1)\Theta=0.$$

Since Θ and $P_m(\mu)$ differ only by a constant factor, this equation may be written:

$$(1-\mu^2)\frac{d^2P_m(\mu)}{d\mu^2}-2\mu\frac{dP_m(\mu)}{d\mu}+m(m+1)P_m(\mu)=0.$$

Differentiate n times with respect to μ by Leibniz' theorem (§ 37.I):

$$\therefore\ (1-\mu^2)\frac{d^{n+2}P_m(\mu)}{d\mu^{n+2}}-2(n+1)\mu\frac{d^{n+1}P_m(\mu)}{d\mu^{n+1}}$$

$$+[m(m+1)-n(n+1)]\frac{d^nP_m(\mu)}{d\mu^n}=0 \quad . \; (16)$$

which is a differential equation of the second order in $d^nP_m(\mu)/d\mu^n$. Equations (15) and (16) will be identical if $X=d^nP_m(\mu)/d\mu^n$, and hence from (14):

$$\Theta=(1-\mu^2)^{n/2}\,.\,d^nP_m(\mu)/d\mu^n \quad . \; . \; . \; . \; . \; . \; . \; (17)$$

[1] *Phil. Mag.*, 1891, **32**, 512 (to $m=7$); Hill, *Trans. Cambr. Phil. Soc.*, 1883, **13**, 273; Byerly, "Fourier's Series and Spherical Harmonics," Boston, 1893, 277; Rayleigh, *Proc. Roy. Soc.*, 1915, **92**, 433.

The function Θ thus obtained is called an *associated Legendre function* of the first kind of degree m and of order n, and it is denoted in standard notation by $P_m^n(\mu)$:

$$P_m^n(\mu)=(1-\mu^2)^{n/2} \, . \, d^nP_m(\mu)/d\mu^n \quad . \quad . \quad . \quad . \quad . \quad . \quad (18)$$

Since $1-\mu^2=1-\cos^2\theta=\sin^2\theta$, (18) can also be written as:

$$P_m^n(\mu)=\sin^n\theta \, . \, d^nP_m(\mu)/d\mu^n \quad . \quad . \quad . \quad . \quad . \quad . \quad . \quad (19)$$

The differential coefficient vanishes for all values of n greater than m (since the function $P_m(\mu)$ is of the mth degree in μ), and hence n, which is integral, has only the values 0, 1, 2, . . . m; also, for each value of m there are $(m+1)$ Legendre functions satisfying (2). The functions of θ and ϕ:

$$\left.\begin{aligned}\cos(n\phi)P_m^n(\mu)&=\cos(n\phi)\sin^n\theta[d^nP_m(\mu)/d\mu^n]\\ \sin(n\phi)P_m^n(\mu)&=\sin(n\phi)\sin^n\theta[d^nP_m(\mu)/d\mu^n]\end{aligned}\right\} \quad . \quad . \quad . \quad (20)$$

are called *tesseral harmonics* of the mth degree and nth order, and there are $(2m+1)$ tesseral harmonics of the mth degree, viz.:

$$\left.\begin{array}{ll} P_m(\mu); & \\ \cos\phi\sin\theta\dfrac{dP_m(\mu)}{d\mu}; & \sin\phi\sin\theta\dfrac{dP_m(\mu)}{d\mu} \\ \cos 2\phi\sin^2\theta\dfrac{d^2P_m(\mu)}{d\mu^2}; & \sin 2\phi\sin^2\theta\dfrac{d^2P_m(\mu)}{d\mu^2} \\ \cos 3\phi\sin^3\theta\dfrac{d^3P_m(\mu)}{d\mu^3}; & \sin 3\phi\sin^3\theta\dfrac{d^3P_m(\mu)}{d\mu^3} \\ \cdots & \cdots \\ \cos(m\phi)\sin^m\theta\dfrac{d^mP_m(\mu)}{d\mu^m}; & \sin(m\phi)\sin^m\theta\dfrac{d^mP_m(\mu)}{d\mu^m} \end{array}\right\} \quad . \quad . \quad . \quad (21)$$

Since $P_m(\mu)$ is of the mth degree, further differentiation reduces it to zero.

For every given energy state of the rotor, given by (6) with $k=m$ (in the present notation):

$$E_m=m(m+1)\boldsymbol{h}^2/8\pi^2I,$$

there are $(2m+1)$ proper functions, which are tesseral harmonics of degree m, so that the rotor with a free axis has $(2m+1)$-fold degeneracy of random space orientation in a centrally symmetrical field, or no field, but in a non-symmetrical perturbing field the terms split into $(2m+1)$ functions, as explained in § 11.

The function obtained by multiplying the tesseral harmonics by arbitrary constants, and adding, is called a *surface spherical harmonic* of degree m:

$$Y_m(\mu,\phi)=\sum_{n=0}^{n=m}\left[A_n\cos(n\phi)\sin^n\theta\frac{d^nP_m(\mu)}{d\mu^n}+B_n\sin(n\phi)\sin^n\theta\frac{d^nP_m(\mu)}{d\mu^n}\right] \quad . \quad (22)$$

A geometrical interpretation of some of these functions is found as follows. The Legendre coefficient of the first kind of degree m is $P_m(\mu)$, which is a polynomial of degree m and has n distinct zero-points between $\mu=-1$ and $\mu=+1$. These nodes, as the graphs in Figs. 5.V–6.V show, are arranged symmetrically about $\mu=0$ (i.e. $\theta=\pi/2$); and on a sphere with the origin at the centre, the function $P_m(\mu)$, or $P_m(\cos\theta)$, vanishes on m circles of latitude with poles at $\theta=0$ and $\theta=\pi$. The circles are symmetrically spaced above and below the equator, and if m is odd the equatorial circle is a nodal circle. The plots also show that there are $2(m-1)$ circles parallel to the nodal circles on which $P_m(\mu)$ has the same absolute value (Fig. 7A.V). This explains why Legendre coefficients of zero order are called *zonal harmonics*. The diameter through the pole is the *axis* of the zonal harmonic.

If n is not zero but is less than m (see below), the functions:

$$(A \cos n\phi + B \sin n\phi) \sin^n \theta \, . \, d^n P_m (\cos \theta)/d(\cos \theta)^n \quad (\cos \theta = \mu) \quad . \; \textbf{(23)}$$

in (22) may be written (§ 49, I) as:

$$\sqrt{(A^2+B^2)} \sin (n\phi+\delta) \sin^n \theta \, . \, d^n P_m(\cos \theta)/d(\cos \theta)^n \quad . \; . \; \textbf{(24)}$$

where $\tan \delta = A/B$. The sine function vanishes for $n\phi = -\delta$ or $\pi - \delta$, corresponding on the sphere with n great circles of longitude (passing through the

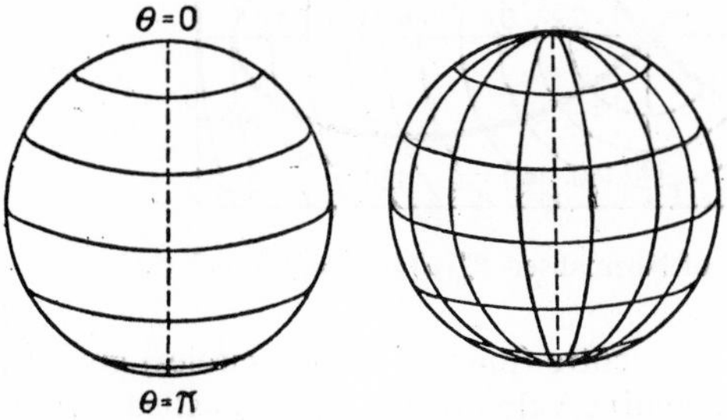

A. Zonal harmonics. B. Tesseral harmonics
FIG. 7.V. Nodal Circles of Spherical Harmonics

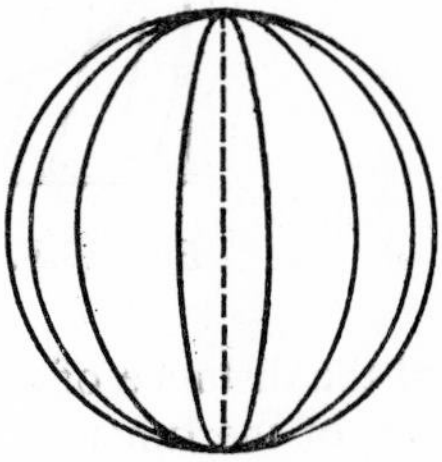

FIG. 8.V. Sectorial Harmonics.

poles), symmetrically distributed, so that the angle between the planes of consecutive circles is π/n. The factor $\sin^n \theta$ vanishes only at $\theta=0$ and $\theta=\pi$. The differential coefficient is the nth derivative of a polynomial of degree m, and thus the highest power of $\mu = \cos \theta$ in it is $(m-n)$; this shows that the function has $(m-n)$ zeros on circles with $\theta=0$ as pole, arranged like the corresponding circles of the zonal harmonics, and cutting them at right angles. The spherical surface is thus divided, as in Fig. 7B.V, by the nodal circles into small four-sided figures, hence the name *tesseral harmonics* (Latin *tessera*, a square block for a tesselated pavement) for these functions. If $n=m$, the differential coefficient becomes a constant, and the spherical harmonic is of the form:

$$\sqrt{(A^2+B^2)} \, . \sin (m\phi+\delta) \sin^m \theta.$$

This vanishes on m great circles passing through the poles $\theta=0$ and $\theta=\pi$, with planes inclined at equal angles π/m and dividing the sphere into $2m$ equal sectors, like sectors of an orange (Fig. 8.V), so that these functions are called *sectorial harmonics*.

The normalising factor [1] for the associated Legendre function $P_m^n(\mu)$ is given by:

$$\frac{1}{N} = \frac{1}{\sqrt{(2\pi)}} \left[\frac{(2n+1)(m-n)!}{2(n+m)!} \right]^{1/2} \quad . \; . \; . \; \textbf{(25)}$$

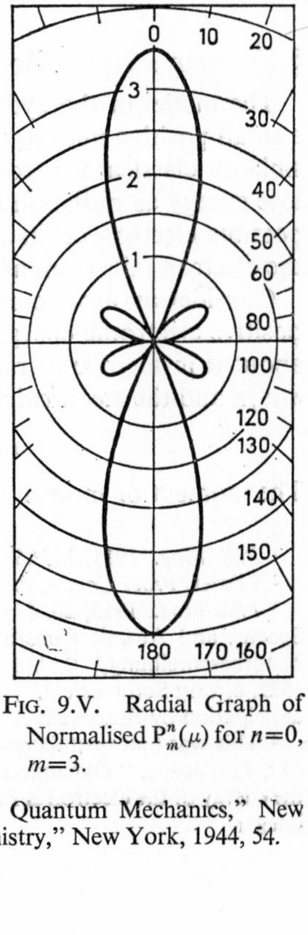

FIG. 9.V. Radial Graph of Normalised $P_m^n(\mu)$ for $n=0$, $m=3$.

[1] For deduction, see Pauling and Wilson, "Introduction to Quantum Mechanics," New York, 1935, 448; Eyring, Walter, and Kimball, "Quantum Chemistry," New York, 1944, 54.

and for $P_3^0(\mu)$ and $P_3^3(\mu)$ it is $[1/\sqrt{(2\pi)}]\sqrt{(7/2)}$, and $[1/\sqrt{(2\pi)}]\sqrt{(7/1440)}$, respectively. (Note that $0!=1$.) The normalised values of the squares of the functions, representing the probabilities of location on the surface of a sphere of unit radius, are $[P_3^0(\cos\theta)]^2/N_0^2$ and $[P_3^3(\cos\theta)]^2/N_3^2$. The values of the functions are $P_3^0(\mu)=\frac{1}{5}(5\mu^3-3\mu)$ and $P_3^3(\mu)=15(1-\mu^2)^{3/2}$, and since $\mu=\cos\theta$ these can easily be calculated for various values of θ. The results, which are then normalised, are plotted in Figs. 9.V–10.V, the angles being marked off on radii,

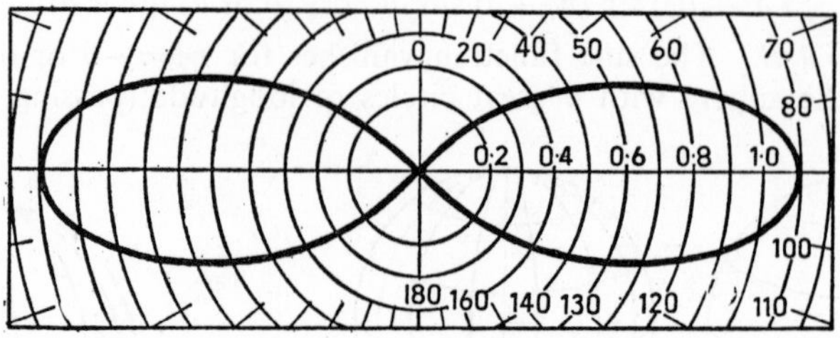

FIG. 10.V. Radial Graph of Normalised $P_m^n(\mu)$ for $n=3$, $m=3$

and the distance of any point from the centre (marked on the circles) gives the value of the function for the corresponding value of θ. This is called a *radial graph*. In the case of a diatomic molecule model, the graphs show that the orientation of the molecular axis is preferred along an axis of symmetry in directions for the maximum of the function. There is a fairly narrow region about the value $\theta=0$ in the first case and $\theta=\pi/2$ in the second case, and this is narrower as $m=n$ increases.

§ 13. Bohr's Atom Model

The model of the hydrogen atom proposed by Rutherford [1] as consisting of a small positive nucleus (proton) with an electron revolving around it, is impossible on classical electromagnetic theory,[2] since the accelerated electron would lose energy as radiation and finally fall into the nucleus. Bohr [3] assumed that possible electron orbits are non-radiating, and radiation is emitted only when the electron falls from an orbit into one nearer the nucleus.

Consider an atom composed of a nucleus of positive charge Ze (e being the positive electronic charge) and an electron of mass m and charge $-e$ revolving about it in a circle of radius a with velocity v. The centripetal force (§ 53.I) mv^2/a and the electrical attraction Ze^2/a^2 are in equilibrium, hence

$$mv^2/a=Ze^2/a^2, \quad \therefore\ mv^2=Ze^2/a \quad \ldots\ldots \quad (1)$$

The moment of momentum of the electron is mva, and it is assumed [4] that this

[1] *Phil. Mag.*, 1911, **21**, 669; previously suggested by Nagaoka, *ibid.*, 1904, **7**, 445.

[2] Eliezer, *Proc. Cambr. Phil. Soc.*, 1943, **39**, 173.

[3] *Phil. Mag.*, 1913, **26**, 476, 857; *Z. Phys.*, 1920, **2**, 422; *J.C.S.*, 1932, 349; "The Theory of Spectra and Atomic Constitution," Cambridge, 1922, 2nd edit., 1924; "Atomtheorie und Naturbeschreibung," Berlin, 1931; Jeans, *J.C.S.*, 1919, **115**, 865; Phillips, *J. Opt. Soc. Amer.*, 1922, **6**, 229; Sommerfeld, "Atomic Structure and Spectrum Lines," 1923, 211; on a supposed anticipation by Boscovich (1758), see Gill, "Roger Boscovich," Dublin, 1941, 22.

[4] This was first postulated by Nicholson, *Month. Not. Roy. Astron. Soc.*, 1912, **72**, 49, 139, 677, 729; Jeans, "Dynamical Theory of Gases," 3rd edit., 1921, 381, 383; Bohr assumed that the energy of the electron is $E=\frac{1}{2}Ze^2/a=\frac{1}{2}nh\tilde{\omega}$, where $\tilde{\omega}$=no. of revolutions per sec. and n is an integer.

is an integral multiple n of $\boldsymbol{h}/2\pi$, where $\boldsymbol{h}$ is Planck's constant:

$$mva=n\boldsymbol{h}/2\pi \quad . \quad . \quad . \quad . \quad . \quad . \quad . \quad . \quad . \quad . \quad (2)$$

$$\therefore \; a^2=n^2\boldsymbol{h}^2/4\pi^2m^2v^2=(n^2\boldsymbol{h}^2/4\pi^2)(1/m^2v^2)$$

$$=(n^2\boldsymbol{h}^2/4\pi^2)(a/Ze^2m), \text{ from (1),}$$

$$\therefore \; a=n^2\boldsymbol{h}^2/4\pi^2e^2Zm \quad . \quad . \quad . \quad . \quad . \quad . \quad . \quad . \quad (3)$$

giving the radii of the possible orbits, with quantum numbers $n=1, 2, 3, \ldots$.

The kinetic energy of the electron is, from (1), $E_k=\frac{1}{2}mv^2=\frac{1}{2}Ze^2/a$, and the potential energy is $E_p=-Ze^2/a$, the potential energy for the electron at an infinite distance from the nucleus being taken as zero ($E_p=0$ as $r\to\infty$); hence $E_p=-2E_k$. The total energy of the electron is:

$$E=E_k+E_p=\tfrac{1}{2}Ze^2/a-Ze^2/a=-Ze^2/2a=-2\pi^2e^4Z^2m/n^2\boldsymbol{h}^2 \quad . \quad (4)$$

from (3).

Bohr assumed, from the quantum theory, that the frequency $\tilde{\nu}$ of radiation emitted when an electron jumps from an orbit in which it has the energy E_1 ($n=n_1$ in (4)) to one in which it has an energy E_2 ($n=n_2$), where $n_1>n_2$, is given by:

$$\boldsymbol{h}\tilde{\nu}=E_1-E_2=(2\pi^2e^4Z^2m/\boldsymbol{h}^2)(1/n_2^2-1/n_1^2) \quad . \quad . \quad . \quad (5)$$

hence if $\nu=\tilde{\nu}/\boldsymbol{c}$ is the wave-number $1/\lambda$ of the emitted radiation:

$$\nu=(2\pi^2e^4m/\boldsymbol{h}^3\boldsymbol{c})Z^2(1/n_2^2-1/n_1^2)=RZ^2(1/n_2^2-1/n_1^2)\ldots \quad . \quad (6)$$

where R is called *Rydberg's number*.[1] For hydrogen ($Z=1$) (5) gives $R=109677{\cdot}76$ cm.$^{-1}$, the value from the hydrogen spectrum being $R=109678{\cdot}18$ cm.$^{-1}$.

Ritz [2] found empirically that the wave numbers of the lines in an atomic spectrum can be represented as the difference of two *terms* R/n^2, where n is integral for hydrogen but not necessarily integral for other atoms; equations (4), (5), and (6) show that the terms represent *energy levels* of the electron in the atom, the (negative) energy in any level being equal to the term multiplied by $\boldsymbol{hc}$. Equation (6) gives (with $Z=1$, $n_2=2$, $n_1=3, 4, 5, \ldots$) the various lines in the Balmer spectrum [3] of hydrogen with great accuracy, and with other values of n_1 and n_2 the lines in the other spectra of atomic hydrogen.

[1] Rydberg, *Compt. Rend.*, 1890, **110**, 394; *Z. phys. Chem.*, 1890, **5**, 227; *K. Svensk. Vetensk. Handl.*, 1890, **23**, No. 11; *Congrès Internat. Phys.*, 1900, **2**, 200; Ostwald's *Klassiker*, 1922 **196**.

[2] *Ann. Phys.*, 1903, **12**, 264; 1908, **25**, 660; *Phys. Z.*, 1905, **9**, 521; Ostwald, *Z. phys. Chem.* 1912, **81**, 121.

[3] The empirical equation for the wave number published by Balmer, *Ann. Phys.*, 1885, **25**, 80, is equivalent to (6). Rydberg, *Z. phys. Chem.*, 1890, **5**, 227, gave the formula $1/\lambda=A-R/(m+\mu)^2$, where A and μ are constants, R is Rydberg's number, and m is an integer. Deslandres, *Compt. Rend.*, 1890, **110**, 748, pointed out that Balmer's formula is a special case of this. See also Rydberg, *Ann. Phys.*, 1896, **58**, 674; Balmer, *ibid.*, 1897, **60**, 380. Information as to the other series will be found in works on spectroscopy: Grotrian, "Graphische Darstellung der Spektren von Atomen und Ionen," 2 vols., Berlin, 1928; Sommerfeld, "Atombau und Spektralinien," Brunswick, 1919, 5th edit., 1931; transl. "Atomic Structure and Spectral Lines," 1923, 3rd edit., 1934, **1**; Fowler, *J.C.S.*, 1928, 764; Swann, *J. Franklin Inst.*, 1928, **205**, 323; Perrin, *Rév. Sci.*, 1928, **66**, 97, 129; Ruark und Urey, "Atoms, Molecules, and Quanta," New York, 1930; Pauling and Goudsmid, "The Structure of Line Spectra," New York, 1930; Gibbs, *Rev. Mod. Phys.*, 1932, **4**, 278; Bacher and Goudsmid, "Atomic Energy States," New York, 1932; White, "Introduction to Atomic Spectra," New York, 1934; Kuhn, "Atmospektren," in *Hand- und Jahrbuch der chem. Phys.*, 1934, **9**, i; Condon and Shortley, "The Theory of Atomic Spectra," Cambridge, 1935; Clark, "The Fine Structure of Matter," 1938, **3** (Quantum Theory of Line Spectra); Shenstone, *Rep. Progr. Phys.*, 1939, **5**, 210.

A static atom, with an attractive force Ze^2/a^2 and a " quantum repulsive force " $(1/ma^3)(nh/2\pi)^2$, proposed by Langmuir,[1] gives equation (5), but has no obvious interpretation.

Actually, the nucleus as well as the electron revolves, and in place of m the reduced mass μ of the electron should be used, given by $1/\mu=1/m_e+1/m_n$, m_e and m_n being the electron and nuclear masses. Since m_e is very small compared with m_n, $\mu\simeq m_e$; the Rydberg number approaches a limiting value[2] $R_e=109737{\cdot}30$ cm.$^{-1}$, the *Rydberg constant*, when $m_n\to\infty$.

§ 14. Sommerfeld's Atom Model

Since the force in both cases is inversely proportional to the square of the distance, the orbit of the electron about the nucleus will be the same as that of a planet round the sun, viz. an ellipse with the nucleus at a focus, and with semi-

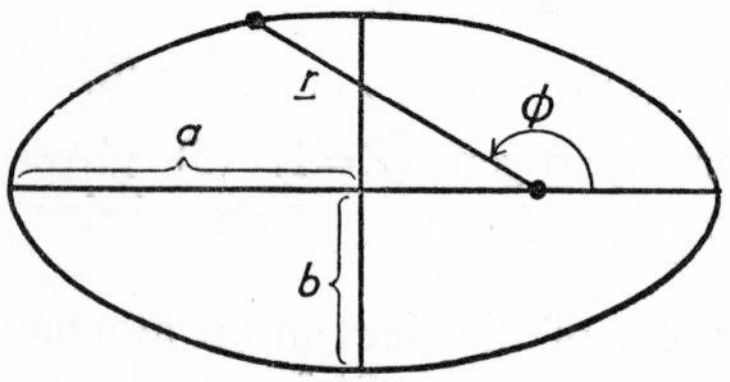

FIG. 11.V. Motion of Electron in an Ellipse

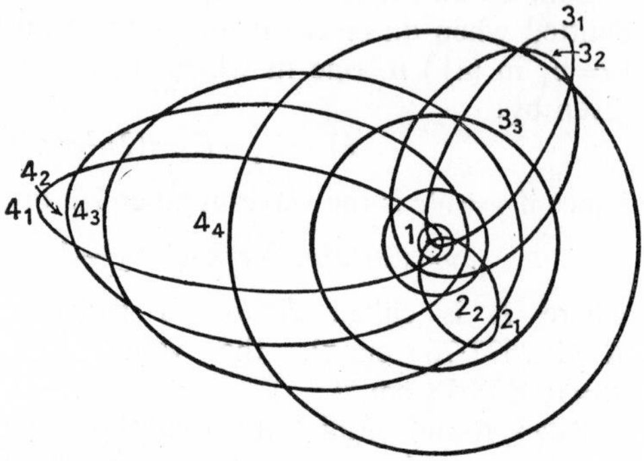

FIG. 12.V. Electron Orbits in Hydrogen Atom

axes a and b ($a>b$). This atom model was investigated by W. Wilson[3] and Sommerfeld.[4]

If r is the radius vector and ϕ the azimuthal angle in the ellipse (Fig. 11.V), the Wilson-Sommerfeld quantisation rule (§19.IV):

$$\oint p\mathrm{d}q=nh$$

gives, since $p_\phi=p=$const. (Kepler's law),

$$\int_0^{2\pi}p_\phi \mathrm{d}\phi=2\pi p=kh$$

where $k=n_\phi$ is the *azimuthal quantum number*. The integral

$$\oint p_r\mathrm{d}r=n_r h$$

is more difficult to find. Since $p_r=m\dot{r}=m(\mathrm{d}r/\mathrm{d}\phi)\dot{\phi}=(p/r^2)(\mathrm{d}r/\mathrm{d}\phi)$

$$\oint p_r\mathrm{d}r=p\int_0^{2\pi}[(\mathrm{d}r/\mathrm{d}\phi)/r]^2\mathrm{d}\phi.$$

[1] *Science*, 1921, **53**, 290; J. J. Thomson, *Phil. Mag.*, 1921, **41**, 510; 1922, **43**, 721; 1922, **44**, 657; Landé, *Z. Phys.*, 1920, **2**, 380.

[2] Du Mond and Cohen, *Rev. Mod. Phys.*, 1948, **20**, 82.

[3] *Phil. Mag.*, 1915, **29**, 795; 1916, **31**, 156.

[4] *Munich Ber.*, 1915, 425, 459; *Ann. Phys.*, 1916, **51**, 1, 125; " Atomic Structure and Spectra Lines," 1923, 233; *Rapport Cons. Phys. Solvay* (1930), 1932, 1; *Naturwiss.*, 1940, **27**, 417; Ishiwara, *Proc. Math. Phys. Soc. Japan*, 1915, **8**, 106; Schwarzschild, *Berlin Ber.*, 1916, 548.

This integral may be found from the orbital equation of the ellipse, and if ϵ is the eccentricity of the ellipse, $1-\epsilon^2=b^2/a^2$,

$$-2\pi p+2(1-\epsilon^2)(a^3/b^3)\pi p=n_r h$$

and the substitution $p(n_\phi h)/2\pi=kh/2\pi$ gives:

$$2(a/b)\pi p=nh, \quad a/b=nh/2\pi p=n/k \quad \ldots\ldots \quad (1)$$

where $n=n_r+n_\phi=n_r+k$ is the total quantum number. When $k=n$ the orbit is a circle. The azimuthal quantum number has the values:

$$k=1, 2, 3, \ldots n.$$

In modern quantum theory, k is replaced by a *serial quantum number* $l=k-1$.

The orbits for the hydrogen atom for $n=1, 2, 3, 4$ are shown in Fig. 12. Since $n_r+k=n$, the energies are still given by Bohr's equation (4), § 13. Sommerfeld showed that, owing to the relativistic change of mass with velocity, the ellipse is not closed but the whole orbit precesses round the nucleus in a circle, and (4), § 13, is then replaced by

$$E=-\frac{2\pi^2 e^4 mZ^2}{n^2h^2}\left[1+\frac{\alpha^2Z^2}{n}\left(\frac{1}{k}-\frac{3}{4n}\right)\right] \quad \ldots\ldots \quad (3)$$

where α is a " fine structure constant "

$$\alpha=2\pi e^2/hc=1/137{\cdot}03 \quad \ldots\ldots \quad (4)$$

which was supposed by Eddington [1] to be 1/137 and to have a special significance in the universe, as well as a function $\frac{1}{2}m^2(m^2+1)$, which with consecutive even numbers gives 10, 136 $(=137-1)$, and even 666 with $m=6$. The interest in this kind of investigation has receded.

§ 15. Electron Spin

Many atomic spectrum lines are actually groups of 2, 3, or more lines very close together (doublets, triplets, etc.). Doublets may be very close, almost unresolvable, but the Tl doublet 5350·5A. and 3775·7A. is very widely separated. Some apparent doublets are really deformed triplets. The association of lines is called a *multiplet*. Compton [2] and Uhlenbeck and Goudsmit [3] assumed that an electron spins about its own axis and there are two directions of spin. The spin momentum is quantised in multiples of $h/2\pi$, and the *spin quantum number* s (sometimes denoted by m_s) has only two values $+\frac{1}{2}$ and $-\frac{1}{2}$. The spin angular momentum contributes to the total angular momentum.

The interaction of spin and orbital momentum may be defined by introducing an *inner quantum number* j, defined by

$$j=l+s \quad \ldots\ldots \quad (1)$$

Since l is integral, and s half-integral, for a single electron j will have half-integral values, multiples of $\frac{1}{2}$. For each value of l there are *two* values of j, $l+\frac{1}{2}$ and $l-\frac{1}{2}$, except when $l=0$, when there is only one value, $+\frac{1}{2}$, since there is no difference between $\pm s$ when $l=0$, there being then no direction of rotation with which to compare s. On the old quantum theory, the angular momentum

1 *Proc. Roy. Soc.*, 1928, **121**, 524; 1929, **122**, 358; 1930, **126**, 696; *Proc. Phys. Soc.*, 1942, **54**, 491; Birge, *Rep. Progr. Phys.*, 1942, **8**, 90.

2 *J. Franklin Inst.*, 1921, **192**, 145.

3 *Naturwiss.*, 1925, **13**, 953; *Nature*, 1926, **117**, 264; the idea of electron spin was at once supported by Bohr, *Nature*, 1926, **117**, 264, but was opposed by Thomas, *ibid.*, 1926, **117**, 514, and Kronig, *ibid.*, 1926, **117**, 550; see Procopiu, *Ann. Sci. Univ. Jassy*, 1913, **7**, 280; Wiśniewski, *Acta Phys. Polon.*, 1937, **6**, 40 (rotation without energy).

vectors are $l(\boldsymbol{h}/2\pi)$, $s(\boldsymbol{h}/2\pi)$, and $j(\boldsymbol{h}/2\pi)$. If the vectors representing l and s are parallel and the rotations in the same sense, l and s add. If s were $-\frac{1}{2}$ its vector would point downwards and be subtracted from l. If $l=0$, the single value of s is $+\frac{1}{2}$ (either sense of rotation). For each value of n there are various possible energy levels corresponding with different values of l. Every l-level, except $l=0$, is split into a fine structure of two levels with slightly different energies.

FIG. 13.V. Angular Momentum Vector

An angular momentum or moment of momentum is a vector quantity and may be represented by a line containing as many units of length as the angular momentum and drawn at right angles to the plane of the orbit in the direction shown in Fig. 13.V, so that the direction is that of the travel of an ordinary cork-screw turned in the direction of the revolution in the orbit.

The new quantum theory (wave mechanics) shows that the *spin angular momentum* is not $s\boldsymbol{h}/2\pi$ but:

$$\sqrt{[s(s+1)]}\,.\,(\boldsymbol{h}/2\pi)=s^*(\boldsymbol{h}/2\pi) \quad . \quad . \quad . \quad . \quad . \quad . \quad (2)$$

where $s^*=\sqrt{[s(s+1)]}$. Similarly, the *orbital angular momentum* is:

$$\sqrt{[l(l+1)]}\,.\,(\boldsymbol{h}/2\pi)=l^*(\boldsymbol{h}/2\pi) \quad . \quad . \quad . \quad . \quad . \quad . \quad (3)$$

where $l^*=\sqrt{[l(l+1)]}$.

The spin and orbital angular momenta combine by vector addition to give a resultant

$$\sqrt{[j(j+1)]}\,.\,(\boldsymbol{h}/2\pi)=j^*(\boldsymbol{h}/2\pi) \quad . \quad . \quad . \quad . \quad . \quad . \quad (4)$$

where $j=l+s$ and $j^*=\sqrt{[j(j+1)]}$.

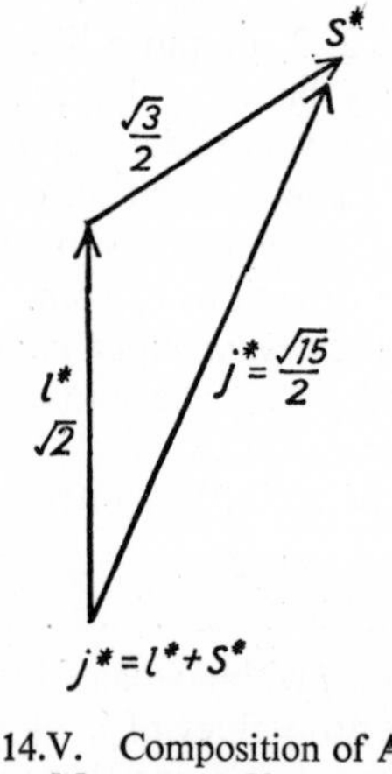

FIG. 14.V. Composition of Angular Momentum Vectors

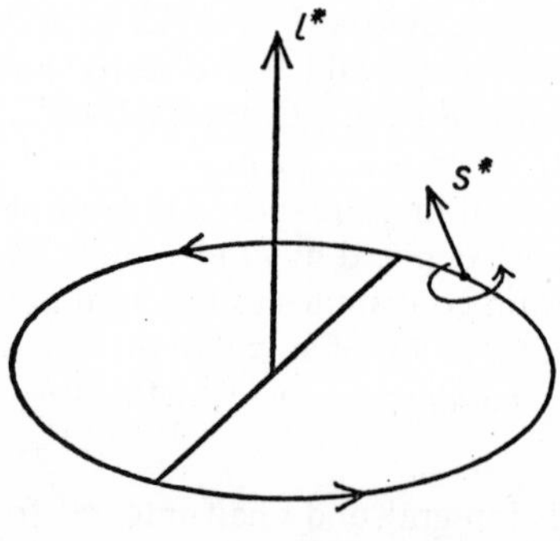

FIG. 15.V. Relation of Orbital and Spin Angular Momentum Vectors

The j-values for the total angular momentum vector on the *old* theory would be, for example, the following multiples of $\boldsymbol{h}/2\pi$:

l	0 (s)	1 (p)	2 (d)	3 (f)
j	1	$\frac{3}{2}$ $\frac{1}{2}$	$\frac{5}{2}$ $\frac{3}{2}$	$\frac{7}{2}$ $\frac{5}{2}$

the l-values being denoted in spectroscopic notation by s, p, d, f, when $l=0$, 1, 2, 3.

On the *new* theory the values will be:

	l	s	j	s^*	l^*	j^*
s	0	$\frac{1}{2}$	$\frac{1}{2}$	$\frac{1}{2}\sqrt{3}$	0	$\frac{1}{2}\sqrt{3}$
p	1	$\begin{cases}+\frac{1}{2}\\-\frac{1}{2}\end{cases}$	$\begin{cases}\frac{3}{2}\\\frac{1}{2}\end{cases}$	$\frac{1}{2}\sqrt{3}$	$\sqrt{2}$	$\begin{cases}\frac{1}{2}\sqrt{15}\\\frac{1}{2}\sqrt{3}\end{cases}$
d	2	$\begin{cases}+\frac{1}{2}\\-\frac{1}{2}\end{cases}$	$\begin{cases}\frac{5}{2}\\\frac{3}{2}\end{cases}$	$\frac{1}{2}\sqrt{3}$	$\sqrt{6}$	$\begin{cases}\frac{1}{2}\sqrt{35}\\\frac{1}{2}\sqrt{15}\end{cases}$

Thus e.g. the vectors $\sqrt{2}(h/2\pi)$ and $\frac{1}{2}\sqrt{3}(h/2\pi)$ must make an angle such that their vector sum has $j^*=\frac{1}{2}\sqrt{15}$ (Fig. 14.V).

Similarly the vectors 0 and $\frac{1}{2}\sqrt{3}(h/2\pi)$ must give a vector resultant with $j^*=\frac{1}{2}\sqrt{3}$. The angles θ can be found graphically or trigonometrically.[1] It will be noticed that the angular momentum vectors are no longer parallel but s^* and l^* make a definite angle θ with one another (Fig. 15.V).

§ 16. Magnetic Quantum Number

To explain the *Zeeman effect*, or the splitting of spectrum lines in a magnetic field,[2] a fourth, *magnetic quantum number*, m, is introduced,[3] which limits the inclination of the electron orbit with respect to the direction of the magnetic field **H**. The orbit precesses round this direction (*Larmor precession*)[4] (Fig. 16.V), and at first it was assumed that there are $2l+1$ possible settings (angles with **H**) for each value of l, giving whole-number projections in the direction of **H**.

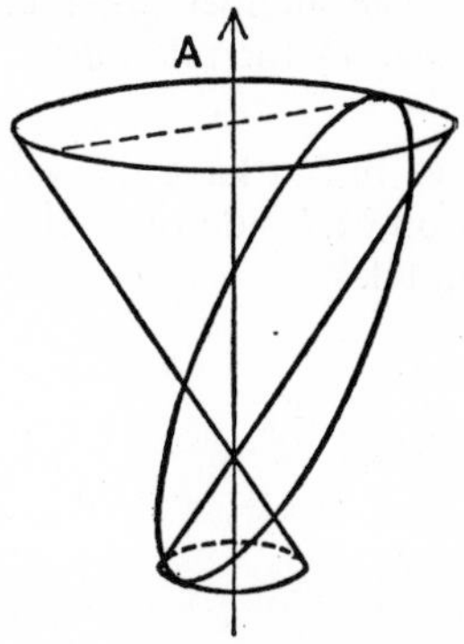

FIG. 16.V. Larmor Precession

In 1896 Zeeman found that spectrum lines are split by a strong magnetic field into polarised components. The source, e.g. a sodium flame, is put in the field, and arrangements made to observe the spectrum (i) across the lines of force, or (ii) (through bored pole-pieces) along them. The effects are:

(i) At *right angles* to the field (Fig. 17.V): the central line π has the same frequency as the line without the field, but is plane polarised in a direction at right angles to the field; two satellite lines, σ_1, σ_2, are plane polarised in the direction of the field. Three lines are seen. The plane of vibration of the electric vector is perpendicular to the plane of polarisation, and hence this direction will be parallel (π) and normal (σ=senkrecht) to the magnetic field, in the two cases.

(ii) *Parallel* to the field (Fig. 18.V; the field now comes forward out of the plane of the paper): the main line disappears and is replaced by two circularly polarised lines symmetrically displaced from the position of the main line. This is the so-called *normal Zeeman effect*, and is shown in strong magnetic fields.

[1] $j(j+1)=l(l+1)+s(s+1)+2\sqrt{[l(l+1)s(s+1)]}\,.\cos\theta$.

[2] Zeeman, *Phil. Mag.*, 1897, **43**, 226; 1897, **44**, 55, 255; *Verslag. K. Akad. Wetens. Amsterdam*, 1897–8, **6**, 13, 99, 260; *Arch. Néerl.*, 1897, **1**, 44, 217; *Z. phys. Chem.*, 1898, **26**, 376; "Researches in Magneto-Optics," 1913; "Magneto-optische Untersuchungen," Leipzig, 1914; Zeeman and de Bruin, *Congr. Internat. Elec.*, 1932, I, No. 29; on the discovery of the Zeeman effect, Onnes, *Physica*, 1921, **1**, 241; for Zeeman effect with H=130,000 gauss, Kapitza and Skinner, *Proc. Roy. Soc.*, 1925, **109**, 224.

[3] Sommerfeld, *Ann. Phys.*, 1916, **51**, 1.

[4] Larmor, *Phil. Mag.*, 1897, **44**, 503

The effect depends on the strength of the field; in weak fields more lines are found (*anomalous Zeeman effect*), and in moderate fields the splitting follows the so-called *Paschen-Back effect*.[1] The details of the explanations of these cases are omitted.[2]

The electron receives energy from the field and each energy level splits into $(2j+1)$ sub-levels. The spectrum lines are also split, but the number of com-

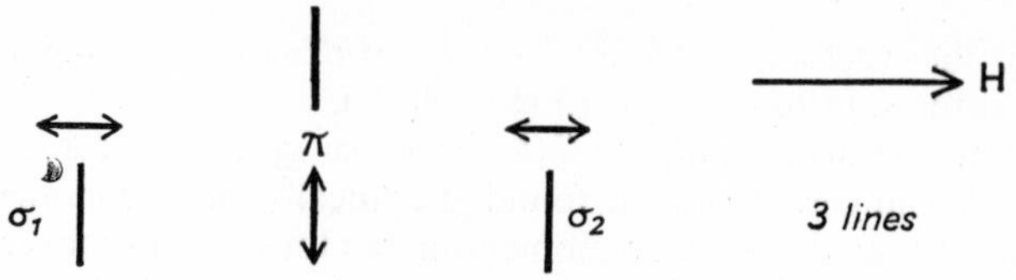

FIG. 17.V. Zeeman Effect. Case (i)

ponents is fewer than would correspond with all possible transitions between levels.

The number $2j+1$ comes about because the magnetic quantum number is given by the relation:

$$-j \leqq m \leqq +j \quad . \quad . \quad . \quad . \quad . \quad . \quad . \quad . \quad . \quad . \quad (1)$$

i.e. m can have the values $-j, -(j-1), -(j-2) \ldots \frac{1}{2} \ldots (j-2), (j-1), j$, i.e. j on *each* side of $\frac{1}{2}$ (the value of j when $l=0$) and the value $\frac{1}{2}$ itself, or $(2j+1)$ in all.

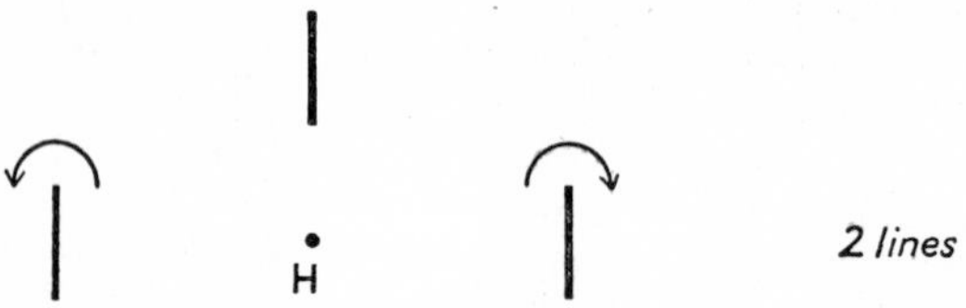

FIG. 18.V. Zeeman Effect. Case (ii)

FIG. 19.V. Stern and Gerlach Experiment

The quantum number m includes the spin quantum number s as well as the serial quantum number l, and s defines the spin moment and l the orbital magnetic moment. A magnetic quantum number:

$$m_l = m - s \quad . \quad . \quad . \quad . \quad . \quad . \quad . \quad . \quad . \quad . \quad (2)$$

will, from (1), have the integral values:

$$m_l = l,\ l-1,\ l-2 \ldots,\ 0,\ -(l-1),\ -l \quad . \quad . \quad . \quad . \quad . \quad . \quad (3)$$

or $(2l+1)$ values in all. E.g. if $l=1$, $m_l=-1, 0, +1$, i.e. 3 values $(2\times 1+1=3)$.

The effect of the magnetic quantum number may be approximately visualised by supposing that in a magnetic field the plane of the electron orbit can be inclined only at certain definite angles with the direction of the field, there being $2j+1$ possible settings in all. The actual details, however, are not very simple;[3] in particular, the angular momentum vector can never point exactly in the direction of the magnetic field.

[1] Paschen and Back, *Ann. Phys.*, 1912, **39**, 897; 1913, **40**, 960; for the whole subject, Back, *Phys. Z.*, 1925, **26**, 833; White, " Introduction to Atomic Spectra," New York, 1934, 215.

[2] See, e.g., Sommerfeld, " Atomic Structure and Spectral Lines," 1923, 294, 384; 3rd edit., 1934, **1**, 321, 474, 489; Landé, in Geiger and Scheel, " Handbuch der Physik," 1929, **21**, 360 f.

[3] See H. E. White, " Introduction to Atomic Spectra," New York, 1934, 215 f.; Herzberg, " Atomic Spectra and Atomic Structure," 1937, 101; Dushman, in H. S. Taylor and Glasstone, " Treatise on Physical Chemistry," 1942, **1**, 273 f.

The discontinuous values of the angle between the electron orbit and the direction of the magnetic field, called *space quantisation*, was experimentally detected by Stern and Gerlach,[1] who found that a beam of silver atoms, when passed through a very inhomogeneous magnetic field (Fig. 19.V) in a vacuum furnace, split into two beams, one on each side of the undeflected beam, and corresponding with two angular positions with respect to the field direction. A similar effect was found with gold and copper, but not with zinc, cadmium or mercury. Since a magnet does not move in a homogeneous magnetic field, it is necessary to have more pull on one pole than the other, i.e. inhomogeneity within atomic dimensions, 10^{-8} cm.

An electron revolving in an orbit of radius a is equivalent to a circular current i or magnetic shell of area A, and by Ampère's theory to a small magnet of moment:

$$\mu = Ai = \pi a^2 i \quad . \quad . \quad . \quad (4)$$

But $i = e \times (1/\text{orbital time}) = ev/2\pi a$, therefore $\mu = \frac{1}{2}eva$. From (2), § 13, $v = \boldsymbol{h}/2\pi ma$, for $n=1$ (smallest orbit),

$$\therefore \ \mu_{B_0} = e\boldsymbol{h}/4\pi m \quad . \quad . \quad . \quad (5)$$

which is called a *Bohr magneton.*[2] In e.m. units it is $9{\cdot}27 \times 10^{-21}$ gauss cm.^{3}, or per mol ($N\mu_{B_0}$) 5582 gauss cm.^{3}. Since mva = orbital angular momentum = p_0

$$\therefore \ \mu_{B_0} = \tfrac{1}{2}(e/m)(\boldsymbol{h}/2\pi) = \tfrac{1}{2}(e/m)p_0 \quad . \quad . \quad . \quad (6)$$

(The Bohr magneton is deduced for the case where the electron has no spin about its own axis.) The *Weiss magneton* [3], 1/4·95 of the Bohr magneton, is not now regarded as having any physical significance.

§ 17. The Hydrogen-like Atom

The theory given in §§ 13–16 is mostly based on the old quantum theory, in which the electron is regarded as a point-charge having a definite velocity (or momentum) and located in a definite plane orbit. Heisenberg's uncertainty principle (§ 14.IV) shows that this picture is unacceptable. The present section deals with the wave-mechanical treatment [4] of a hydrogen-like atom, consisting of a single electron of mass m_1 and charge $-\boldsymbol{e}$ revolving with velocity v about a heavy nucleus of mass m_2 and charge Ze, where Z is the atomic number.[5] The centripetal force of a mass m revolving about a central point is (§ 53.I) mv^2/r, where r is the radius of the electron orbit, assumed circular about the centre of mass. This is balanced by the electrical attraction $-Ze^2/r^2$. The kinetic energy is (§ 13) $T = \frac{1}{2}mv^2 = \frac{1}{2}(Ze^2/r)$. The potential energy is $V = \int_0^\infty (Ze^2/r^2)\mathrm{d}r = -Ze^2/r$, where the value at an infinite distance is arbitrarily taken as zero.

[1] Gerlach and Stern, *Z. Phys.*, 1922, **9**, 349, 353; Stern and Gerlach, *Ann. Phys.*, 1924, **74**, 673; 1925, **76**, 163; Gerlach, *Phys. Z.*, 1923, **24**, 275; Stern, *Z. Phys.*, 1920, **3**, 417; 1921, **7**, 249 (theory); 1926, **39**, 751; Knauer and Stern, *ibid.*, 1926, **39**, 764, 780; Stern, *ibid.*, 1927, **41**, 563; Leu, *ibid.*, 1927, **41**, 551; Dushman, *Chem. Rev.*, 1928, **5**, 164; Specchia, *Nuov. Cim.*, 1935, **12**, 541.

[2] See also Chalmers, *Nature*, 1914, **92**, 687; Vegard, *Phil. Mag.*, 1915, **29**, 651; *Ann. Phys.*, 1917, **53**, 27; Wereide, *ibid.*, 1916, **49**, 976; 1917, **52**, 276, 283, 289; 1917, **53**, 574; 1918, **55**, 589; Cabrera, *An. Fis. Quim.*, 1923, **21**, 505; *Rapp. Cons. Solvay Phys.* (1930), 1932, 81; Pauli, *ibid.*, 175.

[3] Weiss, *J. de Phys.*, 1911, **1**, 900, 965.

[4] Pauling and Wilson, "Introduction to Quantum Mechanics," New York, 1935, 112 Dushman, "The Elements of Quantum Mechanics," New York, 1938, 178; for a different treatment, see Frenkel, "Wave Mechanics. Elementary Theory," Oxford, 1932, 84.

[5] This is the standard symbol, not to be confused with that for the state sum.

(Hence $E=\frac{1}{2}Ze^2/r)-Ze^2/r=-\frac{1}{2}(Ze^2/r)$. The wave equation, (6), § 2, is thus:

$$\partial^2\psi/\partial x^2+\partial^2\psi/\partial y^2+\partial^2\psi/dz^2+(8\pi^2\mu/h^2)(E+Ze^2/r)\psi=0 \quad . \quad (1)$$

where μ is the reduced mass (§ 10), $m_1m_2/(m_1+m_2)$. If r, θ, ϕ, are the polar coordinates of the electron relative to the nucleus and the translational energy of the atom as a whole is left out of account,[1] the wave equation in polar co-ordinates (§ 28.I) is:

$$\frac{1}{r^2}\frac{\partial}{\partial r}\left(r^2\frac{\partial\psi}{\partial r}\right)+\frac{1}{r^2\sin\theta}\frac{\partial}{\partial\theta}\left(\sin\theta\frac{\partial\psi}{\partial\theta}\right)+\frac{1}{r^2\sin^2\theta}\frac{\partial^2\psi}{\partial\phi^2}+\frac{8\pi^2\mu}{h^2}\left(E+\frac{Ze^2}{r}\right)\psi=0 \quad . \quad (2)$$

Assume that the function ψ is separable into three factors:

$$\psi(r,\theta,\phi)=R(r)\,\Theta(\theta)\Phi(\phi) \quad . \; . \; . \; . \; . \; . \; . \; . \quad (2a)$$

$$\therefore\ (\partial\psi/\partial r)=(dR/dr)\Theta\Phi,\quad \partial\psi/\partial\theta=(d\Theta/d\theta)R\Phi,\quad \partial^2\psi/\partial\phi^2=(d^2\Phi/d\phi^2)R\Theta.$$

Substitute in (2) and divide by $R\Theta\Phi$:

$$\therefore\ \frac{1}{Rr^2}\frac{d}{dr}\left(r^2\frac{dR}{dr}\right)+\frac{1}{\Theta r^2\sin\theta}\frac{d}{d\theta}\left(\sin\theta\frac{d\Theta}{d\theta}\right)+\frac{1}{\Phi r^2\sin^2\theta}\frac{d^2\Phi}{d\phi^2}+\frac{8\pi^2\mu}{h^2}\left(E+\frac{Ze^2}{r}\right)=0.$$

Multiply by $r^2\sin^2\theta$:

$$\therefore\ \frac{\sin^2\theta}{R}\frac{d}{dr}\left(r^2\frac{dR}{dr}\right)+\frac{\sin\theta}{\Theta}\frac{d}{d\theta}\left(\sin\theta\frac{d\Theta}{d\theta}\right)+\frac{1}{\Phi}\frac{d^2\Phi}{d\phi^2}+\frac{8\pi^2\mu r^2\sin^2\theta}{h^2}\left(E+\frac{Ze^2}{r}\right)=0$$

If the third term is retained on the left and the others taken over to the right, it is seen that $(1/\Phi)(d^2\Phi/d\phi^2)$, which depends only on ϕ, is equal to terms independent of ϕ, hence both sides of the resulting equation must be equal to the same constant, say to $-m^2$; hence:

$$d^2\Phi/d\phi^2=-m^2\Phi \quad . \; . \; . \; . \; . \; . \; . \; . \; . \quad (3)$$

and after dividing by $\sin^2\theta$:

$$\frac{1}{R}\frac{d}{dr}\left(r^2\frac{dR}{dr}\right)-\frac{m^2}{\sin^2\theta}+\frac{1}{\Theta\sin\theta}\frac{d}{d\theta}\left(\sin\theta\frac{d\Theta}{d\theta}\right)+\frac{8\pi^2\mu r^2}{h^2}\left(E+\frac{Ze^2}{r}\right)=0 \quad . \quad (4)$$

The second and third terms are independent of r, and the first and fourth are independent of θ; hence:

$$\frac{1}{R}\frac{d}{dr}\left(r^2\frac{dR}{dr}\right)+\frac{8\pi^2\mu r^2}{h^2}\left(E+\frac{Ze^2}{r}\right)=\text{const.}=\beta \quad . \; . \; . \quad (5)$$

$$-\frac{m^2}{\sin^2\theta}+\frac{1}{\Theta\sin\theta}\frac{d}{d\theta}\left(\sin\theta\frac{d\Theta}{d\theta}\right)=-\beta \quad . \; . \; . \; . \quad (6)$$

Multiply (5) by R/r^2 and (6) by Θ:

$$\therefore\ \frac{1}{r^2}\frac{d}{dr}\left(r^2\frac{dR}{dr}\right)-\frac{\beta}{r^2}R+\frac{8\pi^2\mu R}{h^2}\left(E+\frac{Ze^2}{r}\right)=0 \quad . \; . \; . \quad (7)$$

and

$$\frac{1}{\sin\theta}\frac{d}{d\theta}\left(\sin\theta\frac{d\Theta}{d\theta}\right)-\frac{m^2\Theta}{\sin^2\theta}+\beta\Theta=0 \quad . \; . \; . \; . \; . \quad (8)$$

Equation (2) is now separated into three ordinary differential equations, (3), (8), and (7), which will be solved in this order. The first two are angular equations, giving spherical harmonics; the third is a radial equation, giving Laguerre functions.

Equation (3) has been shown in (7), § 11, to have the solution

$$\Phi=[1/\sqrt{(2\pi)}]e^{im\phi} \quad . \; . \; . \; . \; . \; . \; . \; . \; . \quad (9)$$

[1] For this, see Pauling and Wilson, reference 4, p. 405.

where m, in order that Φ shall be single valued, must be an integer: $m=0, \pm1, \pm2, \pm3, \ldots$, positive and negative values corresponding with distinct solutions, $1/\sqrt{(2\pi)}$ being the normalising factor. As explained in § 11, the real sine and cosine functions can be used, giving:

$$\left.\begin{array}{c}\Phi_0=1/\sqrt{(2\pi)}, \text{ and} \\ \Phi_{|m|}=[1/\sqrt{(2\pi)}]\cos(|m|\phi) \text{ or } \Phi_{|m|}=[1/\sqrt{(2\pi)}]\sin(|m|\phi)\end{array}\right\} . \quad \textbf{(10)}$$

where $|m|$ is the absolute value of m. There are $(2m+1)$ functions corresponding with the $(2m+1)$ values of m. The integer m, having positive and negative values, is the *magnetic quantum number*, as can be shown by using the symbolic form, § 4, of the wave equation:

$$p_\phi\psi=-(i\boldsymbol{h}/2\pi)(\partial\psi/\partial\phi),$$

where p_ϕ is the angular momentum due to change of ϕ. Since:

$$\psi=\mathrm{R}\Theta\Phi=\text{const. }\mathrm{R}\Theta e^{\pm im\phi},$$

$$\partial\psi/\partial\phi=\pm im\psi,$$

$$-(i\boldsymbol{h}/2\pi)(\partial\psi/\partial\phi)=(-i\boldsymbol{h}/2\pi)(\pm im\psi),$$

$$\therefore\ p_\phi\psi=\pm(\boldsymbol{h}/2\pi)m\psi, \quad \therefore\ p_\phi=\pm m\boldsymbol{h}/2\pi.$$

Since $\boldsymbol{h}/2\pi$ is the unit of angular momentum according to the Nicholson-Bohr theory,[1] m corresponds with the magnetic quantum number (often, as in § 16, written m_l) defining the orientation of the plane of the electron orbit to the direction of a magnetic field.[2]

Equation (8) is solved by putting $\cos\theta=\mu$, and $\sin^2\theta=1-\mu^2$, when $d\Theta/d\theta=(d\Theta/d\mu)(d\mu/d\theta)=-(d\Theta/d\mu)\sin\theta$,

$$\therefore\ \frac{d}{d\mu}\left[(1-\mu^2)\frac{d\Theta}{d\mu}\right]+\left(\beta-\frac{m^2}{1-\mu^2}\right)\Theta=0 \quad . \quad . \quad . \quad . \quad . \quad \textbf{(11)}$$

This is the same as equation (2), § 12, in which λ^2 replaces β, and it is there shown that $\lambda^2=\beta$ must have the value $k(k+1)$, where $k=0, 1, 2, \ldots$,

$$\therefore\ \frac{d}{d\mu}\left[(1-\mu^2)\frac{d\Theta}{d\mu}\right]+\left[k(k+1)-\frac{m^2}{1-\mu^2}\right]\Theta=0.$$

This is the same as (13), § 12, with k in place of m, and m in place of n. Put $k=|m|+l$, where l is a *serial quantum number*, having the values $l=k-|m|=|m|, |m|+1, |m|+2, \ldots$. The function Θ was shown in § 12 to be an associated Legendre function of degree l and order m, given [3] by (18), § 12:

$$\mathrm{P}_l^m(\mu)=(1-\mu^2)^{m/2}\,.\,d^m\mathrm{P}_l(\mu)/d\mu^m.$$

Since the highest term in $\mathrm{P}_l(\mu)$ is μ^l, and this is differentiated m times with respect to μ, it will vanish if $m>l$, so that m cannot exceed l, and consequently m can have the values:

$$m=l, (l-1), (l-2), \ldots, 0, \ldots, -(l-1), -l.$$

The normalised value of Θ can be shown [4] to be:

$$\Theta=\sqrt{\left[\frac{(2l+1)}{2}\frac{(l-|m|)!}{(l+|m|)!}\right]}\mathrm{P}_l^m(\mu) \quad . \quad . \quad . \quad . \quad . \quad \textbf{(11a)}$$

and hence can be found from a table of values of $\mathrm{P}_l^m(\mu)$.

[1] See § 13.

[2] See § 16. The " orbit " picture is not entertained in wave mechanics, where it is replaced by the wave function or " orbital."

[3] Note the change of n to m and of m to l. The symbol μ is used in treatises on spherical harmonics for $\cos\theta$, and need cause no confusion with μ, the reduced mass, used in the equations. If m were used for the latter, there would be confusion with the quantum number m. Pauling and Wilson use $z=\cos\theta$, which could be confused with a coordinate.

[4] Condon and Morse, " Quantum Mechanics," New York, 1929, 55; Pauling and Wilson, " Quantum Mechanics," New York, 1935, 129, 448.

The solution of (7), called the *radial equation*, is also found by the polynomial method. With[1] $\beta=k(k+1)=l(l+1)$, it becomes:

$$\frac{1}{r^2}\frac{d}{dr}\left(r^2\frac{dR}{dr}\right)+\left[\frac{-l(l+1)}{r^2}+\frac{8\pi^2\mu}{h^2}\left(E+\frac{Ze^2}{r}\right)\right]R=0 \quad . \quad . \quad . \quad (12)$$

For quantised orbits E is negative, $-Ze^2/2r$. Put:

$$\alpha^2=-8\pi^2\mu E/h^2, \quad \lambda=4\pi^2\mu Ze^2/h^2\alpha, \quad \rho=2\alpha r \quad . \quad . \quad . \quad (12a)$$

where ρ can vary from 0 to ∞. Then $r=\rho/2\alpha$, $dr=d\rho/2\alpha$, $dR/dr=(1/2\alpha)dR/d\rho$,

$$\therefore \frac{1}{r^2}\frac{d}{dr}\left(r^2\frac{dR}{dr}\right)=\frac{4\alpha^2}{\rho^2}\frac{d}{d\rho}\left(\rho^2\frac{dR}{d\rho}\right),$$

$$-l(l+1)/r^2=-4\alpha^2 l(l+1)/\rho^2$$

$$8\pi^2\mu E/h^2=-\alpha^2$$

$$8\pi^2\mu Ze^2/h^2r=4\alpha^2\lambda/\rho,$$

and by inserting these in (12) and dividing by $4\alpha^2$ it becomes:

$$\left.\begin{aligned} &\frac{1}{\rho^2}\frac{d}{d\rho}\left(\rho^2\frac{dR}{d\rho}\right)+\left[-\frac{1}{4}-\frac{l(l+1)}{\rho^2}+\frac{\lambda}{\rho}\right]R=0,\\ \text{or}\quad &\frac{d^2R}{d\rho^2}+\frac{2}{\rho}\frac{dR}{d\rho}+\left[-\frac{1}{4}-\frac{l(l+1)}{\rho^2}+\frac{\lambda}{\rho}\right]R=0.\end{aligned}\right\} \quad . \quad . \quad . \quad . \quad (13)$$

Since R is a wave function, it must be finite and continuous for all values of ρ and vanish at $\rho\to\infty$ (§ 2). The point $\rho=0$ is a singular point (§ 36.I), as $1/\rho\to\infty$ there. To investigate the behaviour of the function at this point, assume:

$$R=\rho^s F(\rho) \quad . \quad . \quad . \quad . \quad . \quad . \quad . \quad . \quad . \quad . \quad (14)$$

where s is a constant and F may be expressed as a polynomial of the form $F=\Sigma F_n\rho^n$; therefore $R=F_0\rho^s+F_1\rho^{s+1}+\ldots+F_n\rho^{s+n}$,

$$dR/d\rho=sF_0\rho^{s-1}+(s+1)F_1\rho^s+\ldots,$$

and

$$d^2R/d\rho^2=s(s-1)F_0\rho^{s-2}+(s+1)sF_1\rho^{s-1}+\ldots.$$

Substitute in (13):

$$\therefore s(s-1)F_0\rho^{s-2}+(s+1)sF_1\rho^{s-1}+\ldots+2sF_0\rho^{s-2}+2(s+1)F_1\rho^{s-1}+\ldots$$
$$-\tfrac{1}{4}F_0\rho^s-\ldots-l(l+1)F_0\rho^{s-2}-\ldots+\lambda F_0\rho^{s-1}+\ldots=0.$$

The coefficient of $F_0\rho^{s-2}$ is $s(s-1)+2s-l(l+1)=s(s+1)-l(l+1)$. On approaching $\rho=0$, all terms involving powers higher than ρ^{s-2} may be neglected, and if R is to be finite at $\rho=0$, $\rho^{s-2}=1$, i.e. the series must not have any lower powers of ρ than those given by the equation $s(s+1)=l(l+1)$. Of the two solutions of this, $s=l$ and $s=-(l+1)$, only the first is acceptable, since ρ^{-l-1} would become infinite at $\rho=0$. Hence $s=l$, and:

$$R=\rho^l F(\rho) \quad . \quad . \quad . \quad . \quad . \quad . \quad . \quad . \quad . \quad . \quad (15)$$

$$dR/d\rho=l\rho^{l-1}F+\rho^l(dF/d\rho)$$

$$(d^2R/d\rho^2)=l(l-1)\rho^{l-2}F+2l\rho^{l-1}(dF/d\rho)+\rho^l(d^2F/d\rho^2).$$

Substitute in (13) and divide by ρ^l,

$$\therefore \frac{d^2F}{d\rho^2}+\frac{2(l+1)}{\rho}\frac{dF}{d\rho}+\left(\frac{\lambda}{\rho}-\frac{1}{4}\right)F=0 \quad . \quad . \quad . \quad . \quad . \quad (16)$$

[1] Since l, like k, has the values 0, 1, 2, 3, ...

For very large values of ρ, all terms involving $1/\rho$ can be neglected, and the "asymptotic" form of the equation (§ 7) is $d^2F/d\rho^2-F/4=0$, the solution of which (§ 63.I) is:

$$F=C_1e^{-\rho/2}+C_2e^{\rho/2},$$

and in order that F shall not increase indefinitely with ρ (which is positive), the second term must be zero:

$$\therefore\ F=C_1e^{-\rho/2}.$$

The constant C_1 is now (cf. § 7) replaced by a function:

$$L(\rho)=\Sigma a_k\rho^k \quad . \quad . \quad . \quad . \quad . \quad . \quad . \quad . \quad . \quad (17)$$

($a_0\neq 0$) which must be such that F vanishes at $\rho\to\infty$,

$$\therefore\ F=e^{-\rho/2}L \quad . \quad . \quad . \quad . \quad . \quad . \quad . \quad . \quad . \quad (18)$$

$$\therefore\ dF/d\rho=e^{-\rho/2}(dL/d\rho)-\tfrac{1}{2}e^{-\rho/2}L$$

and

$$d^2F/d\rho^2=\tfrac{1}{4}e^{-\rho/2}L-e^{-\rho/2}(dL/d\rho)+e^{-\rho/2}(d^2L/d\rho^2).$$

Substitute in (16) and divide by $e^{-\rho/2}/\rho$,

$$\therefore\ \rho(d^2L/d\rho^2)+[2(l+1)-\rho](dL/d\rho)+(\lambda-l-1)L=0 \quad . \quad . \quad (19)$$

Substitute the series (17) for L and equate coefficients of powers of ρ separately to zero:

$$L=a_0+a_1\rho+a_2\rho^2+\ldots+a_k\rho^k,$$

$$dL/d\rho=\quad a_1+2a_2\rho+\ldots+ka_k\rho^{k-1},$$

$$d^2L/d\rho^2=\quad 2a_2+\ldots\quad +k(k-1)a_k\rho^{k-2},$$

$$\rho(d^2L/d\rho^2)=\quad 2a_2\rho+\ldots\quad +k(k-1)a_k\rho^{k-1},$$

$$[2(l+1)-\rho](dL/d\rho)=2(l+1)a_1+[4(l+1)a_2-a_1]\rho+\ldots+2k(l+1)a_k\rho^{k-1}$$
$$-a_1\rho-2a_2\rho^2-\ldots-ka_k\rho^k$$

$$(\lambda-l-1)L=(\lambda-l-1)(a_0+a_1\rho+a_2\rho^2+\ldots+a_k\rho^k)$$

$$0=(\lambda-l-1)a_0+2(l+1)a_1 \quad \text{for } \rho^0,$$

$$0=(\lambda-l-1-1)a_1+[2\times 2(l+1)+1\times 2]a_2 \quad \text{for } \rho;$$

so that, by inspection, the expression for the coefficient of ρ^k is found to be:

$$(\lambda-l-1-k)a_k+[2(k+1)(l+1)+k(k+1)]a_{k+1}=0.$$

As in previous cases (§§ 7 and 12), the series for F in (18) will not approach zero as $\rho\to\infty$ unless L is a polynomial with a finite number of terms, ending with $k=n_r$, say, hence $\lambda-l-1-n_r=0$, or

$$\lambda=l+1+n_r=n \quad . \quad . \quad . \quad . \quad . \quad . \quad . \quad . \quad . \quad (20)$$

Hence, from (12a): $\lambda^2=n^2=-2\pi^2\mu Z^2e^4/h^2E$, or

$$E=-2\pi^2\mu Z^2e^4/n^2h^2 \quad . \quad . \quad . \quad . \quad . \quad . \quad . \quad . \quad (21)$$

which is the same expression as found by Bohr, (4), § 13, with special assumptions, and n is the *principal* (or *total*) *quantum number*. It is important to notice, however, that a plane orbit is no longer assumed (as it was by Bohr), since the function R has spherical symmetry, i.e. R has the same value, for a given value of r, whatever the values of θ and ϕ, of which it is independent. n_r in (20) is Sommerfeld's (§ 14) *radial quantum number*. The energy levels do not depend on the individual quantum numbers n_r, l, and m, but only on the principal quantum number $n=n_r+l+1$. Since both n_r and l can have only the integral values 0, 1, 2, . . ., it is seen that n can have only the integral values 1, 2, 3, . . ., as was also assumed by Bohr. Including the values of m, the magnetic quantum number, found in (9), the quantum numbers of the electron, apart from the spin quantum number $s=\pm\frac{1}{2}$, which is not considered above, are given by:

$$m=0,\ \pm1,\ \pm2,\ldots,$$
$$l=|m|,\ |m|+1,\ |m|+2,\ldots,$$
$$\text{and } n=l+1\quad l+2,\ l+3,\ \ldots;$$

or, in the usual form: [1]

$$n=1,\ 2,\ 3,\ \ldots;$$
$$l=0,\ 1,\ 2,\ \ldots,\ (n-1);$$
$$m_l=-l,\ -(l-1),\ \ldots,\ -1,\ 0,\ 1,\ \ldots,\ (l-1),\ l,$$

(this value of m being denoted by m_l). There are $(2l+1)$ independent wave functions with given values of n and l, and n^2 wave functions with a given value of n.

§ 18 Laguerre Functions

Now consider the wave function $L(\rho)$ in (17), § 17. Equation (16), § 17, can be written, since $\lambda=n$, from (20), § 17:

$$\rho(d^2F/d\rho^2)+2(l+1)(dF/d\rho)+(n-\rho/4)F=0 \quad . \quad . \quad . \quad . \quad (1)$$

Let $2l+1=p$, and $n+l=k$, then if n is expressed by the identity:

$$n\equiv\tfrac{1}{2}(2n+2l-2l-1+1),$$

it is seen that $n=\frac{1}{2}(2k-p+1)$. Also, $n_r=n-l-1\equiv(n+l)-(2l+1)=k-p$, and (19), § 17, becomes, from (20), § 17:

$$\rho(d^2L/d\rho^2)+(p+1-\rho)(dL/d\rho)+(k-p)L=0 \quad . \quad . \quad . \quad . \quad (2)$$

This differential equation is satisfied by a function called the *associated Laguerre polynomial* [2] of degree $(k-p)$ and order p $(p\leqq k)$, which is denoted by $L_k^p(\rho)$. The *Laguerre polynomial* of zero order is a function of an independent variable x defined by:

$$L_k^0(x)=(-1)^k\left[x^k-\frac{k^2}{1!}x^{k-1}+\frac{k^2(k-1)^2}{2!}x^{k-2}+\ldots+(-1)^k k!\right] \quad . \quad (3)$$

which is the same as:

$$L_k^0(x)=e^x(d^k/dx^k)x^ke^{-x} \quad . \quad . \quad . \quad . \quad . \quad . \quad . \quad . \quad (4)$$

The first five polynomials are found, by putting $k=0, 1, 2, 3, 4$, to be:

$$L_0^0(x)=1 \qquad L_3^0(x)=-x^3+9x^2-18x+6$$
$$L_1^0(x)=-x+1 \qquad L_4^0(x)=x^4-16x^3+72x^2-96x+24.$$
$$L_2^0(x)=x^2-4x+2$$

These polynomials satisfy the differential equation: [2]

$$x(d^2L_k^0/dx^2)+(1-x)(dL_k^0/dx)+kL_k^0=0 \quad . \quad . \quad . \quad . \quad (5)$$

as is seen by substitution of the five special cases given above. By differentiating (5) p times by Leibniz' theorem (§ 37.I), and putting $x=\rho$, equation (2) is found, which is therefore satisfied by the associated Laguerre polynomial:

$$L_k^p(x)=(d^p/dx^p)L_k(x) \quad . \quad . \quad . \quad . \quad . \quad . \quad . \quad . \quad (6)$$

[1] Darwin, *Proc. Roy. Soc.*, 1927, **115**, 1.
[2] Margenau and Murphy, "The Mathematics of Physics and Chemistry," New York, 1943, 77, 122; Wheeler, *Proc. Roy. Irish Acad.*, 1944, **50A**, 7.

For $k=(n+l)$, and $p=(2l+1)$, the associated Laguerre polynomial of degree $(k-p)=(n-l-1)$, and order $p=(2l+1)$, is given by the series:

$$L_{n+l}^{2l+1}(x)=[(n+l)!]^2\left[-\frac{1}{(n-l-1)!(2l+1)!}+\frac{x}{(n-l-2)!(2l+2)!1!}\right.$$
$$\left.-\frac{x^2}{(n-l-3)!(2l+3)!2!}+\ldots+(-1)^{n-l}\frac{x^{n-l-1}}{(n+l)!(n-l-1)!}\right] \quad . \quad (7)$$

The first five polynomials for $2l+1=p=0$ are given above; six more for $p=1$, 2, 3, and $n+l=1$, 2, 3, are:

$L_1^1(x)=1$	$L_3^1(x)=-3x^2+18x-18$
$L_2^1(x)=2x-4$	$L_3^2(x)=-6x+18$
$L_2^2(x)=2$	$L_3^3(x)=-6.$

The solution of (16), § 17, is:

$$F_{nl}=e^{-\rho/2}L_{n+l}^{2l+1}(\rho) \quad . \quad . \quad . \quad . \quad . \quad . \quad . \quad . \quad . \quad (8)$$

and from (15), § 17, the radial function is:

$$R_{nl}=\rho^l F_{nl}=e^{-\rho/2}\rho^l L_{n+l}^{2l+1}(\rho) \quad . \quad . \quad . \quad . \quad . \quad . \quad . \quad . \quad (9)$$

It is convenient to measure r as a fraction of a_0, the radius of the smallest Bohr orbit in the hydrogen atom, which is given by (3), § 13, $a_0=h^2/4\pi^2\mu e^2=$

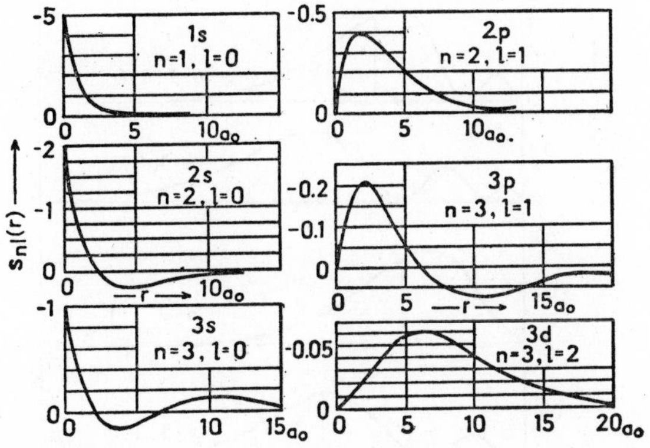

FIG. 20.V. Normalised Radial Functions for Hydrogen Atom

$0{\cdot}52916\times10^{-8}$ cm. From (12), § 17, and (21), § 17, an expression giving ρ in terms of r/a_0 is found:

$$\rho=2Zr/na_0 \quad . \quad . \quad . \quad . \quad . \quad . \quad . \quad . \quad . \quad . \quad (10)$$

The normalising process for the radial function is somewhat involved, and the complicated result only is given here: [1]

$$R_{nl}=\left\{\frac{(n-l-1)!}{2n[(n+l)!]^3}\left(\frac{2Z}{na_0}\right)^3\right\}^{1/2}e^{-\rho/2}\rho^l L_{n+l}^{2l+1}(\rho) \quad . \quad . \quad . \quad . \quad (11)$$

in which ρ can be replaced by the value in (10). Pauling and Wilson,[2] in order to make the functions positive for small values of r, write (11) with a negative sign; this does not, of course, affect the values of R_{nl}^2. In the tables below, their convention is adopted, but in Fig. 20.V the functions are

[1] Condon and Morse, " Quantum Mechanics," New York, 1929, 63; Wintner, *Phys. Rev.*, 1948, **73**, 91.

[2] See Pauling and Wilson, " Introduction to Quantum Mechanics," New York, 1935, 451, where v^s in the second equation should be v^t.

shown[1] with their negative values, plotted against multiples of a_0 for the hydrogen atom ($Z=1$).

The normalised values of R_{nl} are given below [2] for $n=1$, 2, and 3 (the symbols *s* and *p* stand for the values 0 and 1 of *l*). Since the reader may wish to plot these, the third column gives values for the hydrogen atom ($Z=1$), and in plotting, a_0 may be taken as 1:

$n=1$, $l=0$ (1*s* state)	$R_{10}(r)=(Z/a_0)^{3/2}2e^{-\rho/2}$	$(2/a_0^{3/2})e^{-r/a_0}$
$n=2$, $l=0$ (2*s* state)	$R_{20}(r)=\dfrac{(Z/a_0)^{3/2}}{2\sqrt{2}}(2-\rho)e^{-\rho/2}$	$\dfrac{1}{\sqrt{(2)}a_0^{3/2}}(1-r/2a_0)e^{-r/2a_0}$
$n=2$, $l=1$ (2*p* state)	$R_{21}(r)=\dfrac{(Z/a_0)^{3/2}}{2\sqrt{6}}\rho e^{-\rho/2}$	$\dfrac{r}{2\sqrt{(6)}a_0^{5/2}}e^{-r/2a_0}$
$n=3$, $l=0$ (3*s* state)	$R_{30}(r)=\dfrac{(Z/a_0)^{3/2}}{9\sqrt{3}}(6-6\rho+\rho^2)e^{-\rho/2}$	$\dfrac{1}{9\sqrt{(3)}a_0^{3/2}}\left(6-\dfrac{4r}{a_0}+\dfrac{4r^2}{9a_0^2}\right)e^{-r/3a_0}$

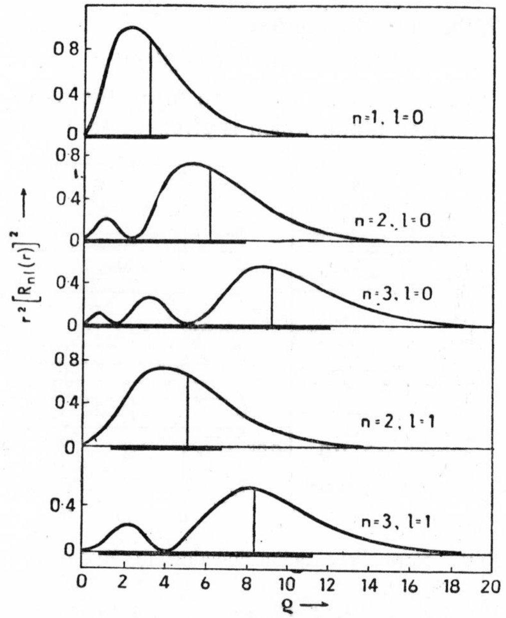

FIG. 21.V. Electron Distribution Function for Hydrogen atom. Abscissae are values of ρ

The charge distribution would be got by plotting the values of R_{nl}^2, but an alternative method is mostly used. In this, a *distribution function* D is defined as follows.[3] The volume of a spherical shell between the radii r and $r+dr$ is $d(4/3)\pi r^3=4\pi r^2dr$, and $4\pi r^2R_{nl}^2dr=Ddr$ is a measure of the charge density (or probability of occurrence of the electron) in a spherical shell of radius r and thickness dr. The significance of such plots, shown in Fig. 21.V, is not very clear, since the zero value at $r=0$ is merely a consequence of the vanishing of r^2, and the electric density is actually a maximum at $r=0$, as will be noted later.

[1] White, "Introduction to Atomic Spectra," New York, 1934, 67; Dushman, "Elements of Quantum Mechanics," New York, 1938, 189. In Fig. 20.V the function $R_{nl}(\rho)$ is denoted by $S_{nl}(r)$ and the abscissae are values of r in multiples of a_0.

[2] Further values in Pauling and Wilson, "Introduction to Quantum Mechanics," 1935, 135.

[3] White, "Introduction to Atomic Spectra," 1934, 66.

§ 19. Angular Functions for the Hydrogen-like Atom

The angular functions $\Theta(\theta)$ and $\Phi(\phi)$ will now be considered. These, it will be remembered, are independent of n, the principal quantum number, but involve the magnetic quantum number m, (10), § 17, or, as it is often called, m_l, the part not involving spin, which is the one considered in the present discussions. The normalised values of Θ and Φ have already been given in § 12 and (9), § 11, and some real values are repeated in the table below. The product $S=\Theta\Phi$ is, as is seen from § 12, a tesseral harmonic function, the values of which are given in the last column. There are $2l+1$ functions for each value of l. Only for an s-electron (l=0) is the value of Θ independent of θ, and is a constant $1/\sqrt{2}=0{\cdot}708$. Hence Θ^2 is also a constant, $\frac{1}{2}$. Since $\Phi=1/\sqrt{(2\pi)}$ is a constant, $\Theta\Phi=1/2\sqrt{\pi}$, and $S^2=1/4\pi$ is a constant.

Electron	l	m	Θ	Φ	$S=\Theta\Phi$
s	0	0	$1/\sqrt{2}$	$1/\sqrt{(2\pi)}$	$1/2\sqrt{\pi}$
p	1	0	$\sqrt{(3/2)}\cos\theta$	$1/\sqrt{(2\pi)}$	$\frac{1}{2}\sqrt{(3/\pi)}\cos\theta$
	1	+1	$\frac{1}{2}\sqrt{(3)}\sin\theta$	$(1/\sqrt{\pi})\cos\phi$	$\frac{1}{2}\sqrt{(3/\pi)}\sin\theta\cos\phi$
		−1		$(1/\sqrt{\pi})\sin\phi$	$\frac{1}{2}\sqrt{(3/\pi)}\sin\theta\sin\phi$
d	2	0	$\frac{1}{2}\sqrt{(5/2)}(3\cos^2\theta-1)$	$1/\sqrt{(2\pi)}$	$\frac{1}{4}\sqrt{(5/\pi)}(3\cos^2\theta-1)$
	2	+1	$\frac{1}{2}\sqrt{(15)}\sin\theta\cos\theta$	$(1/\sqrt{\pi})\cos\phi$	$\frac{1}{2}\sqrt{(15/\pi)}\sin\theta\cos\theta\cos\phi$
		−1		$(1/\sqrt{\pi})\sin\phi$	$\frac{1}{2}\sqrt{(15/\pi)}\sin\theta\cos\theta\sin\phi$
	2	+2	$\frac{1}{4}\sqrt{(15)}\sin^2\theta$	$(1/\sqrt{\pi})\cos 2\phi$	$\frac{1}{4}\sqrt{(15/\pi)}\sin^2\theta\cos 2\phi$
		−2		$(1/\sqrt{\pi})\sin 2\phi$	$\frac{1}{4}\sqrt{(15/\pi)}\sin^2\theta\sin 2\phi$

§ 20. Complete Wave Function for Hydrogen-like Atom

All the functions considered above combine by multiplication to give $\psi=R\Theta\Phi$, called the complete one-electron wave function; such functions do *not* include the electron spin factors. They are the wave-mechanical equivalents of the old electron orbits, and are often called *atomic orbitals.* The wave functions may be denoted by such symbols as ψ_{nlm}, e.g. ψ_{200}, ψ_{210}, ψ_{211} are those for n=2, and the values l=0 and 1, and m=0, 0 and 1, respectively. Those for l=0 and 1 are s and p functions, respectively. The three p functions (for m=0, −1, and +1) are denoted by p_x, p_y, and p_z, respectively, or sometimes by $p\sigma$, $p\pi_-$, and $p\pi_+$ when they are considered with reference to bond-formation in molecules.

By combining the values of Θ and Φ, the spherical wave function $S=\Theta\Phi$, given in the last column of the table in § 19, is obtained. It is usual to normalise these functions conventionally so that the s function is unity, when the p functions must be divided by $1/2\sqrt{\pi}=1/\sqrt{(4\pi)}$; they are then said to be "normalised to 4π." These are given in the following table:

Electron	l	m_l	Function
s	0	0	1
p_x	1	0	$\sqrt{(3)}\cos\theta$
p_y	1	−1	$\sqrt{(3)}\sin\theta\sin\phi$
p_z	1	1	$\sqrt{(3)}\sin\theta\cos\phi$

These results apply to *any* s- and p-electrons in a hydrogen-like atom, since the principal quantum number n does not appear in the spherical wave functions. As a rule, the complete s and p wave-functions for the same value of n show

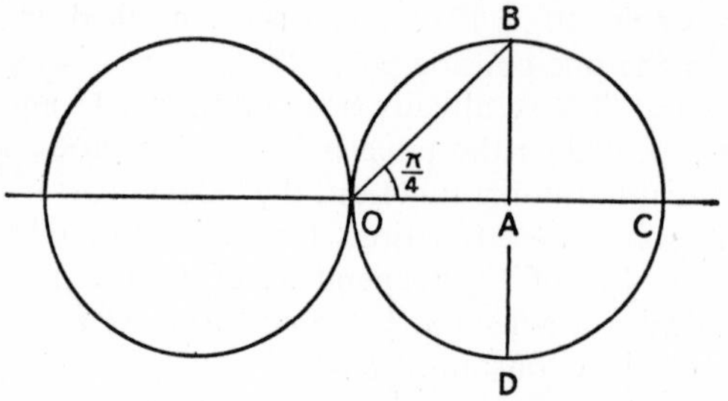

FIG. 22.V. Polar Graph for $\sqrt{(3)} \sin \theta$

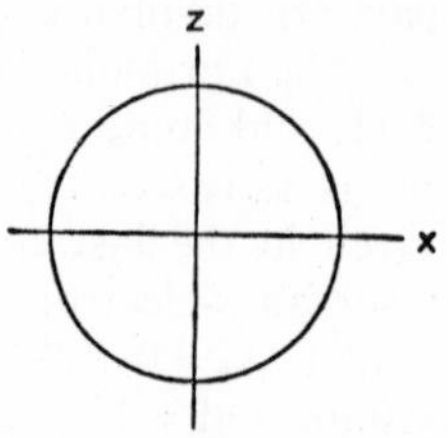

FIG. 23.V. Graph of s Function

approximately the same dependence on r, their radial parts being approximately the same, and the difference is mostly in the angular parts. The charge density of an s-electron ($l=0$) is independent of θ and ϕ and depends only on r, and the wave function is a sphere, which replaces Bohr's circular plane orbit.

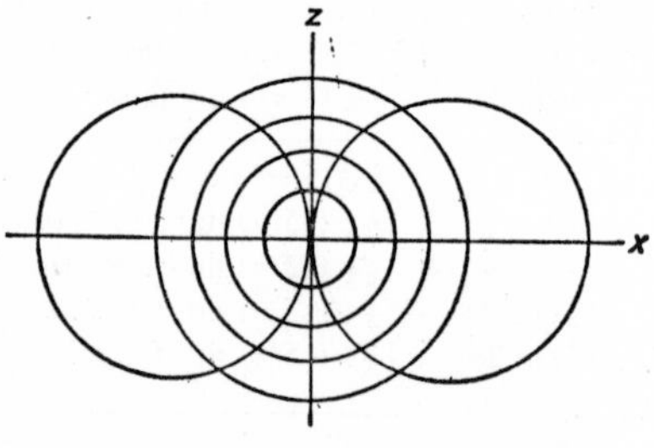

FIG. 24.V. Graph of p_x Function

The construction of the polar graphs is illustrated in Fig. 22.V for $\sqrt{(3)} \sin \theta$. For $\theta=0$, $\sin \theta=1$, therefore $OC=\sqrt{3}$. For $\theta=\pi/2$, $\sin \theta=0$, therefore at O the function is zero. For $\theta=\pi/4$, $\sin \theta=1/\sqrt{2}$. $AB=OA=\frac{1}{2}BD=\frac{1}{2}OC=\frac{1}{2}\sqrt{3}$, therefore $OB^2=OA^2+AB^2=\frac{3}{4}+\frac{3}{4}=\frac{3}{2}$, therefore $OB=\sqrt{3}/\sqrt{2}=\sqrt{(3)} \sin \theta$ for $\theta=\pi/4$. It is clear that the polar graph is a circle for $\theta=0$ to $\theta=\pi/2$, and the continuation to $\theta=2\pi$ gives another circle. The polar graph for $\sqrt{(3)} \cos \theta$ will be that of $\sqrt{(3)} \sin \theta$ turned through

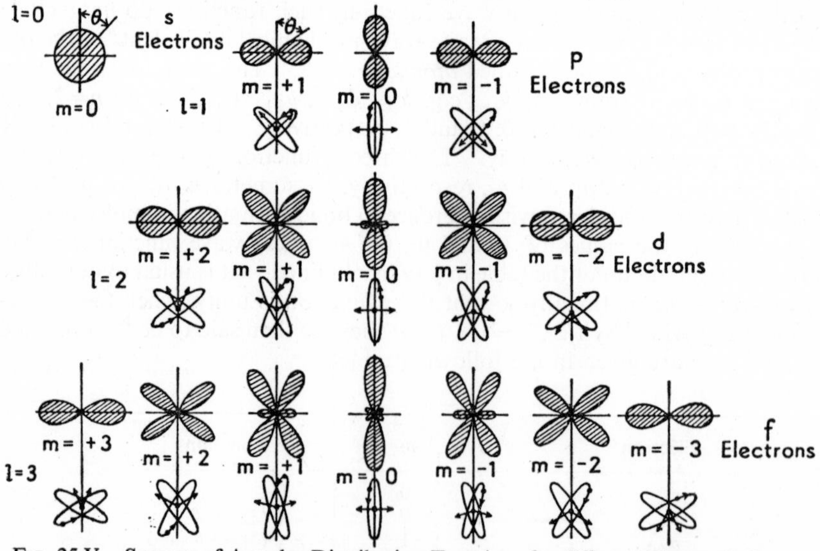

FIG. 25.V. Squares of Angular Distribution Functions for different Electronic States of Hydrogen Atoms

an angle of 90°. In plotting $\sin\theta\cos\phi$, and $\sin\theta\sin\phi$, use may be made of the trigonometrical formulae of § 41.I.

The *s* function ($l=0$) is spherically symmetrical with the value taken as 1 in all directions (Fig. 23.V), the angle being measured as shown in Fig. 22.V; p_x is represented[1] (Fig. 24.V) by two spheres, touching at the origin and with the x axis as an axis of symmetry, with a maximum value (found by putting $\sin\theta=1$ and $\cos\phi=1$) $|p|=\sqrt{3}=1{\cdot}732$ along the x axis; p_y and p_z are similarly represented with maximum values $\sqrt{3}$ along the y and z axes. The *p* functions are, therefore, greater than the *s* function, and it is readily seen from the trigonometry that they are at right angles to one another.

In Fig. 25.V the *squares* of the wave functions, S^2, for $p(l=1)$ and $d(l=2)$ electrons are plotted.[2] In each case the value of S^2 is measured off along a radius vector inclined at an angle θ with the vertical axis, measured clockwise on one side and counterclockwise on the other (Fig. 26.V). The values of S^2 represent the relation of charge density (Schrödinger) or probability of occurrence of an electron (Born) in specified directions. All the areas are projected on the plane $\phi=0$, and the values for plotting are taken from the table in § 19. (Note that $\sin\theta\cos\theta=\frac{1}{2}\sin 2\theta$.) The corresponding Bohr orbits are shown (tilted somewhat out of the normal plane) below each figure. The three-dimensional figures[3] are formed by rotating the figures about the vertical axes; e.g. a dumb-bell shaped figure for $l=1$, $m_l=0$. The values of l give the number of nodal planes or cones in the three-dimensional vibration replacing the Bohr orbit. When $l=0$, there are no nodal planes and there is spherical symmetry, whilst the Bohr orbit for $l=0$ was an elongated ellipse.

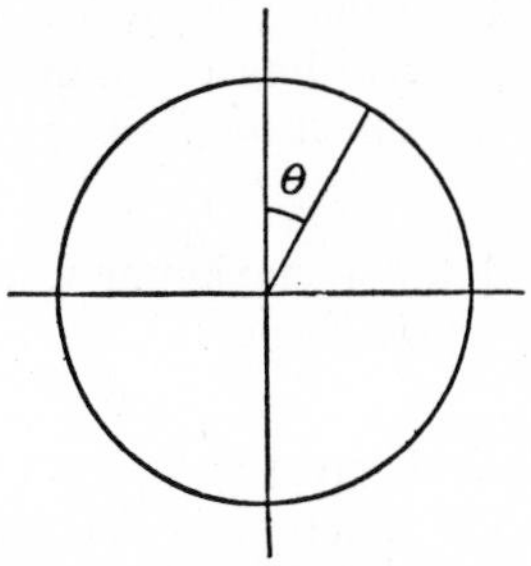

FIG. 26.V

§ 21. Hybridisation of Wave Functions

Since the wave function of a normal state is, in general, a linear combination of functions of states of similar energies, each of which satisfies the wave equation, a combination may be chosen which will minimise the energy, or, when considered in relation to bond formation, will lead to the strongest bond. This process is called[4] *hybridisation*, since it involves the combination of wave functions of different kinds (e.g. *s* and *p* functions). For example, the quadrivalent carbon atom has one *s* function and three *p* functions (p_x, p_y, p_z), and if these have similar energies, each of the four bond-forming functions may be written in the form:

$$\psi_i=a_is+b_ip_x+c_ip_y+d_ip_z$$

where i is 1, 2, 3, or 4. The coefficients a_i, b_i, c_i, and d_i are determined by the normalisation condition, (1), § 5:

$$\int\psi_i\psi_i^*\mathrm{d}v=\int\psi_i^2dv=1,$$

giving $$a_i^2+b_i^2+c_i^2+d_i^2=1;$$

[1] See Pauling and Wilson, "Introduction to Quantum Mechanics," 1935, 150, Figs. 21–6; no description of the figures is given, and exception is sometimes taken to that given above. The wave functions actually extend to infinity, but the angular dependence is representable in the way described.

[2] White, " Introduction to Atomic Spectra," New York, 1934, 63, Fig. 4.3.

[3] Dushman, *J. Chem. Educ.*, 1931, **8**, 1071; Urey, *ibid.*, 1931, **8**, 1114; Hume-Rothery, " Atomic Theory for Students of Metallurgy," 1947, 70, 77 f.

[4] Pauling, *J.A.C.S.*, 1931, **53**, 1367; Hultgren, *Phys. Rev.*, 1932, **40**, 891.

and by the requirement of orthogonality (2), § 5:

$$\int \psi_i \psi_k dv = 0,$$

$$\text{i.e. } a_i a_k + b_i b_k + c_i c_k + d_i d_k = 0,$$

where i and k are 1, 2, 3, and 4, but $i \neq k$.

The values of the wave functions (normalised to 4π) are (§ 20):

$$s=1, \; p_x=\sqrt{(3)} \sin\theta \cos\phi, \; p_y=\sqrt{(3)} \sin\theta \sin\phi, \; p_z=\sqrt{(3)} \cos\theta.$$

Since the direction of the first function is arbitrary, it may be taken along the x axis, when p_y and p_z are zero, and (for $i=1$):

$$\psi_1 = a_1 s + b_1 p_x = a_1 s + \sqrt{(1-a_1^2)} \,.\, p_x,$$

since $a_1^2+b_1^2=1$, therefore $b_1^2=1-a_1^2$.

The value of a_1 which makes the wave function a maximum along the x axis will, according to Pauling, form the strongest bond. The values of s and p_x in this direction ($\theta=0$, $\phi=90°$) are 1 and $\sqrt{3}$, respectively, hence:

$$\psi_1 = a_1 + \sqrt{[3(1-a_1^2)]},$$

and for a maximum value, $d\psi_1/da_1=0$ (§ 9, I), which gives $a_1=\frac{1}{2}$, therefore $b_1=\frac{1}{2}\sqrt{3}$, hence:

$$\psi_1 = \tfrac{1}{2}s + \tfrac{1}{2}\sqrt{(3)} p_x = \tfrac{1}{2} + \tfrac{1}{2}\sqrt{3} \,.\, \sqrt{3} = 2{\cdot}0,$$

which is greater than $\sqrt{3}$, the maximum value of the p_x function.[1]

The function ψ_2 may be chosen to have a maximum in the xz plane, so that p_y makes no contribution. Thus:

$$\psi_2 = a_2 s + b_2 p_x + d_2 p_z,$$

and since the maximum lies in the xz plane, the angle ϕ is 0° or 180°, as is seen from the x, y, z axis system in polar coordinates (Fig. 1.III). $\phi=0$ gives the positive part of the p_x function contributing to ψ_1, so that the negative part, with $\phi=180°$, must be used for ψ_2. Hence $\cos\phi=-1$, and $p_x=-\sqrt{(3)}\sin\theta$, and (since $s=1$, and $p_z=\sqrt{(3)}\cos\theta$):

$$\psi_2 = a_2 - b_2\sqrt{(3)} \sin\theta + d_2\sqrt{(3)} \cos\theta.$$

The normalisation condition is $a_2^2+b_2^2+d_2^2=1$, and the condition for orthogonality (since $d_1=0$) is $a_1a_2+b_1b_2=0$; with the values of a_1 and b_1 found above, these give $a_2=-b_2\sqrt{3}$, and $d_2=\sqrt{(1-4b_2^2)}$,

$$\therefore \; \psi_2 = -b_2\sqrt{3}(1+\sin\theta) + \sqrt{[3(1-4b_2^2)]} \cos\theta.$$

Equating $\partial\psi_2/\partial b_2$ and $\partial\psi_2/\partial\theta$ to zero gives for a maximum (after solving the simultaneous equations): $b_2=-1/2\sqrt{3}$, and $\sin\theta=1/3$, therefore $\theta=19° \; 28'$, or, since $\phi=180°$, the direction of the maximum wave function ψ_2 makes an angle $90°+19° \; 28'=109° \; 28'$ with the x axis or ψ_1, i.e. the regular tetrahedral angle. The values for b_2 and θ give for the maximum, $\psi_2=2{\cdot}0$, the same as ψ_1. From b_2, the values $a_2=\frac{1}{2}$ and $d_2=\sqrt{2}/\sqrt{3}$ are found; hence:

$$\psi_2 = \tfrac{1}{2}s - (1/2\sqrt{3})p_x + (\sqrt{2}/\sqrt{3})p_z.$$

In a similar way it is found that:

$$\psi_3 = \tfrac{1}{2}s - (1/2\sqrt{3})p_x + (1/\sqrt{2})p_y - (1/\sqrt{6})p_z,$$

$$\psi_4 = \tfrac{1}{2}s - (1/2\sqrt{3})p_x - (1/\sqrt{2})p_y - (1/\sqrt{6})p_z,$$

having maximum values of 2·0 in directions making tetrahedral angles with one another and with ψ_1 and ψ_2. The result of hybridisation of s and p functions

[1] This, it will be remembered, is relative to the s function taken as unity.

for the carbon atom thus leads to four equivalent functions, inclined at tetrahedral angles, as in the familiar valency model of the carbon atom. The exact regular tetrahedral angles may be somewhat modified if different atoms or groups are attached to the four bonds, as in CH_3Cl, $CHCl_3$, etc.

The so-called *trigonal hybridisation* arises in the case of a double bond between two carbon atoms, >C=C<. In this case *sp*-hybridisation gives three equivalent (trigonal) wave functions with maxima in one plane, say the *xy* plane, making angles of 120° with one another. Since the p_z functions at right angles to the plane do not contribute, the wave function:

$$\psi_1 = as + bp_x$$

with a maximum in the *x* direction has a part *a* of the *s* function and a part *b* of the p_x function. The *s* function may be regarded as equally divided among

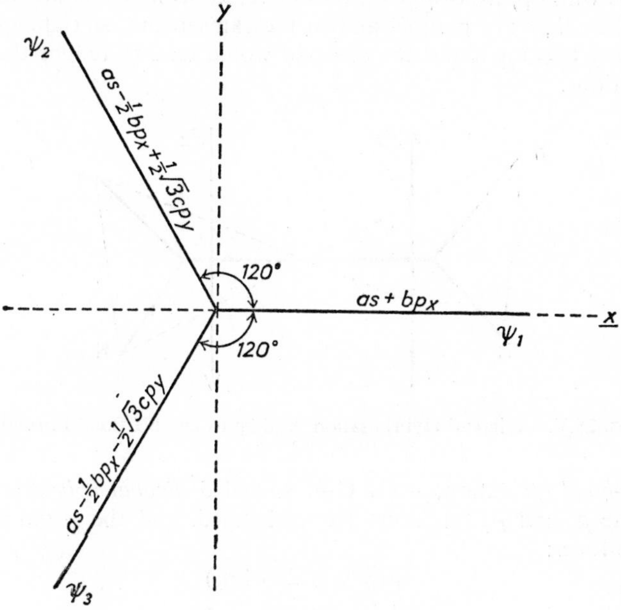

FIG. 27.V. Trigonal Hybridisation

ψ_1, ψ_2, and ψ_3 (*a* the same for all); the negative part of the p_x function and both parts of the p_y are resolved in two directions making angles of 120° with the *x* axis. Then (Fig. 27.V):

$$\psi_2 = as - \tfrac{1}{2}bp_x + \tfrac{1}{2}\sqrt{(3)}cp_y$$
$$\psi_3 = as - \tfrac{1}{2}bp_x - \tfrac{1}{2}\sqrt{(3)}cp$$

The normalisation and orthogonality conditions give $a = 1/\sqrt{3}$, $b = \sqrt{2}/\sqrt{3}$, and $c = \sqrt{2}/\sqrt{3}$, hence:

$$\psi_1 = (1/\sqrt{3})s + (\sqrt{2}/\sqrt{3})p_x$$
$$\psi_2 = (1/\sqrt{3})s - (1/\sqrt{6})p_x + (1/\sqrt{2})p_y$$
$$\psi_3 = (1/\sqrt{3})s - (1/\sqrt{6})p_x - (1/\sqrt{2})p_y$$

the maximum value of each being 1·991.

In double bond formation, >C=C<, the four functions of each carbon atom first form three trigonal hybridised functions, ψ_1, ψ_2, ψ_3, and one unchanged function p_z directed along the z axis at right angles to the plane of the trigonal functions. The two atoms then combine by the pairing of one trigonal function on one atom with another trigonal function on the other atom, these so-called σ-electrons forming a $\sigma\sigma$-bond, and the two p_z functions (so-called π-electrons), with opposite spin values and parallel to each other at right angles to the plane of the trigonal functions, form a $\pi\pi$-bond. The other two trigonal functions on each carbon can form bonds with s functions with opposite spin values on hydrogen atoms by overlapping, and thus the ethylene molecule $\begin{matrix}\mathrm{H}\\ \mathrm{H}\end{matrix}\!\!>\mathrm{C{=}C}<\!\!\begin{matrix}\mathrm{H}\\ \mathrm{H}\end{matrix}$ results (Fig. 28.V).

Free rotation about the double bond is prevented by the tendency of the two p_z functions with opposite spin values to overlap as much as possible, which is the case when they are parallel and in the same plane, at right angles to the xy plane; any twisting about the $\sigma\sigma$-bond would tend to reduce the overlap of the p_z functions.

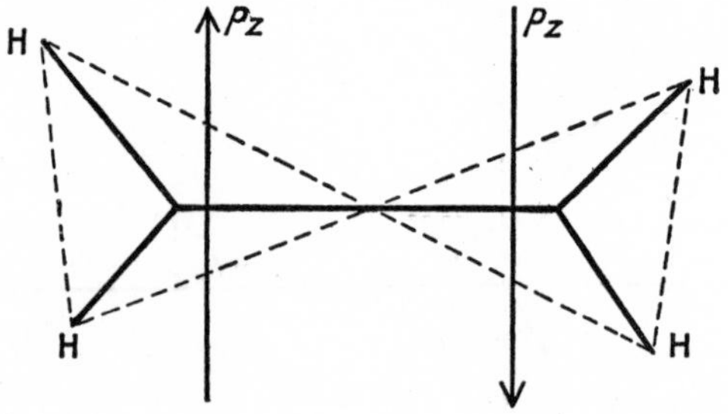

FIG. 28.V. Trigonal Hybridisation, leading to Double Bond Formation

In *triple-bond* formation, —C≡C—, so-called *digonal hybridisation* occurs. In this,[1] the p_y and p_z functions are unchanged, and the s and p_x functions combine to form:

$$\psi_1=\sqrt{(1/2)}(s+p_x)$$
$$\psi_2=\sqrt{(1/2)}(s-p_x)$$

directed in opposite directions along a straight line. In this case there is one $\sigma\sigma$-bond and two $\pi\pi$-bonds.

The extension of the general principles discussed in the present section will be taken up later.

§ 22. Alternative Methods in Quantum Mechanics

Besides the Schrödinger wave-equation method, other methods, which cannot be dealt with here, have been developed in quantum mechanics. Of these, perhaps the most important is the *matrix method*[2] developed by Heisen-

[1] See on the above, Bowen, *Ann. Rep. Chem. Soc.*, 1943, **40**, 12; Coulson, *Quart. Rev. Chem. Soc.*, 1947, **1**, 144; Coulson and Moffitt, *Phil. Mag.*, 1949, **40**, 1.

[2] Swann, *J. Franklin Inst.*, 1928, **205**, 323; Haas, " Materiewellen und Quantanmechanik," Leipzig, 1929, 80; Bloch, " L'Ancienne et la Nouvelle Théorie des Quanta," 1930, 321; Frenkel, Wave Mechanics. Advanced General Theory," Oxford, 1934; Frazer, Duncan, and Collar, " Elementary Matrices," Cambridge, 1938; Margenau and Murphy, " The Mathematics of

berg.[1] As Dushman [2] says, it " is a purely symbolic type of mathematics, and is quite unsuitable for elementary presentation." Dirac's [3] method of the so-called *Poisson brackets* is equally abstruse. All these methods have advantages in some aspects, and can be studied with profit. The matrix method has been largely used in physical chemistry.

Physics and Chemistry," New York, 1943, 287; Eyring, Walter, and Kimball, " Quantum Chemistry," New York, 1944, 129; Glasstone, " Theoretical Chemistry," New York, 1944, 62.

[1] *Z. Phys.*, 1925, **33**, 879; 1926, **38**, 411; 1926, **40**, 501; 1927, **41**, 239; Born and Jordan, *ibid.*, 1925, **34**, 858; Born, Heisenberg, and Jordan, *ibid.*, 1925–6, **35**, 557; von Rachewsky, *ibid.*, 1926, **39**, 153.

[2] " The Elements of Quantum Mechanics," New York, 1938, 19; he gives a brief account of it later, 248 f.

[3] Birtwistle, " The New Quantum Mechanics," Cambridge, 1928, 69; de Broglie, " Théorie de la Quantisation dans la nouvelle Mécanique," 1932, 94; Dirac, " The Principles of Quantum Mechanics," 3rd edit., Oxford, 1947.

SECTION VI

TEMPERATURE

A. THERMOMETRY

§ 1. Thermoregulators

The name " thermostat " was used by Heeren [1] for an arrangement for regulating the heat applied to a water bath by a spirit lamp, the flame of which was deflected into a chimney by an apparatus controlled by an air thermometer in the bath: this was a true thermostat in the modern sense.

Many types of *thermoregulators*, both for gas and electric heating, have been invented,[2] the original gas regulator of Kemp being practically the modern one.

[1] *J. prakt. Chem.*, 1834, **2**, 1. For a furnace with thermostatic control devised by Drebbel (1572–1633), see Gibbs, *Annals of Sci.*, 1948, **6**, 32.

[2] Geer, *J. Phys. Chem.*, 1902, **6**, 85 (bibl.); Kemp, *Chem. Gazette*, 1850, **8**, 184; *Phil. Mag.*, 1850, **36**, 483; Bunsen, q. by Desaga, *Dingl. J.*, 1857, **143**, 342; Herwig, *Ann. Phys.*, 1869, **137**, 19, 592; Reichert, *ibid.*, 1872, **144**, 467; Andreae, *ibid.*, 1878, **4**, 614; Hämmerl, Carl's *Repert. d. Phys.*, 1882, **18**, 309, 441 (bibl.); L. Meyer, *Ber.*, 1883, **16**, 1087; 1884, **17**, 478; Blümcke, *Ann. Phys.*, 1885, **25**, 419; Kahlbaum, *Ber.*, 1886, **19**, 2860; Ostwald, *Z. phys. Chem.*, 1888, **2**, 561; 1900, **35**, 216; Baillé, *Compt. Rend.*, 1894, **118**, 246; *Z. phys. Chem.*, 1894, **14**, 711; Parenty and Bricard, *Compt. Rend.*, 1896, **122**, 919; Thiesen, Scheel, and Sell, *Z. Instr.*, 1896, **16**, 49; Daneel, *Z. Elektrochem.*, 1896, **3**, 81; Gouy, *J. de Phys.*, 1897, **6**, 479 (electric; oscillating contact to±0·0002°); Schaller, *Z. phys. Chem.*, 1898, **25**, 505 (vap. press.); Centnerszwer, *ibid.*, 1898, **26**, 14; Dolezalek, *ibid.*, 1898, **26**, 321 (electric, Hg contact); van't Hoff and Meyerhoffer, *ibid.*, 1898, **27**, 78; Bodenstein, *ibid.*, 1899, **30**, 113 (100°–700°); Marchis, *ibid.*, 1899, **29**, 22; Gumlich, *Z. Instr.*, 1898, **18**, 317 (bimetallic); Rothe, *ibid.*, 1899, **19**, 143 (electric heating, to 500°); Bose, *ibid.*, 1899, **19**, Beibl. 169, 181, 189 (theory); Foote, *Z. phys. Chem.*, 1900, **33**, 749; Duane and Lory, *Amer. J. Sci.*, 1900, **9**, 179; Young, *J.A.C.S.*, 1901, **23**, 327; Knipp, *Phys. Rev.*, 1901, **12**, 47 (bimetallic); Bradley and Browne, *J. Phys. Chem.*, 1902, **6**, 118 (gas; to 0·001°); Kühl, *Z. phys. Chem.*, 1903, **44**, 388 (high temp.); Hahn, *ibid.*, 1903, **44**, 525 (high temp.); Marie and Marquis, *ibid.*, 1903, **45**, 566; Suto, *Z. physiol. Chem.*, 1904, **41**, 363; Dony-Hénault, *Z. Elektrochem.*, 1905, **11**, 3; Lowry, *J.C.S.*, 1905, **87**, 1030; Osborn, *J. Phys. Chem.*, 1905, **9**, 297; Lundén and Tate, *Meddel. Nobelinst.*, 1906, **1**, No. 5; Poda, *Z. angew. Chem.*, 1907, **20**, 2245 (at 15°); Mast, *Science*, 1907, **26**, 554 (Hg-glycerol); Wolff and Waters, *Bur. Stand. Bull.*, 1907, **4**, 1 (33); Fischer and Bobertag, *Z. Elektrochem.*, 1908, **14**, 375 (high temp.); Green, *Chem. News*, 1908, **98**, 49 (toluene); Cohen and Sinnige, *Z. phys. Chem.*, 1909, **67**, 17; Regaud and Fouilland, *Ann. Chim. Anal. Appl.*, 1909, **14**, 14 (Hg); Reid, *Amer. Chem. J.*, 1909, **41**, 148 (electric controlled gas); Poetschke, *J.A.C.S.*, 1909, **31**, 1218 (air expansion); Bousfield, *Trans. Faraday Soc.*, 1911, **7**, 260; *Chem. News*, 1912, **105**, 13 (modified Lowry); Somerville, *Elec. World*, 1911, **57**, 112 (air thermometer); Morgan, *Z. phys. Chem.*, 1911, **78**, 123; Marshall, *Trans. Faraday Soc.*, 1911, **7**, 249; *Chem. News*, 1911, **104**, 295; Cumming, *Trans. Faraday Soc.*, 1911, **7**, 253; *Chem. News*, 1911, **104**, 307; Göpel, *Z. Instr.*, 1912, **32**, Beibl. 209 (air bath); Fletcher and Tyrer, *Proc. Chem. Soc.*, 1912, **28**, 189 (vapour, with manostat); Bodenstein and Kranendieck, *Z. Elektrochem.*, 1912, **18**, 417 (high temp.); Whitaker, *Chem. News*, 1913, **107**, 242 (gas); Jorissen, *Chem. Weekbl.*, 1913, **10**, 532 (safety gas type); Boyd and Atkinson, *Chem. News*, 1913, **108**, 248 (gas); Powell, *J.S.C.I.*, 1914, **33**, 899 (room temp.); Feild, *J.A.C.S.*, 1914, **36**, 72 (vap. press., 0·005°–0·01°); Bunzel and Hesselbring, *J.A.C.S.*, 1914, **36**, 949 (toluene); Siebert, *Chem. Ztg.*, 1914, **38**, 888 (bimetallic); Davis, Putnam, and Jones, *Z. phys. Chem.*, 1915, **90**, 484; Davis, *J.A.C.S.*, 1915, **37**, 1520; Lovelace, Frazer, and Miller, *ibid.*, 1916, **38**, 515; Henning, " Die Grundlagen der Temperaturmessung," Brunswick, 1915, 215; Shaw, *Trans. Roy. Soc. Canada*, 1917, **11**, III, 129; *Amer. Chem. Abstr.*, 1919, **13**, 1778 (toluene); Ray and Reilly, *Chem. News*, 1918, **117**, 181 (general practical hints); Ferguson, *J.A.C.S.*, 1918, **40**, 929 (toluene); Milbauer, *Z. anal. Chem.*, 1918, **57**, 161 (controlling constant-level water bath); Otis, *Science*, 1918, **48**, 425;

Amer. Chem. Abstr., 1919, **13**, 802 (thermocouple control); Hall, *Science*, 1919, **49**, 214 (bimetallic strip); Herrman, *Gen. Elec. Rev.*, 1920, **23**, 57 (*cast* bimetallic strip); King, *J.A.C.S.*, 1920, **42**, 2058 (Hg); Sligh, *ibid.*, 1920, **42**, 60; White, *J. Wash. Acad.*, 1920, **10**, 429 (Hg contact); Othmer, *Ind. Eng. Chem. Anal.*, 1921, **1**, 97 (heavy duty; 4000 watts); Starkey and Gordon, *Ind. Eng. Chem.*, 1922, **14**, 541 (toluene); Winterstein, *Koll. Z.*, 1923, **33**, 112 (Hg, floating contact); Beaver and Beaver, *Ind. Eng. Chem.*, 1923, **15**, 359 (current amplified); Ramberg, *Svensk. Kem. Tid.*, 1924, **36**, 101; Mestresat and Janet, *Bull. Soc. Chim. Biol.*, 1924, **6**, 534 (gas); Bradford, *Biochem. J.*, 1924, **18**, 381 (electric); Murray, *J.C.S.*, 1924, **125**, 461 (gas); Schreiner, Holtsmark, and Trumpy, *Z. Elektrochem.*, 1924, **30**, 293 (photocell control); Smith and Hollister, *Ind. Eng. Chem.*, 1924, **16**, 1162; Fox and Mankudi, *J. Indian Chem. Soc.*, 1925, **2**, 292 (cooled); Roebuck, *Proc. Amer. Acad.*, 1925, **60**, 537; Jaeger and Dykstra, *Z. anorg. Chem.*, 1925, **143**, 233; Sligh, *J. Opt. Soc. Amer.*, 1925, **10**, 691; Roebuck, *ibid.*, 1925, **10**, 679; Leighton, *J. Sci. Instr.*, 1926, **3**, 377 (Hg); Hume, *J.S.C.I.*, 1926, **45**, 246T; Lombard, *Bull. Soc. Chim.*, 1926, **39**, 948 (toluene); Cowperthwaite, *J.A.C.S.*, 1927, **49**, 2255 (graphite heater); Collins, *J. Phys. Chem.*, 1927, **31**, 1097; Lehrman, *Ind. Eng. Chem.*, 1928, **20**, 290 (toluene); Hill, *J. Sci. Instr.*, 1928, **5**, 24; Garrett, *Ind. Eng. Chem. Anal.*, 1928, **10**, 324 (thyratron); Noyes, *J. Opt. Soc. Amer.*, 1928, **17**, 127; Grogan, *J. Sci. Instr.*, 1928, **5**, 217; Black, *ibid.*, 1928, **5**, 376 (bimetallic strip); Robinson, *Ann. Entomol. Soc. Amer.*, 1928, **21**, 607 (Hg-toluene with relay); Čupr, *Z. Elektrochem.*, 1928, **34**, 679; 1931, **37**, 129 (automatic for 20°); van Campen, *ibid.*, 1929, **35**, 265; Nottebohm, *ibid.*, 1929, **35**, 450 (triode valve); Matsui, Oguri, Kambara, and Kato, *J. Soc. Chem. Ind. Japan*, 1929, **32**, Suppl. Bdg. 108B; Durrant, *Engineering*, 1929, **127**, 327 (modif. Haughton-Hanson); Polissar, *J.A.C.S.*, 1930, **52**, 636 (vapour); Beattie and Jacobus, *J. Phys. Chem.*, 1930, **34**, 1254 (photocell); Butterworth and Derratt-Smith, *J. Sci. Instr.*, 1930, **7**, 233 (Ostwald); Evans, *J.S.C.I.*, 1931, **50**, 66 (air thermostat); Adams, *Rev. Sci. Instr.*, 1931, **2**, 187 (Hg); Rieche and Grau, *Z. techn. Phys.*, 1931, **12**, 284 (modif. Kangro); Owen, *J.S.C.I.*, 1931, **50**, 190T (slow *control of rate* of gas heating); Schmitt and Schmitt, *Science*, 1931, **73**, 289 (toluene+thyratron); Schenk, *Ber.*, 1931, **64**, 368 (Hg); Benton, *Gas World*, 1931, **94**, 35 (bimetallic); Stier, *Science*, 1931, **73**, 288 (ice temp.); Coffin, *Canad. J. Res*,. 1931, **5**, 636; 1932, **6**, 417; 1932, **7**, 75; *J.A.C.S.*, 1933, **55**, 3646 (vapour); Durau and Schratz, *Z. phys. Chem.*, 1932, **159**, 115 (±0·001°); Smits and Gerding, *ibid.*, 1932, **160**, 231 (elaborate outfit: photocell, amplifier, and vacuum relay; ±0·0005°); Summers, *Proc. Soc. Chem. Ind. Victoria*, 1931, **31**, 535 (thermionic); Kambara, Oyamada, and Matsui, *J. Soc. Chem. Ind. Japan*, 1931, **34**, Suppl. Bdg. 361; Kambara and Matsui, *ibid.*, 1931, **34**, Suppl. Bdg. 94, 273 (theory); Fuchs, *Chem. Fabr.*, 1932, 49; Lundstrom and Whittaker, *Ind. Eng. Chem. Anal.*, 1932, **4**, 294; Moriguchi, *J. Soc. Chem. Ind. Japan*, 1932, **35**, 377, 441 (Hg); Ferguson, van Lente, and Hitchens, *Ind. Eng. Chem. Anal.*, 1932, **4**, 218 (mercury in steel; valve relay); Ramsey and Watson, *ibid.*, 1932, **4**, 164 (circuit breaker); Roebuck, *Rev. Sci. Instr.*, 1932, **3**, 93 (photoelectric); Rieche, *Z. techn. Phys.*, 1932, **13**, 498 (Pt thermom. and relay); Rosenbohm, *Proc. K. Akad. Wetens. Amsterdam*, 1932, **35**, 876 (triode; no elec. contacts); Nelles and Kistiakowsky, *J.A.C.S.*, 1932, **54**, 2208 (high press.); Korpiun and Goldbach, *Z. Elektrochem.*, 1933, **39**, 755; Van Santen, *Comm. Leiden*, 1933, **227**; Beier and Brintzinger, *Koll. Z.*, 1933, **64**, 173 (air thermostat); Parks, *Ind. Eng. Chem. Anal.*, 1933, **5**, 357 (Hg); Dippel, *Chem. Weekbl.*, 1933, **30**, 193 (5°–20°); Ramsey, *Ind. Eng. Chem. Anal.*, 1933, **5**, 218 (Hg); Stier and Crozier, *J. Gen. Physiol.*, 1933, **16**, 757 (0°+); Woog, Givaudon, and Dayan, *Bull. Soc. Chim.*, 1933, **53**, 240 (to −60°); Lang, *Z. techn. Phys.*, 1933, **14**, 98 (theory); Tian, *J. Chim. Phys.*, 1933, **30**, 132 (theory); Cooke and Swallow, *J.S.C.I.*, 1933, **52**, 1031; Heisig and Cameron, *Ind. Eng. Chem. Anal.*, 1933, **5**, 420; Beattie, *Proc. Amer. Acad.*, 1934, **69**, 389; Bailey, *Science*, 1934, **79**, 277 (expans. gas); Pidgeon, *Canad. J. Res.*, 1934, **10**, 252; Coffin, *Proc. Nova Scotia Inst. Sci.*, 1934, **18**, 213; Lalande, *Bull. Soc. Chim.*, 1934, **1**, 36; *J. Chim. Phys.*, 1934, **31**, 439 (theory and bibl.); Lange and Voos, *Z. techn. Phys.*, 1934, **15**, 323 (photoelectric); Zabel and Hancox, *Rev. Sci. Instr.*, 1934, **5**, 28; Udalow, *Zavodskaya Lab.*, 1935, **4**, 805; Strelkov, *J. Tech. Phys. U.S.S.R.*, 1935, **5**, 1502; Bloxam, *J. Sci. Instr.*, 1935, **12**, 361; Bradfield, *J.S.C.I.*, 1935, **54**, 6T; Folley and Temple, *J. Sci. Inst.*, 1935, **12**, 392 (toluene); Centnerszwer and Szker, *Bull. Soc. Chim.*, 1935, **2**, 495 (toluene, without relay); Gesteau, *Bull. Sci. Pharmacol.*, 1935, **42**, 8; *Bull. Soc. Philomath.*, 1935, **112**, 8 (vap. press.); Benford, *J. Sci. Instr.*, 1936, **13**, 4 (0°–12°); Stiehler, *Science*, 1936, **83**, 40 (copper foil in toluene bulb); Temple, *J. Sci. Instr.*, 1936, **13**, 414 (valve relay); Van de Voorde, *Natuurw. Tijdschr.*, 1936, **18**, 21 (toluene); Negishi, *J.A.C.S.*, 1936, **58**, 2293 (±0·05°); Yee and Davis, *Ind. Eng. Chem. Anal.*, 1936, **8**, 477; Pearson and Norris, *J.S.C.I.*, 1936, **55**, 127T (toluene); Myakov, *J. Exptl. Theor. Phys. U.S.S.R.*, 1937, **7**, 780; Bailey, *Science*, 1937, **86**, 525 (gas); Schwenk and Noble, *J. Phys. Chem.*, 1937, **41**, 809; Briscoe *et al.*, *J.C.S.*, 1937, 1495; Benedict, *Rev. Sci. Instr.*, 1937, **8**, 252 (thyratron); Holmes, *Ind. Eng. Chem. Anal.*, 1937, **9**, 481; Stadler, *Chem. Ztg.*, 1937, **61**, 437; Parkinson, *J. Sci. Instr.*, 1937, **14**, 94 (gas,

The Lowry type, with bulbs, is very good. It is filled by pouring in the mercury, fitting with a cork and tube, inverting, exhausting with a water pump, and opening under toluene, which nearly fills it, the small bubble of air disappearing on standing. The gas connection to a special micro-burner with a mica chimney is made with a small by-pass to keep the flame burning, the mercury level being adjusted at the required temperature. Since the gas tends to bubble past the jet, a pressure regulator (supplied by the gas company) is used. For electric heating, a relay is used (the cheap types stick and are unsatisfactory), contact being made by a platinum wire with a screw adjustment, the heating element being a long carbon-filament stove lamp or other type of resistance heater. The water in the bath is well stirred, and at temperatures over 50° is covered with a layer of suitable oil to check evaporation.

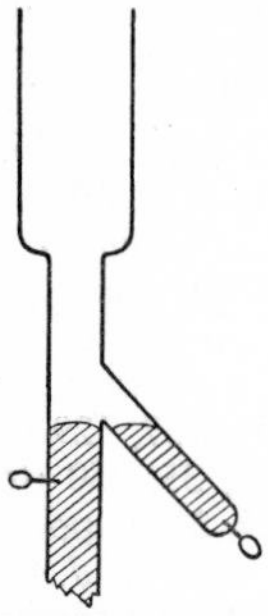

FIG. 1.VI A. Mercury Cut-out for Thermoregulator

To prevent the toluene attacking the mercury, it is refluxed with 1 per cent. sodium amalgam, washed, and distilled, the wet first fraction being rejected.[1] Xylene may be used for higher temperatures.[2]

For approximate work, baths of salt solutions boiling at definite temperatures can be used.[3]

To prevent arcing with a mercury contact, Benrath and Schröder[4] used a sudden cut-out shaped as in Fig. 1.VI A. An oscillating type of mercury contact in which an electrode is kept constantly moving[5] was recommended by Sligh.[6] Sticking of mercury in a capillary is prevented by making contact with it by means of a bent piece of No. 32 nichrom wire.[7]

In the arrangement of Hart and Partington for temperatures of 180°–300° a small furnace was used. The temperature bath, contained in a Pyrex or Hysil beaker suspended from the top of the furnace tube, contained the standardised

to ±0·001°; shape of jet); Gesteau, *J. Pharm. Chim.*, 1937, **26**, 105 (thyratron); Jelinek, *Bull. Soc. Chim.*, 1937, **4**, 1811; Swietoslawski and Pomorski, *Roczn. Chem.*, 1937, **17**, 254 (toluene, cathode-ray relay; 0·001° for days); Van Nes and Tjepkema, *Chem. Weekbl.*, 1938, **35**, 534 (200° ±0·005°); Waddle and Imhoff, *J. Chem. Educ.*, 1938, **15**, 191 (bimetallic helix); Sturtevant, *Rev. Sci. Instr.*, 1938, **9**, 276, 331 (thyratron); *J. Phys. Chem.*, 1941, **45**, 127; Yee, *Ind. Eng. Chem. Anal.*, 1941, **13**, 839 (vap. press.); Fairchild, in " Temperature. Its Measurement and Control," New York, 1941, 587; Hopper and Laby, *Proc. Phys. Soc.*, 1942, **54**, 55; Bancroft, *Rev. Sci. Instr.*, 1942, **13**, 24, 114 (thyratron); Redfern, *Ind. Eng. Chem. Anal.*, 1942, **14**, 64; Gilson and Wooster, *J. Chem. Educ.*, 1942, **19**, 531 (thyratron); Hart and Partington, *J.C.S.*, 1943, 104 (high temp.); Coats, *J. Sci. Instr.*, 1944, **21**, 86 (valve type); Lou and Chen, *ibid.*, 1944, **21**, 88 (electrolytic); Griffin, *Ind. Eng. Chem. Anal.*, 1945, **17**, 671; Stokes, *New Zeal. J. Sci. Tech.*, 1945, **27**B, 75 (toluene-Hg in copper spiral); Harvey, *Ind. Eng. Chem. Anal.*, 1946, **18**, 331 (electronic relay); Wright, *J. Sci. Instr.*, 1947, **24**, 258; Bluethe, *Metal Progr.*, 1947, **52**, 591; Weil, *Compt. Rend.*, 1947, **224**, 810 (±0·0002°); Schwenk, *J. Phys. Chem.*, 1948, **52**, 761; Braude, *J.C.S.*, 1948, 794; summaries in Ostwald-Luther-Drucker, " Physikochemische Messungen," 5th edit., Leipzig, 1931, 119; Haughton, in Glazebrook, " Dict. Applied Physics," 1922, **1**, 1022; P. Griffiths, " Thermostats and Temperature Regulating Instruments," 1934; Ansley, " Temperature Control," 1942; Sturtevant, in Weissberger, " Physical Methods of Organic Chemistry," 1945, **1**, 326; Smith, *J. Sci. Instr.*, 1948, **25**, 16.

[1] Beal and Souther, *J.A.C.S.*, 1927, **49**, 1944.

[2] Burlew, *J.A.C.S.*, 1940, **62**, 681.

[3] For a list, 101°–179·5°, Legrand, *Ann. Chim.*, 1835, **59**, 423.

[4] *Z. anorg. Chem.*, 1927, **161**, 155.

[5] Gouy, *J. de Phys.*, 1897, **6**, 479.

[6] *J.A.C.S.*, 1920, **42**, 60.

[7] Kambara and Matsui, *J.S.C.I. Japan*, 1931, **34** (spec. binding), 94; for tantalum wire (not wetted by mercury) see Jones, Taylor, and Vogel, *J.A.C.S.*, 1948, **70**, 966.

Anschütz thermometer or platinum and platinum-rhodium thermocouple. The readings of the thermometer and couple agreed to 0·1°. The furnace tube was of non-transparent silica in one piece, the upper half of 8 cm. diameter, the lower of 4 cm., and the winding of nichrome wire was covered by a thick layer of heat-resisting cement. A rectangular box of asbestos sheet held the tube and lagging. The temperature regulation was by a mercury-filled regulator, as shown in Fig. 2.VI A, operating a relay which could short-circuit the last 10 ohms of resistance in series with the furnace. Over long periods the temperature control had a maximum variation of ±0·1°, as measured on the thermometer in the bath.

A cement for glass windows in thermostats, which is said [1] to withstand even hot water, is made by rubbing litharge and glycerol with a little water-glass to a

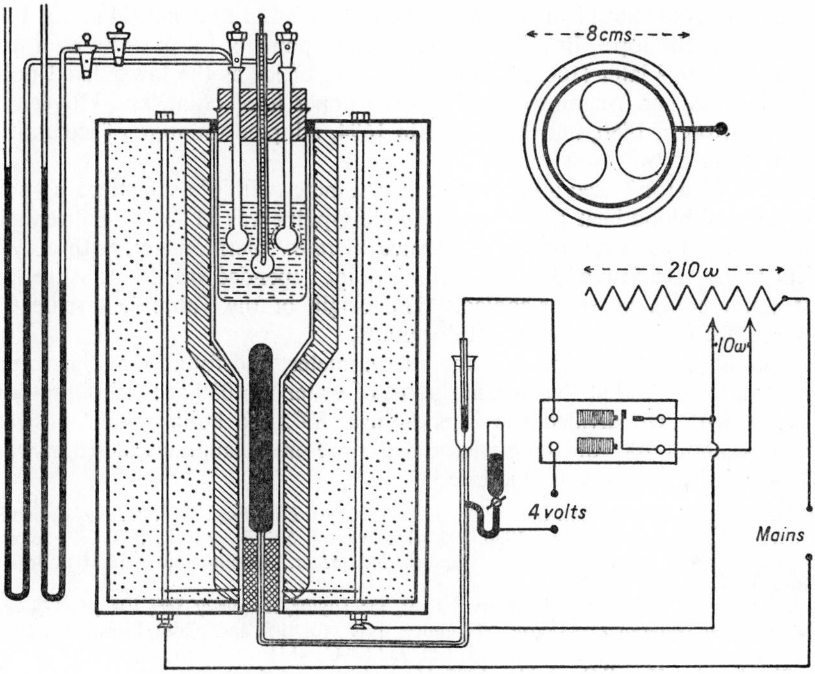

FIG. 2.VI A. High Temperature Thermoregulator

soft paste. It is applied to very clean glass and metal surfaces, and allowed to harden.

The use of resistance thermometers enables temperature control to be achieved by a Wheatstone bridge circuit, the sensitivity being doubled by using two thermometers in opposite arms of the bridge. The bridge output may be used to control the heating current, (*a*) by indicating the D.C. output by a galvanometer which controls the heater by an on-off photocell relay, (*b*) by using the photocell as part of a phase-shifting thyratron circuit, giving continuous control, (*c*) by amplifying the A.C. bridge output and using the product in a phase-shifting thyratron circuit.

With a given installation there is a limit to the sensitivity of a *continuous* control device, beyond which the control causes oscillations of temperature

[1] Arndt, "Phys.-chem. Technik," 2nd edit., 1923, 20 (from F. Köhler, Leipzig).

about an equilibrium point, elaborate mathematical investigations of which have appeared.[1]

§ 2. Mercury Thermometers

A thermoscope used by Galileo before 1597 consisted of a bulb containing air with a vertical tube below containing water or wine, and dipping into a vessel of the liquid.[2] The readings, as Pascal (1643) pointed out, depended on the atmospheric pressure. Jean Rey in 1631 used a water thermoscope. Sealed thermometers containing spirit of wine were used by the Florentine Academicians [3] in 1641, and were improved by Ferdinand II, Duke of Tuscany, about 1644. Some of these thermometers were found in 1829, and there is one in the Cavendish Laboratory, Cambridge.[4] The fixed points were the temperatures of a mixture of ice and salt, and blood heat. Hooke copied one of them received by Boyle in 1661, but his instrument, like most used in England till about 1740, was open at the top. Boyle used the freezing point of oil of anise as a fixed point. Hooke [5] later (1664) adopted the m.p. of ice as the lower fixed point. Fabri in 1669 had " summer heat " as the upper fixed point, and Huygens in 1665, Newton in 1680, and Renaldini in 1694, adopted the m.p. of ice and the b.p. of water as two fixed points.[6]

In 1701 Newton[7] used a linseed oil thermometer with 0° as the freezing-point of water and blood heat 12°, when the boiling-point was 33°–34°. Fahrenheit [8] constructed in 1714 the first useful sealed mercury thermometer, with a cylindrical bulb. He found that the boiling-point depended on the pressure, and that water could be super-cooled. The origin of the Fahrenheit scale (f.p. 32°, b.p. 212°) has been a matter of dispute.[9]

Réaumur [10] used a spirit of wine thermometer, and found that the volume increased from 1000 at the freezing-point of water to 1080 at the boiling-point of the spirit. He divided the interval into 80°; the boiling-point of water would be about 100° on this scale, and the present Réaumur scale (b.p. water 80°) was really proposed by De Luc.[11]

[1] Turner, *Proc. Cambr. Phil. Soc.*, 1936, **32**, 663; *J. Inst. Elec. Eng.*, 1937, **81**, 399; Callendar, Hartree, and Porter, *Phil. Trans.*, 1936, **235**, 415; Ivanoff, *Sci. Progr.*, 1937, **31**, 682; Jelonek, *Proc. Cambr. Phil. Soc.*, 1946, **42**, 62; Carslaw and Jaeger," Conduction of Heat in Solids," Oxford, 1947, 88, 320.

[2] T. Thomson, " Heat and Electricity," 1840, 35; Taylor, *Annals of Sci.*, 1942, **5**, 129.

[3] " Saggi di Natvrali Esperienze," Florence, 1666, fol. I f. and plate; Libri, *Ann. Chim.*, 1830, **45**, 354; Maze, *Compt. Rend.*, 1895, **120**, 732 (0° C.$=13\frac{1}{2}$° on Florentine scale).

[4] Glazebrook, " Heat," Cambridge, 1907, 16; on history of the thermometer see G. Martine, " Essays and Observations on the Construction and Graduation of Thermometers, and on the Heating and Cooling of Bodies," 4th edit., Edinburgh, 1787; Rosenberger, " Geschichte der Physik," Brunswick, 1884, **2**, 163; Bolton, " The Evolution of the Thermometer," Easton, Pa., 1900; Pernet, in Winkelmann, " Handbuch der Physik," 1906, 3, 2, and refs.; K. Meyer, " Die Entwicklung des Temperaturbegriffs," transl. Kolde, *Die Wissenschaft*, Brunswick, 1913, **48**; Brown, *J. Chem. Educ.*, 1934, **11**, 448; Barnett, *ibid.*, 1941, **18**, 358; on thermometer readings by Ismaël Boulliau in 1658, see Maze, *Compt. Rend.*, 1895, **120**, 732.

[5] " Micrographia," 1665, 38.

[6] Crafts, *J. Chim. Phys.*, 1913, **11**, 429.

[7] *Phil. Trans.*, 1701, **22**, 824; transl. in abridged edit., 1809, **4**, 572.

[8] *Phil. Trans.*, 1727, **33**, 1, 78; abridged edit., 1809, **7**, 1, 22.

[9] Muncke, in Gehler, " Physikalisches Wörterbuch," 1839, **9**, 825; Gamgee, *Proc. Cambr. Phil. Soc.*, 1890, **7**, 95 (correcting Tait, and Maxwell); Brown, *J. Chem. Educ.*, 1934, **11**, 448; Cohen and Cohen-de-Meester, q. in *Annals of Sci.*, 1937, **2**, 133, conclude that the scale is an arbitrary modification of one used by Römer in 1708, in which ice and blood temperatures were fixed points.

[10] *Mém. Acad. Sci.*, 1730, 452.

[11] " Recherches sur les Modifications de l'Atmosphère," Geneva, 1772, **1**, 352; Martine, *op. cit.*, ref. 4, 25.

The Centigrade scale was proposed by Celsius,[1] of Uppsala, but he took the freezing-point of water as 100° and the boiling-point (under a pressure of 25 in. 3 lines) as 0°. The present scale (f.p. 0°, b.p. 100°) seems to be due to Linnaeus.[2] The conversion equation for the three scales is: C°/100=R°/80=(F°−32)/180.

The Centigrade scale has been the only legal thermometric scale in Germany since August, 1924, although the Réaumur scale is still used in daily life, as is the Fahrenheit in Great Britain and America.[3]

§ 3. Mercury Thermometer Corrections

The mercury thermometer is very convenient and when carefully constructed, calibrated, and used,[4] is capable of giving measurements to 0·002°–0·001° (Regnault was content with 0·1°). Among the sources of error with an otherwise correctly graduated instrument are (i) the change of volume of the bulb due to varying pressures, both external (atmospheric and hydrostatic pressures) and internal (effect of varying length of mercury column, and whether the instrument is used horizontally or vertically); (ii) the change in ice-point owing to thermal hysteresis of the glass, causing a change in volume of the bulb when the thermometer is heated and then cooled, this change (which may be 0·03°–0·5°) not disappearing until after some days; there may also be a slow continuous change (*secular change*) for several years: [5] for Jena 16^{III} this is

[1] *K. Svenska Vet. Akad. Handl.*, 1742, **3**, 171; Wargentin, *ibid.*, 1749, **10**, 161; see the German transl. by Karsten, 1750, **4**, 197; 1754, **11**, 167.

[2] Arago, " Oeuvres," 1858, **8**, 608; Nordenmark, *Annals of Sci.*, 1937, **2**, 474; the scale is depicted on the plate opposite the title-page of Linnaeus, " Hortus Cliffortianus," Amsterdam, 1737.

[3] Henning, *Naturwiss.*, 1925, **13**, 421.

[4] Pierre, *Ann. Chim.*, 1842, **5**, 427; Regnault, *ibid.*, 1842, **6**, 370; Guillaume, *Trav. et Mém. Bur. Internat. Poids et Més.*, 1886, **5**; 1888, **6**; *Compt. Rend.*, 1891, **112**, 87; " Traité pratique de la Thérmometrie de precision," Paris, 1889; Pernet, *Trav. et Mém. Bur. Internat. Poids et Més.*, 1881, **B 1**; *Wiss. Abhl. Phys.-techn. Reichsanst.*, 1894, **1**; *idem*, in Winkelmann, " Handbuch der Physik," 1906, **3**, 12; Chree, *Phil. Mag.*, 1898, **45**, 205, 299; Chappuis, *Congrès Internat. Phys.*, 1901, **1**, 131; Henning, " Die Grundlagen, Methode, und Ergebnisse der Temperaturmessung," Brunswick, 1915; Higgins, in Glazebrook, " Dict. of Applied Physics," 1922, **1**, 988; *J. Roy. Soc. Arts*, 1926, **74**, 946, 962, 978; Day and Sosman, in Glazebrook, " Dict. of Applied Physics," 1922, **1**, 835; Ostwald-Luther, " Phys.-chem. Messungen," 5th edit., 1931, 101; Hencky, in Eucken and Jakob, " Der Chemie-Ingenieur," 1933, **2**, iii, 82; Sutton, *J. Sci. Instr.*, 1931, **8**, 98 (precision type); Pérard, *Compt. Rend.*, 1933, **196**, 1090 (parallax); on *calibration* see Stewart, Rücker, and Thorpe, *B.A. Rep.*, 1882, 145; Richards and Shipley, *J.A.C.S.*, 1914, **36**, 1; Richards and Jackson, *Z. phys. Chem.*, 1906, **56**, 362 (below 0°); Grundmann, *Glas u. Apparat*, 1936, **17**, 49, 59, 69, 75, 137, 147, 159, 169, 179, 213, 223; 1937, **18**, 21, 33, 43, 65 (construction and calibr.); on *effect of pressure* on bulb see, e.g., Pickering, *Phil. Mag.*, 1887, **23**, 406; on *lag* see Richards, Henderson, and Forbes, *Z. phys. Chem.*, 1905, **52**, 551 (Beckmann thermometer); Harper, *Bur. Stand. Bull.*, 1912, **8**, 659; McLeod, *Phil. Mag.*, 1919, **37**, 134 (in medium changing in temperature at a definite rate); 1922, **43**, 49; Bromwich, *Phil. Mag.*, 1919, **37**, 407; Griffiths and Awbery, *Trans. Faraday Soc.*, 1922, **18**, 243; Yakovleva, *Trav. Inst. Métrol. Stand. U.R.S.S.*, 1936, No. **10**, 58; Lieneweg, *Wiss. Veröffentl. Siemens-Werken*, 1937, **16**, No. iii, 112; 1938, **17**, No. iv, 19; Henning, " Die Grundlagen der Temperaturmessung," Brunswick, 1915, 81; on evaporation of mercury in thermometers, Olivier, *Chem, Weekbl.*, 1917, **14**, 325.

[5] The secular change of zero was first described by Flaugergues, *Ann. Chim.*, 1822, **21**, 330; Muncke, in Gehler's " Physikalisches Wörterbuch," 1839, **9**, 919; Pernet, *Trav. et Mém. Bur. Internat. Poids et Més.*, 1881, B1; Marchis, *Z. phys. Chem.*, 1899, **29**, 1; 1901, **37**, 553, 605; Allihn, *Chem. Ztg.*, 1909, **33**, 130; on elimination of after-effect (Nachwirkung), Kohlrausch and Loomis, *Ann. Phys.*, 1870, **141**, 401; Jaeger and Steinwehr, *Z. phys. Chem.*, 1906, **54**, 428; on " ageing " thermometers, Dickinson, *Bur. Stand. Bull.*, 1906, **2**, 189; Taylor and Noyes, *J. Amer. Ceram. Soc.*, 1944, **27**, 57.

about 0·01° per year; (iii) an emergent stem correction, due to the fact that the mercury in the stem is not at the same temperature as that in the bulb.

The emergent stem correction [1] may be avoided by having the thermometer calibrated so that it reads correctly when completely immersed up to the level of the mercury in the stem at each reading, but this position may not be possible in practice. A correction for the emergent stem can be applied by Kopp's formula:

$$t=t'+\Delta t'; \quad \Delta t'=(t-t'')n\alpha \simeq (t'-t'')n\alpha \quad . \quad . \quad . \quad . \quad (1)$$

where t'=observed temperature, t=true temperature, t''=mean temperature of emergent stem, n=number of emergent degrees on scale (i.e. number of degree marks between level of immersion and level of reading), α=apparent mean coefficient of expansion of mercury in glass, which for most purposes can be taken as $0{\cdot}00016 \simeq 1/6000$ between 0° and 100°. The correction when the thread thermometer [2] is used is given by Adam as $c=(t'-t)/r(m+t-r)$, where t'=apparent temperature, r=number of unimmersed divisions, t=mean temperature of the mercury in these, $m=1/\alpha_0$, where α_0=apparent coefficient of expansion of mercury in glass.

Dimmer [3] found that Kopp's equation (1) gave satisfactory results; t_2=thermometer reading, t_1=temperature of secondary thermometer in air at half the height of the emergent stem, and α is a constant depending on the glass of the thermometer. For solid and hollow thermometers of Jena 16^{III} from −30° to 100° $\alpha=0{\cdot}000156$; for solid thermometers of Jena 59^{III} $\alpha=0{\cdot}000168$, and for hollow thermometers of Jena 59^{III} $\alpha=0{\cdot}0001579$, both from 0° to 400°. Tables calculated by Dimmer are reproduced in Landolt-Börnstein; [4] only the first is given on p. 427, since the corrections are easily calculated from the formula.

The Paris standard thermometers, formerly made by Tonnelot and later by Baudin, in *verre dur*, can, with full precautions, give a reading to 0·002° and sometimes to 0·001°. Barry [5] described a mercury thermometer for the range 15°–21° which can be read to 0·0001°, which he regarded as the limit of precision.

[1] Regnault, *Mém. Acad. Sci.*, 1847, **21**, 225; Kopp, *Ann.*, 1855, **94**, 257; Holtzmann, in Liebig and Poggendorff, "Handwörterb. d. Chemie," 1859, **7**, 368; Landolt, *Ann.*, 1868, Supplb. **6**, 129; Mousson, *Ann. Phys.*, 1868, **133**, 311; Mills, *Chem. News*, 1875, **31**, 234; *Trans. Roy. Soc. Edin.*, 1880, **29**, 567; Thorpe, *J.C.S.*, 1880, **37**, 141; Rimbach, *Ber.*, 1889, **22**, 3072; Guillaume, *Compt. Rend.*, 1891, **112**, 87; *Z. Instr.*, 1893, **13**, 155; Anon, *Z. Instr.*, 1893, **13**, 157; Wüllner, "Lehrbuch der Experimentalphysik," 1896, **2**, 385; Wiebe, *Arch. Néerl.*, 1901, **6**, 323 (hollow stem); Dimmer, *Wien Ber.*, 1917, **122**, II A, 1439, 1629, 1735; Waidner and Mueller, *Ind. Eng. Chem.*, 1921, **13**, 237 (can be erroneous); Berl and Kullmann, *Ber.*, 1927, **60**, 815; Griffiths, "Methods of Measuring Temperature," 1925, 18; Busse, in "Temperature. Its Measurement and Control," New York, 1941, 228; Noyes, *Instruments*, 1942, **15**, 449; *Amer. Chem. Abstr.*, 1943, **37**, 1064, used an exponential formula; Kane and Schuette, *Oil and Soap*, 1943, **20**, 11 (nomogram).

[2] The "thread thermometer" (Fadenthermometer), introduced by Luz in 1784, is a thermometer with a long thin cylindrical bulb which is immersed alongside until the readings (mercury levels) coincide and the bulb is partly immersed and partly exposed; Guillaume, *Z. Instr.*, 1892, **12**, 69; 1893, **13**, 155; Mahlke, *ibid.*, 1893, **13**, 58; Adam, *Z. Instr.*, 1907, **27**, 101; Buckingham, *Bur. Stand. Bull.*, 1912, **8**, 239; Wiebe, *Petroleum* [German], 1912, **7**, 1304; Schlüter, *Chem. Ztg.*, 1915, **39**, 177; *Mitt. Kgl. Materialsprüfungsamt*, 1915, **33**, 505; Henning, "Temperaturmessung," Brunswick, 1915, 81; Ostwald-Luther, "Phys.-chem. Messungen," 5th edit., 1931, 106.

[3] *Wien Ber.*, 1917, **122**, II A, 1439, 1629, 1735; for hollow thermometers see Meissner, *Z. Instr.*, 1909, **29**, 93.

[4] "Tabellen," 5th edit., 1923, **2**, 1212; Romberg's tables, given in the 4th edit., are said by Dimmer to be unreliable. The tables in Landolt-Börnstein have been checked with Dimmer's and found identical, except that the last entry in Table 1 in the column under 50° is 0·78 in Landolt-Börnstein, which is correct, instead of 0·80 in Dimmer.

[5] *J.A.C.S.*, 1920, **42**, 1911.

THERMOMETERS OF JENA 16^{III} GLASS FROM −30° TO 100°

n	t_2-t_1							
	10	20	30	40	50	60	70	80
10	0·02	0·03	0·05	0·06	0·08	0·09	0·11	0·12
20	0·03	0·06	0·09	0·12	0·16	0·19	0·22	0·25
30	0·05	0·09	0·14	0·19	0·23	0·28	0·33	0·37
40	0·06	0·12	0·19	0·25	0·31	0·37	0·44	0·50
50	0·08	0·16	0·23	0·31	0·39	0·47	0·55	0·62
60	0·09	0·19	0·28	0·37	0·47	0·56	0·65	0·75
70		0·22	0·33	0·44	0·55	0·65	0·76	0·87
80			0·37	0·50	0·62	0·75	0·87	1·00
90				0·56	0·70	0·84	0·98	1·12
100					0·78	0·94	1·09	1·25
110						1·03	1·20	1·37
120							1·31	1·50
130								1·62

An important correction for a mercury thermometer is the *zero depression*; the zero (0°) immediately after heating is lower than before heating owing to a lag in recovery of the volume of the bulb. With Jena 16^{III} glass this recovery takes 2–3 days, with some other glasses it may take 10–14 days.[1] It is usual to determine the depression after exposure to steam for 30 minutes and then measure the ice-point immediately afterwards, after cooling in air to 50°. The zero depression is variable until some time after the thermometer has been made, being smaller with a new thermometer. The following table gives the depressions after cooling from the temperature stated.[2]

Glass	25°	50°	100°
Kew	0·04	0·11	0·22
Verre dur	0·02	0·05	0·11
Jena 16^{III}	0·015	0·03	0·07
Jena 59^{III}	0·01	0·02	0·035
Powell's normal ...	0·01	0·02	0·05

An example of a full thermometer correction [3] is the following:

Observed temperature reading	38·85
Ice-point reading	0·15
Emergent stem correction [4]	0·17
∴ first correction 38·85−0·15+0·17=	38·87
Ice-point depression after ½ hour heating in steam (given in thermom. certificate)=0·06°	
∴ depression for 38°=0·06×38/100=0·02	
correction for 0° (from certificate) 0·12° too high	
" " 40° " " 0·13° " "	
∴ scale and zero depression correction=−0·13−(−0·12)−0·02= ...	−0·03
∴ final corrected temperature=	38·84

[1] Höppler, *Chem. Ztg.*, 1933, **57**, 394.
[2] Higgins, in Glazebrook, " Dict. of Applied Physics," 1922, **1**, 1001.
[3] Length of emergent stem 27°, room temperature 18°; correction from Dimmer's tables in Landolt-Börnstein, " Tabellen," 5th edit., 1923, **2**, 1212.
[4] Ostwald-Luther, " Phys.-chem. Messungen," 5th edit., 1931, 110 f.

It is convenient to make a table of the last three corrections conjointly for the range of the thermometer. Taylor and Noyes [1] found that the change of ice-point with time is given by $y=a(1-e^{-mt})$, where a and m are constants. Wiebe [2] corrected for freezing-point depression by having a piece of glass rod inside the bulb containing the mercury.

Edenholm and Olsson [3] used the formula:

$$\Delta t = n_l(t_a - t_e)/(k - n_l + t_e)$$

where t_e=temperature of emergent stem, t_a=observed temperature, n_1=length of emergent stem in degrees, $1/k$=apparent cubic coefficient of expansion. A monogram for the emergent stem correction is described.[4] A proposed [5] vacuum jacket to eliminate stem correction is useless.[6] Specifications for a laboratory thermometer in single degrees from −20° to +150° are given by Collins.[7] Duclaux and Hamelin [8] devised an arrangement for correcting for change of contact angle and electrification of the mercury.

Mercury thermometers filled with carbon dioxide,[9] reading up to 500°, or (now) of borosilicate glass and filled with nitrogen, reading up to 600°, are used. Thermometers containing potassium-sodium alloy [10] (which turns the glass brown), or of quartz containing tin,[11] thallium,[12] or gallium,[13] have only a limited use and are better replaced by thermocouples. Mercury in quartz has been used.[13]

Temp. °C.	Temp. on mercury scale—temp. on gas scale		
	Verre dur	Jena 16^{III} *	Jena 59^{III}
−30	−0·30	−0·32	−0·18
−20	−0·17	−0·19	−0·10
−10	−0·07	−0·08	−0·04
0	0·00	0·00	0·00
+10	0·052	+0·056	+0·024
20	0·085	0·093	0·035
30	0·102	0·113	0·038
40	0·1075	0·120	0·034
50	0·103	0·116	0·026
60	0·0903	0·103	0·016
70	0·072	0·083	0·0076
80	0·050	0·058	0·001
90	0·026	0·030	−0·002
100	0·000	0·000	0·000

* Tubes of this glass have a thin purple line throughout the length.

1 *J. Amer. Ceram. Soc.*, 1944, **27**, 57.
2 *Z. Instr.*, 1910, **30**, 245.
3 *Amer. Chem. Abstr.*, 1936, **30**, 6248.
4 Berl and Kullmann, *Ber.*, 1927, **60**, 815; Somerville, *Ind. Eng. Chem. Anal.*, 1945, **17**, 675; Skau and Wakeham, in Weissberger, " Physical Methods of Organic Chemistry," New York, 1945, **1**, 35.
5 Hahn, *Z. angew. Chem.*, 1914, **27**, i, 24.
6 Dimmer, *Z. angew. Chem.*, 1915, **28**, i, 255.
7 *Ind. Eng. Chem.*, 1921, **13**, 240; on a short thermometer, see Coste, *J.S.C.I.*, 1913, **32**, 341, and discussion.
8 *J. de Phys.*, 1910, **9**, 600.
9 Mahlke, *Ann. Phys.*, 1894, **53**, 965.
10 Baly and Chorley, *Ber*, 1894, **27**, 470.
11 Dufour, *Compt. Rend.*, 1900, **130**, 775; Northrup, *Trans. Faraday Soc.*, 1917, **13**, 212; Anon., *Met. Chem. Eng.*, 1917, **17**, 558 (in graphite to 2000°).
12 McIntosh and Johnson, *J.A.C.S.*, 1912, **34**, 910.
13 Boyer, *Ind. Eng. Chem.*, 1925, **17**, 1252 (to 1000°); *J. Opt. Soc. Amer.*, 1926, **13**, 117; Moreau, *Compt. Rend.*, 1937, **205**, 967.

The differences between the *mercury scale* (1°=0·01×difference in vols. at 0° and 100° extended in both directions) and the *gas scale* (const. vol. hydrogen thermometer) have been investigated by Chappuis [1] and by Thiesen, Scheel, and Sell.[2] The latter give the table, on p. 428, for three kinds of thermometer glass.[3]

§ 4. Beckmann Thermometer

Lord Charles Cavendish [4] and (less obviously) Walferdin [5] first applied the principle used in the Beckmann (or *metastatic*) thermometer, but Beckmann[6] deserves full credit for making a reliable practical instrument available, and it is affectation to call his thermometer by any other name. Its construction and use are well known (Fig. 3.VI A). It has a large bulb and only six degrees on the scale S, which is graduated in $\frac{1}{100}$ degrees, thousandths being read (with a lens) by interpolation. There is a reservoir *b* at the top into which mercury can be driven by warming and then detached by shaking, if higher temperatures are used, or from which mercury can be drawn by inverting and tapping and then warming until the thread in the capillary joins that in *b*. It is best to have separate thermometers for use at widely separated temperatures, so as to avoid the necessity of heating the bulb too much, which introduces errors of change of volume of the bulb.

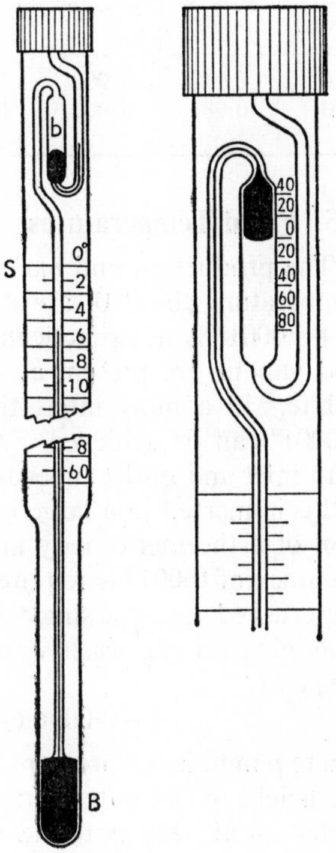

FIG. 3.VI A. Beckmann Thermometer

When a Beckmann thermometer is used account must be taken of the *degree value*, since the quantity of mercury in the bulb is not constant, some being taken out into the upper reservoir when higher temperatures are used. In this case the reading is too small. If the reading is correct at 0°, then at 20° the reading is 20×0·000163=0·003° per degree too small, where 0·000163 is the apparent coefficient of expansion of mercury in glass. The degree factor is thus 1·003, and any measured temperature change must be multiplied by 1·003 to give the correct value. This assumes that the mercury in the capillary is at the same temperature as that in the bulb,

[1] *Trav. et Mém. Bur. Internat. Poids et Més.*, 1888, **6**.

[2] *Z. Instr.*, 1895, **15**, 433; Scheel, *Ann. Phys.*, 1896, **58**, 168; *Z. phys. Chem.*, 1896, **20**, 643.

[3] See Higgins, in Glazebrook, " Dict. of Applied Physics," 1922, **1**, 999.

[4] *Phil. Trans.*, 1757, **50**, 300; abdgd. edit., 1809, **11**, 138 (in full); Menzies, *J.A.C.S.*, 1921, **43**, 2309.

[5] Lottin, Bravais, and Martins, *Compt. Rend.*, 1840, **10**, 289; Walferdin, *ibid.*, 1842, **14**, 63; *Bull. Soc. Geol.*, 1841–2, **13**, 113; Drion, *Ann. Chim.*, 1859, **56**, 5; Wüllner, " Lehrbuch der Experimentalphysik," 1896, **2**, 161.

[6] Beckmann, *Z. phys. Chem.*, 1888, **2**, 638; 1894, **15**, 656; 1896, **21**, 239; 1905, **51**, 329; Grützmacher, *Z. Instr.*, 1896, **16**, 171; *Z. phys. Chem.*, 1896, **21**, 313; 1897, **23**, 365; *Ann. Phys.*, 1899, **68**, 769; Lemke, *Z. Instr.*, 1899, **19**, 33; Schimpff, *Z. phys. Chem.*, 1910, **71**, 257; Kühn, *Chem. Ztg.*, 1912, **36**, 843; 1926, **50**, 437; Disch, *Z. angew. Chem.*, 1913, **26**, 279; Gray, " A Manual of Practical Physical Chemistry," 1914, 48; Féry, *Bull. Soc. Encourag.*, 1914, **113**, 405;

otherwise an emergent stem correction (§ 3) must also be applied, as with all mercury thermometers. It is usually sufficient to take a *decrease* of degree value of 0·001 for every 6° rise in temperature of the stem temperature. E.g. if a measurement is made at 0°, where the degree value is 1·000, and the stem temperature is 15°, the true degree value is $1-15\times0{\cdot}001/6=0{\cdot}997°$. Grützmacher gave the following degree values (reduced to the hydrogen scale): A values are for totally non-immersed mercury thread and B values for totally immersed mercury thread:

Interval	−35° to −30°	0° to 5°	20° to 25°	45° to 50°	95° to 100°	145° to 150°	195° to 200°	245° to 250°
A	0·982	1·000	1·009	1·020	1·037	1·050	1·058	1·060
B	0·981	1·002	1·009	1·016	1·026	1·032	1·033	1·039

§ 5. Fixed Temperatures

The production and *maintenance* of an ice bath within very narrow limits of temperature about 0° are not at all easy; an expert [1] has said that control to $0°\pm0{\cdot}0001°$ is not practicable, and a " triple point bulb," in which ice, water, and vapour are present at $+0{\cdot}0077°$ and 4·57 mm., has been recommended.[2] White,[3] in a most interesting and valuable paper, describes how control to 0·0001° can be achieved. A cell is filled with pure crushed ice and provided with inlet and outlet tubes for washing the ice with pure chilled water, and this cell is immersed in a large ice bath. It may be used to maintain the cold junction of a thermel exactly at 0° over a long period. Roper [4] found that if an accuracy of 0·001° is required, White's apparatus can be simplified: he washed the crushed ice in a single Dewar vessel with chilled pure water (at $0°\pm0{\cdot}1°$), siphoning off the wash water. Beattie, Benedict, and Blaisdell [4] gave for the *ice-point*:

$$-0{\cdot}0098\,(p-760)/760-0{\cdot}0075H/(13{\cdot}6\times760)$$

where p mm. is the pressure at which the water is saturated with air, and H mm. the height of the water surface above the middle point of the platinum thermometer spiral. Moser found the difference between the triple point and the m.p. of ice to water saturated with CO_2-free air to be $0{\cdot}00743\pm0{\cdot}00005°$, and since the melting-point of ice to this water is 0·0024°, the triple point itself is 0·0098°. The effect of dissolved air on the freezing-point of a liquid seems to have been

Fajans and Wüst, " Practical Physical Chemistry," transl. Topley, 1930, 17; Ostwald-Luther, " Phys.-chem. Messungen," 5th edit., 1931, 378; Matsui, Kambara, and Yoshino, *J. Soc. Chem. Ind. Japan*, 1932, **35**, Suppl. Bdg. 313 (calibration); Busse, in " Temperature. Its Measurement and Control," New York, 1941, 228; Reynolds, *Chem. and Ind.*, 1947, 563 (resetting); on Beckmann, *Z. angew. Chem.*, 1923, **36**, 341.

[1] Moser (of the Reichsanstalt), *Ann. Phys.*, 1929, **1**, 341; Waring, *Science*, 1943, **97**, 221.

[2] Moser, *loc. cit.*; Michels and Coeterier, *Proc. K. Akad. Wetens. Amsterdam*, 1927, **30**, 1017.

[3] *Rev. Sci. Instr.*, 1933, **4**, 142; *J.A.C.S.*, 1934, **56**, 20.

[4] *J.A.C.S.*, 1938, **60**, 866; see also Foote and Leopold, *Amer. J. Sci.*, 1926, **11** **[211]**, 42, who say the f.p. of *air-free* water is +0·0023°; Thomas, *Bur. Stand. J. Res.*, 1934, **12**, 313, 323, who says washed commercial ice (excluding the white core) is as good as ice from distilled water; Beattie, Benedict, and Blaisdell, *Proc. Amer. Acad.*, 1937, **71**, 327; Beattie and Blaisdell, *ibid.*, 1937, **71**, 361, 375; Beattie, Tzu-Ching Huang, and Benedict, *ibid.*, 1938, **72**, 137 (triple point 0·00981°); Thomas, in " Temperature. Its Measurement and Control," New York, 1941, 159.

first investigated by Prytz.[1] Stimson[2] found that the pressure and dissolved air together lower the freezing-point about 0·00991° C., so that the triple point is about +0·0100° C. Michels and Coeterier[3] had found the ice-point variable by 0·01° on account of dissolved air, and recommended the triple point +0·007°±0·00023° as standard.

The freezing-points of solutions were proposed as constant temperatures.[4] The *steam bath* for calibrating thermometers described by Regnault is depicted in most textbooks;[5] an improved form was described by Keesom and van der Horst.[6] The temperature of the steam is found by taking the barometric pressure and finding the temperature at which the vapour pressure of water has this value in the tables of vapour pressures, or by using a formula. In Chappius' steam-point apparatus[7] the steam column can be swung into a horizontal position to give the readings for vertical and horizontal positions of the thermometer and thus the internal pressure correction. The influence of pressure has been given[8] as 0·001° per 6 mm. Hg; it may cause errors of more than 0·15° in vacuum distillations.[9]

For the steam-point between 660 and 860 mm. pressure p, Beattie and Blaisdell[10] gave

$$100+0{\cdot}0368578(p-760)-0{\cdot}0_4201591(p-760)^2+0{\cdot}0_71621(p-760)^3.$$

Some fixed points which have been proposed are transition points in systems of salts and water, but as these have been rather differently given by the same experimenters at different times they are not the most accurate standards and are best not used (where only one formula is given, the anhydrous salt is formed):

Na_2SO_4, $10H_2O$	32·383 [11]	Na_2CO_3, $10H_2O \rightarrow 7H_2O$	32·017 [15]
$MnCl_2$, $4H_2O \rightarrow 2H_2O$ ...	58·089±0·005 [12]	NaBr, $2H_2O$	50·674 [16]
$SrCl_2$, $6H_2O \rightarrow 2H_2O$ ...	61·341±0·0007 [13]	$NaNO_3+Na_2SO_4$, $10H_2O$	13·154±0·001 [17]
$SrBr_2$, $6H_2O \rightarrow ?H_2O$ ...	88·62 [13]	Na_2SO_4+NaCl (solid) ...	17·878±0·002 [17]
Na_2CrO_4, $10H_2O \rightarrow 6H_2O$	19·525 [14]	KCl eutectic	−10·645±0·0025 [17]
Na_2CrO_4, $10H_2O \rightarrow 4H_2O$	19·987 [14]	KNO_3 eutectic	− 2·86° [18]
Na_2CrO_4, $6H_2O \rightarrow 4H_2O$	25·90 [14]	$Ba(NO_3)_2$ eutectic ...	− 0·71° [18]

1 *Dansk. Vidensk. Selsk. Forhl.*, 1893, 151; *Ann. Phys. Beibl.*, 1893, **17**, 815.
2 *J. Wash. Acad.*, 1945, **35**, 201.
3 *Proc. K. Akad. Wetens. Amsterdam*, 1927, **30**, 1017.
4 Prytz, *Z. phys. Chem.*, 1904, **47**, 729.
5 Balfour Stewart, "Elementary Treatise on Heat," Oxford, 1888, 11.
6 *Proc. K. Akad. Wetens. Amsterdam*, 1927, **30**, 970; *Comm. Leiden*, **188***a*.
7 Higgins, in Glazebrook, "Dict. of Applied Physics," 1922, **1**, 994 (N.P.L. apparatus also).
8 Loomis, *Ann. Phys.*, 1894, **51**, 500.
9 Smith and Menzies, *Z. phys. Chem.*, 1910, **75**, 498.
10 See note 4 on p. 430.
11 Richards *et al.*, *Z. phys. Chem.*, 1898, **26**, 290 (32·379°); 1903, **43**, 465 (32·383° on H_2 thermom.); Dickinson and Mueller, *Bur. Stand. Bull.*, 1907, **3**, 641; *J.A.C.S.*, 1907, **29**, 1318 (32·384°); Redlich and Loeffler, *Z. Elektrochem.*, 1930, **36**, 716 (32·383°); Hvle, *Chem. Met. Eng.*, 1945, **52**, No. 6, 115; this seems a reliable standard.
12 Richards *et al.*, *Z. phys. Chem.*, 1908, **61**, 313.
13 Richards *et al.*, *J.A.C.S.*, 1918, **40**, 89.
14 Richards *et al.*, *J.A.C.S.*, 1911, **33**, 847; the closeness of the first two transitions makes this an unreliable standard.
15 Richards *et al.*, *J.A.C.S.*, 1914, **36**, 485.
16 Richards *et al.*, *Z. phys. Chem.*, 1906, **56**, 348.
17 Redlich and Löffler, *Z. Elektrochem.*, 1930, **36**, 716.
18 Schoorl, *Chem. Weekbl.*, 1915, **12**, 222.

The determination of temperature from the *solubility* of a salt (e.g. Na_2SO_4),[1] or the use of ice and hydrochloric acid,[2] etc., are inconvenient and unreliable. Fusible metals of the Wood's metal type were proposed as standards by Steinmetz.[3] The transition temperature of CCl_4 seems unsuitable, as it has been given differently by different experimenters.[4] The transition [5] Na_2SO_4, $7H_2O$–Na_2SO_4 at 23·465°±0·004°, is inconvenient.

§ 6. Melting- and Boiling-Points

In the following tables [6] the melting- and boiling-points are given in ° C.:

ELEMENTS

	m.p.	b.p.		m.p.	b.p.
Aluminium	659·8	>2200	Molybdenum	2620	3700
Antimony	630·5	1380	Neon	−248·52	−245·92
Argon	−189·25	−185·85	Nickel	1455	2900
Arsenic	814·5	615 (sublimes)	Niobium	1950	3700
Barium	710	1537	Nitrogen	−210	−195·8
Beryllium	1280	1500	Osmium	2750	>5300
Bismuth	271	1450	Oxygen	−218·4	−183
Boron	2300	2550	Palladium	1553	2200
Bromine	−7·2	58·7	Phosphorus †	44·1	287
Cadmium	320·9	767·3	Platinum	1755	4300
Caesium	28·45	670	Potassium	63·50	757·5
Calcium	851	1439	Radon	−71	−62
Carbon	3500	4200	Rhenium	3167	—
Chlorine	−101·6	−34·6	Rhodium	1970	>2500
Chromium	1900	2200	Rubidium	39·0	700
Cobalt	1495	2900	Ruthenium	2450	>2700
Copper	1083·0	2310	Selenium	220·2	684·8
Fluorine	−217·8	−187	Silicon	1420	2600
Gallium	29·75	>2000	Silver	960·5	1955
Germanium	958·5	2700	Sodium	97·9	882·9
Gold	1063·0	2610	Strontium	800	1366
Hafnium	2200	3200	Sulphur §	112·8	444·60
Helium	−272	−268·87	Tantalum	2850	>4100
Hydrogen *	−259	−252·78	Tellurium	452·5	1390
Indium	155·4	>1450	Thallium	303·5	1475
Iodine	113·9	184·4	Thorium	1845	>3000
Iridium	2440	>4800	Tin	231·84	2260
Iron	1539	2450	Titanium	1800	>3000
Krypton	−157	−152·9	Tungsten	3390	5900
Lead	327·4	1620	Uranium	1689	3500?
Lithium	180	1336	Vanadium	1710	3000
Magnesium	651	1100	Xenon	−111·5	−107·1
Manganese	1260	1900	Zinc	419·4	920
Mercury	−38·90	356·95	Zirconium	1600	>2900

* Deuterium, m.p. −254·5, b.p. −249·6. † White. § Rhombic.

[1] Richards *et al.*, *J.A.C.S.*, 1918, **40**, 164.

[2] Richards *et al.*, *Z. phys. Chem.*, 1906, **56**, 362.

[3] *J.A.C.S.*, 1918, **40**, 96; for a long table of fixed points, see Burgess, *Amer. Chem. Abstr.*, 1912, **6**, 2881; *J. Chim. Phys.*, 1913, **11**, 529.

[4] McCollough and Phipps, *J.A.C.S.*, 1928, **50**, 2213 (−48·45° ±0·02°); Skau and Meier, *ibid.*, 1929, **51**, 3517 (−47·55° ±0·12°); Johnston and Long, *ibid.*, 1934, **56**, 31 (−47·665°); Hicks, Hooley, and Stephenson, *ibid.*, 1944, **66**, 1064; Davidson, Argersinger, and Michaelis, *J. Phys. Chem.*, 1948, **52**, 332 (−47·8°).

[5] Washburn and Clem, *J.A.C.S.*, 1938, **60**, 754.

[6] Landolt-Börnstein, "Tabellen," 5th edit., 1923, 313 (elements), 335 (inorganic compounds), 366 (organic compounds); 1931, Ergänzsbd. **2**, i, 229; Weygand, *Hand u. Jahrb.*

Hume-Rothery [1] found that the b.ps. of elements are given by $T_b N^4 V^3/m = C \simeq 55$, where N=principal quantum number (§§ 14–17.V) of the valency electron, V=ionising potential of the valency electron, m=atomic weight. The melting- and boiling-points of elements are periodic functions of the atomic weights.[2] Increased density in allotropic forms is accompanied by increased m.p.[3] All solids which do not decompose can be melted and boiled in the electric arc furnace.[4] Some carbides have the highest m.ps. of any substances known, about 4100° K.[5] and this has been related to the valencies of the two elements forming the binary compound:

	LiF	MgO	TiN	NbC
m.p. ° K.	1115	2920	3200	4100

For the same valencies, the m.p. of the binary compound AB is highest for a given relation between the atomic or ionic volumes of the constituents, in many cases one of approximate equality. A small volume of one ion compared with the volume of the other ion leads to low m.p., the anion volume being of major importance. For low m.p. gases (HCl, etc.) the anion volume is overwhelmingly large in comparison with the cation volume. The m.p.s of elements are functions

chem. Phys., **2**, iiiC, 104; Partington, "A Textbook of Inorganic Chemistry," 1946, 410; b.ps. of metals, van Laar, *Chem. Weekbl.*, 1936, **33**, 215 (Zn 907°, Cu 2369°); for plot of m.p. and b.p. of elements against atomic number, see Fischer, *J. prakt. Chem.*, 1941, **158**, 200; Renaud, *Bull. Soc. Chim.*, 1945, **12**, 1060; m.ps. of pure elements, Guertler and Pirani, *Z. Metallkde*, 1919, **11**, 1; *Amer. Chem. Abstr.*, 1920, **14**, 664 (tables); of salts, Hüttner and Tammann, *Z. anorg. Chem.*, 1905, **43**, 215; Roberts, *Phys. Rev.*, 1924, **23**, 383; barium, Hartmann and May, *Z. anorg. Chem.*, 1929, **185**, 167 (m.p. 658°); Guntz (m.p. 850°); boron, Cueilleron, *Compt. Rend.*, 1944, **219**, 209, m.p. pure B, 2000°–2075°; carbon, Crookes, *Chem. News*, 1906, **92**, 147; La Rosa, *Ann. Phys.*, 1909, **30**, 369; 1910, **34**, 4; 1911, **36**, 841; Watts and Mendenhall, *ibid.*, 1911, **35**, 783; Thiel and Rittner, *Z. anorg. Chem.*, 1923, **132**, 153; Kohn and Gucker, *Z. Phys.*, 1924, **27**, 305; chromium, Grube and Knabe, *Z. Elektrochem.*, 1936, **42**, 793; cobalt, van Dusen and Dahl, *Bur. Stand. J. Res.*, 1947, **39**, 291; deuterium, Scott, Brickwedde, Urey, and Wahl, *J. Chem. Phys.*, 1934, **2**, 454 (b.p. 23·5° K., triple pt. 18·58° K.); fluorine, Kanda, *Bull. Chem. Soc. Japan*, 1937, **12**, 511 (m.p. −218°); gallium, Roeser and Hoffmann, *Bur. Stand. J. Res.*, 1934, **13**, 673 (m.p. 29·780°); gold, Holborn and Day, *Ann. Phys.*, 1901, **4**, 99 (m.p, 1063·9°); hydrogen, Heuse and Otto, *Ann. Phys.*, 1931, **9**, 486 (b.p. −253·78°); iridium. Henning and Wensel, *Bur. Stand. J. Res.*, 1933, **10**, 809 (f.p. 2454°); iron, Roeser and Wensel, *Bur. Stand. J. Res.*, 1941, **26**, 273; lithium, Hartmann and Schneider, *Z. anorg. Chem.*, 1929, **180**, 275; krypton, Allen and Moore, *J.A.C.S.*, 1931; **52**, 2522; mercury, Heuse and Otto, *Ann. Phys.*, 1931, **9**, 486 (m.p. −38·832°); Henning, *ibid.*, 1914, **43**, 282; nickel, Wensel and Roeser, *Bur. Stand. J. Res.*, 1930, **5**, 1309; van Dusen and Dahl, *Bur. Stand. J. Res.*, 1947, **39**, 291; niobium, Wensel and Roeser, *Bur. Stand. J. Res.*, 1930, **5**, 1309; nitrogen, Aoyama and Kanda, *J. Chem. Soc. Japan*, 1934, **55**, 15 (b.p. −195·79°); oxygen, Heuse and Otto, *Ann. Phys.*, 1931, **9**, 486 (b.p. −182·962°); Aoyama and Kanda, *J. Chem. Soc. Japan*, 1934, **55**, 15 (b.p. −182·98°); platinum, Ribaud and Mohr, *Compt. Rend.*, 1931, **192**, 37 (m.p. 1762°); Schofield, *Proc. Roy. Soc.*, 1934, **146**, 793; Hoffmann and Tingwalt, *Phys. Z.*, 1934, **35**, 434 (f.p. 1773·8° ±1°); rhenium, Agte, Alterthum, Becker, Heyne, and Moers, *Naturwiss.*, 1931, **19**, 108; *Z. anorg. Chem.*, 1931, **196**, 129; selenium, de Selincourt, *Proc. Phys. Soc.*, 1940, **52**, 348 (b.p. 684·8°); silicon, Gayler, *Nature*, 1938, **142**, 478 (m.p. 1415°); strontium, Trautz and Kiphan, *Z. anal. Chem.*, 1929, **78**, 350 (m.p. 797°); Hartmann and May, *Z. anorg. Chem.*, 1929, **185**, 167 (m.p. 752°); tellurium, Kracek, *J.A.C.S.*, 1941, **63**, 1989 (m.p. 449·8°); titanium, Waggaman and Gee, *Chem. Eng. News*, 1948, **26**, 377 (m.p. 1725°); xenon, Allen and Moore, *J.A.C.S.*, 1931, **52**, 2522; zirconium, Waggaman and Gee, *op. cit.* (m.p. 1860° ?).

[1] *J. Phys. Chem.*, 1940, **44**, 808.

[2] Biltz, *Z. Elektrochem.*, 1913, **19**, 613; Ono, *Proc. Phys. Math. Soc. Japan*, 1919, **1**, 251; Renaud, *Bull Soc. Chim.*, 1945, 1060.

[3] Mohr, *Ann.*, 1872, **62**, 61.

[4] Moissan, *Compt. Rend.*, 1906, **142**, 189, 425, 673; *Ann. Chim.*, 1906, **8**, 145.

[5] Friederich and Sittig, *Z. anorg. Chem.*, 1925, **144**, 169; 1925, **145**, 251; Friederich, *Z. Phys.*, 1925, **31**, 813; on refractory nitrides, see Friederich and Sittig, *Z. anorg. Chem.*, 1925, **143**, 293; for the fusion and evaporation of carbon, see, e.g., Alterthum, *Z. tech. Phys.*, 1925, **6**, 540.

of the forces by which the atoms are held together by valency electrons: the highest m.p.s occur at places where metals change to non-metals in the Periodic Table.[1] Ruff[2] found no regular relation of the b.p. with the mass of the central atom, the atomic volume, or the number of atoms in the molecule. The most important factors for volatility are the minimum negative charge on the central atom and the symmetry of the molecule, high symmetry favouring volatility.

The relation between melting-point and the valency forces between the atoms was clearly stated by Nernst,[3] the high m.p. of diamond, for example, being attributed to the strong chemical valency bonds between the carbon atoms, and the low m.ps. of the inert gases to the weak van der Waals forces between their atoms.

INORGANIC COMPOUNDS

	m.p.	b.p.		m.p.	b.p.
HCN[4]	−13·24	25·70	KCl	768	1417
HF[5]	−83	19·4	LiBr	535	1310
PCl_3[6]	−92	76	NaBr	766	1393
$POCl_3$	1·25	107·2	KBr	748	{1376, 1381}
POF_3[7]	−39·4	−39·8			
$SiCl_4$	−68·7	57·0	LiI	450	1170
$TiCl_4$	−25	136·4	NaI	660	1300
$SnCl_4$	−33	114·1	KI	682	1330
$GeCl_4$	−49·5	86·5			
$AsCl_3$	−16	130	Li_2CO_3	735	—
$AsBr_3$	32·8	221	Na_2CO_3	853	—
$SbCl_3$	73	222	K_2CO_3	894	—
$SbBr_3$	96·6	283			
			CuCl	430	1367
Hg_2Cl_2	525	383	CuBr	488	1345
Hg_2I_2	290	310	CuI	588	1293
$HgCl_2$	280	302	AgCl	449	1554
$HgBr_2$	238	320	AgBr	419	—
HgI_2	257	350	AgI	556	—
PbF_2	818	1290	CaF_2	1330	2451
$PbCl_2$	498	954	$CaCl_2$	774	—
$PbBr_2$	373	916	$CaBr_2$	760	812
PbI_2	393	950	CaI_2	740	—
TlCl	451	708	$AlCl_3$	190	—
TlBr	463	—		(2·5 atm.)	
TlI	446	800	$AlBr_3$	97·5	265
			AlI_3	191	>350
LiF[8]	840	1676			
NaF	992	1695	Li_2SO_4	859	—
KF...	846	1505	Na_2SO_4	897	—
LiCl	614	1382	K_2SO_4	1074	—
NaCl	803	{1430, 1441}	Rb_2SO_4	1074	—
			Cs_2SO_4	1019	—

[1] See note 2 on p. 433.
[2] *Ber.*, 1919, **52**, 1223 (tables of b.ps. of salts).
[3] " Vorträge über die kinetische Theorie der Materie und der Elektrizität " (Wolfskehl Samml., Göttingen), Leipzig and Berlin, 1914, 63; Mazzucchelli, *Gazz.*, 1920, **50**, i, 93.
[4] Giauque and Ruhrwein, *J.A.C.S.*, 1939, **61**, 2626.
[5] Wöhler and Jung, *Z. phys. Chem.*, 1933, **21**B, 31.
[6] Biltz and Jeep, *Z. anorg. Chem.*, 1927, **162**, 33.
[7] Booth and Dutton, *J.A.C.S.*, 1939, **61**, 2937.
[8] Boiling-points of alkali halides, von Wartenberg and Schulz, *Z. Elektrochem.*, 1921, **27**, 568.

In the following table $\rho_4{}^{15}$ is the density in g./ml. at 15°, $n_D{}^{15}$ the refractive index for the sodium line at 15°; H_α is the hydrogen line 6563 A.

ORGANIC COMPOUNDS *

	m.p.	b.p.	$\rho_4{}^{15}$	$n_D{}^{15}$
acetaldehyde, CH_3CHO	−123·5 [75]	20·2	0·7834 (20°)	1·33157 (20°)
acetic acid, CH_3COOH	16·7	118·5	1·05148 (18°)	1·37182 (20°)
acetic anhydride, $(CH_3CO)_2O$ ...	−73	139·5	1·0876	1·39038 (20°)
acetone, $(CH_3)_2CO$	−94·6 [75]	56·48 [71]	—	—
	—	56·20 [2]	0·79597 [2]	1·36157 [2]
acetophenone	19·655 [4]	202·0 [6]	1·0238 (25°) [4]	1·53427 (19·1°)
acetyl chloride, CH_3COCl ...	−112	51	1·03236 [6]	1·5363 [6]
allyl alcohol, $CH_2{:}CH.CH_2OH$ ...	(glassy)	97·0 [3]	0·85511 [3]	1·41175 (Hα) [3]
iso-amyl acetate, $CH_3COOC_5H_{11}$	—	142·0	0·8764 (20°)	1·40143 (18·1°)
n-amyl alcohol, $C_5H_{11}OH$ ...	−73·85 [3]	138·25 [3]	0·81837 [3]	1·41173 [3]
iso-amyl alcohol, $C_5H_{11}OH$ ...	−117·2 [75]	131·6 (765 mm.)	0·81289	1·4084 (17·8°)
tert-amyl alcohol, $C_5H_{11}OH$ ...	−11·9 [75]	101·8	0·812	—
anethole	22·5	235·2	0·98556 (21·6°)	1·5624 (12°)
aniline, $C_6H_5NH_2$	−6·1 [5]	184·40 [5]	1·02613 [5]	1·58872 [5]
	−5·98 [66]	—	—	—
anisole, $C_6H_5.OCH_3$	−37·5 [6]	153·80 [6]	0·99858 [6]	1·51961 [6]
anthracene	217·5	333·9 [61]	1·25 (20°)	—
	(213)		—	—
anthraquinone	286 (subl.)	376·8 [61]		
benzaldehyde, C_6H_5COH ...	−26	179·1 (751·3 mm.)	1·0504	1·54629 (17·6°)
benzene, C_6H_6	5·51 [58]	80·093 [58]	—	—
	5·49 [7]	80·2 [11]	0·8791 (20°) [11]	1·50439 [10]
	5·58 [8]	80·110 [57]	—	—
	5·483 [9]	80·08 [10]	0·88420 [10]	1·49794 (25°) [11]
	5·50 [10]	—	0·87367 (25°) [58]	—
	5·48 [11]	—	—	—
	5·493 [9, 12]	—	—	—
	5·7 [68]	—	—	—
	5·85 [54]	—	—	—
benzoic acid	122·36 [59]	250·03 [61]	—	—
benzonitrile, C_6H_5CN	−12·9 [75]	—	—	—
	−13·8 [5]	191·10 [5]	1·00948 [5]	1·53056 [5]
†benzophenone, $(C_6H_5)_2CO$ ...	47·8 [15]	305·44 [15]	—	—
	—	305·9 [61]	—	—
benzoyl chloride, C_6H_5COCl ...	−0·5	198	—	—
benzyl alcohol, $C_6H_5CH_2OH$ ...	−15·3 [6]	205·45 [6]	1·04927 [6]	1·54259 [6]
bromobenzene, C_6H_5Br ...	−30·6 [10]	156·15 [10]	1·50170 [10]	1·56252 [10]
bromoform, $CHBr_3$	8·05 [2]	149·55 [2]	2·90350 [2]	1·60053 [2]
α-bromonaphthalene, $C_{10}H_7Br$ ...	6·10 [13]	277 [13]	1·4834	1·6582
	6·20 [13a]		(20°) [13a]	(20°) [13a]
butane (*see* hydrocarbons, below)				
n-butyl alcohol, C_4H_9OH	−90·2 [2]	118·0 [2]	0·81337 [2]	1·40118 [2]
	−79·9 [75]	—	—	—

* See pp. 440–2 for footnotes.

† The α-form.

ORGANIC COMPOUNDS—*continued*

	m.p.	b.p.	$\rho_4{}^{15}$	$n_D{}^{15}$
iso-butyl alcohol, C_4H_9OH	glassy [2]	108·10 [2]	0·80576 [2]	1·39768 [2]
	−108 [75]	—	—	—
sec-butyl alcohol, C_4H_9OH	−114·7 [75]	99·50 [2]	0·81088 [2]	1·39946 [2]
tert-butyl alcohol, C_4H_9OH	25·55 [14]	82·50 [14]	0·7762 (30°) [14]	—
n-butyric acid, $C_3H_7.COOH$	−5·50 [3]	164·05 [3]	0·96286 [3]	1·39803 (Hα) [3]
iso-butyric acid, $C_3H_7.COOH$	−46·1 [14]	154·70 [14]	0·95296 [14]	1·39525 [14]
camphor (*d*), $C_{10}H_{16}O$	180	209	—	—
carbazole, $(C_6H_4)_2NH$	240·3 [61]	354	—	—
carbon disulphide, CS_2	−112 [1]	46·25 [2,18]	1·27055 [2]	1·63189 [2]
	−116·8 [2]	46·85 [71]	—	1·63149 [71]
	−111·8 [16]	—	—	—
	−111·99 [17]	—	—	—
carbon tetrachloride, CCl_4	−22·85 [16]	76·75 [10, 18]	1·60370 [10]	1·46305 [10]
	−22·9 [18]	—	—	—
	−22·95 [10]	—	—	—
carbonyl chloride, $COCl_2$	−104 [75]	8·2 (756·4 mm)	1·432 (0°)	—
1, 2, 4-carvacrol, $CH_3.C_6H_3(OH)CH(CH_3)_2$	0·5	237·9	0·981	—
chloral, $CCl_3.CHO$	−57·5	97·7	1·5121 (20°)	1·4557 (20°)
chlorobenzene, C_6H_5Cl	−45·2 [16, 18]	132·00 [10, 18]	1·11172 [10]	1·52748 [10]
	−45·1 [10]	—	—	—
	−45·35 [16]	—	—	—
chloroform, $CHCl_3$	−63·5 [10, 16, 18]	61·20 [10, 18]	1·49845 [10]	1·44858 [10]
	−63·7 [1]	—	—	—
	−63·2 [20]	—	—	—
	−63·45 [16]	—	—	—
α-chloronaphthalene, $C_{10}H_7Cl$	—	262·7	1·19382 (20°)	1·6332 (20°)
β-chloronaphthalene, $C_{10}H_7Cl$	56	264·3	1·2656 (16°)	—
o-chlorotoluene, C_7H_7Cl	−34	159·5	1·0785 (20°)	1·52221 (25°)
m-chlorotoluene	−47·8	162·2 (756·5 mm.)	1·07166 (20°)	1·5214 (19°)
p-chlorotoluene	—	161·8	1·0700 (20°)	1·51895 (25°)
cineol, $C_{10}H_{18}O$	0·9 [69]	176·4	0·9294	1·45839 (20°)
cinnamic acid, $C_6H_5CH{:}CH.COOH$	133	300	—	—
a-citral, $C_9H_{15}.CHO$	—	228	0·8868 (20°)	1·4875 (20°)
o-cresol, $CH_3.C_6H_4.OH$	30·95	190·67	1·0458 (25°)	1·5453 (20°)
m-cresol, $CH_3.C_6H_4.OH$	11·95 [13]	202·70 [13]	1·03803 [13]	1·54318 [13]
p-cresol, $CH_3.C_6H_4.OH$	37	202·32 [21]	1·0341 (20°)	1·5395 (20°)
cyclobutane, C_4H_8	−50 [75]	11·12	0·7038 (0°)	1·3752 (0°)
cyclohexane, C_6H_{12}	6·40 [10]	80·80 [10]	0·78310 [10]	1·42886 [10]
cyclohexanol, $CH_2{:}(CH_2.CH_2)_2{:}CHOH$	23·9 [75]	—	—	—
	25·15 [13]	161·10 [13]	0·94155 (30°) [13]	1·46477 (25°) [13]
cyclohexanone, $CH_2{:}(CH_2.CH_2)_2{:}CO$	−15·0 [75]	—	—	—
	−16·4 [13]	155·65 [13]	0·95099 [13]	1·45203 [13]
1, 4-cymene, $CH_3.C_6H_4.CH(CH_3)_2$	−51	177·3	0·8570 (20°)	1·4926 (13·7°)
cis-decalin	−36	193	0·8952	1·48054 (20°)
trans-decalin	—	185	0·8695 (20°)	1·46958 (20°)
p-dichlorobenzene, $C_6H_4Cl_2$	53·13 [67]	174	—	—
dimethylamine, $NH(CH_3)_2$	−92·19 [22, 23]	6·88 [23]	0·6804 (0°)	1·350 (17°)
dimethylaniline, $C_6H_5N(CH_3)_2$	2·45 [5]	194·15 [5]	0·96012 [5]	1·56083 [5]

ORGANIC COMPOUNDS—*continued*

	m.p.	b.p.	ρ_4^{15}	n_D^{15}
o-dinitrobenzene, $C_6H_4(NO_2)_2$ ...	116·93	318·14	—	—
m-dinitrobenzene, $C_6H_4(NO_2)_2$ ...	89·59 [24]	302·6	—	—
p-dinitrobenzene, $C_6H_4(NO_2)_2$ ...	173·5	299	—	—
1–4 dioxane, $O<(CH_2.CH_2)_2>O$...	11·80 [13]	101·40 [13]	1·03916 [13]	1·42436 [13]
diphenyl, $C_6H_5.C_6H_5$	69·0 [15]	254·93 [15]	—	—
diphenylamine, $(C_6H_5)_2NH$ ...	52·98	302	—	—
4, 4′-dipyridyl, $C_5H_4N.C_5H_4N$ ...	112	304·8	—	—
ether, $(C_2H_5)_2O$ ... stable	−116·3 [2, 16]	34·60 [2]	0·71925 [2]	1·35555 [2]
	−117·6 [20]	34·50 [70]	—	—
metastable	−123·3 [2]	—	—	—
	−123·7 [20]	—	—	—
	−123·6 [1, 20]	—	—	—
	−123·3 [16]	—	—	—
ethyl acetate, $CH_3COOC_2H_5$ ...	−82·4	77·06	0·9005 (20°)	1·37257 (20°)
ethyl alcohol, C_2H_5OH	−114·6	78·319 [60]	0·78992 (20°) 0·789344 (20°)	1·36170 (20°) 1·36232 (20°)
ethylamine, $C_2H_5NH_2$	−112 [75]	16·6	0·7059 (0°)	—
ethyl benzoate, $C_6H_5COOC_2H_5$ ...	−34·7 [5]	212·45 [5]	1·05112 [5]	1·50748 [5]
ethyl bromide, C_2H_5Br	−117·8 [75]	—	—	—
	−119·0 [10]	38·40 [10]	1·47080 [10]	1·42756 [10]
ethyl chloride, C_2H_5Cl	−136·4 [13]	12·30 [13]	0·90280 [13]	—
ethyl formate, $HCOOC_2H_5$ ...	−79·4 [8]	54·15 [3]	0·92892 [3]	1·36047 (Hα) [3]
ethyl iodide, C_2H_5I	−111·1 [2]	72·30 [2]	1·94707 [2]	1·51682 [2]
	−105 [75]	—	—	—
ethyl malonate, $CH_2(COOC_2H_5)_2$	−51·5 [14]	199·30 [14]	1·06040 [14]	1·41393 (Hα) [14]
ethyl tartrate (*d*), $C_4H_4O_6(C_2H_5)_2$	17	280	—	—
ethylene bromide, $C_2H_4Br_2$ ...	10·00 [10]	131·70 [10]	2·1911 [10]	1·54160 [10]
ethylene chloride, $C_2H_4Cl_2$ ...	−35·5 [2]	83·50 [2]	1·26000 [2]	1·44759 [2]
ethylene oxide, C_2H_4O	−111·7 [13]	10·7 [13]	0·89713 (0°) [13]	—
1, 4, 3-eugenol,* $C_3H_5.C_6H_3(OH)OCH_3$	10·3	253	1·071	1·5416 (19·4°)
fluorobenzene, C_6H_5F	−41·9 [6]	84·85 [6]	1·03091 [6]	1·46837 [6]
formamide	2·55 [6]	—	1·13756 [6]	1·44911 [6]
formic acid, $HCOOH$	8·25	100·7	1·22647	1·37137 (20°)
fumaric acid, $COOH.CH:CH.COOH$	286·5	290	—	—
	—	77·0 (37 mm.)	—	—
furfural, $C_4H_3O.CHO$	−31	161·7 [64]	1·1563 (25°)	1·52608 (20°)
glutaric acid, $CH_2(CH_2COOH)_2$	97·5	304	—	—
glycol, $(CH_2OH)_2$	−12·6 [6]	197·85 [6]	1·11710 [6]	1·43312 [6]
glycerol, $HO.CH_2.CHOH.CH_2.OH$	18·07 [65]	290	1·26443 [6]	1·47319 [6]
o-guiacol, $HO.C_6H_4.OCH_3$ ...	32	205·1	1·1287 (21·4°)	—
indene, C_9H_8	−2	182·4	1·0059 (4°)	1·5711 (12·7°)
indole, C_8H_7N	52·5	254	—	—
iodobenzene, C_6H_5I	−28·5 [75]	—	—	—
	−31·35 [3]	188·45 [3]	1·83829 [3]	1·61559 (Hα) [3]
d-limonene, $C_{10}H_{16}$	−96·9	177·7	0·846	1·4749
maleic acid, $COOH.CH:CH.COOH$	130·5	—	—	—
mannitol, $C_6H_{14}O_6$	166·05 [72]	—	—	—
d-menthol, $C_{10}H_{19}OH$	43·5	216·4	—	—
menthyl benzoate, $C_{17}H_{24}O_2$ ...	54·5	—	—	—
1, 3, 5-mesitylene, $C_6H_3(CH_3)_3$ ...	−46	164·6	0·8634 (20°)	1·49804 (17·1°)
mesityl oxide, $C_6H_{10}O$	−59	128·39	0·86532 (20°)	1·44582 (16·4°)

* Oil of cloves.

ORGANIC COMPOUNDS—*continued*

	m.p.	b.p.	ρ_4^{15}	n_D^{15}
methyl acetate, CH_3COOCH_3 ...	−98·05	57·0	0·9337 (20°)	1·36143(20°)
	−98·7	—	—	—
methyl alcohol, CH_3OH	−97·8 [25]	64·72	0·7952	1·3312
	−97·88 [26]	—	—	—
	−97·68 [27]	—	—	—
methyl aniline, $C_6H_5NHCH_3$ ...	−57 (?)	196·25 [5]	0·99018 [5]	1·57367 [5]
methyl benzoate, $C_6H_5COOCH_3$ ...	−12·4 [5]	199·50 [5]	1·09334 [5]	1·51924 [5]
methyl bromide, CH_3Br	−93	4·5	1·732 (0°)	—
			—	—
methyl chloride, CH_3Cl	−97·72 [29]	−24·09 [51]	—	—
	−91·5 [52]	−23·73	—	—
methyl iodide, CH_3I	−64·4 [75]	—	—	—
	−66·45 [14]	42·50 [14]	2·29300 [14]	1·52900 (Hα) [14]
methyl ether, $(CH_3)_2O$	−138·5 [52]	−24·9	—	—
methyl formate, $HCOOCH_3$ ...	−99·75	31·85	0·9742 (20°)	1·34332 (20°)
methyl salicylate, $HO.C_6H_4.COOCH_3$	−8·6	223·3	1·1850(20·2°)	1·53773(18·1°)
methylamine, CH_3NH_2	—	−6·7 [51]	—	—
	−93·46 [28]	−6·32 [28]	—	—
methylene bromide, CH_2Br_2 ...	−52·7 [3]	96·95 [3]	2·50986 [3]	1·54012 (Hα)
methylene chloride, CH_2Cl_2 ...	−96·8 [3]	39·95 [3]	1·33479 [3]	1·42466 (Hα) [3]
methylene iodide, CH_2I_2	α 5·54 [30]	180	3·3345 [3] *	1·74428 [3]
	5·60 [3]	—	—	—
	β 6·01 [30]	—	—	—
	6·10 [3]	—	—	—
naphthalene, $C_{10}H_8$...	80·05 [15]	217·68 [15]	—	—
	—	218·06 [31]	—	—
	—	218·0 [10]	—	—
	—	217·96 [61]	—	—
	—	217·97 [63]	—	—
α-naphthol, $C_{10}H_7OH$	96	288	—	—
β-naphthol, $C_{10}H_7OH$	122	294·9	—	—
α-naphthylamine, $C_{10}H_7NH_2$ ...	50	300·8	—	—
β-naphthylamine, $C_{10}H_7NH_2$ ...	112	306·1	—	—
nitrobenzene, $C_6H_5NO_2$	5·70 [32, 5]	210·80 [5]	1·20824 [5]	1·55457 [5]
	5·76 [33]	—	—	—
	5·83 [8]	—	—	—
nitroethane, $C_2H_5NO_2$	−90 [75]	114·5	1·0461 (25°)	1·39007(24·3°)
nitromethane, CH_3NO_2	−28·6 [3]	101·25 [3]	1·14476 [3]	1·38139 (Hα) [3]
p-nitrotoluene, $CH_3 . C_6H_4 . NO_2$...	51·65 [13]	238·50 [13]	1·12259 (55°) [13]	1·53818 (55°) [13]
palmitic acid, $C_{16}H_{32}O_2$ ...	62·65 [54]	—	—	—
phenanthrene, $(C_6H_4CH)_2$ ...	99·6	340·2	—	—
phenetole, $C_6H_5OC_2H_5$	−30·2	170·35	0·9666(20·2°)	1·5076 (21°)
phenol, C_6H_5OH	† 40·75 [13]	182·20 [13]	1·05446 (45°)	1·54027 (45°) [13]
	40·6 [75]	—	—	—
phenylacetic acid, $C_6H_5CH_2COOH$	76·7	265·5	—	—
phorone, $C_9H_{14}O$	28	197·2 (743·3 mm.)	0·8850 (20°)	1·4998 (20°)
phthalic anhydride, $C_6H_4<(CO)_2>O$	130·95 [73]	295·09 [61]	—	—
	131·6	—	—	—

* Coefficient of expansion, 0·0$_3$81.

† Literature values, 33·9°–43°.

ORGANIC COMPOUNDS—*continued*

	m.p.	b.p.	ρ_4^{15}	n_D^{15}
α-picoline, C_6H_7N	−69·9	129 [22]	0·950	1·50293(16·7°)
α-pinene,* $C_{10}H_{16}$	−50	156·2	0·859 (20°)	1·46634(18·1°)
piperidine, $CH_2<(CH_2.CH_2)_2>NH$	−10·5 [13]	106·40 [13]	0·86591 [13]	1·45515 [13]
	—	106·5 [22]	—	—
	—	106·3 (751 mm.)	—	—
piperonal, $C_8H_6O_3$	37	263	—	—
propionic acid, C_2H_5COOH ...	−22 [75]	—	—	—
	−20·8	140	0·9916 (20°)	1·38736(19·9°)
propionitrile, C_2H_5CN	−91·9 [14]	97·20 [14]	0·78673 [14]	1·36641 (Hα) [14]
n-propyl alcohol, C_3H_7OH ...	−127 [75]	—	—	—
	glassy [14]	97·15 [14]	0·80749 [14]	1·38501 (Hα) [14]
iso-propyl alcohol, C_3H_7OH ...	−89·5 [14]	82·40 [14]	0·78916 [14]	1·37719 (Hα) [14]
n-propyl bromide, C_3H_7Br ...	−110·0 [10]	71·00 [10]	1·35965 [10]	1·43695 [10]
n-propyl chloride, C_3H_7Cl ...	−122·8	46·60	0·890 (20°)	1·38838 (20°)
n-propyl ether, $(C_3H_7)_2O$	−122	—	0·7360 (20°)	1·38318(14·5°)
n-propyl iodide, C_3H_7I	−101·3 [14]	102·45 [14]	1·75840 [14]	1·50448 (Hα) [14]
iso-propyl iodide, C_3H_7I	−90·1 [14]	89·45 [14]	1·71371 [14]	1·49763 (Hα) [14]
pyridine, C_5H_5N	−41·8 [13]	115·50 [13, 22]	0·98783 [13]	1·51247 [13]
	—	115·2 [35,55]	—	—
pyrrole, C_4H_5N	—	130·5	0·948 (20°)	1·50347(19·7°)
quinoline, C_9H_7N	−15·0 [75]	—	—	—
	−15·6 [13]	237·10 [13]	1·09771 [13]	1·62928 [13]
iso-quinoline, C_9H_7N	24·6	238	1·0925 (20°)	1·62233(25·1°)
salicylaldehyde, $C_6H_4(OH)COH$ ...	−7	196·5	1·669 (20°)	—
salol, $C_{13}H_{10}O_3$	42·5	173/12 mm.	—	—
skatole, C_9H_9N	95	266·2	—	—
styrene, C_8H_8	30·7 [76]	144	0·9073(19·9°)	1·54849(16·6°)
succinic acid, $C_2H_4(COOH)_2$ ...	182·8	235	—	—
tartaric acid, $C_4H_6O_6$	170	—	—	—
terebene, $C_{10}H_{16}$	—	156	—	—
α-terpineol, $C_{10}H_{17}OH$	35	218	—	—
tetrachloroethylene, $(CCl_2)_2$ ...	−22·35	121·1	1·63109	1·50566 (20°)
tetralin, $C_{10}H_{12}$	−31 [75]	—	0·9731(15·1°)	1·5434 (20°)
	−35·0	207·3	—	—
tetramethylmethane, $C(CH_3)_4$ ...	—	146·4 [74]	0·7524 (ρ_4^{20}) [74]	1·4200 (n_D^{20}) [74]
thiophen, C_4H_4S	−38·30 [56]	84·12 [56]	1·0573 (25°)	1·52989 (18°)
thymol, $C_{10}H_{14}O$	51·5	231·5	0·9689(24·4°)	1·5189(24·4°)
toluene, $C_6H_5CH_3$	−95·01 [10]	110·70 [18]	0·87160 [10] †	1·49985 [10]
	—	110·58 [10]	—	—
	−95·1 [18, 36]	110·80 [10, 36]	—	—
	−97 to −99 [20]	—	—	—
o-toluidine, $C_7H_7NH_2$	−16·4 [5]	200·40 [5]	1·00279 [5]	1·57486 [5]
m-toluidine, $C_7H_7NH_2$	−31·25 [5]	203·40 [5]	0·99302 [5]	1·57021 [5]
p-toluidine, $C_7H_7NH_2$	43·75 [13]	200·55 [13]	0·96589 (45°) [13]	1·55344 (45°) [13]

* Oil of turpentine.

† At 0° 0·8854, and 25° 0·8622: see footnote 19; Smith and Wojciechowski, *Roczn. Chem.*, 1936, **16**, 104, give ρ_4^{25}=0·86172.

ORGANIC COMPOUNDS—*continued*

	m.p.	b.p.	$\rho_4{}^{15}$	$n_D{}^{15}$
trichloroethylene, C_2HCl_3 ...	−86·4	87	—	—
triethylamine, $N(C_2H_5)_3$	−114·7 [3]	89·35 [3]	0·73255 [3]	1·40133 (Hα) [3]
urethane, $C_3H_7O_2N$	48·7	184	—	—
o-xylene, $C_6H_4(CH_3)_2$	−25·34 [37]	142·5	0·8804 (20°)	1·50265 (20°)
	−25·22 [10]	144·41 [10]	—	—
m-xylene, $C_6H_4(CH_3)_2$	−17·89 [37]	139·15	0·8641 (20°)	1·49962(14·9°)
p-xylene, $C_6H_4(CH_3)_2$	+13·28 [10]	—	—	—
	13·23 [37]	138·40 [10]	0·86535 [10]	1·49860 [10]
	13·35 [10]	138·36 [10]	—	—

HYDROCARBONS [50]

	m.p.	b.p.	$\rho_4{}^{15}$	$n_D{}^{15}$
methane, CH_4	−182·5 [38]	−161·4 [39]	—	—
ethane, C_2H_6	−183·3 [40]	−89·1 [40]	—	—
propane, C_3H_8	−187·7 [41]	−42·1 [41]	—	—
	−187·1 [53]	−42·17 [53]	—	—
	—	−41·14 [42]	—	—
n-butane, C_4H_{10}	−138·3 [43]	−0·5 [43]	—	—
n-pentane, C_5H_{12}	−129·7 [44]	36·0 [44]	—	—
	−129·1 [6]	36·10 [6]	0·63114 [6]	1·36033 [6]
iso-pentane, C_5H_{12}	−159·6 [18,10]	27·95 [18, 10]	0·62470 [10]	1·35796 [10]
	−159·9 [39]	27·89 [39]	—	—
	−160·0 [62]	—	—	—
n-hexane, C_6H_{14}	−95·0 [36]	68·80 [36, 2]	0·66380 [2]	1·37787 [2]
	−95·39 [39]	68·72 [39]	—	—
	−95·1 [2]	—	—	—
n-heptane, C_7H_{16}	−90 [6]	98·35 [6]	0·68785 [6]	1·39002 [6]
	−90·6 [36]	98·4 [36]	—	—
n-octane, C_8H_{18}	−57·3 [36]	125·80 [36, 2]	0·70637 [2]	1·40007 [2]
	−57·0 [2]	—	—	—
	−56·8 [75]	—	—	—
n-nonane, C_9H_{20}	−53·9 [36]	150·7 [36]	0·71780 (20°)	1·40563 (20°)
	−53·7 [39]	—	—	—
ethylene, C_2H_4	−169·4 [45]	−103·9 [45]	—	—
propylene, C_3H_6	−185·2 [46]	−47·6 [47]	—	—
acetylene C_2H_2	−81·0 [48]	−83·6 [48] (sublimes)	—	—
isoprene, C_5H_8	−146·8 [49]	34·07 [49]	0·7003	1·42207(18·3°)

[1] Henning, *Ann. Phys.*, 1914, **43**, 282.

[2] Timmermans and Martin, *J. Chim. Phys.*, 1928, **25**, 411 (also values for other compounds; see also Timmermans, *Bull. Soc. Chim. Belg.*, 1911, **25**, 300; 1914, **27**, 334; *Proc. Roy. Dublin Soc.*, 1912, **13**, 310, for values for several organic liquids).

[3] Timmermans and Mme. Hennaut-Roland, *J. Chim. Phys.*, 1930, **27**, 401; 1932, **29**, 529 (also values for other compounds; see table in *Amer. Chem. Abstr.*, 1931, **25**, 2038).

[4] Morgan and Lammert, *J.A.C.S.*, 1924, **46**, 881.

[5] Timmermans and Hennaut-Roland, *J. Chim. Phys.*, 1935, **32**, 589 (also values for other compounds); Bingham and van Klooster, *J. Phys. Chem.*, 1920, **24**, 1, found b.p. of aniline 182·75°.

[6] Timmermans and Hennaut-Roland, *J. Chim. Phys.*, 1935, **32**, 501 (also values for other compounds).

[7] Menzies and Lacoss, *J. Phys. Chem.*, 1932, **36**, 1967.

[8] Masson, *Nature*, 1931, **128**, 726; Oliver, Eaton, and Huffman, *J.A.C.S.*, 1948, **70**, 1502 (m.p. 5·53).

[9] Richards and Shipley, *J.A.C.S.*, 1914, **36**, 1825 (H_2 thermom.); J. Meyer, *Z. phys. Chem.*, 1915, **90**, 721.

[10] Timmermans and Martin, *J. Chim. Phys.*, 1926, **23**, 733 (also values for other compounds); Gibbons *et al.*, *J.A.C.S.*, 1946, **68**, 1130; Streiff *et al.*, *Bur. Stand. J. Res.*, 1947, **38**, 53.

[11] Cohen and Buij, *Z. phys. Chem.*, 1937, **35** B, 270; Smith, *Bur. Stand. J. Res.*, 1941, **26**, 129.

[12] Richards, Carver, and Schumb, *J.A.C.S.*, 1919, **41**, 2019 (saturated with air).

[13] Timmermans and Hennaut-Roland, *J. Chim. Phys.*, 1937, **34**, 695; Gordon and Giauque, *J.A.C.S.*, 1948, **70**, 1506 (m.p. −138·30).

[13a] Jones and Lapworth, *J.C.S.*, 1914, **105**, 1804.

[14] Timmermans and Delcourt, *J. Chim. Phys.*, 1934, **31**, 85 (also values for other compounds, including several nitriles).

[15] Jaquerod and Wassmer, *J. Chim. Phys.*, 1904, **2**, 53; *Ber.*, 1904, **37**, 2531 (H_2 thermom.).

[16] Timmermans, *Comm. Leiden*, 1928, Suppl. **64***a*; Skau, *J. Phys. Chem.*, 1933, **37**, 609; Johnston and Long, *J.A.C.S.*, 1934, **56**, 31.

[17] Brown and Manov, *J.A.C.S.*, 1937, **59**, 500.

[18] Timmermans, van der Horst, and Onnes, *Compt. Rend.*, 1922, **174**, 365; Hicks, Hooley, and Stephenson, *J.A.C.S.*, 1944, **66**, 1064; Davidson, Argersinger, and Michaelis *J. Phys. Chem.*, 1948, **52**, 332.

[19] Burlew, *J.A.C.S.*, 1940, **62**, 690.

[20] Archibald and McIntosh, *J.A.C.S.*, 1904, **26**, 305.

[21] Gibbs, *J.A.C.S.*, 1927, **49**, 839, 2118.

[22] Riley and Bailey, *Proc. Roy. Irish Acad.*, 1929, **38**B, 450.

[23] Aston, Eidinoff, and Forster, *J.A.C.S.*, 1939, **61**, 1539.

[24] McCamish and Salathe, *J.A.C.S.*, 1928, **50**, 1785.

[25] Parks, *J.A.C.S.*, 1925, **47**, 338.

[26] Kelley, *J.A.C.S.*, 1929, **51**, 180 (157·22° K. misprinted for 175·22° K.).

[27] Roper, *J.A.C.S.*, 1938, **60**, 1693.

[28] Aston, Siller, and Messerly, *J.A.C.S.*, 1937, **59**, 1743.

[29] Messerly and Aston, *J.A.C.S.*, 1940, **62**, 886.

[30] Stone, *J.A.C.S.*, 1932, **54**, 112.

[31] Crafts, *J. Chim. Phys.*, 1913, **11**, 429 (N_2 thermom.).

[32] Hansen, *Z. phys. Chem.*, 1904, **48**, 592.

[33] Cohen and te Bokhorst, *Z. phys. Chem.*, 1934, **24** B, 241.

[34] Cook, *J.A.C.S.*, 1937, **59**, 2661.

[35] Constam and White, *Amer. Chem. J.*, 1903, **29**, 1.

[36] Smittenberg, Hoog, and Henkes, *J.A.C.S.*, 1938, **60**, 17.

[37] Pitzer and Scott, *J.A.C.S.*, 1943, **65**, 803.

[38] Parks and Huffman, *Ind. Eng. Chem.*, 1931, **23**, 1138.

[39] Doss, " Physical Constants of the Principal Hydrocarbons," New York, 1942, **1** f.

[40] De Witt and Kemp, *J.A.C.S.*, 1937, **59**, 273.

[41] Kemp and Egan, *J.A.C.S.*, 1938, **60**, 1521.

[42] Harteck and Edse, *Z. phys. Chem.*, 1938, **182**, 220.

[43] Aston and Messerly, *J.A.C.S.*, 1940, **62**, 1917.

[44] Mair, *Bur. Stand. J. Res.*, 1932, **9**, 457; Messerly and Kennedy, *J.A.C.S.*, 1940, **62**, 2988.

[45] Kistiakowsky *et al.*, *J.A.C.S.*, 1935, **57**, 65.

[46] Powell and Giauque, *J.A.C.S.*, 1939, **61**, 2366.

[47] Lamb and Roper, *J.A.C.S.*, 1940, **62**, 806.

[48] Morehouse and Maass, *Canad. J. Res.*, 1931, **5**, 306.

[49] Bekkedahl, Wood, and Wojciechowski, *Bur. Stand. J. Res.*, 1936, **17**, 883.

[50] See Ref. 39; Edgar and Calingaert, *J.A.C.S.*, 1929, **51**, 1540 (isom. heptanes); Signaigo and Cramer, *ibid.*, 1933, **55**, 3327 (isom. mono- and di-alkyl cyclohexanes); Schmerling, Friedman, and Ipatieff, *ibid.*, 1940, **62**, 2446 (3 hexanes, 1 heptane, 3 octanes); Egloff, " Physical Constants of Hydrocarbons," New York, 1939; Rossini *et al.*, *Bur. Stand. Circ.*, 1947, **461** (Selected Values of Properties of Hydrocarbons); for m.ps. and b.ps. generally, see: Carnelley, " Melting and Boiling Point Tables," 2 vols., 1885–7; Landolt-Börnstein, " Tabellen," 5th edit., 1923, 366 (organic compounds); Ergzb. **1**, 1927; Ergzb. **2**, i, 1931, 229; " Chemischer Taschenbuch " (annual); Kempf and Kulter, " Schmelzpunktstabellen zur organischen Molekular-Analyse," Brunswick, 1928; Deffet, *Bull. Soc. Chim. Belg.*, 1931, **40**, 385; Van Nostrand's " Chemical Annual," 1935, 196 f.; Beilstein, " Handbuch der organischen Chemie " (several vols.); Weissberger and Proskauer, " Solvents," Oxford, 1935.

[51] Gibbs, *J.A.C.S.*, 1905, **27**, 851.

52 Baume, *Compt. Rend.*, 1909, **148**, 1322.
53 Hicks-Bruun and Bruun, *J.A.C.S.*, 1938, **58**, 810.
54 Partington and Stratton, *Phil. Mag.*, 1924, **48**, 1085.
55 Middleton and Partington, *Nature*, 1938, **141**, 516.
56 Fawcett and Rasmussen, *J.A.C.S.*, 1945, **67**, 1705.
57 Swietoslawski and Usakiewicz, *Roczn. Chem.*, 1933, **13**, 495.
58 Wojciechowski, *Roczn. Chem.*, 1936, **16**, 524; Smith and Matheson, *Bur. Stand. J. Res.*, 1938, **20**, 641.
59 Schwab and Wichers, *Bur. Stand. J. Res.*, 1940, **25**, 747.
60 Swietoslawski, Zmaczynski, and Usakiewicz, *Compt. Rend.*, 1932, **194**, 357.
61 Marti, *Bull. Soc. Chim. Belg.*, 1930, **39**, 590.
62 Timmermans, *Comm. Leiden*, 1928, Suppl. **64*a***.
63 Eppley, *J. Franklin Inst.*, 1928, **205**, 383.
64 Evans and Aylesworth, *Ind. Eng. Chem.*, 1926, **18**, 24.
65 Samsoen, *Compt. Rend.*, 1926, **182**, 846.
66 Applebey and Davies, *J.C.S.*, 1925, **127**, 1836 ($\rho_4^{20}=1\cdot01236$; $n_D^{20}=1\cdot58685$).
67 Cooper, *Canad. Chem. Met.*, 1925, **9**, 59.
68 Meldrum, *Chem. News*, 1916, **113**, 266; begins to freeze at 3·9° but does not solidify completely; m.p. 5·7°.
69 Fawsitt and Fischer, *J. Roy. Soc. N.S. Wales*, 1917, **51**, 467.
70 Wade and Finnemore, *J.C.S.*, 1909, **95**, 1842; sp. gr. 15°/15°=0·71994.
71 Vecino y Varona, *An. Fis. Quim.*, 1913, **11**, 498.
72 Braham, *J.A.C.S.*, 1919, **41**, 1707.
73 Monroe, *Ind. Eng. Chem.*, 1919, **11**, 1116; Debeau, *J.A.C.S.*, 1946, **68**, 2725.
74 Horton, *J.A.C.S.*, 1947, **69**, 182.
75 Stull, *Ind. Eng. Chem.*, 1947, **39**, 540.
76 Guttman, Westrum, and Pitzer, *J.A.C.S.*, 1943, **65**, 1246.

§ 7. The Platinum Resistance Thermometer

The measurement of temperatures from the resistance R of a platinum wire was proposed by Siemens,[1] who gave the formula $R=\alpha T^{1/2}+\beta T+\gamma$, and was taken up again, at the suggestion of J. J. Thomson, by Callendar,[2] who

1 *Ann. Phys.*, 1861, **113**, 91; *Proc. Roy. Soc.*, 1871, **19**, 443 (brief abstract of lecture); *Phil. Mag.*, 1871, **42**, 150; *B.A. Rep.*, 1874, 242.

2 *Phil. Trans.*, 1887, **178**, 161; *Phil. Mag.*, 1891, **32**, 104; 1892, **33**, 220; 1899, **47**, 191; Shaw, *B.A. Rep.*, 1888, 590; Griffiths, *Proc. Roy. Soc.*, 1890, **48**, 220; *Phil. Trans.*, 1891, **182**, 43; *Nature*, 1895, **53**, 39; Callendar and Griffiths, *Phil. Trans.*, 1891, **182**, 119; Griffiths and Clark, *Phil. Mag.*, 1892, **34**, 515; Heycock and Neville, *J.C.S.*, 1895, **67**, 160; Holborn and Wien, *Ann. Phys.*, 1896, **59**, 213 (low temps.); Wade, *Proc. Cambr. Phil. Soc.*, 1898, **9**, 526; Jaeger and Diesselhorst, *Berlin Ber.*, 1899, 719; *Wiss. Abhl. Phys. techn. Reichsanst.*, 1900, **3**, 269; Holborn and Day, *Ann. Phys.*, 1900, **2**, 505; Chree, *Proc. Roy. Soc.*, 1900, **67**, 3; Chappius and Harker, *Phil. Trans.*, 1900, **194**, 37; *Trav. et Mém. Bur. Internat. Poids et Més.*, 1902, **12**; Holborn and Henning, *Ann. Phys.*, 1901, **6**, 242 (b.p. O_2—182·79°); 1911, **35**, 761 (comparison of Pt with N_2, H_2, and He thermoms. at 200°—450°); Jaeger and Steinwehr, *Verhl. d. D. Phys. Ges.*, 1903, **5**, 353; Harker, *Phil. Trans.*, 1904, **203**, 343, Waidner and Dickinson, *Phys. Rev.*, 1904, **19**, 51; Travers and Gwyer, *Z. phys. Chem.*, 1905, **52**, 437; Stern, *ibid.*, 1909, **65**, 667; Waidner and Burgess, *Bur. Stand. Bull.*, 1909, **6**, 149; Beckmann and Wäntig, *Z. anorg. Chem.*, 1910, **67**, 17; Burgess, *J. Chim. Phys.*, 1913, **11**, 529; Henning, *Ann. Phys.*, 1913, **40**, 635; 1913, **41**, 1064; 1914, **43**, 282 (H_2 and Pt. at 0° to −193°); Holborn, *Z. Electrochem.*, 1915, **21**, 559; Hoffmann and Meissner, *Z. Instr.*, 1915, **35**, 41 (compar. with H_2 thermom.); Warburg, *Ann. Phys.*, 1915, **48**, 1034 (P.T.R. fixed points); Henning, " Die Grundlagen der Temperaturmessung," Brunswick, 1915, 90, 101; McInnes and Braham, *J.A.C.S.*, 1917, **39**, 2110; Robinson, in " Pyrometry Sympos. Vol.," *Amer. Inst. Min. Met. Eng.*, New York, 1920, 450; Frey, *ibid.*, 458; Gillis, *Bull. Soc. Chim. Belg.*, 1921, **30**, 51 (standardising); Sligh, *Bur. Stand. Bull.*, 1921, **17**, 49; Griffiths, in Glazebrook, " Dict. of Applied Physics," 1922, **1**, 693; Manley, *Phil. Mag.*, 1922, **43**, 95; Davis and Cooper, *Ind. Eng. Chem.*, 1924, **16**, 579; Elliott, *J. Phys. Chem.*, 1924, **28**, 611; Lang, *J. Sci. Instr.*, 1925, **2**, 228 (Callendar form, wound on mica cross); Knoblauch and Hencky, " Anleitung zu genauen technischen Temperaturmessungen," Munich and Berlin, 1926, 2nd edit., 1930; Beattie, Jacobus, and Gaines, *Proc. Amer. Acad.*, 1930, **66**, 167 (full of details of mica cross); Redlich and Löffler, *Z. Elektrochem.*, 1930, **36**, 716; Hall, *J. Sci. Instr.*, 1933, **10**, 4 (precision form, wound on quartz in sealed envelope); Mueller, in " Temperature. Its Measurement and Control," New York, 1941, 162; Hoge,

developed it into a successful method. In its present form it corresponds with a standard scale. According to Callendar [1] the temperature *pt* on the " platinum scale " is defined by:

$$pt = 100(R - R_0)/(R_{100} - R_0) \quad . \quad . \quad . \quad . \quad . \quad . \quad . \quad (1)$$

where R_0, R_{100}, and R are the resistances of a pure platinum wire at 0°C., 100° C., and the temperature to be measured. The denominator, $R_{100} - R_0$, is called the *fundamental interval* of the thermometer. If t is the temperature measured on the standard gas scale, it is found experimentally that between 0° C. and 600° C.:

$$R = R_0(1 + at + bt^2) \quad . \quad . \quad . \quad . \quad (2)$$

where a and b are constants for a given specimen of platinum. For $t = 100$:

$$R_{100} = R_0(1 + 100a + 10^4 b) \quad . \quad . \quad . \quad (3)$$

Substituting R and R_{100} from (3) and (2) in (1) gives:

$$pt = 100(at + bt^2)/(100a + 10^4 b)$$

$$\therefore \; t - pt = [10^4 b/(a + 100b)][t/100 - (t/100)^2]$$

$$= \delta[t/100 - (t/100)^2] \quad . \quad . \quad . \quad . \quad (4)$$

where $\delta = 10^4 b/(a + 100b)$ is a constant for a given platinum wire.

The value of δ can be found accurately by measuring R at the boiling-point of sulphur ($t = 444{\cdot}60°$); for most purposes δ can be taken as 1·50. The correction $(t - pt)$ is small and negative between 0° and 100°; on either side it rises rather rapidly.[2] The value of t may be calculated [3] from *pt* by equation (4), or, more conveniently, tables [4] may be used.

The platinum wire should not be thinner than 0·05 mm. nor thicker than 0·2 mm. diameter and it should be annealed at a temperature not lower than 660°. Matsui and Kambara [5] found it necessary to anneal the wire fourteen times at 400°–600° to obtain a constant value of R_0. Keesom and Dammers [6] found the optimum annealing temperature 800°–850°. The purity of the platinum should be such that R_{100}/R_0 is not less than 1·390 and $R_{444 \cdot 6}/R_0$ not less than 2·645. The wire is wound as a spiral on a cross of mica plates contained in a tube (Fig. 4.VI A) and it is attached to thicker leads, which, for temperatures below 600°, may be of silver. The resistance [7] of the coil is 2·56 or

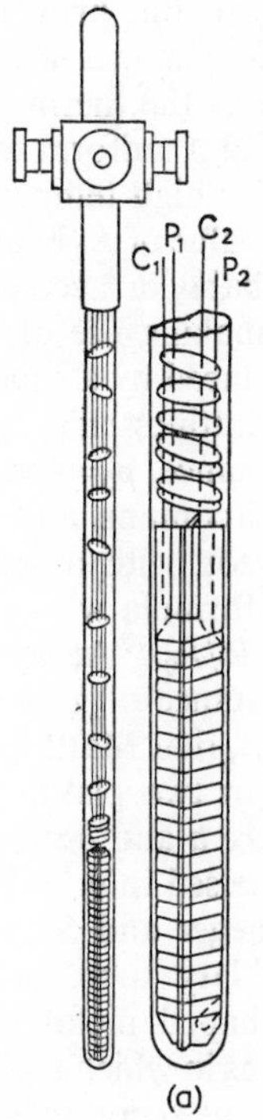

FIG. 4.VI A. Platinum Resistance Thermometer

ibid., 141; Wood and Cork, " Pyrometry," 2nd edit., New York, 1941, 88; Stull, *Ind. Eng. Chem. Anal.*, 1946, **18**, 234 (general). Mercury in a glass tube was used by Jaeger and von Steinwehr, *Ann. Phys.*, 1914, **43**, 1165; for other metals used at low temperatures, see § 19.VI C.

[1] Smith, *Proc. Amer. Acad.*, 1907, **42**, 421, could not confirm Callendar's equation.

[2] Sligh, *J.A.C.S.*, 1921, **43**, 470.

[3] Hoare, *J. Sci. Instr.*, 1929, **6**, 99; *Phil. Mag.*, 1929, **7**, 384; Callendar, *Phil. Mag.*, 1932, **14**, 729.

[4] Callendar and Hoare, " Correction Tables for Use with Platinum Resistance Thermometers," 1933. It should be noted that some writers use a value of δ which is 10^{-4} times that defined by Callendar, and sometimes it is given a negative sign.

[5] *J. Soc. Chem. Ind. Japan*, 1930, **33**, suppl. bind. 401, 403.

[6] *Physica*, 1935, **2**, 1051, 1080 (*Comm. Leiden* **239** *d–e*).

[7] For the optimum resistance, see Michels and Geels, *Proc. K. Akad. Wetens. Amsterdam*, 1928, **31**, 485.

25·6 ohms, when the fundamental interval is 1 or 10 ohms. The leads are kept apart by passing through holes in a number of mica discs which also prevent convection currents, and in some cases the tube may be sealed to prevent ingress of moisture. The mica dehydrates at 1000° and becomes white and brittle, but is still satisfactory in this condition. To prevent errors due to the unequal heating of the leads and the possible temperature difference at the junction of the thick and thin wires, *compensating leads* are used. These consist of lengths of the same thick wire as those connected with the coil, but these are joined to a *short* piece of the thin wire, placed near the junction of the main coil and its leads. The compensating leads C_1C_2 are connected in the opposite arm of the Wheatstone bridge from the main coil P_1P_2, and hence the resistance (including all its changes with temperature) of the leads is automatically subtracted from that of the thermometer, and the resistance measured is that of the part of the coil at a uniform temperature between the ends.

For high temperatures (1100°) Moser [1] used wires of 0·5–0·6 mm. diameter, the value of R_0 being 0·13–0·25 ohms. The ice-point R_0 usually alters somewhat, probably on account of small changes in purity of the wire. He eliminated these by making use of Matthiessen's [2] rule that the change of resistance of a metal produced by a small amount of impurity is almost independent of temperature.

Matthiessen's law, that $\alpha\rho_0$=const., where α=temperature coefficient of resistance, ρ_0=specific resistance, was confirmed for small amounts of titanium in zirconium, and *vice versa*, by de Boer and Clausing.[3] Henning,[4] for comparison with a standard platinum thermometer in the range 20°–70° K. used the formula $w'-w=(273-T)\{A-[B/(T+10)]\}$, where A and B are constants, $w=R_t/R_0$. At very low temperatures, Matthiessen's rule does not apply to the resistance of gold and silver.[5] Van Itterbeek and de Greve [6] found, with thin films, that Matthiessen's rule is obeyed by copper and silver, but not by lead.

For two platinum thermometers, Tory [7] used the formula $pt=pt_1+apt_1+b$, where a and b are constants. The relations used in low temperature work are discussed in § 19.VI C.

Jaeger and Steinwehr [8] passed the thin platinum wire through a thin glass capillary tube, or covered it with shellac varnish and passed it through a U-shaped metal tube. The wire must be supported free from strain,[9] and forms in which a platinum spiral is fused on the inside of a quartz tube (Heraeus) are not accurate[10]: it is also not satisfactory to wind it on a form and cover it with varnish, although this can be done with lead.[11] Dickinson and Mueller [12] put the wire between two thin sheets of mica enclosed in a thin-walled flat metal box. A disturbing cause of error is the electrical conductivity through the glass of the apparatus.[13]

1 *Ann. Phys.*, 1930, **6**, 852; cf. Stern, *Z. phys. Chem.*, 1909, **65**, 667.
2 *Ann. Phys.*, 1860, **110**, 190; 1861, **112**, 353; 1862, **116**, 369; 1864, **122**, 19 (47); see Guertler, *Phys. Z.*, 1908, **9**, 29; Partington, in Taylor, " Treatise on Physical Chemistry," 1931, **1**, 617; derivations in Dube, *Proc. Cambr. Phil. Soc.*, 1938, **34**, 559.
3 *Physica*, 1930, **10**, 267; another confirmation by Geiss and van Liempt, *Z. Phys.*, 1927, **41**, 867.
4 *Naturwiss.*, 1928, **16**, 617; see § 19.VI C.
5 De Haas and van den Berg, *Physica*, 1934, **1**, 1115; 1936, **3**, 440; 1937, **4**, 683.
6 *Physica*, 1944, **11**, 78.
7 *Phil. Mag.*, 1900, **50**, 421; Nernst, *Berlin Ber.*, 1911, 306.
8 *Verhl. d. D. Phys. Ges.*, 1903, **5**, 353; *Ann. Phys.*, 1906, **21**, 23; *Z. Instr.*, 1906, **26**, 237.
9 Roebuck, *J. Opt. Soc. Amer.*, 1922, **6**, 865.
10 Henning, *Z. Elektrochem.*, 1921, **27**, 494.
11 Schimank, *Ann. Phys.*, 1914, **45**, 706; Simon and Zeidler, *Z. phys. Chem.*, 1926, **123**, 383.
12 *Bur. Stand. Bull.*, 1907, **3**, 641.
13 Hoge, *Bur. Stand. J. Res.*, 1942, **28**, 489.

An objection to the Callendar form, which is prominent in most physico-chemical work, is its large temperature lag. A much improved type devised by Dickinson and Mueller [1] has the platinum wound on a flat mica strip enclosed in a flat silver tube, from which it is insulated by strips of mica. For higher temperatures, silica tubes are used.[2] In general, the platinum thermometer for ordinary work is troublesome and, unless great care is used, liable to error, and it is not much used in physico-chemical work, thermocouples being preferred.[3]

An important source of error in platinum thermometry is due to the heating of the coil by the current used to measure its resistance; a current of 0·01 amp. with a thermometer of the usual construction with 0·15 mm. wire produces a rise of temperature of 0·16°–0·17°, and unless great care is taken with this matter the supposed accuracy of the readings may be quite illusory. In the case of

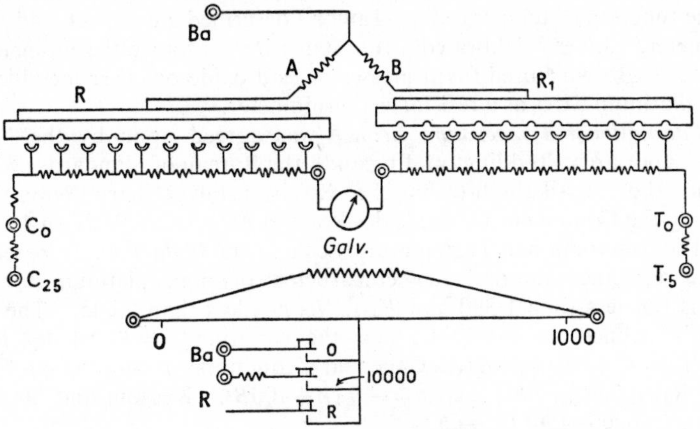

FIG. 5.VI A. Mueller Bridge

very fine wires the heating by the current is most disturbing and productive of error, and every care must be taken to avoid it.

Special bridges are necessary for use with platinum thermometers.[4] Dickinson and Mueller's [5] bridge circuit is shown in Fig. 5.VI A. The balance is adjustable

[1] *Bur. Stand. Bull.*, 1907, **3**, 641; cf. Callendar, *Phil. Trans.*, 1902, **199**, 55; Jaeger and Steinwehr, *Z. phys. Chem.*, 1905, **53**, 153; 1906, **54**, 428. Other constructions: (*a*) *flat coil*: Keyes, Townshend, and Young, *J. Math. Phys. Mass. Inst. Tech.*, 1922, **1**, 243 (somewhat anomalous unless carefully annealed); strain-free type, Sligh, *Bur. Stand. Bull.*, 1922, **17**, 49; (*b*) *coiled-coil* (Pt+10 per cent. Rh): Meyers, *Bur. Stand. J. Res.*, 1932, **9**, 807; Southard and Milner, *J.A.C.S.*, 1933, **55**, 4384; details of construction of Pt thermometers: Sligh, *J.A.C.S.*, 1921, **43**, 470; a simple home-made type is described by de Leeuw, *Z. phys. Chem.*, 1911, **77**, 284; for modern types, see Mueller, in " Temperature. Its Measurement and Control," New York, 1941, 162.

[2] Haagen, *Z. angew. Chem.*, 1907, **20**, 565.

[3] Cf. Kuenen and Robson, *Phil. Mag.*, 1902, **3**, 149; White, *J.A.C.S.*, 1914, **36**, 1856, 1868; Moser, *Ann. Phys.*, 1929, **1**, 341 (Pt thermom. for very accurate work); Bylewski, *Roczn. Chem.*, 1931, **11**, 552 (to ±0·001° at 0°–250°).

[4] For the Callendar-Griffiths bridge, see *Electrician*, 1908, **60**, 477.

[5] *Bur. Stand. Bull.*, 1907, **3**, 641; Mueller, *ibid.*, 1917, **13**, 547; the bridge calibration is described by Griffiths, in Glazebrook, " Dict. of Applied Physics," 1922, **1**, 702 (from which Fig. 5.VI A is taken); other bridges, see, e.g. Callendar, *Phil. Trans.*, 1902, **199**, 55; Edwards, *Proc. Amer. Acad.*, 1905, **40**, 549; Northrup, *Trans. Amer. Inst. Elec. Eng.*, 1906, **25**, 466, 473; Smith, *Phil. Mag.*, 1912, **24**, 541; Harper, *Bur. Stand. Bull.*, 1915, **11**, 259 (296); Sligh, *ibid.*, 1922, **17**, 49; Eppley, *Rev. Sci. Instr.*, 1932, **3**, 687; Matsui and Kambara, *J. Soc. Chem. Ind. Japan*, 1930, **33**, suppl. bind. 401, 403; Kuroda and Yumen, *ibid.*, 1936, **39**, suppl. bind. 472; Eggers,

at three points, where the contact resistance is so placed as to have the minimum effect on the accuracy. The slide wire consists of 11 turns of manganin wound spirally on a marble cylinder, providing a continuous scale 240 in. long, ten turns equivalent to one step of the rheostat R_1. Half the additional turn is located at the high, and the other half at the low, end of the scale, providing for 1 turn slide wire$=0{\cdot}01$ ohm$\simeq0{\cdot}1°$ C. if $R_0\simeq25{\cdot}3$ ohms; $\frac{1}{5}$ div.$\simeq\frac{1}{50}$ in.$\simeq0{\cdot}0001°$. The slide wire contact is in series with the battery; the contacts of the rheostats R and R_1 are each in series with a ratio coil of 200 ohms; R provides coarse adjustment, R_1 is for fine adjustment. R_1 is composed of ten 0·1-ohm coils, R of ten 1-ohm coils. An additional 0·5-ohm resistance extends the range an additional 5°, making 115° in all. This resistance is included in the circuit at will and is connected in series with R_1 between the posts T_0 and $T_{.5}$.

The use of nickel wire below 500° was proposed by del Regno [1]; the resistance is a cubic function of temperature. Taylor [2] described a compact lead filament thermometer. Jones [3] calibrated a tungsten wire resistance thermometer from 0° to 3350°. Brown [4] used fused masses of lead oxide or other metallic oxides between platinum wires as a resistance thermometer.

The *International Temperature Scale* [5] was agreed upon by the National Physical Laboratory (Teddington, England), the Bureau of Standards (Washington) and the Physikalisch-technische Reichsanstalt (Charlottenburg), and adopted by the Conférence Générale des Poids et Mésures in Paris on 4 October, 1927. The International Temperature Scale from 0°–660° C. is based on a platinum resistance thermometer constructed of pure platinum for which R_{100}/R_0 is not less than 1·390 and $R_{444\cdot6}/R_0$ not less than 2·645. The b.p. of sulphur is defined as 444·60° C. and the equation $R=R_0(1+At+Bt^2)$, or $(R-R_0)/R_0=At+Bt^2$, then gives Callendar's equation [6] $t-pt=\delta(t-100)t$, with $pt=(R-R_0)/100(R_{100}-R_0)$, and $\delta=-B/(A+100B)$. Keesom and Dammers [7] studied the range $-190°$ to $+660°$.

Another formula given by Henning [8] for *two* platinum thermometers in the interval 20°–80° K. is:

$$R/R_0-R'/R_0'=(273-T)[A-B/(T+10)]$$

where A and B are constants, determined at the b.p.s of hydrogen and oxygen. Southard and Milner [9] give data for 14°–109° K. by the constant volume hydrogen thermometer, and show that they agree with Henning's formula. Henning [10] proposed a more accurate formula than Callendar's parabolic equation (2):

$$R=R_0(1+at+bt^2+ct^4)$$

Arch. Tech. Messen, 1941, **117**, T39; Guillien, *Compt. Rend.*, 1943, **216**, 521; see the useful summary by Griffiths in Glazebrook, " Dict. of Applied Physics," 1922, **1**, 697; " Methods of Measuring Temperature," 1925, 30; Stack, *Gen. Elec. Rev.*, 1948, **51**, No. 7, 17. Special bridges are supplied by the Cambridge Scientific Instrument Co., and by Leeds and Northrup.

[1] *Rend. Fis. Mat. Accad. Napoli*, 1926, **32**, 194.

[2] *Phys. Rev.*, 1925, **26**, 841.

[3] *Phys. Rev.*, 1926, **28**, 202.

[4] *Phys. Rev.*, 1915, **5**, 126; 1915, **6**, 499; 1917, **9**, 205.

[5] Burgess, *Bur. Stand. J. Res.*, 1928, **1**, 635; Henning and Otto, *Z. Phys.*, 1928, **49**, 742; Focken, *N. Zeal. J. Sci. Techn.*, 1934, **15**, 423; Wensel, *Bur. Stand. J. Res.*, 1939, **22**, 375.

[6] Hoare, *Phil. Mag.*, 1929, **7**, 584; δ is here 10^{-4} times δ in (4).

[7] *Physica*, 1935, **2**, 1051, 1080 (*Comm. Leiden*, **239** *d–e*).

[8] *Naturwiss.*, 1928, **16**, 617; Henning and Otto, *Z. ges. Kälte-Ind.*, 1932, **39**, 86; cf. Henning and Heuse, *Z. Phys.*, 1924, **23**, 95; Loomis and Walters, *J.A.C.S.*, 1925, **47**, 2851; Heuse and Otto, *Ann. Phys.*, 1931, **9**, 486.

[9] *J.A.C.S.*, 1933, **55**, 4384 (with correction tables for *pt* to °K.); Blue and Hicks, *ibid.*, 1937, **59**, 1962.

[10] *Z. Phys.*, 1924, **23**, 95.

in which the constant c may have the same value for all samples of pure platinum, in which case calibration at three points is sufficient. A simpler formula given by Van Dusen,[1] valid from −40° to −190°, is

$$t=(1/\alpha)(R/R_0-1)+\delta(t/100-1)(t/100)+\beta(t/100-1)(t/100)^3$$

the last term being negligible above 0° C., when the equation reduces to Callendar's.

§ 8. Fixed Temperature Points

In the graduation of thermometers the melting-point of ice (0° C.) and the boiling-point of water at 760 mm. pressure (100° C.) are used as fixed points; at p mm. pressure the b.p. of water is taken as $100{\cdot}000+0{\cdot}0367(p-760)-0{\cdot}0_423(p-760)^2$. For higher temperatures, other fixed points are used, the most important being the boiling-point of sulphur, which is taken [2] by international convention as:

$$444{\cdot}60+0{\cdot}0909(p-760)-0{\cdot}0_448(p-760)^2$$

where p is the atmospheric pressure in mm. Hg. The sulphur is boiled in a porcelain or silica tube inside which is a cylindrical shield with a conical part at the top which fits the tube of the thermometer (which may be a thermocouple or a platinum resistance thermometer) and prevents radiation loss and the flow of condensed liquid sulphur over the lower part of the thermometer.[3]

Other fixed points are the boiling-point of naphthalene:

$$217{\cdot}96+0{\cdot}208(t+273{\cdot}2)\log(p/760),$$

the boiling-point of benzophenone:

$$305{\cdot}9+0{\cdot}194(t+273{\cdot}2)\log(p/760),$$

and the freezing-points of pure metals:

Sn, 231·85°	Zn, 419·45°	Au, 1063°
Cd, 320·9°	Sb, 630·5°	* Cu, 1083°
Pb, 327·3°	Ag, 960·5°	Pd, 1555°

* In a reducing atmosphere. The silver and gold points are international standards.[4]

Finck and Wilhelm [5] for the effect of pressure on b.p. gave:

$$t_{p\,\text{mm.}}=t_{760}+A(t_p+273{\cdot}1)\log(p/760)$$

	t_{760}	A
Naphthalene	217·95	0·2075
Benzophenone	305·84	0·194
Anthracene:		
Kahlbaum's ...	340·36	0·201
another specimen ...	339·87	0·201

[1] *J.A.C.S.*, 1925, **47**, 326; Yost, Garner, Osborne, Rubin, and Russell, *ibid.*, 1941, **63** 3488.

[2] Burgess, *Bur. Stand. J. Res.*, 1928, **1**, 635; valid for 695–805 mm.; cf. Eumorfopoulos, *Proc. Roy. Soc.*, 1914, **90**, 189 (444·61°).

[3] Henning, "Temperaturmessung," 1915, 258; Mueller and Burgess, *J.A.C.S.*, 1919, **41**, 745 (standard apparatus); Beattie, Benedict and Blaisdell, *Proc. Amer. Acad.*, 1937, **71**, 361 (precision apparatus); Barber, *J. Sci. Instr.*, 1937, **14**, 227; Blaisdell and Kaye, in "Temperature. Its Measurement and Control," New York, 1941, 127 (S 444·7°; Hg 356·7°).

[4] For m.p. of silver, see Roeser and Dahl, *Bur. Stand. J. Res.*, 1933, **10**, 661; for the scale from 660°–1063°, Roeser, *Bur. Stand. J. Res.*, 1929, **3**, 343.

[5] *J.A.C.S.*, 1925, **47**, 1577 (full tables). On calibration, see Van Dusen, *J.A.C.S.*, 1925, **47**, 326; Loomis and Walters, *ibid.*, 1926, **48**, 3101 (solid CO_2 −78·51°, b.p. O_2 −183·00°); Southard and Milner, *ibid.*, 1933, **55**, 4384; Niven, *Canad. J. Res.*, 1936, **14A**, 1; Hoge and Brickwedde, *Bur. Stand. J. Res.*, 1942, **28**, 217 (−190° to 445°).

Swietoslawski [1] selects for the b.ps. of water from 660–860 mm. Hg:

mm. Hg	b.p. ° C.	mm. Hg	b.p. ° C.
660	96·096	780	100·729
680	96·914	800	101·443
700	97·712	820	102·142
720	98·492	840	102·828
740	99·255	860	103·500

Moser [2] gave for the b.p. at 680–780 mm. Hg, accurate to 0·001°:

$$t=100{\cdot}000+0{\cdot}03687(p-760)-0{\cdot}0_{4}22(p-760)^2.$$

Michels, Blaisse, Ten Seldam, and Wouters [3] gave:

$$t=100+0{\cdot}0369736(p-760)-0{\cdot}0_{4}19590(p-760)^2$$

$$t=100+0{\cdot}0370083(p-760)-0{\cdot}0_{4}19380(p-760)^2-0{\cdot}0_{7}120(p-760)^3 \text{ to } 0{\cdot}001°.$$

Zmaczynski and Bonhoure [4] gave:

$$100+36{\cdot}8863\times10^{-3}(p-760)-20{\cdot}017\times10^{-6}(p-760)^2+15{\cdot}33\times10^{-9}(p-760)^3.$$

Boiling-points given by Smith and Matheson [5] are:

benzene: $80{\cdot}094+0{\cdot}042683(p-760)-0{\cdot}0_{4}2199(p-760)^2+0{\cdot}0_{7}250(p-760)^3$.

n-heptane: $98{\cdot}413+0{\cdot}044849(p-760)-0{\cdot}0_{4}2344(p-760)^2+0{\cdot}0_{7}145(p-760)^3$.

Eppley [6] gave for naphthalene at $p=842-704$ mm. (b.p. at 760 mm.= 217·973°):

$$\log t=0{\cdot}2024 \log p+1{\cdot}755102.$$

The freezing-point of silver is sensitive to oxygen which dissolves in the fused metal on exposure to air.[7] Melting-points of salts for calibration purposes given by Roberts [8] include (° C.):

NaCl, 800·4°   KCl, 770·3° Na_2SO_4, 884·7° K_2SO_4, 1069·1°

§ 9. Thermocouples

From 660° (when the standard platinum resistance thermometer scale ends), the International Temperature Scale is defined [9] as far as 1063° C., when the optical scale begins (§ 13.VI B), by the e.m.f. of a thermocouple of pure platinum, such that R_{100}/R_0 is not less than 1·390, and an alloy of platinum with 10 per cent. of rhodium. This couple must give an e.m.f. not less than 10200 nor greater than 10400 international microvolts with one junction at 0° and the other at the f.p. of gold (1060°), and the wire diameter must be between 0·35 and

1 In Weissberger, "Physical Methods of Organic Chemistry," New York, 1945, **1**, 57.

2 *Ann. Phys.*, 1932, **14**, 790.

3 *Physica*, 1943, **10**, 613.

4 *Compt. Rend.*, 1937, **205**, 1222; see also Zmaczynski and Bouhoure, *Compt. Rend.*, 1929, **189**, 1069; *J. de Phys.*, 1930, **1**, 285; Osborne and Meyers, *Bur. Stand. J. Res.*, 1934, **13**, 1; Smith, Keyes, and Gerry, *Proc. Amer. Acad.*, 1934, **69**, 137; Beattie, Blaisdell, Kaye, Gerry, and Johnson, *ibid.*, 1937, **71**, 371; Zmaczynski and Moser, *Phys. Z.*, 1939, **40**, 221.

5 *Bur. Stand. J. Res.*, 1938, **20**, 641.

6 *J. Franklin Inst.*, 1928, **205**, 383.

7 Roeser and Dahl, *Bur. Stand. J. Res.*, 1933, **10**, 661.

8 *Phys. Rev.*, 1924, **23**, 386; see p. 434.

9 Burgess, *Bur. Stand. J. Res.*, 1928, **1**, 635.

0·65 mm. Agreement to 0·1° was finally reached in comparative tests in the National Physical Laboratory, the Reichsanstalt, and the Bureau of Standards.[1]

To the mathematically minded, this composite definition of temperature will appear very inelegant, but it is of the same character as the definition of all exact working standards (such as electrical units) " where *experimental precision* is the primary consideration and logical exactness is made secondary." [2]

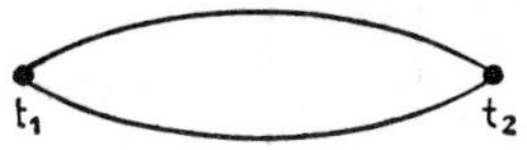

FIG. 6.VI A. Thermocouple

The electromotive force generated when *two* junctions of two wires of different metals are at different temperatures (Fig. 6.VI A) t_1 and t_2, discovered by T. J. Seebeck [3] in 1821, gives a very convenient method of measuring temperature differences. Since it is not altered if other metals are interposed in the circuit the two junctions may be connected by copper leads (Fig. 7.VI A) to a potentiometer and the cold junction t_2 kept immersed in melting ice or at a suitable constant temperature (e.g. in a metal block), the hot junction t_1 being in the system in which the temperature is to be measured. Base metal couple junctions are soldered, platinum and platinum alloys are melted together in the oxyhydrogen flame or (for use below 1000°) soldered with gold. A fuller description of thermo-electricity will be given later and the present account is limited to the use of thermocouples for measuring temperature. By connecting several couples in series the e.m.f. is correspondingly multiplied, and such *thermopiles* are generally used, except with wires of platinum and platinum alloys, with which single couples are the rule. The general name " thermel " for thermocouple and thermopile was suggested by White.[4]

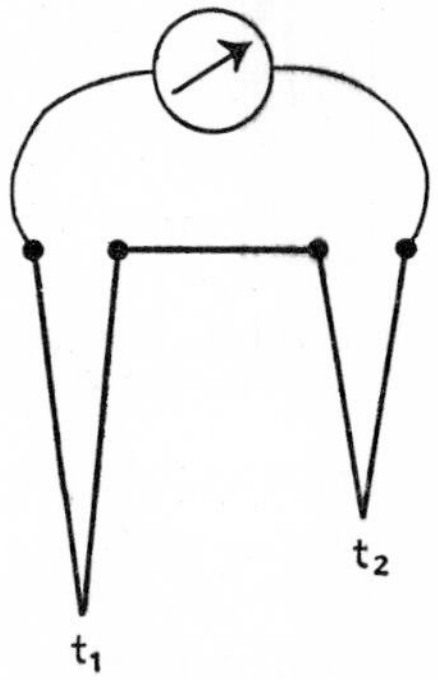

FIG. 7.VI A. Thermocouple Circuit

A six-junction copper-constantan thermopile is shown [5] in Fig. 8.VI A; this combination is much used, and it shows no appreciable hysteresis.[6] The wires for the couples should be suitably annealed; platinum and platinum alloy wires may be annealed by heating to bright redness by an electric current. The thermo-e.m.f. between a hard and soft wire of the same metal may be [7] about $1·1 \times 10^{-6}$ volt/1°.

When the e.m.f. of a couple with the cold junction at a constant temperature (say 0°) is plotted against the temperature t of the hot junction it first increases, then reaches a maximum (at the so-called neutral temperature), and then decreases again: at a certain high temperature it becomes zero and then negative, i.e. the

[1] Roeser, Schofield, and Moser, *Ann. Phys.*, 1933, **17**, 243.

[2] Day and Sosman, in Glazebrook, " Dict. of Applied Physics," 1922, **1**, 838; cf. Henning, " Die Grundlagen der Temperaturmessung," Brunswick, 1915, 110; Wood and Cork, " Pyrometry," 2nd edit., New York, 1941, 33; Roeser, in " Temperature. Its Measurement and Control," New York, 1941, 180 (theory); Scott, *ibid.*, 206; Aston, *ibid.*, 219 (low temps.).

[3] *Abhl. K. Akad. Wiss. Berlin*, 1822–3 (1825), 265–374 (read 1821–2); 1825 (1828), 71; Ostwald's *Klassiker*, 1895, **63**, 70; *Ann. Phys.*, 1823, **73**, 115 (Döbereiner), 430 (Oersted); Yelin, *ibid.*, 1823, **73**, 415; Fourier and Oersted, *Ann. Chim.*, 1823, **22**, 375; Muncke, in Gehler, " Physikalisches Wörterbuch," 1836, **6**, ii, 710; Antinori and Santi Linara, *Compt. Rend.*, 1837, **4**, 520; *Ann. Phys.*, 1837, **40**, 642.

[4] *Science*, 1922, **55**, 617.

[5] Hart, *Thesis*, London, 1941, 18–23.

[6] Richards and Richter, *J.A.C.S.*, 1917, **39**, 231; Griffiths, " Methods of Measuring Temperature," 1925, 61; *ibid.*, " Pyrometry," 1926, 31.

[7] Tammann and Baudel, *Ann. Phys.*, 1933, **16**, 120.

direction of the e.m.f. is reversed. Avenarius,[1] from experiments of Lord Kelvin,[2] found that the curve is a parabola symmetrical about the ordinate through the neutral temperature, $e=bt+ct^2$, where t is reckoned from the cold junction temperature.

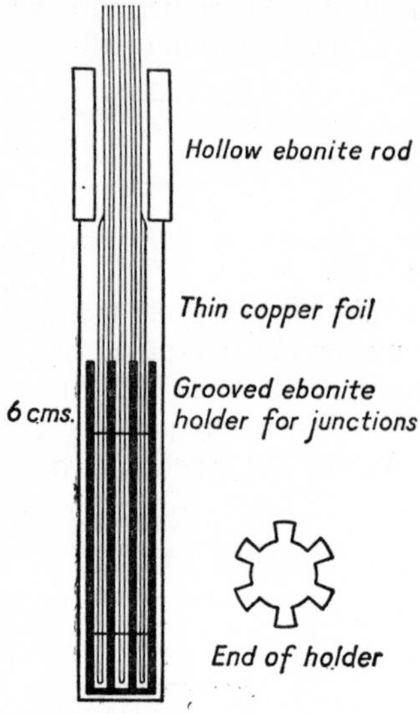

FIG. 8.VI A. Six-junction Thermopile

The thermoelectric power should be defined either as the mean value for 1° over a specified range of temperature, or as the value for 1° difference at a specified temperature: for Pt–(Pt+10 per cent. Rh) the mean value per 1° over the range 0°–100° is 4·74 mv., the values per 1° at 0° and 100° being 4·3 m.v. and 5·18 m.v., respectively.[3]

Copper-constantan couples give 40 microvolts per 1° difference but cannot safely be used in air above 350°, in vacuum perhaps [4] to 600°.

Ahlberg and Lundberg [5] found for a copper-constantan couple in the range 2° to 90° K.:

$$e=A+BT^2+CT^3+DT^4,$$

and for a particular couple and e in microvolts, $A=6039{\cdot}9$, $B=-1{\cdot}5475\times10^{-1}$, $C=6{\cdot}2064\times10^{-4}$, $D=-1{\cdot}5652\times10^{-6}$. For two different couples the differences in voltage are approximately proportional to the average voltage. Nernst,[6] for the range 15°–273° K., used:

$$e=31{\cdot}32T\log(1+T/90)+1{\cdot}0\times10^{-7}T^4 \text{ microvolts.}$$

Eastman and Rodebush [7] used the formula $e=e_0-aT^n (a>0)$ for copper-constantan, but it is of doubtful utility. Adams and Johnston [8] used a cubic equation, $e=A+BT+CT^2+DT^3$. Between 0° and 350°, with a hot junction temperature of t, the best formula for the e.m.f. of a copper-constantan couple is: [9]

$$e=At+B(1-e^{-ct}),$$

where A, B and c are constants, but in practice it is usual to make use of the tables for typical couples given by Adams [10] and prepared by using the formula

[1] *Ann. Phys.*, 1863, **119**, 406; 1864, **122**, 193; 1873, **149**, 372; Tait, *Trans. Roy. Soc. Edin.*, 1872–3, **27**, 125.

[2] *Phil. Trans.*, 1856, **146**, 649; "Math. and Phys. Papers," Cambridge, 1884, **2**, 189. For thermo-electric properties of crystals, see Voigt, "Lehrbuch der Kristallphysik," Leipzig, 1928, 534.

[3] Würschmidt, *Z. Metallkde.*, 1924, **16**, 271.

[4] Klinkhardt, *Ann. Phys.*, 1927, **84**, 167. It is not recommended for such temperatures.

[5] *J.A.C.S.*, 1935, **57**, 2722.

[6] Nernst and Schwers, *Berlin Ber.*, 1914, 355.

[7] *J.A.C.S.*, 1918, **40**, 489.

[8] *Z. anorg. Chem.*, 1911, **72**, 11.

[9] Adams and Johnston, *Amer. J. Sci.*, 1912, **33**, 534; *J. Wash. Acad. Sci.*, 1912, **2**, 275; Adams, *J.A.C.S.*, 1914, **36**, 65.

[10] Adams, *J. Wash. Acad. Sci.*, 1913, **3**, 469; *J.A.C.S.*, 1915, **37**, 481; "Pyrometry Sympos. Vol.," Amer. Inst. Min. Met. Eng., New York, 1920, 165; White, *J.A.C.S.*, 1914, **36**, 2292; Keyes *et al.*, *J. Math. Phys. Mass. Inst.*, 1922, **1**, 243; Anfilogoff, *Thesis*, London, 1932, 177; Hart, *Thesis*, London, 1941, 18 f. A short selection of papers on the Cu-constantan couple includes: Adams, *J.A.C.S.*, 1915, **37**, 481 (construction); Randall and Vanselow, *ibid.*, 1924, **46**, 2418; Giauque, Buffington, and Schulze, *ibid.*, 1927, **49**, 2343 (comparison with H_2 thermom. 15°–283° K.); Giauque, Johnston and Kelley, *ibid.*, 1927,

with average values of A, B and c for different wires. The values of e for a given couple found at various fixed points are subtracted from the tabulated values and the values of Δe plotted against the thermocouple reading. From this curve and the standard tables the temperature corresponding with a thermocouple reading is readily found.

Although an accuracy of 0·0001° is claimed with copper-constantan couples,[1] others [2] find only 0·0005°. A 2000-junction iron-constantan thermocouple embedded in vaseline was said [3] to attain an accuracy of at least 0·0001°.

Norbury [4] proposed the formula $e=-a+bT+c10^{-aT}$. Southard and Andrews [5] for a copper-constantan couple at low temperatures found $e=e_0-0{\cdot}447T^{1{\cdot}699}$, and gave a deviation curve. Jaeger and Rosenbohm [6] found $t=0{\cdot}00279698e-0{\cdot}0_8629e^2$ (e in mv.) at high temperatures (to 960°). Holman [7] found that the e.m.f. of a platinum metal couple between 0° and $t°$ could be represented by the formula $e=mt^n$, where m and n are constants, or $\log e=n \log t+\log m=a \log t+b$. For Pt and (Pt+10 per cent. Rh) $a=1{\cdot}2196$, $b=0{\cdot}302$ with e in microvolts. A large collection of important data on various thermocouples was given by Barus,[8] but his e.m.f. standard (Daniell cell) is somewhat ambiguous.

Simple thermocouples may replace mercury thermometers in many laboratory operations,[9] but they lack portability and require auxiliary apparatus which may not be available. An ingenious way of making a large number of couples (4000) is to electroplate copper on one side of a constantan spiral.[10]

A platinum-palladium couple was used by Becquerel;[11] the couple formed of pure platinum and platinum-rhodium (10 per cent.) alloy was introduced by Le Chatelier,[12] whose excellent work has not received sufficient credit, and was marketed by Heraeus in Germany from about 1890.[13] Barus,[14] and Roberts

49, 2367 (do.); Southard and Milner, *ibid.*, 1933, **55**, 4384 (do.); Roeser and Wensel, *Bur. Stand. J. Res.*, 1935, **14**, 247; Roeser and Dahl, *ibid.*, 1938, **20**, 337; Scatchard, Raymond, and Gilman, *J.A.C.S.*, 1938, **60**, 1275 (sensitive to 0·001°, reading to 0·01°); Burlew and Smith, *ibid.*, 1940, **62**, 701; Lancaster and Brunot, *Gen. Elec. Rev.*, 1942, **45**, 649.

1 White, *Phys. Rev.*, 1910, **31**, 135.

2 White, Dickinson, and Mueller, *Phys. Rev.*, 1910, **31**, 159; White, *J.A.C.S.*, 1914, **36**, 2292.

3 Lange and Streeck, *Z. phys. Chem.*, 1931, **157**, 1; Damköhler and Weinzierl, *ibid.*, 1933 **167**, 71; for a 100-element set, see Karagunis, Hawkinson, and Damköhler, *ibid.*, 1930, **151**, 433; a 1300-element set, Whitelow and Felsing, *J.A.C.S.*, 1944, **66**, 2028; Cu-constantan couple for low temp., see Slizkovskaya, *J. Chem. Ind. U.S.S.R.*, 1937, **14**, 576.

4 *Phil. Mag.*, 1926, **2**, 1188.

5 *J. Franklin Inst.*, 1929, **207**, 323; Wiebe and Brevoort, *Bur. Mines Rep. Invest.*, 1931, **3077**.

6 *Proc. K. Akad. Wetens. Amsterdam*, 1927, **30**, 905.

7 *Phil. Mag.*, 1896, **41**, 465; *Proc. Amer. Acad.*, 1896, **31**, 193, 234; Holman, Lawrence, and Barr, *ibid.*, 218.

8 *U.S. Geol. Survey Bull.*, 1889, **8**, No. 54 (a 306-pp. paper on high temperature measurement, with a very full bibliography); for thermo-e.m.fs. of alloys, see Pélabon, *Compt. Rend.*, 1923, **176**, 1305; van Aubel, *Bull. Acad. Roy. Belg.*, 1926, **12**, 559; for historical information, see Steinmann, *Arch. Sci. Phys. Nat.*, 1900, **9**, 413.

9 Minor, *Phys. Rev.*, 1918, **11**, 479; Foote, Harrison, and Fairchild, in "Pyrometry Sympos. Vol.," Amer. Inst. Min. Met. Eng., 1920, 74.

10 Wilson and Epps, *Proc. Phys. Soc.*, 1920, **32**, 326.

11 *Ann. Chim.*, 1863, **68**, 49 (on high temp. measurement generally, including optical methods); cf. *ibid.*, 1826, **31**, 37 (high temps.).

12 *Bull. Soc. Chim.*, 1887, **47**, 2; *J. de Phys.*, 1887, **6**, 23; cf. Day, Clement, and Sosman, *J. de Phys.*, 1912, **2**, 727, 831, 899.

13 Holborn and Day, *Ann. Phys.*, 1900, **2**, 505.

14 *Phil. Mag.*, 1892, **34**, 1, 376; cf. *U.S. Geol. Survey Bull.*, 1889, **8**, No. 54, 48; this couple was first used by Tait, *Trans. Roy. Soc. Edin.*, 1872–3, **27**, 125.

Austen,[1] used platinum and platinum+20 per cent. iridium, which gives a higher e.m.f. than the Pt-(Pt+Rh) couple but tends to disintegrate at very high temperatures.[2] The Pt and Pt-Rh (10 per cent.) couple can be used up to 1600°, and with 13 per cent. Rh up to 1773°.[3] A couple of iridium and iridium with 10 per cent. of ruthenium [4] can be used up to 2000°, with suitable precautions. At the highest temperatures a couple of tungsten and tungsten-molybdenum was proposed,[5] but this could be used only if protected from contact with atmospheric oxygen. The self-registering Pt-(Pt+Rh) couple was introduced by Kurnakow.[6]

With platinum-platinum+rhodium couples constructed on International specifications the e.m.f. at $t°$ hot junction temperature (cold junction 0°) is given [7] by $e=A+Bt+Ct^2$, where the constants A, B, and C are determined from e at the f.p.s of antimony (630·5°), silver (960·5°), and gold (1063°). Tables like those for copper-constantan couples can be used. Day and Sosman [8] gave $e=-169+7{\cdot}57t+0{\cdot}002648t^2-0{\cdot}0_6 4724t^3$ microvolts, but for the highest accuracy they found it necessary to include a term in t^4.

It is important to notice, in using older experimental data, that the Pt-(Pt+Rh) thermocouples standardised by the Reichsanstalt between 1894 and 1st April, 1901, were based on a scale determined by Holborn and Wien,[9] and rather seriously inaccurate (8° at 500°); a better scale was introduced by Holborn and Day [10] in 1899.

A convenient method of calibrating thermocouples at high temperatures is to take readings when a metal wire of known m.p. (e.g. silver or gold), placed near the hot junction, just melts and so interrupts a current passing through it.[11] A gas-tight furnace for calibrating thermocouples was described by Niven.[12]

The " hot " junction of the couple (or, more accurately, the one measuring the temperature) must be sufficiently immersed in the system—the further the better—since otherwise conduction of heat along the wires to the colder (or from the hotter) parts outside will tend to cause too low (or too high) a reading.[13] For the same reason, thin wires should be used.

The size of the wires really depends on a proper balance between low electrical resistance (leading to increased sensitivity of the galvanometer) and low thermal conduction, as well as on possible restriction of the allowable thermal capacity of the part of the couple inside the apparatus.[14] One (or both) of the wires of

1 Stansfield, *Phil. Mag.*, 1898, **46**, 59.

2 Holborn and Austin, *Berlin Ber.*, 1903, 245.

3 Barker, *Wire Ind.*, 1943, **10**, 163.

4 Heraeus, in Le Chatelier and Boudouard, " High Temperature Measurements," transl. Burgess, New York, 1904, 168; Arndt, " Phys.-chem. Technik," 2nd edit., 1923, 356; Müller, *Ann. Phys.*, 1930, **7**, 48, used Ir+10 per cent. Rh and Ir+10 per cent. Ru to 1800°.

5 Pirani and Wangenheim, *Z. techn. Phys.*, 1925, **6**, 358.

6 *Z. anorg. Chem.*, 1904, **42**, 184.

7 Barus, *U.S. Geol. Survey Bull.*, 1889, **8**, No. 54, 67; Matsui, *J. Soc. Chem. Ind. Japan*, 1929, **32**, Suppl. Bdg., 12; Roeser, *Bur. Stand. J. Res.*, 1929, **3**, 343.

8 Day, Sosman, and Allen, *Amer. J. Sci.*, 1910, **29**, 93.

9 *Ann. Phys.*, 1895, **56**, 360.

10 *Berlin Ber.*, 1899, 691; *Ann. Phys.*, 1900, **2**, 505; 1903, **12**, 447, 666.

11 Holborn and Wien, *Ann. Phys.*, 1892, **47**, 107; Holborn and Day, *ibid.*, 1899, **68**, 817; 1900, **2**, 505 (524); D. Berthelot, *Compt. Rend.*, 1898, **126**, 473; Loebe, *Z. Elektrochem.*, 1907, **13**, 592, 699; Holborn, *ibid.*, 1907, **13**, 646; Sosman, *Amer. J. Sci.*, 1910, **30**, 1; cf. Grubitsch, *Chem. Fabr.*, 1941, **14**, 319.

12 *Canad. J. Res.*, 1936, **14** A, 177; for calibration in lower temperature range, see Monack, *Chem. Met. Eng.*, 1931, **38**, 416.

13 Wood and Cork, " Pyrometry," New York, 1927, 60.

14 Whipp, *Phil. Mag.*, 1934, **18**, 745; Gucker, Pickard, and Planck, *J.A.C.S.*, 1939, **61**, 459.

the couple may be insulated in a silica capillary tube, or a series of short silica tubes strung on. The junction may be fused in the oxy-hydrogen blowpipe or arc welded.[1] Rodebush and Dixon [2] found the temperatures 20°–30° too low at high temperatures if a couple was loosely inserted in a silica sheath, and they recommend that it should be fused into a drawn-out silica tip.

The constancy of the cold junction temperature is one of the conditions which must be rigorously achieved at any cost of trouble, and the practice recommended and used by Eucken,[3] that this temperature can be allowed to drift, and an extrapolation made in the hope that an observed linear drift implies one in the cold junction, must not be followed if reasonably accurate results are aimed at. Eucken's results (sometimes with errors of 20 per cent.) for specific heats at low temperatures are affected by his ill-defined temperature scale, and the apparent agreement of some with the correct values is due to a balancing of errors.[4]

Adler [5] checked the equalisation of the temperature of the cold junction with the environment by putting it inside a mercury thermometer bulb and noting when the mercury level was steady (electric contacts): this method could be suitably modified. Burying the cold junction 10 ft. deep in the earth inside a building was used for technical thermocouples by Whipple.[6] At high temperatures, the " cold " junction may be immersed in steam or other vapour.[7] It may also be put in a copper block, the temperature of which is read by a thermometer.[8] Retzow [9] gave corrections for cold-junction temperature in the cases of linear, quadratic, and cubic relations between e.m.f. and temperature. The effect of impurities on platinum-platinum+rhodium couples was investigated by Fairchild and Schmitt.[10]

A suitable potentiometer circuit [11] is necessary for the thermocouple and great care is necessary to prevent insulation leaks in the couple circuit, particularly if electrical heating is used (this is preferably by A.C.),[12] and stray e.m.f.s from metallic contacts in the circuit at different temperatures, particularly between copper and brass (3·4 microvolts per 1°).[13] Some general references [14] on the

1 Coats, *J.A.C.S.*, 1926, **48**, 2130.

2 *J.A.C.S.*, 1925, **47**, 1036.

3 Wien-Harms, " Handbuch der Experimentalphysik," 1929, **8**, i, 69, where the correct judgment of White, *J.A.C.S.*, 1918, **40**, 1887, is called in question; on a method for keeping the cold junction at constant temperature see White, *Rev. Sci. Instr.*, 1934, **5**, 269; on the large errors in some of Eucken's results, see Lewis and Gibson, *J.A.C.S.*, 1917, **39**, 2554; Giauque and Wiebe, *ibid.*, 1929, **51**, 1441.

4 Giauque and Johnston, *J.A.C.S.*, 1929, **51**, 2300; Wiebe, Hubbard, and Brevoort, *ibid.*, 1930, **52**, 611; Wiebe and Brevoort, *ibid.*, 1930, **52**, 622; for eliminating effect of cold junction, see Kuntze, *Z. Verein. D. Ing.*, 1941, **85**, 703.

5 *Ann. Phys.*, 1904, **15**, 1026.

6 *Trans. Faraday Soc.*, 1917, **13**, 253.

7 Ruff and Bormann, *Z. anorg. Chem.*, 1914, **88**, 365.

8 Forster, *Meteorol. Z.*, 1942, **59**, 298.

9 *Z. techn. Phys.*, 1929, **10**, 164.

10 *Chem. Met. Eng.*, 1922, **26**, 158.

11 Randall, Bichowsky, and Rodebush, *J.A.C.S.*, 1916, **38**, 1266.

12 White, *J.A.C.S.*, 1914, **36**, 1856, 1868, 2292, 2313 (precision apparatus); *idem* in. " Temperature. Its Measurement and Control," New York, 1941, 265.

13 Walger and Lorenz, *Z. techn. Phys.*, 1930, **11**, 242; on mercury contacts, see Lange and Messner, *Z. Elektrochem.*, 1927, **33**, 431.

14 Holborn and Wien, *Ann. Phys.*, 1892, **47**, 107 (corrected in Winkelmann, " Handbuch der Physik," 1906, **3**, 147); 1895, **56**, 360 (high temp.); McCrae, *Ann. Phys.*, 1895, **55**, 95 (m.p. salts); Czermak, *ibid.*, 1895, **56**, 353 (0·1 mm. wires); White, *Phys. Rev.*, 1906, **23**, 449; 1910, **31**, 135; *Amer. J. Sci.*, 1909, **28**, 474; *J.A.C.S.*, 1914, **36**, 1856, 1868, 2229, 2313; Knopp, *Phys. Z.*, 1909, **10**, 439; Darling, *J. Roy. Soc. Arts*, 1910, **59**, 133, 149, 180, 194; 1915, **63**, 590 (thermocouples and general pyrometry); *Trans. Faraday Soc.*, 1917, **13**, 344 (base metal couples); White, Dickinson, and Mueller, *Phys. Rev.*, 1910, **31**, 159; Magnus, *Ann. Phys.*,

construction and use of thermocouples may be consulted. Besides the common copper-constantan, and platinum-platinum+rhodium couples, and the antimony-bismuth couples used in thermopiles and instruments for measuring radiant heat (§ 5.VI B), various special couples have been used, including some described in the section on low temperatures (§ 19.VI C).

The so-called "chromel-alumel" couple,[1] made from the alloys nickel and chromium, and nickel and aluminium, respectively, can be used to 1370°. Its e.m.f. deviates [2] from a linear relation to temperature by as much as 25 per cent. from 0° to −200° (as much as copper-constantan), but at high temperatures (to 900°) only by less than 5 per cent. Constantan-chromel couples have been used.[3] Nichrome-constantan has some advantages.[4] Couples from metals having transition temperatures (Fe, Ni) are not very satisfactory.[5]

Some couples described are: platinum-iron,[6] copper-German silver,[7] copper-iron,[8] iron-constantan,[9] iron-nickel-cobalt alloys,[10] silver-constantan,[11] platinum with gold, silver, iridium, ruthenium, rhodium, and platinum+palladium,[12] platinum-steel (or nickel steel),[13] nickel-copper,[14] nickel-silver,[15] tungsten-tungsten+molybdenum,[16] tellurium-constantan,[17] bismuth-silver, and

1910, **31**, 597; Flügel, *Z. phys. Chem.*, 1912, **79**, 577 (useful); Burgess, *J. Chim. Phys.*, 1913, **11**, 529; Foote, Harrison, and Fairchild, *Met. Chem. Eng.*, 1918, **18**, 343, 403 (standardising all types of couples); Hoffman and Schulze, *Elektrotechn. Z.*, 1920, **41**, 427; Griffiths, in Glazebrook, "Dict. of Applied Physics," 1922, **1**, 901; Gmelin, *Ann. Phys.*, 1925, **76**, 198 (industrial); Goedecke, *Siebert Festschr.* [Hanau], 1931, 72; Snethlage, *Chem. Weekbl.*, 1932, **29**, 557 (dtm. freezing-points); Grüneisen and Reddemann, *Ann. Phys.*, 1934, **20**, 834 (calibration); Tournay, *Bull. Soc. Chim.*,1937, **4**, 1482; Roeser and Wensel, in "Temperature. Its Measurement and Control," New York, 1941, 284 (calibration); Blackie, *J. Sci. Instr.*, 1941, **18**, 113; Rowse, *ibid.*, 1941, **18**, 240; Lancaster and Brunot, *Gen. Elec. Rev.*, 1942, **45**, 649 (calibration); Cichelli, *Ind. Eng. Chem.*, 1948, **40**, 1032.

1 Lohr, *Bull. Amer. Inst. Min. Met. Eng.*, 1919, 1837; Quiggle, Tongberg, and Fenske, *Ind. Eng. Chem.*, 1937, **29**, 827 (chromel-alumel; copper-copel).

2 Spooner, *J. Franklin Inst.*, 1919, **181**, 509.

3 Mason, *Rev. Sci. Instr.*, 1944, **15**, 205.

4 Hoffmann and Schulze, *Elektrotechn. Z.*, 1920, **41**, 427 (to 1200°); Mandelkar and Banerjea, *Current Sci.*, 1938, **6**, 447 (to 800°).

5 Stone, *Trans. Faraday Soc.*, 1918, **13**, 348.

6 Pouillet, *Compt. Rend.*, 1836, **3**, 782.

7 Wroblewski, *Ann. Phys.*, 1885, **25**, 371 (liquid N_2 temp.); Hoffmann and Schulze, *Elektrotechn. Z.*, 1920, **41**, 427.

8 Rosenthal, *Berlin klin. Wochenschr.*, 1893, **30**, 911; *Ann. Phys. Beibl.*, 1894, **18**, 446.

9 Holborn and Wien, *Ann. Phys.*, 1896, **59**, 213; Rubens, *Z. Elektrochem.*, 1898, **5**, 281; de Forest Palmer, *Phys. Rev.*, 1905, **21**, 65; Hunter, *J. Phys. Chem.*, 1906, **10**, 330.

10 Kowalke, *Trans. Amer. Electrochem. Soc.*, 1913, **24**, 377.

11 Gier and Boelter, in "Temperature. Its Measurement and Control," New York, 1941, 1284.

12 Holborn and Day, *Ann. Phys.*, 1900, **2**, 505 (Pd couples require two formulae for temperature range); Jaeger and Rosenbohm, *Proc. K. Akad. Wetens. Amsterdam*, 1941, **44**, 144 (ruthenium).

13 Belloc, *Compt. Rend.*, 1902, **134**, 105.

14 Pécheux, *Compt. Rend.*, 1906, **143**, 397.

15 Von Hevesy and Wolff, *Phys. Z.*, 1910, **11**, 473; Wöhler and Lund, *Z. Elektrochem.*, 1918, **24**, 261.

16 Bristol, *Trans. Amer. Soc. Mech. Eng.*, 1906, **27**, 552; Pirani and von Wangenheim, *Z. techn. Phys.*, 1925, **6**, 358; Morugina, *ibid.*, 1926, **7**, 486 (W-Mo, W-Ta); Watson and Abrams, *Trans. Amer. Electrochem. Soc.*, 1928, **54**, 19 (W-graphite); Van Liempt, *Rec. Trav. Chim.*, 1929, **48**, 585 (W-Mo, W-PtRh, Mo-PtRh, to 1600°); Binnie, *J. Inst. Fuel*, 1932, **5**, 211 (W-Mo, wires 0·4 mm. diam., 1200°–1600°: 8 microvolt/1° at 1600°); Osann and Schroeder, *Arch. Eisenhüttenw.*, 1933, **7**, 89.

17 Lewitsky and Lukomsky, *Phys. Z.*, 1929, **30**, 203 (Te-Bi); Lange and Heller, *ibid.*, 1929, **30**, 419 (Te-Pt); Ketelaar, *Rec. Trav. Chim.*, 1941, **60**, 523. For Pt-$SnSe_2$, Pélabon, *Ann. de Phys.*, 1915, **3**, 97.

bismuth—(bismuth+6 per cent. tin),[1] *Kovar* (Fe, Ni, Co alloy).[2] Up to 2000°, combinations of graphite with silicon carbide or tungsten have been used.[3]

Bidwell [4] found a large but erratic e.m.f. between carbon and graphite rods. A platinum-carbon couple agreed with the Avenarius law.[5] Shearer [6] found that thermocouples of platinum or platinum-rhodium against Nernst mass (§ 2.VI B) had an e.m.f. 40 times that of platinum against platinum-rhodium at 20°–980°. Alloys of platinum with 4·5 or 8 per cent. of rhenium against pure platinum, or rhodium with 40 per cent. iridium against pure iridium, can be used [7] up to 2000°: the e.m.f. of the latter is a linear function of temperature from 0° to 2000°.

Some characteristic data for important thermocouples are given in the following table: [8]

Couple	Usual temp. range ° C.	E.m.f. mv. per junction. with cold junction at 0° C.			
		−200°	+100°	+300°	+1000°
Pt-Pt+Rh	0 to 1450	—	0·643	2·315	9·57
Chromel P-alumel ...	−200 to 1200	−5·75	4·10	12·21	41·31
Fe-constantan	−200 to 750	−8·27	5·40	16·56	58·22
Cu-constantan	−200 to 350	−5·54	4·28	14·86	—

B. HIGH TEMPERATURES

§ 1. Combustion Furnaces

Small pieces of platinum and rhodium can be melted in a small coke blast furnace,[9] and Deville [10] melted platinum in a good wind furnace. Retort (gas carbon, especially if blown with oxygen, gives a very high temperature.[11]

1 Coblentz, *J. Franklin Inst.*, 1913, **176**, 671.

2 Mason, *Rev. Sci. Instr.*, 1937, **8**, 265.

3 Fitterer, *Amer. Inst. Min. Met. Eng.*, 1933, Contrib. **42** (C-SiC couple 300 mv./1°, the largest recorded); Schulze, *Chem. Ztg.*, 1938, **62**, 285; Losana, *Amer. Chem. Abstr.*, 1942, **36**, 6844; Busch, Schmid, and Spöndlin, *Helv. Phys. Acta*, 1947, **20**, 461 (SiC-Pt or Cu).

4 *Phys. Rev.*, 1914, **3**, 450; for W-graphite, Watson and Abrams, *Trans. Amer. Electrochem. Soc.*, 1928, **54**, 19.

5 La Rosa, *Nuov. Cim.*, 1916, **12**, 284.

6 *Phys. Rev.*, 1912, **34**, 238.

7 Goedecke, *Siebert Festschr.* [Hanau], 1931, 72; *Chem. Fabr.*, 1932, **5**, 361; Feussner, *Elektrotechn. Z.*, 1933, **54**, 155.

8 Sturtevant, in Weissberger, "Physical Methods of Organic Chemistry," New York, 1945, **1**, 322; for various metals for couples, cf. Hunter and Jones, in "Temperature. Its Measurement and Control," New York, 1941, 1227; Lohr, Hopkins, and Andrews, *ibid.*, 1232.

9 Faraday, "Chemical Manipulation," 1842, 96.

10 Deville and Debray, *Ann. Chim.*, 1859, **56**, 385; 1861, **61**, 5; *Ann.*, 1859, **111**, 209; 1860, **114**, 78; Becquerel, *Ann. Chim.*, 1863, **68**, 49 (gas carbon in air reaches 1300°–1400°); V. Meyer and Langer, "Pyrochemische Untersuchungen," Brunswick, 1885; V. Meyer, *Ber.*, 1896, **29**, 850.

11 Deville, Leçons sur la Dissociation, in "Leçons de Chimie professées en 1864–5," Paris, 1866, 308; V. Meyer and von Recklinghausen, *Ber.*, 1897, **30**, 1926 (1500° with air); Holborn and Day, *Ann. Phys.*, 1899, **68**, 817 (air-blown retort carbon in Deville furnace reaches 1720°); Thompson, *Proc. Soc. Chem. Ind. Victoria*, 1932, **32**, 693 (temp. reached 1500°–1600° in a few minutes, later 1700°–1800°).

Aluminium burning in oxygen[1] gives a very high temperature. The old Berzelius spirit lamp gives a higher temperature than an ordinary Bunsen gas burner, and the Mitscherlich lamp,[2] in which oxygen is passed into an ether flame, readily melted platinum and quartz. A petroleum-oxygen blowpipe[3] in a zirconia tube reaches 2600° C., which is higher than an iron thermit temperature (2400° C.).[4] The various types of gas furnaces (e.g. Fletcher's with draught, or bellows-blast) and especially the Perrot gas furnace[5] may reach 1650°–1700°, and 1900° with water-gas, although Crafts[6] found the highest useful temperature only about 1350°. The Fletcher furnace with pre-heated air reaches 1250°.[7] The oxy-hydrogen (or oxy-coal gas) blowpipe (about 2800°), with which Hare[8] melted platinum, rhodium, and iridium, and the oxy-acetylene blowpipe (3100°–3315°), which can be used in a zirconia tube,[9] are well known. The atomic hydrogen blowpipe (" welding torch ") of Langmuir[10] is useful for special purposes, since it gives a flame free from oxygen, the heat developed being due to the recombination of hydrogen atoms formed from a jet of molecular hydrogen by an arc between tungsten electrodes.

An electrically pre-heated gas blowpipe was described by Guntz.[11] Coolidge[12] used an acetylene-air blowpipe for working Pyrex glass. Hauser and Rie[13] dispersed liquid hydrocarbon in hydrogen gas and surrounded the 1-m. long luminous flame with an oxygen mantle, so reaching 3000°. A gas-oxygen furnace with zirconia lining was described by Podszus.[14] A general review of the production of high temperatures (including blowpipes, thermit, and electrical) was given by Darling.[15] Rosenhain and Coad-Pryor[16] described a fairly

1 Zengelis, *Z. phys. Chem.*, 1903, **46**, 287.

2 Berzelius, " Lehrbuch der Chemie," 3rd edit., Dresden and Leipzig, 1841, **10**, 329; Griffin, " Chemical Recreations," 10th edit., 1860, **2**, 189.

3 Von Wartenberg, Linde, and Jung, *Z. anorg. Chem.*, 1928, **176**, 349.

4 Chabrié, *Compt. Rend.*, 1909, **145**, 188; von Wartenberg and Wehner, *Z. Elektrochem.*, 1936, **42**, 293.

5 V. and C. Meyer, *Ber.*, 1879, **12**, 1112; Nilson and Pettersson, *Z. phys. Chem.*, 1889, **4**, 206; Biltz and V. Meyer, *Ber.*, 1889, **22**, 725; Foerster, *Z. anorg. Chem.*, 1895, **8**, 274; Biltz, *Z. phys. Chem.*, 1896, **19**, 387; Heinecke, *Z. Elektrochem.*, 1911, **17**, 438; Parmentier, *Ann. Chim.*, 1911, **22**, 417 (Méker gas furnace); von Frerichs, *Z. angew. Chem.*, 1916, **29**, i, 367; Bigot, *Chim. et Ind.*, 1919, **2**, 27 (1400° with recuperator; 1750° in 5½ hours with new gas furnace); Mylius, *Sprechsaal*, 1931, **64**, 225 (1650° with laboratory gas furnace). For gas tube furnaces, see Roscoe and Schorlemmer, " Treatise on Chemistry," 1885, **3**, i, 53; for a simple crucible furnace, Le Chatelier and Boudouard, " High Temperature Measurements," transl. Burgess, New York, 1904, 159. For a gas tube furnace for 1175°–1300°, see Slooff, *Chem. Weekbl.*, 1938, **35**, 104; do. for 1100°, Van den Berg, *ibid.*, 1934, **31**, 24.

6 *Compt. Rend.*, 1880, **90**, 183, 309.

7 Holborn and Wien, *Ann. Phys.*, 1892, **47**, 107; Lorenz, *Z. anorg. Chem.*, 1893, **3**, 290; Heyn and Bauer, " Metallographie," 1909, **1**, 73; gas heated magnesia furnace, Baum, *Ann. Phys.*, 1939, **34**, 377.

8 *Phil. Mag.*, 1847, **31**, 357; E. F. Smith, " The Life of Robert Hare," Philadelphia, 1917; Hare also used an electric furnace in 1839, *J. Phys. Chem.*, 1917, **21**, 607; Deville and Debray, *Ann. Chim.*, 1859, **56**, 385; 1861, **61**, 5; *Ann.*, 1859, **111**, 209; 1860, **114**, 78.

9 Ludwig, *Elektrotechn. Z.*, 1913, **34**, 886; Zumstein, *Phys. Rev.*, 1926, **27**, 562 (carbon tube); Ruff, Ebert, and Stephan, *Z. anorg. Chem.*, 1929, **180**, 215;

10 *Science*, 1925, **62**, 463; *J. Western Soc. Eng.*, 1926, **31**, 373; *Gen. Elec. Rev.*, 1926, **29**, 153, 160; *Ind. Eng. Chem.*, 1927, **19**, 667; Alexander, *Gen. Elec. Rev.*, 1926, **59**, 169; Ribaud, *Chim. et Ind.*, 1936, **35**, 3; Van den Bold and Smit, *Physica*, 1946, **12**, 475.

11 *Bull. Soc. Chim.*, 1934, **1**, 259.

12 *J.A.C.S.*, 1921, **43**, 1319.

13 *Wien Ber.*, 1920, **129**, IIA, 539.

14 *Z. angew. Chem.*, 1919, **32**, i, 146.

15 *J. Roy. Soc. Arts*, 1918, **66**, 621, 635, 649.

16 *Engineering*, 1919, **107**, 702; Scott and Freeman, *Bur. Stand. Bull.*, 1919, **15**, 317; " Pyrometry Sympos. Vol." (Amer. Inst. Min. Met. Eng.), New York, 1920, 214.

small gas recuperative furnace, with a lining of 5 per cent. of china clay and 95 per cent. of silicon carbide applied as a wash or dusted on. A rotating gas tube furnace was described by Pannetier.[1]

§ 2. Electric Furnaces

Although very high temperatures can be produced by chemical means, nearly all modern apparatus for the development of high temperatures (up to nearly 3000° C.) uses some form of electric heating. This is much easier to control and the apparatus is generally more compact than with other types of heating. The following summary deals with various types of electric furnaces.[2] Many references are to relatively early publications, and indicate the pioneer work in this field. Recent papers describe electric heating devices practically identical with older apparatus described in greater detail in earlier papers; references are given to modern sources when these are likely to afford help in the construction of furnaces. Many commercial types of electric furnace are on the market, and no attempt is made to cover this field.[3]

A very useful type is the electrically heated *tube furnace*,[4] in which a refractory tube is heated by a spiral of wire or strip wound on it, the whole being enclosed in an outer casing filled with suitable lagging such as magnesia, kieselguhr, Alundum grains, bauxite, etc. With platinum winding the insulating lagging must be free from iron; Alundum and magnesia are most suitable. Porcelain tubes begin to conduct at 1500°,[5] and also corrode platinum at high temperatures. Unglazed porcelain covered with a layer of a paste of pure magnesia and pure alumina [6] may be used, or magnesia tubes.[7] At very high temperatures tubes of zirconia (m.p. 2900°) [8] have been used. Alundum is very porous. Non-porous alumina tubes can be made by glazing the outside with an oxy-hydrogen flame.[9] At temperatures below 1000° a Vitreosil tube

1 *Chim. et Ind.*, 1946, **57**, 250.

2 Bredig, "Chemie der extremen Temperaturen," Leipzig, 1901; *idem, Phys. Z.*, 1901, **2**, 418, 433; Wright, "Electric Furnaces and their Industrial Applications," 1904; Havard, "Refractories and Furnaces," New York, 1912; Jaeger, "Eine Anleitung zur Ausführung exakter phys.-chem. Messungen bei höheren Temperaturen," Groningen, 1913; Arndt, "Handbuch der phys.-chem. Technik," 1915, 30, 790, 2nd edit., 1923, 36, 869; Symposia, *Trans. Faraday Soc.*, 1917, **13**, 205; 1919, **14**, 70; Pring, "The Electric Furnace," 1921; Moffett, "The Electric Furnace," 1921; Lebeau, "Fours Électrique et Chimie," Paris, 1924; Griffiths, "Methods of Measuring High Temperatures," 1925, 166; *idem*, "Pyrometry . . . with Notes on Electric Furnaces," 1926, 108; Müller, in Geiger and Scheel, "Handbuch der Physik," 1926, **11**, 340; Cohn, *Z. techn. Phys.*, 1928, **9**, 110; von Wartenberg, in Wien-Harms, "Handbuch der Experimentalphysik," 1929, **9**, i, 1; Pirani, "Elektrothermie," Berlin, 1930; Fehse, in Ullmann, "Enzyklopädie der technischen Chemie," 1931, **8**, 162; Ostwald-Luther-Drucker, "Physikochemische Messungen," 5th edit., 1931, 151 (brief); Ruff, *Chim. et Ind.*, 1936, **35**, 255; Thompson, "Theoretical and Applied Electrochemistry," 3rd edit., New York, 1939; much information on laboratory and technical electric furnaces is contained in earlier volumes of *Z. Elektrochem.*

3 Brauer and Reitstötter, "Elektrische Öfen," Leipzig, 1934–6.

4 Friedrich, *Metallurgie*, 1907, **4**, 778; 1908, **5**, 703; Day and Clement, *Amer. J. Sci.*, 1908, **26**, 405; Berry, *Ind. Eng. Chem.*, 1910, **2**, 255; Ubbelohde, *Z. Elektrochem.*, 1911, **17**, 1002; crucible furnace, Day and Allen, *Z. phys. Chem.*, 1906, **54**, 1.

5 Pirani and von Siemens, *Z. Elektrochem.*, 1909, **15**, 969.

6 Guntz, *J. Chim. Phys.*, 1903, **1**, 177 (resistance furnaces).

7 Mehl, Whitten, and Smith, *Ind. Eng. Chem.*, 1925, **17**, 1171; Barrett and Holbrook, *Ind. Eng. Chem. Anal.*, 1938, **10**, 9 (MgO crucibles); on the electrical conductivity of MgO at high temps., Saklatwalla, *Z. Elektrochem.*, 1907, **13**, 589.

8 Cohn, *Z. techn. Phys.*, 1928, **9**, 110.

9 Adcock and Turner, *J. Sci. Instr.*, 1930, **7**, 327; on Alundum, Anon., *Met. Chem. Eng.* 1911, **9**, 225, and trade literature.

with nichrome winding is satisfactory.[1] For temperatures higher than this (when Vitreosil crystallises, and also attacks platinum) gas-tight tubes of Pythagoras mass with platinum strip winding[2] are suitable, but this material tends to crack. The so-called Pythagoras mass (Haldenwanger, Spandau, Berlin) is composed of an aluminous clay or kaolin and a felspar flux, and softens only at 1800°. The so-called Marquardt mass (m.p. 1825°), a Berlin porcelain, contains pure clay and alumina: Schwarz and Reidt[3] found the most refractory composition (m.p. over 1920°) contained 22 of kaolin, 68 of alumina, and 10 of felspar. The coefficient of linear expansion increases with the alumina content.

Thin platinum strip winding is best for high temperatures and the cost, after allowance for platinum scrap, is moderate. Up to 2000° iridium (m.p. 2350°) can be used,[4] but is difficult to work and is generally used as a tube about 2 mm. thick; it disintegrates rapidly in air, although this can be prevented by repeatedly coating the metal with magnesia and dilute magnesium chloride.

Up to 2500° molybdenum (m.p. 2620°) and tungsten (m.p. 3390°) wire windings[5] may be used, but they have the great disadvantage of oxidising very

[1] Partington and Shilling, *Trans. Faraday Soc.*, 1923, **18**, 387; devitrification above 1300°, Crookes, *Proc. Roy. Soc.*, 1912, **86**, 406; *Chem. News*, 1912, **105**, 205.

[2] Shilling and Partington, *Phil. Mag.*, 1928, **6**, 920; King and Partington, *ibid.*, 1930, **9**, 1020; platinum wire, strip and tube furnaces, Lummer and Kurlbaum, *Ann. Phys.*, 1901, **5**, 829; Berthelot, *Ann. Chim.*, 1902, **26**, 58; Haagn, *Z. Elektrochem.*, 1902, **8**, 509; Kalähne, *Ann. Phys.*, 1903, **11**, 257; Guntz, *J. Chim. Phys.*, 1903, **1**, 177, 607; Hutton and Patterson, *Trans. Faraday Soc.*, 1905, **1**, 187; on high temps., Ruff, 15 *Congr. Chim. Ind.* (Brussels), 1935, lxviii; Ribaud, *ibid.*, lix.

[3] *Z. anorg. Chem.*, 1929, **182**, 1; Bouthron and Durrer, *ibid.*, 1931, **198**, 141; on refractories, see also Hahn, *Z. phys. Chem.*, 1903, **44**, 513; Goecke, *Metallurgie*, 1911, **8**, 667; Ruff, *Z. Elektrochem.*, 1914, **30**, 356; *Metall u. Erz*, 1924, **21**, 272; Ruff, Sieferheld, and Bruschke, *Z. anorg. Chem.*, 1914, **86**, 389; Ruff and Lauschke, *ibid.*, 1914, **87**, 198; 1916, **97**, 73 (ZrO_2); Podszus, *Z. angew. Chem.*, 1917, **30**, 17; 1919, **32**, 146 (ZrO_2); Kanolt, *J. Franklin Inst.*, 1919, **188**, 489; Dana and Foote, *Chem. Met. Eng.*, 1920, **22**, 23, 63 (tables); Andersen, *Norg. Geol. Undersökelske*, 1922, No. **101** (oxides); Cohn, *Z. techn. Phys.*, 1928, **9**, 110 (ThO_2, m.p.$>$ 3000°); von Wartenberg and Werth, *Z. anorg. Chem.*, 1930, **189**, 178; Ruff, Ebert, and von Wartenberg, *ibid.*, 1931, **196**, 335 (ZrO_2-BeO); von Wartenberg and Gurr, *ibid.*, 1931, **196**, 374; von Wartenberg and Reusch, *ibid.*, 1932, **207**, 1 (m.p.s BeO 2530°, La_2O_3 2315°, Gd_2O_3 1740°, ThO_2 3050°, Cr_2O_3 2275°); 1932, **208**, 380; von Wartenberg and Prophet, *ibid.*, 1932, **208**, 369; von Wartenberg, Reusch, and Saran, *ibid.*, 1937, **230**, 257; von Wartenberg and Eckhardt, *ibid.*, 1937, **232**, 179; Clausing, *ibid.*, 1932, **204**, 33 (m.p. ZrO_2 *c.* 2715°, m.p. HfO_2 *c.* 2775°); Ruff, Ebert, and Loerpabel, *ibid.*, 1932, **207**, 308 (ZrO_2); Ebert and Cohn, *ibid.*, 1933, **213**, 321 (ZrO_2 and MgO); Ruff, Ebert, and Krawczynski, *ibid.*, 1933, **213**, 333 (MgO, CaO, BeO); Dawihl and Schröter, *ibid.*, 1937, **233**, 178 (m.p. TiO_2 1750°); Koeppel, "Feuerfeste Baustoffe," Leipzig, 1938; Wood and Cork, "Pyrometry," 2nd edit., New York, 1941, 224; Geller, *Bur. Stand. J. Res.*, 1941, **27**, 555 (resist. furnace, 1800°–2000°); Cohn, in "Temperature. Its Measurement and Control," New York, 1941, 764; refractory (1400°) sillimanite porcelain tubes can be sealed to glass: Dalton, *J.A.C.S.*, 1935, **57**, 2150; on sealing mica to glass or metal, Doual, *Rev. Sci. Instr.*, 1942, **13**, 266; quartz to Pyrex glass, Benson, *ibid.*, 1942, **13**, 267 (fused AgCl); for similar joins, see § 13, VII A.

[4] Nernst, *Z. Elektrochem.*, 1903, **9**, 622; *Z. anorg. Chem.*, 1906, **49**, 213; Nernst and von Wartenberg, *Z. phys. Chem.*, 1906, **56**, 534; Waidner and Burgess, *Bur. Stand. Bull.*, 1907, **3**, 163; Friedrich, *Metallurgie*, 1908, **5**, 703 (tube); von Wartenberg, *Naturwiss.*, 1943, **31**, 307.

[5] Von Wartenberg, *Z. Elektrochem.*, 1909, **15**, 866; *Verhl. d. D. Phys. Ges.*, 1910, **12**, 121; Fischer and Tiede, *Ber.*, 1911, **44**, 1717; King, *Astrophys. J.*, 1911, **34**, 37 (pressure furnace); Winne and Dantsizen, *Trans. Amer. Elektrochem. Soc.*, 1911, **20**, 287; Tiede and Birnbräuer, *Z. anorg. Chem.*, 1914, **87**, 129; Oesterheld, *Z. Elektrochem.*, 1915, **21**, 54; Ruder, *Bull. Amer. Inst. Min. Eng.*, 1918, No. **134**, 585; *Trans. Amer. Inst. Min. Eng.*, 1918, **59**, 162; *Chem. Zentr.*, 1919, IV, 1038; Jackson and Morgan, *Ind. Eng. Chem.*, 1921, **13**, 110; von Wartenberg, Broy, and Reinecke, *Z. Elektrochem.*, 1923, **29**, 214 (pressure furnace); Fehse, *Z. techn. Phys.*, 1924, **5**, 473; *idem*, "Elektrische Öfen mit Heizkörpern aus Wolfram" (Samml. Vieweg, **90**); Prescott, *J.A.C.S.*, 1926, **48**, 2534 (W rod); Schumacher, *ibid.*, 1926, **48**, 396 (W ribbon

easily at high temperatures, and must be used in vacuum, an inert gas (e.g. 25 per cent. H_2 and 75 per cent. N_2), or methyl alcohol vapour. Tantalum (m.p. 3030°) wire on a magnesia tube in vacuum,[1] and Nernst mass [2] (zirconia, etc.), have been used. Heating wire (Ni) may be wound on a porcelain " lantern " instead of tubes [3] (up to 500°).

For moderate temperatures pure nickel (m.p. 1450°; 0·5 or 1 mm.) or nichrome (m.p. 1550°) or similar alloy wire windings are suitable. As a general rule, the diameter of the wire should not be less than 0·00025*t* mm., where *t* is the temperature which the wire must reach. (This is always higher than the heated space of the furnace).[4] One m. of 0·5 mm. nickel wire at room temperature has a resistance of 0·6 ohm and at 900° of 2·8 ohms, hence for a voltage of 110 to obtain 5 amps., which heats it to redness, a length of (110/5)÷2·8=8 in. of wire is required. If wound on a 25-mm. diam. tube with windings 1·5 mm. apart, 100 windings or 15 cm. of tube will be needed. Similar calculations may be made in designing tube furnaces with other kinds of wire,[5] e.g. nichrome (80 per cent. Ni and 20 per cent. Cr, specific resistance 108 microhms per cm. cube, temperature coefficient 0·00012), which can be used up to 900° in air and to 1100° if air is practically excluded,[6] but the life is only a few hours at 1300.°

S.W.G.	18	20	22	24	28	30	36
Diameter, inches ...	0·048	0·036	0·028	0·022	0·0148	0·0124	0·0076
Ohms per foot at 800° ...	0·301	0·534	0·883	1·43	3·16	4·53	12·5
Amps at 800°	15	10	7·8	4·8	2·8	2·0	1·29

The heat developed per sec. is i^2R joules$=i^2R\times0{\cdot}2387$ g.cal.; e.g. for 5 amp. in 22 ohms, $5^2\times22\times0{\cdot}2387=131$ g.cal.

The drop in temperature at the ends of a heated tube due to increased heat losses may be compensated by spacing the windings or by putting on additional windings at the ends.[7] Since the voltage of a public supply is liable to fluctuate

to 2500°); Cohn, *Z. techn. Phys.*, 1928, **9**, 110 (also zirconium; bibl. all types); tungsten can be sealed into quartz: Coehn, *Naturwiss.*, 1915, **3**, 610.

1 Saklatvalla, *Dissert.*, Berlin Techn. Hochschule, 1908.

2 Nernst, *Z. Elektrochem.*, 1899, **6**, 41; Nernst and Reynolds, *Gött. Nachr.*, 1900, 328; Reynolds, *Dissert.*, Göttingen, 1902; *Ann. Phys. Beibl.*, 1904, **28**, 121; Harker, *Chem. News*, 1912, **106**, 85, 97; on making Nernst rods, Griffiths, *Phil. Mag.*, 1925, **50**, 263.

3 Weigert, *Ann. Phys.*, 1907, **24**, 55.

4 Day and Allen, *Z. phys. Chem.*, 1905, **54**, 1; Doeltz and Graumann, *Metallurgie*, 1907, 419–421, 468; Poole, *Phil. Mag.*, 1914, **27**, 58.

5 On some other types of resistance tube furnaces, see Kalähne, *Ann. Phys.*, 1903, **11**, 257 (Ni wound tube); Morse and Frazer, *Amer. Chem. J.*, 1904, **32**, 93; Loewenstein, *Z. phys. Chem.*, 1906, **54**, 707; von Wartenberg, *ibid.*, 1906, **56**, 513; Friedrich, *Metallurgie*, 1907, **4**, 778; 1908, **5**, 345; von Hevesy and Lorenz, *Z. Elektrochem.*, 1910, **16**, 185; *Z. phys. Chem.*, 1910, **74**, 443; Berry, *Ind. Eng. Chem.*, 1910, **2**, 255 (wire wound); Gillett, *J. Phys. Chem.*, 1911, **15**, 213; Slade, *Proc. Roy. Soc.*, 1912, **87**, 519; Wolf and Müller, *Z. Elektrochem.*, 1914, **20**, 1; Morey, *J.A.C.S.*, 1914, **36**, 215; Dubsky, *Ber.*, 1917, **50**, 1713 (nichrome); Klemm and Rockstroh, *Z. anorg. Chem.*, 1926, **152**, 235; Tammann furnace for vacuum, Wever and Reinecken, *ibid.*, 1926, **151**, 349; White, *Z. anorg. Chem.*, 1911, **69**, 305, 331 (Pt to 1600°); Roberts and Morey, *Rev. Sci. Instr.*, 1930, **1**, 576 (Pt–Rh strip micro); Voos, *Z. anorg. Chem.*, 1935, **222**, 201 (vacuum); Truesdale and Waring, *J.A.C.S.*, 1941, **63**, 1610.

6 Oxidation and scaling of nickel: Carpenter, *Metallurgie*, 1909, **6**, 94; protection by carbon packing, Ubbelohde, *Z. Elektrochem.*, 1911, **17**, 1002; or by hydrogen, Selbert, *Chem. Ztg.*, 1911, **35**, 443; for a nichrome-wound *vacuum* furnace (to 1000°), Kelley, *Ind. Eng. Chem. Anal.*, 1932, **4**, 391.

7 Holborn and Day, *Ann. Phys.*, 1899, **68**, 817; Holborn and Henning, *ibid.*, 1907, **23**, 809; Meissner, *Wien Ber.*, 1906, **115**, II A, 847; Hempel, *Z. angew. Chem.*, 1910, **23**, 289.

by ±10 volts, some kind of current regulation is necessary if a uniform temperature is to be maintained over several hours.[1] The so-called "barretter" device depends on the heat loss from an iron wire in hydrogen,[2] as used with the Nernst lamp.

Tube furnaces with wire resistance heating and other types may operate in vacuum [3] or under pressure.[4] A tube of platinum with 20 per cent. rhodium was used in a vacuum furnace.[5] Electrically heated crucible furnaces have been described,[6] and furnaces heated by Nernst mass.[7]

Gray [8] obtained greater uniformity of temperature by winding the resistance wire longitudinally on an iron tube. Mellor [9] controlled temperatures to 1300° by a quartz air thermometer acting on a mercury cut-out in a U-tube. A uniform rate of *rise* of temperature of a furnace was achieved by Vallet [10] by varying the distance of copper plates in copper sulphate solution, used as a resistance, together with a mercury thermoregulator in an auxiliary furnace. Radiation from resistance furnaces was studied by Fitzgerald.[11] Douglas [12]

[1] Hahn, *Z. phys. Chem.*, 1903, **44**, 513; Bodenstein and Pohl, *Z. Elektrochem.*, 1905, **11**, 373; Kolowrat, *J. de Phys.*, 1909, **8**, 495; Schuen, *Elektrochem. Z.*, 1911, **17**, 301; Bodenstein and Kranendieck, *Z. Elektrochem.*, 1912, **18**, 417; Haughton and Hanson, *J. Inst. Met.*, 1915, **14**, 145; 1917, **18**, 173; White and Adams, *Phys. Rev.*, 1919, **14**, 44; Fairchild and Foote, in "Pyrometry Sympos. Vol.," Amer. Inst. Min. Met. Eng., New York, 1920, 435; Roberts, *J. Wash. Acad.*, 1921, **11**, 401; *J. Opt. Soc. Amer.*, 1922, **6**, 965; 1925, **11**, 171; Adams, *J. Opt. Soc. Amer.*, 1924, **9**, 599; Adcock, *J. Sci. Instr.*, 1925, **2**, 273 (gas thermom.); Simon and Fischer, *Z. anorg. Chem.*, 1927, **162**, 279; Dittler, *ibid.*, 1928, **174**, 342; Haughton, *J. Sci. Instr.*, 1932, **9**, 310; Kambara and Matsui, *J. Soc. Chem. Ind. Japan*, 1933, **36**, suppl. bdg. 134 (to 1000°); Bubam and Brintzinger, *Chem. Fabr.*, 1933, **6**, 265 (Hg reg. to 500° ±1°); Warren, *Ind. Eng. Chem. Anal.*, 1933, **5**, 285 (1000°); thyratron regulator to 800°, Zabel and Hancox, *Rev. Sci. Instr.*, 1934, **5**, 28; Ewell and Hardy, *J.A.C.S.*, 1941, **63**, 3460 (photo-cell: "a few degrees at 250°–400° for a day"); Roberts, in "Temperature. Its Measurement and Control," New York, 1941, 604; Thomas and Egloff, *ibid.*, 617. Commercial voltage regulators for A.C. are available.

[2] Gati, *Phys. Z.*, 1909, **10**, 897; Kempe, *ibid.*, 1910, **11**, 331; Anfilogoff, *Thesis*, London, 1932, 183; for simpler devices, Förster and Gruner, *Z. Elektrochem.*, 1935, **41**, 9; Hart and Partington, *J.C.S.*, 1943, 104.

[3] Bolton, *Z. Elektrochem.*, 1905, **11**, 45; Soddy, *Proc. Roy. Soc.*, 1907, **78**, 429; von Wartenberg, *Verhl. d. D. Phys. Ges.*, 1910, **12**, 121; Weiss and Neumann, *Z. anorg. Chem.*, 1910, **65**, 248; Ruff, *Ber.*, 1910, **43**, 1564; Tiede and Birnbräuer, *Z. anorg. Chem.*, 1914, **87**, 129; Oesterheld, *Z. Elektrochem.*, 1915, **21**, 54 (tungsten tube furnace); Booth and Ward, *Ind. Eng. Chem. Anal.*, 1932, **4**, 199 ("globar" heater; to 1000°–1500° ±5°).

[4] Boeke, *Z. anorg. Chem.*, 1906, **50**, 244; Nernst and Jost, *Z. Elektrochem.*, 1907, **13**, 521; Haber and Le Rossignol, *ibid.*, 1908, **14**, 181, 513; Hutton and Petavel, *Phil. Trans.*, 1908, **207**, 421; Smyth and Roberts, *J.A.C.S.*, 1920, **42**, 2582.

[5] Slade, *Proc. Roy. Soc.*, 1912, **87**, 519 (horizontal tube); Sosman and Hostetter, *J. Wash. Acad.*, 1915, **5**, 277; *Z. Elektrochem.*, 1915, **21**, 495 (vertical tube); Alcock, Peiser, Pont, and Swallow, *J. Sci. Instr.*, 1947, **24**, 297 (Pt–Rh).

[6] Friedrich, *Metallurgie*, 1907, **4**, 778; Pip, *Z. Elektrochem.*, 1910, **16**, 664; Calhane and Bard, *Chem. Met. Eng.*, 1912, **10**, 461; Askenasy, *Metallurgie*, 1914, **20**, 253; Jänecke, *ibid.*, 1917, **23**, 49; Anon., *Elec. Rev.*, 1919, **84**, 342 (muffle and crucible); Hecht, *Chem. Ztg.*, 1920, **44**, 956 (crucible); Siebert, *ibid.*, 1921, **45**, 772 (muffle); Endell, *Z. angew. Chem.*, 1922, **35**, 31 (muffle); Biltz and Meger, *Z. anorg. Chem.*, 1928, **176**, 23; Smith and Hardy, *ibid.*, 1935, **223**, 1.

[7] Tingwaldt, *Phys. Z.*, 1935, **36**, 627; for "kryptol" heater, see Friedrich, *Metallurgie*, 1907, **4**, 778.

[8] *J. Wash. Acad.*, 1912, **2**, 248; 1914, **4**, 134; *Bur. Stand. Bull.*, 1914, **10**, 451.

[9] *Trans. Ceramic Soc.*, 1907, **7**, 114; Bluethe, *Metal Progr.*, 1947, **52**, 591 (electronic circuit).

[10] *Bull. Soc. Chim.*, 1936, **3**, 103; cf. Fairchild, Harrison, and Foote, *Bull. Amer. Inst. Min. Met. Eng.*, 1919, 2631; *Mining and Met.*, 1919, 312.

[11] *Met. Chem. Eng.*, 1910, **8**, 317.

[12] *Q.J. Geol. Soc.*, 1907, **63**, 145.

used an electrically heated platinum ribbon for melting fragments of rocks. The volatilisation of platinum metals in electric furnaces was described by Crookes.[1] An electric vacuum furnace for 2000° with a tungsten coil was described by Chaudron and Garvin;[2] Winne and Dantsizen[3] used an electrically heated molybdenum or tungsten ribbon furnace, and molybdenum and tungsten[4] and tantalum[5] tube furnaces have been used.

For temperatures over 2500° only carbon is suitable; the m.p. of graphite (the only form stable at high temperatures) being[6] in the region of 3800° C. In this case the carbon heater must be in a vacuum or inert gas or protected from oxidation by an exterior coke packing. Despretz[7] electrically melted silicon, boron, titanium and molybdenum, and claimed to have softened a carbon rod by a current from 500–600 Bunsen cells in an atmosphere of nitrogen so that it bent and even melted to globules—although the last is uncertain and may have been due to impurities.

In Tucker's[8] furnace a carbon tube of 54 cm. length, 25 mm. inner and 38·5 mm. outer diameter, thinned to 31 mm. in the middle 9 cm., was packed round with coke. With 330 amps. at 6 to 8 volts, 1200° was reached in 4 min.; with 600 amps. and 15 volts, 1860° in 11 min.; and with 850 amps. and 15 volts, 2950° in 14 mins. Carbon tube vacuum furnaces[9] (Ruff type) have been much

[1] *Proc. Roy. Soc.*, 1912, **86**, 461; *Chem. News*, 1912, **105**, 229, 241.

[2] *Chim. et Ind.*, 1923, **9**, 647.

[3] *Chem. News*, 1912, **105**, 75.

[4] Compton, *J. Opt. Soc. Amer.*, 1922, **6**, 910; Duffendack, *Phys. Rev.*, 1922, **20**, 665; Lebeau and Picon, *Compt. Rend.*, 1924, **178**, 1151; Duffendack and Black, *Phys. Rev.*, 1929, **34**, 35.

[5] Fredenhagen, *Phys. Z.*, 1913, **14**, 1047.

[6] Ryschkewitsch, *Z. Elektrochem.*, 1925, **31**, 54; Ryschkewitsch and Merck, *ibid.*, 1926, **32**, 42; König, *Naturwiss.*, 1947, **34**, 108.

[7] *Compt. Rend.*, 1849, **28**, 755; 1849, **29**, 48, 545, 709; 1850, **30**, 367.

[8] *Electrochem. and Metall. Ind.*, 1907, **5**, 227; an electrically heated carbon tube furnace for black-body radiation was used by Lummer and Pringsheim, *Verhl. d. D. Phys. Ges.*, 1903, **5**, 3; Harker and Kaye, *Proc. Roy. Soc.*, 1912, **86**, 379; Hemsalech, *Phil. Mag.*, 1918, **36**, 214; King, *Astrophys. J.*, 1908, **28**, 300; 1913, **37**, 119, 238; Silundum tube furnace, Sieverts and Krumbhaar, *Z. phys. Chem.*, 1910, **74**, 284.

[9] Arsem, *Trans. Amer. Electrochem. Soc.*, 1906, **9**, 153; *J.A.C.S.*, 1906, **28**, 921; Pring and Hutton, *J.C.S.*, 1906, **89**, 1591; Hanemann, *Z. Elektrochem.*, 1908, **14**, 695; Heyn and Bauer, "Metallographie," 1909, **1**, 75; Ruff, *Ber.*, 1910, **43**, 1564; *Z. anorg. Chem.*, 1913, **80**, 373; *Z. Elektrochem.*, 1912, **18**, 164; 1914, **20**, 177; 1924, **30**, 356; Goecke, *Metallurgie*, 1911, **8**, 667; *Z. angew. Chem.*, 1911, **24**, 1459; Forsythe, *Astrophys. J.*, 1911, **34**, 353; Harker, *Chem. News*, 1912, **106**, 85, 97; *Nature*, 1912, **89**, 514, *Trans. Faraday Soc.*, 1917, **12**, 3; Humfrey, *Iron and Steel Carnegie Schol. Mem.*, 1912, **4**, 80 (simple type); Fischer and Ploetze, *Z. anorg. Chem.*, 1912, **75**, 1 (pressure); Stähler and Elbert, *Ber.*, 1913, **46**, 2060 (pressure); Seiferheld and Suda, *Z. anorg. Chem.*, 1913, **82**, 373; Kanolt, *ibid.*, 1914, **85**, 1; Tiede and Birnbräuer, *ibid.*, 1914, **87**, 129 (C rod); Ruff and Bormann, *ibid.*, 1914, **88**, 365; Wolf and Müller, *Z. Elektrochem.*, 1914, **20**, 1; Rydt, *ibid.*, 1914, **20**, 185; Jänecke, *ibid.*, 1915, **21**, 439; Askenasy and Grude, *Z. Elektrochem.*, 1922, **28**, 130; Anon., *ibid.*, 1922, **28**, 181 (C tube furnace for mech. press.); Lebeau and Picon, *Compt. Rend.*, 1924, **178**, 1151 (C tube, 2400°); Bryan, Mehring, and Ross, *Ind. Eng. Chem.*, 1924, **16**, 82 (Arsem type); Partington and Anfilogoff, *Trans. Faraday Soc.*, 1925, **21**, 360 (Ruff vac. type); Tammann and Löwenstein, *Z. anorg. Chem.*, 1926, **154**, 173 (C tube furnace to 3300°); Prescott and Hincks, *J.A.C.S.*, 1927, **49**, 2744; Lorenz and Woolcock, *Z. anorg. Chem.*, 1928, **176**, 289; Eitel and Spaliks, *ibid.*, 1929, **183**, 263 (Ruff type); Brantley and Beckman, *J.A.C.S.*, 1930, **52**, 3956 (C tube); Arndt and Pollack, *Z. anorg. Chem.*, 1931, **201**, 81 (C rod); Brunner, *Z. Elektrochem.*, 1932, **38**, 55; Podszus, *Z. anorg. Chem.*, 1933, **211**, 41 (C rod); Evans, *Rev. Sci. Instr.*, 1933, **4**, 391 (vacuum); Mayers, *J.A.C.S.*, 1939, **61**, 2053; for carbon crucible furnace, see Bonna and Lakoyer, *Z. Elektrochem.*, 1897, **3**, 479; carbon powder resistance furnace, Simonis, *Stahl u. Eisen*, 1907, **27**, 739; on "Kryptol" resistance, Buss, *Prometheus*, 1904, **15**, 551, and "Kryptol" furnace, Leroux, *Chem. Ztg.*, 1908, **32**, 1137. For electric and thermal conductivity of carbon, see Cellier, *Ann. Phys.*, 1897, **61**, 511; *Z. phys. Chem.*, 1897, **22**, 636.

used. The thin graphite tube (or spiral) turned from a rod, which may be slotted to increase its resistance, is usually supported vertically between water-cooled copper, bronze, or brass leads, and the parts of the carbon in contact with these may be copper-plated by electrolysis. Very heavy currents at low voltages (e.g. from transformers) are needed, and at temperatures above 2700° there is appreciable volatilisation of the carbon tube, which also becomes very friable. A zig-zag of carbon rods [1] has been used, and an electric cupola furnace described.[2]

In vacuum furnaces continued pumping is needed, as gas is continuously evolved from the heated carbon. A carbon crucible may be supported inside the tube on a magnesia rod, and the outside of the tube sighted by an optical pyrometer through a water-cooled glass window in the furnace jacket. A horizontal carbon tube vacuum furnace, requiring 200 amp. at 30 volts for 2000°, 380 amp. for 2500°, and 500 amp. for 2800° (which at temperatures of 2400°–2500° can operate for several hours) was described by Wolf and Müller.[3] A thick slotted tube, 30 cm. long, 5 cm. outer and 2 cm. inner diameter, was used, with graphite pieces for leads, one screwed in and the other a sliding fit. Surrounding the furnace tube were two concentric carbon tubes, slit down the length and held together by graphite rings. The outer case had a water-cooled jacket. A graphite plate furnace was used by Hemsalech [4] (250 amp.; 3000°). Acheson graphite is more permanent in use than ordinary carbon, but has a better conductivity and needs heavier currents. Silit (containing silicon carbide) tubes can be used up to 1400°.

For the highest temperatures (3000°) the carbon *arc furnace* is practically the only available form. The electric arc between carbon poles was first produced by Davy [5] as "a light so vivid that even the sunlight compared with it appeared feeble." The classical form is that of Moissan,[6] in which two horizontal carbon rods lie in grooves cut in a block of limestone [7] and are covered by another block of limestone, a cavity being formed between the two blocks in which the arc is struck. Very heavy currents are necessary. Such furnaces are in general suited only to qualitative and preparative work, as it is very difficult to determine the temperature and the material is very liable to contamination by carbon.

Heating by *cathode rays* has been used.[8] The latest type of furnace, which requires very expensive apparatus (£750–£3000) but is very efficient, is the high frequency *induction furnace*,[9] in which eddy-currents are induced by an

[1] Hempel, *Ber.*, 1890, **23**, 3388; 5 *Int. Kongr. angew. Chem.*, Berlin, 1903, **1**, 715; Oberhoffer *Stahl u. Eisen*, 1907, **27**, 1764; Finkelstein, *Ber.*, 1906, **39**, 1585; carbon rings, Rosenhain and Coad-Pryor, *Trans. Faraday Soc.*, 1918, **14**, 264.

[2] Schweitzer, *Z. Elektrochem.*, 1926, **32**, 98.

[3] *Z. Elektrochem.*, 1914, **20**, 1.

[4] *Phil. Mag.*, 1920, **39**, 241.

[5] "Elements of Chemical Philosophy," 1812, 152; *Phil. Trans.*, 1821, **111**, 425 (10-cm.-long arc from 2000 cells); "Works," 1840, **4**, 110; **6**, 230.

[6] Moissan, "The Electric Furnace," transl. de Moulpied, 1904; Heusler, *Z. anorg. Chem.*, 1896, **11**, 293; 1897, **14**, 172; Küster and Dolezalek, *Z. Elektrochem.*, 1897, **3**, 329; Pfleger, *ibid.*, 1897, **4**, 12 (large arc furnaces); Anon., *Engineering*, 1906, **81**, 381; Clerc and Minet, *Compt. Rend.*, 1908, **146**, 227; Ruff and Wunsch, *Z. anorg. Chem.*, 1914, **85**, 292; Steiner, *Z. Elektrochem.*, 1941, **47**, 581 (lab. types).

[7] The m.p. of lime (CaO) is 2575°: Schumacher, *J.A.C.S.*, 1926, **48**, 396.

[8] Von Wartenberg, *Ber.*, 1907, **40**, 3287; Fischer, *Z. anorg. Chem.*, 1912, **81**, 170; Tiede, *Ber.*, 1913, **46**, 2229; Gerdien and Riegger, *Wiss. Veröff. Siemens-Konzern*, 1923, **3**, 226; Klinkhardt, *Z. Elektrochem.*, 1926, **32**, 534; Trombe, *Bull. Soc. Chim.*, 1934, **1**, 159, 262.

[9] Northrup, *Trans. Faraday Soc.*, 1917, **13**, 212; *Trans. Amer. Electrochem. Soc.*, 1919, **35**, 69, 158; *J. Franklin Inst.*, 1923, **195**, 665; Ribaud, *Compt. Rend.*, 1925, **180**, 1733; *Chim. et*

alternating magnetic flux in a mass of metal supported in a refractory crucible in a vacuous tube.

Most high-temperature electric furnaces require heavy currents which cannot be taken from the town supply, but require special dynamos or (when A.C. is supplied) transformers. For such currents special resistances are needed. A useful type consists of lead plates in running water.[1] A copper spiral tube cooled by running water and provided with a sliding contact[2] can also be used. A useful type consists of horizontal brass tubes cooled by flowing water and fixed on insulators on a wall, the tubes being connected by suitable bends, and with sliding contacts.[3] For smaller units a resistance composed of plates of carbon in a rack, compressed by a screw to alter the resistance,[4] is useful.

McLennan and McLay[5] used a horizontal carbon tube as an electrode, arcing to a lower electrode from the middle. An enclosed micro-resistance furnace with a carbon rod was used for the sublimation of alloys by Fletcher,[6] a carbon spiral resistance furnace was described by Tarrant,[7] and a carbon muffle furnace by Siebert.[8]

The *burning-glass*, a lens or mirror concentrating sunlight, is one of the oldest means of attaining high temperatures, and the method of concentration of radiation could no doubt find useful modern applications.[9] A small vacuum furnace heated by a burning-glass was described by Stock and Heynemann.[10] Temperatures above 4000° still await investigation.[11]

§ 3. Measurement of High Temperatures[12]

An early method for the measurement of high temperatures was the *pyrometer*

Ind., 1936, **35**, 3; Fischer, *Z. techn. Phys.*, 1926, **7**, 513; *Z. angew. Chem.*, 1927, **40**, 1301; Strutt, *Ann. Phys.*, 1927, **82**, 605; Burch and Davis, *Phil. Mag.*, 1926, **1**, 768; Cain and Peterson, *Trans. Amer. Electrochem. Soc.*, 1925, **48**, 199; von Wartenberg, in Wien-Harms, " Handbuch der Experimentalphysik," 1929, **9**, i, 1; Leitgebel, *Z. anorg. Chem.*, 1931, **202**, 305; Boericke and Bangert, *Ind. Eng. Chem. Anal.*, 1944, **16**, 302; Aitchison and Crouchley, *J. Sci. Instr.*, 1945, **22**, 176; Stauffer, Fox, and Di Pietrow, *Ind. Eng. Chem.*, 1948, **40**, 820; Stansel, *Gen. Elec. Rev.*, 1948, **51**, No. 2, 44.

1 Thiele, *Z. Elektrochem.*, 1910, **16**, 442; Partington and Anfilogoff used iron plates in water in wooden tubs; the water soon boils and must be renewed.

2 Friedrich, *Metall und Erz*, 1913, **10**, 511.

3 This arrangment was used for *c.* 100 amps. by Partington and Shilling; constantan strips, Feussner, *Elektrotechn. Z.*, 1899, **20**, 611, 632.

4 Engelmann, *Onderzoekingen gedaan in het physiol. Lab. te Utrecht*, 1887, **10**, 169; *Arch. Néerl.*, 1888, **22**, 145; Hoffmann, *Elektrotechn. Z.*, 1937, **58**, 1111, 1138.

5 *Trans. Roy. Soc. Canada*, 1925, **19**, III, 89.

6 *J.C.S.*, 1913, **103**, 2097.

7 *Trans. Faraday Soc.*, 1920, **15**, Pt. III, 83.

8 *Chem. Ztg.*, 1921, **45**, 772.

9 Ribaud, *Chim. et Ind.*, 1936, **35**, 3; for the Florentine lens (used by Davy and Faraday), Martin, *J. Sci. Instr.*, 1931, **8**, 379; for Lavoisier's large lens, Lowry, " Historical Introduction to Chemistry," 1915, 100; Trombe, Foëx, and la Blanchetais, *Ann. Chim.*, 1947, **2**, 385; Trombe, *Research*, 1948, **1**, 393 (" solar furnace ").

10 *Ber.*, 1909, **42**, 2863 (melting Si crystals).

11 Finkelnburg, *Naturwiss.*, 1944, **32**, 105.

12 Weinhold, *Ann. Phys.*, 1873, **49**, 186 (bibl. of various methods); Barus, On the Thermoelectric Measurement of High Temperatures, *Bull. U.S. Geol. Survey*, Washington, 1889, **8**, No. 54; " Die physikalische Behandlung und Messung hoher Temperaturen," Leipzig, 1892; *Congrès Internat. Phys.*, 1901, **1**, 148; Le Chatelier and Boudouard, " Températures élevées," Paris, 1900; transl. Burgess, " High Temperature Measurement," 2nd edit., New York, 1904; new edit., Burgess and Le Chatelier, " The Measurement of High Temperatures." 3rd edit., New York, 1912; " Die Messung hoher Temperaturen," Berlin, 1913;

of Wedgwood,[1] depending on the contraction of a prism of baked clay after strong heating; the length was measured by a gauge. The results were very crude: the m.p. of iron was found to be 12,000° C., which is 10,500° too high! The Daniell [2] pyrometer depended on the expansion of a metal bar. The bar is contained in a tube of clay and graphite and pushed to the bottom. Above it is a porcelain index-rod in contact with the bar and kept somewhat tight by a collar. As the bar expands the index is forced out, but on cooling it remains in place and its position can be found. The motion of the index is the difference between the expansion of the bar and that of the tube. A graphite bar has been used.[3]

In the *meldometer* of Joly [4] the melting-point of a solid was found by heating it on a platinum ribbon, heated electrically and stretched by a spring, the extension of the strip being measured by an eye-piece and micrometer screw. The *micropyrometer* of Burgess [5] is an adaptation of Joly's meldometer in which the temperature of the heated platinum strip is determined by a small disappearing-filament pyrometer sighted on it, this being adjusted like a microscope on its stand.

Prinsep [6] exposed a series of small flattened beads of gold-silver alloys of known composition on a cupel and found which melted: the melting-points of the alloys were determined by an air thermometer with a gold bulb. *Seger cones*,[7] used in determining temperatures in porcelain kilns, etc., consist of small cones of various clay bodies, which soften and bend over at various temperatures. Brearley and Moorwood [8] used cast cylinders of salts or alloys instead of Seger cones. Skirrow [9] described a works apparatus depending on the release of a wire, embedded in a solid in an iron tube, on melting of the solid. The so-called *acoustic thermometer* [10] depends on the change of the wave-length of sound in air with change of temperature.

Day and Sosman, High Temperature Gas Thermometry, *Carnegie Inst.*, Washington, 1911, **157**; Griffiths and Schofield, *Trans. Faraday Soc.*, 1917, **13**, 222; Foote, Fairchild, and Harrison, Pyrometric Practice, *Bur. Stand. Bull.*, 1921 (Dept. Commerce), Tech. Pap. **170**—a 326-pp. general article; Wood and Cork, "Pyrometry," New York, 1927, 2nd edit., 1941; Lax and Pirani, in Ullmann, "Enzyklopädie der techn. Chemie," 1932, **9**, 773; Forsythe (edit.), "Measurement of Radiant Energy," New York, 1937.

[1] *Phil. Trans.*, 1782, **72**, 305; 1784, **74**, 358; abdgd. edit., 1809, **15**, 278, 571; an extract in book form, "Description and Use of a Thermometer for Measuring the Higher Degrees of Heat," 1784, was translated into French and German; Guyton de Morveau, *Ann. Chim.*, 1803, **46**, 276; 1810, **73**, 254; 1810, **74**, 18, 129; 1811, **78**, 73; 1814, **90**, 113, 225; Lucas, *Z. phys. Chem.*, 1905, **52**, 327.

[2] *J. Roy. Inst.*, 1821, **11**, 309; *Phil. Trans.*, 1830, **120**, 257; "Introduction to the Study of Chemical Philosophy," 2nd edit., 1843, 111.

[3] Winkler, *Z. anal. Chem.*, 1880, **19**, 63; Beckert, *ibid.*, 1882, **21**, 248.

[4] *Proc. Roy. Irish Acad.*, 1891, **2**, 38; Wilson and Gray, *Phil. Trans.*, 1894, **185**, 361; Ramsay and Eumorfopoulos, *Phil. Mag.*, 1896, **41**, 360; Anon., *Electrician*, 1908–9, **62**, 469, 721.

[5] *J. Wash. Acad.*, 1913, **3**, 7; 1914, **4**, 566; *Phys. Z.*, 1913, **14**, 158.

[6] *Phil. Trans.*, 1828, **118**, 79; *Ann. Chim.*, 1829, **41**, 247; Steinmetz, *J.A.C.S.*, 1918, **40**, 96; Prinsep's results are very accurate and are still used; similar experiments by Erhard and Shertel, *Jahrb. f. Berg-u. Hütten-Wesen in Sachsen*, 1879, 154.

[7] Seger, *Thonindustr. Ztg.*, 1886, 135, 145, 168; Louth and Vogt, *Bull. Soc. Chim.*, 1886, **46**, 786; Walkin, *Trans. Faraday Soc.*, 1917, **13**, 330; Dana and Foote, *ibid.*, 1919, **15**, 186 (m.ps. at high temps.); Kanolt, *J. Franklin Inst.*, 1919, **188**, 489.

[8] *J. Iron Steel Inst.*, 1907, **73**, 261; Anon., *Met. Chem. Eng.*, 1915, **13**, 192 (218°–1329°); Nehls, *Elec. World*, 1915, **65**, 124.

[9] *J.S.C.I.*, 1908, **27**, 434.

[10] Cagniard de la Tour and Demonferrand, *Compt. Rend.*, 1837, **4**, 28; Mayer, *Ann. Phys.*, 1873, **148**, 287; Quincke, *ibid.*, 1897, **63**, 66.

The determination of the *vapour density* of mercury [1] or iodine [2] has been used to measure high temperatures. A calorimetric method was used by Carnelley and Williams [3] to find the melting-points of many salts, but the results are inaccurate.

Pyrometers depending on the change of viscosity of a gas with temperature (proposed by Barus), such as Callendar's *transpiration balance*, have been used.[4] D. Berthelot [5] measured the change of refractive index of a gas. The change of colour of solids, e.g. applied as paints to metals, has often been used.[6]

For temperatures above a red heat, a *thermocouple* or platinum *resistance thermometer* (§ 7.VI A) can be used; for the highest temperatures some form of *optical pyrometer*, depending on the laws of radiation, is applied (§ 13). Special precautions must be used in determining the temperatures of flowing gases by means of thermocouples.[7]

The history of high-temperature gas thermometry may be summarised as follows: [8]

1828 const. press., gold bulb [9]
1836 const. press., platinum bulb [10]
1847 const. press., platinum bulb.[11]
1853 const. vol.[12]
1857 vap. dens. of iodine.[13]
1861 const. press.[14]
1863 const. press., platinum bulb.[15]
1863 const. press. and vol., glazed porcelain bulb.[16]
1879 const. press., porcelain bulb.[17]
1882 const. press., porcelain bulb.[18]

[1] Regnault, *Ann. Chim.*, 1861, **63**, 39.

[2] Deville and Troost, *Ann. Chim.*, 1860, **58**, 257 (results vitiated by the dissociation of iodine).

[3] Carnelley and Williams, *J.C.S.*, 1876, **29**, 489; 1877, **32**, 365; 1878, **33**, 273, 281; Violle, *Compt. Rend.*, 1877, **85**, 543; Hoadley, *J. Franklin Inst.*, 1882, **84**, 91, 169, 252.

[4] Barus, *Ann. Phys.*, 1889, **36**, 358; Callendar, *Nature*, 1899, **59**, 494, 519; Job, *Compt. Rend.*, 1902, **134**, 39.

[5] *Compt. Rend.*, 1895, **120**, 831; 1898, **126**, 410, 473; *Ann. Chim.*, 1902, **26**, 58; Kennard, in " Temperature. Its Measurement and Control," New York, 1941, 685.

[6] See e.g. Naeser, *Mitt. K. Wilh. Inst. Eisenforsch. Düsseldorf*, 1930, **12**, 299; Penzig, *Chem. Fabr.*, 1939, **12**, 358; Déribéré and Buccar, *Chim. et Ind.*, 1941, **46**, 607; Schmidt, *Z. techn. Phys.*, 1942, **23**, 88; Guthmann, *Stahl u. Eisen*, 1942, **62**, 477; and patents, e.g. I. G. Farben, Fr. P. 822308 (1937); Tyte, *Proc. Inst. Mech. Eng.*, 1945, **152**, 226; Partington, *Nature*, 1947, **159**, 784.

[7] Schmidt, *Z. techn. Phys.*, 1926, **7**, 518; Guillon, *Chaleur et Ind.*, 1926, **7**, 395.

[8] Barus, *U.S. Geol. Survey Bull.*, 1889, **8**, No. 54 (on the Thermo-electric Measurement of High Temperatures; with very complete summary of early work); Day and Sosman, in Glazebrook, " Dict. of Applied Physics," 1922, **1**, 857.

[9] Prinsep, *Phil. Trans.*, 1828, **118**, 79; *Ann. Chim.*, 1829, **41**, 247.

[10] Pouillet, *Compt. Rend.*, 1836, **3**, 782.

[11] Regnault, *Mém. Acad. Sci.*, 1847, **21**, 163.

[12] Silbermann and Jacquelin, *Bull. Soc. Encouragem.*, 1853, **52**, 108.

[13] Deville and Troost, *Compt. Rend.*, 1857, **45**, 821; 1859, **49**, 239; *Ann. Chim.*, 1860, **58**, 257 (results falsified by dissociation $I_2 \rightleftharpoons 2I$).

[14] Regnault, *Ann. Chim.*, 1861, **63**, 39.

[15] Becquerel, *Ann. Chim.*, 1863, **68**, 49.

[16] Deville and Troost, *Compt. Rend.*, 1863, **57**, 894, 897; 1864, **59**, 162; reply by Becquerel, *ibid.*, 1863, **57**, 902, 925, 936.

[17] Erhard and Schertel, *Jahrb. f. Berg. u. Hüttenwesen in Sachsen*, 1879, 154.

[18] Violle, *Compt. Rend.*, 1882, **94**, 720.

1889 const. press., platinum bulb.[1]
1892 const. vol., porcelain bulb.[2]
1899 const. vol., porcelain and platinum bulbs (latter preferred).[3]
1904 const. vol., porcelain bulb.[4]
1905 quartz-glass bulb.[5]
1906 const. vol., various bulbs (Ir, Pt and Pt alloys with Ir and Rh).[6]
1908–12 const. vol., platinum-iridium bulb filled with nitrogen.[7]

The *Wiborgh pyrometer* [8] is a gas thermometer type.

§ 4. Radiant Heat

Those parts of the spectrum which lie beyond the visible at the red end [9] constitute *radiant heat* or *infra-red radiation.* They differ from light only in having a longer wave-length (λ), which is measured in Ångström units (A.= 10^{-8} cm.), or for longer waves in millimicrons ($m\mu=10^{-6}$ mm.) or microns ($\mu=10^{-3}$ mm.). The instruments for measuring radiant heat [10] are briefly described in § 5.

According to Draper [11] a solid body begins to emit red light (appearing to the eye as a faint "ghostly" grey)[12] at 525°; the brightness or intensity rises rapidly with increasing temperature, and in addition to an increase of total radiation the distribution in the spectrum (on which the colour depends) changes with rise of temperature, the intensity of short waves (violet) increasing more rapidly than that of long waves (red). Hyde and Forsythe[13] fixed the limit of visibility at the red end of the spectrum at $\lambda=0{\cdot}75\mu$. Amerio [14] pointed out that Draper's law (which he said is incorrect) had been stated previously by Wedgwood.[15] Tammann, Neubert, and Boehme,[16] and Tammann and Boehme,[17] found the emission of grey light to occur at variable temperatures with various

1 Barus, *U.S. Geol. Survey Bull.*, 1889, **8**, No. 54 (313 pp.); *Amer. J. Sci.*, 1894, **48**, 332.
2 Holborn and Wien, *Ann. Phys.*, 1892, **47**, 107; 1895, **56**, 360.
3 Holborn and Day, *Ann. Phys.*, 1899, **68**, 817; *Amer. J. Sci.*, 1899, **8**, 165.
4 Harker, *Phil. Trans.*, 1904, **203**, 343.
5 Jaquerod and Perrot, *Arch. Sci. Phys. Nat.*, 1905, **20**, 28, 128, 454, 506.
6 Holborn and Valentiner, *Berlin Ber.*, 1906, 811; *Ann. Phys.*, 1907, **22**, 1; spectrophotometer.
7 Day and Clement, *Amer. J. Sci.*, 1908, **26**, 405; Day, Sosman, and Allen, *ibid.*, 1910, **29**, 93; *Carnegie Inst. Publ.*, 1911, **157**; Day and Sosman, *Z. anorg. Chem.*, 1911, **72**, 1; *J. de Phys.*, 1912, **2**, 727, 831, 899; *Ann. Phys.*, 1912, **38**, 849.
8 *Jern-Kontorets Annaler*, 1888, **43**, 97; *J. Iron and Steel Inst.*, 1888, ii, 110; Rhodin, *Trans, Faraday Soc.*, 1917, **13**, 260.
9 Discovered by Scheele, "Chemical Observations and Experiments on Air and Fire," transl. Forster, 1780, 66; investigated by Herschel, *Phil. Trans.*, 1800, **90**, 255, 284, 437; Cornell, *Annals of Sci.*, 1938, **3**, 119; for a historical account, see Whewell, "History of the Inductive Sciences," 1857, **2**, 382.
10 Lummer, "Die Ziele der Leuchttechnik," Munich, 1903; Pringsheim, *Z. Elektrochem.*, 1903, **9**, 716; Graetz, in Winkelmann, "Handbuch der Physik," 1906, **3**, 241; Poynting and Thomson, "Heat," 1911, 220; Jellinek, "Physikalische Chemie der Gasreaktionen," Leipzig, 1913, 505 f.; Preston, "Theory of Heat," 3rd edit., 1919, 554; Planck, "Theorie der Wärmestrahlung," 4th edit., Leipzig, 1921; Griffiths, in Glazebrook, "Dict. of Applied Physics," 1923, **3**, 699; Wien and Müller, in Wien-Harms, "Handbuch der Experimentalphysik," 1929, **9**, i, 347; H. A. Taylor, in H. S. Taylor, "Treatise on Physical Chemistry," 1931, **2**, 1519.
11 *Phil. Mag.*, 1847, **30**, 345; "Scientific Memoirs," New York, 1878, 23.
12 Weber, *Ann. Phys.*, 1887, **32**, 256; Emden, *ibid.*, 1889, **36**, 214; Lummer, *ibid.*, 1897, **62**, 14.
13 *Astrophys. J.*, 1915, **42**, 285.
14 *Nuov. Cim.*, 1904, **8**, 313.
15 *Phil. Trans.*, 1784, **74**, 358; 1786, **76**, 390; 1792, **82**, 28.
16 *Ann. Phys.*, 1932, **15**, 317.
17 *Ann. Phys.*, 1933, **17**, 863; Balarew and Karabaschew, *Koll. Z.*, 1934, **68**, 261.

oxides and sulphides, as low as 210° for some oxides. The temperature is lowered by 50°–150° by powdering and it is dependent on the chemical composition.

The so-called *colour scale* of temperature, due to Pouillet,[1] depends on the colour of the light emitted by a glowing body; each of the entries should really refer to a range of temperature, and the results depend on personal factors and on the emissivity of the surface of the hot body:

° C.	° F.	Colour of Light
532	990	Dark blood-red, black-red, incipient red.
566	1050	Dark red, blood-red, low red.
635	1175	Dark cherry-red, incipient cherry-red.
682	1250	Medium cherry-red.
746	1375	Cherry, full red.
835	1550	Light cherry, bright cherry, light red.
899	1650	Orange, salmon.
941	1725	Light orange, light salmon.
996	1825	Yellow.
1079	1975	Light yellow.
1205	2200	White.

That radiant heat showed the same properties of reflexion, refraction, interference, double refraction, and polarisation as light was proved experimentally by Forbes, Melloni,[2] and De la Provostaye and Desains,[3] in a series of investigations with relatively simple apparatus, and most subsequent work has been a refinement of this. As Rayleigh[4] pointed out, Young[5] in 1807 had clearly stated that heat and light are modifications of the same " motion," differing only in frequency.

The quantitative study of radiation provides information as to how the radiant energy is partitioned among the wave-lengths, and how change of temperature affects this partition. Strictly speaking, radiation should be studied in a vacuum, but as air absorbs very little ordinary radiant heat, a good deal of information can often be obtained by working in air.

One of the earliest known laws of radiation, the *theory of exchanges*, stated by Prevost[6] (of Geneva) in 1791, directs attention to the radiating body, and asserts that *each body radiates energy to, and also absorbs energy from, other*

1 *Compt. Rend.*, 1836, **3**, 782; White and Taylor, *Metallographist*, 1900, **3**, 41; Howe, *ibid.*, 1900, **3**, 43; Mellor, " The Crystallisation of Iron and Steel," 1918, 24.

2 Forbes, *Phil. Mag.*, 1835, **6**, 134, 205 (polarisation); Melloni, *Ann. Chim.*, 1836, **61**, 375; 1838, **68**, 107; *Ann. Phys.*, 1835, **35**, 112 (apparatus).

3 *Ann. Chim.*, 1848, **22**, 358; 1849, **27**, 109; 1850, **28**, 252; 1850, **30**, 159, 276; 1851, **32**, 112; 1852, **34**, 192; Knoblauch, *Ann. Phys.*, 1847, **70**, 337; 1847, **71**, 1; 1847, **74**, 161; *Ann. Chim.*, 1860, **59**, 493, and many later papers; Seebeck, *Ann. Phys.*, 1849, **77**, 574 (diffraction by grating); Desains, *Compt. Rend.*, 1866, **62**, 1277; 1877, **84**, 1056 (polarisation); Hussell, *Ann. Phys.*, 1891, **43**, 498 (rotation of plane of polarisation by quartz); Elliott and Ambrose, *Nature*, 1947, **159**, 641; Elliott, Ambrose, and Temple, *J. Opt. Soc. Amer.*, 1948, **38**, 212 (polarisation by pile of selenium films).

4 *Phil. Mag.*, 1889, **27**, 265.

5 " Lectures on Natural Philosophy," 1807, **1**, 638.

6 *Obs. sur la Phys.*, 1791, **38**, 314; " Du Calorique Rayonnant," Paris, 1809; Supplement: " Exposition Élémentaire des Principes qui servent de Base à la Théorie de la Chaleur Rayonnante," Geneva, 1832; a " Recherches Physico-Mécanique sur la Chaleur " was published at Geneva, " aux dépens de l'Auteur," in 1792; Mach, " Die Principien der Wärmelehre," Leipzig, 1896, 125; Guye, *Arch. Sci. Phys. Nat.*, 1912, **33**, 469; Cornell, *Annals of Sci.*, 1936, **1**. 217, where early work on radiant heat is summarised.

bodies. If a body radiates more energy than it receives, its temperature falls; if it receives more than it radiates, its temperature rises. If a number of bodies all at the same temperature are enclosed in a space impervious to heat, the energies radiated and received by each body exactly balance, and there is no change in temperature of any of the bodies. The system is thus in temperature equilibrium.

Experiments made by Leslie [1] with a tin cube, filled with hot water, having faces in different conditions (black, polished, roughened, papered, etc.) and with the various faces turned in succession towards a differential air thermometer having a blackened bulb, showed that *good emitters are also good absorbers.* Quantitative experiments with a thermopile by Melloni [2] confirmed this. A body at every temperature thus emits the same kind of radiation as it absorbs. Bodies which at high temperatures are transparent (hot glass, Bunsen flame) emit practically no light, and if a body absorbs only one kind of radiation it emits only this kind when incandescent (e.g. sodium vapour and radiation of $\lambda=0{\cdot}589\mu$). This is the principle of the detection of elements in the sun from the dark Fraunhofer absorption lines in the spectrum.[3]

A gas exposed to intermittent infra-red radiation emits a sound the intensity of which is proportional to the absorption; the effect has been used in gas analysis.[4]

The relations between *diathermancy* (transmissibility for radiant heat) and chemical composition were investigated by Schulz-Sellack,[5] Nichols,[6] Zsigmondy,[7] and Friedel: [8] the modern aspect, involving a study of absorption bands, will be considered later.

§ 5. Kirchhoff's Law

The fundamental law of heat radiation, arrived at qualitatively by De la Provostaye and Desains,[9] and more precisely formulated by Balfour Stewart,[10] was given a mathematical form by Kirchhoff,[11] after whom it is generally called.

[1] " An Experimental Inquiry into the Nature and Propagation of Heat," 1804, 1 f., 22; Ritchie, *Phil. Trans.*, 1827, **117**, 139; Wiedeburg, *Ann. Phys.*, 1898, **66**, 92.

[2] *Ann. Chim.*, from 1831; *Ann. Phys.*, 1832–53; Taylor's *Scientific Memoirs*, 1837, **1**, 1, 39, 325, 383, 388; 1841, **2**, 141; Melloni, " La Thermochrôse ou la Coloration Calorifique," Naples, 1850; Cornell, *Annals of Sci.*, 1938, **3**, 402; see also Tyndall, " Contributions to Molecular Physics in the Domain of Radiant Heat. A Series of Memoirs published in the Philosophical Transactions and Philosophical Magazine, with Additions," 1872; *Phil. Mag.*, 1861, **22**, 169, 273; 1862, **23**, 252; 1863, **26**, 30, 44; 1864, **28**, 81, 438, 508.

[3] Kirchhoff, *Phil. Mag.*, 1860, **20**, 1, from a letter to him from W. Thomson quoting unpublished teachings of Stokes; Tait, " Recent Advances in Physical Science," 2nd edit., 1876, 191; *idem*, art. Radiation in " Ency. Brit.," 9th edit., 1886, **20**, 212.

[4] Tyndall, *Proc. Roy. Soc.*, 1881, **31**, 307; Röntgen, *Ber. Oberhess. Ges. Natur-u. Heilkde.*, 1881, **20**, 19, 52; Heine, *ibid.*, 1882, **21**, 17; Röntgen, *Ann. Phys.*, 1881, **12**, 155; Veingerov, *Zavodskaya Lab.*, 1947, **13**, 426.

[5] *Ann. Phys.*, 1870, **139**, 182.

[6] *Phys. Rev.*, 1893, **1**, 1.

[7] *Ann. Phys.*, 1893, **49**, 531, 535; 1896, **57**, 639; *Z. phys. Chem.*, 1896, **20**, 634.

[8] *Ann. Phys.*, 1895, **55**, 453.

[9] *Ann. Chim.*, 1850, **30**, 431; 1863, **67**, 5; *Compt. Rend.*, 1853, **36**, 84; 1853, **37**, 168.

[10] *Proc. Roy. Soc. Edin.*, 1858, **22**, 1, 59; *Proc. Roy. Soc.*, 1860, **10**, 385, 503; *Phil. Mag.*, 1860, **20**, 169, 534; 1861, **21**, 391; *Ann. Chim.*, 1861, **62**, 188 (Kirchhoff); " An Elementary Treatise on Heat," 5th edit., Oxford, 1888, 196; Rayleigh, *Phil. Mag.*, 1900, **49**, 539; 1901, **1**, 98; " Scientific Papers," Cambridge, 1903, **4**, 483, 494, who says Stewart's work was insufficiently appreciated on the Continent; cf. Stokes, " Math. and Phys. Papers," 1904, **4**, 127 f., 136; Schuster, *Nature*, 1925, **115**, 87.

[11] *Berlin Ber.*, 1860, 783 (read 11 Dec. 1859; abstract only); *Ann. Phys.*, 1860, **109**, 275; *Phil. Mag.*, 1860, **20**, 1; 1861, **21**, 241; *Ann. Chim.*, 1861, **62**, 160; " Ges. Abhl.," 1882, 571;

Consider an enclosure (cavity; German, *Hohlraum*) heated in a furnace until it is incandescent, and let it contain pieces of glass, silver, and coke (supposed not to burn but to be heated to redness), etc. Through a small hole, the interior of the cavity appears uniformly bright, and the different bodies inside cannot be distinguished. If, however, the pieces of coke and glass are quickly taken out of the cavity, the black coke shines much more brightly than the glass, as it emits much more radiation. The same holds for the coke and the piece of silver. Thus, the feebler emissive powers of the glass and silver are completely compensated in the cavity by the glass freely transmitting radiation from the hot wall behind it, and the silver freely reflecting radiation from the hot wall in front of it. The black, opaque coke neither transmits nor reflects radiation, and as the flux of radiation is the same at all points and in every direction inside the cavity, the black body must provide the whole of its contribution by radiation alone. The brightness of the cavity itself is unchanged if the black body is taken out.

From this experiment the following important consequences follow. If a *perfectly black body* is one which absorbs all radiation falling on it and neither reflects nor transmits any, then:

(1) " If a space is bounded by bodies of equal temperature, and if no radiation can penetrate through these bodies, then every bundle of rays inside the cavity is constituted, as to quality and intensity, as if it came from a perfectly black body at the same temperature, and is, therefore, independent of the nature and form of the bodies, and depends only on the temperature." [1]

(2) At a given temperature the radiation from a perfectly black body (usually called *black-body radiation*, sometimes [2] *full radiation*) is the maximum possible; i.e. no body can be brighter at a given temperature, by pure temperature radiation, than a perfectly black body.

(3) Inside an equally heated enclosure, the differences in radiation from the most different bodies completely vanish.

The fact that an enclosure behaves as a perfectly black body is also proved by the absorption of radiation by it at low temperatures as well as emission at high temperatures. Through a small hole in the wall of a cool cavity, the interior appears perfectly black, although it may be of polished silver. A ray penetrating inside is, by successive reflexions (which may be irregular scattering) finally completely absorbed; since the reflexion is never perfect and there is a little absorption on each, no reflected ray penetrates outside the enclosure (Fig. 1.VI B).

Since all natural bodies reflect to some extent, the practical realisation of a perfectly black *body* is difficult. Carbon and platinum black do not reflect visible rays, and absorb those of longer wave-length, but carbon burns at 400°, and platinum black is converted into ordinary grey platinum at 600°. A

Cotton, *Astrophys. J.*, 1899, **9**, 237; Pringsheim, *Z. wiss. Photogr.*, 1903, **1**, 360; Féry, *Ann. Chim.*, 1909, **17**, 267; Meslin, *J. de Phys.*, 1912, **2**, 557; Richarz, *Z. wiss. Photogr.*, 1912, **11**, 254; Preston, " Theory of Heat," 1919, 556; a proof for separate wave-lengths was given by Evans, *Proc. Amer. Acad.*, 1910, **46**, 97; for experiments, see Schaum and Wüstenfeld, *Z. wiss. Photogr.*, 1911, **10**, 213; a complete summary of *all* the laws of radiation is given by Bauer, *Ann. Chim.*, 1913, **29**, 5, 244, 372; Voigt, *Phys. Z.*, 1912, **13**, 848 (heterogeneous bodies); Jäger, *Wien Ber.*, 1915, **124**, IIA, 305; for a refined deduction of Kirchhoff's law using integral equations, Hilbert, *Phys. Z.*, 1912, **13**, 1056; 1913, **14**, 592.

[1] Kirchhoff, *Ann. Phys.*, 1860, **109**, 275; *Phil. Mag.*, 1860, **20**, 1; Wien, *Ann. Phys.*, 1894, **52**, 132; the *Phil. Mag.* translation is somewhat freer than the above.

[2] Callendar, *Phil. Mag.*, 1913, **26**, 787; 1914, **27**, 870.

refractory body, such as brick or fireclay, coated with ferric or uranium oxide, or manganese dioxide, behaves approximately as a black body, but by far the best experimental black body is a cavity with a small aperture. Such cavities were used at temperatures of −180° to +1400° by Wien and Lummer [1] and Lummer and Pringsheim.[2] The one for use at high temperatures (Fig. 2.VI B), used by Lummer and Kurlbaum [3] consisted of a porcelain tube fitted with diaphragms and with a thermocouple at the closed end, the whole being enclosed in a wider porcelain tube with a platinum resistance heater. The interior was

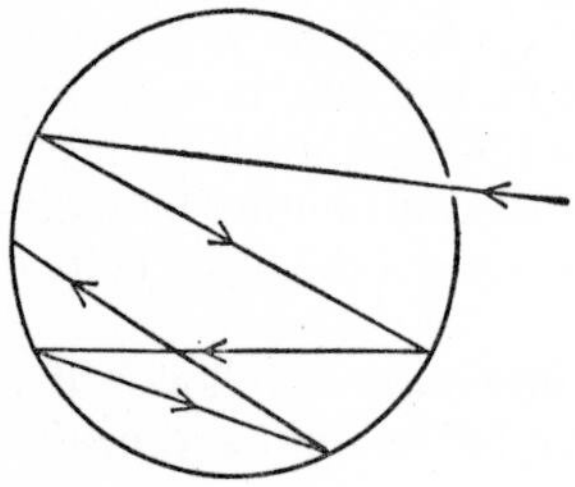

FIG. 1.VI B. Black-body Cavity

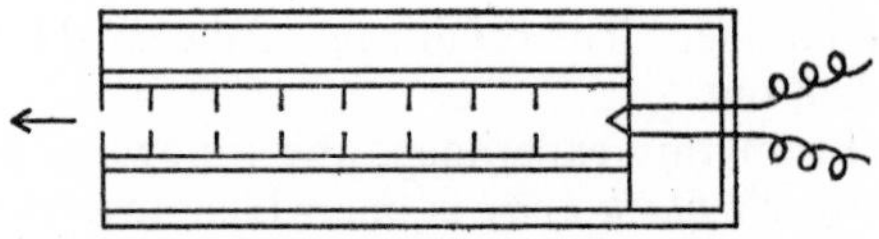

FIG. 2.VI B. Lummer and Kurlbaum Black Body

blackened (probably unnecessarily) by oxides of chromium, nickel, and cobalt. With the radiation emitted from the aperture at the open end, the laws of black-body radiation were established. Other types of black body used include a cavity in a Nernst heater,[4] and a molybdenum wire 12 cm. long and 1·4 mm. diam. with a boring 0·5 mm. diam. and 1 mm. deep, heated in nitrogen.[5] Rubens and Hoffmann [6] investigated the radiation from black carbon and platinum surfaces, and studied the effect of the thickness of the black substance.

The intensity of radiation is measured by a special *thermopile* [7] (or its modi-

[1] *Ann. Phys.*, 1895, **56**, 451; Ostwald's *Klassiker*, 1929, **228**. The first experiments of this type were made by Christiansen, *Ann. Phys.*, 1884, **21**, 364, and Boltzmann, *ibid.*, 1884, **22**, 31, who used Leslie cubes with zig-zag sides, and perforated with small holes, respectively, as black bodies. St. John, *Ann. Phys.*, 1895, **56**, 433; Wilson, *Astrophys. J.*, 1899, **10**, 80; Buckley, *Phil. Mag.*, 1927, **4**, 753; 1928, **6**, 447.

[2] *Ann. Phys.*, 1897, **63**, 395; *Verhl. d. D. Phys. Ges.*, 1899, **1**, 23, 215.

[3] Lummer and Kurlbaum, *Ann. Phys.*, 1901, **5**, 829; Valentiner, *ibid.*, 1910, **31**, 275; Pirani, *Verhl. d. D. Phys. Ges.*, 1911, **13**, 19 (carbon tube); Parmentier, *Ann. Chim.*, 1911, **22**, 417; Stubbs, *Proc. Roy. Soc.*, 1913, **88**, 195; Keene, *ibid.*, 1913, **88**, 49; 1915, **91**, 190; Coblentz, *Bur. Stand. Bull.*, 1914, **10**, 1; Roberts, *J. Opt. Soc. Amer.*, 1925, **10**, 723; Mendenhall, *Phys. Rev.*, 1929, **34**, 502; Ribaud and Nikitine, *Compt. Rend.*, 1929, **188**, 618; *Ann. de Phys.*, 1929, **11**, 451; Ribaud and Mohr, *Compt. Rend.*, 1931, **192**, 37; von Wartenberg and Wehner, *Z. Elektrochem.*, 1936, **42**, 293 (to 3900°). A correction is applied for the departure from perfect blackness due to the finite size of the aperture.

[4] Kurlbaum and Günther-Schulze, *Verhl. d. D. Phys. Ges.*, 1903, **5**, 428 (to 2150°); Ornstein, Vermeulen, and Wouda, *Proc. K. Akad. Wetens. Amsterdam*, 1930, **33**, 985 (Ni body).

[5] Pirani and Altertum, *Z. Elektrochem.*, 1933, **29**, 5; Nothdurft and Wielenberg, *Phys. Z.*, 1942, **43**, 138 (tungsten tube to 2500° K.).

[6] *Berlin Ber.*, 1922, 424.

[7] Hutchins, *Amer. J. Sci.*, 1887, **34**, 466; Boys, *Phil. Trans.*, 1889, **180**, 159 (radiomicrometer; really invented by D'Arsonval); Paschen, *Ann. Phys.*, 1893, **48**, 272; Wilson and Gray, *Phil. Trans.*, 1894, **185**, 361; Rubens, *Z. Instr.*, 1898, **18**, 65; Rubens and Aschkinass, *Ann. Phys.*, 1898, **65**, 241; Coblentz, *Bur. Stand. Bull.*, 1908, **4**, 391; 1913, **9**, 7; 1914, **11**, 131; 1916, **12**, 503; 1918, **14**, 507; 1921, **17**, 187; *J. Opt. Soc. Amer.*, 1921, **5**, 259; 1923, **7**, 439; *J. Franklin Inst.*, 1911, **172**, 559; 1913–14, **175**, 151, 497; *J. Wash. Acad.*, 1913, **3**, 357; 1914, **4**, 511; *Phys. Z.*, 1913, **14**, 683 (Bi–Ag couple); Coblentz, in Glazebrook, " Dict. of Applied Physics," 1923, **4**, 541; Lebedew, *Ann. Phys.*, 1908, **9**, 209 (vacuum thermocouple); Yakovlev, *J. Russ. Phys. Chem. Soc.*, 1912, **44**, 459 (P) (astatic radiomicrometer); Drecq, *Compt. Rend.*, 1914, **158**, 1019 (Bi–Ag couple); Jones and Guy, *Chem. News*, 1912, **106**, 212, 225 (radiomicrometer):

fication in the *radiomicrometer*), or by a *bolometer* [1] (βολαὶ ἡλίου, sun-beams) using the change of resistance of a very thin blackened platinum or other metal strip or wire on which radiation is incident. A flat-surfaced pile (Melloni type) of bismuth–tin and antimony–tin alloys was described by Spence.[2] Extremely fine wires for thermocouples were made by Pfund [3] by throwing molten metal from a crucible on to a large glass plate and picking off the filament. Soldering 0·02-mm. iron and constantan wires for vacuum thermopiles is described.[4] Burger and van Cittert [5] used antimony and bismuth deposited on thin mica by evaporation in vacuum; rapid thermopiles have antimony and bismuth deposited on thin cellulose nitrate films.[6] The use of a bolometer in measuring solar radiation originated with Svanberg [1] (" galvanic differential thermometer "); it was improved by Langley [1] (" actinic balance"). Lummer and Kurlbaum [1] used rolled Wollaston wire and mention that Julius had separated the nickel plating from a teapot to get a film 1/500 mm. thick.[7] Moll and Burgers [8] used constantan–manganin foil rolled to 1 to 4μ for a vacuum thermopile. Brockman [9] used a bolometer of nickel foil 0·1μ thick, the nickel being plated on copper which was anodically dissolved by electrolysis in cyanide solution. Hopkinson [10] described a bolometer for use in exploding gas mixtures.

Ann. Phys., 1914, **43**, 555; Schaeffer, Paulus, and Jones, *J.A.C.S.*, 1915, **37**, 776 (radiomicrometer); Moll, *Proc. K. Akad. Wetens. Amsterdam*, 1913, **16**, 568; *Verslag. K. Akad. Wetens. Amsterdam*, 1913, **22**, 614; *Proc. Phys. Soc.*, 1923, **35**, 257; *Z. Phys.*, 1925, **32**, 575; *Physica*, 1926, **6**, 233; Johansen, *Phys. Z.*, 1913, **14**, 998; Van Reesema, *Proc. K. Akad. Wetens. Amsterdam*, 1918, **20**, 566; Witt, *Phys. Z.*, 1920, **21**, 374 (radiomicrometer); Hase, *Z. Phys.*, 1923, **15**, 52 (vacuum thermopile); Witt, *ibid.*, 1924, **28**, 236 (construction of couples and bolometers); Moll and Burgers, *ibid.*, 1925, **32**, 575; Badger, *J. Opt. Soc. Amer.*, 1927, **15**, 370 (single couples); for vacuum thermopiles see Firestone, *Rev. Sci. Instr.*, 1930, **1**, 630; Cartwright, *ibid.*, 1930, **1**, 592; 1932, **3**, 73 (bismuth–tellurium); Brackett and McAlister, *ibid.*, 1930, **1**, 181; Jaffray, *Compt. Rend.*, 1931, **193**, 926; Strong, *Rev. Sci. Instr.*, 1932, **3**, 65; Beckmann and Dickinson, *J.A.C.S.*, 1930, **52**, 124; Leighton and Leighton, *J. Phys. Chem.*, 1932, **36**, 1882; Jones, *J. Sci. Instr.*, 1937, **14**, 83; Roess and Dacus, *Rev. Sci. Instr.*, 1945, **16**, 164 (sensitive single Bi–Sb vacuum couple); Morpurgo and Silver, *Gas Research Board Comm.*, 1947, **35**; Simpson, Sutherland, and Blackwell, *Nature*, 1948, **161**, 281 (lead selenide); see also Weigert, " Optische Methoden der Chemie," 1927, 295.

1 Svanberg, *Ann. Phys.*, 1851, **84**, 411; Langley, *Amer. J. Sci.*, 1881, **21**, 187; Lummer and Kurlbaum, *Ann. Phys.*, 1892, **46**, 204; Paschen, *ibid.*, 1892, **47**, 272; Kurlbaum, *ibid.*, 1894, **51**, 591; 1897, **61**, 417; *Phys. Z.*, 1900, **2**, 147; Kayser, " Handbuch der Spektroskopie," 1900, **1**, 651; Warburg, Leithäuser, and Johansen, *Ann. Phys.*, 1907, **24**, 25 (vacuum bolometer); Coblentz, *Bur. Stand. Bull.*, 1908, **4**, 391; 1913, **9**, 7, 283; Burgess and Foote, *ibid.*, 1910, **12**, 91; Leimbach, *Ann. Phys.*, 1910, **33**, 308 (linear bolometer with strip 0·00028 mm. thick); Kerkhof, *ibid.*, 1938, **31**, 315 (vacuum bolometer); Shive, *J. Appl. Phys.*, 1947, **18**, 398 (lag); for a supraconducting bolometer (NbN), Milton, *Chem. Rev.*, 1946, **39**, 419. For a comparison of the emissive and absorptive powers of soot and platinum black at lower temperatures, see Kurlbaum, *Ann. Phys.*, 1899, **67**, 846; the reflecting power of carbon was measured by Aschkinass, *Ann. Phys.*, 1905, **18**, 373, cf. *ibid.*, 1905, **17**, 960, for metals; for emissivity of graphite, Prescott and Hincke, *Phys. Rev.*, 1928, **31**, 130. See also § 17.

2 *Phys. Rev.*, 1910, **31**, 666.

3 *Phys. Rev.*, 1912, **34**, 228.

4 Johnston, *Ann. Phys.*, 1910, **33**, 517; Harris, *Phys. Rev.*, 1934, **45**, 635; Pearson, *Rev. Sci. Instr.*, 1936, **7**, 108; Pfund, *ibid.*, 1937, **8**, 417. The writer soldered much thinner wires laid on a sheet of glass backed with black paper, using strong illumination reflected from the wires, and an observation lens.

5 *Z. Phys.*, 1930, **66**, 210.

6 Thompson, *Ann. Rep. Chem. Soc.*, 1945 (publ. 1947), **42**, 9 (bibl.); Harris, *J. Opt. Soc. Amer.*, 1946, **36**, 597; Niven, *Canad. J. Res.*, 1946, **24** A, 93.

7 On electrolytic removal of silver from Wollaston wire, see Partington, *Proc. Roy. Soc.* 1921, **100**, 27; *Z. Phys.*, 1930, **60**, 420.

8 See note 7 on p. 470.

9 *J. Opt. Soc. Amer.*, 1946, **36**, 32.

10 *Proc. Roy. Soc.*, 1907, **79**, 138; 1910, **84**, 155.

Modifications of Crookes's radiometer (§ 7.VII J) have been used [1] to measure the intensity of radiation. Coblentz [2] found the sensitivity of a thermopile proportional to the square root of the surface.

Let radiation of wave-length λ fall on a body, then the ratio of the radiation absorbed to the total incident radiation is called the *absorptive power* (or *absorptivity*) a_λ of the body for the radiation of the particular wave-length:

$$a_\lambda = \text{absorbed radiation}/\text{total incident radiation}.$$

For a perfectly black body, $a_\lambda=1$, by definition, for all values of λ. For all other bodies $a_\lambda<1$, some radiation being reflected or transmitted.

If a body at a given temperature emits into a vacuum from unit area in unit time an amount of energy $e_\lambda d\lambda$ in a range of wave-lengths between λ and $(\lambda+d\lambda)$, the limiting value of e_λ when $d\lambda \to 0$ is called the *emissive power* or *emissivity* of the body at the given temperature T for the given wave-length λ, and is a function of λ and T as well as of the nature of the body and of its surface. A flux of 1 g.cal./cm.² has been called a langley (ly),[3] the time unit being added (e.g. ly/min.).

In a uniformly heated *enclosure* the radiation is uniform, and independent of the nature of the walls or contents. Hence, if dq is the heat *received* per sec. per cm.² by any one body, this is the same for all the bodies. If a body absorbs a fraction a_λ of this, i.e. $a_\lambda dq$, it must reflect or transmit $dq(1-a_\lambda)$, and as the total energy emitted per sec. per cm.² is equal to that received:

$$dq(1-a_\lambda)+e_\lambda d\lambda = dq \quad . \quad . \quad . \quad . \quad . \quad . \quad . \quad . \quad . \quad (1)$$

For a black body, $a_\lambda=1$, and if E_λ is the emissive power of a black body, (1) becomes:

$$E_\lambda d\lambda = dq \quad . \quad . \quad . \quad . \quad . \quad . \quad . \quad . \quad . \quad . \quad (2)$$

From (1) and (2):

$$(1-a_\lambda)E_\lambda + e_\lambda = E_\lambda \quad . \quad . \quad . \quad . \quad . \quad . \quad . \quad . \quad . \quad (3)$$

$$\therefore\ e_\lambda = a_\lambda E_\lambda, \quad \text{or} \quad e_\lambda/a_\lambda = E_\lambda \quad . \quad . \quad . \quad . \quad . \quad . \quad . \quad . \quad (4)$$

Hence at constant λ and T *the ratio* e_λ/a_λ *is the same for all bodies and is equal to the emissive power of a perfectly black body.* This is called *Kirchhoff's law.*[4] It applies only when e_λ depends solely on the body and not on the incident radiation, and would not apply to a fluorescent body.[5]

Bodies other than black bodies reflect radiation, and if they do not transmit radiation, the *reflecting power* or *reflectivity* for a given wave-length is obviously:

$$R_\lambda = 1 - a_\lambda \quad . \quad . \quad . \quad . \quad . \quad . \quad . \quad . \quad . \quad . \quad (5)$$

∴ from (3):

$$E_\lambda R_\lambda + e_\lambda = E_\lambda \quad . \quad . \quad . \quad . \quad . \quad . \quad . \quad . \quad . \quad (6)$$

which shows that if radiation lost by reflection is restored, the body emits black-body radiation. This will occur in an enclosure.

The effect of a polarising body such as tourmaline, giving a different emissivity

[1] Jordan, *Proc. Phys. Soc.*, 1912, **25**, 66; Klumb and Schwarz, *Z. Phys.*, 1944, **122**, 418 (as manometer).

[2] *Phys. Z.*, 1914, **15**, 453.

[3] *Nature*, 1947, **160**, 326.

[4] Experimental verification by Bouman, *Verslag. K. Akad. Wetens. Amsterdam*, 1897, **5**, 438; *Ann. Phys. Beibl.*, 1897, **21**, 589; Rosenthal, *Ann. Phys.*, 1899, **68**, 783; Pflüger, *ibid.*, 1902, **7**, 806. See, on definitions of emissivity, etc., and statement of Kirchhoff's law, Ives, *Astrophys. J.*, 1917, **45**, 39.

[5] Wensel, in "Temperature. Its Measurement and Control," New York, 1941, **3**.

in different directions (as though it had different temperatures) was experimentally confirmed.[1] Kent [2] suggested that Kirchhoff's law might not hold when energy is transmitted by conduction by molecular or electronic impacts between two media in contact; in that case the sum of the radiation and the transmitted energies would be zero, but this might not be true for each separately.

§ 6. Intensity of Emission

Radiation in an enclosure is equally distributed in all directions, or is perfectly diffused. Consider a small element of area ds of a radiating body. The energy of wave-lengths between λ and $\lambda+\mathrm{d}\lambda$ emitted per sec. from ds inside a thin cone of solid angle dω (see § 8. III) at right angles to ds will be proportional to ds, dω, and dλ, or equal to:

$$K_\lambda \mathrm{d}s\mathrm{d}\omega\mathrm{d}\lambda \qquad (1)$$

where K_λ is a constant for a given λ, depending only on the nature of the body and on the temperature,[3] called the *intensity of emission*. The energy emitted

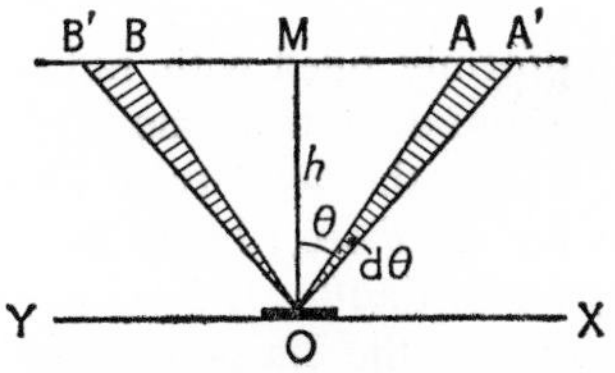

FIG. 3.VI B. Intensity of Emission

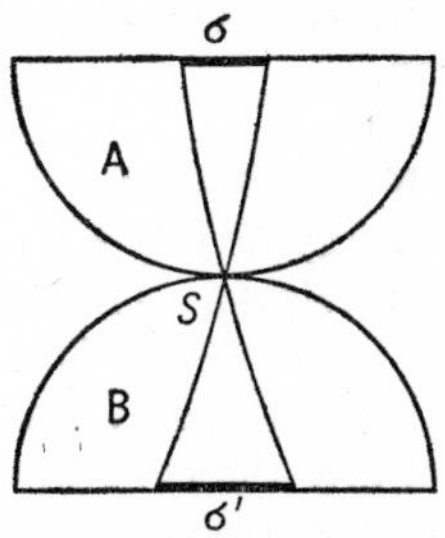

FIG. 4.VI B. Effect of Refractive Index on Radiation Intensity

per sec. in a narrow cone of solid angle dω with its axis making an angle θ with the normal OM to ds at O (Fig. 3.VI B) will be[4] $K_\lambda \cos\theta \mathrm{d}s\mathrm{d}\omega\mathrm{d}\lambda$, since the "opening" of the cone, or the projected area of the radiating surface as seen along the axis of the cone, will now be d$\omega \cos\theta$. The solid angle of the funnel-shaped cones shaded as AA′OB′B (where OA′ or OB′ makes an angle $\theta+\mathrm{d}\theta$ with OM) is (§ 8.III) $\mathrm{d}\omega=2\pi \sin\theta\mathrm{d}\theta$, and the total emission from ds per sec., which is equal to $e_\lambda \mathrm{d}\lambda\mathrm{d}s$, is found by integrating the expression

$$2\pi K_\lambda \cos\theta \sin\theta \, \mathrm{d}s\mathrm{d}\lambda\mathrm{d}\theta \qquad (2)$$

[1] Kirchhoff, *Ann. Phys.*, 1860, **109**, 275 (299); Balfour Stewart, *Phil. Mag.*, 1861, **21**, 391; Pflüger, *Ann. Phys.*, 1902, **7**, 806; Jaeger and Šimek, *Verslag. K. Akad. Wetens. Amsterdam*, 1914, **22**, 762; *Proc. K. Akad. Wetens. Amsterdam*, 1914, **16**, 799.

[2] *Phil. Mag.*, 1917, **33**, 223.

[3] Preston, "Theory of Heat," 1919, 558 (who uses i for K).

[4] This so-called *cosine law* is due to Lambert, "Photometria sive de Mensvra et Gradibvs Lvminis, Calorvm, et Vmbrae," Aug. Vindel., 1760, 26; Ostwald's *Klassiker*, 1892, **31–33**; **31**, 22; **33**, 75; it is called *Lambert's law*. It was confirmed by Melloni by directing the conical receiver of a thermopile towards a radiating surface inclined at various angles, when the radiation received was constant. It is subject to some exceptions when the reflecting power of the surface depends on the direction of incidence: Lommel, *Ann. Phys.*, 1880, **10**, 449; *Munich Ber.*, 1887, 95; Seeliger, *ibid.*, 1888, 201; Christiansen, *Ann. Phys.*, 1884, **21**, 364; Ångström, *ibid.*, 1885, **26**, 253; Uljanin, *ibid.*, 1897, **62**, 528 (bibl.); Koláček, *ibid.*, 1898, **64**, 398; Wright, *ibid.*, 1900, **1**, 17; Lummer and Reiche, *ibid.*, 1910, **33**, 857; Féry and Drecq, *Compt. Rend.*, 1912, **155**, 1239; King, *Phil. Mag.*, 1912, **23**, 237; Zwikker, *Proc. K. Akad. Wetens. Amsterdam*, 1927, **30**, 853.

over the *hemisphere*, i.e. θ from 0 to $\pi/2$ (see § 8.III):

$$\therefore\ e_\lambda \mathrm{d}s\mathrm{d}\lambda = 2\pi K_\lambda \mathrm{d}s\mathrm{d}\lambda \int_0^{\pi/2} \sin\theta \cos\theta \mathrm{d}\theta$$

$$\therefore\ e_\lambda = \pi K_\lambda \quad . \quad . \quad . \quad . \quad . \quad . \quad . \quad . \quad . \quad . \quad (3)$$

If the radiation intensity in vacuum is K, that in a medium of relative refractive index n was shown theoretically by Clausius [1] to be n^2K and this was afterwards proved experimentally.[2] Let A and B (Fig. 4.VI B) be two perfectly reflecting hemispheres filled with two media of different refractive indices, communicating through a small hole of area s. At the centres of A and B let there be small perfectly black surfaces σ and σ', making angles α and β with the centre of s. Rays emitted outside these solid angles are reflected back to σ and σ' and absorbed. From Snell's law of refraction, since $\sin\alpha \simeq \alpha$, $\sin\beta \simeq \beta$, the index of refraction ratio is $n = \alpha/\beta$, and since the areas are proportional to the squares of the linear dimensions, $\sigma/\sigma' = n^2$. If K is the intensity of emission (per cm.^{2}) in A, and K' that in B, and if a fraction R is reflected at s and $(1-R)$ transmitted, then radiation equilibrium between σ and σ' requires that $K\sigma(1-R) = K'\sigma'(1-R)$, therefore $K(\sigma/\sigma') = Kn^2 = K'$, which is Clausius's equation.

§ 7. Energy Density

The *energy density* [3] ρ per cm.^{3} in a space uniformly filled with radiation is found as follows. The energy radiated per sec. from ds in the cone is given by (2), § 6. Also, $OA = OM/\cos\theta = h/\cos\theta$, and if $\boldsymbol{c}$ is the velocity of light, the time taken for energy leaving ds to reach A is $h/\boldsymbol{c}\cos\theta$ sec.; hence the energy sent out into the cone in this time is $2\pi K_\lambda(h/\boldsymbol{c})\sin\theta \mathrm{d}s\mathrm{d}\lambda\mathrm{d}\theta$. If h is very small the energy between the planes A′B′ and XY due to the emission from ds is found by integration between the limits $\theta=0$ and $\theta=\pi/2$ (the rotation about OM is already given by the factor 2π):

$$2\pi K_\lambda(h/\boldsymbol{c})\mathrm{d}s\mathrm{d}\lambda \int_0^{\pi/2} \sin\theta \mathrm{d}\theta = 2\pi K_\lambda(h/\boldsymbol{c})\mathrm{d}s\mathrm{d}\lambda \quad . \quad . \quad . \quad . \quad (1)$$

But if $\rho_\lambda \mathrm{d}\lambda$ is the energy of wave-lengths between λ and $\lambda + \mathrm{d}\lambda$ per cm.^{3}, the space between the planes (away from the edges) contains for each element ds the energy $\rho_\lambda \mathrm{d}\lambda h \mathrm{d}s$. Since there is equilibrium, as much energy returns to ds as leaves it per sec., hence if (1) is *doubled* it can be equated to $\rho_\lambda \mathrm{d}\lambda h\mathrm{d}s$, hence: [4]

$$\rho_\lambda = 4\pi K_\lambda/\boldsymbol{c} = 4e_\lambda/\boldsymbol{c} \quad . \quad . \quad . \quad . \quad . \quad . \quad . \quad . \quad (2)$$

The *total* energy of all wave-lengths emitted per sec. per cm.^{2} is:

$$E = \int_0^\infty e_\lambda \mathrm{d}\lambda = \pi \int_0^\infty K_\lambda \mathrm{d}\lambda = (c/4)\int_0^\infty \rho_\lambda \mathrm{d}\lambda = \rho c/4 \quad . \quad . \quad . \quad (3)$$

from (2), and (3), § 6, where ρ is the *total* radiant energy density (all wave-lengths) in black-body radiation at a given temperature:

$$\rho = \int_0^\infty \rho_\lambda \mathrm{d}\lambda \quad . \quad . \quad . \quad . \quad . \quad . \quad . \quad . \quad . \quad . \quad (4)$$

[1] *Ann. Phys.*, 1864, **121**, 1; Bartoli, *Nuov. Cim.*, 1879, **5**, 265; Balfour Stewart, " Elementary Treatise on Heat," Oxford, 1888, 211; Planck, " Theorie der Wärmestrahlung," 4th edit., Leipzig, 1921, 35.

[2] Quintus Icilius, *Ann. Phys.*, 1866, **127**, 30; Smoluchowski, *Compt. Rend.*, 1896, **123**, 230; Dunoyer, *Ann. Chim.*, 1906, **9**, 30.

[3] W. Thomson (Lord Kelvin), *Phil. Mag.*, 1855, **9**, 36; " Math. and Phys. Papers," 1884, **2**, 28; Tumlirz, *Ann. Phys.*, 1889, **38**, 640.

[4] Wien, *Ann. Phys.*, 1894, **52**, 132 ($\psi = 4\pi\epsilon/c$; the value of (3) is sometimes denoted by S).

Pokrowski [1] supposed that there is an upper limit of energy density corresponding with a temperature of 3×10^{12} deg., with a frequency of 10^{23} and wavelength 3×10^{-5} A.

§ 8. Radiation Pressure

Maxwell showed from the electromagnetic theory of light [2] that light (or radiation) incident on a surface exerts a very small pressure on it. The radiation from the sun exerts a pressure of $\frac{1}{2}$ mg. per m.[2] of the earth's surface. If the radiation is perfectly diffuse (as in black-body radiation) the radiation pressure on any surface, in dynes per cm.^{2}, is equal to one-third the total energy density in ergs per cm.^{3}:

$$p = \tfrac{1}{3}\rho \quad . \; . \; . \; . \; . \; . \; . \; . \; . \; . \quad (1)$$

The existence of radiation pressure was proved experimentally by Lebedev and by Nichols and Hull. It should be noticed that (1) differs from the gas equation, § 2.III, $p = \frac{2}{3}E_k$, where E_k is the kinetic energy per unit vol., in having the factor $\frac{1}{3}$ instead of $\frac{2}{3}$. Thus, Newton's corpuscular theory of light would make the radiation pressure double the true value. The factor $\frac{2}{3}$ refers to perfectly reflected particles, and the factor $\frac{1}{3}$ to perfectly reflected radiation, or perfectly diffuse radiation partly or wholly emitted by the wall, i.e. in all cases when the radiation leaving the wall is the same as the incident radiation.[3]

§ 9. Stefan-Boltzmann Radiation Law

In 1879 Stefan [4] showed that all the experiments published to that time were in agreement with the law that *the intensity of radiation emitted by a body is proportional to the fourth power of the absolute temperature.* If e is the total emissive power:

$$e = \sigma T^4 \quad . \; . \; . \; . \; . \; . \; . \; . \; . \; . \quad (1)$$

where σ is a constant depending only on the nature of the body. For a perfectly black body ($e = E$), σ is called *Stefan's constant*. If the body is in an enclosure of temperature T_0 the net emission is $\sigma(T^4 - T_0{}^4)$. Mendenhall [5] says Stefan deduced his law " from a discussion of bad observations on imperfect radiators, for which it does not hold "; he made use of some observations by Tyndall [6] on radiation from a platinum spiral.

Bartoli [7] had previously pointed out that a cycle in which radiation is brought from a lower to a higher temperature would contradict the second law of thermodynamics unless radiation exerts a pressure, as Maxwell had supposed (§ 8). This result was put into a quantitative form by Boltzmann [8] (who

1 *Z. Phys.*, 1928, **51**, 730.

2 Maxwell, " Treatise on Electricity and Magnetism," Oxford, 1873, **2**, 391, 3rd edit., 1892, **2**, 440; Jeans, " The Mathematical Theory of Electricity and Magnetism," Cambridge, 1908, 145, 531; Planck, " Theorie der Wärme," 1930, 164; Stokes, *Nature*, 1947, **160**, 532.

3 Wertheimer, *Verhl. d. D. Phys. Ges.*, 1919, **21**, 435; Stewart, *Phys. Rev.*, 1925, **26**, 491.

4 *Wien Ber.*, 1879, **79**, II, 391; confirmed by Graetz, *Ann. Phys.*, 1880, **11**, 913.

5 " Pyrometry Sympos. Volume," Amer. Inst. Min. Met. Eng., 1920, 63.

6 *Ann. Phys.*, 1865, **124**, 36; Wüllner, " Lehrbuch der Experimentalphysik," 1896, **2**, 215; Satterly, *Nature*, 1946, **157**, 737; Partington, *ibid.*, 1946, **157**, 879; Davies, *ibid.*, 1946, **157**, 879.

7 " Sopra i Movimenti prodotti della Luce e dal Calore," Florence, 1876; *Nuov. Cim.*, 1884, **15**, 193; *Repert. Phys.*, 1885, **21**, 198; Straneo, *Nuov. Cim.*, 1924, **1**, 345.

8 *Ann. Phys.*, 1884, **22**, 31, 291, 616; Galitzin, *ibid.*, 1892, **47**, 479; Wien, *Ann. Phys.*, 1893, **49**, 632; Guillaume, *Arch. Sci. Phys. Nat.*, 1894, **31**, 121; Larmor, " Aether and Matter," Cambridge, 1900, 137; *Nature*, 1900–1, **63**, 216; " Math. and Phys. Papers," Cambridge, 1929, **2**, 431, 446; Lorentz, *Proc. K. Akad. Wetens. Amsterdam*, 1901, 3, 436, 607; Michelson,

pointed out that it applied to *black-body* radiation), and he was so able to deduce Stefan's equation (1), which is hence usually called the Stefan-Boltzmann law, after both distinguished physicists. The simplest method of deduction [1] is based on Clapeyron's equation (6), § 41.II.

Consider a vacuous cylinder with perfectly reflecting walls, fitted with a perfectly reflecting piston B (Fig. 5.VI B). Let the base A of the cylinder be formed of a black body at an absolute temperature T. The black body is in equilibrium with radiation of density ρ in the volume V of the cylinder, and a pressure $p=\frac{1}{3}\rho$ is exerted on the piston. If the piston be drawn out through a small volume δV, the work done is $p\delta V$, and more radiation enters to fill the volume δV to density ρ. The black body thus loses heat $\delta q=l_v\delta V$ at constant temperature, where l_v is the latent heat of expansion of radiation in the vacuum. If $\delta V=1$ cm.^{3} the heat taken from A is equal to the sum of the increase of energy in the cavity and the work of expansion, $l_v=\rho+\frac{1}{3}\rho=\frac{4}{3}\rho$, and by Clapeyron's equation:

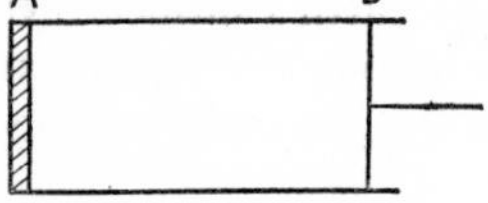

FIG. 5.VI B. Expansion Cylinder for Radiation

$$l_v=T(\mathrm{d}p/\mathrm{d}T)_v, \quad \therefore\ (4/3)\rho=T(\mathrm{d}/\mathrm{d}T)(\rho/3)$$

$$\therefore\ (4/3)\rho=(1/3)T(\mathrm{d}\rho/\mathrm{d}T)$$

$$T(\mathrm{d}\ln\rho/\mathrm{d}T)=(\mathrm{d}\ln\rho/\mathrm{d}\ln T)=4$$

$$\mathrm{d}\ln\rho=4\mathrm{d}\ln T$$

$$\ln\rho=4\ln T+\text{const.}$$

$$\rho=kT^4 \quad \ldots\ldots\ldots\ldots \quad (2)$$

where k is a constant depending only on the units of energy and temperature. Although T is here the temperature of a material black body in equilibrium with radiation, it can (and later will) be identified with the temperature of the radiation itself in vacuum.[2]

Stefan's law was confirmed for black-body radiation by Schleiermacher,[3] and fully by Lummer and Pringsheim.[4] It should be carefully noted that the T^4-law applies only to radiation from a perfectly black body; for many metals the intensity of radiation is more nearly proportional to T^5 (see § 17). The calculated and observed absolute temperatures found by Lummer and Pringsheim, given in their table on p. 477,[5] fully confirmed Stefan's law.

J. Russ. Phys. Chem. Soc., 1902, **34**, 155 (P); Kohl, *Ann. Phys.*, 1902, **8**, 575; Buckingham, *Phys. Rev.*, 1903, **17**, 277; Pellat, *J. de Phys.*, 1903, **2**, 484; Cantor, *Ann. Phys.*, 1906, **20**, 333; Rayleigh, *Nature*, 1913, **92**, 527; Bauer, *Ann. Chim.*, 1913, **29**, 5, 244, 372; Jellinek, " Physikalische Chemie der Gasreaktionen," 1913, 274; Brillouin, *Ann. de Phys.*, 1914, **1**, 163 (who points out that the energy of radiation could be completely converted into work by adiabatic expansion to absolute zero); Jeans, " Dynamical Theory of Gases," 3rd edit., Cambridge, 1921, 366.

1 Haber, " Thermodynamics of Technical Gas Reactions," 1908, 282.

2 Wien, *Ann. Phys.*, 1908, **25**, 5, mentions that Lord Kelvin never brought himself to believe that radiation could have a temperature apart from matter.

3 *Ann. Phys.*, 1885, **26**, 287; Wien and Lummer, *ibid.*, 1895, **56**, 451; Wilson, *Astrophys. J.*, 1899, **10**, 80.

4 *Ann. Phys.*, 1897, **63**, 395 (100°–1300°); 1900, **3**, 159; *Verhl. d. D. Phys. Ges.*, 1899, **1**, 23, 215; Kurlbaum, *Ann. Phys.*, 1898, **65**, 746 (0°–100°); Lummer, *Congrès. Internat. Phys.*, 1901, **2**, 41; Valentiner, *Ann. Phys.*, 1910, **31**, 275 (to 1600°); Mendenhall and Forsythe, *Phys. Rev.*, 1914, **4**, 62 (1063°–1549°); see Griffiths, in Glazebrook, " Dict. of Applied Physics," 1922, **1**, 663.

5 The original German is given: Siedetopf=vessel of boiling water; Salpeterkessel=fused-nitre pot; Chamotteofen=fireclay furnace. Lummer and Pringsheim used gas thermometry up to 1150° and the temperatures are probably correct to 3°; at higher temperatures

Black Body	Abs. Temp. Obs.	Abs. Temp. Calc.
Siedetopf	373·1	374·6
Salpeterkessel ...	492·5	492·0
"	723·0	724·3
"	745	749·1
Chamotteofen ...	789	778
Salpeterkessel ...	810	806·5
"	868	867·1
Chamotteofen ...	1092	1074
"	1112	1095
"	1378	1379
"	1470	1468
"	1497	1488
"	1535	1531

Since the radiation pressure is $p=\frac{1}{3}\rho$, it follows [1] that $p=\frac{1}{3}kT^4$. Stefan's law is usually applied to the emission of radiation per sec. from 1 cm.^{2} of the *surface* of a black body, in which case E is obtained from ρ by (3), § 7, $E=\rho c/4$,

$$\therefore\ E=kT^4c/4=\sigma T^4 \qquad (3)$$

where σ is called *Stefan's constant*. The usually accepted value [2] is $\sigma=5{\cdot}75\times10^{-5}$ erg cm.$^{-2}$ sec.$^{-1}$ deg.$^{-4}$. (In optical pyrometry the radiation intensity E is often denoted by I.)

The radiating body of temperature T will usually be radiating to surroundings of temperature T_0, in which case $E=\sigma(T^4-T_0^4)$. If $(T-T_0)=\delta T$ is small, $(T^4-T_0^4)=(T_0+\delta T)^4-T_0^4\simeq 4T_0^3\delta T$, which is proportional to δT or $(T-T_0)$, when T_0 is approximately constant. This is the so-called Newton's law (which really applies to cooling in moving air).[3]

they extrapolated thermocouple e.m.f.-temperature curves, and their temperatures would not be quite correct.

[1] Galitzin, *Ann. Phys.*, 1892, **47**, 479; Pellat, *J. de Phys.*, 1903, **2**, 484, and Michaud, *J. Chim. Phys.*, 1938, **35**, 99, by a different deduction, found $p=\frac{1}{3}kT^4+CT$, but on Maxwell's theory the integration constant C is zero.

[2] Kurlbaum, *Ann. Phys.*, 1898, **65**, 746; *Verhl. d. D. Phys. Ges.*, 1912, **14**, 576 (summary); Todd, *Proc. Roy. Soc.*, 1909, **83**, 19 ($5{\cdot}48\times10^{-5}$ ergs); Bauer and Moulin, *Compt. Rend.*, 1909, **149**, 988; 1910, **150**, 167; *J. de Phys.*, 1910, **9**, 468 ($5{\cdot}3\times10^{-12}$ watts); Féry, *Compt. Rend.*, 1909, **148**, 777, 915; Royds, *Phil. Mag.*, 1911, **21**, 167; Féry and Drecq, *J. de Phys.*, 1911, **1**, 551; 1913, **3**, 380 ($6{\cdot}33\times10^{-12}$ watts); Puccianti, *Nuov. Cim.*, 1912, **4**, 322 ($6{\cdot}0-6{\cdot}3\times10^{-12}$ watts); Westphal, *Verhl. d. D. Phys. Ges.*, 1912, **14**, 987 ($5{\cdot}54\times10^{-12}$ watts); Shakespear, *Proc. Roy. Soc.*, 1912, **86**, 180 ($5{\cdot}67\times10^{-12}$ watts); Valentiner, *Ann. Phys.*, 1912, **39**, 489 ($5{\cdot}58\times10^{-12}$ watts); Gerlach, *ibid.*, 1912, **38**, 1; 1913, **41**, 99; 1913, **42**, 1163, 1167 ($5{\cdot}803\times10^{-12}$ watts); Paschen, *ibid.*, 1913, **38**, 30; Kurlbaum and Valentiner, *ibid.*, 1913, **41**, 1059; Westphal, *Verhl. d. D. Phys. Ges.*, 1913, **15**, 897 ($5{\cdot}57\times10^{-12}$ watts); Keene, *Proc. Roy. Soc.*, 1913, **88**, 49 ($5{\cdot}90\times10^{-5}$ erg); 1915, **91**, 190—copper sphere receiver; Mendenhall and Forsythe, *Phys. Rev.*, 1914, **4**, 62; Coblentz, *Phys. Z.*, 1914, **15**, 762; *Phys. Rev.*, 1916, **7**, 694; *Proc. Nat. Acad.*, 1917, **3**, 504; *Bur. Stand. Bull.*, 1916, **12**, 553; 1920, **15**, 529, 617; *idem*, in Glazebrook, "Dict. of Applied Physics," 1923, **4**, 541 ($5{\cdot}72\times10^{-5}$ ergs); Millikan, *Phil. Mag.*, 1917, **34**, 1 (adopts $5{\cdot}72\times10^{-5}$ ergs); Kussmann, *Z. Phys.*, 1924, **25**, 58 ($5{\cdot}795\times10^{-12}$ watts); Hoare, *Phil. Mag.*, 1928, **6**, 828; 1932, **13**, 380; 1932, **14**, 445 ($5{\cdot}742\times10^{-5}$); Mendenhall, *Phys. Rev.*, 1929, **34**, 502 ($5{\cdot}79\times10^{-12}$ watts); Wensel, *Bur. Stand. J. Res.*, 1939, **22**, 375 ($5{\cdot}33$ to $5{\cdot}96\times10^{-5}$ ergs; mean $(5{\cdot}69\pm0{\cdot}13)\times10^{-5}$ ergs); Kaye and Laby, "Tables of Physical and Chemical Constants," 1941, 75, give values from 5·7 to $5{\cdot}79\times10^{-5}$ ergs; Birge, *Rep. Progr. Phys.*, 1942, **8**, 90, takes $5{\cdot}672_8\times10^{-5}$, and Du Mond and Cohen, *Rev. Mod. Phys.*, 1948, **20**, 82, take $5{\cdot}6724\times10^{-5}$, erg cm.$^{-2}$ deg.$^{-4}$ sec.$^{-1}$.

[3] Newton's law will be considered in § 3. IX M, Vol. II.

§ 10. Wien's Displacement Law

As the temperature of a solid body rises, the colour of the radiation emitted shifts from red, through yellow, to dazzling bluish-white. Pouillet [1] attempted to lay down a scale of high temperatures from the colour of the radiation, from dull red at 600° to dazzling white at 1600° (§ 4). At each temperature, the *maximum* radiation, distributed over the wave-lengths, occurs for a particular wave-length, and it is clear that this wave-length of the maximum will move from the red towards the violet end of the spectrum as the temperature increases. Earlier workers located the maximum in sunlight in the infra-red, but this result depended on the absorption and dispersion of the glass prisms used, and Draper,[2] using a ruled glass grating, showed that the maximum is in the yellow part of the visible spectrum. A great advance was made by Lummer and Pringsheim [3] by finding the distribution of energy in the spectrum of black-body radiation at different temperatures. The curves (Fig. 6.VI B) giving the emissive powers e_λ in c.g.s. units plotted against the wave-lengths λ in $\mu(=10^{-4}$ cm.) show the shift of λ_m, the wave-length of the maximum, towards shorter wave-lengths with rising temperature. The locus of the maxima is shown by the dotted curve and λ_m plotted against T gives a curve which resembles a hyperbola, so that a relation:

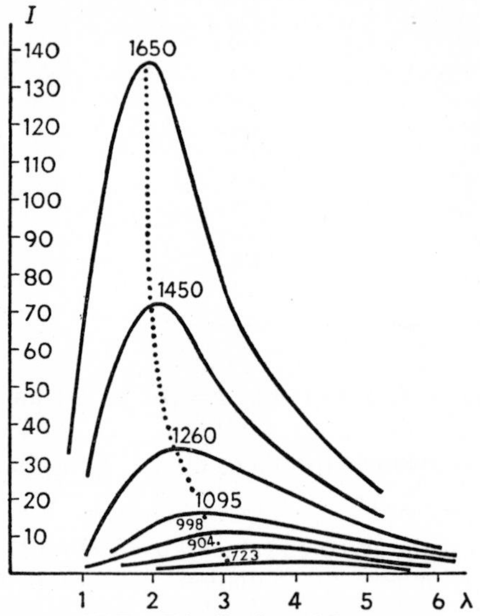

FIG. 6.VI B. Distribution of Energy over Wave-lengths at different Temperatures

$$\lambda_m T_m = \text{const.} = b$$

might be anticipated. This is *Wien's Law*, which is confirmed experimentally, and was also deduced theoretically by Wien [4] in 1893. The following simple deduction is sufficient for our purpose.[5]

[1] *Compt. Rend.*, 1836, **3**, 782.

[2] *Phil. Mag.*, 1857, **13**, 153; "Scientific Memoirs," 1878, 97.

[3] *Verhl. d. D. Phys. Ges.*, 1899, **1**, 23; 1900, **2**, 163; Graetz, in Winkelmann, "Handbuch der Physik," 1906, **3**, 388.

[4] *Berlin Ber.*, 1893, 55; *Ann. Phys.*, 1894, **52**, 132; 1896, **58**, 662; "Enzykl. d. math. Wiss.," 1909, **5**, iii, 282; Oswald's *Klassiker*, 1929, **228**; confirmed experimentally by Paschen, *Ann. Phys.*, 1897, **60**, 662.

[5] See, e.g., Paschen, *Astrophys. J.*, 1895, **2**, 202; 1899, **10**, 40; Paschen and Wanner, *ibid.*, 1899, **9**, 300; Very, *ibid.*, 1895, **2**, 316; 1896, **4**, 38; 1899, **10**, 208; Thiesen, *Verhl. d. D. Phys. Ges.*, 1900, **2**, 65; Larmor, *Nature*, 1900–1, **63**, 216; *Proc. Roy. Soc.*, 1909, **83**, 82; "Ency. Brit.," 11th edit., 1911, **22**, 785; "Math. and Phys. Papers," Cambridge, 1929, **2**, 217; Cantor, *Ann. Phys.*, 1906, **20**, 333; Reiche, *ibid.*, 1908, **25**, 521; Saurel, *Phys. Rev.*, 1910, **30**, 350, 356; Buckingham, *Phil. Mag.*, 1912, **23**, 920; Westphal, *Verhl. d. D. Phys. Ges.*, 1914, **16**, 93; Salpeter, *Phys. Z.*, 1914, **15**, 764; Dempster, *ibid.*, 1914, **15**, 694; Preston, "Theory of Heat," 1919, 569; Jeans, "Dynamical Theory of Gases," 3rd edit., 1921, 368; Planck, "Theorie der Wärmestrahlung," 4th edit., 1921, 69; Jellinek, "Physikalische Chemie der Gasreaktionen," 1913, 280; Brillouin, *Ann. de Phys.*, 1914, **1**, 163; Henning, "Die Grundlagen der Temperaturmessung," Brunswick, 1915, 132; Wood, *Phil. Mag.*, 1918, **35**, 190; Urbach, *Wien Ber.*, 1930, **139**, IIA, 473; Lohr, *Z. Phys.*, 1936, **103**, 454; Hercus, *Nature*, 1948, **162**, 143.

Consider a definite amount of radiation enclosed in a rectangular box with reflecting walls and with sides x, y, z, which can expand or contract so that the box always remains similar to itself; i.e. if δx, δy, δz, are *small* displacements *per sec.* of three sides, the opposite sides remaining fixed, then:

$$\delta x/x=\delta y/y=\delta z/z \quad . \quad . \quad . \quad . \quad . \quad . \quad . \quad . \quad (1)$$

Any ray just reflected from the moving face perpendicular to the x axis must travel along a path l to the opposite face, and back along a path l, before the next reflexion, and if α is the angle made by the ray with the x axis (Fig. 7.VI B):

$$l\cos\alpha=x, \quad l=x/\cos\alpha.$$

The total path traversed per sec. is [1] $2l=2x/\cos\alpha$, the time taken to traverse this is $2x/\boldsymbol{c}\cos\alpha$, where $\boldsymbol{c}$=velocity of light, and hence the numbers of reflexions per sec. is $\boldsymbol{c}\cos\alpha/2x$. For rays reflected from faces normal to the y and z axes, the corresponding values are $\boldsymbol{c}\cos\beta/2y$, and $\boldsymbol{c}\cos\gamma/2z$, where β and γ are the angles between the rays and the axes.

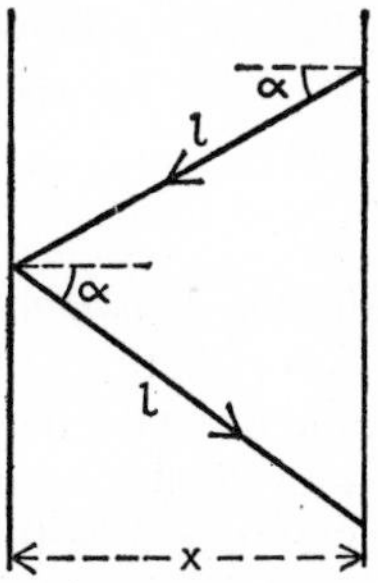

FIG. 7.VI B

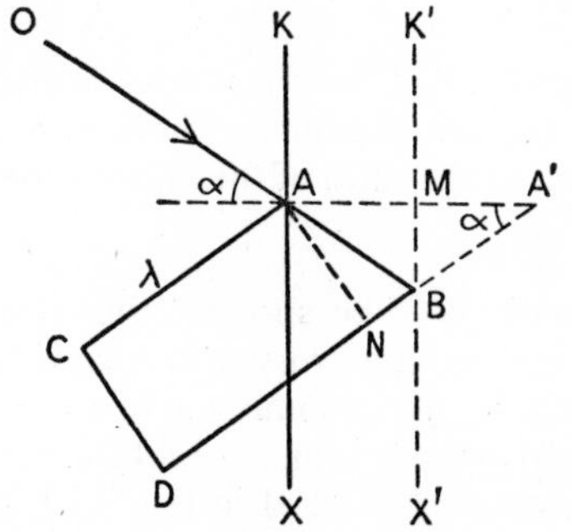

FIG. 8.VI B. Reflexion from Moving Mirror

Consider a ray OA of wave-length λ incident at A (Fig. 8.VI B) at an angle α on the face KX perpendicular to the x axis, KX being in motion from left to right with a constant velocity u. When the crest of the reflected ray reaches C, where AC=λ, the next crest will be at A, but this must now travel along AB to overtake the receding reflecting surface at K'X', the ray being reflected along BD. The distance between the first and second crests is increased from AC to (AB+BD), and the increase in wave-length is $\delta\lambda_x'$=(AB+BN), where AN is perpendicular to BD. Hence if A' is the image of A in K'X':

$$\delta\lambda_x'=\text{AB}+\text{BN}=\text{AA}'\cos\alpha=2\text{AM}\cos\alpha.$$

The time taken for the ray to travel AC is equal to the time taken by the reflecting surface to travel over AM, and if the time taken by the second ray to travel over AB (which is small compared with AC) is neglected:

$$\text{AM}/u=\lambda/\boldsymbol{c}, \quad \therefore \ \text{AM}=u\lambda/\boldsymbol{c}$$

$$\therefore \ \delta\lambda_x'=2\lambda u\cos\alpha/\boldsymbol{c}.$$

This change of wave-length occurs at *each* reflexion, hence the total change of wave-length per sec. is found by multiplying it by the number of reflexions per sec.:

$$\therefore \ \delta\lambda_x=\Sigma\delta\lambda_x'=(2\lambda u\cos\alpha/\boldsymbol{c})[(\boldsymbol{c}\cos\alpha)/2x]=(\lambda u\cos^2\alpha)/x$$

$$\therefore \ \delta\lambda_x=\lambda\cos^2\alpha(\delta x/x),$$

[1] Actually the second path is $(x+\delta x)/\cos\alpha$, but as the ray moves with the very great velocity $\boldsymbol{c}$, δx is negligible in comparison with x.

since $u=\delta x$. Similarly:

$$\delta\lambda_y=\lambda\cos^2\beta(\delta y/y)$$

$$\delta\lambda_z=\lambda\cos^2\gamma(\delta z/z).$$

The total change of wave-length is

$$\delta\lambda=\lambda[(\delta x/x)\cos^2\alpha+(\delta y/y)\cos^2\beta+(\delta z/z)\cos^2\gamma]$$

$$\therefore\ \delta\lambda=\lambda\delta x/x \quad . \quad . \quad . \quad . \quad . \quad . \quad . \quad , \quad . \quad . \quad (2)$$

from (1), and (6), § 78.I ($\cos^2\alpha+\cos^2\beta+\cos^2\gamma=1$). Since $xyz=V$, the volume of the box,

$$yz\delta x+zx\delta y+xy\delta z=\delta V$$

$$\therefore\ \delta V/V=\delta x/x+\delta y/y+\delta z/z=3\delta x/x$$

$$\therefore\ \delta\lambda/\lambda=\delta\ln\lambda=\tfrac{1}{3}\delta V/V=\tfrac{1}{3}\,\delta\ln V$$

$$\therefore\ \ln\lambda=\tfrac{1}{3}\ln V+\text{const. or } \lambda V^{-1/3}=\text{const.}$$

$$\therefore\ \lambda/\lambda_0=(V/V_0)^{1/3} \quad . \quad . \quad . \quad . \quad . \quad . \quad . \quad . \quad (3)$$

Since $(V/V_0)^{1/3}=r/r_0$, where r is the length of a side of the box, it follows that when the box expands without altering its shape, the ratio of the wave-lengths is equal to the ratio of the *linear* dimensions of the cavity:

$$\lambda/\lambda_0=r/r_0 \quad . \quad . \quad . \quad . \quad . \quad . \quad . \quad . \quad . \quad . \quad (4)$$

It must now be shown [1] that if black-body (full) radiation is *adiabatically* expanded or compressed in a *reflecting* box, it remains full radiation. If this were not so, the introduction of a speck of black carbon would bring the radiation to the thermodynamic equilibrium of full radiation without change of energy (the changes produced in the black speck are quite negligible), and as this is a spontaneous change there will be an increase of entropy (§ 51.II). Leaving in the black speck, the volume change is adiabatically reversed and the original volume restored. Since the radiation pressure depends only on the *total* energy density ρ, the work of expansion is equal and opposite to the work of compression, and as no heat has entered or left, the energy is unchanged and so, by Stefan's law, is the temperature. The process has thus been completely reversed without any changes occurring in external bodies. This contradicts the assumption of a finite entropy increase on bringing in the black speck, hence there cannot be such an increase, i.e. full radiation after adiabatic compression or expansion in a reflecting box remains full radiation, which was to be proved.

The total energy in the box is $V\rho$, where ρ is the energy density, and the work done in the adiabatic expansion is (since $p=\frac{1}{3}\rho$):

$$p\mathrm{d}V=-\mathrm{d}(V\rho)=-V\mathrm{d}\rho-\rho\mathrm{d}V=\tfrac{1}{3}\rho\mathrm{d}V,$$

$\therefore\ V\mathrm{d}\rho+\frac{4}{3}\rho\mathrm{d}V=0$, and on division by $V\rho$ this gives $\mathrm{d}\rho/\rho+\frac{4}{3}\mathrm{d}V/V=0$. By integration $\ln\rho+\frac{4}{3}\ln V=\text{const.}$, therefore:

$$\rho/\rho_0=(V_0/V)^{4/3}=(r_0/r)^4=(\lambda_0/\lambda)^4 \quad . \quad . \quad . \quad . \quad . \quad (5)$$

by (4). But Stefan's law, (2), § 9, gives $\rho/\rho_0=(T/T_0)^4$, $\therefore\ T/T_0=\lambda_0/\lambda$, or:

$$\lambda T=\text{const.} \quad . \quad . \quad . \quad . \quad . \quad . \quad . \quad . \quad . \quad . \quad (6)$$

[1] Planck, "Theorie der Wärmestrahlung," 4th edit., 1921, 70; Darwin, in Glazebrook, "Dict. of Applied Physics," 1923, **4**, 566, pointed out that some part of the walls must reflect *diffusely*, otherwise the directions of some parts of the radiation will be changed and it will no longer be completely isotropic; Planck, *op. cit.*, 72, specified "white" walls, which is the same thing.

which is Wien's displacement law. If λ is in cm., the best value [1] of the constant is 0·2897 cm. deg.

From (3), § 6, $E_\lambda=\pi K_\lambda$ ($e_\lambda=E_\lambda$ for full radiation), and (2), § 7, $\rho_\lambda=4\pi K_\lambda/c$, it follows that $\rho_\lambda d\lambda$ is proportional to $E_\lambda d\lambda$. From (5)

$$E_\lambda d\lambda/E_{\lambda_0}d\lambda_0=(\lambda_0/\lambda)^4 \quad . \quad . \quad . \quad . \quad . \quad . \quad . \quad . \quad (7)$$

Since, from (5), $\lambda+d\lambda=(r/r_0)(\lambda_0+d\lambda_0)$ and $\lambda=(r/r_0)\lambda_0$, therefore:

$$d\lambda=(r/r_0)d\lambda_0=(\lambda_0/\lambda)d\lambda_0 \quad . \quad . \quad . \quad . \quad . \quad . \quad . \quad . \quad (8)$$

and from (7) and (8):

$$E_\lambda/E_{\lambda_0}=(\lambda_0/\lambda)^5, \quad \text{or } E_\lambda\lambda^5=\text{const.} \quad . \quad . \quad . \quad . \quad . \quad . \quad (9)$$

Hence from (6):

$$E_\lambda=C_1\lambda^{-5}f(\lambda T) \quad . \quad . \quad . \quad . \quad . \quad . \quad . \quad . \quad . \quad . \quad (10)$$

where C_1 is an absolute constant and $f(\lambda T)$ is some unknown function of (λT) considered as a *single* parameter.

§ 11. Optical Pyrometry

The principle of optical pyrometry is the great increase in the visible radiation intensity with temperature. Red light is usually measured. The relative intensities of light of wave-length $\lambda=0{\cdot}656\mu$ at different temperatures are: 1000° C. 1, 1500° C. 130, 2000° C. 2100. The first application of optical pyrometry was made by Becquerel.[2] Lummer and Kurlbaum [3] found that the intensity of light from heated platinum was given by $(I_1/I_2)=(T_1/T_2)^x$, where x varied from 30 to 14 over the temperature range 900° to 1900° abs. (In what follows, E is denoted by I, as is usual in pyrometry.) Since the intensity varies with the nature of the heated surface (Pt, Fe, MgO, C, etc.), and as some flames (e.g. the Bunsen flame) hardly radiate at all, the heated source must be as nearly as possible a black body, the radiation from which is a function of temperature only. This is ensured by causing the radiation to proceed from a small aperture in a hollow opaque enclosure or cavity heated by the given source. In general, the temperature as determined by an optical pyrometer is *lower* than the true temperature (" black-body temperature ") by an amount depending on the departure from black-body radiation of the radiation from the source.

As compared with, for example, the platinum resistance thermometer, radiation pyrometry " has a sufficiently sound and well-established theoretical basis to have attained a practically independent status," and in high temperature regions, where gas thermometry " is losing its precision, but where the total radiation thermometer is gaining precision or at least holding its own, the gas thermometer will reach a point where it can no longer compete with its rival." [4]

[1] Lummer and Pringsheim, *Verhl. d. D. Phys. Ges.*, 1899, **1**, 23; 1900, **2**, 163, found 0·2876; Lummer, *Congrès Internat. Phys.*, 1901, **2**, 41; Pirani and Meyer, *Verhl. d. D. Phys. Ges.*, 1912, **14**, 576; see Wensel, *Bur. Stand. J. Res.*, 1939, **22**, 375; Dunnington, *Rev. Mod. Phys.*, 1939, **11**, 65; Du Mond and Cohen, *ibid.*, 1948, **20**, 82, give 0·289715 cm. deg. Kaye and Laby, " Tables of Physical and Chemical Constants," 10th edit., 1948, 80, 129, 139; Tables of E_λ, $N_\lambda=E_\lambda/h\nu$ (=number of photons emitted per sec. in the range λ to $\lambda+d\lambda$ in solid angle 2π), $\int_0^\infty E_\lambda d\lambda$ and $\int_0^\infty N_\lambda d\lambda$ are given by Lowan and Blanck, *J. Opt. Soc. Amer.*, 1940, **30**, 70; for a brief discussion of the values of the radiation constants, see Dushman, in Taylor and Glasstone, " Treatise on Physical Chemistry," 1942, **1**, 198.

[2] *Ann. Chim.*, 1863, **68**, 49–143 (full bibl.); Le Chatelier, *Compt. Rend.*, 1892, **114**, 214.

[3] *Verhl. d. D. Phys. Ges.*, 1900, **2**, 89.

[4] Day and Sosman, in Glazebrook, " Dict. of Applied Physics," 1922, **1**, 862; on optical pyrometry, see Henning, " Die Grundlagen der Temperaturmessung," Brunswick, 1915, 128; *idem*, in Geiger and Scheel, " Handbuch der Physik," 1926, **9**, 540; Burgess and Foote,

The fundamental laws used in radiation pyrometry are Stefan's law, that the energy intensity I of radiation from a black body is proportional to the fourth power of the absolute temperature (§ 9), and Wien's displacement law (§ 10) that when the temperature increases the wave-length of every monochromatic radiation (i.e. one of given λ) decreases in such a way that the product of the wave-length and absolute temperature is constant, $\lambda T=\lambda_0 T_0$, in particular that $\lambda_m T=\text{const.}=A$, for the wave-length of maximum energy λ_m. A combination of the two laws gives $I_m T^{-5}=\text{const.}=B$, or $I_m=BT^5$, where I_m is the maximum intensity corresponding with λ_m. If the radiation is not from a black body, $I_m T^{-\alpha}=\text{const.}$, where for polished platinum, e.g. $\alpha=6$ (see § 17). From theoretical reasoning which cannot be considered satisfactory [1] Wien (1896) deduced the formula:

$$I_\lambda=C_1\lambda^{-5}e^{-c_2/\lambda T} \quad . \quad . \quad . \quad . \quad . \quad . \quad . \quad . \quad (1)$$

where I is the intensity corresponding with the spectrum region between λ and $\lambda+d\lambda$, and C_1 and c_2 are constants.

Fig. 6.VI B shows results of Lummer and Pringsheim; I is proportional to the intensity, λ is in μ, and the temperatures are given over the curves. Wien's assumptions are very artificial and unlikely, and Rayleigh (1900) said that Wien's formula, " reviewed from the theoretical side, . . . is little more than a conjecture." Wien's formula shows that the intensity of radiation of a given wave-length reaches a maximum at a certain temperature, and then decreases, and Rayleigh seems to have considered this an objection. It had, however, been found experimentally by Violle [2] in 1879.

Wien's formula was deduced in a different way by Planck.[3] It was found [4] to hold for $\lambda=9{\cdot}2\mu$ to $\lambda=0{\cdot}5\mu$ and temperatures of 100°–1300° C. It holds fairly well in the visible spectrum, but it shows deviations at very high temperatures and long wave-lengths.[5] Rayleigh [6] by an application of the principle of equipartition of energy (§ 20.IV) found the equation:

$$I_\lambda=ckT\lambda^{-4}=kT\nu^4/c^3 \quad . \quad . \quad . \quad . \quad . \quad . \quad . \quad . \quad (2)$$

where ν=frequency, c=velocity of light, k=Boltzmann's constant. This was found to hold for long waves, but failed in other regions.

Bur. Stand. Bull., 1916, **12**, 91; Foote, *Trans. Faraday Soc.*, 1917, **13**, 238; Optical Pyrometry Symposium, *ibid.*, 1917, **13**, 205; Amer. Inst. Min. and Met. Eng., " Pyrometry," Symposium Volume, New York, 1920; Griffiths, in Glazebrook, " Dict. of Applied Physics," 1922, **1**, 643, 663; Gibson, *ibid.*, 1923, **4**, 737 (spectro-photometry); Walsh, " Photometry," London, 1926, 126; Brodhun, in Geiger and Scheel, " Handbuch der Physik," 1928, **19**, 468 (photometry); Mendhousse, *Ann. de Phys.*, 1931, **16**, 209 (full review of all methods); Ribaud, " Traité de Pyrométrie Optique," Paris, 1931.

[1] *Ann. Phys.*, 1896, **58**, 662; cf. Michelson, *Phil. Mag.*, 1888, **25**, 425; *Phys. Z.*, 1901, **2**, 576. For some discussions and criticisms of Wien's deduction and formula, see Rayleigh, *Phil. Mag.*, 1900, **49**, 539; " Scientific Papers," 1903, **4**, 483; Planck, *Ann. Phys.*, 1900, **1**, 69; 1900, **3**, 764; Wien, *ibid.*, 1900, **3**, 530; 1901, **4**, 422; Lummer and Jahnke, *ibid.*, 1900, **3**, 283; Jahnke, Lummer, and Pringsheim, *ibid.*, 1901, **4**, 225; Wood, *Phil. Mag.*, 1918, **35**, 190; Jeffreys, *ibid.*, 1918, **35**, 410.

[2] *Compt. Rend.*, 1879, **88**, 171; cf. Larmor, *Proc. Roy. Soc.*, 1909, **83**, 82; " Math and Phys. Papers," Cambridge, 1929, **2**, 217, 396.

[3] *Ann. Phys.*, 1900, **1**, 69, 719; Syrkin, *Z. Phys.*, 1925, **31**, 836 for another deduction.

[4] Paschen, *Ann. Phys.*, 1896, **58**, 455; 1897, **60**, 662; 1901, **6**, 646; Paschen and Wanner, *Berlin Ber.*, 1899, 5, 405, 959; Wanner, *Ann. Phys.*, 1900, **2**, 141; Féry, *Ann. Chim.*, 1909, **17**, 267; Baisch, *Ann. Phys.*, 1911, **35**, 543 (for $0{\cdot}334\mu$).

[5] Lummer and Pringsheim, *Verhl. d. D. Phys. Ges.*, 1899, **1**, 215; 1900, **2**, 163.

[6] *Phil. Mag.*, 1900, **49**, 539; *Nature*, 1905, **72**, 54, 243; Jeans, *Phil. Mag.*, 1905, **10**, 91; *Phys. Z.*, 1908, **9**, 853.

Planck,[1] at first empirically but very soon after by the introduction of the quantum theory (§ 15.IV), found the equation:

$$I_\lambda = C_1\lambda^{-5}/(e^{c_2/\lambda T}-1) \quad . \quad . \quad . \quad . \quad . \quad . \quad . \quad . \quad (3)$$

which reduces to Wien's for short wave-lengths and to Rayleigh's for long wave-lengths, and was found[2] to agree with experiment over the whole range of wave-lengths. The deduction of this is given in § 12.

The wave-length for which I_λ is a maximum is found from $(dI_\lambda/d\lambda)=0$. By differentiation of (3) it is found (if $c_2/\lambda_m T=\beta$) that $e^{-\beta}+\beta/5-1=0$, or $5(1-e^{-\beta})=\beta$. The *two* roots of this equation[3] are $\beta=0$, which corresponds with $\lambda_m \to \infty$ and is without physical significance, and $\beta=4{\cdot}9651$. Thus $\lambda_m T=c_2/\beta$ is constant, in agreement with Wien's displacement law (§ 10). The value of $\lambda_m T=b$ can thus be calculated from c_2 and β, i.e. from $\boldsymbol{k}$, $\boldsymbol{c}$, $\boldsymbol{h}$, and β, and Planck found 0·288 cm. deg. Lummer and Pringsheim[4] found experimentally 0·294 and Paschen[5] 0·292. Although the accuracy of Planck's formula was called in question by Nernst and Wulf,[6] it was fully confirmed by newer measurements of Rubens and Michel.[7]

H. F. Weber[8] had proposed a radiation formula:

$$e_\lambda = c\pi(1/\lambda^2)e^{(aT-1/b^2T^2\lambda^2)} \quad . \quad . \quad . \quad . \quad . \quad . \quad . \quad . \quad (4)$$

for the energy e_λ radiated per sec. per cm.^{2} of a body at a temperature T, λ being the wave-length, c is the " emission constant," a is the " temperature constant" 0·0043, the same for all bodies, b a constant called the " luminous power " (Leuchtvermögen). The formula was used for T varying from 0° to 1775° C. and λ from 0·0004 to 0·015 mm. The total radiation is given by:

$$E = cb(\pi\sqrt{\pi}/2)e^{aT}\,.\,T = CTe^{aT} \quad . \quad . \quad . \quad . \quad . \quad . \quad (5)$$

where C is a constant. The results are not so good as those with Stefan's equation.[9]

Callendar[10] (whose attitude towards fundamentals was heterodox) tried to establish the formulae:

$$E/v+p = Cv^3(T+bv)e^{-bv/T} \quad . \quad . \quad . \quad . \quad . \quad . \quad . \quad . \quad (6)$$

$$\text{and } E+pv = \sigma b^3v^2T(1+bv/T)e^{-bv/T} \quad . \quad . \quad . \quad . \quad . \quad (7)$$

1 *Verhl. d. D. Phys. Ges.*, 1900, **2**, 202 (formula), 237 (deduction); Ostwald's *Klassiker*, 1923, **206**; *Ann. Phys.*, 1901, **4**, 553; 1901, **6**, 818; tables of Planck's function, Moon, *J. Math. Phys. Mass. Inst. Techn.*, 1937, **16**, 133.

2 Lummer and Pringsheim, *Verhl. d. D. Phys. Ges.*, 1900, **2**, 163; *Ann. Phys.*, 1901, **6**, 192; Rubens and Kurlbaum, *ibid.*, 1901, **4**, 649; Paschen, *ibid.*, 1901, **4**, 277.

3 Jellinek, " Physikalische Chemie der Gasreaktionen," Leipzig, 1913, 354; Planck, " Theorie der Wärmestrahlung," 1921, 183, who gives only the second root; Richtmayer and Kennard, " Introduction to Modern Physics," New York, 1942, 203; Smith, *Phil. Mag.*, 1942, **33**, 775; for solution by successive approximations, see Haskins, *Phys. Rev.*, 1914, **3**, 476.

4 *Ann. Phys.*, 1901, **6**, 192.

5 *Ann. Phys.*, 1901, **6**, 646.

6 *Verhl. d. D. Phys. Ges.*, 1919, **21**, 294.

7 *Berlin Ber.*, 1921, 590; *Phys. Z.*, 1921, **22**, 569; Michel, *Z. Phys.*, 1922, **9**, 285.

8 *Berlin Ber.*, 1888, 933; *Z. phys. Chem.*, 1888, **2**, 967 (abstr.); Petavel, *Proc. Roy. Soc.*, 1898, **63**, 403; *Phil. Trans.*, 1898, **191**, 501, thought his measurements on the emissivity of incandescent bright platinum confirmed Weber's formula; Compan, *Compt. Rend.*, 1901, **133**, 813, 1202, thought Weber's equation better than Stefan's at −182·5° to 302°.

9 Graetz, *Ann. Phys.*, 1889, **36**, 857; Paschen, *ibid.*, 1893, **49**, 50; 1896, **58**, 455.

10 *Phil. Mag.*, 1913, **26**, 787; 1914, **27**, 870; *Nature*, 1913, **92**, 450, 553; for other formulae, see Byk, *Ann. Phys.*, 1913, **42**, 1417; Brillouin, *Ann. de Phys.*, 1914, **1**, 13, 163, 433; Tolman, *Phys. Rev.*, 1914, **3**, 244; Ratnowsky, *Verhl. d. D. Phys. Ges.*, 1915, **17**, 64; Nernst and Wulf, *ibid.*, 1919, **21**, 294.

where σ=Stefan's constant, ν=frequency, E=radiant energy per mol, such that $pv=RT$, p=radiation pressure and v=volume (E/v=energy density), and b and C are constants, b being $h/k=E/R\nu$ (h=Planck's constant, k=Boltzmann's constant).

Charlier [1] proposed the formula:

$$E_\lambda = cT^5 e^{-[\ln(\lambda T/b)]^2/2\sigma_1^2} \quad \ldots \ldots \ldots \quad (8)$$

where b, c, and σ_1 are constants. An attempt to deduce a formula without the quantum hypothesis was made by Walker.[2]

Priest [3] gave the empirical formula:

$$E_\lambda = D_1 T^5 e^{-D_2[A^{-1/3}-(\lambda T)^{-1/3}]^2} \quad \ldots \ldots \ldots \quad (9)$$

where D_1 and D_2 are constants, and A is the Wien displacement law constant (§ 10), $\lambda_m T=A$.

§ 12. Planck's Radiation Formula

It was shown in § 78, I, that for a system of plane stationary waves of length λ and frequency $\nu=c/\lambda$, where c=velocity, the number of modes of vibration (proper vibrations) with frequencies in the range ν to $\nu+d\nu$ is, for a volume V:

$$dn = 4\pi V\nu^2 d\nu/c^3$$

or for unit volume:

$$dn = 4\pi\nu^2 d\nu/c^3 \quad \ldots \ldots \ldots \quad (1)$$

This refers to *longitudinal* vibrations in a medium in which the wave velocity is c, and also to a single frequency ν. For a range of frequencies each equation is replaced by a sum of an infinite number of terms for which ν varies from 0 to ∞, i.e. by a Fourier's series (§ 73.I). Radiation in a vacuous cavity does not consist of longitudinal vibrations but of *transverse* vibrations at right angles to the direction of propagation of the ray OS (Fig. 39.I). Every ray having transverse vibrations in a plane at right angles to OS can, however, be compounded of two rays polarised at right angles and with independent phases, and hence a longitudinal wave train of given frequency and direction must now be replaced by *two* transverse wave trains of equal frequency, and the number of proper vibrations per cm.[3] is double that of (1); hence if c=velocity of light in vacuum:

$$dn = (8\pi/c^3)\nu^2 d\nu \quad \ldots \ldots \ldots \quad (2)$$

Rayleigh [4] and Jeans [5] assumed the principle of equipartition of energy and attributed the energy kT to each proper vibration (§ 20.IV), thus finding for the energy density of radiation of frequency ν:

$$\rho_\nu d\nu = (8\pi/c^3)\nu^2 d\nu \,.\, kT = (8\pi\nu^2 kT/c^3)d\nu \quad \ldots \quad (3)$$

Planck [6] assumed that the energy of an electromagnetic wave system in a

[1] *Arkiv Mat. Astron. Fys.*, 1912, **7**, No. 31; 1913, **9**, No. 11.

[2] *Proc. Roy. Soc.*, 1914, **89**, 393; cf. de Boissoudy, *J. de Phys.*, 1913, **3**, 385, 649; Bauer, *ibid.*, 1913, **3**, 641; Lewis and Adams, *Phys. Rev.*, 1914, **4**, 331.

[3] *Phys. Rev.*, 1919, **13**, 314.

[4] *Phil. Mag.*, 1900, **49**, 539.

[5] *Phil. Mag.*, 1905, **10**, 91; the factor 8π was first given correctly by Jeans, and was accepted by Rayleigh; cf. Carwile, *Phil. Mag.*, 1938, **25**, 926.

[6] *Ann. Phys.*, 1901, **4**, 553; "Theorie der Wärmestrahlung," 1921, 183. On Planck's radiation equation, including alternative deductions, see also Frank, *Phys. Z.*, 1912, **13**, 506; Poincaré, *J. de Phys.*, 1912, **2**, 5; Wolfke, *Verhl. d. D. Phys. Ges.*, 1913, **15**, 1123, 1215; 1914, **16**, 4; *Phys. Z.*, 1914, **15**, 308; Goldhammer, *ibid.*, 1913, **14**, 1185; de Boissoudy, *J. de Phys.*, 1913, **3**, 385, 649; Bauer, *ibid.*, 1913, **3**, 641; Krutow, *Phys. Z.*, 1914, **15**, 133, 363; Brillouin,

vacuous cavity is quantised in the same way as the energy of a linear harmonic oscillator, (9), § 16.IV, omitting the zero-point energy: [1]

$$\bar{\epsilon}=h\nu/(e^{h\nu/kT}-1) \quad . \quad . \quad . \quad . \quad . \quad . \quad . \quad . \quad (4)$$

By combining (2) and (4) the energy density of equilibrium (black-body) radiation in the frequency range ν to $\nu+d\nu$ is found to be:

$$\rho_\nu d\nu=\frac{8\pi h\nu^3}{c^3}\frac{1}{(e^{h\nu/kT}-1}d\nu \quad . \quad . \quad . \quad . \quad . \quad . \quad . \quad . \quad (5)$$

The total energy density for all frequencies is:

$$\rho=\int_0^\infty \rho_\nu d\nu=\frac{8\pi h}{c^3}\int_0^\infty \frac{\nu^3 d\nu}{e^{h\nu/kT}-1}$$

$$=\frac{8\pi(kT)^4}{c^3h^3}\int_0^\infty \frac{x^3dx}{e^x-1}=\frac{8\pi^5k^4}{15c^3h^3}T^4 \quad . \quad . \quad . \quad . \quad . \quad (6)$$

where $x=h\nu/kT$, $\nu^3=x^3(kT)^3/h^3$, $d\nu=(kT/h)dx$. Equation (6) is the Stefan-Boltzmann radiation equation (2), § 9, with the constant k as determined by Planck. The evaluation of the integral [2] is carried out by expanding $(e^x-1)^{-1}$ by division:

$$1/(e^x-1)=e^{-x}+e^{-2x}+e^{-3x}+\ldots$$

and integrating

$$\int_0^\infty x^3(e^{-x}+e^{-2x}+e^{-3x}+\ldots)dx$$

term by term, making use of the results:

$$\int_0^\infty x^3e^{-nx}dx=6/n^4$$

$$1+1/2^4+1/3^4+1/4^4+\ldots=\pi^4/90.$$

At low frequencies and high temperatures (5), with $h\to 0$, gives the Rayleigh-Jeans equation (3); at high frequencies, unity in the denominator is negligible in comparison with the exponential, giving the Wien formula: [3]

$$\rho_\nu d\nu=(8\pi h\nu^3/c^3)e^{-h\nu/kT}d\nu \quad . \quad . \quad . \quad . \quad . \quad . \quad . \quad . \quad (7)$$

Ann. de Phys., 1914, **1**, 13; *J. de Phys.*, 1914, **4**, 681; Livens, *Phil. Mag.*, 1914, **28**, 648; Einstein *Phys. Z.*, 1917, **18**, 12; Flamm, *ibid.*, 1918, **19**, 116; Bichowski, *Phys. Rev.*, 1917, **10**, 92; 1918, **11**, 58: Tolman, *ibid.*, 1918, **11**, 261; Kunz, *Phil. Mag.*, 1923, **45**, 300; Einstein and Ehrenfest, *Z. Phys.*, 1923, **19**, 301 (generalisation of Einstein's deduction); Planck, *Ann. Phys.*, 1924, **73**, 272 (nature of radiation); Schidlof, *Arch. Sci. Phys. Nat.*, 1924, **6**, 281, 381; Heitler, *Z. Phys.*, 1925, **34**, 526 (modified Einstein deduction); Eddington, *Phil. Mag.*, 1925, **50**, 803 (modified Einstein deduction); Saha and Sur, *Phil. Mag.*, 1926, **1**, 890; Syrkin, *Z. Phys.*, 1925, **31**, 836; Westphal, *ibid.*, 1925, **33**, 557; Schaposchnikoff, *ibid.*, 1928, **51**, 895; Sturm, *ibid.*, 1928, **51**, 287 (generalised Planck formula); Forsythe, *J. Opt. Soc. Amer.*, 1928, **16**, 307; Császár, *Naturwiss.*, 1942, **30**, 265; for attempted deductions without quantum theory, see Page, *Phys. Rev.*, 1916, **7**, 229; Swann, *Phil. Mag.*, 1917, **33**, 64; Nagaoka, *Proc. Phys. Math. Soc. Japan*, 1917, **9**, 200; Bružs, *Acta Univ. Latviensis*, 1929, **20**, 433; Schweikert, *Z. Phys.*, 1932, **76**, 679; Lewis, *Proc. Phys. Soc.*, 1947, **59**, 34.

[1] Otherwise there would be an infinite density of electromagnetic energy at $T=0$. The *theoretical* justification for the omission of the zero-point energy is still unknown, but it obviates one of the "diseases of infinity": Born, "Experiment and Theory in Physics," Cambridge, 1943, 35.

[2] See Jellinek, "Physikalische Chemie der Gasreaktionen," Leipzig, 1913, 353; Planck "Theorie der Wärmestrahlung," Leipzig, 1921, 183.

[3] *Ann. Phys.*, 1896, **58**, 662.

The (more satisfactory) deduction from Bose-Einstein statistics, which applies to photons (§ 31.IV), proceeds as follows.[1] The frequency range from 0 to ∞ is divided into regions such as ν_r to $\nu_r+d\nu_r$, and the number of stationary waves in this range is a_r. The total energy is $E=\Sigma n_r\epsilon_r=\Sigma n_r(\boldsymbol{h}\nu_r)=\text{const.}$ The condition $N=\Sigma n_r$, however, drops out. The entropy is

$$S=\boldsymbol{k}\Sigma[a_r \ln (1+n_r/a_r)+n_r \ln (a_r/n_r+1)],$$

as in (15), § 33.IV. For equilibrium (black-body) radiation, this is a maximum and since $S=\boldsymbol{k} \ln W$, $\delta \ln W=0$ corresponds with $\delta S=0$, with the subsidiary condition $\delta E=0$.

$$\begin{aligned}(\partial S/\partial n_r)&=\boldsymbol{k}(\partial/\partial n_r)[a_r \ln (1+n_r/a_r)+n_r \ln (a_r/n_r+1)]\\ &=\boldsymbol{k}[a_r/(a_r+n_r)+\ln (a_r/n_r+1)-a_r/(a_r+n_r)]\\ &=\boldsymbol{k} \ln (a_r/n_r+1),\end{aligned}$$

and $\partial E/\partial n_r=\boldsymbol{h}\nu_r$; hence, by the method of undetermined multipliers (§ 8.IV; $\lambda=0$):

$$\boldsymbol{k} \ln (1+a_r/n_r)-\boldsymbol{k}\mu \boldsymbol{h}\nu_r=0, \text{ where } \mu=1/\boldsymbol{k}T,$$

$$\therefore\ n_r/a_r=1/(e^{\boldsymbol{h}\nu_r/\boldsymbol{k}T}-1) \quad . \quad . \quad . \quad . \quad . \quad . \quad . \quad . \quad \textbf{(8)}$$

Drop the suffix r. The number of photons in the given frequency range is, from (2):

$$n d\nu=8\pi V(\nu^2/\boldsymbol{c}^3)d\nu(e^{\boldsymbol{h}\nu/\boldsymbol{k}T}-1)^{-1} \quad . \quad . \quad . \quad . \quad . \quad . \quad \textbf{(9)}$$

and the energy density ρ_ν is found by multiplying the number per cm.³ by the energy $\boldsymbol{h}\nu$ of each:

$$\rho_\nu d\nu=(n d\nu/V)\boldsymbol{h}\nu \quad . \quad . \quad . \quad . \quad . \quad . \quad . \quad . \quad . \quad \textbf{(10)}$$

Hence, by substituting from (9) in (10), equation (5) results.

§ 13. Optical Pyrometers

In optical pyrometry practice a standard of intensity is used, and the brightness of the photometric field illuminated by the red light emitted by the body (or passing a light filter) is varied until its intensity is equal to that of the standard. The variation may be effected by (i) an iris diaphragm (Le Chatelier), (ii) an absorbing wedge (Féry), (iii) a polarising device (Wanner), or (iv) varying the standard light in a known way (Holborn and Kurlbaum, Morse).[2] Besides this photometric method, others have been used:

(i) The ratio of the intensities of two wave-lengths in the emitted radiation is measured. Crova [3] (1878) chose the red ($\lambda=676$) and the green ($\lambda=523$), making one equal by a variable diaphragm and comparing the intensities of the other. Violle [4] found that the variation in intensity for $\lambda=0{\cdot}656\mu$ (red) and $\lambda=0{\cdot}482\mu$ (blue) for radiation from platinum was only 1:14 for a rise in temperature of 700°, so that the method is not very sensitive.

(ii) The upper wave-length limit of the spectrum, proposed by Crova,[5] was shown by Hempel [6] to give only crude results.

[1] Tolman, "Statistical Mechanics," Oxford, 1938, 382; Mayer and Mayer, "Statistical Mechanics," New York, 1940, 369 (followed above).

[2] For a bibliography of pyrometers, see Hadfield, *Trans. Faraday Soc.*, 1918, **13**, 362; for a general review, see Henning, "Die Grundlagen der Temperaturmessung," Brunswick, 1915, 128, 170, 177; Wood and Cork, "Pyrometry," 2nd edit., New York, 1941.

[3] *Compt. Rend.*, 1878, **87**, 322; see the references to Crova's papers in Le Chatelier and Boudouard, "High Temperature Measurements," transl. Burgess, New York, 1904, 329.

[4] *Compt. Rend.*, 1879, **88**, 171; 1881, **92**, 866, 1204.

[5] *J. de Phys.*, 1878, **7**, 357.

[6] *Z. angew. Chem.*, 1901, **14**, 237.

(iii) The use of Wien's displacement law with *monochromatic* radiation, either in the form $\lambda_m T$=const., or $T=C\sqrt[5]{}/I_m$; this requires elaborate apparatus.

(iv) The measurement of *total* radiation and the use of Stefan's law; this is the commonest method, but it presupposes a black-body source.

By substitution of $\nu=c/\lambda$ in (5), § 12, it is found that:

$$\rho_\nu d\nu=\frac{8\pi h}{\lambda^3}\frac{1}{(e^{hc/k\lambda T}-1)}d\nu.$$

The replacement of ν by λ, however, requires the replacement of $d\nu$ by $d\lambda$. Since $d\nu=-(c/\lambda^2)d\lambda$, then if $d\nu$ and $d\lambda$ are both taken positive (since when ν increases λ decreases):

$$\rho_\lambda d\lambda=\frac{8\pi hc}{\lambda^5}\frac{1}{(e^{hc/k\lambda T}-1)}d\lambda.$$

Hence Planck's radiation equation may be written in the form:

$$I_\lambda=C_1\lambda^{-5}/(e^{c_2/\lambda T}-1) \quad . \quad . \quad . \quad . \quad . \quad . \quad . \quad . \quad (1)$$

where C_1 and c_2 are constants. The values $C_1=3{\cdot}71\times10^{-5}$ erg cm.$^{-2}$ sec.$^{-1}$ and $c_2=1{\cdot}433$ cm. deg. may be adopted. Values of c_2 varying from 1·430, found by Rubens and Michel (1921–2), to 1·436, found by Wensel (1939), have been used.[1] If the unit is the micron (=10^{-4} cm.) deg. the value for cm. deg. is multiplied by 10^4.

Stefan's law gives for the *total* emission in ergs per cm.^{2} per sec.:

$$I=\sigma T^4 \quad . \quad . \quad . \quad . \quad . \quad . \quad . \quad . \quad . \quad . \quad . \quad (2)$$

where $\sigma=5{\cdot}75\times10^{-5}$ erg cm.$^{-2}$ sec.$^{-1}$ deg.$^{-4}$.

The ratio of two intensities for the same wave-length is given by (1) as:

$$I_1/I_2=(e^{c_2/\lambda T_2}-1)/(e^{c_2/\lambda T_1}-1)$$

and in the visible spectrum and at temperatures attainable in the laboratory the effect of neglecting -1 in each expression on the right corresponds with an error in T of less than 1° at a temperature of 1500°. Thus, with sufficient approximation:

$$I_1/I_2=e^{c_2/\lambda T_2}/e^{c_2/\lambda T_1} \quad . \quad . \quad . \quad . \quad . \quad . \quad . \quad . \quad (3)$$

$$\text{or} \quad 1/T_2-1/T_1=(\lambda/c_2)\ln(I_1/I_2) \quad . \quad . \quad . \quad . \quad . \quad (4)$$

[1] Buckingham and Dellinger, *Bur. Stand. Bull.*, 1911, **7**, 393; Pirani and Meyer, *Verhl. d. D. Phys. Ges.*, 1912, **14**, 429; Coblentz, *J. Wash. Acad.*, 1913, **3**, 177; *Bur. Stand. Bull.*, 1914, **10**, 1 (1·4456); Warburg, Leithäuser, Hupka, and Müller, *Berlin Ber.*, 1913, 35; *Ann. Phys.*, 1913, **40**, 609 (1·437); Haskins, *Phys. Rev.*, 1914, **3**, 476 (1·460); Warburg and Müller, *Ann. Phys.*, 1915, **48**, 410 (1·430); Dellinger, *Bur. Stand. Bull.*, 1917, **13**, 535; Mendenhall, *Phys. Rev.*, 1917, **10**, 515 (1·440); Roeser, *Bur. Stand. Bull.*, 1918, **14**, 237 (1·434); Nernst and Wulf, *Verhl. d. D. Phys. Ges.*, 1919, **21**, 294; Rubens and Michel, *Berlin Ber.*, 1921, 590; *Phys. Z.*, 1921, **22**, 569 (1·430); Michel, *Z. Phys.*, 1922, **9**, 285 (1·427); Henning, *Z. Elektrochem.*, 1924, **30**, 309, 396; Wensel, *Bur. Stand. J. Res.*, 1939, **22**, 375; *idem*, in "Temperature. Its Measurement and Control," New York, 1941, 3; Forsythe, *ibid.*, 1115. The National Physical Laboratory (England) chose the value $c_2=1{\cdot}4350$ to correspond with the m.p. of palladium as 1555° C., and the Bureau of Standards (U.S.A.) to correspond with the m.p. of gold as 1063° C. The two scales give agreement to a degree or two over the range 1000°–2400° C. (see Wood and Cork, "Pyrometry," New York, 2nd edit., 1941, 10). Du Mond and Cohen, *Rev. Mod. Phys.*, 1948, **20**, 82, give $8\pi hc=4{\cdot}9902\times10^{-15}$ erg cm., $c_2=hc/k=1{\cdot}43847$ cm. deg., and $\sigma=5{\cdot}6724\times10^{-5}$ erg cm.$^{-2}$ sec.$^{-1}$ deg.$^{-4}$, pointing out that the International Temperature Scale is based on $c_2=1{\cdot}432$ cm. deg.

Wien's formula thus holds with sufficient approximation for $\lambda T < 3000\mu$, and since the longest wave-length used in optical pyrometry is less than $0{\cdot}7\mu$, it is valid for the whole practical range of temperature.[1] Equation (4) gives a linear relation between log I and $1/T$ for a given wave-length:

$$\log I = K_1 - K_2(1/T) \quad . \quad . \quad . \quad . \quad . \quad . \quad . \quad (5)$$

Plots of log I against $1/T$ are called *isochromatics*. Equation (5) is commonly used in calibrating optical pyrometers, the constants K_1 and K_2 being found by measurements at two standard temperatures.

The International Temperature Scale (1927) [2] is defined above the f.p. of gold by the ratio of the intensity I_2 of monochromatic visible radiation of wave-length λ cm. emitted by a black body at the temperature t_2° C. to the intensity I_1 of radiation of the same wave-length emitted by a black body at the gold point (1063° C.) by means of the formula:

$$\ln \frac{I_2}{I_1} = \frac{c_2}{\lambda}\left(\frac{1}{1336} - \frac{1}{t+273}\right)$$

the constant c_2 being taken as 1·432 cm. deg. This equation is valid if $\lambda(t+273)$ is less than 0·3 cm. deg. As secondary points, the f.ps. of palladium (1555° C.) and tungsten (3400° C.) are specified, but the last is not so certain as the others.

In calibrating total radiation pyrometers, the Bureau of Standards used an electrically heated nickel strip, 17 cm. × 13 cm. × 0·015 cm., mounted between water-cooled brass clamp terminals, the strip having a firm and uniform black coat of nickel oxide deposited by heating in air. The radiation is not completely black-body, but a calibrated instrument is used as a comparative standard. The strip can be used indefinitely to 1300°; cooling from 500° to room temperature must be slow, to prevent flaking of the oxide film.

§ 14. Féry's Optical Pyrometer

This [3] makes use of Stefan's formula. A metal or silvered or gilt glass concave mirror M, is contained in a metal tube T movable by a rack and pinion,

[1] Shook, *Met. Chem. Eng.*, 1912, **10**, 238, 334, 416, 478; Griffiths, in Glazebrook, " Dict. of Applied Physics," 1922, **1**, 644; " Methods of Measuring High Temperatures," 1925, 118; Day and Sosman, in Glazebrook, " Dict. of Applied Physics," 1922, **1**, 862; Coblentz, *ibid.*, 1923, **4**, 541. If $\lambda = 6{\cdot}58 \times 10^{-5}$ cm. (red light) and the upper limit of T is 4000° K., $e^{c_2/\lambda T} = 230$, which is large compared with 1; Wood and Cork, " Pyrometry," 2nd edit., 1941, 103, 149. Birge, *Rep. Progr. Phys.*, 1942, **8**, 90, took $c_2 = 1{\cdot}4384$ cm. deg., and Wien's displacement law constant $c_2/4{\cdot}965114 = 0{\cdot}28971_8$ cm. deg.; cf. Wensel, *Bur. Stand. J. Res.*, 1939, **22**, 375; Van Dusen and Dahl, *Science*, 1947, **106**, 428 ($c_2 = 1{\cdot}438$ cm. deg.); on calibration of optical and general pyrometers, see Held, *Chaleur et Ind.*, 1930, **11**, 473; Hoffman and Tingwaldt, " Optische Pyrometrie," Brunswick, 1938; Parlee, *Canad. Chem. Process Ind.*, 1942, **26**, 230.

[2] Burgess, *Bur. Stand. J. Res.*, 1928, **1**, 635; Roeser, *ibid.*, 1929, **3**, 343 (660°–1063°); Wensel, *ibid.*, 1939, **22**, 375.

[3] Thwing, *Phys. Rev.*, 1908, **26**, 190; Burgess, *Bur. Stand. Bull.*, 1909–10, **6**, 111; Anon., *Electrician*, 1909, **63**, 293; Féry and Chéneveau, *J. de Phys.*, 1910, **9**, 397; Féry and Drecq, *ibid.*, 1911, **1**, 551; Gillette, *J. Phys. Chem.*, 1911, **15**, 213; Randolph and Overholser, *Phys. Rev.*, 1913, **2**, 144; Millochau, *Compt. Rend.*, 1914, **159**, 171; Burgess and Foote, *Bur. Stand. Bull.*, 1914, **11**, 41; 1915, **12**, 91; Burgess and Waltenberg, *ibid.*, 1914, **11**, 591; Coblentz, *ibid.*, 1916, **12**, 533; Keinath, *Elektrotechn. Z.*, 1921, **42**, 1384; Forsythe, *J. Opt. Soc. Amer.*, 1925, **10**, 19 (general on optical pyrometers); Philpot, *J. Sci. Instr.*, 1926, **3**, 366 (distance from source); for errors, e.g. due to absorption by lenses, etc., see Miething, *Wiss. Veröffentl. Siemens Konz.*, 1928, **6**, 135; Fidge, *Chem. Eng. Mining Rev.*, 1931, **23**, 189 (radiation pyrometry); Gourevitch and Lerner, *Zavodskaya Lab.*, 1946, **12**, 292; Volochine and Gerard, *Chim. et Ind.*, 1947

and an eye-piece views through a hole in the mirror a small diaphragm D in the form of two halves of a metal mirror inclined at a small angle (Fig. 9.VI B). The small blackened receiving surface R, to which is attached one junction of a thermocouple, is placed immediately in front of a small aperture in D, and M is adjusted so that the image of the radiating body is focused on the hole in D. This will be the case when the two halves of the image formed on the two parts of D form an undisplaced circle *a*, otherwise they will be displaced, as in *b*. The other (cold) junction of the thermocouple is shielded from radiation by enclosing it in a box.

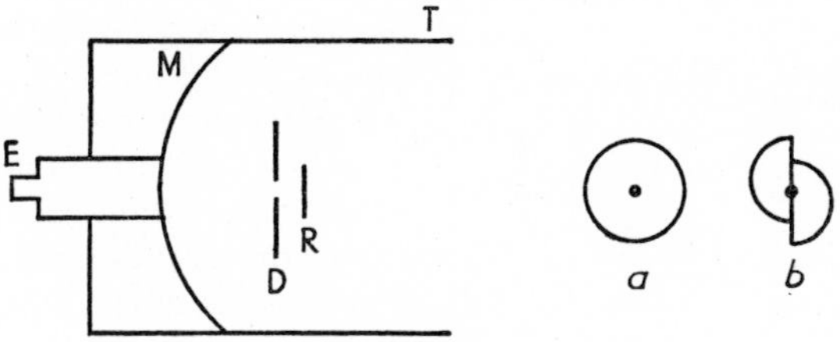

FIG. 9.VI B. Féry Optical Pyrometer

If the aperture in D is filled by the image, the reading is independent of the distance from the radiating body. For, the thermocouple reading depends only on the *intensity* of radiation $K=\rho c/4\pi$ erg. cm.$^{-2}$ sec.$^{-1}$, falling on the aperture, and both the energy received by M and the area of the hole in D are inversely proportional to the square of the distance from the radiating body, so that K, the energy received per unit area, is constant. In order that the image shall fill the aperture (usually 1·5 mm. diam.) the source must have a minimum diameter at each distance, given in a table supplied with the instrument or easily calculated if the focal length of M is known.

The instrument must be calibrated to give readings of the millivoltmeter attached to the thermocouple against temperatures. Sometimes a bi-metallic spiral attached to a pointer replaces the thermocouple.

§ 15. The Disappearing Filament Pyrometer

This was used in a crude form as far back as 1888; it was improved by Morse about 1902, who used a carbon filament lamp in a metal tube through which the hot body was sighted, the current in the lamp being varied until the lamp filament and hot body appeared equally bright, and the filament merged into the brightness of the source.[1] Holborn and Kurlbaum [2] added an objective and eye-piece, so that an image of the furnace is projected in the plane of the lamp filament, and hence the fatigue of the eye in looking at two objects at

57, 567; Griffiths, in Glazebrook, " Dict. of Applied Physics," 1922, **1**, 669; Griffiths, " Methods of Measuring Temperature," 2nd edit., 1925, 93 f.; Wood and Cork, " Pyrometry," 2nd edit., New York, 1941, 149; for transmissibility of glasses for infra-red, see Liana, *Compt. Rend.*, 1925, **180**, 578.

[1] Burgess and Waltenberg, *Z. anorg. Chem.*, 1913, **80**, 361; *Bur. Stand. Bull.*, 1914, **11**, 591; Burgess, *J. Wash. Acad.*, 1913, **3**, 7; *Phys. Z.*, 1913, **14**, 158 (micro-type); Forsythe, *Astrophys. J.*, 1916, **43**, 295; *Trans. Faraday Soc.*, 1920, **15**, pt. iii, 21.

[2] *Ann. Phys.*, 1903, **10**, 225; Nernst, *Phys. Z.*, 1906, **7**, 380; Henning, " Temperaturmessung," Brunswick, 1915, 170; Henning and Heuse, *Z. Phys.*, 1924, **29**, 157.

different distances is avoided. In modern types, a red light-filter glass is fixed in the eye-piece; this makes the radiation approximately monochromatic, and the scale of the instrument can be extrapolated on the basis of Wien's law, (5), § 13.

The pyrometer (Fig. 10.VI B) consists of an arrangement in which an image of the radiating surface S is formed by a lens into a plane in which the filament F of an incandescent electric lamp is situated. The image and filament are focused in an eye-piece E, in front of which is a piece of red glass G which transmits only a very narrow band of wave-lengths, so that Wien's equation applies. The filament current is adjusted by a resistance and ammeter until the filament is invisible on the background of the image of the source, when $I_1=I_2$. If the filament is too hot, it appears brighter than its background; if too cool, darker. The instrument is calibrated by the ammeter readings up to the m.p. of gold by direct observation of a black body (cavity or incandescent strip); at higher temperatures either a suitable coloured glass filter or a rotating sector between the instrument and source are used.[1] In interpolation between two calibration temperatures not too far apart, the lamp current i is related to the temperatures by the equation $\log i=a+b \log T$, where a and b are constants (b being very nearly unity) which can be found from known temperature (m.p.) standards. As supplied, the ammeter scale reads temperatures directly, two scales being used, one for use without, and one with a filter. This type of pyrometer is very handy and easy to use and with suitable precautions can give accurate results. The disappearing filament and Féry pyrometers give the same results, within the range of experimental error (about 5°) up to 2820° C.

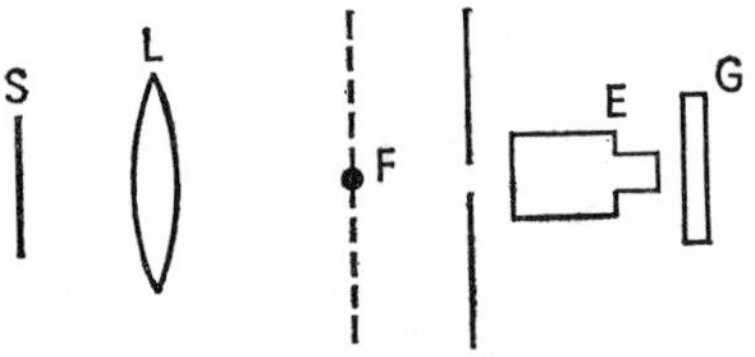

FIG. 10.VI B. Disappearing Filament Pyrometer

It is important to remember that this type of pyrometer does not really give the temperature of the source, but merely compares brightnesses: a cold mirror reflecting rays from a hot body would be recorded as having the temperature of the latter. It is, therefore, important to make sure that the body is not reflecting radiation from a hotter source.[2] The same applies to other optical pyrometers.

[1] Waidner and Burgess, *Bur. Stand. Bull.*, 1904, **1**, 189; Henning, *Z. Instr.*, **1910**, **30**, 61; Foster, *J. Franklin Inst.*, 1910, **169**, 391; Mendenhall, *Phys. Rev.*, 1911, **33**, 74; Fisher, *Met. Chem. Eng.*, 1913, **11**, 532 (Shook pyrometer); Mendenhall and Forsythe, *Phys. Rev.*, 1914, **4**, 62; Worthing and Forsythe, *ibid.*, 1914, **4**, 163; *Gen. Elec. Rev.*, 1917, **20**, 749; *Chem. Met. Eng.*, 1920, **22**, 1211 (calibration); *Trans. Amer. Inst. Min. Met. Eng.*, 1936, **120**, 171; Hyde, Cady, and Forsythe, *Astrophys. J.*, 1915, **42**, 303; Forsythe, *ibid.*, 1916, **43**, 295; Foote, *Trans. Faraday Soc.*, 1918, **13**, 238; Forsythe, *ibid.*, 1919, **15**, 20; *Chem. Met. Eng.*, 1920, **22**, 1211; *J. Opt. Soc. Amer.*, 1925, **10**, 19; 1928, **16**, 307; *idem.* in "Pyrometry Sympos. Vol.," Amer. Inst. Min. Met. Eng., New York, 1920, 291; Foote and Fairchild, *ibid.*, 324; Bash, *ibid.*, 352; Henning, *Phys. Z.*, 1919, **20**, 34; Fairchild, *Phys. Rev.*, 1921, **18**, 116; Fairchild and Hoover, *J. Opt. Soc. Amer.*, 1923, **7**, 543; Schofield and Gall, *J. Sci. Instr.*, 1924, **1**, 193; Henning, *Z. Elektrochem.*, 1924, **30**, 309; von Wartenberg and Moehl, *Z. phys. Chem.*, 1927, **128**, 445; Fairchild, Hoover, and Peters, *Bur. Stand. J. Res.*, 1929, **2**, 930; Egerton and Milford, *Proc. Roy. Soc.*, 1930, **130**, 111; Mendhousse, *Ann. de Phys.*, 1931, **16**, 209; Roeser, Caldwell, and Wensel, *Bur. Stand. J. Res.*, 1931, **6**, 1119; Milford, Bracey, Cunnold, and Egerton, *J. Sci. Instr.*, 1935, **12**, 80; Cunnold, *Proc. Roy. Soc.*, 1935, **152**, 64; Stott, *J. Sci. Inst.*, 1937, **14**, 370; Harrison and Wanamaker, *Rev. Sci. Instr.*, 1941, **12**, 120; Freivert, *Compt. Rend. U.R.S.S.*, 1944, **43**, 237 (600°–700°); Barber, *J. Iron Steel Inst.*, 1945, **42**, 171; Land and Lund, *ibid.*, 1947, **156**, 75 (photoelectric barrier cell); on the Schofield-Griffiths pyrometer, see Griffiths, "Pyrometry, . . . with Notes on Electric Furnaces," 1926, 93.

[2] Wood and Cork, "Pyrometry," New York, 2nd edit., 1941, 133.

§ 16. The Wanner Pyrometer

This is an adaptation[1] of the König[2] spectrophotometer. It depends on the alteration of intensity of a selected spectral portion of the radiated light, which is compared with the brightness of a small incandescent electric lamp illuminating a matt glass surface. The alteration of intensity is effected by means of a pair of polarising prisms, the intensity of the light polarised by the first (Rochon) prism being suitably reduced by rotation of the second (Nicol) prism. The angle of rotation is read off on a divided circular brass scale, over which an arm attached to the eye-piece rotates (Fig. 11.VI B). The instrument is

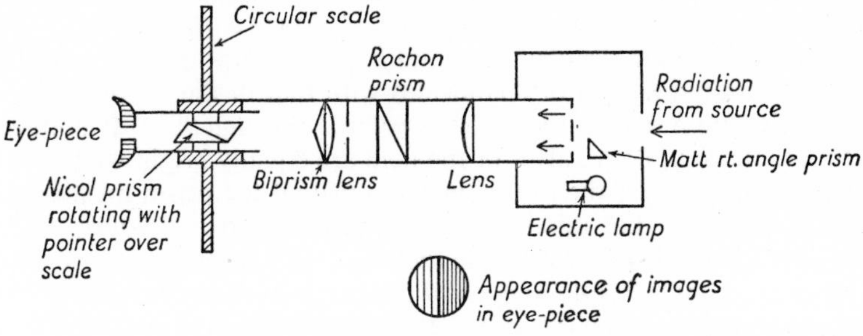

FIG. 11.VI B. Wanner Pyrometer

calibrated, and temperatures are read off from a table directly from the angle of rotation. Usually, the red part of the spectrum (0·656μ) is selected by a prism in the instrument.[3] The standard electric lamp must be carefully compared from time to time with a Hefner-Alteneck amyl acetate standard lamp to correct for errors due to the variations in the electric lamp filament.

[1] Wanner, *Ann. Phys.*, 1900, **2**, 141; *Phys. Z.*, 1900, **1**, 226; 1902, **3**, 112; Lummer and Pringsheim, *Verhl. d. D. Phys. Ges.*, 1901, **3**, 36; Hartmann, *Phys. Rev.*, 1904, **19**, 452; Holborn, *Engineering*, 1907, **84**, 345; Hildebrand, *Z. Elektrochem.*, 1908, **14**, 349; Shook, *Phys. Rev.*, 1910, **31**, 342; Fisher, *Met. Chem. Eng.*, 1913, **11**, 532; Henning, "Temperaturmessung," Brunswick, 1915, 177; Anon., *Iron Age*, 1917, **100**, 243; Griffiths and Schofield, *Trans. Faraday Soc.*, 1917, **13**, 222; Daeves, *Stahl u. Eisen*, 1922, **42**, 121; Hoffmann, *Z. Phys.*, 1926, **37**, 60; Brodhun and Hoffmann, *ibid.*, 1926, **37**, 137.

[2] *Ann. Phys.*, 1894, **53**, 785; Lummer and Brodhun, *Z. Instr.*, 1892, **12**, 132; Holborn and Valentiner, *Ann. Phys.*, 1901, **22**, 1; Gillette, *J. Phys. Chem.*, 1911, **15**, 213 (bibl.); Müller, *Ann. Phys.*, 1930, **7**, 9 (bibl.); Lewin, *Z. techn. Phys.*, 1932, **13**, 497 (micro-pyrometer). On photometry, Tudor, in Glazebrook, "Dict. of Applied Physics," 1923, **4**, 410; Gibson, *ibid.*, 1923, **4**, 737; for Carcel oil lamp, Violle, *Ann. Chim.*, 1884, **3**, 373; Rosa and Crittenden, *J. Wash. Acad.*, 1914, **4**, 280 (inaccurate); for Hefner-Alteneck standard amyl acetate lamp, Hefner-Alteneck, *Berlin Ber.*, 1902, 980; for standard lamps (Carcel, Hefner-Alteneck, Harcourt pentane), Anon., *Electr. Rev.*, 1898, **42**, 759; Violle, *Éclair. Élec.*, 1900, **24**, 420; Liebenthal, *J. Gasbeleucht.*, 1906, **49**, 559; Dow, *Elec. Rev.*, 1906, **59**, 491; Laporte and Jouaust, *Bull. Soc. Int. Élec.*, 1906, **6**, 375; Perot and Laporte, *Compt. Rend.*, 1906, **143**, 743; Hyde, *Bur. Stand. Bull.*, 1907, **3**, 65; Glazebrook, *Electrician*, 1908, **61**, 922; *Nature*, 1909, **80**, 374; Paterson, *Phil. Mag.*, 1909, **18**, 263; Rosa and Crittenden, *Trans. Illum. Eng. Soc.*, 1910, **5**, 753; *J. Wash. Acad.*, 1914, **4**, 280; *Bur. Stand. Bull.*, 1914, **10**, 557 (Hefner better than pentane); Butterfield, Haldane, and Trotter, *Illum. Eng.* (London), 1911, **4**, 509 (corrections for atm. press. and humidity); Gerlach, *Phys. Z.*, 1913, **14**, 577; 1921, **21**, 299 (total radiation from Hefner lamp); Coblentz, *Bur. Stand. Bull.*, 1914, **11**, 87; Crittenden and Taylor, *Bur. Stand. Bull.*, 1914, **10**, 391 (pentane lamp); Liebenthal, *Z. Instr.*, 1923, **43**, 209 (effect of atm. pressure on Hefner lamp); Brodhun, in Geiger and Scheel, "Handbuch der Physik," 1928, **19**, 478; on acetylene flame as standard, Violle, *Compt. Rend.*, 1895, **122**, 79; Féry, *ibid.*, 1898, **126**, 1192; on standards of illumination, Walsh, "Photometry," 1926, 126 (bibl., 62 refs.).

[3] Nernst and von Wartenberg, *Verhl. d. D. Phys. Ges.*, 1906, **8**, 48, 146, used the sodium line region, and calibrated against the m.p. of gold; the relation $I \propto \tan^2 \vartheta$ was only approximately true; cf. Henning, *Z. Elektrochem.*, 1924, **30**, 309, 396.

The standard light and that from the hot source pass through two circular apertures and then through a lens which makes both beams parallel. They then pass through a Rochon polarising prism and *each* is transmitted as two beams polarised at right angles. A biprism lens then splits each image into two semicircles, making a total of eight beams. From these beams six are screened off and two remain, one from each pair, which are polarised at right angles, and are in juxtaposition. These pass through a Nicol prism, eye-piece, and red glass screen, and by rotating the prism the beams are adjusted to equal intensity of the two semicircles in juxtaposition. If ϑ_1, ϑ_2 are the angles of rotation of the Nicol prism to produce equality of the standard with two plane polarised sources of intensities I_1, I_2, then $I_1/I_2=\tan^2\vartheta_1/\tan^2\vartheta_2$.

If the two sources are denoted by α and β, then α appears dark and β bright when the vibration direction of β coincides with that of the Nicol prism, and α appears bright and β dark if the prism is rotated through 90°. If both sources are of equal intensity, both halves of the field are equally bright when the prism is rotated through 45°; if the intensities are unequal the prism must be rotated through an angle ϑ. Let this be ϑ_1 with the standard and source α, and ϑ_2 with the standard and source β. The *amplitude* of β after passing through the Nicol prism at an angle ϑ is $A_\beta'=A_\beta\cos\vartheta$ (since it is 1 for $\vartheta=0$ and 0 for $\vartheta=90°$), and that of α is $A_\alpha'=A_\alpha\sin\vartheta$ (since it is 0 for $\vartheta=0$ and 1 for $\vartheta=90°$). Since the *intensities* are proportional to the squares of the amplitudes, $I_\beta'=I_\beta\cos^2\vartheta$ and $I_\alpha'=I_\alpha\sin^2\vartheta$. For equal brightness of the two halves of the field $I_\alpha'=I_\beta'$, therefore $I_\beta\cos^2\vartheta=I_\alpha\sin^2\vartheta$, or $I_\beta/I_\alpha=\tan^2\vartheta$. If α is the standard source, and β the variable source, then $I_{\beta_1}/I_{\beta_2}=\tan^2\vartheta_1/\tan^2\vartheta_2$, as stated.

For monochromatic radiation, Wien's formula gives:

$$I_1/I_2=e^{(c_2/\lambda)(1/T_2-1/T_1)}=\tan^2\vartheta_1/\tan^2\vartheta_2$$

$$\therefore\ 2(\ln\tan\vartheta_1-\ln\tan\vartheta_2)=(c_2/\lambda)(1/T_2-1/T_1)$$

$$\therefore\ \ln\tan\vartheta=a+b/T,$$

where a and b are constants.

From c_2, λ, and one value of ϑ corresponding with a known temperature T, the values of a and b can be found. Actually, the calibration is made against a black body over a range of temperature.

E.g. for the m.p. of gold ($T_1=1336$) $\vartheta_1=26{\cdot}6°$. After inserting a smoked glass screen of factor 147 the angle $\vartheta_2=28{\cdot}5°$ was found for the source. If the selected wave-length is the sodium line, $\lambda=5893$ A.$=5{\cdot}893\times10^{-5}$ cm., a reduction factor of 0·995 was necessary for standardisation with red light. Hence:

$$\log[\tan^2(0{\cdot}995\times28{\cdot}5°)\times147]-\log[\tan^2(0{\cdot}995\times26{\cdot}6°)]$$
$$=[1{\cdot}432/(5{\cdot}893\times10^{-5})]\times0{\cdot}4343(1/1336-1/T_2)\quad\therefore\ T_2=1865°\text{ K.}$$

Instead of taking a single wave-length λ, the formula may be considered to apply to the *total* brightness H of the visible spectrum with an average $\lambda=0{\cdot}6\mu=6\times10^{-5}$ cm. If $H_1=1$ is the standard brightness of the amyl acetate lamp and T_1 the corresponding black-body temperature, then: [1]

$$\ln H=(1{\cdot}432/6\times10^{-5})(1/T_1-1/T_2)=\alpha(1-T_1/T_2),$$

where α is a constant $=1{\cdot}432T_1/\lambda$.

[1] Rasch, *Ann. Phys.*, 1904, **14**, 193; Haber, "Thermodynamics of Technical Gas Reactions," 1908, 288; Griffiths, in Glazebrook, "Dict. of Applied Physics," 1922, **1**, 662.

On an absorbing wedge pyrometer, see Le Chatelier, *J. de Phys.*, 1892, **1**, 185; Féry, *ibid.*, 1904, **3**, 32; Le Chatelier and Boudouard, "High Temperature Measurements," transl. Burgess, New York, 1904, 208, used an adjustable aperture (" cat's eye ").

In taking the temperature of a *metal* surface, the Wanner pyrometer must be sighted on it normally, since light emitted at an angle to the normal is appreciably polarised.

Smoked glass of varying opacity may be prepared. Dufour [1] with a 72 cm.^{2} plate of glass found that 0·3 mg. of soot slightly darkened it, 4·9 mg. made it possible to view the sun through it, 14·5 mg. made it opaque to sunlight. If the density of soot is 1·4 these correspond with thicknesses of 0·0003, 0·0005 and 0·0014 mm. The absorption of glasses coloured with metallic oxides depends on the composition of the (colourless) glass.[2] Jena red glass (e.g. 4512) is often used.[3]

Naeser [4] isolated red and green light by filters and then re-combined them to form white light for comparison. Lindemann and Keeley [5] used a photo-electric-cell radiation pyrometer using two colour bands. Wensel and Roeser,[6] in finding the m.p. of nickel, compared the brightness of red light $\lambda=0{\cdot}6533\mu$ emitted by black-body cavities in freezing nickel and gold. Foote, Mohler, and Fairchild [7] pointed out that an absorbing glass for use with an optical pyrometer should follow the transmissivity formula $t=e^{ac_2\lambda}$, where c_2 is Wien's constant. This can be attained by combining black and coloured glasses. Rosengarten [8] found the transmissivity of glasses for the *infra-red* rays practically constant over the temperature range 40°–460°.

§ 17. Departure from Black-body Emission

One source of error in optical pyrometry is the departure of the radiating surface from a black-body state, to which the laws used apply. The emissivity of a surface is the ratio of the emissive power K to that of a black body for the same wave-length and temperature, and if the emissivity differs appreciably from unity the apparent temperature shown by an optical pyrometer (the so-called *brightness temperature*) is not the same as the true temperature, the difference being greater for bright metallic or white surfaces of good reflective power.

Crova [9] tried to find the wave-length for which the brightness ratio was equal to the intensity ratio. Violle [10] found that the intensity of radiation from platinum up to its m.p. was given by:

$$I=mTb^{T^2}a^T \quad . \quad . \quad . \quad . \quad . \quad . \quad . \quad . \quad . \quad (1)$$

[1] *Arch. Sci. Phys. Nat.*, 1896, **1**, 220.

[2] Zsigmondy, *Ann. Phys.*, 1901, **4**, 60; Rasch, *Ann. Phys.*, 1904, **14**, 193; Pirani, *Verhl. d. D. Phys. Ges.*, 1913, **15**, 826; Pirani and Loebe, *ibid.*, 1915, **17**, 47; Fedotieff and Lebedeff, *Z. anorg. Chem.*, 1924, **134**, 87; Brode, *J.A.C.S.*, 1933, **55**, 939 (Co glass).

[3] Peychès, *J. de Phys.*, 1932, **3**, 486.

[4] *Stahl u. Eisen*, 1929, **49**, 464.

[5] *Proc. Phys. Soc.*, 1925, **38**, 69; Barber, *J. Iron Steel Inst.*, 1945, **42**, 171; Lund, *J. Sci. Instr.*, 1947, **24**, 95.

[6] *Bur. Stand. J. Res.*, 1930, **5**, 1309; for platinum m.p. 1772° by a similar method, see Hoffmann, *Z. Phys.*, 1924, **27**, 285.

[7] *J. Wash. Acad.*, 1917, **7**, 545.

[8] *Phys. Rev.*, 1920, **16**, 173; for transmissivity of substances, including coloured glasses, see Coblentz, Emerson, and Long, *Bur. Stand. Bull.*, 1919, **14**, 653; Forsythe, *J. Opt. Soc. Amer.*, 1921, **5**, 85 (colour glass screens for pyrometry); 1925, **10**, 19 (absorbing screens); transmissivity of red glass, Hyde, Cady, and Forsythe, *Astrophys. J.*, 1915, **42**, 294; *Phys. Rev.*, 1915, **6**, 70; on coloured glasses, Weyl, *J. Soc. Glass Techn.*, 1943, **27**, 133, 265; 1944, **28** 158, 267, 276; 1945, **29**, 289; 1946, **30**, 91; glasses absorbing ultraviolet, Crookes, *Phil. Trans.*, 1914, **214**, 1.

[9] *Compt. Rend.*, 1881, **93**, 512; Rasch, *Ann. Phys.*, 1904, **14**, 193; Foote, *Bur. Stand. Bull.*, 1916, **12**, 483; Foote and Fairchild, *ibid.*, 1916, **13**, 137.

[10] *Compt. Rend.*, 1881, **92**, 866, 1204; *Ann. Chim.*, 1884, **3**, 373; *J. de Phys.*, 1888, **7**, 193; *Phil. Mag.*, 1884, **17**, 563 (abstr.).

where $b=0{\cdot}9999938$, $a=1{\cdot}03550-13\lambda$ (λ=wave-length in mm.), and m=constant. From molten platinum the radiation was nearly a thousand times that from molten silver. Violle adopted the radiation from 1 cm.[2] of liquid platinum at its freezing-point as a standard of brightness.

A modification of Wien's formula, (1), § 11:

$$I_\lambda=C_1'\lambda^{-a}e^{-c_2'/\lambda T} \quad . \quad . \quad . \quad . \quad . \quad . \quad . \quad . \quad . \quad (2)$$

has been used [1] to represent the energy distribution in radiation from metals. For platinum, Paschen found $a=6{\cdot}4$, and Lummer and Pringsheim 6·0, while McCauley could not find any constant value of a which satisfied (2), or a modified Planck's equation (3), § 11:

$$I_\lambda=C_1\lambda^{-a}/(e^{c_2'/\lambda T}-1) \quad . \quad . \quad . \quad . \quad . \quad . \quad . \quad . \quad (3)$$

If e is the total emissivity of an approximately non-selective surface at temperature T, and S is the apparent temperature observed with a total radiation pyrometer, then (§ 9):

$$E=\sigma(S^4-T_0^4)=e\sigma(T^4-T_0^4)$$

where σ is Stefan's constant. Thus:

$$e=(S^4-T_0^4)/(T^4-T_0^4)\simeq(S/T)^4 \quad . \quad . \quad . \quad . \quad . \quad . \quad . \quad (4)$$

above 600°, when the term in T_0 can be omitted. Actually, an arbitrary coefficient b should replace 4.

Del Regno [2] determined the emissivity of bismuth and nickel; for nickel (344°–643°), $E=kT^n$, where $n=4{\cdot}588\pm0{\cdot}031$, in agreement with values found by Suydam (4·648), Schmidt and Futhermann (4·81) and Barnes (4·77). The emissivities of gold and copper undergo discontinuous change at the melting point.[3] The average emissivities of some solid surfaces for radiation of $\lambda=0{\cdot}65\mu$ as fractions of the black-body emissivity are given below.[4] The figures for liquid surfaces are approximately the same.

Carbon, 0·85	Iridium, 0·3	Nickel, 0·35	Rhodium, 0·3
Copper, 0·1	Iron, 0·35	Nickel, oxidised, 0·9	Silver, 0·1
Copper, oxidised, 0·7	Iron, oxidised, 0·95	Palladium, 0·35	Slag (average), 0·65
Gold, 0·15	Nichrome, 0·9	Platinum, 0·35	Thoria, 0·6
			Tungsten, 0·45

Johnston and Marshall [5] found that radiation from a 0·6–1·2 mm. drilling in nickel was black-body radiation up to high temperatures; that from a 1·8 mm.

[1] McCauley, *Astrophys. J.*, 1913, **37**, 164; Henning, "Temperaturmessung," Brunswick, 1915, 187; Foote and Fairchild, *J. Wash. Acad.*, 1916, **6**, 193; Foote, *ibid.*, 1916, **6**, 317, 323; Forsythe, *Phys. Rev.*, 1917, **10**, 395; Hyde, *Gen. Elec. Rev.*, 1917, **20**, 819; Griffiths, in Glazebrook, "Dict. of Applied Physics," 1922, **1**, 655, for further details of the distribution of energy in radiation from metals, and correction to black-body temperature, for metals, oxides, etc. For Nernst filaments, see Kurlbaum and Günther-Schulze, *Verhl. d. D. Phys. Ges.*, 1903, **5**, 428. On emissibilities see Coblentz, *Bur. Stand. Bull.*, 1911, **7**, 243; 1913, **9**, 81 (metals, oxides, etc.; dependence on thickness); Hyde, *Astrophys. J.*, 1912, **36**, 89 (metals); Randolph and Overholser, *Phys. Rev.*, 1913, **2**, 144 (oxidised metals); Bidwell, *ibid.*, 1914, **3**, 439 (metals at 700°–1700°); Burgess and Foote, *Bur. Stand. Bull.*, 1914, **11**, 41 (iron and nickel oxides); Foote, *ibid.*, 1915, **11**, 607 (platinum); Hulbert, *J. Franklin Inst.*, 1916, **182**, 695 (tungsten); Worthing, *Phys. Rev.*, 1917, **10**, 377 (tungsten); *idem*, in "Temperature. Its Measurement and Control," New York, 1941, 1165; Zwikker, *Physica*, 1925, **5**, 249, 319 (tungsten); 1927, **7**, 71 (molybdenum); Polak, *Z. techn. Phys.*, 1927, **8**, 307; Ornstein, *Physica*, 1936, **3**, 561 (tungsten); Price, *Nature*, 1946, **157**, 765; *Proc. Phys. Soc.*, 1947, **59**, 118, 131; Weil, *ibid.*, 1947, **59**, 781.

[2] *Atti R. Accad. Lincei*, 1929, **10**, 77 (Bi); 1930, **11**, 989 (Ni).

[3] Stubbs and Prideaux, *Proc. Roy. Soc.*, 1912, **87**, 451; Stubbs, *ibid.*, 1913, **88**, 195.

[4] Kaye and Laby, "Tables of Physical and Chemical Constants," 10th edit., 1948, 62.

[5] *J.A.C.S.*, 1940, **62**, 1382.

drilling was less than black-body radiation at 1100°, and at 1600° the apparent temperature was 20° in error. The total emissive power of nickel [1] is proportional to $T^{4\cdot45}$ below the Curie point and $T^{5\cdot15}$ above it; the maximum of emissive power lies above the Curie point at $\lambda_m T^{0\cdot78}=0\cdot060$ and its height is proportional to $T^{5\cdot86}$.

The total radiation at 1000°–2000° from Nernst mass (for Nernst lamp rods) and uranium oxide (U_3O_8) was measured by Wiegand,[2] who pointed out that oxides of high emissivity are good conductors of electricity. Hagen and Rubens [3] found good agreement with metals with a formula deduced by Planck:[4] $E'=36\cdot5\sqrt{(\sigma/\lambda)}$, where E'=ratio of emissivity to that of a black-body taken as 100, σ=electric conductivity in ohm^{-1} for a rod 1 m. long and 1 mm.^{2} section, λ=wave-length in μ. Deviations from the Hagen-Rubens equation were found in the far infra-red by Ornstein [5] and Price; [6] the latter found that, for a given wave-length characteristic of each metal, the emissivity and reflectivity are constant over a wide range of temperature. A more accurate equation used by Hagen and Rubens is: [7]

$$E'=0\cdot365(\sigma/\lambda)^{1/2}-0\cdot0667(\sigma/\lambda)+0\cdot0091(\sigma/\lambda)^{3/2} \quad . \quad . \quad . \quad (5)$$

where σ is the specific electric conductivity.

Petavel [8] found for the total heat loss per cm.^{2} per sec. from platinum in gases at high pressure:

$$E=ap^{\alpha}+bp^{\beta}\vartheta \quad . \quad . \quad . \quad . \quad . \quad . \quad . \quad . \quad (6)$$

where p=pressure in atm., ϑ=temperature difference, and a, b, α, β are constants.

Foote [9] defined the "colour temperature," T', of a non-black body by the emissivity equation:

$$E=E'e^{c_2p/\lambda}e^{q/T} \quad . \quad . \quad . \quad . \quad . \quad . \quad . \quad . \quad . \quad . \quad (7)$$

where E', p, and q are constants and $1/T=1/T'+p$. The colour temperature is the temperature at which the ratio of intensities in the radiation from a given body is the same as the ratio of intensities for the same two wave-lengths in the radiation from a black body; it is larger than the true temperature.[10] The change of colour-scale temperature as a function of temperature was discussed by Judd.[11] The "brightness scale" depends on the use of the colour temperature, and if T' is the colour temperature at a wave-length λ and e_λ is the emissivity of the non-black body, at the same wave-length, then: [12]

$$1/T=1/T'+(\lambda/c_2)\ln e_\lambda \quad . \quad . \quad . \quad . \quad . \quad . \quad . \quad (8)$$

The brightness temperatures for $\lambda=6\cdot65\times10^{-5}$ corresponding with the true temperature of 1400° for some metals are: [13] W 1330°, Mo 1316°, Ni 1315°, Pt

1 Cennamo, *Nuov. Cim.*, 1941, **18**, 19.
2 *Z. Phys.*, 1924, **30**, 40.
3 *Berlin Ber.*, 1903, 269; 1909, 478; Foote, *J. Wash. Acad.*, 1915, **5**, 1; Hase, *Z. Phys.*, 1923, **15**, 54.
4 *Berlin Ber.*, 1903, 278.
5 *Physica*, 1936, **3**, 561.
6 *Nature*, 1946, **157**, 765; *Proc. Phys. Soc.*, 1947, **59**, 118, 131.
7 Henning, *Jahrb. Radioakt. Elektronik*, 1920, **17**, 30.
8 *Phil. Trans.*, 1901, **197**, 229.
9 *J. Wash. Acad.*, 1916, **6**, 193, 317, 323.
10 Hyde, Cady, and Forsythe, *J. Franklin Inst.*, 1916, **181**, 418 (carbon and tungsten); *Phys. Z.*, 1917, **10**, 395.
11 *J. Opt. Soc. Amer.*, 1933, **23**, 7.
12 Hyde, in "Pyrometry Sympos. Vol.," Amer. Inst. Min. and Met. Eng., New York, 1920, 285; Worthing, *ibid.*, 367.
13 Forsythe, *Phys. Rev.*, 1931, **38**, 1247; *idem* in "Internat. Crit. Tables," 1929, **5**, 238, 245; Caldin, *Proc. Phys. Soc.*, 1945, **57**, 440.

1296°. In all cases, the total emissive power approaches that of a black body at very high temperatures.

The Féry total radiation pyrometer is most affected by deviation from Stefan's law. By way of correction, the reflecting power can be measured [1] or other methods used.[2] Lummer [3] assumed a law of total emissive power (all wave-lengths) $E=\sigma' T^n$ similar to Stefan's and determined σ' and n empirically, but this formula holds only over a limited range of T. Helfgott [4] modified Stefan's law by multiplication by a factor $(1-e^{-\alpha T})$, where α is an empirical constant:

$$E=(1-e^{-\alpha T})\sigma T^4 \simeq k\sigma T^5 \quad . \quad . \quad . \quad . \quad . \quad . \quad . \quad (9)$$

and this holds for many metals. The true and apparent temperatures for tungsten filaments have been carefully investigated,[5] and a tungsten lamp can be used as a temperature standard. Schumacher [6] corrected the temperature of a tungsten strip up to 2500° C. by the formula:

$$1/T-1/T_{\text{obs.}}=(\lambda/c_2)(\ln e_\lambda+\ln A) \quad . \quad . \quad . \quad . \quad . \quad (10)$$

where λ is the wave-length in μ, e_λ the spectral emissivity for tungsten for wave-length λ and temperature T, A is the transmission coefficient, 0·92 for tungsten, and c_2 is Wien's constant, 14,330.

The optical temperatures of a blackened quartz vessel were investigated by Ruff and Mugdan.[7] There are also likely to be small differences in temperature between the surface and interior of a radiating body unless this is in a constant temperature enclosure,[8] but these are appreciable only at relatively low temperatures. The use of band spectra in measuring high temperatures was discussed by Knauss and McKay.[9]

§ 18 Flame Temperatures

Wedgwood [10] found that air at such a high temperature that it raised gold foil to bright redness did not itself emit any light. Iodine vapour becomes luminous

[1] Holborn and Henning, *Berlin Ber.*, 1905, 311; Coblentz, *Bur. Stand. Bull.*, 1920, **16**, 249; Henning, *Z. Elektrochem.*, 1924, **30**, 309, 396; Zwikker, *Physica*, 1925, **5**, 249, 319; Mendhousse, *Ann. de Phys.*, 1931, **16**, 209; Ackerlein, *Z. techn. Phys.*, 1929, **10**, 129, described the correction of optical temperature when the reflecting power of an object in a furnace is known; for reflectivity of incandescent tungsten, Weniger and Pfund, *Phys. Rev.*, 1919, **14**, 427.

[2] Pirani, *Verhl. d. D. Phys. Ges.*, 1910, **12**, 301, 1054; 1911, **13**, 19; and ref. 13, p. 495.

[3] *Elektrotechn. Z.*, 1902, **23**, 787, 806; Rasch, *Ann. Phys.*, 1904, **14**, 193; Suydam, *Phys. Rev.*, 1915, **5**, 497; Utterback, *ibid.*, 1929, **34**, 785.

[4] *Z. Phys.*, 1928, **49**, 555.

[5] Langmuir, *Phys. Rev.*, 1913, **2**, 329; Langmuir and Mackay, *ibid.*, 1914, **4**, 377; Langmuir, *ibid.*, 1915, **6**, 138; 1916, **7**, 302; Worthing, *ibid.*, 1917, **10**, 377; Hyde, *Gen. Elec. Rev.*, 1917, **20**, 819; Hyde, Cady, and Forsythe, *Phys. Rev.*, 1917, **10**, 395; Nutting, *J. Opt. Soc. Amer.*, 1923, **7**, 399; Lax and Pirani, *Z. Phys.*, 1924, **22**, 275; Forsythe and Worthing, *Astrophys. J.*, 1925, **61**, 146; Jones, *Phys. Rev.*, 1926, **28**, 203; Griffiths, "Pyrometry with Notes on Electric Furnaces," 1926, 100 (standard tungsten lamp); Zwikker, *Proc. K. Akad. Wetens. Amsterdam*, 1926, **29**, 792; Jones and Langmuir, *Gen. Elec. Rev.*, 1927, **30**, 310, 354, 408; Langmuir, MacLane, and Blodgett, *Phys. Rev.*, 1930, **35**, 478; Djoudat, *Rev. Opt.*, 1937, **16**, 401; Estey, *J. Opt. Soc. Amer.*, 1938, **28**, 293; Reiman, *Phil. Mag.*, 1938, **25**, 834; Brinkman, Rutgers, and De Vos, *Rev. Opt.*, 1948, **27**, 426; on a supposed difference between true and black-body temperatures of metals, see Pirani, *Verhl. d. D. Phys. Ges.*, 1910, **12**, 301, 1054; 1911, **13**, 19; Mendenhall, *Astrophys. J.*, 1911, **33**, 91.

[6] *J.A.C.S.*, 1926, **48**, 396; Walsh, "Photometry," 1926, 137; Ure and Tolman, *J.A.C.S.*, 1929, **51**, 974; Wensel, Judd, and Roeser, *Bur. Stand. J. Res.*, 1934, **12**, 527; Garelli, *Nuov. Cim.*, 1943, **1**, 101.

[7] *Z. anorg. Chem.*, 1921, **116**, 147.

[8] Kurlbaum, *Ann. Phys.*, 1900, **2**, 546.

[9] *Phys. Rev.*, 1937, **52**, 1143.

[10] *Phil. Trans.*, 1792, **82**, 270; abridged edit., 1809, **17**, 215; Smithells, *Phil. Mag.*, 1894, **37**, 245.

below the temperature at which glass shows a red heat.[1] Pringsheim [2] supposed that the emission of light by vapours of salts in a flame is due to chemical action; he obtained " cool flames." Nernst [3] found that radiation from hot gases is considerable, and obeys Stefan's law. The determination of the temperatures of flames is a special branch of high-temperature study.[4] Of various methods, mention may be made of the use of:

(i) wire resistance thermometers in the flame,[5] with suitable correction for heat loss;

(ii) platinum and platinum-rhodium thermocouples, with extrapolation to zero thickness of wire or other correction for heat loss; [6]

(iii) temperature of reversal of sodium lines; a flame coloured with sodium vapour is placed between an incandescent body and a spectroscope, and the bright sodium lines change to dark lines when the temperature of the incandescent body passes upwards through the temperature of the flame.[7]

Some values of flame temperatures quoted (in ° C.) are:

Bunsen, fully aerated ...	1871°	Acetylene flame	2548° (1937°) [8]
„ insufficient air ...	1812°	Oxy-coal gas blowpipe ...	2200°
„ alcohol	1862°	Oxy-hydrogen blowpipe ...	2420°
Alcohol flame	1705°	Oxy-acetylene explosion [9]	3000°–4000°
Hydrogen flame in air ...	1900°		

[1] Salet, *Compt. Rend.*, 1872, **74**, 1249; *Ann. Phys.*, 1872, **147**, 319.

[2] *Ann. Phys.*, 1892, **45**, 428; 1893, **49**, 347; 1894, **51**, 441; Paschen, *ibid.*, 1893, **50**, 408; 1894, **51**, 1, 40; 1894, **52**, 209. According to Bonhoeffer, *Z. Elektrochem.*, 1936, **42**, 448, chemiluminescence is generally negligible.

[3] *Phys. Z.*, 1904, **5**, 777; *Z. phys. Chem.*, 1905, **53**, 124.

[4] Haber, " Thermodynamics of Technical Gas Reactions," 1908, 279; Amerio, *Atti. Accad. Torino*, 1906, **41**, 328, 1054 (black-body radiation); Bauer, *Compt. Rend.*, 1909, **148**, 908, 1756 (radiation); *Le Radium*, 1909, **6**, 110, 360; *Ann. Chim.*, 1913, **29**, 5, 244, 372; Schwarz, *Chaleur et Ind.*, 1926, **7**, 613; Henning and Tingwaldt, *Z. Phys.*, 1928, **48**, 805 (C_2H_2 3100°); Ellis and Morgan, *Trans. Faraday Soc.*, 1932, **28**, 826; Lewis, Seaman, and Jones, *J. Franklin Inst.*, 1933, **215**, 149 (mixtures; cf. Payman, *J.C.S.*, 1919, **115**, 1446); Brevoort, *Rev. Sci. Instr.*, 1936, **7**, 342; Lewis and von Elbe, " Combustion, Flame, and Explosion in Gases," Cambridge, 1938; *idem*, in " Temperature. Its Measurement and Control," New York, 1941, 707; Jost, " Explosions- und Verbrennungsvorgänge in Gasen," Berlin, 1939; Ribaud and Laure, *Rev. Opt.*, 1940, **19**, 123, 220.

[5] Nichols, *Phys. Rev.*, 1900, **10**, 234 (C_2H_2 1900°); Hopkinson, *Proc. Roy. Soc.*, 1906, **77**, 387; David and Jordan, *Phil. Mag.*, 1934, **18**, 238; David, *ibid.*, 1935, **20**, 65; *Engineer*, 1941, **172**, 186.

[6] Waggener, *Ann. Phys.*, 1896, **58**, 579; Berkenbusch, *ibid.*, 1899, **67**, 649; Nichols, *J. Franklin Inst.*, 1900, **150**, 356 (374); White and Traver, *J.S.C.I.*, 1902, **21**, 1012; Baikov, *Chem. Ztg.*, 1904, **28**, 1107; Haber and Richardt, *Z. anorg. Chem.*, 1904, **38**, 5; Haber, " Thermodynamics of Technical Gas Reactions," 1908, 292; Ellis, *Photogr. J.*, 1935, **75**, 482.

[7] Kurlbaum, *Phys. Z.*, 1902, **3**, 332; Féry, *Compt. Rend.*, 1903, **137**, 909; Loomis and Perrott, *Ind. Eng. Chem.*, 1928, **20**, 1004; Griffiths and Awbery, *Gas J.*, 1928, **183**, 596; *Gas World*, 1928, **89**, 261; *Proc. Roy. Soc.*, 1929, **123**, 401; Jones, Lewis, Friauf, and Perrott, *J.A.C.S.*, 1931, **53**, 3992; Lewis and von Elbe, *Phil. Mag.*, 1935, **20**, 44; " Combustion, Flame, and Explosion in Gases," Oxford, 1938, 399; *J. Appl. Phys.*, 1940, **11**, 698; Ribaud, *Compt. Rend.*, 1937, **205**, 901; *Chaleur et Ind.*, 1937, **18**, 235, 295; Kinosita and Kenzi, *Proc. Phys. Math. Soc. Japan*, 1941, **23**, 646; on flame temperatures calculated from heats of combustion, see Goodenough and Felbeck, *Bull. Univ. Illinois Eng. Expt. Station*, 1924, **139**; Coheur, *Rev. Univers. Mines*, 1938, 650; David, *Engineer*, 1941, **172**, 186, says the method gives too high values.

[8] Heinrich, *Phys. Z.*, 1926, **27**, 287.

[9] Klibanov, *Amer. Chem. Abstr.*, 1943, **37**, 2974, found 3128°–3200°.

The temperature of the electric arc is estimated [1] as about 3500° and of the sun [2] as 6000°.

Loomis and Perrott [3] compared the brightness of an electrically heated tungsten band with that of a flame charged with sodium vapour. Schack [4] found that the optical temperature of the carbon particles in a luminous hydrocarbon flame was practically equal to the flame temperature. Senftleben and Benedict [5] determined optically the temperature of a thin gold or platinum wire heated in the flame. Lochte-Holtgreven and Maecker [6] gave the carbon arc temperature as 7600°, and said it can reach 8700° with over-run arcs. Zel'dovich and Leipunsky [7] estimated that temperatures of 30,000° K. and 43,000° K., respectively, are attained in mercury vapour compressed by powerful shock-waves produced by shooting into it projectiles with speeds of 2500 m./sec. and 3000 m./sec. Alentsev, Belyaev, Sobolev, and Stepanov [8] by optical (luminosity) methods found the explosion temperatures for liquids and solids of the order of 3000° K. The temperatures attained in nuclear fission (" atomic bomb ") are supposed to be extraordinarily high.[9]

§ 19. High-temperature Melting-points

Several methods have been used in determining melting-points at temperatures above 500°, when the usual methods are no longer applicable.[10]

(1) *Change of form methods.*—In these, a piece of the solid is heated until it flows, and when this is perceived visually the temperature is taken. In the case of metals, a coherent oxide film may hold the melted metal in its original form, or the metal may sublime through the film, as was found by Arndt [11] with calcium and magnesium, respectively. He found the m.p. of calcium by placing a piece of the metal over a slit in a sheet of iron, putting a 5 g. iron cylinder over the calcium, and heating in an evacuated porcelain tube in a vertical platinum-wound tube furnace, the upper end of the tube having a glass window; when the calcium melted, the iron weight was seen to fall, and the temperature was determined by a thermocouple, protected by a thin porcelain tube, below the plate.

Day and Allen [12] heated long, thin splinters of felspars resting horizontally in small platinum crucibles, but found that even after three hours at 1225° they had not sagged, although on cooling they were found to have been fused; in this

1 Waidner and Burgess, *Phys. Rev.*, 1904, **19**, 241; von Engel and Steenbeck, *Naturwiss.*, 1931, **19**, 212, found the arc temperature 2827°–4977°; Barbanti-Silva and Ligabu, *Nuov. Cim.*, 1941, **18**, 361, gave 4200°–5000°; Mannikopff, *Z. Phys.*, 1943, **120**, 228, calculated the arc temperature in air as 7000° K.

2 Stheiner, " Strahlung und Temperatur der Sonne," Leipzig, 1899 (5400°–6200°); Rosenberg, in Geiger and Scheel, " Handbuch der Physik," 1928, **19**, 50 (6000°). The radiation from the sun is estimated as $5{\cdot}9 \times 10^{27}$ g.cal. per minute.

3 *Ind. Eng. Chem.*, 1928, **20**, 1004.

4 *Z. techn. Phys.*, 1925, **6**, 530.

5 *Phys. Z.*, 1918, **19**, 180.

6 *Z. Phys.*, 1937, **105**, 1; Griffith, *B.A. Rep.*, 1923, 430, mentioned 8600° K. for an arc in gas at 80 atm. pressure.

7 *J. Exptl. Theor. Phys., U.S.S.R.*, 1943, **13**, 181; *J. Phys. U.S.S.R.*, 1943, **7**, 245.

8 *J. Exptl. Theor. Phys. U.S.S.R.*, 1946, **16**, 990.

9 Smythe, *Rev. Mod. Phys.*, 1945, **17**, 351.

10 Arndt, " Phys.-chem. Technik," 2nd edit., 1923, 372 f.; Dana and Foote, *Chem. Met. Eng.*, 1920, **22**, 23, 63 (tables of m.ps. metals, oxides, salts, refractories, and bibl.); Mendhousse, *Ann. de Phys.*, 1931, **16**, 209.

11 *Ber.*, 1904, **37**, 4733.

12 *Z. phys. Chem.*, 1906, **54**, 1 (32).

case the liquid has a very high viscosity. The m.p. was found by holding the temperature near the supposed m.p. for a long time, then taking the crucible rapidly from the furnace and finding, by the glassy appearance and by the lack of crystalline structure shown by a polarising microscope, if the solid had been fused. Doelter [1] used a crystallographic microscope, with a water-cooled objective focused on the substance supported on a small quartz tray in a small platinum-wound vertical tube furnace (15 mm. wide tube) below the microscope objective, and closed above by a quartz window. The temperature was determined by a thermocouple below the quartz tray. The measurements could go up to 1380°. Mendenhall and Ingersoll [2] observed the fusion of small beads of rhodium and iridium put on a glowing Nernst mass, calibrating with beads of gold and platinum, and determining the temperature optically.

(2) *Flow methods.*—Waidner and Burgess [3] heated about 1 mg. of powdered substance on a strip of platinum foil 6 cm. long, 4 mm. wide, and 0·02 mm. thick, heated by an electric current, and observed this through a microscope. When the substance was seen to melt, a second observer read the temperature of the strip by an optical pyrometer, a correction to black-body temperature being applied. To prevent oxidation, Burgess [4] enclosed the strip in an inclined tube with a mica window, and passed dry hydrogen free from oxygen through the tube (Fig. 12.VI B). The observation microscope M and disappearing filament pyrometer T were sighted on the incandescent strip S through the window. A fresh strip was used for each experiment. The m.ps. of several metals were found, the pyrometer being calibrated by the m.p. of platinum taken as 1753°. The accuracy was estimated at 5°, but the values for nickel and cobalt were too low, probably on account of some alloying with the platinum.

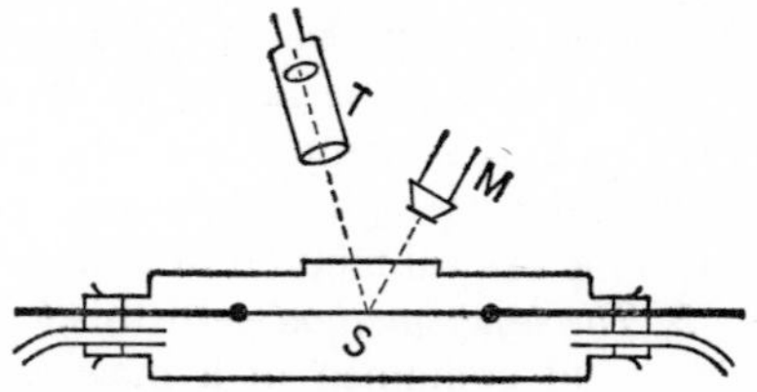

FIG. 12.VI B. Burgess Melting-point Apparatus

Von Wartenberg [5] heated an agglomerated rod of tungsten, supported on a magnesia crucible fixed to the end of an iron tube, and made the anode, in a vacuous vessel, by bombardment with cathode-rays from a strip of platinum foil covered with alkaline earth oxides and heated electrically (Wehnelt cathode). The temperature of the tungsten was observed electrically through the window by a Wanner pyrometer; the moment of fusion could be seen in the pyrometer. With Wien's constant c_2=14,370, the m.p. of tungsten was 2970°.

Pirani and Meyer,[6] by using a mercury arc for heating the tungsten, found 3100°–3205°; Langmuir,[7] by measuring the brightness of the surfaces of tungsten electrodes in an atmosphere of nitrogen when one electrode fused in an alternating current arc between them, found 3270°. The metal used by earlier workers may have contained carbon.

(3) *Electrical contact method.*—A platinum wire is covered with powdered material which is an insulator and is immersed in mercury. The wire and mercury are made parts of an electrical circuit including a bell. The mercury

1 *Wien Ber.*, 1906, **115**, I, 1329; *Z. Elektrochem.*, 1906, **12**, 617.
2 *Phys. Rev.*, 1907, **25**, 1.
3 *Phys. Rev.*, 1906, **22**, 359 (abstr.).
4 *Bur. Stand. Bull.*, 1907, **3**, 345.
5 *Ber.*, 1907, **40**, 3287; *Verhl. d. D. Phys. Ges.*, 1910, **12**, 121 (reflexion coeff. of W).
6 *Verhl. d. D. Phys. Ges.*, 1912, **14**, 426.
7 *Phys. Rev.*, 1915, **6**, 138.

is heated, and when the substance melts the platinum and mercury make contact, a current passes, and the bell rings; then the temperature of the mercury is taken.[1] This method has been little used, but seems capable of improvement, with the use of a fusible metal bath.

(4) *The wire method.*—This method has often been used in various forms.[2] In one, two platinum wires are soldered with a piece of gold and put in circuit with a galvanometer; when the gold melts the current is interrupted and the temperature is read by a thermocouple with the hot junction near the gold. In another method, a piece of gold is used to solder the junction of a platinum metal thermocouple; on heating slowly in the furnace there is an arrest in the e.m.f. because the temperature is constant when the gold is melting, and the thermocouple reading gives the m.p. directly. In another method, the melting of an electrically heated wire is observed visually.

Forsythe used the wire method to find the m.p. of tungsten, a 0·014 mm. wire being heated electrically in a vacuum carbon tube furnace, the temperature of the outside of the carbon tube being found optically by a pyrometer, and the fusion of the wire being indicated by an electric bell and relay. Pirani and Meyer observed the fusion of an electrically heated wire or band of tungsten visually, and Langmuir used the method with tungsten. In the case of oxidisable metals, a high vacuum or inert atmosphere is necessary, and with thin wires the optical method of determining temperature is difficult.

5. *The lever method.*—In this,[3] a metal or other rod rests on the surface of the metal contained in a magnesia or other crucible, under a flux, and the rod, which is suitably weighted, is connected with a lever arm carrying a pointer moving over a scale. When the metal melts, the rod sinks in it and the pointer moves. The temperature is then read by a thermocouple in the crucible.[4] The rod may rest on the solid flux, when two movements are seen, the first due to the melting of the flux and the second to the melting of the metal.

6. *The cooling curve method.*—This gives the freezing-point. A relatively large amount of material is fused in a crucible suitably protected from the atmosphere, and a thermocouple is immersed in the melt. On slow cooling, the temperature sinks regularly until solidification begins, when there is an arrest, due to the evolution of the latent heat of fusion. Usually the liquid supercools, and on solidification the temperature runs up to the freezing-point, and then remains constant. Porcelain, platinum, graphite, or magnesia crucibles are used, or a graphite crucible " brasqued " inside with a magnesia lining. The metal is protected from oxidation by a flux, a layer of carbon, or an inert

[1] Löwe, *Dingl. J.*, 1871, **201**, 250; cf. Washburn and Smith, *Bur. Stand. J. Res.*, 1929, **2**, 787.

[2] Holborn and Wien, *Ann. Phys.*, 1892, **47**, 107 (132); Holborn and Day, *ibid.*, 1900, **2**, 505; 1901, **4**, 99; Holborn and Henning, *Berlin Ber.*, 1905, 311; Harker, *Proc. Roy. Soc.*, 1905, **76**, 235; Nernst and von Wartenberg, *Verhl. d. D. Phys. Ges.*, 1906, **8**, 48; Shukov and Kurbatov, *J. Russ. Phys. Chem. Soc.*, 1907, **39**, 1546 (C); Holborn and Valentiner, *Ann. Phys.*, 1907, **22**, 1; Loebe, *Z. Elektrochem.*, 1907, **13**, 592; Biltz, *Z. anorg. Chem.*, 1908, **59**, 273; Sosman, *Amer. J. Sci.*, 1910, **29**, 93; 1910, **30**, 1; Forsythe, *Astrophys. J.*, 1911, **34**, 353; Pirani and Meyer, *Verhl. d. D. Phys. Ges.*, 1912, **14**, 426; Langmuir, *Phys. Rev.*, 1915, **6**, 138; Ornstein, Vermeulen, and Wouda, *Proc. K. Akad. Wetens. Amsterdam*, 1930, **33**, 985; Mendhousse, *Ann. de Phys.*, 1931, **16**, 209.

[3] Holborn and Day, *Ann. Phys.*, 1900, **2**, 505; Muthmann and Weiss, *Ann.*, 1904, **331**, 1.

[4] See also Stock, *Ber.*, 1917, **50**, 156; Wick and Barchfeld, *Chem. Fabr.*, 1928, **1**, 281. A similar method was used at very low temperatures by Travers and Jaquerod, *Z. phys. Chem.*, 1903, **45**, 449, to find the m.p. of hydrogen. A glass rod dipped into liquid hydrogen in a tube and had an iron spiral at the upper end. As long as the hydrogen was liquid, the rod could be drawn out by a solenoid round the iron, but when it solidified the rod was held fast in the solid.

gas atmosphere. The method has often been used for metals.[1] The thermocouple junction in the metal must then be suitably protected, e.g. by narrow unglazed porcelain or quartz tubes.

The method may also be used for salts (which may supercool strongly), when the thermocouple can generally be used unprotected. On account of the poor thermal conductivity of salts, the rate of cooling must be very slow, and a fairly large quantity must be used. The method has been used in the Geophysical Laboratory, Washington, for the determination of the melting-points of silicates.[2] In this case, the poor thermal conductivity and small velocity of crystallisation make the determination difficult. The arrest in the heating curve is then more suitable than that in the cooling curve, whilst for metals the opposite is true. Two types of crucible were used, one holding about 100 c.c. and the other only about 1 c.c., each having some advantages and disadvantages. The sources of error were discussed by White.

7. *Black-body methods.*—These make use of the principle that a cavity pierced by a small hole emits radiation practically identical with that which would be emitted by a perfectly black body at the same temperature, and if bodies inside the cavity are at the same temperature as the cavity they cannot be seen on looking into it through the hole.[3] Such a cavity has been used in determining melting-points of metals, usually in the form of wires, an electrically heated carbon tube being used, or concentric porcelain tubes with diaphragms and heated electrically by windings of platinum strip.[4] Other optical methods of determining melting-points involve the optical observation of a small hollow sight-tube or other black body in the solidifying fused metal,[5] sighting on a bubble blown in the mass of fused metal at the end of a tube,[6] observation on a hollow perforated metal filament heated electrically,[7] sighting on the inside of a strip of metal folded to a wedge of small angle and heated electrically; [8] in these cases the correction of the optical temperature for deviation from black-body conditions is, in general, negligible.

[1] Heycock and Neville, *J.C.S.*, 1895, **67**, 160; Holborn and Day, *Ann. Phys.*, 1900, **2**, 505; 1901, **4**, 99; for a volume (dilatometer) method, Ssobolewa, *Z. phys. Chem.*, 1903, **42**, 75.

[2] White, *Phys. Rev.*, 1907, **25**, 331; *Z. anorg. Chem.*, 1911, **69**, 305, 331; Day and Sosman, *Z. anorg. Chem.*, 1911, **72**, 1; Johnston and Adams, *ibid.*, 1911, **72**, 11 (effect of pressure); see also Tammann, *ibid.*, 1905, **47**, 289; Jänecke, *Z. phys. Chem.*, 1915, **90**, 257, 265, 280; Arndt and Kunze, *Z. Elektrochem.*, 1917, **18**, 994.

[3] Wien and Lummer, *Ann. Phys.*, 1895, **56**, 451; Roberts, *J. Opt. Soc. Amer.*, 1925, **10**, 723; Buckley, *Phil. Mag.*, 1928, **6**, 447; Price, *Nature*, 1946, **157**, 765.

[4] Wien and Lummer, *Ann. Phys.*, 1895, **56**, 451; Lummer and Pringsheim, *ibid.*, 1897, **63**, 395; Waidner and Burgess, *Bur. Stand. Bull.*, 1907, **3**, 163; Coblentz, in Glazebrook, "Dict. of Applied Physics," 1923, **4**, 541 (bibl.); Cohn, *Z. techn. Phys.*, 1928, **9**, 110 (high temp. furnaces); Fairchild, Hoover, and Peters, *Bur. Stand. J. Res.*, 1929, **2**, 931; Sosman, *Ind. Eng. Chem.*, 1931, **23**, 1369 (control of high temps.).

[5] Kanolt, *Bur. Stand. Bull.*, 1914, **10**, 295; Schofield, *Proc. Roy. Soc.*, 1929, **125**, 517; 1934, **146**, 792; 1936, **155**, 301; Fairchild, Hoover, and Peters, *Bur. Stand. J. Res.*, 1929, **2**, 931 (Au, Pd); Ribaud and Nikitine, *Compt. Rend.*, 1929, **188**, 618; Liebmann, *Z. Phys.*, 1930, **63**, 404 (bibl.; radiation from colourless oxides); Egerton and Milford, *Proc. Roy. Soc.*, 1930, **130**, 111; Wensel and Roeser, *Bur. Stand. J. Res.*, 1930, **5**, 1309 (Pt cylinder black body); Roeser, Caldwell, and Wensel, *ibid.*, 1931, **6**, 1119 (ThO_2 black body); Mendhousse, *Ann. de Phys.*, 1931, **16**, 209; Henning and Wensen, *Ann. Phys.*, 1933, **17**, 620 (m.p. iridium 2454°); Wensel, Judd, and Roeser, *Bur. Stand. J. Res.*, 1934, **12**, 527 (Pt, Rh, Ir).

[6] Jenkins and Gayler, *Proc. Roy. Soc.*, 1930, **129**, 91.

[7] Worthing, *J. Franklin Inst.*, 1916, **181**, 417; *Phys. Rev.*, 1917, **10**, 377; Pirani and Alterthum, *Z. Elektrochem.*, 1923, **29**, 5; Agte, Alterthum, Becker, Heyne, and Moers, *Naturwiss.*, 1931, **19**, 108; *Z. anorg. Chem.*, 1931, **196**, 129.

[8] Féry, *Compt. Rend.*, 1909, **148**, 777, 915; Mendenhall, *Astrophys. J.*, 1911, **33**, 91; Coblentz, *Bur. Stand. Bull.*, 1913, **9**, 81; Spence, *Astrophys. J.*, 1913, **37**, 194; Egerton and Milford, *Proc. Roy. Soc.*, 1930, **130**, 111.

C. LOW TEMPERATURES

§ 1 The Liquefaction of Gases [1]

Loukianos (Lucianus) in his satirical "True History" (*Vera Historia*),[2] composed about 150 A.D., relates that the inhabitants of the Moon drank air compressed to a dew-like liquid in goblets; and some poetical references to "liquid air" have been detected in Virgil (*c.* 50 B.C.).[3] Van Helmont (*d.* 1644) supposed that the "atoms" of *gas* can condense to minute liquid drops by intense cold,[4] but Boerhaave [5] found that only moisture deposits from air on cooling, and he doubted if air is capable of being solidified by the most intense cold or greatest degree of compression. Amontons and Black both considered that air might be a body of a high degree of volatility, capable of liquefaction or even solidification by sufficiently strong cooling,[6] and steam has many properties of air. Lavoisier, also, clearly recognised [7] that gases differ from vapours only in being further from their temperatures of liquefaction, and in "the absence of a sufficient degree of heat . . . would revert to the liquid state, and produce new liquids of the properties of which we cannot at present form the most remote idea." Dalton [8] also supposed we might expect from analogy with vapours that "a still greater pressure would succeed in giving the attractive force [between the particles of gases] the superiority [over the repulsive], when the elastic fluid would become a liquid or solid."

Ammonia was said by Van Marum and Paets van Trovstwyk [9] to be completely liquefied by compressing to about 3 atm. (the result was due to the presence of moisture in the gas),[10] and it was liquefied by cooling in a freezing mixture at $-40°$ (crystalline calcium chloride and ice) by Guyton de Morveau.[11] Fourcroy and Vauquelin [12] failed to liquefy hydrogen chloride, hydrogen sulphide and sulphur dioxide by such cooling, although sulphur dioxide (first liquefied by cooling by Monge and Clouet [13]) is easily liquefied in a freezing mixture of ice and salt ($-18°$). Chlorine, hydrogen chloride, and sulphur

1 Sloane, "Liquid Air and the Liquefaction of Gases," 1899; Alt, "Die Kälte," Leipzig 1910; Dewar, "Ency. Brit.", 1911, **16**, 744; Ewing, in Glazebrook, "Dict. of Applied Physics," 1922, **1**, 564; Claude, "Air liquide, Oxygène, Azote, Gaz rares," 2nd edit. (D'Arsonval), Paris, 1926; transl. Cottrell, "Liquid Air, Oxygen, and Nitrogen," 1913; Meissner, in Geiger and Scheel, "Handbuch der Physik," 1926, **11**, 272; von Wartenberg, in Wien-Harms, "Handbuch der Experimentalphysik," 1929, **9**, i, 33 (low temps.); Lenz, *ibid.*, 1929, **9**, i, 47 (liquefaction and separation); M. and B. Ruhemann, "Low Temperature Physics," Cambridge, 1937; *idem*, "The Separation of Gases," Oxford, 1940; Faraday Soc. discussion on the production and utilisation of cold, *Trans. Faraday Soc.*, 1922, **18**, 139 f.

2 "Works," transl. Fowler and Fowler, Oxford, 1905, **2**, 145.

3 "Georgics," i, 404 (apparet liquido sublimis in aëra Nisius); "Aeneid," vi, 202 (liquidumque per aëra lapsae); cf. Lippmann, *Chem. Ztg.*, 1931, **55**, 819; *Nature*, 1931, **128**, 666.

4 "Ortus Medicinae," Amsterdam, 1652, 66; Partington, *Annals of Science*, 1936, **1**, 359.

5 "Elementa Chemiae," Leyden, 1732, **1**, 429; "Elements of Chymistry," 1734, 105.

6 Mach, "Principien der Wärmelehre," Leipzig, 1900, 179.

7 "Traité de Chimie," 1789, 31; "Elements of Chemistry," 1799, 77.

8 "New System of Chemical Philosophy," 1808, **1**, i, 148.

9 Description de quelques Appareils Chimiques Nouveaux, *Verhandelingen Teyler's Genootschap*, Haarlem, 1798; *Ann. Phys.*, 1799, **1**, 145.

10 Cohen and Cohen-de Meester, *Verhandelingen aangeboden aan P. Zeeman*, Hague, 1935, 395.

11 *Ann. Chim.*, 1799, **29**, 290.

12 *Ann. Chim.*, 1799, **29**, 281.

13 Lavoisier, "Traité élémentaire de Chimie," 1789, 244 (Clouet); Nicholson, "Dict. of Chemistry," 1795, **2**, 925; Fourcroy, "Systéme des Connaissances Chimiques," 1801, **2**, 74 (Monge).

dioxide were liquefied by Northmore [1] in 1806 by compression into a strong glass receiver. He used a condensing pump, but with carbon dioxide the receiver exploded. When 2 pints of chlorine were compressed to $2\frac{1}{4}$ cu. in. a very volatile yellow fluid separated.

When Faraday [2] began his work (at Davy's suggestion) in 1823, therefore, a number of other experimenters (whom he does not mention) had forestalled him with several gases, notably chlorine. He used the combined effects of pressure and cold—which bring the molecules closer together, and also decrease their velocity—by sealing up in one leg of a V-shaped tube (Fig. 1.VI C) [3] the materials which can generate the gas (e.g. chlorine hydrate by warming), and cooling the other leg in a freezing mixture. In this way he liquefied chlorine, sulphur dioxide, hydrogen sulphide, carbon dioxide, nitrous oxide, euchlorine ($Cl_2 + ClO_2$), ammonia, and cyanogen, and in the same way Davy [4] liquefied hydrogen chloride. Davy also [5] made some interesting prophecies about the future use of liquefied gases. Dove [6] *calculated* the temperatures at which gases should liquefy at 1 atm. pressure (the correct figures are in brackets): N_2O −158° (−89°), CO_2 −156° (−78°), HCl −130° (−85°), NH_3 −53° (−33°) by comparison with steam. If t_1, t_2 are the temperatures at which a liquid has pressures p_1, p_2, and t_1', t_2' are the temperatures for steam, then $t_1 - t_2 = t_1' - t_2'$.

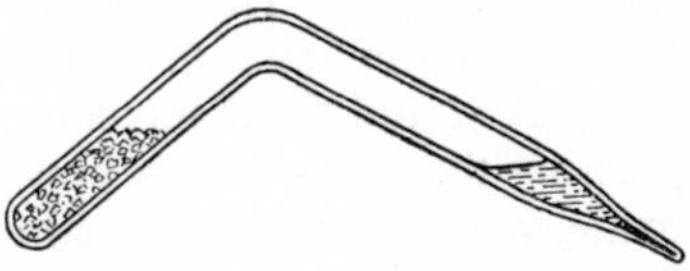

FIG. 1.VI C. Faraday's Tube

After Faraday's work, many other experimenters used higher pressures and obtained larger quantities of the liquids, although Colladon,[7] who used a bent tube cooled at the sealed end into which gas was compressed, failed to liquefy air at 400 atm. at −30°. Thilorier [8] made a notable advance by obtaining large amounts of liquid carbon dioxide by what was essentially Faraday's method. The gas was generated in a cast-iron vessel and the liquid condensed in another cast-iron vessel cooled in a freezing mixture. Thilorier's apparatus was generally used, but one of them burst in a lecture demonstration and killed the assistant, Hervey,[9] so that Mareska and Donny [10] made the apparatus of lead-lined copper; wrought iron was also used, which was reasonably safe. Thilorier [8] was the first to obtain solid carbon dioxide by allowing the liquid to escape into a brass box (a flannel bag, used by Bianchi [11] about 1869, is better), and by

1 *Nicholson's J.*, 1805, **12**, 368; 1806, **13**, 233; *Alembic Club Repr.*, 1904, **12**, 69. Northmore says he was in touch with the "chemical operator" at the Royal Institution. For a simple apparatus for liquefaction by piston compression in a tube, see Benedicks, *Phys Z.*, 1910, **11**, 547.

2 *Phil. Trans.*, 1823, **113**, 160, 189; "Researches in Chemistry and Physics," 1859, 85, 89; *Alembic Club Reprint*, 1904, **12**, where an historical summary by Faraday, from *Quart. J. Sci.*, 1824, **16**, 229, is given.

3 Even in his "Chemical Manipulation," 1842, 424, where directions for making the tubes are given, Faraday does not give a figure.

4 *Phil. Trans.*, 1823, **113**, 164; "Works," 1840, **6**, 264.

5 *Phil. Trans.*, 1823, **113**, 199; "Works," 1840, **6**, 266.

6 *Ann. Phys.*, 1831, **23**, 290.

7 Pictet, *Ann. Chim.*, 1878, **13**, 145 (226); Wroblewski and Olszewski, *Ann, Phys.*, 1883, **20**, 243.

8 *Ann. Chim.*, 1835, **60**, 427, 432 (no description of apparatus); [Liebig], *Ann.*, 1839, **30**, 122 (description of apparatus, and lithographed plate).

9 Aimé, *Ann. Chim.*, 1843, **8**, 275; Natterer, *J. prakt. Chem.*, 1844, **31**, 375.

10 *Bull. Acad. Roy. Belg.*, 1843, **10**, 75; *Mém. Couronn. Acad. Roy. Bruxelles*, 1845, **18**, vi; Bloxam, "Chemistry," 1883, 82; Roscoe and Schorlemmer, "Treatise on Chemistry," 1920, **1**, 811.

11 Landolt, *Ber.*, 1884, **17**, 309; Hempel, *ibid.*, 1898, **31**, 2993, used a linen bag.

mixing it with ether obtained a refrigerating mixture at −78°, the temperature of which could be lowered to −110° by rapid evaporation under reduced pressure. Landolt [1] compressed the snow-like solid into sticks like blackboard chalk, sp. g. 1·2, and the modern "dry ice," in the form of blocks of compressed solid carbon dioxide, is now largely used industrially.[2]

Bussy [3] liquefied sulphur dioxide by cooling in a mixture of ice and salt, and in the cold produced by the rapid evaporation of the liquid he liquefied chlorine and ammonia, and solidified chlorine, ammonia, and cyanogen. Faraday,[4] using Thilorier's mixture in a vacuum, liquefied several gases. In the cooling mixture at atmospheric pressure Cl_2, C_2N_2, NH_3, H_2S, HI, HBr, CO_2, and Cl_2O liquefied; by cooling in the mixture in vacuum and compressing the gases with a powerful pump all the gases mentioned, and nitrous oxide, were solidified, and ethylene, phosphine, and silicon fluoride were liquefied. Six gases (oxygen, nitrogen, hydrogen, carbon monoxide, nitric oxide, and coal gas—containing methane)—the so-called "permanent gases"—resisted liquefaction at this low temperature and pressures of 500–700 lb. per sq. in. Berthelot [5] found that oxygen is not liquefied at 780 atm.

The Vienna physicist, J. O. Natterer, who prepared liquid nitrous oxide in quantity in 1844,[6] subjected the permanent gases to enormous pressures (up to 3600 atm.) by means of an ingenious Kraft's compressing pump, but without success. The reason for this failure became clear as a result of the work of Andrews,[7] who showed that *each gas has a critical temperature, above which it cannot be liquefied by pressure,* however high. The realisation that *strong cooling* was necessary in the case of the permanent gases led to the liquefaction of oxygen in 1877 independently by Cailletet [8] and by Pictet.[9] In 1878 Natterer reached a temperature of −140° by the rapid evaporation of a mixture of liquid nitrous oxide and carbon dioxide. Cailletet (who was an ironmaster, not a professional scientist) announced his result in a letter to Deville of 2 December, which was read to the Academy on 24 December; Pictet (professor of physics at Geneva, later in Berlin) sent his in a telegram to the secretary of the Academy on 22 December, and this also was read on 24 December.

§ 2. Cailletet's Method

The principle of Cailletet's method was to allow a portion of gas, strongly compressed to a pressure p_1 in a strong glass capillary tube over mercury at an absolute temperature T_1, to expand suddenly to atmospheric pressure p_2 by opening a valve, so as to release the mercury. The expansion of the gas was

[1] Landolt, *Ber.*, 1884, **17**, 309; Hampel, *ibid.*, 1898, **31**, 2993.

[2] Littler, *J.S.C.I.*, 1932, **52**, 533R.

[3] *Ann. Chim.*, 1824, **26**, 63; also describing the freezing of mercury, and making ice in a red-hot platinum dish containing liquid SO_2 in the spheroidal state.

[4] *Phil. Trans.*, 1845, **135**, 155; *Ann. Chim.*, 1845, **15**, 257; "Researches in Chemistry and Physics," 1859, 96; *Alembic Club Reprint*, 1904, **12**, 33

[5] *Ann. Chim.*, 1850, **30**, 237.

[6] *J. prakt. Chem.*, 1844, **31**, 375; 1845, **35**, 169 (apparatus); 1852, **56**, 126; 1855, **94**, 436; *Ann. Phys.*, 1844, **62**, 132; *Wien Ber.*, 1850, **5**, 351; 1851, **6**, 557; 1854, **12**, 199; cf. Addams, *B.A. Rep.*, 1839, **7**, 70; Mitchell, *Amer. J. Sci.*, 1839, **35**, 346; Aimé, *Ann. Chim.*, 1843, **8**, 275, also tried high pressures.

[7] In Miller, "Elements of Chemistry," 3rd edit., 1863, **1** ("Chemical Physics"), 328; *Phil. Trans.*, 1869, **159**, 575; 1876, **166**, 421.

[8] *Compt. Rend.*, 1877, **85**, 1213, 1217, 1270; *Ann. Chim.*, 1878, **15**, 132; on Louis Cailletet, 1832–1913, see Mathias, *Rev. Gén. Sci.*, 1913, **24**, 174.

[9] *Compt. Rend.*, 1877, **85**, 1214, 1220; 1878, **86**, 37, 106; *Ann. Chim.*, 1878, **13**, 145; *Arch. Sci. Phys. Nat.*, 1878, **61**, 16.

approximately adiabatic (i.e. no heat was transferred to or from the surroundings; see § 4.II); hence, from (17), § 4.II, $Tv^{\gamma-1}$=const., and as pv/T=const.:

$$(p_1/p_2)^{(\gamma-1)/\gamma}=T_1/T_2 \quad . \quad . \quad . \quad . \quad . \quad . \quad . \quad . \quad . \quad (1)$$

where T_2 is the final absolute temperature after adiabatic expansion, and $\gamma=c_p/c_v$,

$$\therefore \log(T_1/T_2)=[(\gamma-1)/\gamma]\log(p_1/p_2) \quad . \quad . \quad . \quad . \quad (2)$$

The cooling effect in adiabatic expansion is due to the *external work* done by the gas in expanding against the atmospheric pressure, energy being taken from the gas. The effect depends on the value of γ; for most diatomic permanent gases (H_2, O_2, N_2, CO, NO), γ is approximately 1·4, hence (2) becomes:

$$\log T_1-\log T_2=0{\cdot}286(\log p_1-\log p_2) \quad . \quad . \quad . \quad . \quad (3)$$

from which T_2 is easily calculated if p_1 and p_2 (measured in the same units, e.g. atm.) and T_1 are known. E.g. at 50 atm. initial pressure at 20° C. and 1 atm. final pressure, the final temperature is −177° C. The cooling effects fall off at lower initial temperatures, which sets a limit to the method. The theoretical cooling is never attained, on account of the *rapid* exchange of heat between the warmer walls of the capillary and the cold gas.

Cailletet's apparatus is shown in Fig. 2.VI C. The compressor is a special pump containing water. The piston in the pump is operated by a lever, the fine adjustment of pressure (indicated on a Bourdon manometer) by screwing in a piston in a side barrel of the pump by means of a wheel. The water from the pump passes by the steel tube TU to the steel cylinder B containing mercury below, and this mercury is driven into the glass Cailletet tube TT, which contains the gas, and ends above in a thick-walled capillary (which may be graduated). The capillary is surrounded by a glass water bath M (which may contain a cooling mixture), and a bell-jar C, which offers some protection in case of a burst, but mainly serves to prevent atmospheric moisture condensing on the outside of the cooled tube M. When the gas is strongly compressed, a valve on the pump is opened, when the pressure falls suddenly to 1 atm., the gas in the tube T thus suddenly expanding. By compressing oxygen, carbon monoxide, and nitrogen to about 200–300 atm. at room temperature, and then releasing the pressure, Cailletet saw a fog of liquid droplets form in the tube, but this rapidly disappeared and he was unable to obtain any liquid in bulk. He thought he saw a trace of fog with hydrogen, but he could not have liquefied this gas with the arrangement used. Liquid oxygen in bulk was first obtained by Pictet, with a much more complicated apparatus working on a different principle.

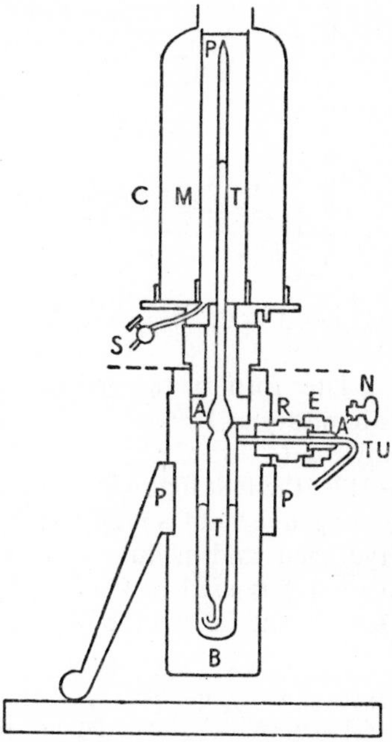

FIG. 2.VI C. Cailletet's Apparatus

§ 3. Pictet's Method

The principle of Pictet's [1] method is the so-called *cascade process.* By evaporating liquid sulphur dioxide (easily liquefied by compression to about 2½ atm. at 15°) under reduced pressure, the temperature drops to a point (−65° to −75°) at which carbon dioxide in a tube surrounded by the liquid sulphur dioxide is liquefied by a moderate pressure. By rapidly evaporating the liquid carbon dioxide (or a mixture of carbon dioxide and sulphur dioxide) [2] under reduced pressure, the temperature attained (−150°) drops below the critical temperature of oxygen, which then liquefies under moderate pressure (12 atm. at −150°) in a tube surrounded by the liquid carbon dioxide. By the rapid evaporation of liquid oxygen, the temperature can be reduced to −220°, but as the critical temperature of hydrogen (−241°) is still lower, this gas cannot be liquefied by Pictet's method.

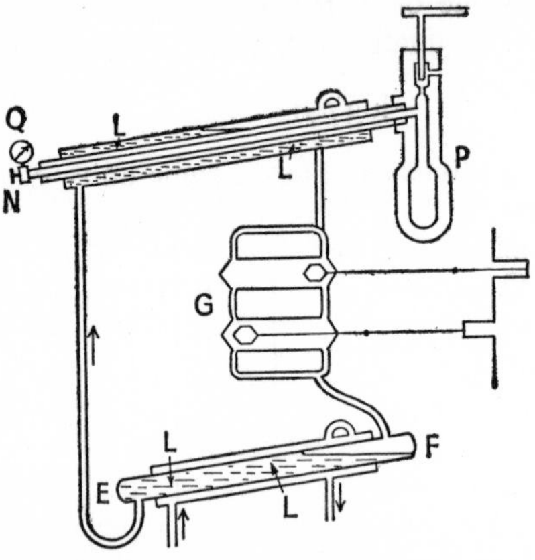

FIG. 3.VI C. Pictet's Apparatus

The temperature attained by the evaporation of a liquid depends on the pressure and is equal to the boiling-point of the liquid at that pressure. By protecting the liquid by heat insulation and *maintaining* a low pressure by means of a pump, a low temperature can therefore be reached if the liquid does not freeze. The last limitation makes it necessary to use several liquids and to drop the temperature in successive steps, hence the name " cascade process." The later form of the process was used by Kamerlingh Onnes in the Cryogenic Laboratory at Leyden.[3] In this the steps are methyl chloride (−24° to −90°), ethylene (−103°·7 to −165°: first used by Olszewski), and oxygen (−183° to −217°: the first figure in all cases gives the b.p. at 1 atm.). The liquid used for cooling must not solidify, and this limits the temperature to its triple point. Hydrogen and helium cannot be liquefied by this method. The cascade method was used in Cracow by Wroblewski [4] and Olszewski,[5] in London by Dewar,[6] and in Berlin by Pictet.

1 *Compt. Rend.*, 1877, **85**, 1214, 1220; 1878, **86**, 37, 106; *Ann. Chim.*, 1878, **13**, 145; *Z. kompr. u. flüss. Gase*, 1903, **7**, 1, 17, 37, 52.

2 The so-called " Pictet's liquid " is a mixture of liquid sulphur dioxide and carbon dioxide: see Blümcke, *Ann. Phys.*, 1888, **34**, 10; 1889, **36**, 911; Pictet, *ibid.*, 1888, **34**, 734.

3 *Verslag. K. Akad. Wetens. Amsterdam*, 1894–5, **3**, 164 (*Comm. Leiden* **14**); *Proc. K. Akad. Wetens. Amsterdam*, 1900, **2**, 129, 437 (*Comm. Leiden*, **51**, **54**); 1903, **5**, 502, 628 (*Comm. Leiden* **83**); 1904, **6**, 668 (*Comm. Leiden* **87**); 1906, **8**, 77, 79, 82 (*Comm. Leiden* **94**); 1907, **9**, 156 (*Comm. Leiden* **94** *f*); 1909, **11**, 883 (*Comm. Leiden* **109**); *Comm. Leiden*, 1922, Suppl. **45** (summary); 1926, **158** (summary); *Trans. Faraday Soc.*, 1922, **18**, 145; Crommelin, *ibid.*, 1922, **18**, 175; Henning, *Z. Instr.*, 1913, **33**, 33.

4 Wroblewski and Olszewski, *Ann. Phys.*, 1883, **20**, 243; Wroblewski, *Compt. Rend.*, 1883, **97**, 1553; *Ann. Phys.*, 1885, **25**, 371; 1885, **26**, 134; Wroblewski and Olszewski later on worked independently, and to some extent in rivalry. They say, *Ann. Phys.*, 1883, **20**, 243, tha Cailletet showed his method freely to others. On Olszewski (1846–1915), see Onnes, *Chem. Ztg.*, 1915, **39**, 517.

5 Olszewski, *Ann. Phys.*, 1889, **37**, 337; 1905, **17**, 987; *Phil. Mag.*, 1895, **39**, 188 (summary and list of papers); *Bull. Acad. Polon.*, 1908, 375 (historical; bibl., illustr.); *Z. kompr. u. flüss. Gase*, 1912, **14**, 93, 111, 127.

6 *Phil. Mag.*, 1884, **18**, 210 (where the apparatus is very insufficiently described); Liveing and Dewar, *ibid.*, 1892, **34**, 205; 1893, **36**, 328; Dewar and Fleming, *ibid.*, 1892, **34**, 326;

The important data are:

	b.p.	triple pt.
Methyl chloride ...	−24·09°	−102·9°
Ethylene	−103·7°	−169°
Oxygen	−182·95°	−218·4°

A diagram of Pictet's apparatus is shown in Fig. 3.VI C. Oxygen was generated by heating potassium chlorate in the iron retort P, connected with the copper tube N about 4 m. long, with a valve at the lower end, and a Bourdon manometer Q. The tube N was cooled by liquid carbon dioxide LL evaporating at about −140°, the vapour being re-liquefied by compression by a pump G into a copper tube EF surrounded by liquid sulphur dioxide evaporated at −65° by another pump. The oxygen in N was thus cooled below its critical temperature (−119°) and liquefied under pressure. On opening the valve at N, a lustrous jet of liquid oxygen issued with great violence. Some of the liquefaction was probably due to the extra cooling by adiabatic expansion on opening the valve, the initial pressure being about 475 atm. (much above the critical pressure of oxygen.

Pictet [1] claimed that by generating hydrogen in the apparatus by heating sodium formate with caustic soda, a " grey mist " and a " steel-blue jet " issued from N on opening the valve and " rattled on the floor like small shot;" hence he thought he had obtained solid hydrogen. This was impossible, as its critical temperature could not have been reached, and the effect was probably due to impurity in the gas.

In Olszewski's apparatus, oxygen at 100 atm. pressure was contained in a 10-lit. iron bottle, connected by a valve and metal tube with a 400-c.c. iron cylinder and a manometer. The cylinder was contained in a Dewar vessel filled with liquid ethylene taken from an iron cylinder cooled in ice and salt, the liquid passing through a spiral cooled in a mixture of carbon dioxide and ether maintained at −100° by pumping. The liquid ethylene in the Dewar vessel was evaporated by a pump and the cold produced liquefied the oxygen. The liquid oxygen was let out to atmospheric pressure (when the temperature fell to −181·4°) through a valve and collected in a triple-walled Dewar vessel.

The cascade process (step by step cooling) is very efficient: in the Leyden apparatus, using ammonia, ethylene, and methane, the energy consumption for 1 kg. of liquid nitrogen from gas at 1 atm. and 25° C. is 463 k.cal., as compared with 894 k.cal. by the Linde process (§ 5) and 751·2 k.cal. by the Claude process (§ 4).[2] A simple ethylene liquefier (without a compressor) was described by Clusius and Riccoboni.[3]

§ 4. Claude's Process

The possibility of cooling a gas by allowing it to do *external* work in an engine or turbine was recognised by Onnes and by Lord Rayleigh,[4] and was

Proc. Roy. Soc., 1898, **63**, 256; *J.C.S.*, 1898, **73**, 528 (liq. H_2); *Proc. Roy. Inst.*, 1899–1901, **16**, 1, 212, 473, 730; Clerke, *ibid.*, **16**, 699; Armstrong, *ibid.*, 1908, **19**, 354 (portr. of Dewar); on the polemic between Dewar (who disclosed his methods only incompletely, as if he wished to prevent their use by others) and Olszewski, see Olszewski, *Nature*, 1895, **51**, 245; Muir (who gives priority to Olszewski), *ibid.*, 1895, **51**, 364, 388; Dewar, *ibid.*, 1895, **51**, 245, 365, 413; *Phil. Mag.*, 1895, **39**, 298. Dewar did not agree to supply liquid hydrogen in Ramsay's work on the inert gases, and Travers set up a second apparatus in London for its production.

[1] *Compt. Rend.*, 1878, **86**, 106.

[2] Keesom, *Comm. Leiden*, 1933, Suppl. **76a**.

[3] *Z. phys. Chem.*, 1937, **38** B, 81.

[4] Onnes, *Comm. Leiden*, 1896, **23**; *Ann. Phys. Beibl.*, 1896, **20**, 518 (*experiments* with hydrogen); Rayleigh, *Nature*, 1898, **58**, 199; " Scientific Papers," 1903, **4**, 360 (suggestion only).

applied by Claude [1] in a process for the liquefaction of air. The moderately compressed air, after purification from moisture and carbon dioxide in the usual way, is divided into two parts. One part passes through an expansion engine, which cools the gas by extracting heat from it for conversion into work, and the other part is cooled by the cold air from the engine in a heat interchanger, and then expands through a valve, when it liquefies. The lubrication of the pistons was a difficulty; liquid nitrogen was used by Claude, but in some forms of compressor a piston with a small clearance and not lubricated is used. Claude also made use of the fact, first noticed by Wroblewski,[2] that air liquefies in fractions of different composition when progressively cooled.

§ 5. Liquefaction of Gases by the Joule-Thomson Effect

The cooling produced by the Joule-Thomson effect, unlike that in adiabatic expansion, is due to the *internal work* performed against the attractions of the molecules. This was first used for large-scale liquefaction by Linde [3] in Germany, and by Hampson [4] in England, in 1895. The equation given by Linde for the lowering of temperature by the Joule-Thomson effect (§ 24.VII A) is:

$$\Delta T = 0{\cdot}276 \Delta p (273/T)^2 \quad \ldots\ldots\ldots \quad \textbf{(1)}$$

where T is the initial absolute temperature. If $\Delta p = 50 - 1 = 49$ atm., the initial temperatures of +20°, 0°, −20°, −60°, −100°, and −140°, give final temperatures of +8·3°, −13·5°, −35·7°, −82·2°, −133·7°, and −197°; i.e. the effect increases at lower temperatures. If air at −20° expands from 50 atm. to 1 atm. it is cooled to −36°. If this cools a second portion of air to −36°, it is cooled on expansion to −54°, and this is repeated to temperatures of −101°, −136°, and −190°, when the air liquefies at atmospheric pressure. This cumulative cooling is achieved, according to an invention of Siemens (1857), by letting the cold expanded air sweep over the outer surface of a metal tube bringing the compressed air to the expansion jet.

Linde's apparatus is shown diagrammatically in Fig. 4.VI C. Air freed from dust and carbon dioxide, taken in on the low-pressure side of the two-stage compressor,[5] is compressed to 20 atm. Its heat is removed by passing through a metal spiral in water, and the air is then compressed to 200 atm. on the high-pressure side. This compressed air, again cooled in a metal spiral, goes

[1] *Compt. Rend.*, 1905, **141**, 823; Claude, "Liquid Air, Oxygen, and Nitrogen," transl. Cottrell, 1913; *Trans. Faraday Soc.*, 1922, **18**, 139.

[2] *Ann. Phys.*, 1885, **26**, 134.

[3] *Germ. Pat.* 88824 (5 June, 1895, with full description of Joule-Thomson effect); *Ann. Phys.*, 1896, **57**, 328; *Z. phys. Chem.*, 1896, **20**, 638; *Engineer*, 1896, **82**, 509; *Z. ges. Kälte-Ind.*, 1897, **4**, 7, 23; *Ber.*, 1899, **32**, 925; Schröter, *Z. Verein D. Ing.*, 1895, **39**, 1157; Lorenz, *Civilingenieur*, 1895, **41**, 633; *Z. ges. Kälte-Ind.*, 1897, **4**, 49 (theory); D'Arsonval, *Compt. Rend.*, 1898, **126**, 1683; Cottrell, *J. Phys. Chem.*, 1906, **10**, 264; Bradley and Hale, *ibid.*, 1906, **10**, 275; Rožič, *Wien Ber.*, 1906, **115**, IIA, 1559; Brot, *Bull. Soc. Encourag.*, 1914, **113**, 16; Hausen, "Geschichte der Ges. für Lindes Eismachinen," 1929; on Linde, see Hausen, *Z. techn. Phys.*, 1932, **13**, 250 (portrait); *Z. ges. Kälte-Ind.*, 1935, **42**, 209; for summary of gas liquefaction methods, see Teichmann, "Komprimierte und verflüssigte Gase," Halle, 1908; Plank, *Phys. Z.*, 1920, **21**, 150 (tables for cooling by adiabatic expansion and Joule-Thomson effect); Burton, Smith, and Wilhelm, "Phenomena at the Temperature of Liquid Helium," New York, 1940, 13 f.

[4] *Brit. Pat.*, 10165 (23 May, 1895: although antedating Linde's patent, this prescribes only "the usual cycle of compression, cooling, and expansion" and "heat interchange"); *Nature*, 1896, **53**, 513; Tilden, *Rev. Gén. Sci.*, 1896, **7**, 329; Kausch, *Z. kompr. flüss. Gase*, 1902, **5**, 171, 185; 1902, **6**, 33; Buckingham, *Bur. Stand. Bull.*, 1909, **6**, 125 (theory).

[5] On gas compressors, see e.g. Ernst, *Ind. Eng. Chem.*, 1926, **18**, 664; Tongue, "The Design and Construction of High Pressure Chemical Plant," 1934.

through a water-separator, which is an empty steel cylinder in which the water used to lubricate the vulcanite packing of the compressor pistons is separated. The moisture is then removed by passing through a drier containing calcium chloride (or is dried by refrigeration), and the dried air passes into the inner coil of three concentric metal tubes, which are surrounded by heat-insulating packing. This air at $-20°$ then expands to 20 atm. through a needle-valve and cools by the Joule-Thomson effect to about $-78°$. This cold air then rises through the second tube and cools the air coming down the inner tube. The air at 20 atm. and about $-20°$ goes back to the high-pressure compressor cylinder. The cooling effect accumulates until the air liquefies and the needle-

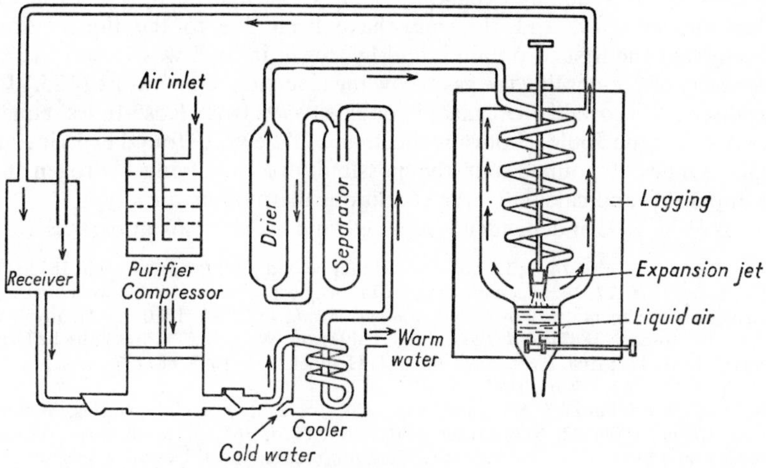

FIG. 4.VI C. Liquefaction of Air

valve is then adjusted so that two-thirds of the air passes out through the second tube to the compressor, and one-third expands to atmospheric pressure, partly liquefies, and partly passes out to the free air through the third tube of the spiral. The liquid air collects in a Dewar vessel and can be withdrawn through a valve.

In Hampson's apparatus,[1] which is more convenient for smaller-scale laboratory work than Linde's, air from a two-stage compressor passes through a water-separator, and a drier containing solid caustic soda, into the liquefier. This contains two or four metal tubes in parallel wound into a close spiral and ending in an expansion valve, controlled from outside by a screw. The upper part of the spiral is heat-insulated by raw-wool packing, and the lower part is contained in a large Dewar vessel. The cooled expanded air (from 180–200 atm. to 1 atm.) sweeps over the metal spiral, and escapes at atmospheric pressure, passing to the pre-purifier, containing moist slaked lime on trays. To avoid breakage, the inner vessel of the Dewar is joined to the valve by an elastic glass spiral.

The possibility of *collecting* liquefied gases was first realised by the invention of the well-known double-walled vacuum vessel (" Dewar vessel " or " thermos

[1] See Travers, " Study of Gases," 1901, 192; Allen and Ambler, *Phys. Rev.*, 1902, **15**, 181; Olszewski, *Ann. Phys.*, 1903, **10**, 768; for regenerator coils, Travers, Gwyer, and Usher *Smithsonian Misc. Coll.*, 1907, **49**, Pt. II, No. 1652; for laboratory liquid oxygen apparatus, Akhumov, *Zavodskaya Lab.*, 1935, **4**, 1510; Keyes, *Chem. Rev.*, 1946, **39**, 449.

flask ") by Dewar [1] in 1892. In this there is a high vacuum between the glass walls, which are silvered on the inside to cut down heat transmission by radiation. Dewar found the rate of heat transmission at −180° proportional to the cube of the absolute temperature.[2] Large metal vessels [3] holding a gallon or two are used, the vacuum being maintained by a tube of absorbent charcoal open to the annular space and cooled in the liquid air or oxygen in the inner vessel —also a device invented by Dewar.[4] The lecture experiments with liquid air and liquid oxygen need not be described.[5]

§ 6. Liquid Hydrogen

Wroblewski, by suddenly expanding compressed hydrogen, saw a fog which vanished immediately, and this may have been due to the liquefaction of hydrogen,[6] but the first to obtain liquid hydrogen in bulk was Dewar in 1895.[7] The necessity of pre-cooling the gas below the inversion temperature (§ 25.VII A), was realised: Witkowski [8] calculated for this −79° from Rose-Innes' equation (§ 24.VII A) for the Joule-Thomson effect, and Olszewski [9] found experimentally −80·5°. Onnes [10] pointed out the possibility of liquefying hydrogen in the Linde apparatus and calculated the conditions thermodynamically.

Travers [11] in 1901 independently devised and worked an apparatus for the

[1] *Proc. Roy. Inst.*, 1893, **14**, 1; Dewar claimed that he had used the *principle* in 1873 (*Trans. Roy. Soc. Edin.*, 1876, **27**, 167, vacuum jacketed brass calorimeter). Double-walled *unsilvered* vacuum vessels are mentioned by Violle, *Compt. Rend.*, 1882, **94**, 1510; D'Arsonval, *ibid.*, 1898, **126**, 1683 (used in 1887); *J. de Phys.*, 1898, **7**, 497; and Weinhold, " Physikalische Demonstrationen," 1881, 479; *Ann. Phys.*, 1898, **66**, 544; Hempel, *ibid.*, 1899, **68**, 137.

[2] Cf. Pictet, *Z. phys. Chem.*, 1895, **16**, 417.

[3] Griffiths, *Trans. Faraday Soc.*, 1922, **18**, 224; for 2-lit. porcelain vessels, Beckmann, *Z. angew. Chem.*, 1909, **22**, 673; Moser, *ibid.*, 1919, **32**, i, 365; on large Pyrex vessels, see Phipps, Cox, and Shaw, *J.A.C.S.*, 1931, **53**, 1365; for losses in metal Dewar vessels, see Briggs, *Proc. Roy. Soc. Edin.*, 1921, **41**, 97; Briggs and Mollinson, *ibid.*, 1923, **43**, 160; conduction of heat down necks of ditto, Hogg, *Trans. Faraday Soc.*, 1924, **20**, 327; liquid oxygen in aircraft, Grayson-Smith and Findlay, *Chem. Rev.*, 1946, **39**, 397; Giauque, *Rev. Sci. Instr.*, 1947, **18**, 852 (Jena glass less permeable to helium than Pyrex); Haynes and Scott, *Science*, 1948, **107**, 301 (silvering).

[4] *Proc. Chem. Soc.*, 1896, **11**, 229; *J.C.S.*, 1898, **73**, 528; *Compt. Rend.*, 1898, **126**, 1408; 1904, **139**, 261.

[5] Dewar, *Proc. Roy. Inst.*, 1894–5, **14**, 1, 393, 665; *Amer. J. Sci.*, 1901, **12**, 168; Pictet and Altschul, *Z. phys. Chem.*, 1894, **5**, 386; Pictet, *Compt. Rend.*, 1894, **119**, 527; *J. Roy. Soc. Arts*, 1911, **59**, 678; Ladenburg, *Ber.*, 1898, **31**, 1968; Tripler, *Chem. News*, 1898, **77**, 113; Sloane, " Liquid Air and the Liquefaction of Gases," 1899; Hardin, " The Rise and Development of the Liquefaction of Gases," New York, 1899; Kastle, *Amer. Chem. J.*, 1900, **23**, 50; D'Arsonval, *Ann. Chim.*, 1902, **26**, 433; Bleekrode, *Ann. Phys.*, 1903, **12** 218; Nowicki and Mayer, " Flüssige Luft," 2nd edit., Leipzig, 1906; Claude, " Liquid Air, Oxygen, and Nitrogen " (transl. Cottrell), 1913; Ewing, in Glazebrook, " Dict. of Applied Physics," 1922, **1**, 564; Cady, *J. Chem. Educ.*, 1931, **8**, 1027; Partington, " Text Book of Inorganic Chemistry," 1946, 141. See also C. G. von Wirkner, " Geschichte und Theorie der Kälteerzeugung," Hamburg, 1897. For a summary and bibliography of low temperatures from 1890, see Shearer, *Phys. Rev.*, 1902, **15**, 243; to 1900, Bredig, *Phys. Z.*, 1901, **2**, 418, 433; on change of colour of solids at low temperatures, Obriemow and de Haas, *Proc. K. Akad. Wetens. Amsterdam*, 1928, **31**, 353.

[6] Pictet, *Z. phys. Chem.*, 1895, **16**, 417.

[7] *Proc. Chem. Soc.*, 1896, **11**, 229 (lecture of 1895); *J.C.S.*, 1898, **73**, 528; *Proc. Roy. Inst.*, 1899–1901, **16**, 1, 212, 473 (solid H_2), 730 (the date is often given as 1898).

[8] *Bull. Acad. Polon.*, 1898, 282.

[9] *Ann. Phys.*, 1902, **7**, 818.

[10] *Verslag. K. Akad. Wetens. Amsterdam*, 1895–6, **4**, 236 (*Comm. Leiden* **23**); *Ann. Phys. Beibl.*, 1896, **20**, 518.

[11] *Phil. Mag.*, 1901, **1**, 411; *Z. phys. Chem.*, 1901, **37**, 100; " Study of Gases," 1901, 196; *Trans. Faraday Soc.*, 1922, **18**, 199.

liquefaction of hydrogen, which he described in detail, and Olszewski [1] in 1902 also described an apparatus, which he improved in 1903, so that in 1906 Graetz [2] could say that " it is not difficult to obtain liquid hydrogen in not inconsiderable quantities." A simplification and modification of Travers' apparatus was described by Nernst [3] in 1911; it was constructed and sold by his mechanic, Hoenow, for 250 marks (£12 10*s*.), and the author saw it in

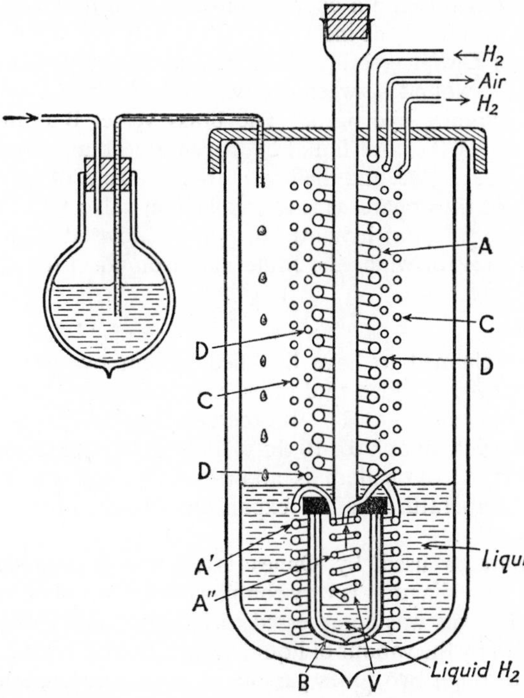

FIG. 5.VI C. Nernst's Apparatus for Liquefaction of Hydrogen

successful operation in the Berlin laboratory in 1912, when a litre or more of liquid hydrogen was regularly made daily for research purposes.

In Nernst's apparatus (Fig. 5.VI C) compressed hydrogen (either from a cylinder or, more economically, from a compressor) enters through the copper coil A and passes through an extension A′ of the coil immersed in liquid air in a large Dewar vessel. The cooled gas then passes through an extension A″ of the

[1] *Ann. Phys.*, 1903, **10**, 768; 1903, **12**, 196.

[2] In Winkelmann, " Handbuch der Physik," 1906, **3**, 896.

[3] *Z. Elektrochem.*, 1911, **17**, 735; for other apparatus, see Onnes, *Proc. K. Akad. Wetens. Amsterdam*, 1900, **2**, 129 (*Comm. Leiden*, **51**); 1926, **29**, 1176 (*Comm. Leiden*, **158**); *Comm. Leiden*, 1922, Suppl. **45**; Olszewski, *Ann. Phys.*, 1903, **10**, 768; 1903, **12**, 196; *Z. kompr. flüss. Gase*, 1912, **14**, 93, 111, 127; Lilienfeld, *Z. kompr. flüss. Gase*, 1911, **13**, 35, 165; Meissner, *Verhl. d. D. Phys. Ges.*, 1913, **15**, 540; *Z. Phys.*, 1923, **18**, 12; Latimer, Buffington, and Hoenshel, *J.A.C.S.*, 1925, **47**, 1571; Ruhemann, *Z. Phys.*, 1930, **65**, 67 (small scale); Simon, Cooke, and Pearson, *Proc. Phys. Soc.*, 1935, **47**, 678; Fischer, *Z. ges. Kälte-Ind.*, 1935, **42**, 174 (calculations); Keyes, Gerry, and Hicks, *J.A.C.S.*, 1937, **59**, 1426 (desorption from charcoal included in cooling effect; theory); Ahlberg, Estermann, and Lundberg, *Rev. Sci. Instr.*, 1937, **8**, 422 (1 lit. liquid per hour from cylinder gas without compressor); Starr, *ibid.*, 1941, **12**, 193; Blanchard and Bittner, *ibid.*, 1943, **13**, 394; Hilsch, *Ann. Phys.*, 1942, **42**, 165; Gilbert and Rossol, *Helv. Phys. Acta*, 1945, **18**, 343; de Sorbo, Milton, and Andrews, *Chem. Rev.*, 1946, **39**, 403; Fairbank, *Rev. Sci. Instr.*, 1946, **17**, 473 (small H_2 liquefier); Jones, Larsen, and Simon, *Research*, 1948, **1**, 420.

coil, composed of two coils in parallel inside a small Dewar tube completely enclosed in a brass vessel B, which can be taken off to get at the Dewar tube. At the end of this coil is a very carefully made expansion valve V, operated from outside. In the tube A″ the previously cooled gas is further cooled by cold expanded gas from the valve sweeping over the outside, and finally the hydrogen liquefies, the liquid collecting in the small Dewar vessel. The cold hydrogen gas passes out through a copper coil C wound in close contact with the coil A, and takes heat from the incoming hydrogen in the latter. The liquid air boiling in the outer Dewar vessel gives off cold air which passes out through another copper coil D, wound between the two coils A and C, and also takes up heat from the incoming hydrogen. The brass vessel B is in two pieces screwed together. 300–400 c.c. of liquid hydrogen are obtained per hour with a gas velocity of 2–3 c.c. per sec. and the use of about 300 c.c. of liquid air. The most important part of the apparatus is the expansion valve V. The theory of the efficiency of hydrogen (and helium) liquefiers [1] shows that the maximum effect occurs at pressures for which the Joule-Thomson effect $(dT/dp)_H = 0$.

§ 7. Liquid Helium

Although Dewar [2] claimed to have liquefied helium by simply cooling in liquid hydrogen, Olszewski [3] failed to do this, and concluded that the temperature of liquefaction was below −271°. It is certain that the first to make liquid helium was Kamerlingh Onnes,[4] on 10 July, 1908. The maximum inversion temperature (§ 25.VII A) of helium is about −173°, and the gas must be cooled below this temperature before expansion, which must then cool it below −267·8°.

The original apparatus used by Onnes is shown *diagrammatically* [5] in Fig. 6.VI C (the complete diagram is very complicated). A volume of 200 lit. of helium was used. The gas was compressed to 100 atm., and passed through a water separator cooled by the vapour of liquid air in a Dewar vessel. The cooled helium gas divided through two tubes passing to regenerative coolers, the first cooled by helium vapour from the liquefier and the second by hydrogen vapour. The two streams of gas combined and passed through charcoal in a tube immersed in liquid air, to remove traces of air from the helium. The gas then

[1] Keesom, *Comm. Leiden*, 1928, Suppl. **65***f.*

[2] *J.C.S.*, 1898, **73**, 528; *Ann. Chim.*, 1898, **14**, 145.

[3] *Ann. Phys.*, 1896, **59**, 184; 1905, **17**, 994.

[4] *Nature*, 1908, **78**, 370; *Compt. Rend.*, 1908, **147**, 421; *Proc. K. Akad. Wetens. Amsterdam*, 1908, **11**, 108 (*Comm. Leiden*, **108**); 1926, **29**, 1176 (*Comm. Leiden*, **158**); *Comm. Leiden*, 1910, Suppl. **21***a*; *ibid.*, 1922, Suppl. **45**; *Trans. Faraday Soc.*, 1922, **18**, 145; Crommelin, *ibid.*, 1922, **18**, 175; for other descriptions of helium liquefaction, see Meissner (Reichsanstalt apparatus), *Naturwiss.*, 1925, **13**, 695; *Phys. Z.*, 1926, **26**, 689; 1928, **29**, 610; McLennan, *Nature*, 1923, **112**, 135; Ruhemann, *Z. Phys.*, 1930, **65**, 67 (small scale); Simon and Ahlberg, *ibid.*, 1933, **81**, 816; Kapitza, *Proc. Roy. Soc.*, 1934, **147**, 189; Rollin, *Proc. Phys. Soc.*, 1936, **48**, 18; Kürti, Lainé, Rollin, and Simon, *Compt. Rend.*, 1936, **202**, 1421; Dixit, *Current Sci.*, 1938, **6**, 589; Sellier, *Z. kompr. flüss. Gase*, 1941, **36**, 13, 39; Schallmach, *J. Sci. Instr.*, 1943, **20**, 195; Van Itterbeek, *Meded. K. Vlaam. Acad. Wetens.*, 1943, No. 10; *Bull. Intern. Inst. Froid*, 1943, **24**, Annex 9 (Louvain liq. He app.).

An apparatus in which liquid helium temperatures are attained without complete liquefaction of the helium was described by Seiler, *Z. Elektrochem.*, 1941, **47**, 116; *Ann. Phys.*, 1941, **39**, 129; on the manipulation of liquid helium, Meissner, Polanyi, and Schmid, *Z. Phys.*, 1930, **66**, 477; Van Itterbeek, *Nature*, 1939, **143**, 560; *Physica*, 1939, **6**, 728; Simon, *ibid.*, 1940, **7**, 502; Anon., *Nature*, 1947, **160**, 736 (Collins app.).

[5] Burton, Smith, and Wilhelm, " Phenomena at the Temperature of Liquid Helium," New York, 1940, 24, Fig. 8; for later apparatus, see Keesom, " Helium," Amsterdam, 1942, 150 f., 155 (solid He).

passed through a spiral cooled in liquid air, through a regenerator C cooled by hydrogen vapour, a spiral D cooled to −258° in liquid hydrogen, and then through a regenerator spiral A cooled by helium vapour. (In the actual apparatus, A and C were vertical and not side by side, as shown.)

The helium was then expanded through a valve V, and partly liquefied in an unsilvered Dewar tube E, the helium vapour passing from B through a regenerator (not shown) back to the compressor. The liquid hydrogen (20 lit. were

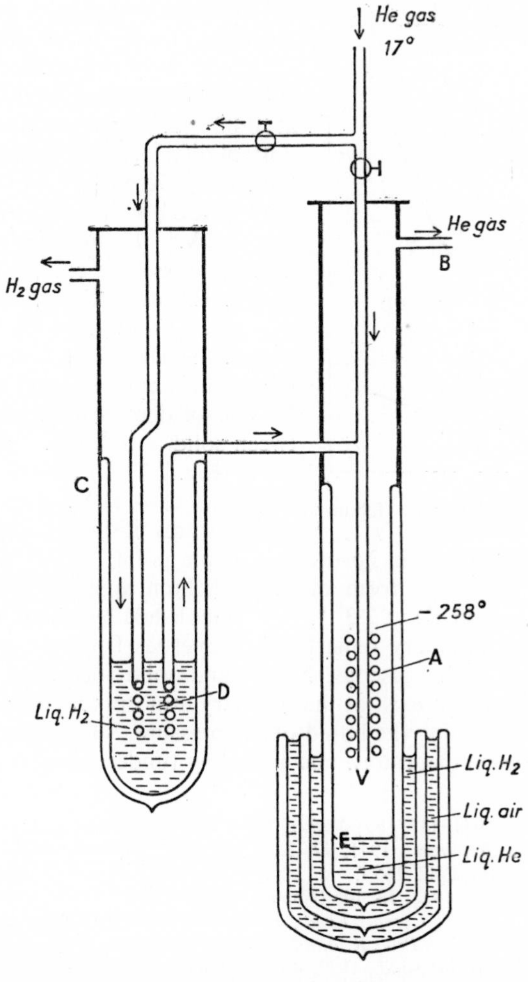

FIG. 6.VI C. Liquefaction of Helium (diagrammatic)

used) was contained in a Dewar vessel cooled in liquid air, and could be siphoned to surround the cooling spiral D. The height of liquid hydrogen was checked by a helium gas thermometer in C, with a metal capillary passing to a mercury manometer. This liquid hydrogen was under the reduced pressure of 6 cm. Hg (−258°), the vapour being drawn off by a pump. The bulb of a second helium gas thermometer, containing gas below atmospheric pressure, was immersed in the liquid helium collecting in the Dewar vessel E, surrounded by a second one containing liquid hydrogen, which was in turn surrounded by a third one containing liquid air. These were unsilvered and the whole was surrounded by a vessel of alcohol to prevent deposition of moisture.

The liquid was kept in a Dewar vessel immersed in another containing liquid hydrogen, and this in turn in a third Dewar vessel containing liquid nitrogen. In his first experiments Onnes obtained 60 c.c. of liquid helium. By reducing the pressure to 3 cm. Hg he reached a temperature of $-271 \cdot 6°$.

In an apparatus designed by Kapitza [1] liquid hydrogen is not used for pre-cooling, but liquid air or nitrogen, the first temperature drop being effected in an expansion engine (§ 4) to below the inversion point, after which the Joule-Thomson effect is used.

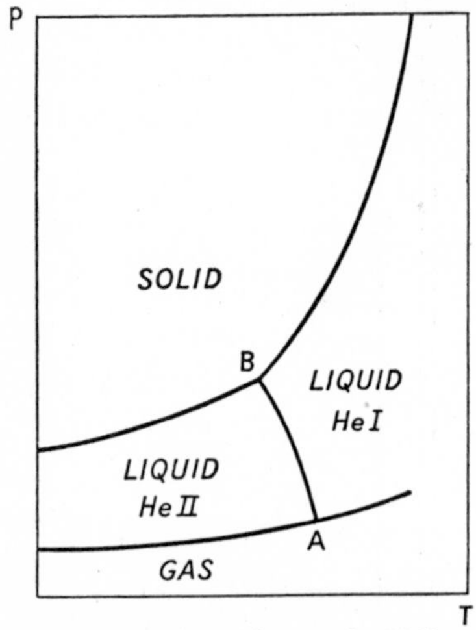

FIG. 7.VI C. Phase Diagram for Helium

Onnes found that liquid helium boiling at 0·82° K. under reduced pressure did not solidify.[2] Solid helium was first obtained by Keesom [3] by a method previously used with hydrogen by Onnes and van Gulik.[4] Helium was compressed in a narrow brass tube cooled in liquid helium, and at 130 atm. the tube became blocked by solid. In a glass tube with a magnetic stirrer, the latter was found to stick when the strongly cooled liquid was compressed. No line of demarcation could be seen between solid and liquid. The solidification curve (Fig. 7.VI C) was traced from 1·1° K. (20 atm.) to 4·2° K. (140 atm.). At low temperatures it bends and tends to run horizontal, and helium has no ordinary triple point. At B there is a change of slope, when a second form of liquid helium appears.[5] The triple point (solid, liquid I, liquid II) at 2·3° K. was established by a cooling curve.

Helium thus shows very remarkable properties from the point of view of phase transitions. The gaseous, liquid, and solid forms are all known, but the solid form does not exist at the ordinary atmospheric pressure, and can be obtained only by cooling the liquid under pressure. The liquid can, therefore, exist at very low temperatures, and probably (under the very low pressure of

1 *Proc. Roy. Soc.*, 1934, **147**, 189; *Nature*, 1934, **133**, 708; Hausen, *Z. ges. Kälte-Ind.*, 1941, **48**, 24; Lane, *Rev. Sci. Instr.*, 1941, **12**, 326; Meissner, *Phys. Z.*, 1942, **43**, 261; Keesom, "Helium," Amsterdam, 1942, 165 f.

2 *Trans. Faraday Soc.*, 1922, **18**, 145 (*Comm. Leiden*, **159**).

3 *Nature*, 1926, **118**, 81; *Compt. Rend.*, 1926, **183**, 26, 189 (*Comm. Leiden*, 1926, **184***b*); *Natuurw. Tijds.*, 1929, **11**, 65; *Proc. K. Akad. Wetens. Amsterdam*, 1932, **35**, 136 (*Comm. Leiden*, **219***a*; 0·7° K.); *Z. ges. Kälte-Ind.*, 1933, **40**, 49; Simon, Ruhemann, and Edwards, *Z. phys. Chem.*, 1929, **2** B, 340; 1929–30, **6** B, 62; on Keesom (with portrait), Verschaffelt, *Physica*, 1929, **9**, 1.

4 *Comm. Leiden*, 1926, **184***a*; van Gulik and Keesom, *ibid.*, 1928, **192***b*; Keesom and Lisman, *ibid.*, 1931, **213***e*; 1932, **221***a*.

5 Keesom and Wolfke, *Comm. Leiden*, 1927, **190***b*; Keesom and Clusius, *ibid.*, 1931, **216***b*; 1932, **219***e*, *f*; Keesom, *ibid.*, 1932, Suppl. **71***e*; Keesom and Keesom, *ibid.*, 1932, **221***d*; 1933, **224***d*, Suppl. **75***a*, **76***b*; *Physica*, 1933, **1**, 128; 1935, **2**, 557; 1936, **3**, 105, 359; Keesom and Taconis, *ibid.*, 1937, **4**, 28, 256; Simon, *Nature*, 1934, **133**, 529; Kaischew and Simon, *ibid.*, 1934, **133**, 460; Schubnikow and Kikoin, *Sow. Phys. Z.*, 1936, **10**, 119; Bijl, *Physica*, 1937, **4** 329; Allen and Jones, *Nature*, 1939, **143**, 227; Satterly, *Rev. Mod. Phys.*, 1936, **8**, 347 (diagram); Burton, Smith, and Wilhelm, "Phenomena at the Temperature of Liquid Helium." New York, 1940, 60. See §8. VIII E, Vol. II.

the vapour) it could exist at absolute zero. Helium does not, therefore, show a triple point, since the fusion and evaporation curves never intersect.

Still more remarkable is the existence of two different kinds of *liquid* helium, called He I and He II, which differ in density, surface tension, viscosity, dielectric constant, thermal conductivity, etc.,[1] one form changing sharply into the other at a so-called Λ-point of 2·19° K. Just below this point the specific heat curve rises steeply; just above it, the curve falls again to a normal value.

§ 8. Low-temperature Baths (Cryostats)

Low-temperature thermostats, or *cryostats*, for various temperatures are described. At 0° ice is used;[2] for temperatures below 0° various freezing mixtures are formed by mixing ice with different salts,[3] the commonest being ice and common salt (−18°).[4] A mixture of 3 parts of $CaCl_2,6H_2O$ and 2 parts of dry snow reaches −40° C., when mercury (m.p. −38·9°) freezes.[5] Snow or ice and concentrated hydrochloric acid can be used,[6] and a mixture of Glauber's salt ($Na_2SO_4,10H_2O$) and concentrated hydrochloric acid (−18·6°).[7] The eutectic mixtures or " cryogens " of ice and various salts were investigated by Guthrie,[8] covering the range −9·85° to −24·9°; the theory of freezing mixtures was discussed by Porter and Gibbs.[9] Mixtures of crystals of washing soda ($Na_2CO_3,10H_2O$) with nitrates of copper, lead, bismuth, and aluminium, liquefy and produce temperatures as low as −18°.[10]

For lower temperatures, solid carbon dioxide is very convenient. The dry solid is a poor conductor of heat. Awbery[11] found that the temperature of solid carbon dioxide crushed into small pieces may fall to −95·5° by evaporation, and is not constant throughout the mass. The solid is usually made into a paste with a liquid such as ether, acetone, alcohol, toluene,[12] or trichlorethylene.[13] Prevention of frothing in solid CO_2-acetone baths was described by McGregor.[14]

According to Cailletet and Colardeau[15] solid carbon dioxide in air has a

1 Ehrenfest, *Comm. Leiden*, 1933, Suppl. **75b**; Keesom and Keesom, *Proc. K. Akad. Wetens. Amsterdam*, 1933, **36**, 612; London, *Phys. Rev.*, 1938, **54**, 947; *J. Phys. Chem.*, 1939, **43**, 49; Keesom, " Helium," Amsterdam, 1942, 218, 220, 255 f.; Kapitza, *J. Phys. U.S.S.R.*, 1944, **5**, 59; Landau, *ibid.*, 1944, **5**, 71; Anon, *Nature*, 1947, **160**, 736.

2 Morse, *Amer. Chem. J.*, 1911, **45**, 383; Cohen, *Z. phys. Chem.*, 1911, **75**, 475; Foote and Akerlof, *Ind. Eng. Chem. Anal.*, 1931, **3**, 389; see § 5. VI A.

3 Réaumur, *Mém. Acad. Sci.*, 1734, 167; Walker, *Phil. Trans.*, 1788, **78**, 395; 1789, **79**, 199; 1795, **85**, 270; 1801, **91**, 120; abdgd. edit., 1809, **16**, 501, 579; **17**, 560.

4 Archibald, *J.A.C.S.*, 1932, **54**, 3886; Gortner, *Science*, 1914, **39**, 584, found −21°; cryostat, Walton and Judd, *J. Phys. Chem.*, 1914, **18**, 717.

5 Graham, " Elements of Chemistry," 2nd edit., 1850, **1**, 46, 218.

6 Witz, *Compt. Rend.*, 1876, **82**, 329; Pfaundler, *J.C.S.*, 1876, **30**, i, 867; ii, 39.

7 Szydlowski, *Wien Ber.*, 1907, **116**, IIA, 855.

8 *Phil. Mag.*, 1875, **49**, 269; 1876, **1**, 49. Gay-Lussac, *Ann. Chim.*, 1822, **21**, 82, was able to freeze mercury by a mixture of ice and salt in vacuum, the water vapour being absorbed by sulphuric acid.

9 *Phil. Mag.*, 1922, **44**, 787.

10 Walton, *Phil. Mag.*, 1881, **12**, 290.

11 *J. Sci. Instr.*, 1932, **9**, 200.

12 *Ether* was used by Faraday (§ 1); *acetone* by D'Arsonval, *Compt. Rend.*, 1901, **133**, 980; *toluene* by Trautz and Gerwig, *Z. anorg. Chem.*, 1924, **134**, 409; Cameron, *Rev. Sci. Instr.*, 1933, **4**, 610; Denslow, *Chemist-Analyst*, 1937, **26**, 33.

13 Beatty, *Science*, 1946, **103**, 235.

14 *Science*, 1945, **102**, 648.

15 *Compt. Rend.*, 1886, **106**, 1489, 1631; cf. Landolt, *Ber.*, 1884, **17**, 309; Lorenz, *Z. ges. Kälte-Ind.*, 1896, **3**, 148, 191, 211, 231; Mollier, *ibid.*, 1896, **3**, 63, 90; Du Bois and Wills, *Verhl. d. D. Phys. Ges.*, 1899, **1**, 168; Behn, *Ann. Phys.*, 1900, **3**, 733; Travers and Gwyer, *Z. phys. Chem.*, 1905, **52**, 433 (who say ether is no better than alcohol); Thiel and Caspar,

temperature of $-60°$ and in vacuum $-76°$; a paste with ether has a temperature of $-77°$ in air and $-103°$ in vacuum. With other liquids the temperatures in air are: CH_3Cl $-82°$, SO_2 $-82°$, amyl acetate $-78°$, PCl_3 $-76°$, absolute alcohol $-72°$, $C_2H_4Cl_2$ $-60°$. In vacuum these mixtures mostly solidify. Methyl chloride alone can be used [1] to $-38°$.

The temperatures given by Cailletet and Colardeau are all too high: some other results are: (i) solid carbon dioxide *in air* $-78{\cdot}16°$,[2] $-78{\cdot}34°$,[3] $-78{\cdot}2°$,[4] $-80°$,[5] $-79°$,[6] $-78{\cdot}4°$,[7] $-78{\cdot}35°$,[8] $-78{\cdot}483°$;[9] (ii) solid carbon dioxide and *alcohol* $-78{\cdot}6$,[10] $-78{\cdot}34$;[7, 8] (iii) solid carbon dioxide and *ether* $-79°$,[6] $-78{\cdot}26°$,[2] $-79{\cdot}5$.[11] Du Bois and Wills,[12] with solid carbon dioxide under 5-mm. pressure, obtained a temperature of $-124°$. Carbon disulphide frozen in liquid air [13] has a temperature of $-112°$, and liquid methane $-164°$.

For still lower temperatures, liquid oxygen, nitrogen, or air can be used. Normal liquid air has a temperature [14] of $-194{\cdot}4°$ (not $-193°$ as commonly stated), but its temperature, of course, depends on its composition. Behn and Kiebitz [15] measured the temperature of liquid air by its density, found by a series of small calibrated silica glass floats, using Baly's [16] figures for the relation between composition and boiling-point. On the International Temperature Scale the b.p. of oxygen at a pressure of p mm. is: [17]

$$-182{\cdot}970+0{\cdot}0126\,(p-760)-0{\cdot}0_565\,(p-760)^2.$$

The b.p. of nitrogen at 760 mm. is [18] $-195{\cdot}81°$ or [19] $-195{\cdot}787°$. The triple points (solid+liq.+gas) are: [18] oxygen $54{\cdot}24\pm0{\cdot}04°$ K., $p=1{\cdot}20\pm0{\cdot}05$ mm.; nitrogen $63{\cdot}09°$ K., $p=93{\cdot}91\pm0{\cdot}05$ mm., or [19] $-219{\cdot}994°$ C. and $9{\cdot}401$ cm. Hg.

In low-temperature cryostats, some kind of low-freezing-point liquid, generally a mixture, [20] is used. *Liquid air* (or oxygen or nitrogen) cooling,[21] usually

ibid., 1914, **86**, 257; Thiel and Schulte, *ibid.*, 1920, **96**, 312; Michels, Blaisse, and Koens *Physica*, 1942, **9**, 356.

1 Moissan, *Compt. Rend.*, 1901, **133**, 786; Cohen and Olie, *Z. phys. Chem.*, 1910, **71**, 394.

2 Regnault, *Ann. Chim.*, 1849, **26**, 257.

3 Zeleny and Zeleny, *Phys. Z.*, 1906, **7**, 716.

4 Zeleny and Smith, *Phys. Z.*, 1906, **7**, 667.

5 Pictet, *Arch. Sci. Phys. Nat.*, 1878, **61**, 16; *Ann. Phys. Beibl.*, 1878, **2**, 131.

6 Villard and Jarry, *Compt. Rend.*, 1895, **120**, 1413.

7 Holborn, *Ann. Phys.*, 1901, **6**, 242.

8 Average value adopted by Thiel and Caspar, *Z. phys. Chem.*, 1914, **86**, 257 (bibl. of 14 authors); Thiel and Schulte, *ibid.*, 1920, **96**, 312; Kannuluik and Law, *J. Sci. Instr.*, 1946, **23**, 154.

9 Heuse and Otto, *Ann. Phys.*, 1931, **9**, 486; in *ibid.*, 1932, **14**, 185, they give $-78{\cdot}471°$; Aoyama and Kanda, *J. Chem. Soc. Japan*, 1934, **55**, 15, found $-78{\cdot}51°$; for apparatus for dry-ice cooling, see Brown, *J. Franklin Inst.*, 1945, **240**, 487.

10 Ladenburg and Krügel, *Ber.*, 1899, **32**, 1818.

11 Archibald and McIntosh, *J.A.C.S.*, 1904, **26**, 305.

12 *Verhl. d. D. Phys. Ges.*, 1899, **1**, 168.

13 Stock, *Ber.*, 1913, **46**, 1971.

14 Keyes, *J.A.C.S.*, 1941, **63**, 3545.

15 *Ann. Phys.*, 1903, **12**, 421.

16 *Phil. Mag.*, 1900, **49**, 517; for modern values, see Dodge and Dunbar, *J.A.C.S.*, 1927, **49**, 591; for temperatures below the b.p. of oxygen, Hoge, in "Temperature. Its Measurement and Control," New York, 1941, 141.

17 Burgess, *Bur. Stand. J. Res.*, 1928, **1**, 635; Heuse and Otto, *Ann. Phys.*, 1932, **14**, 185 (b.p. $-182{\cdot}965°$; N_2 $-195{\cdot}814°$; CO $-191{\cdot}484°$); Anon., *Nature*, 1949, **163**, 427.

18 Justi, *Ann. Phys.*, 1934, **10**, 983.

19 Keesom and Bijl, *Proc. K. Akad. Wetens. Amsterdam*, 1937, **40**, 235; *Physica*, 1937, **4**, 305 (bibl.).

20 Ruhemann and Lichter, *Sow. Phys. Z.*, 1934, **6**, 139; Ruhemann, Lichter, and Komarow, *ibid.*, 1935, **8**, 326.

21 Plotnikow, *Z. phys. Chem.*, 1905, **53**, 605; McIntosh and Steele, *ibid.*, 1906, **55**, 129;

applied to some low-freezing-point liquid such as pentane (when precautions must be taken to avoid explosions from the mixing of the oxygen with pentane vapour) is common. For still lower temperatures, *liquid hydrogen* [1] is used, and at still lower temperatures *liquid helium*.[2] For various kinds of *low temperature cryostats*, reference must be made to the literature.[3] A *constant* triple point of hydrogen is only found with a small amount of liquid present, otherwise there is a temperature gradient in the liquid.[4]

Between the temperatures of liquid nitrogen and hydrogen and liquid hydrogen and helium, there are gaps not covered by other liquid gases. Temperatures in the second of these ranges may be attained by Simon's [5] *desorption method.*

Stoltzenberg, *ibid.*, 1910, **71**, 649; Stock, *Ber.*, 1913, **46**, 1971; Henning, *Z. Instr.*, 1913, **33**, 33; Germann, *Phys. Z.*, 1913, **14**, 857; Holst and Hamburger, *Z. phys. Chem.*, 1916, **91**, 513; Holborn and Otto, *Z. Phys.*, 1924, **30**, 320; Jackson, *J. Sci. Instr.*, 1925, **2**, 158; Walters and Loomis, *J.A.C.S.*, 1925, **47**, 2302 (to −180°); Patterson, *Phil. Mag.*, 1926, **2**, 383; Southard and Andrews, *J. Franklin Inst.*, 1929, **207**, 323; Egerton and Ubbelohde, *Trans. Faraday Soc.*, 1930, **26**, 236; MacGillivray and Swallow, *J. Sci. Instr.*, 1930, **7**, 257; Scott and Brickwedde, *Bur. Stand. J. Res.*, 1931, **6**, 401; Shepherd, *ibid.*, 1938, **21**, 831; Peters, *Chem. Fabr.*, 1934, **7**, 47; Baldeschwieler and Wilcox, *Ind. Eng. Chem. Anal.*, 1939, **11**, 221; for a constant temperature apparatus in dry air at −180°, see Cioffi and Taylor, *J. Opt. Soc. Amer.*, 1922, **6**, 906; Bose, *Indian J. Phys.*, 1947, **21**, 275.

[1] Onnes, *Proc. K. Akad. Wetens. Amsterdam*, 1902, **5**, 505, 628 (*Comm. Leiden*, **83**); 1905–6, **8**, 75, 77, 79, 82 (*Comm. Leiden*, **94**); 1917, **19**, 1049 (*Comm. Leiden*, **151***a*); Nernst, *Z. Elektrochem.*, 1911, **17**, 735; Latimer, Buffington, and Hoenshel, *J.A.C.S.*, 1925, **47**, 1571; Ruhemann, *Z. Phys.*, 1930, **65**, 67; Aoyama and Kanda, *J. Chem. Soc. Japan*, 1934, **55**, 23 (−250°).

[2] Onnes, *Proc. K. Akad. Wetens. Amsterdam*, 1911–12, **14**, 204 (*Comm. Leiden*, **123***a*); *Z. angew. Chem.*, 1913, **26**, iii, 813; Onnes and Crommelin, *Proc. K. Akad. Wetens. Amsterdam*, 1921, **23**, 1185 (*Comm. Leiden*, **154***c*); Mendelssohn, *Z. Phys.*, 1931, **73**, 482; Justi, *Ann. Phys.*, 1931, **9**, 570; Daunt and Mendelssohn, *Proc. Phys. Soc.*, 1938, **50**, 525; Alekseev and Shalnikov, *J. Exptl. Theor. Phys. U.S.S.R.*, 1946, **16**, 361.

[3] D'Arsonval, *Compt. Rend.*, 1901, **133**, 980; Timmermans, *Proc. Roy. Dublin Soc.*, 1912, **13**, 310; von Siemens, *Ann. Phys.*, 1913, **42**, 871; Henning, *Z. Instr.*, 1913, **33**, 33; Cardoso, *Arch. Sci. Phys. Nat.*, 1913, **36**, 97; 1915, **29**, 400; *J. Chim. Phys.*, 1915, **13**, 312; Meissner, *Ann. Phys.*, 1915, **47**, 1001; Stock, *Ber.*, 1920, **53**, 751; Henning and Stock, *Z. Phys.*, 1921, **4**, 226; Maass and Wright, *J.A.C.S.*, 1921, **43**, 1098; Taylor and Smith, *ibid.*, 1922, **44**, 2450; Keyes, Taylor, and Smith, *J. Math. Phys. Mass. Inst. Techn.*, 1922, **1**, 211; Walters and Loomis, *J.A.C.S.*, 1925, **47**, 2302 (liq. air; short bibl.); Trautz and Gerwig, *Z. anorg. Chem.*, 1925, **146**, 1; Jackson, *J. Sci. Instr.*, 1925, **2**, 158; Sligh, *J. Opt. Soc. Amer.*, 1925, **10**, 691; Meissner, in Geiger and Scheel, "Handbuch der Physik," 1926, **11**, 272; Dana, Burdick, and Timm, *Refrig. Eng.*, 1926, **12**, 387; Kanolt, *Bur. Stand. Bull.*, 1926, **20**, 619 (*Sci. Pap.* No. 520); Simon *et al.*, *Ber.*, 1927, **60**, 568; 1928, **61**, 2173; Maass and Barnes, *J.A.C.S.*, 1927, **49**, 360; Andrews and Southard, *J. Franklin Inst.*, 1929, **207**, 323; Zintl, *Ber.*, 1930, **63**, 234; Schattenstein, *Z. anorg. Chem.*, 1930, **193**, 187 (32 refs.); *Z. Elektrochem.*, 1934, **40**, 653; Bartlett *et al.*, *J.A.C.S.*, 1930, **52**, 1363; Scott and Brickwedde, *Bur. Stand. J. Res.*, 1931, **6**, 401; Monosson and Pleskow, *Z. phys. Chem.*, 1931, **156**, 176; Feher, *Z. Elektrochem.*, 1932, **38**, 53; Lundström and Whittaker, *Ind. Eng. Chem. Anal.*, 1932, **4**, 294; Romberg, *Chem. Fabr.*, 1932, 89; Kambara and Matsui, *J. Soc. Chem. Ind. Japan*, 1933, **36**, suppl. bdg. 134; Deitz, *J.A.C.S.*, 1933, **55**, 472 (Al block); Southard and Brickwedde, *ibid.*, 1933, **55**, 4378; Lalande, *J. Chim. Phys.*, 1934, **31**, 439 (theory and bibl.); Adenstedt, *Ann. Phys.*, 1936, **26**, 69; Heisig, *Ind. Eng. Chem. Anal.*, 1936, **8**, 149 (solid CO_2, +25° to −75°); Blaisse, Cooke, and Hull, *Physica*, 1936, **6**, 231; Ruhemann, "Low Temperature Physics," Cambridge, 1937; Blue and Hicks, *J.A.C.S.*, 1937, **59**, 1962; Kurte and Voana, *Zavodskaya Lab.*, 1937, **6**, 107; Booth and Bozorth, *Ind. Eng. Chem.*, 1937, **29**, 470; Roper, *J.A.C.S.*, 1938, **60**, 1693; Thode, *ibid.*, 1940, **62**, 581; "Temperature: its Measurement and Control in Science and Industry," New York, 1941; Tarbutton, Egan, and Frary, *J.A.C.S.*, 1941, **63**, 1782; Van Itterbeek and de Bock, *Physica*, 1946, **12**, 163; Aston and Fink, *Chem. Rev.*, 1946, **39**, 357; Collins, *Phys. Rev.*, 1946, **70**, 98 (He cryostat); *Rev. Sci. Instr.*, 1947, **18**, 157; Tunnicliff, *Anal. Chem.*, 1948, **20**, 962.

[4] Messerly, *J.A.C.S.*, 1941, **63**, 1487.

[5] *Z. ges. Kälte-Ind.*, 1927, **34**, 217; *Phys. Z.*, 1926, **27**, 790; 1934, **87**, 815; Justi, *Ann. Phys.*, 1931, **9**, 570 (50° K. to 112° K.); *Z. Phys.*, 1933, **87**, 273; Van Itterbeek and Vereycken, *Physica*, 1936, **3**, 954.

Helium is adsorbed on charcoal in a vessel cooled in liquid hydrogen, with helium gas in a space between the two to conduct away the heat liberated. This gas is then pumped out, leaving a non-conducting gap, and the helium is desorbed from the charcoal by powerful pumping, when the temperature can be lowered as far as the boiling-point of helium. By adsorbing under pressure,[1] the heat absorbed in expansion is also utilised, and the temperature can be lowered to 1·5 K. Another type of apparatus, working on the principle of a micro-Linde apparatus,[2] will bridge both gaps.

§ 9. Very Low Temperatures

Since about 1930 there have been great advances in the attainment of very low temperatures, with a corresponding increase of knowledge in many directions. It was well said by M. and B. Ruhemann [3] that: "Half a century's experience has taught us that as long as we are in a position to attain yet lower temperatures, there will always be something of interest to study there, even if it is but those processes with the help of which the temperature has been lowered. No one seriously believes that because five-thousandths of a degree is the lowest limit hitherto reached, there is no point in attempting to go farther."

By the rapid evaporation of liquid helium, Keesom [4] in 1932 reached the temperature of 0·71° K., but a limit was set to this method by the circumstances: (i) at very low temperatures the vapour pressure of liquid helium is lower than the pressure attainable by the best vacuum pump, (ii) the heat entering the system from the surroundings may reach the maximum amount of heat which can be extracted by the evaporating liquid. Temperatures below this point, and closely approaching absolute zero, were first attained by the new method of *adiabatic demagnetisation* due to Debye [5] and Giauque.[6]

§ 10. Magnetic Susceptibility

Of the theory of magnetic susceptibility, only enough will be given here as is required to make clear the method of attaining very low temperatures.[7]

1 Mendelssohn, *Z. Phys.*, 1931, **73**, 482.

2 Ruhemann, *Z. Phys.*, 1930, **65**, 67; "Low Temperature Physics," Cambridge, 1937, 49; cf. Crawhall, "Very Low Temperatures," 1936 (Sci. Mus., London), 4, 8.

3 "Low Temperature Physics," 1937, preface.

4 *Proc. K. Akad. Wetens. Amsterdam*, 1932, **35**, 136.

5 *Ann. Phys.*, 1926, **81**, 1154 (theory); 1938, **32**, 85.

6 *J.A.C.S.*, 1927, **49**, 1864, 1870.

7 Gans, *Ann. Phys.*, 1915, **49**, 149 (theory of dia-, para-, and meta-magnetism); Eger, *Z. Metallkde*, 1914, **5**, 278; 1914, **6**, 89; 1914, **7**, 93; 1919, **10**, 82 (metals and alloys); Reiche, *Ann. Phys.*, 1917, **54**, 401 (old quantum theory of paramagnetism); "Report of the Committee on Theories of Magnetism of the National Research Council," Washington, 1922; Weiss and Foëx, "Le Magnétisme," Paris, 1926; E. C. Stoner, "Magnetism and Atomic Structure," 1926; "Magnetism," 1930, 3rd edit., 1946; "Magnetism and Matter," 1934; Cabrera, *J. de Phys.*, 1927, **8**, 257; *An. Fis. Quim.*, 1928, **26**, 50; Stoner, *Sci. Progr.*, 1927, **21**, 600; *Proc. Phys. Soc.*, 1930, **42**, 358; Allen, *ibid.*, 1930, **42**, 372; Powell, *ibid.*, 1930, **42**, 390; Bates, *ibid.*, 1930, **42**, 441; Congress on Magnetism, 6e *Conseil Solvay* (*Physique*), 1932; Van Vleck, "Theory of Electric and Magnetic Susceptibilities," Oxford, 1932; reports by various authors in *Rapport Cons. Solvay Phys.* (1930), Paris, 1932; summary of Leiden work by Gorter, *Arch. Mus. Teyler*, 1933, **7**, 183; Grimm and Wolf, Magnetochemie, in Geiger and Scheel, "Handbuch der Physik," 1933, **24**, ii, 1119; Bhatnagar and Mathur, "Physical Principles and Applications of Magneto-Chemistry," 1935; Klemm, "Magnetochemie," Leipzig, 1936; for several papers on magnetism, see *Sci. Rep. Tôhoku Imp. Univ.*, 1936, *Honda Anniversary Volume*; Jellinek, "Lehrbuch der physikalischen Chemie," 1937, **5**, 629; Robey and Dix, *J. Chem. Educ.*, 1937, **14**, 414; Bhatnagar, *Sci. and Culture*, 1938, **3**, 466; Selwood, "Magnetochemistry," New

In 1778 Brugman,[1] of Leiden (where much of the latest work on the subject has been done), noticed that a floating piece of bismuth is *repelled* by a pole of a magnet, and Becquerel [2] found that antimony repels, and is repelled by, a magnetic pole. Faraday [3] (who quite inadequately mentions the earlier workers) used a powerful electromagnet, and found that all substances are acted upon, some being attracted and called by him *paramagnetic*, others repelled and called *diamagnetic*. Tyndall's researches on "magnecrystallic action" were summarised by Bragg.[4] If the pole strength of a bar magnet of length l and cross-section a is m, the magnetic moment is ml, and the quotient of this by the volume, or the moment per cm.^{3}, is called the *intensity of magnetisation* (or magnetic polarisation),[5] $J=ml/al=m/a$ (=pole strength÷area of pole surface). If this were due to the material of the magnet being put into a magnetic field of strength **H**, the ratio $J/\mathbf{H}=\kappa$ is called the *magnetic susceptibility* of the material. The dimension of κ is a volume; if J is in c.g.s. units and **H** in ørsteds, κ is in cm.^{3} The ørsted is $0{\cdot}4\pi ni$, where n=turns of wire per cm. on a solenoid, i=current in amp.

The field strength **H** may be defined by the number of magnetic lines of force crossing 1 cm.^{2} of area in the field in vacuum. Inside the material put into the field this number will be different, and is equal to the *magnetic induction* **B**. Since each unit pole generates 4π lines of force:

$$\mathbf{B}=\mathbf{H}+4\pi J \qquad (1)$$

$$\therefore\ \mathbf{B}/\mathbf{H}=1+4\pi J/\mathbf{H}=1+4\pi\kappa.$$

The unit of **B** is the gauss. The ratio **B**/**H** is called the *permeability* μ, hence:

$$\mu=1+4\pi\kappa \qquad (2)$$

The unit [6] of μ is [gauss]/[ørsted]. If $\mathbf{B}>\mathbf{H}$ it follows that $\mu>1$, hence κ is positive for paramagnetic substances; if $\mathbf{B}<\mathbf{H}$, $\mu<1$ and κ is negative for

York, 1943; Klemm, *Z. Elektrochem.*, 1945, **51**, 14 (review; inorganic compounds); Müller, *ibid.*, 1945, **51**, 23 (review; organic compounds); Ray and Sahu, *J. Indian Chem. Soc.*, 1946, **23**, 161 (salts); Bozorth, *Rev. Mod. Phys.*, 1947, **19**, 29; for the physical aspects of magnetism, see, e.g., F. Auerbach, in L. Graetz, "Handbuch der Elektrizität und des Magnetismus," Leipzig, 1920, **4**, 1, 711; Auerbach, "Modern Magnetics," transl. Booth, 1925; Schmidt, in Chwolson, "Lehrbuch der Physik," 2nd edit., 1927, **4**, ii, 424; Geiger and Scheel, "Handbuch der Physik," 1927, **15**, 147 (Steinhaus), 222 (Gumlich); 1927, **16**, 679 (Steinhaus), 688 (Gumlich); Peddie, "Molecular Magnetism," 1929; Klemm, *Z. angew. Chem.*, 1931, **44**, 250; 1935, **48**, 617; Vogt, Magnetismus der metallischen Elemente, in *Ergebn. d. exakt. Naturwiss.*, 1932, **11**, 323; Kussmann, *Z. Metallkde.*, 1933, **25**, 259; 1934, **26**, 25; Gmelin, "Handbuch der anorganischen Chemie," 8th edit., 1934, **59** A, 1421; Vogt, *Z. angew. Chem.*, 1935, **48**, 734; Sugden, *J.C.S.*, 1943, 328; summary of earlier magneto-chemical papers by Cabrera, *J. Chim. Phys.*, 1918, **16**, 444.

[1] "Magnetismus seu de affinitatibus magneticis observationes," Leiden, 1779; Poggendorff, *Ann. Phys.*, 1827, **10**, 293; Henrichson, *ibid.*, 1888, **34**, 180.

[2] Becquerel, *Ann. Chim.*, 1827, **36**, 337; Le Baillif, *Bibl. Univers.*, 1829, **40**, 82.

[3] *Phil. Trans.*, 1846, **136**, 21; 1851, **141**, 7; *Phil. Mag.*, 1847, **31**, 401; *Ann. Phys.*, 1847, **70**, 24; 1848, **73**, 256; 1851, **82**, 327; Plücker, *Ann. Phys.*, 1848, **73**, 549; Weber, *ibid.*, 1848, **73**, 241 (theory of magnetism).

[4] *Proc. Roy. Inst.*, 1927, **25**, 161; Tyndall, *Phil. Trans.*, 1855, **145**, 1; 1856, **146**, 237; "Researches on Diamagnetism and Magnecrystallic Action," 1870; for magnetic properties of crystals, see Voigt, "Lehrbuch der Kristallphysik," Leipzig, 1928, 468, 505; Krishnan *et al.*, *Phil. Trans.*, 1933, **231**, 235; 1935, **234**, 265; 1936, **235**, 343; Lonsdale, *Sci. Progr.*, 1938, **32**, 677; Selwood and Parodi, *J. Chem. Educ.*, 1947, **23**, 574.

[5] The symbol M is sometimes used for J, and the symbol σ is sometimes used for the surface density of magnetisation; in the case considered this is identical with J; for another use, see § 14.

[6] On the "dimensions" of μ, etc., see e.g. Kennelly, *Proc. Amer. Phil. Soc.*, 1931, **70**, 103; 1.33, **72**, 39; Kaye and Laby, "Tables of Physical and Chemical Constants," 1948, 8.

diamagnetic substances. The relation of *para*- and *dia*-magnetism to the ratio **B**/**H** was explained by Faraday. For dia- and para-magnetic materials, κ is a constant; for ferromagnetic materials it depends on **H**. The susceptibility κ is the moment per cm.³; the *mass susceptibility* (susceptibility *per gram*) is $\chi=\kappa/\rho$, where ρ=density in g./cm.³, and the *molar susceptibility* $\chi_m=M\chi=M\kappa/\rho=\kappa V_m$, where M=molar weight, and V_m=molar volume.[1]

§ 11. Curie's Law

It has long been known that the strength of a magnet decreases at higher temperatures, and at a red heat a steel magnet loses its magnetism. A very simple law relating the magnetic susceptibility to the absolute temperature was discovered by Curie:[2] $\chi=C/T$, where C is a constant. Curie's law applies strictly only to a dilute system such as a paramagnetic gas (of which very few, notably O_2 and NO, are available). Curie himself tested the law with the results of Wiedemann[3] and of Plesser[4] on solutions of paramagnetic salts. Wiedemann measured the force F of attraction in a magnetic field **H** and verified the formula $F=aM\mathbf{H}^2$, where a is the mass of the body and M the moment induced by unit field. He showed for various salts that the moment (which, in arbitrary units, he called the *specific magnetism*) is proportional to the concentration, as had been found before by Plücker (1848), the magnetism (or diamagnetism) of the solvent being involved additively. The product of the specific magnetism by the molecular weight, or the *molecular magnetism*, was found to be the same for different salts of a metal with the same valency:

	Chloride	Nitrate	Sulphate	Mean
Ferrous	38·58	38·62	39·04	38·7
Ferric	96·33	94·10	92·97	94·5

In this case, for equal weights of metal, the ferric salts are 1·24 times as magnetic as the ferrous. The same values were found for crystalline salts. Complex salts (e.g. ferro- and ferri-cyanides) gave much smaller values, $K_4Fe(CN)_6$ being, as Faraday had found, diamagnetic. Wiedemann found that the magnetism of solutions decreased with rise of temperature, and for different substances by the same fraction of the value at 0° for 1° rise in temperature. If $M_0=100$, then $M_t=100-0{\cdot}325t$, the coefficient being nearly the same as that giving the decrease of electrical conductivity of a pure metal with rise of temperature. Curie in all cases found approximate agreement with his law, but the ranges of temperature were fairly small.

Onnes[5] made the important suggestion that crystalline salts, in which the paramagnetic ions are largely " diluted " with diamagnetic ions and molecules of water of crystallisation, might be expected to behave like dilute solutions,

1 Van Vleck uses χ for κ and $\chi_{\text{mol.}}$ for χ_m.

2 *Compt. Rend.*, 1892, **115**, 1292; 1894, **118**, 1134; *Ann. Chim.*, 1895, **5**, 289–405; " Oeuvres," Paris, 1908, 232; Larmor, " Mathematical and Physical Papers," Cambridge, 1929, **2**, 115, 735; Kanzler, *Ann. Phys.*, 1939, **36**, 38 (compressed O_2); Burris and Hause, *J. Chem. Phys.*, 1943, **11**, 442 (O_2, NO).

3 *Ann. Phys.*, 1865, **126**, 1; 1868, **135**, 177; 1878, **7**, 45; 1887, **32**, 452; earlier experiments by Plücker, *ibid.*, 1848, **74**, 321; 1854, **91**, 1; 1886, **27**, 376, used the magnetic balance method usually attributed to Gouy, *Compt. Rend.*, 1889, **109**, 935. Bequerel, *Ann. Chim.*, 1850, **28**, 282; 1851, **32**, 68; 1855, **44**, 209, also made many measurements. For permeabilities at low temperatures, see Dewar and Fleming, *Proc. Roy. Soc.*, 1896–7, **60**, 57.

4 *Ann. Phys.*, 1890, **39**, 336; Henrichsen, *ibid.*, 1888, **34**, 180; 1892, **45**, 38, made many measurements with organic compounds.

5 Onnes and Perrier, *Comm. Leiden*, 1911, **122a**.

and Onnes and Oosterhuis confirmed Curie's law for ferric alum between 14·7° K. and 290° K., in which interval χ varies from 30×10^{-6} to 600×10^{-6}, but χT is constant at about 880×10^{-5} to $\pm0{\cdot}5$ per cent. Similar results were found by Jackson [1] for hydrated manganese ammonium sulphate; by Onnes, Perrier, and Oosterhuis [2] for hydrated gadolinium sulphate; by Leiterer [3] for chromium salts; and by Giauque and MacDougall [4] for gadolinium phosphomolybdate. By using this device, the magnetic moments of many paramagnetic ions have been determined. The absorption spectra show that the rare earth ions behave, in fact, like ions in the gaseous state under the influence of external electric fields.[5] Oxley [6] explained deviations from Curie's law by the formation of aggregates of particles.

§ 12. Weiss's Law

For many paramagnetic substances $1/\chi$ is a linear function of temperature, as required by Curie's law, but on extrapolation to $T=0$, the line does not pass through the origin as Curie's law requires, but cuts the temperature axis at some point above or below the absolute zero. This behaviour is shown by compressed and liquid oxygen, many concentrated solutions, and many crystalline salts.

This result may, as Weiss [7] showed, be represented by the equation:

$$\chi=C/(T-\Theta) \quad \text{or} \quad 1/\chi=T/C-n$$

where Θ (sometimes denoted by Δ) is the temperature of intersection of the $1/\chi$ line with the T axis, and is called the *Curie point*, and $n=\Theta/C$. The table below gives some values [8] of Θ, and it is seen that the agreement is often unsatisfactory, probably owing to the presence of traces of impurities.

$Fe_2(SO_4)_3$	$CuSO_4$	$CoSO_4$	$MnSO_4$	$FeSO_4$	$FeCl_2$	$MnCl_2$	$NiCl_2$
−79·5 (T.)	−72 (I.)	−29·9 (T.)	−19·0(T.)	−16·0 (I.)	+20·4	+3·1 (T.)	+70·0(I.)[a]
−73·0 (I.)					(W. & W.)	+21·0 (I.)	+94·0 (I.)[b]
							+77·6 (T.)
							+67·0(W.)

a Below 220° K. *b* Above 220° K.

Weiss's law was verified by Jackson and Onnes [9] for crystals at low temperatures. The Curie point may be expected to be sharply defined; an interval of temperature has been ascribed to inhomogeneity of material.[10] A supposed

[1] *Phil. Trans.*, 1923, **224**, 1.

[2] Onnes and Perrier, *Comm. Leiden*, 1911, **122***a*; 1914, **139***a*; Oosterhuis, *ibid.*, 1914, **139***b*; Perrier and Onnes, *ibid.*, 1914, **139***c*: Oosterhuis, *Phys. Z.*, 1913, **14**, 862; Foëx, *Compt. Rend.*, 1913, **157**, 1145.

[3] *Z. phys. Chem.*, 1936, **36** B, 325.

[4] *J.A.C.S.*, 1938, **60**, 376.

[5] Freed and Spedding, *J.A.C.S.*, 1930, **52**, 3747; Spedding and Nutting, *ibid.*, 1933, **55**, 496; see § 17.

[6] *Proc. Cambr. Phil. Soc.*, 1912, **16**, 486.

[7] *Compt. Rend.*, 1907, **144**, 25; *Ann. de Phys.*, 1914, **1**, 134; summary by Stern, *Phys. Z.*, 1911, **12**, 935; *Z. Phys.*, 1920, **1**, 147; Kunz, *Phys. Rev.*, 1915, **6**, 113; Honda, *Sci. Rep. Tôhoku Imp. Univ.*, 1932, **21**, 332; Gorter, *Phys. Z.*, 1932, **33**, 546. On Weiss, see Foëx, *Ann. de Phys.*, 1945, **20**, 111.

[8] From Ishiwara (I.), *Sci. Rep. Tôhoku Imp. Univ.*, 1914, **3**, 303; Honda and Ishiwara, *ibid.*, 1915, **4**, 215; Théodoridès (T.), *Arch. Sci. Phys. Nat.*, 1921, **3**, 5, 137; *J. de Phys.*, 1922, **3**, **1**; Woltjer (W.), *Comm. Leiden*, 1923, **167***b*; Woltjer and Wiersma (W. and W.), *ibid.*, 1929, **201***a*; and Laurent, *J. de Phys.*, 1938, **9**, 331 ($NiCl_2$); cf. Guha, *Nature*, 1945, **155**, 364.

[9] *Compt. Rend.*, 1923, **177**, 154; *Proc. Roy. Soc.*, 1923, **104**, 671; Jackson, *Phil. Trans.*, 1923, **224**, 1; 1926, **226**, 107.

[10] Kussmann and Schulze, *Phys. Z.*, 1937, **38**, 42.

displacement of the Curie point by tension [1] is non-existent.[2] Some empirical equations relating specific heat to the Curie point were given by Ashworth.[3]

De Klerk [4] found that $CuK_2(SO_4)_2,6H_2O$ obeys Weiss's law below 1°K. with $\Theta=0{\cdot}052$, and the specific heat satisfies the $1/T^2$ law.

Weiss explained his law by assuming that when the paramagnetic ions are not in the condition of an ideal gas, the effect of the influence of adjacent particles is equivalent to a *molecular field* $\mathbf{H}_m$ set up by interaction, proportional to the intensity of magnetisation J and acting in the same direction as the applied magnetising field $\mathbf{H}$, but in either the same or the opposite sense. The *effective field* is thus:

$$\mathbf{H}_e=\mathbf{H}+\mathbf{H}_m=\mathbf{H}+cJ$$

where c is a constant. If the mean magnetic moment per *mol* in a field $\mathbf{H}$ is $\bar{\sigma}=N\mu$, where μ=molecular moment, N=Avogadro's number, then since J is the moment per cm.^{3}, $J=\bar{\sigma}/V_m$, where V_m is the molar volume: [5]

$$\mathbf{H}_e=\mathbf{H}+c\bar{\sigma}/V_m=\mathbf{H}+c'\bar{\sigma}$$

where $c'=c/V_m$. Substituting the effective field instead of $\mathbf{H}$ in Curie's law gives:

$$\bar{\sigma}=C(\mathbf{H}+\mathbf{H}_m)/T=C(\mathbf{H}+c'\bar{\sigma})/T$$

and thus

$$\chi_m=C/(T-c'C)=C/(T-\Theta)$$

where $\chi_m=\bar{\sigma}/\mathbf{H}$ is the molar susceptibility and $\Theta=c'C$. Since Θ may be positive or negative, this must also hold for c', i.e. the molecular field may either increase or decrease the effect of the *external* magnetising field.

By considering the exchange effect (resonance) between neighbouring ions, Heisenberg [6] deduced Weiss's law by quantum mechanics, but the subject still admits of progress and, as van Vleck [7] said: " the perfectionist will not get the same comfort from magnetochemistry as he does from spectroscopy."

§ 13. Measurement of Magnetic Susceptibilities

Various methods of determining magnetic susceptibilities have been used.[8] The classical method, used by Plücker and Gouy, and improved by Curie and

[1] Ray-Chaudhuri, *Z. Phys.*, 1931, **71**, 473.

[2] Englert, *Z. Phys.*, 1935, **97**, 94.

[3] *Nature*, 1928, **121**, 323; on *ferro-* and *para-magnetic Curie points*, see Cabera, *An. Fis. Quim.*, 1924, **22**, 463; 1928, **26**, 50; *J. de Phys.*, 1925, **6**, 241, 273; Cabrera and Palacios, *An. Fis. Quim.*, 1926, **24**, 297; Forrer, *Compt. Rend.*, 1929, **188**, 1242; on *diamagnetism*, Debye, in Marx, " Handbuch der Radiologie," Leipzig, 1925, **6**, 668; Bieler, *J. Franklin Inst.*, 1927, **203**, 211; Klemm, " Magnetochemie," 1936, 160, 196; Kremann and Pestemer, " Zusammenhänge zwischen physikalischen Eigenschaften und chemischer Konstitution," 1937, 159; Cabrera, *J. Chim. Phys.*, 1941, **38**, 1; Smith, *Sci. Progress*, 1946, **34**, 764.

[4] *Physica*, 1946, **12**, 513; correcting Casimir, de Klerk, and Polder, *ibid.*, 1940, **7**, 737.

[5] See § 10; it will be noted that $\bar{\sigma}$ (mostly used in the literature) replaces $\chi_m\mathbf{H}$.

[6] *Z. Phys.*, 1928, **49**, 619.

[7] *J. Phys. Chem.*, 1944, **48**, 235; on the doubtful physical significance of Θ see Penney and Schlapp, *Phys. Rev.*, 1932, **41**, 194; Selwood, *J.A.C.S.*, 1933, **55**, 3161 (who found different values of Θ with different compounds of Nd).

[8] Plücker, *Ann. Phys.*, 1854, **91**, 1; Wiedemann, *ibid.*, 1865, **127**, 1; Quincke, *Ann. Phys.*, 1885, **24**, 347; 1888, **34**, 401; Königsberger, *ibid.*, 1898, **66**, 698; Gouy, *Compt. Rend.*, 1889, **109**, 935; du Bois, *Congrès Internat. Phys.*, 1900, **2**, 460; Chéneveau, *Phil. Mag.*, 1910, **20**, 357; Honda, *Ann. Phys.*, 1910, **32**, 1027; Owen, *ibid.*, 1912, **37**, 657; Foëx, *Ann. de Phys.*, 1921, **16**, 174; Driggs and Hopkins, *J.A.C.S.*, 1925, **47**, 363; Decker, *Ann. Phys.*, 1926, **79**, 324; Aharoni and Simon, *Z. phys. Chem.*, 1929, **4 B**, 175; Almeda, *An. Fis. Quim.*, 1947, **43**, 421; and literature in § 10.

Chéneveau, measures the pull on a small rod of substance, or a powder or liquid in a small glass tube, hanging vertically from a balance in the *inhomogeneous* field in the pole-gap of a circular permanent magnet. In the Weiss-Foëx method, the substance is fixed at the end of a horizontal rod with a bifilar suspension, the movement of which tilts a mirror. Electromagnets are now generally used. In Quincke's method, used for liquids, the rise (or fall) of liquid in a tube in the air-gap is measured. In some cases very large magnets have been used, e.g. the Leiden magnet giving a field of 30,000 ørsted [1] across a pole gap of 16 mm. and using 450 kw. In low-temperature work,[2] very narrow Dewar vessels with very thin walls are used, including double and triple vessels blown in one piece with silvered walls and with a total diameter less than 2 cm. Very ingenious adaptations of the apparatus include one in which a horizontal metal tube containing the substance, e.g. a compressed gas, suspended by two V-shaped pairs of thin wires, moves horizontally in the magnetic field (Foëx method), the whole being enclosed in a horizontal cryostat through which a current of cold gas is passed. In another, the vertical tube containing the specimen is hung from floats in mercury, in a vacuous case, weights being put on the top, after the principle of Nicholson's hydrometer. When a large magnet is not available, a small solenoid immersed in liquid hydrogen (to reduce the resistance), with a strong current applied only for about a second to minimise heating, has been used by Ahroni and Simon. [3] Air-free water is generally used as a standard substance: its mass (diamagnetic) susceptibility, found by several recent workers whose results are in good agreement, is $-0{\cdot}720\times10^{-6}$, and the temperature coefficient [4] is $(1/\chi)\mathrm{d}\chi/\mathrm{d}t=2{\cdot}9\times10^{-4}$ at 5°, and $0{\cdot}62\times10^{-4}$ at 70°.

§ 14. Langevin's Formula

Langevin's formula [5] (σ_∞ being the value of σ for $\mathbf{H}\to\infty$):

$$\sigma/\sigma_\infty=\coth a-1/a;\ a=\mu\mathbf{H}/kT \quad . \quad . \quad . \quad . \quad . \quad . \quad (1)$$

was deduced on classical grounds for the change of paramagnetic susceptibility with temperature; the literal application of it would contradict the Nernst heat theorem, which requires a steeper approach to saturation.[6]

In Langevin's calculation, atoms of permanent moment μ are supposed to make angles θ with a magnetic field $\mathbf{H}$. The energy of each is $-\mu\mathbf{H}\cos\theta$.

[1] Since 1930 the name *ørsted* (or *oersted*) (ø) has been used for the c.g.s. unit of field strength **H**, the older name *gauss* being given to the unit of induction **B**.

[2] Onnes and Perrier, *Comm. Leiden*, 1911, **122***a*; 1914, **139** *a, c, d*; Onnes and Oosterhuis *ibid.*, 1913, **134***d*; Oosterhuis, *ibid.*, 1914, **139***b*; Woltjer, *ibid.*, 1923, **167***b*; *Proc. K. Akad Wetens. Amsterdam*, 1925, **28**, 536 (*Comm. Leiden*, **173***b*); Woltjer and Onnes, *Comm. Leiden*, 1923, **167***c*; *Proc. K. Akad. Wetens. Amsterdam*, 1925, **28**, 544 (*Comm. Leiden*, **173c**); Wiersma and Woltjer, *Comm. Leiden*, 1929, **201***c*; Woltjer and Wiersma, *Proc. K. Akad. Wetens. Amsterdam*, 1929, **32**, 735 (*Comm. Leiden*, **201***a*); de Haas, Wiersma, and Capel, *ibid.*, 1929, **32**, 739 (*Comm. Leiden*, **201***b*); Woltjer, Coppoolse, and Wiersma, *Comm. Leiden*, 1929, **201***d*; Wiersma, de Haas, and Capel, *ibid.*, 1931, **212***b*, **215***b*; Wiersma, " Eenige Onderzoekingen over Paramagnetisme," 's Gravenhage, 1932; de Haas and Wiersma, *Comm. Leiden*, 1932, Suppl. **74***b*, 36; brief summary in Ruhemann, " Low Temperature Physics," Cambridge, 1937, 207; Casimir, " Magnetism and Very Low Temperatures," Cambridge, 1941; for a summary of earlier work, see " Het Natuurkundig Laboratorium der Rijksuniversiteit te Leiden in de Jaren 1904–1922," Leyden, 1922, 233 f.; Gorter, *Arch. Mus. Teyler*, 1933, **7**, 183.

[3] See note 8, p. 522.

[4] Auer, *Ann. Phys.*, 1933, **18**, 593.

[5] *Ann. Chim.*, 1905, **5**, 70; for coth *x* see § 47.I.

[6] Debye, in Marx, " Handbuch der Radiologie," Leipzig, 1925, **6**, 668; *Ann. Phys.*, 1926, **81**, 1154.

The area cut off a sphere of unit radius by a strip of width $d\theta$ is (Fig. 8.VI C) $(2\pi \sin\theta)d\theta$, and by Boltzmann's equation (24), § 8.IV, the number of molecular magnets with axes directed in this solid angle is:

$$A'e^{\mu H \cos\theta/kT} \cdot 2\pi \sin\theta d\theta = Ae^{\mu H \cos\theta/kT} \sin\theta d\theta$$

where A' and A are constants. The moment in this direction is:

$$Ae^{\mu H \cos\theta/kT}\mu \cos\theta \sin\theta d\theta.$$

The mean moment is:

$$\bar{\mu} = \int_0^{\pi} Ae^{\mu H \cos\theta/kT}\mu \cos\theta \sin\theta d\theta \Big/ \int_0^{\pi} Ae^{\mu H \cos\theta/kT} \sin\theta d\theta.$$

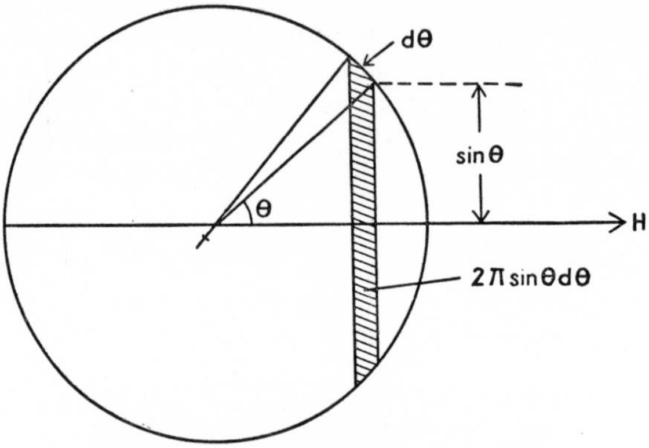

FIG. 8.VI C. Molecular Dipole in Field

Put $\mu H/kT = a$, $\cos\theta = x$, therefore $-\sin\theta d\theta = dx$, when:

$$\bar{\mu} = \mu \int_{-1}^{+1} e^{ax} x dx \Big/ \int_{-1}^{+1} e^{ax} dx = \mu\left(\frac{e^a + e^{-a}}{e^a - e^{-a}} - \frac{1}{a}\right) = \mu\,(\coth a - 1/a).$$

For

$$\int_{-1}^{+1} e^{ax} dx = (1/a)\Big[e^{ax}\Big]_{-1}^{+1} = (e^a - e^{-a})/a \quad . \quad . \quad . \quad . \quad . \quad (2)$$

and, by integration by parts (§ 19.I)

$$\int e^{ax} x dx = xe^{ax}/a - (1/a)\int e^{ax} dx = xe^{ax}/a - (e^{ax}/a^2)$$

$$\therefore \int_{-1}^{+1} e^{ax} x dx = \Big[xe^{ax}/a - e^{ax}/a^2\Big]_{-1}^{+1} = (e^a + e^{-a})/a + (e^{-a} - e^a)/a^2 \quad . \quad (3)$$

Divide (3) by (2), giving $(e^a + e^{-a})/(e^a - e^{-a}) - 1/a$. Hence (the value of coth a being inserted), equation (1) follows. With $\sigma = N\mu$ this gives Langevin's equation, the value μ corresponding with saturation, i.e. with σ_∞. If a is small, the exponentials under the integrals may be expanded and $1 + ax$ only retained, when the integrations easily give:

$$\bar{\mu} = \tfrac{1}{3}a\mu = \mu^2 H/3kT. \quad . \quad . \quad . \quad . \quad . \quad . \quad . \quad . \quad . \quad (4)$$

The calculation on the basis of quantum mechanics [1] shows that the shape of the saturation curve depends on the nature of all the lower energy levels, and

[1] Van Vleck, *Phys. Rev.*, 1927, **29**, 727; 1927, **30**, 31; 1928, **31**, 587; "Theory of Electric and Magnetic Susceptibilities," Oxford, 1932, 30, 181; Niessen, *Phys. Rev.*, 1929, **34**, 253; Freed and Kasper, *J.A.C.S.*, 1930, **52**, 4671; for older literature on the theories of magnetism, see various authors in *Bull. Nat. Res. Council*, 1922, **3**, No. 18.

no general formula can be derived; the approach to saturation, however, is steeper than Langevin's formula predicts.

A test of Langevin's formula by Woltjer and Onnes [1] with gadolinium sulphate, $Gd_2(SO_4)_3,8H_2O$, was made using fields up to 22,000 ø and low temperatures attainable with liquid helium. The resulting curve (Fig. 9.VI C), in which $(\sigma/\sigma_\infty)\times 5564/6\times 10^{23}$ is plotted against a, where σ_∞ is the saturation value, shows that Langevin's curve is followed up to 85 per cent. of saturation. The actual points, however, show a rather steeper approach to saturation than the curve.

Other experiments of this type are wanting, but an approach to the subject is possible in another direction, viz. from the *Faraday effect*,[2] the rotation of the

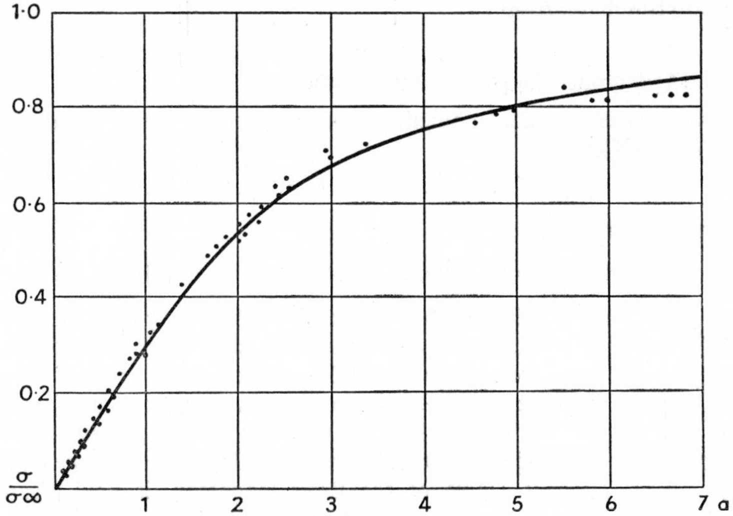

FIG. 9.VI C. Curve of Langevin's Equation with Experimental Points

plane of polarisation of plane polarised light passing through a substance placed in a magnetic field. This is not confined to liquids, but is also shown by transparent solids—it was discovered by Faraday with heavy glass. H. Becquerel [3] had shown that it is connected with the magnetic properties of the substance, and Kundt [4] that thin transparent films of ferromagnetic metals show a strong magnetic rotary power which is not proportional to the field strength but shows saturation. If it is *assumed* that the magnetic rotary power ω is proportional to the susceptibility σ, it will be connected with $\mathbf{H}/T$ by a Langevin formula: experiments by J. Becquerel [5] with field strengths up to 27,000 ø

[1] *Comm. Leiden*, 1923, **167***c*; van der Handel, *Physica*, 1941, **8**, 513.

[2] Faraday, *Phil. Trans.*, 1846, **136**, 1; see Vol. II.

[3] *Ann. Chim.*, 1877, **12**, 5; *Compt. Rend.*, 1897, **125**, 679.

[4] *Ann. Phys.*, 1884, **23**, 228.

[5] Becquerel *et al.*, *Comm. Leiden*, 1928, **191c**, **193***a*; 1929, **199***a*, *b*, **204***a*, *b*; 1929, Suppl. **68** *a*, *b*, *c*; 1930, **211***a*, *b*, *c*; 1931, **218***a*; 1932, Suppl. **78***a*; 1934, **231***a*; *Z. Phys.*, 1928, **52**, 678; 1929, **52**, 678; 1929, **57**, 11; 1929, **58**, 205; *J. de Phys.*, 1928, **9**, 346; *Compt. Rend.*, 1928, **186**, 1720; 1929, **188**, 1156; 1930, **191**, 782; 1934, **198**, 1400, 1849, 1987; *Proc. K. Akad. Wetens. Amsterdam*, 1929, **32**, 590 (*Comm. Leiden*, **199***b*), 1199; 1930, **33**, 913 (*Comm. Leiden*, **211***a*; bibl.); *Physica*, 1934, **1**, 383; 1936, **3**, 1133; 1937, **4**, 345; 1940, **7**, 705, 711, 945; de Haas and Gorter, *Proc. K. Akad. Wetens. Amsterdam*, 1930, **33**, 1101 (*Comm. Leiden*, **210***d*); Gorter, Dijkstra, and Groendijk, *Physica*, 1940, **7**, 625; Eisses, Groendijk, and Gorter, *ibid.*, 1940, **7**, 865.

and temperatures as low as 1·3° K., mostly with the mineral tysonite (La, Ce)F_3, and ethylsulphates of rare earths, showed that magnetic saturation is reached with strong fields and low temperatures. The values of ω for saturation depended on the temperature and on the frequency of the light. The rotational power depends on the absorption bands of the crystals, the absorption differing for two beams of light circularly polarised in opposite directions. The curves in general resemble that for gadolinium sulphate, and are in agreement with the formula of Kramers [1] for the case of a rare earth ion excited only in the ground state:

$$\omega = A \tanh (\mu \mathrm{H}/kT) + B\mathrm{H}$$

where, at low temperatures, A and B are functions of wave-length only. For erbium ethylsulphate, $B=0$.

§ 15. The Quantum Theory of Magnetism

The *mechanical* angular momentum of an electron with serial quantum number l (§ 14.V) is:

$$p_l = \sqrt{[l(l+1)]} \,.\, (h/2\pi) \quad (l=0, 1, 2, 3, \ldots) \quad . \quad . \quad . \quad . \quad (1)$$

The magnetic moment due to this is:

$$M_l = \tfrac{1}{2}(e/mc)p_l = \tfrac{1}{2}(e/mc)(h/2\pi)\sqrt{[l(l+1)]} = \sqrt{[l(l+1)]} \,.\, \mu_{0B} \quad . \quad (2)$$

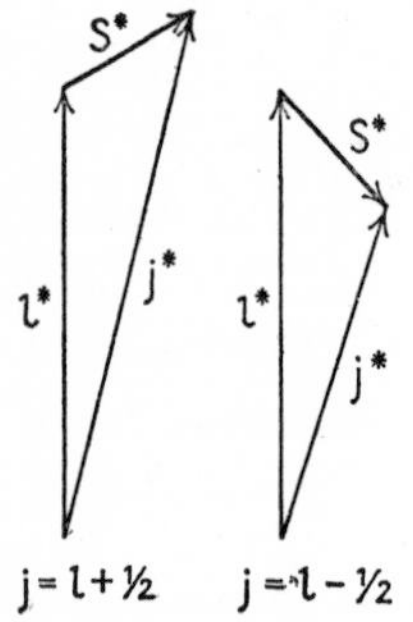

FIG. 10.VI C.

where $\mu_{0B} = eh/4\pi mc$ is the *Bohr magneton*, this being the moment of the magnetic shell equivalent to the electron revolving in the smallest Bohr orbit of the hydrogen atom [2] (viz. orbital, not electron spin). In e.m. units it is $9{\cdot}273 \times 10^{-21}$ erg ørsted^{-1}, or per mol ($N\mu_{0B}$) 5586 erg ørsted^{-1} mol^{-1}. The *Weiss magneton*,[3] which is 1/4·95 of the Bohr magneton, is now regarded as having no theoretical significance.

For the *spin* of the electron the angular momentum is, similarly:

$$p_s = \sqrt{[s(s+1)]} \,.\, (h/2\pi) \quad (s=\tfrac{1}{2}) \quad . \quad . \quad . \quad (3)$$

but the expression $M_s = \tfrac{1}{2}(e/mc)p_s$ for the corresponding magnetic moment gives only half the correct result, hence:

$$M_s = 2[\tfrac{1}{2}(e/mc)p_s] = (eh/4\pi mc)\sqrt{[4s(s+1)]} = \sqrt{[4s(s+1)]} \,.\, \mu_{0B} = 2\sqrt{[s(s+1)]} \,.\, \mu_{0B} \quad . \quad (4)$$

The two vectors $l^*(h/2\pi)$ and $s^*(h/2\pi)$, where:

$$l^* = \sqrt{[l(l+1)]} \text{ and } s^* = \sqrt{[s(s+1)]}$$

couple according to the following rules.[4] For a *single* electron they combine vectorially to give a vector $j^*(h/2\pi)$, where:

$$j^* = \sqrt{[j(j+1)]}$$

[1] *Proc. K. Akad. Wetens. Amsterdam*, 1929, **32**, 1176; 1930, **33**, 959; *Physica*, 1934, **1**, 182.

[2] Bohr, *Phil. Mag.*, 1913, **26**, 476, 857; Chalmers, *Nature*, 1914, **92**, 687; Vegard, *Phil. Mag.*, 1915, **29**, 651; *Ann. Phys.*, 1917, **53**, 27; Wereide, *Ann. Phys.*, 1916, **49**, 976; 1917, **52**, 276, 283, 289; 1917, **53**, 574; 1918, **55**, 589; Cabrera, *An. Fis. Quim.*, 1923, **21**, 505; *Rapp. Cons. Solvay*, Paris (1930), 1932, 81; Pauli, *ibid.*, 1932, 175.

[3] Weiss, *J. de Phys.*, 1911, **1**, 900, 965, and many later papers.

[4] Herzfeld, *Phys. Z.*, 1925, **26**, 824; Rabinowitsch, *Z. Elektrochem.*, 1933, **39**, 702.

and $j=l\pm s=l\pm\frac{1}{2}$. For $l=0$, 1, 2, there are the cases (Fig. 10.VI C):

$l=0,\ s=\frac{1}{2}$; $\quad j=\frac{1}{2},\ l^*=0$; $\quad s^*=\sqrt{3}/2,\ j^*=\sqrt{3}/2$;
$l=1,\ s=\frac{1}{2}$; $\quad j=\frac{1}{2}$ or $\frac{3}{2},\ l^*=\sqrt{2}$; $\quad s^*=\sqrt{3}/2,\ j^*=\sqrt{3}/2$ or $\sqrt{15}/2$;
$l=2,\ s=\frac{1}{2}$; $\quad j=\frac{3}{2}$ or $\frac{5}{2},\ l^*=\sqrt{6}$; $\quad s^*=\sqrt{3}/2,\ j^*=\sqrt{15}/2$ or $\sqrt{35}/2$.

For *more than one electron*, the corresponding expressions are:

$$S^*=\sqrt{[S(S+1)]} \quad S=0,\ \tfrac{1}{2},\ 1,\ \tfrac{3}{2}\ \ldots$$
$$L^*=\sqrt{[L(L+1)]} \quad L=0,\ 1,\ 2,\ \ldots.$$

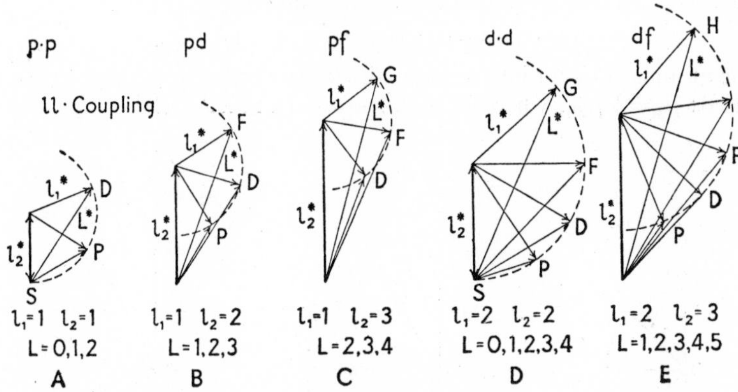

FIG. 11.VI C.

For *two* outer electrons with $l_1=1$ and $l_2=1$, $l_1^*=\sqrt{2}$ and $l_2^*=\sqrt{2}$, and the orientation is such that $L^*=\sqrt{[L(L+1)]}$, i.e. $L^*=0$, $\sqrt{2}$, and $\sqrt{6}$, since L is 0, 1, and 2. The other cases are shown in Fig. 11.VI C: [1]

$l_1=1, l_2=1$	$l_1=1, l_2=2$	$l_1=1, l_2=3$	$l_1=2, l_2=2$	$l_1=2, l_2=3$
$L=0, 1, 2$	$L=1, 2, 3$	$L=2, 3, 4$	$L=0, 1, 2, 3, 4$	$L=1,2,3,4,5.$

For the *spin* vectors for *two* outer electrons, $S^*=\sqrt{[\frac{1}{2}(\frac{1}{2}+1)]}=\sqrt{3}/2$ or zero, and the S^* values combine vectorially so that the resultant is 0 or $\sqrt{2}$, as shown in Fig. 12.VI C. The combination of the L^* and S^* vectors takes place, in

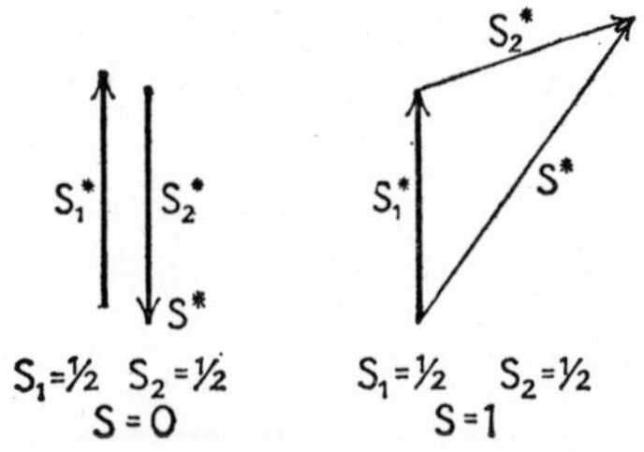

FIG. 12.VI C

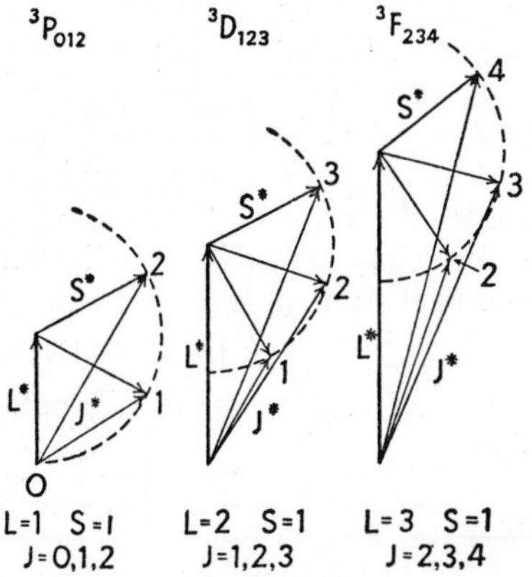

FIG. 13.VI C

[1] White, "Introduction to Atomic Spectra," New York, 1934, 121, 155, 184, 215.

so-called Russell-Saunder's coupling,[1] as shown in Fig. 13.VI C, to give a vector J^* $(h/2\pi)$, where:

$$L=1,\ S=1;\ J=0,\ 1,\ 2;\ L^*=\sqrt{2},\ S^*=\sqrt{2};\ J^*=\sqrt{[J(J+1)]}=0,\ \sqrt{2},\ \text{or}\ \sqrt{6}.$$

The orientation of J^* in a not too strong magnetic field is such that its projection $m=J^* \cos \vartheta$ in the direction of the field (ϑ=angle between the magnetic axis and the field) is integral (Fig. 14.VI C). The *magnetic moment*, μ, of the atom may now be compounded of the component moments μ_J as follows.

If $S=0$ then $J=L$, and every value of L corresponds with only one state (*singlet*). In this case for all atoms at all temperatures:

$$\mu=\sqrt{[J(J+1)]}\ .\ \mu_{0B}=\sqrt{[L(L+1)]}\ .\ \mu_{0B}.$$

If the atom is brought into a magnetic field its moment parallel to the field is quantised: $\mu_m=M\mu_{0B}$, where $M=-J,\ -(J-1),\ldots,J$. (Note that this is not

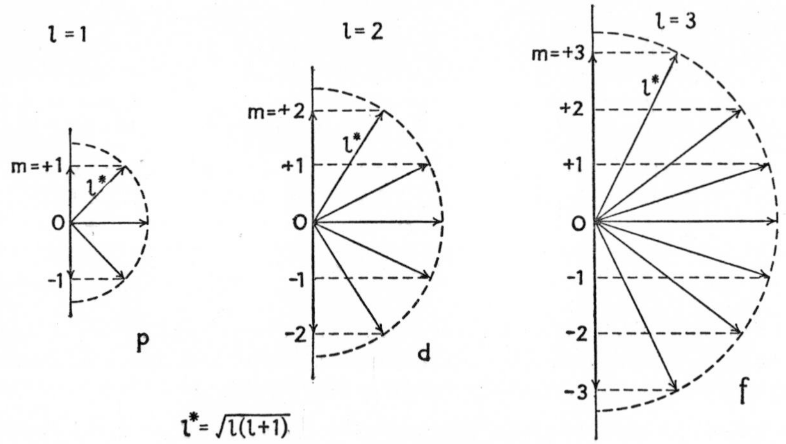

FIG. 14.VI C. Space Quantisation

$\sqrt{[M(M+1)]}$, since there is now a *fixed* axis, that of the applied field). The *average value* of μ_m is given by the usual statistical equation:

$$\bar{\mu}_m=\Sigma M\mu_{0B}e^{\mathbf{H}\mu_{0B}M/kT}/\Sigma e^{\mathbf{H}\mu_{0B}M/kT} \quad . \quad . \quad . \quad . \quad . \quad . \quad (5)$$

where the sums are from $M=-J$ to $M=+J$. The *molar susceptibility* χ_m is defined by $N\bar{\mu}_m=\chi_m\mathbf{H}$, where N is Avogadro's number.

The evaluation of the expression (5) is tedious but simple. The projection of J^* on the direction of $\mathbf{H}$ is given by $m=J^* \cos \vartheta$. For each atom there are $2J+1$ orientations (all positive and negative values of J, and zero). The *potential energy* of the atomic magnet is $-\mu\mathbf{H} \cos \vartheta$, where μ is the moment, and the number of atoms oriented in a given direction ϑ at a given temperature and field strength is given by Boltzmann's equation (§ 8.IV) as:

$$[A'/(2J+1)]e^{-\epsilon/kT}=Ae^{-\epsilon/kT}=Ae^{\mu\mathbf{H}\cos\vartheta/kT}$$

where A' is a constant, independent of ϑ. The average value of $\mu \cos \vartheta$ is then

$$\overline{\mu \cos \vartheta}=\Sigma(\mu \cos \vartheta)e^{\mu\mathbf{H}\cos\vartheta/kT}/\Sigma e^{\mu\mathbf{H}\cos\vartheta/kT}$$

[1] In this, the s vectors of all the electrons $(s_i.h/2\pi)$ combine to form a resultant S^*, and independently all the l vectors $(l_i.h/2\pi)$ form a resultant L^*. The two resultants S^* and L^* then combine vectorially to form a resultant J^*. (S^*, L^*, and J^* are quantum numbers multiplying $h/2\pi$ to give the magnitudes of the corresponding vectors.)

where the sums are taken from $-J$ to $+J$. Since $\cos\vartheta = m/J^* = m/\sqrt{[J(J+1)]}$, and μ is a constant:

$$\therefore\ \overline{\mu\cos\vartheta} = \mu\Sigma\{m/\sqrt{[J(J+1)]}\}e^{\beta m/\sqrt{[J(J+1)]}}/\Sigma e^{\beta m/\sqrt{[J(J+1)]}}$$

where $\beta = \mu\mathbf{H}/kT$. For small values of $\mathbf{H}$ the exponentials may be expanded and only the first term retained ($e^x = 1+x$):

$$\therefore\ \overline{\mu\cos\vartheta} = \mu\Sigma\{m/\sqrt{[J(J+1)]}\}.\{1+\beta m/\sqrt{[J(J+1)]}\}/\Sigma\{1+\beta m/\sqrt{[J(J+1)]}\} \quad (6)$$

The denominator in (6) can be written:

$$\Sigma\{1+\beta m/\sqrt{[J(J+1)]}\} = (2J+1)+\{\beta/\sqrt{[J(J+1)]}\}[J+(J-1), \ldots +0, -(J-1)-J] = 2J+1$$

since J is kept intact but m varied from $-J$ to $+J$, giving $(2J+1)$ terms, and the sum in square brackets is zero. The numerator is:

$$\Sigma\{m/\sqrt{[J(J+1)]}\}\{1+\beta m/\sqrt{[J(J+1)]}\} = \Sigma\{m/\sqrt{[J(J+1)]}\}+\Sigma[\beta m^2/J(J+1)]$$
$$= \{1/\sqrt{[J(J+1)]}\}[J+(J-1), \ldots +0, -(J-1)-J]+[\beta/J(J+1)]\Sigma m^2$$
$$= [\beta/J(J+1)]\Sigma m^2.$$

Now $\sum_0^n x^2 = (2n+1)n(n+1)/6$, both for integral values of x and values which are odd multiples of $\frac{1}{2}$; hence:

$$[\beta/J(J+1)]\Sigma m^2 = [\beta/J(J+1)]\,.\,2(2J+1)J(J+1)/6 = (\beta/3)(2J+1)$$

(the multiple 2 coming from the sets of positive and negative values of J). Hence:

$$\overline{\mu\cos\vartheta} = \tfrac{1}{3}\mu\beta(2J+1)/(2J+1) = \mu\beta/3 = \mu^2\mathbf{H}/3kT.$$

Since $\overline{\mu\cos\vartheta} = \bar{\mu} = \chi_m\mathbf{H}/N$

$$\therefore\ \chi_m = \mu^2N/3kT = (\mu N)^2/3kNT = (\mu N)^2/3\boldsymbol{R}T = C/T$$

where $C = (N\mu)^2/3\boldsymbol{R}$ is the Curie constant,

$$\therefore\ N\mu = \sqrt{(3\boldsymbol{R}C)} \quad . \quad . \quad . \quad . \quad . \quad . \quad . \quad . \quad . \quad (7)$$

This is identical with the classical Langevin equation (see § 14) and differs from the equation found from the *old* quantum theory. All these equations hold also for the case $L=0$, therefore $J=S$ (S-terms).

For *multiplet terms*, with all the atoms practically in the ground states, each component is defined by S, L, and J. The atom precesses round the direction of the vector J^*, but on account of the "double" magnetism of the spins (see above) the direction of the resultant moment μ is usually different from that of J^*.

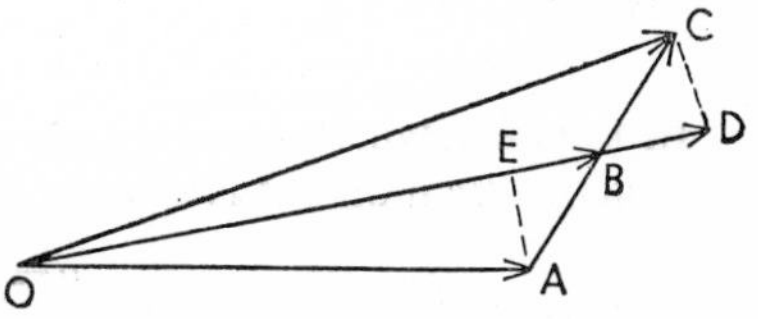

FIG. 15.VI C.

In Fig. 15.VI C, OA is the mechanical orbital impulse vector $L^* = \sqrt{[L(L+1)]}\,.\,\boldsymbol{h}/2\pi$ drawn as $\sqrt{[L(L+1)]}$ units, AB is mechanical spin vector $S^* = \sqrt{[S(S+1)]}\,.\,\boldsymbol{h}/2\pi$ drawn as $\sqrt{[S(S+1)]}$ units, and OB the resultant total mechanical impulse vector $\sqrt{[J(J+1)]}\,.\,\boldsymbol{h}/2\pi$. Now L^* produces a moment $\sqrt{[L(L+1)]}\,.\,\boldsymbol{eh}/4\pi mc = \sqrt{[L(L+1)]}$, which is drawn from O and of the same length as OA (actually it is in the opposite direction), and S^* produces a moment $2\sqrt{[S(S+1)]}\,.\,\boldsymbol{eh}/4\pi mc$ drawn as 2AB=AC. The resultant moment is represented by OC.

$$\mathrm{OA}=\sqrt{[L(L+1)]}(e\boldsymbol{h}/4\pi mc)=\mu_L$$

$$\mathrm{AC}=2\mathrm{AB}=\mu_S=2\sqrt{[S(S+1)]}(e\boldsymbol{h}/4\pi mc)$$

$$\mathrm{OC}=\mu=\sqrt{(\mu_L^2+\mu_S^2-2\mu_L\mu_S\cos\mathrm{OAC})}$$

$$\cos\mathrm{OAC}=\cos\mathrm{OAB}=(\mathrm{OA}^2+\mathrm{AB}^2-\mathrm{OB}^2)/2\mathrm{OA}\,.\,\mathrm{OB}$$

$$=\frac{L(L+1)+S(S+1)-J(J+1)}{2\sqrt{[L(L+1)]}\,.\,\sqrt{[S(S+1)]}}$$

$$\therefore\ \mathrm{OC}=\mu=\sqrt{[2J(J+1)+S(S+1)-L(L+1)]}\,.\,(e\boldsymbol{h}/4\pi mc).$$

Of the total moment μ, on account of precession of μ_L and μ_S about the direction of J^*, only the projection OE of μ_L=OA on OB, and the projection ED of μ_S=AC on OB, come in. Their sum, OE+ED=OD, is also the projection of μ=OC on OB, i.e. μ_J, therefore μ_J=OD=OA cos AOB+2AB cos OBA.

The two cosines are again given from the mechanical impulses in the triangle OAB and the result is:

$$\mu_J=\mathrm{OD}=\sqrt{[J(J+1)]}\left[1+\frac{J(J+1)+S(S+1)-L(L+1)}{2J(J+1)}\right](e\boldsymbol{h}/4\pi mc)$$

$$=g\sqrt{[J(J+1)]}\,.\,\mu_{\mathrm{OB}} \quad \ldots\ldots\ldots \quad (8)$$

where $g=1+[J(J+1)+S(S+1)-L(L+1)]/2J(J+1)$

is called *Landé's splitting factor*,[1] and arises from the "double" spin magnetism.

Such an atom in a magnetic field is subject to two effects:

(i) If a directional force is exerted by the field during the precession, the latter is deformed and a component in the direction of the field, proportional to **H**, appears, viz. $\chi_{2m}=\mathbf{H}\alpha$, where α is the constant of *induced magnetism* (analogous to induced electric polarisation);

(ii) a temperature-dependent magnetic polarisation χ_{1m}, obeying Curie's law but with μ_J in place of μ, appears:

$$\chi_{1m}=(N\mu_{\mathrm{OB}})^2g^2J(J+1)/3\boldsymbol{R}T=(N\mu_J)^2/3\boldsymbol{R}T=C/T$$

$$N\mu_J=\sqrt{(3\boldsymbol{R}C)}.$$

The total susceptibility is given by a formula analogous to Debye's for the electric polarisation:

$$\chi_m=\chi_{1m}+\chi_{2m}=(N\mu_J^2+3\boldsymbol{k}T\alpha)/3\boldsymbol{k}T.$$

In the case where $L=S\neq0$, $J=0$, the mechanical impulses cancel, but as the spin *magnetic* moment is double the orbital, there is a residue:

$$\mu=\mu_{\mathrm{OB}}\sqrt{[S(S+1)]}.$$

The atom then has no *permanent* magnetic moment ($\mu_J=0$ for $J=0$), since the direction of μ in the atom is completely indefinite, and there is no orientation of μ in a magnetic field. (This is related to Heisenberg's uncertainty principle, § 14.IV). The whole paramagnetism then depends on the induced moment (e.g. Eu^{+++}).

The above case refers to "wide multiplets," when $\Delta\epsilon_J\gg\boldsymbol{k}T$, where $\Delta\epsilon_J$ is the energy difference between the ground state and the higher level for a multiplet component. For "narrow multiplets" the relation $\Delta\epsilon_J\simeq\boldsymbol{k}T$ may apply, in which case there is a distribution of the atoms among the different

[1] Landé, *Z. Phys.*, 1923, **15**, 189.

multiplet components according to their Boltzmann factors and statistical weights (§ 9.IV), and a statistical mean is taken:[1]

$$\chi_m=\chi_{2m}+\chi_{1m}=N\frac{\Sigma\alpha_J(2J+1)e^{-\epsilon_J/kT}}{\Sigma(2J+1)e^{-\epsilon_J/kT}}+\frac{(N\mu_{0B})^2}{3RT}\frac{\Sigma g_J J(J+1)(2J+1)e^{-\epsilon_J/kT}}{\Sigma(2J+1)e^{-\epsilon_J/kT}}$$

in which all J values from $|L-S|$ to $L+S$ are taken, and $(2J+1)$ is the statistical weight for a state with the total impulse quantum number J. In such cases, owing to an appreciable χ_{2m} term, Curie's law need not be obeyed strictly.

In the other extreme case of very small multiplet splitting, $\Delta\epsilon_J \ll kT$, all the Boltzmann factors are practically unity, and the division of χ_m into χ_{1m} and χ_{2m} loses its meaning, on account of very weak coupling of L^* and S^*. The two moments μ_L and μ_S now precess independently, and there are two separate equations for χ_m:

$$\chi_{Sm}=(N\mu_{0B})^2 \,.\, 4S(S+1)/3RT$$

$$\chi_{Lm}=(N\mu_{0B})^2 \,.\, L(L+1)/3RT$$

$$\therefore\ \chi_m=\chi_{Sm}+\chi_{Lm}=[(N\mu_{0B})^2/3RT][4S(S+1)+L(L+1)]=C/T.$$

The magnetic moment (in Bohr magnetons) of paramagnetic ions of the transition metals is given approximately by:

$$\mu_B=\sqrt{[4S(S+1)+L(L+1)]}$$

where S is the resultant spin ($2S$ is the number of unpaired electrons, each with spin $\frac{1}{2}$) and L is the resultant orbital angular momentum. Except with cobalt, however, the interaction and perturbing effects of the other ions in the solution or crystal cancel out most of the L contribution, since the electrons of the incomplete $3d$ shell are outermost, and this so-called "quenching" of orbital momentum leaves only the electron spin effect to be considered[2]: $\mu_B=\sqrt{[S(S+1)]}$. If the number of *unpaired* electrons is n, the relation $S=\frac{1}{2}n$ gives $\mu_B=\sqrt{[n(n+2)]}$.

The values of μ_B so calculated for simple salts and oxides are in good agreement with experiment. For complex compounds, e.g. cobaltammines, the electronic levels are rearranged and the ion may be diamagnetic. In the case of rare earths the incomplete shell is $4f$, and as this is screened by the $5p$ and $5s$ shells outside it, the moment is no longer accounted for by S alone.

The agreement with some metallic oxides is good only if μ_B is calculated from the measured molar susceptibility χ_m by Weiss's formula:[3]

$$\mu_B=2{\cdot}839\sqrt{[\chi_m(T-\Theta)]},$$

where Θ is a characteristic temperature, instead of Curie's formula:

$$\mu_B=2{\cdot}839\sqrt{(\chi_m T)}.$$

Diatomic molecules have the quantum numbers Λ=the projection of L on the molecular axis, giving Σ, Π, Δ . . . states with Λ=0, 1, 2, . . ., and Σ=the projection of S along the molecular axis.

1 Van Vleck, *Phys. Rev.*, 1927, **30**, 31; 1928, **31**, 587; Bhatnagar and Mathur, "Physical Principles and Applications of Magneto-chemistry," 1935, 161.

2 Cabrera and Duperier, *J. de Phys.*, 1925, **6**, 121; Cabrera, *ibid.*, 1925, **6**, 241, 273; Bose *Z. Phys.*, 1927, **43**, 864; Stoner, *Proc. Leeds Phil. Soc.*, 1930, **2**, 56; Pauling, *J.A.C.S.*, 1931, **53**, 1392; "The Nature of the Chemical Bond," 1939, 107; Fahlenbrach, *Ann. Phys.*, 1932, **14**, 524; von Auwers and Kühlwein, *ibid.*, 1933, **17**, 107, 121.

3 Bhatnagar *et al.*, *J.C.S.*, 1939, 1433. The residual paramagnetism in La··· compounds is perhaps due to a surface effect: Haller and Selwood, *J.A.C.S.*, 1939, **61**, 85; for Nd···, see Selwood, *ibid.*, 1931, **53**, 1799; Fritsch, *Ann. Phys.*, 1941, **39**, 31 (Eu sulphate to 20° K.).

The angular momentum (moment of momentum) J is formed by combining the angular momenta of orbit, spin, and nuclear rotation, and there are two main cases:

(*a*) a strong coupling between orbit and spin, when J is the resultant of nuclear momentum, Λ and Σ;

(*b*) a weak coupling between orbit and spin, when J is formed by vectorial addition of these; this case always holds when $\Lambda=0$ (Σ-states):

(i) ground level of type $^1\Sigma$, i.e. $\Lambda=\Sigma=0$; corresponds with diamagnetic substances;

(ii) ground level a Σ-term but $\Sigma\neq0$; case (*b*) holds, the term is a narrow multiplet, and the moment is due to spin only:

$$\chi=4\mu_{0B}{}^2\Sigma(\Sigma+1)/3kT \quad . \quad . \quad . \quad . \quad . \quad (9)$$

(iii) $\Lambda\neq0$. Case (*b*):

$$\chi=(\mu_{0B}{}^2/3kT)[4\Sigma(\Sigma+1)+\Lambda^2] \quad . \quad . \quad . \quad (9a)$$

(iv) $\Lambda\neq0$. Case (*a*). If the ground multiplet is narrow in comparison with kT, (9) again holds, but if wide

$$\chi=(\mu_{0B}{}^2/3kT)(2\Sigma+\Lambda)^2 \quad . \quad . \quad . \quad . \quad . \quad (9b)$$

It is noteworthy that the paramagnetic susceptibility of bivalent rare earth ions approaches that of the tervalent ion of the element of next higher atomic number, e.g. Sa$^{\cdot\cdot}$=Eu$^{\cdot\cdot\cdot}$; in each case the electronic arrangement is the same.[1]

In practice an *effective moment* μ_{eff} is calculated from χ by Curie's law, i.e. neglecting α, and this is equal to the true moment μ only for singlet terms. For other cases:

$\mu_{eff}=\sqrt{(\mu_J{}^2+3kT\alpha)}$ for wide multiplets.

μ_{eff}=sum over multiplets for medium multiplets.

$\mu_{eff}=\sqrt{(\mu_L{}^2+\mu_S{}^2)}$ for narrow multiplets (independent of T).

For the case when the orbital angular momentum is "quenched," J=S, and $g=2$, and (8) and (5) (with the inclusion of g in the exponent) show that the state sum [2] is:

$$Z=\sum_{M=-S}^{M=S} e^{2M\mu_{0B}\mathbf{H}/kT}=\sum_{M=-S}^{M=S} e^{2Mx}$$

where $x=\mu_{0B}\mathbf{H}/kT$, and Z is a function of $\mathbf{H}$ and T. The series is a geometrical progression, the sum of which is:

$$Z=\frac{e^{(2S+1)x}-e^{-(2S+1)x}}{e^x-e^{-x}}=\frac{\sinh[(2S+1)x]}{\sinh x} \quad . \quad . \quad . \quad . \quad (10)$$

The sum of the geometrical progression starts from the first term $a=e^{-2Sx}$; the number of terms is $n=2S+1$ (i.e. all + and − values of S plus zero); the common ratio is $r=e^{2x}$ (since successive values of S differ by unity). Hence the sum is:

$$a\frac{1-r^n}{1-r}=e^{-2Sx}\cdot\frac{1-e^{2x(2S+1)}}{1-e^{2x}}=\frac{e^{-2Sx}-e^{(2S+2)x}}{1-e^{2x}}$$

[1] Hughes and Pierce, *J.A.C.S.*, 1933, **55**, 3277; Selwood, *ibid.*, 1933, **55**, 4869; 1934, **56**, 2392.

[2] For further details on this section, see Fowler and Guggenheim, "Statistical Thermodynamics," 1939, 608 f.; Aston, in Taylor and Glasstone, "Treatise on Physical Chemistry," 1942, **1**, 627 f. The quantum number is denoted by s to distinguish it from the entropy *S*.

Multiply numerator and denominator by $-e^{-x}$, and (10) follows, with (§ 47.I) $\frac{1}{2}(e^x - e^{-x}) = \sinh x$. The entropy due to the spin orientation is given by (28), § 8.IV:

$$S = \boldsymbol{R}[\ln Z + (T/Z)(dZ/dT)].$$

By inserting the values of Z and dZ/dT, it is found that

$$S = \boldsymbol{R}\left\{\ln \frac{\sinh[(2S+1)x]}{\sinh x} - (2S+1)x \coth[(2S+1)x] + x \coth x\right\} \quad . \quad \textbf{(11)}$$

(the two meanings of S in this and subsequent equations must not be confused) where $\coth x = \cosh x/\sinh x$. If **H**, and hence x, are small

$$S = \boldsymbol{R}\{\ln(2S+1) - \tfrac{1}{6}[4S(S+1)x^2]\}$$

and if $\mathbf{H}=0$, i.e. in the absence of an external magnetic field

$$S = \boldsymbol{R}\ln(2S+1)$$

as is obvious, since there are $2S+1$ orientations of spin of equal energy.

Equation (10) is true only when the external magnetic field is large compared with the effect of the charged ions in the crystal (" internal Stark effect ") and the interaction between spins. The former was considered by Van Vleck and Penny,[1] but the results are tentative and will not be discussed here. The effect is to remove part of the entropy at absolute zero, and it seems probable that the whole of this entropy vanishes.

When a paramagnetic substance in an S-state (real or effective) is magnetised at low temperature, (11) shows that there is a decrease of entropy, the consequent heat liberation from which may be conducted away by a bath of helium boiling under reduced pressure. The substance is then thermally isolated, and the field is removed. If this is a reversible adiabatic change, the entropy is constant, and since practically no heat enters from outside, the temperature falls. If (11) were true to the absolute zero, it would theoretically be possible to reduce the temperature to absolute zero, but this contradicts Nernst's heat theorem and complicating effects appear at very low temperatures.

§ 16. Ferromagnetism

In the case of *ferromagnetic* metals (iron, cobalt, nickel, Heusler alloys), which show the phenomena of *saturation*, *spontaneous magnetism*, and *hysteresis*,[2] Weiss's equation holds at temperatures higher than the (positive) Curie point Θ, which was thus regarded as marking the transition between ferromagnetism (below Θ) and paramagnetism (above Θ). Weiss explained ferromagnetism by assuming a term in the molecular field which was independent of field strength, leading to spontaneous magnetisation in " elementary groups " of atoms. In the absence of a field, these groups are oriented irregularly, the resulting magnetisation being inappreciable, but they are oriented by a very small field and so the typical magnetisation curves are deducible. This is essentially the same as Ewing's theory.[3]

The physical significance of these positive Curie points was doubtful when the susceptibilities of many substances which followed Weiss's law accurately

1 *Phil. Mag.*, 1934, **17**, 961; Hebb and Purcell, *J. Chem. Phys.*, 1937, **5**, 338.

2 The name *ferromagnetism* is now coming to mean *any* case where the susceptibility depends on the field strength.

3 Ewing, " Magnetic Induction in Iron and other Metals," 3rd edit., 1900; *Proc. Roy. Soc.*, 1922, **100**, 449; *Proc. Phys. Soc.*, 1930, **42**, 355; Fleming, " Magnets and Electric Currents," 3rd edit., 1914; Spooner, " Properties and Testing of Magnetic Materials," New York, 1927; Wall, " Applied Magnetism," 1927; S. R. Williams, " Magnetic Phenomena, an Elementary Treatise," New York, 1931; Gmelin, " Handbuch der anorganischen Chemie," 8th edit., 1934, **59** A, 1429 (and bibliography).

down to liquid-air temperature were found to show marked deviations at lower temperatures, although the Curie point was still at a much lower temperature. The curve then rises above the extrapolated Weiss line ($1/\chi$ against T) and bends down again, forming a " hook." This effect is called the *cryomagnetic anomaly* and is established for a number of substances.[1] The " ferromagnetic " Curie point Θ_F has thus been defined as the temperature at which the body begins to deviate from the Weiss line and show ferromagnetic properties, but it is usually taken as the point where the curve actually cuts the T axis, and this may differ from the " paramagnetic " Curie point Θ_P extrapolated from Weiss's formula. Θ_F may be greater or less than Θ_P, and may even be negative when Θ_P is positive. The Θ_F point is more sharply defined by anomalies in specific heats (see Vol. II). The behaviour is different from that of ferromagnetic *metals* in the relation between χ and **H**. Above Θ_F, χ is independent of **H** but Weiss's formula ceases to hold at appreciably higher temperatures.

Landau [2] explained this difference quantitatively by the assumption that interaction forces *in* the layers of paramagnetic ions in crystals orient their moments in one direction, whilst the weaker forces *between* the layers orient adjacent layers in opposite directions, and as large fields are required to reverse this, no permanent magnetism occurs.

The cases of oxygen and nitric oxide, both paramagnetic, are very interesting. Van Vleck [3] deduced the equation for NO:

$$\chi=N\Theta^2/3kT;\quad \Theta^2=4\mu_B{}^2(1-e^{-x}+xe^{-x})/(x+xe^{-x});\quad x=\boldsymbol{h}\Delta\nu/\boldsymbol{k}T$$

where $\Delta\nu$ is the frequency difference between the two $^2\Pi$ levels and $x=173{\cdot}2/T$. The equation was found [4] to agree with experiment from 113° K. to 292° K.

In the case of liquid oxygen diluted with liquid nitrogen, Perrier and Onnes [5] found a deviation from Curie's law (which oxygen gas obeys at ordinary pressure [6]), but Weiss's law is obeyed. Compressed oxygen gas obeys neither law. This was explained by Lewis [7] on the assumption of a polymerisation to diamagnetic O_4, increasing with pressure in the gas, or concentration in the liquid mixtures, and this was shown by Wiersma and Gorter [8] to explain the dependency of the Curie constant C on pressure. The assumption is also in agreement with the absorption spectrum.[9]

[1] $NiCl_2$, $CoCl_2$, $FeCl_2$, $CrCl_3$: Woltjer and Onnes, *Comm. Leiden*, 1925, **173***b*, *c*; Woltjer and Wiersma, *ibid.*, 1929, 201*a*; on specific heats, see Trapeznikowa and Schubnikow, *Nature*, 1934, **134**, 378; *Sow. Phys. Z.*, 1935, **7**, 66, 255; Trapeznikowa, Schubnikow, and Miljutin, *ibid.* 1936, **9**, 237; Kürti, Lainé, Rollin, and Simon, *Compt. Rend.*, 1936, **202**, 1576; 1937, **204**, 754; 1939; **208**, 173; Trapeznikowa and Miljutin, *Sow. Phys. Z.*, 1937, **11**, 55; Schubnikow and Schalyt, *ibid.*, 1937, **11**, 566; de Haas and Schultz, *Physica*, 1939, **6**, 481; de Haas, Schultz, and Koolhaas, *ibid.*, 1940, **7**, 57; Schultz, *ibid.*, 1940, **7**, 413; Van Dijk and Keesom, *ibid.*, 1940, **7**, 970 ($FeNH_4$ alum; anomal. max. at 3·6° K.).

[2] *Sow. Phys. Z.*, 1933, **4**, 675; Schultz, *Physica*, 1940, **7**, 413.

[3] *Phys. Rev.*, 1928, **31**, 587.

[4] Wiersma, de Haas, and Capel, *Comm. Leiden*, 1930, **212***b*; de Haas and Wiersma, *ibid.* 1932, Suppl. **74***b*, 36 (NO).

[5] *Comm. Leiden*, 1914, **139***d*.

[6] Onnes and Oosterhuis, *Comm. Leiden*, 1913, **134***c*; Wiersma and Gorter, *Physica*, 1932, **12**, 316.

[7] *J.A.C.S.*, 1924, **46**, 2027.

[8] *Physica*, 1932, **12**, 316.

[9] Salow and Steiner, *Nature*, 1934, **134**, 463; Guillien, *Compt. Rend.*, 1934, **148**, 1223, 1486; Prikhotko, Ruhemann, and Federitenko, *Sow. Phys. Z.*, 1935, **7**, 410; cf. Becquerel, *Le Radium*, 1908, **5**, 5; Van Vleck, " Electric and Magnetic Susceptibilities," Oxford, 1932, 89. For the detection of liquid oxygen in liquid nitrogen by the magnetic susceptibility, see Kapitsa and Milner, *J. Sci. Instr.*, 1937, **14**, 201.

§ 17. Magneto-thermal Effect

If a magnetic field is applied to a paramagnetic substance which contains atoms, ions, or molecules in degenerate states, these are split into Zeeman components of smaller statistical weight (see § 9.IV). The weight g in the ground level gives, at low temperatures, a term $\boldsymbol{R} \ln g$ per mol to the entropy S, and hence in the magnetic field the entropy is decreased. In an adiabatic enclosure (for which S is constant) this loss of magnetic entropy is compensated by a gain of thermal entropy, and there is a rise of temperature from T_1 to T_2 such that $\int_{T_1}^{T_2} (C/T)\mathrm{d}T$ (where C=heat capacity) is equal to the loss of magnetic entropy. When the field is removed, a corresponding fall of temperature occurs. This provides a means of attaining very low temperatures.

The *magneto-thermal effect* (which Weiss called the *magneto-caloric effect*) [1] $\mathrm{d}T/\mathrm{d}\mathbf{H}$ can be calculated by thermodynamics as follows.[2] To produce a change of magnetisation $\mathrm{d}\sigma$ the field *does* work $\mathbf{H}\mathrm{d}\sigma$, and in all practical cases any changes of volume and pressure can be disregarded. Hence, if l is the latent heat:

$$\delta q = \mathrm{d}E - \mathbf{H}\mathrm{d}\sigma \quad . \quad . \quad . \quad . \quad . \quad . \quad . \quad . \quad . \quad (1)$$

$$\delta q = C\mathrm{d}T + l\mathrm{d}\sigma \quad . \quad . \quad . \quad . \quad . \quad . \quad . \quad . \quad . \quad (2)$$

$$\therefore \ \mathrm{d}E = C\mathrm{d}T + l\mathrm{d}\sigma + \mathbf{H}\mathrm{d}\sigma$$

and since $\mathrm{d}E$ is a perfect differential, Euler's criterion (§ 27.I) gives:

$$(\mathrm{d}C/\mathrm{d}\sigma)_T = (\mathrm{d}l/\mathrm{d}T)_\sigma + (\mathrm{d}\mathbf{H}/\mathrm{d}T)_\sigma \quad . \quad . \quad . \quad . \quad . \quad . \quad . \quad (3)$$

By dividing (2) by T:

$$\mathrm{d}S = \delta q/T = (C/T)\mathrm{d}T + (l/T)\mathrm{d}\sigma \quad . \quad . \quad . \quad . \quad . \quad . \quad . \quad (4)$$

and since $\mathrm{d}S$ is a perfect differential:

$$(1/T)(\mathrm{d}C/\mathrm{d}\sigma)_T = (\mathrm{d}/\mathrm{d}T)(l/T)_\sigma \quad . \quad . \quad . \quad . \quad . \quad . \quad . \quad (5)$$

therefore from (3) and (5):

$$l = -T(\mathrm{d}\mathbf{H}/\mathrm{d}T)_\sigma \quad . \quad . \quad . \quad . \quad . \quad . \quad . \quad . \quad . \quad (6)$$

which corresponds with Clapeyron's equation (5), § 41. II, and could, as explained there, be at once written down as a result of the generalised Clapeyron diagram. Since $l/T = (\mathrm{d}q/\mathrm{d}\sigma)_T/T = (\mathrm{d}S/\mathrm{d}\sigma)_T$, and since it follows from a generalised Maxwell's relation (3), § 48.II, that $(\mathrm{d}S/\mathrm{d}\sigma)_T = (\mathrm{d}\mathbf{H}/\mathrm{d}T)_\sigma$, this is an alternative very direct deduction of (6). By replacing σ by $\chi\mathbf{H}$ (§ 12) this gives:

$$(\mathrm{d}S/\mathrm{d}\mathbf{H})_T = \mathbf{H}(\mathrm{d}\chi/\mathrm{d}T)_\mathbf{H} \quad . \quad . \quad . \quad . \quad . \quad . \quad . \quad . \quad (6)$$

which is a useful equation, but involves the assumption of Curie's law (§ 11).

From (1), per mol:

$$(\mathrm{d}q/\mathrm{d}T)_\mathbf{H} \equiv C_\mathbf{H} = (\mathrm{d}E/\mathrm{d}T)_\mathbf{H} - \mathbf{H}(\mathrm{d}\sigma/\mathrm{d}T)_\mathbf{H}$$

[1] Weiss, *J. de Phys.*, 1921, **2**, 161; Debye, in Marx, " Handbuch der Radiologie," Leipzig, 1925, **6**, 742.

[2] W. Thomson, *Phil. Mag.*, 1878, **5**, 4; " Mathematical and Physical Papers," 1882, **1**, 291, 315; Weiss and Piccard, *J. de Phys.*, 1917, **7**, 103; Weiss, *ibid.*, 1921, **2**, 161; Weiss and Forrer, *Ann. de Phys.*, 1926, **5**, 153; Giauque, *J.A.C.S.*, 1927, **49**, 1870; Ahrens, *Ann. Phys.*, 1934, **21**, 169 (high temps.); Stoner, *Phil. Mag.*, 1935, **19**, 565; 1937, **23**, 833; *Phil. Trans.*, 1936, **235**, 165; *Proc. Roy. Soc.*, 1939, **169**, 339; a magneto-thermal equation for supraconducting states is considered in Vol. II; Giauque and MacDougall, *J.A.C.S.*, 1935, **57**, 1175; Honda and Hirone, *Nature*, 1936, **137**, 492; Epstein, " Textbook of Thermodynamics," 1937, 352; Dixit, *Current Sci.*, 1938, **6**, 589; van Laer, *Physica*, 1939, **6**, 1; J. K. Roberts, " Heat and Thermodynamics," 1940, 117.

and for an adiabatic change ($dS=0$), (4) gives:

$$(C_H/T)=-(l/T)(d\sigma/dT)_S,$$

$\therefore$ from (6): $$C_H=-l(d\sigma/dT)_S=T(dH/dT)_\sigma(d\sigma/dT)_S.$$

Again:

$$dS=(dS/dH)_T dH+(dS/dT)_H dT$$

and for adiabatic conditions $dS=0$:

$$(dT/dH)_S=-(dS/dH)_T/(dS/dT)_H$$
$$=-H(d\chi/dT)_H/(dS/dT)_H, \text{ from (6)}$$
$$=-(d\sigma/dT)_H/(1/T)(dq/dT)_H$$
$$\therefore (dT/dH)_S=-(T/C_H)(d\sigma/dT)_H \quad . \ . \ . \ . \ . \ (7)$$

giving the magneto-thermal effect. Since $d\sigma/dT<0$, it follows that $(dT/dH)_S>0$, i.e. the temperature falls when the field is decreased. At low temperatures, $d\sigma/dT$ becomes large, and (unless there is a cryomagnetic anomaly, § 16) C_H becomes small, hence the cooling effect becomes large at very low temperatures. If Curie's law (§ 11) is valid:

$$\sigma=\chi H=CH/T \quad \therefore (d\sigma/dT)_H=-CH/T^2 \quad . \ . \ . \ . \ (8)$$

$\therefore$ by substituting in (7) and assuming C_H constant:

$$T(dT/dH)_S=CH/C_H, \quad \therefore \int_{T_1}^{T_2} TdT=\int_0^H (CH/C_H)dH$$
$$\therefore \tfrac{1}{2}(T_2^2-T_1^2)=\tfrac{1}{2}(T_2+T_1)(T_2-T_1)=\tfrac{1}{2}(CH^2/C_H).$$

If T_2-T_1 is small, $\frac{1}{2}(T_2+T_1)$ can be put equal to the average temperature T, and hence:

$$T_2-T_1=(1/2C_H)(CH^2/T) \quad . \ . \ . \ . \ . \ . \ . \ (9)$$

Values of T_2-T_1 calculated from (9) at room temperature are very small even with large fields. In general, however, C_H is not constant, as assumed, but decreases considerably with temperature. For small values of C_H, (9)—which then does not really apply, as it was deduced on an incorrect assumption—gives quite large values of T_2-T_1.

A new magneto-thermal effect, periodic heating and cooling when a ferromagnetic single crystal is rotated in a strong magnetic field at low temperature, was deduced, and experimentally verified with nickel at liquid nitrogen temperature, by Akulov and Kirensky.[1]

A thermodynamic deduction of Curie's law (§ 11) was given by Larmor.[2] By taking the system round a small Carnot cycle, as in Clapeyron's deduction (§ 41.II), the heat absorbed at T is $-H\delta J$, and the work in the cycle is $-\delta H\delta J$ (the p and v coordinates being replaced by H and J). Hence $-\delta H\delta J=-(H\delta J)\delta T/T$. If κ, the susceptibility, is constant at constant temperature, $H=J/\kappa$,

$$\therefore \delta H=[Jd(1/\kappa)/dT]\delta T=H\delta T/T$$

$$\therefore d(1/\kappa)=(H/J)dT/T=(1/\kappa)dT/T, \text{ or } d\ln(1/\kappa)=d\ln T,$$

$\therefore \ln(1/\kappa)=\ln T+\text{const.}$, or $\ln(1/\kappa T)=\text{const.}$, $\therefore \kappa=C/T$, where C is a constant. This is Curie's law.

[1] *J. Phys. U.S.S.R.*, 1940, **3**, 31.

[2] "Mathematical and Physical Papers," Cambridge, 1929, **2**, 115, 729, 736; Stoner, *Phil. Mag.*, 1935, **19**, 565.

The magneto-thermal effect may be deduced [1] by a slight generalisation of equation (2a), § 3.II, and equation (10), § 21.II. In:

$$\delta q = c_v dT + l_v dv = c_v dT + [(dE/dv)_T + p]dv$$

v must be replaced by σ and p by $-\mathbf{H}$, $c_v = (dE/dT)_v$ becoming $(dE/dT)_\sigma$:

$$\delta q = (dE/dT)_\sigma dT + [(dE/d\sigma)_T - \mathbf{H}]d\sigma$$

$$\therefore\ dS = \delta q/T = (1/T)(dE/dT)_\sigma dT + [(1/T)(dE/d\sigma)_T - \mathbf{H}/T]d\sigma.$$

Since dS is a perfect differential, $d^2S/dTd\sigma = d^2S/d\sigma dT$, and differentiation of the coefficient of dT with respect to σ gives the same result as differentiation of the coefficient of $d\sigma$ with respect to T (§ 27.I),

$$\therefore\ \frac{d}{d\sigma}\left[\frac{1}{T}\left(\frac{dE}{dT}\right)_\sigma\right] = \frac{d}{dT}\left[\frac{1}{T}\left(\frac{dE}{d\sigma}\right)_T - \frac{\mathbf{H}}{T}\right] \quad \ldots\ldots (10)$$

$$\therefore\ (1/T)(dE/d\sigma)_T - \mathbf{H}/T = -f(\sigma) \quad \text{and} \quad (dE/d\sigma)_T = g'(\sigma)$$

on integration, where f and g′ denote functions of σ. Hence:

$$\mathbf{H} = Tf(\sigma) + g'(\sigma) \quad \ldots\ldots\ldots (11)$$

The complete theory of the magnetothermal effect would lead too far from the scope of the present chapter. It may be mentioned that the molar entropy decrease due to an applied field **H** is, for a gadolinium salt, equal to: [2]

$$\Delta S_0^{\mathbf{H}} = R\left[\ln \Sigma \cosh(gjM\mathbf{H}\cos\theta/RT) - \ln 4 - (gjM\mathbf{H}/RT)\frac{\Sigma \cos\theta \sinh(gjM\mathbf{H}\cos\theta/RT)}{\Sigma \cosh(gjM\mathbf{H}\cos\theta/RT)}\right] \quad . (12)$$

where, for the Gd‴ ion in the ^{3}S state, $g=2$=ratio of magnetic to mechanical moment, j=S (quantum number)$=7\times\frac{1}{2}$=total momentum, M=molar Bohr magneton, and the summation requires four values of cos θ, viz. 1, 5/7, 3/7, 1/7, negative values being included by using the hyperbolic functions (see § 47.I).

Bates and Edmondson [3] found an abnormally large temperature change with cobalt in small fields.

§ 18. Realisation of Very Low Temperatures

Debye [4] and Giauque [5] suggested that the magneto-thermal effect could be used in attaining temperatures below the lowest (0·7° K.) reached with liquid helium. The ions of paramagnetic salts such as gadolinium sulphate, iron ammonium sulphate, and potassium chromium sulphate, owing to the spin magnetism, behave like small magnets which, in ordinary conditions, are in a state equivalent to a random orientation. If the salt is cooled to the lowest temperature attainable with liquid helium (0·7° K.), and then subjected to a powerful magnetic field, the spin components are orientated, the entropy decreases, and heat is evolved, which is removed by the cooling bath. When the temperature has

1 Halpern, *Ann. Phys.*, 1932, **12**, 169; Debye, *Phys. Z.*, 1934, **35**, 923.

2 Giauque and Clark, *J.A.C.S.*, 1932, **54**, 3135; cf. Spedding, *Phys. Rev.*, 1931, **38**, 2080; Spedding and Nutting, *ibid.*, 2294; Selwood, " Magnetochemistry," New York, 1943, 89.

3 *Proc. Phys. Soc.*, 1947, **59**, 329; Bates and Harrison, *ibid.*, 1948, **60**, 213, 225; Bates and Davis, *ibid.*, 1948, **60**, 307.

4 *Ann. Phys.*, 1926, **81**, 1154; *Phys. Z.*, 1934, **35**, 923; *Z. techn. Phys.*, 1934, **15**, 499; Squire, in " Temperature. Its Measurement and Control," New York, 1941, 745.

5 *J.A.C.S.*, 1927, **49**, 1864, 1870; Hebb and Purcell, *J. Chem. Phys.*, 1937, **5**, 338; Dixit, *Current Sci.*, 1938, **6**, 589. For thermal insulation at 1° K. (as little as 1 erg/min.) see Cooke and Hull, *Proc. Roy. Soc.*, 1942, **181**, 83.

fallen again to 0·7° K. the field is suddenly switched off. The resulting change from ordered to disordered orientation causes an increase of entropy (§ 5.IV) and the temperature falls to about 0·015° K. By using very powerful magnetic fields a temperature as low as about 0·003° K. was reached. For the measurement of these very low temperatures, only the change in magnetic susceptibility of some paramagnetic salts can be used. According to Curie's law, the suceptibility is inversely proportional to the absolute temperature. The susceptibility is measured by means of two coils wound round the tube containing the paramagnetic substance (Fig. 16.VI C). Through one coil, an alternating current is passed, and the induced current in the other coil depends on

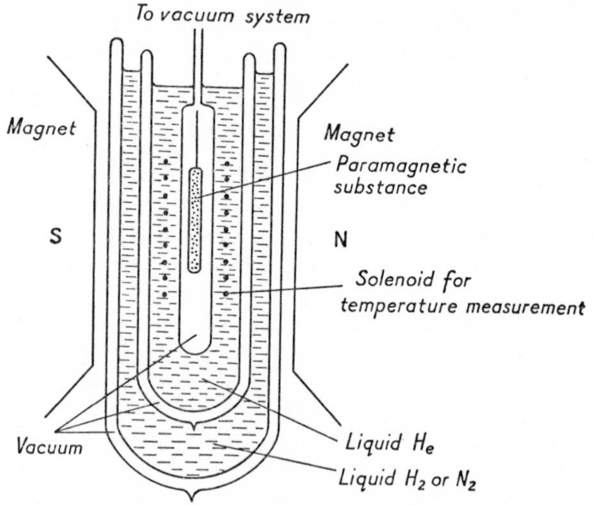

FIG. 16.VI C. Production and Measurement of Very Low Temperatures

the magnetic susceptibility of the crystal core. This induced current is amplified and measured, and from it the temperature of the crystal can be calculated. There is, however, considerable difficulty in linking up this low-temperature scale with the gas thermometer scale.

The experimental realisation of very low temperatures by the magneto-thermal method is due to Giauque, MacDougall, and Clark,[1] at Berkeley, California; de Haas and Wiersma [2] at Leiden; and Kürti and Simon [3] at

[1] Giauque and Clark, *J.A.C.S.*, 1932, **54**, 3135; Giauque and MacDougall, *Phys. Rev.*, 1933, **43**, 768; 1933, 44, 235; 1935, **47**, 885; *J.A.C.S.*, 1935, **57**, 1175; MacDougall and Giauque, *ibid.*, 1936, **58**, 1032; Hebb and Purcell, *J. Chem. Phys.*, 1937, **5**, 338 (bibl.); Van Vleck, *ibid.*, 1938, **6**, 81; Giauque, Stout, Egan, and Clark, *ibid.*, 1941, **63**, 405; Stout and Giauque, *ibid.*, 1941, **63**, 714.

[2] De Haas, *Proc. K. Akad. Wetens. Amsterdam*, 1932, **35**, 136; *Nature*, 1933, **132**, 372; *Naturwiss.*, 1933, **21**, 732; de Haas and Wiersma, *Physica*, 1935, **2**, 335; 1937, **3**, 491; Crawhall, "Very Low Temperatures," (Sci. Mus.) 1936; Ruhemann, "Low Temperature Physics," Cambridge, 1937; Casimir, de Haas, and de Klerk, *Physica*, 1939, **6**, 255; Casimir, de Klerk, and Polder, *ibid.*, 1940, **7**, 737; Van Lammeren, "Technik der tiefen Temperaturen," Berlin, 1941; van Dijk, *Physica*, 1946, **12**, 371; Luttinger and Tisza, *Phys. Rev.*, 1946, **70**, 954; de Klerk, *Physica*, 1946, **12**, 513; Weissman, *Amer. J. Phys.*, 1947, **15**, 451; Alekseyevsky and Migunov, *J. Phys. U.S.S.R.*, 1947, **11**, 95; de Klerk, Steenland, and Gorter, *Nature*, 1948, **161**, 678 (0·003° K.).

[3] Kürti, *Z. phys. Chem.*, 1933, **20** B, 305; Kürti and Simon, *Naturwiss.*, 1933, **21**, 178; *Physica*, 1934, **1**, 1107; *Nature*, 1934, **133**, 907; *Proc. Roy. Soc.*, 1935, **149**, 152; 1935, **151**, 610; 1935, **152**, 21; *Phil. Mag.*, 1938, **26**, 849; Kürti, Rollin, and Simon, *Physica*, 1936, **3**, 266; Kürti,

Oxford. The American workers used gadolinium sulphate as the paramagnetic substance, but this is not really very suitable, and de Haas and Wiersma found that chrome alum is much better. Kürti and Simon used much simpler apparatus, and their lowest temperature (0·05° K.) did not attain [1] that (0·0044° K.) reached at Leiden with a mixture of 1 part of chrome alum diluted with 14·4 parts of potash alum. Giauque's results, with gadolinium sulphate, were less striking. In the Leiden method, the salt was cooled by liquid helium at low pressure in the magnetic field (30,000 øersted), then the whole apparatus was swung out of the pole gap to reduce the field to zero, and the temperature measured by determining the susceptibility by an induction method with a solenoid. Kürti and Simon, with only a few c.c. of liquid helium, used the salt in a thin sealed glass bulb containing 1 c.c. of helium gas, and cooled it in liquid helium at as low a temperature as possible. The field was applied and the heat evolved was removed in about 3 min. The field was switched off and the condensation of the helium gas produced a hard vacuum in the bulb, and, as there was very little thermal contact between the loosely packed salt and the tube, a very low temperature was reached. With about 0·001° K. the limit of the magneto-thermal method is reached, and any further progress would probably involve the utilisation of the random distribution of *nuclear* spins.[2]

§ 19. Measurement of Low Temperatures

The measurement of low temperatures is carried out in various ways. For approximate work down to liquid-air temperature a thermometer containing *pentane* is used.[3] As the liquid becomes viscous at low temperatures the bulb should be gradually lowered into the cooling bath, taking care not to immerse the stem until the bulb is thoroughly cooled. The total volume change from 30° to −189° is about a quarter of the volume at 30°.

Vapour pressure thermometers [4] are very convenient. A pure liquid, the

Lainé, Rollin, and Simon, *Compt. Rend.*, 1936, **202**, 1576; Kürti, Lainé, and Simon, *ibid.*, 1937, **204**, 754; 1939, **208**, 173; Simon, *J. Inst. Met.*, 1941, **67**, 325; Ashmead, *Nature*, 1939, **143**, 853.

[1] Newer calculations suggest that the temperature reached was actually 0·0034° K.; Hebb and Purcell, *J. Chem. Phys.*, 1937, **5**, 338. The calculated Curie point is 0·0013° K. For a discussion of earlier doubts whether such low temperatures had been reached, see Burton, Smith, and Wilhelm, "Phenomena at the Temperature of Liquid Helium," New York, 1940, 236.

[2] Debye, *Phys. Z.*, 1934, **35**, 923; Kürti and Simon, *Nature*, 1935, **135**, 31; *Proc. Roy. Soc.*, 1935, **149**, 152.

[3] Kohlrausch, *Ann. Phys.*, 1897, **60**, 463; Holborn and Henning, *ibid.*, 1901, **6**, 242; Baudin, *Compt. Rend.*, 1901, **133**, 1207; Rothe, *Z. Instr.*, 1904, **24**, 47; Beckmann and Waentig, *Z. anorg. Chem.*, 1910, **67**, 17; Scheel, *Z. angew. Chem.*, 1919, **32**, 347 (general on temperature measurement); ether and chloroform thermometers had been used (not for low temperatures) by Joule and Thomson: see W. Thomson, "Mathematical and Physical Papers," 1890, **3**, 142; and an alcohol thermometer by Angot, *J. de Phys.*, 1891, **10**, 399; see Wroblewski, *Ann. Phys.*, 1885, **25**, 371.

[4] W. Thomson, "Ency. Brit.," 9th edit., 1878, art. "Heat"; "Math. and Phys. Papers," 1890, **3**, 156; 1911, **5**, 88, 90, 113; Stock and Nielsen, *Ber.*, 1906, **39**, 2066 (liq. O_2); Onnes and Braak, *Proc. K. Akad. Wetens. Amsterdam*, 1908, **11**, 333 (*Comm. Leiden*, **107***a*; O_2); von Siemens, *Ann. Phys.*, 1913, **42**, 871 (O_2, N_2, CO_2, CS_2); Thiel and Caspar, *Z. phys. Chem.*, 1914, **86**, 257; Thiel and Schulte, *ibid.*, 1920, **96**, 312; Henning, *Z. Elektrochem.*, 1921, **27**, 494; 1922, **28**, 248; Henning and Stock, *Z. Phys.*, 1921, **4**, 226; Menzies, *J.A.C.S.*, 1921, **43**, 2309, 2314; *Proc. Nat. Acad.*, 1921, **7**, 81; Stock, Henning, and Kuss, *Ber.*, 1921, **54**, 1119; Stock, *Z. Elektrochem.*, 1923, **29**, 354; Henning and Heuse, *Z. Phys.*, 1924, **23**, 105; Henning, *Z. Phys.*, 1927, **40**, 775; Giauque, Johnston, and Kelley, *J.A.C.S.*, 1927, **49**, 2367 (H_2);

vapour pressure of which at various temperatures is known, is contained along with its pure vapour in a bulb connected with a mercury manometer. The bulb is immersed in the bath and the pressure read on the manometer. The bulb may be filled with a gas (O_2, N_2, etc.) which liquefies when sufficiently cooled. In the case of helium, used at very low temperatures, it must be noted that there is a discontinuity in the vapour-pressure curve at 2·19° K., owing to the existence of two forms of liquid helium, with a transition-point (Λ-point) at that temperature (§ 7); hence [1] two vapour-pressure formulae, one above 2·19° K.:

$$\log p_{\text{cm.}} = -3{\cdot}024/T + 2{\cdot}208 \log T + 1{\cdot}217,$$

and one below 2·19° K.:

$$\log p_{\text{cm.}} = -3{\cdot}859/T + 0{\cdot}922 \log T + 2{\cdot}035$$

or

$$\log p \text{ mm.} = -3{\cdot}018/T + 2{\cdot}484 \log T - 0{\cdot}00297T^4 + 1{\cdot}197$$

must be used. For other liquids the Nernst vapour-pressure formula (also used for helium by Onnes):

$$\log (p/p_c) = 2{\cdot}5 \log (T/T_c) - 0{\cdot}53(T_c/T) + 0{\cdot}59,$$

where p_c and T_c are the critical values, may be used. Another formula due to Nernst is:

$$\log p = -a/T + 1{\cdot}75 \log T - cT + k$$

with the following constants [2] (p in mm. Hg; $T = t°$ C.+273·1):

Substance	B.p. °C.	Range in °C.	a	$c \times 10^3$	k
CS_2	+46·2	+12 to −25	1682·38	5·2980	5·44895
SO_2	−9·99	−11 to −62	1561·36	6·1757	6·20476
NH_3	−33·36	−35 to −80	1393·60	5·7034	5·89654
CO_2	−78·52	−80 to −110	1279·11	2·0757	5·85242
HCl	−85·03	−87 to −118	905·53	5·0077	4·65739
PH_3	−87·43	−90 to −132	845·57	6·1931	4·61480
C_2H_4	−103·72	−110 to −141	834·13	8·3753	5·32340
CH_4	−161·37	−162 to −170	472·47	9·6351	4·60175
O_2	−182·97	−183 to −205	379·95	9·6219	
N_2	−195·78	−195 to −205	301·91	9·0272	

The most recent values for the b.ps. of hydrogen and helium are: [3] H_2 −252·762° C. and He −268·928° C. The vapour pressures of liquid helium have been determined [3] for use in thermometry from 1° to 4·2° K., but the results are not quite consistent, and there is the complication of the existence of two forms of liquid helium.

Keesom, *Comm. Leiden*, 1929, **202***b*, *c* (He to 0·84° K.); Heuse and Otto, *Ann. Phys.*, 1931, **9**, 486; 1932, **14**, 185; Henning and Otto, *Phys. Z.*, 1936, **37**, 633; Andersen, *Rev. Sci. Instr.*, 1946, **17**, 12 (CO_2; ±0·02°).

[1] Ruhemann, "Low Temperature Physics," Cambridge, 1937, 61.

[2] Stock, Henning, and Kuss, *Ber.*, 1921, **54**, 1119; different values are given in a table (containing some errors) by Ebert, in Drucker and Proskauer, "Phys.-chem. Taschenbuch," Leipzig, 1923, **2**, 266.

[3] Schmidt and Keesom, *Physica*, 1937, **4**, 963, 971; *Comm. Leiden*, **250***b*, *c*; Bleaney and Simon, *Trans. Faraday Soc.*, 1939, **35**, 1205; Burton, Smith, and Wilhelm, "Phenomena at the Temperature of Liquid Helium," New York, 1940, 54.

In 1921 the Reichsanstalt adopted [1] the following low temperature standards: 0° C.=273·20° K. (see § 18.VII A). Freezing-point of mercury −38·89° C. Sublimation temperature in ° C. of solid carbon dioxide at p mm. pressure near 760 mm.:

$$-78{\cdot}52+1{\cdot}595\times10^{-2}(p-760)-1{\cdot}1\times10^{-5}(p-760)^2$$

Boiling-point of oxygen in ° C. near 760 mm. pressure:

$$-182{\cdot}97+1{\cdot}258\times10^{-2}(p-760)-0{\cdot}79\times10^{-5}(p-760)^2$$

Boiling-point of hydrogen in ° C. near 760 mm. pressure:

$$-252{\cdot}80+0{\cdot}45\times10^{-2}(p-760).$$

The International Temperature Scale [2] is defined by a platinum resistance thermometer between 0° and −190° C. by the formula:

$$R_t=R_0[1+At+Bt^2+C(t-100)t^3]$$

with the constants R_0, A, and B found from the ice, steam, and sulphur points, and the additional constant C from the b.p. of oxygen at 1 atm. pressure, taken as −182·970° C. on the gas scale; at p mm. pressure the b.p. is

$$t_p=-182{\cdot}970+0{\cdot}0126(p-760)-0{\cdot}0_565(p-760)^2.$$

The steam point at p mm. pressure is:

$$t_p=100{\cdot}000+0{\cdot}0367(p-760)-0{\cdot}0_423(p-760)^2,$$

and the sulphur point:

$$t_p=444{\cdot}600+0{\cdot}0909(p-760)-0{\cdot}0_448(p-760)^2.$$

The temperatures so defined differ [3] by less than 0·1° from the gas scale between −183° and −39°.

For measurements of low temperatures the Société Internationale du Froid defined [4] the International Helium Scale as a helium constant-volume gas thermometer with 1 m. Hg pressure at 0° and corrected by the constants A, B, and C in the characteristic equation for helium determined at Leiden (§ 10.VII A)

$$pv=A(1+B/v+C/v^2+\ldots).$$

At temperatures below the boiling-point of helium, the vapour pressure of liquid helium was used at Leiden to define temperature.

That Callendar's platinum thermometer formula fails at low temperatures was proved by Holborn,[5] Meilink,[6] Onnes *et al.*,[7] and Henning.[8] Henning

[1] *Z. Elektrochem.*, 1923, **29**, 90; cf. Holborn, *ibid.*, 1915, **21**, 559.

[2] Burgess, *Bur. Stand. J. Res.*, 1928, **1**, 635; Roeser, *ibid.*, 1929, **3**, 343; Henning and Otto, *Z. Phys.*, 1928, **48**, 742; *Phys. Z.*, 1936, **37**, 601; Michels, Blaisse, and Koens, *Physica*, 1942, **9**, 356; Anon., *Nature*, 1949, **163**, 427.

[3] Heuse and Otto, *Ann. Phys.*, 1931, **9**, 486; 1932, **14**, 181, 185; Keesom and Dammers, *Physica*, 1935, **2**, 1051, 1080; Henning and Heuse, *Z. Phys.*, 1924, **23**, 105, pointed out that the Leiden and Reichsanstalt scales differed by the former being a few hundredths of a degree higher; Aston and Fink, *Chem. Rev.*, 1946, **39**, 357.

[4] Keesom, *Comm. Leiden*, 1929, Suppl. **67***b*; *Physica*, 1929, **9**, 385, who says the scale is defined to ±0·02° at the best; cf. Jacyna, *Bull. Acad. Polon.*, 1937A, 260.

[5] *Ann. Phys.*, 1901, **6**, 242.

[6] *Proc. K. Akad. Wetens. Amsterdam*, 1902, **4**, 495 (*Comm. Leiden*, **77**); 1905, **7**, 290 (*Comm. Leiden*, **93**).

[7] Onnes and Clay, *Proc. K. Akad. Wetens, Amsterdam*, 1907, **9**, 207, 213 (*Comm. Leiden*, **95** *c*, *d*); *Ann. Phys. Beibl.*, 1907, **31**, 772); Onnes and Tuyn, *Proc. K. Akad. Wetens. Amsterdam*, 1907, **10**, 207 (*Comm. Leiden*, Suppl. **58**); Onnes, Braak, and Clay, *ibid.*, 1907–8, **10**, 422 (*Comm. Leiden*, **101***a*).

[8] *Ann. Phys.*, 1913, **40**, 635; *Z. Instr.*, 1914, **34**, 116; Heuse and Otto, *Ann. Phys.*, 1932, **14**, 181, 185; Henning and Otto, *Phys. Z.*, 1936, **37**, 601, 639.

found that the calculated temperature is too low below $-40°$, and at $-193°$ it is 2° in error. He found that the platinum temperatures pt' given by different specimens of platinum wire could be reduced to a standard platinum temperature pt by Nernst's [1] formula $pt'-pt=cpt(pt-100)$, where c is a constant for a given wire. Zernike [2] for the resistance of platinum at low temperatures used $R=C\tau/(1+a\tau+b\tau^2+c\tau^3)+r$, where $\tau=0{\cdot}01T$; C, a, b, and c are constants, and r is the part due to impurities. Henning and Otto [3] used a 5-constant equation for the platinum thermometer in the region 14°–80° K. Henning,[4] for comparison with a standard platinum thermometer in the region 20°–70° K. used the formula $w'-w=(273-T)[A-B/(T+10)]$, where $w=R_t/R_0$, and A and B are constants. De Haas and de Boer [5] found that the electrical resistance of platinum at very low temperature cannot be represented by any simple function of the temperature.

Between the b.ps. of oxygen ($-190°$) and hydrogen ($-259°$), Henning and Otto [6] used for the platinum resistance thermometer

$$R_T/R_{0°\,C.}=a+(bT+cT^2)\mathrm{D}(100/T)+(d+cT-cT^2)\mathrm{D}(230/T),$$

where D is the Debye function of the specific heat (see §3.IX N, Vol. II):

$$\mathrm{D}(x)=\frac{3}{x^3}\int_0^x \frac{\xi^3 d\xi}{e^{\xi}-1} \quad (x=\Theta/T;\ \text{here } \Theta=100 \text{ or } 230)$$

which is tabulated. Keesom [7] found that this gives a maximum difference from the helium gas thermometer of 0·05°. A simpler empirical formula used by Keesom is:

$$\log T=a+b\log(10^3 r')+cr'$$

where $r'=R_T/R_{0°\,C.}-R_{0°\,K.}/R_{0°\,C.}$ is the resistance ratio corrected for the effects of impurities in the platinum by subtracting the value extrapolated to 0° K.; it gives results correct to $\pm 0{\cdot}07°$.

The platinum resistance thermometer cannot be used at temperatures [8] below 10° K., since then the resistance of platinum, which is lower the purer the specimen, becomes almost independent of temperature. Lead [9] can be used to 7° K., when it becomes supraconductive (§16.IX O, Vol. II). An inaccurate temperature scale for the lead thermometer found by Eucken was corrected by Latimer and Hoenshel and by Clusius,[10] and care should be taken to use the new figures. The lead thermometer is now practically obsolete. A copper thermometer has been used,[11] also constantan and

[1] *Berlin Ber.*, 1911, 306.
[2] *Proc. K. Akad. Wetens. Amsterdam*, 1916, **18**, 914.
[3] *Z. ges. Kälte-Ind.*, 1932, **39**, 86.
[4] *Naturwiss.*, 1928, **16**, 617.
[5] *Physica*, 1934, **1**, 609.
[6] *Phys. Z.*, 1936, **37**, 639.
[7] Keesom and Bijl, *Physica*, 1936, **3**, 418; 1937, **4**, 305; Keesom and Tuyn, *Comm. Leiden* 1936, Suppl. **78**.
[8] Holborn and Henning, *Ann. Phys.*, 1911, **35**, 761; comparison of Pt and He gas thermometers $-190°$ to $-258°$, see Keesom and Bijl, *Physica*, 1936, **3**, 418.
[9] Onnes and Clay, *Proc. K. Akad. Wetens. Amsterdam*, 1907, **10**, 207 (*Comm. Leiden*, **95c**); and papers listed in §11.IX M, Vol. II.
[10] Eucken and Schwers, *Verhl. d. D. Phys. Ges.*, 1913, **15**, 578; Latimer and Hoenshel, *J.A.C.S.*, 1926, **48**, 19; Clusius, *Z. phys. Chem.*, 1929, **3** B, 41; Clusius and Vaughen, *Z. ges. Kälte-Ind.*, 1929, **36**, 215.
[11] Siemens, *Ann. Phys.*, 1861, **113**, 91; *Proc. Roy. Soc.*, 1871, **19**, 443; Dewar, *Proc. Roy. Soc.*, 1901, **68**, 360; Onnes and Holst, *Proc. K. Akad. Wetens. Amsterdam*, 1914, **17**, 508 (*Comm. Leiden*, **142a**); Meissner, *Verhl. d. D. Phys. Ges.*, 1914, **16**, 262; Darling, *Proc. Phys. Soc.*,

manganin,[1] but the best material for very low temperatures is unannealed phosphor bronze.[2]

The sensitivity of some samples of phosphor bronze (not all are suitable for the purpose of thermometry) seems to be due to the accidental or intentional inclusion of small amounts of supraconducting lead in the metal, which causes a rapid fall of resistance, without actual supraconductivity, as the temperature is reduced.[3] Unannealed phosphor-bronze gives a reproducible and almost linear change of resistance with temperature between 4·2° K. and 0·99° K. Gold wire has been used instead of platinum.[4] An advantage of gold over platinum is that it can be obtained purer, has a resistance-temperature curve better suited to interpolation, and has a lower inflexion point in the resistance curve.

In temperature measurements in strong magnetic fields, such as are used to produce low temperatures by the magneto-thermal effect (§ 18), it is important to remember that the resistance of metal wires changes in a magnetic field,[5] so that non-magnetic carbon or Indian-ink resistance thermometers have been used in such fields.[6] Austin and Pierce [7] measured temperatures from 18° to −200° by the change of refractive index of silica glass with temperature. Radiation thermopiles for liquid-air temperature are described.[8]

Thermocouples have been used in low-temperature measurements. Dewar and Fleming [9] showed that the ordinary parabolic formula (§ 9.VI A) fails at low temperatures, especially for iron, antimony, and bismuth against lead. Dewar [10] used platinum–German silver couples to −250°; Pellat [11] used iron–zinc, and iron–constantan or steel–constantan couples have been used by several experimenters.[12] The common copper–constantan couple can be used if suitably calibrated.[13] Silver–gold couples [14] have some advantages. Nernst

1921, **33**, 138; Gibson and Giauque, *J.A.C.S.*, 1923, **45**, 93; Maier, *J. Phys. Chem.*, 1930, **34**, 2861; Giauque and Stout, *J.A.C.S.*, 1936, **58**, 1144.

1 Onnes and Braak, *Proc. K. Akad. Wetens. Amsterdam*, 1908, **10**, 204; Onnes and Clay, *ibid.*, 1908, **10**, 200, 207 (*Comm. Leiden*, **99** *a–c*); Onnes and Holst, *ibid.*, 1914, **17**, 508 (*Comm. Leiden*, **142** *a*, *c*).

2 Keesom and Van den Inde, *Comm. Leiden*, 1929, **203***c*; 1932, **219***b*; Southard and Milner, *J.A.C.S.*, 1933, **55**, 4384; Babbitt and Mendelssohn, *Phil. Mag.*, 1935, **20**, 1025; Van Laer and Keesom, *Physica*, 1935, **5**, 541; Allen and Shire, *Nature*, 1937, **139**, 878 (to 0·027° K.); Van Dijk, Keesom, and Steller, *Physica*, 1938, **5**, 625 (to 0·25° K.)

3 Burton, Smith, and Wilhelm, "Phenomena at the Temperature of Liquid Helium," New York, 1940, 56.

4 Dewar, *Proc. Roy. Soc.*, 1901, **68**, 360; Giauque and Wiebe, *J.A.C.S.*, 1928, **50**, 101; Schäfer, *Z. phys. Chem.*, 1937, **36** B, 85.

5 Kapitza, *Proc. Roy. Soc.*, 1929, **123**, 292; 1930, **126**, 683; Stout and Barieau, *J.A.C.S.*, 1939, **61**, 238 (Au and Ag at 1·5° to 20° K.); Giauque and Stout, *ibid.*, 1940, **62**, 3516 (manganin).

6 Giauque, Stout, and Clark, *Ind. Eng. Chem.*, 1936, **28**, 743 (bibl.); *J.A.C.S.*, 1938, **60**, 1053; Van Dijk, Keesom, and Steller, *Physica*, 1938, **5**, 625; Fairbank and Lane, *Rev. Sci. Instr.*, 1947, **18**, 525.

7 *Physics*, 1935, **6**, 43.

8 Cartwright, *Rev. Sci. Instr.*, 1933, **4**, 382.

9 *Phil. Mag.*, 1895, **40**, 95.

10 *Proc. Roy. Soc.*, 1905, **76**, 316.

11 *Compt. Rend.*, 1901, **133**, 921.

12 Holborn and Wien, *Ann. Phys.*, 1896, **59**, 213; Ladenburg and Krügel, *Ber.*, 1899, **32**, 1818; Onnes, Clay, and Crommelin, *Proc. K. Akad. Wetens. Amsterdam*, 1907, **9**, 180, 199, 367, 403 (*Comm. Leiden*, **95***a*, *b*, *c*, *d*).

13 Giauque, Buffington, and Schulze, *J.A.C.S.*, 1927, **49**, 2343; Aston, Willinghanz, and Messerly, *ibid.*, 1935, **57**, 1642 (table for 12° to 273° K.).

14 Onnes and Clay, *Proc. K. Akad. Wetens. Amsterdam*, 1907, **9**, 213 (*Comm. Leiden*, **95***f*); 1908, **11**, 344 (*Comm. Leiden*, **107***b*); Borelius, Keesom, Johanson, and Linde, *Comm. Leiden*, 1932, **217** *d*, *e*.

and Schwers [1] give for the e.m.f. of a copper–constantan couple between 10° and 100° K.:

$$e = 31{\cdot}12 T \log(1 + T/90) + 10^{-7} T^4 \text{ microvolts.}$$

The copper–constantan and iron–constantan couples are useful down to −190° C. or 83° K. Between 5° and 14° K. there are no fixed points, and a helium gas thermometer or some resistance thermometer or thermocouple compared with it is most suitable. Keesom and Matthijs [2] used alloys of gold and copper with various metals (the best being gold with about 2 per cent. of cobalt) against a standard silver alloy with 0·37 atomic per cent. of copper, down to 2·5° K.

§ 20. Measurement of Very Low Temperatures

The measurement of *very low* temperatures (below 1° K.) is possible only by the effect on the magnetic susceptibility, χ, of a paramagnetic salt which obeys Curie's law [3] (§ 11): $\chi = C/T$, where C is a constant. Gadolinium sulphate $Gd_2(SO_4)_3,8H_2O$ was first used, or caesium titanium alum, but potassium chromium alum is better. Curie's law is verified for the substances down to, say, 1° K., and is then *assumed* to hold to the lowest temperatures measured, say 0·01° K.

In Fig. 17.VI C the entropy S of a paramagnetic substance is plotted against temperature for zero magnetic field strength ($\mathbf{H}=0$). The temperature T_0 is (i) high enough to be measured by a gas thermometer, (ii) low enough to make the entropy due to ordinary vibrations in the crystal lattice negligible. The entropy at T_0 and $\mathbf{H}=0$ will then be due only to the multiplicity g due to the degeneracy of energy levels (§9.IV), and equal to $\mathbf{R} \ln g$ per g.atom. If Nernst's heat theorem (§ 69.II) applies, this multiplicity will be resolved at the absolute zero, when $g=1$ and the entropy is zero. The curve will, therefore, fall off at lower temperatures, as shown. If the specific heat is measured, the value of $\mathrm{d}E/\mathrm{d}T^*$ is known, where T^* is the temperature measured magnetically on the assumption of Curie's law. The shape of the curve may be found by a series of adiabatic demagnetisations along vertical lines descending from various values of the field strength, $\mathbf{H}_1$, $\mathbf{H}_2$ . . ., and thus T_1^*, T_2^* . . . found. The slope $\mathrm{d}S/\mathrm{d}T^*$ is thus found, and the thermodynamic temperature at any point of the curve is then given, from (2), § 35.II, i.e. $T = (\mathrm{d}E/\mathrm{d}S)$, by:

$$T = (\mathrm{d}E/\mathrm{d}T^*)_{\mathbf{H}=0} / (\mathrm{d}S/\mathrm{d}T^*)_{\mathbf{H}=0}.$$

In determining the quantity of energy required to warm the substance, this was supplied in the form of γ-rays from radioactive material. A plot of T^* and the time of irradiation was converted into a curve between E and T^* by using the condition that the Curie and absolute scales must coincide at the higher temperatures.[4]

[1] *Berlin Ber.*, 1914, 354.

[2] *Physica*, 1935, **2**, 623; *Comm. Leiden*, **238***b*.

[3] Keesom, *J. de Phys.*, 1934, **5**, 373; *Phys. Z.*, 1934, **35**, 928; *Physica*, 1935, **2**, 805; 1936, **3**, 491; De Haas and Wiersma, *ibid.*, 1935, **2**, 335; 1936, **3**, 491; Kürti, Lainé, and Simon, *Compt. Rend.*, 1937, **204**, 754; 1939, **208**, 173; Kürti and Simon, *Phil. Mag.*, 1938, **26**, 840, 849; Jacyna, *Bull. Acad. Polon.*, 1937 A, 260; Jacyna, Malis, and Obnorsky, *ibid.*, 1938 A, 33; Giauque and Stout, *J.A.C.S.*, 1939, **61**, 1384; Casimir, de Klerk, and Polder, *Physica*, 1940, **7**, 737; Giauque, Stout, Egan, and Clark, *J.A.C.S.*, 1941, **63**, 405; Van Dijk, *Physica*, 1941, **8**, 67; 1943, **10**, 248; 1946, **12**, 371 (0·25°–1·5° K.); general reviews in Ruhemann, " Low Temperature Physics," 1937, 245; Dixit, *Current Sci.*, 1938, **6**, 589 (59 refs.); Giauque, *Nature*, 1939, **143**, 623; Powell, *Rep. Progr. Phys.*, 1939, **5**, 164; Roberts, " Heat and Thermodynamics," 1940, 120; Luttinger and Tisza, *Phys. Rev.*, 1946, **70**, 954; de Klerk, *Physica*, 1946, **12**, 513; de Klerk, Steenland, and Gorter, *Nature*, 1948, **161**, 678 (0·005° K.).

[4] Burton, Smith, and Wilhelm, " Phenomena at the Temperature of Liquid Helium," New York, 1940, 228.

Even when the susceptibility is not known as a function of temperature, and hence Curie's law cannot be used in the calculation, it is still possible to use the following method, due to Keesom. If temperature-entropy curves (which need not be known) are supposed to be drawn through the horizontal $T=T_0$, and cutting this at 1 and 2 for field strengths $\mathbf{H}_1$ and $\mathbf{H}_2$, and if the verticals through $\mathbf{H}_1$ and $\mathbf{H}_2$ meet the curve for $\mathbf{H}=0$ at 3 and 4, as shown in Fig. 17.VI C, the quantity of heat required to pass from 4 to 3 can be found by using an arbitrary thermometer which can be used to locate the point 3. If an adiabatic demagnetisation is carried out from $\mathbf{H}_2$ to $\mathbf{H}_1$, i.e. from point 2 to point 5, the quantity of heat q_1 required to pass from 5 to 1 at the field strength $\mathbf{H}_1$ may be found. Since $q=\int T dS$, the quantities of heat are proportional to the areas and hence T_2/T_0=(area 3687)/(area 1287). If $\mathbf{H}_1$ and $\mathbf{H}_2$ are nearly equal, this ratio is very nearly the same as (area 3487)/(area 1587) $=q_2/q_0$. (In the figure, where $\mathbf{H}_1$ and $\mathbf{H}_2$ are widely separated, for clearness, this is obviously wide of the mark, but if the verticals through $\mathbf{H}_1$ and $\mathbf{H}_2$ come closer together, the equality of the two ratios of the areas will be approached.) Since T_0, q_0, and q_2 are known, T_2 (equal in the limit to T_1) can be calculated.

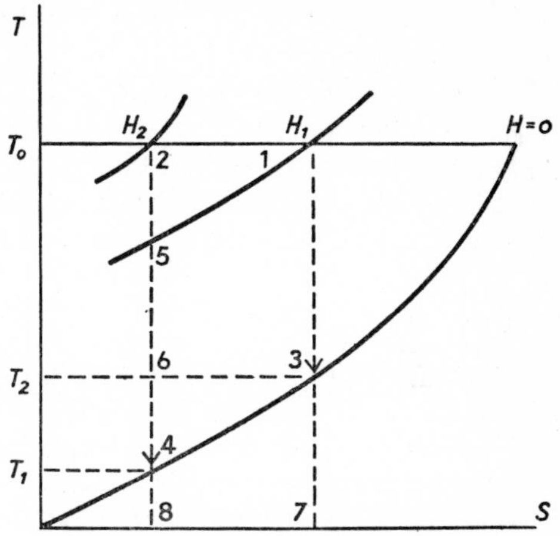

FIG. 17.VI C. Entropies as Functions of Temperature in a Magnetic Field

Another method, used by de Haas and Wiersma, depends on their observation that adiabatic demagnetisation of caesium titanium alum, from various high field strengths, produced no change in molar magnetic moment $\sigma=\sigma_0^2\mathbf{H}/3\boldsymbol{R}T$, where $\sigma_0=\mu N$, μ being the atomic magnetic moment and N Avogadro's number. If $\mathbf{H}_1$, T_1, and $\mathbf{H}_2$, T_2, are two points on two known saturation curves at helium temperatures, for which σ has a value σ_0 remaining constant in demagnetisation, and if $(dE/d\sigma)_T=g'(\sigma)$, where E is the energy and g' is a function of σ, then $g'(\sigma)=g'(\sigma_0)=g'$ can be calculated from $\mathbf{H}_1$, $\mathbf{H}_2$, T_1, and T_2; and if $\mathbf{H}_b$, T_b, and $\mathbf{H}_e$, T_e, are the field strengths and temperatures at the beginning and end of a demagnetisation experiment, then it can be shown that $T_e/T_b=(\mathbf{H}_e-g')/(\mathbf{H}_b-g')$, and, as T_b, $\mathbf{H}_e$, $\mathbf{H}_b$, and g' are known, T_e can be calculated.

For two points on the saturation curve ($\sigma=\sigma_0$=const.) (11), § 17, gives:

$$\mathbf{H}_1=T_1 f(\sigma_0)+g'(\sigma_0)$$
$$\mathbf{H}_2=T_2 f(\sigma_0)+g'(\sigma_0)$$
$$\therefore\ g'(\sigma_0)=[T_1T_2/(T_2-T_1)](\mathbf{H}_1/T_1-\mathbf{H}_2/T_2).$$

Since σ is constant during demagnetisation (magnetisation independent of $\mathbf{H}$), and f and g' are constants for the conditions of experiment used by de Haas and Wiersma, therefore $(\mathbf{H}-g')/T=f$, therefore $(\mathbf{H}_b-g')/T_b=(\mathbf{H}_e-g')/T_e$, or $T_e/T_b=(\mathbf{H}_e-g')/(\mathbf{H}_b-g')$, which is the formula just given.

To measure temperatures below 1° K., Lawson and Long [1] used the Brownian movement of a quartz crystal bar.

[1] *Phys. Rev.*, 1946, **70**, 220, 977; Brown and MacDonald, *ibid.*, 1946, **70**, 976.

SECTION VII

THE PROPERTIES OF GASES

A. PRESSURE-VOLUME-TEMPERATURE RELATIONS OF GASES. EXPERIMENTAL

§ 1. The Material Nature of Air

The material nature of air was recognised by the Greek philosophers [1] Anaxagoras (498–428 B.C.) and Empedokles (*fl.* 472 B.C.) who quote an experiment in which a pipette-like vessel (*klepshydra*) is plunged mouth downwards into water, which does not enter unless a vent is made in the top of the vessel for the escape of air. Philo of Byzantium (250 B.C.?) in his *De Ingeniis Spiritualibus* (known only in a Latin translation from an Arabic version) [2] describes the experiment with a flask, and also the ascent of water into a vessel of air in which a candle has burnt out.[3] The first experiment is described by Hero of Alexandria (A.D. 50?) in his *Pneumatica*.[4] Menon,[5] a pupil of Aristotle, says that a bladder weighs less when blown up with air than when deflated, but Simplikios (Simplicius) [6] in the 6th century A.D., who quotes the experiment from a (lost) work of Ptolemaios the astronomer, "On Weights," says he tried the experiment and found no change in weight, hence air has no weight when weighed in air. Cardan [7] much later proposed to weigh air by inflating a bladder with it and weighing. Lucretius [8] inferred that air has weight. The loss of weight of a body when weighed in air, and the variation according to the density of the air, are clearly stated in the "Book of the Balance of Wisdom" by the Greek, al-Khāzini [9] (12th century A.D.). Galileo,[10] in 1628, published a

[1] Burnet, "Early Greek Philosophy," 1920, 197 (E.), 251 (A.).

[2] Printed in Hero of Alexandria, "Opera," edit. Schmidt, Leipzig, 1899, **1**, 460.

[3] In Hero of Alexandria, "Opera," edit. Schmidt, Leipzig, 1899, **1**, 476; the same experiment is described by Fludd, "Utriusque Cosmi Maioris . . . Historia," Oppenheim, 1617, 471.

[4] Thevenot, "Veterum Mathematicorum Opera," Paris, 1693, 145; "The Pneumatics of Hero of Alexandria," transl. Greenwood and edit. Woodcroft, 1851, 2; Hero of Alexandria, "Opera," edit. Schmidt, Leipzig, 1899, **1**, 4.

[5] See Partington and McKie, *Annals of Sci.*, 1938, **3**, 2.

[6] Commentary on Aristotle's *De Coelo*, edit. Heiberg, Berlin, 1894, 17.

[7] "De Rerum Varietate," lib. i, cap. 8; Basel, 8vo, 1557, 86.

[8] Young, "Lectures on Natural Philosophy," 1845, **1**, 12.

[9] Khanikoff, *J. Amer. Orient. Soc.*, 1860, **6**, 1; on similar work by al-Bīrūnī, see Clement-Mullet, *J. Asiat.*, 1858, **11**, 379; Sarton, "Introduction to the History of Science," 1931, **2**, 216.

[10] "Discorsi e Demonstrationi Matematiche intorno a due nuoue Scienci," Leyden, 1628, 81; "Opere," Bologna, 1655, **2**, 59; Ostwald's *Klassiker*, 1890, **11**, 69; transl. Weston, "Mathematical Discourses concerning Two New Sciences relating to Mechanicks and local Motion in four Dialogues," London, 1730 (and 2nd edit. 1734), 118; new transl. by Crew and De Salvio, "Dialogues concerning Two New Sciences," New York, 1924; Jean Rey, in 1630, "Recerche de la cause pour laquelle l'Estain & le Plomb augmente de Poids quand on les calcine," Bazas, 1630 (Paris, 1777, 35), proposed to weigh air by compressing it into a vessel, but it is doubtful if he tried the experiment.

rough determination of the specific gravity of air by compressing it into a globe and weighing, finding it (water=1) 1/400=0·0025, whilst Boyle[1] in 1660 found 1/938=0·00106, and in 1666, 1/900=0·0011; the correct figure is 0·001293 at S.T.P.

§ 2. The Barometer

The recognition of the density of the air played an important part in the invention of the barometer. It had been found that a pump would not lift water higher than 34 ft., and hence the old explanation that the water rose because "Nature abhors a vacuum" got into difficulties. Galileo's pupil, Torricelli,[2] in 1643 showed that mercury in a vertical tube sealed at one end sank to a height of 30 in., leaving a vacuous space above, and he suggested that the mercury column in this apparatus, which Boyle[3] named a *barometer* (*βάρος*, weight, *μέτρον*, a measure), is sustained by the pressure of the atmosphere on the surface of the mercury in the open dish in which the tube stands. Torricelli's experiment was reported by Mersenne to Pascal, and a description of it was published in Pascal's posthumous work,[4] edited by Perier. The experiment had been suggested by Descartes[5] in 1631.

Pascal, in his "New Experiments concerning the Vacuum"[6] (1647), had pointed out that, as the densities of mercury and water are in the approximate ratio 13·5:1, a water column of 34 ft. should be upheld by the atmospheric pressure. He found this to be so by using a 46-ft. tube supported on the side of a house, the level being read from an upper window, and with other liquids the height was inversely proportional to the density. Perier[7] in 1647 repeated Torricelli's experiment (at Pascal's suggestion) at the foot and summit of the Puy-de-Dôme mountain, and found, as Pascal predicted, that the mercury sank with increasing altitude, when the air became increasingly rarefied. Townley[8]

[1] "New Experiments Physico-Mechanicall, Touching the Spring of the Air," 1660; "Works," 1744, **1**, 56; "Hydrostatical Paradoxes," 1666; "Works," 1744, **2**, 417; Musschenbroek, "The Elements of Natural Philosophy," transl. Colson, 1744, **2**, 164, gave 1/800.

[2] Letter to Ricci of 11th June, 1644; Torricelli, "Opere," edit. Loria and Vassura, Faenza, 1919, **3**, 186–88 (cf. pp. 198, 211); transl. in I. H. B. and A. G. H. Spiers, "The Physical Treatises of Pascal," New York, 1937, 163; cf. de Waard, "L'Expérience Barométrique," Thouars, 1936, 110; the actual experiments were made by Torricelli's pupil Viviani.

[3] "New Experiments and Observations Touching Cold," 1665, 27; "Works," 1744, **2**, 244; for history of the barometer, see De Luc, "Recherches sur les Modifications de l'Atmosphère," Geneva, 1772, **1**, 5 f.

[4] "Traitez de l'Eqvilibre des Liqvevrs et de la Pesantevr de la Masse de l'Air," Paris, 1663, preface, fol. viii, and pp. 92, 105, 176; transl. Spiers, "The Physical Treatises of Pascal," New York, 1937, 49; Mach, "The Science of Mechanics," 1893, 114.

[5] "Oeuvres," Paris, 1824, **6**, 204; 1825, **10**, 344, 351 (letters of 1649 to Carcavi); see Duhem, *Rev. Gén. Sci.*, 1906, **17**, 769, 809.

[6] "Discovrs dv Vvide svr les Experiences de Monsievr Paschal, et le traicté de Mr. Pierius . . .," Roven, 1648; "Experiences Novvelles tovchant le Vvide . . . Dedié à Monsievr Pascal . . . Par le sievr B. P. son fils," Paris, 1647; "Observation tovchant le Vvide, fait povr la Premier fois en France . . . par Monsievr Petit," Paris, 1647; Pascal, "Oeuvres," 1908, **2**, 53; Thurot, *J. de Phys.*, 1872, **1**, 171 (Torricelli's expt.), 267 (*horror vacui*); Adam, *Rev. Philosoph.*, 1887, **24**, 612; 1888, **25**, 65 (Pascal and Descartes); Duhem, *Rev. Gén. Sci.*, 1905, **16**, 599; 1906, **17**, 769, 809 (Pascal and hydrostatics; attempts to weigh air from Cardan to Descartes); Milhaud, *Rev. Sci.*, 1907, **7**, 769 (Pascal's experiments on the vacuum); Leavenworth, "A Methodological Analysis of the Physics of Pascal," New York, 1930, 74 f., 92 f.; Maire, "L'Oeuvre Scientifique de Blaise Pascal," 1912.

[7] Letter of 1644 in Pascal, "Traitez de l'Eqvilibre des Liqvevrs," Paris, 1663, 176; Spiers, "The Physical Treatises of Pascal," New York, 1937, 103.

[8] Boyle, "Works," edit. Birch, 1744, **1**, 98.

(at Boyle's suggestion) repeated the experiment, with a similar result, on Winter Hill, near Chorley, in Lancashire.

The barometer experiment, as Boyle [1] says, was explained differently by some philosophers, such as Hobbes and Franciscus Linus, who postulated an invisible " cord " or *funiculum* stretching from the surface of the mercury to the top of the tube and supporting the mercury column; these *plenists* still maintained that an extended vacuum was impossible, whilst the *vacuists* (Guericke, Pascal, and Boyle) believed that a vacuum could be produced in a suitable apparatus, and tried to prove this experimentally.

The various forms of barometers (the siphon barometer, usually credited to Hooke, seems really to have been invented by Torricelli in 1644), and the necessary corrections, are described in works on Physics.[2]

Very pure mercury wets (but does not adhere to) clean gas-free glass, giving a flat surface in a barometer.[3] The fact that the mercury in a completely filled barometer tube does not always sink to the barometric level on inverting the tube, but remains filling the tube, was known to Boyle: the height of the column may [4] exceed 2 m.

The coefficient of expansion of mercury at room temperature is 0·0001817, and if β is that of the scale (assumed correct at 0°) the corrected barometer reading at 0° is $B_0=B_t[1-(0{\cdot}0001817-\beta)t]$. The values of β are for ordinary glass 0·00001, brass 0·00002, steel 0·000012. Correction tables are generally used [5] and one may conveniently be hung near the barometer.

In calculating the absolute pressure in dynes/cm.^{2} from the reading of a barometer (or mercury manometer, § 7) it is necessary to know not only the density of mercury (§ 7) but also the value of the acceleration of gravity, g, at a given place. This depends on the latitude ϕ and the height h above sea-level. The meniscus correction is considered in § 7.

The variation of g, the acceleration of gravity, with the height h m. above sea-level and latitude $\phi°$ is given by some form of an equation due originally to Clairaut (1743) and modified, e.g. by Helmert [6] (1901):

$$g=978{\cdot}030(1+0{\cdot}005302\sin^2\phi-0{\cdot}0_57\sin^2 2\phi)-0{\cdot}0_33086h.$$

[1] " New Experiments Physico-Mechanical touching the Spring and Weight of the Air proposed by Mr. Boyle . . . against the Objections of Franciscus Linus," London, 1662; " Works," edit. Birch, 1744, **1**, 76.

[2] Koch, *Ann. Phys.*, 1895, **55**, 391; 1899, **67**, 485; Prytz, *Z. Instr.*, 1896, **16**, 178; Shields, *Phil. Mag.*, 1896, **41**, 406 (temperature correction); Collie, *J.C.S.*, 1895, **67**, 128; Travers, " Study of Gases," 1901, 143; Woringer, *Z. phys. Chem.*, 1901, **38**, 326; Auerbach, in Winkelmann, " Handbuch der Physik," 1908, **1**, ii, 1289; Green, *Chem. News*, 1908, **98**, 49 (temperature compensated); Morrison, *Proc. Roy. Soc. Edin.*, 1910, **30**, 386; Stillman, *Bur. Stand. Bull.*, 1914, **10**, 371 (setting Hg surface to ivory point); Cintra do Prado, *An. Acad. Brasil Cienc.*, 1941, **13**, 337 (corrections); Levanto, *Ann. Acad. Sci. Fenn.*, 1941, **1**A, No. 8; Satterly, *J. Roy. Astron. Soc. Canada*, 1944, **38**, 21; for a full description of barometer corrections, see Beattie, Benedict, and Blaisdell, *Proc. Amer. Acad.*, 1937, **71**, 327.

[3] Schumacher, *J.A.C.S.*, 1923, **45**, 2255; Baker, *Science*, 1928, **67**, 74; Manley, *Phil. Mag.*, 1928, **5**, 958.

[4] Pizzarello, *Nuov. Cim.*, 1898, **8**, 266; McKie, *Sci Progr.*, 1936, 55.

[5] See e.g. Landolt-Börnstein, " Tabellen," 5th edit., 1923, 68 (also to sea-level and lat. 45°); Ostwald-Luther, " Phys.-chem. Messungen," 5th edit., 1931, 202; for a mechanical correcting device, see Shields, *Phil. Mag.*, 1896, **41**, 406.

[6] See e.g. Glazebrook, " Dict. of Applied Physics," 1922, **1**, 587; Landolt-Börnstein, " Tabellen," 5th edit., 1923, 25; Newman and Searle, " Properties of Matter," 1928, 50; Kaye and Laby, " Tables," 10th edit., 1948, 19; no two works of reference agree on the formula. Jeffreys, *Nature*, 1948, **162**, 915, gives $g_0=978{\cdot}0373$, and g at Teddington 981·1807, at Washington 980·0831, and at Potsdam 981·2606.

The value of g (to two decimal places) in London is 981·20, in Oxford 981·21, in Cambridge 981·26, in Paris 980·94, in Washington 980·10, etc. The standard value of g_0 for $\phi=45°$ from Helmert's formula is 980·616; the value accepted has varied, and at present 980·629 is taken [1] (§ 1.VII D). A more accurate formula by Heiskanen [2] (1924) is:

$$g_0=978{\cdot}052[1+0{\cdot}005285 \sin^2 \phi-0{\cdot}0_5 7 \sin^2 2\phi+0{\cdot}0_4 19 \cos^2 \phi \cos 2(\lambda-17°)]$$

for $h=0$, and $g=g_0-0{\cdot}0_3 3086h$; λ is the degree of east longitude.

§ 3. Units of Pressure

The natural *unit of pressure* [3] is unit force acting uniformly and normally on unit area. In the c.g.s. system this is 1 dyne per cm.^{2}, called a *barye*, but as this is a very small unit, 10^6 dynes per cm.^{2}, called a *bar*, is used; a *millibar* is 0·001 bar. By Richards the bar (10^6 dynes per cm.^{2}) was called a megabar [4] (a bar being 1 dyne per cm.^{2}, which is here called a barye), and a millibar was called a kilobar. The bar (10^6 dynes per cm.^{2}) is equivalent to 750·06 mm. Hg of the standard barometer (acceleration of gravity $g=980{\cdot}665$) or 0·98703 atm., and is sometimes (to add to the unfortunate confusion) called a "c.g.s. atmosphere." Since the utility of the convenient names "bar" and "atmosphere" has now been completely vitiated, they are best avoided altogether, the pressure being given in other, unambiguous, units. The original definition of the bar as 10^6 dynes per cm.^{2} has been restored by international convention, but still another name, the *microbar*, has been introduced for the barye (1 dyne per cm.^{2}).[5]

The *normal atmosphere* has been defined as the pressure of a mercury column of 760 mm. with a density of mercury of 13·59509 g. cm.$^{-3}$ in a place with $g=980{\cdot}665$ cm. sec.$^{-2}$; this is equal to 1,013,249 dyne cm.$^{-2}$. The standard value of g has since been changed to 980·629 cm. sec.$^{-2}$, and the normal atmosphere defined (independently of barometric height) as a pressure of 1,013,250 dyne cm.$^{-2}$.

In laboratory or technical preparative chemistry, pressures from 10^{-2} to $10^{-3\cdot7}$ mm. Hg are common, 10^{-6} mm. occurs in electronic practice, 10^{-9} mm. is the present lower limit of pressure attainable; at this nadir of pressure there are still about $10^{19}\times10^{-9}/760\simeq10^9$, or 1,000,000,000 molecules per cm.^{3}. Hickman proposed a low-pressure notation similar to the pH scale, pm being the exponent of 10 in the mm. Hg pressure, e.g. 10^{-9} mm. is pm$=-9$; 760 mm.$=10^{2\cdot88}$ mm. is pm$=2{\cdot}88$, etc. The mm. Hg unit is quite unnecessarily called a *torr* (after Torricelli) in some German works.[6] A very confusing unit proposed by Townsend [7] takes the logarithm of the pressure in torrs in a completely negative form and multiplies it by -10, e.g. if $p=2\times10^{-5}$ mm.,

[1] Moles, *J. Chim. Phys.*, 1937, **34**, 49; Clark, *Proc. Roy. Soc.*, 1946, **186**, 192, says 980·62 was adopted in 1941; Birge, *Rep. Progr. Phys.*, 1942, **8**, 90, takes 980·616 for $\phi=45°$.

[2] Landolt-Börnstein, "Tabellen," 1931, Ergzb., **2**, i, 17; Berroth, in Geiger and Scheel, "Handbuch der Physik," 1926, **2**, 463.

[3] Sometimes, incorrectly, the whole force on an area (called a "thrust" by Briggs and Bryan, "Matriculation Hydrostatics," 1896, 71) is called "pressure." On exact pressure units, see Onnes and Keesom, "Encycl. d. math. Wiss.," 1912, **5**, i, 615 (*Comm. Leiden*, 1912, Suppl. **23**).

[4] Richards and Stull, *Z. phys. Chem.*, 1904, **49**, 9; all Richards' papers contain this name; for the confusion, see report on A.E.F. units, *Verhl. d. D. Phys. Ges.*, 1913, **15**, 143.

[5] McAdie, *Phys. Rev.*, 1919, **13**, 285, proposed a bar of 1 dyne/cm.^{2} and a kilobar of 1,000 of these; Whipple, *Proc. Phys. Soc.*, 1919, **31**, 237; Meyers and Jessup, *Bur. Stand. J. Res.*, 1931, **6**, 1061.

[6] For another "tor"=10 baryes, see de Baillhache, *Rev. Gén. Sci.*, 1913, **24**, 17.

[7] *Nature*, 1945, **155**, 545; Feinberg, *ibid.*, 1945, **156**, 85; Wylie, *ibid.*, 1945, **156**, 85.

log $2\times10^{-5}=\bar{5}\cdot301=-4\cdot699=47$ units. The *micron* unit of pressure is 10^{-3} mm. Hg.[1]

As Meldrum [2] said, if "science is measurement" then it "has little to do with definitions of time and space in the abstract. The man of science proceeds by defining standards, which serve in the measurement of time and space." The same applies to "matter," and "when a body is divested, in thought, of all those qualities which, according to the teachings of modern science, are in their nature phases of motion, the residue is not matter, but mass." [3] The name "somatology" (σῶμα, body) proposed by Leslie [4] for the subject generally called "properties of matter," has not been adopted.

The British standard atmosphere [5] is the pressure of a column of mercury at 32° F. which is 29·905 in. in height at sea-level and in the latitude of Greenwich, near London. This is approximately 14·7 lb. wt. per in.^{2} (76 cm.=29·921 in.), and since no work of high accuracy is expressed in British units, this will suffice. The obsolete *line*=1/12 in.=0·08333 in.=0·21167 cm. is used in some older barometric data.

Some comparisons of metric and other units [6] are:

1 foot=0·3048010 metre   1 yard [7]=0·91439862 m.

1 cu. in. =16·387 cu. cm.

1 cu. ft.=28315 ml. (1 ml.=0·001 lit.).

1 English gallon=4·5435 lit.

1 U.S.A. gallon=3·7853 lit.

1 lb. avoirdupois [5]=453·6 gm.

1 lb. U.S.=1/2·20462 kg.

Some metric units in metre, metric ton, etc., units are:

1 *sthène*=force giving 1 metric ton an acceleration of 1 m. sec.$^{-2}$ =1000 *newtons*.

1 *pièze*=pressure of 1 sthène m.$^{-2}$.

The *microgram* $\gamma=10^{-6}$ g.=0·001 mg.

1 Dushman, *Ind. Eng. Chem.*, 1948, **40**, 778.

2 "Avogadro and Dalton," Edinburgh, 1906, 53.

3 Stallo, "Concepts of Modern Physics," 1882, 25.

4 "Elements of Natural Philosophy," Edinburgh, 1823, **1**, 6.

5 Gould, *Proc. Roy. Soc.*, 1946, **186**, 171, 195.

6 Everett, "Units and Physical Constants," 1879; "Illustrations of the C.G.S. System of Units," 5th edit., 1902; F. M. Perkin, "The Metric and British System of Weights, Measures, and Coinage," 1907; Partington and Shilling, "Specific Heats of Gases," 1924, 27; Wallot, in Geiger and Scheel, "Handbuch der Physik," 1926, **2**, 1; Henning and Jaeger, *ibid.*, 487; Block, "Messen und Wägen," Leipzig, 1928; Kaye and Laby, "Tables of Physical and Chemical Constants," 1948, 4; Kennelly, "Vestiges of Pre-Metric Weights and Measures," New York, 1928, gives interesting examples of how metric weights have been given old names, and how trade is still carried on in old units. In my time (1912) in Berlin, groceries were sold by the Pfund (=500 g.), or its "Viertel" or "Halbes-Viertel" (=62·5 g.), and paid for in "Thaler" and "Grosschen." On units, see "Computer's Handbook," Meteorological Office, 1917; Trotter, *Electrician*, 1919, **82**, 300 (British units); history of the metric system, Guillaume, *Bull. Soc. Internat. Élec.*, 1908, **8**, 27; on A.E.F. units (including γ=0·001 mg.), *Verhl. d. D. Phys. Ges.*, 1913, **15**, 143; E. E. A. in Glazebrook, "Dictionary of Applied Physics," 1922, **1**, 580; on changes in standard kg. weights over a period of over 100 years, see Siertsema, *Physica*, 1928, **8**, 37; Anon., *Nature*, 1946, **157**, 538 (British units).

7 Sears and Barrell, *Phil. Trans.*, 1932, **231**, 75; 1934, **233**, 143; Sears, *Proc. Roy. Soc.*, 1946, **186**, 152.

Prefixes used in the metric system are:

T	tera	10^{12}	h	hecto	10^2	m	milli	10^{-3}
G	giga	10^9	D	deca	10^1	μ	micro	10^{-6}
M	mega	10^6	d	deci	10^{-1}	n	nano	10^{-9}
k	kilo	10^3	c	centi	10^{-2}	p	pico	10^{-12}

§ 4. Measurements of Heights by the Barometer

Halley [1] measured heights barometrically by arbitrary calibration against measured heights; according to Auerbach [2] this method was proposed by Pascal. The atmospheric pressure decreases with height according to a formula given by Halley and by Laplace [3] (for deduction, see § 19.III), the so-called *barometer formula.* If p_0=pressure at sea-level, p that at a height h cm., ρ_0=density of air at sea-level in g./cm.³, then:

$$p = p_0 e^{-hg\rho_0/p_0} \quad (1)$$

or, since $p_0 v_0 = p_0/\rho_0 = RT/M$, where M=mol. wt. of air=29·00,

$$p = p_0 e^{-hgM/RT} \quad (2)$$

For a gas composed of one kind of molecule, of mass m, $M=Nm$ and $\boldsymbol{R}=N\boldsymbol{k}$ (N=Avogadro's number, $\boldsymbol{k}$=Boltzmann's constant),

$$\therefore \; p = p_0 e^{-hgm/\boldsymbol{k}T} \quad (2a)$$

This assumes that M, and hence the composition of the air, is constant, but owing to the different masses of the molecules of oxygen and nitrogen there should be a tendency for the atmosphere to be enriched with nitrogen at high altitudes; owing to mixing by convection, winds, etc., the composition is almost constant [4] up to a height of 20 km., and only at altitudes above 29 km. is a change in composition found experimentally.[5] G. Johnstone Stoney [6] calculated that light molecules, such as hydrogen, should escape from the upper atmosphere into space against gravitational attraction; owing to its smaller gravitating mass, the moon has lost its atmosphere. Jeans,[7] however, showed that the earth should be able to retain hydrogen and all other gases.

§ 5. Boyle's Law

The invention of the *air pump* by Otto von Guericke,[8] Burgomaster of Magdeburg, about 1650, gave an impetus to experiments on the " vacuum " (actually a low atmospheric pressure), and noteworthy in this connection is

[1] *Phil. Trans.*, 1720, **31**, 116; abridged edit., 1809, **6**, 496.

[2] Winkelmann, " Handbuch der Physik," 1891, **1**, 547.

[3] Halley, *Phil. Trans.*, 1685, **16**, 104; abridged edit., 1809, **3**, 300; Laplace, " Mécanique Céleste," bk. X, ch. 4; " Oeuvres," 1880, **4**, 290, 294; Angot, *Compt. Rend.*, 1898, **126**, 826.

[4] Yost and Russell, " Systematic Inorganic Chemistry," New York, 1944, 1.

[5] Paneth, *Nature*, 1937, **139**, 181; Carpenter, *J.A.C.S.*, 1937, **59**, 358.

[6] Of Atmospheres upon Planets and Satellites, in *Trans. Roy. Dublin Soc.*, 1897, **6**, 305; Bryan, *Phil. Trans.*, 1900, **196**, 1.

[7] Jeans, " Dynamical Theory of Gases," Cambridge, 3rd edit., 1921, 339; Vassy, *Le Vide*, 1948, **3**, 375 (stratosphere).

[8] " Experimenta Nova Magdeburgica de Vacuo Spatio," Amsterdam, 1672; Rodwell, *Chem. News*, 1864, **9**, 14; Schimank, *Z. techn. Phys.*, 1936, **17**, 209; Kossel, *ibid.*, 1936, **17**, 345 (portraits). See Partington, " Short History of Chemistry," 1947, Fig. 37, p. 68. On the date of invention of von Guericke's pumps, and supposed extant examples, see Gerland, *Ann. Phys.*, 1883, **19**, 534; Berthold, *ibid.*, 1883, **20**, 345; 1895, **54**, 724; 1916, **51**, 881; Poggendorff, " Histoire de la Physique," 1883, 258, 286; Rosenberger, " Geschichte der Physik," Brunswick, 1884, **2**, 142.

Boyle's work.[1] He had an improved pump constructed, and showed that a barometer contained in a receiver fell as the air pressure was reduced, until the mercury-level in the tube fell nearly to that in the trough. A criticism of Boyle's views by Hobbes and Linus [2] called forth in 1662 a reply [3] from Boyle, in which he first announced the famous *Boyle's Law.* In the course of experiments made in 1661, he examined both the effect of pressures higher than atmospheric on the volume of air enclosed in the shorter sealed limb of a U-tube, by pouring mercury into the long open limb of the tube, and also the effect of pressures less than atmospheric (the " debilitated force "), by using a straight glass tube, closed at one end and containing about a 1-in. length of air confined over mercury; the tube could be raised in a vessel of mercury until the air expanded to 32 in. The pressures used varied in both sets of experiments from 3 cm. to 300 cm. of mercury. The " hypothesis that supposes the pressures and expansions [volumes] to be in reciprocal proportion," Boyle says, was suggested to him by Richard Townley, after an examination of Boyle's results. This is *Boyle's law:*

$$pv=\text{const.} \qquad (1)$$

which was much later extended to other gases than air [4]: *the volume of a given mass of gas at constant temperature is inversely proportional to the pressure.*

If $v-v'=\Delta v$, $p-p'=\Delta p$, then [5] $\Delta v/v=\Delta p/p$.

On 2 August, 1661, Hooke made some experiments which confirmed Townley's hypothesis, and on 11 September, 1661, Croone and Boyle communicated some experiments to the Royal Society.[6] In his publication of 1662, after describing the making of the siphon tube and the bringing of the included air to atmospheric pressure by inclining the tube till the mercury was at the same level on both sides, Boyle says:

" This done we began to pour quicksilver into the longer leg of the syphon, which by its weight pressing up that in the shorter leg did by degrees straighten the included air; and continuing this pouring of quicksilver till the air in the shorter leg was by condensation reduced to take up but half the space it possessed (I say possessed, not filled) before; we cast our eyes upon the longer leg of the glass, on which was likewise pasted a list of paper carefully divided into inches and parts,[7] and we observed not without delight and satisfaction that the quick-

[1] " New Experiments Physico-Mechanicall, Touching the Spring of the Air," 1660; " Works," edit. Birch, 1774, **1**, 1; James, *Sci. Progr.*, 1928–9, **23**, 263.

[2] According to Polvani, *Nuov. Cim.*, 1924, **1**, 1, Franciscus Linus was Francis Hall, b. London 1595, d. 1673. On Hobbes, see Rodwell, *Chem. News*, 1864, **9**, 242.

[3] " A Defence of the Doctrine touching the Spring and Weight of the Air proposed by Mr. Boyle . . . against the Objection of Franciscus Linus," 1662, pt. I, chapt. 5; " Works," edit. Birch, 1744, **1**, 76. A full quotation and tables from the original are given by Tait, " Properties of Matter," 4th edit., 1899, 162 f., 328 f., who emphasised that Boyle also used pressures *less* than atmospheric, sometimes credited to Mariotte; extracts in Harper's *Scientific Memoirs*, New York, 1899, **5**. Boyle's priority over Mariotte was pointed out by Muncke, in Gehler's " Physikalisches Wörterbuch," 1828, **4**, 1026, 1028, who says Boyle's publication was almost certainly known to Mariotte.

[4] Mayow, " Tractatus Quinque Medico-Physici," Oxford, 1674, ch. ix; *Alembic Club Reprint*, 1907, **17**, 113, had proved this experimentally for some gases, which he found are compressed to the same extent as air.

[5] Rebenstorff, *Chem. Ztg.*, 1908, **32**, 570.

[6] Rodwell, *Chem. News*, 1864, **9**, 14, 26, 50, 242; 1864, **10**, 74, 195, 208; 1865, **11**, 38, 74, 160, 291; 1865, **12**, 62, 74, 293; 1866, **14**, 51. Boyle's law was stated, as a *hypothesis*, before 1663 by Pascal, who says of a balloon of air, " il deuroit s'élargir à proportion de ce qu'il seroit moins chargé ": " Traitez de l'Eqvilibre des Liqvevrs et de la Pesantevr de la Masse de l'Air," Paris, 1663, 50; Spiers, " The Physical Treatises of Pascal," New York, 1937, 30.

[7] Into eighths, as is stated earlier. For simple demonstration apparatus for Boyle's law.

silver in that longer part of that tube was 29 inches higher than the other. . . . Here the same air being brought to a degree of density about twice as great as that it had before, obtains a spring twice as strong as formerly."

Although Boyle's law might [1] be called "Townley's law" (see above), the name "Mariotte's law," formerly more used on the Continent, has litttle justification, since Mariotte [2] published it seventeen years after Boyle, and (although he does not mention Boyle) he makes no claim to an independent discovery, as he could, in fact, hardly do, since Boyle's publications were well known in France. Mariotte used the same explanation of the pressure or "spring" of the air, by comparing it with little fleeces of wool or tiny coiled springs, as had been given by Boyle; [3] the same explanation had, in fact, been given long before by Hero of Alexandria [4] (A.D. 50?) and by Descartes.[5] Descartes himself preferred a kinetic explanation, based on his famous theory of vortices, and very well summarised by Boyle: [6] "by the restless agitation of that celestial matter [the ether] wherein the particles swim, are so whirled round that each corpuscle endeavours to beat off all others from coming within the little sphere requisite to its motion about its own centre."

§ 6. Deviations from Boyle's Law

Until late in the eighteenth century, when other gases besides air were characterised by Black, Cavendish, and Priestley, Boyle's law was applied only to atmospheric air. It was realised that more accurate experiments were necessary to test its strict validity. Van Musschenbroek,[7] Sulzer,[8] and Robison [9] obtained no very definite results: the first found air *less* compressible than Boyle's law requires, and attributed this to the finite volume of the molecules. In 1799 Van Marum [10] pointed out the first decisive deviation from Boyle's law in the case of ammonia at high pressure (which finally liquefied it), and similar experiments with other easily condensable gases (hydrogen sulphide, cyanogen,

see e.g. Humphreys, *Phys. Rev.*, 1900, **10**, 123; Rogers, *ibid.*, 1900, **11**, 112; Williams, *ibid.*, 1900, **11**, 255; Reiff, *Verhl. d. D. Phys. Ges.*, 1906, **8**, 526; Dehn, *J.A.C.S.*, 1908, **30**, 578.

[1] Eggert, "Physical Chemistry," 1932, 12.

[2] "Discours sur la Nature de l'Air," Paris, 1679; reprint, 1923; "Oeuvres," Leyden, 1717, **1**, 149; Mariotte says experiments were made by Hubin and himself; McKie, *Endeavour*, 1948, **7**, 148.

[3] "New Experiments Physico-Mechanicall, Touching the Spring of the Air," 1660; "Works," edit. Birch, 1744, **1**, 8.

[4] "Pneumatica," in "Opera," edit. Schmidt, Leipzig, 1899, **1**, 8; transl., edit. Woodcroft, 1851, 3 ("when any force is applied to it, the air is compressed, and . . . falls into the vacant spaces from the pressure exerted on its particles: but when the force is withdrawn, the air returns again to its former position from the elasticity of its particles, as is the case with horn shavings and sponge [τοῖς τῶν κεράτων συμβαίνει ξέσμασι καὶ τοῖς ξηροῖς σπόγγοις], which, when compressed and set free again, return to the same position and exhibit the same bulk.")

[5] "Principia Philosophiae," Amsterdam, 1644, lib. iv, cap. 46, p. 218; transl., "Oeuvres," edit. Cousin, Paris, 1824, **3**, 369 ("aër . . . ejus particulæ ferè omnes sint flexiles, instar mollium plumularum vel tenium funiculorum . . . "like small feathers or thin strings . . .": he is speaking of the dilatation by heat rather than resistance to compression). Pascal, "Traitez de l'Eqvilibre des Liqvevrs," Paris, 1663, 48; Spiers, "The Physical Treatises of Pascal," New York, 1937, 29, speaks of the air being like a great mass of wool, compressed by the weight of the upper layers.

[6] "New Experiments Physico-Mechanicall," 1660; "Works," 1744, **1**, 8.

[7] "Introductio ad Philosophiam Naturalem," Leiden, 1762, **2**, 858; "The Elements of Natural Philosophy," transl. Colson, London, 1744, **2**, 181.

[8] *Hist. Acad. Berlin*, 1753, 114.

[9] "System of Mechanical Philosophy," edit. Brewster, Edinburgh, 1822, **3**, 635 f.

[10] *Ann. Phys.*, 1799, **1**, 145.

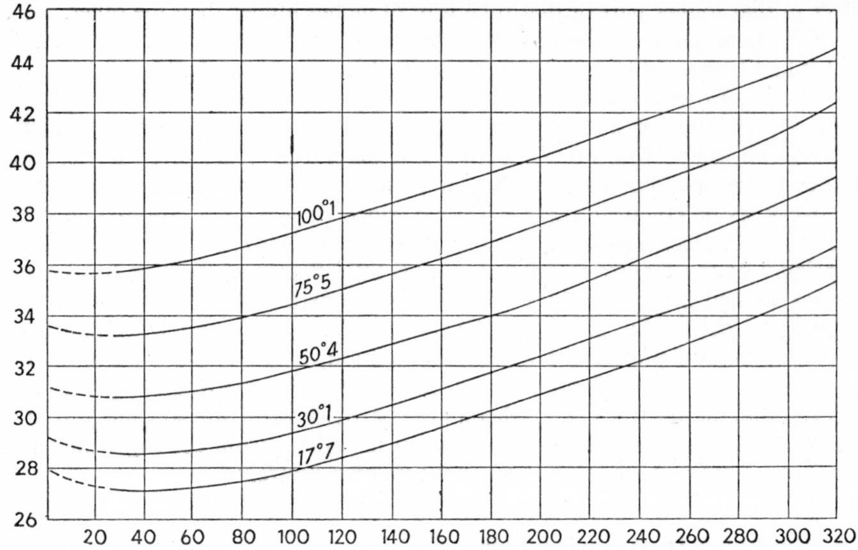

FIG. 1.VII A. Results of Amagat for Nitrogen

etc.) showed that as the pressure increases the value of pv decreases, i.e. the gas is *more* compressible (v smaller for a given p) than it should be according to Boyle's law. In the case of air, the deviation begins to be appreciable only above 20 atm.[1]; with sulphur dioxide (which liquefies under 2·5 atm. pressure

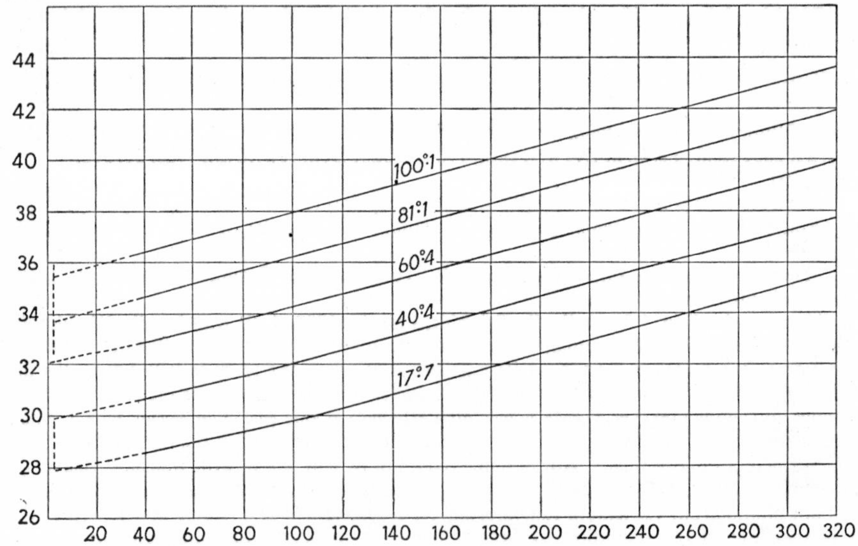

FIG. 2.VII A. Results of Amagat for Hydrogen

[1] Gilbert, *Ann. Phys.*, 1799, **1**, 145 (" not every gas obeys Mariotte's law," NH_3 does not); Oersted and Schwendsen, *Edin. J. Sci.*, 1826, **4**, 224; Despretz, *Ann. Chim.*, 1827, **34**, 335, 443; *Compt. Rend.*, 1842, **14**, 239; Arago and Dulong, *Ann. Chim.*, 1830, **43**, 74; *Bull. Soc. Encourag.*, 1830, **29**, 295; *Mém. Acad. Sci.*, 1831, **10**, 193; Magnus, *Compt. Rend.*, 1842, **14**, 165; Pouillet, *Compt. Rend.*, 1847, **24**, 915; " Élémens de Physique Expérimentale," 6th edit., Paris, 1853, **1**, 121. For a simple demonstration apparatus, see Famiglini, *Nuov. Cim.*, 1922, **23**, 393.

at 15°) the deviation is easily recognised in an ordinary Boyle's-law tube. Experiments at higher pressures with so-called " permanent gases " (i.e. those not liquefied by the application of pressure unless they are strongly cooled) were made by Regnault,[1] Natterer [2] (who reached 3,000 atm.), Cailletet,[3] and especially Amagat.[4]

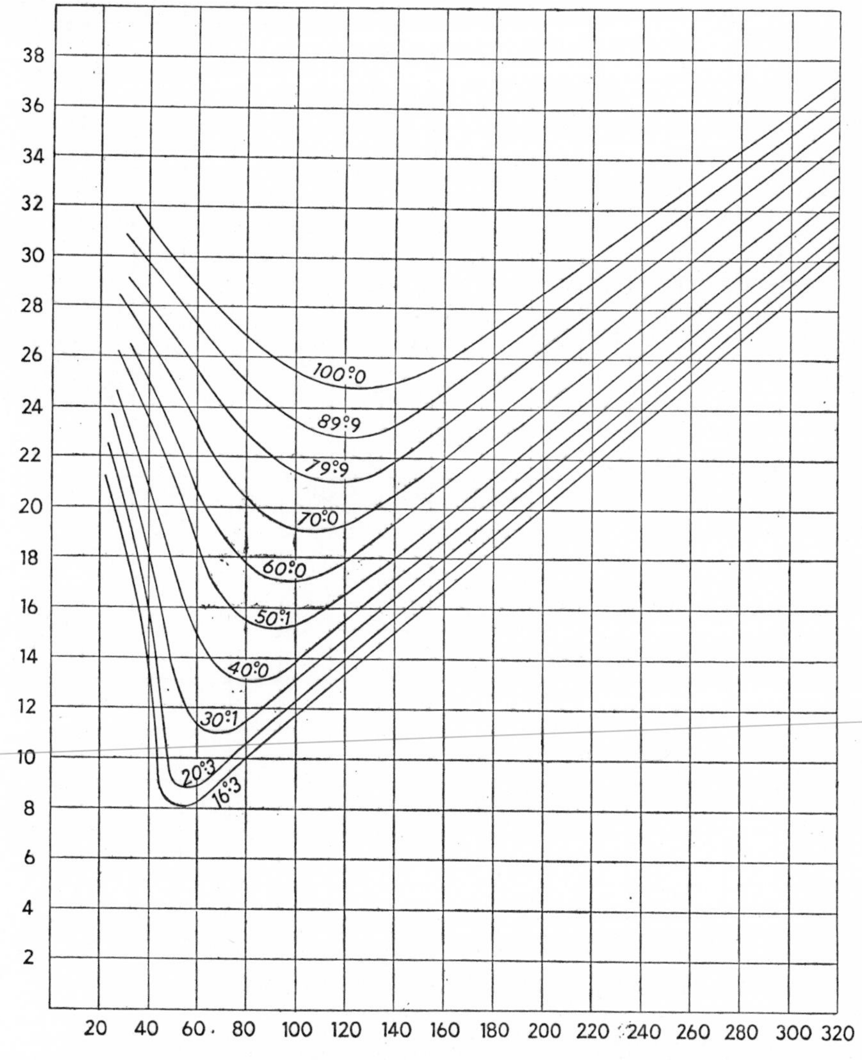

FIG. 3.VII A. Results of Amagat for Ethylene

[1] *Mém. Acad. Sci.*, 1847, **21**, 1, 329; 1862, **26**, 229; " Relation des Expériences," 3 pts., 1847–62–70, and plates; Henri Victor Regnault, b. Aix-la-Chapelle, 1810, d. 1878; Henning, *Phys. Z.*, 1910, **11**, 770.

[2] *Ann. Phys.*, 1844, **62**, 132; 1855, **94**, 436; *J. prakt. Chem.*, 1844, **31**, 375; 1845, **35**, 169; 1852, **56**, 126; *Ann.*, 1845, **54**, 254; *Wien Ber.*, 1850, **5**, 351; 1851, **6**, 557; 1854, **12**, 199; Natterer was a medical student when he began this work.

[3] *Compt. Rend.*, 1870, **70**, 1131; 1879, **88**, 61; 1880, **90**, 210 (mixtures); 1891, **112**, 764; *J. de Phys.*, 1879, **8**, 267; *Ann. Chim.*, 1880, **19**, 386.

[4] *Compt. Rend.*, 1869, **68**, 1170; 1870, **71**, 67; 1871, **73**, 183; 1872, **75**, 479; 1876, **82**, 914; 1879, **88**, 336; 1879, **89**, 437; 1880, **90**, 995; 1880, **91**, 428; 1881, **93**, 306; 1882, **94**, 847; 1882,

Natterer first showed that *pv*, after decreasing with rise of pressure up to a point, afterwards increases with all gases; Regnault had found this only with hydrogen, which he ironically called [1] " plus que parfait." Thus, all gases at

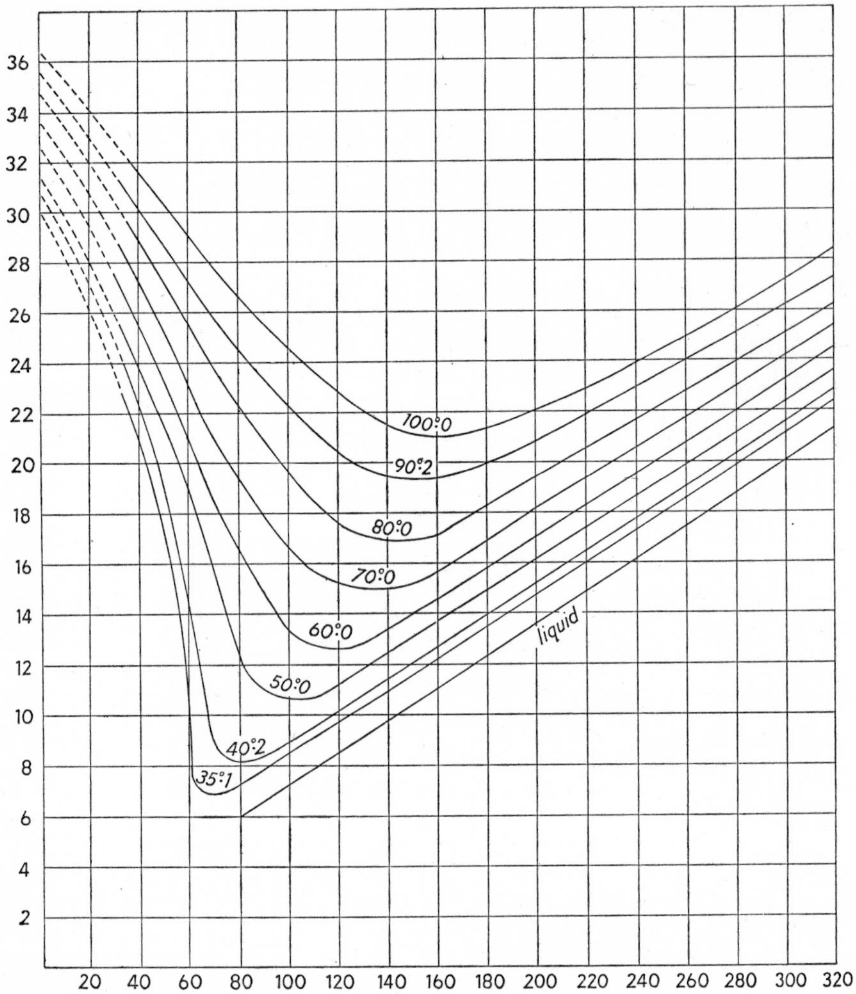

FIG. 4.VII A. Results of Amagat for Carbon Dioxide

95, 281, 638; 1888, **107**, 522; 1890, **111**, 871; 1898, **127**, 88; *Ann. Chim.*, 1873, **28**, 274; 1873, **29**, 246; 1876, **8**, 270; 1880, **19**, 345; 1881, **22**, 353; 1883, **28**, 456, 464, 480, 500; summary in *ibid.*, 1893, **29**, 68; *Arch. Sci. Phys. Nat.*, 1869, **35**, 169; 1871, **40**, 320; 1871, **41**, 365; *Phys. Z.*, 1901, **1**, 530; *Congrès Internat. Phys.*, 1901, **1**, 550; Amagat and Décombe, " La Statique des Fluides," Paris, 1917; see also Winkelmann, *Ann. Phys.*, 1878, **5**, 92 (C_2H_4); Roth, *ibid.*, 1880, **11**, 1 (CO_2, SO_2, NH_3, C_2H_4); Koch, *ibid.*, 1908, **27**, 311 (air); Koch and Wagner, *ibid.*, 1909, **31**, 31; Holborn *et al.*, *ibid.*, 1915, **47**, 1089 (air, A, He); 1920, **63**, 674 (H_2 at 0°, 50°, and 100° at 20–100 atm.); on interpolating *pv* for even *volumes*, see Bridgeman, *J.A.C.S.*, 1927, **49**, 1130. Extracts from Amagat's papers are given in Harper's *Scientific Memoirs*, New York, 1899, **5**. Of Emile-Hilaire Amagat (1840–1915), Guye, *J. Chim. Phys.*, 1915, **13**, 260, says: " Complètement indépendant des influences des écoles, Amagat a imprimé à toute son oeuvre une originalité particulière . . . En toutes circonstances, ce savant évite les chemins battus, pour ouvrir une voie qui est bein à lui."

[1] *Mém Acad. Sci.*, 1847, **21**, 402.

sufficiently high pressures become less compressible than according to Boyle's law. Hydrogen at ordinary temperatures, and also helium and neon, show this at pressures of the order of 1 atm.

Some results of Amagat are shown in Figs. 1–5.VII A; the values of *pv* are taken as ordinates for the mass of gas used, and pressures in m. Hg as abscissae. The minimum value of *pv* occurs at different pressures for different gases and at different temperatures for the same gas. At 0° it occurs at 100 atm. for air and nitrogen, 200 atm. for oxygen, 35 atm. for carbon dioxide, and 44 atm. for ethylene. The minimum is most marked near the critical temperature of the gas, and at temperatures well above this it becomes less appreciable; with hydrogen at 0° (critical temperature −241°) it has disappeared. Hydrogen

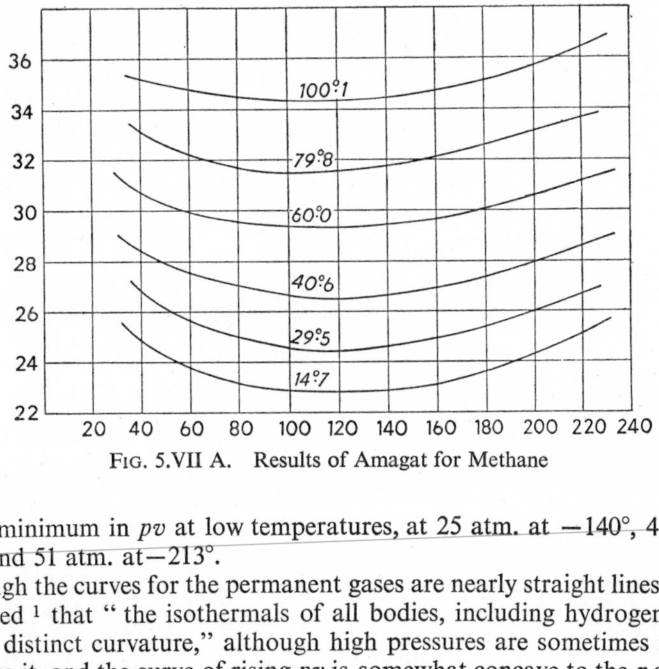

FIG. 5.VII A. Results of Amagat for Methane

shows a minimum in *pv* at low temperatures, at 25 atm. at −140°, 45 atm. at −195°, and 51 atm. at−213°.

Although the curves for the permanent gases are nearly straight lines, Amagat emphasised [1] that " the isothermals of all bodies, including hydrogen, show a perfectly distinct curvature," although high pressures are sometimes necessary to disclose it, and the curve of rising *pv* is somewhat concave to the *p* axis. The results depend on the temperature; Fig. 4.VII A for carbon dioxide at 40°–100° shows that the dip towards lower values of *pv* becomes less and less pronounced at higher temperatures. The fact that hydrogen also shows a minimum value of *pv* at low temperatures, although a very flat one, was proved by Witkowski [2] and by Kamerlingh Onnes and collaborators.[3]

1 *Phil. Mag.*, 1901, **2**, 651.

2 *Phil. Mag.*, 1896, **41**, 288; 1896, **42**, 1; Wroblewski, *Monatsh.*, 1889, **9**, 1067.

3 Onnes and Braak, *Proc. K. Akad. Wetens. Amsterdam*, 1907, **9**, 754; 1907–8, **10**, 204, 413 (*Comm. Leiden*, 1907, **97***a*, **99***a*, **100***a*); de Haas, *ibid.*, 1912, **14**, 101; 1912–13, **15**, 295, 299 (*Comm. Leiden*, 1912, **127***a*, *b*); Onnes and de Haas, *ibid.*, 1912–13, **15**, 405 (*Comm. Leiden*, **127***c*); Onnes, Dorsman and Holst, *ibid.*, 1915, **18**, 458 (*Comm. Leiden*, **146***a*, H_2); Onnes, Crommelin, and Smid, *ibid.*, 1915, **18**, 465 (*Comm. Leiden*, 1915, **146***b*, H_2); Crommelin and Smid, *ibid.*, 1915, **18**, 472 (*Comm. Leiden*, **146***c*) (pressure balance); Kuypers and Onnes, *Arch. Néerl.*, 1923, **6**, 277 (*Comm. Leiden*, **165***a*, O_2); Onnes and Penning, *ibid.*, 1924, **7**, 157 (*Comm. Leiden*, **165***b*); Penning and Onnes, *ibid.*, 1924, **7**, 166 (*Comm. Leiden*, **165***c*, He); Penning, *ibid.*, 1924, **7**, 172 (*Comm. Leiden*, **166**); see the summary in " Het Natuurkundig Laboratorium der Rijksuniversiteit te Leiden in de Jaren 1904–22," Leyden, 1922.

In Despretz's apparatus, the gases were confined over mercury in glass tubes and the whole placed in a vessel of water to which pressure was applied by a screw plunger. Pouillet first used a metal compression chamber with a screw plunger, the capillary tube containing the gas projecting from the chamber. Dulong and Arago applied pressure directly by a mercury column, but they failed to find any deviations from Boyle's law. Natterer compressed the gas into a wrought-iron vessel by a pump, the pressure being transmitted by mercury to a loaded piston which acted as a manometer. The lower surface of the gas-piston was hollowed and the edges, ground to razor sharpness, formed a thin ring of metal which was pressed by the liquid against the cylinder walls and so formed a tight joint.

The first really accurate measurements were by Regnault, who confined the gas at atmospheric pressure in a vertical piezometer tube 3 m. long and 10 mm. diameter, over mercury (Fig. 6.VII A). This tube was surrounded by a water-jacket and communicated with a water compression pump by which mercury

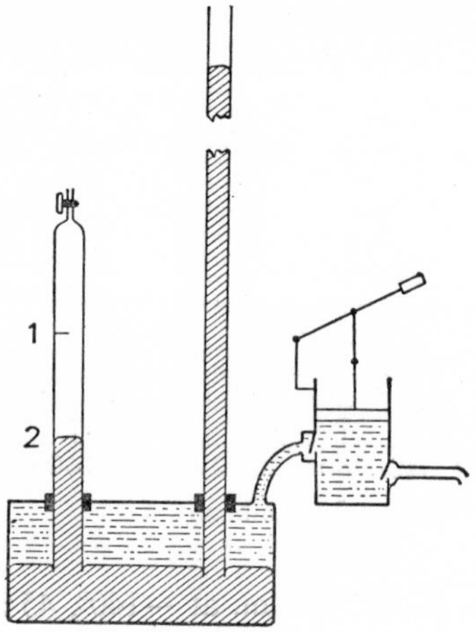

FIG. 6.VII A. Regnault's Apparatus (diagrammatic)

FIG. 7.VII A. Cailletet tube

could be forced into it, and with a long vertical manometer, consisting of a series of glass tubes, 24 m. long, in which mercury rose when the pump was operated until a final pressure of about 30 atm. was reached. The gas was first compressed to half its volume, and the pressure (*c.* 4 atm.) read. Fresh gas was then pumped in to restore the original volume under 2 atm. pressure, then this was again compressed to half, and the process of adding gas and compressing to half the volume was repeated until the maximum pressure was reached. The manometer was read to 0·5 mm.

Cailletet confined a fixed quantity of gas over mercury in a special compression tube terminating above in a graduated capillary (Fig. 7.VII A) and dipping below into mercury, and pressure was applied by a screw with a capstan wheel. At first the pressure was determined by the rise of mercury in a thermometer, enclosed in the pressure vessel, owing to compression of the bulb. In later apparatus, the tube containing the gas was completely enclosed in a steel vessel connected by a long flexible steel tube with an open vessel of mercury. The tube was wound on a vertical drum 2 m. in diameter, and the case containing the compression tube was lowered into an artesian well. The inside of the gas compression tube had a thin film of gold deposited on it, and the height to which this was dissolved off by the mercury gave the final volume of the gas. The pressure was measured by a vertical mercury manometer column, which sometimes reached 500 m. Cailletet invented a very compact and powerful pump for forcing water into an apparatus, the pressure then being transmitted to the gas through mercury (Fig. 2.VI C). The Cailletet pump, made by Ducretet et Cie, Paris, easily reaches 1,000 atm. or more.[1]

Amagat used pressures in his later experiments which reached 3,000 atm. at 15°–260°, and for many years his work stood alone in the field of such pressures. Up to 450 atm. he used a strong glass capillary tube, 1 mm. internal and 1 cm. external diam., enlarged below and containing mercury. It was surrounded by a metal water-jacket with windows at intervals.[2] The tube was fixed in a compression block, and pressure was applied by pumping in glycerol, which forced mercury into the tube and compressed the gas. The mercury levels were observed visually through the windows. The pressure was measured by the height of mercury in an open vertical tube of steel, which finally reached a length of 340 m. and was fixed to a mine-shaft. A fixed mass of gas was used, the volume being read on the capillary. At higher pressures, the piezometer tube was enclosed in a steel pressure cylinder so that it was compressed both internally and externally by pumping in water. The volume was measured by having platinum wires sealed through the capillary, and when the mercury meniscus touched these an electric current flowed, this increasing abruptly as successive wires made contact. This method is due to Tait.

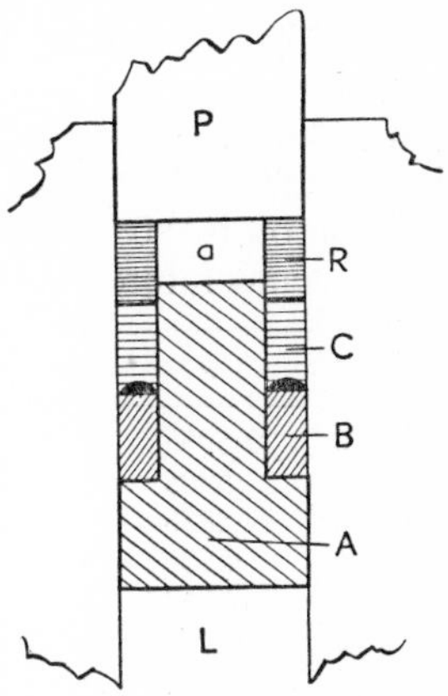

FIG. 8.VII A. Bridgman's apparatus

After Amagat, the use of high pressures was resumed by Bridgman,[3] who went to about three times the highest pressures of 3,000 atm. reached by the French pioneer. (Bridgman's work was partly on the compressibility of liquids and solids.) In Bridgman's apparatus (Fig. 8.VII A) the piston P presses on the inner piston A by a ring of hard steel R, a ring of soft steel C, and a rubber packing B, the thrust being communicated to the liquid L. The shaft of A enters the ring R, but there is a space *a* between P and A. The upward thrust of the liquid on A is compensated by the pressure of the packing on the flange of A, which is greater than the pressure on the upper surface of A, so that liquid does not leak past B.[4] A mixture of treacle and glycerol was used to lubricate the pistons.

The advantage of very deep pistons without packing for compressors was pointed out by Joule.[5] Hydrogen at high pressures penetrates and bursts

[1] Cailletet, *Ann. Chim.*, 1878, **15**, 132; Cohen and Sinnige, *Z. phys. Chem.*, 1909, **67**, 1; Cohen and de Boer, *ibid.*, 1913, **84**, 32.

[2] On a pressure window, see Roebuck and Miller, *Rev. Sci. Instr.*, 1939, **10**, 179.

[3] See e.g. *Proc. Amer. Acad.*, 1909, **44**, 201, 221; 1911, **47**, 321; 1924, **59**, 171 (He, A, H_2, N_2, NH_3); 1935, **70**, 1; " The Physics of High Pressure," 1931, 30, 98 f.; *Rev. Mod. Phys.*, 1946, **18**, 1.

[4] See also Petavel, *Engineering*, 1907, **84**, 97 (calibration of pressure gauges, etc.); Adams, Williamson, and Johnston, *J.A.C.S.*, 1919, **41**, 12; Ernst, *Ind. Eng. Chem.*, 1926, **18**, 664; Keyes, *ibid.*, 1931, **23**, 1375; Tongue, " The Design and Construction of High Pressure Chemical Plant," 1934 (compressors, etc.); Newitt, " The Design of High Pressure Plant and the Properties of Fluids at High Pressures," Oxford, 1940; Werescayin and Zelinsky, *Bull. Acad. Sci. U.R.S.S.*, 1943(6), 443; Comings, *Ind. Eng. Chem.*, 1947, **39**, 948 (bibl.).

[5] *Manch. Mem.*, 1862, **3**, 5; "Scientific Papers," 1884, **1**, 531.

ordinary steel.[1] By using small pistons of "Carboloy," Bridgman[2] reached pressures of 250,000 kg./cm.^{2}. At pressures of 100,000 kg./cm.^{2} he used Duprene for packing, as this does not harden like rubber.[3] Basset[4] claimed to have reached gas pressures of 5,000 kg./cm.^{2} at 1,000°. Poulter and Buckley[5] used diamond windows for pressures up to 21,500 atm.

§ 7 Manometers

The simple *manometer* (Latin *manus*, force; Greek *μέτρον*, a measure) consists of a U-tube[6] containing a suitable liquid, such as water, mercury (which is very dense, causing insensitivity), α-bromonaphthalene, dibutyl phthalate,[7] amyl phthalate ($\rho=1{\cdot}0$ at 25°), nonylic acid,[8] octane,[9] carbon tetrachloride,[10] olive oil,[11] etc. The density of α-bromonaphthalene[12] at 25° is 1·48834 and changes by 0·00101 per 1°. The coefficient of expansion of paraffin oil is[13] $0{\cdot}0_3 7643$ at room temperature (16°). Densities of mercury in g./ml., temperatures on the hydrogen scale, are[14] 13 plus the decimal in the table:

t° C.	ρ	t° C.	ρ	t° C.	ρ	t° C.	ρ
0	0·5955	20	0·5462	40	0·4973	60	0·4486
2	·5905	22	·5413	42	·4924	62	·4437
4	·5856	24	·5364	44	·4875	64	·4389
6	·5806	26	·5315	46	·4826	66	·4340
8	·5757	28	·5266	48	·4778	68	·4292
10	·5708	30	·5217	50	·4729	70	·4243
12	·5659	32	·5168	52	·4680	80	·4001
14	·5609	34	·5119	54	·4632	90	·3711
16	·5560	36	·5070	56	·4583	100	·3518
18	·5511	38	·5022	58	·4534		

1 Bridgman, *Rec. Trav. Chim.*, 1923, **42**, 568.

2 *Phys. Rev.*, 1940, **57**, 342; *Rev. Mod. Phys.*, 1946, **18**, 1.

3 *Proc. Amer. Acad.*, 1945, **76**, 1, 9.

4 *Compt. Rend.*, 1930, **191**, 928; for 25,000 kg./cm.^{2} see *idem*, *Chim. et Ind.*, 1928, Spec. No. (April), 148; for 15,000 kg./cm.^{2}, *Compt. Rend.*, 1927, **185**, 343; for 300,000 kg./cm.^{2}, *Chim. et Ind.*, 1945, **53**, 303.

5 *Phys. Rev.*, 1932, **41**, 364.

6 On mercury manometers: Lala, *Ann. Fac. Sci. Toulouse*, 1891, **5**, G; Rayleigh, *Proc. Roy. Soc.*, 1893, **53**, 134; Villard, *Ann. Chim.*, 1897, **11**, 289 (open and closed ends); Holborn and Day, *Ann. Phys.*, 1899, **68**, 821; Brady, *J. Franklin Inst.*, 1919, **187**, 499; Mülhaeuser, *Metall u. Erz*, 1919, **16**, 101, 147; Swan, *J.A.C.S.*, 1925, **47**, 1341; Hartshough, *Science*, 1925, **26**, 160; Hagen, *Z. techn. Phys.*, 1927, **8**, 599; *Phys. Z.*, 1927, **28**, 735; Hickman, *J. Opt. Soc. Amer.*, 1929, **18**, 305 (0·01–5 mm.); Melville, *J.C.S.*, 1931, 2509; Martin and Collie, *ibid.*, 1932, 2658; Lane, Hammerschlag, and Roehl, *J.A.C.S.*, 1932, **54**, 1020; van Santen, *Comm. Leiden*, 1934, **227** (calibration); Roebuck and Cram, *Rev. Sci. Instr.*, 1937, **8**, 215; A. B. Hart, *Thesis*, London, 1941; Werner, *Ind. Eng. Chem. Anal.*, 1945, **17**, 805; for a barometer-manometer independent of atmospheric pressure variations, see Lawson, *Wien Ber.*, 1915, **124**, IIA, 669.

7 Hickman and Weyerts, *J.A.C.S.*, 1930, **52**, 4714; Malmberg and Nicolas, *Rev. Sci. Instr.*, 1932, **3**, 440.

8 Drucker, Jiméno, and Kangro, *Z. phys. Chem.*, 1915, **90**, 513.

9 Jaeger, *Z. anorg. Chem.*, 1917, **101**, 30.

10 Henry, *Compt. Rend.*, 1912, **155**, 1078; for tetralin, see Hull, *J. Sci. Instr.*, 1936, **13**, 165.

11 Frowein, *Z. phys. Chem.*, 1887, **1**, 5: $\rho=0{\cdot}917$ at 20°, coefficient of expansion 0·000798; precision oil manometer, Chadwick and Palkin, *Ind. Eng. Chem. Anal.*, 1938, **10**, 399; cf. Palkin, *ibid.*, 1935, **7**, 434.

12 Timmermans and Hennaut-Roland, *J. Chim. Phys.*, 1937, **34**, 695; Roozeboom, *Z. phys. Chem.*, 1889, **4**, 81; Bodenstein, *Z. Elektrochem.*, 1918, **24**, 186, who gives the densities 1·4894 at 13·72°, 1·4844 at 16·9°, and 1·4814 at 19·00°, and $\rho_{15}=\rho_t[1-0{\cdot}0015(t-15)]$; Biltz and Meinecke, *Z. anorg. Chem.*, 1923, **131**, 1.

13 Lundal, *Ann. Phys.*, 1898, **66**, 741.

14 Chappuis, *Trav. et Mém. Bur. Internat. Poids et Més.*, 1917, **16**.

The effect of temperature is given by (0°—100°):

$$\rho_t = \rho_0/(1+1{\cdot}816904\times10^{-4}t-2{\cdot}951266\times10^{-9}t^2+1{\cdot}14562\times10^{-10}t^3).$$

Various types of manometers are described in the literature; [1] a few of the most useful forms are briefly reviewed here.

A correction for the volume of the mercury meniscus in a glass tube is necessary in accurate work. This deviates from a spherical shape. In the table [2] the values of *f* (cm.), the ratio of the volume of the meniscus to its lower section, are given for tubes (Jena normal glass) of radius *R* cm., where δ=ratio of height of meniscus above the lower section to *R*:

R	δ=0·05	0·1	0·15	0·20	0·25	0·30	0·35	0·40
0·05	0·00126	0·00252	0·0038	0·00506	0·00637	0·00773	0·0091	0·0107
0·1	0·00252	0·00504	0·0076	0·0102	0·0128	0·0155	0·0183	0·0213
0·15	0·00376	0·00756	0·01145	0·0153	0·01925	0·02325	0·0274	0·0318
0·2	0·00505	0·0103	0·0155	0·0206	0·0257	0·0310	0·0366	**0·0426***
0·25	0·00655	0·0131	0·01965	0·02615	0·0327	0·0393	**0·0462***	**0·0536***
0·3	0·0080	0·0159	0·0239	0·0320	**0·0401***	**0·0483***	**0·0566***	**0·0657***
0·35	0·00935	0·0188	0·0283	**0·0384***	**0·0489***	**0·0592***	**0·0700***	**0·0815***
0·4	0·01085	0·0218	**0·0331***	**0·0453***	**0·0583***	**0·0737***	**0·0904***	—

(Starred values show important deviations from a spherical meniscus.)

For most purposes Winkler's corrections are sufficient. For a tube of radius *R* mm., *t* mm. is subtracted from the reading of the top of the meniscus when this is dry, and *f* mm. when it is moist:

R	2	4	6	8	10	12
t	0·4	0·58	0·60	0·56	0·50	0·43
f	0·54	0·71	0·75	0·71	0·65	0·56

Bunsen [3] obtained a flat mercury surface by covering the meniscus with mercuric chloride solution: twice the space between the curved surface and the flat surface was taken as the correction when the tube was used in the inverted position. This correction is not satisfactory for wide tubes.

In calibrating the volume of a capillary by weighing mercury threads, it is necessary to correct for the non-planar shape of the ends of the mercury column, and this can be done if the volumes of the meniscus caps at each end are known. Scheel and Heuse [4] and Palacios [5] determined this for mercury in air, and the volume in mm.³ is (to 2 per cent.):

$$\phi = xy(2{\cdot}77x - 4{\cdot}5y^{-0{\cdot}13}),$$

[1] Baume, *J. Chim. Phys.*, 1908, **6**, 1; Auerbach, in Winkelmann, " Handbuch der Physik," 1908, **1**, 1311; Jakeman, in Glazebrook, " Dict. of Applied Physics," 1922, **1**, 623; Arndt, " Handbuch der phys.-chem. Technik," 1923, 247 f.; Haehnel, in Stähler, " Arbeitsmethoden der anorganischen Chemie," 1925, **2**, ii, 1291; Ostwald-Luther-Drucker, " Phys.-chem. Messungen," 1931, 195 f.; Ebert, in Eucken and Jakob, " Der Chemie-Ingenieur," 1933, **2**, iii, 1; for Barcroft differential manometer, Gibson, *Biochem. J.*, 1947, **41**, 44.

[2] Mendeléeff and Gutkowsky, *J. Russ. Phys. Chem. Soc.*, 1877, **8**, 212; *Ann. Phys. Beibl.*, 1877, **1**, 455 (table); Onnes and Schalkwijk, *Proc. K. Akad. Wetens. Amsterdam*, 1901, **3**, 421, 481; *Comm. Leiden*, 1901, **67**; abstr. in *Z. phys. Chem.*, 1903, **42**, 114; for corrections for mercury and water meniscuses see Winkler, *Z. anal. Chem.*, 1901, **40**, 403; *Z. angew. Chem.*, 1903, **16**, 718; abstr. in *J. Chim. Phys.*, 1905, **3**, 277; Germann, *ibid.*, 1914, **12**, 66; Goig, *An. Fis. Quim.*, 1931, **29**, 189; Cawood and Patterson, *Trans. Faraday Soc.*, 1933, **29**, 514.

[3] " Gasometry," transl. Roscoe, 1857, 32.

[4] *Ann. Phys.*, 1910, **33**, 291 (table); Lohnstein, *ibid.*, 1910, **33**, 296; cf. Maltézos, *Compt. Rend.*, 1894, **118**, 583.

[5] *An. Fis. Quim.*, 1919, **17**, 275; *Phys. Z.*, 1923, **24**, 151; cf. Onnes and de Haas, *Proc. K.*

where x=radius in mm., y=meniscus height in mm. In narrow tubes, the meniscus may be taken approximately as a hemisphere of radius x.

The sticking of mercury in gauges, etc., was investigated by Moser.[1] Methods of filling U-gauges, closed at one end, with mercury are described.[2] Another type of gauge uses the variation in length of a column of air between two columns of mercury in a capillary tube.[3] In Töpler's differential manometer, a drop of xylene is contained in a very flat nearly horizontal U-tube with gas pressures on both sides.[4]

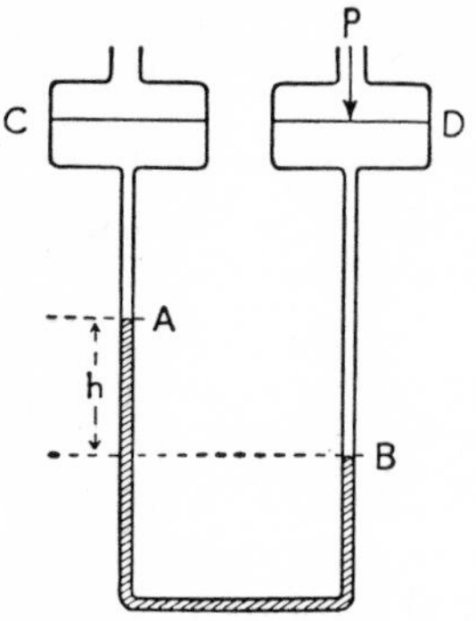

FIG. 9.VII A. Huygens' Manometer

A sensitive mercury U-tube manometer (Δp ±0·01 mm.) has tungsten wires in the mercury and the change of resistance due to the change of shape of the meniscus is measured.[5] If mercury in a manometer comes in contact with platinum (e.g. in electric contacts) it may be necessary to take account of the small solubility of platinum in mercury (0·0205 atomic per cent. at 16·5° to 1·77 at 200°),[6] which would slightly increase its density. Faraday's statement [7] that gas can pass between the mercury and glass of a containing vessel standing in a mercury trough, was found by Dixon [8] to be untrue if the glass and mercury are clean, as Faraday himself implies. To keep a mercury surface clean it may be covered with syrupy metaphosphoric acid. Most workers tap the manometer smartly with a piece of soft wood before taking a reading. Keesom, van der Horst, and Taconis [9] read the mercury miniscus by an X-ray shadowgraph.

In the *Huygens* (or Kretz, or Chattock) *manometer* [10] two liquids of different densities meet in a bent tube (Fig. 9.VII A) at the interfaces A and B, the heavier

Akad. Wetens. Amsterdam, 1912, **15**, 405 (*Comm. Leiden*, **127***c*); Verschaffelt, *ibid.*, 1919, **21**, 836; Cawood and Patterson, *Trans. Faraday Soc.*, 1933, **29**, 514 (bibl.); on meniscus correction, see also Guye, *J. Chim. Phys.*, 1907, **5**, 203; Germann, *ibid.*, 1914, **12**, 66; *J.A.C.S.*, 1914, **36**, 2456; Kistemaker, *Physica*, 1945, **11**, 270, 277; a full description of barometer corrections is given by Beattie, Benedict, and Blaisdell, *Proc. Amer. Acad.*, 1937, **71**, 327.

1 *Ann. Phys.*, 1877, **160**, 138.

2 Swan, *J.A.C.S.*, 1925, **47**, 1341; Weatherill, *ibid.*, 1925, **47**, 1947.

3 Tammann and Nernst, *Z. phys. Chem.*, 1892, **9**, 1.

4 *Ann. Phys.*, 1896, **57**, 472; Foch, *Ann. Chim.*, 1913, **29**, 597 (optical reading).

5 Klumb and Haase, *Z. techn. Phys.*, 1932, **13**, 272; same type with electrolyte solution and platinum wires, see Smith, *J. Opt. Soc. Amer.*, 1926, **12**, 655.

6 Plaskin and Suvorovskaya, *J. Phys. Chem. U.S.S.R.*, 1941, **15**, 978; tantalum is not wetted by mercury, Jones, Taylor, and Vogel, *J.A.C.S.*, 1948, **70**, 966.

7 " Chemical Manipulation," 1842, 343, 554.

8 *Chem. News*, 1886, **54**, 227 (Davy, in 1826, had also found this).

9 *Physica*, 1934, **1**, 324.

10 Kretz, in Jamin, " Cours de Physique," 1882, **1**, i, 218; Töpler, *Ann. Phys.*, 1895, **56**, 609; Smits, *Arch. Néerl.*, 1898, **1**, 97; *Z. phys. Chem.*, 1902, **39**, 385; for a differential paraffin oil manometer for low pressures, see Bleier and Kohn, *Monatsh.*, 1899, **20**, 505, 909; Battelli, *Nuov. Cim.*, 1901, **1**, 5, with mercury, aniline, and water, 100 times as sensitive as mercury; Chattock, Walker, and Dixon, *Phil. Mag.*, 1901, **1**, 79; Smith, *Engineering*, 1910, **90**, 144; Henry, *Compt. Rend.*, 1912, **155**, 1078; *J. de Phys.*, 1913, **3**, 652 (sensitive form); Pannell, *Engineering*, 1913, **96**, 343; Druker, Jiméno, and Kangro, *Z. phys. Chem.*, 1915, **90**, 513; Mülhaeuser, *Metall u. Erz*, 1919, **16**, 101, 147; Jakeman, in Glazebrook, " Dict. of Applied Physics," 1922, **1**, 640; Duncan, *J. Sci. Instr.*, 1927, **4**, 376; Darbord, *Compt. Rend.*, 1929, **188**, 50; Owen, *Phil. Mag.*, 1930, **10**, 544; Pearson, *Z. phys. Chem.*, 1931, **156**, 86; Topley and Smith, *J. Sci. Instr.*, 1931, **8**, 194; Dickens and Greville, *Biochem. J.*, 1933, **27**, 213 (const. vol.); Vincent, *Proc. Phys. Soc.*, 1933, **45**, 808; Ståhlane, *J. Sci. Inst.*, 1934, **11**, 79 (±0·01 mm.

liquid being in this tube and the lighter above it on both sides. If the densities are ρ_a and ρ_b ($\rho_a > \rho_b$) and if an increase of pressure p mm. Hg on the right causes a difference of level h, the difference of level in the wide reservoirs C and D will be h/a, where a=ratio of cross-section of reservoir to that of the tube. Then, if a is much larger than h, $13{\cdot}56p=h(\rho_a-\rho_b)+(h/a)\rho_b \simeq h(\rho_a-\rho_b)$. Thus, $h=13{\cdot}56p/(\rho_a-\rho_b)$, and if ρ_a and ρ_b are nearly the same this is large. E.g. with moist aniline $\rho_a=1{\cdot}022$ and water $\rho_b=0{\cdot}998$ at 20°, then $h=(13{\cdot}56/0{\cdot}024)p=565p$, so that a pressure change of 1 mm. Hg produces a change of level in the manometer of 565 mm.

Amagat [1] calibrated his manometers by means of very long mercury columns. One was fixed to a church spire at Lyons, two others were in mine shafts 400 m. and 500 m. deep. Cailletet [2] used a mercury manometer of steel tube, 4·5 mm. bore, fixed to the Eiffel Tower in Paris, 300 m. high. High-pressure mercury gauges with closed ends should contain nitrogen, since air causes slow oxidation of the mercury and the gas volume thus changes.[3]

A manometer used by Holborn and Henning [4] consists of a mercury reservoir Q (Fig. 10.VII A), which has to withstand the high gas pressure transmitted to the mercury surface through the tube J_3, and from which a vertical steel tube LL′, 12 m. long, 6 mm. wide, and 1 mm. thick, projects. On every 2 m. of this was a stopcock leading to a 2-m.-long vertical glass tube (G_1 to G_6). When the mercury had risen into a part of the steel tube communicating with one of these glass tubes, the stopcock was opened and the mercury level read in the glass tube. Since mercury is oxidised by air at high pressure, the tube should be filled with nitrogen.

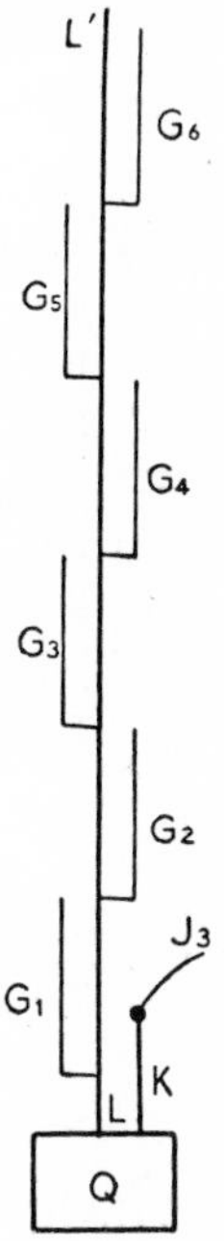

FIG. 10.VII A. Holborn and Henning's Manometer

An explosion of a pressure mercury manometer used with ammonia gas was recorded.[5]

Instead of using the very long open manometers employed by Regnault, Amagat, etc., Kamerlingh Onnes [6] invented a shortened form which can be used up to 100–200 atm. It consists of a number of thick-walled glass siphon manometers connected in series with mercury columns of about 4 atm. in each, the upper end of each being connected by steel capillary tube with the lower part of the next, and the last one open to the air. By an arrangement

water); Beeck, *Rev. Sci. Instr.*, 1935, **6**, 399; Röbbelen, *Z. techn. Phys.*, 1936, **17**, 95 (micromanometer depending on a capillary meniscus); 1937, **18**, 11; Cope and Houghton, *J. Sci. Instr.*, 1936, **13**, 83; Holmes and Emmett, *J. Phys. Chem.*, 1947, **51**, 1262; Young and Taylor, *Ind. Eng. Chem. Anal.*, 1947, **19**, 133; Brow and Schwertz, *Rev. Sci. Instr.*, 1947, **18**, 183; South Met. Gas Co., *Gas J.*, 1948, **253**, 318.

[1] *Ann. Chim.*, 1893, **29**, 68; Koch and Wagner, *Ann. Phys.*, 1909, **31**, 31. On similar long manometers at Manchester, St. Étienne, etc., see Anon., *Engineer*, 1913, **115**, 535.

[2] *Compt. Rend.*, 1891, **112**, 764; *Z. kompr. Gase*, 1897, **1**, 88; *J. Phys. Chem.*, 1897, **1**, 738 (abstr.).

[3] Kuenen and Robson, *Phil. Mag.*, 1902, **3**, 149; Cardoso and Levi, *J. Chim. Phys.*, 1921–2, **19**, 244.

[4] *Ann. Phys.*, 1908, **26**, 833.

[5] Sampey, *Chem. Eng. News*, 1947, **25**, 2138.

[6] *Proc. K. Akad. Wetens. Amsterdam*, 1899, **1**, 213 (*Comm. Leiden*, **44**); 1906, **8**, 75, 77, 79, 82 (*Comm. Leiden*, **94***b–e*); Schalkwijk, *ibid.*, 1901, **3**, 421, 484; 1902, **4**, 23 (*Comm. Leiden*, **67**, **70**); Meyers and Jessup, *Bur. Stand. J. Res.*, 1931, **6**, 1061 (bibl.); Hunt and Larsen, *J. Phys. Chem.*, 1934, **38**, 801; Roebuck and Cram, *Rev. Sci. Instr.*, 1937, **8**, 215 (200 atm.).

of steel stopcocks the air pressures in the upper and lower parts of the tubes are gradually built up with compressed air, and the total pressure to be measured is then the sum of the pressures in the tubes, i.e. the sum of the mercury columns. E.g. with a pressure of 42 atm., there will be eleven columns of 4 atm. in the closed tubes and a column of 2 atm. in the last tube with one side open to the atmosphere. Certain corrections for the temperature of the mercury and the weight of the compressed air are applied.

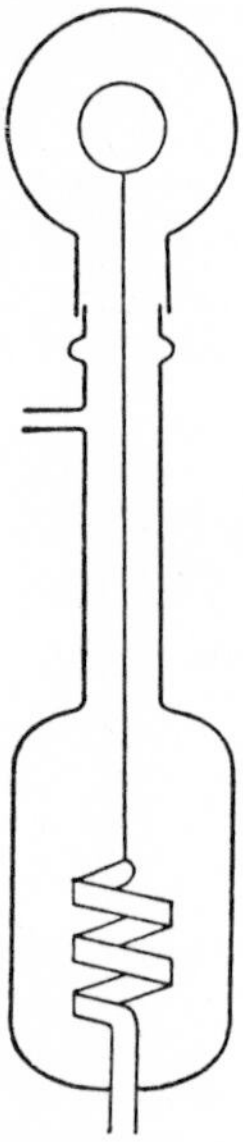

FIG. 11.VII A. Spiral Manometer

A manometer depending on the change of volume of the bulb of a mercury thermometer when exposed to pressure (" manomètre à écrasement ") suffers from the defect of change of zero.[1] An interferometer method, depending on the change of refractive index of water by pressure, was used up to 270 atm. by van Doren, Parker, and Lotz.[2] A differential manometer accurate to 1 in 1,000 at 3,000 lb./in.^{2} was described by Boyd.[3]

The *Bourdon gauge* [4] is very much used for high-pressure measurement (e.g. with oxygen cylinders). It consists of a hook-shaped metal tube (German-silver or steel) of elliptical cross-section, which may be filled with paraffin oil, and when pressure is applied to the interior the tube stretches and the free end moves. The motion is approximately proportional to the pressure and is registered by a pointer-hand on a circular scale operated by wheel-work. Such gauges have been known to burst and cause fatal accidents, and they should be tested from time to time. They also show some elastic after-effect.

The Spurge manometer uses the elastic deformation of a hollow metal cylinder or shell.[5] Baume and Robert [6] measured pressure changes by the change in volume of a *thin* thermometer bulb containing mercury and exposed to the gas.

For high pressures, a bifilar steel spiral capillary, which may form part of the gas supply system, has been used.[7]

The *spiral manometer* [8] operates on the principle of the Bourdon gauge. It consists of a spiral of thin-walled tube of elliptical section, of glass or quartz (which shows no elastic after-effect), with a small mirror attached by a fibre to the closed end. The whole is enclosed in a tube in which a compensating gas pressure, read on a mercury manometer, is maintained (Fig. 11.VII A), the spiral

[1] Cardoso, *J. Chim. Phys.*, 1921–2, **19**, 217.

[2] *J.A.C.S.*, 1921, **43**, 2497.

[3] *J.A.C.S.*, 1930, **52**, 5102; another was described by Wildhagen, *Z. angew. Math. Mech.*, 1923, **3**, 181.

[4] Bourdon, *Compt. Rend.*, 1853, **37**, 656; Barus, *Phil. Mag.*, 1891, **31**, 400; made by Bourdon, of Paris, Gindre Frères & Cie, of Lyons, and Schäffer and Budenburg, of Magdeburg. On calibration see Wagner, *Ann. Phys.*, 1904, **15**, 906; temperature correction, Jakeman, in Glazebrook, " Dict. of Applied Physics," 1922, **1**, 633; correction for elastic after-effect, Bennewitz, *Phys. Z.*, 1921, **22**, 329; theory, Lorenz, *Z. Verein D. Ing.*, 1910, **54**, 1865; *Phys. Z.*, 1917, **18**, 117; Wohlfarth, *Z. techn. Phys.*, 1924, **5**, 361; Koppl, *Rev. Sci. Instr.*, 1947, **18**, 850 (quartz); Wuest, *Die Technik*, 1948, **3**, 23.

[5] Anon., *Engineer*, 1913, **115**, 535.

[6] *Compt. Rend.*, 1919, **168**, 1199; Baume, *Bull. Soc. Chim.*, 1922, **31**, 129.

[7] Simon, Ruhemann, and Edwards, *Z. phys. Chem.*, 1929, **6** B, 62.

[8] Ladenburg and Lehmann, *Verhl. d. D. Phys. Ges.*, 1906, **8**, 20; *Ann. Phys.*, 1906, **21**, 305; Johnson, *Z. phys. Chem.*, 1908, **61**, 457; Johnson and McIntosh, *J.A.C.S.*, 1909, **31**, 1138; Bodenstein *et al.*, *Z. Elektrochem.*, 1908, **14**, 544; 1909, **15**, 244; 1910, **16**, 961; 1913, **19**, 836; 1916, **22**, 327; 1917, **23**, 105; *Z. phys. Chem.*, 1909, **69**, 26; Preuner and Schupp, *Z. phys. Chem.*, 1909, **68**, 129; Preuner and Brockmöller, *ibid.*, 1912, **81**, 129; Rassow, *Z. anorg. Chem.*, 1920, **114**, 117; Stirnemann, *N. Jahrb. Min.*, 1925, *B. Bd.* **52** A, 334; Davies, *Z. phys. Chem.*,

manometer being used as a null instrument. The quartz apparatus may also be used to read by direct deflexion, and up to high pressures (with less sensitivity).

The *disc manometer* operates on the principle of the aneroid barometer (invented and named by Vidi [1]). It can be used for high or low pressures and consists of a circular disc, usually of metal, of thickness appropriate to the pressures measured, sometimes corrugated, and clamped round the edge in a suitable box. The pressure (liquid or gaseous) is applied to one side and causes the disc to bulge, the motion being transmitted to a pointer; or else a small mirror is fastened to the disc and a beam of light reflected from it to a scale or, when the apparatus is to be used for very rapid pressure changes, on to a camera with a revolving film.[2] An error is due to elastic after-effect, but this is not appreciable in the single deflexions of a steel membrane in explosion measurements (Pier, Bjerrum). A differential disc gauge causing a change of capacity of an electric condenser [3] has been described. A silica membrane,[4] and a glass membrane platinised so that its motion breaks an electric circuit,[5] have been used.

Gillespie and Frazer [6] adapted the membrane gauge for higher temperatures by attaching a vertical glass thread to the centre, projecting in a tube outside a heating chamber, and read the movement of the end of the thread by a microscope. A glass diaphragm gauge, compensated by a measured air pressure on the other side, can be used with gases which attack mercury.[7] An organic film causing interference fringes in its motion [8] is sensitive to 0·003 mm. Hg.

The *spoon gauge* [9] consists of a thin glass bulb, one side of which has been

1928, **134**, 57; Daniels, *J.A.C.S.*, 1928, **50**, 1115 (bibl); Braune and Knoke, *Z. phys. Chem.*, 1931, **152**, 409; Robert, *Helv. Phys. Acta*, 1936, **9**, 405; Arii and Kawabata, *Bull. Inst. Phys. Chem. Res. Tokyo*, 1938, **17**, 299; Nitta and Seki, *J. Chem. Soc. Japan*, 1941, **62**, 581 (in Japanese); Vaughan, *Rev. Sci. Instr.*, 1947, **18**, 192; Yorke, *J. Sci. Instr.*, 1948, **25**, 16.

[1] *Compt. Rend.*, 1847, **24**, 975; Wohlfarth, *Z. techn. Phys.*, 1924, **5**, 361; Klemenc, *J.A.C.S.*, 1925, **47**, 2173; Fredenhagen, *Z. anorg. Chem.*, 1932, **210**, 210; 1934, **218**, 161; recording diaphragm gauge for high pressures, Smith, *J. Sci. Instr.*, 1940, **17**, 242; 1947, **24**, 134 (160 ±0·4 lb./in.^{2}); Kleiber, *Rev. Sci. Instr.*, 1945, **16**, 79. The idea of the aneroid barometer was proposed by Leibniz in 1697 in a letter to Papin: Fleckenstein, *Experientia*, 1946, **2**, 262.

[2] Kohlrausch, *Ann. Phys.*, 1869, **136**, 618; Röntgen, *ibid.*, 1873, **148**, 580; Hansemann, *ibid.*, 1884, **21**, 545; Wien, *ibid.*, 1889, **36**, 834; Dieterici, *ibid.*, 1893, **50**, 47; 1897, **62**, 616; 1899, **67**, 859; Martens, *Z. Verein D. Ing.*, 1909, **53**, 747; Pier, *Z. phys. Chem.*, 1908, **62**, 385; Scheel and Heuse, *Verhl. d. D. Phys. Ges.*, 1909, **11**, 1; *Z. Instr.*, 1909, **29**, 14; Bjerrum, *Z. phys. Chem.*, 1912, **79**, 513; 1912, **81**, 281; sensitive membrane manometers: Fry, *Phil. Mag.*, 1913, **25**, 494 (0·001 dyne/cm.^{2}); Seeliger and Lentow, *Z. techn. Phys.*, 1920, **1**, 20; *Phys. Z.*, 1926, **27**, 732; Bennewitz, *Phys. Z.*, 1921, **22**, 329; Kornfeld and Klingler, *Z. phys. Chem.*, 1929, **4** B, 37 (Pt foil); Sommerfeld, *ibid.*, 1931, **155**, 208; Fischer, *Chem. Fabr.*, 1933, 377; Kürti, *Z. phys. Chem.*, 1933, **20** B, 305 (0·02 mm. Ag foil); Allsop, *Safety in Mines Res. Board*, 1925, No. **16** (electron tube type); Moser, *Ann. Phys.*, 1932, **14**, 790 (high temp.); Caldwell and Fiock, *Bur. Stand. J. Res.*, 1941, **26**, 175.

[3] Whiddington, *Phil. Mag.*, 1920, **40**, 634; Whiddington and Hare, *ibid.*, 1923, **46**, 607; Karrer, Johnston, and Wulf, *Ind. Eng. Chem.*, 1922, **14**, 1015; Daniels, *J.A.C.S.*, 1928, **50**, 1115; Olson and Gunn, *ibid.*, 1929, **51**, 2378; Hirst and Olson, *ibid.*, 1929, **51**, 2398; Lilly, *Rev. Sci. Instr.*, 1942, **13**, 34; Gilson, *Science*, 1942, **95**, 513 (photocell); Matheson and Eden, *Rev. Sci. Instr.*, 1948, **19**, 502.

[4] Stock and Gibson, *Ber.*, 1912, **45**, 3527; Smith and Taylor, *J.A.C.S.*, 1924, **46**, 1393; Kenty, *Rev. Sci. Instr.*, 1940, **11**, 377 (bibl.).

[5] Daniels and Bright, *J.A.C.S.*, 1920, **42**, 1131; 1921, **43**, 53; Harvey and Shuette, *ibid.*, 1926, **48**, 2065; silvered collodion was used by Lafay, *Compt. Rend.*, 1909, **149**, 1115; and Villey, *ibid.*, 1910, **151**, 65.

[6] *J.A.C.S.*, 1936, **58**, 2260.

[7] Baume and Robert, *Compt. Rend.*, 1919, **168**, 1199; Klemenc, *J.A.C.S.*, 1925, **47**, 2173.

[8] Tobias, *Rev. Sci. Instr.*, 1942, **13**, 232.

[9] Gibson, *Dissert.*, Breslau, 1911; *Proc. Roy. Soc. Edin.*, 1913, **33**, 1; Jackson, *J.C.S.*, 1911, **99**, 1066; Scheffer and Treub, *Z. phys. Chem.*, 1912, **81**, 308; Norrish, *J.C.S.*, 1925, **127**, 2316; Rushton and Daniels, *J.A.C.S.*, 1926, **48**, 384; Geddes and Mack, *ibid.*, 1930, **52**, 4372;

thickened and collapsed inward by melting, so that the whole resembles a very thick spoon (Fig. 12.VII A). A thin glass fibre pointer is attached to the end. Pressure causes deformation and motion of the pointer, observed with a microscope. On account of ease of breakage it is best used as a null instrument, a compensating and manometrically measured air pressure being applied outside the gauge.

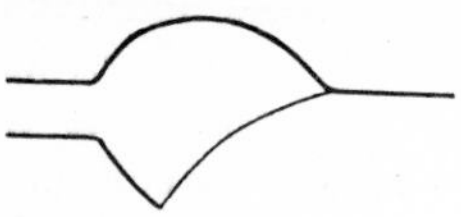

FIG. 12.VII A. Spoon Gauge

The "clicking manometer" or "click gauge" consists [1] of a thin blown bulb flattened by heating in a flame so that a small wrinkle results; change of pressure causes a clicking noise as the uneven glass diaphragm passes a critical position. A pressure difference of 0·2 mm. at 1 atm. is recorded. It seems to be rather troublesome to work, and usually operates only in one direction.

An "optical lever" manometer consists [2] of a U-tube with a steel float on the mercury, which on moving tilts a mirror pivoted on two knife-edges and so reflects a beam of light. A fairly wide (44-mm. diam.) tube is used to avoid capillary depression. The sensitivity is $0{\cdot}0_3 1$ mm. Hg and an accuracy of $0{\cdot}0_3 2$ mm. Hg is claimed. In Barus's and Roseveare's apparatus,[2] interferometry is used. A Michelson interferometer optical pressure gauge was devised by Manley [3] for measurements from 0·0001 to 20 mm. Hg. An X-ray shadow manometer for pressures to 3μ Hg was used by Kistemaker.[4]

A low-pressure manometer consisting of a graphite plate resting (and making a gas-tight seal) on a vertical glass tube evacuated below, and supported by a quartz fibre carrying an iron weight actuated by a magnet, and hung from an arm (Fig. 13.VII A), was used by Rodebush and Coons.[5]

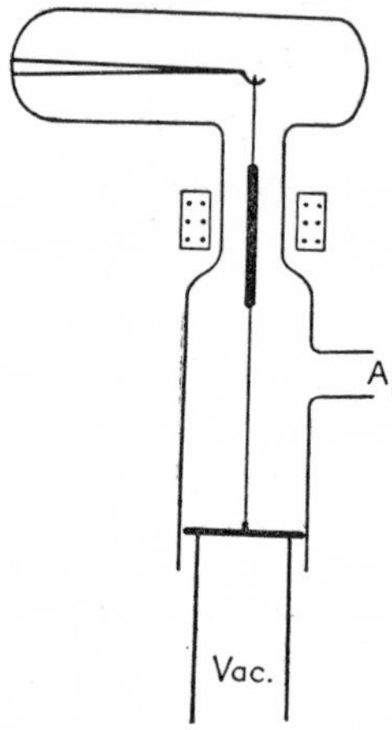

FIG. 13.VII A. Manometer of Rodebush and Coons

For the measurement of high pressures Amagat [6] used an improved form of the so-called *Desgoffe manometer*, really invented (he says) by Galey-Cazalat,

Foord, *J. Sci. Instr.*, 1934, **11**, 126; Henry, *Bull. Soc. Chim. Belg.*, 1935, **44**, 311; Thompson and Linnett, *Trans. Faraday Soc.*, 1936, **32**, 681; Lewis and Style, *Nature*, 1937, **139**, 631; Helm and Mack, *J.A.C.S.*, 1937, **59**, 60; Southard and Nelson, *ibid.*, 1937, **59**, 911; Gucker and Munch, *ibid.*, 1937, **59**, 1275; Berl, Rueff, and Carpenter, *Ind. Eng. Chem. Anal.*, 1938, **10**, 220; Stoddart, *J.C.S.*, 1944, 388.

[1] Smith and Taylor, *J.A.C.S.*, 1924, **46**, 1393; Yost and Kircher, *ibid.*, 1930, **52**, 4680; Nester, *ibid.*, 1931, **53**, 1811; Yost and Claussen, *ibid.*, 1933, **55**, 885; Negishi, *ibid.*, 1936, **38**, 2293.

[2] Prytz, *Ann. Phys.*, 1905, **16**, 735; Knudsen, *ibid.*, 1910, **33**, 1435; Schrader and Ryder, *Phys. Rev.*, 1919, **13**, 321; Barus, *Proc. Nat. Acad.*, 1921, **7**, 71; Carver, *J.A.C.S.*, 1923, **45**, 59; Roseveare, *ibid.*, 1932, **54**, 202; Henry, *Bull. Soc. Chim. Belg.*, 1931, **40**, 657; Newbury and Utterback, *Rev. Sci. Instr.*, 1932, **3**, 593; for other types of low-pressure, etc., manometers, see Guéritot, *Compt. Rend.*, 1913, **156**, 1974 (thermo-electric); Verbeek, *Chem. Ztg.*, 1913, **37**, 1338, 1361; Trombe, *Bull. Soc. Chim.*, 1934, **1**, 160, 408 (bell floating in mercury); Hindley, *J. Sci. Instr.*, 1947, **24**, 295 (bells, torsion balance; 2×10^{-4} mm.).

[3] *Proc. Phys. Soc.*, 1928, **40**, 57.

[4] *Physica*, 1946, **12**, 217.

[5] *J.A.C.S.*, 1927, **49**, 1953; Daniels, *ibid.*, 1928, **50**, 1115 (diagrams of 12 types of gauge); Rodebush and Henry, *ibid.*, 1930, **52**, 3159.

[6] *Ann. Chim.*, 1893, **29**, 68; see also Wroblewski, *Wien Ber.*, 1888, **97**, II A, 1321; Witkowski, *Phil. Mag.*, 1896, **41**, 288; 1896, **42**, 1; Tammann, *Ann. Phys.*, 1899, **68**, 553; Wagner, *ibid.*,

which is a kind of reversed hydraulic (Bramah) press. The pressure acts on a small piston (with molasses packing) which is in contact with a large piston (with castor-oil packing) in a vessel below in which is a liquid communicating with a mercury gauge (Fig. 14.VII A, simplified). If p is the pressure read on the mercury manometer and a, A, the areas of the small and large pistons, the pressure applied to the small piston is pA/a.

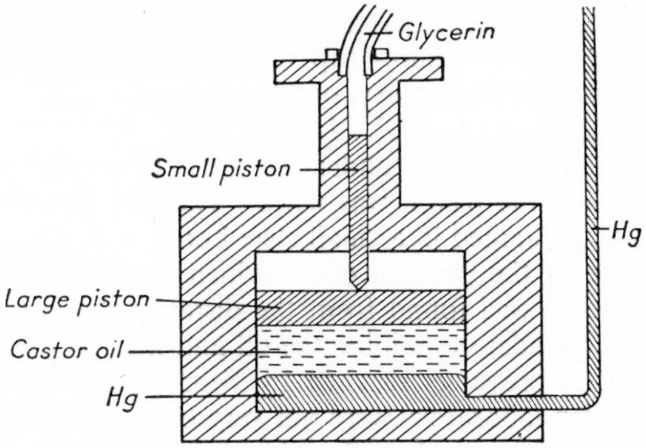

FIG. 14.VII A. Desgoffe Manometer

Holborn and others [1] used up to 250 kg./cm.^{2} a Stückrath's *pressure balance*, consisting of a piston working in a steel cylinder containing castor oil and bearing at the top against a spindle carrying a frame loaded with weights. The motion of the piston is registered by suitable apparatus. Pressures of 100 kg./cm.^{2} can be measured to 0·012 per cent.

Amsler's *pendulum manometer* [2] consists of a cylinder containing oil, the piston of which presses against a heavy pendulum, the weight of which can be adjusted by a sliding weight. The pressure is determined (sensibility about 0·4 kg.) by the displacement of the pendulum.

Bridgman's *absolute manometer* [3] for pressures up to 6,800 kg./cm.^{2}, and in modified form up to 12,000 kg./cm.^{2}, was a combination of an Amagat's

1904, **15**, 906; Knoblauch, Linde, and Klebe, *Forsch. Gebiet. Ingenieurwesens*, Berlin, 1905, Heft **21**, 33, 57 (steam); Martens, *Z. Verein D. Ing.*, 1909, **53**, 747; Koch and Wagner, *Ann. Phys.*, 1910, **31**, 31; Kohnstamm and Walstra, *Verslag. K. Akad. Wetens. Amsterdam*, 1913, **22**, 679; Cardoso, *J. Chim. Phys.*, 1921–2, **19**, 217 (small type); see, on high-pressure manometers, Bridgman, "The Physics of High Pressure," 1931, 60.

1 Holborn and Baumann, *Ann. Phys.*, 1910, **31**, 945; Holborn and Schultze, *ibid.*, 1915, **47**, 1089; Holborn, *ibid.*, 1917, **54**, 503; 1924, **75**, 276; Michels, *ibid.*, 1924, **73**, 577; [Stückrath] *Z. Instr.*, 1894, **14**, 307; Meissner, *ibid.*, 1910, **30**, 137; Wiebe, *ibid.*, 1910, **30**, 205; Dimmer, *ibid.*, 1915, **35**, 245; Richards, *Z. phys. Chem.*, 1908, **61**, 77; Cohen *et al.*, *ibid.*, 1910, **75**, 257; 1919, **93**, 421; Wohlfarth, *Z. techn. Phys.*, 1924, **5**, 361; the instrument was made by Stückrath, Friedenau.

2 Jänecke, *Z. phys. Chem.*, 1915, **90**, 257; on piston gauges and pressure balances see also: Jakeman, in Glazebrook, "Dict. of Applied Physics," 1922, **1**, 630; Schalkwijk, *Proc. K. Akad. Wetens. Amsterdam*, 1901, **3**, 421, 481; 1902, **4**, 23, 107; *Comm. Leiden*, 1901, **67**; Kohnstamm and Walstra, *Proc. K. Akad. Wetens. Amsterdam*, 1914, **16**, 754, 822; 1914, **17**, 203, 217 (3,000 atm.); *Verslag. K. Akad. Wetens. Amsterdam*, 1914, **22**, II, 679, 808, 1366; Crommelin and Smid, *Ann. Phys.*, 1916, **51**, 621; Smid, *ibid.*, 1916, **51**, 635 (calibration of Schäffer and Budenburg pressure balance); *Comm. Leiden*, 1915, **146***c*; Keyes and Brownlee, *J.A.C.S.*, 1918, **40**, 25; Keyes and Felsing, *ibid.*, 1919, **41**, 589; Smith and Taylor, *ibid.*, 1923, **45**, 2107; 1924, **46**, 342; Michels, *Ann. Phys.*, 1923, **72**, 285; 1924, **73**, 577; Beattie, *J.A.C.S.*, 1924, **46**, 342; Keyes and Dewey, *J. Opt. Soc. Amer.*, 1927, **14**, 491; Bridgeman, *J.A.C.S.*, 1927, **49**, 1174 (fixed pt., liq. CO_2, 34·4009 atm. at 0°, or 26144·7 mm. Hg, g=980·665 cm. sec.$^{-2}$); Michels and Gibson, *Ann. Phys.*, 1928, **87**, 850; Bartlett, Cupples, and Tremearne, *J.A.C.S.*, 1928, **50**, 1275; Beattie and Edel, *Ann. Phys.*, 1931, **11**, 633; Meyers and Jessup, *Bur. Stand. J. Res.*, 1931, **6**, 1061 (bibl.); Beattie and Bridgeman, *Ann. Phys.*, 1932, **12**, 827; Keyes, *Proc. Amer. Acad.*, 1933, **68**, 505; Beattie, *ibid.*, 1934, **69**, 389; Benedict, *J.A.C.S.*, 1937, **59**, 2224, 2233; Vereshchagen and Aleksandrov, *J. Tech. Phys. U.S.S.R.*, 1939, **9**, 348; Burlew, *J.A.C.S.*, 1940, **62**, 681, 696.

3 *Proc. Amer. Acad.*, 1909, **44**, 201, 221; 1911, **47**, 321; 1924, **59**, 171; 1935, **70**, 1.

manometer with a pressure balance. A small piston (1·59 mm. diam.) moved in a massive steel block with a clearance of 0·0025 mm., bearing above on a wider piston carrying a frame loaded with weights. An accuracy of 0·1 per cent. was attained and a sensitivity of 2 kg./cm.^{2} at 7,000 kg./cm.^{2} pressure. The pistons were lubricated with a mixture of treacle and glycerol. To measure very high pressures (up to 15,000 kg./cm.^{2}) Bridgman [1] used the change of resistance of mercury, or [2] the change of resistance of manganin, a method used originally by Lisell.[3] The pressures were applied by paraffin oil, which remained sufficiently liquid under the great compression, and an ingenious method of sealing the piston was used. The gas, already compressed to 2,000 kg./cm.^{2}, was contained in a small steel bomb with a valve which opened when the pressure of the paraffin oil in which it was immersed exceeded this value. The volume was found from the distance the compressing piston was driven into the cylinder containing the oil and the gas bomb.

The pressures reached by Kamerlingh Onnes and his collaborators in the Leiden laboratory were not very high, but the measurements were made at low temperatures, when the gases would liquefy if high pressures were used, and precision was aimed at. From the numerous publications a representative selection only can be given here.[4]

It is obvious from the above summary that many types of manometer are available for moderate and high pressures, and if the designs suitable for use at very low pressures (considered in Section VII J) are included the range of choice is considerable. As a general rule, the simplest apparatus which fulfils the requirements of a particular investigation should be chosen, due regard being paid to the rest of the apparatus. If, for example, the manometer is required to record the pressure of a gas at a fairly high temperature, some design (such as the spoon-gauge) which can be enclosed in a constant-temperature space will be best. If accurate readings of pressure at room temperature are to be made, some form of simple U-type will probably be best, in which case great care should be taken in the choice of the manometric liquid, the density and coefficient of expansion of which must be accurately determined. For high pressures, a study of the publications listed which cover this field will enable a suitable choice to be made. Elaborate apparatus, with electrical contacts and parts which may easily get out of order, should be avoided. Manometers of the Bourdon type should be frequently recalibrated.

Although several manometric liquids have been mentioned, many more will suggest themselves. The chief property of a manometric liquid which should be considered is its volatility; a liquid having an appreciable vapour pressure at the temperature of the manometer must not be used.

[1] *Proc. Amer. Acad.*, 1909, **44**, 201, 221; first used by de Forest Palmer, *Amer. J. Sci.*, 1898, **6**, 451, to 3,500 atm.

[2] *Proc. Amer. Acad.*, 1911, **47**, 321, 335; 1914, **49**, 627; 1924, **59**, 173; 1935, **70**, 1.

[3] Lisell, *Dissert.*, Upsala, 1903; *Ann. Phys. Beibl.*, 1903, **27**, 852; Lindeck, *Z. Instr.*, 1908, **28**, 229; Lafay, *Compt. Rend.*, 1909, **149**, 566 (Pt, Hg, manganin); *Ann. Chim.*, 1910, **19**, 289; Biron, *J. Russ. Phys. Chem. Soc.*, 1910, **42**, 223 (P); *Ann. Phys. Beibl.*, 1911, **35**, 746; Jaeger and Steinwehr, *Z. Phys.*, 1922, **9**, 201; Bridgman, "The Physics of High Pressure," 1931, 70; Ziklis, *J. Techn. Phys. U.S.S.R.*, 1945, **15**, 960. It should be noted that the results of Lussana, *Nuov. Cim.*, 1903, **5**, 305; 1918, **15**, 130, were in error, since he did not use manganin in the experiments.

[4] Onnes, *Proc. K. Akad. Wetens. Amsterdam*, 1900, **2**, 29 (*Comm. Leiden*, **50**); 1900, **2**, 437 (*Comm. Leiden*, **54**; Hg compr. pump); Onnes and Braak, *ibid.*, 1901, **3**, 299 (*Comm. Leiden*, **60**); Onnes and Hyndman, *ibid.*, 1901, **3**, 621 (*Comm. Leiden*, **69**); Gzn, *Z. phys. Chem.*, 1902, **39**, 14 (HCl, C_2H_6; bibl.); Schalkwijk, *Proc. K. Akad. Wetens. Amsterdam*, 1902, **4**, 107 (*Comm. Leiden*, **70**: H_2 to 60 atm.); 1903, **5**, 636 (*Comm. Leiden*, **84**: volumeter); Onnes

§ 8. Manostats

The *manostat*, or pressure regulator of Moitessier,[1] consists (Fig. 15.VII A) of a weighted bell inverted over a mixture of 2 parts of glycerol and 1 part of water. The gas enters by a tube inside the bell and leaves by another tube which is closed at the top by a valve operated by a rod from the bell, which is lifted when

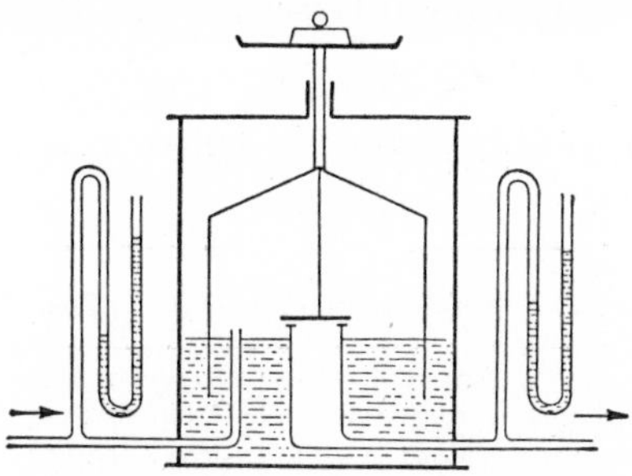

FIG. 15.VII A. Manostat

the latter rises. The pressure is adjusted by weights in a pan at the top of the bell. The adjustment is to 0·5 mm. of water pressure. In Giroud's apparatus a weighted membrane is used. Other types of manostat, some for reduced pressures, are described by Lothar Meyer,[2] Perkin,[3] Smits,[4] Drucker,[5] Scheel

and Hyndman, *ibid.*, 1902, **4**, 761 (*Comm. Leiden*, **78**); Keesom, *ibid.*, 1904, **6**, 532, 541, 554, 565 (*Comm. Leiden*, **88**, O_2+CO_2); Onnes and Braak, *ibid.*, 1907, **9**, 754, 775 (*Comm. Leiden*, **97***a*; *Ann. Phys. Beibl.*, 1907, **31**, 933: H_2); 1907–8, **10**, 204, 413, 419, 429, 743 (*Comm. Leiden*, **99***a*, **100***a*, **100***b*, **102***d*; deviations from Boyle's law; H_2); Onnes, *ibid.*, 1907–8, **10**, 445, 741 (*Comm. Leiden*, **102***a*, *c*; He); Onnes and de Haas, *ibid.*, 1912, **15**, 295 (*Comm. Leiden*, **127***a*; H_2); Onnes, Crommelin, and Smid, *ibid.*, 1915, **18**, 465 (*Comm. Leiden*, **146***b*; H_2); Onnes and Crommelin, *ibid.*, 1915, **18**, 515 (*Comm. Leiden*, **147***d*; Ne); Crommelin, Martinez, and Onnes, *ibid.*, 1919, **22**, 108 (*Comm. Leiden*; 1921, **154***a*; Ne); Kuenen, Verschoyle, and Urk, *ibid.*, 1923, **26**, 49 (O_2+N_2); Kuypers and Onnes, *Arch. Néerl.*, 1923, **6**, 277 (*Comm. Leiden*, **165***a*; O_2); Martinez and Onnes, *ibid.*, 1923, **6**, 253 (*Comm. Leiden*, **164**; H_2, He); Onnes and Penning, *ibid.*, 1924, **7**, 157, 166 (*Comm. Leiden*, **165***b*, *c*; H_2, He); Penning, *ibid.*, 1924, **7**, 172 (*Comm. Leiden*, **166**; isochores of air); van Urk and Nijhoff, *Comm. Leiden*, 1924, **169***c* (O_2); Kuypers, *ibid.*, 1924, **169***b* (O_2); Onnes and Kuypers, *ibid.*, 1924, **169***a* (O_2); Onnes and van Urk, *ibid.*, 1924, **169***d* (N_2); van Urk, *ibid.*, 1924, **169***e* (N_2); Boks and Onnes, *ibid.*, 1924, **170***a* (He); Onnes and Boks, *ibid.*, 1924, **170***b* (He); Crommelin and Swallow, *4th Internat. Congr. Refrig.*, 1924, **1**, 53*a* (*Comm. Leiden*, 1925, **172***a*; H_2); van Agt and Onnes, *Proc. K. Akad. Wetens. Amsterdam*, 1925, **28**, 674 (*Comm. Leiden*, **176***b*; H_2, He); Nijhoff and Keesom, *ibid.*, 1925, **28**, 963 (*Comm. Leiden*, **179***b*, O_2); 1928, **31**, 404 (*Comm. Leiden*, **188***b*; He); Nijhoff, Keesom, and Iliin, *ibid.*, 1928, **31**, 408 (*Comm. Leiden*, **188***c*); Nijhoff and Keesom, *ibid.*, 1928, **31**, 410, 413 (*Comm. Leiden*, **188***d*; H_2); Nijhoff, Gerver, and Michels, *ibid.*, 1930, **33**, 72 (CO_2 0°–100°, 2,000 atm.); Michels and Michels, *Physica*, 1934, **1**, 587 (N_2); Michels and Lenssen, *J. Sci. Instr.*, 1934, **11**, 345 (to 3,000 atm.); Michels, Wouters, and de Boer, *Physica*, 1936, **3**, 585, 597 (N_2); Keesom and Walstra, *ibid.*, 1940, **7**, 985 (He, low temp.); Michels and Goudeket, *ibid.*, 1941, **8**, 347 (H_2 to 3,000 atm.); Michels and Wouters, *ibid.*, 1941, **8**, 923 (He to 200 atm., 0°–150°); Kistemaker and Keesom, *ibid.*, 1946, **12**, 227 (He, low temp.); on Kamerlingh Onnes (1853–1926) see Mathias, *Rev. Gén. Sci.*, 1926. **37**, 294; Keesom, *Physica*, 1926, **6**, 81; de Haas-Lorentz, *Naturwiss.*, 1926, **14**, 441.

[1] Stansfield, *Trans. Faraday Soc.*, 1911, **7**, 116; Collins, *Chem. News*, 1912, **105**, 244; *Z. Instr.*, 1912, **32**, 305; cf. Mathews and Faville, *J. Phys. Chem.*, 1918, **22**, 1; Arndt, " Handbuch der physikal.-chem. Technik," 1923, 173 f.; Smith, *Ind. Eng. Chem.*, 1924, **16**, 22; Carroll, Rollefson, and Mathews, *J.A.C.S.*, 1925, **47**, 1785, 1791; Coffin, *ibid.*, 1933, **55**, 3646; Campbell and Dulmage, *ibid.*, 1948, **70**, 1723.

[2] *Ann.*, 1873, **165**, 303.

[3] *J.C.S.*, 1881, **53**, 689.

[4] *Z. phys. Chem.*, 1900, **33**, 565.

[5] *Z. phys. Chem.*, 1910, **74**, 612.

and Heuse,[1] Beckmann,[2] Speranski,[3] Beckmann and Liesche,[4] and Ruff and Hartmann.[5] Manostats for high pressures are described by Cohen and de Boer[6] and Hershberg and Huntress,[7] and for low pressures by Soller, Goldwasser, and Beebe.[8] A Cartesian diver type was first used by Caswell.[9]

§ 9. Results of Compressibilities of Gases at High Pressures

TABLE I

Values of *PV* found by Amagat[10] (value at 0° C. and 1 atm.=1.)

Oxygen

P atm.	100	200	300	400	500	600	700	800	900	1000
0°	0·9265	0·9140	0·9625	1·0515	1·1560	1·2690	1·3855	1·5030	1·6200	1·7355
15·65°	1·0045	0·9945	1·0420	1·1250	1·2270	1·3370	1·4515	1·5660	1·6820	1·7980
99·50°	1·3750	1·4000	1·4530	1·5320	1·6220	1·7200	1·8270	1·9340	2·0415	2·1510
199·50°	—	1·8190	1·8850	1·9610	2·0500	2·1420	2·2415	2·3430	2·4465	—

Nitrogen

P atm.	100	200	300	400	500	600	700	800	900	1000
0°	0·9910	1·0390	1·1360	1·2570	1·3900	1·5260	1·6615	1·7980	1·9340	2·0685
16·03°	1·0620	1·1145	1·2105	1·3290	1·4590	1·5945	1·7290	1·8655	2·0015	2·1360
99·45°	—	1·4890	1·5905	1·7060	1·8275	1·9545	2·0865	2·2200	2·3540	—
199·50°	—	1·9065	2·0145	2·1325	2·2570	2·3840	2·5125	2·6400	2·7715	—

Hydrogen[11]

P atm.	100	200	300	400	500	600	700	800	900	1000
0°	1·0690	1·1380	1·2090	1·2830	1·3565	1·4315	1·5045	1·5775	1·6490	1·7200
15·50°	1·1290	1·1980	1·2685	1·3410	1·4150	1·4890	1·5620	1·6340	1·7060	1·7760
99·25°	—	1·5135	1·5860	1·6590	1·7310	1·8040	1·8760	1·9490	2·0210	2·0930
200·25°	—	1·8840	1·9560	2·0300	2·1050	2·1762	2·2480	2·3200	2·3915	—

1 *Ann. Phys.*, 1912, **37**, 79.
2 *Z. phys. Chem.*, 1912, **79**, 565.
3 *Z. phys. Chem.*, 1913, **84**, 160.
4 *Z. phys. Chem.*, 1914, **88**, 13.
5 *Z. anorg. Chem.*, 1924, **133**, 29; see also Stephenson, *J. Phys. Chem.*, 1907, **11**, 107; Miller, *ibid.*, 1907, **11**, 392; Joseph, *Proc. Chem. Soc.*, 1914, **30**, 254; Dawson, *Ind. Eng. Chem.*, 1924, **16**, 160; *J. Phys. Chem.*, 1925, **29**, 1408; Johnson, *J.C.S.*, 1931, 2523; Martin and Collie, *ibid.*, 1932, 2658; Trombe, *Bull. Soc. Chim.*, 1938, **5**, 710; Thelin, *Ind. Eng. Chem. Anal.*, 1941, **13**, 908; Oliver and Bickford, *Rev. Sci. Instr.*, 1945, **16**, 130; Donahoe, Russell, and Van der Werf, *Ind. Eng. Chem. Anal.*, 1946, **18**, 156; Spardo, Vix, and Gastrock, *ibid.*, 1946, **18**, 214; Goodwin, *J. Chem. Educ.*, 1947, **24**, 511; Campbell and Dulmage, *Anal. Chem.*, 1948, **70**, 1723.
6 *Z. phys. Chem.*, 1913, **84**, 32.
7 *Ind. Eng. Chem. Anal.*, 1933, **5**, 344.
8 *J.A.C.S.*, 1936, **58**, 1703; 1938, **60**, 1265.
9 *Phil. Trans.*, 1704, **24**, 1597 ("baroscope"); Dubrovin, *Instruments*, 1933, **6**, 194 (low-pressure gauge); Germann and Gagos, *Ind. Eng. Chem. Anal.*, 1943, **15**, 285; Gilmont, *ibid.*, 1946, **18**, 633.
10 *Ann. Chim.*, 1893, **29**, 68.
11 Amagat says he prepared his hydrogen by heating "oxalic acid" with soda lime; he

TABLE I—*continued*

Air

P atm.	100	200	300	400	500	600	700	800	900	1000
0°	0·9730	1·0100	1·0975	1·2145	1·3400	1·4700	1·6020	1·7345	1·8640	1·9920
15·70°	1·0460	1·0855	1·1740	1·2835	1·4110	1·5375	1·6670	1·8000	1·9300	2·0600
99·40°	1·4030	1·4670	1·5585	1·6625	1·7815	1·9060	2·0300	2·1555	2·2830	2·4150
200·4°	—	1·8860	1·9865	2·0960	2·2110	2·3300	2·4515	2·5750	2·7000	2·8280

Carbon Dioxide

P atm.	100	200	300	400	500	600	700	800	1000
0°	0·2020	0·3850	0·5595	0·7280	0·8905	1·0495	1·2055	1·3580	1·6560
20°	0·2285	0·4190	0·5985	0·7710	0·9380	1·0995	1·2590	1·4170	1·7160
40°	0·3090	0·4675	0·6485	0·8230	0·9900	1·1570	1·3190	1·4790	1·7800
60°	0·6610	0·5425	0·7100	0·8840	1·0540	1·2190	1·3825	1·5435	1·8475
80°	0·8725	0·6600	0·7900	0·9560	1·1240	1·2900	1·4535	1·6140	1·9210
100°	1·0300	0·8145	0·8900	1·0385	1·2005	1·3655	1·5285	1·6890	1·9990
198°	1·5820	1·4960	1·4935	1·5630	1·6775	1·8120	1·9560	2·1080	—
258°	1·8470	1·8040	1·8200	1·8830	—	—	—	—	—

The compressibilities of air [1] and hydrogen [2] were measured by Witkowski, his values for hydrogen being particularly good, and he also worked down to very low temperatures. The values found by Amagat [3] and by Witkowski are given (with some abridgement) in tables II and III ($PV=1$ at 0° and 1 atm. in III).

TABLE II

Relative Volumes (Amagat). Volume at 0° C. and 1 atm. = 1,000,000.

Atm.	Oxygen			Air			Nitrogen			Hydrogen		
	0°	99·5°	199·5°	0°	99·4°	200·4°	0°	99·45°	199·5°	0°	99·25°	200·25°
100	9265	13750	12000	9730	14030	—	9910	—	—	1069	—	—
200	4570	7000	9095	5050	7335	9430	5195	7445	9532	5690	7567	9420
300	3208	4843	6283	3658	5195	6622	3786	5301	6715	4030	5286	6520
400	2629	3830	4902	3036	4156	5240	3142	4265	5331	3207	4147	5075
500	2314	3244	4100	2680	3563	4422	2780	3655	4514	2713	3462	4210
600	2117	2867	3570	2450	3177	3883	2543	3258	3973	2387	3006	3627
700	1981	2610	3202	2288	2900	3502	2374	2980	3589	2150	2680	3211
800	1880	2417	2929	2168	2694	3219	2247	2775	3300	1970	2436	2900
900	1800	2268	2718	2071	2537	3000	2149	2616	3079	1835	2244	2657
1000	1736	2151	—	1992	2415	2828	2068	—	—	1725	2093	—
1500	1526	—	—	—	—	—	—	—	—	1380	—	—
2000	1408	—	—	—	—	—	—	—	—	1194	—	—

probably meant *formic* acid, and Wroblewski, *Wien Ber.*, 1888, **97**, IIA, 1321, says the gas would contain about 20 per cent. of carbon monoxide; Balandin and Freidlin, *J. Gen. Chem. U.S.S.R.*, 1936, **6**, 868, say the method gives pure H_2, free from CO.

[1] *Phil. Mag.*, 1896, **41**, 288; 1896, **42**, 1 (values for +16°, −136°, and −140° also given; for air at 0° to −79° to 200 atm., see Koch, *Ann. Phys.*, 1908, **27**, 311). Thermodynamic functions of air were calculated from Witkowski's data by Clausius's equation (§ 28.VII C) by Fouché, *Compt. Rend.*, 1919, **169**, 1089, 1158.

[2] *Bull. Acad. Polon.*, 1905, **6**, 305; Landolt-Börnstein, " Tabellen," 5th edit., 1923, 105.

[3] *Ann. Chim.*, 1893, **29**, 68.

TABLE III

Values of PV for Air and Hydrogen (Witkowski)

Atm.		100°	0°	−35°	−78·5°*	−103·5°†	−130°	−145°‡	−183°	−205°	−212°
1	air	1·367	1·0000	0·8716	0·7119	0·6202	0·5229	0·4679	—	—	—
	H_2	1·3661	1·0000	—	0·7180	0·6189	—	0·4611	0·3283	0·2470	0·2207
10	air	1·3678	0·9951	—	—	—	—	—	—	—	—
	H_2	1·3721	1·0055	—	0·7228	0·6232	—	0·4635	0·3284	0·2427	0·2145
20	air	1·3691	0·9897	—	0·6778	0·5697	0·4410	0·3447	—	—	—
	H_2	1·3789	1·0118	—	0·7282	0·6279	—	0·4661	0·3272	0·2373	0·2065
30	air	1·3704	0·9842	—	0·6599	0·5417	0·3936	0·2444§	—	—	—
	H_2	1·3858	1·0181	—	0·7336	0·6327	—	0·4689	0·3270	0·2321	0·1997
40	air	1·3725	0·9793	—	0·6423	0·5125	0·3329	—	—	—	—
	H_2	1·3927	1·0245	—	0·7391	0·6376	—	0·4721	0·3270	0·2288	0·1946
50	air	1·3754	0·9754	0·8288	0·6252	0·4839	0·2544	—	—	—	—
	H_2	1·3996	1·0309	—	0·7445	0·6427	—	0·4758	0·3278	0·2275	0·1928
60	air	1·3784	0·9723	0·8219	0·6089	0·4567	0·2013	—	—	—	—
	H_2	1·4064	1·0373	—	0·7501	0·6478	—	0·4801	0·3296	0·2275	0·1928
70	air	1·3821	0·9701	0·8158	0·5937	0·4318	0·1989	—	—	—	—
80	air	1·3866	0·9688	0·8105	0·5796	0·4103	0·2043	—	—	—	—
90	air	1·3908	0·9681	0·8058	0·5680	0·3948	—	—	—	—	—
100	air	1·3951	0·9681	0·8023	0·5600	0·3881	—	—	—	—	—
110	air	1·4004	0·9690	0·8006	0·5544	0·3877	—	—	—	—	—
120	air	1·4065	0·9710	0·8006	0·5520	0·3914	—	—	—	—	—
130	air	—	0·9738	—	0·5528	0·3981	—	—	—	—	—

* −77° for H_2. † −104° for H_2. ‡ −147° for H_2. § 29 atm.

TABLE IV[1]

Values of PV in Amagat units (P atm.; unit mass of gas = mass of 1 lit. at S.T.P.). Observers: A = Amagat, B = Bartlett, H = Holborn, O = Onnes, S = Schalkwijk, ST = Smith and Taylor, V = Verschoyle, W = Witkowski. Values collected by Bartlett *et al.*, 1930.

Nitrogen

Atm.	+20°	−25°	−50°	−70°
1	1·0735	0·9082	0·8162	0·7432
25	1·0685 (V)	0·8910 (H)	0·7900 (H)	0·7044 (H)
	1·0689 (O)	—	—	—
	1·0695 (H)	—	—	—
50	1·0667 (V)	0·8780 (O)	0·7680 (O)	0·6747 (B)
	1·0668 (O)	0·8780 (H)	0·7672 (H)	0·6680 (O)
	1·0646 (ST)	—	—	0·6680 (H)
	1·0672 (H)	—	—	—

[1] Bartlett, Hetherington, Kvalnes, and Tremearne, *J.A.C.S.*, 1930, **52**, 1363, where values for 75, 125, 150, and 300 atm. are also given; Bartlett, Cupples, and Tremearne, *ibid.*, 1928, **50**,

TABLE IV—*continued*

Nitrogen—continued

Atm.	$+20°$	$-25°$	$-50°$	$-70°$
100	1·0745 (B)	0·8676 (B)	0·7438 (B)	0·6362 (B)
	1·0737 (V)	0·8677 (H)	0·7407 (H)	0·6290 (H)
	1·0766 (H)	—	—	—
	1·0796 (A)	—	—	—
	1·0693 (ST)	—	—	—
200	1·1320 (B)	0·9151 (B)	0·7854 (B)	0·6823 (B)
	1·1297 (V)	—	—	—
	1·1332 (A)	—	—	—
400	1·3467 (B)	1·1445 (B)	1·0334 (B)	0·9477 (B)
	1·3468 (A)	—	—	—
500	1·4761 (A)	1·2798 (B)	1·1748 (B)	1·0914 (B)
600	1·6098 (B)	1·4186 (B)	1·3159 (B)	1·2331 (B)
	1·6115 (A)	—	—	—
800	1·8817 (B)	1·6958 (B)	1·5928 (B)	1·5111 (B)
	1·8822 (A)	—	—	—
1000	2·1481 (B)	1·9600 (B)	1·8573 (B)	1·7783 (B)
	2·1527 (A)	—	—	—

1275. Amagat's and Holborn's values are interpolated from observations at 0° and 15°–16°, and at 50°, 0°, −50°, and −100°, respectively. According to Deming and Shupe, *J.A.C.S.*, 1931, **53**, 843, the temperatures given above, from Bartlett *et al.*, as −25°, −50°, and −70°, should be −24·99°, −49·93°, and −69·90°, respectively, for the H_2 table. Lala, *Ann. Fac. Sci. Toulouse*, 1891, **5**, G3 (gases and mixtures); Kuenen, *Arch. Néerl.*, 1893, **26**, 354, 392 (CH_3Cl); Amagat, *Ann. Chim.*, 1893, **29**, 68; Leduc, *ibid.*, 1898, **15**, 5; *Compt. Rend.*, 1909, **148**, 407 (several gases, 0–3 atm.); Verschaffelt, *Proc. K. Akad. Wetens. Amsterdam*, 1899, **1**, 329 (*Comm. Leiden*, 1899, **47**) (CO_2+H_2); Ramsay and Travers, *Z. phys. Chem.*, 1901, **38**, 641 (675) (He, Ne, A, Kr, Xe); Onnes and Boudin, *Proc. K. Akad. Wetens. Amsterdam*, 1901, **3**, 299 (*Comm. Leiden*, 1901, **60**); Schalkwijk, *ibid.*, 1902, **4**, 23, 107 (*Comm. Leiden*, 1902, **70**); Witkowski, *Bull. Acad. Polon.*, 1905, **6**, 305; Onnes and Braak, *Proc. K. Akad. Wetens. Amsterdam*, 1907, **9**, 754 (*Comm. Leiden*, **97***a*); 1907–8, **10**, 204 (*Comm. Leiden*, **99***a*), 413 (*Comm. Leiden*, **100***a*), 419 (*Comm. Leiden*, **100***b*); *ibid.*, 1907–8, **10**, 743; *Verslag. K. Akad. Wetens. Amsterdam*, 1908, **16**, 501, 817 (*Comm. Leiden*, 1908, **102***d*) (He); Kohnstamm and Walstra, *Proc. K. Akad. Wetens. Amsterdam*, 1914, **17**, 203 (values marked **); Onnes, Crommelin, and Smid, *Comm. Leiden*, 1915, **146***b* (recalculated by Michels and Gerver, *Ann. Phys.*, 1933, **16**, 745); Holborn *et al.*, *Ann. Phys.*, 1915, **47**, 1089; 1920, **63**, 674; *Z. Phys.*, 1925, **33**, 1; 1926, **38**, 359; Holborn and Schultze, *Ann. Phys.*, 1915, **47**, 1089 (air, He, A; 0°–200°); Keyes and Felsing, *J.A.C.S.*, 1919, **41**, 589; Holborn, *Ann. Phys.*, 1920, **63**, 674 (H_2); Holborn and Otto, *Z. Phys.*, 1922, **10**, 367 (H_2, O_2, He); 1925, **33**, 1 (air, O_2, N_2, Ne, He); Kuypers and Onnes, *Arch. Néerl.*, 1923, **6**, 277 (O_2); Smith and Taylor, *J.A.C.S.*, 1923, **45**, 2107; 1926, **48**, 3122; Crommelin and Swallow, *4th Internat. Congr. Refrig.*, 1924, **1**, 53*a* (*Comm. Leiden*, **172***a*); Verschoyle, *Proc. Roy. Soc.*, 1926, **111**, 552; [Pickering], *Bur. Stand. Circ.*, 1926, No. **279** (extensive data); Sameshima, *Bull. Chem. Soc. Japan*, 1926, **1**, 41 (C_2H_2, to 12 atm. at 0° and 25°); Crommelin and Watts, *Proc. K. Akad. Wetens. Amsterdam*, 1927, **30**, 1059 (*Comm. Leiden*, **189***c*) (C_2H_4); Keyes and Burks, *J.A.C.S.*, 1927, **49**, 1403; 1928, **50**, 1100 (CH_4 and CH_4+N_2); Shidei, *Bull. Chem. Soc. Japan*, 1928, **3**, 25 (HCl); Nijhoff and Keesom, *Proc. K. Akad. Wetens. Amsterdam*, 1928, **31**, 410, 413; Goig, *Compt. Rend.*, 1929, **189**, 246 (CO, 53–127 atm.); Botella, *An. Fis. Quim.*, 1929, **27**, 315 (CO 0°–20°, to 50 atm.); Nijhoff, *Comm. Leiden*, 1929, Suppl. **64***c* (He, H_2), **64***f* (O_2, N_2); Heuse and Otto, *Ann. Phys.*, 1929, **2**, 1012; Bartlett, Hetherington, Kvalnes, and Tremearne, *J.A.C.S.*, 1930, **52**, 1374 (O_2); Basset and Dupinay, *Compt. Rend.*, 1930, **191**, 1295 (N_2+H_2 to 5,000 atm.); Freeth and Verschoyle, *Proc. Roy. Soc.*, 1931, **130**, 453 (CH_4); Dodge, *Ind. Eng. Chem.*, 1932, **24**, 1353 (review); Beattie, *Proc. Amer. Acad.*, 1934, **64**, 389; Johnston and Weimer, *J.A.C.S.*, 1934, **56**, 625 (N_2O and NO); Michels and Michels, *Physica*, 1934, **1**, 587 (N_2); Beattie, Hadlock, and Poffenberger, *J. Chem. Phys.*, 1935, **3**, 93 (C_2H_6); Michels and Nederbraght, *Physica*, 1935, **2**, 1000 (CH_4, 20–80 atm.); Michels and Michels, *Proc. Roy. Soc.*, 1936, **153**, 201, 211 (CO_2 to 3,000 atm.); Michels, de Gruyter, and Niesen, *Physica*, 1936, **3**, 346 (C_2H_4 to 270

TABLE IV—*continued*

Hydrogen

Atm.	+20°	−25°	−50°	−70°
1	1·0732	0·9085	0·8170	0·7438
25	1·0887 (S)	0·9230 (B)	0·8307 (B)	0·7566 (B)
	1·0889 (V)	0·9240 (W)	0·8330 (W)	0·7580 (W)
	1·0889 (H)	—	—	—
	1·0885 (W)**	—	—	—
50	1·1049 (S)	0·9384 (B)	0·8447 (B)	0·7703 (B)
	1·1053 (V)	0·9374 (H)	0·8447 (H)	0·7695 (H)
	1·1048 (H)	0·9382 (W)	0·8450 (W)	0·7710 (W)
	1·1049 (W)**	—	—	—
100	1·1391 (B)	0·9706 (B)	0·8756 (B)	0·8003 (B)
	1·1382 (S)	0·9695 (H)	0·8754 (H)	0·7980 (H)
	1·1383 (V)	—	—	—
	1·1402 (O)	—	—	—
	1·1384 (H)	—	—	—
	1·1464 (A)	—	—	—
	1·1385 (A)**	—	—	—
200	1·2079 (B)	1·0383 (B)	0·9411 (B)	0·8640 (B)
	1·2054 (V)	—	—	—
	1·2154 (A)	—	—	—
	1·2094 (A)**	—	—	—
400	1·3511 (B)	1·1808 (B)	1·0832 (B)	1·0075 (B)
	1·3578 (A)	—	—	—
	1·3545 (A)**	—	—	—
500	1·4240 (B)	1·2542 (B)	1·1568 (B)	1·0804 (B)
	1·4320 (A)	—	—	—
	1·4274 (A)**	—	—	—
600	1·4958 (B)	1·3272 (B)	1·2301 (B)	1·1555 (B)
	1·5057 (A)	—	—	—
	1·5006 (A)**	—	—	—
800	1·6391 (B)	1·4717 (B)	1·3755 (B)	1·3018 (B)
	1·6504 (A)	—	—	—
	1·6450 (A)**	—	—	—
1000	1·7795 (B)	1·6139 (B)	1·5185 (B)	1·4443 (B)
	1·7923 (A)	—	—	—
	1·7885 (A)**	—	—	—

Holborn [1] represented his results with hydrogen to 100 atm. by the equations:

$$0^\circ \; pv=0{\cdot}99918+0{\cdot}0_381613/v+0{\cdot}0_51220/v^2$$

$$50^\circ \; pv=1{\cdot}18112+0{\cdot}0_210505/v+0{\cdot}0_51015/v^2$$

$$100^\circ \; pv=1{\cdot}36506+0{\cdot}0_212450/v+0{\cdot}0_51240/v^2.$$

atm.); Michels, Wouters, and de Boer, *ibid.*, 1936, **3**, 585 (N_2); Beattie, Gouq-Jen Su, and Simard, *J.A.C.S.*, 1939, **61**, 926 (C_2H_6); Kelso and Felsing, *ibid.*, 1940, **62**, 3132, 3529 (hydrocarbons); V. Fischer, *Ann. Phys.*, 1941, **39**, 272; Kritschewsky and Levchenko, *Acta Physicochim. U.R.S.S.*, 1941, **14**, 271 (binary and ternary mixtures of N_2, H_2, and CH_4); Michels and Goudeket, *Physica*, 1941, **8**, 347 (H_2); Michels and Wouters, *ibid.*, 923 (He); Beattie, Ingersoll, and Stockmayer, *J.A.C.S.*, 1942, **64**, 548 (*iso*butene); Vaughan and Collins, *Ind. Eng. Chem.*, 1942, **34**, 885 (C_3H_8, *iso*-C_5H_{12}); Felsing and Watson, *J.A.C.S.*, 1943, **65**, 780, 1889 (hydrocarbons); Michels, Geldermans, and de Groot, *Physica*, 1946, **12**, 105 (C_2H_4 to 3,000 atm.); Meyers, *Bur. Stand. Bull.*, 1948, **40**, 457 (O_2); for N_2 see also Keyes, Smith, and Joubert, *J. Math. Phys. Mass. Inst.*, 1922, **1**, 191; Onnes and Van Urk, *Comm. Leiden*, 1924, **169***d*; Kvalnes and Gaddy, *J.A.C.S.*, 1931, **53**, 395 (to 1000 atm.); Benedict, *ibid.*, 1937, **59**, 2224, 2233; Otto, Michels, and Wouters, *Phys. Z.*, 1934, **35**, 97; Maron and Turnbull, *J.A.C.S.*, 1942, **64**, 44.

[1] *Ann. Phys.*, 1920, **63**, 674.

The following figures[1] show the volumes occupied by 1 volume of gas at 16° C. at the stated pressure when released to 1 atm. pressure:

Atm.	50	100	120	150	200
H_2	48·5	93·6	111·3	136·3	176·4
N_2	50·5	100·6	120·0	147·6	190·8
Air	50·9	101·8	121·9	150·3	194·8
O_2	—	105·2	—	—	212·6
O_2 at 0° C.	52·3	107·9	128·6	161·9	218·8
CO_2	69	477*	485*	498*	515*

* Liquid at pressures above 90 atm.

Some values of pv (=1 at 0° and 1 kg./cm.²) found by Bridgman[2] are:

p kg./cm.²	2,000	4,000	6,000	8,000	10,000	13,000	15,000
He 65°	—	2·64	3·33	3·98	4·60	5·52	6·11
H_2 65°	2·54	3·83	5·08	6·23	7·29	8·66	—
N_2 68°	—	5·82	7·95	9·94	11·91	14·70	16·50

The intermediate values for H_2 at 65° are:

p	3,000	5,000	7,000	9,000	11,000	12,000
pv	3·18	4·50	5·65	6·17	7·80	8·25

Michels, Nijhoff, and Gerver[3] found that the compressibilities of hydrogen at 0°–100° and 1 to 1,000 atm. could be represented by $(pv)_t^p=(pv)_0^p+\alpha t$, where α is a function of pressure, having the values: 0 atm. 0·003661, 500 atm. 0·003745, 1,000 atm. 0·003698. The values of pv (1 at 1 atm. and 0°) are:

Atm.	0°	25°	50°	75°	100°
0	0·9993	1·0908	1·1823	1·2739	1·3654
100	1·0639	1·1569	1·2501	1·3429	1·4358
200	1·1328	1·2269	1·3203	1·4137	1·5071
400	1·2761	1·3703	1·4635	1·5577	1·6513
600	1·4221	1·5157	1·6081	1·7022	1·7955
800	1·5668	1·6593	1·7512	1·8452	1·9380
1000	1·7086	1·8008	1·8917	1·9856	2·0784

Amagat's results for hydrogen and nitrogen to 5,000 atm. were confirmed by Basset and Dupinay.[4] Volumes of H_2, N_2, and CO, and mixtures of N_2+3H_2,

[1] Cochrane, in "Physical and Chemical Data of Nitrogen Fixation" (H.M. Stationery Office), 1918, 5; cf. Stewart, *J. Amer. Soc. Mech. Eng.*, 1908, **30**, 1361; Bartlett, *et al.*, *J.A.C.S.*, 1928, **50**, 1275; 1930, **52**, 1363, 1374, for higher pressures. See the collection of data in Winkelmann, "Handbuch der Physik," 1908, **1**, ii, 1257; Graetz, *ibid.*, 1906, **3**, 1111; Landolt-Börnstein, "Tabellen," 5th edit., 1923, 103; "Internat. Crit. Tables," **3**, 3f.; Pickering, *Bur. Stand. Misc. Publ.*, 1925, **71**.

[2] *Proc. Amer. Acad.*, 1924, **59**, 171.

[3] *Ann. Phys.*, 1932, **12**, 562.

[4] *Compt. Rend.*, 1930, **191**, 1295.

at −70° to +300° and 1–1,000 atm. were given (with charts) by Dilley.[1] Results found by Bridgman [2] are:

p kg./cm.^{2}	H_2 c.c./g. at 30°	H_2 c.c./g. at 65°	He c.c./g. at 65°	N_2 c.c./g. at 68°	A Δv c.c./g. at 55°	NH_3 Δv c.c./g. at 30°
2,000	13·89	—	—	—	−0·083	−0·217
3,000	11·64	12·17	5·54	1·29	0·000	0·000
4,000	10·52	11·03	4·77	1·20	+0·049	+0·120
5,000	9·80	10·29	4·31	1·14	0·085	0·200
6,000	9·29	9·73	4·00	1·09	0·112	0·261
7,000	8·87	9·29	3·77	1·06	0·134	0·310
8,000	8·55	8·96	3·59	1·03	0·152	0·348
9,000	8·26	8·71	3·44	1·00	0·167	0·380
10,000	8·01	8·49	3·32	0·982	0·180	0·409
11,000	7·78	8·29	3·21	0·964	0·190	0·436
12,000	7·55	8·12	3·13	0·948	0·201	0·461
13,000	7·32	7·96	3·06	0·933	0·209	—
14,000	—	—	2·99	0·920	0·217	—
15,000	—	—	2·94	0·908	0·224	—

The compressibility of ammonia gas is shown [3] below, the values of V ml./g. at the given temperatures corresponding with the pressures in atm. in the table. The results were represented by a Beattie-Bridgeman equation (§ 38.VII C) with the following constants (NH_3=17·0311; atm., lit./mol, $T=t°$ C.+273·13): $\boldsymbol{R}$ 0·08206, A_0 2·3930, a 0·17031, B_0 0·03415, b 0·19112, c 476·87×10^4.

V ml./g.	90	80	60	40	20
300° C.	29·84	33·45	44·18	65·03	123·10
250° C.	27·01	30·27	39·83	58·26	108·18
200° C.	24·15	27·01	35·40	51·29	92·57
150° C.	21·23	23·70	30·86	44·11	76·24
100° C.	18·24	20·28	26·12	36·47	58·28

The compressibility of helium from −70° to 200° and up to 1,000 atm. pressure can be represented (PV in Amagat units) by the equations: [4]

$$-70° \quad PV=0{\cdot}7438+0{\cdot}0_3 5322P-0{\cdot}0_7 4332P^2$$
$$-35° \quad PV=0{\cdot}8721+0{\cdot}0_3 5296P-0{\cdot}0_7 4336P^2$$
$$0° \quad PV=1{\cdot}00059+0{\cdot}0_3 5217P-0{\cdot}0_7 3876P^2$$
$$50° \quad PV=1{\cdot}18480+0{\cdot}0_3 51043P-0{\cdot}0_7 35308P^2$$
$$100° \quad PV=1{\cdot}3664+0{\cdot}0_3 50442P-0{\cdot}0_7 34889P^2$$
$$200° \quad PV=1{\cdot}73284+0{\cdot}0_3 47795P-0{\cdot}0_7 22518P^2.$$

1 *Chem. Met. Eng.*, 1931, **38**, 280.

2 *Proc. Amer. Acad.*, 1923–4, **59**, 173; Δv gives the *change* of volume from the volume at 3,000 kg./cm.^{2} taken as unity. Several characteristic equations (van der Waals, Tumlirz, Keyes, Becker) were tested. The observed volumes were smaller than the calculated at high pressures, which " is to be ascribed to the compression of the atoms."

3 Beattie and Lawrence, *J.A.C.S.*, 1930, **52**, 6; Meyers and Jessup, *Refrig. Eng.*, 1925, **11**, 345; compressibility of N_2–H_2–NH_3 mixtures at high temperatures, Kazarnovsky, Simonov, and Aristov, *J. Phys. Chem. U.S.S.R.*, 1940, **14**, 774; Kazarnovsky and Sidorov, *ibid.*, 1947, **21**, 1363.

4 Wiebe, Gaddy, and Heins, *J.A.C.S.*, 1931, **53**, 1721 (*P* in atm.); cf. Michels and Wouters, *Physica*, 1941, **8**, 923 (0°–150°).

The compressibility of carbon monoxide is shown below,[1] the values of PV being in Amagat units (unit mass of gas= 1 lit. at S.T.P.):

P atm.	−50°	−25°	0°	50°	100°	200° C.
1	0·8162	0·9082	1·0000	1·1836	1·3671	1·7336
50	0·7622	0·8768	0·9796	1·1826	1·3837	1·7758
100	0·7264	0·8592	0·9745	1·1955	1·4062	1·8146
200	0·7656	0·9022	1·0200	1·2561	1·4794	1·9090
400	1·0285	1·1403	1·2487	1·4716	1·6963	2·1380
600	1·3225	1·4282	1·5256	1·7378	1·9557	2·3923
800	1·6100	1·7153	1·8064	2·0144	2·2244	2·6602
1000	1·8871	1·9935	2·0827	2·2879	2·4935	2·9264

Carbon monoxide is slightly more compressible than nitrogen at lower pressures and slightly less at higher pressures, the difference being less at higher temperatures. This would be expected from the values of the critical temperatures (CO −139·0°, N_2 −147·1°). Verschoyle's results with CO–N_2–H_2 mixtures were recalculated by Fischer.[2]

§ 10 Virial Coefficients

The experimental results on compressibilities of gases are usually represented by empirical equations, and these are of two main types. The Leiden school [3] uses the so-called *virial equation* in which PV is expressed as a series in which the terms involve powers of the reciprocal of the volume multiplied by coefficients which are functions of temperature:

$$PV=A_v+B_v(1/V)+C_v(1/V)^2+D_v(1/V)^4+E_v(1/V)^6+F_v(1/V)^8+ \quad . \quad (1)$$

where A_v, B_v, C_v, D_v, E_v, F_v are the first, second, third, fourth, etc., *virial coefficients*, D_v, E_v, and F_v being usually very small below 1 atm. The value of PV is taken as 1 at 1 atm. pressure. The use of odd exponents of $1/V$ adds nothing to the accuracy. The virial coefficients are represented by polynomials as functions of temperature, usually reduced temperature, $\vartheta=T/T_c$. The physical interpretation of the second virial coefficient B_v and its relation to van der Waals's constants a and b, was considered by Jones.[4] Michels and Goudeket [5] found that the number of terms taken in the power series can affect the value of the virial coefficient B. Holborn and his collaborators [6] at the Reichsanstalt use an equation in ascending powers of the pressure:

$$PV=A_p+B_pP+C_pP^2+D_pP^4+E_pP^6+ \ldots \quad . \quad (2)$$

in which the value of PV is taken as unity at a pressure of 1 m. of mercury. A_p, B_p, C_p, D_p . . . are also called virial coefficients. Equation (2) does not

[1] Selected from data given by Bartlett, Hetherington, Kvalnes, and Tremearne, *J.A.C.S.*, 1930, **52**, 1374; cf. Scott, *Proc. Roy. Soc.*, 1929, **125**, 330; Botella, *An. Fis. Quim.*, 1929, **27**, 315; Goig, *Compt. Rend.*, 1929, **189**, 246.

[2] *Ann. Phys.*, 1938, **31**, 531.

[3] Onnes, *Arch. Néerl.*, 1901, **6**, 874 (*Comm. Leiden*, **74**); *Proc. K. Akad. Wetens. Amsterdam*, 1902, **4**, 125 (*Comm. Leiden*, 1902, **71**); Keesom, *Comm. Leiden*, 1912, Suppl. **25**; Onnes and Keesom, " Enzykl. d. math. Wiss.," 1912, **5**, x, 728; Onnes and Crommelin, *Proc. K. Akad. Wetens. Amsterdam*, 1912, **15**, 273, 452 (*Comm. Leiden*, **128a**); Bakker, *Z. phys. Chem.*, 1916, **91**, 641; on various forms of virial equation see Core, *Phil. Mag.*, 1923, **46**, 256; Hirschfelder, Ewell, and Roebuck, *J. Chem. Phys.*, 1938, **6**, 205.

[4] *Proc. Cambr. Phil. Soc.*, 1924, **22**, 105; for further discussion, see § 42.VII C.

[5] *Physica*, 1941, **8**, 347; Michels and Michels, *ibid.*, 1941, **8**, 587.

[6] Holborn and Otto, *Z. Phys.*, 1924, **23**, 77; 1924, **30**, 320; 1925, **33**, 1; 1926, **38**, 359.

hold at very high pressures,[1] and an equation with many constants need not be accurate if the functional relation is unsuitable.[2]

If P is in m. Hg, V in lit. of gas such that $V=1$ when $P=1$, the values of the coefficients for nitrogen are:

	A_p	B_p	C_p
0° C.	1·000	$-0{\cdot}61\times10^{-3}$	$5{\cdot}4\times10^{-6}$
50° C.	1·184	$-0{\cdot}015\times10^{-3}$	$3{\cdot}8\times10^{-6}$
100° C.	1·37	$+0{\cdot}36\times10^{-3}$	$3{\cdot}15\times10^{-6}$

The values of the second virial coefficient B for several gases for 1 atm. pressure (B_0), with the molar volume of the ideal gas=22·4156 lit., were given by van Laar.[3] The temperature variation of the virial coefficient B for helium was calculated from the Joule-Thomson effect by Whitelaw; [4] the virial coefficients for helium at 2·6°–4·2° K. were determined by Keesom and Kraak.[5] Keesom and Walstra [6] determined the isotherms of helium at liquid helium temperature.

Equation (1) is sometimes written as:

$$PV=A(1+B/V+C/V^2+D/V^4+E/V^6+F/V^8).$$

Thiesen [7] proposed the equation:

$$p=rT\rho(1+\theta_1\rho+\theta_2\rho^2+\theta_3\rho^3+\ldots)$$

where r=gas const. per g., $1/V=\rho$=density, and θ_1, θ_2, θ_3, . . . are functions of temperature. Thus:

$$\rho=\frac{p}{rT}\left(1-\frac{\theta_1}{T}\cdot\frac{p}{r}+\frac{2\theta_1^2-\theta_2}{T^2}\cdot\frac{p^2}{r^2}-\frac{5\theta_1^3-5\theta_1\theta_2+\theta_3}{T^3}\cdot\frac{p^3}{r^3}\cdots\right).$$

Maron and Turnbull [8] found that over a wide range of pressure and temperature an equation:

$$PV=RT+\alpha_1P+\alpha_2P^2+\alpha_3P^3+\alpha_4P^4$$

was necessary, where:

$\alpha_1=a_1+a_2/T+a_3/T^3$, $\alpha_2=b_1/T^2+b_2/T^4+b_3/T^6$, $\alpha_3=c_1/T^2+c_2/T^4+c_3/T^6$, and $\alpha_4=d_1/T^2+d_2/T^4+d_3/T^6$.

The virial equation giving PV as a polynomial in the density up to ρ^8 fails to represent the isothermals of carbon dioxide and ethylene in the critical region, and $(d^2p/dT^2)_v$, which is negative at high temperatures over the whole density range, becomes positive near the critical density and temperature.[9] Similar results were found for nitrogen.[10]

1 A. and C. Michels, *Proc. Roy. Soc.*, 1937, **160**, 348; Benedict, *J.A.C.S.*, 1937, **59**, 2224, 2233.
2 Keyes, *J.A.C.S.*, 1921, **43**, 1452.
3 *J. Chim. Phys.*, 1919, **17**, 266.
4 *Physica*, 1934, **1**, 749.
5 *Proc. K. Akad. Wetens. Amsterdam*, 1934, **37**, 746; *Physica*, 1935, **2**, 37 (*Comm. Leiden* 1935, **234***e*).
6 *Physica*, 1940, **7**, 985; 1947, **13**, 225; correcting Onnes and Boks.
7 *Ann. Phys.*, 1885, **24**, 467.
8 *J.A.C.S.*, 1942, **64**, 44.
9 Michels and Gibson, *Ann. Phys.*, 1928, **87**, 850 (Ne to 500 atm.); Michels, de Gruyter, and Niesen, *Physica*, 1936, **3**, 346 (C_2H_4); A. and C. Michels, *Proc. Roy. Soc.*, 1937, **160**, 348.
10 Benedict, *J.A.C.S.*, 1937, **59**, 2224.

A very complicated equation was used for nitrogen at high pressures by Benedict:[1] $PV=P_0V_0+\beta d$, where P_0V_0=ideal value, d=density in Amagat units (density of gas at S.T.P.=1) and:

$$\beta=p+qd+rd^4+(T/100)(s+td+ud^2)+(100/T)v+(100/T)^3d^3w\,.\,10^{-xd^2},$$

where P is in atm., V in Amagat units (vol. of gas at S.T.P.=1), $T=t°$ C.+273·20 and the constants are:

$p=-1·66453$	$s=0·67617$	$v=-1·21342$
$q=-1·35938$	$t=0·91512$	$w=107·03$
$r=11·3200$	$u=2·06932$	$x=6·975$

Another equation used for nitrogen by Benedict[2] [$x=\sqrt[3]{(1000/P)}$] is:

$$10^3V=(3·54842+0·0_35881T-(4·6131/\sqrt{T})x-(2·40797+0·0_219102T)x^2$$
$$+(-0·48596+0·0_257846T+8·2630/\sqrt{T}-6·0483/T)x^3.$$

Rozen,[3] for high pressures, used $PV=A+BP+CT$. Michels, Wouters, and de Boer[4] used $P(V-\alpha)=A+\beta\rho+\gamma\rho^2+\delta\rho^3$.

§ 11. Compressibility of Gases at Low Pressures

It was, apparently, first suggested by Regnault that at very low pressures *all* gases should obey Boyle's law (cf. § 6). Some anomalous results at low pressures,[5] e.g. a break in the pressure-volume curve for oxygen at 0·7 mm. Hg pressure found by Battelli, were later shown by careful experiments by Lord Rayleigh[6] and others to be due to experimental errors, and there is no doubt that at sufficiently small pressures all gases obey Boyle's law within the very small limits of experimental error. Rayleigh worked with two ranges of pressure, 1·5–0·02 mm. and 150–75 mm., and with both ranges he concluded that no deviation from Boyle's law was perceptible to 1 in 10,000 with hydrogen, nitrogen, air, oxygen, and argon. Oxygen showed no anomalies. The deviation in the pressure range 1·5–0·02 mm. was less than 0·5 in 1,000 for the gases. In the range 150–75 mm. the deviations were less than 0·2 in 1,000 for hydrogen, air, oxygen, and argon, but nitrous oxide showed deviations of 0·6 in 1,000.

If p_0v_0 is the limiting value of pv for zero pressure ($p\to 0$), when the gas obeys Boyle's law, the deviation from Boyle's law at moderate pressures (up to about 6 atm.) can be represented, as Regnault found, by the equation (A=const.):

$$1-pv/p_0v_0=Ap \quad . \quad . \quad . \quad . \quad . \quad . \quad . \quad . \quad (1)$$

1 Benedict, *J.A.C.S.*, 1937, **59**, 2224.

2 *J.A.C.S.*, 1937, **59**, 2233.

3 *J. Phys. Chem. U.S.S.R.*, 1946, **20**, 333.

4 *Physica*, 1936, **3**, 585.

5 Siljeström, *Ann. Phys.*, 1874, **151**, 451, 573; *Ber.*, 1875, **8**, 576; Mendeléeff and Kirpitschoff, *Bull. Acad. Sci. St. Petersb.*, 1874, **19**, 469; *Ber.*, 1874, **7**, 1339; Mendeléeff, *Ann. Chim.*, 1874, **2**, 427; 1876, **9**, 111; Amagat, *ibid.*, 1876, **8**, 270; Krajewitsch, *J. Russ. Phys. Chem. Soc.*, 1882, **14**, 198; *Repert. Phys.*, 1883, **19**, 118; *Ann. Phys. Beibl.*, 1885, **9**, 315; Bohr, *Ann. Phys.*, 1886, **27**, 459; Fuchs, *Ann. Phys.*, 1888, **35**, 431; van der Ven, *ibid.*, 1889, **38**, 302; Baly and Ramsay, *Phil. Mag.*, 1894, **38**, 301; Battelli, *Nuov. Cim.*, 1901, **1**, 5, 81; *Phys. Z.* 1901, **2**, 409; 1901, **3**, 17; Bestelmeyer and Valentiner, *Ann. Phys.*, 1904, **15**, 61.

6 *Phil. Trans.*, 1901, **196**, 205; 1902, **198**, 417; 1905, **204**, 351; *Proc. Roy. Soc.*, 1904, **73**, 153; *Z. phys. Chem.*, 1901, **37**, 713; 1902, **41**, 71; 1905, **52**, 705; see also Thiesen, *Ann. Phys.*, 1901, **6**, 280; Hering, *ibid.*, 1906, **21**, 319; Scheel and Heuse, *Verhl. d. D. Phys. Ges.*, 1909, **11**, 1, and the references in § 15, VII D; Onnes, *Proc. K. Akad. Wetens. Amsterdam*, 1907–8, **10**, 445, 741(*Comm. Leiden*, 1907–8, **102***a*, *c*; H_2, He); Onnes and Braak, *ibid.*, 1907, **9**, 754 (*Comm. Leiden*, 1907, **97**); 1907–8, **10**, 204, 413, 419 (*Comm. Leiden*, 1907, **100***a*, *b*); for He at 2·7–1·7° K., Kistemakers and Keesom, *Physica*, 1946, **12**, 227.

§ 12. Vacuum Pumps

The old types of air pump[1] had a piston and valves similar in principle to those of the water lift-pump, but the valves were much lighter (e.g. oiled silk flaps) so that they were raised by fairly small pressures of air. These were improved by Geryk by making the piston descend at the bottom of the stroke into oil, thus eliminating clearance and giving a much better vacuum. The Gaede piston oil pump gave a vacuum of $0{\cdot}0_45$ mm. directly.[2] Such pumps are still used, generally power-driven, for producing the preliminary vacuum (or, as is said, as " backing pumps ") for the newer types of high vacuum pumps, some of which do not operate unless the pressure is first reduced to the order of 1 mm. or less. The modern pumps[3] are of various types. The newer types of rotary oil-sealed pumps, which are very compact and efficient, require no backing but exhaust rapidly from atmospheric pressure to 10^{-3} to 10^{-5} mm. with pumping speeds of 0·5–100 lit./sec. They work on the principle[4] shown in Fig. 16.VII A. An eccentric rotor 2 rotates anti-clockwise in the body 1 of the pump. The rotor is slotted and two blades 3,3 are pressed outwards by a spring *s* so that they rotate continuously with the rotor and press against the walls of the cylindrical cavity in the body of the pump. Air is drawn through the suction orifice 4 and expelled through the exhaust valve 5. All working parts run in special high vacuum oil in an outer case, which ensures lubrication and sealing and prevents friction and air-leakage. Such pumps are either one or two-stage; in the latter two single pumps are connected in series. The vacuum is of the order

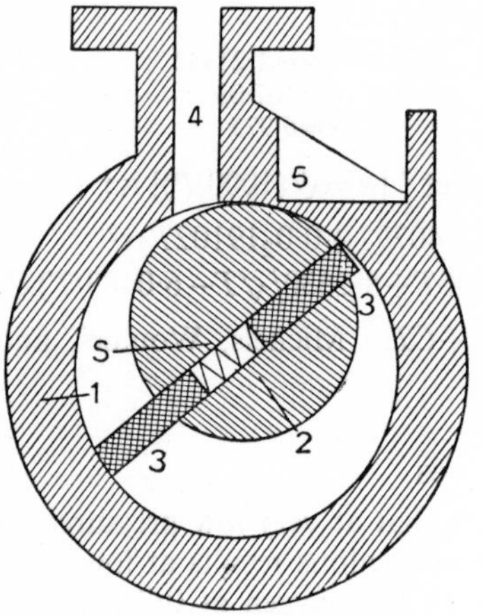

FIG. 16.VII A. Rotary Pump

[1] Rosenberger, " Geschichte der Physik," Brunswick, 1884, **2**, 124, 145 f., 206 f. (historical); Auerbach, *Ann. Phys.*, 1890, **41**, 364 (theory of piston pump); Auerbach, in Winkelmann, " Handbuch der Physik," 1908, **1**, ii, 1316; Anon., " Ency. Brit.," 11th edit., 1911, **22**, 645; Arndt, " Handbuch der phys.-chem. Technik," Stuttgart, 1915, 63; 2nd edit., 1923, 83; Glazebrook, " Dict. of Applied Physics," 1922, **1**, 2; Schleede, in Stähler, " Arbeitsmethoden der anorganischen Chemie," 1925, **2**, ii, 1119; Veil, *Rev. Gén. Sci.*, 1928, **39**, 10; Ostwald-Luther, " Phys.-chem. Messungen," 5th edit., Leipzig, 1931, 253; Pingriff, *School Sci. Rev.*, 1940, **21**, 1078; Justi, *Elektrotechn. Z.*, 1943, **64**, 285 (historical); Sullivan, *Rev. Sci. Instr.*, 1948, **19**, 1.

[2] Gaede, *Phys. Z.*, 1913, **14**, 1238.

[3] Dushman, *Gen. Elec. Rev.*, 1920, **23**, 493, 605, 672; " Production and Measurement of High Vacuum," Schenectady, 1922; suppl. in *J. Franklin Inst.*, 1931, **211**, 689; Dunoyer, " La Technique du Vide," Paris, 1924; " Vacuum Practice," 1926; Newman, " The Production and Measurement of Low Pressures," 1925; Götze, " Physik und Technik des Hochvakuums," Brunswick, 1926; Kaye, " High Vacua," 1927; Holland-Merten, " Die Vakuumtechnik," Erfurt, 1936; Moench, " Vakuumtechnik im Laboratorium," Weimar, 1937; Yarwood, " High Vacuum Technique," 2nd edit., New York, 1945; L. H. Martin and R. D. Hill, " A Manual of Vacuum Practice," Melbourne, 1947; Jnanananda, " High Vacua," 1947; Dushman, *Ind. Eng. Chem.*, 1948, **40**, 778; Weingartner, *ibid.*, 1948, **40**, 780; Normand, *ibid.*, 1948, **40**, 783; Mellen, *ibid.*, 1948, **40**, 787; Jacobs, *ibid.*, 1948, **40**, 791; Dayton, *ibid.*, 1948, **40**, 795; a French journal, *Le Vide*, commenced in 1946. Comparison of pumps, Scheel and Heuse, *Z. Instr.*, 1909, **29**, 46. For a reciprocating piston mercury pump (to 0·0001 atm.), see Bianu, *Bull. Sect. Sci. Acad. Roumaine*, 1916–17, **5**, 58; rocking crescent-shaped mercury pump (Roden pump), Anon, *Engineering*, 1909, **88**, 735.

[4] See Young, " Lectures on Natural Philosophy," 1845, 256, plate xxiii, fig. 315; Fischer, *Verhl. d. D. Phys. Ges.*, 1905, **7**, 383; *Phys. Z.*, 1905, **6**, 868.

of 0·0001 mm. Fischer[1] found that one pump reduced the pressure to 0·015 mm. (the vapour pressure of the oil), and two in series to 0·00015 mm. The modern "Hyvac" pump is an improvement on this type. These pumps have largely replaced the older types of mercury-seal[2] or rotary[3] "molecular" Gaede pumps.

For still higher vacuum some type of vapour-stream or diffusion pump,[4] invented by Gaede and Langmuir and improved by others, is used. These are of glass, silica, or metal (steel) and various models are available. They produce a vacuum of 10^{-6} to 10^{-8} mm. They all require some type of backing pump; for some types (glass and silica pumps) a good water pump is sufficient, but for all types a rotary oil-sealed pump of the type described above is preferable. The Volmer type is inexpensive and very handy and efficient. The diffusion pumps use mercury, special (*Apiezon*) oil of very low vapour pressure,[5] pure esters, or silicone fluids,[6] boiled in a vessel and the vapour made to

[1] *Verhl. d. D. Phys. Ges.*, 1905, **7**, 383; *Phys. Z.*, 1905, **6**, 868.

[2] Gaede, *Z. Elektrochem.*, 1905, **11**, 873; *Phys. Z.*, 1905, **6**, 758; 1907, **8**, 852; Jones, *Phys. Rev.*, 1921, **18**, 332.

[3] Gaede, *Verhl. d. D. Phys. Ges.*, 1912, **14**, 775; *Phys. Z.*, 1912, **13**, 864; *Electrician*, 1912, **70**, 48; *Ann. Phys.*, 1913, **41**, 337; Goes, *Phys. Z.*, 1913, **14**, 170; Glazebrook, " Dict. of Applied Physics," 1922, **1**, 18; von Friesen, *Rev. Sci. Instr.*, 1940, **11**, 362.

[4] Gaede, *Ann. Phys.*, 1915, **46**, 357; *Z. techn. Phys.*, 1923, **9**, 337; Langmuir, *Phys. Rev.*, 1916, **8**, 48 (mentioning Gaede); *J. Franklin Inst.*, 1916, **182**, 719; Stimson, *J. Wash. Acad.*, 1917, **7**, 477 (2-stage); Crawford, *Phys. Rev.*, 1917, **10**, 557; Kraus, *J.A.C.S.*, 1917, **39**, 2183; Baker, *Phys. Rev.*, 1917, **10**, 642; Knipp, *ibid.*, 1917, **9**, 311; 1918, **12**, 492; Jones and Russell, *ibid.*, 1917, **10**, 301; Crawford, *ibid.*, 1917, **10**, 557; Schrader and Sherwood, *ibid.*, 1918, **11**, 134; 1918, **12**, 70; Volmer, *Ber.*, 1919, **52**, 804; *Z. angew. Chem.*, 1921, **34**, 149; Magnus, *Ber.*, 1919, **52**, 1194; Gehrts, *Z. techn. Phys.*, 1920, **1**, 61; Palacios, *An. Fis. Quim.*, 1920, **18**, 331; Jones, *Gen. Elec. Rev.*, 1920, **23**, 605, 672; *Phys. Rev.*, 1921, **18**, 332; *J. Opt. Soc. Amer.*, 1923, **7**, 537; Kurth, *Science*, 1921, **54**, 608; Knipp, *ibid.*, 1922, **55**, 183; Dushman, "Production and Measurement of High Vacuum," Schenectady, 1922, 57; Loosli and Lauster, *Z. techn. Phys.*, 1923, **4**, 392; Ebert, *Z. Phys.*, 1923, **19**, 206 (pumping speed); Waran, *J. Sci. Instr.*, 1923, **1**, 51; Blanchard, *Ann. Chim. Anal.*, 1923, **5**, 274; Backhurst and Kaye, *Phil. Mag.*, 1924, **47**, 918, 1016; Rutherford, *Engineering*, 1924, **117**, 365; Hauff and Buest, *Elektrotechn. Z.*, 1924, **45**, 661; *Licht u. Lampe*, 1924, 104; Stintzing, *Z. phys. Chem.*, 1924, **108**, 70; Romanoff, *J. Russ. Phys. Chem. Soc.*, 1925, **57**, 124 (P); Parsons, *J. Sci. Instr.*, 1925, **2**, 293 (large steel Hg vap. pump); Molthan, *Phys. Z.*, 1925, **26**, 712 (theory); *Z. Phys.*, 1926, **39**, 1; *Z. techn. Phys.*, 1926, **7**, 377, 452; Kaye, *J. Roy. Soc. Arts*, 1926, **74**, 991, 1011, 1030; *Engineering*, 1926, **121**, 240, 308, 366, 367; *Phil. Mag.*, 1926, **1**, 349 (metal pump); Dunoyer, *Compt. Rend.*, 1926, **182**, 686; *J. de Phys.*, 1926, **7**, 69; Ansiau, *Compt. Rend.*, 1931, **192**, 670; Becker and Jaycox, *Rev. Sci. Instr.*, 1931, **2**, 773; Matricon, *J. de Phys.*, 1932, **3**, 127 (theory; formulae); Munch, *Science*, 1932, **76**, 170; Hickman, *J. Franklin Inst.*, 1932, **213**, 119; Estermann and Byck, *Rev. Sci. Instr.*, 1932, **3**, 482 (high speed Hg vap.); Boddy, *ibid.*, 1934, **5**, 278; Henry, *Bull. Soc. Chim. Belg.*, 1935, **44**, 307; Klumb, *Elektrotechn. Z.*, 1936, **57**, 1445 (high vac. pumps); Westin and Ramm, *K. Norsk. Vidensk. Selsk. Skrift.*, 1936, No. **9** (high vac. technique); Thermal Syndicate, *J. Sci. Instr.*, 1937, **14**, 32 (silica pump for high fore-pressure); Abbott, *Rev. Sci. Instr.*, 1942, **13**, 187 (fusible metal); Anderson and Emmett, *J. Phys. Chem.*, 1947, **51**, 1308 (Stimson pump); Jaeckel, *Z. Naturforsch.*, 1947, **2** A, 666 (theory); Anon., *J. Sci. Instr.*, 1948, **25**, 245; Liebmann, *ibid.*, 1948, **25**, 186.

[5] Burch, *Nature*, 1928, **122**, 729; *Proc. Roy. Soc.*, 1929, **123**, 271; von Brandenstein and Klumb, *Phys. Z.*, 1932, **33**, 88 (dibutyl phthalate—dissolves gases too readily; paraffin); Mills, *Rev. Sci. Instr.*, 1932, **3**, 309 (oils, etc.); Klumb and Glimm, *Phys. Z.*, 1933, **34**, 64; Edwards, *Rev. Sci. Instr.*, 1935, **6**, 145; Amdur, *ibid.*, 1936, **7**, 395; Gatt, *J. Techn. Phys. U.S.S.R.*, 1936, **6**, 1292; Klumb, *Z. techn. Phys.*, 1936, **17**, 201; Burch and van Dijck, *J.S.C.I.*, 1939, **58**, 39 T; Fawcett, *ibid.*, 43 T; Burrows, *ibid.*, 50 T; Jewell, Mead, and Phipps, *ibid.*, 56 T; Wang, *Ind. Eng. Chem. Anal.*, 1945, **17**, 670; Bachman, *Rev. Sci. Instr.*, 1945, **16**, 153; Ray and Sengupta, *Indian J. Phys.*, 1945, **19**, 138 (theory); Blears, *Proc. Roy. Soc.*, 1946, **188**, 62 (effect of oils); Alexander, *J. Sci. Instr.*, 1946, **23**, 11 (theory; new high-speed pump); Avery and Witty, *Proc. Phys. Soc.*, 1947, **59**, 1016 (theory); Jacobs and Kappf, *Ind. Eng. Chem.*, 1948, **40**, 842 (theory); Gibson, *Rev. Sci. Instr.*, 1948, **19**, 276.

[6] Hickman and Sandford, *J. Phys. Chem.*, 1930, **44**, 627, 637; *Rev. Sci. Instr.*, 1930, **1**, 140;

entrain air or gas (already at low pressure). The mercury or oil, etc., vapour is then condensed by cooling and the entrained gas pumped off by the backing pump. The liquid runs back into the boiler. Mercury is now little used, as compared with oils.

Fig. 17.VII A shows the principle of a modern form (the Kaye metal pump). The mercury or oil is contained in the boiler S, heated by gas or electrically. The vapour rises through the tube *a* and is deflected downwards through the narrow annular space *ee*, which is of the order of the mean free path at the working pressure. The preliminary exhaustion is maintained by the backing pump through V. The gas molecules diffuse from H, the high vacuum side, which is connected by a flange with the vacuum line, which must be of wide-bore tubing (not less than 2 cm. diam.), and contains a glass or steel mercury trap [1] of the form shown in Fig. 18.VII A, immersed in liquid air to remove any mercury vapour, when mercury is used in the boiler. The gas is carried along with the vapour, and the latter is condensed on the cooled walls by an annular water cooler K, the liquid draining back into the boiler S. The gas is removed through V by the backing pump. Any trace of vapour diffusing upwards is condensed by a second cooling jacket L and by the trap. Very pure mercury must be used and a special grade of oil for the oil pumps, which are not quite so easy to operate as the mercury pumps, but under favourable conditions will give lower pressures. The pumps may be used singly or two-stage (usually of different types). The pumping speed may be from a few lit. to over 1,000 lit. per sec. per unit.[2]

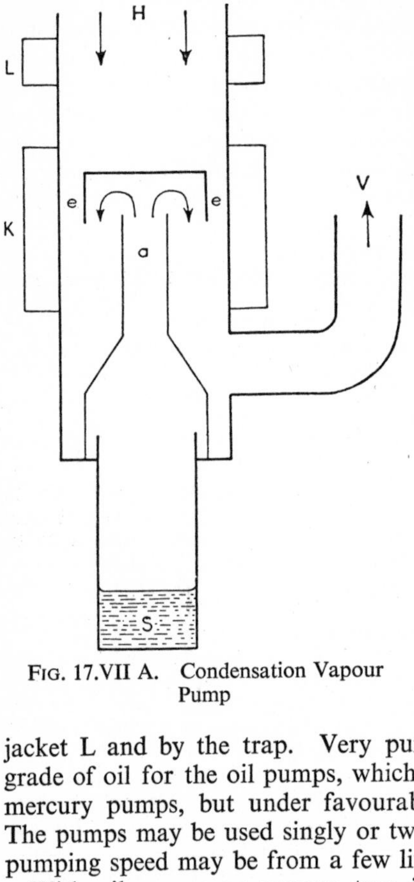

FIG. 17.VII A. Condensation Vapour Pump

With oil pumps no vapour trap is necessary, according to Hickman and Sandford,[3] whilst Mills [4] says it is. Becker and Jaycox [5] with an oil pump and an active charcoal trap replacing a liquid air trap obtained a vacuum of 2×10^{-8} mm. A solvent trap for use in evaporation with an oil pump is described by

Baxter and Hickman, *J. Franklin Inst.*, 1936, **221**, 215, 383; Malter and Marcuvitz, *Rev. Sci. Instr.*, 1938, **9**, 92 (modif. Hickman pump); Burrows, *J. Sci. Instr.*, 1943, **20**, 21, 77; Hickman, *Chem. Rev.*, 1944, **34**, 51 (bibl.); *Nature*, 1945, **156**, 635; *Ind. Eng. Chem.*, 1947, **39**, 686; Brown, *Rev. Sci. Instr.*, 1945, **16**, 316; Ray and Sengupta, *Nature*, 1945, **156**, 636; Witty, *J. Sci. Instr.*, 1945, **22**, 201; silicone fluids for use in pumps are supplied by Dow-Corning, Michigan, and Albright and Wilson, Oldbury, England.

1 For influence of traps on vacuum, see Guichard, *Bull. Soc. Chim.*, 1917, **21**, 237; Fredlund, *Arkiv. Mat. Astron. Fys.*, 1937, **26** A, No. 6; for spiral vane trap, Humphreys and Watson, *Rev. Sci. Instr.*, 1937, **8**, 263 (oil diffusion pump).

2 On measurement of pumping speed, see Dayton, *Ind. Eng. Chem.*, 1948, **40**, 795 (bibl.).

3 *Rev. Sci. Instr.*, 1930, **1**, 140.

4 *Rev. Sci. Instr.*, 1932, **3**, 309.

5 *Rev. Sci. Instr.*, 1931, **2**, 773.

Askew and Bourdillon.[1] Poindexter [2] used a sodium trap with a mercury-vapour pump. Bumping of mercury in the pump is prevented by first exposing the metal to hydrogen sulphide at atmospheric pressure.[3]

The principle of the pump is described by Langmuir as follows.[4] The mercury (or oil) molecules are rapidly condensed on the cool walls near the mercury (or oil) vapour outlet and the condensed, cooled liquid does not re-evaporate to any appreciable extent. The gas molecules diffusing in from the space to be exhausted collide with the mercury (or oil) molecules rushing to the jet and acquire a velocity component which removes them rapidly from the vicinity of the jet. The gas passing on, which accumulates to a higher pressure, is continuously removed by the backing pump. The diffusion pump may be modified [5] so as to determine gases evolved from a system being pumped off.

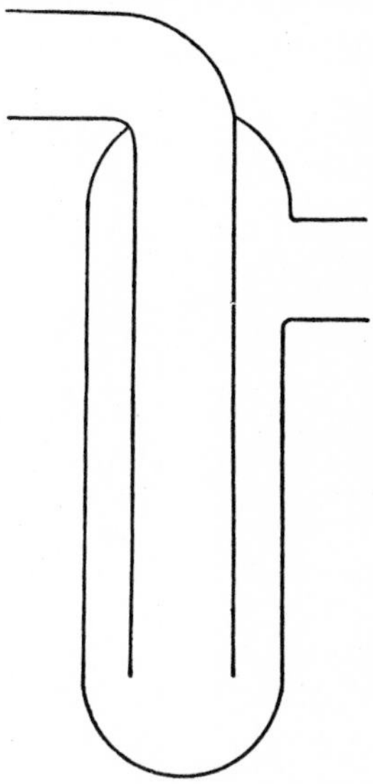

FIG. 18.VII A. Vapour Trap

A "high duty" mercury-vapour diffusion pump described by Gaede and Keesom [6] dealt with 130 lit. of air and 420 lit. of helium *per sec.* with a vacuum of 0·15 mm. Very large high-vacuum apparatus (for separation of uranium isotopes) is described by Colaico and Hopper.[7] According to Ramsauer [8] the present limit of low pressure of 10^{-9} mm. Hg might perhaps be extended to 10^{-40} mm. by using liquid helium, with the vapour pumped off under low pressure, for cooling the charcoal bulb.

Since some of the older pumps are still useful, a few words will be said about them in conclusion.

The mercury pump of Geissler [9] (1858), used to exhaust electrical discharge tubes, consisted of a barometer tube with a bulb at the top provided with a 3-way tap and a mercury reservoir attached by rubber tubing below. The bulb was filled with mercury, air escaping through the tap. Then the tap was opened to the vessel to be exhausted and the reservoir lowered, and the process repeated.

A mercury pump which has been extensively used and is still sometimes

[1] *J. Sci. Instr.*, 1932, **9**, 280.

[2] *J. Opt. Soc. Amer.*, 1924, **9**, 629 (no liquid air required); Hughes and Poindexter, *Phil. Mag.*, 1925, **50**, 423 (potassium).

[3] Adam and Balson, *J.C.S.*, 1941, 620.

[4] Cf. Ray and Sengupta, *Nature*, 1945, **155**, 727.

[5] Johnson, *J. Franklin Inst.*, 1928, **205**, 99; Vacher and Jordan, *Bur. Stand. J. Res.*, 1931, **7**, 375 (Stimson pump); Chipman and Fontana, *Ind. Eng. Chem. Anal.*, 1935, **7**, 391; Holm and Thompson, *Bur. Stand. J. Res.*, 1941, **26**, 245; Derge, *Metals Tech.*, 1943, **10**, T.P. 1544; Naughton and Uhlig, *Ind. Eng. Chem. Anal.*, 1943, **15**, 750; Puddington, *ibid.*, 1944, **16**, 592.

[6] *Proc. K. Akad. Wetens. Amsterdam*, 1928, **31**, 985 (*Comm. Leiden*, **195***a*).

[7] *Westinghouse Engr.*, 1946, **6**, 103.

[8] *Chem. Fabr.*, 1937, **10**, 391; for a review of high-vacuum technology, Morse, *Ind. Eng. Chem.*, 1947, **39**, 1064; various authors, *ibid.*, 1948, **40**, 778 f.; *Chem. and Ind.*, 1948, S. 3 f.

[9] Poggendorff, *Ann. Phys.*, 1862, **117**, 610; Auerbach, in Winkelmann, "Handbuch der Physik," 1908, **1**, ii, 1321 (also other types); a mercury pump on the principle of Geissler's had been used by the Florentine Academicians, "Saggi di Natvrali Esperienze," Florence, 1666, fol. xxvi f., LIV, and plates; see also Joule, "Scientific Papers, 1884, **1**, 623.

employed is that of Töpler.[1] In the Töpler pump (Fig. 19.VII A) the gas is exhausted from E by alternately raising and lowering by hand the mercury reservoir R connected to the tube *ab* of barometric length. On raising R, mercury enters B, and the glass valve *v* closes the entrance to E by rising on the mercury, which also forms a tight liquid seal round the upper part of *v*. The gas in B is forced out through *ef* and bubbles through mercury in the pot M. On lowering R a vacuum is formed in B, and as the mercury falls *v* drops and gas from E passes into B. The process is repeated until the limit of exhaustion (0·02–0·01 barye) is reached. The pump is tiring in use and involves much manual labour. In the later stages, R must be raised slowly, since a rush of mercury will drive *v* so forcibly against its seat that the tube is fractured. An advantage of the Töpler pump is that the gas pumped off may be collected in M, and, if required, circulated round a system. For this purpose, however, the Sprengel pump is usually more convenient.

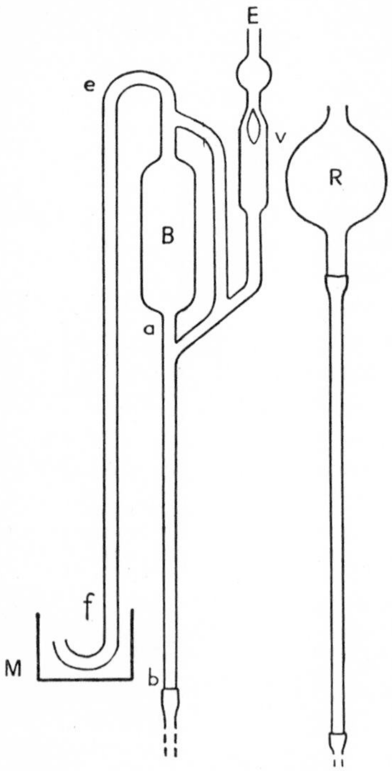

FIG. 19.VII A. Töpler Pump

The Sprengel pump [2] is of the barometer type also, but differs from the Geissler and Töpler pumps in having no upper bulb. Mercury is run from an upper reservoir down a vertical fall tube longer than barometric length, having a side tube near the top. The mercury breaks into columns, between which air bubbles are trapped and carried down, escaping under mercury into which the fall tube dips. An automatic form of Sprengel pump is very convenient, the mercury being raised in an air-lift by a water-pump

[1] Töpler, *Dingl. J.*, 1862, **163**, 426; on an old type used by Swedenborg see Gren, *J. der Phys.*, 1791, **4**, 407; Wiedemann, *Ann. Phys.*, 1880, **10**, 208; Neesen, *ibid.*, 1880, **11**, 522; 1895, **55**, 733; 1896, **58**, 415; 1897, **61**, 414; 1902, **7**, 693; Schuller, *ibid.*, 1881, **13**, 528; Greiner and Friedrich, *ibid.*, 1886, **29**, 672; S. P. Thompson, *J. Soc. Arts*, 1887, **36**, 20 (historical); Usagen, *J. Russ. Phys. Chem. Soc.*, 1890, **2**, 229 (P); Raps, *Ann. Phys.*, 1891, **43**, 629; 1892, **47**, 377; Morley, *Amer. J. Sci.*, 1894, **47**, 439; Wood, *Ann. Phys.*, 1896, **58**, 205; Jaumann, *Z. Instr.*, 1897, **17**, 243 (automatic); *Ann. Phys.* 1897, **61**, 204 (regulator); Travers, "Study of Gases," 1901, 3; Phillips, *Phil. Mag.*, 1904, **8**, 218 (automatic); Pauli, *Z. Instr.*, 1906, **26**, 251; de Lury, *Phys. Rev.*, 1907, **25**, 495; Grimsehl, *Verhl. d. D. Phys. Ges.*, 1907, **9**, 466; *Phys. Z.*, 1907, **8**, 762; von Reden, *Phys. Z.*, 1909, **10**, 316; *Elektrochem. Z.*, 1909, **16**, 98 (rocking type); Klein, *Compt. Rend.*, 1909, **148**, 1181; *J. de Phys.*, 1910, **9**, 44; Steele, *Chem. News*, 1910, **102**, 53; *Phil. Mag.*, 1910, **19**, 863 (automatic); Antropoff, *Chem. Ztg.*, 1910, **34**, 979; Johnson, *J.A.C.S.*, 1912, **34**, 909; Pamfil, *J. Chim. Phys.*, 1913, **11**, 801 (automatic); Maass, *J.A.C.S.*, 1915, **37**, 2654 (automatic); 1919, **41**, 53 (automatic); 1920, **42**, 2571 (with H_2SO_4 in place of Hg); Bianu, *Bull. Soc. Sci. Acad. Roum.*, 1916, **5**, 58; Stock, *Z. Elektrochem.*, 1917, **23**, 35 (automatic); Stedman, *Trans. Roy. Soc. Canada*, 1921, **15**, 93; Porter, *Ind. Eng. Chem.*, 1924, **16**, 731; Weaver and Shepherd, *J.A.C.S.*, 1928, **50**, 1829; Taylor, *ibid.*, 1930, **52**, 3576; Williamson, *Rev. Sci. Instr.*, 1932, **3**, 782 (automatic); Saffert and Wustrow, *Z. Elektrochem.*, 1934, **40**, 231; Puddington, *Ind. Eng. Chem. Anal.*, 1945, **17**, 592.

[2] Sprengel, *J.C.S.*, 1865, **18**, 9 (from Odling's laboratory, St. Bartholomew's Hospital; the original Sprengel pump taken by Odling to Oxford has disappeared); Gimingham, *Proc. Roy. Soc.*, 1876, **25**, 396 (from Crookes's laboratory); von Babo, *Ann. Phys. Beibl.*, 1879, **3**,

vacuum, this device being due to von Babo (Fig. 20.VII A). The fall tube tends to crack owing to "hammering" of the mercury in high vacuum. A very small Sprengel fall pump using very little mercury (8–20 ml.) was described by Beutell.[1] Although very many special and expensive types of pump are on the market, and new types appear almost daily, it is not at all necessary to use these, and an experimenter who has moderate skill in glass-blowing can easily produce an efficient pump on the Sprengel principle at very small expense. The simple hard-glass or quartz mercury vapour pumps with a water filter-pump backing, are also perfectly satisfactory for nearly every purpose. The increasing tendency to use more and more elaborate and expensive apparatus, which is fostered by manufacturers and advertisers, is often quite unnecessary, and it is perhaps most evident in the field of low pressure research. Many of the papers in the references will give valuable hints on making simple apparatus.

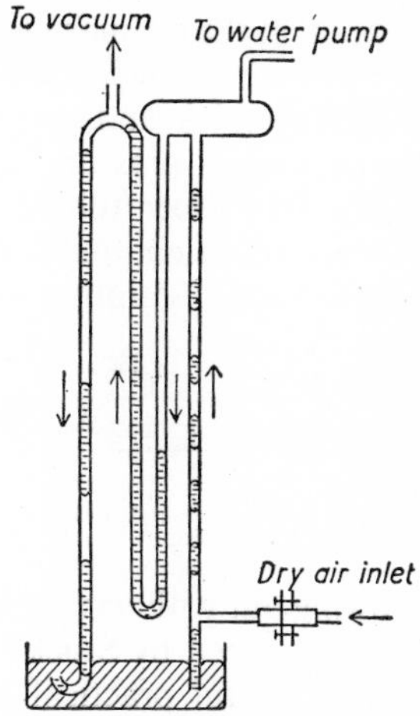

FIG. 20.VII A. Sprengel-von Babo Pump

§ 13. Vacuum Technique

It is perhaps worth mentioning that thick, strong glass vessels, such as desiccators, may burst with great violence when standing in an evacuated state, the pieces of glass being projected to great distances with sufficient force to bore into wooden doors, etc. They should be protected in strong wooden boxes with an opening above for the leading tube and stopcock.[2]

It is impossible to obtain a really high vacuum unless the glass vessel is heated, whilst exhausted, to the highest temperature possible without collapse, in order to drive off the condensed film of moisture (see § 6.III); if part is afterwards sealed off by melting, some moisture is driven off the glass melted. This can be reduced by first heating the sealing place to as high a temperature as possible for some time previous to sealing, and finally melting off as quickly as possible.[3] The use of charcoal (previously strongly heated in a vacuum),

738 (with figure); Narr, *Ann. Phys.*, 1885, **25**, 542; Prytz, *ibid.*, 1891, **42**, 191 (simple intermittent type); Wells, *Ber.*, 1891, **24**, 1037; Kahlbaum, *Ann. Phys.*, 1894, **53**, 199; 1901, **6**, 590 (modified von Babo type); Krafft, *Ber.*, 1895, **28**, 2583; 1896, **29**, 1316 (2-fall von Babo type); Boltwood, *Amer. Chem. J.*, 1897, **19**, 76; Müller, *Ann. Phys.*, 1897, **60**, 82; 1898, **65**, 476 (2-fall type); Friedrichs, *ibid.*, 1897, **62**, 383 (automatic); Donle, *Z. Instr.*, 1900, **20**, 78; *Ann. Phys.*, 1903, **10**, 313 (automatic von Babo type); Kahlbaum, Roth, and Siedler, *Z. anorg. Chem.*, 1902, **29**, 177 (Kahlbaum type); Pollock, *J. Proc. Roy. Soc. N.S. Wales*, 1907, **41**, 140; Guichard, *Bull. Soc. Chim.*, 1909, **5**, 571 (simple type); Hansen, *Z. angew. Chem.*, 1909, **22**, 337; Keyes, *J.A.C.S.*, 1909, **31**, 1271; Zehnder, *Ann. Phys.*, 1910, **33**, 646 (modified Kahlbaum's); Williams, *Amer. J. Sci.*, 1911, **32**, 13 (chain and bucket); Odell, *J.A.C.S.*, 1911, **33**, 56 (Boltwood type); Ranque, *Compt. Rend.*, 1921, **172**, 1653; Chen, *Science*, 1923, **58**, 18; Manley, *Proc. Phys., Soc*, 1924, **36**, 291; 1925, **37**, 142; Broom and Travers, *Proc. Roy. Soc.*, 1932, **135**, 512 (continuous); Castro, *Bull. Soc. Encourag. Ind. Nat.*, 1933, **132**, 187; Reynolds, *Chem. and Ind.*, 1947, 176 (modified Sprengel).

[1] *Chem. Ztg.*, 1910, **34**, 1342, and Rep. 181; Beutell and Oberhoffer, *ibid.*, 1919, **43**, 705; Greiner and Friedrichs, *Z. angew. Chem.*, 1921, **34**, i, 46; Arndt, "Handbuch der phys.-chem. Technik," 2nd edit., 1923, 90.

[2] Lehmann, *Ann. Phys.*, 1902, **7**, 1; Gibson, *J.S.C.I.*, 1932, **51**, 1064; Mann, *ibid.*, 1933, **52**, 13; McDermott, *ibid.*, 1933, **52**, 82.

[3] Dushman, "Production and Measurement of High Vacuum," Schenectady, 1922, 156 f.

in a bulb cooled in liquid air, introduced by Dewar,[1] is a well-known adjunct to high-vacuum technique; silica gel has also been used.

If the vessel exhausted has eventually to be sealed off, a constriction in the tube is necessary; a bore of 3 mm. is the widest which can be sealed off under vacuum in the ordinary way, but with special sealing devices a maximum bore of 1 cm. can be sealed.

Special thick and soft rubber tubing is used for high vacuum connections: the ordinary " pressure tubing " used with water pumps is not suitable. Pauli [2] made the rubber tubing vacuum tight by bathing it (externally) in a molten mixture of picein and lanoline, hanging it up, and carefully brushing it over with a flame. Painting with cellulose lacquer (which must not crack on bending) can also be used. The tubing should be dried out in a warm cupboard for a few days before use.[3]

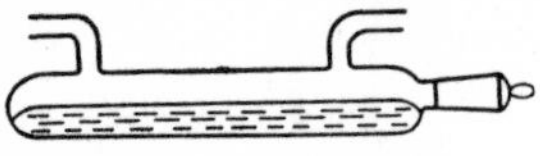

FIG. 21.VII A. P_2O_5 Tube

Willard [4] used a valve consisting of a glass capillary sealed by a graded seal into an outer quartz tube: the glass was closed by melting, heating being effected outside the quartz tube, and opened by blowing out with gas pressure while soft. A mercury trap obviating stopcocks was developed by Stock,[5] and a greaseless stopcock by Ramsperger.[6]

Very useful practical hints, including making joints, glass-blowing, etc., in connection with vacuum pumps, are given by Zehnder.[7] Usually, a P_2O_5 drying tube, of horizontal type (Fig. 21.VII A), which may be provided with a stirrer,[8] is included between the pump and the system evacuated. Various pumps for circulating gases are described.[9]

A hemispherical ground glass joint for vacuum systems was described by Rubens and Henderson,[10] flexible metal tubes, and metal joints and valves for vacuum by Duran,[11] and a non-lubricated all-glass vacuum valve by Vaughan.[12]

[1] Dewar, " Conferences. Special Loan Collection of Scientific Apparatus " [South Kensington Museum], 1876, 155; *Proc. Roy. Soc.*, 1904, **74**, 126; Claude and Lévy, *Compt. Rend.*, 1906, **142**, 876; Merton, *J.C.S.*, 1914, **105**, 645 (finely divided copper); Dushman, *Gen. Elec. Rev.*, 1921, **24**, 436; " Production and Measurement of High Vacuum," 1922, 123 f. (also calcium, etc.); Collie, *Proc. Phys. Soc.*, 1934, **46**, 252 (charcoal and liq. H_2); Zamenhof, *Physica*, 1939, **6**, 47 (charcoal; silica gel).

[2] *Z. Instr.*, 1910, **30**, 133.

[3] Mündel, *Z. phys. Chem.*, 1913, **85**, 435.

[4] *J.A.C.S.*, 1935, **57**, 2328.

[5] Stock and Priess, *Ber.*, 1914, **47**, 3109; Stock, *Z. Elektrochem.*, 1917, **23**, 33; 1933, **39**, 256; *Ber.*, 1925, **58**, 2058; Bodenstein, *ibid.*, 1918, **51**, 1640; Wolf and Reichel, *Z. Elektrochem.*, 1933, **39**, 143; Schumb and Crane, *J.A.C.S.*, 1936, **58**, 2649; Burg and Schlesinger, *ibid.*, 1940, **62**, 3425.

[6] *J.A.C.S.*, 1929, **51**, 2132; Yee and Reuter, *ibid.*, 1931, **53**, 2645 (greaseless diaphragm valve); Lockenvitz, Hughes, Lipson, and Olewin, *Rev. Sci. Instr.*, 1948, **19**, 272 (bellows valve); Kurie, *ibid.*, 1948, **19**, 485 (seals and valves).

[7] Lehmann, " Physikalische Technik," Halle, 1885; Zehnder. *Ann. Phys.*, 1903, **10**, 623; Mönch, *Chem. Ztg.*, 1936, **60**, 465; Burrows, *J. Sci. Instr.*, 1943, **20**, 21, 77.

[8] Moles, *An. Fis. Quim.*, 1911, **9**, 214; Dennis, *J.A.C.S.*, 1925, **47**, 797.

[9] Rubber-tubing pump, Prytz, *Z. Instr.*, 1905, **25**, 193; Rollett, *Z. phys. Chem.*, 1942, **191**, 251; water pump, Fischer and Ringe, *Ber.*, 1908, **41**, 2017; mercury pumps, Liebert, *Chem. Weekbl.*, 1911, **8**, 342; Scheel and Heuse, *Ann. Phys.*, 1913, **40**, 473; spiral tube pump, von Wartenberg, *Z. Elektrochem.*, 1913, **19**, 482; electromagnetic circulating pumps, Livingstone, *J. Phys. Chem.*, 1929, **33**, 955; Brenschede, *Z. phys. Chem.*, 1936, **178**, 74; Marshall, *J. Sci. Instr.*, 1947, **24**, 192.

[10] *Rev. Sci. Instr.*, 1939, **10**, 49.

[11] *Z. Phys.*, 1934, **89**, 143, 148, 152.

[12] *Rev. Sci. Instr.*, 1945, **16**, 254; for vacuum valves, see Geissmann, *Phys. Z.*, 1943, **44**, 268; for a wide-bore high-vacuum cut-off, Schmitt, *Rev. Sci. Instr.*, 1937, **8**, 68; a " vacuum

Seals between porcelain and metal are described by Schad,[1] and Pyrex glass seals by Fraenckel.[2] The nickel steel called *kovar* is used for seals into glass.[3]

Rubber tubing and stoppers which have stuck to glass tubing may be softened and removed after heating by passing steam through the glass tube.[4]

Adsorption of water vapour on glass is prevented by covering the glass with a hydrophobic unimolecular film by washing with a 0·05 per cent. solution of "Cetavlon." [5] Testing for leakage in high-vacuum systems may be carried out with a mass spectrometer.[6]

Special mercury-sealed stopcocks are generally used for vacuum work [7]; a stopcock with the conical barrel inverted to withstand internal *pressure* without blowing out was devised by Dixon and Edgar.[8]

Many varieties of tap greases or lubricants have been used. The so-called "Ramsay lubricant" is blended from rubber and vaseline.[9] Travers [10] heated 2 parts of soft rubber clippings, 1 part of vaseline, and $\frac{1}{8}$ part of hard paraffin wax in a basin on a sand-bath, stirring until the rubber dissolved. Zintl and Goubeau [9] heated purified beef suet at 150° for 30 minutes, added an equal weight of Para rubber, heated at 150° till homogeneous, and then at 200° for 2 hours. For exposure to chlorine, etc., a paraffin-base grease may be heated

door," Mehl and Smith, *Ind. Eng. Chem. Anal.*, 1925, **17**, 598; on high-vacuum technique and measurement, Rabe, *Z. angew. Chem.*, 1910, **23**, 20 (stopcocks with square bore); Bodenstein, *Ber.*, 1918, **51**, 1640 (stopcocks, valves, etc.); Garner, *J.S.C.I.*, 1920, **39**, 347 T (metal-glass disc connector); Schirmann, *Phys. Z.*, 1926, **27**, 659 (all aspects, incl. stopcocks and sealing off); Peters, *Z. angew. Chem.*, 1928, **41**, 509; Richards, *Rev. Sci. Instr.*, 1931, **2**, 49 (pressure control); Ptizyn, *J. Techn. Phys. U.S.S.R.*, 1932, **2**, 651.

[1] *Sprechsaal*, 1938, **71**, 139; silica to metal, Buttolph, *J. Opt. Soc. Amer.*, 1925, **11**, 549 (bibl.); Oliver, *J. Sci. Instr.*, 1928, **5**, 9; Morris, *ibid.*, 1934, **11**, 232.

[2] *Rev. Sci. Instr.*, 1936, **7**, 395; quartz to Pyrex with fused silver chloride, Palmer, *Phys. Rev.*, 1934, **45**, 556; Weber and Bazzoni, *Rev. Sci. Instr.*, 1937, **8**, 170; Benson, *ibid.*, 1942, **13**, 267; with a sealing glass, Dale and Stanworth, *J. Soc. Glass Techn.*, 1945, **29**, 77; with Wood's fusible metal, Mach, *Z. Instr.*, 1893, **13**, 428; Welo, *J. Opt. Soc. Amer.*, 1924, **8**, 453; Lux, *Z. anorg. Chem.*, 1935, **226**, 21; for glass to porcelain, Suë, *Bull. Soc. Chim.*, 1946, 410.

[3] Scott, *J. Franklin Inst.*, 1935, **220**, 733; on sealing metals to glass, see Shaw, *Proc. Phys. Soc.*, 1912, **24**, 95 (metals to glass); Schaller, *Z. Instr.*, 1914, **34**, Beibl., 130 (graded glass to quartz seals for metal wires); vacuum-tight lead seals in glass and silica, Sand, *Proc. Phys. Soc.*, 1914, **26**, 127; McKelvy and Taylor, *J.A.C.S.*, 1920, **42**, 1364 (glass to metal; bibl.); sealing base metals in glass, Scott *et al.*, *J. Amer. Inst. Elec. Eng.*, 1923, **42**, 877; for some practical recipes for platinising glass, see Taylor, *J. Opt. Soc. Amer.*, 1929, **18**, 138; de Laszlo, *J. Sci. Instr.*, 1933, **10**, 296 (copper to glass tubes); for vacuum joints in metal apparatus, Archer, *J. Sci. Instr.*, 1936, **13**, 161; Rinck, *Bull. Soc. Chim.*, 1937, **4**, 199 (metal wires in glass); for glass to metal joints (theory), Redston and Stanworth, *J. Soc. Glass Techn.*, 1945, **29**, 48; Douglas, *ibid.*, 1945, **29**, 92; for *copper* mirrors, Chattaway, *J.C.S.*, 1908, **93**, 270; "Discussion on the Making of Reflecting Surfaces," Physical Society and Optical Society, 1920 (including silvering); Eyber, *Chem. Ztg.*, 1927, **51**, 4; Barnard, *Science*, 1927, **66**, 330; on ordinary glass and silica working, Threlfall, "On Laboratory Arts," 1898; on attaching glass to steel tubing by coppering and soldering, Onnes, *Proc. K. Akad. Wetens. Amsterdam*, 1905, **8**, 75 (*Comm. Leiden*, **94***b*).

[4] Skazin, *Canad. J. Res.*, 1934, **10**, 592; on loosening "seized" stopcocks, Bailey, *Ind. Eng. Chem.*, 1932, **4**, 324; Friedrichs, *Chem. Fabrik.*, 1933, **6**, 40; Robinson, *Chemist Analyst*, 1947, **36**, 70.

[5] Norrish and Russell, *Nature*, 1947, **160**, 57.

[6] Jacobs, *Ind. Eng. Chem.*, 1948, **40**, 791.

[7] Thiele and Eckard, *Ann. Phys.*, 1901, **6**, 428; Randall and Bichowsky, *J.A.C.S.*, 1915, **37**, 137; Trivelli, *J.S.C.I.*, 1928, **47**, 496R.

[8] Dixon and Edgar, *Phil. Trans.*, 1905, **205**, 169; Randall and Bichowsky, *loc. cit.*

[9] Shepherd and Ledig, *Ind. Eng. Chem.*, 1927, **19**, 1059; Zintl and Goubeau, *Z. anorg. Chem.*, 1927, **163**, 105; Boughton, *J.A.C.S.*, 1930, **52**, 4858; Cacciapuoti, *Rivista Nuov. Cim.*, 1943, **1**, 56 (various).

[10] "Study of Gases," 1901, 24.

in chlorine,[1] e.g. a mixture of 3 parts of stearin and 2 of paraffin for 4–5 hours in chlorine at 150°–180°, and then for a day in vacuum at the same temperature. " Perchlornaphthalene " can be used with chlorine and bromine at higher temperatures.[2] " Apiezon " oil can be blended with rubber.[3] For corrosive substances, deliquesced phosphorus pentoxide can be used, the dry tap barrel being dipped into P_2O_5 and then breathed upon. Various lubricants with metaphosphoric acid base have been proposed.[4] In contact with grease-solvents (e.g. benzene) lubricants such as treacle,[5] fused dextrose and glycerol,[6] a mixture of dextrin, mannitol, and glycerol,[7] a mixture of concentrated sulphuric acid and aluminium sulphate,[8] etc., and amalgams on silvered stopcocks,[9] have been used.

Faraday's[10] cement consists of 5 parts of resin, 1 of yellow wax, and 1 of red ochre melted together; for higher pressures, half the amount of wax is used;[11] it is softer if more wax is used. Roth[12] cemented Cailletet tubes with a mixture of 2 parts of resin strongly heated, into which 1 part of cuttings of old rubber tubes or stoppers was stirred. Marine glue[13] contains rubber, petroleum and asphaltum, Chatterton's compound and de Khotinsky cement are special preparations. Of sealing wax, the black English variety is the best.[14] Picëin[15] is a black pitch-like cement, but rather soft for pressure sealings. Glass to metal joints[16] are necessary in pressure work.

§ 14. Low-pressure Manometers

The simple U-shaped manometer for oil, α-bromonaphthalene, mercury, etc., needs no description;[17] some special types will be described in connection with

[1] Wourtzel, *J. Chim. Phys.*, 1913, **11**, 29; Bodenstein and Dux, *Z. phys. Chem.*, 1913, **85**, 297 (beeswax and lanoline chlorinated at 150°); Biltz and Meinecke, *Z. anorg. Chem.*, 1923, **131**, 1.

[2] For higher temperature lubricants, see Puddington, *J.A.C.S.*, 1943, **65**, 990 (metallic soaps); silicone greases for use at higher temperatures (Dow-Corning, Michigan; supplied in England by Edwards), Bass, *Chem. and Ind.*, 1947, 171, 189; various authors, *Ind. Eng. Chem.*, 1947, **39**, 1364 f.

[3] Slee, *Chem. Trade J.*, 1932, **90**, 380; for greases (aliphatic diesters+lithium stearate, etc.) for low temperatures, see Hain, Jones, Merker, and Zisman, *Ind. Eng. Chem.*, 1947, **39**, 500.

[4] Bodenstein and Fink, *Z. phys. Chem.*, 1907, **60**, 1; Wöhler, Plüddemann, and Wöhler, *Ber.*, 1908, **41**, 703; Stephens, *J.A.C.S.*, 1930, **52**, 635; Boughton, *ibid.*, 1930, **52**, 2814; Pinkus, *Bull. Soc. Chim. Belg.*, 1934, **43**, 462.

[5] Möller, *Ann. Phys.*, 1902, **7**, 256.

[6] Tyrer, *J.C.S.*, 1911, **99**, 1633.

[7] Meloche and Fredrich, *J.A.C.S.*, 1932, **54**, 3264.

[8] Traube, *Ber.*, 1913, **46**, 2513.

[9] Boughton, *J.A.C.S.*, 1930, **52**, 2421, 4335, 4858 (various); Francis, *Rev. Sci. Instr.*, 1933, **4**, 615 (various); Wagner, *Oesterr. Chem. Ztg.*, 1940, **43**, 229; Herrington and Starr, *Ind. Eng. Chem. Anal.*, 1942, **14**, 62 (starch and glycerol).

[10] Faraday, " Chemical Manipulation," 1842, 489; *Phil. Trans.*, 1845, **135**, 155.

[11] Bradley and Browne, *J. Phys. Chem.*, 1904, **8**, 37.

[12] *Ann. Phys.*, 1880, **11**, 1.

[13] Heat 10 pts. asphalt and 10 pts. gutta-percha at 150°–180° and stir well. Add a little powdered resin, 1 pt. oil of turpentine and 1 pt. of coal tar. To soften, stir in some asphalt varnish mixed with turpentine.

[14] Mündel, *Z. phys. Chem.*, 1913, **85**, 435; white sealing wax is often used for pressure joints.

[15] Walter, *Ann. Phys.*, 1905, **18**, 860.

[16] McKelvy and Taylor, *J.A.C.S.*, 1920, **42**, 1364 (bibl.); Dundon, *ibid.*, 1923, **45**, 716; Meyers, *ibid.*, 1923, **45**, 2135; Ridyard, *ibid.*, 1924, **46**, 287; on brass-glass joint with sealing wax, McBain and Britton, *ibid.*, 1930, **52**, 2198; on fixing tubes in Cailletet apparatus, Bradley and Browne, *J. Phys. Chem.*, 1904, **8**, 37; Cardoso, *J. Chim. Phys.*, 1912, **10**, 470; calibrating tubes, Hulett, *Z. phys. Chem.*, 1900, **33**, 237; see the section on critical constants, § 4.VII B. For laboratory waxes and cements in general, see Walden, *J. Sci. Instr.*, 1936, **13**, 345.

[17] See § 7; Travers, " Study of Gases," 1901, 141; Auerbach, in Winkelmann, " Handbuch

apparatus for particular measurements, and only manometers for the measurements of low pressures will be described here. Some special types (Knudsen absolute manometer, Pirani gauge, etc.) for *very* low pressures are described in Section VII J.

A much-used manometer for low-pressure measurements is the McLeod gauge.[1] In its simplest form this consists of a glass bulb A (Fig. 22.VII A) of known volume (e.g. 500 ml.) surmounted by a graduated capillary tube *a*, also of known volume and each division corresponding with 0·001 ml. The bulb is connected below by a long vertical glass tube and rubber pressure tubing with a mercury reservoir B. From the tube at *b* below the bulb A a side tube branches into *c* and *d*, joining again at *e*, which is connected with the vessel in which the pressure is to be measured. The tube *c*, which is close to and parallel to *a*, may also be graduated or (usually) backed by a graduated scale. When the reservoir B is raised a volume of gas at the low pressure x is trapped in A and the mercury then rises in the bulb and in the tubes *c* and *d*. The gas in A is then further compressed into the capillary *a* and its volume is read off. Suppose it is $v=0{\cdot}010$ml. The level of the mercury in *c* (and *d*) is higher than that in *a*; suppose the *difference* of level is $\delta=5{\cdot}3$mm. Then Boyle's law gives $\delta\times V=x\times v$, therefore $x=\delta(v/V)=5{\cdot}3\times(0{\cdot}01/500)=0{\cdot}000106$ mm. Pressures down to 0·00001 mm. can be measured.

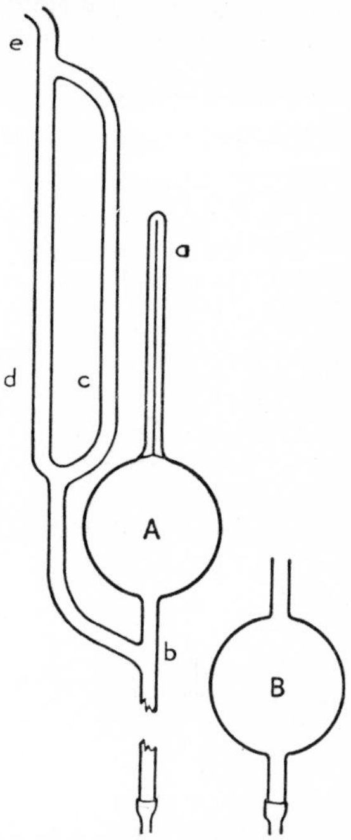

FIG. 22.VII A. McLeod Gauge

If the tubes *a* and *c* are of different bores there is a correction for capillary depression; as this is considerable for narrow tubes it is often eliminated by making *a* and *c* from the same tubing. Klemenc and Bankowski [2] found the

der Physik," 1908, **1**, ii, 1311; Dushman, " Production and Measurement of High Vacua," Schenectady, 1922, 86; Arndt, " Phys.-chem. Technik," 2nd edit., 1923, 209; Ostwald-Luther, " Phys.-chem. Messungen," 5th edit., 1931, 195; Newman, " The Production and Measurement of Low Pressures," 1925; Kaye, *J. Roy. Soc. Arts*, 1926, **74**, 991, 1011, 1030; Ríus, *An. Fis. Quim.*, 1947, **42**, 106 (4-arm gauge).

[1] McLeod, *Phil. Mag.*, 1874, **48**, 110; Crookes, *Phil. Trans.*, 1881, **172**, 387; Baly and Ramsay, *Phil. Mag.*, 1894, **38**, 301; Brush, *ibid.*, 1897, **44**, 415; *Science*, 1898, **7**, 730; Zehnder, *Ann. Phys.*, 1903, **10**, 623; Wohl and Losanitsch, *Ber.*, 1905, **38**, 4149; Hering, *Ann. Phys.*, 1906, **21**, 319; Ubbelohde, *Z. angew. Chem.*, 1906, **19**, 753; Baume, *J. Chim. Phys.*, 1908, **6**, 1; Guichard, *Bull. Soc. Chim.*, 1911, **9**, 435 (influence of moisture); Gaede, *Ann. Phys.*, 1913, **41**, 289; Reiff, *Z. Instr.*, 1914, **34**, 97; Bailey, *Chem. News*, 1920, **120**, 302; Dushman, *Gen. Elec. Rev.*, 1920, **23**, 731, 847; Hay, *J. Opt. Soc. Amer.*, 1923, **7**, 1015; Smith and Taylor, *J.A.C.S.*, 1924, **46**, 1393; Harrington, *J. Opt. Soc. Amer.*, 1924, **9**, 469; Duffendack and Schaefer, *ibid.*, 1924, **9**, 689; Shirai, *Bull. Chem. Soc. Japan*, 1926, **1**, 109; Bless, *Science*, 1928, **68**, 38; Clarke, *J. Sci. Instr.*, 1928, **5**, 126 (calibration); Taylor, *J.A.C.S.*, 1928, **50**, 2937 (dtm. permanent gas in condensible vapour, e.g. air in H_2O vapour); Brunner, *Helv. Chim. Acta*, 1930, **13**, 915; Hickman, *J. Phys. Chem.*, 1930, **34**, 627; Pearson, *Z. phys. Chem.*, 1931, **156**, 86; Booth, *Ind. Eng. Chem. Anal.*, 1932, **4**, 380; Ramaswamy, *Phil. Mag.*, 1932, **14**, 96 (calibration); MacDougall, *J.A.C.S.*, 1936, **58**, 2588; Flosdorf, *Ind. Eng. Chem. Anal.*, 1938, **10**, 534; Keevil, Errington, and Newman, *Rev. Sci. Instr.*, 1941, **12**, 609 (measuring small volumes); *Ind. Eng. Chem. Anal.*, 1942, **14**, 542 (olive oil); Le Roy, *ibid.*, 1945, **17**, 652; Flosdorf, *Chem. Met. Eng.*, 1945, **52**, No. 11, 102; Balson, *Trans. Faraday Soc.*, 1947, **43**, 48; for a very complicated set-up with Apiezon-B oil displaced by a plunger in a 300 ml. bulb, instead of mercury, see Bannon, *Rev. Sci. Instr.*, 1943, **14**, 6.

[2] *Naturwiss.*, 1934, **22**, 10.

capillary depression for mercury in 30-mm. tubes only 0·002 mm., and in 40-mm. tubes it was less than 0·0002 mm. The McLeod gauge may be made more compact [1] by dispensing with the long vertical tube and levelling bulb and replacing them by a vessel of mercury which is connected with an air pump for reducing the pressure; by cautiously admitting air to this vessel the mercury is driven from it into the bulb *a* and tubes *c* and *d*.

The manometer and mercury must be very clean and dry. The effect of the vapour pressure of mercury and of grease on joints, etc., in the use of the McLeod gauge requires careful consideration. The vapour pressures remain constant during the compression into *a*; they are of the order of 10^{-3} mm. and the same on both sides of the mercury in *a* and *c*, hence the pressure reading gives the permanent gas pressure only. The total pressure in the apparatus, however, includes the mercury pressure, which has the following values about room temperature: [2]

t° C.	0	5	10	16	20	25	30
p mm.	0·00019	0·00025	0·0005	0·0012	0·0013	0·0017	0·0029

or is given by the formula:

$$\log p_{\text{mm.}} = 15{\cdot}24431 - 3623{\cdot}932/T - 2{\cdot}367233 \log T.$$

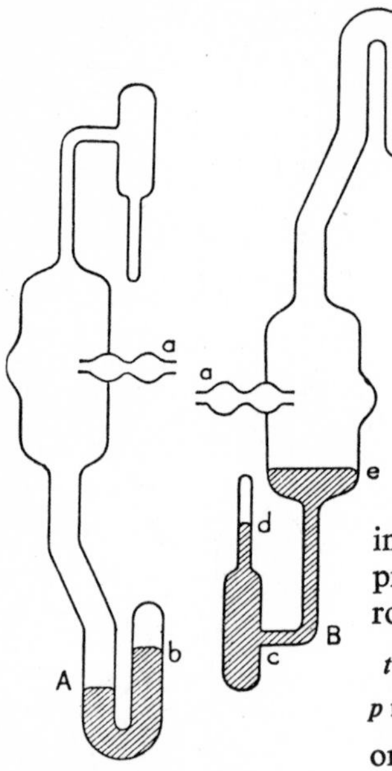

FIG. 23.VII A. Vacuoscope

By careful drying of the manometer and gas, pressures of 10^{-5} mm. can be measured quite exactly.[3]

A combination of a McLeod and membrane gauge was used by Yamasaki and Yosida.[4] The sticking of mercury in the closed capillary of the McLeod gauge at pressures below 10^{-3} was studied with tubes of various materials and forms by Hagen,[5] who utilised it to measure low pressures. A combination of a McLeod and Pirani gauge was used by Pfund [6] and Cox.[7] Klayrfeld,[8] with a McLeod gauge and an electric discharge tube, measured pressures down to 5×10^{-8} mm.

A convenient manometer using the principle of the McLeod gauge is the *vacuoscope* [9] (Fig. 23.VII A), a small glass gauge into which 8–13 ml. of pure

[1] Ubbelohde, *Z. angew. Chem.*, 1906, **19**, 753; 1907, **20**, 2172; 1908, **21**, 976, 1454; Hartmann, *ibid.*, 1908, **21**, 439; Reiff, *ibid.*, 1908, **21**, 977; Druecker, Jiméno, and Kangro, *Z. phys. Chem.*, 1915, **90**, 513; Underwood, *J. Opt. Soc. Amer.*, 1929, **19**, 78; Martin, *Phil. Mag.*, 1930, **9**, 97; Peters and Lohmar, *Z. phys. Chem.*, 1937, **180**, 58; Bourstein, *Zavodskaya Lab.*, 1946, **12**, 382.

[2] Hertz, *Ann. Phys.*, 1882, **17**, 193; Kaye and Laby, "Tables of Physical and Chemical Constants," 1948, 55; the values given by Regnault, *Mém. Acad. Sci.*, 1862, **26**, 339 (506) are much larger, those of Morley, *Z. phys. Chem.*, 1904, **49**, 95, are somewhat smaller, than Hertz's (the value at 16° given is from Morley); Knudsen, *Ann. Phys.*, 1910, **33**, 1435.

[3] Scheel and Heuse, *Verhl. d. D. Phys. Ges.*, 1908, **10**, 785; 1909, **11**, 1; *Z. Instr.*, 1909, **29**, 14.

[4] *Proc. Phys. Math. Soc. Japan*, 1933, **15**, 400.

[5] *Phys. Z.*, 1926, **27**, 47; cf. Rieger, *Z. techn. Phys.*, 1920, **1**, 16; Simon, *ibid.*, 1924, **5**, 221.

[6] *Phys. Rev.*, 1921, **18**, 78.

[7] *J. Opt. Soc. Amer.*, 1924, **9**, 569 (to 10^{-9} mm.).

[8] *J. Russ. Phys. Chem. Soc.*, 1925, **57**, 129 (P).

[9] Von Meyeren, *Z. phys. Chem.*, 1932, **160**, 273; for similar apparatus, see Karrer, *Phys.*

mercury is introduced, with the apparatus horizontal, through *a*, which is afterwards connected by pressure tubing to the evacuated system. In position A, if the closed limb *b* is first completely filled with mercury, it acts as a short barometer, the difference of levels being read with a cathetometer. At low pressures, position B is used, the gas in *c* being forced into the capillary *d*. Since the level at *e* in the wide tube is practically constant, *d* can be graduated to read the pressure (from 0·005 mm.) directly. The *total* pressure is shown, as with the McLeod gauge.

A manometer for low pressures suggested by Langmuir [1] used the damping of the vibrations of a thin (0·01–0·001 mm.) quartz fibre fixed at one end, or of a bifilar pendulum of two thin quartz fibres supporting a small weight. Knudsen used a small glass sphere on a quartz thread; if P=frictional force on surface moving with a tangential velocity of 1 cm./sec., p=gas pressure in dynes/cm.^{2}, T=absolute temperature, M= mol. wt. of gas, then $M=522{\cdot}25\times10^6T(P/p)^2$. A vibrating quartz plate or horizontal rod suspended by a quartz thread has also been used.[2] The Pirani gauge, depending on the variation of thermal conductivity of a gas, and other gauges, suitable for very low pressures, are described in Section VII J. A vacuum indicator [3] for low pressures depends on the flow of heat across the space in a Dewar vessel connected with the apparatus; the thermal conductivity of a gas depends on the pressure when this is very low (§ 4.VII J). The Edelmann manometer described by Heis [4] consists of two cups suspended on a rod hanging from a fibre suspension, like an anemometer.

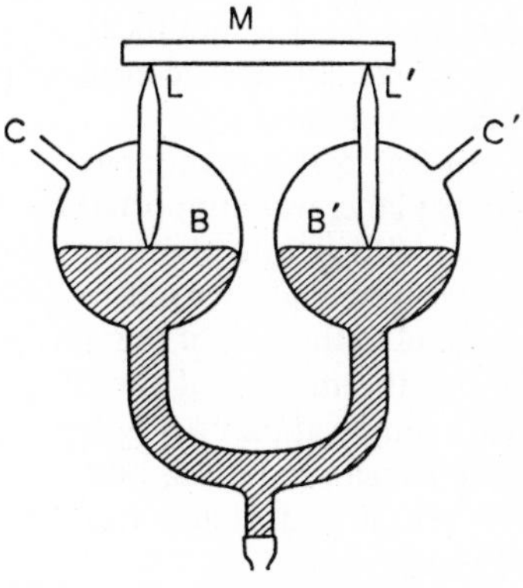

FIG. 24.VII A. Rayleigh Manometer

In his experiments on Boyle's law at low pressures (§ 11) Rayleigh [5] used (for the range 0·02–1·5 mm.) the manometer shown in Fig. 24.VII A, which indicated pressures to 1/2000 mm. Hg. Two bulbs B and B′ had sealed glass

Rev., 1915, **6**, 49; *J.A.C.S.*, 1918, **40**, 928; *J. Franklin Inst.*, 1918, **185**, 555; Hamlin, *J.A.C.S.*, 1925, **47**, 709; Hartshough, *Science*, 1925, **62**, 160 (tilting type); Demontvignier, *Bull. Soc. Chim.*, 1927, **41**, 1244; Moser, *Phys. Z.*, 1935, **36**, 1; Ievlev, *Zavodskaya Lab.*, 1946, **12**, 831.

1 Langmuir, *J.A.C.S.*, 1913, **35**, 105; Haber and Kerschbaum, *Z. Elektrochem.*, 1914, **20**, 296; Knudsen, *Ann. Phys.*, 1914, **44**, 525; *Ann. Phys. Beibl.*, 1915, **39**, 763 (dtm. of mol. wts.); Henglein, *Z. anorg. Chem.*, 1922, **123**, 137; Coolidge, *J.A.C.S.*, 1923, **45**, 1637 (can be used at 0·1–1 mm.); 1924, **46**, 680; Coolidge and Coolidge, *ibid.*, 1927, **49**, 101; King, *Proc. Phys. Soc.*, 1925, **38**, 80; Brüche, *Phys. Z.*, 1925, **26**, 717; *Ann. Phys.*, 1926, **79**, 695; Burk, *J. Phys, Chem.*, 1927, **31**, 590; Martin, *Phil. Mag.*, 1930, **9**, 97.

2 Brüche, *Phys. Z.*, 1925, **26**, 717; King, *Proc. Phys. Soc.*, 1925, **38**, 80; Nikliborc, *Acta Phys Polon.*, 1935, **4**, 85; 1937, **6**, 19.

3 Herzog and Scherrer, *Helv. Phys. Acta*, 1933, **6**, 277.

4 *Phys. Z.*, 1924, **25**, 326; for micro-manometer (bells on torsion balance), 2×10^{-4} mm., see Hindley, *J. Sci. Instr.*, 1947, **24**, 295; for strain-sensitive resistance wire stretched by bellows, Keenan and McIntosh, *Rev. Sci. Instr.*, 1948, **19**, 336.

5 *Phil. Trans.*, 1901, **196**, 205; 1902, **198**, 417; 1905, **204**, 351; *Z. phys. Chem.*, 1901, **37**, 713; 1902, **41**, 71; 1905, **52**, 705; *Proc. Roy. Soc.*, 1904, **73**, 153; Thiesen, *Z. Instr.*, 1886, **6**, 89; Morley and Brush, *Amer. J. Sci.*, 1902, **13**, 455; Tower, *J.A.C.S.*, 1908, **30**, 1219; Scheel and Heuse, *Z. Instr.*, 1909, **29**, 344; *Ann. Phys.*, 1909, **29**, 723; Maier, *ibid.*, 1910, **31**, 423; Mündel, *Z. phys. Chem.*, 1913, **85**, 435; Frazer and Lovelace, *J.A.C.S.*, 1914, **36**, 2439; *Z. phys. Chem.*, 1915, **89**, 155; Schrader and Ryder, *Phys. Rev.*, 1919, **13**, 321; Schibata and Mori, *J. Chem. Soc. Japan*, 1933, **54**, 44 (in Japanese); on low-pressure measurements, see Etzrodt, *Chem. App.*, 1938, **25**, 321.

points which at L and L′ supported a small table M. The bulbs were connected with two vessels, between which the pressure difference was measured, by tubes C and C′. By suitably inclining the whole manometer, the mercury levels in B and B′ were brought to the glass points, and from the angle of tilt, measured by reflexion from a mirror attached to M, the pressure difference could be calculated. In the second apparatus, pressures of 75 mm. and 150 mm. were exactly maintained by contact of mercury with glass points 75 mm. apart. Hering [1] used a modification suggested by Paschen in which, instead of tilting the gauge, an electric contact is screwed down until it touches the mercury and makes a circuit.

In Rayleigh's manometer the platform M, carrying the mirror at right angles to its plane, was supported by three points L L′, two on one bulb and one on the other, fitting into three holes in the platform. The mirror, stand, and manometer were rigidly fixed to a board which could be rotated on a horizontal axis parallel to the face of the mirror, lying approximately in the mirror surface and at about the middle of the height of the operative part of the apparatus. This very simple apparatus is capable of giving results of great precision with suitable care in manipulation, and could find more extensive use. The form described by Scheel and Heuse has perhaps the most convenient equipment for tilting the apparatus.

§ 15. Charles's Law

The expansion of air on heating was demonstrated by the bubbling of air from a bent tube with one end in water and the other connected with a globe of air by Philo of Byzantium (250 B.C.?) [2] and Hero of Alexandria (A.D. 50); [3] the latter made use of air expanded by heating to perform curious tricks, such as opening the doors of a temple when fire was kindled on an altar containing a concealed air vessel, the expanded air driving water into buckets drawing on cords. Experiments on expanding air are mentioned by Baptista Porta (1589),[4] Galileo [5] (1603), Cornelius Drebbel (1608),[6] and Fludd (1617).[7] Van Helmont [8] used an air thermoscope to indicate changes of temperature. Amontons [9] found that equal masses of air gave changes of pressure at constant volume in the same ratio at two temperatures, whatever the initial pressure, so that the same rise in temperature produces the same increase of pressure at constant volume. He calculated that air would exert no pressure if cooled below the freezing-point of water by about $2\frac{1}{2}$ times the range of temperature between the freezing- and boiling-points of water (i.e. at −250° C.; Lambert [10]

1 *Ann. Phys.*, 1906, **21**, 319; cf. Mündel, ref. 5, p. 591.

2 In Hero of Alexandria, "Opera," edit. Schmidt, Leipzig, 1899, **1**, 474.

3 Hero of Alexandria, "Pneumatica," lib. ii, cap. 8; "Opera," edit. Schmidt, Leipzig, 1899, **1**, 225.

4 "Magia Naturalis," Naples, 1589, lib. xix, cap. 3; Leyden, 1650, p. 635.

5 Rosenberger, "Geschichte der Physik," Brunswick, 1884, **2**, 18; Taylor, *Annals of Sci.*, 1942, **5**, 129.

6 "Ein kurzer Tractat von der Natur Der Elementen," Leyden, 1608, fol. a_8v; Burckhardt, *Ann. Phys.*, 1868, **133**, 680; Hoefer, "Histoire de la Chimie," 1869, **2**, 128; Jaeger, "Cornelis Drebbel en zijn Tijdgenooten," Groningen, 1932; Tierie, "Cornelis Drebbel," Amsterdam, 1932; Gibbs, *Annals of Sci.*, 1948, **6**, 32.

7 "Utriusque Cosmi Majoris . . . Historia," Oppenheim, 1617, 203–4.

8 "Ortus Medicinae," Amsterdam, 1648, 64; Partington, *Annals of Sci.*, 1936, **1**, 359.

9 *Hist. Acad. Sci.* (Paris), 1699, 101; 1702, 1; 1703, 6; *Mém. Acad. Sci.*, 1699, 112; 1702, 155; 1703, 101; Hauksbee, "Physico-Mechanical Experiments," 1709, 170; De Luc, "Recherches sur les Modifications de l'Atmosphère," Geneva, 1772, **2**, 60.

10 "Pyrometrie, oder vom Maase des Feuers und der Wärme," Berlin, 1779, 29, 40, 74;

by more accurate experiments obtained a result which located this " absolute zero " at −274°). Boerhaave [1] concluded that " air of unequal masses but of the same density, is always expanded in the same measure by the same degree of fire; so that these expansions . . . are always proportional to the augmentation of heat."

Priestley [2] from " a very coarse experiment " concluded that " fixed and common air were expanded alike with the same degree of heat," and although Berthollet, Monge, and others,[3] found different degrees of expansion for different gases, this law of equal expansions was proved by Charles [4] in 1787 and Volta [5] in 1793.

Dalton [6] in 1801 suspected that the experiments giving different expansions for different gases were vitiated by neglecting to dry the gases,[7] and his own experiments showed that " all elastic fluids, under the same pressure, expand equally by heat." Gay-Lussac [8] used a glass bulb containing the dried gas with a long narrow neck containing a drop of mercury to confine the gas. The bulb and tube were laid horizontally in melting ice and then in boiling water, and the increase in volume found from the movement of the drop of mercury, allowance being made for the expansion of the glass bulb. Gay-Lussac stated his results in terms of a *coefficient of expansion* α, giving the increase in volume at constant pressure for 1° rise in temperature as a fraction of the initial volume at 0° C.:

$$V_t = V_0(1+\alpha t), \quad \therefore \alpha = (V_t - V_0)/V_0 t \quad . \quad . \quad . \quad . \quad (1)$$

where t=final temperature. He found that α was very nearly the same for various gases, the values varying from 0·003740 to 0·003757. The mean value 0·00375 is too high.

Dalton [6] at first found that 1000 measures of air at 55° F., when corrected for the expansion of the glass, become 1,325 at 212° F., but later (from other experiments) he says [9] 1000 measures at 32° F. become 1376 at 212° F., according to his own and Gay-Lussac's experiments. Regnault [10] says Rudberg finished his second memoir (see below) by an important remark, already made by

Mach, " Die Principien der Wärmelehre," Leipzig, 1896, 9. For older references, see Muncke, in Gehler, " Physikalisches Wörterbuch," 1841, **10**, 933 f.

1 " Elementa Chemiae," Leyden, 1732, **1**, 458.

2 " Experiments and Observations on Air," Birmingham, 1790, **2**, 448.

3 De Morveau, " Encyclopédie Méthodique," Chimie, 1786, **1**, 678 f.

4 Quoted by Gay-Lussac, *Ann. Chim.*, 1802, **43**, 137 (157); Charles did not publish his experiments, but communicated the results to Gay-Lussac, who seems to have been the first to refer the expansions to a standard initial volume and temperature, e.g. 0° C.

5 *Annali di Chimica*, 1793, **4**, 227; " Opere," 1816, **3**, 329 (coefficient for air=0·003662). Volta's paper is entitled: " Memoria sulla uniforme dilatazione Dell'Aria per ogni grade di calore, cominciando sotto la temperature del ghiaccio fin sopra quella dell' ebolizione dell' acque," and he was the first to *publish* the law; Charles preceded him by six years in *experiments*; Guareschi, *Archiv Gesch. Naturwiss. Technik*, 1914–15, **5**, 142, 209; Guye, *J. Chim. Phys.*, 1917, **15**, 471; Aumerio, *Nuov. Cim.*, 1928, **5**, 39.

6 *Manch. Mem.*, 1802, **5**, 595; *Ann. Phys.*, 1803, **12**, 310; Ostwald's *Klassiker*, 1894, **44**; Harper's *Scientific Memoirs*, 1902, " The Expansion of Gases by Heat," edit. Randall; Dixon, *Manch. Mem.*, 1891, **4**, 36; James, *Sci. Progr.*, 1929–30, **24**, 57.

7 Flaugergues, *J. de Phys.*, 1813, **77**, 273, and quoted in Gehler's " Physikalisches Wörterbuch," 1825, **1**, 637, found that moist air expands by heat rather more than dry; on coefficients of expansion of moist gases, see Amagat, *Compt. Rend.*, 1872, **74**, 1299.

8 *Ann. Chim.*, 1802, **43**, 137; *Ann. Phys.*, 1803, **12**, 257; Biot, " Traité de Physique," 1816, **1**, 182, and plate III; Ostwald's *Klassiker*, 1894, **44**.

9 " New System of Chemical Philosophy," 1808, **1**, 19.

10 *Mém. Acad. Sci.*, 1847, **21**, 15 (23).

Gilbert,[1] viz. that Dalton's and Gay-Lussac's results differ appreciably, since the former refers to an initial volume at 55° F. instead of 32°. Preston[2] says Regnault [who quotes Dalton accurately] was misled, as it was supposed that Dalton took the initial volume as 1000 at 32° F. instead of 55° F., whereas Dalton expressly says in 1802 that when the volume was 1000 at 55° F. it was 1325 at 212° F., and he mentions in 1808 that he had not the means of finding the volume at 32° F. According to Preston, this gives the coefficient of expansion as 0·00373, which is nearly the same as 0·00375, the mean of Gay-Lussac's experiments. Dalton's figures, however, give the following result: 55° F.= 12·8° C., 212° F.=100° C. If V_0 is the initial volume at 32° F. or 0° C., $1000=V_0(1+12{\cdot}8\alpha)$, and $1325=V_0(1+100\alpha)$, whence $\alpha=0{\cdot}00391$, and not 0·00373, and it seems as if Gilbert and Regnault are correct.[3]

Although Gay-Lussac's value 0·00375 was apparently confirmed by an indirect method by Dulong and Petit,[4] Magnus[5] pointed out a source of error which vitiated Gay-Lussac's results and has frequently turned up in other researches,[6] the authors of which are apparently still unaware of it. This is the leakage of gas past a *thread* of mercury used to confine it in a glass tube; Magnus by this method found results varying from 0·00355 to 0·00387. Regnault,[7] using a mercury thread as in Gay-Lussac's apparatus, found that if the initial reading at 0° of the mercury index was 152·7, the reading was 534·5 at 100°, and on cooling again to 0° it was 154·5, the barometer being sensibly constant.

Better results were obtained by Rudberg,[8] who found $\alpha=0{\cdot}00365$ for air, and also measured the increase of pressure at constant volume. The *pressure coefficient* β is then defined by:

$$P_t=P_0(1+\beta t) \quad \ldots \quad (2)$$

where P_0, P_t are the pressures at 0° and t° at constant volume. If V_0 is the volume at 0° and t° and if the gas obeys Boyle's law, then if the pressure were reduced to P_0 at t° the volume would become:

$$V_t=P_tV_0/P_0, \quad \therefore \text{ from (1) } P_tV_0/P_0=V_0(1+\alpha t)$$

$$\therefore P_t=P_0(1+\alpha t) \quad \ldots \quad (3)$$

Hence, from (2) and (3) it follows that:

$$\alpha=\beta \quad \ldots \quad (4)$$

but this is true only if Boyle's law holds, and will not be exactly correct for actual gases.

On the Fahrenheit scale the initial volume is at 32° F. (not 0° F.), and the ideal coefficient of expansion on that scale, α_F, is related to that on the Centigrade scale, α_C, by the equation:[9]

$$\alpha_F=\tfrac{5}{9}\alpha_C=\tfrac{5}{9}\times(1/273)=1/490 \quad \ldots \quad (5)$$

[1] *Ann. Phys.*, 1803, **14**, 266.

[2] "Theory of Heat," 1894, 191; still in the 3rd edit., 1919, 197.

[3] Joule, *Manch. Mem.*, 1858 (1860), **15**, 143; "Scientific Papers," 1884, **1**, 384.

[4] *Ann. Chim.*, 1818, **7**, 113; Ostwald's *Klassiker*, 1894, **44**; T. Thomson, "Heat and Electricity," 1840, 6, says Prout in unpublished experiments found 0·0036861 for air.

[5] *Ann. Phys.*, 1842, **55**, 1; 1842, **57**, 177; Ostwald's *Klassiker*, 1894, **44**.

[6] See Kuenen and Visser, *Proc. K. Akad. Wetens. Amsterdam*, 1913–14, **16**, 75 (*Comm. Leiden*, 1913, **138**); Noyes, *J.A.C.S.*, 1925, **47**, 1942, used a mercury thread in what was claimed to be an accurate differential air thermometer; for a demonstration apparatus, Dehn, *J.A.C.S.*, 1908, **30**, 578.

[7] *Ann. Chim.*, 1842, **4**, 43; *Mém. Acad. Sci.*, 1847, **21**, 15.

[8] *Ann. Phys.*, 1837, **41**, 271; 1838, **44**, 119; Taylor's *Scientific Memoirs*, 1841, **2**, 507; Ostwald's *Klassiker*, 1894, **44**; Winkelmann, "Handbuch der Physik," 1906, **3**, 112.

[9] Baynes, in O. E. Meyer, "Kinetic Theory of Gases," 1899, 29.

Dalton seems to have assumed that the increase in volume per 1° at any temperature is a constant fraction α of the volume at that temperature, not at 0°C., $dV/dt=\alpha V$, therefore $dV/V=\alpha dt$, therefore (see §§ 13, 18.I):

$$V=V_0 e^{\alpha t}=V_0(1+\alpha t+\tfrac{1}{2}\alpha t^2+\ldots).$$

If terms in the second and higher powers of t are neglected, Dalton's and Gay-Lussac's statements are identical.[1]

The mean of all Rudberg's results for air was $\alpha=0{\cdot}003646$. Magnus found[2] the values of β: air 0·0036678, H_2 0·0036594, CO_2 0·0036937, SO_2 0·0038591.

The equality of α and β (assumed by earlier experimenters) is not exact, as is seen from the following more accurate figures[3] (0°–100°):

	Air	H_2	CO_2	CO	N_2O	SO_2
$\alpha\times10^6$	3670	3661	3710	3669	3719	3903
$\beta\times10^6$	3665	3667	3688	3667	3676	3845

Hoffmann,[4] for air, found $\alpha-\beta=0{\cdot}0_5123$. Measurements of α and β were made by Regnault[5] (five methods), Amagat,[6] Jolly,[7] Chappuis,[8] Kuenen and Randall,[9] Onnes and Boudin,[10] Travers, Senter, and Jaquerod,[11] Richards and Mark,[12] Makower and Noble,[13] Pier,[14] Henning and Heuse,[15] Heuse and Otto,[16] Day and Clement,[17] Day and Sosman,[18] Eumorfopoulos,[19] Cath and Onnes,[20] and Keesom and Van der Horst.[21]

1 Schreber, *Ann. Phys.*, 1898, **64**, 163; 1898, **66**, 118; 1898, **65**, 648; *Z. phys. Chem.*, 1898, **26**, 751; *Phys. Z.*, 1915, **16**, 327; Auerbach, *Ann. Phys.*, 1898, **64**, 754; Peczalski, *Compt. Rend.*, 1914, **158**, 1164; *J. de Phys.*, 1914, **4**, 286; Weber, *Phys. Z.*, 1915, **16**, 19; Mewes, *Z. Sauerstoff Stickstoff Ind.*, 1918, **10**, 93; 1919, **11**, 13.

2 Corrected by Winkelmann, "Handbuch der Physik," 1906, **3**, 112, for the temperature scale.

3 Regnault, *Mém. Acad. Sci.*, 1847, **21**, 15.

4 *Ann. Phys.*, 1898, **66**, 224.

5 *Ann. Chim.*, 1842, **4**, 5; 1842, **5**, 52; *Mém. Acad. Sci.*, 1847, **21**, 15; Ostwald's *Klassiker*, 1894, **44**; Winkelmann, "Handbuch der Physik," 1906, **3**, 115.

6 *Ann. Chim.*, 1873, **29**, 246.

7 *Ann. Phys.*, 1874, Pogg. Jubelbd., 82; Recknagel, *Ann. Phys.*, 1864, **123**, 115; Mendeléeff, abstr. in *Ber.*, 1875, **8**, 1681; 1876, **9**, 1311; 1877, **10**, 81.

8 *Trav. et Mém. Internat. Bur. Poids et Més.*, 1888, **6**; Chappuis and Harker, *ibid.*, 1902, **12**; 1907, **13**; Chappuis, *Arch. Sci. Phys. Nat.*, 1888, **20**, 5, 153, 248; *Phil. Mag.*, 1900, **50**, 433.

9 *Proc. Roy. Soc.*, 1895, **59**, 60 (He, A).

10 *Proc. K. Akad. Wetens. Amsterdam*, 1901, **3**, 299 (*Comm. Leiden*, **60**) (H_2).

11 *Phil. Trans.*, 1903, **200**, 105; *Z. phys. Chem.*, 1903, **45**, 385, 416, 435.

12 *Proc. Amer. Acad.*, 1902–3, **38**, 415; 1905, **41**, 117; *Z. phys. Chem.*, 1903, **43**, 475.

13 *Proc. Roy. Soc.*, 1903, **72**, 379.

14 *Z. phys. Chem.*, 1908, **62**, 385 (Cl_2).

15 *Z. Phys.*, 1921, **5**, 285; *Z. Elektrochem.*, 1921, **27**, 494; 1922, **28**, 248; Heuse, *Z. Phys.*, 1926, **37**, 157.

16 *Ann. Phys.*, 1929, **2**, 1012.

17 *Amer. J. Sci.*, 1908, **26**, 405.

18 *Amer. J. Sci.*, 1912, **33**, 517; *Ann. Phys.*, 1912, **38**, 849.

19 *Proc. Roy. Soc.*, 1914, **90**, 189.

20 *Arch. Néerl.*, 1922, **6**, 1 (*Comm. Leiden*, **156***a*).

21 *Proc. K. Akad. Wetens. Amsterdam*, 1927, **30**, 970 (*Comm. Leiden*, **188***a*); for helium, see Keesom, Van der Horst, and Taconis, *Physica*, 1934, **1**, 324.

§ 16. Measurements of the Coefficients α and β

One form of apparatus used by Regnault [1] for the determination of α, which can also be used as a constant-pressure air thermometer, is shown diagrammatically in Fig. 25.VII A. The dry gas is contained in the bulb A and tube B over dry mercury. A is first immersed in ice at 0° and the mercury brought to a level *a* in B so that the difference of level in B and C is very small, h mm., the barometer reading being H mm. The bulb is then surrounded by steam at the temperature t (approximately 100°) and the levels again adjusted at *b*, with the small difference h', the barometer reading being H'.

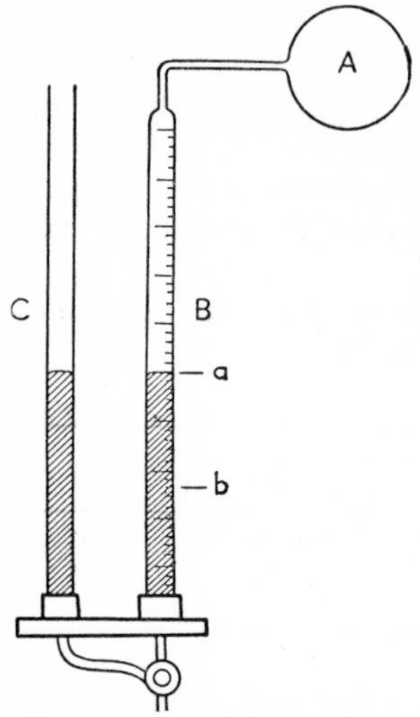

FIG. 25.VII A. Regnault's Apparatus

If V_0 is the volume of the bulb at 0°, v_1 the volume of the stem and tube to the mark *a*, v_2 the volume of the tube between *a* and *b*, then if the gas were all at the same temperature, its volume at 0° would be V_0+v_1 and at t would be $(V_0+v_1+v_2)(1+gt)$, where g is the coefficient of cubical expansion of glass. If the pressure were constant:

$$(V_0+v_1)(1+\alpha t)=(V_0+v_1+v_2)(1+gt).$$

But if the volume v_1 is at the temperature t_1, v_2 at t_2, and the initial and final pressures are $(H+h)$ and $(H'+h')$, the equation $pv/(1+\alpha t)=$const., for a fixed mass of gas (§ 21), gives:

$$[V_0(1+gt)/(1+\alpha t)+v_1(1+gt_1)/(1+\alpha t_1)+v_2(1+gt_2)/(1+\alpha t_2)](H'+h')$$
$$=[V_0+v_1(1+gt_1)/(1+\alpha t_1)](H+h),$$

$\therefore\ 1+\alpha t=(H'+h')(1+gt)/D$, where D stands for:

$$[H+h+v(H+h)/V_0(1+\alpha t_1)-v(H'+h')/V_0(1+\alpha t_1)-v'(H'+h')/V_0(1+\alpha t_2)],$$

where $v=v_1(1+gt_1)$ and $v'=v_2(1+gt_2)$. In the denominator, D, an approximate value of α is first substituted, then the value found from the equation. The new value of α may be resubstituted if necessary. Accurate determinations of V_0, v_1, v_2 (which are found by weighing mercury), and of t_1 and t_2, the manometer temperatures (read from a well-stirred water jacket), are necessary.

The theory of an apparatus containing gas with parts at different temperatures is important in gas thermometry and in many other experiments.[2] A mass m_1 of gas of mol. wt. M in a volume v_1 at a temperature T_1 exerts a pressure (§ 21) $p=(m_1RT_1/Mv_1)$, therefore $pv_1/T_1=m_1\boldsymbol{R}/M$. If the pressure is the same throughout, $p\Sigma(v_1/T_1)=(\boldsymbol{R}/M)\Sigma m_1$. If the gas is contained in another volume v_1' at a temperature T_1' and pressure p', $p'\Sigma(v_1'/T_1')=p\Sigma(v_1/T_1)$.

Barus [3] gave the general equation:

$$\Sigma\left[V\left(p'\cdot\frac{1+gt'}{1+\alpha t'}-p\cdot\frac{1+gt}{1+\alpha t}\right)\right]=A.$$

[1] *Mém. Acad. Sci.*, 1847, **21**, 15 (168); for a simple apparatus, see Schiff, *Z. phys. Chem.*, 1887, **1**, 68; Adams, *Phys. Rev.*, 1900, **10**, 178 (H_2SO_4 gauge).

[2] Voigt, " Thermodynamik," Leipzig, 1903, **1**, 6; Fischer, *Z. anorg. Chem.*, 1929, **184**, 333; Allen, *J.A.C.S.*, 1934, **56**, 2053.

[3] *U.S. Geol. Survey Bull.*, 1889, **8**, No. 54, 188, 210, where full details of calculations are given.

where V is a zero volume at the temperatures t' (t_1', t_2', . . .) and pressure p', and temperatures t (t_1, t_2, . . .) and pressure p, α is the coefficient of expansion of the gas (assumed ideal), g the coefficient of cubic expansion of the bulb, stem, etc., and A is proportional to the excess of volume at t' over that of a fixed mass of gas at t. In the constant volume apparatus, $A=0$, in the constant pressure apparatus $p'=p$.

In measurements of the pressure coefficient β, Regnault kept the mercury level constant at a mark a, which must be on the wide part of the tube, no consistent results being obtainable when it was on the capillary tube. (A fixed glass point, brought to contact with the adjustable mercury surface, as used by Brodie,[1] is preferable to a mark.) If the bulb is in ice and the barometer reading is H and the manometer reading h, and the corresponding readings are H' and h' with the bulb in steam at the temperature t (approximately 100°), then if V_0 is the volume of the bulb at 0° and v_1 the volume of the stem and tube up to the mark a, the equation for β is (if the manometer temperature is the same t_1 throughout, otherwise v_1 may be suitably corrected by multiplication by $(1+gt_1)$ and $(1+gt_2)$, as above):

$$[V_0+v_1/(1+\beta t_1)](H+h)=[V_0(1+gt)/(1+\beta t)+v_1/(1+\beta t_1)](H'+h'),$$

$$\therefore\ 1+\beta t=(1+gt)(H'+h')/D$$

$$D=H+h-v_1(H'+h'-H-h)/V_0(1+\beta t_1),$$

where, as before, an approximate value of β can be used in the denominator.[2]

Regnault found the following values of α at 1 atm. pressure (he found it very difficult to dry sulphur dioxide thoroughly):

Air	0·0036706	SO_2	0·0039028	C_2N_2	0·0038767
H_2	0·0036613	CO	0·0036688		
CO_2	0·0037099	N_2O	0·0037195		

In another method Regnault admitted dry air to a bulb of known volume heated in a steam bath, the pressure being atmospheric. The tip of the stem was then sealed, and after cooling the bulb was inverted in mercury and the tip broken off. The mercury entering the bulb was determined by weighing, and thence the change in volume of the gas between steam and air temperatures was calculated. Regnault found that the mercury rushing into the bulb on breaking the tip was apt to carry some outer air with it, which he supposed came from a film of air between the glass tube and the mercury, so that he surrounded the tube with an amalgamated brass collar which made contact with the mercury.

§ 17. Values of α and β

Regnault [3] found that β for air increased gradually as the pressure increased, indicating a deviation from Boyle's law, and the increase of β for carbon dioxide with pressure was larger than for air.[4] Regnault found that $1+100\alpha$ for air at 0° increased from 1·36706 at 760 mm. to 1·36964 at 2620 mm., and $1+100\beta$ from 1·36482 at 110 mm. to 1·37091 at 3656 mm. A correction pointed out by Mendeléeff,[5] for latitude and the absolute expansion of mercury, applied to the pressure coefficient β, makes the results of different observers more concordant.

1 *Phil. Trans.*, 1872, **162**, 435.
2 Porter, in Glazebrook, " Dict. of Applied Physics," 1922, **1**, 885.
3 *Ann. Chim.*, 1842, **4**, 5; Penning, *Arch. Néerl.*, 1924, **7**, 172 (various gases).
4 Regnault, *Mém. Acad. Sci.*, 1847, **21**, 110, 119; 1862, **26**, 565.
5 *Ber.*, 1877, **10**, 81.

Some accurate values of α and β for the range 0°–100° at the pressures stated are given in the table below.[1] Keyes [2] suggested that the values of α found with glass bulbs may be too high because an adsorbed moisture or gas film is partly driven off by heating, and he considered that results with metal and silica bulbs are more accurate. He remarked that Holborn and Henning [3] found for nitrogen a mean value of α of 0·0036703 in a glass bulb and 0·0036684 in a silica bulb, at 620 mm. I have no personal experience in this work, but on reading the various publications I have formed the opinion that figures after the fifth place (i.e. 0·1 per cent. accuracy) are significant only in unusually accurate experiments.

Coppock and Whytlaw-Gray,[4] who used a modification of Callendar's apparatus (§ 19) found irregular results with glass bulbs with easily condensable gases, and found results in good agreement with those of previous workers when they used silica bulbs. Regnault found that $\alpha > \beta$ for a gas more compressible than the ideal, and $\alpha < \beta$ for hydrogen, which is less compressible.[5]

Gas	p mm.	$\alpha \times 10^6$	Observer	p_0 mm.	$\beta \times 10^6$	Observer
He (0°–100°)	504·8	3658·9	Henning and Heuse (1921)	504·8	3659·5	Henning and Heuse (1921)
	520·5	3660·3	”	520·5	3659·9	”
	760·1	3659·1	”	760·1	3659·8	”
	1102·9	3658·2	”	1102·9	3660·1	”
	1116·5	3658·1	”	1116·5	3660·0	”
				760	3661·1	Cath and Onnes; Keesom *et al.* (1922–7)
				700	3662·55	Travers, Senter, and Jaquerod (1903)
				500	3662·8	”
H_2	760	3661	Regnault (1847)	760	3667	Regnault (1847)
	1000	3660·04	Chappuis (1903)	1000	3662·54	Chappuis (1903)
	762	3660·92	Richards and Mark (1903–5)			
	1095·3	3659·0	Henning and Heuse (1921)	1000	3662·7	Onnes and Boudin (1901)
	508·2	3660·2	”	700	3662·55	Travers, Senter, and Jaquerod (1903)
				1095·2	3662·3	Henning and Heuse (1921)
				508·2	3661·2	”
N_2	1000	3673·13	Chappuis (1903)	550	3668	Day and Clement (1908)
	1387	3677·5	”	985	3673	”
	760	3669·8	Eumorfopoulos (1914)	500	3668·46	Chappuis and Harker (1902)
	1105·3	3674·2	Henning and Heuse (1921)	760	3668	Regnault (1847)
	511·4	3667·9	”	1000	3674·4	Chappuis (1903)

[1] See also Landolt-Börnstein, " Tabellen," 5th edit., 1923, **1**, 114 f.; 1931, Ergzb. **2**, i, 67.
[2] *J.A.C.S.*, 1921, **43**, 1452.
[3] *Ann. Phys.*, 1911, **35**, 761.
[4] *Proc. Roy. Soc.*, 1934, **143**, 487.
[5] Moutier, " Thermodynamique," 1885, 42.

Gas	p mm.	$\alpha\times10^6$	Observer	p_0 mm.	$\beta\times10^6$	Observer
N_2	220·3	3663·0	Henning and Heuse (1921)	793·5	3671·8	Chappuis (1903)
				530·8	3668·3	Chappuis (1903)
				1105·3	3675·2	Henning and Heuse (1921)
				511·4	3667·5	,,
				220·3	3662·6	,,
O_2				500	3671·7	Makower and Noble (1903)
				700	3674	,,
Air	760	3670	Regnault (1847)	760	3665	Regnault (1847)
	760	3670·8	Eumorfopoulos (1914)	1000	3674·4	Chappuis
	1000	3672·8	Chappuis (1914)			
CO	760	3669	Regnault (1847)	760	3667	Regnault (1847)
	760	3674	Coppock and Whytlaw-Gray (1934)			
Cl_2	760	3883	Pier (1908)	760	3807	Pier (1908)
C_2N_2	760	3877	Regnault (1847)	760	3829	Regnault (1847)
CO_2	760	3710	Regnault (1847)	760	3688	Regnault (1847)
	761	3728·2	Richards and Mark (1903–5)	999	3726·2	Chappuis (1914)
	999	3741·4	Chappuis (1914)			
	1377	3770·3	,,			
	518	3707·8	,,			
	760 (12°–48°)	3725	Coppock and Whytlaw-Gray (1934)			
SO_2	760	3903	Regnault (1847)	760	3845	Regnault (1847)
NO	760	3679	Coppock and Whytlaw-Gray (1934)			
N_2O	760	3719	Regnault (1847)	760	3676	Regnault (1847)
SF_6	760 (12°–48°)	3808	Coppock and Whytlaw-Gray (1934)			
$(CH_3)_2O$	760 (12°–48°)	3920	Coppock and Whytlaw-Gray (1934)			

The *effect of pressure* on the values of α and β was investigated by Regnault,[1] and at much higher pressures by Andrews [2] and by Amagat.[3] The general result was that, for gases more compressible than according to Boyle's law, the coefficient of expansion is increased, for gases less compressible it is decreased, by increase of pressure. Some of Amagat's figures for α for carbon dioxide at 0°–10°, $\alpha=(1/V)\,.\,\Delta V/\Delta t$, are:

p atm.	75	100	200	500	1000
$\alpha\times10^5$	654	544	416	253	175

1 *Mém. Acad. Sci.*, 1847, **21**, 96; 1862, **26**, 565.
2 *Phil. Trans.*, 1876, **166**, 421.
3 *Compt. Rend.*, 1892, **115**, 771, 919, 1041, 1238; *Ann. Chim.*, 1893, **29**, 68; the unit of volume is the volume at the lower temperature.

and for β for nitrogen at 0°–100°, $\beta=(1/p) \cdot \Delta p/\Delta t$:

p atm.	100	200	300	400	500	600
$\beta\times10^5$	462	537	582	595	596	597

and for nitrogen at 0°–16° at very high pressures:

p atm.	1000	1200	1500	1800	2000	2400	2800
$\beta\times10^5$	550	510	471	475	468	448	424

Henning and Heuse [1] found the following effects of pressure (p mm. Hg):

N_2	$\alpha\times10^7=36604+0{\cdot}117p$	$\beta\times10^7=36604+0{\cdot}134p$
H_2	$\alpha\times10^7=36604-0{\cdot}012p$	$\beta\times10^7=36604+0{\cdot}017p$
He	$\alpha\times10^7=36604-0{\cdot}019p$	$\beta\times10^7=36604-0{\cdot}004p$

These give $1/T_0=0{\cdot}0036604$, therefore $T_0=273{\cdot}20°$ K. for the absolute temperature of 0° C., which is probably about 0·05° to 0·10° too high (§ 18).

The *effect of increase in temperature* is generally to lower the coefficient of expansion α or of tension β.[2] The following values of $\beta\times10^5$ for ethylene (p_0=37 atm.) were found by Amagat:

t° interval	0°–20°	20°–40°	40°–60°	60°–80°	80°–100°	100°–137·5°	137·5°–198·5°
$\beta\times10^5$	838	694	610	553	489	424	366

§ 18. Absolute Zero of Temperature

If equation (1), § 15, remained true at all temperatures, the volume V_t should become zero for a temperature $t=-1/\alpha$, or, since α is approximately 1/273 for a permanent gas, at a temperature −273° C. This is called the *absolute zero.* Similarly (3), § 15, shows that the pressure should vanish at −273° C., which is a more intelligible result. These equations hold for the so-called *ideal* (or *perfect*) *gas,* for which α or β can be calculated (see § 30.VII C) from the observed values for an actual gas. The following values of the absolute temperature T_0 of 0° C. have been so found:

273·09	D. Berthelot, *Z. Elektrochem.*, 1904, **10**, 621.
273·13	Eumorfopoulos, *Proc. Roy. Soc.*, 1914, **90**, 189 (const. press. N_2 thermometer; Joule-Thomson effect).
273·20	Henning and Heuse, *Z. Phys.*, 1921, **5**, 285; Henning, *Z. Elektrochem.*, 1921, **27**, 494; 1922, **28**, 248 (H_2, He, N_2); Heuse, *Z. Phys.*, 1926, **37**, 157.
273·09	Keesom and Onnes, *Arch. Néerl.*, 1925, **9**, 114, with a long critical discussion of all experimental values.
273·12–273·13	Smith and Taylor, *J.A.C.S.*, 1923, **45**, 2125.
273·16	Heuse and Otto, *Ann. Phys.*, 1929, **2**, 1012 (He, H_2, N_2); 1930, **4**, 778 (Ne); Holborn and Otto, *Z. Phys.*, 1924, **30**, 320; 1925, **33**, 1; 1926, **38**, 359 (A, H_2, O_2, N_2).
273·207	Neusser, *Phys. Z.*, 1932, **33**, 76.
273·16±0·02	Roebuck, *Phys. Rev.*, 1936, **50**, 370.
273·14	Keesom, van der Horst, and Taconis, *Physica*, 1934, **1**, 324; Keesom, *Comm. Leiden*, 1936, Suppl. **80***a*.
273·144	Keesom and Tuyn, *Trav. et Mém. Bur. Internat. Poids et Més.*, 1936, **20**; *Comm. Leiden*, Suppl. **78** (copious bibl.); Keesom and Bijl, *Physica*, 1937, **4**, 305.

[1] *Z. Elektrochem.*, 1921, **27**, 494; 1922, **28**, 248; peculiar results at low pressures found by Melander, *Ann. Phys.*, 1892, **47**, 135, may have been due to moisture.

[2] Hirn, "Théorie Mécanique de la Chaleur," Paris, 1862, 307, 367; Amagat, *locc. cit.* For calculations by van der Waals's equation, see § 11.VII C. V. Meyer and Langer, *Ber.*, 1885, **18**, 1501; "Pyrochemische Untersuchungen," Brunswick, 1885, 5; found that O_2, N_2, CO_2, and SO_2 approximately obey Gay-Lussac's law up to 1700° C.

273·16	Kinoshita and Oishi, *Phil. Mag.*, 1937, **24**, 52 (He, Ne, H_2, N_2).
273·16	Committee on Low Temperature, National Research Council, U.S.A., 1938; Birge, *Rep. Progr. Phys.*, 1942, **8** 90.
273·165±0·015	Beattie, in " Temperature. Its Measurement and Control," New York. 1941, 74.
273·170	Roebuck and Murrell, in " Temperature. Its Measurement and Control," New York, 1941, 60.
273·15	de Groot, *Nederl. Tidjschr. Natuurkde.*, 1942, **9**, 497; *Amer. Chem. Abstr.*, 1944, **38**, 3884; Beattie and Edwards, *J.A.C.S.*, 1948, **70**, 3382 (adopted by International Conference).

The value 273·16° is suggested,[1] but the second decimal, it is clear, is doubtful to at least 0·03°, and **273·1**° seems the most probable value [2] to the accuracy attainable. *Absolute* temperatures to three decimal places are unjustifiable, especially when no value of T_0 is given.[3] Centigrade temperature may be known to three or four decimal places. It may be noted that in meterorology $x°$ a. is often used for $x°$ K. (=Kelvin, see § 37.II), although the latter symbol was adopted by the Association Internationale du Froid.[4] Marvin [5] and Whipple [6] proposed an " approximate " absolute scale of $t°$ C.+273·0.

Although the absolute zero has been regarded as a mathematical fiction, thermodynamics and experiment (Section VI C) show that it is a physical reality,[7] although the concept of zero-point energy (§ 11.IV) has made it less easy to understand kinetically than formerly.

§ 19. Air Thermometers

The air thermometer for moderate temperatures has often been used.[8] After Regnault's work, the most significant improvement was introduced by Deville and Troost (1864), and Callendar (1891), in the use of a compensation for the connecting tubes not in the heated zone by having on the other side of the manometer a sealed duplicate of these tubes, without a bulb, which was situated alongside the actual connecting tubes. Any pressure changes in the latter were duplicated in the " dummy " system, and by acting on the other side of the manometer compensated the change in the actual measuring system.

1 Kaye and Laby, " Tables of Physical and Chemical Constants," 1941, 54; 1948, 59; Birge, *Rep. Progr. Phys.*, 1942, **8**, 90.

2 Batuecas, *Z. phys. Chem.*, 1939, **183**, 438.

3 Several papers in *J.A.C.S.* since 1920 contain such data.

4 *Chem. Ztg.*, 1911, **35**, 3. On the Fahrenheit scale, the absolute temperature is found by adding 459·44 to °F.: " Dict. of Applied Physics," 1922, **1**, 585.

5 *Science*, 1918, **47**, 267.

6 *Proc. Phys. Soc.*, 1919, **31**, 237.

7 O. E. Meyer, " Kinetic Theory of Gases," 1899, 29; Dushman, *Gen. Elec. Rev.*, 1915, **18**, 93, 238.

8 Flaugergues, *J. de Phys.*, 1813, **77**, 273; Regnault, *Ann. Chim.*, 1842, **5**, 83; Balfour Stewart, *Phil. Trans.*, 1863, **153**, 425; Deville and Troost, *Compt. Rend.*, 1864, **59**, 162; Berthelot, *Ann. Chim.*, 1868, **13**, 135; *Phil. Mag.*, 1868, **35**, 423; Jolly, *Ann. Phys.*, Poggendorff Jubelbd., 1874, 82; Callendar, *Phil. Trans.*, 1887, **175**, 161; *Proc. Roy. Soc.*, 1891–2, **50**, 247 (compensation for connecting tubes); 1914, **90**, 189; Bottomley, *Phil. Mag.*, 1888, **26**, 149; Mazzotto, *Nuov. Cim.*, 1891, **29**, 142; Holborn and Wien, *Ann. Phys.*, 1892, **47**, 107; 1895, **56**, 360; V. Meyer and Riddle, *Ber.*, 1893, **26**, 2443; 1894, **27**, 766; V. Meyer, Riddle, and Lamb, *ibid.*, 1894, **27**, 3129 (high temp.); L. Meyer, *Ber*, 1893, **26**, 1047; Erskine Murray, *J. Phys. Chem.*, 1897, **1**, 714; Holborn and Day, *Ann. Phys.*, 1899, **68**, 817 (to 1150°); 1900, **2**, 505; Kapp, *ibid.*, 1901, **5**, 905; Travers, " Study of Gases," 1901, 151 (Callendar's); Holborn and Valentiner, *Ann. Phys.*, 1907, **22**, 1; Eumorfopoulos, *Proc. Roy. Soc.*, 1908, **81**, 339; Miller, *Phil. Mag.*, 1910, **20**, 296; Day, Sosman, and Allen, " High Temperature Gas Thermometry," Carnegie Inst., Washington, 1911; Henning, *Z. Elektrochem.*, 1913, **19**, 185; Madsen and Herber, *Gas J.*, 1920, **151**, 338 (differential); Noyes, *J.A.C.S.*, 1925, **47**, 1942.

The *constant pressure* gas thermometer developed by Callendar is represented in its final form by the apparatus (Fig. 26.VII A) used by Eumorfopoulos, whose work was of a high standard. T is the thermometer bulb of Jena 6 III glass connected by capillary tubes with a tap A and second bulb E and by a tap M to the gauges, described below. E is connected with an inlet for mercury at L and an outlet at K. The reservoir H was used in setting up the apparatus but not in the actual experiments. G is a small air-trap. Alongside this thermometric system was the compensating system of tubes, exactly similar except that the bulb T is missing, so that the capillary tube passed straight across from D to B and thence to a stopcock alongside A; it contained a bulb similar to and alongside E. The two systems were connected together by the gauges shown in Fig. 27.VII A. NOP is a rough-adjustment mercury gauge, NQP a fine-adjustment oil gauge, and O and Q are three-way taps. The plane of Fig. 27.VII A is at

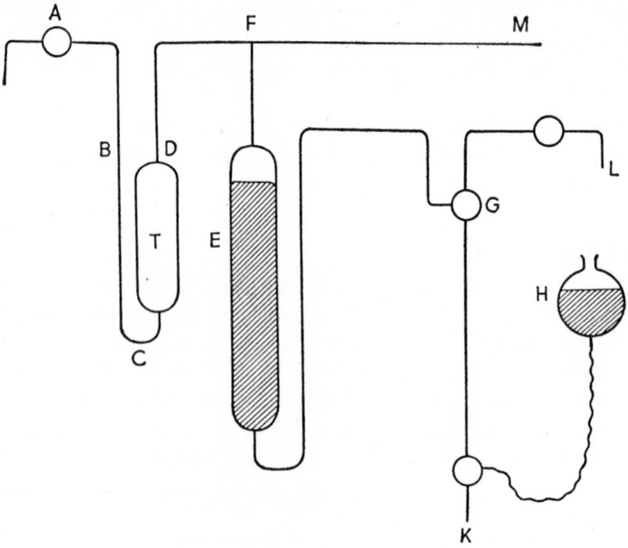

FIG. 26.VII A. Constant Pressure Gas Thermometer (Eumorfopoulos)

right angles to that of Fig. 26.VII A. The air in T is limited towards A by a mercury thread in the horizontal tube, and towards the gauges by the mercury and oil they contain, while E, which was always immersed in ice along with the similar compensating bulb, contains a variable amount of mercury, also occupying the capillary tubes to the outlets at H, K, and L. The standard pressure on the thermometer side was adjusted to the air pressure on the compensating side in the bulb corresponding with E, the two masses of air being as nearly equal as possible. Pressure differences were read on the oil gauge to 0·001 cm. by a microscope. The open end of each mercury delivery tube was cut off and ground at 45°. The volume of the bulb T was accurately measured. The two E bulbs were kept at 0° C. $=T_0$° K. When T was heated to any desired temperature T, mercury was added or removed through L, and this mercury was weighed.[1] The volume change was calculated from this weight of mercury.

[1] The paper does not give this information, but it is contained in Callendar's paper, *Phil. Trans.*, 1887, **178**, 161. On correction of gas thermometer scale, see Callendar, *Proc. Phys. Soc.*, 1901–3, **18**, 282. On a modification of Callendar's apparatus, see Coppock and Whytlaw-Gray, *Proc. Roy. Soc.*, 1934, **143**, 487.

In a discussion of the relative merits of (1) the constant-pressure and (2) the constant-volume gas thermometer, Day and Sosman [1] remarked that (1) has been almost entirely used by Callendar and his associates, and has never been really developed above the b.p. of sulphur. It has been claimed that it has the advantages that (i) the apparatus and calculations are simple, (ii) the internal pressure on the bulb does not increase with the temperature, and hence the expansion of the bulb due to this does not arise, and (iii) the accuracy is limited only by the precision with which weighings can be made. Its disadvantages, recognised by Callendar and by Eumorfopoulos, are (i) a permanent change in the volume of the bulb after each exposure to higher temperatures, (ii) changes and uncertainties in the coefficient of expansion of the bulb material (chiefly glass and porcelain),[2] and (iii) inexact knowledge of the coefficient of expansion of mercury through an adequate temperature range. These errors can be greatly reduced by a judicious selection of the bulb material and careful study.

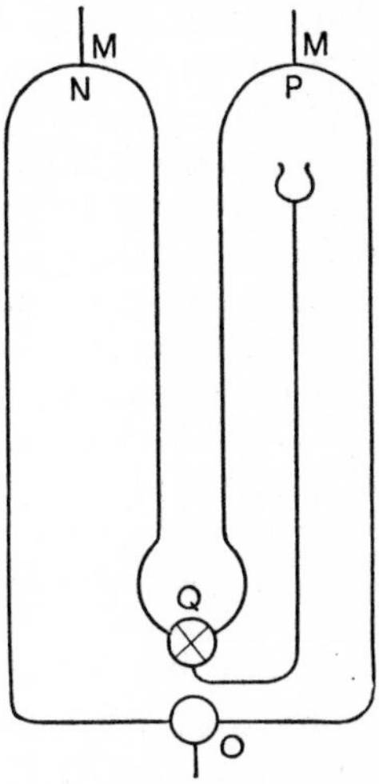

FIG. 27.VII A. Gauges for Constant Pressure Gas Thermometer

In the case of (2) there are three primary correction factors in which sources of error may lie: [3] (i) the dead space ratio (unheated part to heated part), which introduces quite large corrections at higher temperatures, e.g. for the ratio 0·01 at 500° it brings in 13° and at 1000°, 44°; (ii) the thermal expansion of the bulb, most appreciable with glass and platinum–iridium, for both of which it amounts to about 5° at 500°, but small with fused silica; (iii) the expansion of the bulb due to internal pressure, quite a small correction, not amounting to 1° even at 1500°.

The dead-space ratio can be reduced to quite small values, and its temperature and volume determined with sufficient accuracy to make it only a minor source of error. The expansion coefficient of the bulb is the most serious source of error, and difficulties arise in the crystallisation of glass and silica at high temperatures, the volatilisation of iridium from the alloy with platinum at high temperatures, etc. Day and Sosman emphasised that the most essential experimental precaution is uniformity of temperature of the bulb, which requires a large heating space; a space sufficient to enclose a 200-ml. bulb, all of which is to have a temperature of 1500°±5°, has probably never been available. Temperature control of the long manometer columns is also necessary, since pressures of 2 or 3 atm. may be developed.

Reading a mercury level by an image of a point reflected in a surface was used by Gay-Lussac; [4] it is doubtful if the complicated electrical contacts proposed [5] have any advantage when the surface is available for visual

[1] In Glazebrook, " Dict. of Applied Physics," 1922, **1**, 867.

[2] Callendar, *Proc. Roy. Soc.*, 1908, **81**, 363.

[3] Henning, " Die Grundlagen der Temperaturmessung," Brunswick, 1915, 30 (const. vol.), 57 (const. press).

[4] In Biot, " Traité de Physique," 1816, **1**, 291; Brodie, *Phil. Trans.*, 1872, **162**, 435; Knudsen, *Ann. Phys.*, 1910, **33**, 1435; Ostwald-Luther-Drucker, " Physiko-chemische Messungen," 5th edit., Leipzig, 1931, 197.

[5] Richards and Mark, *Z. phys. Chem.*, 1903, **43**, 475; Maier, *Ann. Phys.*, 1910, **31**, 423; Carver, *J.A.C.S.*, 1923, **45**, 59; Ewald, *Z. Instr.*, 1927, **47**, 97.

inspection. A differential air thermometer for low temperatures was described by Noyes.[1]

§ 20. Gas Thermometers

The constant-volume hydrogen thermometer was used as a precision standard, adopted as international, by Chappius.[2] It consisted of a 1·039 lit. platinum–iridium alloy cylindrical bulb, 110 cm. long and 36 mm. outer diam., with 1 mm. thick walls, connected with a mercury manometer by a platinum capillary tube, 1 m. long and 0·7 mm. bore. A barometer dipped into the open limb of the mercury manometer; in the closed limb, connected with the bulb, the mercury level was brought into coincidence with a fine point near the top so that the dead space (gas) in the manometer was less than 1/1000 of the volume of the bulb; a correction for this and for the expansion of the bulb was applied, and an accuracy of 0·002° between −20° and +100° was claimed. With this thermometer, four mercury in glass thermometers were standardised from 5° to 78°, and became " the custodians of the international temperature scale from 0° to 100°, and all other standard thermometers in the world's various national bureaus of standards have been calibrated by comparison with these four." [3]

The gas thermometer with platinum–iridium, platinum–rhodium, iridium, glass, glazed porcelain, and quartz bulbs containing hydrogen (which permeates platinum and quartz at higher temperatures), helium (which permeates quartz at quite low temperatures), or nitrogen, has been used at high temperatures (Day and Sosman used nitrogen in a platinum–rhodium bulb up to 1600°).[4] Hydrogen and helium thermometers have been used at low temperatures.[5] In this case precautions to minimise thermal diffusion (§ 16.III) are necessary.

[1] *J.A.C.S.*, 1925, **47**, 1942.

[2] *Trav. et Mém. Bur. Internat. Poids et Més.*, 1888, **6**; 1907, **13**; *Arch. Sci. Phys. Nat.*, 1888, **20**, 5; *Phil. Mag.*, 1900, **50**, 433; W. Thomson, " Math. and Phys. Papers," 1890, **3**, 182; 1911, **5**, 99 (const. p H_2); Harker and Chappuis, *Phil. Trans.*, 1900, **194**, 37; Buckingham, *Bur. Stand. Bull.*, 1907, **3**, 237 (correction to thermodynamic scale); Henning, *Z. Elektrochem.*, 1913, **19**, 185; " Die Grundlagen der Temperaturmessung," 1915, 30; Burgess, *Phys. Z.*, 1913, **14**, 152; Preston, " Theory of Heat," 3rd edit., 1919, 138 (formula); Henning, in Geiger and Scheel " Handbuch der Physik," 1926, **9**, 521.

[3] Day and Sosman, in Glazebrook, " Dict. of Applied Physics," 1922, **1**, 848.

[4] Callendar, *Proc. Roy. Soc.*, 1891, **50**, 247; *Phil. Mag.*, 1899, **48**, 519 (const. press.); Holborn and Wien, *Ann. Phys.*, 1892, **47**, 107; 1895, **56**, 360; Holborn and Day, *ibid.*, 1899, **68**, 817; 1900, **2**, 505; Travers, Senter, and Jaquerod, *Z. phys. Chem.*, 1903, **45**, 416; Jacquerod and Perrot, *Compt. Rend.*, 1904, **138**, 1032; Jaquerod and Wassmer, *J. Chim. Phys.*, 1904, **2**, 53; Holborn and Valentiner, *Ann. Phys.*, 1907, **22**, 1; Day and Clement, *Amer. J. Sci.*, 1908, **26**, 405; Day and Sosman, *ibid.*, 1910, **29**, 93; 1912, **33**, 517; *Ann. Phys.*, 1912, **38**, 849; *Carnegie Inst. Publ.*, 1911, **157**; Holborn and Henning, *Ann. Phys.*, 1911, **35**, 761; Henning, *Z. Elektrochem.*, 1913, **19**, 185; Henning and Heuse, *Z. Phys.*, 1921, **5**, 258; Aoyama and Kanda, *J. Chem. Soc. Japan*, 1934, **55**, 15 (H_2 low temp.).

[5] Onnes and Boudin, *Proc. K. Akad. Wetens. Amsterdam*, 1900, **3**, 299 (*Comm. Leiden*, **60**; H_2); Onnes and Meilink, *ibid.*, 1902, **4**, 495 (*Comm. Leiden*, **70**; Pt and H_2 thermoms.); Keesom, *ibid.*, 1903, **6**, 541 (*Comm. Leiden*, **88**; O_2 and CO_2); Meilink, *ibid.*, 1904, **7**, 290 (*Comm. Leiden*, **93**; Pt and H_2 thermoms.); Onnes and Braak, *ibid.*, 1906–7, **9**, 367 (*Comm. Leiden*, **95***e*, H_2); 1907, **9**, 775 (*Comm. Leiden*, **97***b*, H_2); 1907–8, **10**, 429 (*Comm. Leiden*, **101***b*, H_2), 589 (*Comm. Leiden*, **102***b*, He), 743 (*Comm. Leiden*, **102***d*, gas thermoms.); Onnes and Clay, *ibid.*, 1907–8, **10**, 200 (*Comm. Leiden*, **99***b*, Pt calibr.), 422 (*Comm. Leiden*, **101***a*, H_2); Onnes and Braak, *ibid.*, 1908, **11**, 333 (*Comm. Leiden*, **107***a*, O_2 v. pr. thermom.); Onnes, *ibid.*, 1909, **12**, 175 (*Comm. Leiden*, **112**; He temps. by He gas thermom.); Onnes, *ibid.*, 1911, **13**, 1093 (*Comm. Leiden*, **119**; He temps.); 1911, **14**, 678 (*Comm. Leiden*, **124***b*); Onnes and Holst, *ibid.*, 1914, **17**, 501 (*Comm. Leiden*, **141***a*, Pt and H_2); " Sur la Thérmometrie des basses Températures," *Comm. Leiden*, 1913, Suppl. **34***a*; Onnes and Weber, *ibid.*, 1915, **18**, 493 (*Comm. Leiden*, **147***b*, He temp. with He gas thermom.); Blue and Hicks, *J.A.C.S.*, 1937,

Jacyna [1] claimed that the constant-pressure helium thermometer is more accurate than the constant-volume at temperatures higher than −100° C.

The calculation of the correction for a constant-pressure or constant-volume gas thermometer is now usually made by the so-called virial equation (§ 10) in the form $PV=RT(1+B_v/V)\simeq RT+B_vP$, where B_v is a second virial coefficient, determinable experimentally or from the characteristic equation. If α and β are the mean coefficients of expansion and pressure (§ 16) for an actual gas, and γ the value of α or β for the ideal gas (for which both are equal), then, if t_α and t_β are the Centigrade temperatures found by the constant-pressure and constant-volume gas thermometers, respectively, it is easily shown [2] that:

$$t-t_\alpha=(\alpha-\gamma)t/\gamma-(T_0B_t-TB_0)/V_0,$$
$$t-t_\beta=(\beta-\gamma)t/\gamma-(B_t-B_0)T/V_0,$$

where t is the *thermodynamic* Centigrade temperature. For the helium constant-volume thermometer the correction is (necessarily) zero at 0° and 100° C., has a small negative value between 0° and 100°, and an increasing positive value below 0° and above 100°.

The International Committee on Weights and Measures in 1887 adopted as a temperature scale the Centigrade constant-volume hydrogen scale with an initial pressure of 1000 mm. Hg, this being called the *normal hydrogen scale*. For temperatures below 0° C. a Centigrade constant-volume *helium scale* with an initial pressure of 1000 mm. Hg was used. For temperatures above 100° C. the constant-volume *nitrogen scale* with an initial pressure of 500 mm. Hg was largely used. These different scales are not actually consistent in forming a continuous range, and none gives exactly the temperature as defined on the so-called *absolute* or *thermodynamic scale*. The details of the way in which the corrections have been found will be mentioned later; here the corrections only are given.

In 1922, Day and Sosman [3] gave the limits of divergence of gas temperatures (various types of thermometers) from thermodynamic absolute temperatures as follows:

° C.	Δ	° C.	Δ
−250	0·05	200	0·05
−100	0·02	400	0·1
0	0·003	1000	1·0
50	0·006	1500	2·0
100	0·01		

The corrections which must be *added* to the readings of gas thermometers (derived from the assumption that the gas obeys Boyle's law and Charles's law) in order to reduce them to the thermodynamic scale (§ 36.II) are given below.[4]

59, 1962 (He to 11° K.); Schmidt and Keesom, *Physica*, 1937, **4**, 963, 971 (*Comm. Leiden*, **250***b*, *c*); Woodcock, *Canad. J. Res.*, 1938, **16** A, 133 (He).

[1] *Bull. Acad. Polon.*, 1937 A, 97.

[2] Burton, Smith, and Wilhelm, " Phenomena at the Temperature of Liquid Helium," New York, 1940, 38 f.

[3] Glazebrook, " Dict. of Applied Physics," 1922, **1**, 846.

[4] Calculated from measurements of departure from Boyle's law by Holborn and Otto, *Z. Phys.*, 1924, **30**, 320; 1925, **33**, 1; 1926, **38**, 359; cf. Burgess, *J. Chim. Phys.*, 1913, **11**, 529; for H_2 thermometer, see Onnes and Braak, *Proc. K. Akad. Wetens. Amsterdam*, 1907, **9**, 775 (*Comm. Leiden*, **97***b*); 1907–8, **10**, 204 (*Comm. Leiden*, **101**); Giauque, Buffington, and Schulze,

The initial pressure of gas at 0° C. is 1000 mm. Hg. The values at constant volume below −180° C. agree with the results of Onnes; they are larger for hydrogen and helium thermometers than earlier measurements indicated, but the differences between the two sets of corrections (these and the earlier ones) are of the order of the experimental errors. Except when − is given, the sign is +. Slightly different values are given by Keesom and Tuyn.[1]

I. *Constant Pressure*				II. *Constant Volume*			
t° C.	He	H_2	N_2	*t*° C.	He	H_2	N_2
450	0·012	—	0·670	450	0·061	—	0·190
400	·010	—	·550	400	·046	—	·150
350	·008	—	·430	350	·034	—	·110
300	·006	—	·320	300	·023	—	·080
250	·004	·035	·225	250	·015	·032	·050
200	·002	·020	·132	200	·008	·017	·027
150	·001	·008	·056	150	·003	·007	·011
100	·000	·000	·000	100	·000	·000	·000
50	·000	−0·003	−0·025	50	−0·001	−0·002	−0·004
0	·000	·000	·000	0	·000	·000	·000
−25	·001	·007	·039	−25	·002	·003	·006
−50	·002	·018	·112	−50	·004	·006	·015
−75	·004	·032	·228	−75	·006	·010	·029
−100	·006	·052	·399	−100	·009	·015	·052
−125	·011	·084	·686	−125	·013	·021	·084
−150	·018	·139	—	−150	·018	·028	—
−175	·028	·230	—	−175	·023	·037	—
−200	·046	·368	—	−200	·028	·047	—
−225	·077	—	—	−225	·034	·060	—
−250	·195	—	—	−250	·043	—	—
−260	·500	—	—	−260	·048	—	—

Thus if the constant-pressure N_2 thermometer reading (based on the equation in § 16) is 150°, the true thermodynamic temperature is 150·056°.

§ 21. The General Gas Law

Consider a fixed mass of a gas in the state P_1, V_1, t_1 and let it be converted into the state P_2, V_2, t_2 in two stages:

(i) While the temperature remains constant at t_1 change the pressure from P_1 to P_2 and let the volume become V. From Boyle's law, $P_1V_1=P_2V$, therefore $V=P_1V_1/P_2$ (1).

J.A.C.S., 1927, **49**, 2343; Giauque, Johnston, and Kelley, *ibid.*, 1927, **49**, 2367 (adsorption on bulb at low temps.); Southard and Milner, *ibid.*, 1933, **55**, 4384; on He thermometer from 12° K. see Aston, Willihnganz, and Messerly, *ibid.*, 1935, **57**, 1642; on comparison of H_2 and He thermometers, see Cath and Onnes, *Comm. Leiden*, 1922, **156*a***; on low-temp. gas thermometry, see Henning, *Ann. Phys.*, 1913, **40**, 635; 1913, **41**, 1064; 1914, **43**, 282; *Z. phys.*, 1921, **5**, 264; Heuse and Otto, *Ann. Phys.*, 1931, **9**, 486.

[1] *Comm. Leiden*, 1936, Suppl. **78**. Precision constant-volume and constant-pressure gas thermometry was fully discussed by Beattie, Jacobus, Gaines, Benedict, and Blaisdell, *Proc. Amer. Acad.*, 1941, **74**, 327; Beattie, Benedict, and Kaye, *ibid.*, 1941, **74**, 343; Beattie, Blaisdell, Kaye, Gerry, and Johnson, *ibid.*, 1941, **74**, 371 (coeff. expans. and compressibility of vitreous silica and thermal expansion of mercury); Beattie, Blaisdell, and Kaye, *ibid.*. 1941, **74**, 389 (capillary depression of mercury); Keyes, in "Temperature. Its Measurement and Control," New York, 1941, 45 (*pv* values); Cragoe, *ibid.*, 89 (criticism of Holborn and Otto's unit).

(ii) While the pressure remains constant at P_2 change the temperature from t_1 to t_2. The volume then changes to V_2 and by Charles's law, $V_2/V=(1+\alpha t_2)/(1+\alpha t_1)$ (2), where α is the coefficient of expansion. From (1) and (2):

$$V_2 \,.\, P_2/P_1V_1=P_2V_2/P_1V_1=(1+\alpha t_2)/(1+\alpha t_1).$$

If $t_1=0°$ C., $t_2=t°$ C., $PV/P_0V_0=1+\alpha t$, or

$$PV=P_0V_0(1+\alpha t)=(P_0V_0/\alpha)(1/\alpha+t) \quad . \; . \; . \; . \; . \quad (3)$$

For 1 g. of gas, P_0V_0/α has a constant value (since P_0V_0 is constant, by Boyle's law), which Clapeyron [1] denoted by R; to avoid confusion with the molar gas constant $\boldsymbol{R}$ it will here be denoted by r:

$$PV=r(t+1/\alpha) \quad . \; . \; . \; . \; . \; . \; . \; . \; . \quad (4)$$

He took $1/\alpha=267$ from Gay-Lussac's experiments, but the accurate value for an ideal gas (§ 18) is 273·1, hence:

$$PV=r(t+a)=r(t+273{\cdot}1)=rT \quad . \; . \; . \; . \; . \; . \quad (5)$$

where[2] $a=1/\alpha$, and $T=t+273{\cdot}1$ is the absolute temperature on the ideal Centigrade gas scale (see § 36.II). The value of r is a characteristic constant for each gas; if $P=1$ atm., $t=0$, then $r=v/273{\cdot}1$, where v is the specific volume at S.T.P.

It is obviously possible to choose masses $M_1, M_2, \ldots$ of different gases for which $M_1r_1=M_2r_2=\ldots=$const., at a given temperature and pressure, since then V is proportional to the mass. If the mass in g. of any one standard gas is fixed, the Mr values of all other gases are equal to that for the chosen mass of standard gas. If the latter is chosen as 32·0000 g. of oxygen in the ideal state at S.T.P. (see § 15.VII D), called the *molar weight* of oxygen, the masses M_1, $M_2 \ldots$, in g. of the other gases (also in the ideal state) are then called their *molar weights*. If this value of Mr is denoted by $\boldsymbol{R}$, then for a molar weight of *any* ideal gas:

$$PV=\boldsymbol{R}T \quad . \; . \; . \; . \; . \; . \; . \; . \; . \; . \; . \quad (6)$$

where $\boldsymbol{R}$ is called the *general gas constant.* Equation (6) is due to Horstmann [3] (who wrote it $up=RT$). For n molar weights, or *mols*,[4] at the same pressure and temperature, the volume is n times that of 1 mol, i.e. is equal to nV, hence (6) becomes:

$$PV=n\boldsymbol{R}T \quad . \; . \; . \; . \; . \; . \; . \; . \; . \; . \quad (7)$$

At 273·09° K. and under 1 atm. pressure the volume of 1 mol of ideal gas,

[1] *J. de l'École Polytechn.*, 1834, **14**, 153; Taylor's *Scientific Memoirs*, 1837, **1**, 347; Guldberg, *Förhl. Vidensk.-Selsk. Christiania*, 1867, 140, 159; Ostwald's *Klassiker*, 1903, **139**, 6; Hoppe, *Z. Elektrochem.*, 1919, **25**, 216, 324, traced the symbol R back to Newton's viscosity formula, R (resistance)$=\alpha c/r$, where c=velocity, and showed that the kinetic theory values (see §1.VII F), $nmcl/3=\alpha$, where l=mean free path (§ 20.III) and $l\simeq r$, give $R=pv/T$. This is quite accidental, however.

[2] Clausius, *Ann. Phys.*, 1850, **79**, 368, who took $a=273$; " The Mechanical Theory of Heat," 1879, 41. The symbol R for *unit mass* is still used in many physical works, and Jeans, " The Kinetic Theory of Gases," 1940, 28, used it for Boltzmann's constant (§ 1.IV), the gas constant per *molecule*, $\boldsymbol{k}=\boldsymbol{R}/N$.

[3] *Ann.*, 1873, **170**, 192; Ostwald's *Klassiker*, 1903, **137**, 31; Kleeman, *Z. Elektrochem.*, 1931, **37**, 77, 371, suggested $pV^{1+\alpha}=\boldsymbol{R}T^{1+\beta}$, where α and β are small positive quantities.

[4] Ostwald, " Outlines of General Chemistry," 3rd edit., transl. Taylor, 1912, 41 (" mol "); Nernst, " Theoretical Chemistry," transl. Tizard, 1911, 40 (" mol "); the name " mole " is often used, since it gives the international pronunciation.

the *molar volume*, is (§14.VII D) $V_m=22{\cdot}414$ lit., therefore[1] $\boldsymbol{R}=PV/T=1\times 22{\cdot}414/273{\cdot}09=0{\cdot}08207$ lit. atm./1° C. mol.

In other units (see §13, II) the values per mol are: $\boldsymbol{R}=82{\cdot}07$ ml. [" c.c. "] atm./1° C.=84801 g.cm./1° C.=1·9875 g.cal./1° C.=8316 abs. joules/1° C.= 8312 internat. joules/1° C.

Corrections of gaseous volumes to standard temperature and pressure[2] (0° C. and 760 mm. Hg barometer) are conveniently made by using (7) in this form, or (as the mass of gas is fixed) by $p_1v_1/T_1=p_2v_2/T_2$. If the volume and pressure units are chosen arbitrarily, the last form is true for all units. E.g. 500 ml. of air at 15° C. and 750 mm. pressure become v_0 ml. at S.T.P., where $750\times 500/288=760v_0/273$, therefore $v_0=467{\cdot}7$ ml. Apparatus for the automatic reduction of a gas volume to S.T.P., apparently first used by Davy,[3] has often been described.[4] Nomographic charts[5] can be used in calculations.

The deviations from the ideal gas laws may become very marked at very high pressures or even at fairly high pressures at low temperatures. Bridgman[6] found $pV/\boldsymbol{R}T=13{\cdot}2$ for nitrogen at 65° C. and 15,000 kg./cm.^{2} (theoret.= 1 at 0° C.), and Buchmann[7] found values of $pV/\boldsymbol{R}T$ up to 12·5 for helium at 13·5° to 20·4° abs. and 200 kg./cm.^{2} A convenient function for showing the deviations from the ideal state is[8] $\alpha=\boldsymbol{R}T/p-V$, for 1 mol, which is zero in the ideal state. The " residual," α, is well adapted to graphical methods, especially if a reduced equation (§ 16, VII C), is used.[9] If α_r, α_c are the reduced and critical values of α ($\alpha_r=\alpha/\alpha_c$):

$$V/\alpha_c=(\boldsymbol{R}T_c/p_c\alpha_c)(\vartheta/\pi)-\alpha_r,$$

where $\pi=p/p_c$ and $\vartheta=T/T_c$. The ratio $\boldsymbol{R}T_c/p_c\alpha_c$ is practically constant for a series of hydrocarbons. The values of α_r are plotted against those of π.

[1] Holborn, *Z. Phys.*, 1921, **6**, 69 (0·08204; 1·986 g.cal./1°); " Internat. Crit. Tables," 1926, **1**, 17 (0·08206, $8{\cdot}313\times 10^7$ ergs/1°, with $g=980{\cdot}665$); Partington, " Chemical Thermodynamics," 1940, 214; Birge, *Rep. Progr. Phys.*, 1942, **8**, 90 (0·08205; $8{\cdot}31436\times 10^7$ ergs/1°; 1·98646 g.cal./1°—the last two decimal places are superfluous); Moles, *Compt. Rend.*, 1942, **214**, 424 (0·082056, with $T_0=273{\cdot}15°$; $V_m=22{\cdot}4137$ lit.); de Groot, *Nederl. Tijdschr. Natuurkde.*, 1942, **9**, 497; *Amer. Chem. Abstr.*, 1944, **38**, 3884 (1·98725 g.cal./1°; $V_m=22{\cdot}414$, as used by Guye and Batuecas, *Helv. Chim. Acta*, 1922, **5**, 532). Since $\boldsymbol{R}$ always refers to 1 mol it seems superfluous to specify this, but cf. Butkow, *Sow. Phys. Z.*, 1937, **12**, 485. The distinction between " molecular weight " and " mol," made by Pohl, *Phys. Z.*, 1942, **43**, 531; Westphal, *ibid.*, 1942, **43**, 329; Duncanson, *Phil. Mag.*, 1944, **35**, 73, 81, seems unimportant.

[2] See e.g. Partington and Stratton, " Intermediate Chemical Calculations," 1946, 4; Meyer, *J. Chem. Educ.*, 1946, **21**, 31.

[3] *J. Roy. Inst.*, 1800, **1**, 45; " Works," 1839, **2**, 232.

[4] Hall, *Quart. J. Sci.*, 1818, **5**, 52; Faraday, " Chemical Manipulation," 1842, 386; Barnes, *J.C.S.*, 1881, **39**, 462; Vernon Harcourt, *Proc. Roy. Soc.*, 1882, **34**, 166 (" aerorthometer "); Kreusler, *Ber.*, 1884, **17**, 29; Winkler, *ibid.*, 1885, **18**, 2533; Lunge, *ibid.*, 1890, **23**, 440; Japp, *J.C.S.*, 1891, **59**, 894; Than, *Z. phys. Chem.*, 1896, **20**, 307; Davis, *J.A.C.S.*, 1908, **30**, 971; Deming, *ibid.*, 1917, **39**, 2145; for tables for reduction of (dry) gas volumes to S.T.P. see Landolt-Börnstein, " Tabellen," 5th edit., 1923, 50.

[5] Farmer, *Analyst*, 1910, **35**, 308; Wendriner, *Z. angew. Chem.*, 1914, **27**, i, 183 (logarithmic method); Fenby, *Chem. News*, 1917, **116**, 5 (slide rule); Cosens, *Proc. Cambr. Phil. Soc.*, 1922, **21**, 228; Eck and Kayser, *Z. Verein D. Ing.*, 1925, **69**, 871 (plot of $pV=\boldsymbol{R}T$ on triangular axes); Liesche, *Chem. Fabr.*, 1928, **161**, 228, 241, 359, 392; Bagg, *Gas J.*, 1931, **196**, 730; *Trans. Inst. Chem. Eng.*, 1932, **10**, 172; Allcock and Jones, " The Nomogram," London, 1932; Patton, *Chem. Met. Eng.*, 1934, **41**, 488; Mairs, " Construction of Nomographic Charts," Scranton, Pa., 1939; Partington and Stratton, " Intermediate Chemical Calculations," 1946, 222; Burrows, *Ind. Eng. Chem.*, 1946, **38**, 472; Davey, *Gas World*, 1947, **126**, 182, 412, 524.

[6] " The Physics of High Pressure," 1931, 109.

[7] *Z. phys. Chem.*, 1933, **163**, 461.

[8] Deming and Shupe, *Phys. Rev.*, 1931, **37**, 638; 1931, **38**, 2245 (tables).

[9] Edminster, *Ind. Eng. Chem.*, 1938, **30**, 352.

For methane, Keyes and Burks [1] found the values of v ml./g.:

p atm.	0°	50°	100°	150°	200°
40	32·297	39·418	46·474	52·486	60·486
30	42·003	51·809	61·510	71·139	80·752
20	60·129	75·980	91·240	106·540	121·806
10	107·950	145·076	181·840	218·122	254·266

Rozen [2] expressed the deviations from the ideal state by the differences of the magnitudes $T(\mathrm{d}p/\mathrm{d}T)_v/p$, $p(\mathrm{d}v/\mathrm{d}T)_p/R$, and $p^2(\mathrm{d}v/\mathrm{d}p)_T/RT$ from ± 1.

§ 22. The Law of Partial Pressures

If the volumes $v_1, v_2, v_3, \ldots$ of various ideal gases, all at the same temperature and pressure, are mixed, the total volume V of the mixture is the sum of the volumes of the separate gases each at the same pressure and temperature as the mixture:

$$V = v_1 + v_2 + v_3 + \ldots = \Sigma v_1 \quad \ldots \ldots \quad (1)$$

Boyle's law shows that the total pressure P of the mixture is the sum of the pressures which the separate gases would exert if each occupied the total volume of the mixture at the same temperature:

$$P = p_1 + p_2 + p_3 + \ldots = \Sigma p_1 \quad \ldots \ldots \quad (2)$$

The *partial pressure* p_1, etc., of any gas is the pressure this gas would exert if it alone occupied the whole volume of the mixture at the same temperature, hence (2) expresses the fact that *the total pressure is the sum of the partial pressures.* This holds approximately also for vapours mixed with permanent gases, e.g. water vapour in air. The results are only approximations for actual gases.

The *law of partial pressures* (2) was discovered by Dalton [3] in the autumn of 1801, and stated by him [4] as follows:

> " When two or more mixed gases acquire an equilibrium, the elastic energy of each against the surface of the vessel or of any liquid, is precisely the same as if it were the only gas present occupying the whole space, and all the rest were withdrawn."

He also [5] stated it in the form:

> " When a vessel contains a mixture of two . . . elastic fluids, each acts independently upon the vessel, with its proper elasticity, just as if the other were absent,"

and Henry [6] in the concise form that " every gas is a vacuum to every other gas."

[1] *J.A.C.S.*, 1927, **49**, 1403; 1928, **50**, 1100.
[2] *J. Phys. Chem. U.S.S.R.*, 1945, **19**, 469.
[3] *Nicholson's J.*, 1801, **5**, 241; *Manch. Mem.*, 1802, **5**, 535; *Ann. Phys.*, 1803, **12**, 385; 1803, **15**, 1; " New System of Chemical Philosophy," 1808, **1**, i, 150; Partington, *Annals of Science*, 1939, **4**, 245.
[4] " New System of Chemical Philosophy," 1808, **1**, i, 191.
[5] " New System of Chemical Philosophy," 1808, **1**, i, 154.
[6] *Nicholson's J.*, 1804, **8**, 297.

Dalton's law was misunderstood and criticised when it was put forward,[1] the chief reason being the hypothesis used by Dalton, and taken by him from Newton (§ 23), that gaseous pressure is a result of the self-repulsion of particles of gases, since the law seemed to require that particles of different gases do not repel one another.

If v_1, v_2 are the volumes of the separate, unmixed, gases under the total pressure P of the mixture, and V is the volume of the mixture, then $pv_1=p_1V$ and $Pv_2=P_2V$, hence:

$$v_1/v_2=p_1/p_2 \quad \ldots \ldots \ldots \quad (3)$$

where p_1 and p_2 are the partial pressures.

Dalton's law of partial pressures is a special case of a general law [2] that in any gas mixture each single gas behaves, with respect to all its properties, as if it alone were present in the total space, under a pressure equal to its partial pressure.

The law of partial pressures applies (as Dalton pointed out) to *vapours*, e.g. to water vapour in the atmosphere. The law is only approximate.[3] Fuchs [4] found that when nitrogen is mixed with nitrous oxide, carbon dioxide, or oxygen; nitrous oxide with carbon dioxide, or oxygen; and oxygen with carbon dioxide, then in every case there is an expansion ($V>\Sigma v_1$), which is greater the more the two gases differ in physical properties. The volume change reaches a maximum with mixtures containing more than 50 per cent. of the gas with the lower critical temperature, but nearer the 1:1 ratio the more the two gases resemble one another. Schulze [5] found an increase of pressure on mixing two *vapours* (CS_2 and ether).

Amagat [6] and Leduc [7] found the experimental results more closely represented by the law that *the volume of a mixture of gases is the sum of the volumes of the component gases each at the temperature and pressure of the mixture* (equation (1)), but Masson and Dolley [8] found for binary mixtures of oxygen or nitrogen with acetylene that this gives less good results than the partial pressure law, a result which is unusual. Townend and Bhatt,[9] with mixtures of hydrogen and carbon monoxide at 0° and 25°, up to 600 atm., found the maximum deviation from the Amagat-Leduc law only 2·5 per cent., whereas the deviation from the law of partial pressures reached 25 per cent. The observed volume was larger than the calculated. The volumes of N_2, H_2, and CO, and the mixture N_2+3H_2 at $-70°$ to $+300°$ and 1–1000 atm. were given (with charts) by Dilley.[10]

If two gases are mixed, the volume change can be calculated from the coefficients of deviation from Boyle's law shown by the separate gases and by the

[1] Summary in Partington, *Annals of Science*, 1939, **4**, 245; cf. Bunsen, "Gasometry," transl. Roscoe, 1857, 130; Lamont, *Ann. Phys.*, 1863, **118**, 168; O. E. Meyer and Springmühl, *ibid.*, 1873, **148**, 526; Kedrov, *J. Phys. Chem. U.S.S.R.*, 1930, **1**, 433; Foà, *Chem. and Ind.*, 1946, 97.

[2] Ostwald, "Outlines of General Chemistry," 1895, 117.

[3] Gay-Lussac and Clement, *Ann. Chim.*, 1815, **95**, 311; Regnault, *Mém. Acad. Sci.*, 1862, **26**, 679; Krönig, *Ann. Phys.*, 1864, **123**, 299; Troost and Hautefeuille, *Compt. Rend.*, 1876, **83**, 333, 975; Cailletet, *J. de Phys.*, 1880, **9**, 192; Andrews, *Phil. Trans.*, 1887, **178**, 45; Braun, *Ann. Phys.*, 1888, **34**, 943; Margules, *Wien Ber.*, 1889, **98**, IIA, 883; *Ann. Phys.*, 1891, **42**, 348; Galitzine, "Das Daltonsche Gesetz," Strasburg, 1890; *Gött. Nachr.*, 1890, 22; *Ann. Phys.*, 1890, **41**, 588, 770; Lala, *Compt. Rend.*, 1890, **111**, 819; 1891, **112**, 426; *Ann. Fac. Sci. Toulouse*, 1891, **5**, G3.

[4] *Z. phys. Chem.*, 1918, **92**, 641.

[5] *Z. anorg. Chem.*, 1921, **118**, 223.

[6] *Ann. Chim.*, 1880, **19**, 345 (384); *Compt. Rend.*, 1898, **127**, 88.

[7] *Compt. Rend.*, 1898, **126**, 218, 1859; 1898, **127**, 88; Foà, *Chem. and Ind.*, 1946, 97.

[8] *Proc. Roy. Soc.*, 1923, **103**, 524.

[9] *Proc. Roy. Soc.*, 1931, **134**, 502.

[10] *Chem. Met. Eng.*, 1931, **38**, 280.

mixture,[1] but the mixture rule does not apply accurately to the compressibilities between 1 and 2 atm. Berthelot found small increases in pressure Δp on mixing two gases at constant temperature and volume. By considering the separate gases expanded to a large volume (when they obey Boyle's law), mixing, and bringing the mixture to the given volume, the value of Δp was calculated, and compared with measurements by Sacerdote: [2]

	Δp mm. calc.	Δp mm. obs.
SO_2+CO_2	1·52	1·36
Air	0·01	0
H_2+O_2	0·17	0·21
CO_2+N_2O	—	0·08

The compressibility of a mixture was calculated from those of its components, and the results agreed with experiment.

The deviations from (1) or (2) with actual gas mixtures make the partial pressures only fictitious quantities,[3] and the theoretical treatment, involving intermolecular forces, becomes complicated. At low temperatures the cohesive and repulsive forces between the molecules may balance one another and the deviations become negligible; in some cases the observed pressure may exceed the sum of the pressures at the same molecular concentration and temperature.[4] In the present section only the experimental results [5] will be considered; the theory is dealt with later (§ 35.VII C). The deviation from the additive relation (1) may be expressed as $\Delta v=(V-\Sigma v_1)/\Sigma v_1$, at a given pressure p (1 atm. in the table below), where V is the volume of the mixture; and the

p atm.	Per cent. ethylene									
	24·74		49·95		59·86		70·72		90·06	
	$100\Delta v$	Δp	$100\Delta v$	Δp	$100\Delta v$	Δp	$100\Delta v$	Δp	$100\Delta v$	Δp
30	2·15	0·75	2·7	0·85	3·2	0·9	3·1	0·7	1·25	0·45
40	3·35	1·05	5·3	1·6	5·5	1·6	5·5	1·4	2·7	0·7
50	5·0	1·7	8·4	2·7	9·1	2·7	9·35	2·25	5·35	1·2
60	7·7	2·35	13·7	3·9	15·4	4·0	16·4	3·55	11·1	1·8
70	10·75	3·35	21·5	5·45	25·1	5·7	28·1	4·85	22·8	1·95
80	11·75	4·3	24·0	6·8	28·0	6·35	31·3	5·25	21·3	0·75
90	11·1	5·2	21·6	7·65	24·5	7·25	25·5	4·9	11·1	−1·0
100	9·9	6·05	17·95	8·0	19·0	7·1	18·2	4·0	3·7	−3·0
110	8·7	6·6	14·3	8·15	14·1	6·7	11·6	2·7	−0·05	−5·25
120	7·5	—	10·9	—	9·7	—	6·4	—	−2·05	−8·05
125	6·9	—	9·35	—	7·7	—	4·55	—	−2·65	−9·05

[1] Berthelot, *Compt. Rend.*, 1898, **126**, 1703, 1857; 1899, **128**, 820, 1159; Berthelot and Sacerdote, *ibid.*, 1899, **128**, 820.

[2] *J. de Phys.*, 1899, **8**, 319.

[3] Jakob, *Z. Phys.*, 1927, **41**, 737, 739; Gillespie, *Phys. Rev.*, 1930, **36**, 121; Beattie, *ibid.*, 1930, **36**, 132.

[4] Lennard-Jones, *Nature*, 1927, **119**, 459; Jakob, *Z. Phys.*, 1927, **41**, 737, 739 (He+Ne).

[5] Braun, *Ann. Phys.*, 1888, **34**, 943; Margules, *Wien Ber.*, 1889, **98**, IIA, 883; on heat of mixing, *ibid.*, 1888, **97**, IIA, 1399; van der Waals, "Die Continuität," Leipzig, 1900, **2**, 50 f.,

deviation from (2) by $\Delta p = \Sigma p_1 - P$, where P is the pressure of the mixture. Some values for mixtures of argon and ethylene found by Masson and Dolley and Tanner and Masson at 24·95° are shown in the table; except at higher pressures the deviations are positive (P less than Σp_1, etc.).

The following values of $100\Delta v$ were found for mixtures [1] (N_2+3H_2) by Bartlett, Cupples, and Tremearne: [2]

p atm.	0°	50°	99·85°	198·9°	299·8°
50	0·58	0·29	0·25	−0·05	—
100	1·34	0·74	0·47	0·14	−0·06
200	1·66	1·07	0·68	0·23	−0·07
300	1·65	0·83	0·66	0·16	0·01
400	1·34	0·70	0·60	−0·20	−0·08
600	0·78	0·54	0·33	0·04	0·05
800	0·64	0·28	0·19	−0·15	0·08
1000	0·21	0·03	0·00	−0·27	0·28

The deviations become small as the temperature increases. Equation (1) is very closely followed, whilst there were large deviations from (2), e.g. at 50° the pressure for a given volume was 977 atm., whilst the sum of the partial pressures was only 750 atm.

At constant temperature the pressure exerted by one constituent of the gaseous mixture was found to be given with good accuracy by the product of its mol fraction and the pressure it would exert as a pure gas at a molecular concentration equal to the total molecular concentration of the mixture, i.e. in this case:

$$(pv/p_0v_0)_m = \tfrac{1}{4}[3(pv/p_0v_0)_{H_2} + (pv/p_0v_0)_{N_2}] \quad . \quad . \quad . \quad . \quad (4)$$

v in each term representing the same molecular volume, and hence the gases are present in identical molecular concentrations. Krichevsky [3] found the rule of Bartlett, Cupples, and Tremearne gave better agreement at high pressures than that of Lewis and Randall (§ 62.II), but still better agreement was found with the rule of Gilliland [4] that the slopes of the isochores (v const.) of the mixture are the averages of the slopes of the components at the same molar concentration. Bolshakov [5] found that the Lewis and Randall rule held well at 200° to 1000 atm. for nitrogen–hydrogen mixtures.

If p_1 is the partial pressure of a component of a gas mixture, then:

$$p_1 = n_1RT/V \quad . \quad . \quad . \quad . \quad . \quad . \quad . \quad . \quad . \quad . \quad (5)$$

66 f.; Kuenen, "Verdampfung und Verflüssigung von Gemischen," Leipzig, 1906, 99; Verschaffelt, *Arch. Néerl.*, 1906, **11**, 403 (*Comm. Leiden*, Suppl. **13**); Kuenen, Verschoyle, and van Urk, *Comm. Leiden*, 1922, **161**; Masson and Dolley, *Proc. Roy. Soc.*, 1923, **103**, 524; Trautz *et al.*, *Z. anorg. Chem.*, 1926, **150**, 277; 1929, **179**, 1; Verschoyle, *Proc. Roy. Soc.*, 1926, **111**, 552; Maass and Mennie, *ibid.*, 1926, **110**, 198; Lennard-Jones and Cook, *ibid.*, 1927, **115**, 334 (theory only); Bartlett *et al.*, *J.A.C.S.*, 1927, **49**, 65, 687, 1955; 1928, **50**, 1275; 1930, **52**, 1363; Gibby, Tanner, and Masson, *Proc. Roy. Soc.*, 1929, **122**, 283 (H_2+He); Scott, *ibid.*, 1929, **125**, 330 (H_2+CO); Tanner and Masson, *ibid.*, 1930, **126**, 268; Edwards and Roseveare, *J.A.C.S.*, 1942, **64**, 2816.

1 The very close validity of (1) for such mixtures had previously been reported by Cochrane in "Physical and Chemical Data of Nitrogen Fixation," H.M. Stationery Office, 1918, 6.

2 *J.A.C.S.*, 1928, **50**, 1275.

3 *J. Phys. Chem. U.S.S.R.*, 1937, **9**, 659; *J.A.C.S.*, 1937, **59**, 2733.

4 *Ind. Eng. Chem.*, 1936, **28**, 212 (17 refs.).

5 *Acta Physicochim. U.R.S.S.*, 1945, **20**, 259; measurements of partial molal volumes and fugacities at 0°–200° up to 1000 atm.

But if p is the total pressure of the mixture:

$$pV=\Sigma n_1RT \quad \ldots \ldots \ldots \ldots (6)$$

Hence, from (5) and (6):

$$p_1=(n_1/\Sigma n_1)p=N_1p \quad \ldots \ldots \ldots (7)$$

where N_1 is the *mol fraction* of the first gas.

Penning [1] regarded the Amagat-Leduc law as so exact that he used it to check the accuracy of his experiments on gas mixtures. In an elaborate research Trautz and Emert [2] measured the increases in pressure resulting from the mixing of several pairs of gases both at 1 atm. and higher pressures. They calculated the a and b values by van Laar's equation (§ 34.VII C) and from van der Waals's equation, and with these values of a and b they calculated the pressures of the mixtures. They found that Dalton's law did not hold with the pressures so corrected.

Edwards and Roseveare [3] calculated the second virial coefficient (§ 10.VII A) B_m for a mixture: $PV=RT+B_mP$, by the equations:

$$P(v_1/n_1)=RT+B_1P, \quad P(v_2/n_2)=RT+B_2P,$$
$$P[v_m/(n_1+n_2)]=RT+B_mP \quad \ldots \ldots \ldots (8)$$

where n_1, n_2 mols of separate gases, occupying volumes v_1, v_2 are mixed at the pressure P and constant temperature T, and v_m is the volume occupied by the mixture. The volume change on mixing is:

$$\Delta v=v_m-(v_1+v_2)=(n_1+n_2)B_m-n_1B_1-n_2B_2 \quad \ldots \ldots (9)$$

or in terms of mol fractions N $(n=n_1+n_2)$:

$$\Delta v/n=B_m-N_1B_1-N_2B_2 \quad \ldots \ldots \ldots (10)$$

Justi [4] used the equation $pV=RT+Bp$ for each component and for binary mixtures found (x=mol fraction; $x_1+x_2=1$):

$$B_m=x_1B_{11}+x_1x_2\beta+x_2B_{22} \quad \ldots \ldots \ldots (11)$$

where $\beta=2B_{12}-B_{11}-B_{22}$ is a measure of the deviation from the law of additive volumes. The change of volume on mixing, ΔV, is always positive and reaches a maximum of $\beta/4$ for $x_1=0{\cdot}5$. Ternary mixtures of He, H_2, A at 25° were also considered. Deviations from Dalton's law by reacting gases (HCl and CH_3OH vap., HCl and H_2O vap.) were investigated by Shidei.[5] They are larger than with non-reacting gases. Van Lerberghe and Schouls [6] used concentrations n_1/V and n_2/V and wrote:

$$p=p_1+p_2+B_{12}n_1n_2/V^2 \quad \ldots \ldots \ldots (12)$$

where p_1, p_2 are the pressures of the pure gases at the given concentrations and B_{12} is a function of temperature. Lennard-Jones and Cook,[7] for molecules with symmetrical force fields, deduced:

$$B_m=N_1^2B_1+2N_1N_2B_{12}+N_2^2B_2 \quad \ldots \ldots (13)$$

1 *Arch. Néerl.*, 1923, **7A**, 172 (*Comm. Leiden*, **166**).
2 *Z. anorg. Chem.*, 1926, **150**, 277 (bibl.).
3 *J.A.C.S.*, 1942, **64**, 2816.
4 *Forsch. Gebiete Ingenieurw.*, 1944, **15**, No. 1, 18.
5 *Mem. Coll. Sci. Kyoto Imp. Univ.*, 1925, 97; *Sexagint*, 1927, 143; *Bull. Chem. Soc. Japan*, 1928, **3**, 25.
6 *Bull. Acad. Roy. Belg.*, 1929, **15**, 583, where fugacities (§ 36.VII C) are also calculated.
7 *Proc. Roy. Soc.*, 1927, **115**, 334.

where B_{12} is a second virial coefficient representing only the interaction of unlike molecules. Since:

$$\Delta v/nN_1N_2=2B_{12}-(B_1+B_2) \quad . \quad . \quad . \quad . \quad . \quad . \quad (14)$$

the value of B_{12} may be calculated if B_1 and B_2 are known.

§ 23. Joule's Law

The pressure of a gas was formerly explained by static repulsive forces acting between the molecules at rest and transmitted to the walls of the vessel, and Newton,[1] by assuming repulsive forces inversely proportional to the distance between the molecules, was able to show that the gas would obey Boyle's law. It follows, however, that a gas expanding into a vacuous vessel without doing external work should become heated if there are repulsive forces between the molecules, and cooled if there are attractive forces, since in the first case internal work is done and converted into heat energy, and in the second case internal work is spent and its equivalent is taken as heat from the gas.

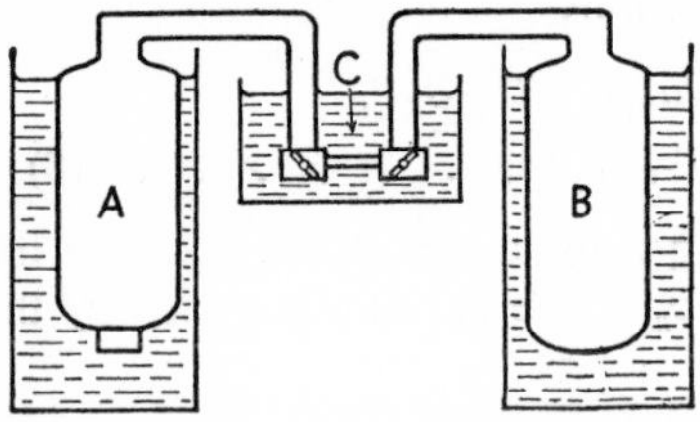

FIG. 28.VII A. Joule's Experiment

Gay-Lussac,[2] from some approximate experiments, concluded that there is no appreciable alteration of temperature in such a case. He allowed air, carbon dioxide, and oxygen to rush from one globe into a vacuous globe, and observed the changes of temperature by two mercury thermometers placed at the centres of the globes. The cooling in the first globe was very nearly equal to the heating in the second globe, the maximum change of temperature being less than 1° C. The results depended on the positions of the thermometers, and incorrect conclusions were drawn from the experiments.

Joule [3] used two copper vessels A and B (Fig. 28.VII A), the first containing air at 25 atm. pressure and the second vacuous, immersed in a can of water surrounded by an air-jacket. On opening the taps C connecting the vessels, expansion occurred, but after stirring the water its temperature was found to be unchanged. Hence, Joule concluded that " no change of temperature occurs when air is allowed to expand without developing mechanical power," i.e. without doing external work, and this indicates that the gas molecules exert no appreciable attractive or repulsive forces on one another.

The globes and taps were then placed in three separate cans of water, as shown, and the experiment repeated. A fall of 0·595° *per kg. of water* occurred in A, a rise of 0·606° in B, and a rise of 0·078° in C. Within the limits of error, the same amount of heat is absorbed by the air expanding from A and doing work as is evolved by the compression of the air in B.

Since the air in Joule's experiment did no net *external* work,[4] $w=0$, and since

1 " Principia," Book ii, prop. 23, theorem 18; London, 1687, 301.

2 *Mém. Soc. Arcueil*, 1807, **1**, 180; *Ann. Phys.*, 1808, **30**, 249; Harper's *Scientific Memoirs*, New York, 1898, **1**; cf. Leslie, " Experimental Enquiry into the Nature and Propagation of Heat," 1804, 533.

3 *Phil. Mag.*, 1845, **26**, 369; " Scientific Papers," 1884, **1**, 172; on the *kinetic theory* of the Joule experiment, see Natanson, *Compt. Rend.*, 1888, **107**, 164; *Ann. Phys.*, 1889, **37**, 341; Fireman, *J. Phys. Chem.*, 1902, **6**, 463; Parts, *Svensk. Kem. Tids.*, 1944, **56**, 348.

4 The misinterpretation of the experiment by H. S. Taylor, " Treatise on Physical Chemistry " New York, 1931, **1**, 46, is a common error of beginners.

no heat was absorbed or emitted to the surroundings, $q=0$; it follows from (2), § 16.II, that:

$$\Delta E=q-w=0 \quad \dots \dots \dots \quad (1)$$

i.e. *the energy at constant temperature is independent of the volume*:

$$(dE/dV)_T=0 \quad \dots \dots \dots \quad (2)$$

This is called *Joule's law* and it follows by thermodynamics for any ideal gas, defined by the equation $PV=RT$. This was proved in § 54.II.

The *Joule effect* [1] is the cooling of unit mass of gas for unit volume expansion when the energy remains constant, i.e. $(dT/dV)_E$. This is found as follows. From (1), and (2a), § 3.II:

$$dE=\delta q-\delta w=(c_v dT+l_v dV)-PdV=0,$$

$$\therefore\ c_v(dT/dV)_E=-(l_v-P).$$

But from Clapeyron's equation (5), § 41.II:

$$l_v=T(dP/dT)_V,$$

$$\therefore\ (dT/dV)_E=-(1/c_v)[T(dP/dT)_V-P]=-(T^2/c_v)(d/dT)(P/T)_V \quad . \quad (3)$$

which obviously vanishes when, at constant volume (k=const.):

$$(dP/dT)_V=P/T, \quad \text{or } (d \ln P/d \ln T)_V=1; \quad \text{or } P=kT \quad . \ . \quad (4)$$

The Joule effect for a gas which dissociates with absorption of heat (e.g. $N_2O_4 \rightleftharpoons 2NO_2$) should be greater than for an ordinary imperfect gas.[2]

The energy of a gas as a function of pressure, $(dE/dp)_T$, was determined by Rossini and Frandsen [3] by a calorimetric method suggested by Washburn.[4] At 301° K. the coefficient was practically constant up to 40 atm. and in joule atm.$^{-1}$ mol^{-1} was: $-6{\cdot}08$ for air, $-6{\cdot}51$ for oxygen, and $-6{\cdot}51-11{\cdot}0x-11{\cdot}0x^2$ for mixtures of oxygen and carbon dioxide containing a mol fraction x of the latter. A steel bomb electrically heated by a resistance spiral was used.

§ 24. The Joule-Thomson Effect

Since Joule's thermometer would not record temperature changes in the water corresponding with changes of less than 1·88° *in the air*, the experiments were not sensitive enough to decide whether the law (2), § 23, holds accurately or not. (In Gay-Lussac's experiments the temperatures were measured in the gases, and were constant to 0·1°.) William Thomson (later Lord Kelvin) in 1851 suggested modifications in the method, and in 1852–62 he and Joule carried out (in Joule's brewery in Salford, near Manchester) the so-called " porous plug " experiment.[5] A stream of gas under constant pressure higher

[1] Hirn, " Théorie Mécanique de la Chaleur," 1862, 103; Cazin, *Ann. Chim.*, 1870, **19**, 5; Parenty, *ibid.*, 1896, **8**, 5; 1897, **12**, 289; Rose-Innes, *Phil. Mag.*, 1900, **50**, 251; 1901, **2**, 130 (theory); Rudge, *ibid.*, 1909, **18**, 159; Worthing, *Phys. Rev.*, 1911, **32**, 245; 1911, **33**, 217; Keyes and Sears, *Proc. Nat. Acad.*, 1925, **11**, 38; Shiba, *Bull. Inst. Phys. Chem. Res. Tokyo*, 1928, **33**, 357, 576; Bennewitz and Andreewa, *Z. phys. Chem.*, 1929, **141**, 37; Bennewitz and Windisch, *ibid.*, 1933, **166**, 401; Drzewiecki, *Compt. Rend.*, 1931, **192**, 1024; Michels, Wouters, and de Boer, *Physica*, 1936, **3**, 597, who calculated $(dE/dP)_T$ for N_2 to 3000 atm.; Roebuck and Murrell, in " Temperature. Its Measurement and Control," New York, 1941, 60; Baker, *Phys. Rev.*, 1943, **64**, 302.

[2] Brass and Tolman, *J.A.C.S.*, 1932, **54**, 1003.

[3] *Bur. Stand. J. Res.*, 1932, **9**, 733.

[4] *Bur. Stand. J. Res.*, 1932, **9**, 521.

[5] Joule and Thomson, *Phil. Mag.*, 1852, **4**, 481; *Phil. Trans.*, 1853, **143**, 357; 1854, **144**, 321; 1862, **152**, 579; Thomson, " Mathematical and Physical Papers," 1882, **1**, 333, 337, 415; Joule, " Scientific Papers," 1887, **2**, 216, 231, 247, 342; Harper's *Scientific Memoirs*, New York, 1898, **1** (also Gay-Lussac's paper); on theory, see Schiller, *Ann. Phys.*, 1890, **40**, 149;

than atmospheric was forced continuously through a porous plug of cotton-wool or silk supported in a heat-insulating boxwood tube. The temperatures of the gas before and after the plug were determined by thermometers, and, after various corrections, the change in temperature of the gas in passing through the plug was found. Suppose a volume V_1 of unit mass of gas at a temperature T is pressed by a piston A under a pressure P_1 through the plug at C, the gas on the other side of C expanding to a volume V_2 under a pressure P_2 by pushing out a piston B (Fig. 29.VII A).

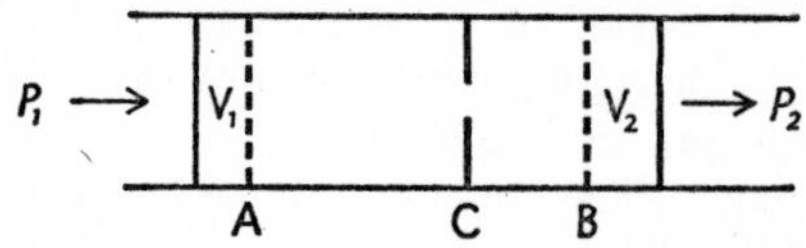

FIG. 29.VII A. Porous Plug Experiment

The net work done by the gas is $w=P_2V_2-P_1V_1$. If E_1 and E_2 are the energies of unit mass before and after passing the plug, $\Delta E=E_2-E_1$, and if q is the heat absorbed from outside: [1]

$$q=\Delta E+w=E_2-E_1+P_2V_2-P_1V_1=H_2-H_1 \quad . \quad . \quad . \quad (1)$$

where H is the heat content (§ 17.II), $H=E+PV$.

The experiment, however, is so arranged that $q=0$, therefore $H_2-H_1=0$. (Note that in this case P is not constant.) If the changes are very small:

$$\mathrm{d}H=\mathrm{d}(E+PV)=\mathrm{d}E+P\mathrm{d}V+V\mathrm{d}P=0 \quad . \quad . \quad . \quad (2)$$

where $\mathrm{d}V\mathrm{d}P$ is neglected as of the second order (§ 4.I) The energy change is the same, for the same change of state, whether the process is carried out irreversibly, as in the plug experiment, or reversibly, and hence q in (1) can be calculated for the reversible case. From (2a), § 3.II:

$$\delta q=c_v\mathrm{d}T+l_v\mathrm{d}V.$$

From (5), § 41.II:

$$l_v=T(\mathrm{d}P/\mathrm{d}T)_V, \text{ and } \mathrm{d}V=(\mathrm{d}V/\mathrm{d}T)_P\mathrm{d}T+(\mathrm{d}V/\mathrm{d}P)_T\mathrm{d}P,$$

$$\therefore\ \delta q=c_v\mathrm{d}T+T(\mathrm{d}P/\mathrm{d}T)_V[(\mathrm{d}V/\mathrm{d}T)_P\mathrm{d}T+(\mathrm{d}V/\mathrm{d}P)_T\mathrm{d}P]=0 \quad . \quad (3)$$

From (2b), § 3.II:

$$\delta q=c_p\mathrm{d}T+l_p\mathrm{d}P,$$

hence the first two terms on the right of (3) are equal to $c_p\mathrm{d}T$. From (2c), § 5.II:

$$(\mathrm{d}P/\mathrm{d}T)_V(\mathrm{d}V/\mathrm{d}P)_T=-(\mathrm{d}V/\mathrm{d}T)_P \quad . \quad . \quad . \quad . \quad (4)$$

Hence equation (3) can be written as:

$$\delta q=c_p\mathrm{d}T-T(\mathrm{d}V/\mathrm{d}T)_p\mathrm{d}P=0 \quad . \quad . \quad . \quad . \quad . \quad . \quad . \quad (5)$$

Since, from (2), § 16.II, $\delta q=\mathrm{d}E+P\mathrm{d}V$, it follows from (2) and (5) that:

$$-V\mathrm{d}P=c_p\mathrm{d}T-T(\mathrm{d}V/\mathrm{d}T)_P\mathrm{d}P,$$

$$\therefore\ c_p\mathrm{d}T+[V-T(\mathrm{d}V/\mathrm{d}T)_P]\mathrm{d}P=0,$$

$$\therefore\ (\mathrm{d}T/\mathrm{d}P)_H=(1/c_p)[T(\mathrm{d}V/\mathrm{d}T)_P-V] \quad . \quad . \quad . \quad . \quad (6)$$

Preston, "Theory of Heat," 1894, 699; Buckingham, "An Outline of the Theory of Thermodynamics," New York, 1900, 127; *Bur. Stand. Bull.*, 1907, **3**, 237; Clark, *Trans. Roy. Soc. Canada*, 1924, **18**, III, 293; Wensel, in "Temperature. Its Measurement and Control," New York, 1941, 3; Roebuck and Murrell, *ibid.*, 60.

[1] The *kinetic* energy of the gas passing the plug is assumed to be converted, by friction, into heat in the gas after the plug; this may not always have been the case: see Keyes, *J.A.C.S.*, 1921, **43**, 1452. Callendar's name "adiathermal" for an irreversible adiabatic process of this kind, *Phil. Mag.*, 1903, **5**, 48, is superfluous, since "adiabatic" covers all cases of $q=0$, the reversible process being isentropic (§ 34.II). Porter, *Trans. Faraday Soc.*, 1922, **18**, 139; "Thermodynamics," 1931, 59, calls $pdv-\mathrm{d}(pv)=-vdp$ "the work that fails to be done (or shirk)."

A more concise deduction of (6) is the following:

$$dH = (dH/dT)_P dT + (dH/dP)_T dP$$
$$= c_p dT + (dH/dP)_T dP = 0$$
$$\therefore \ (dT/dP)_H = -(dH/dP)_T / c_p \quad . \quad . \quad . \quad . \quad . \quad . \quad (7)$$

But

$$dH = d(E+PV) = dE + PdV + VdP = TdS + VdP$$

from (3), § 43.II, therefore $(dH/dP)_T = T(dS/dP)_T + V$, and from Maxwell's equation (4), § 48.II:

$$(dS/dP)_T = -(dV/dT)_P$$
$$\therefore \ (dH/dP)_T = -T(dV/dT)_P + V \quad . \quad . \quad . \quad . \quad . \quad (8)$$

By substituting from (8) in (7), equation (6) follows. The coefficient $(dT/dP)_H$ gives the change in temperature per atm. pressure change of the gas in passing through the plug, and is called the *Joule-Thomson effect*. It is independent of the mass of gas, since for a mass m g., mc_p replaces c_p and mV replaces V, and m cancels in (6).

For an ideal gas, $PV = \boldsymbol{R}T$, therefore $V = \boldsymbol{R}T/P$, therefore $T(dV/dT)_P = \boldsymbol{R}T/P = V$, and hence from (6) the Joule-Thomson effect vanishes.

It should be noticed that the Joule-Thomson effect vanishes not only for an ideal gas under *all* conditions, but also for *any* gas under such special conditions that $T(dV/dT)_P - V = 0$, or $(dV/dT)_P = V/T$, or:

$$(d \ln V / d \ln T)_P = 1 \quad . \quad . \quad . \quad . \quad . \quad . \quad . \quad . \quad (9)$$
$$\text{or } V = kT \quad . \quad . \quad . \quad . \quad . \quad . \quad . \quad . \quad . \quad (10)$$

at constant pressure, k being a constant.

The Joule-Thomson effect involves (i) the deviation of the gas from Boyle's law, expressed by the *external work*, and (ii) the usually larger effect due to the separation of the molecules under the influence of attractive forces, expressed by the *internal work*.[1]

Using initial pressures of 1·43, 2·26 and 8·18 atm. and the final pressure 1 atm., Joule and Thomson found for air the fall of temperature 0·108°, 0·363° and 1·10° respectively; for hydrogen they found at 6·8° a small *heating* effect of 0·18° for 6 atm. pressure difference, or 0·03° per atm. Olszewski [2] found that this changed to a cooling effect if the temperature was −80·5°, a so-called *inversion point*, but this depends on the pressure (see § 6.VI C).

The *cooling* effect ΔT was found experimentally to be proportional to the pressure difference ΔP and inversely proportional to the square of the absolute temperature. For air, if T is the initial absolute temperature and ΔP is in atm.

$$\Delta T = 0{\cdot}276(273/T)^2 \times \Delta P.$$

Measurements and calculations of the Joule-Thomson effect for various gases have been made,[3] and it has an important application in the liquefaction

[1] Hausen, *Z. techn. Phys.*, 1926, **7**, 444; these are sometimes confused in the literature; for H_2 and He, (i) outweighs (ii).

[2] *Ann. Phys.*, 1902, **7**, 818; *Phil. Mag.*, 1902, **3**, 535; 1907, **13**, 722; *Bull. Acad. Polon.*, 1906, 792; Keyes, Gerry, and Hicks, *J.A.C.S.*, 1937, **59**, 1426.

[3] Joule and Thomson, ref. 5, p. 615; Hirn, "Théorie Mécanique de la Chaleur," 1862, 103; Sutherland, *Phil. Mag.*, 1886, **22**, 81; Natanson, *Ann. Phys.*, 1887, **31**, 502; 1888, **33**, 683 (theory); Bouty, *J. de Phys.*, 1889, **8**, 20; Rose-Innes, *Phil. Mag.*, 1898, **45**, 227; 1899, **48**, 286; 1900, **50**, 251; 1901, **2**, 130; 1903, **6**, 353; 1908, **15**, 301; Love, *ibid.*, 1899, **48**, 106; van der Waals, " Continuität," Leipzig, 1899, **1**, 119; Grindley, *Phil. Trans.*, 1900, **194**, 1; Olszewski, *Ann. Phys.*, 1902, **7**, 818; *Phil. Mag.*, 1902, **3**, 535; Bevan, *Proc. Cambr. Phil. Soc.*, 1903, **12**, 127; Callendar, *Phil. Mag.*, 1903, **5**, 48; Griessmann, *Forschungsarb. Gebiet Ingenieurwes.*,

of gases (see § 5.VI C). For the experimental data and curves, reference is made to the original papers.

In a type of apparatus for measuring the Joule-Thomson effect (Hausen) the porous plug was of asbestos pressed between two perforated plates of ebonite or (for higher temperatures) porcelain; it was 40 mm. diam. and 23 mm. thick.

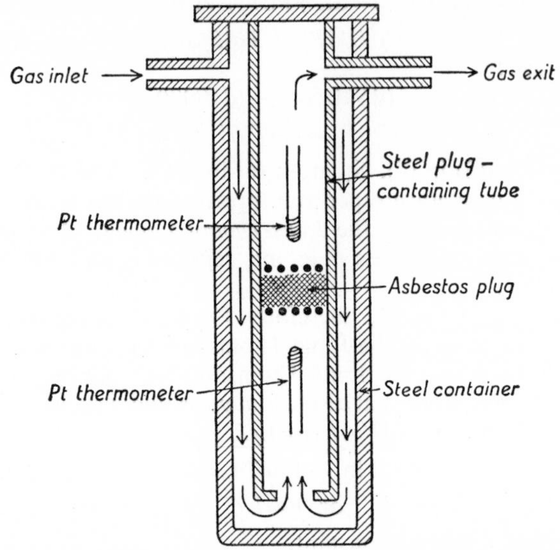

FIG. 30.VII A. Hausen's Apparatus for Joule-Thomson Effect

1904, **13** ,1; Kester, *Phys. Rev.*, 1905, **21**, 260; *Phys. Z.*, 1905, **6**, 44 (CO_2); Peake, *Proc. Roy. Soc.*, 1905, **76**, 185; Porter, *Phil. Mag.*, 1906, **11**, 554; Dodge, *J. Amer. Soc. Mech. Eng.*, 1907, **28**, 1265; 1908, **30**, 1227; Bradley and Hale, *Phys. Rev.*, 1909, **29**, 258; Dalton, *Proc. K. Akad. Wetens. Amsterdam*, 1909, **11**, 863, 874 (*Comm. Leiden*, 1909, **109***a* and *c*) (reduced virial equation); Rudge, *Phil. Mag.*, 1909, **18**, 159; *Proc. Cambr. Phil. Soc.*, 1910, **16**, 48; Vogel, *Munich Ber.*, 1909, Abhl. 1; *Ann. Phys. Beibl.*, 1909, **33**, 967; *Forschungsarb. Gebiet Ingenieurwes.*, 1911, Nos. **108–9**, 1; Burnett and Roebuck, *Phys. Rev.*, 1910, **30**, 529; Jenkin and Pye, *Phil. Trans.*, 1914, **213**, 67; 1915, **215**, 353 (CO_2); Plank, *Phys. Z.*, 1914, **15**, 904; Noell, *Forschungsarb. Gebiet Ingenieurwes.*, 1916, **184** (air); Schulze, *Ann. Phys.*, 1916, **49**, 569, 585; Jakob, *ibid.*, 1918, **55**, 527; *Phys. Z.*, 1921, **22**, 65; Hoxton, *Phys. Rev.*, 1919, **13**, 438 (bibl.); Keyes, *J.A.C.S.*, 1921, **43**, 1452; Meissner, *Z. Phys.*, 1923, **18**, 12; Burnett, *Phys. Rev.*, 1923, **22**, 590; *Bur. Stand. Circ.*, 1923, **142** (NH_3); *Univ. Wisc. Bull., Eng. Ser.*, 1926, **9**, No. 6; Perry, *J. Phys. Chem.*, 1924, **28**, 1108, 1338 (He); Seligmann, *Z. techn. Phys.*, 1925, **6**, 237; Hausen, *ibid.*, 1926, **7**, 371, 444; *Z. Verein D. Ing.*, 1926, **70**, 266; *Sci. Abstr.*, 1926, **29**, 428; *Forschungsarb. Gebiet Ingenieurwes.*, 1926, **274** (air); Roebuck, *Proc. Amer. Acad.*, 1925, **60**, 537; 1930, **64**, 287 (see errors in these papers corrected in *J. Chem. Phys.*, 1940, **8**, 627); Roebuck and Oesterberg, *Phys. Rev.*, 1933, **43**, 60; 1934, **45**, 332; 1934, **46**, 785; 1935, **48**, 450; *J.A.C.S.*, 1938, **60**, 341; Roebuck, Murrell, and Miller, *ibid.*, 1942, **64**, 400; Roebuck and Oesterberg, *J. Chem. Phys.*, 1938, **6**, 205; 1940, **8**, 627; Eumorfopoulos and Rai, *Phil. Mag.*, 1926, **2**, 961; Bridgeman, *Phys. Rev.*, 1929, **34**, 527 (air); Huang, Liu, and Fu, *Z. Phys.*, 1936, **100**, 594 (CO_2 from Beattie-Bridgeman equation); Gusak, *Sow. Phys. Z.*, 1937, **11**, 60 (N_2); Weng Wen-Po, *Phil. Mag.*, 1938, **26**, 225; Verschaffelt, *Bull. Acad. Roy. Belg.*, 1938, **24**, 825; 1940, **26**, 193; *Wis. Natuurkde. Tijdsch.*, 1941, **10**, 173; Collins and Keyes, *J. Phys. Chem.*, 1939, **43**, 5 (steam); Dorsey, "Properties of Ordinary Water Substance," New York, 1940, 119 (H_2O); Zelmanov, *J. Phys. U.S.S.R.*, 1940, **3**, 43; *Foreign Petrol. Technol.*, 1941, **9**, 429 (He at low temp.); Budenholzer, Botkin, Sage, and Lacey, *Ind. Eng. Chem.*, 1942, **34**, 878 ($CH_4+C_3H_8$); Sage, Botkin, and Lacey, *Amer. Inst. Min. Met. Eng.*, 1942, Tech. Publ. **1504**; Keenan and Kaye, *J. Appl. Mechanics*, 1943, **10** A, 123; Buckingham and Corner, *Proc. Roy. Soc.*, 1947, **189**, 118 (calc.); de Groot and Geldermans, *Physica*, 1947, **13**, 538 (C_2H_4, calc.); de Groot and Michels, *ibid.*, 1948, **14**, 218 (CO_2).

The gas passed down an annular space between the wall of the steel containing vessel and the inner tube containing the plug. Before and after the plug were two platinum resistance thermometers, enclosed in double concentric wooden tubes to prevent heat loss (Fig. 30.VII A). In Burnett and Roebuck's apparatus the gas passed radially through the walls of porous material.

The values of $\Delta T/\Delta p=\Delta t/\Delta p$ for carbon dioxide for an initial pressure up to 6 atm. found by Joule and Thomson (calculated by Kester) are:

CO_2											
$t°$	0	10	20	30	40	50	60	70	80	90	100
$\Delta t/\Delta p$	1·35	1·24	1·14	1·05	0·96	0·89	0·83	0·76	0·71	0·66	0·62
„ (K.)	1·46	1·32	1·20	1·11	1·04	0·99	0·95	0·91	0·87	0·83	0·80

The last line gives Kester's values for an initial pressure up to 40 atm. Joule and Thomson's results for other gases are:

	Air				H_2	
$t°$	7·1	39·5	92·8	$t°$	6·8	90·1
$\Delta t/\Delta p$	0·26	0·23	0·15	$\Delta t/\Delta p$	−0·030	−0·044

The effect of pressure is shown by results for air at 0° found by Dalton (D.) and Vogel (V.); the initial pressure is stated:

p atm.	5	10	15	20	30	40	60	80	100	140	160
$\Delta t/\Delta p$ (D.)	0·226	0·251	0·259	0·262	0·264	0·231	—	—	—	—	—
„ (V.)	—	—	—	0·260	—	0·243	0·225	0·208	0·191	0·157	0·139

Kester found $\Delta t/\Delta p$ for CO_2 at 22° given by $1{\cdot}187°+0{\cdot}0015p$.

The equation $\mathrm{d}H=0$ can be written:

$$(\mathrm{d}H/\mathrm{d}T)_p\mathrm{d}T+(\mathrm{d}H/\mathrm{d}p)_T\mathrm{d}p=0 \quad . \quad . \quad . \quad . \quad . \quad . \quad . \quad (11)$$

Suppose, as in technical gas liquefaction, the final pressure p_2 and the initial temperature T_1 are fixed. Then:

$$(\mathrm{d}H_2/\mathrm{d}T_2)_p\mathrm{d}T_2+(\mathrm{d}H_1/\mathrm{d}p_1)_T dp_1=0 \quad . \quad . \quad . \quad . \quad . \quad (12)$$

The minimum final temperature is obviously found when:

$$(\mathrm{d}H_1/\mathrm{d}p_1)_T=0 \quad . \quad . \quad . \quad . \quad . \quad . \quad . \quad . \quad . \quad (13)$$

and as this is independent of p_2, the assumption of a fixed end-pressure is unnecessary, the choice of p_1 as a root of (13) giving a maximum cooling for all values of p_2, if p_1-p_2 is not too small. Equation (6) is easily transformed by the equations of § 5I.I, into:

$$(\mathrm{d}T/\mathrm{d}p)_H=[T(\mathrm{d}p/\mathrm{d}T)_v+v(\mathrm{d}p/\mathrm{d}v)_T]/c_p(\mathrm{d}p/\mathrm{d}v)_T \quad . \quad . \quad . \quad (14)$$

and for the differential inversion point this is zero. Thus (13) and (14) show that, for a given initial temperature, the optimum cooling in the integral Joule-Thomson effect occurs at the same pressure as the inversion in the differential effect.[1] If the substance obeys the van der Waals equation this pressure is determined by the reduced form (§ 16.VII C):

$$\pi_i=24[\sqrt{(3\vartheta_i)}-\vartheta_i/2-9/8] \quad . \quad . \quad . \quad . \quad . \quad . \quad . \quad . \quad (15)$$

where $\pi=p/p_c$, $\vartheta=T/T_c$, p_c and T_c being the critical values.

The Joule-Thomson effect has often been used [2] to calculate the absolute temperature of 0° C., but it always gives values which are too high, above 273·1

1 Epstein, "Textbook of Thermodynamics," New York, 1937, 73.

2 Boltzmann, *Ann. Phys.*, 1894, **53**, 948; Rose-Innes, *Phil. Mag.*, 1900, **20**, 251; Callendar, *ibid.*, 1903, **5**, 48; Buckingham, *ibid.*, 1903, **6**, 518; Roebuck, *Phys. Rev.*, 1936, **50**, 370 (273·16±0·02).

and sometimes as high as 273·36, so that it is not a reliable method.[1] The Joule-Thomson effects for methane-nitrogen mixtures were calculated by the Beattie-Bridgeman equation (§ 38.VII C) by Perry and Hermann.[2]

The Joule and Joule-Thomson effects for gases obeying Bose-Einstein and Fermi-Dirac statistics (§ 36.IV) were considered by Singh.[3] They are of opposite signs.

It is important to notice that the Joule-Thomson effect is not solely due to deviation of the gas from Boyle's law; this would produce a very much smaller temperature change. Another mistake [4] is to regard the Joule-Thomson cooling as due to adiabatic expansion (i.e. *external* work). It is true that adiabatic conditions are assumed in the deduction, but the work done by the gas in expanding in the plug is given to it on the inlet side of the plug, and (apart from the small deviation from Boyle's law) these two amounts of work are equal, so that no net external work is done.

Joule and Thomson found that the observed fall in temperature for air was 9 to 10 times that which would be produced by the deviation from Boyle's law. It is found that pv changes by about 1/2500 for a change of pressure of 1 atm. at room temperature. Hence if P, V are the initial and p, v the final pressure and volume for 1 g. of substance:

$$PV=pv[1-(P-p)/2500p],$$

$$\therefore\ PV-pv=(P-p)v/2500.$$

This is the external work done due to the deviation from Boyle's law. By dividing this by the specific heat of air the fall in temperature is found. The conditions are neither constant pressure nor constant volume, but $c_p=0{\cdot}239$ may be taken.

There is no reason to suppose that there is ever a *repulsion* between gas molecules, and difficulty may be felt in understanding the heating effect which occurs with hydrogen. This is due to the fact that, since the molecular attraction is very small with hydrogen, the internal work is very small and would produce only a very small cooling effect. With hydrogen, at ordinary pressures, and other gases at *high* pressures (§ 9.VII A), $PV>pv$, hence the *external* work $pv-PV$ is negative, i.e. net work is done *on* the gas during the expansion. This will increase the energy of the gas (since no exchange of heat with the surroundings occurs), and it becomes warmer. This heating effect outweighs the cooling due to internal work, and the result is a small heating effect.

If $PV=pv$ (the gas obeys Boyle's law) or $PV<pv$ (the gas more compressible than an ideal gas),[5] there will always be cooling if there is any attraction between the molecules, and for equal attractions the cooling will be greater in the case $PV<pv$ (when some external work is done) than in the case $PV=pv$ (when no external work is done).

Joule and Thomson found that the cooling effect $-(\mathrm{d}T/\mathrm{d}P)_H=\Delta T$ was inversely proportional to the square of the absolute temperature, or if a is a constant, $\Delta T=a/T^2$. Rose-Innes [6] proposed the formula: $\Delta T=a/T-b$, where a and b

[1] Keyes, *J.A.C.S.*, 1920, **42**, 54; 1921, **43**, 1452; 1924, **46**, 1584; misprint in 1921 paper corrected by Smith and Taylor, *ibid.*, 1923, **45**, 2125.

[2] *J. Phys. Chem.*, 1935, **39**, 1188; cf. Hirschfelder and Roseveare, *ibid.*, 1939, **43**, 15.

[3] *Indian J. Phys.*, 1940, **14**, 459; Srivastava, *Proc. Nat. Inst. Sci. India*, 1938, **4**, 75; Kothari, *ibid.*, 1938, **4**, 69.

[4] See, e.g., Lowry and Sugden, " Class Book of Physical Chemistry," 1943, 44.

[5] It must be remembered that $P>p$, so that the change from p to P is the *compression.*

[6] *Phil. Mag.*, 1898, **45**, 227; Lehfeldt, *ibid.*, 363.

are constants;[1] for hydrogen $a=64\cdot1$ and $b=0\cdot331$, which give an inversion temperature of 193·7° K. Love[2] showed that Clausius's characteristic equation (§ 28.VII C) gives $\Delta T=a/T^2-b$, where a and b are constants, and this is in better agreement than Joule and Thomson's formula for carbon dioxide.

Measurements of the Joule-Thomson effect for *liquid* oxygen and nitrogen[3] have been used to calculate the heat content H. Regnault[4] worked with *isothermal* gas expansions, and (after overcoming great experimental difficulties) found results in agreement with those in the adiabatic expansion.

§ 25. The Inversion Curve

The Joule-Thomson effect for hydrogen changes from a slight warming at ordinary temperature to a cooling below −80·5° at 113 atm. initial pressure, this being an *inversion point* at which the effect is zero. This makes it possible to liquefy hydrogen by expansion provided it is first strongly cooled (§ 6.VI C). The inversion temperature for helium is as low as −240° C. The inversion temperature of a gas depends on the pressure, so that it is more correct to speak of an *inversion curve*, giving pairs of values of pressure and temperature for each gas for which the Joule-Thomson effect vanishes. This occurs, by (7), § 24, when:

$$(\mathrm{d}V/\mathrm{d}T)_P=V/T, \quad \text{or} \quad (\mathrm{d}\ln V/\mathrm{d}\ln T)_P=1 \quad \ldots \quad (1)$$

Assume that the gas obeys van der Waals's equation:[5]

$$(P+a/V^2)(V-b)=\boldsymbol{R}T \quad \ldots \quad (2)$$

which (by multiplying out and dividing by P) may be put in the form:

$$V-b=\boldsymbol{R}T/P-a/PV+ab/PV^2,$$

and put $V=\boldsymbol{R}T/P$ in the *correction terms*, then:

$$V=\boldsymbol{R}T/P-a/\boldsymbol{R}T+abP/\boldsymbol{R}^2T^2+b \quad \ldots \quad (3)$$

$$\therefore\ (\mathrm{d}V/\mathrm{d}T)_P=\boldsymbol{R}/P+a/\boldsymbol{R}T^2-2abP/\boldsymbol{R}^2T^3 \quad \ldots \quad (4)$$

From (6), § 24, for the Joule-Thomson effect:

$$\mathrm{d}T=(1/C_p)[T(\mathrm{d}V/\mathrm{d}T)_P-V]\mathrm{d}P,$$

(where $C_p=Mc_p$ is the molecular heat, since V is now the molar volume), (3) and (4) give:

$$\mathrm{d}T=(2a/\boldsymbol{R}T-3abP/\boldsymbol{R}^2T^2-b)(1/C_p)\mathrm{d}P \quad \ldots \quad (5)$$

Neglect the second term in brackets as small compared with the other two, then:

$$\mathrm{d}T=(2a/\boldsymbol{R}T-b)(1/C_p)\mathrm{d}P,$$

giving on integration:

$$C_p(T_1-T_2)=(2a/\boldsymbol{R}T-b)(P_1-P_2) \quad \ldots \quad (6)$$

The inversion point occurs when $\mathrm{d}T=0$ in (5),

$$\therefore\ 2a/\boldsymbol{R}T-3abP/\boldsymbol{R}^2T^2-b=0,$$

$$\text{or } (T-a/\boldsymbol{R}b)^2=a^2/\boldsymbol{R}^2b^2-3aP/\boldsymbol{R}^2 \quad \ldots \quad (7)$$

$$\therefore\ T\simeq 2a/\boldsymbol{R}b \quad \ldots \quad (8)$$

1 Keyes, *J.A.C.S.*, 1921, **43**, 1452, claimed that all reliable experiments led to this relation.
2 *Phil. Mag.*, 1899, **48**, 106; Leduc, *Compt. Rend.*, 1899, **128**, 88.
3 Rodebush, Andrews, and Taylor, *J.A.C.S.*, 1925, **47**, 313.
4 *Compt. Rend.*, 1869, **69**, 780; *Mém. de l'Inst.*, 1870, **3 7**, II, 579; Buckingham, *Phil. Mag.*, 1903, **6**, 518; *Nature*, 1907, **76**, 493.
5 For inversion curve of CO_2 with the equation $(p+a/T^nv^2)(v-b)=\boldsymbol{R}T$ see Schulze, *Ann. Phys.*, 1916, **49**, 585.

By plotting T against P from (7), a parabola is obtained, all points inside which represent a cooling effect and all points outside a heating effect; this is the inversion curve.

It is more convenient [1] to use equation (1) in the reduced form (§ 16.VII C):

$$\vartheta(d\phi/d\vartheta)_\pi - \phi = 0 \qquad (9)$$

($\phi = v/v_c$, $\pi = p/p_c$, $\vartheta = T/T_c$). Differentiate the reduced van der Waals's equation:

$$(\pi + 3/\phi^2)(3\phi - 1) = 8\vartheta \qquad (10)$$

with respect to ϑ (π constant) and substitute from (9), when:

$$-8\vartheta/(3\phi-1) + 6(3\phi-1)/\phi^2 = 0.$$

Hence at an inversion point:

$$\vartheta_i = 3(3\phi-1)^2/4\phi^2 \qquad (11)$$

or by elimination of ϑ:

$$\pi_i = 9(2\phi-1)/\phi^2 \qquad (12)$$

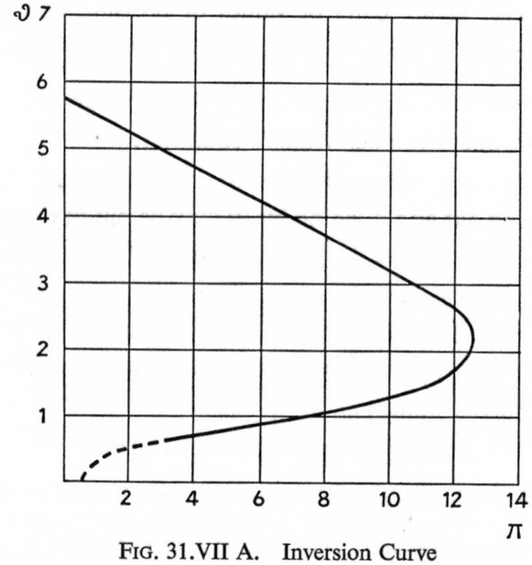

FIG. 31.VII A. Inversion Curve

For all pressures from 0 to $9P_c$ (12) has two real roots, and there are *two* inversion temperatures within this region for each pair of values of P and V, these temperatures ranging from a little below, to 6·7 times, the critical temperature. At pressures higher than $9P_c$ there is no inversion point. Eliminating ϕ leads to:

$$\vartheta_i = 3[1 \pm \tfrac{1}{6}\sqrt{(9-\pi)}]^2$$

again giving two inversion points, depending on the pressure.

The experimental results of the compressibilities of carbon dioxide and nitrous oxide gave identical inversion curves, this agreeing with the law of corresponding states (see Fig. 31.VII A), but the curve was not that predicted by van der Waals's theory. Davis found the same reduced curves for five gases, including water vapour.

[1] Berthelot, *Compt. Rend.*, 1900, **130**, 1379; *J. de Phys.*, 1903, **2**, 186; Porter, *Phil. Mag.*, 1906, **11**, 554; 1910, **19**, 888; *Proc. Roy. Soc.*, 1914, **89**, 377; Dickson, *Phil. Mag.*, 1908, **15**, 126; Davis, *Proc. Amer. Acad.*, 1910, **45**, 243.

Jakob[1] found the following empirical equation for the reduced inversion curve for air, hydrogen, oxygen, nitrogen, carbon dioxide, and ethylene:

$$\pi = 23{\cdot}37 - 1{\cdot}174x\vartheta - 178{\cdot}6/x^2\vartheta^2 \quad \ldots \ldots \quad (13)$$

where $x = RT_c/P_cV_c = 82{\cdot}07T_c/MP_cv_c$, v_c=critical volume in ml. per g., and M=mol. wt.

The values of the Joule and Joule-Thomson effects may also be found from Berthelot's equation (and from any characteristic equation which leads to these effects). From (14), § 30.VII C, the Joule effect (E const.) is found to be:

$$dT_E = (RT_c/C_vP_c)(27/32)\tau^2 dP \quad \ldots \ldots \quad (14)$$

and from (15), § 30.VII C the Joule-Thomson effect (H constant) is:

$$dT_H = (9RT_c/128P_cC_p)(1-18\tau^2)dP \quad \ldots \ldots \quad (15)$$

($\tau = T_c/T$). Other characteristic equations may be used in a similar way.

B. CRITICAL PHENOMENA

§ 1. The Critical State

When a liquid in contact with its vapour in a closed vessel is heated, so that excess of liquid is always present, the vapour pressure increases. It might be supposed that this increase of pressure would go on continuously with rise in temperature until extremely high pressures would be reached. James Watt in 1783[2] had found by calculation based on his experiments that at a sufficiently high temperature and pressure the latent heat of water would vanish, the specific volumes of water and steam would become equal, and the water would "become an elastic fluid nearly as specifically heavy as water," but he thought it would be converted into air. König[3] pointed out that G. Schmidt[4] in 1823 had said "temperatures may be imagined (even if not definitely realised) for which the densities of steam and water are the same: would heat become latent in such a formation of vapour?" He did not carry the idea further. Cagniard de la Tour[5] heated alcohol, ether, and other liquids in sealed glass tubes, and found that the increase in pressure reached a sharp limit, when the liquid meniscus suddenly disappeared:

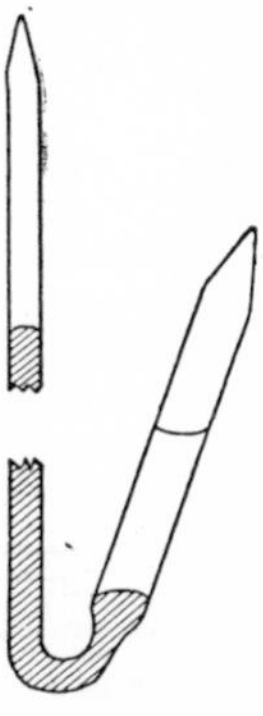

FIG. 1.VII B. Cagniard de la Tour Tube

> "The liquid, after assuming about double its original volume, completely disappeared and was converted into a vapour so transparent that the tube seemed quite empty, but on letting it cool for a moment a very thick fog formed, after which the liquid reappeared in its former state."

1 *Phys. Z.*, 1917, **18**, 421; 1921, **22**, 65; cf. Plank, *ibid.*, 1914, **15**, 904; 1916, **17**, 521; 1917, **18**, 33, 291; 1920, **21**, 150; *Z. ges. Kälte-Ind.*, 1920, **27**, 1; Schames, *Phys. Z.*, 1917, **18**, 30; Joffe, *Phys. Rev.*, 1946, **70**, 766 (maximum inversion temperatures, He 62·7° K. or 60·1° K., Ne *c.* 250° K.).

2 Muirhead, "Correspondence of the late James Watt," 1846, 6.

3 *Ann. Phys.*, 1931, **11**, 985.

4 *Ann. Phys.*, 1823, **75**, 343 (354).

5 *Ann. Chim.*, 1822, **21**, 127, 178; 1823, **22**, 410; Brewster, *Edin. N. Phil. J.*, 1823, **9**, 94, 268, 400, noticed similar phenomena with liquid inclusions (CO_2) in quartz crystals; cf. Sajontschewsky, *Ann. Phys. Beibl.*, 1879, **3**, 741; Cailletet and Colardeau, *Compt. Rend.*, 1891, **112**, 563.

Cagniard de la Tour then used a bulb containing liquid and vapour (Fig. 1.VII B) and measured the temperatures and pressures at which the meniscus vanished; this was at 200° with ether, 259° with alcohol, 275° with carbon disulphide, and 362° with water. He must be considered the discoverer of the *critical state.*

Similar observations were made by Drion [1] in 1859, with ethyl chloride (110°) and sulphur dioxide (240°), and Mendeléeff [2] in 1861, who called the temperature at which a " liquid changes to vapour regardless of pressure and

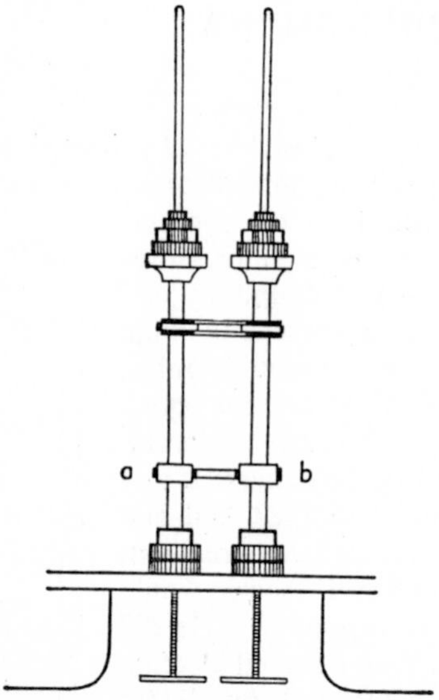

FIG. 2.VII B. Andrews' Critical Point Apparatus. Complete apparatus showing outer Copper Tubes, with Capillary Tubes projecting above and Compressing Screws below

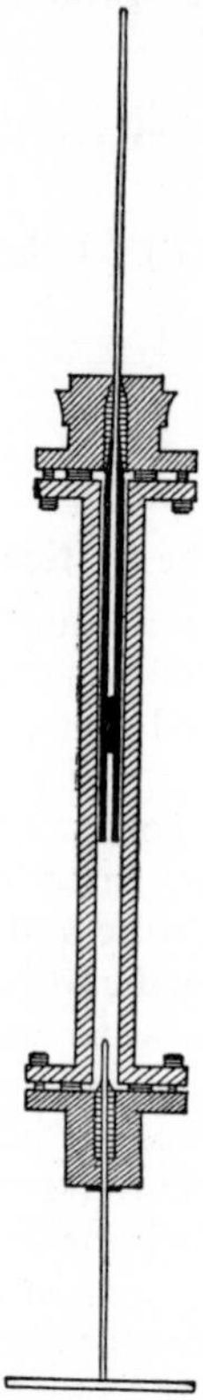

FIG. 3.VII B. Sections o Tubes, showing lower part of Gas Tube with Mercury Seal

volume " its *absolute boiling-point*, at which " the cohesion and heat of vaporisation become zero." This name is likely to be confused with the boiling-point on the absolute scale, i.e. b.p. in ° C.+273. Mendeléeff's approach was the decrease of surface tension of a liquid with temperature.

Such observations as Cagniard de la Tour's obviously point to the conclusion reached by Faraday [3] that at the Cagniard de la Tour temperature, " or one a little higher, it is not likely that any increase of pressure, except perhaps one exceedingly great, would convert the gas into a liquid "; " permanent " gases

[1] *Ann. Chim.*, 1859, **56**, 5.

[2] *Ann.*, 1861, **119**, 1; *Ann. Phys.*, 1870, **141**, 618; " Principles of Chemistry," 3rd edit., 1905, **1**, 132.

[3] *Phil. Trans.*, 1845, **135**, 155; " Researches in Chemistry and Physics," 1859, 116.

might then " be brought into the state of very condensed gases, but not liquefied." Berthelot [1] also concluded that " pressure alone cannot bring about the liquefaction of a gas in certain conditions of temperature," but the full study of

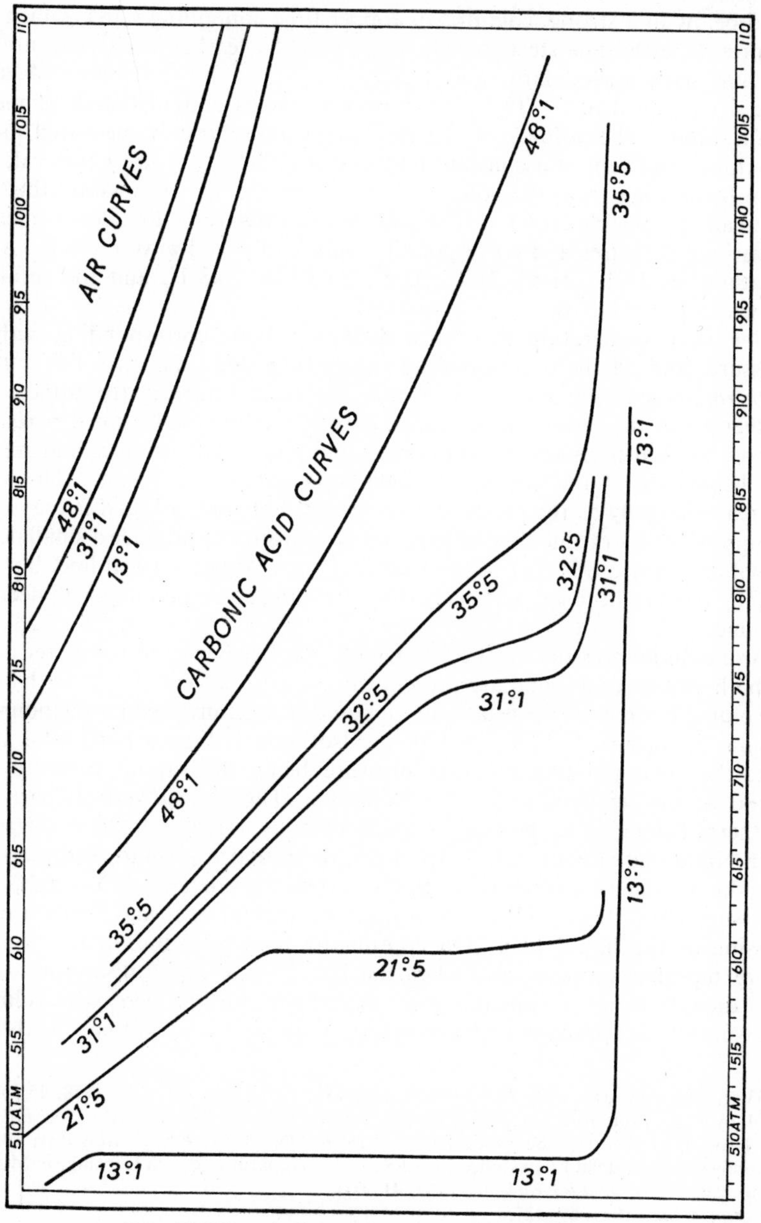

FIG. 4.VII B. Andrews' Curves for Carbon Dioxide

critical phenomena, which are of such fundamental importance in the properties of gases and liquids, was first made by Thomas Andrews,[2] whose work was

[1] *Ann. Chim.*, 1850, **30**, 237.

[2] First announced in Miller, " Chemical Physics. Elements of Chemistry," 3rd edit.,

based on an observation of Thilorier[1] that the coefficient of expansion of *liquid* carbon dioxide between 0° and 20° was four times that of the gas.

Andrews used the apparatus shown in Figs. 2 and 3.VII B. The gas (carbon dioxide) was contained in a tube *a*, ending above in a sealed capillary tube and fixed below in a strong, cold-drawn copper tube containing water, which could be pressed in by fine steel screws, made tight by leather washers saturated in vacuum with melted lard, and tightly pressed in brass flanges. A similar tube *b* contained air.[2] The gas or air was enclosed by a thread of mercury in the tube. The volume of the capillary was accurately measured and the apparatus was kept at a constant temperature. The pressure p was calculated from Boyle's law from the volume of the air (at the higher pressures this would cause an appreciable error).[3] The volume v of the carbon dioxide was measured at various pressures and corresponding values of p and v were plotted at temperatures of 17·1°, 21·5°, 31·1°, 32·5°, 33·5°, and 48·1°, and the results are shown in Fig. 4.VII B.

For each temperature there is a definite volume corresponding with each pressure, and all the corresponding values of p and v lie on a line called an *isotherm*, connecting points for which the temperature is the same. These isotherms, at the lower temperatures, consist of three well-defined parts. The almost vertical parts on the left correspond with small volumes and represent the behaviour of the substance when it is completely liquid. The volume decreases slightly as the pressure is increased, but since a liquid is only slightly compressible a large increase of pressure is necessary to produce a small decrease in volume, hence this part of the isotherm is an almost vertical line, but slopes slightly from right to left with increasing pressure, corresponding with decreasing volume.

At a definite pressure on the falling side, vapour begins to form, and as soon as both vapour and liquid are present the pressure cannot change with increase in volume but remains constant, more liquid being converted into vapour as the volume is increased. This part of the isotherm is thus a horizontal straight line, the corresponding constant pressure being the vapour pressure of the liquid at the temperature of the isotherm. The almost vertical part of the isotherm belonging to the liquid should meet the horizontal part corresponding with liquid and vapour at a sharp angle; the rounded form in Andrews' curves was due to a small amount of air in the carbon dioxide used.[4] Young's[5] curves for isopentane (Fig. 5.VII B) show quite horizontal lines and sharp breaks on passing to the liquid line. On continually increasing the volume more and more liquid evaporates, and when the last drop of liquid disappears the carbon dioxide is now completely gaseous and with further increase in volume the pressure drops approximately according to Boyle's law, so that this third part

1863, **1**, 328; Andrews, *Phil. Trans.*, 1869, **159**, 575; 1876, **166**, 421; 1887, **178**, 45 (posthum. publ. by Tait); *Proc. Roy. Soc.*, 1875, **23**, 514; *J.C.S.*, 1870, **23**, 74; *Proc. Roy. Soc. Edin.*, 1909, **21**, 1 (publ. by Knott); "Scientific Papers," 1889, 296, 333; Ostwald's *Klassiker*, 1902, **132**; "Conferences. Special Loan Collection of Scientific Apparatus [South Kensington Museum]," 1876, 150; Plank, *Z. Elektrochem.*, 1935, **41**, 804.

[1] *Ann. Chim.*, 1835, **60**, 427.

[2] Andrews also used an iron apparatus filled with mercury, which is less compressible than water, but then had difficulties with the packing; "Scientific Papers," 1889, 336; the original apparatus is in the Science Museum, South Kensington; see photograph in Edser, "Heat for Advanced Students," 1899, 206.

[3] See Knott, *Nature*, 1908, **78**, 262; *Proc. Roy. Soc. Edin.*, 1909, **30**, 1.

[4] Kuenen, "Die Zustandsgleichung der Gase und Flüssigkeiten," Brunswick, 1907, 36.

[5] "Stoichiometry," 1918, 116, Fig. 22.

of the isotherm, shown on the right, is approximately a rectangular hyperbola. The horizontal line meets this in a sharp angle, as shown.

By starting with gaseous carbon dioxide and increasing the pressure these changes occur in the reverse order. At first the pressure increases with decreasing volume until *liquefaction* begins, when the isotherm becomes horizontal. As long as liquid and gas (or vapour) are both present it remains horizontal, but when the last bubble of gas has liquefied and the carbon dioxide is all liquid, the isotherm turns sharply upwards and becomes a nearly vertical line.

At higher temperatures the isotherm has the same general form, but since at each pressure the volume of the liquid is slightly larger at a higher temperature

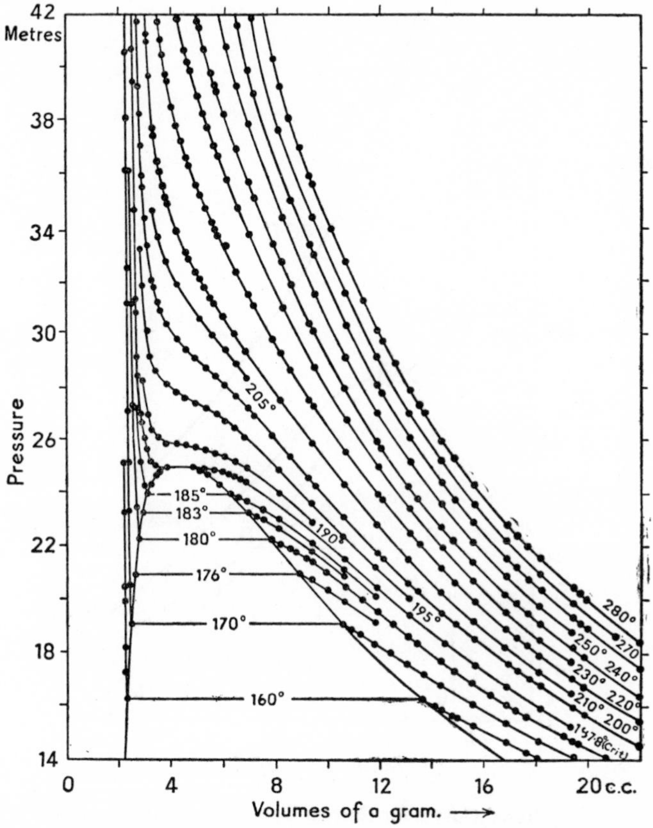

FIG. 5.VII B. Young's Curves for Isopentane

the liquid isotherm starts to the right of the previous one. Since also the vapour pressure is higher at the higher temperature, the horizontal part of the isotherm starts higher up than previously. The horizontal part becomes progressively shorter as the temperature increases. All these features appear in the isotherms for 17·1° and 21·5°; on the 31·1° isotherm the sharp break of the horizontal part on the right has become rounded, but this is due to the presence of air.

At a certain temperature the two ends of the horizontal isotherm approach so closely that they meet, and this means that the densities of the liquid and gas (or vapour) have become identical, i.e. these two states have become identical. This occurs on the 32·5° isotherm, on which the sharp breaks on the right and the left have both disappeared and the curve has no finite horizontal portion, but runs for an instant horizontal, the curvature changing, as shown. This corresponds with a *point of inflexion* (§ 10.I) and was called by Andrews the *critical point* (it may be called the "liquid-gas critical point"), and 32·5° the *critical temperature.*

At the critical temperature, therefore, liquid and vapour are identical and Andrews assumed that the substance is then in a definite *critical state.* At the critical point the separation of liquid from vapour, or the evaporation of liquid to vapour, to form a *heterogeneous* mixture of liquid and vapour is no longer possible, but the transition from vapour to liquid, or *vice versa,* occurs continuously. The proximity to the critical point is still shown by a change of

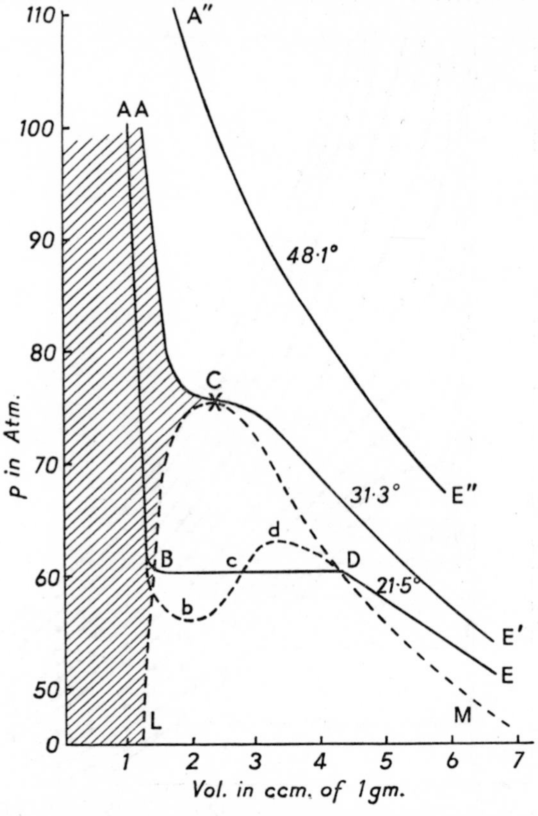

FIG. 6.VII B. Andrews' Curves for Carbon Dioxide, showing Regions of Existence of States.

curvature on the 33·5° isotherm, but on the 48·1° isotherm all trace of it has disappeared and the curve throughout is that of a gas.

The cloudy appearance of the liquid just as the meniscus vanishes at the critical point and the remarkable striations seen just above the critical point are described and illustrated by Andrews [1] (see § 2).

Andrews thus showed that, at a certain temperature, carbon dioxide passes *continuously* from the liquid to the gaseous state, and no increase of pressure would cause liquefaction, or separation into liquid and vapour, as long as the

1 "Scientific Papers," 1889, 337, Figs. 1 and 2; he correctly says they are due to "the great changes of density which slight changes of pressure or temperature produce." See also the figures in Harand, *Monatsh.*, 1935, **65**, 153.

temperature is at or above this critical temperature. In his first announcement [1] he says: " there exists for every liquid a temperature at which no amount of pressure is sufficient to retain it in the liquid form." Corresponding with the critical temperature is a *critical pressure*, which is the upper limit of the pressures causing liquefaction (separation into liquid and vapour) with rising temperature, i.e. the highest pressure under which liquid can form or exist. The volume of 1 g. of substance at the critical temperature and pressure is the *critical volume*, and its reciprocal is the *critical density*. These constants are usually denoted by t_c, p_c, v_c, and ρ_c.

The critical temperature divides the state of *vapour*, which can be liquefied (converted into vapour and liquid) by increase of pressure, below the critical temperature, from the state of *gas*, above the critical temperature, which cannot be liquefied by increase of pressure.

The critical state was found by Andrews for carbon dioxide, nitrous oxide, hydrogen chloride, ammonia, ether, and carbon disulphide, and he concluded that it is a general property of liquids. This has since been confirmed for a large number of substances. If the ends of the horizontal isotherms are joined, the dotted curve in Fig. 6.VII B is obtained, with a maximum at the critical point. Inside this curve [2] every point represents a mixture of liquid and vapour; outside it and to the left is liquid as far as the critical isotherm, and on the right is vapour below the critical isotherm and gas above it.

§ 2. Continuity of Liquid and Gaseous States

If the region of heterogeneous states (liquid and vapour) inside the limiting curve is not entered, it is possible to convert a liquid into a vapour, or a vapour into a liquid (where " vapour " may include " gas ") without any visible separation of one from the other, i.e. the appearance of a meniscus. This is a *continuous transition of state*. To do this, the liquid is taken, represented by a point to the left of the region of heterogeneous states and of the critical isotherm. The temperature and pressure are raised together so that the substance still remains in the homogeneous region until the temperature is higher than the critical point; by increasing the volume but maintaining the temperature above the critical value, we pass from left to right across the critical isotherm into the gas region, and by lowering the temperature and pressure, so as always to keep out of the region of heterogeneous states, we reach the vapour by again crossing the critical isotherm. The reverse process of converting the vapour *continuously* into liquid may obviously be carried out by raising the temperature above the critical temperature, compressing until the critical isotherm is crossed into the liquid region, and then lowering the temperature and pressure. As Andrews [3] said: " the ordinary gaseous and ordinary liquid states are only widely separated forms of the same condition of matter, and may be made to pass into one another by a series of gradations so gentle that the passage shall nowhere present any interruption or breach of continuity . . . the gas and liquid are only distant stages of a long series of continuous physical changes."

Van't Hoff [4] showed that phosphonium iodide, which dissociates on heating

[1] Miller, " Elements of Chemistry," 1863, **1**, 328.

[2] On various curves joining states with different properties *inside* this region, see Amagat, *J. de Phys.*, 1892, **1**, 288; Raveau, *ibid.*, 1892, **1**, 461; Mathias, *ibid.*, 1900, **9**, 479; Onnes and Keesom, " Enzykl. d. math. Wiss.," 1912, **5**, i, 665 and the instructive Fig. 14 there.

[3] " Scientific Papers," 1889, 342 (lecture in 1871); the same in rather different words in the paper of 1869, *ibid.*, 316.

[4] *Ber.*, 1885, **18**, 2088.

at atmospheric pressure, shows a critical point at 50°–51° and 80–90 atm. when heated in a sealed tube.

The molecular explanation of the critical phenomena is, qualitatively, fairly obvious. Above the critical temperature, the kinetic energy of the molecules is so large in comparison with the attractive forces of cohesion that the molecules seldom or never remain attached to one another, and the cohesive forces are greatly weakened. This agrees with the facts that (i) the surface tension vanishes at the critical point, and (ii) with rise of temperature the latent heat of evaporation l_e of a liquid, representing the work done in separating the molecules under the influence of cohesive forces, becomes progressively smaller and probably vanishes at the critical temperature. This would follow from the Clapeyron-Clausius equation (see § 7.VIII L, Vol. II); when the specific volumes v_l and v_g of liquid and vapour become equal at the critical point:

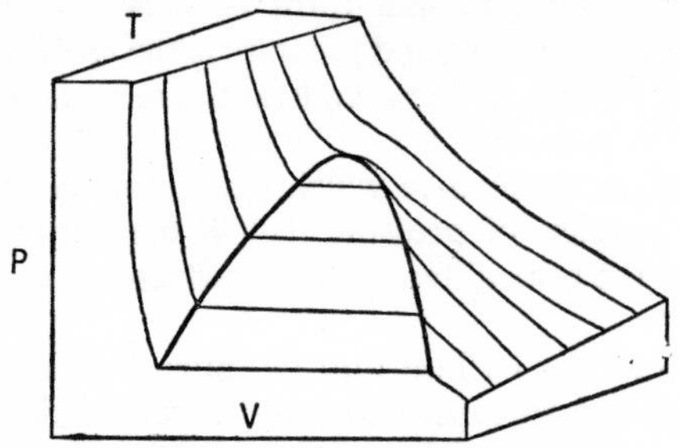

FIG. 7.VII B. Space Model of Pressure, Volume, and Temperature

$$l_e = T(\mathrm{d}p/\mathrm{d}T)(v_g - v_l) = 0.$$

A space-model [1] of the p, v curves with temperature as a third axis [2] gives a clear view of the whole range of behaviour of a fluid to pressure and temperature (Fig. 7.VII B). The figure is self-explanatory.

Jamin [3] plotted p against *density* instead of volume, and Wroblewski [4] proposed to call lines of equal density *isopycnics* (πυκνός, compact). By plotting p against T for equal densities he found no discontinuity at the critical temperature.

§ 3. Supposed Anomalies in Critical Phenomena

The continuous conversion of liquid into vapour at the critical point, and the resulting identity of these two states, is convincingly shown in an experiment of Nadejdine.[5] In this, liquid is contained with vapour in a sealed tube supported on a knife-edge at its centre and balanced by suitable weights so as to be horizontal when empty (Fig. 8.VII B). The liquid at one end tilts the tube down by its weight. On raising the temperature, the densities of liquid and vapour become identical at the critical point and the tube swings into a horizontal position. This has been used as a method for determining critical temperatures.

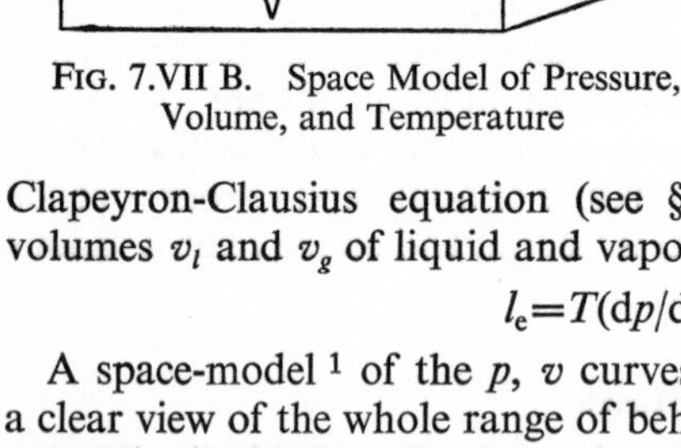

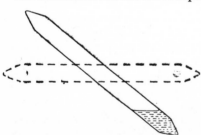

FIG. 8.VII B. Nadejdine's Experiment

[1] First constructed by James Thomson, *Proc. Roy. Soc.*, 1871, **20**, 1 (wood models); see Andrews, "Scientific Papers," 1889, 340; J. Thomson, "Collected Papers in Physics and Engineering," Cambridge, 1912, 276 f. (incl. unpublished material).

[2] See Ostwald, "Lehrbuch der allgemeinen Chemie," 1911, **2**, ii, 342, 347.

[3] *Compt. Rend.*, 1883, **97**, 10; *J. de Phys.*, 1883, **2**, 389.

[4] *Ann. Phys.*, 1886, **29**, 428; cf. Hirsch, *ibid.*, 1899, **69**, 456, 837; 1900, **1**, 655.

[5] *Bull. Acad. St. Petersb.*, 1885, **30**, 327; *Ann. Phys. Beibl.*, 1885, **9**, 721; Bond and Williams, *J.A.C.S.*, 1931, **53**, 34 (HF).

Jamin,[1] in a criticism of Andrews' results, argued that the so-called critical point is merely the temperature at which a meniscus vanishes because the densities of liquid and *saturated* vapour, which have been changing in opposite directions with rise of temperature, accidentally become equal. Cailletet and Colardeau,[2] however, pointed out that, if this is so, an increase of pressure should cause the liquid to appear in the *upper* part of the tube and the vapour below, which is not the case; other objections were answered by Stoletow.[3]

Cailletet and Colardeau [4] then sealed up liquid carbon dioxide and concentrated sulphuric acid in a circular tube and heated above the critical point. They found that even a little above the critical point the sulphuric acid showed a difference of level, indicating that the liquid still remained somewhat denser than the vapour. Battelli [5] found that when ether contained in one of two communicating vessels was heated above the critical temperature, and the whole apparatus then uniformly cooled, the liquid reappeared in the vessel which originally contained it, indicating that the liquid was still present above the critical temperature.

De Heen,[6] Zambiasi,[7] and Dwelshauvers-Dery,[8] by measurements of critical density, concluded that this is not a unique constant, but depends on the mass of the substance, and de Heen (who emphasised that the critical point has no significance unless liquid and vapour are present) supposed that the critical temperature is a transition temperature at which two different species of molecules, the polymerised *liquidogen* molecules of the liquid and the simple *gasogen* molecules of the vapour (these names are due to Traube [9]) become miscible, and the transition from liquidogen to gasogen molecules, according to Traube, is not instantaneous.

Galitzine [10] by measurements of refractive index also found variable densities above the critical temperature. Verain [11] found that the curves for the dielectric constant of liquid and gaseous carbon dioxide met at the critical point with a common tangent. Teichner [12] found large density differences in different parts of a tube above the critical temperature by means of small glass floats of different densities, all fairly near the critical density, which had been sealed up in the

1 *Compt. Rend.*, 1883, **96**, 1448; 1883, **97**, 10.

2 *J. de Phys.*, 1889, **8**, 389; *Compt. Rend.*, 1892, **115**, 13; *Ann. Chim.*, 1892, **25**, 519.

3 *J. Russ. Phys. Chem. Soc.*, 1893, **25**, 303 (P); 1894, **26**, 26 (P); cf. Saposhnikov, *ibid.*, 1924 **56**, 581 (P); Ramsay, *Phil. Mag.*, 1894, **37**, 215.

4 *Ann. Chim.*, 1889, **18**, 269; Hannay and Hogarth, *Proc. Roy. Soc.*, 1880, **30**, 178; Hagenbach, *Ann. Phys.*, 1901, **5**, 276.

5 *Ann. Chim.*, 1893, **29**, 400; *Phil. Mag.*, 1894, **38**, 245; cf. Ramsay and Young, *Phil. Mag.*, 1894, **38**, 569.

6 *Bull. Acad. Roy. Belg.*, 1892, **24**, 96, 267; 1893, **25**, 695; 1894, **27**, 348, 580, 885; 1894, **28**, 46; 1896, **31**, 147, 379; 1897, **33**, 119; 1908, 512; *Phil. Mag.*, 1894, **37**, 424.

7 *Atti R. Accad. Lincei*, 1892, **1**, 423; 1893, **2**, 21; 1895, **4**, ii, 127.

8 *Bull. Acad. Roy. Belg.*, 1896, **30**, 570; 1896, **31**, 277; Traube, *ibid.*, 1902, 319.

9 *Ann. Phys.*, 1902, **8**, 267; *Phys. Z.*, 1903, **4**, 569; *Z. anorg. Chem.*, 1903, **37**, 225; 1904, **38**, 399; *Z. phys. Chem.*, 1907, **58**, 475; *Verhl. d. D. Phys. Ges.*, 1913, **15**, 1219; *Trans. Faraday Soc.*, 1938, **34**, 1234; cf. Mathias, *Compt. Rend.*, 1903, **136**, 545; *J. de Phys.*, 1903, **2**, 172; Lehmann, *Ann. Phys.*, 1906, **20**, 77; 1907, **22**, 469; Fuchs, *ibid.*, 1906, **21**, 393, 814; 1907, **23**, 385; Hein, *Z. phys. Chem.*, 1914, **86**, 385; Bennewitz and Splittgerber, *ibid.*, 1926, **124**, 49; Bennewitz and Windisch, *ibid.*, 1933, **166**, 401; Clarke, *Chem. Rev.*, 1938, **23**, 1.

10 *Ann. Phys.*, 1893, **50**, 521; Galitzine and Wilip, *Bull. Acad. St. Petersb.*, 1899, **11**, 117; *Congrès Internat. Phys.*, 1900, **1**, 668; *Z. phys. Chem.*, 1901, **37**, 126 (abstr.); cf. Chappuis, *Compt. Rend.*, 1894, **118**, 976; Schames, *Elster-Geitel Festschr.*, 1915, 287.

11 *Compt. Rend.*, 1912, **154**, 345; the curves are not very convincing.

12 *Ann. Phys.*, 1904, **13**, 595; Traube and Teichner, *Z. Elektrochem.*, 1903, **9**, 618 (and discussion); *Ann. Phys.*, 1904, **13**, 611.

tube; each sphere floated in a horizontal level where the density was equal to its own. Wilip [1] thought the liquid was transformed into a fine state of subdivision and persisted as such above the critical point.

Hein [2] found that the meniscus in a tube containing liquid and gaseous carbon dioxide disappears on heating when the mean density is 0·341–0·589 or 0·735–1·269 times the critical density. There were, however, variations of density in the tube, made evident by the different positions taken up by a number of small spheres of different density, as used by Teichner.

That a large part of these supposed anomalies is due to non-uniformity of temperature [3] and most of the rest probably to impurities [4] seems established beyond reasonable doubt. Since the compressibility is very large at the critical point ($dp/dv=0$) the influence of weight is important, and by inverting the tube [5] or using a stirrer [6] the differences of density due to any cause may be removed. In a very convincing experiment Ramsay [7] showed that in a circular tube just below the critical temperature droplets of liquid ether float in the vapour as a cloud, showing that the densities of liquid and vapour are almost identical, and on very slight further heating to the critical temperature the two states became identical. Bradley, Browne, and Hale [6] found the temperatures of disappearance of the meniscus with carbon dioxide differed by only 0·08°.

The *opalescence* at the critical point, observed by Andrews (§ 1) and many later workers,[8] is due to minute differences in density in various parts of the

[1] *Acta Comment. Univ. Dorpatensis*, 1924, **6** A, No. 2; Swietoslawski, "Ebulliometric Measurements," New York, 1945, 186, 190.

[2] *Z. phys. Chem.*, 1914, **86**, 385.

[3] Stoletow, *Fortschr. Phys.*, 1892, **48**, ii, 190; *J. Russ. Phys. Chem. Soc.*, 1893, **25**, 303 (P); 1894, **26**, 26 (P); Kuenen, *Z. phys. Chem.*, 1893, **11**, 38; Villard, *J. de Phys.*, 1894, **3**, 441; *Ann. Chim.*, 1897, **10**, 387; Altschul, *Chem. Ztg.*, 1895, **19**, Suppl., 65; Young, *J.C.S.*, 1897, **71**, 446; *J. Chim. Phys.*, 1906, **4**, 425; "Stoichiometry," 1918, 118; von Hirsch, *Ann. Phys.*, 1900, **1**, 655; Onnes, *Proc. K. Akad. Wetens. Amsterdam*, 1901, **3**, 628 (*Comm. Leiden*, **68**); Onnes and Villars, *ibid.*, 1907–8, **10**, 215 (*Comm. Leiden*, **98**); Travers and Usher, *Proc. Roy. Soc.*, 1906, **78**, 247; *Z. phys. Chem.*, 1906, **57**, 365; Piazzo, *An. Soc. Cient. Argentina*, 1941, **132**, 245.

[4] Knietsch, *Ann.*, 1890, **259**, 100; *Z. phys. Chem.*, 1895, **16**, 731; Ramsay and Young, *Phil. Mag.*, 1894, **37**, 215, 503; Ramsay, *Z. phys Chem.*, 1894, **14**, 486; Villard, *J. de Phys.*, 1894, **3**, 441; *Ann. Chim.*, 1897, **10**, 387; von Wesendonck, *Z. phys. Chem.*, 1894, **15**, 262; *Ann. Phys.*, 1895, **55**, 577; Pictet and Altschul, *Z. phys. Chem.*, 1895, **16**, 26; von Hirsch, *Ann. Phys.*, 1899, **69**, 456; 1900, **1**, 655; de Heen, *Bull. Acad. Roy. Belg.*, 1907, 859.

[5] Gouy, *Compt. Rend.*, 1892, **115**, 720; 1893, **116**, 1289; Villard, *ibid.*, 1895, **120**, 182; 1895, **121**, 115; Mathias, "Le Point Critique des Corps Purs," 1904.

[6] Kuenen, *Proc. K. Akad. Wetens. Amsterdam*, 1893–4, **2**, 85; 1894–5, **3**, 19, 57; *Arch. Néerl.*, 1893, **26**, 354; *Z. phys. Chem.*, 1893, **11**, 38; "Die Zustandsgleichung," Brunswick, 1907, 40; Bradley, Browne, and Hale, *Phys. Rev.*, 1904, **19**, 258; 1908, **26**, 470; 1908, **27**, 90.

[7] *Z. phys. Chem.*, 1894, **14**, 486; von Wesendonck, *ibid.*, 1894, **15**, 262; Cardoso, *J. Chim. Phys.*, 1912, **10**, 470.

[8] Andrews, "Scient. Papers," 1889, 337; Avenarius, *Ann. Phys.*, 1874, **151**, 303; Galitzine, *ibid.*, 1893, **50**, 521; Konowalow, *ibid.*, 1903, **10**, 360; 1903, **12**, 1160; Travers and Usher, *Proc. Roy. Soc.*, 1906, **78**, 247; *Z. phys. Chem.*, 1907, **57**, 365; von Wesendonck, *Verhl. d. D. Phys. Ges.*, 1908, **10**, 483; Rothmund, *Z. phys. Chem.*, 1908, **63**, 54; Keesom, *Ann. Phys.*, 1911, **35**, 591; Ostwald, *ibid.*, 1911, **36**, 848; Onnes and Keesom, "Enzykl. d. math. Wiss.," 1912, **5**, i, 796; Cardoso, *J. Chim. Phys.*, 1912, **10**, 470; 1915, **13**, 414; Ornstein, *Proc. K. Akad. Wetens. Amsterdam*, 1912, **15**, 54; Ornstein and Zernike, *ibid.*, 1914–15, **17**, 793; *Phys. Z.*, 1926, **27**, 761; Schidloff, *Arch. Sci. Phys. Nat.*, 1915, **39**, 25; Zernike, *Proc. K. Akad. Wetens. Amsterdam*, 1916, **18**, 1250; *Arch. Néerl.*, 1918, **4**, 74; Lorentz, "Les Théories Statistique en Thermodynamique," Leipzig and Berlin, 1916, 44; Davis, *J.A.C.S.*, 1916, **38**, 1166; Roozeboom, "Die heterogenen Gleichgewichte," 1918, **2**, ii, 81; Martin, *J. Phys. Chem.*, 1922, **26**, 471; Raman and Ramanathan, *Phil. Mag.*, 1923, **45**, 113; Audat, *J. de Phys.*, 1924, **5**, 193; Stewart, *J. Opt. Soc. Amer.*, 1925, **11**, 581; Kar, *Phys. Z.*, 1926, **27**, 380; 1927, **28**, 710; *Phil. Mag.*, 1927, **3**, 601; Raman, *ibid.*, 1927, **4**, 447; Schroer, *Z. phys. Chem.*, 1929, **140**, 241; Placzek, *Phys. Z.*,

substance caused by [1] variations of the order of magnitude contemplated in Maxwell's Distribution Law (§ 10.III). F. B. Young [2] found that the opalescence with ether persists even in tubes of 0·15 mm. inner diameter, and the point of maximum opalescence seemed to depend mainly on the mean specific volume of the fluid. Cardoso [3] found with several gases, opalescence regions of about 0·5°, but Audant [4] found a range of 3°. Opalescence is *not* observed with oxygen.[5] Friedländer [6] found no electrophoresis of the opalescence, whilst actual drops would be expected to move in an electric field.

Smoluchowski showed that the probability $W(v)$ that N molecules should have a specific volume v, where v_0 is the normal specific volume, is

$$W(v)=be^{N/kT}\int_{v_0}^{v}(p-p_0)\mathrm{d}v,$$

where b is a constant, k is Boltzmann's constant, and p, p_0 are the pressures corresponding with v, v_0. From this he (and more simply Schidloff) found the mean square deviation from the average density $\delta^2=kT/Nv_0^2(1-\partial p/\partial v)_T$. It is large when $\mathrm{d}p/\mathrm{d}v$ is small, i.e. near the critical point.

If I_0 and I_s are the intensities of the incident and scattered light:

$$I_s/I_0=kT\kappa_T(n^2-1)^2(n^2+2)^2[V\pi^2(1+\cos^2\theta)/18d^2\lambda^4],$$

where κ_T=isothermal compressibility, n=refractive index, V=vol. of liquid, d=distance at which I_s is observed, θ=angle between incident and scattered beams.

Another form of the Einstein-Smoluchowski equation (which is given differently by every author who quotes it) for the fraction of the incident light scattered per unit volume per unit solid angle, is: [7]

$$I_s/I_0=(\pi^2RT\kappa/18N\lambda^4)(n^2-1)^2(n^2+2)^2,$$

where N=Avogadro's number. If the observed depolarisation for the transversely scattered wave is r, this expression requires multiplication [8] by $6(1+r)/(6-7r)$; for Rayleigh scattering $r=0$.

Smoluchowski actually gave the formula for the mean deviation from the average density as $\bar{\delta}=\sqrt{(2\omega p\beta/V\pi)}$, where $\beta=-(1/v)(\mathrm{d}v/\mathrm{d}p)_T$, V=normal given volume, ω=molecular volume corresponding with the pressure p. Einstein found:

$$I_0/I_s=\frac{M''}{N}\cdot\frac{v(\mathrm{d}D/\mathrm{d}k)}{\mathrm{d}\ln p''/\mathrm{d}k}\left(\frac{2\pi}{\lambda}\right)^4\frac{\phi}{(4\pi D)^2}\cos^2\theta,$$

1930, **31**, 1052; Vaidyanathan, *Indian J. Phys.*, 1930, **5**, 501; Rocard, *J. de Phys.*, 1933, **4**, 165; Parthasarathy, *Indian J. Phys.*, 1934, **8**, 275; *J. Univ. Bombay*, 1936, **5**, ii, 34; Sata and Kimura, *Bull. Chem. Soc. Japan*, 1935, **10**, 409 (mixtures); Yvon, *Compt. Rend.*, 1936, **201**, 1099; Todes and Zeldovich, *Acta Physiocochim. U.R.S.S.*, 1942, **16**, 26; Markwood, *J. Franklin Inst.*, 1947, **244**, 92 (historical; equations).

1 Smoluchowski, *Ann. Phys. Boltzmann Festschr.*, 1904, 626; *Ann. Phys.*, 1908, **25**, 205; *Bull. Acad. Polon.*, 1911, 493; *Phil. Mag.*, 1912, **23**, 165; *Phys. Z.*, 1912, **13**, 1069; Einstein, *Ann. Phys.*, 1910, **33**, 1275; for further theoretical papers, see ref. 8, p. 632.

2 *Proc. Roy. Soc.*, 1906, **78**, 262; *Chem. News*, 1906, **94**, 149; *Phil. Mag.*, 1910, **20**, 793.

3 *Arch. Sci. Phys. Nat.*, 1912, **34**, 20.

4 *Compt. Rend.*, 1920, **170**, 1573.

5 Cardoso, *Arch. Sci. Phys. Nat.*, 1914, **38**, 78, 137; Onnes, Dorsman, and Holst, *Proc. K. Akad. Wetens. Amsterdam*, 1915, **17**, 950.

6 *Z. phys. Chem.*, 1901, **38**, 385.

7 Raman, *Nature*, 1921, **108**, 402; Krishnan, *Phil. Mag.*, 1925, **50**, 697; Cabannes, *J. de Phys.*, 1927, **8**, 321.

8 Cabannes and Ganzet, *J. de Phys.*, 1925, **6**, 182.

where M''=mol. wt. of second component, v=sp. vol. of first component, ϕ=irradiated volume, N=Avogadro's number, D=dielectric constant, p''=partial pressure of second component, k=mass of second component mixed with unit mass of the first.

A revision of Einstein's theory was given by Rocard,[1] who omitted the factor $[(D+2)/3]^2$ in one of Einstein's equations: $(\partial D/\partial v)^2=(D-1)^2(D+2)^2/9v^2$, where $(D-1)v/(D+2)$=const. Shaposhnikov [2] criticised the theory; he thought the *adiabatic* compressibility should be used.

Debye [3] defined a *turbidity* $\tau=(8\pi/3)Nk\mu^2$, $k=2\pi/\lambda$, λ=wave-length in vacuum, μ=electric moment in field of intensity 1, N=number of particles per cm.^{3}. The loss of intensity in the direction of propagation is $-d\tau/dx=\tau I$. If c=concentration in g./cm.^{3}, $\tau=cHM$, where M=mol. wt., $H=(32\pi^3/3)(n_0^2/N\lambda^4)[(n-n_0)/c]^2$, where N=Avogadro's number, n_0, n=refractive indices of medium and suspension. There may be a depolarisation factor $(6-7r)/(6+3r)$.

Cabannes [4] found:

$$R=J/EV=3\pi^2[(n^2-1)^2/\lambda^4N][(1+\rho)/(6-7\rho)],$$

where J is the intensity diffused at right angles, E is the intensity of the unpolarised beam, n=refractive index, N=number of molecules in a volume V, ρ is the ratio of the intensities at right angles to, and parallel to, the original beam. This subject will be considered in Vol. II.

Callendar [5] found that on heating water which had been deprived of every trace of dissolved air in a quartz tube the meniscus vanished at 374°, but a difference in density between the parts which had been occupied by liquid and vapour persisted up to nearly 380° in favourable conditions. The density of the liquid was determined by sealing a known weight of water in a tube of known volume and heating till the meniscus just reached the top of the tube. The density of the vapour was determined by sealing up a known smaller amount of liquid and heating till the last drop of liquid vanished. These densities were then plotted against temperature and the curves shown in Fig. 9.VII B obtained. The values for the liquid above 374° were found by observing the line of demarcation between liquid and vapour, which (on account of differences in density) could still be observed after the meniscus had disappeared. The extrapolated vapour curve met the liquid curve at a little above 380°. A trace of dissolved air made observations in the " unstable " region (above 374°) impossible.

It is clear that this method of experimenting differs from that generally used in determining critical temperatures, in which the aim is to eliminate all such differences in density,[6] and the interpretation of the results is correspondingly difficult. The sharp discontinuity in angle of liquid and vapour curves at 380° is quite different from the rounded maxima found by other experimenters; these, according to Callendar, are due to traces of dissolved air. It should be noted that Callendar's characteristic equation for steam (§ 32.VII C) does not agree with the existence of a critical point.

[1] *Ann. de Phys.*, 1928, **10**, 116, 181 (bibl., 118 refs., and abstracts).
[2] *Amer. Chem. Abstr.*, 1925, **19**, 1653.
[3] *J. Phys. Chem.*, 1947, **51**, 18.
[4] *J. de Phys.*, 1920, **1**, 129.
[5] *Proc. Roy. Soc.*, 1928, **120**, 460; *Engineering*, 1928, **126**, 594, 625, 671.
[6] Eversheim, *Ann. Phys.*, 1904, **13**, 492, had emphasised that this is necessary; Kennedy, *J.A.C.S.*, 1929, **51**, 1360, found different values for t_c for CO_2 according as a sharp or diffuse meniscus was used as a criterion.

Callendar calculated the values of the heat content $H=E+PV$ from his equation:

$$H=(n+1)rT-(n+1)(a/T^n)p+bp+\beta$$
$$a/T^n=[r(\mathrm{d}T/dp)_H+b/(n+1)]/[1-(np/T)(\mathrm{d}T/\mathrm{d}p)_H],$$

where $n=10/3$, b=vol. of 1 g. liquid, $r=R/M$=gas constant per g., and β is the only unknown constant and must be determined experimentally. The values of H were plotted at various temperatures against the saturation pressure (Fig. 10.VII B), and again the liquid and vapour curves met at a sharp angle at 380·5°; at 374°, where the curves for water containing a trace of air coalesced in a rounded maximum, there was still a latent heat. Callendar's curious results were not confirmed by Egerton and Callendar,[1] Koch,[2] and Eck; [3] the last two measured

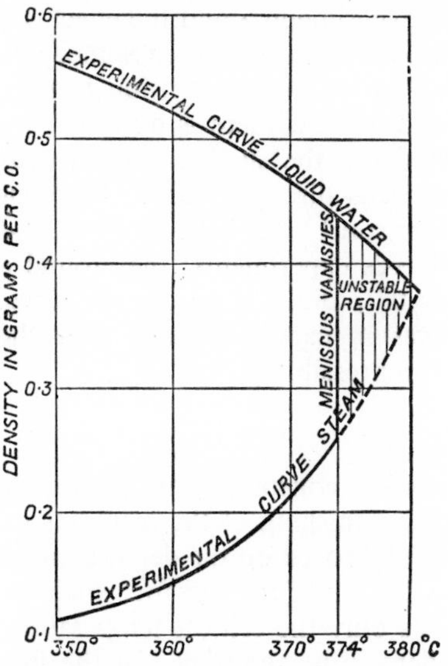

FIG. 9.VII B. Callendar's Curves for Densities of Liquid Water and Steam

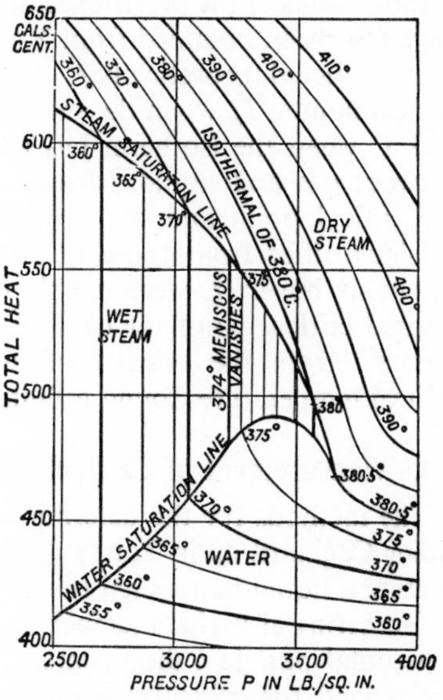

FIG. 10.VII B. Callendar's Curves for Total Heat of Water and Steam

the volumes of liquid and vapour from 350° to the critical temperature 374·2°, and considered that Callendar's results were due to dissolved air.

The question of the persistence of liquid above the critical temperature was opened again by Maass,[4] who believed the experimental results show that (i) a liquid has a structure due to certain regularities of molecular distribution, which structure tends to be broken down by rise of temperature and decrease of density, (ii) at the critical temperature the " normal density " of the liquid has

[1] *Phil. Trans.*, 1932, **231**, 147.

[2] *Forschungsart. Gebiet. Ingenieurw.*, 1932, **3** A, 189.

[3] *Phys. Z.*, 1939, **40**, 3; cf. Dorsey, " Properties of Ordinary Water Substance," New York, 1940, 557 f.

[4] Tapp, Steacie, and Maass, *Canad. J. Res.*, 1933, **9**, 217; Winkler and Maass, *ibid.*, 1933, **9**, 613; Edwards and Maass, *ibid.*, 1935, **12**, 357; Maass and Geddes, *Phil. Trans.*, 1937, **236**, 303; Maass, *Chem. Rev.*, 1938, **23**, 17; Dacey, McIntosh, and Maass, *Canad. J. Res.*, 1939, **17** B, 206, 241; Clark, *Trans. Roy. Soc. Canada*, 1915, **9**, iii, 43; 1924, **18**, iii, 329; *Chem. Rev.*, 1938, **23**, 1; Harvey, *Phys. Rev.*, 1934, **45**, 848; 1934, **46**, 441; Swietoslawski, *Bull. Acad. Polon.*, 1938 A, 304; *Koll. Z.*, 1939, **86**, 145; "Ebulliometric Measurements," New York, 1945, 186; Ruedy, *Canad. J. Res.*, 1938, **16** A, 89; cf. Ostwald, *Koll. Z.*, 1933, **64**, 50.

decreased to a point beyond which the structure rapidly diminishes, and (iii) the liquid state of aggregation can exist above this temperature when the density is increased by pressure so as to bring about a necessary concentration. In the experiments, a density difference varying from 10 per cent. for ethylene to 50 per cent. for methyl chloride persisted above the critical temperature and could not be destroyed by stirring, but with rise of temperature above the critical point the density difference disappeared. When the substance was now cooled, the density difference did not reappear, so that the heterogeneous state is obviously metastable. Again, if the upper part of the tube, after heating above the critical temperature, is cooled so as to reverse the density difference and promote mixing by convection, the density difference disappears, although this does not happen with mechanical stirring, even after six hours.

Indications of the persistence of the liquid state above the critical temperature have also been obtained from X-ray scattering experiments,[1] and the effect has been predicted theoretically.[2] Brescia,[3] on the basis of this theory, assumed two critical points, T_m when the meniscus vanishes and the surface tension is zero, and T_c when the isotherm has a point of inflexion and there is no difference between gas and liquid. Rice [4] discussed in detail the surface tension near the critical point and the temperature of meniscus disappearance. His conclusions differ from those of Mayer and Harrison.[5] Michels, Blaisse, and Michels,[6] however, were unable to repeat Maass's experiments; they found a normal critical point for carbon dioxide at 31·03°, and a good critical curve. Noury,[7] from the velocity of ultrasonic waves in carbon dioxide near the critical temperature, found a finite adiabatic compressibility.

§ 4. Measurement of Critical Constants

The methods for the determination of the critical constants [8] are essentially either Cagniard de la Tour's (§ 1), based on the vanishing of the meniscus on heating a liquid in a sealed tube, or Andrews' (§ 1), based on the determination of isotherms at various temperatures and the selection of the one for which the horizontal part just disappears. The first gives only the critical temperature, the second the critical pressure and critical density in addition. In the first method the difference in density between liquid and vapour can be followed by an interferometer, depending on differences of refractive index; in this way Chappuis [9] found 31·40° for the critical temperature of carbon dioxide, as compared with 31·35° found by Amagat by the isotherm method.

The tubes for the meniscus method should be of fairly thick wall (1–2 mm.), of hard glass, carefully sealed, and precautions should be taken to avoid the

[1] Spangler, *Phys. Rev.*, 1934, **46**, 698; Barnes, *Chem. Rev.*, 1938, **23**, 29 (bibl.).

[2] Mayer, *J. Chem. Phys.*, 1937, **5**, 67; Mayer and Ackermann, *ibid.*, 1937, **5**, 74; Mayer and Harrison, *ibid.*, 1938, **6**, 87; Harrison and Mayer, *ibid.*, 1938, **6**, 101.

[3] *J. Chem. Phys.*, 1946, **14**, 501; *J. Chem. Educ.*, 1947, **24**, 123.

[4] *J. Chem. Phys.*, 1947, **15**, 314 (bibl.).

[5] *J. Chem. Phys.*, 1938, **6**, 87, 101; see also Krichevsky and Rosen, *Acta Physicochim. U.R.S.S.*, 1947, **22**, 153.

[6] *Proc. Roy. Soc.*, 1937, **160**, 358.

[7] *Compt. Rend.*, 1946, **223**, 377.

[8] Mathias, *Congrès Internat. Phys.*, 1901, **1**, 615; "Le Point Critique des Corps purs," Paris, 1904, 38 f., 66 f., 115 f.; Traube, *Ann. Phys.*, 1902, **8**, 267; Graetz, in Winkelmann, "Handbuch der Physik," 1906, **3**, 840; Cardoso, *J. Chim. Phys.*, 1912, **10**, 470; Klemensciewicz, in Stähler, "Arbeitsmethoden der anorganischen Chemie," 1913, **3**, i, 193; Hein, *Z. phys. Chem.*, 1914, **86**, 385; Siebert and Burrell, *J.A.C.S.*, 1915, **37**, 2683; Young, "Stoichiometry," 1918, 159; Harand, *Monatsh.*, 1935, **65**, 153.

[9] *Compt. Rend.*, 1894, **118**, 976; Amagat, *ibid.*, 1892, **114**, 1093.

entry of air or foreign gas in filling.[1] The liquid may be stirred by a glass tube in which an iron wire is enclosed and moved by an external electromagnet. The tube may be heated in a liquid or vapour bath,[2] or a copper block.[3]

With water, which attacks glass at high temperatures, a quartz tube is used.[4] The tubes need not be very thick: a tube of 1·5-mm. thick walls and 7-mm. bore withstands 100 atm., but with ammonia (p_c=115 atm.) 2–2·5-mm. walls and 2–3-mm. bore were necessary, and many tubes burst.[5] According to Moissan[6] tubes of internal diameter 1·5–6-mm. and external diameter 6–10 mm., respectively, withstand 200–300 atm., but explosions with pressures exceeding 100 atm. must always be expected. A micro-method of determining the critical temperature can be used with very small quantities of material,[7] and would probably minimise the danger of bursting tubes.

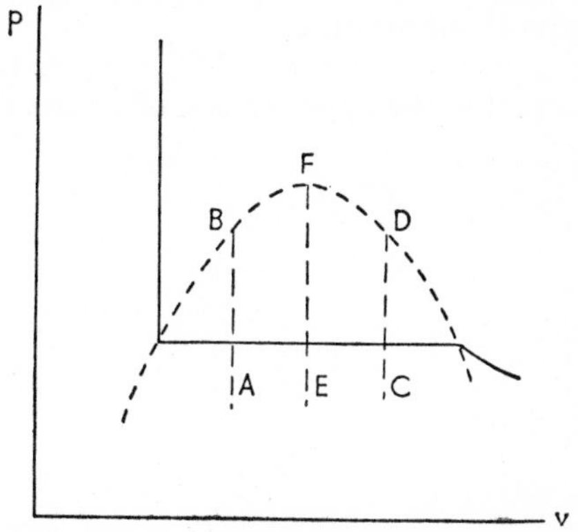

FIG. 11.VII B. Boundary Curve (BFD) of Liquid and Vapour States. Liquid to the left of F and Vapour to the right

If we begin with a mass of substance and vapour in the heterogeneous region at A (Fig. 11.VII B) and raise the temperature at constant total volume, we move along a vertical AB (v constant) until B is reached. At this point the substance is all liquid, i.e. the meniscus has moved up to the top of the tube and no disappearance of the meniscus can be seen on further increase of temperature. If we start at C, the meniscus moves *down* the tube until at D the substance is all gaseous, and the meniscus disappears at the bottom of the tube, although the critical point F is not reached. By starting at E, the critical point F is reached, and here *the meniscus disappears in the middle of the tube*, since just before this the densities of liquid and vapour are equal. In other cases the meniscus may disappear at some other point in the tube where the density, because of the gradient of density in the tube, happens to be equal to the critical density.[8] In

1 Amagat, *Compt. Rend.*, 1892, **114**, 1093; Bradley, Browne, and Hale, *Phys. Rev.*, 1904, **19**, 258; 1908, **26**, 470; 1908, **27**, 90; Travers and Usher, *Z. phys. Chem.*, 1907, **57**, 365; Young, *Phil. Mag.*, 1910, **20**, 793; Cork, *Rev. Sci. Instr.*, 1930, **1**, 563.

2 Altschul, *Z. phys. Chem.*, 1893, **11**, 577; Gouy, *J. de Phys.*, 1897, **6**, 479; Centnerszwer, *Z. phys. Chem.*, 1903, **46**, 427; Jaquerod and Wassmer, *J. Chim. Phys.*, 1904, **2**, 52; Drucker, *Z. phys. Chem.*, 1910, **74**, 612; Des Coudres, *Leipzig Ber.*, 1910, **62**, 296 (high temp.); Beckmann, *Z. phys. Chem.*, 1912, **79**, 565; Young, *Phil. Mag.*, 1910, **20**, 793; Onnes and Mathias, *Proc. K. Akad. Wetens. Amsterdam*, 1911, **13**, 939 (*Comm. Leiden*, **117**) (low temp.).

3 Hackspill and Mathieu, *Bull. Soc. Chim.*, 1919, **25**, 482; Rassow, *Z. anorg. Chem.*, 1920, **114**, 117.

4 Traube and Teichner, *Ann. Phys.*, 1904, **13**, 620; Rassow, *loc. cit.*; Schröer, *Z. phys. Chem.*, 1927, **129**, 79; 1941, **49** B, 271; Callendar, *Proc. Roy. Soc.*, 1928, **120**, 460.

5 Stock and Hofmann, *Ber.*, 1903, **36**, 895.

6 *Compt. Rend.*, 1901, **133**, 768. On calibration of capillary tubes, see Isaac and Masson, *J. Phys. Chem.*, 1924, **28**, 166; Botella, *An. Fis. Quim.*, 1929, **27**, 315. For rotating bomb method, see Ipatieff and Monroe, *Ind. Eng. Chem. Anal.*, 1942, **14**, 171.

7 Harand, *Monatsh.*, 1935, **65**, 153; Kopper, *Z. phys. Chem.*, 1936, **175**, 469; Kennedy, *J.A.C.S.*, 1929, **51**, 1360, found no effect of tube diam. from 0·004 to 2 mm. for CO_2.

8 Ramsay, *Proc. Roy. Soc.*, 1880, **30**, 323; 1880, **31**, 194; Hannay, *ibid.*, 1880, **30**, 484; Gouy, *Compt. Rend.*, 1892, **115**, 720; 1893, **116**, 1289; Galitzin, *J. de Phys.*, 1892, **1**, 474; Stoletow, *Fortschr. Phys.*, 1892, **48**, ii, 190; Battelli, *Ann. Chim.*, 1893, **29**, 400; von Hirsch,

practice, it is found that the critical temperature is insensitive to the method of filling.[1]

Sajontschewski,[2] and Cailletet and Colardeau,[3] showed that when pressure is plotted against temperature for different amounts of liquid in a tube of fixed volume, the vapour-pressure curves are all identical (AK, Fig. 12.VII B) so long as both liquid and vapour are present, but at the critical point K, when only one phase is present, the curves diverge, each mass of substance giving its own curve. This will be a continuation of the vapour-pressure curve if the volume is the critical volume. This behaviour can be used to determine the critical temperature.

The *critical pressure* alone [4] can be measured by a method used by Altschul.[5] Liquid in the upper 15 cm. of a glass tube 30 cm. long and 1 mm. bore is con-

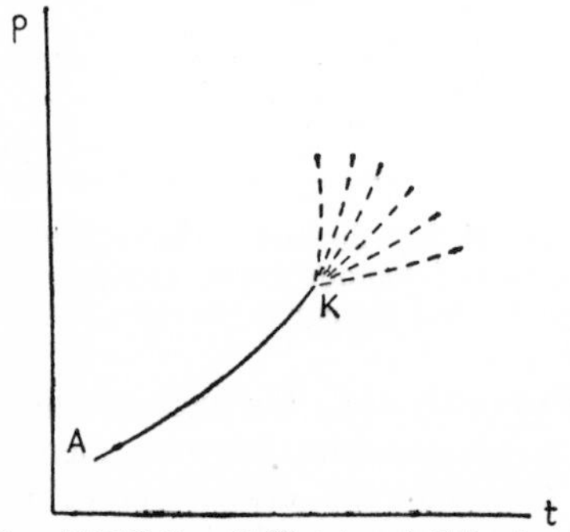

FIG. 12.VII B. Cailletet and Colardeau's Curves

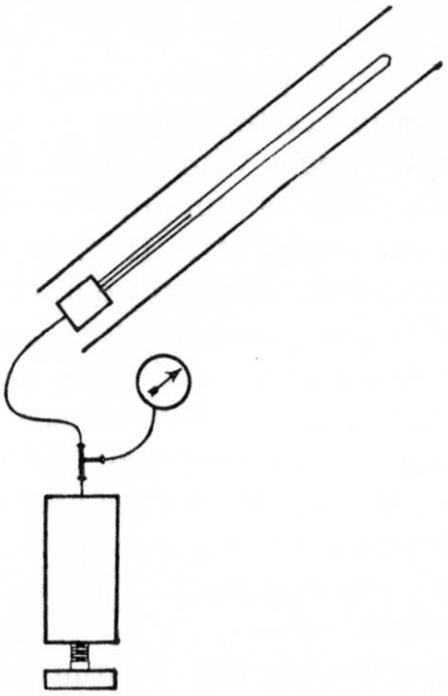

FIG. 13.VII B. Altschul's Critical Pressure Apparatus

nected by mercury in a metal tube with a screw pump filled with paraffin oil and with a pressure gauge (Fig. 13.VII B). The upper 5–7 cm. of the tube is heated in a wider tube over the critical temperature, when vapour forms in the upper part of the tube and liquid remains in the cooler lower part if the pressure is below the critical pressure. The mercury is below the heated portion. The pressure is now increased until the meniscus in the tube vanishes. This occurs

Ann. Phys., 1899, **69**, 456; 1900, **1**, 655; Centnerszwer, *Z. phys. Chem.*, 1903, **46**, 427; 1904, **49**, 199; Mathias, "Le Point critique des Corps purs," 1904; F. B. Young, *Phil. Mag.*, 1910, **20**, 793; Hein, *Z. phys. Chem.*, 1914, **86**, 385; S. Young, "Stoichiometry," 1918, 166; Audant, *Compt. Rend.*, 1920, **170**, 1573; Riesenfeld and Schwab, *Z. phys.*, 1922, **11**, 12.

[1] Avenarius, *Ann. Phys.*, 1874, **151**, 303; Küster, Meyerhoffer, and Abegg, *Z. Elektrochem.*, 1902, **8**, 113; Schröer, *Z. phys. Chem.*, 1929, **140**, 241, 379; Kennedy, *J.A.C.S.*, 1929, **51**, 1360.

[2] *Ann. Phys. Beibl.*, 1879, **3**, 741.

[3] *Compt. Rend.*, 1891, **112**, 563, 1170; *J. de Phys.*, 1891, **10**, 333; *Ann. Chim.*, 1892, **25**, 519; Altschul, *Z. phys. Chem.*, 1893, **11**, 577; Küster, Meyerhoffer and Abegg, *Z. Elektrochem.*, 1902, **8**, 113; Trautz and Adler, *Phys. Z.*, 1934, **35**, 446, 711; Eucken, *ibid.*, 1934, **35**, 708; Krüger, *ibid.*, 1936, **37**, 56; for a method in which liquid in a sealed tube is unequally heated, see W. Thomson, *Nature*, 1880, **23**, 87; "Math. and Phys. Papers," 1911, **5**, 107.

[4] In Andrews' method it is determined along with the critical temperature.

[5] *Z. phys. Chem.*, 1893, **11**, 577 (details in Ostwald-Luther, "Physiko-chem. Messungen," 1931, 303); Ferretto, *Gazz.*, 1900, **30**, i, 296; Guye and Mallet, *Arch. Sci. Phys. Nat.*, 1902, **13**, 30, 129, 274, 462; Centnerszwer, *Z. phys. Chem.*, 1904, **49**, 199.

at the critical pressure, since the meniscus will form in that part of the tube where the temperature corresponds with a vapour pressure equal to that applied by the pump. On increasing the pressure the meniscus rises towards the higher temperature end of the tube, but disappears when it reaches the part of the tube which is at the critical temperature. Special apparatus is necessary for substances (e.g. N_2O_4) which attack mercury.[1]

§ 5. Law of Rectilinear Diameter

The determination of *critical volume* or *critical density* is difficult and is usually made by the so-called *rectilinear diameter method* of Cailletet and

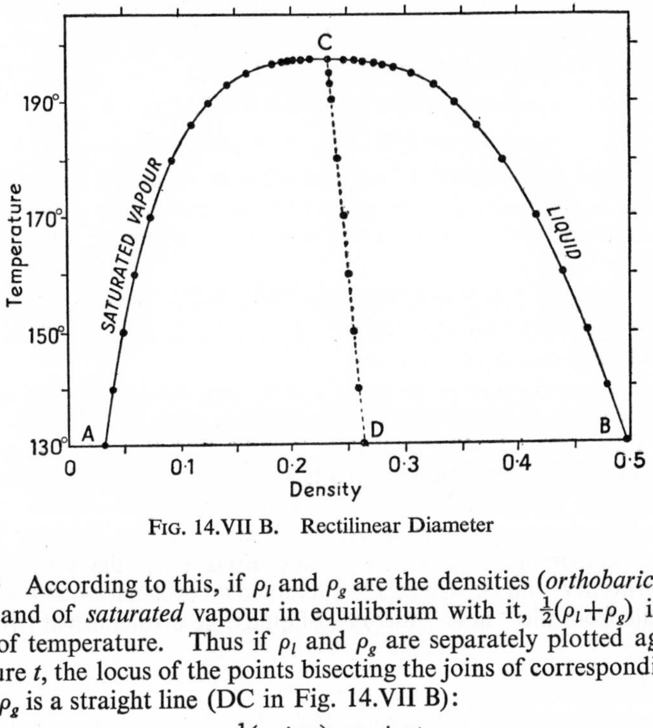

FIG. 14.VII B. Rectilinear Diameter

Mathias.[2] According to this, if ρ_l and ρ_g are the densities (*orthobaric densities*) of liquid and of *saturated* vapour in equilibrium with it, $\frac{1}{2}(\rho_l+\rho_g)$ is a linear function of temperature. Thus if ρ_l and ρ_g are separately plotted against the temperature t, the locus of the points bisecting the joins of corresponding values of ρ and ρ_g is a straight line (DC in Fig. 14.VII B):

$$\tfrac{1}{2}(\rho_l+\rho_g)=\rho_0+at \quad \dots\dots\dots \quad (1)$$

where ρ_0 is the *mean* density of liquid and vapour at 0° C. and a is a constant. At the critical temperature $\rho_l=\rho_g=\rho_c$, therefore $\frac{1}{2}(\rho_l+\rho_g)=\rho_c$,

$$\therefore\ \rho_c=\rho_0+at_c \quad \dots\dots\dots \quad (2)$$

1 Bennewitz and Windisch, *Z. phys. Chem.*, 1933, **166**, 401.

2 *J. de Phys.*, 1886, **5**, 549; *Compt. Rend.*, 1886, **102**, 1202; 1887, **104**, 1563; Mathias, *ibid.*, 1892, **115**, 35; 1899, **128**, 1389; *J. de Phys.*, 1893, **2**, 5; *Z. phys. Chem.*, 1893, **11**, 429; "Le Point critique des Corps purs," 1904; Young, *Phil Mag.*, 1892, **34**, 503; *J.C.S.*, 1897, **71**, 446; *Proc. Roy. Dublin Soc.*, 1910, **12**, 374; "Stoichiometry," 1918, 154, 168; Young and Thomas, *Phil. Mag.*, 1892, **34**, 507; van Laar, *Z. phys. Chem.*, 1893, **11**, 661; Bakker, *ibid.*, 1895, **18**, 645; Donnan, *Nature*, 1895, **42**, 619; von Hirsch, *Ann. Phys.*, 1899, **69**, 456; 1900, **1**, 655; Batschinski, *Z. phys. Chem.*, 1902, **41**, 741; von Jüptner, *ibid.*, 1912, **80**, 299; 1913, **85**, 1; Herz and Neukirch, *ibid.*, 1923, **104**, 433; Ter-Gazarian, *J. Chim. Phys.*, 1906, **4**, 140; 1908, **6**, 492; 1909, **7**, 273; Prud'homme, *ibid.*, 1919, **17**, 377, 534; Cardoso, *ibid.*, 1927, **24**, 65, 77; Bichowsky and Gilkey, *Ind. Eng. Chem.*, 1931, **23**, 366; Rotinjanz and Nagornow, *Z. phys. Chem.*, 1934, **169**, 20; for tables of values of ρ_l and ρ_g see Valentiner, Landolt-Börnstein, "Tabellen," 5th edit., 1923, 271.

This corresponds with the point where the straight line joining the bisections (the so-called *rectilinear diameter*) cuts the U-shaped curve of ρ_l and ρ_g at the critical point C.

The *separate* curves for the densities of liquid and saturated vapour were found to be parabolas, the equations being, for the *vapours*:

$$N_2O: \quad \rho_g=0{\cdot}5099-0{\cdot}00361t-0{\cdot}0714\sqrt{(36{\cdot}4-t)} \quad (-28° \text{ to } +33{\cdot}9°)$$
$$C_2H_4: \quad \rho_g=0{\cdot}1929-0{\cdot}00188t-0{\cdot}0346\sqrt{(9{\cdot}2-t)} \quad (-30° \text{ to } +8{\cdot}9°)$$
$$CO_2: \quad \rho_g=0{\cdot}5668-0{\cdot}00426t-0{\cdot}084\sqrt{(31-t)} \quad (-29{\cdot}8° \text{ to } +30{\cdot}2°).$$

Lowry and Erickson [1] found for carbon dioxide:

$$\rho_l=0{\cdot}4683+0{\cdot}001442(t_c-t)+0{\cdot}1318\sqrt[3]{(t_c-t)}$$
$$\rho_g=0{\cdot}4683+0{\cdot}001442(t_c-t)-0{\cdot}1318\sqrt[3]{(t_c-t)},$$

and Quinn and Wernimont [2] for nitrous oxide:

$$\rho_l=0{\cdot}459+0{\cdot}00111(t_c-t)+0{\cdot}1222\sqrt[3]{(t_c-t)}$$
$$\rho_g=0{\cdot}459+0{\cdot}00111(t_c-t)-0{\cdot}1222\sqrt[3]{(t_c-t)}.$$

In many cases this empirical law of rectilinear diameters holds with great accuracy, but sometimes over a large range of temperature the diameter shows a slight curvature and is then represented by a parabolic (or even cubic) equation: [3]

$$\tfrac{1}{2}(\rho_l+\rho_g)=\rho_0+at+bt^2+ct^3 \quad \ldots\ldots \quad (3)$$

Cardoso [4] found, with very pure sulphur dioxide, no curvature of the diameter near the critical point, previously reported.[5]

If the line is extrapolated to $t=-273°$, or the absolute zero, ρ will be half the density of the liquid if it could exist at the absolute zero, since the density of the vapour is then zero. In this way it is found [6] that the ratio of the critical volume to the volume at absolute zero is 3·6 to 4 (see § 10). Mathias [7] found that a increases with molecular weight in homologous series. A semi-theoretical deduction of the law of rectilinear diameter was given by Vasilescu-Karpen.[8] Timmermans [9] found large deviations from the simple law and included terms in t^2 and t^3. Cremer [10] attempted an explanation of the Cailletet-Mathias rule from the "hole" theory of liquids: he distinguished two types of

[1] *J.A.C.S.*, 1927, **49**, 2729.

[2] *J.A.C.S.*, 1929, **51**, 2002.

[3] Thorpe, *J.C.S.*, 1880, **37**, 141; Young, *Phil. Mag.*, 1900, **50**, 291; "Stoichiometry," 1918, 156; Timmermans, *Proc. Roy. Dublin Soc.*, 1912, **13**, 310; Mathias, Onnes, and Crommelin, *Compt. Rend.*, 1913, **156**, 129 (argon); Weber, *Kgl. Dansk. Vidensk. Selsk. mat. fys. Meddel.*, 1920, **3**, No. 4; Mathias, *Onnes Festschr.*, 1922, 165; *Phys. Ber.*, 1923, **4**, 701; Mathias, Crommelin, and Onnes, *Ann. de Phys.*, 1922, **17**, 442 (A), 455 (N_2), 463 (H_2O); 1923, **19**, 231, 239 (Ne); Mathias and Onnes, *ibid.*, 1922, **17**, 416 (O_2); Mathias, Crommelin, Onnes, and Swallow, *ibid.*, 1926, **5**, 359 (He); Mathias, Crommelin, and Watts, *Compt. Rend.*, 1927, **185**, 1240; *Proc. K. Akad. Wetens. Amsterdam*, 1927, **30**, 1054; *Comm. Leiden*, **189***a* (C_2H_4); Onnes, Crommelin, and Mathias, *Ann. de Phys.*, 1929, **11**, 344 (C_2H_4); Mathias, Bijleveld, and Grigg, *Compt. Rend.*, 1932, **194**, 1708 (CO); Mathias and Crommelin, *Ann. de Phys.*, 1936, **5**, 137 (CO, He); Mathias, Crommelin, and Meihuizen, *ibid.*, 1937, **8**, 467 (Kr); Mathias, *Compt. Rend.*, 1937, **204**, 1097 (curvature).

[4] *J. Chim. Phys.*, 1927, **24**, 65, 77.

[5] Cardoso, *Compt. Rend.*, 1911, **153**, 257; *Arch. Sci. Phys. Nat.*, 1912, **34**, 127.

[6] Davis, *Phil. Mag.*, 1912, **24**, 415; Gay, *Compt. Rend.*, 1914, **158**, 34; Lorenz, *Z. anorg. Chem.*, 1916, **94**, 240.

[7] *Comm. Leiden*, 1929, Suppl. **64***b*.

[8] *Bull. Sect. Sci. Acad. Roumaine*, 1923, **8**, 175.

[9] *Proc. Roy. Dublin Soc.*, 1912, **13**, 310; *Bull. Soc. Chim. Belg.*, 1923, **32**, 299.

[10] *Z. phys. Chem.*, 1944, **193**, 287; already by Eyring, *J. Chem. Phys.*, 1936, **4**, 283.

thermal expansion, a linear (predominating at lower temperatures) and an exponential (predominating at higher temperatures).

Van Laar [1] modified the law of rectilinear diameter, and found for the density at T° K. $\rho_T = \rho_0(1-\alpha T)$, where ρ_0=density at 0° K. and $\alpha = [\gamma/(1+\gamma)T_c]$. For normal substances $\gamma = 0{\cdot}9$, hence $\alpha = 1/2{\cdot}1T_c$, therefore $\rho_T = \rho_0(1-T/2{\cdot}1T_c)$, from which the density at absolute zero may be calculated. The equation does not hold for fused salts. The law of rectilinear diameter holds for liquid helium.[2]

Von Jüptner [3] and Mathias [4] proposed $\frac{1}{2}(\rho_l+\rho_g)/\rho_c = 1+a(1-\vartheta)$, where $\vartheta = T/T_c$ and a is a characteristic function of the critical temperature. According to Mathias, $a = bT_c^n$, where b and n are constants, the value of n being very close to $\frac{1}{4}$. Mebius [5] proposed $\frac{1}{2}(\rho_l^{2/3}+\rho_g^{2/3})$=const., independent of temperature.

§ 6. Critical Data

In the following table [6] ρ_l is the density of the saturated liquid, t_c° C. and p_c atm. are the critical temperature and pressure, ρ_c in g/ml. is the critical density.

The specification of the critical volume varies in the literature; it is sometimes (as here) in ml. per g., sometimes (as in Landolt-Börnstein, " Tabellen ") as a fraction v_c' (usually also written v_c) of the volume of the same mass existing in the state of ideal gas at S.T.P.; the two values are, of course, quite different. If M=mol. wt. in the gaseous state, $v_c' = Mv_c/22415$.

Substance	ρ_l g./ml.	ρ_c g./ml.	t_c° C.	p_c atm.
He	0·154 [1] *	0·066 [2]	−268 [1]	2·3 [1]
	0·126 (−268·9°) [59]	0·0693 [58]	−267·9 [58]	
H_2	0·0700 (−252·5°) [3] 0·07086 [86]	0·031 [4]	−242 [5]	12·80 [4]
	$0{\cdot}084404-0{\cdot}0_3223T-0{\cdot}0_42183T^2$ [60]	—	—	—
	$1/\rho_l = 5{\cdot}2269[1+0{\cdot}01715(T-20{\cdot}5)]$ [71]	—	−239·91 [4]	—
Ne	1·24 [6]	0·484 [7]	−228·35 [4]	29 [1]
	1·204 at b.p.; 1·248 at −245·9° [61]	—	−228·71 [60]	26·86 [4]
N_2	$1{\cdot}165-0{\cdot}00458T$ [3, 8, 72]	0·311 [7]	−146 [10]	35·0 [10]
	$1{\cdot}1604-0{\cdot}00455T$ [9, 59]	—	−144·7 [83]	33·65 [83]
	0·885 at b.p. [13]	0·31096 [9]	−147·13 [11]	33·5 [11]
	0·7914 at b.p. [87]	—	—	—

* See pages 643–4 for footnotes.

[1] *Z. anorg. Chem.*, 1925, **146**, 263; Herz, *ibid.*, 1925, **149**, 230.
[2] Mathias, Crommelin, Onnes, and Swallow, *Ann. de Phys.*, 1926, **5**, 359.
[3] *Z. phys. Chem.*, 1908, **63**, 355.
[4] *Onnes Festschr.*, 1922, 165; *Phys. Ber.*, 1923, **4**, 701.
[5] *Arkiv Mat. Astron. Fys.*, 1915, **10**, Nos. 19, 20 (tables of T_c and p_c).
[6] For collections of data see Heilborn, *Z. phys. Chem.*, 1891, **7**, 601 (bibl.); Mathias, " Le Point Critique des Corps purs," Paris, 1904, 175 f.; Herzog, *Z. Elektrochem.*, 1909, **15**, 345 (crit. densities); Baume, *J. Chim. Phys.*, 1911, **9**, 282; van der Waals, *Proc. K. Akad. Wetens. Amsterdam*, 1911, **13**, 1211; Cardoso, *Arch. Sci. Phys. Nat.*, 1912, **34**, 20; Mathews, *J. Phys. Chem.*, 1913, **17**, 181; van Laar, *J. Chim. Phys.*, 1920, **18**, 273; Keesom, *Onnes Festschr.*, 1922, 89; *Phys. Ber.*, 1923, **4**, 613; Valentiner, in Landolt-Börnstein, " Tabellen," 5th edit., 1923, 253, and supplements; Pickering, *J. Phys. Chem.*, 1924, **28**, 97; *Bur. Stand. Bull.*, 1926, **21**, 597; Germann and Pickering, " Internat. Crit. Tables," 1928, **3**, 248; Fales and Shapiro, *J.A.C.S.*, 1936, **58**, 2418; Kremann and Pestemer, " Zusammenhänge zwischen physikalischen Eigenschaften und chemischer Konstitution," Dresden, 1937.

Substance	ρ_l g./m.	ρ_c g./ml.	t_c° C.	p_c atm.
CO	1·142−0·00420*T* [8]	0·311 [12]	−138·7 [83]	34·6 [12, 83]
	—	0·301 [75,78]	−139·5 [13]	35·5 [13]
	—	—	−140·23 [75]	34·53 [75]
	—	—	−140·21 [77]	34·529 [77]
O_2	1·576−0·00481*T* [3, 8, 72]	0·4299 [14]	−118·8 [15]	50·8 [15]
	1·124 at b.p. [13]	—	−118·0 [83]	49·30 [83]
	1·1316 at b.p. [88]	—	−118·82 [11]	—
A	1·969−0·00650*T* [8]	0·531 [16]	−117·4 [17]	52·9 [17]
NO	1·269 (−150·2°) [18]	0·52 [7]	−93·5 [15]	71·2 [15]
	—	—	−92·9 [18]	64·6 [18]
CH_4	0·466 (−164°) [19]	0·162 [12]	−82·9 [12, 83]	45·6 [12, 83]
	—	—	−81·8 [15]	54·9 [15]
Kr	2·15 (−146°) [20]	0·78 [7]	−62·5 [17]	54·3 [17]
SiH_4 ...	0·68 (−185°) [62]	—	−0·5 [21]	—
C_2H_4 ...	—	0·22 [7]	9·50 [22, 23]	50·8 [22]
	—	—	9·6 [88]	50·65 [23]
Xe	3·52 (−102°) [20]	1·155 [7]	14·7 [17]	57·2 [17]
	—	—	16·6 [24]	58·2 [24]
CO_2	1·990−0·00375*T* [25]	0·449 [26]	31·00 [22, 49]	73·0 [22, 49]
	—	—	30·96 [73, 74]	—
C_2H_6	—	0·21 [7]	32·1 [22]	49·0 [22]
	—	0·203 [66]	32·37 [66]	48·20 [66]
	—	—	31·03 [82]	—
C_3H_8	—	—	92·6 [67]	45·34 [67]
	—	—	96·81 [81]	42·01 [81]
$C_4H_{10}(n)$ ...	—	0·225 [68]	152·0 [68]	37·47 [68]
$C_7H_{16}(n)$ ...	—	0·241 [69]	267·0 [69]	27·00 [69]
iso-Butene $(CH_3)_2C:CH_2$	—	0·235 [70]	144·73 [70]	39·48 [70]
C_2H_2 ...	1·065−0·00234*T* [27]	0·231 [7]	36·5 [27, 28]	61·6 [27, 28]
	—	0·314 [27]	35·5 [28]	61·7 [28]
N_2O	1·2257 (−89·4°) [63]	0·454 [23, 29]	36·50 [22, 23]	71·95 [22]
	—	—	—	71·65 [23]
PH_3	0·894−0·0080*T* [30]	0·30 [7]	51·3 [31]	64·5 [31]
HCl	1·706−0·00276*T* [19]	0·42 [7]	51·8 [31]	83·6 [31]
	—	—	51·4 [32]	81·55 [32]
	—	—	51·1 [34]	80·49 [34]
HBr	2·936−0·00380*T* [30]	—	91·3 [33]	84·4 [34]
	—	—	90 [34]	—
HI	3·795−0·00420*T* [30]	—	150·7 [33]	—
	—	—	150 [34]	80·8 [34]
HF	—	—	230 [35]	—
HCN ...	—	0·195 [36]	183·5 [36]	53·2 [36]
	—	—	—	50·0 [88]
H_2S	1·328−0·00171*T* [19]	—	100·4 [22]	89·3 [22]
	—	—	—	89·05 [23]
$(CH_3)_2O$ ...	—	0·271 [7, 37]	126·90 [38, 39, 40]	52·0 [38, 39, 40]
	—	—	126·6 [88]	58·2 [88]
	—	—	128·3 [28]	59·8 [28]
NH_3	1·022−0·00145*T* [19]	0·236 [41]	132·3 [42]	109·6 [42]
	—	—	132·9 [43]	112·3 [43]
H_2Se	2·12 (−42°) [64]	—	138 [44]	91 [44]
CH_3Cl ...	—	0·37 [7]	143·2 [33]	65·9 [38]
F_2	—	—	−129 [45]	55 (calc.) [45]
Cl_2	2·132−0·00241*T* [46]	0·573 [47]	144 [47]	76·1 [47]
	—	—	146 [46]	—
CH_3NH_2 ...	—	—	155 [48]	—

Substance	ρ_l g./ml.	ρ_c g./ml.	t_c° C.	p_c atm.
SO_2	2·122−0·00232*T* [19]	0·513 [49]	157·15 [49]	77·65 [49]
	—	—	157·2 [31]	78·0 [31, 38]
SO_3	—	0·633 [84]	218·3 [84]	83·8 [84]
NOCl ...	2·010−0·00242*T* [50]	—	167·0 [50]	92·4 (calc.) [50]
N_2O_4 ...	2·060−0·00209*T* [65]	0·570 [51]	158·2 [52]	100 [52]
$COCl_2$ ...	—	0·52 [53]	182 [53]	56 [53]
	—	—	181·7 [88]	—
SiF_4	—	—	−14·15 [54]	36·7 [54]
Hg	—	5·0 [55, 56]	1450 [55, 56]	1036 [55, 56]
S	—	—	1040 [56]	—
I_2	—	—	553 [56]	—
P	—	—	720·6 [57]	—
OsO_4... ...	—	—	405 [76]	—
BCl_3	—	—	178·8 [79]	—
$SiCl_4$	—	—	233·6 [79]	—
O_3 [85]	$1/\rho_l=0{\cdot}51193+0{\cdot}0_2 4559T+0{\cdot}0_5 3929T^2$	0·537	−5	66

[1] Onnes, *Compt. Rend.*, 1908, **147**, 421; *Proc. K. Akad. Wetens. Amsterdam*, 1909, **12**, 175.
[2] Onnes, *Proc. K. Akad. Wetens. Amsterdam*, 1911–12, **14**, 678; *Comm. Leiden*, 1912, **124** *b*.
[3] Dewar, *Proc. Roy. Soc.*, 1904, **73**, 244.
[4] Onnes, Crommelin, and Cath, *Proc. K. Akad. Wetens. Amsterdam*, 1917, **19**, 1058 (Ne); 1917–18, **20**, 178 (H_2); *Comm. Leiden*, 1917, **151** *b*, *c*.
[5] Olszewski, *Ann. Phys.*, 1895, **56**, 133; 1905, **17**, 986.
[6] Rudorf, *Phil. Mag.*, 1909, **17**, 795.
[7] "International Critical Tables," 1928, **3**, 248.
[8] Baly and Donnan, *J.C.S.*, 1902, **81**, 907.
[9] Mathias, Onnes, and Crommelin, *Proc. K. Akad. Wetens. Amsterdam*, 1914, **17**, 953; *Comm. Leiden*, 1914, **145** *c*.
[10] Olszewski, *Compt. Rend.*, 1884, **98**, 913.
[11] Onnes, Dorsman, and Holst, *Proc. K. Akad. Wetens. Amsterdam*, 1914, **17**, 950; *Comm. Leiden*, 1914, **145** *b*.
[12] Cardoso, *Arch. Sci. Phys. Nat.*, 1913, **36**, 97; *Atti R. Accad. Lincei*, 1914, **24**, i, 1056; *J. Chim. Phys.*, 1915, **13**, 312.
[13] Olszewski, *Ann. Phys.*, 1887, **31**, 58.
[14] Mathias and Onnes, *Proc. K. Akad. Wetens. Amsterdam*, 1911, **13**, 939; *Comm. Leiden*, **117**.
[15] Olszewski, *Compt. Rend.*, 1885, **100**, 350, 940.
[16] Mathias, Onnes, and Crommelin, *Proc. K. Akad. Wetens. Amsterdam*, 1912, **15**, 667; *Comm. Leiden*, 1912, **131***a*; cf. Mathias, Onnes, and Crommelin, *Compt. Rend.*, 1913, **156**, 129; Mathias and Crommelin, *Comm. Leiden*, 1924, Suppl. **52** (table).
[17] Ramsay and Travers, *Proc. Roy. Soc.*, 1900, **67**, 329; Onnes and Crommelin, *Proc. K. Akad. Wetens. Amsterdam*, 1911–12, **14**, 158; *Comm. Leiden*, **121***b*.
[18] Adwentowski, *Bull. Acad. Polon.*, 1909, 742.
[19] Baume and Perrot, *Compt. Rend.*, 1911, **152**, 1763.
[20] Ramsay and Travers, *Z. phys. Chem.*, 1901, **38**, 641 (688).
[21] Ogier, *Compt. Rend.*, 1879, **88**, 236.
[22] Cardoso, Arni, and Bell, *Arch. Sci. Phys. Nat.*, 1910, **30**, 432.
[23] Cardoso and Arni, *J. Chim. Phys.*, 1912, **10**, 504.
[24] Patterson, Cripps, and Whytlaw-Gray, *Proc. Roy. Soc.*, 1912, **86**, 579.
[25] Behn, *Ann. Phys.*, 1900, **3**, 733.
[26] Dorsman, *Dissert.*, Amsterdam, 1908, q. by Jellinek, "Lehrbuch der physikalischen Chemie," 1928, **1**, 385.
[27] McIntosh, *J. Phys. Chim.*, 1907, **11**, 306.
[28] Cardoso and Baume, *Compt. Rend.*, 1910, **151**, 141; *J. Chim. Phys.*, 1912, **10**, 509.
[29] Villard, *Compt. Rend.*, 1894, **118**, 1096.

30 Steele, McIntosh, and Archibald, *Z. phys. Chem.*, 1906, **55**, 129; for errors in this work, see Pearson and Robinson, *J.C.S.*, 1934, 880; for AsH_3, $\rho_l=1{\cdot}409-0{\cdot}0036t°$ C.; Corriez and Gross, *Bull. Soc. Chim.*, 1948, 203.

31 Briner, *J. Chim. Phys.*, 1906, **4**, 477; *Mém. Soc. Phys. Nat.* (Geneva), 1907, **35**, 681.

32 Cardoso and Germann, *J. Chim. Phys.*, 1912, **10**, 517.

33 Estreicher, *Z. phys. Chem.*, 1896, **20**, 605.

34 Drozdowski and Pietrzak, *Bull. Acad. Polon.*, 1913 A, 219.

35 Bond and Williams, *J.A.C.S.*, 1931, **53**, 34.

36 Bredig and Teichmann, *Z. Elektrochem.*, 1925, **31**, 449; Partington and Carroll, *Phil. Mag.*, 1925, **49**, 665.

37 Cardoso and Coppada, *J. Chim. Phys.*, 1923, **20**, 337.

38 Baume, *J. Chim. Phys.*, 1908, **6**, 1.

39 Cardoso and Bruno, *J. Chim. Phys.*, 1923, **20**, 347.

40 Briner and Cardoso, *J. Chim. Phys.*, 1908, **6**, 641.

41 Berthoud, *J. Chim. Phys.*, 1918, **16**, 429; *Helv. Chim. Acta*, 1918, **1**, 84.

42 Jaquerod, *Mém. Soc. Phys. Nat.* (Geneva), 1907, **35**, 686.

43 Cardoso and Giltay, *J. Chim. Phys.*, 1912, **10**, 514.

44 Wroblewski, *Monatsh.*, 1888, **9**, 1067; Olszewski, *Bull. Acad. Polon.*, 1890, 57; *Ann. Phys. Beibl.*, 1890, **14**, 896.

45 Cady and Hildebrand, *J.A.C.S.*, 1930, **52**, 3839.

46 Knietsch, *Ann.*, 1890, **259**, 100.

47 Pellaton, *J. Chim. Phys.*, 1915, **13**, 426.

48 Vincent and Chappuis, *J. de Phys.*, 1886, **5**, 58.

49 Cardoso, *Compt. Rend.*, 1911, **153**, 257; *Arch. Sci. Phys. Nat.*, 1912, **34**, 127; Cardoso and Bell, *J. Chim. Phys.*, 1912, **10**, 497.

50 Briner and Pylkoff, *J. Chim. Phys.*, 1912, **10**, 640; Francesconi and Bresciani, *Atti R. Accad. Lincei*, 1903, **12**, ii, 75, found $t_c=163°$ to 164°.

51 Bennewitz and Windisch, *Z. phys. Chem.*, 1933, **166**, 401.

52 Scheffer and Treub, *Z. phys. Chem.*, 1913, **81**, 308.

53 Germann and Taylor, *J.A.C.S.*, 1926, **48**, 1154.

54 Booth and Swinehart, *J.A.C.S.*, 1935, **57**, 1337.

55 Weber, *Kgl. Dansk. Vidensk. Selskab. mat. fys. Meddel.*, 1920, **3**, No. 4.

56 Other values are proposed by Koenigsberger, *Chem. Ztg.*, 1912, **36**, 1321 (p_c 1000 atm.); Menzies, *J.A.C.S.*, 1913. **35**, 1065 (tube burst at 1275°); Cenac, *Ann. Chim.*, 1913, **29**, 298 (calc. 2500°–3000°); Bender, *Phys. Z.*, 1915, **16**, 246; 1918, **19**, 410 ($t_c=1400°$, $\rho_c=4{\cdot}5$); van Laar, *Proc. K. Akad. Wetens. Amsterdam*, 1917, **20**, 138 ($T_c=1172°$ K., $p_c=180$ atm., $\rho_c=3{\cdot}3$ g./ml.); Ariès, *Compt. Rend.*, 1918, **166**, 334 ($t_c=1077°$, $p_c=420$ atm.); Rassow, *Z. anorg. Chem.*, 1920, **114**, 117; G. Meyer, *Phys. Z.*, 1921, **22**, 76 ($t_c=1474°$); Jouniaux, *Bull. Soc. Chim.*, 1924, **35**, 1293 ($t_c=1325°$); Bernhardt, *Z. techn. Phys.*, 1925, **26**, 265 (with $t_c=1650°$ calculated p_c as 3000–3500 atm.); Birch, *Phys. Rev.*, 1932, **41**, 641 ($t_c=1460°$, $p_c=1640$ kg./cm.^{2}).

57 Marckwald and Helmholz, *Z. anorg. Chem.*, 1922, **124**, 81.

58 Mathias, Crommelin, Onnes, and Swallow, *Ann. de Phys.*, 1926, **5**, 359.

59 Onnes, q. in " Internat. Critical Tables," 1928, **3**, 20.

60 Onnes and Crommelin, *Proc. K. Akad. Wetens. Amsterdam*, 1913, **16**, 245; *Comm. Leiden*, **137***a*.

61 Onnes and Crommelin, *Proc. K. Akad. Wetens. Amsterdam*, 1915, **18**, 515; *Comm. Leiden*, **147***d*.

62 Stock and Somiesky, *Ber.*, 1916, **49**, 111.

63 Grunmach, *Ann. Phys.*, 1904, **15**, 401.

64 De Forcrand and Fonzes-Diacon, *Compt. Rend.*, 1902, **134**, 171.

65 Pascal and Garnier, *Bull. Soc. Chim.*, 1919, **25**, 309.

66 Beattie, Gouq-Jen Su, and Simard, *J.A.C S*, 1939, **61**, 924.

67 Siebert and Burrell, *J.A.C.S.*, 1915, **37**, 2683.

68 Beattie, Simard, and Gouq-Jen Su, *J.A.C.S.*, 1939, **61**, 24.

69 Beattie and Kay, *J.A.C.S.*, 1937, **59**, 1586.

70 Beattie, Ingersoll, and Stockmayer, *J.A.C.S.*, 1942, **64**, 546.

71 Heuse, *Z. phys. Chem.*, 1930, **147**, 288.

72 Onnes, *Proc. K. Akad. Wetens. Amsterdam*, 1915, **17**, 950.

73 Kennedy and Meyers, *Refrig. Eng.*, 1928, **15**, 125; Kennedy, *J.A.C.S.*, 1929, **51**, 1360.

74 Poettmann and Katz, *Ind. Eng. Chem.*, 1945, **37**, 847.

75 Mathias and Crommelin, *Ann. de Phys.*, 1936, **5**, 137.

76 Ogawa, *Bull. Chem. Soc. Japan*, 1931, **6**, 302.

77 Crommelin, Bijleveld, and Brown, *Proc. K. Akad. Wetens. Amsterdam*, 1931, **34**, 1314.
78 Mathias, Bijleveld, and Grigg, *Compt. Rend.*, 1932, **194**, 1708.
79 Parker and Robinson, *J.C.S.*, 1927, 2977.
80 Crommelin, *Rec. Trav. Chim.*, 1923, **42**, 814 (*Comm. Leiden*, **162**).
81 Beattie, Poffenberger, and Hadlock, *J. Chem. Phys.*, 1935, **3**, 96.
82 Michels, Blaisse, and Michels, *Proc. Roy. Soc.*, 1937, **160**, 358.
83 Cardoso, *Arch. Sci. Phys. Nat.*, 1915, **39**, 400.
84 Berthoud, *Helv. Chim. Acta*, 1922, **5**, 513.
85 Riesenfeld and Schwab, *Ber.*, 1922, **55**, 2088; *Z. Phys.*, 1922, **11**, 12 (p_c calc. 64·8–92·3 atm.); Riesenfeld, *Z. Elektrochem.*, 1923, **29**, 119.
86 Augustin, *Leipzig Ber.*, 1914, **65**, 229.
87 Drugman and Ramsay, *J.C.S.*, 1900, **77**, 1228.
88 Stull, *Ind. Eng. Chem.*, 1947, **39**, 540.

Critical temperatures of deuterium compounds [1] are:

	DCl	DBr	DI	D_2S	D_2Se	D_3N	D_3P	D_3As
t_c° C.	50·3	88·8	148·6	99·1	139·2	132·3	50·4	98·9

Selected values of critical constants of hydrocarbons [2] are:

	Mol. wt.	T_c° K.	p_c atm.	V_c ml./mol.
Methane	16·03	191·1	45·8	99
Acetylene	26·02	309·1	61·7	113·2
Ethylene	28·03	282·8	50·7	133·4
Ethane	30·05	305·2	48·8	137·0
Propylene	42·05	364·8	45·0	181·6
Propane	44·06	369·9	42·01	195·0
Isobutane	58·08	407·1	37·0	249·0
n-Butane	58·08	426·0	36·0	250·0
Isopentane	72·09	460·9	32·92	307·6
n-Pentane	72·09	470·3	33·0	310·9
Benzene [3]	78·05	561·6	47·7	256·2
Cyclohexane	84·09	554·1	40·6	308·7
Di-isopropyl	86·11	500·5	30·6	357·1
n-Hexane	86·11	507·9	29·5	367·2
n-Heptane...	100·12	540·0	26·8	427·0
Di-isobutyl	114·14	549·9	24·5	482·0
n-Octane	114·14	569·3	24·6	490·0

Critical temperatures (t_c° C.) of sulphur compounds determined by Ferretto [4] are:

Mercaptan C_2H_5SH	228	Methyl ethyl sulphide $CH_3.S.C_2H_5$	259·66
dimethyl sulphide $(CH_3)_2S$ ...	231·2	*iso*amyl hydrosulphide [5] $C_5H_{11}SH$	*c.* 334°
diethyl sulphide $(C_2H_5)_2S$ ...	284·67		

1 Kopper, *Z. phys. Chem.*, 1936, **175**, 469.
2 Edminster, *Ind. Eng. Chem.*, 1938, **30**, 352; the abs. value of 0° C. is not stated; note that critical volumes are *per mol*; see also Corcoran, Bowles, Sage, and Lacey, *ibid.*, 1945, **37**, 825; Poettmann and Katz, *ibid.*, 1945, **37**, 847 (bibl.); Corner, *Trans. Faraday Soc.*, 1945, **41**, 617.
3 Gornowski, Amick, and Hixson, *Ind. Eng. Chem.*, 1947, **39**, 1348, found T_c=562·6° K., p_c=48·7 atm., v_c=3·36 ml./g.
4 *Gazz.*, 1900, **30**, i, 296.
5 From mixtures, by Pawlewski's rule (§ 12).

The values for the critical constants of some substances liquid (naphthalene is solid) at room temperature are given in the following table: [1]

	t_c° C.	p_c atm.	ρ_c g./ml.		t_c° C.	p_c atm.	ρ_c g./ml.
Acetone	235·0	47	0·268	Chlorobenzene ...	359·2	44·6	0·365
Ether [2]	193·8	35·6	0·262	Bromobenzene ...	397·0	44·6	0·486
Alcohol	243·1	63·1	0·275	Fluorobenzene ...	286·6	44·6	0·354
Aniline	426	52·4	—	Toluene	320·6	41·6	0·292
Benzene	288·5	47·7	0·304	Carbon disulphide ...	273·1	73	—
Chloroform	263	55	0·516	Methyl alcohol [4] ...	240·0	78·7	0·272
Ethyl chloride ...	187·2	52	0·33	Water [5]	374·1	218	0·313
Naphthalene [3] ...	478·5	40·7	0·314	Heavy water D_2O [6] ...	371·5	218·6	0·363

§ 7. Guldberg's Rule

In cases where the critical constants are unknown, *approximate* values may be calculated from a number of empirical or semi-empirical equations, and since these are often very useful, a fairly complete selection will be given. In some cases they depend on applications of the Law of Corresponding States (§ 16.VII C). The best known of these rules, proposed independently by Guldberg [7] and by Guye,[8] states that the absolute b.p. at 1 atm. pressure, T_b, is approximately two-thirds of the absolute critical temperature:

$$T_b = \tfrac{2}{3} T_c \quad \quad (1)$$

In homologous series the ratio T_b/T_c may vary from 0·58 for the initial to 0·70 for the final members, but the average value is about $\frac{2}{3}$=0·666. For low b.p.

[1] Pawlewski, *Ber.*, 1883, **16**, 2633; Heilborn, *Z. phys. Chem.*, 1890, **6**, 578; 1891, **7**, 601; Vespignani, *Gazz.*, 1903, **33**, i, 73; Graetz, in Winkelmann, " Handbuch der Physik," 1906, **3**, 860; Young, *Proc. Roy. Dublin Soc.*, 1910, **12**, 374; " Stoichiometry," 1918, 170; Berthoud, *J. Chim. Phys.*, 1917, **15**, 3; Landolt-Börnstein, " Tabellen," 5th edit., 1923, 253; Germann and Pickering, " Internat. Crit. Tables," 1928, **3**, 248.

[2] See Schröer, *Z. phys. Chem.*, 1929, **140**, 241, 379.

[3] Schröer, *Z. phys. Chem.*, 1941, **49** B, 271, found t_c=480°, p_c=42 kg./cm.^{2}, ρ_c=0·314 g./ml.

[4] Salzwedel, *Ann. Phys.*, 1930, **5**, 853, found p_c=99 atm.

[5] For critical constants for water, see, e.g., Cailletet and Colardeau, *Compt. Rend.*, 1891, **112**, 1170; *J. de Phys.*, 1891, **10**, 333 (t_c=332·5°); Knipp, *Phys. Rev.*, 1900, **11**, 129; Traube and Teichner, *Ann. Phys.*, 1904, **13**, 621 (t_c=374°); Davis, *Phys. Rev.*, 1909, **29**, 81; Rassow, *Z. anorg. Chem.* 1920, **114**, 117; Schröer, *Z. phys. Chem.*, 1927, **129**, 79; 1941, **49** B, 271; Harand, *Monatsh.*, 1934, **65**, 153; Keyes, Smith, and Gerry, *Proc. Amer. Acad.*, 1935, **69**, 137; Osborne, Stimson, and Ginnings, *Bur. Stand. J. Res.*, 1937, **18**, 389; 1939, **23**, 261; Eck, *Phys. Z.*, 1939, **40**, 3 (t_c=374·2°, p_c=225·5 kg./cm.^{2}, v_c=3·0656 ml./g.); Dorsey, "Properties of Ordinary Water Substance," New York, 1940, 558 (t_c=374·15°, p_c=218·39 atm., v_c=3·1 cm.^{3}/g.).

[6] Riesenfeld and Cheng, *Z. phys. Chem.*, 1935, **28** B, 408; 1935, **30** B, 61; Eck, *Phys. Z.*, 1939, **40**, 3 (t_c=371·5°, p_c=221·5 kg./cm.^{2}, v_c=2·74 ml./g.).

[7] *Z. phys. Chem.*, 1890, **5**, 374.

[8] *Bull. Soc. Chim.*, 1890, **4**, 262; on the rule see also Heilborn, *Z. phys. Chem.*, 1890, **6**, 578; Kurbatow, *J. Russ. Phys. Chem. Soc.*, 1908, **40**, 813 (C); Leduc, *Compt. Rend.*, 1913, **156**, 65; Boutaric, *Ann. Chim.*, 1914, **1**, 437; Ferguson, *Phil. Mag.*, 1915, **29**, 599; Lorenz, *Z. anorg. Chem.*, 1916, **94**, 240, 255, 265; 1918, **103**, 243; Herz, *ibid.*, 1916, **94**, 1; 1916, **95**, 253; 1916, **96**, 289; van Laar, *ibid.*, 1918, **104**, 81; Jorissen, *ibid.*, 1918, **104**, 157; Walden, *ibid.*, 1920, **112**, 225; Kistiakowsky, *J. Chim. Phys.*, 1927, **24**, 309; Stephenson, *Chem. News*, 1931, **143**, 135 (gives $T_b = \frac{4}{5} T_c$); for summary of methods of calculating all critical constants, see Mathias, " Le Point Critique des Corps purs," Paris, 1904, 146 f.

gases the ratio is abnormal: for helium it is 0·998. Livingstone [1] proposed the linear relation:

$$t_c = a + bt_b \quad . \quad . \quad . \quad . \quad . \quad . \quad . \quad . \quad . \quad (2)$$

where a and b are constants. A deduction of Guldberg's rule from Trouton's rule (see § 14.VIII L, Vol. II) was given by Green.[2]

Prud'homme [3] found $T_c = \frac{1}{2}T_b + \sqrt{(T_b^2/4 + KT_b)}$, where $1/K \simeq 0{\cdot}00409$. Bagge and Harteck [4] found for inert gases $T_c = -274{\cdot}5 + 6860/E_j eV$, where E_j= ionising potential, V=interaction potential between two inert gas atoms.

The absolute b.p. at 10–20 mm. is [5] about $\frac{1}{2}T_c$, and the ratio of b.ps. at 20 and 760 mm. is [6] $T_{20}/T_{760} = 0{\cdot}78$. If T_0 is the b.p. in a cathode-ray vacuum, then [7] $T_{15} = 1{\cdot}22T_0$, $T_0 = \frac{2}{3}T_{760}$, and $T_0 = \frac{2}{5}T_c$. Van Laar and Lorenz [8] concluded that the ratio T_{20}/T_c is 0·485 for normal substances. Lautié [9] proposed $4(T_c/T_b) + 10(T_b/T_c) = 12{\cdot}69$. Lorenz and Herz [10] found better agreement with Guldberg's rule if the b.ps. were at equal fractions (1/33, or better 1/50) of the critical pressure.

McCrae [11] calculated the critical temperature of carbon as follows. The m.p. of oxygen is 50° K. and its critical temperature 155·8° K. Over the average temperature range 0°–50° K., i.e. at 25° K., the atomic heat of oxygen is assumed to be 6·4 (Dulong and Petit value). From Weber's results, it is assumed that the atomic heat of carbon would be 6·4 at 2000° K., hence the critical temperature is (155/25)×(2000+273)=14,000° K. Crookes [12] estimated T_c as 5800° K. and p_c as 2320 atm.

Pawlewski [13] proposed the formula $T_c - T_b = t_c - t_b$=const., for homologous series. Isomeric esters have equal or nearly equal critical temperatures, but this is not true for other isomers (e.g. alcohols). Compounds containing double bonds between carbon atoms have much higher critical temperatures than isomers without double bonds. The first relation is illustrated by the short table for esters:

	Ethyl formate	Propyl formate	Methyl acetate	Ethyl acetate	Butyl acetate	Methyl propionate	Ethyl butyrate	Ethyl isobutyrate	Propyl isobutyrate
t_b	55·7	85·1	57·1	75·0	123·7	80·0	121·7	108·6	133·4
t_c	238·6	267·4	239·8	256·5	305·9	262·7	304·3	290·4	316·0
$t_c - t_b$	182·9	182·3	182·7	181·5	182·2	182·7	182·6	181·8	182·6

For other compounds the differences vary from 150° to 210°, and Ostwald [13]

[1] *J. Phys. Chem.*, 1942, **46**, 340.
[2] *J.A.C.S.*, 1924, **46**, 544.
[3] *J. Chim. Phys.*, 1920, **18**, 94.
[4] *Z. Naturforsch.*, 1946, **1**, 481.
[5] Herz, *Z. anorg. Chem.*, 1916, **96**, 289.
[6] Jorissen, *Z. anorg. Chem.*, 1918, **104**, 157.
[7] Hansen, *Z. phys. Chem.*, 1910, **74**, 65; Walden, *Z. anorg. Chem.*, 1920, **112**, 225, 312.
[8] *Z. anorg. Chem.*, 1925, **142**, 189.
[9] *Compt. Rend.*, 1934, **199**, 932; *Bull. Soc. Chim.*, 1935, **2**, 2234.
[10] *Z. anorg. Chem.*, 1921, **115**, 100.
[11] *Chem. News*, 1906, **94**, 314.
[12] *Chem. News*, 1906, **92**, 147.
[13] *Kosmos* (Lwow), 1881, **6**, 498; 1882, **7**, 1; *Ber.*, 1882, **15**, 460, 2460; 1883, **16**, 2633; Nadejdine, *J. Russ. Phys. Chem. Soc.*, 1882, **14**, 536 (P); 1883, **15**, 25 (P); *Ann. Phys. Beibl.*,

pointed out that the difference is not constant for boiling-points at pressures other than atmospheric.

§ 8. Critical Temperature and Chemical Composition

Many attempts have been made to relate the critical temperature of a compound to its molecular weight, M, and to the molecular structure, or to the number of atoms, n, in the molecule. Lautié [1] attempted to express T_c as a sum of increments characteristic of the atoms and bonds in a molecule: for details the originals should be consulted. For normal paraffins, C_nH_{2n+2}, Ferguson [2] found $T_c n^g = hT_b$, where g and h are constants; Merckel,[3] $\log T_c = 0{\cdot}159 \log [(n-1)^2-(n-1)+1]+2{\cdot}4957$. Pawlow [4] proposed $T_c = 1{\cdot}6167M\sqrt{n}$. Watson [5] from Trouton's rule found $T_b/T_c = 0{\cdot}283(M/\rho_b)^{0\cdot13}$, where ρ_b=density of liquid at b.p.; Chen and Hu,[6] $T_c/T_b = 10^{1\cdot59/\sqrt{M}}$, ($M \log T_c + 6{\cdot}4\sqrt{M}$) being additive. Corner [7] proposed four empirical formulae for extrapolating the critical temperatures of paraffin hydrocarbons C_nH_{2n+2}, including $T_c/T_b = A+B \log (T_c/V_c)+Cn$, and $\log T_c = A+B \log (n-c)$, where A, B, c, and C are constants. Lautié,[8] for normal liquids, found $T_c/\sqrt{(M)}+2500\sqrt{(M)}/T_c = 101$, and $T_c = 1{\cdot}2T_b+10\sqrt{M}+20$.

A relation with the coefficient of expansion of the liquid at 0° C. (α_0), viz.[9] $t_c = 0{\cdot}3/\alpha_0$, or at 20° C. (α_{20}), viz.[10] $T_c = \frac{1}{2}(1/\alpha_{20}+293)$, has been proposed. The last is a modification (T=293) of an equation $\alpha_T = 1/(2T_c - T)$, proposed independently by Oswald [11] and Davies.[12] De Kolossowsky [13] found $\alpha_b T_c = 0{\cdot}86$ and $\alpha T_c = 0{\cdot}77$, where α_b=coefficient of expansion at the b.p., and α that at the temperature $0{\cdot}6T_c$. Thorpe and Rücker [14] found $T_c = (T_b x - 273)/1{\cdot}995(x-1)$, where x=vol. at b.p./vol. at 0° C.; and if ρ_1, ρ_2 are the densities of the liquid at the abs. temperatures T_1, T_2, then $T_c = (T_2\rho_1 - T_1\rho_2)/A(\rho_1-\rho_2)$, where A is 1·974 to 1·995.

Prud'homme [15] found some relations between the absolute critical temperatures of binary and ternary compounds: the differences for CS_2-CO_2 and COS$-$CO are equal, $T_c(H_2O) = 2T_c(HCl)$, etc. The critical temperature of an inorganic compound is the sum of simple multiples or fractions of those of its elements, those of metals being ignored.

Trautz [16] believed that the values of T_c/M (where M=mol. wt.) for gases and vapours are in the ratios of whole numbers, and the critical pressures also approximate to whole number ratios:

1883, **7**, 678 (const.=156·6° for homologues C_nH_{2n}); Schuck, *J. Russ. Phys. Chem. Soc.*, 1882, **14**, 157 (P); Bartoli, *Nuov. Cim.*, 1885, **16**, 74; Ferretto, *Gazz.*, 1900, **30**, i, 296; for fuller tables, see Ostwald, " Lehrbuch der allgemeinen Chemie," 1910, **1**, 341.

1 *Compt. Rend.*, 1934, **199**, 932; *Bull. Soc. Chim.*, 1935, **2**, 155, 2234; 1936, **3**, 1689; 1943, **10**, 44; *J. Chim. Phys.*, 1937, **34**, 452; see also " Parachor," § 5.VIII G, Vol. II..

2 *Phil. Mag.*, 1915, **29**, 599.

3 *Proc. K. Akad. Wetens. Amsterdam*, 1937, **40**, 164.

4 *J. Russ. Phys. Chem. Soc.*, 1917, **49**, 322 (C).

5 *Ind. Eng. Chem.*, 1931, **23**, 360.

6 *J. Chinese Chem. Soc.*, 1943, **10**, 208, 212.

7 *Trans. Faraday Soc.*, 1945, **41**, 617; *Proc. Cambr. Phil. Soc.*, 1946, **42**, 328.

8 *Bull. Soc. Chim.*, 1936, **3**, 2337.

9 Sibaiya, *Current Sci.*, 1938, **6**, 329.

10 Herz, *Z. anorg. Chem.*, 1920, **112**, 278; *Z. Elektrochem.*, 1921, **27**, 125.

11 *Compt. Rend.*, 1912, **154**, 61.

12 *Phil. Mag.*, 1912, **23**, 657.

13 *J. de Phys.*, 1925, **6**, 99; *J. Chim. Phys.*, 1927, **24**, 56.

14 *J.C.S.*, 1884, **45**, 133; Herz, *Z. phys. Chem.*, 1921, **97**, 376.

15 *Bull. Soc. Chim.*, 1925, **37**, 1330.

16 *Ann. Phys.*, 1931, **8**, 267, 433; Watson, *Ind. Eng. Chem.*, 1931, **23**, 360.

	T_c	M	T_c/M	Ratio	p_c	Ratio
CH_4 ...	190·6	16·03	11·89	2·002	54·9	1·01
NH_3 ...	405·5	17·03	23·81	3·002	113	2·08
OH_2 ...	647·1	18·02	35·93		217·5	4

Jatkar and Lakshminarayanan [1] found:

(i) for aromatic substances free from halogens and sulphur $T_c=1{\cdot}41T_b+66-r(0{\cdot}383T_b-93)$ where r=ratio of number of non-cyclic carbon atoms to the total number of carbon atoms in the compound;

(ii) for all compounds other than aromatics and free from halogens and sulphur $T_c=1{\cdot}027T_b+159$;

(iii) for compounds containing halogens and sulphur $T_c=1{\cdot}41T_b+66-11F$, where F=total number of fluorine atoms in the molecule;

(iv) for compounds boiling below 235° K., $T_c=1{\cdot}70T_b-2$.

Grunberg and Nissan [2] found for normal paraffin hydrocarbons that T_c^3 is proportional to the molecular weight; the increment of T_c^3 for $-CH_2$ is $2{\cdot}7\times10^7$.

§ 9. Critical Temperature and Melting-point

The ratio of the critical temperature and the m.p. (abs.), T_c/T_m, varies from 1·7 to 3·06 for various groups of substances; [3] the value of T_m/T_c varies from 0·3 to 0·5, the average value [4] being $\frac{2}{5}=0{\cdot}4$. Lorenz [5] found $T_b/T_c=0{\cdot}64$, $T_m/T_c=0{\cdot}44$, $T_b/T_m=1{\cdot}471$, $T_m/T_b\simeq T_b/T_c\simeq\frac{2}{3}$; for groups of substances, Lorenz and Herz [6] found for T_m/T_b: elements 0·5583, inorganic compounds 0·7183, organic compounds 0·5839, with an average value of 0·62. The value of T_c-T_m, giving [7] the "range of existence of the liquid state," is arbitrary,[8] since T_m depends on pressure and the triple point does not limit the liquid state at the lower temperature.

Prud'homme [9] proposed a "Rule of Three Temperatures," $T_m+T_b\simeq T_c$, which was criticised by van Laar [10] as purely accidental: it is, however, generally a good approximation.[11] Porlezza [11] obtained it from the relation $T_m/T_c+T_b/T_c=1{\cdot}04\simeq1$. He regarded it as a deduction from the law of corresponding states, and as more accurate than the formula of Lorenz,[12] deduced from Guldberg's rule, $T_b/T_c\simeq\frac{2}{3}$ (§ 7), viz., $T_b/T_c=(T_m/T_c)\times(T_b/T_c)$, which gives $\frac{2}{3}\times\frac{2}{3}+\frac{2}{3}=1{\cdot}11$.

[1] *J. Indian Inst. Sci.*, 1946, **28** A, **1**.
[2] *Nature*, 1948, **161**, 170.
[3] Clark, *Amer. Chem. J.*, 1896, **18**, 618; *Z. phys. Chem.*, 1896, **21**, 183; van Laar, *Ann. Phys. Boltzmann Festschr.*, 1904, 316 (metals); Lorenz and Herz, *Z. anorg. Chem.*, 1921, **116**, 103; van Laar, *ibid.*, 1925, **149**, 324 (T_c and p_c for alkali halides).
[4] Onnes and Keesom, "Enzykl d. math. Wiss.," 1912, **5**, i, 867.
[5] *Z. anorg. Chem.*, 1916, **94**, 240, 255, 265; 1918, **103**, 243; Van Liempt, *ibid.*, 1920, **111**, 280, found $T_m/T_c=0{\cdot}476$.
[6] *Z. anorg. Chem.*, 1922, **122**, 51.
[7] Herz, *Z. Elektrochem.*, 1918, **24**, 48, 139; Meyer, *ibid.*, 1918, **24**, 138.
[8] Bruni, *Atti R. Accad. Lincei*, 1918, **27**, ii, 394.
[9] *J. Chim. Phys.*, 1920, **18**, 270, 307, 359; 1921–2, **19**, 188; 1924, **21**, 243; *Ann. Chim.*, 1921, **15**, 212.
[10] *J. Chim. Phys.*, 1921–2, **19**, 3.
[11] Porlezza, *Nuov. Cim.*, 1923, **25**, 291; Taft and Stareck, *J. Phys. Chem.*, 1930, **34**, 2307.
[12] *Z. anorg. Chem.*, 1916, **94**, 240, 255, 265; 1918, **103**, 243.

§ 10. Empirical Equations for Critical Volumes

According to Lorenz [1] the ratio of the specific volume at the boiling-point to that at the critical temperature is $v_b/v_c=0{\cdot}376$, and that at the melting-point $v_m/v_c=0{\cdot}321$, for inorganic and organic substances. Herzog,[2] from Avenarius's formula for the thermal expansion of a liquid, $v=a-b\log(t_c-t)$, where a and b are constants (see § 4.VIII C, Vol. II), deduced for the critical density:

$$\rho_c=\rho_t[0{\cdot}906-0{\cdot}233\log(t_c-t)],$$

or with slightly greater accuracy:

$$\rho_c=\rho_T\{0{\cdot}900-0{\cdot}227\log[T_c-T+(T_c/T)^4]\}.$$

The critical density is approximately one-third of the density ρ_0 of the liquid at atmospheric pressure at absolute zero,[3] or $1/2{\cdot}66$ of the density at the boiling-point.[4] Lorenz [5] found $\rho_0=\rho_T(0{\cdot}77+0{\cdot}64T/T_b)$, and van Laar [6] $\rho_T=\rho_0(1-T/2{\cdot}1T_c)$.

A simple empirical formula for the critical density which gives good results in many cases [7] is $\rho_t=\rho_c+\sqrt{(\beta\tau)}$, where β is a constant and τ is the temperature reckoned below a characteristic temperature t_1, $\tau=t_1-t$; e.g. for $CH_3COC_2H_5$ t_1 is 272·5, CH_3COOH 355, *n*-pentane 221. This is modified to $\rho_t=\rho_c[1+2{\cdot}73\sqrt{(T/T_0)}]$, where $T_0=1{\cdot}05T_c$, T=temp. of observation reckoned below T_c. Ferguson and Kennedy [8] found $\rho_c=0{\cdot}3592\rho_r$, where ρ_r is the density at the reduced temperature $\vartheta=T/T_c=0{\cdot}6$. Jatkar and Lakshminarayanan [9] found $V_c=(0{\cdot}377[P]+11{\cdot}0)^{1{\cdot}25}$, where $[P]$ is the parachor. Grunberg and Nissan [10] for normal paraffin hydrocarbons found $\rho_c\simeq0{\cdot}23$ g./ml.

Timmermans [11] confirmed the rule $\rho_m/\rho_c=\rho_c/\rho_g$, where ρ_m is the maximum density (e.g. as calculated by an extension of the law of rectilinear diameter, § 5) and ρ_g is the density at the critical temperature calculated for the ideal gas state. Young [12] had calculated from van der Waals's equation that $\rho_c/\rho_g=\frac{8}{3}\sqrt{2}=3{\cdot}77$, and found that this is nearly true except for alcohols and acetic acid, which have values from 4 to nearly 5.

Herz [13] assumed that if M_c and M_b are the mol. wts. at the critical temperature and the b.p., $(M_c/\rho_c)/(M_b/\rho_b)$=const.$=K$. For halogen substituted benzenes he assumed $M_c=M_b$, and hence found $K=\rho_b/\rho_c=2{\cdot}69$. Thus, in general $M_c/M_b=2{\cdot}69\rho_c/\rho_b$. This, however, was practically unity both for "normal",

1 *Z. anorg. Chem.*, 1916, **94**, 240; Herz, *Z. Elektrochem.*, 1919, **25**, 215; Lorenz and Herz, *Z. anorg. Chem.*, 1924, **138**, 331.

2 *Z. Elektrochem.*, 1909, **15**, 345; Rudorf, *ibid.*, 1909, **15**, 746.

3 Mathias, *Ann. Fac. Sci. Toulouse*, 1892, **5**; Guldberg, *Z. phys. Chem.*, 1895, **16**, 1; 1900, **32**, 116 ($\rho_0/\rho_c=3{\cdot}75$); *Z. anorg. Chem.*, 1898, **18**, 87; Lorenz, *Z. anorg. Chem.*, 1916, **94**, 240 ($\rho_0/\rho_c=3{\cdot}75$).

4 Walden, *Z. phys. Chem.*, 1908–9, **65**, 129, 257; 1909, **66**, 385; *Z. Elektrochem.*, 1908, **14**, 712; Lorenz, *Z. anorg. Chem.*, 1916, **94**, 240 ($\rho_0/\rho_b=1{\cdot}41$); Herz, *Z. phys. Chem.*, 1921, **98**, 175; 1923, **104**, 433; Schwab, *Z. Phys.*, 1922, **11**, 188 ($\rho_c/\rho_b=2{\cdot}665$); Kistiakowsky, *J. Chim. Phys.*, 1927, **24**, 309 (ρ_b/ρ_c varied from 2·60 to 2·69 for 28 liquids).

5 *Z. anorg. Chem.*, 1916, **94**, 240.

6 *Z. anorg. Chem.*, 1925, **146**, 283.

7 Saslawsky, *Z. phys. Chem.*, 1924, **109**, 111; Lorenz and Herz, *Z. anorg. Chem.*, 1924, **138**, 331; criticised by van Laar, *ibid.*, 1924, **140**, 52.

8 *Trans. Faraday Soc.*, 1935, **31**, 1000.

9 *J. Indian Inst. Sci.*, 1946, **28** A, 1.

10 *Nature*, 1948, **161**, 170.

11 *Bull. Soc. Chim. Belg.*, 1923, **32**, 299.

12 *Phil. Mag.*, 1892, **33**, 153; 1892, **34**, 503; *Chem. News*, 1898, **7**, 200; "Stoichiometry," 1918, 208.

13 *Z. anorg. Chem.*, 1921, **115**, 237; cf. Predwoditelew, *Z. Phys.*, 1926, **36**, 557.

and "associated" liquids, and the same result was found with densities at $\frac{7}{12}T_c$ instead of at the normal b.p. $\simeq\frac{2}{3}T_c$. This result was regarded as an empirical rule not necessarily implying a law of corresponding states.

Porlezza [1] proposed a "rule of four volumes" (V_m at m.p., V_b at b.p., V_0 at 0° K., V_c critical volume), $V_0/V_c+V_m/V_c+V_b/V_c=0{\cdot}96\simeq1$, so that $V_0+V_m+V_b=V_c$. Each member V_0/V_c, etc., in the first equation is $\frac{1}{3}$. Swientoslawski [2] found that ρ_c/ρ_T is a function of T/T_c increasing with molecular weight and association.

Ter Gazarian at first [3] considered that at temperatures equally removed from the critical temperatures, members of homologous series have equal densities, but he later [4] modified this to the general rule that the ratios of numbers representing any physical property at two temperatures is a linear function of the difference of temperatures, on the analogy of Ramsay and Young's rule (see § 8.VIII K, Vol. II), $r_2=r_1+c(t_2-t_1)-at$.

Lautié [5] gave for the molar volume at the b.p. V_b for normal liquids:

$$\frac{T_c}{T_c-T_b}\log 24\frac{T_c-T_b}{V_b}\simeq 2{\cdot}9 \text{ to } 3{\cdot}1.$$

An important equation for the critical volume was based by Mathias [6] on the law of rectilinear diameter (§ 5); at such temperatures that the density of the vapour can be neglected in comparison with that of the liquid this gives $\rho_c=\rho/2(2-T/T_c)$, where ρ is the density at the temperature T. The complete equation is $(\rho_l+\rho_g)/2\rho_c=2-T/T_c=2-\vartheta$, where $\vartheta=T/T_c$. Jüptner [7] replaced this by $\frac{1}{2}(\rho_l+\rho_g)=a-b\vartheta$, where a and b are constants, or $(\rho_l+\rho_g)/2\rho_c=1+a'(1-\vartheta)$, where a'=const., and found:

$$\rho_l=\rho_c K[(1-\vartheta)+(1-\vartheta)^{1/3}+\vartheta]$$

where K is an empirical constant, varying from 1·657217 for *p*-xylene to 2·17134 for propionic acid. The accuracy is good, except for alcohols, which may show 5 per cent. deviation or more. Herz [8] found $T_c(\rho_c/M)^{1/3}$=const.

For most liquids (H_2, He, Ne, and PH_3 give lower values) the reduced density at the b.p. is $\rho_b/\rho_c=2{\cdot}68$; also $\rho_b/\rho_c=0{\cdot}422 \log p_c$ (atm.)$+1{\cdot}981$ holds for normal and associated liquids (CS_2, HCN, CH_3CN, and C_2H_5CN are abnormal). The results $v_c=2{\cdot}68/\rho_b$ and b (van der Waals constant)$=1{\cdot}22/\rho_b$ follow. If α=coefficient of expansion at the b.p., $T_c=T_b+(0{\cdot}254/\alpha)(1+0{\cdot}122M/T_b{}^2\rho_b\alpha)$. All these relations are true to 2 to 3 per cent.[9]

According to D. Berthelot [10] the molar critical volume M/ρ_c is 1/3·6 times the molar volume of an ideal gas at the critical temperature and pressure, i.e. (with p_c in atm.) in lit.:

$$\frac{M}{\rho_c}=\frac{22{\cdot}4}{3{\cdot}6}\cdot\frac{T_c}{273}\cdot\frac{1}{p_c}.$$

1 *Nuov. Cim.*, 1923, **25**, 305.
2 *Roczn. Chem.*, 1921, **1**, 276, 297.
3 *J. Chim. Phys.*, 1908, **6**, 492.
4 *J. Chim. Phys.*, 1909, **7**, 233; *Compt. Rend.*, 1911, **153**, 871, 1071.
5 *Compt. Rend.*, 1936, **202**, 753.
6 *Compt. Rend.*, 1893, **117**, 1082; "Le Point Critique des Corps purs," 1904, 164.
7 *Z. phys. Chem.*, 1910, **73**, 173; 1913, **85**, 1; Timmermans, *Proc. Roy. Dublin Soc.*, 1912, **13**, 310.
8 *Z. anorg. Chem.*, 1925, **150**, 385.
9 Benson, *J. Phys. Chem.*, 1948, **52**, 1060.
10 *Compt. Rend.*, 1898, **128**, 553, 607; Dieterici, *Ann. Phys.*, 1899, **69**, 685, gave 1/3·7.

With the equation of Mathias, $\rho_c=\rho/2(2-T/T_c)$, this gives for the molar weight of the *liquid*:

$$M=11{\cdot}4\rho T_c/p_c(2-T/T_c).$$

Some values of M calculated by this formula are:

SO_2 65·1	CS_2 73·4	C_6H_5F 99	C_2H_5OH 51·6 (46)
Ether 76·1	$SnCl_4$ 252·4	NH_3 19·2	H_2O 25·1 (18)
CCl_4 152·3	C_2H_5Cl 63·5	CH_3COOH 80·6 (60)	
$CHCl_3$ 114·5	C_6H_6 79·2	CH_3OH 45·8 (32)	

Except in the last four cases (normal molar wts. in brackets), known on other grounds to be associated, the agreement is good. Herz [1] found satisfactory agreement at moderately high temperatures for both normal and associated liquids. Kam [2] supposed that the critical density ρ_c is two-thirds of the density of an ideal gas exerting the pressure p_c at the temperature T_c, but this does not agree with Berthelot's results.

Substitution of Guldberg's relation (§ 7), $T_b/T_c=0{\cdot}67$ in Berthelot's equation gives $M=11{\cdot}4\rho_bT_c/p_c(2-0{\cdot}67)=9\rho_bT_c/p_c$. Schuster [3] modified Berthelot's equation to:

$$M=C\rho T_c/p_c[1-\surd(1-\vartheta)-\tfrac{1}{2}(1-\vartheta)]^3,$$

where $\vartheta=T/T_c$ and C, a constant, is approximately $2\times11{\cdot}4$. With Guye's equation [4] $R_L=1{\cdot}8T_c/p_c$, where R_L=molar refractivity=$(n^2-1)M/(n^2+2)\rho$, Berthelot's equation gives [5] $M=5\rho_bR_L$, or $M/\rho_b=V_b$ (molar vol. at b.p.)$=5R_L$. This holds approximately for simple aliphatic compounds but not for halogen substitution products or aromatic, heterocyclic, and inorganic compounds.

	Ethyl formate	Amyl acetate	Octane	Ethyl ether	Ethyl iodide	Chloroform	Aniline	CCl_4	CS_2
M/ρ_b	84·7	175·0	186·6	106·4	86·1	83·4	106·4	103·7	62·1
$5R_L$	90·05	181·0	195·8	112·6	121·5	107·0	152·9	132·6	105·9

Schaposchnikow [6] proposed $\rho=n\rho'+b$, where ρ and ρ' are the densities of two liquids at temperatures equidistant from the critical points, $(T_c-T)=(T_c'-T')$, and n and b are constants.

§ 11. Empirical Equations for Critical Pressures and Relations among Critical Constants

A few equations for the critical pressure are available, but in many cases this appears in equations which also contain the critical temperature or the critical volume, or both (notably in the form p_cv_c/T_c). Since v_c and T_c can be found by independent equations, as explained above, any equations containing them along with p_c are really means of determining the last.

[1] *Z. Elektrochem.*, 1923, **29**, 394; Timmermans, *Bull. Soc. Chim. Belg.*, 1923, **32**, 299, found deviations.

[2] *Phil. Mag.*, 1916, **31**, 22.

[3] *Ber.*, 1925, **58**, 2183; *Z. anorg. Chem.*, 1925, **146**, 299; *Z. Elektrochem.*, 1926, **32**, 46, 155.

[4] *Compt. Rend.*, 1890, **110**, 141; 1894, **119**, 852; *Ann. Chim.*, 1890, **21**, 206, 211; *Arch. Sci. Phys. Nat.*, 1890, **23**, 197, 204; 1894, **31**, 38; *Z. phys. Chem.*, 1890, **6**, 372.

[5] Herz, *Z. phys. Chem.*, 1922, **101**, 54.

[6] *Z. phys. Chem.*, 1905, **51**, 542.

Walden [1] gave an empirical formula $p_cV_b/T_b=12{\cdot}46$ (p_c in atm., V_b=molar volume at the abs. b.p. T_b), and also $p_c=6{\cdot}5\sigma_b/\log T_b-0{\cdot}012T_b$, where σ_b is the surface tension at the b.p.

Natanson [2] proposed (p_c in atm.) $\rho_c=0{\cdot}044p_c/T_c$; Ferguson and Kennedy [3] $\rho T=0{\cdot}7804M/p_c$ (ρ=density at temperature T); Lautié [4] $p_cV_b/(T_c-T_b)=24$, or $p_cM_b/(T_c-T_b)\rho_b$, and: [5]

$$xp_cv_c/T_c=(25{\cdot}2+4{\cdot}0617\times10^{-4}T_c^2)/(1+1{\cdot}925\times10^{-5}T_c^2)$$

where x is the association factor at the critical point. For many liquids $x=1$; for water it is 1·4. Lautié and Artières [6] found that the " critical product " p_cv_c of a series of normal halogen compounds is a linear function of that of the corresponding inert gases. Partington [7] proposed the formula (p_c atm.):

$$n=0{\cdot}642+0{\cdot}00116p_c+0{\cdot}0_4399p_c^2,$$

where n is the exponent in the formula for the viscosity of a gas, $\eta_T=\eta_0(T/273)^n$. Schuster [8] gave the formula:

$$v_c=(RT_c/8p_c)(3+0{\cdot}038\sqrt{T_c})/(1+0{\cdot}038\sqrt{T_c}),$$

which gives fairly good results in some cases, but not in others, and he represented the critical volume as the sum of contributions of the atoms in the molecule. Jatkar and Lakshminarayanan [9] found $p_c=20{\cdot}8T_c/(V_c-8)$.

According to Guye [10] the *critical coefficient* $K=T_c/p_c$ is related to the molar refractivity $R_L=(M/\rho)(n^2-1)/(n^2+2)$, where n=refractive index extrapolated to $\lambda=\infty$ by Cauchy's equation, by the equation $K=R_L/1{\cdot}8$, therefore $p_c=1{\cdot}8T_c/R_L$. For a compound, K is the sum of the values for the separate atoms, augmented in some cases by coefficients depending on the mode of linkage: C 1·35, H 0·57, O 0·87, O″ 1·27, Cl 3·27, Br 4·83; $I^{=}$6·88, $I^{\equiv}$1·03.

Dutoit and Friderich [11] gave the formulae $p_c=11{\cdot}1\sigma_b/\sqrt[3]{V_m}$, where σ_b=surface tension, V_m=molar volume, at the b.p. T_b (abs.); and $p_c=(T_b/Mv)[13{\cdot}8+(Mv/100)]$, ($p_c$ atm.), and the first equation was tested by Guye and Baud.[12]

Boutaric [13] proposed the equation $T_c/p_c=0{\cdot}1176M/\rho_b$ (ρ_b=density at b.p. in g./ml., p_c in atm.), and since Lorenz [14] found $\rho_b/\rho_c=2{\cdot}66$, this gives $T_c/p_c=0{\cdot}04421M/\rho_c$. Herz [15] modified Boutaric's equation to $M=22{\cdot}62T_c\rho_c/p_c$. He started [16] with the equation [17] $M=AK\rho_c$, where $K=T_c/p_c$ (atm.), and, since $A=21{\cdot}55$ to $21{\cdot}86$, he put it equal to Trouton's coefficient $Ml_e/T_b=22$. Thus $l_e=p_cT_b/T_c\rho_c$, and since $T_b/T_c\simeq0{\cdot}66$, therefore $l_e=0{\cdot}66p_c/\rho_c$. By

1 *Z. phys. Chem.*, 1909, **66**, 385.
2 *J. de Phys.*, 1895, **4**, 219.
3 *Trans. Faraday Soc.*, 1935, **31**, 1000.
4 *Compt. Rend.*, 1934, **199**, 932; 1935, **200**, 455.
5 *Bull. Soc. Chim.*, 1936, **3**, 1136.
6 *Bull. Soc. Chim.*, 1937, **4**, 664.
7 *Trans. Faraday Soc.*, 1922, **17**, 734.
8 *Z. Elektrochem.*, 1926, **32**, 46, 155, 191.
9 *J. Indian Inst. Sci.*, 1946, **28 A**, 1.
10 *J. de Phys.*, 1890, **9**, 312; *Ann. Chim.*, 1890, **21**, 211; Guye and Friderich, *Arch. Sci. Phys. Nat.*, 1900, **9**, 505.
11 *Arch. Sci. Phys. Nat.*, 1898, **5**, 574; 1900, **9**, 105.
12 *Arch. Sci. Phys. Nat.*, 1901, **11**, 449, 537.
13 *Compt. Rend.*, 1912, **155**, 1080.
14 *Z. anorg. Chem.*, 1916, **94**, 240; Herz, *ibid.*, 1921, **116**, 250; Lorenz and Herz, *ibid.*, 1921, **116**, 103.
15 *Z. Elektrochem.*, 1920, **26**, 109; *Z. anorg. Chem.*, 1921, **116**, 250.
16 *Z. Elektrochem.*, 1919, **25**, 323.
17 Prud'homme, *J. Chim. Phys.*, 1913, **11**, 589.

substituting $\rho_b/\rho_c=2{\cdot}66$, from Lorenz,[1] in Boutaric's equation he found $T_c/p_c=0{\cdot}1176M/2{\cdot}66\rho_c$, therefore $M=22{\cdot}62T_c\rho_c/p_c$.

The integrated Clapeyron-Clausius equation (see § 7.VIII L, Vol. II) gives:

$$Ml_e=2{\cdot}303\boldsymbol{R}\frac{T}{T_b-T}\log\frac{p_b}{p}=4{\cdot}606\frac{TT_b}{T_b-T}\log\frac{p_b}{p},$$

and with $l_e=p_cT_b/T_c\rho_c$ this gives:

$$Mp_c/T_c\rho_c=4{\cdot}606\frac{T}{T_b-T}\log\frac{p_b}{p}.$$

With $\boldsymbol{R}=82{\cdot}07$ ml. atm./1°, the average value (§ 20.VII C) of $\boldsymbol{R}T_c\rho_c/Mp_c$ is 3·63, hence $M=22{\cdot}62T_c\rho_c/p_c$ approximately, as given by Boutaric's equation. Prud'homme [2] gave the same formula.

Van der Waals's equation gives $v_c=\frac{3}{8}\boldsymbol{R}T_c/p_c$, hence v_cp_c/T_c should be constant for normal substances and equal to $0{\cdot}0_393$. Herz's equation $l_e=p_cT_b/T_c\rho_c$ then gives [3] $l_e=0{\cdot}0_393/\rho_cv_c$, where v_c=critical volume,[4] and Trouton's rule, $Ml_e/T_b=21$, gives $0{\cdot}0_393M/\rho_cv_c\simeq21$.

Prud'homme [5] gave the formula $(T_c-T_b)p_c^{\,n}$=const., where n is a constant. A formula proposed by Mathias,[6] $p_c=a+b/(n+3)$, where a and b are constants and n is the number of carbon atoms in the molecule in homologous series, was not confirmed by Berthoud.[7]

Fielding [8] found for inorganic compounds $T_c=1{\cdot}714T_b+3{\cdot}3$ and $(T_c-X)/\sqrt{p_c}$ =const., where X is a constant for different groups of substances, and $(T_c+236{\cdot}9)/\sqrt{p_c}=70{\cdot}9$ for elements, but these equations were not confirmed by Moles.[9] Since van der Waals's equation (§ 7.VII C) gives $T_c/\sqrt{p_c}=8\sqrt{a}/\sqrt{(27\boldsymbol{R})}$, Fielding's equation $(T_c-X)/\sqrt{p_c}$=const.$=K$ implies [10] an approximate constancy of $\sqrt{a}$. G. G. Longinescu [11] found $T_c/\rho_c\sqrt{n}=450$, where n=number of atoms in the molecule, and a theoretical interpretation was given by I. N. Longinescu.[12] Herz [13] found $T_c/np_c=0{\cdot}90$, $T_c/Zp_c=0{\cdot}44$, $v_c/Z=0{\cdot}00044$, $1000v_c=T_c/p_c$ (p_c atm., v_c=fraction of ideal gas volume at S.T.P.), where Z is the sum of the valencies. For compounds free from nitrogen, Jorissen [14] found $n=193M^2/T_b^{\,2}\rho_b$, and with $T_b/T_c\simeq\frac{2}{3}$, this gives $n=434M^2/T_c^{\,2}\rho_b$.

Mathias [15] pointed out relations between the critical constants and molar weights M in homologous series; Bulatow,[16] for aliphatic esters, found

1 *Z. anorg. Chem.*, 1916, **94**, 240.

2 *Bull. Soc. Chim.*, 1922, **31**, 295; 1926, **39**, 145.

3 Herz, *Z. Elektrochem.*, 1920, **27**, 26.

4 In all these equations v_c is the fraction of the *ideal* gas volume at S.T.P. as unit, p_c is in atm., and ρ_c in g./ml.

5 *J. Chim. Phys.*, 1920, **18**, 94.

6 *Compt. Rend.*, 1893, **117**, 1082.

7 *J. Chim. Phys.*, 1917, **15**, 3.

8 *Chem. News*, 1918, **117**, 379 (tables of data).

9 *J. Chim. Phys.*, 1919, **17**, 415.

10 Friend, *Chem. News*, 1921, **129**, 219.

11 *J. Chim. Phys.*, 1903, **1**, 259.

12 *J. Chim. Phys.*, 1929, **26**, 314; Barbulescu, *Bul. Soc. Stiinte Cluj*, 1936, **8**, 462; *Brit. Chem. Abstr.*, 1937, A I, 230; *J. Chim. Phys.*, 1938, **35**, 27.

13 *Z. anorg. Chem.*, 1920, **109**, 293; 1920, **111**, 52; 1920, **114**, 153; *Z. Elektrochem.*, 1921, **27**, 373.

14 *J. Chim. Phys.*, 1920, **18**, 25.

15 *Compt. Rend.*, 1893, **117**, 1082; " Le Point Critique des Corps purs," 1904, 161.

16 *J. Russ. Phys. Chem. Soc.*, 1899, **31**, 69 (P); *Ann. Phys. Beibl.*, 1899, **23**, 754 (unit of v_c=ideal gas volume at S.T.P.).

$v_c=0{\cdot}000178M-0{\cdot}0034$, and $t_c=122{\cdot}5+1{\cdot}5M$. Merckel [1] found for normal paraffins (C_nH_{2n+2}) $\log p_c=-0{\cdot}346 \log [(n+2)^2-(n+2)+1]+2{\cdot}0747$.

Herz [2] pointed out that t_c increases but p_c decreases, with increase in the number of carbon atoms in homologous series. For compounds of C, H, O, and N (but not those containing sulphur or halogens) T_c/p_c divided by the number of valencies (C=4, N=3, O=2, H=1) is constant and is approximately 0·44, but is larger for associated compounds, and slightly larger for many aliphatic compounds. The quotient by the number of atoms in the molecule is not constant. For aromatic compounds better results are found if the valency of carbon is taken as 3, in agreement with modern ideas of the structure of graphite, from which they are derived. The constant is then 0·49 for both aliphatic and aromatic compounds.[3]

Telang [4] found p_c (cm. Hg)$=1251T_c/[P]$, where $[P]$ is the parachor (see p. 648), and Syrkin [5] $\mu=3{\cdot}58\times10^{-21}\sqrt{(T_cv_c)}=1{\cdot}66\times10^{-20}T_c/\sqrt{p_c}\simeq3{\cdot}82\times10^{-20}\sqrt{(T_cv_b)}$ (p_c atm.), where μ=dipole moment. Some ill-defined relations between the critical constants and the electronic structures of atoms and molecules have been proposed.[6] The construction of a critical pressure chart described by Hooks and Kerze [7] was based on the equation proposed by Meissner and Redding,[8] p_c being found from T_c and v_c, with v_c calculated from the critical parachor.

Batschinski [9] proposed for the critical temperature (or, as he calls it, *meta-critical temperature*, since the liquid may contain molecules of different complexity) the formula $T_c=16{\cdot}31(\eta T^3)^{2/7}/\rho_c^{1/7}$, where η=viscosity, the product ηT^3 being constant for *normal* liquids, supposed to be a sensitive indication of association. This does not hold for associated liquids, when T_c must be replaced by a "metacritical" *variable* temperature T_c', which is calculated from the above formula. He calculated the degree of association x from a modified Ramsay and Shields' formula, $\sigma(xMv)^{2/3}=2{\cdot}12(T_c'-T-6)$, where σ=surface tension, and found values of x much higher than those calculated by Ramsay and Shields. According to Stakhorsky [10] the metacritical temperature is given by $T'=T/[1-(0{\cdot}17/\alpha T)]$, where α is the coefficient of expansion of the liquid at $T°$ K. Grunberg and Nissan [11] found for normal paraffins $\eta_c=K(\rho_c^{2/3}/M^{1/6})T_c^{1/2}$ where K is a universal constant.

§ 12. Critical Temperatures of Solutions

The *critical temperature of a liquid mixture* was represented by Strauss [12] by the equation:

$$t_c=[at_{c_1}+(100-a)t_{c_2}]/100 \quad . \quad . \quad . \quad . \quad . \quad . \quad . \quad . \quad (1)$$

where t_{c_1} and t_{c_2} are the critical temperatures of the components and a the

[1] *Proc. K. Akad. Wetens. Amsterdam*, 1937, **40**, 164; another formula for p_c is given by Pedrero, *An. Fis. Quim.*, 1936, **34**, 173.
[2] *Z. anorg. Chem.*, 1920, **109**, 293.
[3] *Z. anorg. Chem.*, 1920, **114**, 153.
[4] *J. Indian Chem. Soc.*, 1942, **19**, 366.
[5] *Z. anorg. Chem.*, 1928, **174**, 47.
[6] Woolsey, *J.A.C.S.*, 1937, **59**, 1577.
[7] *Chem. Eng.*, 1946, **53**, No. 11, 163.
[8] *Ind. Eng. Chem.*, 1942, **34**, 521.
[9] *Z. phys. Chem.*, 1902, **40**, 629; 1911, **65**, 665; 1913, **82**, 86, 90; Tyrer, *ibid.*, 1912, **80**, 50.
[10] *Ukrain. Chem. J.*, 1928, **3**, Sci. Pt. 457.
[11] *Nature*, 1948, **161**, 170.
[12] *J. Russ. Phys. Chem. Soc.*, 1880, **12**, 207 (P); 1882, **14**, 510 (P); *J. de Phys.*, 1880, **10**, 420 (alcohol and ether); *Ann. Phys. Beibl.*, 1882, **6**, 282; 1883, **7**, 676.

percentage of the first component. The rule was found by Pawlewski [1] (Pavlevsky) and others [2] to hold fairly well in many cases (also for several components), although some exceptions occur,[3] the observed values being both higher and lower than the calculated.

Percentages		t_c obs.	t_c calc.
Alcohol	Ether		
0	100	193·5	—
22·83	77·17	200·4	204·5
45·67	54·33	212·1	215·7
52·97	47·03	216·2	219·1
100	0	241·9	—
Benzene	Ether		
100	0	296·4	—
47·26	52·74	242·3	242·1
36·04	63·96	231·4	230·6
28·36	71·64	224·5	223·7
14·23	85·77	209·9	208·1
0	100	193·5	—
Ether	Acetone		
0	100	234·4	—
6·6	93·4	230·1	231·6
14·1	85·9	227·3	228·4
30·7	69·3	218·4	221·3
100	0	191·8	—

If some experiments by Cailletet and Hautefeuille [4] are correct, the critical temperature of some gas mixtures can lie outside the interval between those of the components. Dewar [5] found the critical temperature for a mixture of carbon monoxide and acetylene lower than that of either constituent, and the same was found for nitrous oxide and ethane by Kuenen.[6]

The Strauss-Pawlewski rule probably holds with close approximation in those cases where no change in molecular complexity occurs in mixing; [7] an examina-

[1] *Kosmos* (Lwow), 1881, **6**, 498; 1882, **7**, 1; *Ber.*, 1882, **15**, 460, 2460; 1890, **23**, 3752.

[2] Ramsay, *Proc. Roy. Soc.*, 1880, **31**, 194; Blümcke, *Z. phys. Chem.*, 1890, **6**, 153; 1891, **8**, 554; 1892, **9**, 78; Gilbaut, *ibid.*, 1897, **24**, 410; Schmidt, *Ann.*, 1891, **266**, 266; Pictet, *Compt. Rend.*, 1895, **120**, 64; Dwelshauers-Dery, *Bull. Acad. Roy. Belg.*, 1895, **29**, 277; Levi-Bianchini, *Atti R. Accad. Lincei*, 1904, **13**, ii, 174; Friedrichs, *J.A.C.S.*, 1913, **35**, 1866; *Z. anorg. Chem.*, 1913, **84**, 373; Kurata and Katz, *Trans. Amer. Inst. Chem. Eng.*, 1942, **38**, 995 (hydrocarbon mixtures); Klinkenberg, *Chem. Weekbl.*, 1947, **43**, 816.

[3] Ansdell, *Proc. Roy. Soc.*, 1882, **34**, 113; Galitzine, *Ann. Phys.*, 1890, **41**, 588; Kuenen, *Z. phys. Chem.*, 1893, **11**, 38; 1897, **24**, 667; 1901, **37**, 485; *Phil. Mag.*, 1902, **4**, 116; Quint, *Phys. Z.*, 1899, **1**, 65; Ferreto, *Gazz.*, 1900, **30**, i, 296; van Laar, *Chem. Weekbl.*, 1905, **2**, 223; *Proc. K. Akad. Wetens. Amsterdam*, 1905, **8**, 33, 144, 699; Centnerszwer and Zoppi, *Z. phys. Chem.*, 1906, **54**, 689; Centnerszwer, *ibid.*, 1907, **61**, 356; Wilip, *Acta Comment. Univ. Dorpatensis*, 1924, **6** A, No. 2; Booth and Willson, *J.A.C.S.*, 1935, **57**, 2280 (A and BF_3); Wiebe and Gaddy, *J.A.C.S.*, 1937, **59**, 1984 (H_2+NH_3); Mayfield, *Ind. Eng. Chem.*, 1942, **34**, 843 (hydrocarbons); Diepen and Scheffer, *J.A.C.S.*, 1948, **70**, 4081, 4085.

[4] *Compt. Rend.*, 1881, **92**, 901; cf. Galitzine, *loc. cit.*; Ansdell's experiments with CO_2 and HCl did not agree with it.

[5] *Proc. Roy. Soc.*, 1880, **30**, 538.

[6] *Arch. Néerl.*, 1893, **26**, 354; *Phil. Mag.*, 1895, **40**, 173; 1897, **44**, 174; 1902, **4**, 116.

[7] Young, "Stoichiometry," 1918, 269; Galitzine, *Ann. Phys.*, 1890, **41** 588, thought it held better for liquids than for gases.

tion of the results from this point of view would be interesting, especially a comparison with vapour-pressure data. It should be noted, however, that the critical phenomena for mixtures are more complicated than those of pure substances, and that a mixture has, in theory, no single critical temperature but generally two (see reference 3 on p. 658). The critical temperatures of oxygen and nitrogen, for example, are −118° and −146°, respectively, and the calculated critical temperature of air is −140·8°. Although, in theory, air has no single critical temperature, the observed value is between −140° and −141°.

Merzlin [1] thought the Strauss-Pawlewski rule was a limiting form; a theory based on Stakhorsky's [2] surface-tension equation for mixtures indicated that the critical temperature-composition curve may not be straight, as the rule predicts, but convex or concave to the composition axis.

The *critical pressures* of mixtures have been investigated.[3] The increase in critical pressure is proportional to concentration, the relative lowering of vapour-pressure is zero at the critical point, and the critical part of the boundary curve is given by $p_c = p_{0c} + A(t_c - t_{0c})$, where p_0, t_0 refer to the solvent and A is the quotient of the molecular elevation of critical pressure and the molecular elevation of critical temperature.

Hannay and Hogarth [4] found that several solutions (KI, KBr, $CaCl_2$ in alcohol; $FeCl_3$ in ether; S in CS_2) remained homogeneous above the critical temperature of the solvent. No change of colour of a solution of cobalt chloride in alcohol could be observed on passing through the critical point. Thus, sparingly volatile solids are soluble in gases. Cailletet and Colardeau [5] found that iodine is soluble in *liquid* CO_2 and in the *vapour* above the critical temperature, and similar results were found by other experimenters.

Investigations by Centnerszwer,[6] and Tyrer,[7] on the same subject gave the following results. Centnerszwer found that the critical temperature depends on the mode of filling of the tube, that the solutes raised the critical temperature of the solvent in proportion to the concentration, and the " molecular elevation of critical temperature " was independent of the solute but depended on the solvent. The critical temperature falls with increasing filling of the tube,

[1] *J. Gen. Chem. U.S.S.R.*, 1935, **5**, 1073.

[2] *Z. Elektrochem.*, 1928, **34**, 111; 1929, **35**, 185; see § 19.VIII G, Vol. II.

[3] Zawidski and Centnerszwer, *Ann. Phys.*, 1905, **19**, 426; Centnerszwer and Pakalneet. *Z. phys. Chem.*, 1906, **55**, 303; Centnerszwer and Kalnin, *ibid.*, 1907, **60**, 441.

[4] *Proc. Roy. Soc.*, 1879, **29**, 324; 1880, **30**, 178, 484; *Chem. News*, 1879, **40**, 256; 1880, **41**, 103.

[5] *Compt. Rend.*, 1889, **108**, 1280; *Ann. Chim.*, 1889, **18**, 269; cf. Ramsay, *Proc. Roy. Soc.*, 1880, **30**, 323; *Phil. Mag.*, 1883, **16**, 118; Cailletet and Hautefeuille, *Compt. Rend.*, 1881, **92**, 840; Jamin, *ibid.*, 1883, **96**, 1448; 1883, **97**, 10; Villard, *ibid.*, 1895, **120**, 182; *J. de Phys.*, 1894, **3**, 441; 1896, **5**, 453; *Ann. Chim.*, 1897, **11**, 289; *Z. phys. Chem.*, 1897, **23**, 373; *Chem. News*, 1898, **78**, 297, 309; Schiller, *Ann. Phys.*, 1894, **53**, 396; 1897, **60**, 755; Pictet, *Compt. Rend.*, 1895, **120**, 43, 64; Pictet and Altschul, *Z. phys. Chem.*, 1895, **16**, 26; Altschul, *Z. kompr. Gase*, 1898, **1**, 207; Seitz, *ibid.*, 1899, **2**, 75; Levi-Bianchini, *Atti R. Accad. Lincei*, 1904, **13**, ii, 174; Bertrand and Lecarme, *Compt. Rend.*, 1905, **141**, 320; Raveau, *ibid.*, 1905, **141**, 348; Friedrichs, *Z. anorg. Chem.*, 1913, **84**, 373; Rassow, *Dissert.*, Berlin, 1920; *Z. anorg. Chem.*, 1920, **114**, 117.

[6] *Z. phys. Chem.*, 1903, **46**, 427; 1907, **61**, 356; 1909, **69**, 81; Centnerszwer and Zoppi, *ibid.*, 1906, **54**, 688; Centnerszwer and Kalnin, *ibid.*, 1907, **60**, 441; Centnerszwer and Tetelow, *Z. Elektrochem.*, 1903, **9**, 799; Swietoslawski and Pieszczek, *Bull. Acad. Polon.*, 1937 A, 72; Holder and Maass, *Canad. J. Res.*, 1940, **18** B, 293: Walton and Thomas, *Nature*, 1947, **157**, 232.

[7] *J.C.S.*, 1910, **97**, 621.

whilst with the pure solvent it reaches a maximum. The results agreed with Caubet's theory [1] of binary mixtures.

Tyrer found that the solubility in the vapour is a function of the concentration of the solvent, decreasing considerably when the meniscus disappears, and appreciably just below the critical temperature, when the coefficient of expansion increases. The solubility in the vapour decreases with rise of temperature, when complexes with the solvent are presumably broken down.

Schröer [2] found that the gas phase contains very little salt when the critical point is reached unless the material is well stirred. The relation between the elevation of critical temperature and molar concentration x was found to be $\Delta T_c = x^{1/n} + \text{const.}$, where n is a constant. The temperature-density curve is discontinuous and shows a part independent of density, so that there is a critical zone rather than a critical point.

§ 13. Liquefaction of Gas Mixtures

The phenomena observed in the liquefaction of a mixture of two gases [3] by pressure are much more complicated than those for a single gas. A mixture of 1 vol. of air and 9 vols. of carbon dioxide at 2° C. begins to liquefy at 72 atm. pressure, but at higher pressures at this temperature the liquid diminishes, and disappears again at 149 atm. pressure; liquid does not appear again however high the pressure is taken. On plotting the pressures for the appearance and disappearance of liquid against the temperature the *dew curve* BKCA (Fig. 15.VII B) is obtained. For each temperature, e.g. T_1, below T_0, there are two pressures, p_1 and p_1', between which gas and liquid are present. At T_0 there is only one phase and the point K corresponds with the critical point for a pure substance. Above T_0 no condensation occurs at any pressure.

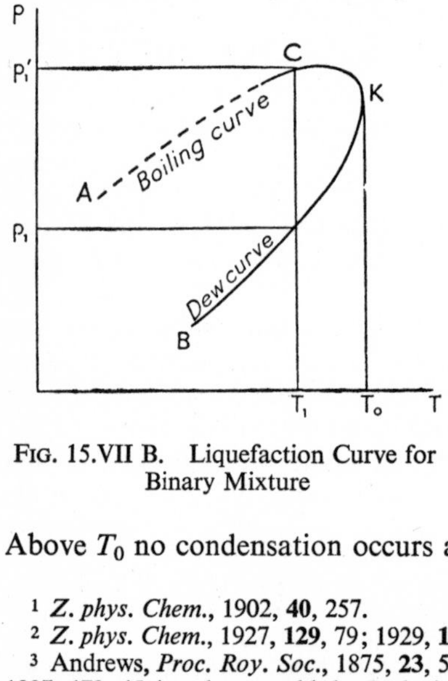

FIG. 15.VII B. Liquefaction Curve for Binary Mixture

[1] *Z. phys. Chem.*, 1902, **40**, 257.

[2] *Z. phys. Chem.*, 1927, **129**, 79; 1929, **142**, 365; Des Coudres, *Ann. Phys.*, 1924, **73**, 289.

[3] Andrews, *Proc. Roy. Soc.*, 1875, **23**, 514; *Phil. Mag.*, 1876, **1**, 78 (CO_2+N_2); *Phil. Trans.*, 1887, **178**, 45 (posthum. publ. by Stokes); *Proc. Roy. Soc. Edin.*, 1899, **30**, 1 (posthum. publ. by Knott); Cailletet, *Compt. Rend.*, 1880, **90**, 210; *J. de Phys.*, 1880, **9**, 192; Hautefeuille and Chappuis, *Compt. Rend.*, 1880, **91**, 815; Cailletet and Hautefeuille, *ibid.*, 1881, **92**, 901; Jamin, *J. de Phys.*, 1883, **2**, 389; Duhem, *J. de Phys.*, 1888, **7**, 198; *Trav. et Mém. Fac. Lille*, 1893, **3**, Nos. 11, 12, 13; "Traité de Mécanique Chimique," 1899, **4**, 61; *J. Phys. Chem.*, 1901, **5**, 91; van der Waals, *Z. phys. Chem.*, 1890, **5**, 133; *Arch. Néerl.*, 1891, **24**, 1; 1897, **30**, 266, 278; "Continuität," Leipzig, 1900, **2**, 112; Kuenen, *Arch. Néerl.*, 1893, **26**, 354; 1900, **5**, 306; *Z. phys. Chem.*, 1893, **11**, 38; 1902, **41**, 43; *J. Phys. Chem.*, 1896–7, **1**, 273; *Phil. Mag.*, 1895, **40**, 173; 1897, **44**, 174; 1902, **4**, 116; *Z. kompr. Gase*, 1898, **1**, 153; Villard, *Ann. Chim.*, 1897, **10**, 387; Verschaffelt, *Proc. K. Akad. Wetens. Amsterdam*, 1898–9, **1**, 288, 323; *Comm. Leiden*, **45**, **47**; *Arch. Néerl.*, 1900, **5**, 644; Hartman, *ibid.*, 1900, **5**, 636; *Proc. K. Akad. Wetens. Amsterdam*, 1900–1, **3**, 66; *Comm. Leiden*, **56**; Caubet, *Compt. Rend.*, 1900, **130**, 167, 828; 1900, **131**, 108, 1200; 1901, **132**, 128; *Z. phys. Chem.*, 1901, **37**, 639; 1902, **40**, 257; 1903, **41**, 115; 1904, **49**, 101; Saurel, *J. Phys. Chem.*, 1901, **5**, 179; Centnerszwer and Zoppi, *Z. phys. Chem.*, 1906, **54**, 689; Kuenen, "Theorie der Verdampfung und Verflüssigung von Gemischen," Leipzig, 1906, 59 f., 108, 216 f.; Bradley, Browne, and Hale, *Phys. Rev.*, 1908, **26**, 470; 1908, **27**, 90; Ostwald, "Lehrbuch der allgemeinen Chemie," 1911, **2**, ii, 652; Kuenen

If T_1 corresponds with the maximum C on the curve, then below T_1 normal condensation (liquefaction) occurs on raising the pressure. Between T_1 and T_0 both normal and *retrograde condensation* (disappearance of liquid with increased pressure) occur. AC is the *boiling curve* and above this the system is liquid. K is called a *plait point*.

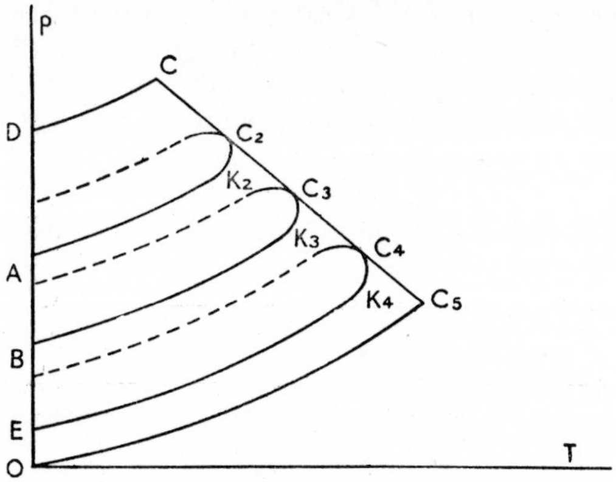

FIG. 16.VII B. Plait-Points in Liquefaction of a Binary Mixture

These phenomena occur only with certain mixtures, and with others outside this range the dew curves are normal. In Fig. 16.VII B, DC and OC_5 represent the curves for these limiting mixtures. The line joining the plait points C_2, C_3, C_4 for various mixtures is the *plait-point curve*. The border curves (full and dotted) gradually narrow as they approach the normal vapour-pressure curves DC and OC_5.

At the plait point the plait point curve seems to form a double cusp of the

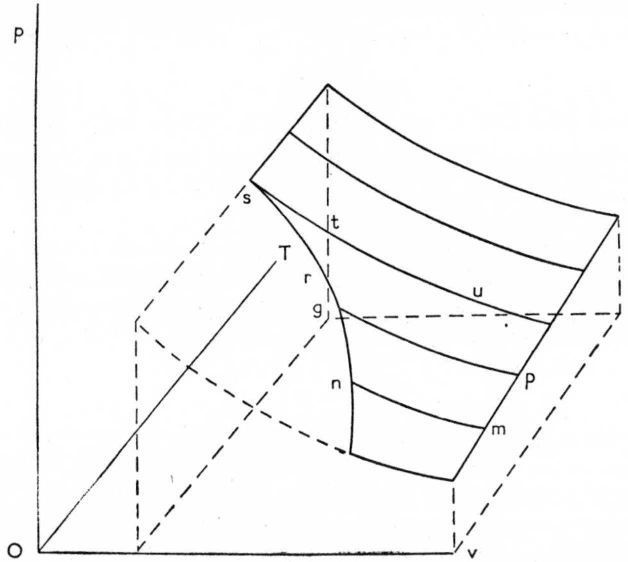

FIG. 17.VII B. Three-dimensional Representation of Liquefaction Curves for a Binary Mixture

second species (§ 59.I). Whether AC_3K_3B really forms a continuous curve so that CC_5 is a tangent to it at C_3, or separate lines forming a spinode or cusp with CC_5 at C_3, has been discussed.

and Clark, *Proc. K. Akad. Wetens. Amsterdam*, 1917, **19**, 1088 (*Comm. Leiden*, **150***b*); Kuenen, Verschoyle, and Van Urk, *ibid.*, 1922, **26**, 49 (*Comm. Leiden*, **161**); Booth and Carter, *J. Phys. Chim.*, 1930, **34**, 2801 (bibl.); Bošnjaković, "Technische Thermodynamik," II Teil, Dresden and Leipzig, 1937; Olds, Sage, and Lacy, *Ind. Eng. Chem.*, 1942, **34**, 1008 (CH_4+i-C_4H_{10}).

The phenomena should be represented in a three-dimensional (p, v, T) diagram (Fig. 17.VII B). The vapour pressures for a given temperature are shown by the curves *mn*, *pg*, etc., and on *mn* liquefaction begins at *n*, on *pg* at the higher pressure *g*. To the right of *ngrs* is gas, to the left liquid. If light fell on the figure in the direction *vO* it would cast a shadow on the *pOT* plane which would be the *vapour-pressure curve*, and the lowest temperature for which the pressure-volume curve *ut* is not cut by *ngrs* is the *critical temperature.*

Some results by Caubet for mixtures of sulphur dioxide and carbon dioxide are given in the table. The sign * denotes the first dew point (1er *point de rosée*), ** the second dew point (2e *point de rosée*).

70°		72°		74·2°	
p atm.	vol. of liq.	*p* atm.	vol. of liq.	*p* atm.	vol. of liq.
61·0	0	60·0	0	75·0	0
66·2	*	70·0	*	78·2	*
69·4	0·066	74·5	0·066	80·6	0·066
77·0	0·164	84·8	0·164	83·4	0·099
83·4	0·250	87·8	0·184	86·2	0·066
87·8	0·428	89·6	0·099	88·0	**
89·6	0·263	89·8	**	93·0	0
90·0	**	95·6	0	105·0	0
91·0	0	105·0	0	—	—
105·0	0	—	—	—	—

C. PRESSURE-VOLUME-TEMPERATURE RELATIONS OF GASES. CHARACTERISTIC EQUATIONS

§ 1. Van der Waals's Equation

So far, consideration has mostly been given to so-called *ideal* (or *perfect*) *gases*, the molecules of which are assumed to be very small compared with the volume of the gas, and between the molecules of which there are supposed to be no forces of attraction and repulsion. The behaviour of such a gas is represented by the equation (§ 21.VII A):

$$pV=RT \quad (1)$$

When a gas below its critical temperature is compressed, it is reduced to a liquid, the volume of which, although much smaller than that of the gas, is finite. Since the liquid volume changes only slightly for a large increase in pressure, it may be assumed that the molecules in the liquid are fairly closely packed and exert large repulsive forces when an attempt is made to bring them closer together. The liquefaction shows that there must also be attractive forces between the molecules, which increase as the volume of the gas (i.e. the distance between its molecules) is reduced.

The very small compressibility of the liquid might be explained by assuming that the molecules are hard elastic spheres, the repulsive force not being operative until the molecules are in contact, and as a first approximation it may be postulated that: (i) the molecules in the gas occupy a small but finite fraction of the total volume, and (ii) there are forces of attraction between the molecules which increase when the distance between them is reduced, i.e. when the volume of the gas is decreased.

The effect of the volume occupied by the molecules in increasing the pressure was recognised by Bernoulli [1] in 1738, in his deduction of Boyle's law from the kinetic theory (§ 1.III). Rankine [2] in 1854 proposed an equation equivalent to:

$$(p+a/V^2T)V=RT \quad \ldots \ldots \quad (2)$$

and Recknagel [3] in 1871 attempted to allow for molecular attraction by assuming that each molecular encounter leads to a temporary retardation of rectilinear motion, and the collision rate on the walls is reduced in proportion to the density; he thus found the equation:

$$pV=RT(1-B/V) \quad \ldots \ldots \quad (3)$$

where B is a function of temperature.

Clausius [4] in 1857 correctly pointed out the two causes for the deviation from Boyle's law, but did not represent them by an equation. This was done by Hirn [5] in 1863, who proposed the equation:

$$p(V-\psi)=RT \quad \ldots \ldots \quad (4)$$

in which he (incorrectly) supposed the constant ψ (*co-volume*) was equal to the "sum of the volumes of all the atoms" (it is a small multiple of this). Hirn also assumed that the molecules attract one another and that this is equivalent to the addition of a term r, "the sum of the internal actions," to the external pressure:

$$(p+r)(V-\psi)=RT \quad \ldots \ldots \quad (5)$$

He supposed that r is an inverse volume function, decreasing rapidly when the volume increases.

None of these early attempts to correct the ideal gas equation gave results of importance. Starting from the same assumptions, J. D. van der Waals [6] in 1873, in what Clausius [4] called "a very interesting paper," deduced the famous equation for an imperfect gas:

$$(p+a/V^2)(V-b)=RT \quad \ldots \ldots \quad (6)$$

[1] "Hydrodynamica," Strasburg, 1738, 200 f.; Du Bois Reymond, *Ann. Phys.*, 1859, **107**, 490; this was emphasised again by Lomonossov, *Novi Comment. Acad. Petropol.*, 1747–8, **1**, 230, 307 (publ. in 1750); Ostwald's *Klassiker*, 1910, **178**; Smith, *J.A.C.S.*, 1912, **34**, 109.

[2] Note to paper by Joule and Thomson, *Phil. Trans.*, 1854, **144**, 336; cf. *ibid.*, 1862, **152**, 579.

[3] *Ann. Phys.*, 1871, *Ergänzbd.* **5**, 563; 1872, **145**, 469; see Clausius, *ibid.*, 1880, **9**, 337; J. J. Thomson, "Watts' Dictionary of Chemistry," edit. Morley and Muir, 1890, **1**, 88: "the collision between two molecules of a gas is the formation and breaking up of a molecular aggregation . . . the time which elapses between the successive aggregations is much smaller in the case of a gas than in that of the liquid or solid."

[4] *Ann. Phys.*, 1857, **100**, 353; 1880, **9**, 337.

[5] *Cosmos* (Paris), 1863, **22**, 283, 413; a "separate" of Hirn's paper is bound in at the end of the second volume of his "Theorie Mécanique de la Chaleur," with a separate title-page dated Paris, 1863, and with the statement "Extrait du Cosmos," in the Cambridge University Library copy. The equation is dealt with on pp. 39 f., especially p. 49, of the reprint. The actual equation given is $(R+P)(V-\psi)=\Theta$. See also Hirn, *Ann. Chim.*, 1867, **10**, 32; 1867, **11**, 5; Dupré, *ibid.*, 1864, **3**, 76; Roth, *Ann. Phys.*, 1880, **11**, 1; Moutier, *Compt. Rend.*, 1867, **64**, 653; 1868, **66**, 344, 606; *Phil. Mag.*, 1868, **35**, 466 (relation of r to composition); Budde, *J. prakt. Chem.*, 1874, **9**, 30.

[6] "Over de continuïteit van den gas- en vloeistoftoestand" (on the continuity of the gaseous and liquid state), *Dissert.*, Leiden, 1873; "Die Continuität des gasförmigen und flüssigen Zustandes," transl. Roth, Leipzig, 1881; Engl. transl. Threlfall and Adair, *Physical Memoirs* (Phys. Soc., Taylor and Francis), 1890, **1**, iii, 333; 2nd enlarged German edit., 2 vols., Leipzig, 1899–1900; "La Continuité des États gazeux et liquide," transl. Dommer and Pomey, Paris, 1896; Kuenen, "Die Zustandsgleichung der Gase und Flüssigkeiten," Brunswick, 1907; "Die Eigenschafte der Gase," 1919; van der Waals, "Die Zustandsgleichung," Nobel lecture, Leipzig, 1911; "Weiteres zur Zustandsgleichung," Leipzig, 1913; the best account of

where a and b are constants taking account of the molecular attractions and the finite size of the molecules, respectively. (Actually, he wrote $(p+a/v^2)(v-b)=(1+a)(1-b)(1+\alpha t)$: see § 3). The main interest of the investigation (as the title of the Dissertation shows) was not so much to find an equation representing the behaviour of imperfect gases as one which includes a description of critical phenomena.

Van der Waals amplified Hirn's equation (5) by showing that (i) ψ is probably *four* times the volume occupied by the molecules, and (ii) r is inversely proportional to the square of the volume, $r=a/V^2$, where a is a constant. This form agrees with an attractive force inversely proportional to the fourth power of the distance (as proposed by Sutherland.)[1] For, the internal work of expansion is $\int(a/V^2)\mathrm{d}V=-a/V+\text{const.}=-a'/r^3+\text{const.}$, where r is here the average distance between the molecules, and this is equal to the increase in potential energy W. But the force is equal to $-\mathrm{d}W/\mathrm{d}r=3a'/r^4$.

The most important features of van der Waals's equation are (i) that it applies also to the liquid state, with the same constants a and b, and (ii) that it gives an account of the critical point. It is, however, only an approximate equation, and, as van der Waals himself pointed out, it deviates more and more from the experimental results as the pressure increases. In spite of its defects it was a very great advance[2] in the theory of gases, and still has a very important practical value. For quick and reasonably accurate orientation in situations where experimental data are lacking, and in giving a qualitative survey of the main properties of gases and liquids, the equation is indispensable, and is likely to remain so. Whether or not it gives a correct picture of the forces acting in a gas is quite another matter, which will receive attention later.[3]

§ 2. Deduction of van der Waals's Equation

The deduction of the equation on a statical basis is simple.[4] Molecules with a finite diameter occupy part of the space available for translatory motion, and hence collide more often with the walls of a container than if they were mere

the equation is given by Onnes and Keesom, Die Zustandsgleichung, *Comm. Leiden*, 1912, **11**, Suppl. **23**, reproducing " Enzykl. d. math. Wiss.," 1912, **5**, i, Heft 5, pp. 615–945; see Guye, *Arch. Sci. Phys. Nat.*, 1889, **22**, 540; Jeans, *J.C.S.*, 1923, **123**, 3398.

[1] Sutherland, *Phil. Mag.*, 1886, **22**, 81; Mellor, *ibid.*, 1902, **3**, 423; Chatley, *Proc. Phys. Soc.*, 1918, **30**, 151; Porter, *Trans. Faraday Soc.*, 1928, **24**, 108; the criticism by Fowler, *Phil. Mag.*, 1922, **43**, 785, that the law of variation only affects the form of a as a function of temperature had already been pointed out by Kleeman, *ibid.*, 1912, **23**, 656; correcting Tyrer *ibid.* 1912, **23**, 101.

[2] According to Thiesen, *Ann. Phys.*, 1897, **63**, 329, van der Waals's equation first became well known after the full abstract in *Ann. Phys. Beibl.*, 1877, **1**, 13–21. There is, however, a long critical account of it by Maxwell in *Nature*, 1874, **10**, 477.

[3] Although Keyes, *J.A.C.S.*, 1929, **51**, 3684, correctly says that the theory of real gases is " a field where an extraordinary amount of illusory theory has been written," it is also one in which the pure mathematician has probably produced less of practical value in proportion to his efforts than any other. A sensible survey of this field in relation to more modern theory is given by Keyes and Felsing, *J.A.C.S.*, 1919, **41**, 589. Smoluchowski (no mean mathematician), *Ann. Phys.*, 1915, **48**, 1098, considered that the " intuitive " method used by van der Waals and his school was often physically more correct than a purely mathematical method, and had the advantage of guarding against gross errors to which the latter was (and is) liable if followed without close relation to the physical results. Several recent mathematical papers have later been followed by admissions of error, and the non-mathematical reader may be deceived by a machinery of rigour which is illusory.

[4] Edser, " Heat for Advanced Students," 1899, 307; Nernst, " Theoretical Chemistry," 1911, 208; Eucken, " Lehrbuch der chemischen Physik," 1930, 175; best of all, Boltzmann, " Vorlesungen über Gastheorie," 1898, **2**, 1 f.; see the rather refined criticism by Fowler, " Statistical Mechanics," Cambridge, 1929, 200 (where other errors are introduced).

points. The pressure is thus *greater* than the ideal pressure. This could be achieved by keeping the pressure ideal but reducing the actual volume V to a smaller value $(V-b)$, where b is a volume correction depending on the molecular size.

A second effect, which makes the observed pressure *smaller* than the ideal pressure, is the attraction between the molecules. A molecule in the interior of the gas is pulled equally in all directions, but one on the surface experiences an unbalanced attraction towards the interior, which decreases its momentum on striking the wall, and hence lowers the pressure. The inward force on unit area of the surface will be proportional to the number of molecules per $cm.^2$ on the surface of the gas, which is proportional to the density ρ, and to the number of molecules per $cm.^3$ in the body of the gas, which is also proportional to ρ; hence the cohesive attraction is proportional to the square of the density,[1] and the net force per $cm.^2$, or the pressure on the wall, is reduced from the ideal value to $p_{id}-a\rho^2$, where a is a constant. The pressure which the gas would exert in the ideal state is thus $p_{obs}+a\rho^2$. The product $(p+a\rho^2)(V-b)$ will therefore correspond with the ideal product $p_{id}V_{id}$, i.e. to RT/M, if unit mass of gas is taken and M=mol. wt. Since $\rho=1/v$ (v=specific vol.):

$$(p+a/v^2)(v-b)=RT/M.$$

By suitable adjustment of the constants a and b, the equation will apply to 1 mol, when:

$$(p+a/V^2)(V-b)=RT.$$

A fuller deduction is achieved by some refinement of detail. The following deduction is based on that given by Boltzmann.[2] It may be noted that for large values of V (small pressures) van der Waals's equation passes into the ideal gas equation as a limiting case, since a/V^2 and b are then negligible, and all characteristic equations for gases in normal conditions must have this property. They should also, if they are to take account of liquefaction, reproduce the critical phenomena, and van der Waals's equation does this at least semi-quantitatively.

Consider a volume V of gas containing N spherical molecules of *diameter* σ, and draw a sphere of *radius* σ round the centre of each molecule. The minimum distance between the molecular centres is σ, so that the centre of any molecule A cannot lie inside the spheres surrounding any of the $N-1$ other molecules B, C, D . . . . The free space available to A is:

$$V-\tfrac{4}{3}(N-1)\pi\sigma^3 \simeq V-\tfrac{4}{3}N\pi\sigma^3 \qquad (1)$$

The probability of finding the centre of A in a specified volume element dV is equal to the ratio of dV to the total available space:

$$dV/(V-\tfrac{4}{3}N\pi\sigma^3) \qquad (2)$$

1 Bakker, *J. Chim. Phys.*, 1906, **4**, 67, states that Sarrau, in the French translation of van der Waals's " Continuity," says this result is in works of Cauchy and Poisson.

2 " Gastheorie," 1898, **2**, 1 f.; Jeans, " Kinetic Theory of Gases," 1940, 64, whose simplified treatment is followed here. Other deductions: Lorentz, *Ann. Phys.*, 1881, **12**, 127; Galitzine, *Z. phys. Chem.*, 1889, **4**, 417; Jäger, *Wien Ber.*, 1896, **105**, II A, 15; van der Waals, *Proc. K. Akad. Wetens. Amsterdam*, 1898, **1**, 138, 468; 1900–01, **3**, 515, 571, 643; *Z. phys. Chem.*, 1899, **30**, 157; 1901, **38**, 257; Lorentz, *Verslag. K. Akad. Wetens. Amsterdam*, 1901, **9**, 572; Happel, *Phys. Z.*, 1909, **10**, 687; Nabl, *Wien Ber.*, 1911, **120**, II A, 851; Wagner, *Ann. Phys.*, 1914, **45**, 1169; Smoluchowski, *ibid.*, 1915, **48**, 1098; Holm, *ibid.*, 1916, **51**, 768 (bibl.); Shaha and Basu, *Phil. Mag.*, 1918, **36**, 199; Haag, *Compt. Rend.*, 1923, **176**, 372; Benumof, *Amer. J. Phys.*, 1948, **16**, 249. It should be noted that van der Waals assumed no static forces between the gas molecules and the wall of the container; this was taken into account by Nabl.

A molecule moving normal to the wall collides with it if, at the beginning of a time interval dt within which it is supposed to undergo collision, its centre lies in a small volume $udAdt$, where u is the normal velocity and dA the element of surface of the wall on which collision occurs. This small volume is now identified with dV. It may lie either inside or outside one of the $N-1$ spheres of radius σ.

Suppose that each sphere is divided into two hemispheres by a plane parallel to the wall of the container. The volume dV cannot be further than $\frac{1}{2}\sigma$ from the wall and, as it cannot lie inside one of the spheres if there is to be a collision, it must lie in the free volume $V-\frac{2}{3}(N-1)\pi\sigma^3 \simeq V-\frac{2}{3}N\pi\sigma^3$ between the nearer hemispheres. The probability that it does so is:

$$(V-\tfrac{2}{3}N\pi\sigma^3)/V \quad . \quad . \quad . \quad . \quad . \quad . \quad . \quad . \quad . \quad (3)$$

and the probability of a collision within the interval dt is, from (2):

$$NdV/(V-\tfrac{4}{3}N\pi\sigma^3) \quad . \quad . \quad . \quad . \quad . \quad . \quad . \quad . \quad . \quad (4)$$

The total probability of a collision is the product of (3) and (4):

$$(NdV/V)[(V-b)/(V-2b)] \quad . \quad . \quad . \quad . \quad . \quad . \quad . \quad . \quad (5)$$

where

$$b=\tfrac{2}{3}N\pi\sigma^3 \quad . \quad . \quad . \quad . \quad . \quad . \quad . \quad . \quad . \quad . \quad (6)$$

Since the total volume occupied by the molecules is $\frac{4}{3}N\pi(\sigma/2)^3=\frac{1}{6}N\pi\sigma^3$, it follows from (6) that the constant b is equal to four times [1] this volume. Since b is small compared with V, the term $(b/V)^2$ can be neglected, and hence by division of (5) the total probability of a collision is found to be:

$$NdV/(V-b) \quad . \quad . \quad . \quad . \quad . \quad . \quad . \quad . \quad . \quad (7)$$

If the molecules occupied no volume this expression would be NdV/V, so that the effect of the finite size of the molecules is to replace the volume V by $(V-b)$, where b is four times the volume of the molecules. The effect of molecular size alone is taken into account in the equation:

$$p(V-b)=RT \quad \text{or} \quad pV \simeq RT(1+b/V) \quad . \quad . \quad . \quad . \quad (8)$$

The correction for intermolecular attraction was deduced by van der Waals by replacing the complicated molecular force field by a simple cohesional force, as in Laplace's theory of liquids (see § 20.VIII G, Vol. II), which force is appreciable only over a very small distance. Each molecule is assumed to be surrounded by an imaginary sphere, outside which the molecules exert no appreciable force on the one at the centre. When the molecule is in the body of the gas, the other molecules fill this sphere of action equally in all directions and their effects thus cancel out, since every molecule has an equidistant partner on an axis of the sphere on the other side of the centre. When the molecule is as near the wall as possible, however, only the other molecules in the hemisphere resting on that side of the wall are acting, and their effect is equivalent to a force

[1] According to O. E. Meyer, "Kinetic Theory of Gases," 1899, 326, 423, b is $4\sqrt{2}$ times the actual volume of the molecules; Jäger, in Winkelmann, "Handbuch der Physik," 1906, **3**, 703; cf. van der Waals, *Arch. Néerl.*, 1877, **12**, 201, 217; *Verslag. K. Akad. Wetens. Amsterdam*, 1898, **7**, 160, 408, 477; *Z. phys. Chem.*, 1899, **30**, 157 (abstr.); *Proc. K. Akad. Wetens. Amsterdam*, 1913, **15**, 903, 971, 1131; republished as "Weiteres zur Zustandsgleichung," Leipzig, 1913; van Laar, *Proc. K. Akad. Wetens. Amsterdam*, 1914, **16**, 44, 808; 1914, **17**, 451; "Die Zustandsgleichung von Gasen und Flüssigkeiten," Leipzig, 1924, 2. On the mean free path and the b correction, see Korteweg, *Arch. Néerl.*, 1877, **12**, 241, 254; Kohnstamm, *Proc. K. Akad. Wetens. Amsterdam*, 1904, **6**, 787, 794; *J. Chim. Phys.*, 1905, **3**, 161.

directed from the wall towards the interior of the gas, and at right angles to the wall, the force components parallel to the wall cancelling, since each has an equal and opposite partner. The whole effect is thus equivalent to a static inward pull on the layer of gas in contact with the wall, tending to drag it away, and hence reducing its pressure on the wall. This force will be proportional to the number of molecules pulled and to the number which pull on each one. Each of these is proportional to the density of the whole gas, and hence the inward force is proportional to the square of the density, or inversely proportional to the square of the volume of a given mass, i.e. to a/V^2, where a is a constant. The actual pressure p on the wall is therefore smaller than the pressure which would be exerted if there were no molecular attraction, and the term a/V^2 must be *added* to the actual (measured) pressure p to get a pressure corresponding with the *ideal* gas:

$$p_{id}=p+a/V^2 \quad \ldots \ldots \ldots \quad (10)$$

This train of argument can be put into the form of multiple integrals without in any way increasing its precision or validity: as Boltzmann [1] said, it would be difficult, by the most subtle considerations, to find a better formula than that which van der Waals arrived at " so to say, by inspiration."

The final equation is, therefore:

$$(p+a/V^2)(V-b)=RT \quad \ldots \ldots \ldots \quad (11)$$

$$\text{or} \quad p+a/V^2=RT/(V-b) \quad \ldots \ldots \ldots \quad (11a)$$

A deduction of van der Waals's equation by statistical methods was given by Ornstein [2] and by Shaha and Basu.[3]

It could be expected that the deduction of van der Waals's equation would be criticized; this happened at the time of its publication,[4] and still continues. It is noteworthy, however, that the utility of the equation and the general truth of its physical bases have always been recognised by physical chemists and physicists of the first rank (Ostwald, van't Hoff, Nernst, T. W. Richards, Rayleigh, Boltzmann, Jeans, etc.). The equation has led to more experimental research (in the properties of fluids) than any other generalisation put forward in the last century, and all the other characteristic equations which have any practical interest go back to the same foundations.

It is shown later (§ 7) that $b=v_c/3$ where v_c=critical volume, and if this is in cm.^{3} and N_L=no. of molecules per cm.^{3} (Loschmidt's number), $b=v_c/3=4N_L(4\pi/3)(\sigma/2)^3$, from which the molecular diameter σ can be calculated. This value will be somewhat different from the value σ_0, corresponding with the zero value of the potential-energy curve (§ 17.IV), which is found from the second virial coefficient on the assumption of resonance forces (§ 45), and also from the value σ_m corresponding with the distance for minimum potential energy for molecules in a crystal lattice. The latter is given, for cubic close-packing, by $(4\pi/3)(\sigma_m/2)^3=0{\cdot}74V_m/N$, where V_m is the molar volume and N is Avogadro's

[1] " Gastheorie," 1898, **2**, 155.

[2] *Proc. K. Akad. Wetens. Amsterdam*, 1912, **14**, 853; *Arch. Néerl.*, 1914, **3**, 179 (Gibbs statistics).

[3] *Phil. Mag.*, 1918, **36**, 199 (from entropy and probability: $S=k \ln W+C$; § 5.IV); Waldmann, *Physica*, 1937, **4**, 1117; Hill, *J. Chem. Educ.*, 1948, **25**, 347.

[4] See Maxwell, *Nature*, 1874, **10**, 477; Tait, *ibid.*, 1891, **44**, 546, 627; 1892, **45**, 199 (criticism); defended by Rayleigh, *ibid.*, 1891, **44**, 499, 597; 1892, **45**, 80; Korteweg, *ibid.*, 1892, **45**, 152, 277; Kohnstamm, *J. Chim. Phys.*, 1905, **3**, 161, 170, 665; 1906, **4**, 102; Metcalf, *J. Phys. Chem.*, 1915, **19**, 705.

number, 0·74 being the space-filling factor. It is found[1] that $\sigma<\sigma_0<\sigma_m$. In A. (10^{-8} cm.):

	He	H_2	O_2	CO_2	Cl_2	CH_4	CCl_4	C_6H_6
$r=\frac{1}{2}\sigma$ ...	2·5	2·6	2·8	3·2	3·4	3·6	3·8	4·1
$r_0=\frac{1}{2}\sigma_0$ ...	2·6	3·5	3·2	3·7	—	—	—	—
$r_m=\frac{1}{2}\sigma_m$ ...	4·0	4·0	3·9	4·1	3·7	4·2	5·4	<5·3

Jablczyński[2] calculated the molecular radii of CO_2, C_2H_4, O_2, N_2, CO, and H_2 on the assumption that b is four times the actual volume of the molecules, and found results almost identical with those calculated by Sutherland from the viscosities (§ 5.VII F). On the assumption that, with diatomic gases, the two atoms rotate so rapidly that they fill the molecular sphere, the radii of the atoms O, N, and H were calculated as half the radii of the molecules O_2, N_2, and H_2, and agreed with the X-ray values. The radius of the CO molecule was successfully calculated from the atomic radii. At very high pressures or low temperatures the molecular volumes decrease, even below the b-values. Broughall[3] calculated the molecular diameter from $\sigma=(3b)^{1/3}/2\pi N_L$, where N_L was taken as $2{\cdot}75\times10^{19}$ at S.T.P.

A more detailed deduction of van der Waals's equation by the method sketched above leads to the equations:[4]

$$pv=RT[1+b/v+\tfrac{5}{8}(b/v)^2+\ldots] \qquad (12)$$

$$(p+a/v^2)v=RT[1+b/v+\alpha_1(b/v)^2+\alpha_2(b/v)^3+\ldots] \qquad (13)$$

where a is assumed to be constant (as before), b is four times the volume of the molecules (assumed spherical), and $\alpha_1, \alpha_2, \ldots$, are new constants: $\alpha_1=5/8=0{\cdot}625$, and $\alpha_2=0{\cdot}2869$. Equation (13) can be written:

$$\begin{aligned} RT&=(p+a/v^2)v/[1+b/v+\alpha_1(b/v)^2+\alpha_2(b/v)^3+\ldots] \\ &\simeq(p+a/v^2)[v-b+(1-\alpha_1)(b^2/v)+(2\alpha_1-\alpha_2-1)(b^3/v^2)+\ldots] \\ &=(p+a/v^2)\{v-b[1-(1-\alpha_1)(b/v)-(2\alpha_1-\alpha_2-1)(b/v)^2+\ldots]\} \\ &=(p+a/v^2\{v-b[1-0{\cdot}375(b/v)+0{\cdot}037(b/v)^2\ldots]\} \qquad (14) \end{aligned}$$

Hence in van der Waals's equation b is replaced by:

$$b'=b[1-0{\cdot}375(b/v)+0{\cdot}037(b/v)^2] \qquad (15)$$

Equation (14) gives better results above the critical temperature than the simple van der Waals equation.

§ 3. Values of the van der Waals Constants *a* and *b*

The values of the constants a and b depend on the nature of the gas and on the quantity of gas considered.[5] If unit volume of gas is taken as the volume in the

[1] Stuart, "Molekülstruktur," 1934, 33; Kremann and Pestemer, "Zusammenhänge zwischen physikalischen Eigenschaften und chemischer Konstitution," 1937, 26.

[2] *Roczn. Chem.*, 1934, **14**, 10.

[3] *Phil. Mag.*, 1921, **41**, 872.

[4] Jäger, *Wien Ber.*, 1896, **105**, II A, 15, 97; Boltzmann, "Vorlesungen über Gastheorie," 1898, **2**, 170; *Proc. K. Akad. Wetens. Amsterdam*, 1899, **1**, 398; van Laar, *Proc. K. Akad. Wetens. Amsterdam*, 1899, **1**, 273; van der Waals, jr., *ibid.*, 1903, **5**, 487; Happel, *Gött. Nachr.*, 1905, 282; *Ann. Phys.*, 1906, **21**, 342; van der Waals, *Arch. Néerl.*, 1912, **1**, 90; Onnes and Keesom, "Enzykl. d. math. Wiss.," 1912, **5**, i, 747. Happel gave $\alpha_2=0{\cdot}288$. See Kuenen, "Die Eigenschaften der Gase" (Ostwald-Drucker, "Handbuch der allgemeinen Chemie," **3**), Leipzig, 1919, 335.

[5] Rücker, *J.C.S.*, 1888, **53**, 256; Häntzschel, *Ann. Phys.*, 1905, **16**, 565; Kuenen, *ibid.*, 1905, **17**, 189; van Laar, *J. Chim. Phys.*, 1916, **14**, 3; "Die Zustandsgleichung," Leipzig,

ideal state at S.T.P., then if V' is the *ratio* of the given volume V ml. to the unit 22,415 ml., *per mol*, then (11), § 2, becomes:

$$(p+a/V'^2)(V'-b)=T/273{\cdot}1 \quad . \quad . \quad . \quad . \quad . \quad . \quad . \quad (1)$$

These are the so-called "normal units." If (with van der Waals and most physicists) the *actual* volume at S.T.P. is taken as the unit, the equation becomes:

$$(p+a/V''^2)(V''-b)=(1+a)(1-b)T/273{\cdot}1 \quad . \quad . \quad . \quad (2)$$

Values of a and b (mostly calculated from critical constants, as explained in § 7) are given both for formula (1) [1] and for formula (2).[2] Since formula (1) is more convenient, the values in the following abbreviated table are for use in it. Pressures are in atm. and V' is the volume *ratio*, the actual volume being 22,415 V' ml. If $a_1=\alpha a$, $b_1=\beta b$, $R_1=\gamma R$, a and b being the values calculated from (2) and $\boldsymbol{R}$ the ordinary gas constant 82·09 ml. atm./1° C. per mol, then the values of α, β, and γ are as follows: [1]

Units	α	β	γ
ml., mm. Hg	760	1	760
lit., atm.	10^{-6}	10^{-3}	10^{-3}
lit., mm. Hg	$7{\cdot}6\times10^{-5}$	10^{-3}	0·760

	H_2 [3]	O_2	N_2	He	Ne	A	Kr	Xe
$10^5 . a$	49	276	277	6·8	42·2	268	462	816
$10^6 . b$	1188	1441	1747	1050	763	1437	1776	2279

	Cl_2	HCl	CO	CO_2	NH_3	N_2O	NO	H_2S
$10^5 . a$	1294	731	296	716	831	754	267	883
$10^6 . b$	2510	1822	1779	1905	1655	1971	1245	1914

	SO_2	CH_4	C_2H_6	C_2H_4	C_2H_2	$(C_2H_5)_2O$	C_6H_6
$10^5 . a$	1338	449	1074	891	875	3464	3727
$10^6 . b$	2516	1910	2848	2551	2293	6002	5369

An attempt to relate the a values to chemical composition was made by Bose and Bose,[4] and Mathews [5] proposed the formula:

$$a=C(Mn)^{2/3} \quad . \quad . \quad . \quad . \quad . \quad . \quad . \quad . \quad . \quad . \quad (3)$$

where M=mol. wt., n=number of valencies in the molecule, and C is a constant, the same for all normal substances.

The following table[1] refers to equation (2); some values are older and

1924, 4; Lorenz, *Z. phys. Chem.*, 1928, **139**, 1; Partington and Tweedy, "Calculations in Physical Chemistry," 1928, 46.

[1] Guye and Friderich, *Arch. Sci. Phys. Nat.*, 1900, **9**, 505; 1902, **13**, 559; *Z. phys. Chem.*, 1901, **37**, 380; Guye and Mallet, *Compt. Rend.*, 1902, **134**, 168; Winkelmann, "Handbuch der Physik," 1906, **3**, 857 f.; van Laar, *J. Chim. Phys.*, 1916, **14**, 3.

[2] Landolt-Börnstein, "Tabellen," 5th edit., 1923, 253 f.

[3] Schalkwijk, *Verslag. K. Akad. Wetens. Amsterdam*, 1901, **10**, 118.

[4] *Z. phys. Chem.*, 1909, **69**, 52.

[5] *J. Phys. Chem.*, 1913, **17**, 154, 183, 252, 331, 337, 481, 520, 603; 1914, **18**, 474; criticised by van Laar, *Z. anorg. Chem.*, 1918, **104**, 77; reply by Mathews, *Verhl. K. Akad. Wetens. Amsterdam*, 1917, **12**, No. 4, giving a large collection of values of *a*.

probably less accurate than those in the preceding table, but a number of *liquids* are included, and the values then refer primarily to their vapours.

Substance	For initial volume at S.T.P.=1		g.mol.		gram	
	a	b	$a\,.\,10^{-6}$	b	$a\,.\,10^{-1}$	b
Hydrogen	0·00038	0·00088	0·211	19·75	516	9·28
Nitrogen	0·00276	0·00166	1·30	37·1	166	1·32
Oxygen	0·00272	0·00142	1·37	31·8	133	0·994
Argon	0·00256	0·00134	1·30	30·82	81·3	0·758
Krypton	0·00460	0·00177	2·32	39·8	34·3	0·485
Xenon	0·00823	0·00231	4·11	51·6	25·1	0·403
Hydrogen chloride	0·00726	0·00180	3·62	40·2	272	1·10
Carbonic oxide ...	0·00274	0·00168	1·38	37·7	176	1·35
Nitric oxide... ...	0·00257	0·00115	1·29	25·9	143	0·862
Carbon dioxide ...	0·00727	0·00192	3·612	42·84	185·7	0·971
Nitrous oxide ...	0·00750	0·00195	3·72	43·4	192	0·987
Sulphur dioxide ...	0·01345	0·00251	6·61	55·7	161	0·870
Ammonia	0·00810	0·00162	4·01	36·0	1386	2·11
n-Pentane	0·04481	0·000743	20·93	160·7	402·5	2·228
*Iso*pentane	0·03829	0·000653	18·07	141·8	347·6	1·966
Hexane	0·05383	0·000820	24·75	175·9	333·6	2·042
Benzene	0·03984	0·00555	18·71	120·3	307·0	1·541
Toluene	0·05240	0·00684	24·08	146·4	283·9	1·590
Fluorbenzene ...	0·04272	0·00596	19·95	128·7	216·2	1·340
Chlorbenzene ...	0·05580	0·00680	25·54	145·5	201·8	1·293
Methyl chloride ...	0·01363	0·00263	6·85	58·27	262·7	1·154
Ethyl chloride ...	0·02264	0·00394	10·92	86·55	262·6	1·342
Water	0·01204	0·00147	5·95	33·60	1830	1·865
Methyl alcohol ...	0·01959	0·00304	9·53	67·05	928·8	2·093
Ethyl alcohol ...	0·02512	0·00385	15·22	84·46	570·0	1·834
Carbon disulphide	0·02412	0·00350	11·63	76·89	159·5	1·010
Stannic chloride ...	0·05926	0·00771	26·94	164·3	39·75	0·631
Ethyl ether ...	0·03688	0·00619	17·44	34·7	317·8	1·818
Ethyl acetate ...	0·04383	0·00654	20·47	141·3	263·9	1·604
Acetic acid ...	0·03737	0·00492	17·60	106·9	488·4	1·780
Acetonitrile ...	0·00370	0·00536	17·59	116·9	104·5	2·847
Methyl ether ...	0·01653	0·00328	8·08	72·5	381	1·574
Methylamine ...	0·01476	0·00276	7·40	61·0	751	1·97
Aniline	0·00567	0·00633	26·51	136·9	319·7	1·583
Anisole	0·00616	0·00744	28·35	159·6	242·6	1·476
Phenetole	0·00786	0·00928	35·20	196·4	236·1	1·609

§ 4. Test of van der Waals's Equation

Regnault [1] represented the results of his experiments on the compressibilities of gases (see § 6.VI A) by the empirical equation:

$$r/m=1-A(m-1)+B(m-1)^2 \quad . \quad . \quad . \quad . \quad . \quad . \quad (1)$$

where $m=V/v$, the ratio of two values of the volume reduced to the same temperature, say 0° C., and $r=p/P$, the ratio of the corresponding pressures, A and B being constants. The volume occupied by a given mass of gas under a pressure $P=1$ m. Hg was taken as unity, $V=1$, and hence (1) can be written:

$$pv=1-A[(1-v)/v]+B[(1-v)/v]^2,$$

$$\text{or} \quad pv+(A+2B)v^{-1}-Bv^{-2}=1+A+B \quad . \quad . \quad . \quad . \quad . \quad (2)$$

[1] *Mém. Acad. Sci.*, 1847, **21**, 329 (421); errata, *ibid.*, 1862, **26**, 925.

This corresponds with van der Waals's equation in the form:

$$(p+av^{-2})(v-b)=R'(1+\alpha t) \quad . \quad . \quad . \quad . \quad . \quad . \quad . \quad (3)$$

where α=coefficient of expansion, for the case when $t=0°$ C., when $1+\alpha t=T/273{\cdot}1$, and p in the correction bp is taken from Boyle's law, $p=PV/v=v^{-1}$, since then (3) becomes:

$$pv+(a-b)v^{-1}-abv^{-2}=R',$$

which is the same as (2) if $(a-b)=(A+2B)$, $ab=B$, and $R'=(1+A+B)$, and a and b can be calculated [1] from A and B. The determination of van der Waals's a and b was discussed by Keyes and Collins.[2] Mollier [3] wrote the equation $pv^2/T=[Rv^2/(v-b)-a/T]$ and if $pv^2=y$ is plotted against T a parabola is obtained.

For carbon dioxide van der Waals [4] gave equation (2), § 3, as:

$$(p+0{\cdot}00874/v^2)(v-0{\cdot}0023)=0{\cdot}00369(273+t° \text{ C.}),$$

where p is in atm. and v in fractions of the volume at S.T.P. The values of p for different values of t are:

$t=0°$	$v=0{\cdot}1$	0·05	0·025	0·01	0·0075	0·005	0·004	0·003
	$p=9{\cdot}4$	19·7	30·3	43·3	37·9	23·2	45·8	466·8
$t=32°$	$v=0{\cdot}1$	0·05	0·025	0·020	0·01	0·0075	0·005	0·004
	$p=10{\cdot}6$	23·4	34·6	41·9	58·7	62·0	67·2	118·5
$t=91°$	$v=0{\cdot}05$	0·04	0·02	0·01	0·0075			
	$p=24{\cdot}5$	30·0	52·6	74·1	86·4			

These three typical isotherms may be plotted (Fig. 1.VII C), the one for 32° being the critical isotherm.

For ethylene the corresponding equation is:

$$(p+0{\cdot}00786/v^2)(v-0{\cdot}0024)=0{\cdot}0037(272{\cdot}5+t° \text{ C.}),$$

and a comparison between observed and calculated values of pv at 20° was made by Baynes,[5] the agreement being satisfactory, especially at high pressures. The value of pv sinks to a minimum between 50 and 85 atm.

p atm.	1000 pv		p atm.	1000 pv	
	obs.	calc.		obs.	calc.
31·58	914	895	133·26	520	520
45·80	781	782	176·01	643	642
72·86	416	387	233·58	807	805
84·16	399	392	282·21	941	940
94·53	413	413	329·14	1067	1067
110·47	454	456	398·71	1248	1254

1 Roth, *Ann. Phys.*, 1880, **11**, 1.

2 *Proc. Nat. Acad.*, 1932, **18**, 328; cf. Neusser, *Phys. Z.*, 1930, **31**, 1041; 1932, **33**, 76.

3 *Phys. Z.*, 1920, **21**, 457.

4 Onnes and Keesom, "Enzykl. d. math. Wiss.," 1912, **5**, i, 675, say it was fortunate for the development of his theory that the critical constants calculated by van der Waals from Regnault's results, which are not very exact, agreed with those found by Andrews.

5 *Nature*, 1880, **23**, 186; the experimental figures are Amagat's. Baynes took the old value 272·5 for the absolute temperature of 0° C. The values of a and b giving good agreement at 20° do not apply accurately to other temperatures; Kuenen, "Die Zustandsgleichung der Gase und Flüssigkeiten," Brunswick, 1907, 81; Onnes and Keesom, *loc. cit.*; Kuenen, "Die Eigenschaften der Gase" (Ostwald-Drucker. "Handbuch der allgemeinen Chemie," **3**), Leipzig, 1919, 251, 257.

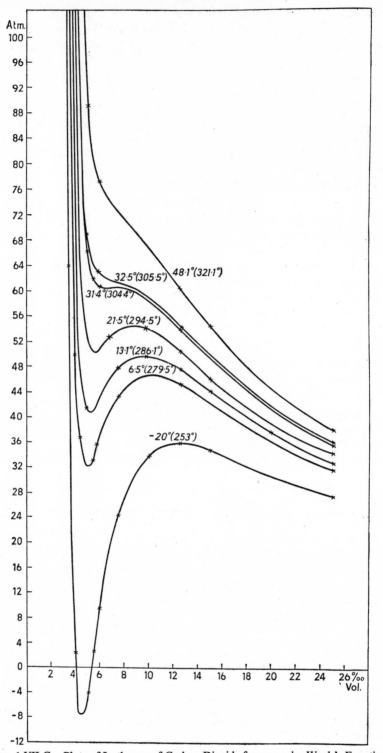

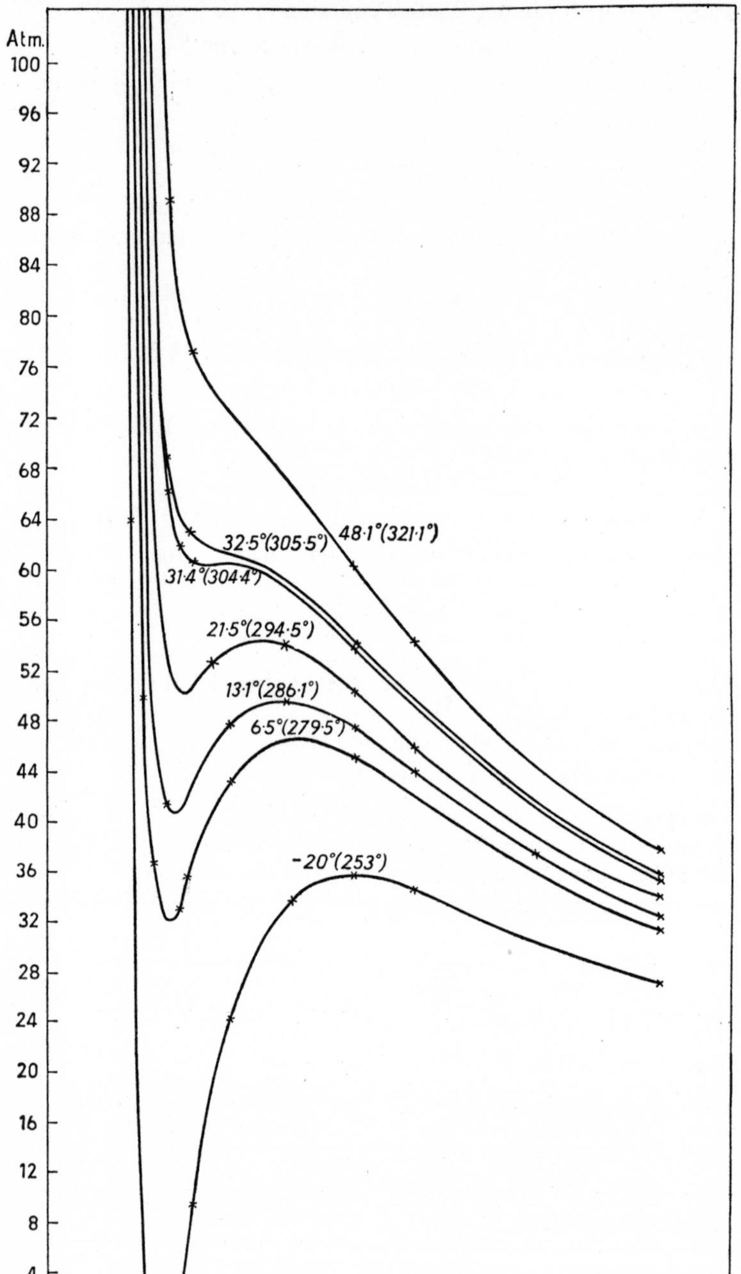

FIG. 1.VII C. Plots of Isotherms of Carbon Dioxide from van der Waals's Equation

§ 5. Form of the van der Waals Isotherms

If van der Waals's equation is written in the form

$$p=\frac{RT}{(v-b)}-\frac{a}{v^2}=\frac{1}{(v-b)}\left[RT-a\frac{(v-b)}{v^2}\right] \quad . \quad . \quad . \quad . \quad (1)$$

it is seen that $p=0$ when $a(v-b)/v^2=RT$. Also, $a(v-b)/v^2$ has a maximum value [1] $a/4b$ when $v=2b$, and is zero when $v=b$. Thus $p=0$ when $a/4b=RT$, or $v=2b$, and the p, v curve will cut the v axis in two real points when $RT<a/4b$. If $RT=a/4b$, the v axis is a tangent to the curve. If the equation in the form:

$$p=RT/(v-b)-a/v^2 \quad . \quad . \quad . \quad . \quad . \quad . \quad . \quad . \quad (2)$$

is differentiated with respect to v, with T constant, it gives:

$$\left(\frac{dp}{dv}\right)_T=-\frac{RT}{(v-b)^2}+\frac{2a}{v^3}=-\frac{1}{(v-b)^2}\left[RT-\frac{2a(v-b)^2}{v^3}\right] \quad . \quad . \quad (3)$$

For sufficiently large values of T the sign of dp/dv will always be negative. If v is small, $(v-b)^2$ will be very small and the curve will retain its negative slope. When T is sufficiently small, dp/dv may be positive for certain values of v.

$2a(v-b)^2/v^3$ has a maximum value, $8a/27b$, when $v=3b$, and the gradient approaches zero when v becomes very large. If RT is greater than $8a/27b$, v increases as p decreases, but if RT is less than $8a/27b$, v decreases with p for small and large values of v, but increases in the neighbourhood of $v=3b$. Thus, p has a maximum or minimum value for any value of v which makes $2a(v-b)^2/v^3$ equal to RT. The value $8a/27b=RT$ corresponds with a point of inflexion (the critical point).

The second differential coefficient is:

$$\left(\frac{d^2p}{dv^2}\right)_T=\frac{2RT}{(v-b)^3}-\frac{6a}{v^4}=\frac{2}{(v-b)^3}\left[RT-\frac{3a(v-b)^3}{v^4}\right] \quad . \quad . \quad . \quad (4)$$

hence there is a point of inflexion when $3a(v-b)^3/v^4$ is equal to RT. The value of $3a(v-b)^3/v^4$ is zero when $v=b$, and is a maximum $3^4a/4^4b$ when $v=4b$. For all values of RT between $2^3a/3^3b$ and $3^4a/4^4b$ there will be two points of inflexion. For values of RT greater than $3^4a/4^4b$ the curve will be a rectangular hyperbola.

§ 6. Virial Form of van der Waals's Equation

Van der Waals's equation may be written in the *virial form* (§ 10.VII A) as follows:

$$(p+a/v^2)(v-b)=RT \quad \therefore \; pv=RT+pb-a/v+ab/v^2.$$

For large volumes the last term can be neglected and $p=RT/v$ put in the correction term pb:

$$pv=RT+(RTb-a)/v;$$

and by comparison with the virial equation (1), § 10.VII A:

$$pv=A_v+B_v/v+C_v/v^2+ \ldots,$$

[1] Let $v=x$ and $a(v-b)/v^2=y$, then $dy/dx=-a/v^2+2ab/v^3$ and for a maximum or minimum (§ 11.I) $dy/dx=0 \;\therefore\; a/v^2=2ab/v^3 \;\therefore\; v=2b$. Substitute in y and this becomes $a/4b$. Also $d^2y/dx^2=2a/v^3-6ab/v^4$ and with $v=2b$ this becomes $-a/8b^3$, i.e. <0, hence the point is a maximum. A similar procedure is adopted for the other cases in the text. See Metcalf, *J. Phys. Chem.*, 1916, **20**, 177; Bagchi, *Indian J. Phys.*, 1940, **14**, 173.

with $A_v=RT$, the second virial coefficient, B_v, is found

$$B_v=RTb-a \quad . \quad . \quad . \quad . \quad . \quad . \quad . \quad . \quad (1)$$

Alternatively, for small pressures, $1/v$ can be put for p/RT in the correction term a/v, giving:

$$pv=RT+(b-a/RT)p \quad . \quad . \quad . \quad . \quad . \quad . \quad . \quad (2)$$

and by comparison with the virial equation (2), § 10.VII A, with $A_p=RT$, it is seen that the second virial coefficient B_p according to van der Waals's equation is:

$$B_p=b-a/RT \quad . \quad . \quad . \quad . \quad . \quad . \quad . \quad . \quad . \quad . \quad (3)$$

A temperature T_B, such that $bRT_B=a$, and $B_p=0$, is called the *Boyle temperature*. At this temperature (2) becomes $pv=RT$, i.e. the gas obeys Boyle's law (although, of course, it is not an ideal gas), the plot of pv against p going through a minimum value and running for a moment horizontal. Since $T_B=a/Rb$ and, as will be shown in § 7, $T_c=8a/27Rb$, it follows that:

$$T_B/T_c=27/8=3{\cdot}375 \quad . \quad . \quad . \quad . \quad . \quad . \quad . \quad (4)$$

The actual values for some gases are given below and it is seen that the agreement is not very good:

He 3·65	Ne 3·00	A 2·73
H_2 3·21	N_2 2·56	O_2 2·72

§ 7. Critical Data from van der Waals's Equation

It was stated in § 1 that van der Waals showed that his equation:

$$(p+a/v^2)(v-b)=RT \quad . \quad . \quad . \quad . \quad . \quad . \quad . \quad (1)$$

applies to liquids as well as gases, that it gives a semi-quantitative explanation of the critical phenomena, and that the same constants a and b apply over the whole range of states. When (1) is multiplied out and rearranged to

$$v^3-[b+(RT/p)]v^2+(a/p)v-ab/p=0 \quad . \quad . \quad . \quad . \quad (2)$$

it is a cubic equation in v (an equation of the third degree, involving v^3 as the highest power of v). For any pair of values of p and T, equation (2) gives three values of v, which are the so-called roots of (2). If these are v_1, v_2, and v_3, the cubic equation may be written as:

$$(v-v_1)(v-v_2)(v-v_3)=0 \quad . \quad . \quad . \quad . \quad . \quad . \quad . \quad (3)$$

since for any *one* of the values v_1, v_2, and v_3, for v, the expression on the left vanishes. Since all magnitudes in (2) are real, the roots must all be real, or else two may be imaginary, since a real magnitude can result only from the multiplication of an even number of imaginary ones.[1] The equation must, therefore, have either one or three real roots, and these must be positive, as a negative volume is meaningless. This result is seen to be satisfied by the graph of (1), e.g. in Fig. 1.VII C, where the curve cuts a horizontal line either in three points or (above the critical temperature) only in one.

At the critical point (2) becomes:

$$v^3-[b+(RT_c/p_c)]v^2+(a/p_c)v-ab/p_c=0 \quad . \quad . \quad . \quad . \quad (4)$$

[1] If X and Y are imaginary, they may be written as $x\sqrt{-1}$ and $y\sqrt{-1}$, where x and y are real, and $\sqrt{-1}$ is imaginary. Since $\sqrt{-1}\times\sqrt{-1}=-1$ is real, it follows that $(\sqrt{-1}\times\sqrt{-1})^n$ is real where n is any integer, i.e. $(\sqrt{-1})^{2n}$ is real, and $2n$ must be even.

and (3), since the three roots are equal ($=v_c$) at the critical point,[1] becomes:

$$(v-v_c)^3=v^3-3v_cv^2+3v_c^2v-v_c^3=0 \quad . \quad . \quad . \quad . \quad . \quad (5)$$

and by equating the coefficients of like powers of v in (4) and (5), it is found that:

$$b+RT_c/p_c=3v_c, \quad a/p_c=3v_c^2, \quad ab/p_c=v_c^3,$$

from which, by algebra, it follows that: [2]

$$v_c=3b, \quad p_c=a/27b^2, \quad T_c=8a/27bR \quad . \quad . \quad . \quad . \quad . \quad (6)$$

$$\therefore\ b=\tfrac{1}{3}v_c=RT_c/8p_c, \quad a=3p_cv_c^2=27R^2T_c^2/64p_c, \quad R=8p_cv_c/3T_c \quad . \quad (7)$$

The same result is found by a more general method,[3] which can be used with any characteristic equation. The theoretical isotherm below the critical temperature is seen from Fig. 2.VII C to be S-shaped and has both a maximum and minimum, in the sense explained in § 9.I. As the critical point is approached, the three points in which the curve cuts any horizontal, come closer together, and at the critical point they coincide. At the critical point, therefore, the curve cuts a horizontal in three coincident points.[4] The critical point is thus a point of inflexion, hence (§ 10.I), since T=const. along an isotherm:

$$(dp/dv)_T=0, \text{ and } (d^2p/dv^2)_T=0 \quad (8)$$

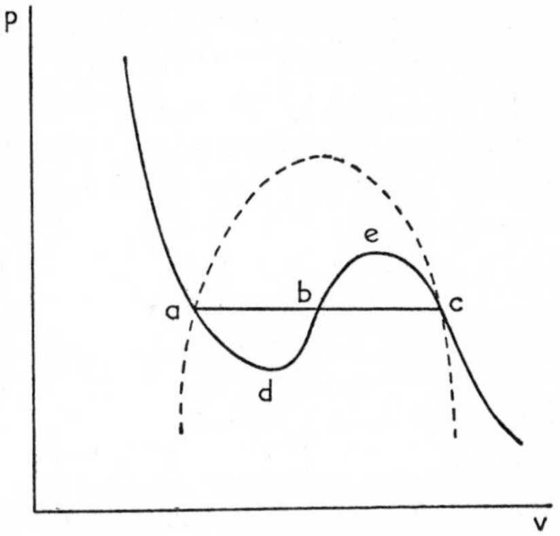

FIG. 2.VII C. Theoretical van der Waals Isotherm below the Critical Temperature

By differentiating van der Waals's equation in the form:

$$p=RT/(v-b)-a/v^2 \quad . \quad . \quad . \quad . \quad . \quad . \quad . \quad . \quad (9)$$

twice with respect to v, it is easily found that:

$$(dp/dv)_T=-RT/(v-b)^2+2a/v^3 \quad . \quad . \quad . \quad . \quad . \quad . \quad (10)$$

$$\text{and} \quad (d^2p/dv^2)_T=2RT/(v-b)^3-6a/v^4 \quad . \quad . \quad . \quad . \quad . \quad (11)$$

From (8), at the critical point:

$$RT/(v-b)^2=2a/v^3 \quad . \quad . \quad . \quad . \quad . \quad . \quad . \quad . \quad (12)$$

$$\text{and} \quad 2RT/(v-b)^3=6a/v^4 \quad . \quad . \quad . \quad . \quad . \quad . \quad . \quad (13)$$

Divide (12) by (13) and put $v=v_c$, then $v_c=3b$, as in (6). Substitute this value of v_c in (12) for v, then $RT_c/(2b)^2=2a/(3b)^3$, therefore $T_c=8a/27bR$, as in (6). Substitute $v=v_c=3b$, and $T_c=8a/27Rb$ in (9), therefore $p_c=RT_c/2b-a/(3b)^2=(R/2b)(8a/27Rb)-a/9b^2=4a/27b^2-a/9b^2=a/27b^2$, as in (6).

[1] The case of equality of *two* roots is investigated by Friderich, *J. Chim. Phys.*, 1906, **4**, 123; and Prud'homme, *ibid.*, 1912, **10**, 636; 1913, **11**, 520; 1916, **14**, 445, who found $p_c=1/4b$, $p_c=a/27b^2$, $T_c=9a/32Rb$. Pinter, *Amer. Chem. Abstr.*, 1943, **37**, 2631, thought T_c may be lower than the temperature of the inflexion isotherm; Verschaffelt, *Arch. Néerl.*, 1907, **12**, 193; *J. de Phys.*, 1923, **4**, 158, developed p in series on the critical isotherm in terms of $(v-v_c)$ and $(T-T_c)$, and found an analytical discontinuity near the critical point.

[2] See, however, Kirajew, *Z. Elektrochem.*, 1927, **33**, 91.

[3] Dickson, *Phil. Mag.*, 1880, **10**, 40; Onnes, *Verl. K. Akad. Wetens. Amsterdam*, 1881, **21**, No. 4, 12; Thiesen, *Ann. Phys.*, 1885, **24**, 467.

[4] Any curve cuts its *tangent* in *two* coincident points.

Some apparent difficulties in this use of van der Waals's equation are discussed by Brennen,[1] who thinks an additional term is necessary.

§ 8. Practical Application of van der Waals's Equation

In the use of van der Waals's equation in the standard form:

$$(p+a/v^2)(v-b)=\boldsymbol{R}T \quad . \quad . \quad . \quad . \quad . \quad . \quad . \quad (1)$$

careful attention must be given to the units. If the quantity of substance is a mol (1 g.mol.) and v is measured in ml., then $\boldsymbol{R}=82{\cdot}09$ ml.atm./1°. If the quantity is n mols, and if v is the actual volume, the molar volume is v/n, and (1) becomes:

$$[p+a/(v/n)^2](v/n-b)=\boldsymbol{R}T,$$

$$\therefore\ (p+n^2a/v^2)(v-nb)=n\boldsymbol{R}T \quad . \quad . \quad . \quad . \quad . \quad . \quad (2)$$

If the volume at S.T.P. is nv_0, where v_0 is the actual molar volume at S.T.P., and the actual volume v at any other temperature and pressure is expressed as a fraction v_1 of this volume at S.T.P., $v_1=v/nv_0$, then:

$$\left(p+\frac{(n^2a/n^2v_0^2)}{v^2/n^2v_0^2}\right)\left(\frac{v}{nv_0}-\frac{nb}{nv_0}\right)=\frac{n\boldsymbol{R}T}{nv_0}$$

$$\therefore\ [p+a/(v_0/v_1)^2](v_1-b/v_0)=\boldsymbol{R}T/v_0=R'T \quad . \quad . \quad . \quad (3)$$

where $R'=\boldsymbol{R}/v_0$. Put:

$$a/v_0^2=a', \text{ and } b/v_0=b' \quad . \quad . \quad . \quad . \quad . \quad . \quad . \quad . \quad (4)$$

$$\therefore\ (p+a'/v_1^2)(v_1-b')=R'T \quad . \quad . \quad . \quad . \quad . \quad . \quad (5)$$

or, if a' and b' are written as a and b, and v_1 as v:

$$(p+a/v^2)(v-b)=R'T \quad . \quad . \quad . \quad . \quad . \quad . \quad . \quad (6)$$

which holds for *any* mass of substance. At 0° C. and 1 atm., $v=1$, therefore $(1+a)(1-b)=273R'$, therefore (6) can be written in the form:

$$(p+a/v^2)(v-b)=(1+a)(1-b)(T/273) \quad . \quad . \quad . \quad . \quad (7)$$

in which p is in atm., v is the *ratio* of the actual volume at p and T to the actual volume at S.T.P., and a and b are constants in units chosen to agree with (7). In this case the values of p_c and v_c are given in terms of a and b as in (6), § 7, but:

$$T_c=8a/27R'b=(8\times 273/27)a/b(1+a)(1-b) \quad . \quad . \quad . \quad . \quad (8)$$

From $p_c=a/27b^2$ and (8), *approximate* values of a and b are found by simply leaving out the expression $(1+a)(1-b)\simeq 1$, viz., $b_0=T_cp_c/8\times 273$, $a_0=27p_cb_0^2$, and then as a second approximation:

$$b=b_0(1+a_0)(1-b_0)\simeq b_0(1+a_0-b_0),$$

is obtained.

Since in (7) the volume is expressed as a fraction of the actual volume at S.T.P., this must be known. The equation with given values of a and b can be used to calculate this volume from the ideal volume. For gases far removed from the ideal state or for liquids, it is better to refer the volumes to the volume

[1] *Proc. Nat. Acad.*, 1929, **15**, 11; cf. Shiba, *Proc. Phys. Math. Soc. Japan*, 1927, **9**, 157. On the calculation of critical constants from a and b values, see, e.g. van Laar, " Die Zustandsgleichung," Leipzig, 1924, 128 f.; *Chem. Weekbl.*, 1933, **30**, 294.

v_0' of an equal mass of the substance in the state of ideal gas at S.T.P., since then comparable values of a and b for all substances can be calculated. In this case, in (6):

$$R' = R/v_0' = R/273R = 1/273,$$

$$\therefore \ (p + a/v^2)(v - b) = T/273 \quad . \ . \ . \ . \ . \ . \ . \ (9)$$

where v is now the *fraction* of the actual volume to the volume of an equal mass of the gas in the ideal state at S.T.P.[1] By substituting $R' = 1/273$ in (7), § 7, the values of a and b in suitable units for use in (9) are:

$$a = [27/64(273)^2](T_c^2/p_c), \quad b = (1/8 \times 273)(T_c/p_c) \quad . \ . \ . \ (\mathbf{10})$$

The volume V of 1 g. of gas in ml. is now to be multiplied by the molecular weight M and divided by 22,415 to find v for use in (9):

$$v = MV/22{,}415 \quad . \ . \ . \ . \ . \ . \ . \ . \ . \ (\mathbf{11})$$

It is clear that the use of van der Waals's constants a and b is liable to cause errors in calculation, and generally the best course is to use the reduced form of the equation, explained in § 16.

§ 9. Metastable States

The complete continuous van der Waals isotherm for temperatures below the critical point is seen from Fig. 2.VII C, to pass through the region (shown dotted) of heterogeneous states (liquid+vapour), to which the equation (limited to homogeneous states) does not apply. The isotherm has an S-shaped form, and the physical meaning, if any, which this part of the curve suggests must be considered.

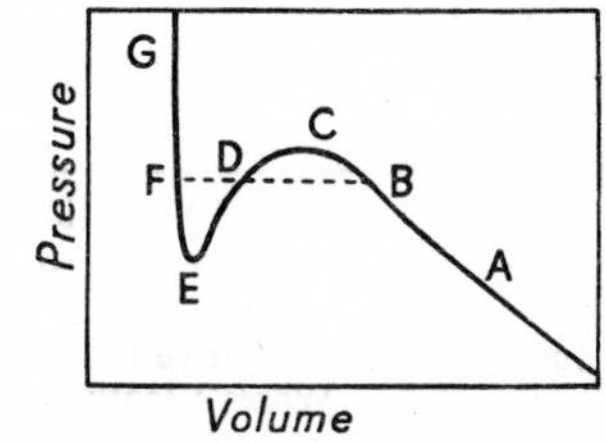

FIG. 3.VII C. Isotherm of Metastable States

Since the stable state of the system in this region is heterogeneous, any such curve must represent *metastable states*. The point F (Fig. 3.VII C) lies on the boundary curve separating liquid from (liquid+vapour), and must represent the liquid state; the point B represents the vapour state. The curve FE represents superheated liquid, since at the temperature corresponding with the isotherm the liquid should, in the stable state, break down into (liquid+vapour). The curve CB represents supercooled vapour, since on decreasing the volume the vapour should partly liquefy in the stable region. The part EDC of the curve can have no physical significance, since along it the pressure would increase along with the volume, a behaviour not known for any actual homogeneous substance.[2] The S-shaped isotherm giving the continuous transition of gaseous and liquid states had been recognised (before the publication of van der Waals's equation) in 1871 by James Thomson,[3] and hence it is often called the *James Thomson isotherm.*

[1] Kuenen, *Ann. Phys.*, 1905, **17**, 189.

[2] Van der Waals, "Continuität," 1899, **1**, 95; Preston, *Phil. Mag.*, 1896, **42**, 231; Tumlirz, *Wien Ber.*, 1905, **114**, II A, 167; Centnerszwer, *Z. phys. Chem.*, 1923, **107**, 81; Larson, *Ind. Eng. Chem.*, 1945, **37**, 1010.

[3] *Proc. Roy. Soc.*, 1871, **20**, 1: Considerations on the Abrupt Change at Boiling or Condensation in reference to the Continuity of the Fluid State of Matter; "Collected Papers in Physics and Engineering," Cambridge, 1912, 278, and unpublished notes, p. 318 f. In Thomson's figure the p and v axes are as shown in Andrews' diagram, Fig. 4.VII B.

Maxwell[1] pointed out that if the substance is supposed to be carried round an isothermal reversible cycle FEDCBF, the work done is zero (§ 30.II). The area of this cycle is thus also zero, hence area FED=area DCB. Thus the horizontal isotherm of real states FB divides the van der Waals isotherm FECB so as to cut off equal areas above and below the horizontal. From this it is, in principle, possible to find the position of the real isotherm FB from the van der Waals isotherm. The ordinate of FB then gives the vapour pressure of the saturated vapour. Smith[2] showed, for alcohol and ether, that the James Thomson isotherm is continuous where it cuts the line of saturated states (liquid+vapour) at D.

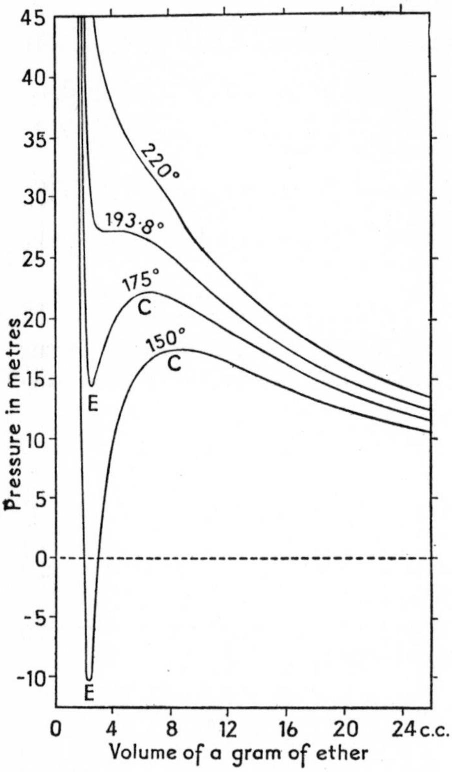

FIG. 4.VII C Negative Pressures on van der Waals's Isotherm

§ 10. Negative Pressures

The van der Waals isotherms at the lower temperatures cross the v axis (Fig. 4.VII C), and the part below the v axis corresponds with a negative pressure. Although this cannot exist for a gas, it may represent a metastable state for a liquid, which would then be in a state of tension. This isotherm, however, turns upwards again and re-crosses the v axis in the direction of increasing pressure, so that it must have a minimum value of the tension, below which presumably the metastable state would break down into liquid and vapour. For carbon dioxide this is $-7{\cdot}8$ atm. at $-20°$.

Negative pressures were first noticed in the non-descent of mercury in a

[1] *J.C.S.*, 1875, **28**, 493; *Nature*, 1875, **11**, 357; "Scientific Papers," 1890, **2**, 407, 418; Moser, *Ann. Phys.*, 1877, **160**, 138; Boltzmann, *Wien Ber.*, 1877, **75**, II, 801; "Wiss. Abhl.," 1909, **2**, 150; Clausius, *Ann. Phys.*, 1880, **9**, 337 (who deduced the result independently); 1881, **14**, 279, 692; Planck, *ibid.*, 1881, **13**, 535; Riecke, *ibid.*, 1894, **53**, 379; 1895, **54**, 739; van der Waals, "Continuität," 1899, **1**, 98; Saurel, *J. Phys. Chem.*, 1899, **3**, 214; Onnes, *Arch. Néerl.*, 1900, **5**, 665 (*Comm. Leiden*, **66**); Hilton, *Phil. Mag.*, 1901, **1**, 579; 1901, **2**, 108; Dieterici, *Ann. Phys.*, 1901, **6**, 861; St. Meyer, *ibid.*, 1902, **7**, 937; Batschinski, *Z. phys. Chem.*, 1902, **41**, 741; Pitsch, *Wien Ber.*, 1904, **113**, II A, 849; Jeans, "Dynamical Theory of Gases," 1904, 132; Dalton, *Phil. Mag.*, 1907, **13**, 517; van der Waals and Kohnstamm, "Lehrbuch der Thermodynamik," 1907, **1**, 35; Smoluchowski, *Ann. Phys.*, 1908, **25**, 205; Amagat, "Notes sur la Physique," 1912, 71; Larmor, *Proc. Math. Soc. London*, 1916, **15**, 182; Metcalf, *J. Phys. Chem.*, 1916, **26**, 177; Järvinen, *Z. phys. Chem.*, 1919, **93**, 743; Leduc, *Compt. Rend.*, 1923, **176**, 1456; Jouguet, *Compt. Rend.*, 1933, **197**, 1705; Decker, *Physica*, 1941, **8**, 59. In later editions of his "Theory of Heat" (4th edit., 1875, etc.) Maxwell does not fix the position of the horizontal line, but Lord Rayleigh, in his edition (1897, 125) refers to the paper in *Nature* of 1875, saying that "it cuts off equal areas from the curve above and below."

[2] *Proc. Amer. Acad.*, 1907, **42**, 421.

barometer tube in which it stands above the normal height (§ 2.VII A), and studied in experiments [1] in which a liquid freed from dissolved air was filled into a tube with a capillary outlet, and the tube heated until the liquid by expansion filled the capillary, which was then sealed off. On cooling, the liquid still filled the tube completely and must have been under tension. Quantitative measurements were made with some liquids (water, alcohol, and ether).[2] In Meyer's apparatus a small glass bulb (Fig. 5.VII C) drawn out below to a fine capillary for filling was attached to a spiral elliptical tube surmounted by a mirror. The spiral tube turned about its axis by pressure change and moved the mirror, a beam of light reflected from which was deflected. The spiral was calibrated against a mercury manometer. A small bubble of vapour remaining after sealing the fine capillary was removed by warming, when the liquid expanded, and on cooling vapour did not reappear. The greatest tensions reached were, 34 atm. for water (24·4°), 39·5 atm. for ethyl alcohol (22·5°), and 72·0 atm. (17·7°) for ether. The value calculated by van der Waals's equation (minimum pressure) for ether at 17·7° is -83 atm. pressure or 83 atm. tension, which is in quite satisfactory agreement. (At the absolute zero the largest theoretical value of the tension is $-a/b^2$, if the volume at $T=0$ is b.) Meyer showed that the compressibility coefficient of a liquid remains the same on passing from pressures to tensions.

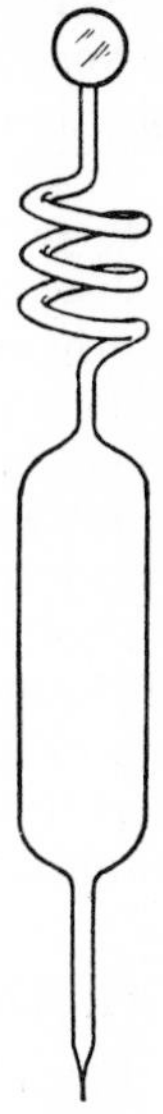

FIG. 5.VII C Meyer's Apparatus

The part of the curve FE, Fig. 3.VII C, corresponds with superheated liquid. In Wismer's experiments [3] the maximum temperatures to which ether could be heated at various pressures without boiling were found to lie on a straight line when plotted against the pressures, and the temperatures were always *higher* than the maximum temperatures given by van der Waals's equation, which should also lie on a curve, not a straight line. It is difficult to believe that these experiments have much quantitative significance.

MacDougall [4] pointed out that the experiments on negative pressures in liquids are difficult to interpret on the basis of van der Waals's theory, since this, and similar ones,[5] assume that there is no attractive force between the

[1] Donny, *Ann. Chim.*, 1846, **16**, 167; Berthelot, *ibid.*, 1850, **30**, 232; 1861, **61**, 468; Moser, *Ann. Phys.*, 1877, **160**, 138; Helmholtz, *Verhl. Berlin Phys. Ges.*, 1887, **6**, 1, 104; "Wiss. Abhl.," 1895, **3**, 264.

[2] Osborne Reynolds, *Manch. Mem.*, 1878, **7**, 1; "Papers on Mechanical and Physical Subjects," Cambridge, 1900, **1**, 231; Stefan, *Ann. Phys.*, 1886, **29**, 655; Worthington, *Phil. Trans.*, 1892, **183**, 355; van der Mensbrugghe, *Bull. Acad. Roy. Belg.*, 1893, **26**, 37; Tumlirz, *Wien Ber.*, 1900, **109**, II A, 837; 1901, **110**, II A, 437; Leduc and Sacerdote, *Compt. Rend.*, 1902, **134**, 589; *Soc. France Phys. Séances*, 1902, 76; Hulett, *Z. phys. Chem.*, 1903, **42**, 353; Ramstedt, *Arkiv Mat. Astron. Fys.*, 1908, **4**, No. 16 (glass spiral gauge; alcohol -10 to -12 atm.); Dixon, *Proc. Roy. Dublin Soc.*, 1909–10, **12**, 60; J. Meyer, Zur Kenntnis des negativen Druckes, *Abhl. D. Bunsen Ges.*, 1911, **6**; *Z. Elektrochem.*, 1911, **17**, 743; 1912, **18**, 709, 744; *Z. phys. Chem.*, 1935, **173**, 106; Budgett, *Proc. Roy. Soc.*, 1911–12, **86**, 25; Skinner and Entwistle, *ibid.*, 1915, **91**, 481; Larmor, *Proc. Math. Soc. London*, 1916, **15**, 182; Skinner and Burfitt, *Proc. Phys. Soc.*, 1919, **31**, 131; Dorsey, "Properties of Ordinary Water Substance," New York, 1940, 179 (bibl.); Vincent, *Proc. Phys. Soc.*, 1941, **53**, 126 (157 atm. by Berthelot's method); 1943, **55**, 41; Vincent and Simmonds, *ibid.*, 1943, **55**, 376 (max. tension *c.* 25 atm.); Zeldovich, *Compt. Rend. U.R.S.S.*, 1943, **18**, 1 (calc. 250 atm. for ether); Scott, Shoemaker, Tanner, and Wendel, *J. Chem. Phys.*, 1948, **16**, 495 (33 atm. by Berthelot's method).

[3] *J. Phys. Chem.*, 1922, **26**, 301; Kenrick, Gilbert, and Wismer, *ibid.*, 1924, **28**, 1297.

[4] *J.A.C.S.*, 1916, **38**, 528.

[5] Dieterici's equation, (6), § 31, does not lead to negative pressures, and those who support it have no option to denying their existence.

fluid molecules and the wall, the only force there (neglecting hydrostatic pressure) being due to the bombardment of the wall by molecules which reach the surface. In the absence of any adhesive force between the fluid and the wall, a negative external pressure is inconceivable. The reality of the negative pressure is, however, demonstrated by experiments and is beyond argument.

An attempt by Wagner [1] to take account of the effect of the walls ended in an equation containing an unknown function, and the very large negative pressures (−352 atm. at 20° for ether) calculated by Döring,[2] seem to be based on faulty theory. Fürth, from the " hole " theory of liquids (see § 1.VIII A, Vol. II), deduced the formula $p_e - p^* = 1{\cdot}3\sigma^{3/2}/\sqrt{(kT)}$, where p_e=vap. press. at temp. T, p^*=hydrostatic pressure, σ= surface tension, k=Boltzmann's constant; and from this Silver calculated 80,000 lb./in.^{2} as the tensile strength of water at room temperature (cf. § 15).

Temperley and Chambers [3] (who found Berthelot's method the best) reached a negative pressure of 40 atm. with water. Good adhesion of liquid to the solid wall of the tube must be attained by suitable experimental details. The effect of dissolved air was studied. Vacuous cavities are formed in corn syrup at the rear of an accelerated rod; [4] in water free from gas-nuclei and dust no cavities were formed up to velocities of 37 m./sec., but in presence of gas-nuclei cavities formed at 3 m./sec.

§ 11. Thermal Coefficients from van der Waals's Equation

From van der Waals's equation:

$$(p+a/v^2)(v-b)=RT$$

a number of thermal coefficients (§ 3.II) and related quantities [5] may be calculated.

(i) For two temperatures at *constant volume*:

$$(p_1+a/v^2)(v-b)=RT, \quad \text{and} \quad (p_0+a/v^2)(v-b)=RT_0$$

where $T_0=273{\cdot}1°$ (0° C.). By subtraction, $(p_1-p_0)(v-b)=R(T_1-T_0)$,

$$\therefore\ p_1-p_0=R(T_1-T_0)/(v-b)=(p_0+a/v^2)(T_1-T_0)/T_0.$$

Hence the *pressure coefficient* (§ 15.VII A) is:

$$\beta=(p_1-p_0)/p_0(T_1-T_0)=(1/T_0)(1+a/p_0v^2) \quad . \ . \ . \quad (1)$$

For the ideal gas this is $1/T_0=1/273{\cdot}1$. Equation (1) shows that β depends on the density but not on the temperature (T_0 is constant). The dependence of β on temperature is discussed in § 17.VII A; β depends slightly on temperature, although Regnault [6] found the variation for most gases to be very small over quite a large temperature range, sulphur dioxide being exceptional. More exact experiments by Chappuis [7] gave for β:

[1] *Ann. Phys.*, 1914, **45**, 1169; *Z. phys. Chem.*, 1920, **96**, 483.

[2] *Z. phys. Chem.*, 1937, **36** B, 371; 1937, **38** B, 292; Fürth, *Proc. Phys. Soc.*, 1940, **52**, 768; *Proc. Cambr. Phil. Soc.*, 1941, **37**, 252, 276, 281; Silver, *Nature*, 1942, **150**, 605.

[3] *Proc. Phys. Soc.*, 1946, **58**, 420; Temperley, *ibid.*, 1946, **58**, 436; 1947, **59**, 199.

[4] Harvey, McElroy, and Whiteley, *J. Appl. Phys.*, 1947, **18**, 162.

[5] Van der Waals, " Continuität," 1899, **1**, 68 f.; Jäger, *Wien Ber.*, 1892, **101**, II, 1675; Jeans, " Dynamical Theory of Gases," 3rd edit., 1921, 135; Carrara, *Nuov. Cim.*, 1923, **26**, 157.

[6] *Mém. Acad. Sci.*, 1847, **21**, 162 (190).

[7] *Trav. et Mém. Bur. Internat. Poids et Mésures*, 1907, **13**.

	N_2 (p_0=1001·9 mm. at 0° C.)	CO_2 (p_0=998·5 mm. at 0° C.)
0°–20°	0·0036754	0·0037335
0°–40°	0·0036752	0·0037299
0°–100°	0·0036744	0·0037262

The value of β for hydrogen, 0·00366254, is very nearly the same as that for the ideal gas, 0·003662 (for T_0=273·1°), so that the Comité Internationale des Poids et Mésures [1] adopted the constant-volume hydrogen thermometer with p_0=1000 mm. as a standard gas thermometer.

(ii) For two temperatures at *constant pressure*:

$$(p+a/v_0^2)(v_0-b)=\boldsymbol{R}T_0, \quad \text{and} \quad (p+a/v_1^2)(v_1-b)=\boldsymbol{R}T_1.$$

Subtract the equations and neglect terms of the second order multiplied by ab:

$$p(v_1-v_0)+a/v_1-a/v_0=\boldsymbol{R}(T_1-T_0)$$
$$\therefore\ (p-a/v_1v_0)(v_1-v_0)=\boldsymbol{R}(T_1-T_0)$$
$$\therefore\ v_1-v_0=\boldsymbol{R}(T_1-T_0)/(p-a/v_1v_0).$$

Hence the coefficient of expansion is:

$$\alpha=(v_1-v_0)/v_0(T_1-T_0)=\boldsymbol{R}/(pv_0-a/v_1). \quad . \quad . \quad . \quad . \quad (2)$$

From the first equation and (2), $\boldsymbol{R}$ can be eliminated:

$$T_0\alpha(pv_0-a/v_1)=(p+a/v_0^2)(v_0-b),$$
$$\therefore\ \alpha=\frac{1}{T_0}\frac{(p+a/v_0^2)(v_0-b)}{pv_0-a/v_1}\simeq\frac{1}{T_0}\frac{pv_0+a/v_0-pb}{pv_0-a/v_1}$$
$$\simeq\frac{1}{T_0}\left[1+\frac{a}{pv_0}\left(\frac{1}{v_0}+\frac{1}{v_1}\right)-\frac{b}{v_0}\right] \quad . \quad . \quad . \quad . \quad . \quad . \quad . \quad . \quad (3)$$

by division, rejecting at each step terms involving ab and a^2.

Equation (3) is more complicated than (1), since it involves both a and b, and depends both on pressure and density ($1/v$), or (by elimination) on one of these and on temperature. For an ideal gas, $a=b=0$ and (3) becomes $\alpha=1/T_0=$ 0·003662, so that $\alpha=\beta$. The dependence of α on pressure and temperature is discussed in § 17.VII A, and is illustrated by the following values: [2]

	N_2 p=1001·9 mm.	CO_2 p=998·5 mm.	CO_2 p=517·9 mm.
0°–20° ...	0·0036770	0·0037603	0·0037128
0°–40° ...	0·0036750	0·0037536	0·0037100
0°–100° ...	0·0036732	0·0037410	0·0037073

An experimental value of β gives a from (1), and from this and an experimental value of α (3) gives b.

To find $(\mathrm{d}p/\mathrm{d}T)_v$, write the van der Waals equation in the form $p+a/v^2=\boldsymbol{R}T/(v-b)$,

$$\therefore\ (\mathrm{d}p/\mathrm{d}T)_v=\boldsymbol{R}/(v-b)=(p+a/v^2)/T \quad . \quad . \quad . \quad . \quad (4)$$

[1] Chappuis, *Trav. et Mém. Bur. Internat. Poids et Mésures*, 1888, **6**; 1907, **13**
[2] Jeans, " Kinetic Theory of Gases," 1940, 81.

To find $(dv/dT)_p$, write the van der Waals equation in the form $pv-pb+a/v=RT$, neglecting the small term $-ab/v^2$; then by differentiation:

$$p(dv/dT)_p-(a/v^2)(dv/dT)_p=R,$$

$$\therefore\ (dv/dT)_p=R/(p-a/v^2) \quad . \quad . \quad . \quad . \quad . \quad . \quad . \quad . \quad (5)$$

(iii) For varying volumes at *constant temperature*, write van der Waals's equation as $p=RT/(v-b)-a/v^2$

$$\therefore\ (dp/dv)_T=-RT/(v-b)^2+2a/v^3,$$

$\therefore$ the *isothermal elasticity* (§ 4.II) is:

$$\epsilon_T=-v(dp/dv)_T=(RT-2a/v)/(v-2b) \quad . \quad . \quad . \quad . \quad (6)$$

(iv) The *Joule effect* is given by (9), § 23.VII A, as:

$$(dT/dv)_E=-(1/c_v)[T(dp/dT)_v-p] \quad . \quad . \quad . \quad . \quad . \quad (7)$$

From (4), $T(dp/dT)_v-p=a/v^2$, therefore:

$$(dT/dv)_E=-(1/c_v)(a/v^2) \quad . \quad . \quad . \quad . \quad . \quad . \quad . \quad . \quad (8)$$

and for a finite volume change, by integration:

$$T_1-T_2=(a/c_v)(1/v_1-1/v_2) \quad . \quad . \quad . \quad . \quad . \quad . \quad . \quad (9)$$

(v) The *Joule-Thomson* effect has been worked out [1] in (5), § 25.VII A, as:

$$dT=(2a/RT-3abp/R^2T^2-b)(dp/C_p) \quad . \quad . \quad . \quad . \quad (10)$$

(vi) The *difference of molecular heats* at constant pressure and at constant volume is given by (2), § 47.II, as:

$$C_p-C_v=T(dp/dT)_v(dv/dT)_p.$$

The values of $(dp/dT)_v$ and $(dv/dT)_p$ are given by (4) and (5) as $(dp/dT)_v=R/(v-b)$, and $(dv/dT)_p=R/(p-a/v^2)$, hence:

$$\begin{aligned}\therefore\ C_p-C_v&=[RT/(v-b)][R/(p-a/v^2)]\\&=R(p+a/v^2)/(p-a/v^2)=R(p+a/v^2)/p(1-a/pv^2)\\&\simeq R(p+a/v^2)(1+a/pv^2)/p\simeq R(1+2a/pv^2)\\&\simeq R(1+2ap/R^2T^2) \quad . \quad . \quad . \quad . \quad . \quad . \quad . \quad . \quad . \quad . \quad . \quad (11)\end{aligned}$$

by division, putting $1/(1-x)\simeq 1+x$ when x is small, neglecting terms in a^2, and substituting $v=RT/p$ in the correction term only.[2]

(vii) For an *adiabatic change* van der Waals [3] deduced the equation:

$$(p+a/v^2)(v-b)^\gamma=\text{const.} \quad . \quad . \quad . \quad . \quad . \quad . \quad . \quad . \quad (12)$$

where $\gamma=c_p/c_v$, and this was used by Boynton [4] in calculating γ from adiabatic expansion experiments. Magyar [5] deduced an adiabatic equation for $\gamma=a+bT$, where a and b are constants $(b<0)$. The thermodynamic functions for a van der Waals gas were calculated by Wang.[6]

[1] For application of Clausius's equation (§ 28) see Korteweg, *Ann. Phys.*, 1881, **12**, 136.

[2] Dalton, *Phil. Mag.*, 1907, **13**, 525, 536; for high pressures, see Godnev, *J. Gen. Chem. U.S.S.R.*, 1931, **1**, 684.

[3] "Continuität," 2nd edit., Leipzig, 1899, **1**, 131.

[4] *Phys. Rev.*, 1901, **12**, 353; see also Perman, Ramsay, and Rose-Innes, *Phil. Trans.*, 1897, **189**, 167 (ether vapour); Worthing, *Phys. Rev.*, 1911, **32**, 243; 1911, **33**, 217 (air and CO_2).

[5] *Z. techn. Phys.*, 1924, **5**, 404.

[6] *Chinese J. Phys.*, 1945, **6**, 27.

§ 12. Van der Waals's Equation for Liquids

Van der Waals's equation should apply also to liquids. In this case the external pressure p may often be neglected in comparison with the internal pressure a/v^2. Another type of equation:[1]

$$(v-b)(B+p)=CT \quad \ldots \ldots \quad (1)$$

where B is the internal pressure and C depends on the nature of the liquid, was shown by Tammann[2] to hold for liquids at high pressures (over 1000 atm.) and not too high temperatures. The constant b is the volume at infinite pressure. Bogdan[3] used equation (1) in the form $(p+K)(v-b)=\boldsymbol{R}T$, where K is the internal pressure, to deduce the Clapeyron-Clausius latent heat equation, putting $l_e=\int_v^V (p+K)\mathrm{d}v$, where v and V are the liquid and vapour volumes. Weiss,[4] from (1), deduced:

$$(p+a/v^n)(v-b)=\xi \boldsymbol{R}T \quad \ldots \ldots \quad (2)$$

with four constants, a, b, n, and ξ.

Ramsay and Young,[5] and Amagat[6] (who emphasised that the relation is not exact, the experimental lines showing a slight curvature), found that the *isochores* (constant-volume lines; Greek χώρα, space)[7] for liquids are fairly accurately given by:

$$p=bT-a \quad \ldots \ldots \quad (3)$$

where a and b are constants (not the van der Waals constants) for each liquid, but Bridgman[8] showed that b is really a function of temperature.

According to Frank and Lei[9] the constants in (3) are given by:

$$b=(\boldsymbol{R}/V_m)e^{\alpha/V^\beta}, \quad a=K/V_m^{\ n}-C/V_m^{\ d} \quad \ldots \ldots \quad (3a)$$

where α, β, n, and d are constants, the last two non-integral, and V_m is the molar volume.

Rose-Innes[10] fitted Young's[11] results with ether and *n*- and *iso*pentane to an equation:

$$p=(\boldsymbol{R}T/v)[1+e/(v+k-g/v^2)]-l/v(v+k) \quad \ldots \quad (4)$$

where e, k, l, and g are constants. This is of the fifth order in v but has only three real roots.

[1] Tumlirz, *Wien Ber.*, 1900, **109**, II A, 837; 1901, **110**, II A, 437; 1909, **118**, II A, 203; Weiss, *Compt. Rend.*, 1918, **167**, 232, 293; Fischer, *Ann. Phys.*, 1922, **69**, 315; 1923, **71**, 591; Brandt, *ibid.*, 1924, **73**, 415 (used f(T) instead of CT); a very complicated equation was later proposed by Tumlirz, *Wien Ber.*, 1921, **130**, II A, 93.

[2] *Gött. Nachr.*, 1911, 527; *Ann. Phys.*, 1912, **37**, 975.

[3] *Ann. Sci. Univ. Jassy*, 1907, **4**, 151.

[4] *Compt. Rend.*, 1918, **167**, 293, 364.

[5] *Z. phys. Chem.*, 1887, **1**, 433.

[6] *Compt. Rend.*, 1892, **115**, 1238; *Ann. Chim.*, 1893, **29**, 505; Keyes and Felsing, *J.A.C.S.* 1919, **41**, 589.

[7] The name *isometric* was proposed by Gibbs, *Trans. Connect. Acad.*, 1873, **2**, 309; "Scientific Papers," 1906, **1**, 1; Ritter, *Ann. Phys.*, 1878, **3**, 447, proposed *isopleres* (Greek πλήρης, filled), and Wroblewski, *Wien Ber.*, 1886, **94**, II, 257, *isopyknics* (Greek πυκνός, dense); the last name is often used as an alternative to isochore, meaning a line of constant density

[8] *Proc. Amer. Acad.*, 1913–14, **49**, 1 (89).

[9] *Phys. Rev.*, 1932, **42**, 893 (gaseous and liquid ethyl ether).

[10] *Proc. Phys. Soc.*, 1897, **15**, 126; 1898, **16**, 11; *Phil. Mag.*, 1897, **44**, 76; 1898, **45**, 102; 1901, **2**, 208.

[11] Rose-Innes and Young, *Phil. Mag.*, 1899, **47**, 353.

	*iso*pentane	ether	*n*-pentane
R	863·56	840·34	863·56
e	7·473	7·485	7·473
k	3·636	3·188	3·135
g	6·2318	4·4539	6·695
l	542800	5095070	5426800

It has often [1] been pointed out that *all* equations of the type $p=Tf(v)+a$ will give $(d^2p/dT^2)_v=0$, and hence from (1), § 49.II, $(dc_v/dv)_T=0$, which can hardly be true for liquids. Equation (3) may apply to liquids better at very high pressures. Webster [2] argued that the equation $v=f(p/T)$ does not lead to the result that the specific heats are independent of pressure.

The various characteristic equations which have been proposed may be divided approximately into three groups: [3]

(i) $p=Tf_1(v)-F_1(v)$, e.g. van der Waals's equation,

(ii) $p=Tf_2(v, T)-F_2(v, T)$,

(iii) $p=Tf_3(v)-F_3(v, T)$, e.g. Clausius's equation,

where f_1, f_2, f_3, F_1, F_2, F_3 denote functions of the quantities in brackets. In (i) p is a linear function of temperature at constant volume, so that $(dp/dT)_v$ is a constant, whereas in (ii) and (iii) it is a function of temperature. Verschaffelt [4] obtained a complicated equation based on the relation $(d^2p/dv^2)_T=0$ at the critical point. Milosavliévitch [5] modified van der Waals's equation, using reduced quantities and an exponential function. For *liquids*, Barus,[6] Amagat,[7] and Ramsay and Young,[8] all found that p is a linear function of T at constant volume, but in the critical region $(dp/dT)_v$ is a function of temperature. For ether *vapour* at 175°–325° Beattie [9] found the isochores to be straight lines up to a concentration of (1/15) g./ml.; with higher concentrations they showed a slight curvature.

Hirschfelder, Stevenson, and Eyring [10] calculated that for closely packed molecules in a liquid, van der Waals's equation takes the form:

$$(p+a/v^2)(v-\phi b^{1/3}v^{2/3})=RT,$$

where $\phi=0·7163$ for body-centred packing of spheres, and $\phi=0·6962$ for face-centred packing of spheres. Bradford [11] deduced $A(p+K)(v-b)=\lambda^2RT$, where K=internal pressure, A=association factor, λ=ratio of most probable molecular velocity in a real fluid to that in an ideal gas.

1 Lévy, *Compt. Rend.*, 1878, **87**, 449, 488; Massieu, *ibid.*, 1878, **87**, 731; Fitzgerald, *Proc. Roy. Soc.*, 1887, **42**, 50; Thiesen, *Ann. Phys.*, 1897, **63**, 329; Wassmuth, *ibid.*, 1909, **30**, 381; Onnes and Keesom, "Enzykl. d. math. Wiss.," 1912, **5**, i, 757; Wicksell, *Phil. Mag.*, 1912, **24**, 869.
2 *Proc. Nat. Acad.*, 1920, **6**, 302.
3 Keyes and Felsing, *J.A.C.S.*, 1919, **41**, 589; 1920, **42**, 106.
4 *Arch. Néerl.*, 1923, **6**, 153.
5 *Compt. Rend.*, 1947, **224**, 1345; 1947, **225**, 671, 1288.
6 *Phil. Mag.*, 1890, **30**, 338.
7 *Ann. Chim.*, 1893, **29**, 505.
8 *Z. phys. Chem.*, 1887, **1**, 433.
9 *J.A.C.S.*, 1924, **46**, 342.
10 *J. Chem. Phys.*, 1937, **5**, 896; Eyring, *J. Phys. Chem.*, 1939, **43**, 37.
11 *Proc. Phys. Soc.*, 1938, **50**, 30; *Phil. Mag.*, 1943, **34**, 433.

Batschinski [1] pointed out that a van der Waals p, v curve cuts the ideal gas curve $pv=RT$ in two points, (i) $v=\infty$, and (ii) $v=k$, for which:

$$bRT/(v-b)=a/v,$$

and he called $1/k$ the *orthometric density*. This was found to be a linear function of temperature, $1/k=1/b-RT/a$. He also [2] found that the equation:

$$v^2(RT-pv)/(v/k-1)=\text{const.},$$

$$\text{or}\quad p=RT-(A-B/v)(v/k-1)/(v^2-s),$$

where A, B, k, and s are constants, agreed with the results for *iso*pentane and ether.

Van der Waals [3] considered that his equation could be used to calculate the coefficients of expansion of liquids. Berger [4] calculated the coefficients of expansion of liquids from the approximate van der Waals equation ($p\simeq0$), $(a/v^2)(v-b)=RT$ as $\alpha=(1/v)(dv/dT)_p=Cw^2/(2-w)$ where $w=v/b$ and $C=Rb/a=\alpha(1+\alpha T)/(1+2\alpha T)^2=8/27T_c$. The values of a and b calculated from α do not agree with those found from the critical constants, but the values of C found from α and T_c are in fair agreement, except for associated liquids. The law of corresponding states (§ 16) is in good agreement if the values of b calculated from α are used. If $p_x=p/(a/b^2)$, $T_x=T/(a/Rb)$, then $(p_x+1/w^2)(w-1)=T_x$, $w=2/[1+\sqrt{(1-4T_x)}]$, which is modified to:

$$w=3/[1+\tfrac{1}{6}\sqrt{(1-\tfrac{27}{8}T_x)}].$$

This gives good results for the coefficient of expansion from the m.p. to the b.p.

An equation suggested by Hall,[5] $a=(\alpha/\kappa)(T-p)v^2$, where α=coefficient of expansion, κ=liquid compressibility, was checked by Smith [6] for alcohol and ether near the b.ps.

For liquids the value of $(dp/dT)_v$, which, from (4), § 11, is equal to $R/(v-b)$, or $(p+a/v^2)/T$, can be written as a/v^2T, the external pressure p being negligible in comparison with the internal pressure a/v^2. If $v=M/\rho$ (M=*normal* mol. wt., ρ=density) is substituted, it is found that $(dp/dT)_v$ so calculated does not always agree with that found from the critical constants with $a=(27/24)RT_cv_c$ (§ 17), and Herzog [7] assumed this to be due to association. By using $R/x(v-b)$ instead of $R/(v-b)$ he calculated the degree of association x for some liquids and found it of the order of 2, agreeing with that found by other methods, e.g. surface tension (§7.VIII G, Vol. II). Reinganum [8] put $a/v^2=T(dp/dT)_v-p$ and found that, near the critical point, $a+m(da/dT)_v=n$, where m and n are constants. Since a/v^2 is supposed to measure the internal pressure, Hildebrand [9] took the value of $T(dp/dT)_v$ as the value of the internal pressure, and made extensive use of this approximation.[10]

[1] *Ann. Phys.*, 1905, **19**, 307.
[2] *Ann. Phys.*, 1905, **19**, 310; 1906, **21**, 1001.
[3] "Continuität," 1899, **1**, 161 f.; *J. Chim. Phys.*, 1904, **2**, 7.
[4] *Z. phys. Chem.*, 1924, **111**, 129; 1925, **115**, 1.
[5] *Ann. Phys., Boltzmann Festschr.*, 1904, 899.
[6] *Proc. Amer. Acad.*, 1907, **42**, 421.
[7] *Z. phys. Chem.*, 1930, **147**, 118.
[8] *Ann. Phys.*, 1905, **18**, 1008.
[9] *J.A.C.S.*, 1919, **41**, 1067; 1921, **43**, 500; "Solubility," New York, 1936; Karpen, *Compt. Rend.*, 1922, **174**, 1693.
[10] See Mortimer, *J.A.C.S.*, 1923, **45**, 633; Glasstone, "Recent Advances in General Chemistry," 1936, 243 f.

§ 13. Variability of van der Waals's *a* and *b* with Pressure and Temperature

Although van der Waals's equation agrees fairly well with Amagat's isotherms (§§ 6, 9.VII A) at higher temperatures, the two "constants" *a* and *b* are really functions of temperature.[1] Van der Waals admitted from the first a variation of *b* with pressure, but regarded *a* as constant. The variation of *b* was represented by:

$$b=b_\infty[1-17b_\infty/32V+0{\cdot}0958(b_\infty/V)^2+\ldots] \quad . \quad . \quad . \quad (1)$$

where b_∞ is the value for $V\to\infty$ or $p=0$.

It would be expected that the (ideal) volume of a gas would be reduced by increasing attraction (*a*) and increased by the volume of the molecules (*b*), hence the ratio *a*/*b* should increase with decreasing molar volume of the actual gas. This is found not to be the case.[2] For carbon dioxide *b* increases with rise of temperature; for helium it decreases. The inconstancy of *b* for carbon dioxide over a wide range of pressure is seen by assuming *a* to be constant at 100° C., and using Amagat's *p* and *v* data to calculate *b* by the equation: [3]

$$(p+0{\cdot}00874/v^2)(v-b)=1{\cdot}00646\times 373/273,$$

where *v* is the ratio of the volume to the actual volume at S.T.P.

p atm.	50	100	300	500	1000
v ...	0·02413	0·01030	0·00297	0·00240	0·000199
b ...	0·00298	0·00276	0·00191	0·00172	0·00156

The isochores (lines of constant volume) calculated from van der Waals's equation and those found experimentally by Ramsay and Young [4] may also be compared.[5] From the complete isotherms for ether (Fig. 4.VII C), for example, the corresponding values of pressure and temperature for each constant value of *v* can be read off outside the heterogeneous region. The plots of these values of *p* against *T* are isochores, and Ramsay and Young found them to be accurately straight lines, as required by van der Waals's equation (v=const.)

$$p=RT/(v-b)-a/v^2=kT-c \quad . \quad . \quad . \quad . \quad . \quad . \quad . \quad (2)$$

where *k* is the tangent of the angle made by the isochore with the *T* axis and

[1] De Heen and Dwelshauvers-Dery, *Bull. Acad. Roy. Belg.*, 1894, **28**, 46; Amagat, *Compt. Rend.*, 1894, **118**, 566; Traube, *Ann. Phys.*, 1897, **61**, 380, 391, 396; 1901, **5**, 548; 1902, **8**, 267; 1907, **22**, 519; *Z. phys. Chem.*, 1909, **68**, 289; van der Waals, *Verslag. K. Akad. Wetens. Amsterdam*, 1898, **7**, 160, 408, 477; *Z. phys. Chem.*, 1899, **31**, 157; 1901, **38**, 257; *Arch. Néerl.*, 1901, **4**, 299; *Ann. Phys., Boltzmann Festschr.*, 1904, 305; *J. Chim. Phys.*, 1904, **2**, 7; Rose-Innes and Young, *Phil. Mag.*, 1899, **47**, 353; Lewis, *Proc. Amer. Acad.*, 1899, **35**, 1; Berthelot, *Compt. Rend.*, 1900, **130**, 115; Reinganum, *Ann. Phys.*, 1905, **18**, 1008; *Z. Elektrochem.*, 1910, **16**, 662; von Jüptner, *Z. phys. Chem.*, 1908, **63**, 579; 1910, **73**, 343; Nabl, *Wien Ber.*, 1911, **120**, II A, 851; Wicksell, *Phil. Mag.*, 1912, **24**, 869 (new equation in series); Wohl, *Z. phys. Chem.*, 1914, **87**, 1; Kam, *Phil. Mag.*, 1916, **31**, 22; 1919, **37**, 65. Onnes and Keesom, "Enzykl. d. math. Wiss.," 1912, **5**, i, 703, pointed out that *a* and *b* are, in general, functions of both *v* and *T*.

[2] Fuchs, *Z. phys. Chem.*, 1913, **84**, 755; on molecular deformation in strongly compressed gases as detected by a change in optical properties, see Michels and de Groot, *Nederland. Tijdschr. Natuurkde.*, 1946, **12**, 77.

[3] Jellinek, "Lehrbuch der physikalischen Chemie," 1928, **1**, 657.

[4] *Phil. Mag.*, 1887, **23**, 435; *Phil. Trans.*, 1887, **178**, 57.

[5] Jellinek, *op. cit.*, 670.

c is the intercept on the *p* axis at $T=0$ (*p* negative). The numerical values of the constants *k* and *c* were not, however, in good agreement with the equation, since *a* varied from 2691×10^3 to 5320×10^3 (*p* in mm. Hg, *v* in ml.) and *b* from 1·47 to 5·60, for a volume range from 3 ml. to 300 ml. The isochores for *iso*-pentane (a normal substance) are not straight but slightly curved.[1]

The variation of *b* with pressure (or volume) was considered by van der Waals.[2] The values of $f=(T_c/p_c)(\mathrm{d}p/\mathrm{d}T)_{T=T_c}=4$, and $g=\boldsymbol{R}T_c/p_cv_c=8/3$ calculated from his equation are in disagreement with experiment. He found that $(f-1)/3=h$ and $g=(8/3)\sqrt{h}$, where *h* is a constant, which for most normal substances is approximately equal to 2. He thence calculated $\mathrm{d}b/\mathrm{d}v$ and $\mathrm{d}^2b/\mathrm{d}v^2$ at the critical point. The assumption of the dependence of *b* alone on temperature and the constancy of *a* is, however, not generally compatible with experimental results.[3]

Herz [4] calculated the values of b_c at the critical point by the equation $b_c=\boldsymbol{R}T_c/8p_c$, and found them proportional to M/ρ_c, where ρ_c is the critical density in g./ml., and there is a relation with the absolute volume of the molecules calculated from the refractive index [5] *n* as $(n^2-1)M/(n^2+2)\rho$. Lorenz and Herz[6] calculated a_0 at 0° K. from the equation of van Laar,[7] $a_0=Av_0\boldsymbol{R}$, as $a_0=A(M/\rho_0)\times82{\cdot}07\times2{\cdot}303$.

Hall [8] calculated *a* from Amagat's experiments on the compressibility of liquids, and compared it with the vapour value, obtaining good agreement with ether but poor agreement with alcohol (an associated liquid). Pavlov,[9] for liquids of the same boiling-point, found $(b-b_1)/(ab-a_1b_1)=12$. Jablczynski [10] concluded that *b* is constant but *a* a function of pressure and temperature for nitrogen, oxygen, ethylene, and carbon dioxide; Neusser [11] that both *a* and *b* decrease with rise of temperature for inert gases. Chatley [12] proposed $a=2a_c(1-T/2T_c)$; Dalton [13] proposed $a=a_ce^{\beta(T_c-T)}$, where $\beta=2{\cdot}48\times10^{-8}$ for *iso*pentane, $\ln a=\alpha-\beta T$, where α and β are constants, for several substances.

Boltzmann and Mache [14] assumed *a* constant, but $b=b_0-c/(v^2+d)$, where b_0, *c*, and *d* are constants. Van der Waals [15] later concluded that the experimental

1 Young, *Proc. Phys. Soc.*, 1895, **13**, 602; "Stoichiometry," 1918, 193; Traube, *Ann. Phys.*, 1897, **61**, 380; 1901, **5**, 548; 1902, **8**, 267; 1907, **22**, 519; *Z. phys. Chem.*, 1909, **68**, 289; Reinganum, *Ann. Phys.*, 1905, **18**, 1008.

2 *Proc. K. Akad. Wetens. Amsterdam*, 1912–13, **21**, 800, 947, 1074; "Weiteres zur Zustandsgleichung," Leipzig, 1913; *Z. Elektrochem.*, 1914, **20**, 142; cf. *Proc. K. Akad. Wetens. Amsterdam*, 1901, **3**, 415, 571, 643; *Arch. Néerl.*, 1901, **6**, 47; *Ann. Phys. Boltzmann Festschr.*, 1904, 305; *J. Chim. Phys.*, 1904, **2**, 7.

3 Happel, *Ann. Phys.*, 1904, **13**, 340; 1906, **21**, 342; 1909, **30**, 175; 1910, **31**, 841; Rudorf, *ibid.*, 1909, **29**, 751; 1910, **31**, 416.

4 *Z. Elektrochem.*, 1923, **29**, 527.

5 Herz, *Z. Elektrochem.*, 1929, **35**, 456.

6 *Z. anorg. Chem.*, 1930, **186**, 164; Lorenz, *Z. phys. Chem.*, 1928, **139**, 1.

7 "Die Zustandsgleichung," Leipzig, 1924, 279.

8 *Ann. Phys. Boltzmann Festschr.*, 1904, 899.

9 *J. Phys. Chem. U.S.S.R.*, 1932, **3**, 448, 455, 477.

10 *Roczn. Chem.*, 1932, **12**, 773; 1933, **13**, 75; *Phys. Z.*, 1932, **33**, 536.

11 *Phys. Z.*, 1930, **31**, 1041; 1932, **33**, 76.

12 *Phil. Mag.*, 1921, **42**, 183.

13 *Trans. Roy. Soc. S. Africa*, 1914, **4**, 123; 1924, **11**, 209.

14 *Trans. Cambr. Phil. Soc.*, 1899, **18**, 91; *Ann. Phys.*, 1899, **68**, 350; Boltzmann, "Wiss. Abhl.," 1909, **3**, 651, 654, 658; cf. Maxwell, *Nature*, 1874, **10**, 477; Tait, *Proc. Roy. Soc. Edin.*, 1886, **33**, 1 (90); Rayleigh, *Nature*, 1891, **44**, 499, 597; 1892, **45**, 80; "Scientific Papers," Cambridge, 1902, **3**, 465, 469; van der Waals, *Proc. K. Akad. Wetens. Amsterdam*, 1899, **1**, 138, 468.

15 *Proc. K. Akad. Wetens. Amsterdam*, 1910, **13**, 107, 491; *Chem. Weekbl.*, 1913, **10**, 628

results could not be explained by the assumption that b was a function of volume, and he adopted the idea of molecular clustering (§ 46) or "quasi-association." Schuster[1] used the formulae $b_b=v_c-(RT_b/B_b)$, $b_c=RT_c/8p_c$, $b_b=0{\cdot}64b_c$, and $v_b-b_b=0{\cdot}23b_c$, where the suffix b refers to the b.p. and c to the critical temperature, and B is the internal pressure. Berthelot[2] used $b_T=b_c[1+0{\cdot}3(T/T_c-1)]$.

Guye[3] calculated the "limiting" values of a and b for easily liquefiable gases from the formulae $a_0=a(T_c/T)^{3/2}$, and $b=b_0[1-(T_c-T)/T_c](1-0{\cdot}0_232229p_c/p)$ and used a_0 and b_0 in reducing gas densities to the ideal state. A much simpler method, used by Kuenen,[4] is described in § 8. Reinganum[5] found that $a+k(\mathrm{d}a/\mathrm{d}T)_v=$const. Pagliani[6] concluded that b in $p(v-b)=$const. for liquids should increase with rise of temperature if v is the volume for $p\to\infty$, but with liquids like ether, the compressibility of which increases rapidly with rise of temperature, b decreases. At a given temperature, b increases with the number of atoms in the molecule, and $\sqrt[3]{(Mb)}$, where $M=$mol. wt., is supposed to be proportional to the molecular diameter.

§ 14. Empirical Formulas for the van der Waals Constants

From the relations of a and b to the critical constants (§ 7), and the numerous empirical formulae for the latter (§§ 7–11.VII B), several empirical equations for a and b may be found, some of which are given here. From the formulae $T_c/np_c=0{\cdot}90$, $T_c/Zp_c=0{\cdot}44$, $v_c/Z=0{\cdot}00044$, $1000v_c=T_c/p_c$ (p_c is in atm., $v_c=$ fraction of the ideal gas volume at S.T.P.), where $n=$no. of atoms in molecule, $Z=$sum of valencies in molecule (for aromatic compounds the valency of carbon is taken as 3), and the equation $(p+a/v^2)(v-b)=T/273$, it is found[7] that $b=(4n/Z)\times10^{-6}=201Z\times10^{-6}$. The equation[8] (which applies only to compounds free from nitrogen) $n=193M^2/T_b^2\rho_b$, where $M=$mol. wt., $T_b=$b.p. abs., $\rho_b=$density at b.p., gives[7] $b=(795{\cdot}16M^2/T_b^2\rho_b)\times10^{-4}$. The equation[9] $M=\rho_bT_c/0{\cdot}1176p_c$, with $T_c=1{\cdot}5T_b$, gives[7] $b=(12354\rho_b/p_c^2)\times10^{-3}$ and $a=(27/64\times273^2)T_c^2/p_c$, or with T_c/p_c in terms of n or Z, $a=5{\cdot}094nT_c\times10^{-6}=2{\cdot}49ZT_c\times10^{-6}=4{\cdot}584n^2p_c\times10^{-6}$. Jorissen's equation[8] gives $a=1474{\cdot}713\times10^{-6}M^2/T_b\rho_b$, and Boutaric's equation,[9] $a=239920\times10^{-6}\rho_bT_b/p_c^2$. Herz's equation[10] $T_c=\frac{1}{2}(1/\alpha_{20}+293)$, where $\alpha_{20}=$coefficient of expansion at 20° C., gives, on substitution in $a=5{\cdot}094nT_c\times10^{-6}$, and division by $b=412n\times10^{-6}$, the equation $\alpha_{20}=1/(a/0{\cdot}00618b-293)$. In these equations b is a fraction of the molar volume in the ideal state at S.T.P. From the equation (§ 11.VII B) $l_e=p_cT_b/T_cp_c$, Herz[11] found $b=T_b/2184l_e\rho_c$, where $l_e=$latent heat of evaporation; and from $l_e=0{\cdot}00093T_b/\rho_cv_c$, he found $b=v_c/2{\cdot}031$. By taking $\rho_cRT_c/Mp_c=3{\cdot}875$ (the usual value is 3·75; § 20), he found $b=0{\cdot}0000216M/\rho_c$, and from $a=27p_cb^2$ it follows that $a=1{\cdot}26\times10^8p_c(M/\rho_c)^2$.

[1] *Ber.*, 1925, **58**, 2183.
[2] *Compt. Rend.*, 1900, **130**, 115.
[3] Friderich and Guye, *Arch. Sci. Phys. Nat.*, 1900, **9**, 505; Guye, *J. Chim. Phys.*, 1905, **3**, 321.
[4] *Ann. Phys.*, 1905, **17**, 189.
[5] *Ann. Phys.*, 1905, **18**, 1008.
[6] *Atti R. Accad. Lincei*, 1901, **10**, ii, 69; *Nuov. Cim.*, 1901, **2**, 122; for ether, see Taylor and Smith, *J.A.C.S.*, 1922, **44**, 2450.
[7] Herz, *Z. anorg. Chem.*, 1920, **109**, 293; 1920, **114**, 153; *Z. Elektrochem.*, 1921, **27**, 373.
[8] Jorissen, *J. Chim. Phys.*, 1920, **18**, 25; Herz, *Z. anorg. Chem.*, 1921, **116**, 250.
[9] Boutaric, *Compt. Rend.*, 1912, **155**, 1080; *Ann. Chim.*, 1914, **1**, 437.
[10] *Z. anorg. Chem.*, 1920, **112**, 278; *Z. Elektrochem.*, 1921, **27**, 125.
[11] *Z. Elektrochem.*, 1920, **27**, 26; 1921, **27**, 373.

Paul [1] deduced the equation:

$$b=\{v''-v'\sqrt{[(v''/v')x]}\}/\{1-\sqrt{[(v''/v')x]}\}$$

where $x=e^{L_e/RT}$, L_e being the latent heat of evaporation per mol, v' and v'' the specific volumes of liquid and gas, and he found the calculated values of b almost independent of temperature. According to Walden,[2] $b_c/V_b=1{\cdot}26$ (V_b=molar vol. at b.p.) for normal liquids, but the ratio falls to 1·13 for substances of low b.p. (N_2, etc.). Gay [3] found v_c/b=const.=3·6 and RT_c/p_cb= const.= 13·65.

Attempts have been made to calculate values of the constants a and b for compound molecules from atomic values. If A is the value of a for the compound $X_mY_pZ_q$ and a the " atomic " value, van Laar [4] proposed the equation:

$$A^{1/2}=ma_X{}^{1/2}+pa_Y{}^{1/2}+qa_Z{}^{1/2},$$

but found that one constant (a_X, a_Y, or a_Z) must be put equal to zero; he suggested that this was because some atoms are " screened " by being inside the molecule. Barbulescu [5] proposed to divide the van der Waals a by the atomic or molecular weight to give a " specific attraction " constant a_s, and found that:

$$A_s^2=ma_{sX}{}^2+pa_{sY}{}^2+qa_{sZ}{}^2.$$

For organic compounds he supposed that $a_{sX}=a_{sY}=a_{sZ}$, and hence if $n=m+p+q\doteq$no. of atoms in molecule:

$$A_s^2=n\bar{a}_s^2$$

where $\bar{a}_s$ is a mean specific factor, approximately $4{\cdot}10\times10^{-3}$ lit.^{2} atm. The values were in fair agreement with those calculated from $a_c=(27/64)(R^2T_c^2/p_c)$ (§ 7).

§ 15. Internal Pressure of a Liquid

Young [6] calculated the internal pressure K in water as about 23,000 atm. Dupré,[7] who recognised, correctly, that there is an expansive pressure opposing the internal pressure and due to the heat motion of the molecules, found the equation $K=l_{ei}/v$, where l_{ei} is the internal latent heat of evaporation and v the sp. vol., and for water he calculated K to be 23,900 atm., in good agreement with Young's value. Rayleigh [8] drew attention to Young's idea of intrinsic pressure (as Rayleigh called the internal pressure), and pointed out that there must be an intrinsic repulsive pressure to balance it, but he did not follow up the suggestion, which was afterwards developed in detail by T. W. Richards.[9]

Geissler [10] proposed the formula $K=S/(V-v)^n$, where V=total molar volume, v=minimum volume, and S and n are constants, and attempted to calculate n

1 *Z. phys. Chem.*, 1939, **183**, 321.
2 *Z. phys. Chem.*, 1909, **66**, 385.
3 *Compt. Rend.*, 1910, **151**, 612; 1911, **153**, 262, 722; 1913, **156**, 1015, 1070; 1913, **157**, 711; 1914, **158**, 34.
4 *J. Chim. Phys.*, 1916, **14**, 3.
5 *Bull Soc. Sci. Cluj*, 1936, **8**, 462; *J. Chim. Phys.*, 1938, **35**, 27.
6 *Phil. Trans.*, 1805, **95**, 71.
7 *Ann. Chim.*, 1864, **2**, 185; Worthington, *Phil. Mag.*, 1884, **18**, 334; see on various calculations of K, Lewis, *Trans. Faraday Soc.*, 1911, **7**, 94; Takénchi, *Proc. Phys. Math. Soc. Japan*, 1931, **13**, 17.
8 *Phil. Mag.*, 1890, **30**, 285, 456; " Scientific Papers," Cambridge, 1902, **3**, 397.
9 See § 4.IX N, Vol. II.
10 *Z. Elektrochem.*, 1918, **24**, 101.

from the critical volume. Schuster[1] from Stefan's formula (see § 6.VIII G, Vol. II) $(K-p)V \simeq KV = Ml_e/2$, and the Clapeyron-Clausius equation (see § 7.VIII L, Vol. II), $Ml_e = RT^2(\mathrm{d}\ln p/\mathrm{d}T)$, found $K=(RT^2/2V_m)(\mathrm{d}\ln p/dT)$, where V_m=molar volume. From van der Waals's vapour-pressure equation (see § 22):

$$\ln(p_c/p)=f(T_c/T-1),$$

where f=const., it follows that:

$$-\mathrm{d}\ln p/\mathrm{d}T=-fT_c/T^2+(T_c/T-1)\mathrm{d}f/\mathrm{d}T \simeq -fT_c/T^2$$

$$\therefore\ K=(RT_c/2V_m)f=(R/2V_m)TT_c\ln(p_c/p)/(T_c-T)$$

$$=41{\cdot}04TT_c\ln(p_c/p)/V_m(T_c-T)$$

if p is in atm. and V_m in ml./mol. (R=82·08). At 1 atm. pressure (b.p.):

$$K_b=41{\cdot}04T_bT_c\ln p_c/V_{bm}(T_c-T_b).$$

The values agree with those calculated by Walden.[2]

Expressions for the internal pressure K are those of Herzog,[3] $K=3{\cdot}7RT/(v-b)$; Herz,[4] $K=a_T/v^2=3p_cT_c\rho^2/\rho_c^2T$, where $a_T=3p_cT_c/\rho_c^2T$ from Clausius's equation (§ 28), $K\alpha$ (α=coefficient of expansion) being approximately 2 but showing some temperature variation; and Bradford,[5] $A(p+K)(v-b)=\lambda^2RT$, where λ is the ratio of the most probable molecular velocity in a real fluid to that in an ideal gas (§ 10.III), and A is an association factor.

Amagat[6] calculated the internal pressure from the semi-empirical equation (§ 12) $K=T(\mathrm{d}p/\mathrm{d}T)_v-p \simeq T(\mathrm{d}p/\mathrm{d}T)_v$. K is then independent of temperature, but is a function of volume, reaching a maximum at a volume ϵ. The co-volume is a function of volume, and:

$$[p+A(v-\epsilon)/v^m][v-\alpha+B(v-\alpha)^n]=RT,$$

where A, B, and α are constants. He also used $K+p=p_cv_c/v$. He compared the internal pressure $K=T(\mathrm{d}p/\mathrm{d}T)_v-p$ with that, $w=\Sigma Rr/3v$, calculated by the virial equation (§ 40), which gives $w=(p_0v_0-pv)/v$. The two values are not in agreement and he gave the preference to w.

Smith[7] showed for alcohol and ether that $a/v^2+p=T(\mathrm{d}v/\mathrm{d}T)_p(\mathrm{d}v/\mathrm{d}p)_T$. It is usually supposed that the internal pressure decreases without limit with rise of temperature, but Leduc[8] concluded that it decreases to a finite limit and does not vanish for $T\to\infty$.

§ 16. The Law of Corresponding States

The van der Waals equation contains three constants, a, b, and R. These may be expressed in terms of the three critical constants p_c, v_c, and T_c by means of equations (7), § 7:

$$b=v_c/3,\quad a=3p_cv_c^2,\quad R=(8/3)p_cv_c/T_c \quad . \quad . \quad . \quad . \quad (1)$$

[1] *Z. anorg. Chem.*, 1925, **146**, 299; *Ber.*, 1925, **58**, 2183.
[2] *Z. phys. Chem.*, 1909, **66**, 385.
[3] *Z. phys. Chem.*, 1930, **149**, 89.
[4] *Z. anorg. Chem.*, 1926, **155**, 323; 1926, **157**, 326.
[5] *Proc. Phys. Soc.*, 1938, **50**, 30; *Phil. Mag.*, 1943, **34**, 433.
[6] *J. de Phys.*, 1894, **3**, 307; *Compt. Rend.*, 1894, **118**, 326, 566; 1895, **120**, 489, 580; 1899, **128**, 538, 649; 1906, **142**, 371; 1909, **148**, 1135; 1911, **153**, 851; 1912, **154**, 909; *J. de Phys.*, 1909, **8**, 617; " Notes sur la Physique," 1912, 85, 98, 103, 110, 117, 124, 129; *Ann. Chim.*, 1913, **28**, 5; Dubief, *Compt. Rend.*, 1926, **182**, 688.
[7] *Proc. Amer. Acad.*, 1907, **42**, 421.
[8] *Compt. Rend.*, 1915, **161**, 97.

When substituted in the van der Waals equation:

$$(p+a/v^2)(v-b)=RT \quad . . . . (2)$$

these give:

$$(p+3p_c v_c^2/v^2)(v-v_c/3)=(8/3)p_c v_c T/T_c \quad . . . . . (3)$$

$$[p/p_c+3(v_c/v)^2](3v/v_c-1)=8T/T_c \quad . . . . . . (4)$$

If the pressure, volume, and temperature are expressed as fractions of the critical values, giving the so-called *reduced pressure*, *reduced volume*, and *reduced temperature*: [1]

$$\pi=p/p_c, \quad \phi=v/v_c, \quad \vartheta=T/T_c \quad . . . . (5)$$

then (4) becomes:

$$(\pi+3/\phi^2)(3\phi-1)=8\vartheta \quad . . . . (6)$$

which is called the *reduced van der Waals's equation.* With appropriate values of π, ϕ, and ϑ this should hold for any mass of any substance. It is assumed, of course, that the molecular state is the same throughout the range of pressure, volume, and temperature, i.e. no association is present. Schames [2] introduced the ratio $k=M/M_0$ of the molecular weight to the ideal gas value, and if k, k_c are the values at a given temperature and the critical temperature, he wrote the reduced equation (6) as:

$$[\phi(k/k_c)-1/3][\pi+3(k-1)/\phi^2\vartheta(k_c-1)]=(8/3)\vartheta.$$

Substances having the same values of π, ϕ, and ϑ are said to be in *corresponding states.*[3] Equation (6) now contains no specific constants of particular substances [4] and should, therefore, be a general equation for all gases and liquids. It is one form of what is called a *law of corresponding states.*

Many other characteristic equations besides van der Waals's, but not all, lead to laws of corresponding states, although the exact form of the equation corresponding with (6) varies from case to case. The general expression of the law of corresponding states is that *all substances should behave alike for the same values of* π, ϕ, *and* ϑ. This is approximately true. The behaviour excludes chemical activity, but is wider than mere pressure, volume, and temperature relations. Equation (12), § 5.II, becomes, in terms of corresponding states, $(d\pi/d\phi)_S=-\gamma\pi/\phi$, where S=entropy and γ is the ratio of specific heats.[5]

The most general form of characteristic equation is:

$$F(p, v, T, c_1, c_2, c_3, \ldots)=0 \quad . . . . (7)$$

where F is a function of the variables p, v, and T, and of $c_1, c_2, c_3, \ldots$, which are constants characteristic of the particular substance, including the molecular weight (since the constant $\boldsymbol{R}$ in the equation $pv=\boldsymbol{R}T$ is the same only for equimolecular amounts). Equation (7) holds, and at the critical point the two equations (8) of § 7:

$$(dp/dv)_T=0, \quad \text{and} \quad (d^2p/dv^2)_T=0 \quad . . . . . (8)$$

1 The symbols π, ϕ, ϑ are those recommended by the committee on symbols, *Trans. Faraday Soc.*, 1910, **5**, 252; the German AEF symbols are p_r, v_r, T_r, Aufschlüsse für Einheiten und Formelgrössen, *Verhl. d. D. Phys. Ges.*, 1910, **12**, 476; also Anglo-American provisional symbols, *J.A.C.S.*, 1914, **36**, 46. Natanson, *Compt. Rend.*, 1889, **109**, 855, called them the *specific* pressure, volume, and temperature.

2 *Ann. Phys.*, 1912, **38**, 830; 1912, **39**, 887; *Verhl. d. D. Phys. Ges.*, 1913, **15**, 1017; *Phys. Z.*, 1913, **14**, 1172.

3 Van der Waals, *Verhl. K. Akad. Wetens. Amsterdam*, 1881, **21**, No. V.

4 The values of p_c, v_c, and T_c are, of course, specific for every substance, so that the calculation of π, ϕ, and ϑ requires a knowledge of these in every case.

5 Bakker, *Z. phys. Chem.*, 1896, **21**, 127, 506.

then allow *three* constants in (7) to be expressed in terms of the critical constants. If the resulting equation is a reduced equation, such as (6) in a special case, it must contain no constants characteristic of the substance; hence (7) can contain only *three* such constants. In this case it can always be written in the form:

$$f(p/p_c, v/v_c, T/T_c)=0, \quad \text{or} \quad f(\pi, \phi, \vartheta)=0 \quad . \quad . \quad . \quad (9)$$

Hence, a characteristic equation leads to a law of corresponding states when it contains only three characteristic constants and shows a critical point.[1] This is the case with van der Waals's equation. Characteristic equations containing more than three constants (e.g. Clausius's and Wohl's) take account of deviations from the law of corresponding states.

§ 17. Tests of the Law of Corresponding States

Experiments to test the law of corresponding states were made by Amagat [2] and Raveau; [3] the latter plotted the logarithms of the reduced pressures and volumes for various substances:

$$\log \phi = \log v - \log v_c = \log v - \text{const.},$$
$$\log \pi = \log p - \log p_c = \log p - \text{const.},$$

for various values of the reduced temperature ϑ according to (6), § 16. The observed values of log p and log v were then plotted on a translucent sheet of paper, and this laid over the first sheet of curves. Since the reduction of log p to log π and of log v to log ϕ requires merely the addition (or subtraction) of a constant, it should be possible to bring the two sets of curves into coincidence merely by shifting one sheet over the other parallel to the axes of p and v. The critical point was brought into coincidence, and it was then found that the two sets of curves did not exactly coincide, but cut one another (Fig. 6.VII C, for CO_2). The reduced van der Waals equation is, therefore, not strictly accurate.

Young,[4] in an extensive series of careful experiments (see § 19), found that the law of corresponding states itself is not rigorously exact. It should not be overlooked, however, that, even in the case of van der Waals's equation, some of the proposed tests are extremely sensitive, and even quite small experimental errors would be greatly magnified in the mathematical treatment used. Very few equations in other branches of science would survive such tests.

[1] Natanson, *Compt. Rend.*, 1889, **109**, 855, 890; *Z. phys. Chem.*, 1892, **9**, 26; Curie, *Arch. Sci. Phys. Nat.*, 1891, **26**, 13; Mathias, *Ann. Fac. Sci. Toulouse*, 1891, **5**, F; Meslin, *Compt. Rend.*, 1893, **116**, 135; Brillouin, *J. de Phys.*, 1893, **2**, 113; Boltzmann, " Gastheorie," 1898, **2**, 27; Hilton, *Phil. Mag.*, 1901, **1**, 579; 1901, **2**, 108; Berthelot, *J. de Phys.*, 1903, **2**, 186; van Iterson, *Z. phys. Chem.*, 1905, **53**, 633; Haig, *Phil. Mag.*, 1908, **16**, 201; Ter Gazarian, *J. Chim. Phys.*, 1909, **7**, 233; von Kaufmann, *Phil. Mag.*, 1915, **30**, 146; Bochet, *Compt. Rend.*, 1924, **178**, 377, 922; Berthelot, *ibid.*, 1924, **178**, 677; Pinter, *Acta Phys. Polon.*, 1935, **4**, 23; *Z. Elektrochem.*, 1937, **43**, 669.

[2] *Compt. Rend.*, 1896, **123**, 30, 83; 1897, **124**, 547; 1913, **156**, 843; *J. de Phys.*, 1897, **6**, 5; *Z. phys. Chem.*, 1897, **23**, 177 (abstr.); " Notes sur la Physique et la Thermodynamique," 1912, 38 f.

[3] *Compt. Rend.*, 1896, **123**, 100; 1920, **171**, 235, 471; *J. de Phys.*, 1897, **6**, 432; Onnes, *Arch. Néerl.*, 1897, **30**, 101; 1900, **5**, 665 (*Comm. Leiden*, **66**); *Ann. Phys. Beibl.*, 1901, **25**, 189; D. Berthelot, *Compt. Rend.*, 1900, **130**, 565, 713; 1900, **131**, 175; *J. de Phys.*, 1901, **10**, 611; Happel, *Ann. Phys.*, 1904, **13**, 340; 1906, **21**, 342; 1909, **30**, 175; 1910, **31**, 841; 1910, **32**, 868; *Phys. Z.*, 1909, **10**, 687; Schaposchnikow, *Z. phys. Chem.*, 1905, **51**, 542; Onnes and Keesom, " Enzykl. d. math. Wiss.," 1912, **5**, i, 697, 727; Kuenen, " Die Eigenschaften der Gase " (Ostwald-Drucker, " Handbuch der allgemeinen Chemie," **3**), Leipzig, 1919, 393; Byk, *Phys. Z.*, 1921, **22**, 15; Schüle, " Technische Thermodynamik," Berlin, 1923, **2**, 110.

[4] Summary in Young, " Stoichiometry," 1918, 200 f.; Surdin, *J. de Phys.*, 1937, **8**, 294, found that a plot of ϕ against ϑ for many liquids gave a good single curve.

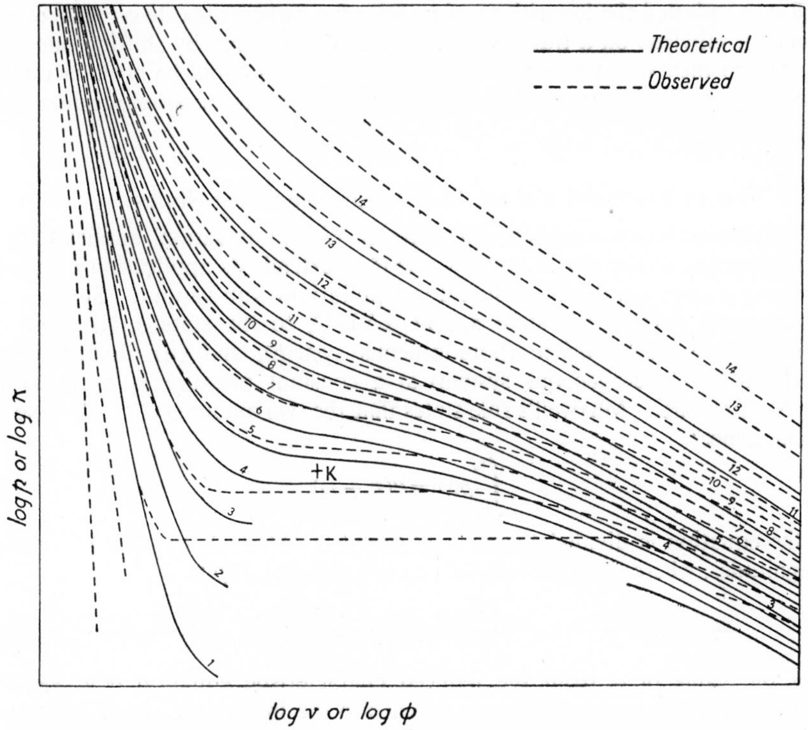

FIG. 6.VII C. Plots of log π against log ϕ for carbon dioxide (K is the critical point). The theoretical and observed curves, although similar in form, cut one another

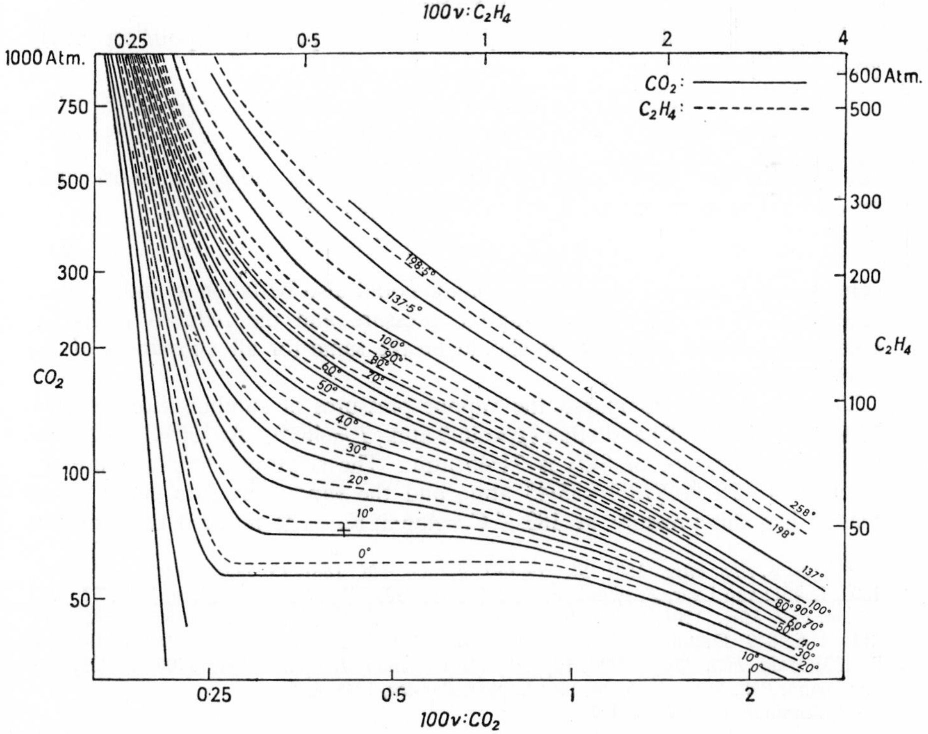

FIG. 7.VII C. Plots of log p against log v for carbon dioxide and ethylene, showing agreement with the Law of Corresponding States

Raveau plotted the logarithms of p and v for carbon dioxide on a sheet, and those for ethylene on a translucent sheet, and found that by shifting one sheet parallel to the axes of p and v the two sets of curves could be brought into an excellent set (Fig. 7.VII C), showing that the *general* law of corresponding states was obeyed.

§ 18. Vapour Pressures and the Law of Corresponding States

The characteristic equation, e.g. van der Waals's equation, applies only to homogeneous states, but Maxwell's rule (§ 9) extends its application to heterogeneous systems composed of liquid in equilibrium with vapour. Suppose the system carried from the state *a*, Fig. 2.VII C, to the state *c*, (i) along the theoretical isotherm *adbec* (homogeneous system), and (ii) along the real isotherm *ac* (heterogeneous system) at a constant pressure *P*, equal to the vapour pressure. Maxwell's rule states that the two amounts of work done are equal, hence:

$$\int_{v_l}^{v_g} p\,dv = P(v_g - v_l).$$

If the equation is divided through by $p_c v_c$ it is obtained in terms of reduced magnitudes, where π_V is the reduced vapour pressure, P/p_c:

$$\int_{\phi_l}^{\phi_g} \pi\,d\phi = \pi_V(\phi_g - \phi_l) \quad . \quad . \quad . \quad . \quad . \quad . \quad . \quad . \quad (1)$$

If the value of π from the reduced characteristic equation (e.g. van der Waals's equation (6), § 16) is introduced into the integral of (1), then on integration an equation containing π_V, ϕ_l, ϕ_g, and ϑ is obtained:

$$\mathrm{F}(\pi_V, \phi_l, \phi_g, \vartheta) = 0 \quad . \quad . \quad . \quad . \quad . \quad . \quad . \quad . \quad . \quad (2)$$

The application of the reduced equation to the liquid and vapour separately gives two equations:

$$\mathrm{f}(\pi_V, \phi_l, \vartheta) = 0 \quad . \quad . \quad . \quad . \quad . \quad . \quad . \quad . \quad . \quad (3)$$

$$\mathrm{f}(\pi_V, \phi_g, \vartheta) = 0 \quad . \quad . \quad . \quad . \quad . \quad . \quad . \quad . \quad . \quad (4)$$

and from the three equations (2)–(4) the values of π_V, ϕ_l, and ϕ_g can, in principle, be determined as functions of the reduced temperature:

$$\pi_V = \mathrm{f}_1(\vartheta),\ \phi_l = \mathrm{f}_2(\vartheta),\ \phi_g = \mathrm{f}_3(\vartheta) \quad . \quad . \quad . \quad . \quad . \quad . \quad (5)$$

(The reduced pressure or reduced volume could also be taken as independent variable.) Thus, the reduced vapour pressure and the reduced molecular volumes of liquid and vapour should be the same for all substances at the same reduced temperature.[1]

Van der Waals[2] compared the vapour pressures of sulphur dioxide (p_c= 78·9 atm., T_c=428·4°) and ether (p_c=36·9 atm., T_c=463°). At 150° C.=423° K., the vapour pressure of SO_2 is 71·45 atm. The corresponding pressure for ether is 71·45×36·9/78·9=33·45 atm., and the vapour-pressure curve shows that it has this pressure at 183·3° C.=456·3° K. The reduced temperatures

1 Clausius, *Ann. Phys.*, 1881, **14**, 279, 692; Planck, *ibid.*, 1881, **13**, 535; Raveau, *J. de Phys.*, 1892, **1**, 461; van Laar, *Z. phys. Chem.*, 1893, **11**, 433, 721; Donnan, *Nature*, 1895, **52**, 619; Hilton, *Phil. Mag.*, 1901, **1**, 579; Ritter, *Wien Ber.*, 1902, **111**, II A, 1046; Pitsch, *ibid.*, 1904, **113**, II A, 849; Dalton, *Phil. Mag.*, 1907, **13**, 517; *Trans. Roy. Soc. S. Africa*, 1914, **4**, ii, 123; Haig, *Phil. Mag.*, 1908, **16**, 201; Ter Gazarian, *J. Chim. Phys.*, 1909, **7**, 233; von Kaufmann, *Phil. Mag.*, 1915, **30**, 146; Decker, *Physica*, 1941, **8**, 59.

2 " Continuität," 1899, **1**, 141.

are 423/428·4=0·987 and 456·3/463=0·986, i.e. practically equal. A complete table shows, however, that the agreement holds only at high pressures.

p atm.	SO_2 $(C_2H_5)_2O$	60 28·4	41·56 19·4	33·95 15·9	22·47 10·5	141·31 6·69	8·43 3·94
$\vartheta=T/T_c$	SO_2 $(C_2H_5)_2O$	0·964 0·963	0·918 0·918	0·894 0·895	0·848 0·849	0·801 0·807	0·754 0·762

§ 19. Young's Experiments on the Law of Corresponding States

The law of corresponding states was tested by Young [1] and co-workers by using vapour-pressure measurements. A selection of the data is given for the substances for which the critical constants [2] are given in Table I.

TABLE I

Substance	Formula	Mol. wt.	t_c° C.	p_c mm. Hg	v_c ml./g.
Fluorobenzene ...	C_6H_5F	95·8	286·55	33910	2·822
Chlorobenzene ...	C_6H_5Cl	112·2	360	33910	2·731
Bromobenzene ...	C_6H_5Br	156·6	397	33910	2·059
Iodobenzene ...	C_6H_5I	203·4	448	33910	1·713
Benzene	C_6H_6	77·84	288·5	36395	3·293
Carbon tetrachloride	CCl_4	153·45	283·15	34180	1·799
Stannic chloride ...	$SnCl_4$	259·3	318·7	28080	1·347
Ether	$(C_2H_5)_2O$	73·84	199·4	27060	3·801
Methyl alcohol ...	CH_3OH	31·93	240·0	59760	3·697
Ethyl alcohol ...	C_2H_5OH	45·90	243·1	47850	6·636
Acetic acid	CH_3COOH	52·86	321·6	43400	2·846

Fluorobenzene was taken as the standard substance. In Table II the ratio of the vapour pressure P to the vapour pressure P' of fluorobenzene at a series of corresponding temperatures ϑ is shown for the other substances in the first table. From the law of corresponding states, the ratio P/p_c should be constant in corresponding states, and for any given substance the ratio P/P' should be constant at various reduced temperatures, i.e. the figures in the vertical columns should be constant for each substance. This is very nearly the case for some substances, but not for others.

In Table III the ratios of the vapour volumes for the substances and fluorobenzene and in Table IV the ratios of the liquid volumes are given for various reduced temperatures. The figures in the vertical columns should again be constant.

The greatest deviations occur with the alcohols and acetic acid, which are regarded as associated substances, the degree of association varying with

[1] *Z. phys. Chem.*, 1887, **1**, 237, 433; 1899, **29**, 193; *J.C.S.*, 1893, **63**, 1191; 1895, **67**, 1071; 1897, **71**, 446; 1898, **73**, 675; 1899, **75**, 873; 1900, **77**, 1126, 1145; 1902, **81**, 783; *Phil. Mag.*, 1892, **33**, 153; 1894, **37**, 1; *Proc. Phys. Soc.*, 1895, **13**, 602; *Proc. Roy. Dublin Soc.*, 1910, **12**, 374; " Stoichiometry," 1918, 200; Dewar, *B.A. Rep.*, 1902, 29; Winkelmann, " Handbuch der Physik," 1906, **3**, 940; graphical applications, Watson, *Ind. Eng. Chem.*, 1943, **35**, 398. On Sidney Young (1857–1937), see Timmermans, *Endeavour*, 1947, **6**, 11.

[2] Young, *Phil. Mag.*, 1892, **34**, 503.

TABLE II

C_6H_5F		C_6H_5Cl	C_6H_5Br	C_6H_5I	C_6H_6	CCl_4	$SnCl_4$	$(C_2H_5)_2O$	CH_3OH	C_2H_5OH	CH_3COOH
T	ϑ										
272·25	0·4866	0·998	0·987	0·985	1·338	1·460	0·706	—	—	—	0·476
338·75	0·6053	1·014	1·008	1·007	1·239	1·253	0·772	0·728	0·579	0·323	0·658
393·25	0·7028	0·998	0·991	0·994	1·163	1·136	0·799	0·758	—	0·587	0·817
444·25	0·7939	0·991	0·996	—	1·120	1·077	0·814	0·775	1·167	0·870	0·956
484·95	0·8666	1·004	—	—	1·102	1·047	0·825	0·795	1·399	1·085	1·083
544·5	0·9729	1·006	—	—	1·078	1·012	0·828	0·800	1·696	1·351	1·248
559·55	1·0000	—	—	—	1·073	1·008	0·828	0·798	1·762	1·411	1·280

TABLE III

C_6H_5F		C_6H_5Cl	C_6H_5Br	C_6H_5I	C_6H_6	CCl_4	$SnCl_4$	$(C_2H_5)_2O$	CH_3OH	C_2H_5OH	CH_3COOH
T	ϑ										
367·3	0·6564	1·118	1·174	1·272	0·842	0·828	1·336	1·101	1·244	2·076	0·894
423·8	0·7571	1·150	1·203	1·281	0·893	0·910	1·313	1·078	0·875	1·284	0·797
460·4	0·8228	1·143	1·189	—	0·923	0·938	1·300	1·054	0·729	1·028	0·745
519·7	0·9287	—	—	—	0·926	0·977	1·262	1·030	0·572	0·763	0·681
555·0	0·9917	—	—	—	—	1·014	—	1·025	0·484	0·648	0·639
559·55	1·0000	—	—	—	0·940	—	—	—	—	—	0·631

TABLE IV

C_6H_5F		C_6H_5Cl	C_6H_5Br	C_6H_5I	C_6H_6	CCl_4	$SnCl_4$	$(C_2H_5)_2O$	CH_3OH	C_2H_5OH	CH_3COOH
T	ϑ										
272·25	0·4866	1·1247	1·1802	1·2761	0·9457	—	1·2657	—	—	—	0·6215
338·75	0·6053	1·1244	1·1798	1·2772	0·9485	1·0267	1·2720	1·0284	0·4152	0·5997	0·6197
393·25	0·7028	1·1236	1·1792	1·2773	0·9484	1·0280	1·2761	1·0290	0·4102	0·5919	0·6196
444·25	0·7939	1·1242	1·1804	—	0·9487	1·0264	1·2786	1·0279	0·4061	0·5867	0·6178
484·95	0·8666	1·1280	—	—	0·9477	1·0270	1·2844	1·0345	0·4040	0·5851	0·6178
544·5	0·9729	—	—	—	0·9489	1·0280	—	1·0421	0·4082	0·5900	0·6227
559·55	1·0000	—	—	—	0·9400	—	—	—	—	—	0·6310

temperature. The remaining substances seem to fall into groups (halogen substituted benzenes; benzene and carbon tetrachloride; stannic chloride and ether).[1]

Another comparison may be made at equal reduced pressures. The reduced volumes [2] of liquid and vapour are given for several substances in Table V for a reduced pressure of $P/p_c=\pi=0{\cdot}08846$ and various reduced temperatures ϑ.

TABLE V

Substance	ϑ	ϕ_l	ϕ_g
Cyclohexane	0·7277	0·4090	27·7
Benzene	0·7282	0·4065	28·3
*iso*pentane	0·7292	0·4085	27·7
n-pentane	0·7331	0·4061	28·4
n-hexane	0·7406	0·4055	29·1
n-heptane	0·7483	0·4029	29·5
n-octane	0·7544	0·4006	29·35
Fluorobenzene	0·7334	0·4067	28·4
Chlorobenzene	0·7345	0·4028	28·5
Bromobenzene	0·7343	0·4024	28·3
Iodobenzene	0·7337	0·4020	28·3
Carbon tetrachloride ...	0·7251	0·4078	27·45
Tin tetrachloride	0·7337	0·4031	28·15
Ether	0·7380	0·4030	28·3
Methyl formate	0·7348	0·4001	29·3
Ethyl formate	0·7385	0·4003	29·6
Methyl acetate	0·7445	0·3989	30·15
Ethyl acetate	0·7504	0·4001	30·25
Acetic acid	0·7624	0·4100	25·4
Methyl alcohol	0·7734	0·3973	34·35
Ethyl alcohol...	0·7794	0·4061	32·15

Herz [3] found that the reduced temperatures at which liquids have equal reduced densities $\rho_r=\rho/\rho_c$ are approximately equal:

ρ_r	$\frac{1}{2}$	$\frac{1}{10}$	$\frac{1}{50}$	2	2·75
ϑ	0·978	0·830	0·697	0·890	0·609

Pall and Maass [4] determined the densities of liquid propylene and methyl ether and found that the law of corresponding states held to 1 in 2000 up to temperatures at least as high as $0{\cdot}96T_c$. Herz [5] did not find the expected regularity with the densities of saturated vapours at $\frac{9}{10}T_c$ and $\frac{2}{3}T_c$.

Table VI gives the reduced vapour pressures $\pi=P/p_c$ for a number of substances at different reduced temperatures.

1 Cf. Herz, *Z. anorg. Chem.*, 1925, **144**, 40; Carroll, *Phil. Mag.*, 1926, **2**, 385.

2 Cf. Meslin, *J. de Phys.*, 1909, **8**, 752; Davis, *Phil. Mag.*, 1912, **23**, 657; Herz, *Z. anorg. Chem.*, 1924, **133**, 177; Salzwedel, *Ann. Phys.*, 1930, **5**, 853; Bauer, Magat, and Surdin, *J. de Phys.*, 1936, **7**, 441, obtained good results with $\vartheta'=(T-T_t)/(T_c-T_t)$, where T_t=abs. triple point, at which solid, liquid, and vapour are in equilibrium.

3 *Z. anorg. Chem.*, 1925, **144**, 40.

4 *Canad. J. Res.*, 1936, **14** B, 96.

5 *Arch. Pharm.*, 1927, **265**, 212.

TABLE VI

ϑ		0·5170	0·6400	0·7334	0·8464
P mm.	Substance	π			
33910	Fluorobenzene	0·00147	0·02241	0·08847	0·2949
33910	Chlorobenzene	0·00149	0·02252	0·08744	0·2956
25210	Propyl acetate	0·00059	0·01404	0·06613	0·2583
25210	Ethyl propionate	0·00059	0·01407	0·06697	0·2585
35180	Methyl acetate	0·00093	0·01765	0·07598	0·2765
30440	Propyl formate	0·00094	0·01799	0·07791	0·2801
25100	*n*-Pentane	0·00154	0·02256	0·08888	0·2960
18730	*n*-Octane	0·00060	0·01406	0·06645	0·2567
34180	Carbon tetrachloride	0·00203	0·02681	0·09801	0·3088

Herz [1] found that the reduced vapour pressures for equal reduced densities of the liquids are approximately equal; for $\rho/\rho_c=2$, $\pi=0{\cdot}464$. For $\rho=2{\cdot}75\rho_c$ the results were less satisfactory, perhaps owing to experimental errors.

Quite appreciable deviations from equality in the vertical columns in Table VI occur even for related substances, such as *n*-pentane and *n*-octane, and methyl and propyl acetates. Non-related substances such as *n*-octane and propyl acetate, and *n*-pentane and chlorobenzene, show almost equal values of π. The possibility of grouping substances from the point of view of corresponding states is thus remote. Herz [2] found, however, that the temperatures at which the vapour pressures are equal fractions of the critical pressure are nearly equal fractions of the critical temperature.

§ 20. Values of the Critical Ratio

Another test of van der Waals's equation may be made as follows.[3] The three equations (6), § 7, give:

$$RT_c=8a/27b=8p_cv_c/3,$$

therefore:

$$RT_c/p_cv_c=8/3=2{\cdot}67 \quad \ldots\ldots \quad (1)$$

The *critical ratio* RT_c/p_cv_c should be a constant for all substances. For one mol of substance, if M is the molecular weight, ρ_c the critical density, and if v_c is in ml. and p_c in atm.:

$$RT_c/p_cv_c=(82{\cdot}1/M)(\rho_cT_c/p_c)=2{\cdot}67 \quad \ldots\ldots \quad (2)$$

The values of (2) for various substances, according to Young and other observers are:

He [4]	H_2	A	O_2	N_2	C[illegible]	SO_2	Xe	Cl_2
3·184	3·28	3·424	3·419	3·421	3·486	3·605	3·605	3·63

i-C_5H_{12}	C_6H_6	*n*-C_5H_{12}	C_6H_5Cl	C_6H_5F	$(C_2H_5)_2O$	C_2H_5OH	H_2O
3·734	3·755	3·762	3·776	3·797	3·814	4·115	4·458

[1] *Z. anorg. Chem.*, 1925, **145**, 378.

[2] *Z. Elektrochem.*, 1930, **36**, 300.

[3] Young, *J.C.S.*, 1897, **71**, 446; *Phil. Mag.*, 1900, **50**, 291; "Stoichiometry," 1918, 218; Dieterici, *Ann. Phys.*, 1904, **15**, 860; Walden, *Z. phys. Chem.*, 1909, **66**, 385 (437); Kleeman, *Phil. Mag.*, 1909, **18**, 901; Kam, *ibid.*, 1916, **31**, 22 (value should be 2·0); Porter, in Glazebrook, "Dict. of Applied Physics," 1922, **1**, 891; Walker, *Phil. Mag.*, 1924, **47**, 111, 513 (value is a function of the length of the molecule).

[4] According to Onnes, *Proc. K. Akad. Wetens. Amsterdam*, 1911, **13**, 1093, the value for helium is the theoretical value 2·68.

The value is always greater than 2·67 and not quite constant, varying from about 3·2 to 3·9 for normal substances, but having larger values (over 4) for associated liquids. A rough average value for normal substances is 15/4=3·75. According to Guye [1] the ratio is:

$$RT_c/p_c v_c = 2{\cdot}648(1+0{\cdot}0_3 9345 T_c) \quad . \quad . \quad . \quad . \quad . \quad . \quad (3)$$

Berthelot (see § 29) put it equal to 32/9=3·56. The value $v_c=3b$ predicted by van der Waals's equation is too large, as is seen by comparison with (1); the observed constant, 3·75, corresponds with $v_c=3\times2{\cdot}67b/3{\cdot}75\simeq2b$, and this is more nearly in agreement with experiment.[2] In a later publication,[3] van der Waals gave reasons for taking $v_c=2{\cdot}13b$.

§ 21. Molar Volume at the Absolute Zero

Another test [4] of van der Waals's equation is the comparison of the calculated values of the molar volume at the absolute zero. It might be assumed that the value of v given by van der Waals's equation, $(p+a/v^2)(v-b)=RT$, would be equal to b at $T=0$, when the factor $(v-b)$ vanishes. The value of the density ρ_0 at the absolute zero can, however, be calculated from the rectilinear diameter equation of Cailletet and Mathias (§ 5.VII B), and if M=mol. wt. then:

$$v_c\rho_0/M = v_c/b = 3 \quad . \quad . \quad . \quad . \quad . \quad . \quad . \quad . \quad . \quad (1)$$

so that the critical volume of all substances should be three times the volume of the same mass at the absolute zero. From some values given below it is seen that the ratio varies between 3·6 and 4, but in view of the wide variation in v_c and ρ_0, the constancy of the ratio must be regarded as very fair.

	v_c ml. per mol	M/ρ_0 ml.	$v_c\rho_0/M$
O_2	74·40	20·8	3·58
CO_2	96	25·5	3·77
$(C_2H_5)_2O$	280	71·7	3·91
C_6H_6	256	70·6	3·63
CCl_4	276	72·2	3·82
Propyl acetate ...	345	86·2	4·00

§ 22. Reduced Vapour-Pressure Equation

A very elegant graphical test of the law of corresponding states is due to Bingham.[5] Van der Waals [6] proposed a semi-empirical vapour-pressure equation:

$$\log(p_c/P) = f(T_c/T-1) = f(1-\vartheta)/\vartheta \quad . \quad . \quad . \quad . \quad . \quad . \quad (1)$$

[1] *Compt. Rend.*, 1891, **112**, 1257; Bogdan, *Z. phys. Chem.*, 1906, **57**, 349.

[2] Walden, *Z. phys. Chem.*, 1909, **66**, 385 (437); Herz, *Z. Elektrochem.*, 1923, **29**, 527.

[3] *Proc. K. Akad. Wetens. Amsterdam*, 1910–11, **13**, 107, 494; on the relation to chemical composition, see MacLeod, *Trans. Faraday Soc.*, 1944, **40**, 439.

[4] D. Berthelot, *Compt. Rend.*, 1900, **130**, 713; Guldberg, *Z. phys. Chem.*, 1900, **32**, 116; van't Hoff, "Vorlesungen über theoretische und physikalische Chemie," Brunswick, 1903, **3**, 21; Mebius, *Arkiv Mat. Astron. Fys.*, 1915, **10**, No. 20.

[5] *J.A.C.S.*, 1906, **28**, 717, 723; Nernst, *Gött. Nachr.*, 1906, 1; "Theoretische Chemie," 7th edit., 1913, 234; Nijhoff, *Comm. Leiden*, 1929, Suppl. **64** *f.*

[6] "Continuität," 2nd edit., 1899, **1**, 147, 158; Dieterici, *Ann. Phys.*, 1904, **15**, 860; Rudorf, *ibid.*, 1909, **29**, 751; 1910, **31**, 416; Venator, *Chem. Ztg.*, 1918, **42**, 194; *Z. phys. Chem.*, 1918, **93**, 242, 245, 247; Berthoud, *J. Chim. Phys.*, 1918, **16**, 245; Herz, *Z. Elektrochem.*, 1919, **25**, 468; Brandt, *Ann. Phys.*, 1924, **73**, 403.

where P=vapour pressure, $\vartheta = T/T_c$, and f is a constant very nearly equal to 3·0. Guye [1] calculated the following values of f:

Benzene	2·89	Propyl formate	3·04
Chlorobenzene	2·95	Methyl acetate	3·07
Carbon tetrachloride	2·81	Propyl acetate	3·22
Ethyl ether	3·00	Methyl propionate	3·13
Fluorobenzene	2·99	Ethyl propionate	3·22
Stannic chloride	3·01	Methyl *iso*butyrate	3·15
Ethyl formate	3·00	Methyl butyrate	3·24
Methyl formate	2·97	Ethyl acetate	3·26

The mean value is 3·06. For water, alcohols, and acetic acid, the value of f is greater than 3·2. At the boiling-point, $T=T_b$, $P=1$ atm., therefore $T_c/T_b = 1+\log p_c/f$.

Bingham, and Nernst, plotted the values of log (p_c/P) against those of $(T_c/T-1)$, and obtained the set of curves shown in Fig. 8.VII C. If the law

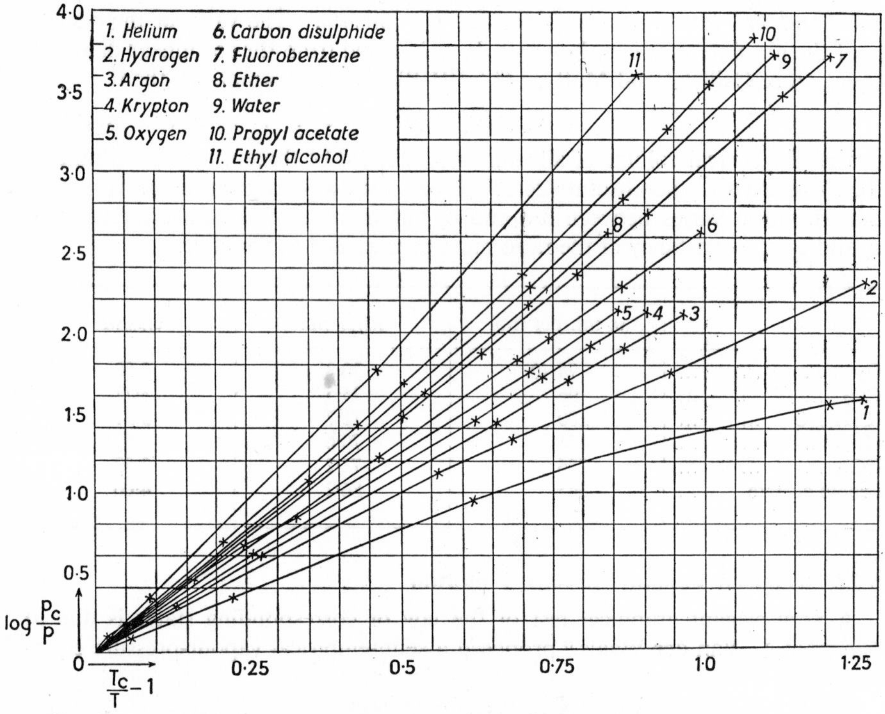

FIG. 8.VII C. Bingham-Nernst plots of log (p_c/P) against $(T_c/T-1)$, where P=vapour pressure, for various substances

of corresponding states holds, all the points should lie on one curve, but each substance has a separate curve, and the curves deviate more and more as T becomes smaller (i.e. $T_c/T-1$ becomes larger). The substances may roughly be divided into three groups, (i) those of small molecular complexity and low critical temperature (hydrogen and helium), (ii) normal liquids such as fluorobenzene and ether, and (iii) associated liquids such as water and alcohol; the separation, however, is not sharp. As a general rule (apart from associated

[1] *Arch. Sci. Phys. Nat.*, 1894, **31**, 463; *Z. phys. Chem.*, 1906, **56**, 461.

liquids), the higher the molecular weight and the larger the number of atoms in the molecule, the steeper is the curve. The deviations from the law of corresponding states shown in these curves are much larger than in the groups of substances selected by Young. Kireev [1] plotted values of $p(\mathrm{d}T/\mathrm{d}p)$ against temperature and found parallel curves for various substances; this is related to the values of the Trouton coefficient (see § 14.VIII L, Vol. II) L_e/T_b, since $p(\mathrm{d}T/\mathrm{d}p)$ is equal to T^2/L_e, from the Clapeyron-Clausius equation.

The coefficient f is not really a constant, but depends somewhat on temperature. Shames [2] found that it has a minimum value for $T \simeq 0{\cdot}8T_c$. Cederberg [3] also assumed that f has a minimum value, and made the further assumptions that (i) the curve of f plotted against ϑ is symmetrical on both sides of the minimum, and (ii) each branch of the curve is an exponential function of ϑ:

$$f = ab^{(\vartheta - y)^2} \quad \ldots\ldots\ldots \quad (2)$$

where a is the minimum value of f, y is the value of ϑ for this minimum, and b is a characteristic constant for each substance. The value of y varied from 0·71 to 0·80. The resulting equation:

$$\ln (p_c/p) = 2{\cdot}303\, ab^{(\vartheta - y)^2} \,.\, (1-\vartheta)/\vartheta \quad \ldots\ldots \quad (3)$$

gave good results with water, but only when an arbitrary value $t_c = 216{\cdot}3°$ was taken for the critical temperature instead of the observed value 374·1°.

Fales and Shapiro [4] pointed out that in some cases (3) does not agree with experiment; (i) for helium and argon f does not assume a minimum value, but decreases steadily with temperature,[5] (ii) the symmetry of the f–ϑ curve is not complete, and (iii) the value of f is very sensitive to errors in T_c and the vapour pressures. They proposed the equation:

$$\ln (p_c/p) = k'(1-\vartheta^2)^{m'}/\vartheta^{n'} \quad \ldots\ldots \quad (4)$$

where k', m', and n' are constants.

Dieterici [6] found that:

$$(\mathrm{d}p/\mathrm{d}T)_{v_c} = \tfrac{1}{2}R/v_c \quad \ldots\ldots\ldots \quad (5)$$

i.e. the value of $(\mathrm{d}p/\mathrm{d}T)_v$ in the critical state is half the value for an ideal gas under the same conditions. Van der Waals [7] and Dieterici [8] found that, at all temperatures, the mean value of $(\mathrm{d}p/\mathrm{d}T)_v$ between two volumes corresponding with saturation (liquid⇌vapour) was equal to the increase of $\mathrm{d}p_s/\mathrm{d}T$, where p_s = vapour pressure. Hence at the critical point:

$$(\mathrm{d}p_s/\mathrm{d}T)_{T_c} = (\mathrm{d}p/\mathrm{d}T)_{v_c} \quad \ldots\ldots\ldots \quad (6)$$

The two equations (5) and (6) give:

$$T_c(\mathrm{d}p/\mathrm{d}T)_c/p_{v_c} = 7{\cdot}4 \quad \ldots\ldots\ldots \quad (7)$$

Since the ratio $T(\mathrm{d}p_s/\mathrm{d}T)(v_g - v_l)/p(v_g - v_l)$ = heat absorbed/work done, in a

[1] *J. Russ. Phys. Chem. Soc.*, 1926, **58**, 856 (C).

[2] *Verhl. d. D. Phys. Ges.*, 1913, **15**, 1017; 1914, **16**, 121; 1916, **18**, 35; *Elster-Geitel Festschr.*, 1915, 287; *Ann. Phys. Beibl.*, 1916, **40**, 7; *Z. Phys.*, 1920, **1**, 198; 1920, **3**, 255; *Phys. Z.*, 1921, **22**, 644 (took $\pi = pv_c/RT_c$, $\vartheta = Tv_c/T_cv_0$, $\phi = v/v_0$, where v_0 = vol. at $p=0$ and $T=0$); Duclaux, *J. Chim. Phys.*, 1943, **40**, 65.

[3] *Arkiv Mat. Astron. Fys.*, 1914, **10**, No. 7.

[4] *J.A C.S.*, 1938, **60**, 784, 794, where the equation is misprinted.

[5] *Ann Phys.*, 1903, **12**, 144.

[6] Onnes, *Comm. Leiden*, 1911, **124***b*.

[7] Q. by Keesom, *Verslag. K. Akad. Wetens. Amsterdam*, 1901–2, **9**, 331 (*Comm. Leiden*, **75**), and Dieterici, *Ann. Phys.*, 1903, **12**, 144.

[8] *Ann. Phys.*, 1901, **6**, 867; 1904, **15**, 860.

Carnot's cycle (§ 32.II), and this should be equal to T/T_c, it follows that $(T/p_s)(dp_s/dT)=7{\cdot}4(T_c/T)$ and hence:

$$p_s=p_c e^{7{\cdot}4(1-T_c/T)}$$

which is the same as van der Waals's vapour-pressure formula (1).

Woolsey [1] found a complicated generalised characteristic equation which leads to a law of corresponding states.

§ 23. Reduced Law of Rectilinear Diameter

A further test of the law of corresponding states is the reduced form of Mathias's [2] law of rectilinear diameter (§ 5.VII B). If $\rho_m=\frac{1}{2}(\rho_l+\rho_g)$ is the mean density of liquid and saturated vapour, then:

$$\rho_m=\rho_c+a(T_c-T) \quad . \quad . \quad . \quad . \quad . \quad . \quad . \quad . \quad . \quad (1)$$

where ρ_c is the critical density and a is a constant. Hence:

$$\rho_m=\rho_c[1+(aT_c/\rho_c)(1-T/T_c)]=\rho_c[1+(aT_c/T)(1-\vartheta)],$$

and if ρ_r is the reduced *mean* density, ρ_m/ρ_c, and $A=aT_c/T$, then:

$$\rho_r=1+A(1-\vartheta) \quad . \quad . \quad . \quad . \quad . \quad . \quad . \quad . \quad . \quad (2)$$

Batschinski [3] deduced this equation from van der Waals's equation and Dupré's vapour-pressure formula (see § 18.VIII J, Vol. II). All substances should give the same straight line with the same value of A. It is found, however, that both the reduced densities of liquid and vapour (the upper and lower parts of the parabolas), and the reduced rectilinear diameters, are not identical for various substances, but the deviation for the diameter is not large (Fig. 9.VII C).

The value of A is found [4] to be very approximately unity, except for low boiling-point gases:

Hydrogen	0·236	Iodobenzene	0·957
Helium	0·255	Fluorobenzene	0·917
Nitrogen	0·685	Carbon tetrachloride	0·918
Oxygen	0·713	Carbon disulphide	0·954
Argon	0·751	*n*-pentane	0·904
Nitrous oxide	0·828	*iso*-pentane	0·892
Carbon dioxide	0·858	*n*-hexane	0·966
Ethylene	1·060	*n*-heptane	1·014
Ammonia	1·002	*n*-octane	1·075
Sulphur dioxide	1·053	Methyl formate	0·997
Chlorine	0·768	Ethyl formate	1·021
Bromine	0·896	Methyl acetate	1·049
Benzene	0·936	Ethyl acetate	1·061
Chlorobenzene	0·956	Ethyl propionate	1·090
Bromobenzene	0·964		

1 *J.A.C.S.*, 1936, **58**, 984, 2229; 1937, **59**, 2743.

2 *J. de Phys.*, 1893, **2**, 224; 1899, **8**, 407; 1905, **4**, 77; see von Hirsch, *Ann. Phys.*, 1899, **69**, 456; van der Waals, *Z. phys. Chem.*, 1901, **36**, 461. Mathias, *Compt. Rend.*, 1891, **112**, 85, confirmed the relation $\rho/\rho_c=f(T/T_c)$ for the densities of the liquid and vapour of SO_2, CO_2, N_2O, and C_2H_4; Onnes and Crommelin, *Proc. K. Akad. Wetens. Amsterdam*, 1913, **15**, 952 (confirmed for argon); Haigh, *Phil. Mag.*, 1908, **16**, 201; Young, *ibid.*, 1908, **16**, 222 (new form of reduced equation); Berthelot, *Compt. Rend.*, 1915, **160**, 657; Surdin, *J. de Phys.*, 1937, **8**, 294.

3 *Z. phys. Chem.*, 1902, **41**, 741.

4 Berthelot, *Compt. Rend.*, 1915, **160**, 675; Mebius, *Arkiv Mat. Astron. Fys.*, 1915, **10**, No. 20; see the table in Jellinek, "Lehrbuch der physikalischen Chemie," 1915, **2**, 99, and § 4.VIII L, Vol. II.

Hence (2) becomes $\rho_r=(2-\vartheta)$, or, if the vapour density is neglected in comparison with the liquid density:

$$\rho_l=2\rho_c(2-\vartheta) \quad . \quad . \quad . \quad . \quad . \quad . \quad . \quad . \quad . \quad (3)$$

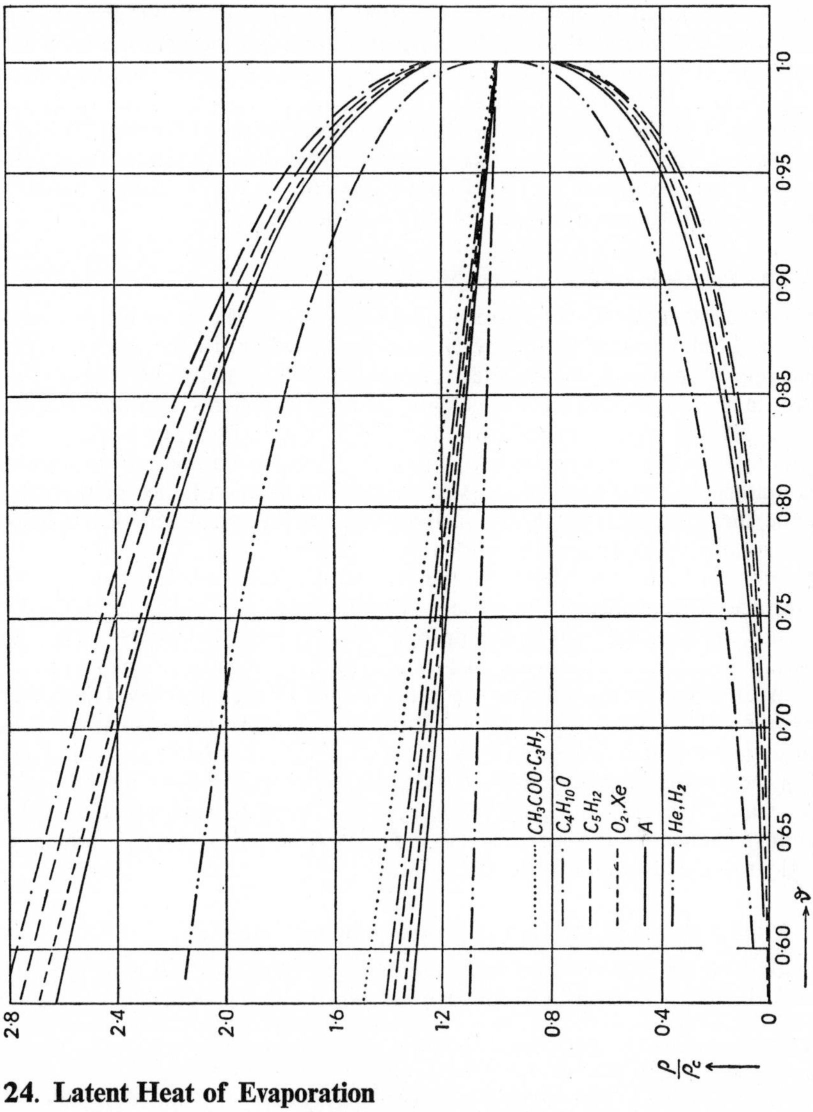

FIG. 9.VII C. Reduced Rectilinear Diameters for Various Substances

§ 24. Latent Heat of Evaporation

Still another test of van der Waals's equation is given by the reduced Clapeyron-Clausius equation (see § 7.VIII L, Vol. II):

$$(L_e/T)=(p_c v_c/T_c)(d\pi/d\vartheta)(\phi_g-\phi_l) \quad . \quad . \quad . \quad . \quad . \quad . \quad (1)$$

found by substituting $p=\pi p_c$, $v=\phi v_c$, and $T=\vartheta T_c$ in the ordinary equation:

$$L_e/T=(dp/dT)(v_g-v_l).$$

The quotient $p_c v_c/T_c$, according to van der Waals's equation, (1), § 20, is $3\boldsymbol{R}/8$, and according to Berthelot's equation, (4), § 29, it is $9\boldsymbol{R}/32$. Hence at corresponding temperatures L_e/T should be the same for all substances. But according to Guldberg's empirical rule (§ 7.VII B) the absolute boiling-point T_b is two-thirds of the absolute critical temperature; hence L_e/T_b=const. If T_b/T_c=const., however, the critical pressures of all substances should be equal, which is not the case.[1]

Darzens [2] deduced the relation $L_e/T_c=f(\vartheta)$, or $L_e/T_b=F(\vartheta)$, but found that the curves of the quotients plotted against ϑ did not coincide and had a point of inflexion at $\vartheta=0{\cdot}75$. The equation L_e/T_b=const.$\simeq$21 is *Trouton's Rule* (see § 14.VIII L, Vol. II), and the value of the constant is very near [3] to 21 for normal liquids. (The modifications [4] of it are considered in § 14.VIII L, Vol. II.)

If, however, the value of p_cv_c/T_c given by van der Waals's equation is substituted in (1) the value of L_e/T_b is found to be only 10·8. A correct value is given by Berthelot's equation (see § 4.VIII L, Vol. II).

§ 25. The Principle of Mechanical Similitude

Onnes [5] derived the law of corresponding states from the principle of mechanical similitude, first proposed by Newton,[6] and related to the theory of the dimensions of physical magnitudes. It may be illustrated [7] by considering two substances the molecules of which are hard elastic spheres with diameters in the ratio $1:l$ and masses in the ratio $1:m$. The dimensions of kinetic energy are [mass][velocity]^2=[mass][length]^2/[time]^2. If equal numbers of molecules are contained in two cubes of sides in the ratio $1:l$, or volumes in the ratio $1:l^3$, the temperatures, which are proportional to the mean kinetic energies, are in the ratio $1:ml^2/t^2$, and the velocities in the ratio $1:l/t$.

The pressures are proportional to the momentum transferred in unit time to unit surface of the walls of the vessel. The momenta are in the ratio $1:ml/t$, and hence the pressures are in the ratio $1:(ml/t)(1/t)(1/l^2)=1:m/lt^2$. The van der Waals forces are in the ratio a/v^2 and a'/v'^2, or $1:(a'/a)(v^2/v'^2)=1:A/l^6$. The attractive forces must be in the ratio $1:m/lt^2$, hence $1:A/l^6=1:m/lt^2$, or $A/l^5=m/t^2$. Thus the volume, temperature, and pressure ratios in two mechanically similar systems are given by $v:v'=1:l^3$; $T:T'=1:ml^2/t^2$; $p:p'=1:A/l^6$.

With the reasonable assumption that the critical states represent mechanically similar states, the critical values for p, v, and T must be substituted in these equations, thence giving $v:v'=v_c:v_c'$, $T:T'=T_c:T_c'$, $p:p'=p_c:p_c'$, which is equivalent to the law of corresponding states.

§ 26. Modifications of the Law of Corresponding States

Kirstine Meyer [8] used as reduced quantities $T_c\div T/K$, $p_c\div p/L$, and $v_c\div v/Q$, where K, L, and Q are constants for each substance. This is equivalent to taking

[1] Kistiakowsky, *J. Chim. Phys.*, 1927, **24**, 309.

[2] *Compt. Rend.*, 1896, **123**, 940; 1897, **124**, 610.

[3] Kurbatow, *J. Russ. Phys. Chem. Soc.*, 1903, **35**, 319; *Chem. Centr.*, 1903, **7**, II, 323, found the average value 20·7±0·8. Kleeman, *Phil. Mag.*, 1909, **18**, 491 (508), deduced $L_e/T=-R+(\vartheta/\pi)\cdot(d\pi/d\vartheta)$=const.; cf. Lewis, *Z. phys. Chem.*, 1911, **78**, 24; 1912, **79**, 185, 196.

[4] The modifications are summarised by Kendall, *J.A.C.S.*, 1914, **36**, 1620.

[5] *Verhl. K. Akad. Wetens. Amsterdam*, 1881, **21**, iv; *Arch. Néerl.*, 1897, **30**, 101; Onnes and Keesom, " Enzykl. d. math. Wiss.," 1912, **5**, i, 694 f.; Bridgman, *Phys. Rev.*, 1914, **4**, 244, and later papers; Weber, *Physica*, 1939, **6**, 551, 563; Trautz, *J. prakt. Chem.*, 1943, **162**, 218.

[6] " Principia," lib. II, sect. vii, prop. 32, theorem 26; Geneva, 1740, **2**, 250.

[7] Onnes and Keesom, Die Zustandsgleichung, *Comm. Leiden*, 1912, **12**, Suppl. 23; " Enzykl. d. math. Wiss.," 1912, **5**, i, 694 f.; Kuenen, " Die Eigenschaften der Gase " (Ostwald-Drucker, " Handbuch der allgemeinen Chemie," **3**), Leipzig, 1919, 393.

[8] *Z. phys. Chem.*, 1900, **32**, 1; 1910, **71**, 325.

a different *unit* for measuring the reduced quantities for each substance, or reckoning from a different zero. By plotting $(p_c-p)/p_c$ against $(T_c-T)/K$, taking K from the values for fluorobenzene as standard, it was found that L was practically unity, so that the characteristic constants could be reduced to two, the quantities for plotting being $(T_c-T)/\tau$, $(p_c-p)/p_c$, and $(v_c-v)/v_m$, where the denominators, τ and v_m, are specific temperature and volume units. Timmermans[1] found that this modification of the law of corresponding states holds at the lowest temperatures.

Byk[2] extended this idea on a quantum basis. The free energy F per mol is reckoned on a specific unit of $\boldsymbol{k}T_c$ per molecule, where $\boldsymbol{k}$ is Boltzmann's constant, and by considering the phase space (§ 14.IV) he found a universal function with a parameter $w=\boldsymbol{h}/m^{1/2}(v_c/N)^{1/3}(\boldsymbol{k}T_c)^{1/2}$, where m is the mass of the molecule, $\boldsymbol{h}$ is Planck's constant, and N is Avogadro's number. For a molecule, in c.g.s. units, $(F/N)/(\boldsymbol{k}T_c)=\mathrm{f}(\phi, \vartheta, w)$, a universal function, where $\phi=v/v_c$ and $\vartheta=T/T_c$. For any magnitude G characterising the state, of dimensions $M^{\mu}V^{\xi}E^{\epsilon}T^{\tau}$ (M=mass, V=volume, E=energy, T=temperature), the magnitude $G/m^{\mu}(\phi/N)^{\xi}(\boldsymbol{k}\vartheta)^{\epsilon}\vartheta^{\tau}=\mathrm{g}(\phi, \vartheta, w)$, is a universal function of ϕ, ϑ, and w. Van der Waals's theory of corresponding states is a limiting case for high molecular weight and high critical volume and temperature; then w is very small, whilst for substances of low molecular weight and critical temperature it is of the order of unity. Byk's theory is, strictly, confined to monatomic substances, or those behaving as monatomic, but the latter can nearly always be assumed. The theory was extended to a number of magnitudes, such as the " constant " f (really variable) of van der Waals's vapour-pressure equation (§ 22), the reclinear diameter (§ 5.VII B), the Eötvös constant for surface energy (see § 7.VIII G, Vol. II), etc. In all cases, the quantity is assumed to follow an equation based on Einstein's equation for the energy of a monatomic solid (§ 16.IV), $\epsilon=\boldsymbol{h}\nu/(e^{\boldsymbol{h}\nu/\boldsymbol{k}T}-1)$ (see § 2.IX N, Vol. II), with w replacing $\boldsymbol{h}\nu/\boldsymbol{k}T$, i.e. $q=\alpha+\beta\delta w/(e^{\delta w}-1)$, where α, β, and δ are constants for each magnitude. The plots of q against $1/w$ pass fairly well through the band of scattered points.

§ 27. Characteristic Equations

Besides van der Waals's equation a great number of other characteristic equations will be found in the literature. Many of these (excluding those which contain unknowable quantities) are modifications of van der Waals's equation in which either a or b, or both, are replaced by functions of volume or temperature, or both; or else the factors $(p+a/v^2)$ and $(v-b)$ receive some additional terms or other alteration. Other equations are quite different in form from van der Waals's. Some of the equations are deduced from theoretical principles, others are empirical; some are of theoretical interest only, either because they are too complicated or contain too many constants to be practically useful, or involve integrals or other mathematical expressions which have not been, or cannot be, expressed in terms of measurable data. Only a few of the more important equations can be considered here, and in most cases the results will merely be stated.[3]

[1] *Proc. Roy. Dublin Soc.*, 1912, **13**, 310.

[2] *Phys. Z.*, 1921, **22**, 15; *Ann. Phys.*, 1913, **42**, 1417; 1921, **66**, 157; 1922, **69**, 161; *Z. phys. Chem.*, 1924, **110**, 291; Clusius, *ibid.*, 1929, **4 B**, 1; de Boer, *Physica*, 1948, **14**, 139, 149.

[3] A list of 56 equations is given by Partington and Shilling, " The Specific Heats of Gases," 1924, 29; see also Graetz in Winkelmann, " Handbuch der Physik," 1906, **3**, 1135; Kuenen, " Die Eigenschaften der Gase " (Ostwald-Drucker, " Handbuch der allgemeinen Chemie," 3), Leipzig, 1919, 376; Chwolson, " Lehrbuch der Physik," 1923, **3**, ii, 335; Pickering, *Bur. Stand. Circ.*, 1926, **279** (700 refs.); Goranson, Thermodynamic Relations in Multicomponent Systems, *Carnegie Inst. Publ.*, 1930, **408**.

Planck,[1] from the fundamental statistical definition of entropy (§ 5.IV), deduced a *canonical equation of state* giving the entropy as a function of energy and volume, $S=f(E,V)$. For a gas consisting of hard elastic spheres and a van der Waals cohesive force this gives:

$$p=(RT/\beta)\ln(1-\beta/v)-\alpha/v^2,$$

where $\beta=2b$, $\alpha=$const., which differs from van der Waals's equation only in terms of the second order in b/v.

§ 28. Clausius's Equation

As an example of a correction of the pressure factor $(p+a/v^2)$ the equation of Clausius [2] may be considered. He supposed that clusters of two or more molecules could be formed temporarily at lower temperatures by collisions, these breaking up more readily at higher temperatures. In such clusters the attractions are much greater than if the molecules were separate in the gas, and hence van der Waals's term a/v^2 is too small at lower temperatures. Clausius also thought the simple inverse proportionality to v^2 required correction. He replaced the van der Waals term a/v^2 by one dependent on temperature, v being also replaced by $(v+c)$:

$$[p+a/T(v+c)^2](v-b)=RT \quad . \quad . \quad . \quad . \quad . \quad . \quad (1)$$

where a, b, and c are positive constants (a is, of course, different from the van der Waals constant). By equating $(dp/dv)_T$ and $(d^2p/dv^2)_T$ to zero, the values of the critical constants can be found from (1) in the same way as from the van der Waals equation (§ 7):

$$v_c=3b+2c; \quad p_c=a/27(b+c)^2T_c; \quad T_c^2=8a/27R(b+c) \quad . \quad . \quad (2)$$

$$a=(27/64)s^2T_cv_c^2; \quad b=v_c(1-s/4); \quad c=v_c(3s/8-1) \quad . \quad . \quad . \quad (3)$$

where $s=RT_c/p_cv_c$ (see § 20).

Sarrau [2] proposed the equation:

$$p=RT/(v-b)-\kappa\epsilon^{-T}/(v+\beta)^2 \quad . \quad . \quad . \quad . \quad . \quad . \quad (4)$$

where b, β, ϵ, κ, and R are constants, and Ariès [2] proposed

$$p=RT/(v-\alpha)-\kappa/T^n(v+\beta)^2 \quad . \quad . \quad . \quad . \quad . \quad . \quad (5)$$

where α, β, R, and n are constants, and κ is either a constant or a function of temperature.

[1] *Berlin Ber.*, 1908, 633; Wassmuth, *Ann. Phys.*, 1909, **30**, 331; *Wien Ber.*, 1913, **122**, II A, 651; for a relativistic treatment, see Jüttner, *Ann. Phys.*, 1911, **34**, 856; 1911, **35**, 145; Westphal, *Verhl. d. D. Phys. Ges.*, 1911, **13**, 590; Weber, *ibid.*, 1911, **13**, 695, 974; Keesom, *Proc. K. Akad. Wetens. Amsterdam*, 1912, **15**, 240 (*Comm. Leiden, Suppl.* **24***a*).

[2] *Ann. Phys.*, 1880, **9**, 337; 1881, **14**, 279, 692; *Ann. Chim.*, 1883, **30**, 448; Dickson, *Phil. Mag.*, 1880, **10**, 40; Planck, *Ann. Phys.*, 1881, **13**, 535; "Thermodynamik," 1911, 13; Fitzgerald, *Proc. Roy. Soc.*, 1887, **42**, 216; Riecke, *Ann. Phys.*, 1895, **54**, 739; modifications by Sarrau, *Compt. Rend.*, 1882, **94**, 639, 718, 845; 1885, **101**, 941, 994, 1145; 1890, **110**, 880 (an error in Sarrau's paper was pointed out by Fouché, *Compt. Rend.*, 1919, **169**, 1089, 1158); Jäger, *Wien Ber.*, 1892, **101**, II A, 1675; Battelli, *Ann. Chim.*, 1892, **25**, 38 (83); 1893, **29**, 239; *Mem. Accad. Torino*, 1893, **43**, 64; 1894, **44**, 57; Onnes, *Arch. Néerl.*, 1897, **30**, 101; Ariès, *Compt. Rend.*, 1916, **163**, 737, 963; 1917, **164**, 261; 1917, **165**, 1088; 1918, **166**, 57, 193, 334, 447, 553, 668, 802, 935; 1918, **167**, 118, 267; 1918, **168**, 204, 444, 714, 930, 1188; 1919, **169**, 216, 602, 1140; "Thérmodynamique. L'équation d'état des fluides," Paris, 1920; summaries in *J. Chim. Phys.*, 1919, **17**, 432; 1920, **18**, 160 (severely criticised by Brandt, *Ann. Phys.*, 1924, **73**, 406); Pochammer, *Ann. Phys.*, 1911, **37**, 103; Holm, *Meddel. Nobelinst.*, 1919, 5, No. 27; *Arkiv Mat. Astron. Fys.*, 1923, **17**, Nos. 1, 20 (bibl.); Webster, *Proc. Nat. Acad.*, 1919, **5**, 286 (complicated general equation with Clausius's as a special form).

Berthelot[1] replaced $(v+c)^2$ in Clausius's equation by $v^2+2lvb+mb^2$, where l and m are constants. Schulze[2] used $(p+a/T^n v^2)(v-b)=RT$, with $n=0{\cdot}348$, for air.

Since Clausius's equation is a cubic equation in v and contains *four* constants, it does not lead to a law of corresponding states. The reduced Clausius equation is:

$$(\pi+3/\vartheta\phi'^2)(3\phi'-1)=8\vartheta \quad . \quad . \quad . \quad . \quad . \quad . \quad . \quad (6)$$

where $\phi'=(v+c)/(v_c+c)$, which still contains a constant c depending on the substance. A plot of the equation for carbon dioxide is given by Planck.[3]

§ 29. Berthelot's Equation

An important modification of Clausius's equation is that of D. Berthelot:[4]

$$(p+a/Tv^2)(v-b)=RT \quad . \quad . \quad . \quad . \quad . \quad . \quad . \quad (1)$$

(a is different from the van der Waals a, here replaced by a/T), which in its reduced form, with $\pi=p/p_c$, $\phi=v/v_c$, and $\vartheta=T/T_c$, is:

$$(\pi+3/\vartheta\phi^2)(3\phi-1)=8\vartheta \quad . \quad . \quad . \quad . \quad . \quad . \quad . \quad (2)$$

By plotting $(d\pi\phi/d\pi)_\vartheta$ against $1/\vartheta=\tau$, and comparing with experimental points, Berthelot found that the constants deduced from equation (1), viz.:

$$a=3p_c v_c^2 T_c, \quad b=v_c/3, \quad R=8p_c v_c/3T_c \quad . \quad . \quad . \quad . \quad (3)$$

did not give satisfactory results, i.e. equation (2) did not fit the observed curves. He found, by arbitrarily altering the constants to

$$a=(16/3)p_c v_c^2 T_c, \quad b=v_c/4, \quad R=(32/9)p_c v_c/T_c \quad . \quad . \quad . \quad (4)$$

that the resulting reduced equation:

$$\left(\pi+\frac{16}{3}\cdot\frac{1}{\vartheta\phi^2}\right)\left(\phi-\frac{1}{4}\right)=\frac{32}{9}\vartheta \quad . \quad . \quad . \quad . \quad . \quad . \quad (5)$$

gave very accurate results at moderate pressures near room temperature. At the critical point, when $\pi=\phi=\vartheta=1$, (5) leads to the impossible result $4{\cdot}75=3{\cdot}56$, so that it is a purely empirical equation which cannot hold near the critical point.[5] This discrepancy in no way reduces the value of equation (5) in regions where it can properly be applied, and is of no practical significance.

By substituting $\pi=p/p_c$, $\phi=v/v_c$, $\vartheta=T/T_c$, $R=(32/9)(p_c v_c/T_c)$, (5) gives:

$$\left(\frac{p}{p_c}+\frac{16}{3}\frac{1}{\vartheta\phi^2}\right)\left(\frac{v}{v_c}-\frac{1}{4}\right)=\frac{32}{9}\frac{T}{T_c}=\frac{RT}{p_c v_c} \quad . \quad . \quad . \quad . \quad . \quad (6)$$

$$\therefore\ pv-\frac{pv_c}{4}+\frac{16}{3}\frac{p_c v}{\vartheta\phi^2}-\frac{4}{3}\frac{p_c v_c}{\vartheta\phi^2}=RT \quad . \quad . \quad . \quad . \quad . \quad (7)$$

All terms on the left except the first are small (as v_c is small compared with v)

[1] *Compt. Rend.*, 1900, **130**, 69 (for liquids).
[2] *Ann. Phys.*, 1916, **49**, 569.
[3] See ref. 2, p. 704.
[4] *J. de Phys.*, 1899, **8**, 263; *Arch. Néerl.*, 1900, **5**, 417; *Z. Elektrochem.*, 1904, **10**, 620; Sur les Thermomètres à Gaz, in *Trav. et Mém. Bur. Internat. Poids et Més.*, 1907, **13**; Partington, "Chemical Thermodynamics," 1913, 160, 2nd edit., 1924, 85; Nernst, "Theoretische Chemie," 8–10th edit., 1921, 254.
[5] Henning, "Temperaturmessung," 1915, 24; Porter, *Phil. Mag.*, 1922, **44**, 1020.

and the last term may be neglected. In these *correction terms* (only), $pv=RT$ can be substituted, (7) then giving:

$$pv=RT[1+v_c/4v-(16/3)(p_c/p\vartheta\phi^2)] \quad . \quad . \quad . \quad . \quad . \quad (8)$$

On substitution from the *approximate* form of (5):

$$\pi\phi=(32/9)\vartheta \quad . \quad . \quad . \quad . \quad . \quad . \quad . \quad . \quad . \quad . \quad (9)$$

in the *correction terms* only, and putting [1] $T_c/T=1/\vartheta=\tau$, (8) gives:

$$pv=RT[1+(9/128)\pi\tau(1-6\tau^2)] \quad . \quad . \quad . \quad . \quad . \quad . \quad (10)$$

Equation (10) shows that for such low temperatures that $6\tau^2>1$ the gas is more compressible than an ideal gas. In the case of hydrogen, T_c is small, and even at fairly low temperatures $6\tau^2<1$, so that this gas is less compressible than an ideal gas (" plus que parfait "). The Boyle point (§ 6) is given by $6\tau^2=1$, therefore $T_B/T_c=\sqrt{6}=2{\cdot}45$, in better agreement with experiment than the van der Waals value, 3·375.

At a given temperature, (10) shows that pv is a linear function of pressure, which is applied in the determination of molecular weights from gas densities (§ 17.VII D). Berthelot used (10) to calculate the value of R (§ 21.VII A).

Equation (10) may be written as:

$$pv=RT+\frac{9}{128}\frac{RT_c}{p_c}(1-6T_c^2/T^2)p \quad . \quad . \quad . \quad . \quad . \quad . \quad (11)$$

so that the second virial coefficient (§ 39.VII A) in $pv=RT+B_pp$ is:

$$B_p=\frac{9}{128}\frac{RT_c}{p_c}(1-6T_c^2/T^2)=\frac{9}{128}\frac{RT_c}{p_c}(1-6\tau^2) \quad . \quad . \quad . \quad (12)$$

Berthelot's original equation (1) may be written in the approximate form:

$$pv=RT+(b-a/RT^2)p \quad . \quad . \quad . \quad . \quad . \quad . \quad . \quad (13)$$

giving the second virial coefficient:

$$B_p=(b-a/RT^2) \quad . \quad . \quad . \quad . \quad . \quad . \quad . \quad . \quad . \quad (14)$$

Schimank [2] believed that Berthelot's equation, although generally good at moderate temperatures, is less accurate at low temperatures; Eucken and co-workers [3] used Callendar's equation (§ 32) for reducing measured specific heats to the ideal state, but others (including later workers) have mostly used Berthelot's equation. The very close agreement found between exact calorimetric entropies reduced to the ideal state by Berthelot's equation and the spectroscopic values [4] (see §§ 26–29.IV), shows that the data used by Eucken are inaccurate, and that the equation in general gives very satisfactory results, even at low temperatures.

[1] Beginners are apt to put $\tau=T/T_c$ instead of $\tau=T_c/T$, and care should be taken not to fall into this trap, which may not be noticed until a large amount of laborious computation is done. Some values of $1-(9/64)\pi\tau(1-6\tau^2)$, a factor often required, are given in Partington and Shilling, " The Specific Heats of Gases," 1924, 28.

[2] *Phys. Z.*, 1916, **17**, 393 (based on Ramsay and Steele's inaccurate vapour densities, § 9.VII D).

[3] Bartels and Eucken, *Z. phys. Chem.*, 1921, **98**, 70; see § 15.VII E; Eucken, in Wien-Harms, " Handbuch der Experimentalphysik," 1929, **8**, 404, 469.

[4] Giauque *et al.*, *J.A.C.S.*, 1928, **50**, 101, 2193; 1929, **51**, 1441, 2300, 3194; 1932, **54**, 2610; 1933, **55**, 4875, etc., who found Eucken's sp. ht. measurements so inaccurate that their correction has no particular interest; Johnston and Weimer, *ibid.*, 1934, **56**, 625; Foz Gazulla and Vidal, *An. Fys. Quim.*, 1947, **43**, 842; Berthelot's equation was verified for ether vapour in some rather crude experiments by Alexander and Lambert, *Trans. Faraday Soc.*, 1941, **37**, 421.

§ 30. Thermal Coefficients from Berthelot's Equation

By multiplying out the reduced Berthelot's equation (5), § 29:

$$\left(\pi+\frac{16}{3}\cdot\frac{1}{\vartheta\phi^2}\right)\left(\phi-\frac{1}{4}\right)=\frac{32}{9}\vartheta \quad . \quad . \quad . \quad . \quad . \quad . \quad . \quad . \quad (1)$$

and neglecting the small term $\frac{4}{3}\vartheta\phi^2$, the approximate equation:

$$\pi\phi-\pi/4+(16/3)/\vartheta\phi=(32/9)\vartheta \quad . \quad . \quad . \quad . \quad . \quad . \quad . \quad (2)$$

is found. Differentiate (2) with respect to ϑ at constant volume ϕ and substitute $\phi-1/4$ from (1), then:

$$(\phi-1/4)(\mathrm{d}\pi/\mathrm{d}\vartheta)_\phi=(16/3)/\phi\vartheta^2+32/9$$

$$(32/9)\vartheta(\mathrm{d}\pi/\mathrm{d}\vartheta)_\phi=[(16/3)/\phi\vartheta^2+32/9][\pi+(16/3)/\vartheta\phi^2]$$

$$=(32/9)\pi[1+(3/2)/\phi\vartheta^2][1+(16/3)/\pi\vartheta\phi^2] \quad . \quad . \quad . \quad . \quad (3)$$

Substitute $1/\phi=(9/32)(\pi/\vartheta)$ from (9), § 29, and use the approximation formula $(1+x)^2\simeq 1+2x$, when x is small compared with unity (§ 4.I); then (3) becomes $(\tau=1/\vartheta)$:

$$(\vartheta/\pi)(\mathrm{d}\pi/\mathrm{d}\vartheta)_\phi=[1+(27/64)\pi/\vartheta^3][1+(27/64)\pi/\vartheta^3]$$

$$=1+(27/32)\pi/\vartheta^3=1+(27/32)\pi\tau^3 \quad . \quad . \quad . \quad (4)$$

Put $\pi=p/p_c$, and $\vartheta=T/T_c$ on the left: then $(T/p)(\mathrm{d}p/\mathrm{d}T)_v=1+(27/32)\pi\tau^3$, and:

$$(1/p)(\mathrm{d}p/\mathrm{d}T)_v=(1/T)[1+(27/32)\pi\tau^3] \quad . \quad . \quad . \quad . \quad (5)$$

giving the pressure coefficient. For the ideal gas $\beta_0=1/T_0$, where T in (5) is T_0, the absolute temperature of 0° C. From Chappuis's measured values of β (§ 17.VII A), Berthelot calculated $T_0=273{\cdot}09$° C. Equation (5) gives the correction for the constant-volume gas thermometer. From (10), § 29:

$$v=(\boldsymbol{R}T/p)[1+(9/128)\pi\tau(1-6\tau^2)]=(\boldsymbol{R}/p)[T+(9/128)\pi T_c(1-6T_c^3/T^2)] \quad . \quad (6)$$

Differentiate with respect to T, keeping p constant, then:

$$(\mathrm{d}v/\mathrm{d}T)_p=(\boldsymbol{R}/p)[1+(108/128)\pi\tau^3] \quad . \quad . \quad . \quad . \quad . \quad (7)$$

$$\alpha=(1/v)(\mathrm{d}v/\mathrm{d}T)_p.$$

Substitute $1/v$ from (10):

$$1/v=(p/\boldsymbol{R}T)[1-(9/128)\pi\tau+(54/128)\pi\tau^3]$$

$$\therefore\ \alpha=(1/T)[1+(108/128)\pi\tau^3][1-(9/128)\pi\tau+(54/128)\pi\tau^3]$$

$$\simeq(1/T)[1-(9/128)\pi\tau(1-18\tau^2)] \quad . \quad . \quad . \quad . \quad . \quad . \quad (8)$$

giving the coefficient of expansion ($\alpha_0=1/T_0$ for the ideal gas), and the correction for the constant-pressure gas thermometer.

In Fig. 10.VII C the values of pv are plotted against p at two temperatures, e.g. 0° C. and 100° C., and at such pressures (0 to 4 or 5 atm., or 200 atm. for H_2) that the curves are straight lines (the slopes of which are greatly exaggerated in the figure). A vertical line through O′, where OO′=1 atm., cuts these lines in A′ and B′. OA′ is drawn and produced to meet BB′ in B″. The line OA′B″ is an isochore (or line of constant volume), since $\tan\alpha=pv/p=v=$const.

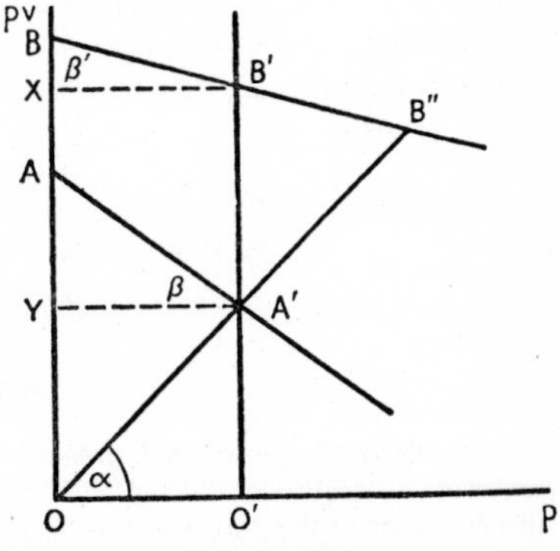

FIG. 10.VII C. Coefficients of Expansion and Pressure, α_0 and β_0, for the Ideal Gas

Draw B'X and A'Y parallel to Op, then the tangents of the angles β and β' between these horizontals and the pv isotherms give $(dpv/dp)_T$.

The coefficient of expansion is:

$$\alpha=1/(t_2-t_1)\,.\,(v_2-v_1)/v_1=1/(t_2-t_1)\,.\,(pv_2-pv_1)/pv_1=1/(t_2-t_1)\,.\,\mathrm{A'B'/O'A'},$$

and the coefficient of pressure is:

$$\beta=1/(t_2-t_1)\,.\,(p_2-p_1)/p_1=1/(t_2-t_1)\,.\,(p_2v-p_1v)/p_1v=1/(t_2-t_1)\,.\,\mathrm{A'B''/OA'}.$$

As p becomes progressively smaller, OA'B'' turns anticlockwise about O, and at $p=0$ it coincides with the axis OB. The intersections A' and B' or B'' then coincide with A and B, and both α and β have the common limit:

$$\alpha_0=\beta_0=1/(t_2-t_1)\,.\,\mathrm{AB/OA},$$

which is obviously the value for the ideal gas. If $t_2-t_1=100$, OA and OB are in the ratio $1/\alpha_0$ to $(1/\alpha_0+100)$, and if $\mathrm{OA}=(pv)_0=1$, then $1:\mathrm{OB}=1:(1+100\alpha_0)$.

For nitrogen, Chappuis found $\alpha=0{\cdot}00367313$ between 0° and 100° and 1 m. Hg pressure, and the values of $(1/p_0v_0)(dpv/dp)_T$ (where p_0v_0 is the ideal gas value) at 0° and 100° were $-0{\cdot}000571$ and $+0{\cdot}000347$. Hence

$$1+100\alpha_0=(1-0{\cdot}000571)\times1{\cdot}367313-0{\cdot}000347=1{\cdot}366185.$$

He also found for an initial pressure of 0·7935 m. Hg, $100\beta=0{\cdot}367180$, $\therefore\ 1+100\beta_0=(1-0{\cdot}000571\times0{\cdot}7935)\times1{\cdot}367180-0{\cdot}000347\times0{\cdot}7935\times1{\cdot}367180=1{\cdot}366184$. By including all Chappuis's measurements with nitrogen and hydrogen, Berthelot calculated $\alpha_0=\beta_0=0{\cdot}00366180$, giving $T_0=1/\alpha_0=273{\cdot}090$. Since the measurements of Chappuis are of great accuracy,[1] even in comparison with more recent work, there is little doubt that this value is one of the best extant.

The *difference of molecular heats* of a gas [2] is from (2), § 47.II:

$$C_p-C_v=T(dp/dT)_v(dv/dT)_p.$$

Substitution from (5) and (7) gives:

$$C_p-C_v=(Tp/T)[1+(27/32)\pi\tau^3](\boldsymbol{R}/p)[1+(108/128)\pi\tau^3]$$
$$=\boldsymbol{R}[1+(27/32)\pi\tau^3][1+(108/128)\pi\tau^3]$$
$$\simeq\boldsymbol{R}[1+(27/16)\pi\tau^3] \quad . \; . \; . \; . \; . \; . \; . \; . \quad (9)$$

neglecting terms of higher orders. (The factor $27/16=27/32+108/128$. Note that $\pi=p/p_c$, and $\tau=T_c/T$.)

From (1) and (2), differentiation and substitution of (9), § 29, in the correction terms gives:

$$(d\pi\phi/d\pi)_\vartheta=(1/4)(1-6\tau^2) \quad . \; . \; . \; . \; . \; . \; . \; . \quad (10)$$
$$[\vartheta(d\pi/d\vartheta)_\phi-\pi]=(32/3)/\vartheta\phi^2=(27/32)\pi^2\tau^3 \quad . \; . \; . \; . \quad (11)$$
$$[\vartheta(d\phi/d\vartheta)_\pi-\phi]=(9/2)\tau^2-1/4 \quad . \; . \; . \; . \; . \; . \; . \quad (12)$$
$$(d\phi/d\pi)_\vartheta=(1/\pi)[1/4-\phi-(3/2)\tau^2] \quad . \; . \; . \; . \; . \; . \quad (13)$$

[1] On Pierre Chappuis, see Guillaume, *Rev. Gén. Sci.*, 1916, **27**, 204. Chappuis's thermometer scales were closely checked and confirmed within a negligible error against the platinum standard thermometer at the National Physical Laboratory; Hall, *Proc. Roy. Soc.*, 1946, **186**, 179, who says (without adequate discussion) that the latest values of T_0 vary from 273·15 to 273·165.

[2] For the calculation with van Laar's equation (§ 34), see van Laar, " Die Zustandsgleichung," Leipzig, 1924, 119.

The *Joule effect* is found from (3), § 23.VII A, and (5), with the approximate substitution $dv=-RTdp/p^2$, as:

$$dT=\frac{RT_c}{C_v}\frac{dp}{p_c}\frac{27}{32}\tau^2 \quad \ldots \ldots \ldots \quad (14)$$

For the *Joule-Thomson effect* (7), and (6), § 24.VII A, give:

$$dT=\frac{9RT_c}{128p_cC_p}(1-18\tau^2)dp \quad \ldots \ldots \quad (15)$$

For CO_2 at 0° C. with $dp=1$ atm., $T_c=304$, $p_c=73$ atm., $R=1{\cdot}984$ g.cal./1°, $C_p=8{\cdot}6$ g.cal., (15) gives:

$$dT=\frac{9\times1{\cdot}984\times304}{128\times73\times8{\cdot}6}\left[1-18\left(\frac{304}{273}\right)^2\right]\times1=-1{\cdot}44°.$$

The observed fall in temperature is 1·46°.

The (theoretical) value of the molecular heat at constant volume C_v of a gas *in the ideal state*, $C_v{}^0$, when $p=0$ or $v\to\infty$, is found as follows.[1] From (11):

$$\vartheta(d^2\pi/d\vartheta^2)_\phi=(d/d\vartheta)[\vartheta(d\pi/d\vartheta)_\phi-\pi]_\phi=-(32/3)/\vartheta^2\phi^2 \quad \ldots \quad (16)$$

From (1), § 49.II:

$$(dC_v/dv)_T=T(d^2p/dT^2)_v=(p_c\vartheta/T_c)(d^2\pi/d\vartheta^2)_\phi$$

$$=-(32/3)p_c/\vartheta^2\phi^2T_c=-(32/3)p_cv_c^2/\vartheta^2v^2T_c \quad \ldots \quad (17)$$

Thus, by integration with respect to v (T constant):

$$C_v=f(v)+(32/3)p_cv_c^2/\vartheta^2T_cv \quad \ldots \ldots \quad (18)$$

where $f(v)$ is a function of volume or a constant. When $v\to\infty$ (i.e. $p\to0$) C_v becomes $C_v{}^0$, therefore $f(v)=C_v{}^0$, or:

$$C_v=C_v{}^0+(32/3)p_cv_c^2/\vartheta^2T_cv.$$

But from (5), § 29, $p_cv_c/T_c=(9/32)R$; also from the approximate equation (9), § 29, $\pi\phi=(32/9)\vartheta$, and with $1/\vartheta=\tau=T_c/T$:

$$C_v=C_v{}^0+(27/32)R\pi\tau^3 \quad \ldots \ldots \ldots \quad (19)$$

Since $C_v{}^0$ refers to an ideal gas, it is a constant (§ 54.II).

The so-called Kellogg characteristic equation: [2]

$$p=RT\rho+(B_0RT-A_0-C_0/T^2)\rho^2+(bRT-a-c/T^2)\rho^3 \quad \ldots \quad (20)$$

where ρ=density, was used by some American workers [3] to find $C_v{}^0$.

§ 31. Dieterici's Equations

Dieterici in 1899 [4] proposed a modification of van der Waals's equation in which the internal pressure is $a/v^{5/3}$ instead of a/v^2. He arrived at this as follows.

[1] Nernst, "Theoretische Chemie," 7th edit., 1913, 241, where most of the equations in this paragraph are given without deduction; deductions in Partington, "Chemical Thermodynamics," 1924, 85; for applications, see Partington, *Proc. Roy. Soc.*, 1921, **100**, 27; Bartels and Eucken, *Z. phys. Chem.*, 1921, **98**, 70 (corrected by Millar, *J.A.C.S.*, 1923, **45**, 874; Giauque and Powell, *J.A.C.S.*, 1939, **61**, 1970, and many other workers; see § 15.VII E.)

[2] Benedict, Webb, and Rubin, *J. Chem. Phys.*, 1940, **8**, 334.

[3] Waddington, Todd, and Huffman, *J.A.C.S.*, 1947, **69**, 22.

[4] *Ann. Phys.*, 1899, **69**, 685; 1901, **5**, 51; 1903, **12**, 144; 1908, **24**, 569; 1911, **35**, 220; 1920, **62**, 75; von Jüptner, *Z. phys. Chem.*, 1910, **73**, 343; MacDougall, *J.A.C.S.*, 1916, **38**, 528; 1917, **39**, 1229; Porter, *Phil. Mag.*, 1922, **44**, 1020; Jellinek "Lehrbuch der physikalischen Chemie," 1928, **1**, 911.

Imagine a slice of 1 cm.^{2} area cut from the bulk of a substance in the critical state, and such that only one molecule can lie in its thickness. Then if there are n molecules in a volume v, the number per cm.^{3} is $n/v=N$, and if it is supposed (with Clausius; § 21.III) that each molecule is surrounded by an imaginary cube of edge λ, then $(n/v)\lambda^3=N\lambda^3=1$ cm.^{3}, and a slice of 1 cm.^{2} cross-section and thickness λ contains $N^{2/3}=(n/v)^{2/3}$ molecules. The internal pressure p_i, expressed by a/v^2 in van der Waals's equation, is the sum of all the forces exerted by the molecules in this slice, and if it is assumed, with van der Waals, that this is inversely proportional to v, this gives:

$$p_i=(n/v)^{2/3}(c/v)=a/v^{5/3} \quad . \quad . \quad . \quad . \quad . \quad . \quad . \quad . \quad (1)$$

where c and a are constants. By substituting (1) in place of a/v^2 in van der Waals's equation it follows that:

$$(p+a/v^{5/3})(v-b)=RT \quad . \quad . \quad . \quad . \quad . \quad . \quad . \quad . \quad (2)$$

By multiplying out, (2) gives:

$$v^{8/3}-[(bp+RT)/p]v^{5/3}+(a/p)v-ab/p=0 \quad . \quad . \quad . \quad . \quad (3)$$

which is of the form $(x=v^{1/3})$ $x^8-\alpha x^5+\beta x^3-\gamma=0$, and can have only three real roots. Lees [1] proposed the equation:

$$(p+ap^{1/3}/Tv^{5/3})(v-b)=RT \quad . \quad . \quad . \quad . \quad . \quad . \quad . \quad . \quad (4)$$

The critical constants are found from (3) by putting $dp/dv=0$ and $d^2p/dv^2=0$ as:

$$v_c=4b,\ p_c=a/4(4b)^{5/3}=a/4v_c^{5/3},\ T_c=15ab/4(4b)^{5/3}R=15ab/4Rv_c^{5/3} \quad (5)$$

and the relation found experimentally by Young (§ 20) follows, viz. $RT_c/p_cv_c=3{\cdot}75$.

This ratio has the following values according to the value chosen as the exponent of v in the internal pressure a/v^n:

n	$\frac{4}{3}$	$\frac{5}{3}$	$\frac{6}{3}$	$\frac{7}{3}$	$\frac{8}{3}$
RT_c/p_cv_c	48/7=6·89	15/4=3·75	8/3=2·66	21/10=2·10	96/55=1·75

A second equation proposed by Dieterici [2] (1899):

$$pe^{a/RTv}(v-b)=RT \quad . \quad . \quad . \quad . \quad . \quad . \quad . \quad . \quad (6)$$

has a theoretical basis. Since it contains three constants, it gives a law of corresponding states. On expanding the exponential function (§ 13.I), (6) gives, for large values of v:

$$p=[RT/(v-b)]e^{-a/RTv}\simeq[RT/(v-b)](1-a/RTv)=RT/(v-b)-a/v(v-b) \ . \quad (7)$$

which is similar to van der Waals's equation, $p=RT/(v-b)-a/v^2$.

The critical constants are found from (6) in the usual way as follows:

$$v_c=2b,\quad p_c=a/4e^2b^2=a/29{\cdot}56b^2,\quad T_c=a/4Rb \quad . \quad . \quad . \quad (8)$$

The value of RT_c/p_cv_c is 3·695. The reduced equation was considered by Porter:

$$\pi=[\vartheta/(2\phi-1)]e^{2-2/\vartheta\phi} \quad . \quad . \quad . \quad . \quad . \quad . \quad . \quad . \quad (6a)$$

A modified Dieterici equation based on the idea of molecular clustering (§ 46) was used for saturated water vapour by Ray.[3]

[1] *Phil. Mag.*, 1924, **47**, 431.
[2] *Locc. cit.*; Peczalski, *Compt. Rend.*, 1913, **156**, 1884; 1913, **157**, 113; MacLeod, *Trans. Faraday Soc.*, 1937, **33**, 694; 1944, **40**, 439, found $v_c\simeq 2b_c$.
[3] *Koll. Z.*, 1931, **57**, 259; 1935, **73**, 269.

MacDougall [1] calculated a and b for carbon dioxide by Dieterici's equation (6) from Amagat's results, finding:

	20°	40°	60°	80°	100°	137°
a	0·00983	0·00919	0·00852	0·00797	0·00749	0·00708
b	0·00202	0·00221	0·00227	0·00228	0·00226	0·00227

(The units are vol. of 1 ml. at S.T.P.=1; b in ml.; a in atm./ml.). Thus, a is really a function of temperature; b also varies somewhat with temperature, but is almost constant above the critical temperature. Neither a nor b depends much on volume.

Thermal coefficients calculated from (6) are: [2]

$$(\mathrm{d}p/\mathrm{d}v)_T = -\frac{p}{v-b}\left[1-\frac{a(v-b)}{v^2RT}\right] \quad (9)$$

$$(\mathrm{d}p/\mathrm{d}T)_v = \frac{p}{T}\left(1+\frac{a}{vRT}\right) \quad (10)$$

$$(\mathrm{d}v/\mathrm{d}T)_p = \frac{R}{p}\mathrm{e}^{-a/vRT}\frac{1+a/vRT}{1-a(v-b)/v^2RT} \quad (11)$$

$$(\mathrm{d}E/\mathrm{d}v)_T = \frac{a\mathrm{e}^{-a/vRT}}{v(v-b)} \simeq \frac{a}{v^2} \quad (12)$$

$$C_p - C_v = R\mathrm{e}^{-a/vRT}\frac{(1+a/vRT)^2}{1-a(v-b)/v^2RT} \simeq R+\frac{2a}{vT} \quad (13)$$

$$\left[\frac{\mathrm{d}(pv)}{\mathrm{d}p}\right]_T = \frac{v^2(bRT-a)+abv}{v^2RT-av+ab} \simeq b-\frac{a}{RT}\,(v \text{ large}) \quad (14)$$

Pinter [3] used the equations:

$$(p \pm r/v^{n-1})(v-b) = RT - a/v + c/v^2 - d/v^3 \pm 1/v^{n-3}$$

with the + sign for even and the − for odd values of n. These give a law of corresponding states.

De Boissoudy,[4] to take account of molecular clustering (§ 46), used:

$$(p + a\mathrm{e}^{k/T}/v^2T^{1/2})(v-b) = RT,$$

where a, k, and b are constants.

Becker,[5] for nitrogen at high pressure (Amagat's results) used:

$$p = (RT/v)[1+(k/v)\mathrm{e}^{k/v}] - a/v^2 + \kappa/v^{\beta+2},$$

where, k, κ, and β are constants ($\beta=5$). If the last term is neglected, k/v put equal to x, and $1+x\mathrm{e}^x=f$, then:

$$p = (T/273)\rho f - a\rho^2,$$

[1] *J.A.C.S.*, 1916, **38**, 528; "Thermodynamics and Chemistry," 3rd edit., New York, 1939 16; Shaxby, *Phil. Mag.*, 1921, **41**, 441; Walker, *ibid.*, 1924, **47**, 111, 513; 1925, **50**, 1244.
[2] MacDougall, *J.A.C.S.*, 1916, **38**, 528.
[3] *Acta Phys. Polon.*, 1935, **4**, 23; *Z. Elektrochem.*, 1937, **43**, 669.
[4] *Compt. Rend.*, 1912, **155**, 704.
[5] *Z. Phys.*, 1921, **4**, 393.

where $\rho = 1/v$, and the equation leads to a critical point. Bridgman[1] found good agreement with the equation with his results for nitrogen. Brenner[2] proposed the equation:

$$(p + ce^{A/T}/V^n)(V - b) = RT$$

where c, A, and n are constants.

§ 32. Callendar's Equation

It has been stated (§ 24.VII A) that the Joule-Thomson effect was found experimentally to be inversely proportional to the square of the absolute temperature, hence:

$$T(\mathrm{d}v/\mathrm{d}T)_p - v = T^2(\mathrm{d}/\mathrm{d}T)(v/T)_p = C_p\alpha/T^2$$

where α is a constant. By integration, $v/T = -C_p\alpha/T^3 + \text{const.}$ For $T \to \infty$ it may be assumed that the ideal state is reached, when $v/T = \boldsymbol{R}/p$, hence:

$$v = \boldsymbol{R}T/p - \beta/T^2$$

where β is a constant. This equation was amplified by Callendar[3] into:

$$(v - b) = \boldsymbol{R}T/p - c_0(T_0/T)^n = V - c \quad . \quad . \quad . \quad . \quad . \quad . \quad (1)$$

$V = \boldsymbol{R}T/p$ is the " theoretical (ideal gas) volume," $T_0 = 273$, n is a constant, and:

$$c = c_0(T_0/T)^n \quad . \quad . \quad . \quad . \quad . \quad . \quad . \quad . \quad . \quad . \quad (2)$$

is a " co-aggregation volume " which is a function of temperature, and, except at moderate pressures, also of pressure. This has been used for steam, but otherwise has found little application. It does not lead to a critical state, which Callendar tried (§ 3.VII B) to show does not exist for water.

Callendar started with Rankine's formula (§ 1), $pv = \boldsymbol{R}T - a/Tv$ and substituted $pv = \boldsymbol{R}T$ in the correction term, giving $v = \boldsymbol{R}T/p - a/\boldsymbol{R}T^2$. He then replaced v by $(v - b)$, and assumed an exponent n in place of 2, giving equation (1) if $a/\boldsymbol{R} = c_0 T_0^n$. From some theoretical considerations[4] he concluded that:

$$n = C_v^0/\boldsymbol{R} \quad . \quad . \quad . \quad . \quad . \quad . \quad . \quad . \quad . \quad . \quad (3)$$

where C_v^0 is the limiting value of C_v for $p = 0$. Thus, for argon and monatomic gases, $n = 1{\cdot}5$, for diatomic gases 2·5, and for triatomic gases (e.g. steam) 3·5; but for carbon dioxide, $n = 2$.

Callendar's equation (1) may be written in the form:

$$pv = \boldsymbol{R}T + p(b - a/\boldsymbol{R}T^n)$$

giving the second virial coefficient (cf. (3), § 6) as:

$$B_p = b - a/\boldsymbol{R}T^n \quad . \quad . \quad . \quad . \quad . \quad . \quad . \quad . \quad . \quad (4)$$

From (1), $pV = \boldsymbol{R}T$, where $V = v - b + c$, hence:

$$V(\mathrm{d}p/\mathrm{d}T)_v + p(\mathrm{d}V/\mathrm{d}T)_v = \boldsymbol{R}$$

$$V(\mathrm{d}^2p/\mathrm{d}T^2)_v + 2(\mathrm{d}V/\mathrm{d}T)_v(\mathrm{d}p/\mathrm{d}T)_v + p(\mathrm{d}^2V/\mathrm{d}T^2)_v = 0.$$

[1] *Proc. Amer. Acad.*, 1923–4, **59**, 173 (209).

[2] *Proc. Nat. Acad.*, 1929, **15**, 11.

[3] *Proc. Roy. Soc.*, 1900, **67**, 266; *Phil. Mag.*, 1903, **5**, 48; " Properties of Steam," 1920, 184; Ewing, "Thermodynamics for Engineers," Cambridge, 1920, 318; Smith, *Proc. Roy. Soc.*, 1931–2, **134**, xviii; Eucken, in Wien-Harms, " Handbuch der Experimentalphysik," 1929, **8**, i, 404.

[4] Those using Callendar's equation for reduction of specific heats to the ideal state (see § 29) overlook this assumption.

From (2):

$$(\mathrm{d}V/\mathrm{d}T)_v=(\mathrm{d}c/\mathrm{d}T)_v=-nc/T \quad \ldots \quad (5)$$

$$\therefore\ (\mathrm{d}^2V/\mathrm{d}T^2)_v=(\mathrm{d}^2c/\mathrm{d}T^2)_v=n(n+1)c/T^2 \quad \ldots \quad (6)$$

Also,

$$(\mathrm{d}p/\mathrm{d}T)_v=(p/T)(1+nc/V) \quad \ldots \quad (7)$$

$$(\mathrm{d}^2p/\mathrm{d}T^2)_v=(pnc/T^2V)(1-n+2nc/V)=(\boldsymbol{R}nc/TV^2)(1-n+2nc/V) \quad . \quad (8)$$

From (1), § 49.II, since $\mathrm{d}v=\mathrm{d}V$ when T is constant:

$$(\mathrm{d}C_v/\mathrm{d}v)_T=(\mathrm{d}C_v/\mathrm{d}V)_T=T(\mathrm{d}^2p/\mathrm{d}T^2)_v=(\boldsymbol{R}nc/V^2)(1-n+2nc/V)$$

$$\therefore\ C_v=C_v{}^0+(\boldsymbol{R}nc/V)(n-1-nc/V) \quad \ldots \quad (9)$$

where $C_v{}^0$ is the ideal gas value, when $V\to\infty$ or $p\to 0$.

Since $V=\boldsymbol{R}T/p$, therefore

$$(\mathrm{d}V/\mathrm{d}T)_p=\boldsymbol{R}/p \quad \ldots \quad (10)$$

and $(\mathrm{d}^2V/\mathrm{d}T^2)_p=0$. Since:

$$(\mathrm{d}^2V/\mathrm{d}T^2)_p=(\mathrm{d}^2v/\mathrm{d}T^2)_p+(\mathrm{d}^2c/\mathrm{d}T^2)_p,$$

$$\therefore\ -(\mathrm{d}^2v/\mathrm{d}T^2)_p=(\mathrm{d}^2c/\mathrm{d}T^2)_p=n(n+1)c/T^2 \quad \ldots \quad (11)$$

From (2), § 49.II:

$$(\mathrm{d}C_p/\mathrm{d}p)_T=-T(\mathrm{d}^2v/\mathrm{d}T^2)_p=n(n+1)c/T$$

$$\therefore\ C_p=C_p{}^0+n(n+1)cp/T \quad \ldots \quad (12)$$

where $C_p{}^0$ is the ideal gas value, when $p\to 0$. Also from (1), and (2), § 47.II:

$$(\mathrm{d}v/\mathrm{d}T)_p=\boldsymbol{R}/p-(\mathrm{d}c/\mathrm{d}T)_p=\boldsymbol{R}/p+nc/T \quad \ldots \quad (13)$$

$$C_p-C_v=T(\mathrm{d}p/\mathrm{d}T)_v(\mathrm{d}v/\mathrm{d}T)_p=\boldsymbol{R}(1+nc/V)^2 \quad \ldots \quad (14)$$

With the special assumption (3), and $C_p{}^0-C_v{}^0=\boldsymbol{R}$, equations (9) and (12) become:

$$C_v=C_v{}^0(1+nc/V)(1-c/V) \quad \ldots \quad (15)$$

$$C_p=C_p{}^0(1+nc/V) \quad \ldots \quad (16)$$

$$\therefore\ C_p/C_v=\gamma=(C_p{}^0/C_v{}^0)/(1-c/V)=\gamma^0/(1-c/V) \quad \ldots \quad (17)$$

Since $v-b=\boldsymbol{R}T/p-c$, therefore:

$$(\mathrm{d}p/\mathrm{d}v)_T=-p^2/\boldsymbol{R}T \quad \ldots \quad (18)$$

$$\text{the isothermal elasticity}=\epsilon_T=-v(\mathrm{d}p/\mathrm{d}v)_T=p^2v/\boldsymbol{R}T=pv/V \quad . \quad (19)$$

$$\text{the adiabatic elasticity}=\epsilon_q=\gamma\epsilon_T=\gamma^0pv/V(1-c/V)=\gamma^0pv/(v-b) \quad . \quad (20)$$

For the entropy, (2b), § 3.II, and (1), § 35.II, give:

$$\mathrm{d}S=C_p\mathrm{d}T/T+l_p\mathrm{d}p/T$$

and since from (4), § 5.II, $l_p=l_v(\mathrm{d}v/\mathrm{d}p)_T$, from (5), § 41.II, $l_v=T(\mathrm{d}p/\mathrm{d}T)_v$, and (2c), § 5.II, $(\mathrm{d}p/\mathrm{d}T)_v(\mathrm{d}v/\mathrm{d}p)_T=-(\mathrm{d}v/\mathrm{d}T)_p$:

$$\mathrm{d}S=C_p\mathrm{d}T/T-(\mathrm{d}v/\mathrm{d}T)_p\mathrm{d}p \quad \ldots \quad (21)$$

$$=(C_p{}^0/T)\mathrm{d}T+n(n+1)cp\mathrm{d}T/T^2-(\boldsymbol{R}/p)\mathrm{d}p-(nc/T)\mathrm{d}p$$

$$=(Cp^0/T)\mathrm{d}T-(\boldsymbol{R}/p)\mathrm{d}p-n\mathrm{d}(cp/T)$$

$$\therefore\ S=S_0+C_p{}^0\ln T-\boldsymbol{R}\ln p-(ncp/T) \quad \ldots \quad (22)$$

For a change of state from (p_1, T_1) to (p_2, T_2):

$$\Delta S = C_p^0 \ln (T_2/T_1) - \boldsymbol{R} \ln (p_2/p_1) - n(c_2p_2/T_2 - c_1p_1/T_1) \quad . \ (23)$$

Put $c_0T_0^n = \text{const.} = C$, then with assumption (3) equation (22) becomes:

$$S = S_0 + (n+1)\boldsymbol{R} \ln T - \boldsymbol{R} \ln p - nCp/T^{n+1}$$
$$= S_0 + \boldsymbol{R} \ln (T^{n+1}/p) - nC(p/T^{n+1})$$

and since in a reversible adiabatic change S is constant

$$p/T^{n+1} = \text{const.} \quad \ldots \ (24)$$

From (1), $p(v-b)/T = \boldsymbol{R} - Cp/T^{n+1}$, hence in such a change:

$$p(v-b)/T = \text{const.} \quad \ldots \ (25)$$

$$\therefore \ (T^{n+1}/p)p(v-b)/T = (v-b)T^n = \text{const.} \quad \ldots \ (26)$$

and by multiplying (25) and (26):

$$p(v-b)^{(n+1)/n} = p(v-b)^{\gamma_0} = \text{const.} \quad \ldots \ (27)$$

$$\text{or} \quad p^n(v-b)^{n+1} = \text{const.} \quad \ldots \ (28)$$

For an isothermal change, from (23):

$$\Delta S_T = \boldsymbol{R} \ln (p_1/p_2) - (p_1 - p_2)nc/T \quad \ldots \ (29)$$

$$q_T = \boldsymbol{R}T \ln (p_1/p_2) - (p_1 - p_2)nc \quad \ldots \ (30)$$

The energy change is given by (3), § 43.II:

$$\mathrm{d}E = T\mathrm{d}S - p\mathrm{d}v.$$

But

$$\mathrm{d}v = (\boldsymbol{R}/p)\mathrm{d}T - (\boldsymbol{R}T/p^2)\mathrm{d}p + (nc/T)\mathrm{d}T \quad \ldots \ (31)$$

$$\therefore \ \mathrm{d}E = (C_p^0 - \boldsymbol{R})\mathrm{d}T + n[(ncp/T)\mathrm{d}T - c\mathrm{d}p]$$
$$= C_v^0\mathrm{d}T - n\mathrm{d}(cp)$$

$$\therefore \ E = E_0 + C_v^0T - ncp \quad \ldots \ (32)$$

The work done in an isothermal change is:

$$w_T = q_T - (\Delta E)_T = \boldsymbol{R}T \ln (p_1/p_2) \quad \ldots \ (33)$$

the same as for an ideal gas.

In the application to steam, the values of c at various temperatures are calculated and subtracted from the ideal volume V to find the actual volume v. Since this is given by:

$$v/V = 1 - (c-b)/V = 1 - (c-b)p/\boldsymbol{R}T \quad \ldots \ (34)$$

it follows that v/V at constant temperature is a linear function of p, and the isotherms are straight lines which radiate from the point $v/V = 1$ for $p = 0$. The observed isotherms found by Amagat and by Young, however, are curves, and the equation cannot be regarded as applying accurately even to steam.

The results for steam can be fairly well represented by a much simpler equation proposed by Tumlirz,[1] holding from $-6°$ to $+231°$, but not quite to the saturation pressure:

$$p(v+b)=kT \quad . \quad . \quad . \quad . \quad . \quad . \quad . \quad . \quad . \quad (35)$$

where b is a constant$=0{\cdot}008402$, and $k=3{\cdot}4348$. A complicated formula was proposed by Naumann,[2] and another later by Tumlirz.[3]

§ 33. Wohl's Equations

Wohl,[4] who considered a large number of possible equations, at first proposed one with three constants, derivable from critical data:

$$(p-c'/v^3)(v-b)=RT-a'/v \quad . \quad . \quad . \quad . \quad . \quad . \quad (1)$$

$$\text{or} \quad p=RT/(v-b)-a'/v(v-b)+c'/v^3 \quad . \quad . \quad . \quad . \quad (2)$$

where a' and c' are temperature functions, which can be *approximately* represented by writing:

$$[p+a/Tv(v-b)-c/T^2v^3](v-b)=RT \quad . \quad . \quad . \quad . \quad . \quad (3)$$

This form is generally known as "Wohl's equation."[5] It reduces to Berthelot's equation at low pressures, gives good results at high pressures, and (as it contains three constants, a, b, and c) takes account of deviations from the law of corresponding states. The third term in the first bracket in (3) represents a *repulsive* pressure between the molecules, not taken into account by van der Waals. In terms of the critical constants:

$$a=6v_c^2p_cT_c, \quad b=v_c/4, \quad c=4v_c^3p_cT_c^2, \quad RT_c/p_cv_c=\tfrac{15}{4}=3{\cdot}75 \quad . \quad (4)$$

In further investigations[6] Wohl proposed the formula ($\tau=T_c/T$):

$$p=RT/(v-b)-a\tau/v(v-b)+c\tau^{4/3}/v^3 \quad . \quad . \quad . \quad . \quad (5)$$

and then:[7]

$$[p+af_1(T)/v(v-b)-cf_2(T)/v^3](v-b)=RT \quad . \quad . \quad . \quad . \quad (6)$$

where a, b, c are constants and $f_1(T)$ and $f_2(T)$ two functions of temperature, which as a first approximation are τ and $\tau^{4/3}$, when:

$$p=RT/(v-b)-a'/Tv(v-b)+c'/T^{4/3}v^3 \quad . \quad . \quad . \quad . \quad (7)$$

Herz[8] compared the results of Berthelot's equation

$$pv=RT[1+0{\cdot}0703(T_cp_c/Tp)(1-6T_c^2/T^2)],$$

and Wohl's equation:

$$pv=RT[1+0{\cdot}0667(T_cp/Tp_c)(1-6{\cdot}40T_c^2/T^2)],$$

for various substances at the saturation vapour pressures. With $R=0{\cdot}08207$

1 *Wien Ber.*, 1899, **108**, II A, 1058, 1395; *Nuov. Cim.*, 1900, **11**, 5; *Ann. Phys. Beibl.*, 1900, **24**, 670, 1265; H. Lorenz, "Technische Wärmelehre," Munich, 1904, 215, 274, 293, 304, 356; Ciampini, *Nuov. Cim.*, 1912, **3**, 101, found this very inaccurate for gases.

2 *Z. phys. Chem.*, 1932, **159**, 135.

3 *Wien Ber.*, 1921, **130**, II A, 93.

4 *Z. phys. Chem.*, 1914, **87**, 1.

5 Nernst, "Theoretische Chemie," 8–10th edit., 1921, 257; Wegscheider, *Z. phys. Chem.*, 1922, **99**, 361; 1928, **135**, 362; Nesselmann, *ibid.*, 1924, **108**, 309 (steam); Herz, *Z. Elektrochem.*, 1926, **32**, 31; Geissler, *ibid.*, 1926, **32**, 217. All Wohl's papers are interesting and informative.

6 *Z. phys. Chem.*, 1921, **99**, 207, 226, 234.

7 *Z. phys. Chem.*, 1928, **133**, 305, 368; 1929, **2 B**, 77.

8 *Z. Elektrochem.*, 1926, **32**, 31; more values are given in the original.

lit. atm./1° and v in lit. he found for benzene the following observed and calculated values of pv from 0·72 to 43 atm.:

T° K.	343·2	363·2	383·2	403·2	423·2	463·2	503·2	523·2	553·2
pv obs.	27·56	28·91	29·71	30·75	30·98	31·23	28·90	26·66	20·27
pv calc. W.	27·42	28·59	29·57	30·36	30·97	31·58	31·39	30·97	29·90
pv calc. B.	27·50	28·60	29·60	30·41	31·04	31·71	31·60	31·24	30·27
p atm.	0·7203	1·337	2·300	3·717	5·704	11·91	22·13	29·23	43·12
RT	28·17	29·81	31·45	33·09	34·73	38·02	41·30	42·94	45·49

Both equations give satisfactory values at lower pressures, but at higher pressures there is a deviation, reaching 6 per cent., and there is little difference between the two equations. For carbon tetrachloride the results are:

T° K.	343·2	373·2	403·2	423·2	443·2	463·2	483·2	523·2
pv obs. ...	27·19	28·72	29·83	30·33	30·78	30·15	29·40	25·86
pv calc. W. ...	27·30	28·91	30·10	30·65	31·00	31·19	31·15	30·49
pv calc. B. ...	27·32	28·94	30·15	30·73	31·10	31·32	31·32	30·77
p atm.... ...	0·808	1·917	3·950	5·993	8·738	12·25	16·79	29·49
RT	28·17	30·63	33·09	34·73	36·37	38·02	39·66	42·94

Similar results were found for many other substances; the results with argon, oxygen, and hydrogen were less satisfactory. The temperature T_m at which pv is a maximum is about 0·8 times the critical temperature (0·771–0·882), except for hydrogen (0·584).

§ 34. Van Laar's Equation

Van Laar,[1] by a virial method (§ 42), found an equation in the form of van der Waals's:

$$[p+(a_g)_T/v^2][v-(b_g)_T]=RT \quad . \; . \; . \; . \; . \; . \; . \quad (1)$$

in which $(a_g)_T$ and $(b_g)_T$ are functions of temperature. If the equation is written in virial form (§ 6), $pv=RT+B/v$, the second virial coefficient is given by:

$$B_T=RT(b_g)_T-(a_g)_T=[RT(b_g)_c-(a_g)_c]e^{\alpha(1/RT-1/RT_c)} \quad . \; . \; . \quad (2)$$

the subscript c denoting a value at the critical temperature,[2] and α is a constant which can be calculated from the values of $(b_g)_c$, $(a_g)_c$, and B_T for *one* temperature. If a_c, b_c are the values at the critical temperature and pressure, $(b_g)_c=\phi_1 b_c$, and $(a_g)_c=\phi_2 a_c$, and if T_B is the Boyle temperature (§ 6), for which pv=const.:

$$T_B=\frac{(a_g)_T}{R(b_g)_T}=\frac{(a_g)_c}{R(b_g)_c}=\frac{\phi_2 a_c}{R\phi_1 b_c} \quad . \; . \; . \; . \; . \; . \; . \quad (3)$$

In many cases ϕ_1 and ϕ_2 are approximately unity. The values of a_c and b_c are:

$$a_c=27T_c^2/64(273)^2p_c, \quad b_c=T_c/8\cdot 273p_c \quad . \; . \; . \; . \quad (4)$$

[1] Van Laar, *J. Chim. Phys.*, 1916, **14**, 3; *Proc. K. Akad. Wetens. Amsterdam*, 1918, **21**, 2, 16; *Z. anorg. Chem.*, 1918, **104**, 57, 77, 81, 98, 105, 134, 145; *Rec. Trav. Chim.*, 1920, **39**, 215, 371; "Die Zustandsgleichung von Gasen und Flüssigkeiten," Leipzig, 1924.

[2] The *pressure* is assumed to be below the critical value.

Examples of the applicability of the equation are: [1]

H_2			CO_2		
T° K.	10^6 B calc.	10^6 B obs.	T° K.	10^6 B calc.	10^6 B obs.
473·34	1278	1280	273·1	−7041	−7041
373·09	934	930 (average)	293·1	−6313	−6416
			303·1	−6000	−6233
293·09	657	657	304·1†	−5972	−5952
237·09	588	585–90	313·1	−5716	−5851
169·55	225	244	330·8	−5268	−5260
133·25	95	112	343·1	−4997	−5100
109·00	6·1	7·3	353·1	−4793	−4903
107·37*	0	0	363·1	−4602	−4698
90·34	−65	−80	373·1	−4424	−4462
77·89	−114	−123	410·1	−3857	−3857
68·47	−153	−173	471·1	−3138	−2965
60·36	−188	−223			
55·77	−209	−245			
33·18†	−336	—			
20·62	−467	−470			
17·77	−518	−490			
15·09	−560	−550			

* Boyle point. † Critical temperature.

Van Laar [2] assumed that b_c (which is 3·5–4 times the actual volume of the molecules) can be additively composed of atomic values: C (aliphatic) 0·00100, C (aromatic, cyclic) 0·00075, H 0·00014, O″ (in acid and ester CO group) 0·00050, other O 0·00070, Cl 0·00115, Br 0·00165, I 0·00220 (for unit of b see § 3). Van Laar's calculations are not wholly acceptable; he calculated [3] values of a for alkali metals and halides from the internal latent heat by the equations:

$$Ml_{ei}=a/v=\boldsymbol{R}T^2(\mathrm{d}\ln p/\mathrm{d}T)=\boldsymbol{R}(A-BT-DT^2),$$

$$\ln p=-A/T-B/\ln T+C-DT,$$

with $B=1{\cdot}25$; $Ml_0=a_0/v_0=\boldsymbol{R}A$, where v_0 is the extrapolated molar volume at 0° K., and l_0 and a_0 are corresponding values. This gives $a_0=A\boldsymbol{R}v_0$, and by subtracting from $\sqrt{a_0}$ the value of $\sqrt{a_0}$ for the halogen, the value for the metal in MeX was found.

§ 35. Gas Mixtures

A theoretical extension of van der Waals's equation to a mixture of two gases was obtained [4] by Lorentz and van der Waals. The form of the equation is

[1] Van Laar, "Die Zustandsgleichung," 1924, 22 (H_2), 32 (CO_2).

[2] *Proc. K. Akad. Wetens. Amsterdam*, 1914–15, **17**, 451, 598, 606; 1915, **18**, 1220; 1916, **19**, 2, 287, 295; 1917–18, **20**, 492, 505; 1919, **21**, 644; *J. Chim. Phys.*, 1916, **14**, 3; *Chem. Weekbl.*, 1918, **15**, 1124; "Die Zustandsgleichung," 1924, 176.

[3] *Z. anorg. Chem.*, 1925, **148**, 235; on calculation of a and b for tungsten and molybdenum, Van Liempt, *Proc. K. Akad. Wetens. Amsterdam*, 1931, **34**, 1032.

[4] Lorentz, *Ann. Phys.*, 1881, **12**, 127, 660; van der Waals, *Compt. Rend.*, 1898, **126**, 1856; *Verslag. K. Akad. Wetens. Amsterdam*, 1898, **6**, 279; 1898, **7**, 239, 270, 469; *Proc. K. Akad. Wetens. Amsterdam*, 1899, **1**, 179, 232, 390; 1912, **14**, 655, 875; 1912, **15**, 602; *Z. phys. Chem.*, 1899, **30**, 159; "Continuität," 2nd edit., 1900, **2**, 2f., 50; *Congrès Internat. Phys.*, 1901, **1**, 583; Happel, *Ann. Phys.*, 1908, **26**, 95.

still $(p+a/v^2)(v-b)=RT$, where v is the molar volume, but the constants a and b are calculated from those of the component gases. If there are N_1 and N_2 mols of the two gases, the mol fractions are:

$$x_1=N_1/(N_1+N_2) \quad \text{and} \quad x_2=N_2/(N_1+N_2)=1-x_1,$$

and if V is the total volume of the mixture Lorentz found:

$$\left.\begin{aligned} v&=V/(N_1+N_2) \\ a&=a_{11}x_1^2+2a_{12}x_1x_2+a_{22}x_2^2 \\ b&=b_{11}x_1^2+2b_{12}x_1x_2+b_{22}x_2^2 \end{aligned}\right\} \quad \dots \dots \quad (1)$$

where the coefficients a_{11}, a_{22}, b_{11}, b_{22} are those of the pure gases, while a_{12} and b_{12} arise from the mutual action of the gases.

For the b constant, Lorentz [1] proposed:

$$\sqrt[3]{b_{12}}=\tfrac{1}{2}(\sqrt[3]{b_{11}}+\sqrt[3]{b_{22}}) \quad \dots \dots \quad (2)$$

whilst van der Waals [1] and D. Berthelot [2] proposed:

$$b_{12}=\tfrac{1}{2}(b_{11}+b_{22}) \quad \dots \dots \quad (3)$$

$$\therefore\ b=b_{11}x_1+b_{22}x_2 \quad \dots \dots \quad (3a)$$

For the a constant, Galitzine [3] and D. Berthelot [2] proposed:

$$a_{12}=\sqrt{(a_{11}a_{22})} \quad \dots \dots \quad (4)$$

$$\therefore\ \sqrt{a}=\sqrt{a_{11}}x_1+\sqrt{a_{22}}x_2 \quad \dots \dots \quad (4a)$$

According to Braune and Strassmann,[4] a_{12} is inversely proportional to T, as in Berthelot's equation (§ 29). The additivity of the b value for a molecule from atomic values [5] may be approximately true, but the additivity of the $\sqrt{a}$ values [6] is much less certain.

Galitzine, in an elaborate investigation, assumed an inverse square law of attraction and Clausius's equation (§ 28), and found (apart from a small correcting factor):

$$a_{12}=\sqrt{(a_1a_2)}, \quad c_{12}=\sqrt{(c_1c_2)},$$

$$b_{12}=\sqrt{[(m_1+m_2)/2m_2]}\sigma'^3\alpha_1, \quad b_{21}=\sqrt{[(m_1+m_2)/2m_1]}\,\sigma'^3\alpha_2,$$

where $\alpha_1=(v_2/v_1)_0$, $\alpha_2=(v_1/v_2)_0$, $\sigma'=(\sqrt[3]{b_1}+\sqrt[3]{b_2})/2$, and m_1, m_2 are the molecular weights. Morino [7] used the equations $\sqrt{a}=x\sqrt{a_A}+(1-x)\sqrt{a_B}$, $b=xb_A+(1-x)b_B$, where x=mol fraction of A, and calculated the critical temperature of a mixture from these.

Lennard-Jones and Cook [8] calculated the second virial coefficient B (§ 6)

[1] See note 4, p. 718.

[2] *Compt. Rend.*, 1898, **126**, 1703; 1899, **128**, 820 (with Sacerdote), 1159.

[3] *Ann. Phys.*, 1890, **41**, 770; Gillespie, *J.A.C.S.*, 1925, **47**, 305; Eucken and Brester, *Z. phys. Chem.*, 1928, **134**, 230; Lorenz, *ibid.*, 1929, **139**, 1; Neusser, *Phys. Z.*, 1934, **35**, 738.

[4] *Z. phys. Chem.*, 1929, **143**, 225.

[5] Guye, *Ann. Chim.*, 1890, **21**, 206; Heilborn, *Z. phys. Chem.*, 1890, **6**, 578; Altschul, *ibid.*, 1893, **11**, 577; Happel, *Ann. Phys.*, 1908, **26**, 95; Batschinski, *Z. phys. Chem.*, 1913, **82**, 86; van Laar, *Proc. K. Akad. Wetens. Amsterdam*, 1914–15, **17**, 451, 598, 606; 1915, **18**, 1220; 1916, **19**, 2, 287, 295; 1917–18, **20**, 492, 505; 1919, **21**, 644; *Z. anorg. Chem.*, 1918, **104**, 57; " Die Zustandsgleichung," Leipzig, 1924, 176–210.

[6] Van Laar, *J. Chim. Phys.*, 1916, **14**, 3; *Chem. Weekbl.*, 1918, **15**, 1124; " Die Zustandsgleichung," Leipzig, 1924, 199, and references in footnote 5; Herz, *Z. Elektrochem.*, 1921, **27**, 125, 373; Lorenz, *Z. phys. Chem.*, 1928, **139**, 1; Herzog, *ibid.*, 1930, **147**, 118.

[7] *Sci. Pap. Inst. Phys. Chem. Res. Tokyo*, Abstr., 1932, **11**, 131.

[8] *Proc. Roy. Soc.*, 1927, **115**, 334; Beattie and Bridgeman, *J.A.C.S.*, 1928, **50**, 3151; Beattie, *ibid.*, 1929, **51**, 19 (found $B=\beta_m/\Sigma(n_1)^2RT$ with the Beattie-Bridgeman coefficient β; § 38); Edwards and Roseveare, *ibid.*, 1942, **64**, 2816.

for a binary mixture with mol fractions x and $(1-x)$ by the equation:

$$B=B_{11}(1-x)^2+2B_{12}x(1-x)+B_{22}x^2 \quad . \quad . \quad . \quad . \quad (5)$$

in which B_{12} depends on the interaction of the two kinds of molecules.

Attempts have been made [1] to correlate volume changes on mixing *liquids* with a and b values from van der Waals's equation.

Kritschewsky and Kazarnowsky [2] proposed the equation (N=mol fraction):

$$p=p_1{}^0N_1+p_2{}^0N_2+\alpha N_1N_2(p_1{}^0-p_2{}^0) \quad . \quad . \quad . \quad . \quad (6)$$

where α is a constant, depending on temperature, and this gave good results with H_2+CO_2 and H_2+N_2. Kritschewsky and Markov [3] extended this to ternary mixtures:

$$p=p_1{}^0N_1+p_2{}^0N_2+p_3{}^0N_3+\alpha_{12}N_1N_2(p_1{}^0-p_2{}^0)+\alpha_{23}N_2N_3(p_2{}^0-p_3{}^0)$$
$$+\alpha_{31}N_3N_1(p_1{}^0-p_3{}^0) \quad (7)$$

and this equation gave good results with $N_2+H_2+CO_2$ mixtures.

For a mixture of N_a molecules of one kind and N_b of another kind, with diameters d_a and d_b, Ursell [4] found the state sum (§ 8.IV):

$$Z=V^{(N_a+N_b)}\Phi \quad . \quad . \quad . \quad . \quad . \quad . \quad . \quad . \quad . \quad (8)$$

where V is the volume and Φ is a function given by:

$$\ln \Phi=-\frac{1}{V}[N_a{}^2(\tfrac{2}{3}\pi d_a{}^3)+N_aN_b(\tfrac{4}{3}\pi d_{ab}{}^3)+N_b{}^2(\tfrac{2}{3}\pi d_b{}^3)]$$
$$-\frac{1}{V^2}[\tfrac{5}{16}N_a{}^3(\tfrac{2}{3}\pi d_a{}^3)^2+4\pi^2N_a{}^2N_bd_a{}^3(\tfrac{2}{9}d_{ab}{}^3-\tfrac{1}{8}d_{ab}{}^2d_a+\tfrac{1}{144}d_a{}^3)$$
$$+\tfrac{5}{16}N_b{}^3(\tfrac{2}{3}\pi d_b{}^3)^2+4\pi^2N_aN_b{}^2d_b{}^3(\tfrac{2}{9}d_{ab}{}^3-\tfrac{1}{8}d_{ab}{}^2d_b+\tfrac{1}{144}d_b{}^3)] \quad . \quad (9)$$

where $d_{ab}=\frac{1}{2}(d_a+d_b)$ is the sum of the radii. If the sizes are the same, $d_a=d_b=d_{ab}=d$, and if $N=N_a+N_b$, $N_a/N=x_a$, $N_b/N=x_b$:

$$\ln \Phi=-\frac{N^2}{V}(x_a+x_b)^3(\tfrac{2}{3}\pi d^3)-\tfrac{5}{16}\frac{N^3}{V^2}(x_a+x_b)^3(\tfrac{2}{3}\pi d^3)^2$$

or, since $x_a+x_b=1$ and $\frac{4}{3}\pi d^3=v$=sphere of exclusion of a molecule (§ 2):

$$\ln \Phi=-\frac{1}{2}\frac{N^2}{V}v-\frac{5}{64}\frac{N^3}{V^2}v^2.$$

The contribution of this to the free energy is (§ 8.IV):

$$-kT\ln \Phi=NkT[\tfrac{1}{2}\frac{N}{V}v+\tfrac{5}{64}\left(\frac{N}{V}\right)^2v^2],$$

and the contribution to the pressure, given by $-(\mathrm{d}F/\mathrm{d}V)_T$ (§ 43.II), is:

$$\frac{NkT}{V}\left(\frac{1}{2}\frac{N}{V}v+\frac{5}{32}\frac{N^2}{V^2}v^2\right).$$

[1] Kremann, Meingast, and Gugl, *Monatsh.*, 1914, **35**, 1235.
[2] *Acta Physicochim. U.R.S.S.*, 1939, **10**, 217 (bibl.); Kazarnowsky, *ibid.*, 1940, **13**, 853.
[3] *Acta Physicochim. U.R.S.S.*, 1940, **12**, 59.
[4] *Proc. Cambr. Phil. Soc.*, 1927, **23**, 685; Fowler, "Statistical Mechanics," 2nd edit., Cambridge, 1936, 241.

The van der Waals co-volume is $b=4N\times\frac{4}{3}\pi(d/2)^3=\frac{1}{2}Nv$, and hence the effect of the excluded volume on the pressure is:

$$\frac{NkT}{V}\left[\frac{b}{V}+\frac{5}{8}\left(\frac{b}{V}\right)^2\right]$$

as found by Boltzmann (§ 2). This type of calculation is full of mathematical pitfalls.[1]

§ 36. Fugacity

The fugacity f of a gas or vapour may be defined [2] as an idealised pressure which makes the equation for an ideal gas, from (5), § 44.II:

$$\mathrm{d}G_i=V_i\mathrm{d}p=RT\mathrm{d}\ln p \quad . \quad . \quad . \quad . \quad . \quad . \quad . \quad . \quad (1)$$

true for an actual gas in the form:

$$dG_a=V_a\mathrm{d}p=RT\mathrm{d}\ln f \quad . \quad . \quad . \quad . \quad . \quad . \quad . \quad . \quad (2)$$

in the sense of the exact relation to the available energy change. The *activity coefficient* γ may then be defined as:

$$\gamma=f/p \quad . \quad . \quad . \quad . \quad . \quad . \quad . \quad . \quad . \quad . \quad . \quad (3)$$

Integration of (1) and (2) gives:

$$RT\ln(p/p^*)=\int_{p^*}^{p}V_i\mathrm{d}p \quad . \quad . \quad . \quad . \quad . \quad . \quad . \quad . \quad (4)$$

$$RT\ln(f/f^*)=\int_{p^*}^{p}V_a\mathrm{d}p \quad . \quad . \quad . \quad . \quad . \quad . \quad . \quad . \quad (5)$$

where p^* is a very low pressure, and: [3]

$$\lim_{p^*\to 0} f^*=p^* \quad . \quad . \quad . \quad . \quad . \quad . \quad . \quad . \quad . \quad . \quad (6)$$

Subtract (4) from (5) and use (6):

$$\therefore\ RT\ln\frac{f}{p}=RT\ln\gamma=\lim_{p^*\to 0}\int_{p^*}^{p}(V_a-V_i)\mathrm{d}p \quad . \quad . \quad . \quad . \quad (7)$$

From (7) the fugacity or the activity coefficient may be found (i) by graphical integration from the known p, V, T data, the volume residual $V_a-V_i=\alpha$ being

[1] Van Rysselberghe and Eisenberg, *J.A.C.S.*, 1939, **61**, 3030; 1940, **62**, 451; Alfrey and Mark, *J. Chem. Phys.*, 1942, **10**, 303; Fuchs, *Proc. Roy. Soc.*, 1943, **181**, 411; Wannier, *ibid.*, 1943, **181**, 409.

[2] Lewis, *Proc. Amer. Acad.*, 1900, **36**, 145 (" escaping tendency "); 1901, **37**, 49 (" fugacity "); *Z. phys. Chem.*, 1900, **35**, 343; 1901, **38**, 205; Lewis and Randall, " Thermodynamics," New York, 1923, 176, 226; Gillespie, *J.A.C.S.*, 1925, **47**, 305; 1926, **48**, 28; Randall and Sosnick, *ibid.*, 1928, **50**, 967; Merz and Whittaker, *ibid.*, 1928, **50**, 1522 (20 per cent. deviation for N_2+3H_2 to 1000 atm.); Essex and Sandholzer, *J. Phys. Chem.*, 1938, **42**, 317 (vapours).

[3] On this condition see Tunell, *J. Phys. Chem.*, 1931, **35**, 2885; on fugacities and their applications, see also Gibson and Sosnick, *J.A.C.S.*, 1927, **49**, 2172 ($C_2H_4+H_2$ only to 50 atm.); Cope, Lewis, and Weber, *Ind. Eng. Chem.*, 1931, **23**, 887; Lewis and Luke, *Trans. Amer. Soc. Mech. Eng.*, 1932, **54**, PME (8), 55; *Ind. Eng. Chem.*, 1933, **25**, 725; Selheimer, Souders, Smith, and Brown, *Ind. Eng. Chem.*, 1932, **24**, 515; Brown, Souders, and Smith, *ibid.*, 1932, **24**, 513; Brown, Lewis, and Weber, *ibid.*, 1934, **26**, 325; Lewis and Kay, *Oil Gas J.*, 1934, **32**, No. 45, 40; Essex and Kelly, *J.A.C.S.*, 1935, **57**, 815 (H_2O and C_2H_5OH vapour mixtures); Keyes, *J.A.C.S.*, 1938, **60**, 1761; Fischer, *Ann. Phys.*, 1939, **36**, 381 (O_2 and N_2); Temkin, *Acta Physicochim. U.R.S.S.*, 1944, **19**, 163; *J. Phys. Chem. U.S.S.R.*, 1945, **19**, 72; Othmer, *Ind. Eng. Chem.*, 1944, **36**, 669 (bibl.); Kirkbride, *Petrol. Refiner*, 1945, **24**, 485; Joffe, *Ind. Eng. Chem.*, 1947, **39**, 837; 1948, **40**, 2439 (hydrocarbons).

plotted against p (this is the most accurate method), or (ii) by substitution in (7) from a characteristic equation, e.g. V_a from Berthelot's equation (§ 29):

$$\frac{pV}{RT}=1+\frac{9}{128}\frac{pT_c}{p_cT}\left(1-6\frac{T_c^2}{T^2}\right) \quad . \quad . \quad . \quad . \quad . \quad . \quad . \quad (8)$$

from which by integration of (7):

$$\ln \gamma=\frac{9}{128}\frac{pT_c}{p_cT}\left(1-6\frac{T_c^2}{T^2}\right) \quad . \quad . \quad . \quad . \quad . \quad . \quad . \quad (9)$$

which is reasonably accurate for most gases up to 100–200 atm. pressure.[1] Substitution for dp in (7) from van der Waals's equation:

$$(p+a/V^2)(V-b)=RT \quad . \quad . \quad . \quad . \quad . \quad . \quad . \quad (10)$$

gives on integration:

$$\ln \gamma=\ln \frac{RT}{p(V-b)}+\frac{b}{V-b}-\frac{2a}{RTV} \quad . \quad . \quad . \quad . \quad . \quad . \quad (11)$$

which, with a and b found from compressibilities, holds for most gases up to about 100 atm. with reasonable accuracy.

Calculations are simplified by the use of reduced γ-curves.[2] Fugacities in mixtures [3] may be calculated on the assumption that the fugacity is equal to the mol fraction times the fugacity of the pure gas at the same temperature and total pressure (*Lewis's fugacity rule*): [4]

$$f_A=N_Af_A^0 \quad . \quad . \quad . \quad . \quad . \quad . \quad . \quad . \quad . \quad . \quad (12)$$

and that Dalton's law of partial pressures holds:

$$p_A=N_AP \quad . \quad . \quad . \quad . \quad . \quad . \quad . \quad . \quad . \quad . \quad (13)$$

where P=total pressure. From (12) and (13):

$$\gamma_A=f_A/p_A=N_Af_A^0/N_AP=f_A^0/P=\gamma_A^0 \quad . \quad . \quad . \quad . \quad . \quad (14)$$

Fugacity along the critical isotherm was considered by Meyers,[5] who found the approximate rule $f\simeq\frac{2}{3}p_c$.

Gay [6] introduced an " expansibility tension," π, which is related to the van der Waals co-volume b and the " heat of idealisation " L_i per mol:

$$\ln \pi=\ln [RT/(V_m-b)]+[b/(V_m-b)](L_i+pV_m-RT)/RT.$$

Krasilshchikov [7] defined the fugacity f by.

$$RT \ln f=RT \ln p+Bp,$$

where $B=b-a/RT$ is the second virial coefficient (§ 6). Up to 100 atm. this held for oxygen to 0·5 per cent., but with carbon dioxide the deviation was 6·5 per cent. Krichevsky and Kasarnovsky [8] pointed out that the usual

[1] Brodsky, *Compt. Rend. U.R.S.S.*, 1942, **36**, 237.
[2] Newton, *Ind. Eng. Chem.*, 1935, **27**, 302; van Lerberghe, *J. Chim. Phys.*, 1934, **31**, 577.
[3] Newton and Dodge, *Ind. Eng. Chem.*, 1935, **27**, 577; Gillespie, *Chem. Rev.*, 1936, **18**, 359; 1941, **29**, 525.
[4] Lewis and Randall, " Thermodynamics," New York, 1923, 226.
[5] *Bur. Stand. J. Res.*, 1942, **29**, 157.
[6] *Compt. Rend.*, 1910, **151**, 612; 1911, **153**, 262, 722; 1913, **156**, 1015, 1070; 1913, **157**, 711; 1914, **158**, 34; *J. Chim. Phys.*, 1912, **10**, 197; the " expansibility tension " was introduced by Guillemin, *Compt. Rend.*, 1904, **138**, 38, as the tendency of a liquid to emit vapour. It is related to the fugacity or escaping tendency.
[7] *J. Phys. Chem. U.S.S.R.*, 1935, **6**, 1362.
[8] *J.A.C.S.*, 1935, **57**, 2168.

integration of fugacity equations by the Gibbs-Duhem equation really assumes constant temperature, and Krichevsky [1] criticised Lewis's fugacity rule.

By the same procedure as was used for an ideal gas (§ 56.II) it is possible to find from van der Waals's equation an expression for the available energy of a mixture (treated as a single gas), and if $n=\Sigma n_1=n_1+n_2$:

$$G=n_1g_1'(T)+n_2g_2'(T)+nRT[\ln(p+a/v^2)-2a/RTv+b/(v-b)] -nTS_0(n_1,n_2) \quad (15)$$

where

$$g_1'(T)=\int C_{p1}dT-T\int(C_{p1}/T)dT+H_{01}-TS'_{01} \quad (16)$$

is a temperature function per mol of separate gas. The entropy of mixing is given by $S_0(n_1, n_2)$ and is evaluated for the case of large volume V, when the gas mixture becomes ideal; in this case (11), § 57.II, gives, if $N_1=n_1/n$, $N_2=n_2/n$ are the mol fractions:

$$S_0(N_1,N_2)=-R(N_1\ln N_1+N_2\ln N_2) \quad (17)$$

Expression (15) differs from that for an ideal gas mixture (6a), § 55.II, only by the omission of a term $nRT\ln p$ and by the third term on the right. Hence:

$$G-G_i=RTn[\ln(1+a/pv^2)-2a/RTv+b/(v-b)].$$

The logarithm is expanded and the volume eliminated by van der Waals's equation, giving:

$$G-G_i=n[p(b-a/RT)+(p/RT)^2a(b-a/RT)] \quad (18)$$

Following Randall and Sosnick [2] a fugacity $f_j=f_j^0N_j$ is defined, where f_j is the fugacity of a gas j in the mixture and f_j^0 its fugacity in the pure state at the same temperature and total pressure. For an ideal gas, $f_j=p_j$, the partial pressure, $p_j=pN_j$.

The fugacity is supposed to be related to the chemical potential $\mu=(dG/dn_1)_{T,p,n_2,\ldots}$ (§ 58.II), by the equation:

$$\mu_2-\mu_1=RT\ln(f_2/f_1),$$

$$\therefore \ln(f_j/pN_j)=\frac{1}{RT}\frac{d(G-G_i)}{dn_j} \quad (19)$$

This holds for all mol fractions, including $N_j=1$, when the left-hand side is identical with $\ln(f_j^0/p)$. By taking differences of the two expressions, and putting $j=1$ (for any particular component), it is found that:

$$\ln(f_1/f_1^0N_1)=(BN_2+CN_3+DN_4+\ldots)/RT \quad (20)$$

which was found by Hildebrand [3] to hold for liquid solutions. Epstein [4] gave the values of the coefficients:

$$B=p[(a_{11}-2a_{12}+a_{22})/RT-(b_{11}-2b_{12}+b_{22})]+(p/RT)^2[(6a_{11}+6a_{12}+a_{22})\times (a_{11}/2RT-b_{11})-(6a_{11}-4a_{12})(a_{12}/2RT-b_{12})+a_{11}(a_{22}/2RT-b_{22})]$$

$$C=4(p/RT)^2[-(2a_{11}-3a_{12}+a_{22})(a_{11}/2RT-b_{11})+(3a_{11}-4a_{12}+a_{22})\times (a_{12}/2RT-b_{12})-(a_{11}-a_{12})(a_{22}/2RT-b_{22})]$$

$$D=3(p/RT)^2(a_{11}-2a_{12}+a_{22})[(a_{11}-2a_{12}+a_{22})/2RT-(b_{11}-2b_{12}+b_{22})],$$

[1] *J.A.C.S.*, 1937, **59**, 2733.

[2] *J.A.C.S.*, 1928, **50**, 965; criticism by Krichevsky, *ibid.*, 1937, **59**, 2733; the fugacity rules are rather crude.

[3] *Proc. Nat. Acad.*, 1927, **13**, 267.

[4] "Textbook of Thermodynamics," New York, 1937, 207; for activity coefficients of binary and ternary *liquid* mixtures, Wohl, *Trans. Amer. Inst. Chem. Eng.*, 1946, **42**, 215.

and showed that the curves for mixtures of ethylene and argon are consistent with these if a_{12} and b_{12} have commensurate values.

Gibbs [1] modified Dalton's law of partial pressures (§ 56.II) to the form: "the pressure in a mixture of different gases is equal to the sum of the pressures of the different gases as existing each by itself at the same temperature and with the same value of its [chemical] potential." Lurie and Gillespie [2] interpreted these pressures as the *equilibrium pressures* p_e, which are to be exerted on the unmixed gases each on one side of a membrane permeable to it alone and on the other side of which is the gas mixture. They showed that the total pressure is the sum of the equilibrium pressures according to the equation:

$$P=p_{e1}+p_{e2}=f_1(T, V/n_1)+f_2(T, V/n_2) \quad . \quad . \quad . \quad . \quad . \quad (21)$$

where V=total volume, n_1, n_2=nos. of mols ($n=n_1+n_2$), where $P=f(T, V/n)$ is the characteristic equation of the gas mixture. Then if f_e is the fugacity of a gas in the mixture and f_m the fugacity of the mixture, both at the total pressure P:

$$RT \ln f_e=\int_0^P (\partial V/\partial n_1-v)dP+RTN_1 \ln f_m \quad . \quad . \quad . \quad . \quad (22)$$

where $N_1=n_1/(n_1+n_2)$ and $v=RT/p$, the value of f_m being calculated from the characteristic equation of the mixture.

§ 37. Keyes's Equation

Keyes [3] proposed the gas equation:

$$p=RT/(v-\beta e^{-\alpha/v})-A/(v+l)^2=RT/(v-\delta)-A/(v+l)^2 \quad . \quad . \quad (1)$$

where $\delta=\beta e^{-\alpha/v}$ is a function of volume and β, α, A and l are constants independent of v and T; for monatomic gases $\alpha=0$. According to Keyes and Marshall [4] the constant A is given in terms of Debye's quadrupole attraction theory (§ 43) by:

$$A=6\pi N\tau^2\alpha/5d^5,$$

where N=Avogadro's number, τ=electric moment of inertia function, α= polarisability, and d=diameter of the molecule.

For *mixtures of gases*, the same equation is used,[5] but the constants are functions of the constants of the separate gases, e.g. for a mixture of two gases:

$$A=(n_1\sqrt{A_1}+n_2\sqrt{A_2})^2$$
$$\beta=n_1\beta_1+n_2\beta_2$$
$$\alpha=n_1\alpha_1+n_2\alpha_2$$
$$l=n_1l_1+n_2l_2,$$

where n_1 and n_2 are numbers of mols (when the constants refer to n_1+n_2 mols

[1] "Scientific Papers," 1906, **1**, 155 f.

[2] *J.A.C.S.*, 1927, **49**, 1146; see Gillespie, *ibid.*, 1925, **47**, 305; 1926, **48**, 28; *Phys. Rev.*, 1929, **34**, 1605; Jellinek, "Lehrbuch der physikalischen Chemie," 1933, **4**, 345.

[3] *Proc. Nat. Acad.*, 1917, **3**, 323; Keyes and Felsing, *J.A.C.S.*, 1919, **41**, 589; 1920, **42**, 106; Keyes, *ibid.*, 1920, **42**, 54; Taylor and Smith, *ibid.*, 1922, **44**, 2450 (ether); 1923, **45**, 2107; 1926, **48**, 3122; Keyes, Smith, and Joubert, *J. Math. Phys. Mass. Inst.*, 1922, **1**, 191; Keyes, Taylor, and Smith, *ibid.*, 1922, **1**, 211; Keyes, Townshend, and Young, *ibid.*, 1922, **1**, 243 (corr. gas thermom.); Beattie, *J.A.C.S.*, 1924, **46**, 342; 1927, **49**, 1123; Keyes and Taylor, *ibid.*, 1927, **49**, 896; Bridgeman, *ibid.*, 1927, **49**, 1130; Keyes and Burks, *ibid.*, 1927, **49**, 1403; Keyes and Marshall, *ibid.*, 1927, **49**, 156.

[4] *J.A.C.S.*, 1927, **49**, 156; values of A for several substances.

[5] Keyes, *J.A.C.S.*, 1927, **49**, 1393; Keyes and Burks, *ibid.*, 1928, **50**, 1100; Keyes and Felsing, *ibid.*, 1939, **61**, 2457; Beattie, Stockmayer, and Ingersoll, *J. Chem. Phys.*, 1941, **9**, 863, 871.

of mixture), or mol fractions (no. of mols÷total no. of mols; when they refer to 1 mol of mixture); hence:

$$p=RT\Sigma n_1/[v-(\Sigma n_1\beta_1)e^{-\Sigma n_1 a_1/v}]-(\Sigma n_1\sqrt{A_1})^2/(v+\Sigma n_1 l_1)^2 \quad . \quad (2)$$

The following are observed and calculated pressures in atmospheres for a mixture of nitrogen and methane containing 30·44 wt. per cent. of methane:

v ml./g.	0°	50°	100°	150°	200°	
30	31·640 31·603	38·172 38·077	44·664 44·551	51·126 51·025	57·591 57·499	obs. calc.
20	46·812 46·732	56·998 56·817	67·146 66·902	77·220 76·987	87·281 87·073	obs. calc.

§ 38. Beattie and Bridgeman's Equation

Beattie and Bridgeman [1] proposed the gas equation:

$$p=RT(1-\epsilon)(v+B)/v^2-A/v^2 \quad . \quad . \quad . \quad . \quad . \quad . \quad (1)$$

where $A=A_0(1-a/v)$, $B=B_0(1-b/v)$, $\epsilon=c/vT^3$, R, c, B_0, b, A_0, and a being constants independent of v and T. For *mixtures of gases* [2] the constants are given by:

$$\left.\begin{array}{l} A_0=(\Sigma n_1\sqrt{A_{01}})^2 \\ a=\Sigma n_1 a_1,\ B_0=\Sigma n_1 B_{01},\ b=\Sigma n_1 b_1 \\ c=\Sigma n_1 c_1,\ \text{and}\ R=\Sigma n_1 R \end{array}\right\} \quad . \quad . \quad . \quad . \quad (2)$$

where (as above) n_1 is either a number of mols or a mol fraction.

In the temperature interval 0°–200°, with a maximum pressure of 216–254 atm., the average percentage deviations for the observed and calculated pressures are given in the following table:

Composition	N_2	69·556 N_2 30·444 CH_4	31·014 N_2 68·986 CH_4	29·69 N_2 70·31 CH_4	CH_4
Percentage deviation ...	0·055	0·547	0·113	0·232	0·066

Maron and Turnbull [3] developed a method of determining the constants of

[1] *J.A.C.S.*, 1927, **49**, 1665; *Proc. Amer. Acad.*, 1928, **63**, 229; *J.A.C.S.*, 1928, **50**, 3133, 3151; *Z. Phys.*, 1930, **62**, 95; Beattie, *Phys. Rev.*, 1928, **31**, 680; 1928, **32**, 691, 699 (mixtures); 1929, **34**, 1615 (heat capac. gases, bibl.); Bridgeman, *ibid.*, 1929, **34**, 527; Gillespie, *J. Phys. Chem.*, 1929, **33**, 354 (C_2H_4); Beattie and Lawrence, *J.A.C.S.*, 1930, **52**, 6; Beattie, *Proc. Nat. Acad.*, 1930, **16**, 14; Scatchard, *ibid.*, 1930, **16**, 811; Deming and Shupe, *J.A.C.S.*, 1930, **52**, 1382; 1931, **53**, 843, 860; Beattie, Hadlock, and Poffenberger, *J. Chem. Phys.*, 1935, **3**, 93 (C_2H_6); Smith, Beattie, and Kay, *J.A.C.S.*, 1937, **59**, 1587 (*n*-heptane); Beattie, Kay, and Kaminsky, *ibid.*, 1937, **59**, 1589 (C_3H_8); Beattie, Simard, and Gouq-Jen Su, *ibid.*, 1939, **61**, 26 (*n*-C_4H_{10}); Gouq-Jen Su and Simard, *ibid.*, 1939, **61**, 926 (C_2H_6); Stockmayer, *J. Chem. Phys.*, 1941, **9**, 863; Beattie, Stockmayer, and Ingersoll, *ibid.*, 1941, **9**, 871; Lashakov, *J. Gen. Chem. U.S.S.R.*, 1941, **18**, No. 19, 17 (CH_3OH vap.); Brown, *Ind. Eng. Chem.*, 1941, **23**, 1536; for calculations, see Hougen and Watson, "Industrial Chemical Calculations," New York, 1931, 63.

[2] Beattie, *J.A.C.S.*, 1929, **51**, 19; Beattie and Ikehara, *Proc. Amer. Acad.*, 1930, **64**, 127; Deming and Shupe, *op. cit.*; Gillespie and Beattie, *J.A.C.S.*, 1930, **52**, 4239; Keyes, *ibid.*, 1938, **60**, 1761.

[3] *Ind. Eng. Chem.*, 1941, **33**, 408; *J.A.C.S.*, 1942, **64**, 44, 2195.

the Beattie-Bridgeman equation from critical data, on the assumption that most gases have the same activity coefficient at the same reduced pressure and temperature, and this procedure has been related to the theoretical equation [1] for a gas at moderate to high densities by Brown.[2] The five constants B_0, A_0, a, b, c of the Beattie-Bridgeman equation are replaced by the constants:

$$\alpha=A_0/RB_0T_c,\ \beta=c/B_0T_c^3,\ \gamma=-b/B_0,\ \delta=a/B_0,$$

and the equation then becomes:

$$\frac{PV}{RT}=\left[1+\left(\frac{B_0}{V}\right)+\gamma\left(\frac{B_0}{V}\right)^2\right]-\alpha\frac{T_c}{T}\left[\frac{B_0}{V}-\delta\left(\frac{B_0}{V}\right)^2\right]$$
$$-\beta\left(\frac{T_c}{T}\right)^3\left(\frac{B_0}{V}\right)\left[1+\frac{B_0}{V}+\gamma\left(\frac{B_0}{V}\right)^2\right] \quad . \quad (3)$$

which compares with the theoretical equation: [1]

$$\frac{PV}{RT}=\mathrm{f}_1\left(\frac{V_0}{V}\right)-\frac{\phi_0}{kT}\mathrm{f}_2\left(\frac{V_0}{V},\frac{\phi_0}{kT}\right),$$

where the first term represents the effect of the volume V_0 of the molecules and the second term gives the effect of the forces between the molecules, ϕ_0 being the minimum potential energy between two molecules.

For the purpose of reduction to the ideal state, Beattie and Bridgeman [3] wrote their equation in the virial form (§ 6):

$$pV=RT+\beta/V+\gamma/V^2+\delta/V^3 \quad . \quad . \quad . \quad . \quad . \quad . \quad (4)$$

where $\beta=RTB_0-A_0-Rc/T^2$; $\gamma=-RTB_0b+A_0a-RB_0c/T^2$; and $\delta=RB_0bc/T^2$. Linhart [4] showed by plotting $1/V$ against $\log p$ that the very simple equation with two constants, K and V_∞ (the value of V when $p\to\infty$):

$$(V_1-V_\infty)/(V_p-V_\infty)=p^K \quad . \quad . \quad . \quad . \quad . \quad . \quad . \quad . \quad (5)$$

gives very good results for various gases, each line being at a given temperature.

The reduced Beattie-Bridgeman equation [5] is ($\pi=p/p_c$, $\phi_0=v/v_{c0}$, $\vartheta=T/T_c$):

$$\pi=\vartheta(1-\epsilon')(\phi_0-B')/\phi_0^2-A'/\phi_0^2 \quad . \quad . \quad . \quad . \quad . \quad (6)$$

where $\epsilon'=c'/\phi_0\vartheta^3$, $A'=A_0'(1-a'/\phi_0)$, $B'=B_0'(1-b'/\phi_0)$, and A_0', a', B_0', b', c' are reduced constants. It should be noted that v_{c0} is an "ideal" critical volume, defined by $v_{c0}=RT_c/p_c$. The reduced constants (independent of the nature of the gas) are $A_0'=0{\cdot}4758$, $a'=0{\cdot}1127$, $B_0'=0{\cdot}18764$, $b'=0{\cdot}03833$, $c'=0{\cdot}05$. The results with seventeen gases agreed to 2 per cent. or less nearly to the critical point. The reduced equation is also written in the forms:

$$\pi=\vartheta/(\beta-\phi_0)-\alpha/\phi_0^2,$$

$$\pi=(\vartheta/\phi_0^2)(\phi_0+B)-A/\phi_0^2, \quad \text{and} \quad B=B_0(1+b/\phi_0),$$

where α and β are universal constants.

[1] Lennard-Jones, *Physica*, 1937, **4**, 941; Lennard-Jones and Devonshire, *Proc. Roy. Soc.*, 1937, **163**, 53; Michels and Michels, *Proc. Roy. Soc.*, 1937, **160**, 348 (CO_2); Michels, Blaisse, and Michels, *ibid.*, 1937, **160**, 358 (CO_2); Michels, Bijl, and Michels, *ibid.*, 1937, **160**, 376; de Boer and Michels, *Physica*, 1938, **5**, 945.

[2] *Ind. Eng. Chem.*, 1941, **33**, 1536.

[3] *J.A.C.S.*, 1928, **50**, 3151.

[4] *J. Phys. Chem.*, 1933, **37**, 645; 1934, **38**, 1091.

[5] Gouq-Jen Su and Chien-Hou Chang, *J.A.C.S.*, 1946, **68**, 1080; *Ind. Eng. Chem.*, 1946, **38**, 800, 802; Jouq-Jen Su, *Ind. Eng. Chem.*, 1946, **38**, 803, 923; Gouq-Jen Su, Peh-Hsi Huang, and Yuan-Mou Chang, *J.A.C.S.*, 1946, **68**, 1403 (gas mixtures); Joffe, *Ind. Eng. Chem.*, 1947, **39**, 837 (gas mixtures).

Beattie and Bridgeman [1] gave values of the constants for ten gases, p being in atm. and v in lit. per mol; $T=t°$ C.+273·13°.

	A_0	a	B_0	b	$c\times10^{-4}$
He ...	0·0216	0·05984	0·01400	0	0·004
Ne ...	0·2125	0·02196	0·02060	0	0·101
A ...	1·2907	0·02328	0·03931	0	5·99
H_2 ...	0·1975	−0·00506	0·02096	−0·04359	0·0504
N_2 ...	1·3445	0·02617	0·05046	−0·00691	4·20
O_2 ...	1·4911	0·02562	0·04624	0·004208	4·80
Air ...	1·3012	0·01931	0·04611	−0·01101	4·34
CO_2 ...	5·0065	0·07132	0·10476	0·07235	66·00
CH_4 ...	2·2769	0·01855	0·05587	−0·01587	12·83
$(C_2H_5)_2O$	31·278	0·12426	0·45446	0·11954	33·33

§ 39. Miscellaneous Characteristic Equations

In the following list, letters other than p, v, and T denote constants or (when stated) functions of temperature and pressure; $\boldsymbol{R}$ is the gas constant, $\boldsymbol{N}$ is Avogadro's number, $\boldsymbol{k}=\boldsymbol{R}/\boldsymbol{N}$ is Boltzmann's constant.

I. Sutherland: [2]

$$p=RT/v-(b-2KRT)/v(v+k).$$

II. Boltzmann and Mache: [3]

$$\text{(i)}\ (pT+a/v)(v-b/3)=R'(v+2b/3)$$

$$\text{(ii)}\ (p+a/v^2)[v-b+c/(v^2+d)]=R'T$$

where $R'=(1+a)(1-b)/273$. In (i), $a=0{\cdot}000874$ and $b=0{\cdot}003283$ for carbon dioxide.

III. Reinganum: [4]

$$(p+a/v^2)v^3/(v-b)^4=\boldsymbol{R}T$$

$a=f_1(v, T)$, $b=f_2(v, T)$, depending on the space-filling, β.

IV. Goebel: [5]

$$\text{(i)}\ p=k_1T/(v-b)-k_2/(v-\alpha)^2$$

$$\text{(ii)}\ p=k_1T/(v-b+cp)-k_2/(v-\alpha)^2$$

based on a specific attraction km_1m_2/r^4, where m_1, m_2 are the molecular masses and r the distance.

[1] *J.A.C.S.*, 1928, **50**, 3133; Deming and Shupe, *ibid.*, 1930, **52**, 1382, for nitrogen, introduced a sixth parameter, a', $A=A_0(1-a/v-a'/v^2)$, and found (g., atm., c.c. units) A_0 1528·6, a 0·2748, a' 0·9084, B_0 1·643, b −0·9235, c 2·2×10⁶; *ibid.*, 1931, **53**, 843, for hydrogen (mol, atm., c.c. units), below the critical density, A_0 124040, B_0 20·22, a 56·18, b −7·22, c 20×10^6; above the critical density, A_0 124040, B_0 17·50, a 56·18, b −19·68, c 20×10^6; *ibid.*, 1931, **53**, 860, for N_2+3H_2 mixtures, below the critical density (mol, atm., c.c. units), A_0 3000×10^2, B_0 25·03, a 21·36, b −15·16, c 16×10^6; above the critical density, A_0 3489×10^2, B_0 21·42 a 28·56, b −30·58, c 16×10^6.

[2] *Phil. Mag.*, 1893, **35**, 211; 1893, **36**, 150.

[3] *Ann. Phys.*, 1899, **68**, 350.

[4] *Dissert.*, Göttingen, 1899; *Chem. Centra.*, 1899, II, 955; *Ann. Phys. Beibl.*, 1900, **24**, 665; *Arch. Néerl.*, 1900, **5**, 574; *Ann. Phys.*, 1901, **6**, 533; 1903, **10**, 334; 1912, **38**, 649; *Phys. Z.*, 1901, **2**, 241; Vogel, *Z. phys. Chem.*, 1910, **73**, 429.

[5] *Z. phys. Chem.*, 1904, **47**, 471; 1904, **49**, 129; 1904, **50**, 238; the second equation does not give p as a linear function of T at constant volume.

V. Järvinen:[1]

$$p=k(RT/v)\sqrt[3]{v}/(\sqrt[3]{v}-\sqrt[3]{b})-a/v^{2\cdot 5}$$

where $k=0{\cdot}845$, $b=\mathrm{f}(T)$, and a specific attraction for like molecules km^2/r^n is assumed, with $n\simeq 5$ (5·5 for mercury).

VI. Plank:[2]

$$p=RT/(v-b)-a_2/(v-b)^2+a_3/(v-b)^3-a_4/(v-b)^4+a_5/(v-b)^5.$$

VII. Joffe:[3]

$$p=RT/(v-b)-a/v(v-b)+c/v(v-b)^2-d/v(v-b)^3+e/v(v-b)^4.$$

VIII. Moulin:[4]

$$p=R(1+\alpha t)/(v-b)-a/v^2+C(1+\alpha t)/(v-b)^3$$

where α=coefficient of expansion, t=temperature centigrade.

IX. Applebey;[5] Shaha and Basu:[6]

$$\text{(i)}\quad p=-(kT/b)\ln[(v-b)/v]-a/v^2$$

$$\text{(ii)}\quad P(v-b)=kT(Pb/kT)/(e^{Pb/kT}-1)$$

where $P=p+a/v^2$. The second equation has a formal resemblance to Planck's radiation formula (§ 12.VI B).

X. Schames:[7]

$$p+a/v^2=RT\mathrm{f}(v)$$

where $a=T\int_{\infty}^{T}\hat{a}\,\mathrm{d}(1/T)_v$, $\hat{a}=-v^2\partial(p/T)_v/\partial(1/T)$.

XI. Kohl:[8]

$$p=T\int \mathrm{d}T(\mathrm{d}v/\mathrm{d}T)_v/T^2+T\mathrm{f}(v).$$

XII. Schreber:[9]

$$v=RT/p+hp^2/T-a/T+c.$$

XIII. Antoine:[10]

$$pv=D(\beta+T),\ \beta=A-B\sqrt{p}.$$

XIV. Vasilev:[11]

$$(RT-pv)v=a-bRT-b^2RT/v,$$

$a=\mathrm{f}_1(T)$, $b=\mathrm{f}_2(T)$.

XV. Pochhammer:[12]

$$\pi=\gamma\vartheta/(\phi-\alpha_1)(1+\beta H)-3H(1+\alpha)^2/(\phi+\alpha)^2,$$

1 *Z. phys. Chem.*, 1913, **82**, 541; 1914, **88**, 428; 1919, **93**, 737, 743; 1921, **97**, 445; 1924, **109**, 275; 1925, **116**, 420; the equation was applied to liquids.

2 *Forschungsarb. Gebiet Ingenieurwes.*, 1936, **7**, 161; used by Ruedy, *Canad. J. Res.*, 1938, **16** A, 89, to explain supposed differences of density at the critical point (see § 3.VI B).

3 *J.A.C.S.*, 1947, **69**, 540.

4 *Bull. Soc. Phys.*, 1900, *Séances* 37; 1906, **2**, 141; by considering the attractions of *atoms* in the molecules.

5 *Phil. Mag.*, 1920, **40**, 197.

6 *Phil. Mag.*, 1920, **39**, 456.

7 *Z. Phys.*, 1920, **3**, 255.

8 *Monatsh. Math. Phys.*, 1912, **23**, 81; 1914, **24**, 159.

9 *Phys. Z.*, 1920, **21**, 430.

10 *Compt. Rend.*, 1891, **112**, 284.

11 *J. Phys. Chem. U.S.S.R.*, 1940, **14**, 1139; 1941, **15**, 239.

12 *Ann. Phys.*, 1912, **37**, 103; the calculated values of ϕ are in good agreement with the observed.

$\pi=p/p_c$, $\phi=v/v_c$, $\vartheta=T/T_c$, $\gamma=RT_c/p_cv_c$, $\alpha_1=(1-2\alpha)/3$, $\beta=3\gamma/8(1+\alpha)-1$, $H=e^{h(1-\pi)}$, where α and h are constants. The equation is a cubic in v and reproduces the critical phenomena like van der Waals's equation.

	Ethyl ether	Ethyl alcohol	*iso*pentane	*n*-pentane
α ...	0·125	0·155	0·113	0·14
h ...	0·28	0·32	0·27	0·29

XVI. Dubief [1] used for Amagat's results for carbon dioxide:

$$(p+a/v^2+\beta/v)\{v-b_0+[c/(v^2+d)]\}=(1-\gamma/v)RT.$$

XVII. Maass and Mennie: [2]

$$(p+A/v^2)v=RT(1+2r/l),$$

where r=molecular radius, l=mean free path, A=constant. This was also written in the form:

$$pv^2-RTv+a-RT\beta(1+C/T)=0,$$

where C is Sutherland's viscosity constant (§ 5.VII F), $\beta=8\sqrt{(2\pi)}r^3N/(1+C/T)$.

XVIII. Cooper and Maass [3] (for CO_2 at low pressures):

$$pv^2+a-RTv-RTb(1+KT_0)/(1+KT)=0,$$

$$\text{or} \quad v(1+KT)(pv-RT)=\lambda T-a,$$

where K is the constant of the viscosity equation (42), § 5.VII F, $\eta=\sqrt{T}(1+KT)$, $\theta=1/T$, $\lambda=a-\epsilon/(\theta-K)$, $\epsilon=Rb_0$.

Jacyna [4] used a complicated equation for helium at high pressures, which was criticized by Rozen.[5] Eucken [6] took the parachor (see § 5.VIII G, Vol. II) as a basis, and extended it by using Richards's equation (see § 4.IX N, Vol. II):

$$p+a/v^n=p_T+c/v^m,$$

where p_T is the thermal pressure, when two very complicated equations resulted, neither of which agreed with experiment under ordinary conditions.

The characteristic equation of a gas at very high temperatures (e.g. in the detonation wave) has been considered.[7]

The methods of calculating the thermodynamic functions of a gas from the characteristic equation follow the lines of § 55.II, but are more intricate. A general procedure for a characteristic equation of the form (cf. § 12):

$$p=T\psi(v)-\phi(v)-f(v, T) \quad . \quad . \quad . \quad . \quad . \quad . \quad (1)$$

where ψ, ϕ, and f stand for known functions, is given by Tzu-Ching Huang.[8]

1 *Compt. Rend.*, 1925, **180**, 1164; 1926, **182**, 688; *J. de Phys.*, 1926, **7**, 402.
2 *Proc. Roy. Soc.*, 1926, **110**, 198.
3 *Canad. J. Res.*, 1932, **6**, 596.
4 In about forty one-page papers from 1924, reference to which are mostly given in *J.A.C.S.*, 1938, **60**, 555.
5 *J. Phys. Chem. U.S.S.R.*, 1941, **15**, 688.
6 *Forschungsarb. Gebiet Ingenieurwes.*, 1941, **12**, 113; *Amer. Chem. Abstr.*, 1944, **38**, 2249.
7 Caldirola, *J. Chem. Phys.*, 1946, **14**, 738; Brinkley, *ibid.*, 1947, **15**, 113; Cook, *ibid.*, 1947, **15**, 518; Paterson, *ibid.*, 1948, **16**, 159.
8 *Phys. Rev.*, 1931, **37**, 1171; *J.A.C.S.*, 1932, **54**, 1024; cf. Wassmuth, *Ann. Phys.*, 1909, **30**, 381.

The thermodynamic equations (§§ 48, 54.II):

$$(\mathrm{d}S/\mathrm{d}v)_T=(\mathrm{d}p/\mathrm{d}T)_v \quad \ldots\ldots\ldots \quad (2)$$

$$(\mathrm{d}E/\mathrm{d}v)_T=T(\mathrm{d}p/\mathrm{d}T)_v-p \quad \ldots\ldots\ldots \quad (3)$$

are used. From (1) by differentiation:

$$(\mathrm{d}p/\mathrm{d}T)_v=\psi(v)-(\mathrm{d}f/\mathrm{d}T)_v \quad \ldots\ldots\ldots \quad (4)$$

and by substitution in (2) and integration:

$$S=\int\psi(v)\mathrm{d}v-\int(\mathrm{d}f/\mathrm{d}T)_v\mathrm{d}v+\beta(T),$$

where $\beta(T)$ is a function of temperature. By substituting (1) and (4) in (3) and integration:

$$E=\int\phi(v)\mathrm{d}v+\int[\mathrm{f}(v, T)-T(\mathrm{d}f/\mathrm{d}T)_v]\mathrm{d}v+\alpha(T),$$

where $\alpha(T)$ is a function of temperature.

The use of the fugacity was explained in § 36, and recent treatments of p, v, T data for gases and vapours are based on it. Curtiss and Hirschfelder [1] estimated gas imperfection by calculating PV/RT from the Clapeyron-Clausius equation (§ 7.VIII L, Vol. II), P being the vapour pressure. For hydrocarbon vapours below the critical point the equation $\mu \log \mu=-\pi \mathrm{f}_{10}$ has been used,[2] in which $\mu=pv/RT$ and f_{10} is a function of the reduced temperature ϑ only.

§ 40. The Virial

A method of dealing with problems of kinetic theory which is especially useful when there are forces acting between the molecules was used by Clausius [3] in 1870. Consider a molecule of mass m with coordinates x, y, z and velocity components $\dot{x}=u$, $\dot{y}=v$, $\dot{z}=w$. Let the components of a force acting on it in the directions x, y, z be X, Y, Z. Since $\mathrm{d}x/\mathrm{d}t=u$, and since *force=mass× acceleration*, i.e. $X=m(\mathrm{d}^2x/\mathrm{d}t^2)=m(\mathrm{d}u/\mathrm{d}t)$, it follows that:

$$\mathrm{d}(mxu)/\mathrm{d}t=mx\,.\,\mathrm{d}u/\mathrm{d}t+mu\,.\,\mathrm{d}x/\mathrm{d}t=Xx+mu^2;$$

$$\mathrm{d}(myv)/\mathrm{d}t=Yy+mv^2;\ \mathrm{d}(mzw)/\mathrm{d}t=Zz+mw^2.$$

By integration between the times $t=0$ and $t=\tau$, where τ is very large compared with the average times between disturbances of the motion of the molecules, and division by τ, the *average* values, denoted as usual by a bar over the symbol, are obtained:

$$\frac{1}{\tau}\int_0^\tau \frac{\mathrm{d}(mxu)}{\mathrm{d}t}\mathrm{d}t=\frac{1}{\tau}\int_0^\tau Xx\mathrm{d}t+\frac{1}{\tau}\int_0^\tau mu^2\mathrm{d}t$$

$$\therefore\ (m/\tau)(x_\tau u_\tau-x_0u_0)=\overline{Xx}+\overline{mu^2}.$$

[1] *J. Chem. Phys.*, 1942, **10**, 491.

[2] Cope, Lewis, and Weber, *Ind. Eng. Chem.*, 1931, **23**, 887; Thomson, *ibid.*, 1943, **35**, 894.

[3] On a Mechanical Theorem applicable to Heat, *Ann. Phys.*, 1870, **141**, 124; *Phil. Mag.*, 1870, **40**, 122; Villarceau, *Compt. Rend.*, 1872, **75**, 232; Baynes, " Thermodynamics," Oxford, 1878, 11; Rayleigh, *Nature*, 1891, **44**, 499, 597; 1892, **45**, 80; *Phil. Mag.*, 1900, **50**, 210; 1905, **9**, 494; " Scientific Papers," Cambridge, 1902, **3**, 465, 469; 1903, **4**, 491; 1912, **5**, 238; *idem* in Maxwell, " Theory of Heat," 1897, 322; Richarz, *Ann. Phys.*, 1892, **47**, 467; Finger, *Wien Ber.*, 1897, **106**, II A, 722; Larmor, *Phil. Trans.*, 1897, **109**, 205; " Math. and Phys. Papers," Cambridge, 1929, **2**, 132 (" a small foundation from which to draw weighty conclusions "); Burbury, " A Treatise on the Kinetic Theory of Gases," Cambridge, 1899, 14; van der Waals, *Proc. K. Akad. Wetens. Amsterdam*, 1899, **1**, 138 (*b* correction); Polvani, *Nuov. Cim.*, 1924, **1**, 1; Milne, *Phil. Mag.*, 1925, **50**, 409 (also true if there are frictional forces proportional to the velocity, as in the Brownian movement); Fock and Krutkow, *Sow. Phys. Z.*, 1932, **1**, 756. According to Villarceau, the theorem was given before Clausius by Jacobi. For the case of a mixture of molecules, see Lorentz, *Ann. Phys.*, 1881, **12**, 127.

When τ is large it seems reasonable to assume that the expression on the left vanishes, since u does not increase without limit and x will not do so in the case of a collection of colliding molecules. By considering also the other two components the three equations:

$$\overline{Xx}+\overline{mu^2}=0, \quad \overline{Yy}+\overline{mv^2}=0, \quad \overline{Zz}+\overline{mw^2}=0,$$

are found, and by addition:

$$(\overline{Xx}+\overline{Yy}+\overline{Zz})+m(\overline{u^2}+\overline{v^2}+\overline{w^2})=0$$

$$\therefore\ (\overline{Xx}+\overline{Yy}+\overline{Zz})+m\overline{c^2}=0,$$

since $\overline{c^2}=\overline{u^2}+\overline{v^2}+\overline{w^2}$. Since equations of this type hold for all the molecules, their sum is also zero, hence:

$$\Sigma(\overline{Xx}+\overline{Yy}+\overline{Zz})+\Sigma m\overline{c^2}=0 \quad \ldots\ldots\ (1)$$

The expression $\Sigma(\overline{Xx}+\overline{Yy}+\overline{Zz})$ (or half its value) was called by Clausius the *virial of the forces* acting on the molecules, and (1) is called the *virial equation.* The term $\Sigma m\overline{c^2}$ is twice the kinetic energy of translation of all the molecules.

Consider N molecules of mass m of an ideal gas contained in a rectangular box of sides x, y, z in the directions of the coordinate axes and with the origin at one corner. Then no forces act on the molecules except when they are colliding with the walls of the box. With the opposite sides of the box parallel to the yz plane and with coordinates $x=0$ and $x=x$, the force (with reference to the coordinate system) on the left-hand side is $p\,.\,yz$, where p is the pressure, and that on the right-hand side is $-p\,.\,yz$ (since it acts in the opposite direction). By considering also the other two pairs of faces, it is found that:

$$\overline{Xx}=p\,.\,yz\,.\,0-p\,.\,yz\,.\,x$$

$$\overline{Yy}=p\,.\,xz\,.\,0-p\,.\,xz\,.\,y$$

$$\overline{Zz}=p\,.\,xy\,.\,0-p\,.\,xy\,.\,z.$$

Hence the virial is $-3p\,.\,xyz=-3pv$, where $v=xyz$ is the volume of the box. Also $\Sigma m\overline{c^2}=Nm\overline{c^2}$, therefore $-3pv+Nm\overline{c^2}=0$, or:

$$p=Nm\overline{c^2}/3=\rho\overline{c^2}/3 \quad \ldots\ldots\ldots\ (2)$$

where ρ=density, which is equation (13), § 8.III.

Ray [1] showed that the virial depends on the origin of the coordinates, when the pressure may vary with the distance from the wall of the vessel, $p=p_0e^{-kh}$. The usual deduction assumes a constant pressure. If an average pressure is defined by $\bar{p}=\iiint p\,\mathrm{d}x\mathrm{d}y\mathrm{d}z$, the virial of the external forces is $(3/2)\bar{p}v$.

If the gas is not ideal, but forces act between the molecules, the virial may be divided into a part due to forces of collision, which has just been shown to be equal to $-3pv$, and a part $\Sigma_i(Xx+Yy+Zz)$ which now refers only to intermolecular forces; hence (where the masses m of the molecules may now be different):

$$\Sigma m\overline{c^2}-3pv+\Sigma_i(Xx+Yy+Zz)=0,$$

$$\text{or}\quad pv=\tfrac{1}{3}\Sigma m\overline{c^2}+\tfrac{1}{3}\Sigma_i(Xx+Yy+Zz) \quad \ldots\ldots\ (3)$$

If the pressure is due only to repulsive forces, as Newton supposed (§ 23.VII A), then:

$$pv=\tfrac{1}{3}\Sigma_i(Xx+Yy+Zz).$$

(Clausius took the virial for *attractive* forces as positive; the convention varies.)

[1] *Bull. Acad. Polon.*, 1929, 233.

Then if the container and gas expanded to n times its linear dimensions, x, y, and z are multiplied by n, and as Boyle's law shows that pv remains constant, X, Y, and Z must be multiplied by $1/n$, i.e. must vary inversely as the distance, as Newton showed. This law, however, cannot be true, since, as Jeans says,[1] " it would make the action of distant parts of the gas preponderate over that of the contiguous parts, and so would not give a pressure which would be constant for a given volume and temperature as we passed from one vessel to another, or even from one part to another of the surface of the same vessel."

Now consider a gas in which the molecules have both kinetic and potential energies. Let there be a pair of molecules distant r apart, with centres at (x, y, z) and (x', y', z'), and with a repulsive force which is some function of the distance, $F(r)$, acting between them. Then:

$$X=F(r) . (x-x')/r, \quad Y=F(r) . (y-y')/r, \quad Z=F(r) . (z-z')/r,$$

the factors of $F(r)$ being the cosines of the angles between the line joining the molecules and the coordinate axes. Hence, $Xx+X'x'=F(r)(x-x')^2/r$, and so on; therefore:

$$(Xx+Yy+Zz)_i=[F(r)/r][(x-x')^2+(y-y')^2+(z-z')^2]=F(r)r,$$

since $(x-x')^2+(y-y')^2+(z-z')^2=r^2$. Hence (3) becomes:

$$pv=\tfrac{1}{3}\Sigma m\overline{c^2}+\tfrac{1}{3}\Sigma\Sigma F(r)r \quad . \quad . \quad . \quad . \quad . \quad . \quad . \quad (4)$$

where the summation is taken over all *pairs* of molecules. If the forces have a potential, V (see § 12, IV):

$$pv=\tfrac{1}{3}\Sigma m\overline{c^2}-\tfrac{1}{3}\Sigma\Sigma(\mathrm{d}V/\mathrm{d}r)r \quad . \quad . \quad . \quad . \quad . \quad . \quad . \quad (5)$$

If both attractive and repulsive forces act:

$$pv=\tfrac{1}{3}\Sigma m\overline{c^2}+\tfrac{1}{3}\Sigma\Sigma F(r)_r r-\tfrac{1}{3}\Sigma\Sigma F(r)_a r \quad . \quad . \quad . \quad . \quad . \quad (6)$$

§ 41. The Molecular Force Field

A deduction of van der Waals's equation by the virial method is possible, but here a more general type of equation will be considered. It is assumed [2] that the molecules are hard, elastic spheres, which are subject to both attractive and repulsive forces, F_a and F_r. These are supposed to be functions of the distance r between the molecules and of the type:

$$\text{repulsive force}=k_1/r^n=k_1r^{-n}=F_r \quad . \quad . \quad . \quad . \quad . \quad (1)$$

$$\text{attractive force}=k_2/r^m=k_2r^{-m}=F_a \quad . \quad . \quad . \quad . \quad . \quad (2)$$

where m, n, k_1, and k_2 are constants. The repulsion exponent determines the " hardness " ($n>14$) or " softness " ($n=9$) of the molecule in collisions, and appears to be greater the higher the electron density on the surface.[3]

The resultant of the attractive and repulsive forces in the gas:

$$k_1/r^n-k_2/r^m$$

[1] Kohnstamm, *J. Chim. Phys.*, 1905, **3**, 665; 1906, **4**, 102; Jeans, " The Kinetic Theory of Gases," 1940, 73; but cf. Stewart, *Phys. Rev.*, 1925, **26**, 491; Fowler, " Statistical Mechanics," 2nd edit., 1936, 287.

[2] Natanson, *Phil. Mag.*, 1892, **33**, 301; Lennard-Jones and Cook, *Proc. Roy. Soc.*, 1926, **112**, 214; Lennard-Jones, *Proc. Phys. Soc.*, 1931, **43**, 461 (bibliography), and Chap. X in Fowler, " Statistical Mechanics," Cambridge, 1929, 2nd edit., 1936, 292 f.; cf. Weinstein, *Ann. Phys.*, 1895, **54**, 544; " Thermodynamik und Kinetik der Körper," 1901, **1**, 44.

[3] Rice, *J.A.C.S.*, 1932, **54**, 4559; Schmidt, *Z. Elektrochem.*, 1936, **42**, 8, where inelastic collisions and the Ramsauer effect (§ 21.III) are also considered.

may be called the *molecular force field*, and it is a function of the distance between the molecules (an *average* distance, of course, since the molecules are in motion), or, in other words, of the total volume of the gas.

The treatment of the molecular field is implicit in the theory of Boscovich [1] (adopted by Priestley, Faraday, Kelvin, etc.) in which material particles are replaced by point *centres of force*, such that an attractive force at relatively large distances is replaced by a repulsive force at small distances. Boscovich assumed that the force could alternate between attraction and repulsion several times as the distance was reduced, finally reaching a very large value of repulsion at a very minute distance. A function having this property was devised by Poynting [2] (mass m distant r from unit mass):

$$F=m(r-a)(r-2a)(r-3a)/r^5.$$

Schofield [3] showed that the cohesion of gas and liquid molecules requires forces of the type k_r/r^n and k_a/r^m, and cannot be explained on the assumption of rigid spheres.

The mathematical machinery, over-simplified to bring it within the power of the methods of mathematics, assumes that (i) the forces act over distances which are rather large compared with the molecular dimensions, and (ii) the force is symmetrical about the molecule, considered as a sphere. If it is assumed that the force acts only over a distance of one or two molecules, and that only binary collisions occur, an equation may be deduced [4] which does not agree with the van der Waals expression a/V^2 for the molecular attraction. Langmuir [5] extended his view of forces acting in adsorption only over a distance of one molecule to liquids, and deduced an equation for the vapour pressure of mixtures of liquids which gives satisfactory results, but no important advance has yet been made in gas theory in this direction.

Boltzmann [6] tried to develop a theory of chemical affinity in which forces act only from small regions of the surfaces of molecules; this removed the over-simple assumption of spherical symmetry, and in Debye's theory of quadrupole attraction [7] such directed forces were introduced to explain gas molecule attractions, but without real success (see § 43).

[1] Roger Joseph Boscovich, S. J., b. Ragusa (Dubrovnik), Dalmatia, 1711, d. Milan, 1787: " Theoria Philosophiæ Naturalis redacta ad Unicam Legem Virium in Natura Existentium," 4to, Venice, 1758, 2nd edit., 1763 (xl+311 pp., 4 plates, 4 unnumb. ll. of list of B.'s works; both editions very rare), 1 f., Fig. 1, plate I; transl. Brewster, " A System of Mechanical Philosophy," 4 vols, Edinburgh, 1822; transl. edit. (with life of B.) by Child, Chicago, 1922; Lord Kelvin, " Baltimore Lectures," 1904, 675, reproducing an [altered] Fig. 1 from Boscovich's " great work "; Chapman, *Nature*, 1940, **146**, 607; Gill, " Roger Boscovich, S. J. (1711–1787) Forerunner of Modern Physical Theories," Dublin, 1941, who mentions (p. 22) the adumbration of Bohr orbits by Boscovich.

[2] In Hastings, " Ency. Religion and Ethics," 1909, **2**, 203; Poynting, " Scientific Papers," 1920, 724.

[3] *Phil. Mag.*, 1928, **5**, 1171; Roop, *Science*, 1916, **43**, 758, assumed a cohesive force for liquid mercury proportional to $1/r^6$; Edser, *B.A. Rep. Coll. Chem.*, 1922, 40, assumed a force proportional to $1/r^8$; see Bradford, *Engineering*, 1933, **135**, 439; *Phil. Mag.*, 1943, **34**, 433; Wheeler, *Indian J. Phys.*, 1934, **8**, 521; *Proc. Indian Acad. Sci.*, 1934, **1** A, 105; *Trans. Nat. Inst. Sci. India*, 1938, **1**, 333.

[4] Fowler, " Statistical Mechanics," Cambridge, 1929, 172.

[5] *Colloid Symposium Monograph*, 1925, **3**, 48; Smyth and Engel, *J.A.C.S.*, 1929, **51**, 2646, 2660.

[6] " Vorlesungen über Gastheorie," 1898, **2**, 177 f., where, incidentally, the " modern " theory of " collisions of the second kind," is developed; see Franck, *Z. Phys.*, 1925, **31**, 411; Born and Volmer, *Z. phys. Chem.*, 1931, **13** B, 299.

[7] *Phys. Z.*, 1920, **21**, 178; 1921, **22**, 302.

Buckingham and Corner [1] assumed long-range attraction proportional to a sum of terms in r^{-6} and r^{-8}, and a short-range repulsion proportional to $e^{-\rho r}$ (ρ=const.), finding a potential energy with four parameters, also giving the depth of the minimum in the curve (§ 17.IV). Quantum corrections were applied and tabulated in the calculation of the second virial coefficient.

§ 42. Deduction of the Characteristic Equation

In the present simplified discussion repulsive forces between the molecules are assumed to be of such a type that when the distance between the centres is greater than σ (the sum of the radii, or the molecular diameter), the repulsive force is negligibly small, whilst for distances less than σ (which corresponds with the contact of hard spheres), say $(\sigma-\delta)$, this force is extremely large. Hence the exponent n in r^{-n} must be a fairly large number. The value of m in r^{-m} is, for the present, left undecided, except that it is assumed to be rather considerably smaller than n; i.e. the attractive forces are supposed to have a larger range than the repulsive forces when $r>\sigma$. When two molecules approach from a large distance, there is first an increasing rather weak attraction, the resultant force then passing through a minimum (i.e. a maximum attraction), and then rising very steeply as a repulsion when r approaches σ.

The virial equation gives:

$$\Sigma m\overline{c^2}+V_p+V_r+V_a=0 \quad \ldots\ldots \quad (1)$$

where V_p, V_r, and V_a are the parts of the virial due to the external pressure, the repulsive forces, and the attractive forces, respectively.[2] For 1 mol of gas (15), § 8.III, gives $Nm\overline{c^2}=3RT$, and V_p has been shown in § 40 to be $-3pv$, hence:

$$3RT+V_r+V_a=3pv \quad \ldots\ldots \quad (2)$$

The calculation of V_r and V_a may be made as follows.[3] Let any two molecules, numbered 1 and 2, of the gas at a given moment be at the points A (x_1, y_1, z_1) and B (x_2, y_2, z_2) in the coordinate system, distant r apart. The components of the forces in the directions x, y, and z are found by multiplying the forces in the direction of r (the line joining the molecules) by the cosines of the angles which r makes with the axes.

The total virial of the repulsive forces has been found in § 40 to be $[F(r)=F]$:

$$V_r=\Sigma\Sigma rF_r \quad \ldots\ldots \quad (3)$$

Similarly, the total virial of the attractive forces is found to be:

$$V_a=\Sigma\Sigma rF_a \quad \ldots\ldots \quad (4)$$

$$\therefore\ 3RT+\Sigma\Sigma rF_r+\Sigma\Sigma rF_a=3pv \quad \ldots\ldots \quad (5)$$

where the sums are to be taken over all *pairs* of molecules.

The number dN of pairs of molecules which, at a given moment, have their centres lying between the distances r and $r+dr$ is found as follows. If two spheres of these radii are drawn around the center of each of the N molecules of the gas, the volume between the spheres is $d(\frac{4}{3}N\pi r^3)=4\pi Nr^2dr$, and the probability that the centre of any molecule is in the space $4\pi r^2dr$ belonging to a

[1] *Proc. Roy. Soc.*, 1947, **189**, 118.

[2] The sign of V_a is *negative* if that of V_r is taken (as usual) positive.

[3] Reinganum, *Phys. Z.*, 1901, **2**, 241; *Ann. Phys.*, 1901, **6**, 533, 549; 1902, **10**, 334; 1908, **28**, 142; 1912, **38**, 649; see the criticism by Kohnstamm, *J. Chim. Phys.*, 1905, **3**, 665; 1906, **4**, 102.

second molecule, *when there are no forces between the molecules*, is $4\pi Nr^2 dr/v$, where v is the total volume of the vessel, and it is assumed that the molecules occupy an inappreciable part of this volume. Hence, the number of *pairs* of molecules required is found by multiplying by $(N-1) \simeq N$ and dividing by 2:

$$dN' = 2\pi N^2 r^2 dr/v \quad . \quad . \quad . \quad . \quad . \quad . \quad . \quad . \quad (6)$$

When there *are* forces between the molecules, Boltzmann's equation, § 19.III, shows that:

$$dN = (2\pi N^2 r^2/v)e^{-\epsilon_p/kT} dr \quad . \quad . \quad . \quad . \quad . \quad . \quad . \quad . \quad (7)$$

where ϵ_p is the potential energy of a molecule resulting from the joint action of F_r and F_a at a given point.

The virial sums may be replaced by integrals:

$$\Sigma\Sigma rF_r = \frac{2\pi N^2}{v}\int_{\sigma-\delta}^{\infty} r^3 F_r e^{-\epsilon_p/kT} dr \quad . \quad . \quad . \quad . \quad . \quad . \quad (8)$$

$$\Sigma\Sigma rF_a = \frac{2\pi N^2}{v}\int_{\sigma}^{\infty} r^3 F_a e^{-\epsilon_p/kT} dr \quad . \quad . \quad . \quad . \quad . \quad . \quad . \quad . \quad (9)$$

From the assumed nature of the repulsive force, the upper limit of integration in (8) can be replaced by σ, since beyond this distance the force is inappreciable. Also (since potential energy = force × distance):

$$\epsilon_p = \int_{\infty}^{\sigma} F_a dr + \int_{\sigma}^{r} F_r dr \quad . \quad . \quad . \quad . \quad . \quad . \quad . \quad . \quad (10)$$

which is to be substituted in (8) and (9).

In the case of (9), since only the attractive force need be considered for $r > \sigma$, only the first term in (10) need be taken, and the integral in (9) must be a function of temperature only (from the factor $1/kT$ in the exponential),

$$\therefore \ \Sigma\Sigma rF_a = (2\pi N^2/v)\phi(T) \quad . \quad . \quad . \quad . \quad . \quad . \quad . \quad . \quad (11)$$

The case of (8) is more difficult. First replace ∞ by σ in the upper limit of integration:

$$\Sigma\Sigma rF_r = \frac{2\pi N^2}{v}\int_{\sigma-\delta}^{\sigma} r^3 F_r e^{-\epsilon_p/kT} dr.$$

Since $\sigma-\delta$ and σ are very close together, r^3 can be replaced by σ^3 (constant) and taken outside the integral sign:

$$\Sigma\Sigma rF_r = \frac{2\pi N^2 \sigma^3}{v}\cdot\int_{\sigma-\delta}^{\sigma} F_r e^{-\epsilon_p/kT} dr.$$

In evaluating the integral, substitute $-\epsilon_p$ from (10):

$$\int_{\sigma-\delta}^{\sigma} F_r e^{-\epsilon_p/kT} dr = \int_{\sigma-\delta}^{\sigma} F_r e^{-J_1/kT} \,.\, e^{-J_2/kT} dr,$$

where $J_1 = \int_{\infty}^{\sigma} F_a dr$ and $J_2 = \int_{\sigma}^{r} F_r dr$.

Since J_1 is a constant, and $J_1/k = \text{const.} = C$:

$$\int_{\sigma-\delta}^{\sigma} F_r e^{-\epsilon_p/kT} = e^{C/T}\int_{\sigma-\delta}^{\sigma} F_r e^{-J_2/kT} dr.$$

To evaluate the integral J_2, put

$$\int_r^\sigma F_r \mathrm{d}r = y, \quad -F_r \mathrm{d}r = \mathrm{d}y$$

$$\int_{\sigma-\delta}^{\sigma} \mathrm{e}^{-y/kT}\mathrm{d}y = \int_0^\infty \mathrm{e}^{-y/kT}\mathrm{d}y = kT$$

(since for $r=\sigma$, $y=0$, and for $r=\sigma-\delta$, $y\rightarrow\infty$),

$$\therefore\ \Sigma\Sigma rF_r = (2\pi N^2\sigma^3/v)\mathrm{e}^{C/T} \,.\, kT = (2\pi N\sigma^3/v)\mathrm{e}^{C/T} \,.\, RT \quad . \quad . \quad (12)$$

The volume of the molecules is $\frac{4}{3}\pi N(\sigma/2)^3 = N\pi\sigma^3/6$. Put

$$4 \,.\, (N\pi\sigma^3/6) = b' \quad . \quad . \quad . \quad . \quad . \quad . \quad . \quad . \quad . \quad (13)$$

$$\therefore\ \Sigma\Sigma rF_r = (3RTb'/v)\mathrm{e}^{C/T} \quad . \quad . \quad . \quad . \quad . \quad . \quad . \quad . \quad (14)$$

From (5), (11), and (14):

$$pv = RT(1 + b'\mathrm{e}^{C/T}/v) + (2\pi N^2/3v)\phi(T) \quad . \quad . \quad . \quad . \quad (15)$$

which is Reinganum's equation. It can be written as:

$$[p - (2\pi N^2/3v^2)\phi(T)]v/(1 + b'\mathrm{e}^{C/T}/v) = RT,$$

and by division and the assumption that $b'\mathrm{e}^{C/T}/v$ is small compared with 1:

$$[p - (2\pi N^2/3v^2)\phi(T)](v - b'\mathrm{e}^{C/T}) = RT \quad . \quad . \quad . \quad . \quad (16)$$

which becomes identical with van der Waals's equation:

$$(p + a/v^2)(v - b) = RT \quad . \quad . \quad . \quad . \quad . \quad . \quad . \quad . \quad (17)$$

if $a = -2\pi N^2\phi(T)/3$ and $b = b'\mathrm{e}^{C/T}$. These, however, are both unknown functions of temperature, and not constants as assumed in (17).

Now return to (7); multiply by $\frac{1}{3}rF(r)$, where $F(r)$ may be taken as the net force acting between the molecules, and integrate over all values of r, then:[1]

$$\tfrac{1}{3}\Sigma\Sigma F(r) \,.\, r = \frac{2\pi N^2}{3v}\int_0^\infty r^3 F(r)\mathrm{e}^{-\epsilon_p/kT}\mathrm{d}r$$

$$= \frac{2\pi N^2}{3v}\int_0^\infty r^3 \frac{\mathrm{d}\epsilon_p}{\mathrm{d}r}\mathrm{e}^{-\epsilon_p/kT}\mathrm{d}r.$$

Equation (5), § 40, with $\frac{1}{3}\Sigma m\overline{c^2} = NkT = RT$ per mol then becomes:

$$pv = RT - \frac{2\pi N^2}{3v}\int_0^\infty r^3 \frac{\mathrm{d}\epsilon_p}{\mathrm{d}r}\mathrm{e}^{-\epsilon_p/kT}\mathrm{d}r$$

$$= RT\left(1 - \frac{2\pi N}{3kTv}\int_0^\infty r^3 \frac{\mathrm{d}\epsilon_p}{\mathrm{d}r}\mathrm{e}^{-\epsilon_p/kT}\mathrm{d}r\right) \quad . \quad . \quad . \quad . \quad . \quad (18)$$

By integration by parts this can be transformed into:

$$pv = RT\left[1 - 2\pi\frac{N}{v}\int_0^\infty (\mathrm{e}^{-\epsilon_p/kT} - 1)r^2\mathrm{d}r\right] \quad . \quad . \quad . \quad . \quad . \quad (19)$$

since

$$\int_0^\infty (1 - \mathrm{e}^{-\epsilon_p/kT})r^2\mathrm{d}r = -\frac{1}{3kT}\int_0^\infty \mathrm{e}^{-\epsilon_p/kT}(\mathrm{d}\epsilon_p/\mathrm{d}r)r^3\mathrm{d}r,$$

[1] The upper limit may be taken as ∞, since all intermolecular forces vanish long before this volume is reached, and the rest of the integration contributes nothing. The lower limit should, actually, be σ, the distance between the molecular centres on contact; Keyes, *J.A.C.S.*, 1928, **50**, 930; on the integrals see Coulson, *Proc. Cambr. Phil. Soc.*, 1942, **38**, 210.

and by comparison with the equation giving the second virial coefficient [1] B:

$$pv=RT(1+B/v) \qquad (20)$$

(where $B=b-a/RT$ according to van der Waals, but where a and b are really functions of temperature) it follows that:

$$B=2\pi N\int_0^\infty(1-e^{-\epsilon_p/kT})r^2dr \qquad (21)$$

In general, $\epsilon_p=\epsilon_r-\epsilon_a$, where r and a refer to repulsions and attractions, respectively. For rigid spheres with an attractive force, and with a minimum distance r_0 between the centres:

$$B=b_0+2\pi N\int_{r_0}^\infty(1-e^{-\epsilon_a/kT})r^2dr \qquad (22)$$

$$a=2\pi NT\int_{r_0}^\infty(e^{-\epsilon_a/kT}-1)r^2dr \qquad (23)$$

and the temperature dependence of a is explained by swarm-formation. At high temperatures $kT\gg\epsilon_a$, and

$$a=(2\pi N/k)\int_{r_0}^\infty-\epsilon_a r^2dr \qquad (24)$$

is then independent of temperature.[2] For rigid spheres of diameter d surrounded by an attractive force field proportional to r^{-s} Keesom [3] found

$$B=\frac{2\pi}{3}Nd^3\left\{1-3\sum_{n=1}^{n=\infty}\frac{(\epsilon/kT)^n}{n![(s-1)n-3]}\right\} \qquad (25)$$

where ϵ is the work done in separating to an infinite distance two molecules initially in contact.

Lennard-Jones [4] assumed the force field $\lambda/r^n-\mu/r^m$, and found:

$$B=\frac{2\pi N}{3}F(y)\left(\frac{\lambda}{n-1}\cdot\frac{m-1}{\mu}\right)^{3/(n-m)} \qquad (26)$$

$$y=\frac{\mu}{(m-1)kT}\left[\frac{(n-1)kT}{\lambda}\right]^{(m-1)/(n-1)} \qquad (27)$$

$$F(y)=y^{3/(n-m)}\left[\Gamma\left(\frac{n-4}{n-1}\right)-\sum_{x=1}^{x=\infty}c_x y^x\right] \qquad (28)$$

$$c_x=\frac{3\Gamma\left[\frac{x(m-1)+n-4}{n-1}\right]}{x![x(m-1)-3]}=\frac{3\Gamma\left[\frac{x(m-1)-3}{n-1}\right]}{x!(n-1)} \qquad (29)$$

[1] Collins and Keyes, *J. Phys. Chem.*, 1939, **43**, 5, wrote this in the form $p=RT/(v-B)$, which is equivalent to the above as far as terms in $1/v^2$. For the *third* virial coefficient, see de Boer and Michels, *Physica*, 1938, **5**, 945; 1939, **6**, 97; 1940, **7**, 369.

[2] Briegleb, *Z. phys. Chem.*, 1933, **23** B, 105; for further consideration of this type of approach, see the brief summary by Orr, *Ann. Rep. Chem. Soc.*, 1940, **37**, 28.

[3] *Proc. K. Akad. Wetens. Amsterdam*, 1912, **15**, 256, 417, 643; 1921, **23**, 939, 943; *Comm. Leiden*, 1912, Suppl. **24** *b*, **25**, **26**; *Phys. Z.*, 1921, **22**, 129, 643; 1922, **23**, 225.

[4] *Proc. Roy. Soc.*, 1924, **106**, 463; Lennard-Jones and Cook, *ibid.*, 1926, **112**, 214; Lennard-Jones, *Proc. Phys. Soc.*, 1931, **43**, 461; section in Fowler, "Statistical Mechanics," 1929, Chapt. X; Keyes, *Chem. Rev.*, 1929, **6**, 175; Lennard-Jones and Devonshire, *Proc. Roy. Soc.*, 1937, **163**, 53; Corner and Lennard-Jones, *ibid.*, 1941, **178**, 401; Hassé and Cook, *Proc. Roy. Soc.*, 1929, **125**, 196, worked out the case $m=5$, $n=9$; see Wheeler, *Trans. Nat. Inst. Sci. India*, 1938, **1**, 333; Powell, *Rep. Progr. Phys.*, 1939, **5**, 164; Linnett, *Trans. Faraday Soc.*, 1940, **36**, 1123; 1942, **38**, 1; Orr, *Proc. Cambr. Phil. Soc.*, 1942, **38**, 224.

Γ denoting the gamma function (§ 54.I), and $x!$ is factorial x. Some comparison with experiments gave quite fair results; for helium $n=14\frac{1}{3}$ and $m=5$ (chosen for convenience, as the integration is then simple) and there is agreement except for one point.[1] There is also agreement with the pairs (n, m) of (9, 5), or (11, 5), or (11, 6). Lennard-Jones and Devonshire showed that such an equation qualitatively represents the critical phenomena.

§ 43. Dipole and Quadrupole Fields

An electric dipole consists of two equal and opposite charges $+e$ and $-e$ separated by a distance l, and the dipole moment is $\mu=el$. By considering a random arrangement of dipole molecules, van der Waals, junr.[2] obtained for the attraction virial an infinite series with $1/T$ in the first term, agreeing with Berthelot's equation (§ 29). Similar series were found, with other assumptions, by Ornstein.[3] Keesom [4] considered the case where the molecules are rigid spheres with a permanent electric dipole of moment μ at the centre of each, obtaining again an infinite series. The mean interaction energy between a pair of dipoles having free rotation and with random orientation of axes is

$$\bar{\epsilon}=-\tfrac{2}{3}\mu^4/kTr^6 \quad . \; . \; . \; . \; . \; . \; . \; . \; . \quad (1)$$

which has the correct dependence on r according to modern views (§ 45), but would not apply to non-polar gases.

Debye [5] considered the interaction between dipoles of moment $\mu_i=\alpha F$ *induced* in molecules of polarisability α in an electric field F, and found for the mean interaction energy:

$$\bar{\epsilon}_i=-2\alpha\mu_i^2/r^6 \quad . \; . \; . \; . \; . \; . \; . \; . \; . \quad (2)$$

again giving the correct dependence on r, but numerically too small. Falkenhagen [6] also considered the attraction of molecular dipoles of electric moment μ, and found for the second virial coefficient:

$$B=(2\pi/3)Nd^3\{1-[b_1(\Theta/T)+b_2(\Theta/T)^2+b_3(\Theta/T)^3+\ldots]\}$$

where d=molecular diameter, $\Theta=\mu^2/d^3k$, and $b_1, b_2, b_3, \ldots$, are polarisability coefficients. Although Eucken and Meyer [7] found remarkable agreement with this theory with measurements of the vapour densities of some organic compounds, the latter had non-polar molecules in many cases, so that the result is not particularly significant.

A theory of molecular attraction depending on the interaction of electric *quadrupoles* was worked out by Debye.[8] He considered a molecule with

[1] In this case, the experiments may be in error and the theory correct; see Anfilogoff, *Thesis*, London, 1932, 140, 319, 364; Partington, *Phys. Z.*, 1933, **34**, 289.

[2] *Proc. K. Akad. Wetens. Amsterdam*, 1900, **3**, 27; *Verslag. K. Akad. Wetens. Amsterdam*, 1901, **9**, 46; 1908, **17**, 130, 391; *Ann. Phys. Beibl.*, 1901, **25**, 346; 1909, **33**, 48, 446.

[3] *Dissert.*, Leiden, 1908; *Proc. K. Akad. Wetens. Amsterdam*, 1908–9, **11**, 116, 526.

[4] *Proc. K. Akad. Wetens. Amsterdam*, 1912, **15**, 256, 417, 643; 1921, **23**, 939, 943; *Comm. Leiden*, 1912, Suppl. **24***b*, **25**, **26**; *Phys. Z.*, 1921, **22**, 129, 643; 1922, **23**, 225; attracting dipoles had been considered by Reinganum, *Ann. Phys.*, 1901, **6**, 533, 549; 1903, **10**, 334; 1908–9, **11**, 132, 315; 1912, **38**, 649; Sutherland, *Phil. Mag.*, 1902, **4**, 625; for Keesom's theory, see Holst, *Proc. K. Akad. Wetens. Amsterdam*, 1917, **19**, 932; *Comm. Leiden*, Suppl. **41** *f.*

[5] *Phys. Z.*, 1920, **21**, 178; 1921, **22**, 302; Jona, *ibid.*, 1919, **20**, 14.

[6] *Phys. Z.*, 1922, **23**, 87; Zwicky, *ibid.*, 1921, **22**, 449.

[7] *Z. phys. Chem.*, 1929, **2** B, 452.

[8] *Phys. Z.*, 1920, **21**, 178; 1921, **22**, 302; Keesom, *Proc. K. Akad. Wetens. Amsterdam*, 1921, **23**, 939, 943; 1922, **24**, 162; *Phys. Z.*, 1921, **22**, 129, 643; Schmick, *Phys. Z.*, 1928, **29**, 633; Syrkin, *Z. phys. Chem.*, 1929, **5** B, 156; Margenau, *Rev. Mod. Phys.*, 1939, **11**, 1 (bibl.).

charge e_k at a point with coordinates ξ_k, η_k, ζ_k. The potential V due to it at a point at a distance r, with coordinates x, y, z, was expanded [1] into a series of powers of $1/r$ and summed over k:

$$V=\Sigma\frac{e_k}{r}+\frac{1}{r^2}\left(\frac{x}{r}\Sigma e_k\xi_k+\frac{y}{r}\Sigma e_k\eta_k+\frac{z}{r}\Sigma e_k\zeta_k\right)$$
$$+\frac{1}{r^3}\left[\tfrac{1}{2}\left(3\frac{x^2}{r^2}-1\right)\Sigma e_k\xi_k^2+\tfrac{1}{2}\left(3\frac{y^2}{r^2}-1\right)\Sigma e_k\eta_k^2+\tfrac{1}{2}\left(3\frac{z^2}{r^2}-1\right)\Sigma e_k\zeta_k^2\right.$$
$$\left.+\frac{3xy}{r^2}\Sigma e_k\xi_k\eta_k+\frac{3yz}{r^2}\Sigma e_k\eta_k\zeta_k+\frac{3zx}{r^2}\Sigma e_k\zeta_k\xi_k\right]+\ldots \qquad (1)$$

The first term is the Coulomb potential due to point charges, the second is the potential due to dipoles; both of these are assumed to be absent, so that only the third term, representing the potential due to quadrupoles, is taken.

The system of coordinates may be laid in the molecule so that:

$$\Sigma e_k\xi_k\eta_k=\Sigma e_k\eta_k\zeta_k=\Sigma e_k\zeta_k\xi_k=0 \qquad (2)$$

and the molecule is then characterised by three principal electric moments of inertia:

$$\Theta_1=\Sigma e_k\xi_k^2,\quad \Theta_2=\Sigma e_k\eta_k^2,\quad \Theta_3=\Sigma e_k\zeta_k^2 \qquad (3)$$

A quadrupole in general has three principal electric moments of inertia; it requires at least four charges. The simplest arrangement is a linear one, which has one electric moment of inertia. The charges are supposed to be arranged on the x axis, a charge $-2e$ at the origin and two charges $+e$ at distances $\pm a$ from the origin (Fig. 11*a*.VII C). Then the coordinates of $-2e$ are $\xi=\eta=\zeta=0$, those of the charges $+e$ are $\xi_1=a$, $\xi_2=-a$, $\eta=\zeta=0$. Hence $\Theta_1=\Sigma e_k\xi_k^2=e(\xi_1^2+\xi_2^2)-2e\times 0=2ea^2$. The arrangement $-e+2e-e$ gives $\Theta_1=-2ea^2$. In this case, $\Theta_2=\Theta_3=0$.

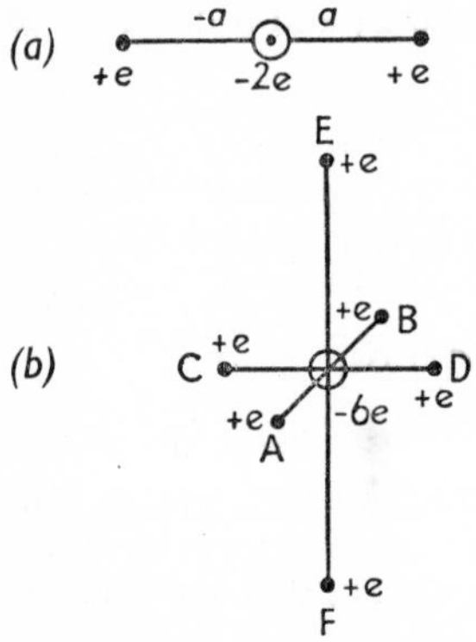

FIG. 11.VII C. Two simple Quadrupole Systems

An arrangement giving three moments is shown in Fig. 11*b*.VII C. There are six positive charges $+e$ at the ends of three axes and a negative charge $-6e$ at the origin. If AB$=2a$, CD$=2b$, EF$=2c$, then $\Theta_1=2ea^2$, $\Theta_2=2eb^2$, $\Theta_3=2ec^2$. Although a dipole is oriented in an electric field, a quadrupole experiences no force or turning moment in a uniform electric field.

If λ, μ denote the dipole and quadrupole moments of a molecule, the mutual energies are: [2]

1. dipole-dipole $E_{dd}=-(\lambda_1\lambda_2/d^3)(2\cos\theta_1\cos\theta_2-\sin\theta_1\sin\theta_2\cos\phi)$,
2. dipole-quadrupole $E_{dq}=-(3\lambda_1\mu_2/2d^4)(-2\cos\theta_1\cos^2\theta_2+\cos\theta_1\sin^2\theta_2+2\sin\theta_1\sin\theta_2\cos\theta_2\cos\phi)$,
3. quadrupole-quadrupole $E_{qq}=(-3\mu_1\mu_2/4d^5)[1-5\cos^2\theta_1-5\cos^2\theta_2-15\cos^2\theta_1\cos^2\theta_2+2(4\cos\theta_1\cos\theta_2-\sin\theta_1\sin\theta_2\cos\phi)^2]$,

[1] Maxwell, "A Treatise on Electricity and Magnetism," Oxford, 1873, **1**, 157, 3rd edit., Oxford, 1892, **1**, 194.

[2] Schmick, *Phys. Z.*, 1928, **29**, 633; on dipole, quadrupole, and octupole fields, see Zwicky, *Phys. Rev.*, 1921, **22**, 449; Kirkwood, *J. Chem. Phys.*, 1934, **2**, 351; McMeekin, Cohn, and Blanchard, *J.A.C.S.*, 1937, **59**, 2717; Moelwyn-Hughes, "Physical Chemistry," Cambridge, 1940, 95.

where d=distance of molecular centres, θ_1 and θ_2=angles between the molecular axes and the x axis, and ϕ=angle which the plane containing the axis of the first molecule makes with the plane containing the second molecule and the x axis. The average energy is then found, for all possible orientations ($d\tau=\sin\theta_1 \sin\theta_2 \, d\theta_1 d\theta_2 d\phi$) as:

$$\bar{E}=\int E e^{-E/kT} d\tau \Big/ \int e^{-E/kT} d\tau.$$

The field due to the quadrupoles is given by $F=-\partial V/\partial r$ and $\overline{F^2}$ (the mean square of the field) was shown by Debye to be $3\tau^2/r^8$, where:

$$\tau^2=\Theta_1{}^2+\Theta_2{}^2+\Theta_3{}^2-(\Theta_1\Theta_2+\Theta_2\Theta_3+\Theta_3\Theta_1) \quad . \quad . \quad . \quad (4)$$

If there are N molecules per cm.³ the mean square electric intensity in the interior of the gas is:

$$\overline{F^2}=N\int_d^\infty 4\pi r^2(3\tau^2/r^8)dr=(12\pi/5)(N\tau^2/d^5) \quad . \quad . \quad . \quad . \quad (5)$$

where d is the molecular diameter. If a molecule of polarisability α is brought into this field, its potential energy would be $-\frac{1}{2}\alpha\overline{F^2}$ if it did not contribute to the field, but as it polarises all the other molecules the work done is twice this expression.

If there are N' molecules in a volume v, $N=N'/v$, and if a further dN' molecules are added the work done is $-(12\pi/5)(\alpha\tau^2/d^5)(N'dN'/v)$, and the total potential energy due to N molecules in a volume v is found by integration to be $-A/v$, where $A=(6\pi/5)(\alpha\tau^2/d^5)N^2$. Comparison with the van der Waals expression $-a/v$ gives:

$$a=(6\pi/5)(\alpha\tau^2/d^5)N^2 \quad . \quad . \quad . \quad . \quad . \quad . \quad . \quad . \quad (6)$$

which gives too large a temperature dependence of a. The polarisability α is found from the molecular refraction R_L by the equation:

$$R_L=(n^2-1)/(n^2+2) \, . \, (M/\rho)=(4\pi/3)N\alpha \quad . \quad . \quad . \quad . \quad . \quad (7)$$

which is true for infinite wave-length; hence:

$$a=(9/10)R_L N\tau^2/d^5 \quad . \quad . \quad . \quad . \quad . \quad . \quad . \quad . \quad (8)$$

The determination of τ is not so simple. Debye [1] calculated it from the broadening of spectrum lines, and assumed $\tau \simeq e(10^{-8})^2=5\times10^{-26}$, where e=electronic charge. The value of b was taken from van der Waals as four times the volume of the molecules, viz. $4N(4\pi/3)(d/2)^3=(2\pi/3)Nd^3$.

The wave-mechanical theory (§ 45) assumes that inert gas molecules are symmetrical, and hence they cannot have quadrupoles. A comparison with experimental data also shows [2] that neither Keesom's (dipole) nor Debye's (quadrupole) theory applies, and the present theory of molecular attraction is based on a theory due to London,[3] in which it is supposed to be due to a wave-mechanical resonance phenomenon.

§ 44. Wave-Mechanical Theory

The resonance attraction has been described [4] as due to " a sympathetic fluctuation of the electron space clouds of the two atoms, which produces in

[1] *Phys. Z.*, 1919, **20**, 160.

[2] Wohl, *Z. phys. Chem.*, 1928, **133**, 305; 1929, **2** B, 77.

[3] *Z. Phys.*, 1930, **63**, 245; *Z. phys. Chem.*, 1930, **11** B, 222; 1936, **33** B, 8; Wohl, *Z. phys. Chem.*, 1931, *Bodenstein Festb.*, 807; Müller, *Proc. Roy. Soc.*, 1936, **154**, 624; Buckingham, *ibid.*, 1937, **160**, 94; Margenau, *Rev. Mod. Phys.*, 1939, **11**, 1.

[4] Lennard-Jones, *Trans. Faraday Soc.*, 1932, **28**, 333; Randall, *J. Phys. Chem.*, 1932, **36**, 2106; Dushman and Seitz, *ibid.*, 1937, **41**, 233; Benumof, *Amer. J. Phys.*, 1948, **16**, 249; correction for non-symmetrical field of H_2 and D_2, see de Boer, *Physica*, 1942, **9**, 363; 1943, **10**, 357.

the atoms effective dipoles tending to move more in phase than out of phase." The resonance energy is (§ 45):

$$\epsilon_a = -(3/4)h\nu_0\alpha^2/r^6 \quad . \quad . \quad . \quad . \quad . \quad . \quad . \quad . \quad (1)$$

where α is the polarisability and ν_0 is the frequency of the oscillating dipole in its lowest energy state. London identified $h\nu_0$ with the ionising potential V_I and found:

$$\epsilon_a = -(3/4)V_I\alpha/r^6 \quad . \quad . \quad . \quad . \quad . \quad . \quad . \quad . \quad (2)$$

which holds only for $r^3 \gg \alpha$. The second virial coefficient is then:

$$B = (2\pi/3)Nd^3[1 - f_1(\Theta/T) - f_2(\Theta/T)^2 - f_3(\Theta/T)^3 - \ldots] \quad . \quad . \quad (3)$$

where $\Theta = (3\alpha^2/4r_0^6k)h\nu_0$, and $f_1, f_2, \ldots$ are numerical coefficients. For two inert gas atoms the full expression for the potential energy is:

$$\epsilon = -(3/4\pi)(h/r_0^6)(e^2/m)^2\sum_j\sum_k f_{j0}f_{k0}/[\tilde{\omega}_{j0}\tilde{\omega}_{k0}(\tilde{\omega}_{j0}+\tilde{\omega}_{k0})] \quad . \quad . \quad (4)$$

where e and m are the electronic charge and mass, j and k relate to the excited states of the two atoms, f_{j0} and f_{k0} are the fictitious oscillator strengths in the dispersion theory, and $\tilde{\omega}_{j0}$ and $\tilde{\omega}_{k0}$ are the transition frequencies from the ground state 0 to the excited states j and k.

A simplified form of London's theory proposed by Slater and Kirkwood[1] replaced the attraction potential (2) by:

$$\epsilon_a = -7\cdot07 \times 10^{-12}\alpha^{3/2}n^{1/2}/r^6 \text{ volt} \quad . \quad . \quad . \quad . \quad . \quad (5)$$

where n is the number of electrons in the outer shell of the molecule; this usually gives much higher values than (2), even when the dispersion energy V_D is used instead of the ionisation potential V_I, as was proposed by London.[2] London, and Wohl,[3] substituted for the repulsion potential the rigid co-volume b_0, which is a good approximation for high temperatures, and if the characteristic equation is in the form $pv/RT = 1 + B/v$, the van der Waals second virial coefficient is $B = b - a/RT$. From (2) and (5):

$$a = 1\cdot152 \times 10^{54}\alpha^2 V_I/b_0 \quad . \quad . \quad . \quad . \quad . \quad . \quad . \quad . \quad (6)$$

$$a = 1\cdot084 \times 10^{43}\alpha^{3/2}n^{1/2}/b_0 \quad . \quad . \quad . \quad . \quad . \quad . \quad . \quad . \quad (7)$$

(V in volts, b_0 in cm.^{3}/mol, a in atm. (cm.^{3}/mol)^2). London put $b_0 = RT_c/8p_c$ (§ 7) and compared the values of a from (6) with the van der Waals value (§ 7), $a = 27R^2T_c^2/64p_c$, obtaining agreement not only with inert gases but also with dipole gases such as HCl, within the rather large (up to 50 per cent.) limits of error.

Wohl pointed out that the van der Waals b_0 value is too small (probably in the ratio 0·75:1), and if the value $4b_0/3$ is used, the calculated a-values are (except for H_2 and He) smaller than the empirical; the agreement is improved when V_D is used instead of V_I, but formula (5) gives still better agreement.[4]

The value of the second virial coefficient, with Slater and Kirkwood's value for the interaction energy, is given by (3) with $\Theta = 9\cdot42 \times 10^{-2}\alpha^{3/2}n^{1/2}/r_0^6k$.

[1] Slater, Kirkwood, and Keyes, *Phys. Rev.*, 1931, **37**, 682; Kirkwood and Keyes, *ibid.*, 1931, **37**, 832; Slater, *ibid.*, 1931, **38**, 237; Herzfeld, *ibid.*, 1937, **52**, 374; van Arkel and de Groot, *Physica*, 1932, **12**, 211; *Rec. Trav. Chim.*, 1932, **51**, 1081; Berger, *Z. phys. Chem.*, 1935, **28** B, 95; Herzfeld, in Geiger and Scheel, "Handbuch der Physik," 1933, **24**, ii, 162; see also de Boer and Michels, *Physica*, 1940, **7**, 369; Ninii, *Ann. Acad. Sci. Fenn.*, 1940, **55** A, No. 8 (liquid mixtures); and for B_{12} for mixtures, Beattie and Stockmayer, *J. Chem. Phys.*, 1942, **10**, 473, 476.

[2] *Z. phys. Chem.*, 1930, **11 B**, 222.

[3] *Z. phys. Chem.* 1931, *Bodenstein Festb.*, 807; 1929, **2 B**, 77.

[4] This is more practical, as it contains only two magnitudes, which are known for many substances.

§ 45. Van der Waals Attraction

The wave-mechanical explanation of van der Waals forces, mentioned in § 44, may be sketched.[1] The treatment is due to London.[2] The material particle (atom or molecule) is supposed to be capable of electric polarisation; when placed in an electric field F a separation of charges occurs with the production of a temporary dipole of moment proportional to F, i.e. $\mu=\alpha F$, where the constant α is the polarisability. The energy of polarisation is:

$$E_p=-\int_0^\mu F\mathrm{d}\mu=-\int_0^F \alpha F\mathrm{d}F=-\tfrac{1}{2}\alpha F^2 \quad . \quad . \quad . \quad . \quad . \quad (1)$$

Consider two identical linear harmonic oscillators arranged as in Fig. 12.VII C with amplitudes a_1 and a_2, and let R be the equilibrium distance between their positive ends; R is supposed to be very large compared with a_1 and a_2. The mutual potential energy of the system is:

$$V=e^2[1/(R+a_2-a_1)-1/(R+a_2) \\ -1/(R-a_1)+1/R] \quad . \quad (2)$$

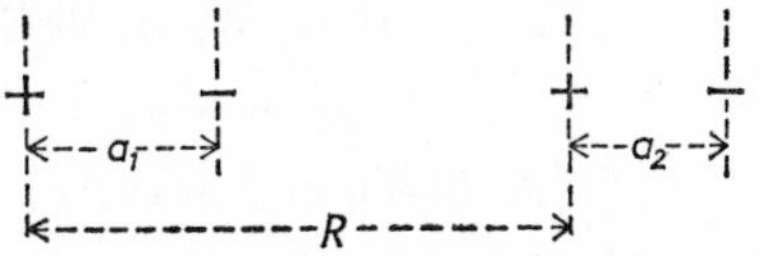

FIG. 12.VII C. Attraction between two Linear Harmonic Oscillators

since e times each term in brackets gives the potential, and this multiplied by e (with the correct sign) gives the potential energy. Divide (2) by R, then as a_1/R and a_2/R are much less than unity a binomial expansion (§ 33.I) is possible:

$$(1+a_2/R)^{-1}=1-a_2/R+(a_2/R)^2-(a_2/R)^3+\ldots$$

$$(1-a_1/R)^{-1}=1+a_1/R+(a_1/R)^2+(a_1/R)^3+\ldots$$

$$[1-(a_1-a_2)/R]^{-1}=1-(a_2-a_1)/R+(a_2^2+a_1^2-2a_1a_2)/R^2-\ldots.$$

By neglecting terms beyond the squares, it is found that:

$$V=-2e^2a_1a_2/R^3 \quad . \quad . \quad . \quad . \quad . \quad . \quad . \quad . \quad . \quad (3)$$

Stopping the series at terms in R^{-2} is equivalent to restricting the forces to dipole interactions, terms involving R^{-4} and R^{-5} corresponding with dipole-quadrupole and quadrupole-quadrupole interaction respectively [3] (§ 43).

If k is the oscillator constant, the potential energy due to the oscillators is $\frac{1}{2}k(a_1^2+a_2^2)$, and if p_1, p_2 are the momenta the kinetic energy is (§ 16.IV) $(1/2\mu')(p_1^2+p_2^2)$, where μ' is the reduced mass (not to be confused with μ, the dipole moment). The total energy is:

$$E=T+V=(1/2\mu')(p_1^2+p_2^2)+(1/2k)(a_1^2+a_2^2)-2e^2a_1a_2/R^3 \quad . \quad (4)$$

The last term in (4) corresponds with an *interaction energy*. For large values of R the last term is negligible and the system consists of two isolated oscillators of frequency (§ 7.V):

$$\nu_0=(1/2\pi)\sqrt{(k/\mu')} \quad . \quad . \quad . \quad . \quad . \quad . \quad . \quad . \quad (5)$$

For smaller values of R the field due to each oscillator acts on the other one, and if a is the displacement, (1) gives:

$$\tfrac{1}{2}ka^2=\tfrac{1}{2}\alpha F^2 \quad . \quad . \quad . \quad . \quad . \quad . \quad . \quad . \quad . \quad (6)$$

[1] The treatment follows Born and Göppert Mayer, in Geiger and Scheel, " Handbuch der Physik," 1933, **24**, ii, 750; Dushman, " Elements of Quantum Mechanics," New York, 1938, 220; Margenau, *Rev. Mod. Phys.*, 1939, **11**, 1 (bibl.).

[2] London, *Z. Phys.*, 1930, **63**, 245; *Z. phys. Chem.*, 1931, **11** B, 222; Hassé, *Proc. Cambr. Phil. Soc.*, 1931, **27**, 66; Fripiat, *Bull. Acad. Roy. Belg.*, 1947, **32**, 465; for extension to symmetrical tops, see Carroll, *Phys. Rev.*, 1938, **53**, 310.

[3] On these terms, see Margenau, *J. Chem. Phys.*, 1938, **6**, 896, also R^{-8} and R^{-10}.

and since the dipole moment is

$$\mu = ae = \alpha F \quad . \quad . \quad . \quad . \quad . \quad (7)$$

$$\therefore \ \alpha = e^2/k \quad . \quad . \quad . \quad . \quad . \quad (8)$$

Now introduce new coordinates [1] in place of a_1 and a_2:

$$q_1 = (1/\sqrt{2})(a_1 + a_2), \quad q_2 = (1/\sqrt{2})(a_1 - a_2) \quad . \quad . \quad . \quad (9)$$

$$\therefore \ a_1 = (1/\sqrt{2})(q_1 + q_2), \quad a_2 = (1/\sqrt{2})(q_1 - q_2) \quad . \quad . \quad . \quad (10)$$

$$2a_1a_2 = q_1^2 - q_2^2 \quad . \quad . \quad . \quad . \quad . \quad (11)$$

From the momentum equation, $p = \mu' v = \mu' \dot{a}$ (where $\dot{a} = \mathrm{d}a/\mathrm{d}t$). Let P be the momentum in terms of the q coordinate:

$$P_1 = \mu' \dot{q}_1 = (\mu'/\sqrt{2})(\dot{a}_1 + \dot{a}_2) = (1/\sqrt{2})(p_1 + p_2),$$

$$P_2 = \mu' \dot{q}_2 = (\mu'/\sqrt{2})(\dot{a}_1 - \dot{a}_2) = (1/\sqrt{2})(p_1 - p_2),$$

$$\therefore \ p_1^2 + p_2^2 = \tfrac{1}{2}[(p_1 + p_2)^2 + (p_1 - p_2)^2] = P_1^2 + P_2^2,$$

$$\therefore \ E = (1/2\mu')(p_1^2 + p_2^2) + (k/2 - e^2/R^3)q_1^2 + (k/2 + e^2/R^3)q_2^2$$

from (4) and (11). The energy is separable into two terms corresponding with two new modes of vibration:

$$\nu_1 = (1/2\pi)\sqrt{[(k/\mu')(1 - 2e^2/kR^3)]} \text{ and } \nu_2 = (1/2\pi)\sqrt{[(k/\mu')(1 + 2e^2/kR^3)]} \quad (12)$$

By putting $2e^2/kR^3 = x$, which is small compared with unity, using the expansions (1), § 33.I:

$$(1 - x)^{1/2} = 1 - x/2 - x^2/8 - \ldots \quad \text{and} \quad (1 + x)^{1/2} = 1 + x/2 - x^2/8 + \ldots$$

and comparing with (5):

$$\nu_1 = \frac{1}{2\pi}\sqrt{\frac{k}{\mu'}}\left(1 - \frac{2e^2}{kR^3} - \frac{e^4}{2k^2R^6} + \ldots\right) = \nu_0\left(1 - \frac{2e^2}{kR^3} - \frac{e^4}{2k^2R^6} + \ldots\right) \quad (13)$$

$$\nu_2 = \frac{1}{2\pi}\sqrt{\frac{k}{\mu'}}\left(1 + \frac{2e^2}{kR^3} - \frac{e^4}{2k^2R^6} + \ldots\right) = \nu_0\left(1 + \frac{2e^2}{kR^3} - \frac{e^4}{2k^2R^6} + \ldots\right) \quad (14)$$

For a single oscillator, from (4), § 16.IV, $E_n = h\nu_0(n + \tfrac{1}{2})$, hence for the two oscillators:

$$E_{n_1 n_2} = h\nu_1(n_1 + \tfrac{1}{2}) + h\nu_2(n_2 + \tfrac{1}{2})$$

$$= h\nu_0\left[n_1 + n_2 + 1 - \frac{2e^2}{kR^3}(n_1 - n_2) - \frac{e^4}{2k^2R^6}(n_1 + n_2 + 1) + \ldots\right] \quad . \quad (15)$$

For $n_1 = n_2 = 0$, with (8):

$$E_{00} = h\nu_0(1 - e^4/2k^2R^6) = h\nu_0(1 - \alpha^2/2R^6) \quad . \quad . \quad . \quad . \quad (16)$$

The coupling energy is, therefore:

$$\Delta E = -h\nu_0\alpha^2/2R^6 \quad . \quad . \quad . \quad . \quad . \quad (17)$$

and the attractive force (shown by the negative sign) is:

$$F_a = \mathrm{d}\Delta E/\mathrm{d}R = -3\alpha^2 h\nu_0/R^7 \quad . \quad . \quad . \quad . \quad (18)$$

i.e. the force is inversely proportional to the seventh power of the distance. London assumed that $h_0\nu$ is equal to the ionisation potential V_i of the atom or molecule.

For the more general case of oscillators in three dimensions, the coordinate

[1] This corresponds with a rotation of the rectangular axes a_1 and a_2 through an angle of 45°; C. Smith, "Conic Sections," 1914, 60.

transformations include terms for y and z of the same form as those for x ($=a$) in (9); the energy is $\frac{3}{2}$ times (17) rather than 3 times, since, of the six frequencies, two pairs occur with identical values:

$$\Delta E=-(3/4)h\nu_0\alpha^2/R^6 \quad \ldots \ldots \quad (19)$$

The results may be related to the van der Waals constants as follows. The general equation for the second virial coefficient is (21), § 42:

$$B=2\pi N\int_0^\infty r^2(1-e^{-E/kT})dr.$$

The repulsive force may be taken approximately as ∞ for $r<r_0$ and 0 for $r>r_0$ (hard spheres) so that the integral from 0 to r_0 is:

$$2\pi N\int_0^{r_0} r^2dr(1-e^{-\infty})=2\pi N\int_0^{r_0} r^2dr=\tfrac{2}{3}\pi Nr_0^3.$$

The attractive force virial coefficient, if $-\frac{3}{4}h\nu_0\alpha^2=\beta$, is:

$$2\pi N\int_{r_0}^\infty r^2(1-e^{\beta r^{-6}/kT})dr\simeq 2\pi N\int_{r_0}^\infty r^2[1-(1+\beta r^{-6}/kT)]dr$$

$$=-2\pi N\int_{r_0}^\infty(\beta r^{-4}/kT)dr=(2\pi N\beta/kT)\int_\infty^{r_0} r^{-4}dr=-(2\pi/3)N\beta/kTr_0^3.$$

The total virial coefficient is:

$$B=(2\pi/3)Nr_0^3-(2\pi/3)N\beta/kTr_0^3 \quad \ldots \ldots \quad (20)$$

The van der Waals virial coefficient is $B=b-a/NkT$, and by comparing the two values of B it is seen that (v_0=volume of molecules):

$$b=(2\pi/3)Nr_0^3=\tfrac{1}{2}v_0 \quad \ldots \ldots \quad (21)$$

$$a=(2\pi/3)N^2\beta/r_0^3 \quad \ldots \ldots \quad (22)$$

If b is assumed known, the values of a given by:

$$a=(4\pi^2/9)N^3\beta/b \quad \ldots \ldots \quad (23)$$

calculated by London for inert gases were found in very good agreement with experimental results. The values of α may be calculated from the molar refraction (§ 43).

The various types of forces acting between atoms, molecules, and ions are assumed to be: [1]

(1) Electrostatic Coulomb forces between ions, deduced from the classica inverse-square law.

(2) Exchange (resonance) forces, very short-range attractions leading to covalent bond formation, deduced from wave-mechanics.

(3) Intermolecular long-range van der Waals attractive forces, leading to deviations from gas laws, forces in liquids, latent heats of evaporation and of sublimation of molecular lattices; these are small compared with (2).

(4) Intramolecular van der Waals forces between atoms and groups, not directly linked, in the same molecule; these generally influence the shape of the molecule, restrict rotation about bond directions, etc.

[1] Briegleb, *Z. phys. Chem.*, 1933, **23 B**, 105; Stuart, "Molekülstruktur," Berlin, 1934, 3 f.; Kremann and Pestemer, "Zusammenhänge zwischen physikalischen Eigenschaften und chemischer Konstitution," 1937, 10; Staverman, *Physica*, 1937, **4**, 1141; Eisenschitz, *Sci. Progr.*, 1947, **35**, 470.

The van der Waals forces (3) and (4) are attributed to the following causes:

(*a*) Electrostatic attractions between dipoles of separate bonds (quadrupoles and multipoles have little effect).

(*b*) Attractions due to polarisation of atoms under the influence of the electric fields of permanent electric moments; these are small.

(*c*) Dispersion (London) attractive forces, due to the rapid changes of electron configuration; these cause the main effect.

(*d*) Resonance repulsions, due to the approach of saturated atoms (e.g. two hydrogen atoms) in a molecule, which cannot form a bond; these may cause steric hindrance.

§ 46. Molecular Clustering

The old idea [1] that the higher compressibility of a gas, as compared with Boyle's law, is due to the formation of " clusters " of molecules, rather than to long-range attractive forces between separate molecules (van der Waals), has often been brought forward. On the basis of the London theory of molecular attraction (§§ 44, 45), which gives a potential energy of the form:

$$\epsilon_p = -k_1/r^6 + k_2/r^n$$

where the second term on the right is a repulsion potential not yet fully understood,[2] and with the assumption of binary clusters, an attempt was made [3] to represent the temperature change of the second virial coefficient B. Schäfer [4] developed a virial equation on wave-mechanical principles, introducing the energy levels of the molecules, and considered its relation to H_2 and D_2, and Mayer [5] worked out so-called " cluster integrals " on a statistical basis.

Many attempts have been made to distribute the " centres " of the London attractive forces in *polyatomic* molecules; they are not central forces of the type k_1/r^m but are composed of highly anisotropic force centres, and in some molecules there are long, extended, electronic oscillators, which cannot be built up additively from smaller units. The problem is one of great complexity [6] and cannot be considered in detail here. The practical application of such conceptions is far from attaining a form suitable for use in applied chemistry.

[1] Recknagel, *Ann. Phys.*, 1871, *Ergzb.* **5**, 563; 1872, **145**, 469; Clausius, *ibid.*, 1880, **9**, 337; Jäger, *Wien Ber.*, 1896, **105**, IIA, 791; Jeans, " Dynamical Theory of Gases," Cambridge, 1904, 73; Bernoulli, *Z. phys. Chem.*, 1909, **65**, 391; Drucker, *ibid.*, 1909, **68**, 616; van der Waals, *Proc. K. Akad. Wetens. Amsterdam*, 1910–11, **13**, 107, 494; Duclaux, *J. de Phys.*, 1924, **5**, 331; 1927, **8**, 336; 1940, **1**, 293; 1947, **8**, 94; *Compt. Rend.*, 1948, **226**, 1113, 2034; Keyes and Taylor, *J.A.C.S.*, 1927, **49**, 896; Keyes and Burks, *ibid.*, 1927, **49**, 1403; Bridgeman, *ibid.*, 1927, **49**, 1130; Eucken, *Z. phys. Chem.*, 1931, *Bodenstein Festb.*, 423; Tonks, *Phys. Rev.*, 1936, **50**, 955; Goodeve, *Nature*, 1937, **140**, 424; Herman, *Compt. Rend.*, 1937, **205**, 1065; de Boer and Michels, *Physica*, 1938, **5**, 945 (quantum correction in He virial coefficient); de Boer, *ibid.*, 1942, **9**, 363; 1943, **10**, 357; Mayer and Harrison, *J. Chem. Phys.*, 1938, **6**, 87; Kahn and Uhlenbeek, *Physica*, 1938, **5**, 399; Rice, *J. Chem. Phys.*, 1942, **10**, 653; Bogolyubov, *J. Phys. U.S.S.R.*, 1946, **10**, 257; Green, *Proc. Roy. Soc.*, 1947, **189**, 103; Eisenschitz, *Sci. Progr.*, 1947, **35**, 470.

[2] Wave mechanics gives $e^{-\rho r}$ instead of r^{-n}, where ρ=const.; Born and Mayer, *Z. Phys.*, 1932, **75**, 1; Mayer and Helmholtz, *ibid.*, 1932, **75**, 19.

[3] Margenau, *Z. Phys.*, 1930, **64**, 584; *Phys. Rev.*, 1930, **66**, 1782; 1943, **63**, 385; 1943, **64**, 131; Wohl, *Z. phys. Chem.*, 1931, **14** B, 36; Briegleb, *ibid.*, 1933, **22** B, 105.

[4] *Z. phys. Chem.*, 1937, **38** B, 187.

[5] *J. Phys. Chem.*, 1939, **43**, 71; Mayer and Mayer, " Statistical Mechanics," New York. 1940, 278, 297, 455.

[6] London, *J. Phys. Chem.*, 1942, **46**, 305.

Berger [1] calculated the attraction energy for a binary mixture and solution from those of its pure components by the formula:

$$\epsilon_{12}=\sqrt{(\epsilon_{11}\epsilon_{22})}=\alpha_1\alpha_2\sqrt{(\phi_1\phi_2)}/(r_1r_2)^3,$$

where α_1, α_2 are the polarisabilities, ϕ_1, ϕ_2 the excitation energies, and r_1, r_2 the distances between the molecular centres, on the basis of London's formula, and a similar expression for Slater and Kirkwood's formula.

The supposed evidence for clustering in NO to N_2O_2 given by Eucken and d'Or [2] is nugatory, since Berthelot's equation (§ 29) represents the results better.[3] Duclaux's results were accepted by Leduc,[4] since they agreed with an equation previously deduced [5] ($\tau=T_c/T$; $A=0{\cdot}0463RT_c/p_cv_c$):

$$pV=RT\{V/(V-A^2)-3{\cdot}160[A/(V+A)^2](4\tau-1)\}.$$

They were, however, criticised by Rocard.[6]

D. DENSITIES AND MOLAR WEIGHTS OF GASES AND VAPOURS

§ 1. Densities of Gases

Otto von Guericke [7] about 1650 showed that a glass globe weighed 2 oz. less when the air in it is exhausted by an air pump, but this method of finding the density of a gas could not give accurate results until a good vacuum could be obtained. Hales [8] weighed a 540 cu. in. jar full of fixed air (CO_2), blew out the the gas with bellows, and weighed again, but found no difference in weight. Hauksbee [9] found the densities of air and water in the ratio of 1:885 by weighing a globe vacuous and full of air. Cavendish [10] determined the densities of fixed air (CO_2) and inflammable air (H_2) by finding the gain and loss in weight, respectively, of a measured bladder inflated with the gases and weighed in air, and also by measuring the volume of gas generated in a vessel and the loss in weight of the vessel. Priestley [11] tried to weigh gases in flasks in which they had been collected over water, and also in bladders, but the results were inaccurate, although they showed that nitrogen is slightly lighter than air.

Better results were obtained by Fontana [12] towards the end of 1779 by weighing

[1] *Z. phys. Chem.*, 1935, **28** B, 95; Hildebrand and Wood, *J. Chem. Phys.*, 1933, **1**, 817; Hildebrand, *J.A.C.S.*, 1935, **57**, 866.

[2] *Gött. Nachr.*, 1932, 107.

[3] Johnston and Weimer, *J.A.C.S.*, 1934, **56**, 625.

[4] *Compt. Rend.*, 1925, **180**, 502.

[5] Leduc, *Compt. Rend.*, 1923, **176**, 830, 1132.

[6] *J. de Phys.*, 1925, **6**, 198.

[7] " Experimenta Nova (ut vocantur) Magdeburgica de Vacuo Spatio," Amsterdam, 1672, 100; Ostwald's *Klassiker*, 1894, **59**, 64; he does not give the size of the globe, but a note in Ostwald's *Klassiker* says it was a " half " or " quarter " chemical receiver.

[8] " Vegetable Staticks," 1727, 184.

[9] *Phil. Trans.*, 1706, **25**, 2221; abdgd. edit., 1809, **5**, 288.

[10] *Phil. Trans.*, 1766, **56**, 141; abdgd. edit., 1809, **12**, 298.

[11] " Experiments and Observations on Air," Birmingham, 1790, **2**, 215; this had been found before by Scheele, " Chemical Observations and Experiments on Air and Fire," 1777, transl. by Forster, London, 1780, 15.

[12] Cavallo, " A Treatise on the Nature and Properties of Air and other Permanently Elastic Fluids," 1781, 422; he found the weights in grains of 1 cu. in. at room temperature and pressure: N_2 0·377, air 0·385.

an exhausted globe fitted with a stopcock (Fig. 1.VII D), filling it with gas by screwing the stopcock to a stopcock at the top of a bell-jar containing the gas over mercury, opening the stopcocks, and weighing the globe filled with gas. Biot and Arago [1] used a 5–6 lit. globe and corrected for air displacement on weighing, residual air, expansion of the globe by temperature, and moisture in the gas; they reduced the barometer to sea-level and latitude 45° and the densities to the standard temperature and pressure. The same method was used with dried gases by later experimenters.[2]

Let V_t=volume of globe in ml. found by weighing full of water at a temperature t, W the weight of the globe filled with dry gas at the barometric pressure p mm. Hg and temperature t, W' the weight of the globe when most of the gas has been removed by pumping to a pressure p' mm. and at temperature t; then the density of the gas in g. per ml. at S.T.P. is:

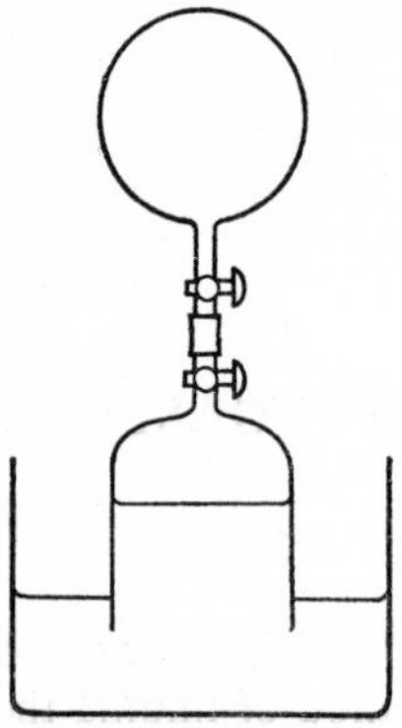

FIG. 1.VII D. Fontana's Gas Density Apparatus

$$\rho=[(W-W')/V_t](1+\alpha t)\,.\,760/(p-p') \quad . \quad (1)$$

where α is the coefficient of expansion of the gas. If W and W' are found at two different temperatures t and t', the expression becomes:

$$\rho=\frac{(W-W')(760/V_t)}{p/(1+\alpha t)-p'[1+\beta(t-t')]/(1+\alpha t')} \quad , \quad (2)$$

where β is the coefficient of cubical expansion of the glass of the globe, and a small correction is then necessary for the different volumes of air (at slightly different densities) displaced by the globe.[3]

The *normal density D* (or sometimes *L*) of a gas is the weight in vacuum in grams of one litre (1000·027 cm.³) of the gas, at 0° C., and 760 mm. Hg at 0° pressure (standard, or normal, temperature and pressure, S.T.P., or N.T.P.) with the mercury column at sea-level and latitude 45°, corresponding with a pressure of 1,013,250 dynes per cm.² The correction to sea-level and latitude 45°, necessitating a knowledge of the acceleration of gravity g at the place of experiment, really affects the pressure exerted by the column of mercury of 760 mm. at 0°, the density of the gas depending on the pressure.[4]

The *relative* (or *vapour*) *density* is the ratio of the weight of any volume of a gas (or vapour) to the weight of an equal volume of a standard gas (e.g. hydrogen, which is the lightest gas), measured and weighed under identical conditions.

[1] *Mém. de l'Inst.*, 1806, **7**, i, 301; Biot, " Traité de Physique," 1816, **1**, 347–98.

[2] Berzelius and Dulong, *Ann. Chim.*, 1820, **15**, 386; Thomson, *Ann. Phil.*, 1820, **15**, 232; 1820, **16**, 161, 241; Prout, *B.A. Rep.*, 1832, 566; Dumas and Boussingault, *Ann. Chim.*, 1841, **3**, 257; Faraday, " Chemical Manipulation," 1842, 387; older values in Poggendorff, *Ann. Phys.*, 1840, **49**, 417; a full table of earlier gas and vapour-density determinations, with references, is given in Lothar Meyer, " Modern Theories of Chemistry," 1888, 37; Muir, " Principles of Chemistry," Cambridge, 1889, 33, 39; and a shorter table in Lowry, " Historical Introduction to Chemistry," 1915, 361; a history of gas density determinations is given by Germann, *J. Phys. Chem.*, 1915, **19**, 437. For values of densities and compressibilities of gases, see Landolt-Börnstein, " Tabellen," 5th edit., 1923, **1**, 269; Ergzb. I, 1927, 160; Ergzb. II, 1931, 205.

[3] Baxter, *J.A.C.S.*, 1921, **43**, 1317.

[4] Guye, *J. Chim. Phys.*, 1913, **11**, 319; Moles, *ibid.*, 1937, **34**, 49. The accepted standard value of g_0 (sea-level and lat. 45°) has varied somewhat (980·665, 980·616, 980·629), the present value being 980·629. Birge, *Rep. Progr. Phys.*, 1942, **8**, 90, took 980·616 for 45° and 980·665 as a " standard " value; Clark, *Proc. Roy. Soc.*, 1946, **186**, 192, said 980·62 was adopted in 1941.

If both gases obey Boyle's and Charles's laws, the relative density is the same at all temperatures and pressures.

§ 2. Densities of Gases by the Globe Method

The experimental accuracy of the globe method was raised to a high standard by Regnault.[1] He introduced two principal improvements: (i) The globe was filled with pure dry gas at 0° C. by finally surrounding it by a large vessel of melting ice, filling it several times with gas and exhausting until the amount of residual air was negligible. The globe was carefully wiped with a damp cloth and hung on one arm of the balance. (ii) Instead of correcting for the volume of air displaced by the globe, which varies with temperature, pressure and moisture, a second *compensating globe*[2] of the same glass, and as equal in volume as possible to the gas globe, was hung on the opposite arm of the balance, (Fig. 2.VII D) and the small weight difference compensated by brass weights, already corrected for air displacement (which in any case is then practically negligible). A small glass bulb was hung on the side of the smaller globe so as compensate to the volumes. If w, w' are the additional weights to balance the globes with the gas pressures p and p', the density of the gas at S.T.P. is:

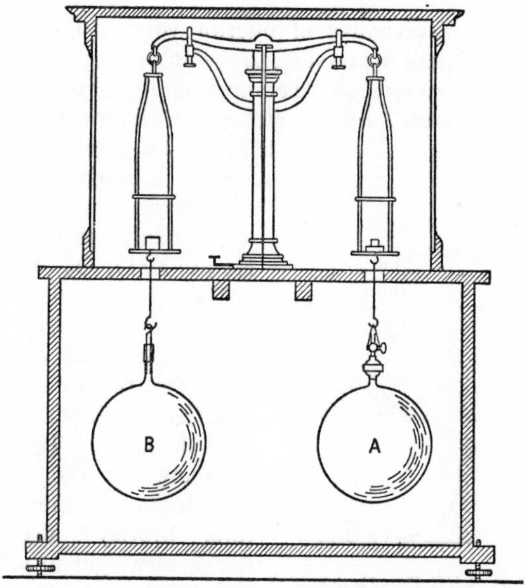

FIG. 2.VII D. Regnault's Gas Density Apparatus. A=gas globe, B=compensating globe

$$[(w-w')/V_0]\,.\,760/(p-p')\;\ldots\ldots\ldots\ldots \quad (1)$$

This requires an accurate determination of the volume V_0 of the globe.[3]

A correction which seems to have been overlooked by Regnault is the

[1] *Mém. Acad. Sci.*, 1847, **21**, 121; *Ann. Phys.*, 1847, **74**, 202; " Cours Élémentaire de Chimie," 4th edit., Paris, 1853, **1**, 144.

[2] According to Miller, " Chemical Physics," 1872, 281, the compensating globe was used previously by Prout " in his careful investigations of the density of the atmosphere " (giving 1·29262 g./lit. at S.T.P., Miller, " Inorganic Chemistry," 1874, 135, almost identical with the modern value). Ostwald, " Lehrbuch der allgemeinen Chemie," 1903, **1**, 168, credited it to Wrede and Svanberg, from Berzelius, *Jahres-Ber.*, 1846, **26**, 29. It is not mentioned in Prout's paper, *B.A. Rep.*, 1832, 566, the only one on the subject by Prout given in the Royal Society " Catalogue of Scientific Papers." This gives the density as 32·7958 grains per 100 cu. in. at 32° F. and 30 in. Hg in London, and mentions a sudden variation to 32·8218.

[3] On the globe method see Guye and Davila, *Mém. Soc. Phys. Nat.* (Geneva), 1907, **35**, 615; Baume, *J. Chim. Phys.*, 1908, **6**, 1; Guye, in Stähler, " Arbeitsmethoden der anorganischen Chemie," 1913, **3**, i, 53; Germann, *J. Chim. Phys.*, 1914, **12**, 66; *J. Phys. Chem.*, 1914, **19**, 437; Schultze, *Ann. Phys.*, 1915, **48**, 269; Scheel, in Geiger and Scheel, " Handbuch der Physik," 1926, **2**, 156; Klemenc and Bankowski, *Z. anorg. Chem.*, 1932, **208**, 348; 1934, **217**, 62; Fischer and Weidmann, *ibid.*, 1933, **213**, 106; Batuecas, *J. Chim. Phys.*, 1935, **32**, 58; Roper, *J. Phys. Chem.*, 1940, **44**, 834; and the references to Moles, etc., below.

contraction or shrinkage of an exhausted globe owing to the pressure of the atmosphere, which makes it displace rather less air than the compensating globe, which is equal in volume to the first globe when this is filled with gas. This shrinkage correction was first pointed out by Agamennone,[1] and independently by Rayleigh,[2] who used it to correct Regnault's results, and Rayleigh determined the correction directly for the globes he used.

Agamennone used Lamé's [3] formula:

$$\Omega=\kappa V[NH-(N+1)H_1+(5/4)(N+1)(H-H_1)]$$

where Ω=change of interior volume V of the globe, H=internal pressure, H_1=external pressure, N=volume of interior of globe/volume of material of walls, and κ=cubical compressibility of the material of the globe.

Regnault's 9·88-lit. globe, with all his other apparatus, had been systematically smashed at Sèvres in 1870 by the German army of occupation, but from the remaining pieces Crafts,[4] using a similar globe, found a correction of $0{\cdot}0_3247$ of the total volume per atm. pressure. The corrections to Regnault's relative densities referred to air=1 were: H_2+0·00317, O_2−$0{\cdot}0_42$, N_2+$0{\cdot}0_41$, CO_2−$0{\cdot}0_49$.

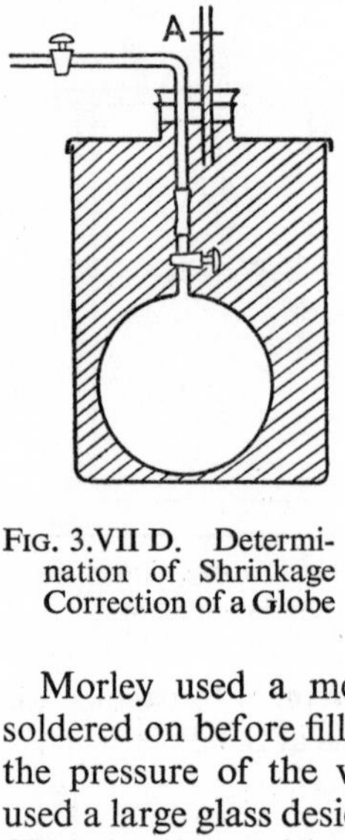

FIG. 3.VII D. Determination of Shrinkage Correction of a Globe

The simplest method of determining the shrinkage of a globe [5] is to enclose it in a metal or glass vessel filled with water, the neck of the globe passing out through a rubber stopper in the lid which also carries a vertical graduated glass tube A partly filled with water (Fig. 3.VII D). The fall of water-level in this tube on pumping out the air from the globe is determined. The apparatus must be kept at a constant temperature. Morley [5] also used two small globes having the same weight in vacuum but differing in volume by the shrinkage of the density globe, and suspended on opposite sides of the balance when the latter was weighed exhausted.

Morley used a metal container, the lid carrying the globe being lightly soldered on before filling up with water, and ran in water from a burette to keep the pressure of the water constant when the globe was exhausted. Travers used a large glass desiccator with a vertical tube and filled with water. Rayleigh filled the globe with air-free water and measured the displacement in the neck when the pressure on the water was reduced to 2/3 atm. (lower pressures caused boiling), either by finding a weight of mercury which gave the same displacement of water or (later) by sealing a narrow calibrated tube to the neck and finding the contraction directly. An allowance was made for the dilation of the water. Rayleigh [6] preferred to measure the *internal* contraction, and Moles and Miravalles [7] found a slightly larger shrinkage by Morley's method, which measures the *external* contraction.

[1] *Atti R. Accad. Lincei*, 1885, **1**, 105.

[2] *Chem. News*, 1888, **57**, 73; *Proc. Roy. Soc.*, 1888, **43**, 356; 1889, **45**, 425 (mentioning Agamennone); 1892, **50**, 448; 1897, **62**, 204; 1904, **73**, 153; 1904, **74**, 181; "Scientific Papers," Cambridge, 1902, **3**, 37, 233, 524; 1903, **4**, 347; 1912, **5**, 201.

[3] "Leçons sur la Théorie Mathématique de l'Élasticité des Corps Solides," 1852, **211** f.

[4] *Compt. Rend.*, 1888, **106**, 1662.

[5] Morley, *Z. phys. Chem.*, 1896, **20**, 83, see Fig. 4 in this paper; Travers, "Experimental Study of Gases," 1901, 119.

[6] *Proc. Roy. Soc.*, 1892, **50**, 448.

[7] *J. Chim. Phys.*, 1924, **21**, 1; confirmed by Beckers, *Bull. Soc Chim. Belg.*, 1929, **38**, 329.

Crafts used a hydrostatic method, weighing the globe nearly filled with water and immersed in water, then exhausting, and finding the weight to be added to bring to equilibrium again. Moles and Miravelles found it difficult to get accurate results by this method.

Rayleigh had compared the shrinkage with the ratio of the volume and weight of the globe, V/w, and Moles and Miravalles found an empirical equation for the contraction of a globe of volume V ml. and weight w g. not counting the stopcock, the correction in grams for 1 lit. of gas at 760 mm. pressure being $15{\cdot}5 \times 0{\cdot}0012 \times 10^{-3}(V/w)$, where 0·0012 is the average weight of 1 ml. of laboratory air, in g. Klemenc and Bankowski [1] wrote this in the form of a compressibility:

$$(1000\Delta V/V\Delta p)_T = -15{\cdot}5(V/w) \quad . \quad . \quad . \quad . \quad . \quad . \quad (3)$$

The tendency has been to reduce the size of the globe used for weighing the gas. Regnault used globes of about 10 lit., the volume of which he determined with great accuracy; Morley [2] used 8–21-lit. globes, Leduc [3] 2·3-lit., Rayleigh [4] 1·8-lit., Guye and Davila [5] 0·38–0·82-lit., Perman and Davis [6] 0·5-lit., and Gray [7] 0·267-lit. According to Guye [8] the change in weight in air on evacuation of a globe of 500–600 ml. of fairly thick glass is not more than 0·02 mg. and hence the shrinkage correction is negligible. In order to keep the air of the balance room fairly dry and prevent condensation of moisture on the globe, Rayleigh [9] hung up a large blanket, which was dried out daily before a fire.

The globe method was refined by Moles,[10] in Madrid, who claimed an accuracy of 1 in 10^5 and adopted the following precautions:

(i) The globe was surrounded by melting ice, the temperature of which was checked by a Beckmann thermometer.

(ii) Rubber connections carrying mercury were dispensed with.

(iii) The mercury in the manometer and gas leading tubes was kept at a constant temperature by water circulating through a thermostat, or by melting ice.

(iv) Mercury was never in contact with tap-grease.

(v) Only pure dry air entered the lower manometer chamber, and the gas pressure in the density bulbs was equalised through a gauge containing Apiezon oil of negligible vapour pressure.

(vi) Oil or mercury fog was prevented from entering the globes by sintered glass filters.

[1] *Z. anorg. Chem.*, 1932, **208**, 348; Beckers, *J.A.C.S.*, 1929, **51**, 2042, for 600–2000 ml, globes (after allowing for tap and neck) found that the constant is about 16·0; he thought the contraction is nearly a linear function of pressure difference.

[2] *Amer. J. Sci.*, 1891, **41**, 220, 276; *Z. phys. Chem.*, 1895, **17**, 87; 1896, **20**, 68, 242, 417; *Smithsonian Contributions to Knowledge*, 1895, **980**, Part 1, 14.

[3] *Compt. Rend.*, 1891, **113**, 186; 1897, **125**, 571; 1898, **126**, 413; *Ann. Chim.*, 1898, **15**, 5; *J. de Phys.*, 1898, **7**, 5, 189.

[4] *Chem. News*, 1893, **67**, 183, 198, 211; *Proc. Roy. Soc.*, 1893, **53**, 134.

[5] *Mém. Soc. Phys. Nat.* (Geneva), 1907, **35**, 615; Guye and Pintza, *ibid.*, 1907, **35**, 594; Jaquerod and Pintza, *ibid.*, 1907, **35**, 589; cf. Guye, *J. Chim. Phys.*, 1906, **4**, 203.

[6] *Proc. Roy. Soc.*, 1906, **78**, 28.

[7] *J.C.S.*, 1905, **87**, 1601; Gray and Burt, *ibid.*, 1909, **95**, 1633.

[8] *J. Chim. Phys.*, 1913, **11**, 275, 319.

[9] *Proc. Roy. Soc.*, 1888, **43**, 356.

[10] *An. Fis. Quim.*, 1937, **35**, 134; *J. Chim. Phys.*, 1937, **34**, 49; *Bull. Soc. Chim. Belg.*, 1938, **47**, 405; *Trans. Faraday Soc.*, 1939, **35**, 1439; Les Déterminations physico-chimiques des Poids Moléculaires et Atomiques des Gaz, *Institut Internationale de Coopération Intellectuelle*, Paris, 1938; R. W. Gray, *Ann. Rep. Chem. Soc.*, 1938, **35**, 131. See references in § 6.

(vii) Adsorption of gas on the inside of the globe was measured for each gas on glass of the same composition as the globe and a correction appropriate to the filling pressure applied.

The gas weighed should be as pure and dry as possible. Formerly, phosphorus pentoxide was used as a drying agent when it did not react with the gas. Morley [1] found that a gas dried by passing *through* 25 cm.^{3} of P_2O_5 powder at the rate of 2 lit. per hr. contains less than 1 mg. of water vapour in 40,000 lit., but contains a trace of P_2O_5 vapour. Cooling in liquid air is much more effective than P_2O_5 at room temperature, so that drying by strong cooling or liquefaction and fractionation is now preferred. The *solidification* of a gas and its purification by sublimation is very effective in removing other gaseous impurities.[2] Ammonia is particularly difficult to dry.[3] Traces of mercury vapour can lead to error, since it is very heavy; it was formerly removed by passing over gold leaf or gold wire-sponge,[4] but strong cooling in a liquid air trap or a sodium or potassium trap (§ 13.VII A) is much better.

Bower [5] found the following weights of water in mg. in 1 lit. of air at 30° after passing over the drying agents stated:

$CaCl_2$ granular ...	1·5	NaOH stick ...	0·80
$CaCl_2$ fused ...	1·25	KOH stick ...	0·014
CaO	0·003	BaO	0·00065

Bircumshaw,[6] for drying, passed a stream of gas through a trap cooled in ice and salt, a trap cooled in solid carbon dioxide and acetone connected with the first trap by a short length of lagged tubing, and then allowed it to pass through a long glass tube to a third cooled trap.

Where high accuracy is not essential, the troublesome shrinkage correction may be avoided by weighing the globe first filled with dry air, oxygen, or carbon dioxide,[7] the density of which is known, and then filled with the other gas; the difference in weights gives the difference in weights of equal volumes V of the gases, where V is the volume of the globe, and if the density of one gas is known, that of the other may be calculated.

According to Guye [8] the film of moisture adsorbed on the inside of the globe is removed by rinsing out *several* times with the gas, since Bunsen [9] found that moisture not so removed is inside the surface of the glass. Experiments on the

[1] *Amer. J. Sci.*, 1885, **30**, 141 (0·28 mg. in 100 lit.); *Z. anal. Chem.*, 1885, **24**, 532; 1888, **27**, 1; *J.A.C.S.*, 1904, **26**, 1171; *J. Chim. Phys.*, 1905, **3**, 240; cf. Dibbits, *Z. anal. Chem.*, 1876, **15**, 121; Baxter and Warren, *J.A.C.S.*, 1911, **33**, 340 ($CaBr_2$, $ZnCl_2$, $ZnBr_2$); Johnson, *ibid.*, 1912, **34**, 911 (Al_2O_3); Smith, *et al.*, *J.A.C.S.*, 1922, **44**, 2255; *Ind. Eng. Chem.*, 1924, **16**, 20 ($Mg(ClO_4)_2$); Moles and Roquero, *An. Fis. Quim.*, 1933, **31**, 11; Lacosse and Menzies, *J.A.C.S.*, 1937, **59**, 2471, found P_2O_5 as effective at 90° as at room temperature; on drying agents, see Yoe, *Chem. News*, 1925, **130**, 340; Ostwald-Luther, "Phys.-chem. Messumgen," 1931, 348 f. and refs; for *theory*, see van Liempt, *Rec. Trav. Chim.*, 1942, **61**, 341; Bocker, *Chim. et Ind.*, 1947, **58**, 31.

[2] Gray, *J.C.S.*, 1905, **87**, 1601; Burt and Edgar, *Phil. Trans.*, 1916, **216**, 393; Bircumshaw, *J.C.S.*, 1930, 2213.

[3] Hart and Partington, *J.C.S.*, 1943, 104; cf. Sancho and Moles, *An. Fis. Quim.*, 1932, **30**, 701.

[4] Crookes, *Phil. Trans.*, 1881, **172**, 387 (gold leaf); Burt and Edgar, *Phil. Trans.*, 1916, **216**, 393; Coolidge, *J.A.C.S.*, 1924, **46**, 680, found it ineffective.

[5] *Bur. Stand. J. Res.*, 1934, **12**, 241; cf. Damiens, *Compt. Rend.*, 1934, **198**, 1233.

[6] *J.C.S.*, 1930, 2213.

[7] Cooke, *Proc. Amer. Acad.*, 1889, **24**, 202 (CO_2); Moissan and Gautier, *Ann. Chim.*, 1895, **5**, 568 (air).

[8] *J. Chim. Phys.*, 1907, **5**, 203.

[9] See § 6.III.

behaviour of fine powders on a glass surface [1] show, however, that this film, not driven off unless the glass is quite strongly heated in vacuum, is actually *on* the surface of the glass. Curry [2] found that gases adsorbed on glass come off below 200° if moisture is excluded, but water changes the nature of the surface. Bartell and Bristol [3] found an adsorbed water film on quartz and Pyrex glass even after standing over fresh P_2O_5, and the film probably penetrates inside the glass.[4]

Tammann and Diekmann [5] found that fine powders on heating seem to " boil " from escape of adsorbed moisture and gas, and a drop of mercury on the surface falls, but rises again on cooling. Pirani [6] removed the water film from the inside of a glass bulb by bombarding with cathode rays and then rinsing with mercury vapour.

The adsorption of gases on glass (cf. § 6.III) was fully studied in the Madrid laboratory in relation to density determinations.[7] Crespi [8] e.g. found that the adsorption of nitrogen on a glass globe of 800–1000 ml. introduces a correction of -6×10^{-4} g./lit. on the normal density.

That the density of a gas is independent of the shape of the vessel in which it is weighed has been proved experimentally.[9]

§ 3. The Volumeter Method

In the volumeter method (already used by Cavendish, see § 1) the volume of gas filling a globe or vessel of accurately known volume at a measured temperature and pressure is weighed in another small bulb or vessel, either a generating apparatus (the loss in weight of which is found) or an absorption apparatus (the gain in weight of which is determined). The difficulty of weighing a large globe or bulb is thus obviated.

This method was used by Morley [10] to find the density of hydrogen. Very pure and dry electrolytic hydrogen was brought in contact with metallic palladium heated in an exhausted glass tube, and the metal allowed to cool in the gas. A large volume of hydrogen was taken up by the metal, and any impurities in the hydrogen were then pumped out. On heating the palladium to dull redness, pure hydrogen was evolved and was received in three large exhausted glass globes of accurately known volume (43·2574 lit.), and the pressure measured by a mercury manometer.

The density of hydrogen chloride was determined by this method by Gray

1 Partington, *Phys. Z.*, 1914, **15**, 601.

2 *J. Phys. Chem.*, 1931, **35**, 859.

3 *J. Phys. Chem.*, 1940, **44**, 89.

4 Bent and Lesnick, *J.A.C.S.*, 1935, **57**, 1246; Dalton, *ibid.*, 1935, **57**, 2150 (H_2O and gases evolved at 1400°).

5 *Z. anorg. Chem.*, 1924, **135**, 194; the phenomenon is described for gypsum by Hooke, " Micrographia," 1665, 41.

6 *Z. Phys.*, 1922, **9**, 327.

7 Crespi and Moles, *An. Fis. Quim.*, 1926, **24**, 210, 452; Crespi, *ibid.*, 1927, **25**, 25; Moles and Crespi, *ibid.*, 1929, **27**, 529; Crespi and Moles, *ibid.*, 1930, **28**, 448; 1931, **29**, 146; Crespi, *ibid.*, 1932, **30**, 520; 1933, **31**, 825; Crespi and Aleixandre, *ibid.*, 1934, **32**, 666; see also Bangham and Burt, *Proc. Roy. Soc.*, 1924, **105**, 481; Moles, Déterminations phys.-chim. des Poids Moléculaires et Atomiques des Gaz, *Institut Internationale de Coopération Intellectuelle*, Paris, 1938, 1, 187.

8 *An. Fis. Quim.*, 1932, **30**, 520.

9 Noyes and Johnson, *J.A.C.S.*, 1916, **38**, 1016.

10 *Z. phys. Chem.*, 1895, **20**, 68, 242. For this method, see Buff, *Ann. Phys.*, 1831, **22**, 242; Marchand, *J. prakt. Chem.*, 1848, **44**, 38; Bodländer, *Z. angew. Chem.*, 1894, **7**, 425; Scheuer, *Compt. Rend.*, 1909, **149**, 599; *Z. phys. Chem.*, 1909, **68**, 575.

and Burt.[1] The pure dry gas was collected in a glass bulb A (Fig. 4.VII D) of accurately known volume (about 450 ml.) which was rigorously dried by evacuating, heating, filling with dry air, and exhausting, repeatedly. The bulb was maintained at 0° and the gas collected at atmospheric pressure, the excess bubbling through concentrated sulphuric acid in *h*. The pressure was read on a standard barometer and reduced to latitude 45° and sea-level.

The air in the capillaries and in the weighed bulb B (*c.* 20 ml.) containing gas-free charcoal was removed by immersing another charcoal bulb C in liquid air, the tap *a* being closed. The tap *c* was then closed, *a* opened and the bulb B immersed in liquid air. All the gas in A condensed on the charcoal in B, which was shut off at *b*, detached from the ground joint and weighed against a compensating bulb. The bulb A could be refilled and the process repeated.

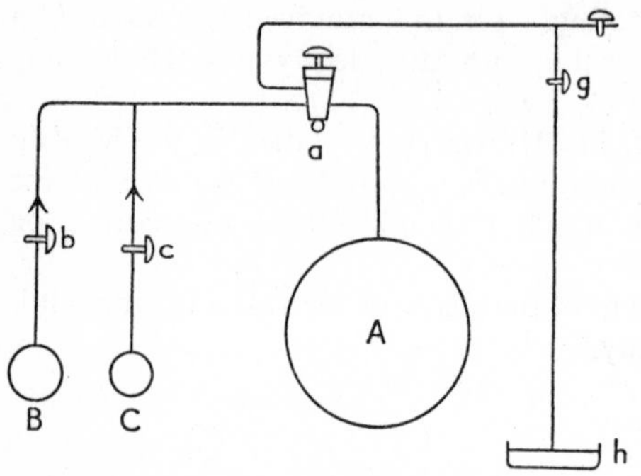

FIG. 4.VII D. Volumeter Method

No shrinkage correction was necessary for the small bulb B but a correction was necessary for gas adsorbed on the walls of A, which passed into B when A became vacuous. This was found to be 0·1235 mm.^{3} per cm.^{2} of wall. A silica bulb A was easier to dry, and no adsorption correction was necessary. A small correction for deviation from Boyle's law was applied in reducing atmospheric pressure to 760 mm.

Joly [2] weighed a gas compressed in a copper globe to 20–30 atm., then allowed it to expand and measured the volume. Occhialini [3] expanded a weighed amount of gas compressed in a 3–10-ml. steel vessel into a 900-ml. glass bulb. Maass and Russell [4] condensed the gas in a small bulb cooled in liquid air, but obtained poor results.

§ 4. Manometric and Buoyancy Methods

The manometric method [5] depends on the measurement of the difference in the weights exerted on a manometric liquid by two different gases under the same pressure contained in two vertical tubes. The manometer may be a slightly bent tube containing a thread of xylene, read microscopically. This is similar to Hare's apparatus for liquids (see § 1.VIII B, Vol. II), and is only a rough method (±5 per cent.).

[1] *J.C.S.*, 1909, **95**, 1633; *Trans. Faraday Soc.*, 1911, **7**, 30; cf. Jaquerod and Pintza, *Compt. Rend.*, 1904, **139**, 129; Guye and Pintza, *ibid.*, 1904, **139**, 677; 1905, **141**, 51; Maass and Russell, *J.A.C.S.*, 1918, **40**, 1847; Maass and Boomer, *ibid.*, 1922, **44**, 1709 (low pressure); Dietrichson, Bircher and O'Brien, *ibid.*, 1933, **55**, 1 (NH_3); Schäfer, *Z. phys. Chem.*, 1937, **36** B, 85 (H_2 and D_2, rather crude); Steurer and Wolf, *ibid.*, 1938, **39** B, 101 (for vapours).

[2] *Phil. Mag.*, 1890, **30**, 379; Karwat, *Chem. Fabr.*, 1941, **14**, 432.

[3] *Nuov. Cim.*, 1912, **4**, 426.

[4] *J.A.C.S.*, 1918, **40**, 1847.

[5] Recknagel, *Ann. Phys.*, 1877, **2**, 291; Müller, *Z. phys. chem. Unterr.*, 1889, **2**, 274; Toepler, *Ann. Phys.*, 1895, **56**, 609; 1896, **57**, 311, 324; Schloesing, *Compt. Rend.*, 1898, **126**, 220, 476, 896; Threlfall, *Proc. Roy. Soc.*, 1906, **77**, 542; Smith, *Engineering*, 1916, **102**, 600; Brady, *J. Franklin Inst.*, 1918, **187**, 501; Blackie, *D.S.I.R. Fuel Techn. Res. Paper*, 1922, **5**; Pollitzer, *Z. angew. Chem.*, 1924, **37**, 459; von Wartenberg, *Z. Elektrochem.*, 1941, **47**, 92; Kahle, *Chem. Techn.*, 1943, **16**, 144; Smith, Eiseman and Creitz, *Bur. Stand. Misc. Publ.*, 1947, M **177**, 76.

Another approximate method (±0·25 per cent.) is Lux's gas balance,[1] consisting of a counterpoised globe which is filled with gas through the hollow balance beam, and the change in weight registered by a pointer at the other end of the beam moving over a graduated scale.

The *buoyancy method*, depending on Archimedes' principle, in which the loss in weight of a glass bulb weighed in the gas is found,[2] was refined by Jaquerod and Tourpain.[3] The same principle is used in some forms of *microbalance*.[4] Gray and Ramsay's balance had a sensibility of 1/500,000 mg., and was used to find the density of 0·1 mm.[3] of radium emanation, weighing less than 0·001 mg. The latest type used for gas density determinations by Roberts, Emeléus, and Briscoe (Fig. 5.VII D) had the beam, suspension fibres and parts of the frame of fused quartz, the bulbs and most of the frame (shown in black) of Pyrex glass. The beam was 50 mm. × 1 mm., the bulbs 19·4 and 13·7 mm. diam., with outer surfaces in the ratio $\sqrt{2}:1$, and since the smaller bulb was pierced on the axis of the beam and exposed both inner and outer surfaces, both had the same exposed surface. A cross-bar of very light quartz rod sealed on at the " centre of surface " was also at the centre of gravity. The final adjustment in air was with rather less than 1 atm. pressure in the glass case (130 × 25 mm.), and the period

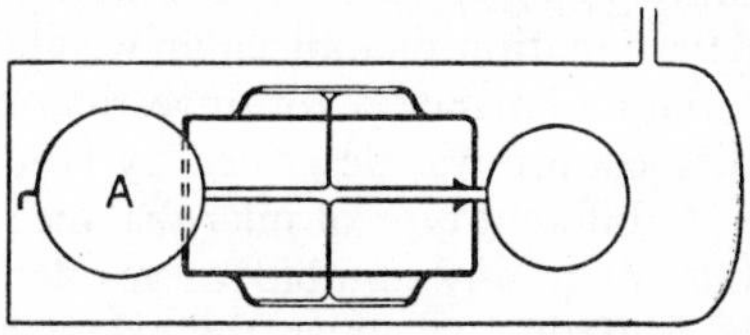

FIG. 5.VII D. Microbalance for Determination of Gas Densities

[1] Lux, *Z. Instr.*, 1885, **5**, 411; 1886, **6**, 255; *Z. anal. Chem.*, 1886, **25**, 3; 1887, **26**, 38; 1890, **29**, 13; " Die Gaswage," Ludwigshafen, 1887; Chandler, *J. Gas Lighting*, 1912, **117**, 26; Arndt, " Handbuch der phys.-chem. Technik," 1915, 181; Duchêne, *J. Usines Gaz*, 1935, **59**, 589; Hales and Moss, *J. Sci. Instr.*, 1935, **12**, 309; Warren, *Rev. Sci. Instr.*, 1936, **7**, 107.

[2] Greenwood, *Phil. Trans.*, 1729, **36**, 184; Lommel, *Ann. Phys.*, 1886, **27**, 144; Bauer, *ibid.*, 1895, **55**, 184 (vapours); Dünwald and Wagner, *Z. anorg. Chem.*, 1931, **199**, 321; Simons, *Ind. Eng. Chem. Anal.*, 1938, **10**, 587; Brandt, *Oel u. Kohle*, 1940, **36**, 134; Cady and Rarick, *J.A.C.S.*, 1941, **63**, 1357 (vapours).

[3] *Compt. Rend.*, 1910, **151**, 666; *Arch. Sci. Phys. Nat.*, 1911, **31**, 20; *J. Chim. Phys.*, 1913, **11**, 3, 268; Edwards, *Bur. Stand. Techn. Paper*, 1917, **89**; *Chem. News*, 1917, **115**, 279; *Ind. Eng. Chem.*, 1917, **9**, 790; Baxter, *J.A.C.S.*, 1921, **43**, 1317; Kerr and Schmidt, *Natural Gas and Gasoline J.*, 1917, **11**, Sept., 260 (microbalance type); Wagner, Bailey, and Eversole, *Ind. Eng. Chem. Anal.*, 1942, **14**, 129 (vapours); Smith, Eiseman, and Creitz, *Bur. Stand. Misc. Publ.*, 1947, M **177** (Instruments for the Determination, Indication, or Recording of the Specific Gravities of Gases).

[4] Warburg and Ihmori, *Ann. Phys.*, 1886, **27**, 481; Ihmori, *ibid.*, 1887, **31**, 1006; Giesen, *ibid.*, 1903, **10**, 830 (gas densities); Nernst, *Gött. Nachr.*, 1903, 75; Nernst and Riesenfeld, *Ber.*, 1903, **36**, 2086; Hunter, *Z. phys. Chem.*, 1905, **53**, 441; Brill and Evans, *J.C.S.*, 1908, **93**,1442; Steele and Grant, *Proc. Roy. Soc.*, 1909, **82**, 580; Gray and Ramsay, *ibid.*, 1911, **84**, 536; Aston, *ibid.*, 1914, **89**, 439; Riesenfeld and Möller, *Z. Elektrochem.*, 1915, **21**, 131; Taylor, *Phys. Rev.*, 1917, **10**, 653; Kramer, *Chem. Ztg.*, 1917, **41**, 773; Guye, *J. Chim. Phys.*, 1918, **16**, 46; Emich, in Abderhalden, " Handbuch der biochemischen Arbeitsmethoden," Berlin and Vienna, 1919, **9**, 55; Pettersson, *Proc. Phys. Soc.*, 1920, **32**, 209; Shaxby, *ibid.*, 1920, **32**, 21; Hartung, *J.C.S.*, 1922, **121**, 682; 1924, **125**, 2198; *Phil. Mag.*, 1922, **43**, 1056; Stock and Siecke, *Ber.*, 1924, **57**, 562; Stock *et al.*, *Z. phys. Chem.*, 1926, **114**, 204; 1926, **119**, 333; 1927, **126**, 172; 1928, **139**, 47; 1933, **167**, 82; Donau, *Mikrochem.*, 1931, **9**, 1; Whytlaw-Gray, Patterson, and Cawood, *Proc. Roy. Soc.*, 1931, **134**, 7; Lehrer and Kuss, *Z. anorg. Chem.*, 1933, **167**, 73; Whytlaw-Gray and Woodhead, *J.C.S.*, 1933, 846; Cawood and Patterson, *Phil. Trans.*, 1937, **236**, 77; Trenner, *J.A.C.S.*, 1937, **59**, 1391; Simons, *Ind. Eng. Chem. Anal.*, 1938, **10**, 587; Roberts, Emeléus, and Briscoe, *J.C.S.*, 1939, 43; Barrett, Birnie, and Cohen, *J.A.C.S.*, 1940, **62**, 2839; Takeda, *Proc. Phys. Math. Soc. Japan*, 1941, **23**, 1020; Koizumi, *J. Chem. Soc. Japan*, 1942, **63**, 1486; Nanjundayya and Ahmad, *Indian J. Agric. Sci.*, 1943, **13**, 649; Gulbransen, *Rev. Sci. Instr.*, 1944, **15**, 201; Gregg, *J.C.S.*, 1946, 561, 563; Grangaud, *Bull. Soc. Chim.*, 1947, 229; Stock and Fill, *Metallurgia*, 1947, **37**, 108; Bose, *Indian J. Phys.*, 1947, **21**, 275.

of oscillation was 10 sec. The bent pointer was attached to the buoyancy bulb and the reading microscope was end-on, viewing through a plate-glass window. A capillary connection led to the pressure system, and pressure differences of 0·002–0·005 mm. were indicated.

The beam is balanced at zero when the gas density in the case exerts a buoyancy effect on the bulb which compensates the net weight, and if two different gases are used an accurate comparison of densities is possible from the pressure ratio $p_1/p_2=\rho_2/\rho_1$. The microbalance method is particularly suited to the determination of molecular weights by the limiting density method (§ 15). A " thermobalance " for investigating loss of weight in chemical reactions of dissociation was described by Honda.[1]

A different type of microbalance (actually used for adsorption measurements, but apparently suitable for gas density work) is the quartz spiral spring balance of McBain,[2] in which the extension of a thin quartz spiral [3] is measured. A heated microbalance was used by Rodebush and Michalek [4] for vapour-density measurements.

§ 5. The Effusion Method

The comparison of gas densities by the effusion method is based on the theory (§ 15.III) that the times for equal volumes of two gases to stream through a small hole in a thin plate, under the same driving pressure, are proportional to the square roots of the densities: [5]

$$t_1/t_2=\sqrt{\rho_1}/\sqrt{\rho_2} \quad \dots \dots \dots \quad (1)$$

The method seems to have been used first by Leslie,[6] but was perfected by Bunsen.[7] The apparatus, or *effusiometer*, devised by Bunsen, may consist of a cylinder (Fig. 6*a*.VII D) having two marks and immersed in water. At the top is a tap opening into a space closed by a thin platinum plate in which a hole is pierced by a fine needle. The tube is filled with gas below the lower mark, the tap opened, and the time for the liquid to rise between the two marks noted. For gases soluble in water, mercury is used as the confining liquid and a float having marks at the upper and lower ends is inside the tube (Fig. 6*b*.VII D). The

[1] *Sci. Rep. Imp. Tôhoku Univ.*, 1915, **4**, 97.

[2] McBain and Bakr, *J.A.C.S.*, 1926, **48**, 690; Newsome, *Ind. Eng. Chem.*, 1928, **20**, 827; *J.S.C.I.*, 1928, **47**, 594; McBain and Britton, *J.A.C.S.*, 1930, **52**, 2198; McBain, Jackman, Bakr, and Smith, *J. Phys. Chem.*, 1930, **34**, 1439.

[3] On winding quartz spiral springs, Sliupas, *Nature*, 1925, **115**, 943; Boys, *ibid.*, 1925, **115**, 944; Smith, *ibid.*, 1925, **116**, 14; Drane, *Phil. Mag.*, 1928, **5**, 559; Cameron, *J.A.C.S.*, 1931, **53**, 2646; Zentner, *J. Phys. Chem.*, 1947, **51**, 927.

[4] *J.A.C.S.*, 1929, **51**, 748.

[5] Bernoulli, " Hydrodynamica," Strasburg, 1738, 224; Graham, *Phil. Mag.*, 1833, **2**, 175; *Phil. Trans.*, 1846, **136**, 573; 1863, **153**, 385; Voss, *Ann. de Phys.*, 1923, **20**, 66.

[6] " An Experimental Inquiry into the Nature and Propagation of Heat," 1804, 534.

[7] " Gasometry," transl. Roscoe, 1857, 121; Schilling, *Dingl. J.*, 1860, **155**, 194; Plattner, *ibid.*, 1878, **229**, 537 (abstr.); Melde, *Ann. Phys.*, 1887, **32**, 659; Timofejew, *Z. phys. Chem.*, 1890, **6**, 586; Freer, *ibid.*, 1892, **9**, 669; Ladenburg, *Ber.*, 1898, **31**, 2508; Emich, *Monatsh.*, 1903, **24**, 747 (high temperatures); Myhill, *Gas World*, 1913, **58**, 763; Debierne, *Ann. de Phys.*, 1915, **3**, 62; Edwards, *Bur. Stand. Techn. Pap.*, 1917, **94**; *Met. Chem. Eng.*, 1917, **16**, 518; Marcus, *Ind. Eng. Chem.*, 1917, **9**, 603; Buckingham and Edwards, *Bur. Stand. Bull.*, 1920, **15**, 573; Eyring, *J.A.C.S.*, 1928, **50**, 2398 (vapours); Kahle, *Z. angew. Chem.*, 1928, **41**, 876; Zipperer and Rottengatter, *Gas u. Wasserfach*, 1930, **73**, 1190; Kretschmer, *Forsch. Gebiet. Ingenieurw.*, 1932, **3** A, 150; Schiller, *ibid.*, 1933, **4** A, 225; Duchêne, *J. Usines Gaz*, 1935, **59**, 589; Wilson, *Proc. Amer. Gas Assoc.*, 1937, **19**, 777; Lehr, *Gas u. Wasserfach*, 1938, **81**, 435; Zipperer and Fischer, *ibid.*, 1938, **81**, 434; Schwietring, *ibid.*, 1942, **85**, 315; Smith, Eiseman, and Creitz, *Bur. Stand. Misc. Publ.*, 1947, M **177**, 130 (Fisher densimeter).

times when the marks appear above the mercury surface (observed through a telescope) are taken. With ordinary apparatus the accuracy is about 2 per cent. If water is used as confining liquid, the measured density is that of the gas saturated with water vapour at the temperature of the experiment. If D is the weight of 1 lit. of dry gas at S.T.P., p the vapour pressure of water in mm. Hg at the temperature t of the experiment, and P the atmospheric pressure, the density of the moist gas in g./lit. is:

$$\frac{273}{(273+t)760}[D(P-p)+0{\cdot}8038p]$$

from which D may be calculated.

Effusion was used by Yamaguchi[1] to determine high temperatures by the equation $t=a+b\sqrt{T}$, where t=effusion time, T=abs. temp., a and b are constants.

Acoustical methods for determining gas and vapour densities, depending on the proportionality of the square of the frequency of the sound emitted by an organ pipe or whistle blown by the gas to the density of the gas, have not been much used.[2]

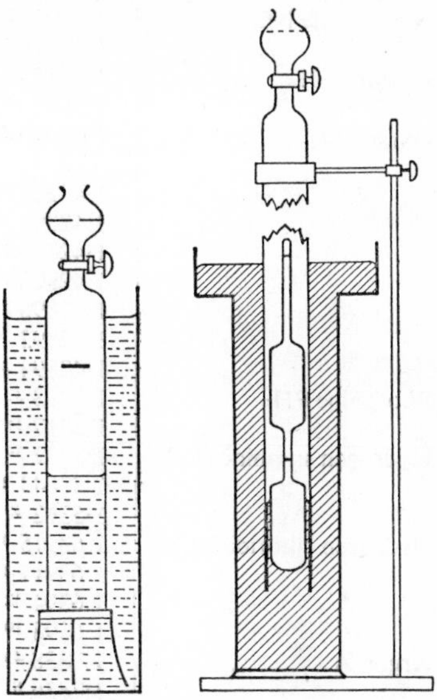

(a) (b)

FIG. 6.VII D. Effusiometers

Kalähne[3] measured gas densities from the change in frequency of a vibrating aluminium tube due to " loading " by the gas.

§ 6. Table of Normal Densities of Gases [1] *

Hydrogen H_2	0·08982 [2]	Carbon monoxide CO ...	1·2504 [17, 19]
	0·08988 [3]		1·25010 [18]
	0·08965 [4]		1·25001 [20]
	0·089873 [5]	Nitrogen N_2	1·2511 [21]
Helium He	0·1782 [6]		1·2503 [18]
	0·1786 [7]		1·2507 [22, 26]
	0·17846 [8, 9]		1·25056 [23]
Methane CH_4	0·7168 [10]		1·25049 [20, 24]
Ammonia NH_3 ...	0·7708 [11]		1·25036 [25]
	0·77077 [12]		1·25046 [27]
	0·77140 [13]	Ethylene C_2H_4 ...	1·2610 [16]
	0·7710 [14]		1·2603 [29]
	0·77126 [15]		1·2604 [14]
Neon Ne	0·9002 [6]		1·26036 [60]
	0·89990 [8, 9]	Air (c. $4N_2+O_2$) ...	1·2933 [2, 30]
Acetylene C_2H_2 ...	1·1791 [16]		1·29316 [18]
	1·1749 [61]		1·29300 [31]
	1·1695 [65]		1·2927 [32]

* See pages 756–7 for footnotes.

1 *Bull. Chem. Soc. Japan*, 1926, **1**, 209.

2 Jahoda, *Wien Anz.*, 1899, **36**, 216; *Wien Ber.*, 1899, **108**, II A, 803; Wachsmuth, *Ann. Phys., Boltzmann Festschr.*, 1904, 923; *Verhl. d. D. Phys. Ges.*, 1905, **7**, 47 (vapours).

3 *Verhl. d. D. Phys. Ges.*, 1914, **16**, 81; *Ann. Phys.*, 1914, **45**, 321.

Air (*c.* $4N_2+O_2$)—*cont.*	1·29308[67]	Carbon dioxide CO_2—*cont*	1·9763[18]
	1·29287[66]		1·9768[11, 18, 40]
Nitric oxide NO ...	1·3402[22, 33]		1·97693[27]
	1·34018[12]		1·97694[45]
Ethane C_2H_6	1·3555[16]		1·97704[46]
	1·3562[10]	Nitrous oxide N_2O ...	1·9777[11, 17]
Oxygen O_2	1·42900[5, 19, 30, 34, 59]		1·9804[46]
			1·97821[45]
	1·42901[63]		1·9781[18]
	1·42891[35]	Methyl ether $(CH_3)_2O$ ...	2·1096[47]
	1·42898[25]	Methyl chloride CH_3Cl	2·3045[47]
	1·42906[12, 31]		2·3084[64]
	1·42896[25]	Propane C_3H_8	1·9149[48]
	1·42892[36]		2·0200[49]
	1·42894[20, 27]	Butane C_4H_{10}	2·6726[49]
Phosphine PH_3 ...	1·5293[37]	Sulphur dioxide SO_2 ...	2·9267[18, 19, 50]
	1·5317[38]		2·92665[27, 28, 47]
Hydrogen sulphide H_2S	1·5392[39]		2·92675[12]
	1·53843[27]	Nitrosyl chloride NOCl	2·9919[51]
	1·5362[40]	Chlorine Cl_2	3·214[52]
Hydrogen chloride HCl	1·63915[41]	Hydrogen bromide HBr	3·6219[53]
	1·63917[12]		3·6397[65]
	1·6394[42]		3·6441[55]
	1·6398[19]		3·64442[54]
Argon A	1·7838[43]	Krypton Kr	3·708[6, 56]
	1·7836[8, 9]		3·733[8, 9]
	1·7809[6, 19]	Silicon fluoride SiF_4 ...	4·693[57]
	1·7816[44]	Hydrogen iodide HI ...	5·7888[58]
	1·7832[62]	Xenon Xe	5·851[6]
Carbon dioxide CO_2 ...	1·9769[17]		5·887[9, 56]

[1] See Landolt-Börnstein, " Tabellen," 5th edit., 1923, 269; Ergzb. I, 1927, 160; Ergzb. II, 1931, 205 (some entries differ slightly from the originals, which are reproduced here); see also ref. 14; Blanchard, *Chem. Met. Eng.*, 1923, **29**, 399.

[2] Leduc, *Compt. Rend.*, 1891, **113**, 186; cf. Broch, *Trav. et Mém. Bur. Internat. Poids et Més.*, 1881, A 51.

[3] Regnault, corrected for shrinkage (but at latitude of Paris) by Rayleigh, *Proc. Roy. Soc.*, 1893, **53**, 134.

[4] Regnault, corrected for shrinkage, and reduced to latitude 45°, by Thomsen, *Z. anorg. Chem.*, 1896, **12**, 1; Moles, *J. Chim. Phys.*, 1937, **34**, 49.

[5] Morley, *Z. phys. Chem.*, 1896, **20**, 68 (130), 242 (271); selected as best value by Guye, *J. Chim. Phys.*, 1907, **5**, 203, and Moles, *ibid.*, 1937, **34**, 49.

[6] Watson, *J.C.S.*, 1910, **97**, 810, 833.

[7] Heuse, *Verhl. d. D. Phys. Ges.*, 1913, **15**, 518.

[8] Moureu, *J.C.S.*, 1923, **123**, 1905.

[9] Allen and Moore, *J.A.C.S.*, 1931, **53**, 2512, 2532.

[10] Baume and Perrot, *Compt. Rend.*, 1909, **148**, 39; *J. Chim. Phys.*, 1909, **7**, 369.

[11] Guye and Pintza, *Mém. Soc. Phys. Nat.* (Geneva), 1907, **35**, 551.

[12] Scheuer, *Wien Ber.*, 1914, **123**, IIA, (i), 931.

[13] Moles and Sancho, *An. Fis. Quim.*, 1934, **32**, 931; 1936, **34**, 865; Moles and Roquero, *ibid.*, 1937, **35**, 263; cf. Moles, *ibid.*, 1926, **24**, 717; Les Déterminations Physico-Chimiques des Poids Moléculaires et Atomiques des Gaz, *Institut Internationale de Coopération Intellectuelle*, Paris, 1938, 39.

[14] Blanchard and Pickering, *Bur. Stand. Bull.*, 1926, **21**, 141 (selected).

[15] Dietrichson, Bircher, and O'Brien, *J.A.C.S.*, 1933, **55**, 1; Dietrichson, Orleman, and Rubin, *ibid.*, 1933, **55**, 14.

[16] Stahrfoss, *Arch. Sci. Phys. Nat.*, 1909, **28**, 384; *J. Chim. Phys.*, 1918, **16**, 175.

[17] Rayleigh, *Proc. Roy. Soc.*, 1898, **62**, 204 (recalculated with air=1·2933).

[18] Leduc, *Ann. Chim.*, 1898, **15**, 5; Pire and Moles, *An. Fis. Quim.*, 1929, **27**, 267; Moles and Salazar, *ibid.*, 1932, **30**, 182.

[19] Guye, *J. Chim. Phys.*, 1907, **5**, 203 (selection of best values).

20 Moles and Crespi, *An. Fis. Quim.*, 1922, **20**, 190 (1·42895); Moles and Gonzalez, *ibid.*, 1922, **20**, 72 (*Mém.*); Moles and Salazar, *ibid.*, 1934, **32**, 954.

21 Rayleigh and Ramsay, *Phil. Trans.*, 1895, **186**, 187.

22 Gray, *J.C.S.*, 1905, **87**, 1601.

23 Moles and Clavera, *J. Chim. Phys.*, 1924, **21**, 10; for summary of Moles' earlier work, see Moles, *Gazz.*, 1926, **56**, 915.

24 Moles and Clavera, *Z. anorg. Chem.*, 1927, **167**, 49.

25 Baxter and Starkweather, *Proc. Amer. Acad.*, 1926, **12**, 699, 703; 1928, **14**, 50.

26 Moles, *J. Chim. Phys.*, 1921–2, **19**, 283.

27 Moles, *Trans. Faraday Soc.*, 1939, **35**, 1439; Moles and Escribano, *Compt. Rend.*, 1938, **207**, 66.

28 Moles, Toral, and Escribano, *Compt. Rend.*, 1938, **206**, 1726.

29 Batuecas, *Helv. Chim. Acta*, 1918, **1**, 136; *J. Chim. Phys.*, 1918, **16**, 322; 1925, **22**, 101; according to Moles and Toral, *Monatsh.*, 1936, **69**, 342, all Batuecas' gas density results are affected by an error in the calculation of a temperature correction.

30 Rayleigh, *Proc. Roy. Soc.*, 1893, **53**, 134.

31 Guye, Kovacs, and Wourtzel, *J. Chim. Phys.*, 1912, **10**, 332 (normal density of Geneva air varies by a fraction of a mg.; cf. Jaquerod and Borel, *Arch. Sci. Phys. Nat.*, 1920, **2**, 411; for Madrid air, Payá and Moles, *An. Fis. Quim.*, 1922, **20**, 247.

32 Germann, *J. Chim. Phys.*, 1914, **12**, 66 (bibl. from Fourcroy, 1791).

33 Guye and Davila, *Mém. Soc. Phys. Nat.* (Geneva), 1907, **35**, 615.

34 Moles, *Compt. Rend.*, 1942, **214**, 424 (1·42901).

35 Moles, *J. Chim. Phys.*, 1921, **19**, 100 (bibl.).

36 Moles and Gonzalez, *J. Chim. Phys.*, 1921–2, **19**, 311; Moles, *Ber.*, 1926, **59**, 740.

37 Ter Gazarian, *J. Chim. Phys.*, 1909, **7**, 337; 1911, **9**, 101.

38 Ritchie, *Nature*, 1929, **123**, 838.

39 Baume and Perrot, *J. Chim. Phys.*, 1908, **6**, 610.

40 Klemenc and Bankowski, *Z. anorg. Chem.*, 1932, **208**, 348.

41 Gray and Burt, *J.C.S.*, 1909, **95**, 1633.

42 Scheuer, *J. Chim. Phys.*, 1910, **8**, 289.

43 Schultze, *Ann. Phys.*, 1915, **48**, 269.

44 Fischer and Froboese, *Ber.*, 1911, **44**, 92.

45 Moles and Toral, *Monatsh.*, 1936, **69**, 342; for CO_2 see also Cooper and Maass, *Canad. J. Res.*, 1931, **4**, 283.

46 Batuecas, *J. Chim. Phys.*, 1931, **28**, 572; *Z. phys. Chem.*, 1931, *Bodenstein Festbd.*, 78.

47 Baume, *J. Chim. Phys.*, 1908, **6**, 1.

48 Batuecas, *J. Chim. Phys.*, 1934, **31**, 165.

49 Timmermans, *J. Chim. Phys.*, 1920, **18**, 133; for *n*-butane, Beckers, *Bull. Soc. Chim. Belg.*, 1927, **36**, 559; 1930, **39**, 470; van Bogaert, *ibid.*, 1927, **36**, 384.

50 Jaquerod and Pintza, *Mém. Soc. Phys. Nat.* (Geneva), 1907, **35**, 589; for SO_2, see Stewart and Maass, *Canad. J. Res.*, 1934, **11**, 530 (50 lit. weighed).

51 Wourtzel, *J. Chim. Phys.*, 1913, **11**, 29.

52 Jaquerod and Tourpain, *J. Chim. Phys.*, 1913, **11**, 3, 269; cf. Partington, *Z. phys. Chem.*, 1930, **7** B, 319; Ross and Maass, *Canad. J. Res.*, 1940, **18** B, 55 (3·212 g./lit.).

53 Moles, *J. Chim. Phys.*, 1916, **14**, 389; 1921–2, **19**, 135.

54 Moles, *Compt. Rend.*, 1916, **163**, 94.

55 Murray, *J. Chim. Phys.*, 1917, **15**, 334; Guye, *ibid.*, 1916, **14**, 361; 1917, **17**, 141; Reiman, *ibid.*, 1917, **15**, 293.

56 Moore, *J.C.S.*, 1908, **93**, 2181.

57 Moles, *J. Chim. Phys.*, 1932, **29**, 53.

58 Moles and Miravalles, *An. Fis. Quim.*, 1926, **24**, 356.

59 Jaquerod and Tourpain, *Arch. Sci. Phys. Nat.*, 1911, **31**, 20.

60 Moles, Toral, and Escribano, *Compt. Rend.*, 1938, **207**, 1044.

61 Sameshima, *Bull. Chem. Soc. Japan*, 1926, **1**, 41.

62 Moles, *Ber.*, 1927, **60**, 134.

63 Baxter and Starkweather, *Proc. Nat. Acad.*, 1924, **10**, 479.

64 Batuecas, *An. Fis. Quim.*, 1925, **23**, 343.

65 Maass and Russell, *J.A.C.S.*, 1918, **40**, 1847.

66 Blanchard, *Chem. Met. Eng.*, 1923, **29**, 399 (adopted value).

67 Moles, Batuecas, and Payá, *An. Fis. Quim.*, 1922, **20**, 34 (Madrid air; maximum deviation 0·0008).

§ 7. Vapour Density

The three main methods, each having particular advantages and disadvantages, used for the determination of the densities of the vapours of liquid or solid substances are:

(i) Dumas' method (1826), in which the weight of a known volume o vapour is found.

(ii) Hofmann's method (1868), in which the volume of vapour produced from a known weight of substance is found.

(iii) Victor Meyer's method (1877), in which the volume of air (or other gas) displaced by the vapour of a known weight of substance vaporised in a suitable vessel is determined.

§ 8. Dumas' Method

In this,[1] a glass bulb of 100–300 ml. has the neck drawn to a point (Fig. 7.VII D). This is weighed, and by warming the bulb and dipping the neck into the liquid, a quantity of liquid more than sufficient to expel all the air from the bulb on vaporisation is drawn in on cooling. The bulb is then immersed by means of a suitable holder of wire springs, or rings on a vertical rod, in water or oil heated in a bath or an iron pot to about 30° above the boiling-point of the liquid. This heating bath must be kept at a constant temperature, read on a thermometer. The neck of the bulb projects above the surface of the heating liquid. A rapid stream of vapour then issues from the bulb, carrying out the air. When this stream of vapour ceases, the point of the neck is sealed by a pointed flame; the temperature of the bath and the barometric pressure are read, and the bulb is removed from the bath, cooled, cleaned, and weighed, the temperature in the balance case and the barometric pressure being again read. The point of the neck of the bulb is scratched with a file, and broken off under the surface of previously boiled water in a dish. Water rushes into the bulb and, if the experiment is successful, fills it completely. The bulb filled with water is weighed on a rough balance.

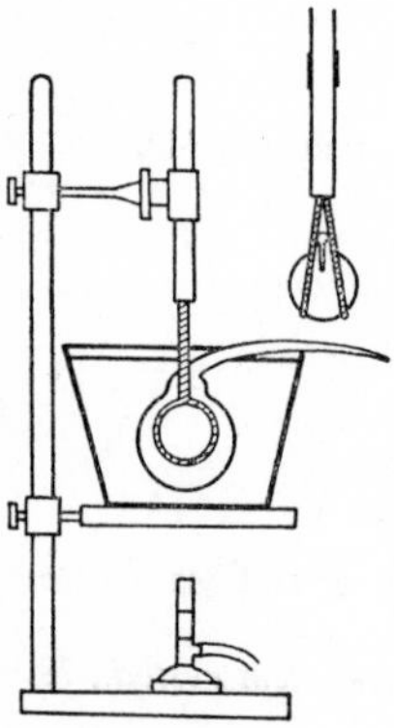

FIG. 7.VII D. Dumas' Vapour Density Apparatus

The method of calculation may be illustrated by an example, in which the vapour density of hexane was determined.

Weight of empty bulb in air=23·449 g.

Weight of bulb + vapour at 15·5°=23·720 g.

Temperature of sealing=110°; barometric pressure=759 mm. Hg, unchanged

[1] Dumas, *Ann. Chim.*, 1826, **33**, 337; *Ann. Phys.*, 1827, **9**, 293; Regnault, *Ann. Chim.*, 1861, **63**, 45; Bunsen, *Ann.*, 1867, **141**, 273; Williams, in Watts, " Dictionary of Chemistry," 1874, **5**, 365; Habermann, *Wien Ber.*, 1876–7, **74**, ii, 423; *Ann.*, 1877, **187**, 341; Pawlewski, *Ber.*, 1883, **16**, 1293 (stoppered bulb); La Coste, *ibid.*, 1885, **18**, 2122; Schall, *ibid.*, 1885, **18**, 2068; Roscoe and Schorlemmer, "Treatise on Chemistry," 1885, **3**, i, 84; Windisch, " Die Bestimmung des Molekulargewichts in theoretischer und praktischer Beziehung," Berlin, 1892, 2nd edit., 1899; *idem*, " Die Praxis der Molekelgewichtsbestimmung," Berlin, 1898; Biltz, " Practical Methods of Determining Molecular Weights," 1899; Haupt, *Z. phys. Chem.*, 1904, **48**, 713; Kohlweiler, *ibid.*, 1920, **95**, 95; Barton and Yost, *J.A.C.S.*, 1935, **57**, 307; Ingle and Cady, *J. Phys. Chem.*, 1938, **42**, 397; Palmer, " Experimental Physical Chemistry," Cambridge, 1941, 19.

throughout the experiment. Capacity of bulb found by weighing full of water=178 ml.

Weight of air displaced by bulb$=178\times(273/288\cdot5)\times0\cdot001293=0\cdot2175$ g.

$\therefore$ weight of vacuous bulb in air$=23\cdot449-0\cdot2175=23\cdot321$ g.

$\therefore$ weight of vapour$=23\cdot720-23\cdot321=0\cdot489$ g.

Volume at S.T.P. of vapour filling bulb at 110° and 759 mm.

$=178\times(273/383)\times(759/760)=126\cdot7$ ml.

$\therefore$ normal density of vapour$=0\cdot489/0\cdot1267=3\cdot86$ g./lit.

Account may be taken of the expansion of the glass bulb on heating. If t'° C. and p' mm. are the temperature and pressure on sealing of the bulb, and t° C. and p mm. those when the bulb filled with vapour is weighed, M is the weight of the bulb filled with water, m the weight of the bulb in air, and m' that of the bulb filled with vapour, then if the densities of air and water are ρ_a and ρ_w, and α is the coefficient of cubical expansion of glass, the vapour density referred to air=1 is:[1]

$$\left.\begin{array}{l}[(m'-m)(\rho_w/\rho_a)+(M-m)]/Q \\ Q=(M-m)(p/p')(1+0\cdot00367t')[1+\alpha(t-t')]/(1+0\cdot00367t)\end{array}\right\} \quad (1)$$

or, approximately:

$$[(m'-m)/(M-m)\rho_a+1](p'/p)(1+0\cdot00367t)/(1+0\cdot00367t') \quad (1a)$$

Brown's formula is:[2]

$$\rho=\frac{W'-W+0\cdot001293VH/[760(1+0\cdot00367t')]-0\cdot001293vH/[760(1+0\cdot00367t')]}{V\left[1+\alpha(t-t')-v\left(1+\dfrac{0\cdot00367(t-t')}{1+0\cdot00367t'}\right)\right]\dfrac{0\cdot001293H}{760(1+0\cdot00367t)}} \quad (2)$$

where W=weight of empty bulb in air, W'=weight of bulb+vapour in air, H=barometric pressure in mm. Hg, V=volume of bulb, v=volume of residual air in bulb when containing vapour, t=temperature of bath, t'=air temperature of weighing, α=coefficient of cubical expansion of glass.

The spherical bulb with the neck approximately at right angles to the vertical of the bulb is not a very convenient form, since part of the neck always projects from the heating bath. A more convenient form[3] consists of a cylindrical bulb, such as a large test-tube, with a vertical neck drawn out at the top, and supported by a handle in a vapour bath (Fig. 8.VII D).

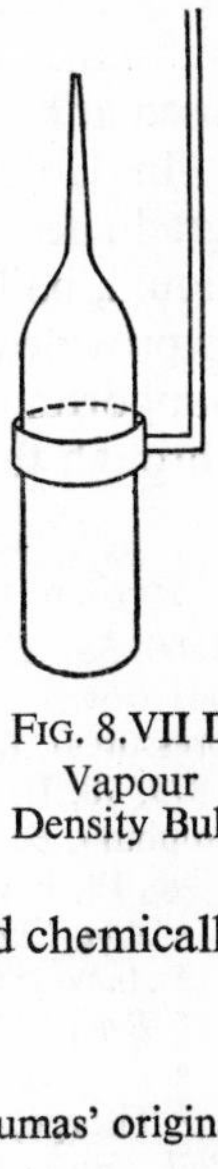

FIG. 8.VII D. Vapour Density Bulb

A curious misunderstanding is the belief that the Dumas method is "obsolete," since it is, in fact, the method most frequently used when results better than those found by the Victor Meyer method are required.[4] With less care it can, of course, give[5] quite inaccurate results. In a modified method[6] the vapour is sealed off and, after cooling, the substance is dissolved and determined chemically

1 Haupt, *Z. phys. Chem.*, 1904, **48**, 713.
2 Brown, *J.C.S.*, 1866, **19**, 72 (tables).
3 Pettersson and Ekstrand, *Ber.*, 1880, **13**, 1191; a vertical neck was used in Dumas' original apparatus, the bulb being spherical.
4 Riesenfeld and Schwab, *Ber.*, 1922, **55**, 2088 (density of ozone).
5 Eucken and Krome, *Z. phys. Chem.*, 1940, **45** B, 175; corrected by Giguère and Rundle *J.A.C.S.*, 1941, **63**, 1135.
6 Jewett, *Phil. Mag.*, 1902, **4**, 546.

in the solution. Schulze [1] condensed the vapour from the bulb in a small connected bulb immersed in liquid air, afterwards sealed off and weighed (cf. § 3).

Modifications of Dumas' method have been used at lower pressures, and at high temperatures [2] with porcelain bulbs heated in the vapours of mercury (357°), sulphur (444·6°), stannous chloride (606°), cadmium (767°), or zinc (918°), boiling in an iron bath, the tip of the bulb (with a vertical neck) projecting through the lid. This neck is sealed with an oxyhydrogen blowpipe. The coefficient of cubical expansion of porcelain may be taken as 0·0000108.

If the substance contains an impurity of higher b.p. this tends to accumulate in the last portions of vapour, and as this is the part weighed the results will be inaccurate in such cases.

§ 9. Hofmann's Method

The principle of this method, the oldest method for determining vapour densities, goes back to Gay-Lussac,[3] whose apparatus comprised a graduated glass tube about 38 cm. long, sealed at one end and filled with mercury, inverted in mercury contained in the lower part of an iron pot. Water was poured into a glass jacket surrounding the tube, and the whole could be heated over a charcoal fire. The water in the jacket was stirred and its temperature read on a thermometer. The substance was weighed in a small thin glass bulb with capillary neck afterwards sealed; this was passed into the tube, and the vapour formed by the bursting of the bulb depressed the mercury. The pressure was suitably measured, and the volume of vapour reduced to S.T.P.

Gay-Lussac's method was improved by Hofmann,[4] Landolt,[5] Grabowski,[6] and others.[7] Hofmann surrounded the graduated tube by a vapour jacket, which gave a more constant temperature than the water bath, and by using a long tube (over 76 cm.), was able to work under reduced pressure, when the substance had a lower b.p. Instead of mercury, Wood's fusible metal can be used at higher temperatures [8] in the tube containing the vapour.

In Hofmann's method, a uniform glass tube about 1 m. long, carefully graduated in ml., is supported in a glass jacket through which the vapour of a liquid, boiling in a separate vessel, is passed (Fig. 9.VII D). The vapour jacket is provided with a side tube near the bottom (or a tube leading through a cork supporting the lower part of the graduated tube), from which the vapour flowing through the jacket passes to a condenser. (If steam is used, it can escape into

[1] *Phys. Z.*, 1913, **14**, 922.

[2] Deville and Troost, *Compt. Rend.*, 1857, **45**, 821; 1859, **48**, 641; 1859, **49**, 239; *Ann. Chim.*, 1860, **58**, 257; *Ann.*, 1860, **113**, 42; Playfair and Wanklyn, *Trans. Roy. Soc. Edin.*, 1861, **72**, 441 (lower pressures); Habermann, *Ann.*, 1877, **187**, 341; *Phil. Mag.*, 1877, **4**, 462 (reduced pressures); Roscoe, *Proc. Roy. Soc.*, 1878, **27**, 426; *Ber*, 1878, **11**, 196; Sommeruga, *Wien Ber.*, 1879, **78**, II, 312; *Ann.*, 1879, **195**, 302 (vapour density of indigo; reduced pressure at b.p. of sulphur); E. and L. Natanson, *Ann. Phys.*, 1886, **27**, 606; Biltz, *Z. phys. Chem.*, 1888, **2**, 921; 1896, **19**, 385; Nilson and Pettersson, *ibid.*, 1889, **4**, 206; Biltz and Pruener, *ibid.*, 1902, **39**, 323.

[3] *Ann. Chim.*, 1811, **80**, 218; Biot, " Traité de Physique," 1816, **1**, 291.

[4] *Ann.*, 1861, *Supplbd.* **1**, 1; *Ber.*, 1868, **1**, 198.

[5] *Ber.*, 1872, **5**, 497.

[6] *Ber.*, 1875, **8**, 1433.

[7] Thorpe, *J.C.S.*, 1880, **37**, 141; Schoop, *Ann. Phys.*, 1881, **12**, 550; Ramsay and Young, *Phil. Trans.*, 1887, **178**, 57; Young and Thomas, *Proc. Phys. Soc.*, 1894–5, **13**, 658; Ramsay and Steele, *Z. phys. Chem.*, 1903, **44**, 348; *Phil. Mag.*, 1903, **6**, 492; Reinganum, *Z. phys. Chem.*, 1904, **48**, 697; Drucker and Ullmann, *ibid.*, 1910, **74**, 567 (influence of adsorption on walls of tube); Egerton, *Chem. News*, 1911, **104**, 259.

[8] Victor Meyer, *Ber.*, 1876, **9**, 1216.

the air.) A thermometer is hung in the vapour jacket, and a suitable stem-correction (§ 3.VI A) is applied. The liquid is weighed in a small stoppered bulb, which it must completely fill. This bulb is passed into the graduated tube and rises to the surface of the mercury. The vapour formed forces out the stopper, and the liquid volatilises completely. The volume of vapour, V ml., the temperature t of the jacket, the barometric pressure, H mm., and the height, h mm., of the mercury in the tube above the level of the trough, are read.

The volume of vapour at S.T.P. is:

$$V_0 = V \cdot 273/(273+t) \cdot (H-h)/760 \text{ ml.} \quad (1)$$

and if m g. is the mass of substance taken, the normal density is

$$D = m \times 1000/V_0 \text{ g./lit.} \quad (2)$$

In accurate work the expansion of the tube, and of the mercury in the heated column, and the vapour pressure of the mercury, must be taken into account. Details are given in the literature cited. Suitable liquids for the vapour jacket are water (b.p. 100°), amyl alcohol (b.p. 131°–132°), aniline (b.p. 184·4°), toluidine (b.p. 202°), ethyl benzoate (b.p. 212·9°), amyl benzoate (b.p. 262°), naphthalene [1] (b.p. 218°), diphenylamine (b.p. 310°), or anthraquinone (b.p. 368°). Brühl [2] found that by using small amounts of substance (0·01 g. minimum) and a long mercury column, so as to evaporate under low pressure, a steam jacket can be used with substances of fairly high b.p.

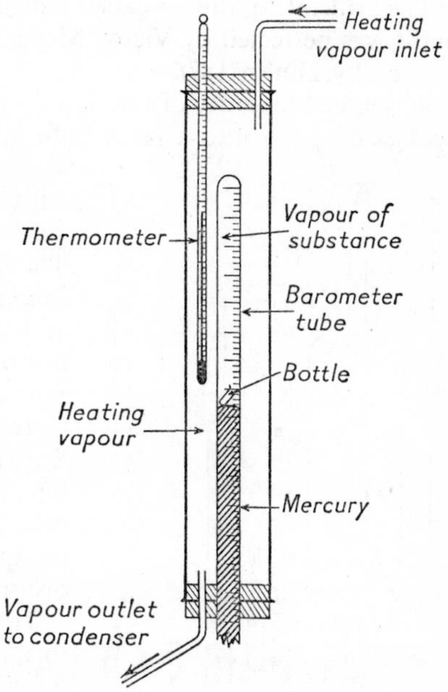

FIG. 9.VII D. Hofmann's Vapour Density Apparatus

The vapour densities found by Ramsay and Steele [3] by a supposedly very accurate form of Hofmann's apparatus were all much greater than those corresponding with the molecular weights, so that they [4] concluded that the vapour-density method could not give accurate values of the molecular weight. Batuecas,[5] who corrected the densities by Berthelot's equation (§ 29.VII C), found, however, that the values found by Ramsay and Steele became less than those corresponding with the molecular weights, which is impossible. He showed that they are vitiated by some obscure experimental error. Ramsay and Steele's conclusion was, therefore, unjustified. Magnus and Schmid [6] used a modified Hofmann apparatus for accurate vapour-density determinations. The vapour volume was kept constant and the pressure measured by a mercury

[1] Grabowski, *Ber.*, 1875, **8**, 1433.
[2] *Ber.*, 1876, **9**, 1368; 1879, **12**, 197.
[3] *Phil. Mag.*, 1903, **6**, 492; *Z. phys. Chem.*, 1903, **44**, 348; there are discrepancies in the two papers, and some arithmetical errors, which are usual in Steele's work; Steele, *J.C.S.*, 1902, **81**, 1076 (compressibility of vapours).
[4] Cf. Leduc, *Ann. Chim.*, 1910, **19**, 441.
[5] *Z. phys. Chem.*, 1939, **183**, 438; errors in Ramsay and Steele's work were pointed out by Guye, *Compt. Rend.*, 1907, **145**, 1330.
[6] *Z. anorg. Chem.*, 1922, **120**, 232; Batuecas, *ibid.*, 1941, **246**, 158 (confirmed; correction for deviation from gas laws).

column kept entirely at a constant temperature by a steam jacket. They found that pv/MT, where M=mol. wt., was a linear function of pressure, and extrapolated to $p=0$ to find the value of M. Lautié [1] used $\rho=a+bp+cp^2$, for $p=300-8000$ mm., for mixed vapours; a is very small and positive.

§ 10. Victor Meyer's Method

The principle of this so-called " displacement method " goes back to Dulong,[2] but it was perfected by Victor Meyer,[3] the present form of the apparatus being devised by him in 1878.

A weighed quantity of the liquid in a small bulb with a stopper or a capillary neck is dropped into a large bulb at the bottom of a vertical tube carrying a side tube delivering into a graduated tube filled with water over a pneumatic trough, or into a gas burette [4] filled with water (Fig. 10.VII D). The large bulb and part of the tube are heated in a glass or metal [5] (e.g. copper) vapour jacket at a temperature which must be higher than the b.p. of the liquid and constant, but need not otherwise be known. A little sand (or mercury) is put into the large bulb to avoid fracture when the small bulb [6] containing the liquid is dropped in. If the upper part of the tube is closed with a rubber stopper, this must be quickly inserted when the small tube is dropped in.

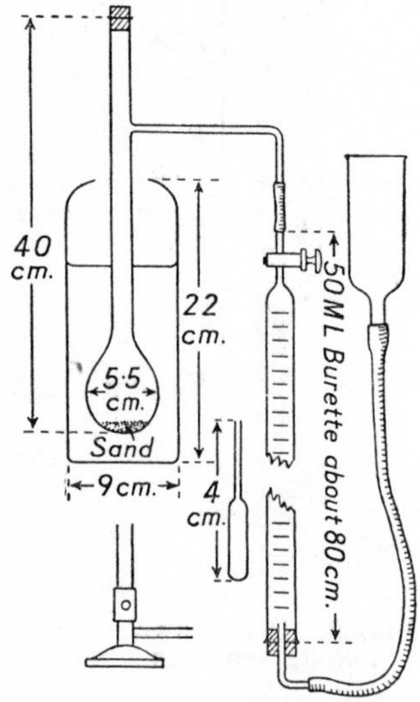

FIG. 10.VII D. Victor Meyer's Vapour Density Apparatus

The bulb of liquid may also be dropped in through a wide stopcock,[7] or by supporting it on a glass rod which is attached to rubber tubing fitted over a small side tube at the top of the vertical tube (which is corked when the tube containing liquid is in position), and then pulling back the glass rod, when the bulb falls.

The liquid vaporises, and the vapour displaces an equal volume of air, which pushes out cool air from the upper part of the tube, and this is collected in the graduated tube or burette. After levelling, the volume of air is read off, the temperature of the water and the barometric pressure being determined. The

1 *Bull. Soc. Chim.*, 1947, 230.

2 Dumas, *Compt. Rend.*, 1874, **78**, 536, who says Dulong had informed him of the method; see Nilson and Pettersson, *Ber.*, 1884, **17**, 987.

3 *Ber.*, 1878, **11**, 1867; V. and C. Meyer, *ibid.*, 1878, **11**, 2253; V. Meyer, *J.C.S.*, 1883, **44**, 618; a different method was used previously by V. Meyer, *Ber.*, 1876, **9**, 1216; 1879, **10**, 2068.

4 Lunge and Neuberg, *Ber.*, 1891, **24**, 729.

5 V. Meyer, *Ber.*, 1886, **19**, 1861; Price, *Chem. News*, 1920, **121**, 249; Patterson, *Ber.*, 1920, **121**, 307.

6 V. Meyer and Pond, *Ber.*, 1885, **18**, 1623; this must *not* be done in determinations at lower pressures: Demuth and V. Meyer, *ibid.*, 1890, **33**, 311.

7 V. Meyer and Pond, *Ber.*, 1885, **18**, 1623; rod in side tube, Biltz, *ibid.*, 1888, **21**, 2776; Biltz and Meyer, *Z. phys. Chem.*, 1888, **2**, 184; opening two pinchcocks on rubber tube, Valente, *Gazz.*, 1881, **11**, 193; for some other methods of dropping the bulb, see Patterson, *Chem. News*, 1908, **97**, 73; Brandenburg, *Chem. Ztg.*, 1909, **33**, 192; Walter, *ibid.*, 1909, **33**, 267; Chapin, *Ind. Eng. Chem.*, 1912, **4**, 684; Evans and Cassaretto, *J. Chem. Educ.*, 1948, **25**, 348.

volume is corrected to S.T.P. with the air dry. This volume of dry air is equal to the volume which the vapour would occupy [1] if it could exist at S.T.P.

If the original Victor Meyer apparatus is used there is an error due to the rise of water in the delivery tube dipping into the pneumatic trough, this tube being full of air when the experiment is finished. By using a delivery tube of suitable diameter with the end immersed to a fixed depth, this may be made to compensate the air displacement due to the insertion of the rubber stopper in the vaporisation tube.[2] This displacement may also be found by a blank experiment.[3] A narrow tube fused into the bottom of the vaporising bulb, through which air can be passed to remove the vapour after an experiment,[4] makes the apparatus fragile and should be avoided.

If the volume of *moist* air collected over water is V ml., measured at a temperature t and barometric pressure H mm., the volume of *dry* air at S.T.P. will be:

$$V_0 = V[273/(273+t)][(H-p)/760] \text{ ml.} \quad . \quad . \quad . \quad . \quad (1)$$

where p is the vapour pressure of water in mm. at $t°$. If the mass of substance taken is m g., the normal vapour density is:

$$D = m \times 1000/V_0 \text{ g./lit.} \quad . \quad . \quad . \quad . \quad . \quad . \quad . \quad . \quad . \quad (2)$$

The vapour density (relative to O=16) may be calculated [5] from the general gas formula $pv=nRT$ (§ 21.VII A); if m g. of vapour occupy v lit. at a pressure of p mm. Hg, the vapour density is $D=m\times 62{\cdot}36T/2pv$.

Equation (2) holds if the vapour-density apparatus is initially filled with dry air; actually it is ordinary air partly saturated with water vapour, so that the correction factor for pressure is $(H-p+p')/760$, where p' is the partial pressure of water vapour in the air filling the Victor Meyer apparatus at the beginning of the experiment.[6] The method is, in any case, only approximate, and the factor $H/760$ is usually quite accurate enough.[7]

Since the vapour is mixed with air in the bulb and its partial pressure is reduced to an unknown amount,[8] the method is not suitable for substances which dissociate on heating, e.g. PCl_5, for which the Dumas method is used.

The liquid in the vapour jacket is usually water, but by using a copper, iron, or aluminium jacket vessel, liquids boiling at higher temperatures may be used, such as those mentioned in § 9, or a fused lead bath can be used.[9]

Matheson and Maass [10] used the apparatus shown in Fig. 11.VII D for determinations at low pressure. The bulb A containing hydrogen was pumped out through *a* to low pressure and heated in a bath. A weighed amount of the

1 See the explanation in Durrant, "General and Inorganic Chemistry," 1939, 76.
2 Pettersson and Ekstrand, *Ber.*, 1880, **13**, 1185.
3 Palmer, "Experimental Physical Chemistry," Cambridge, 1941, 23.
4 Tian, *Bull. Soc. Chim.*, 1926, **39**, 1771; Eucken and Suhrmann, "Physikalisch-chemische Praktikumsaufgaben," Leipzig, 1928, 116.
5 Ostwald, "Principles of Inorganic Chemistry," 1904, 90; Durrant, *Nature*, 1920, **105**, 742.
6 Erdmann, "Lehrbuch der anorganischen Chemie," Brunswick, 1898, 71; Swarts, *Bull. Acad. Roy. Belg.*, 1907, 212; Evans, *J.A.C.S.*, 1913, **35**, 958; Findlay, "Practical Physical Chemistry," 7th edit., 1941, 53.
7 For accurate work, a correction of the vapour density by Berthelot's equation (§ 29.VII C) can be made; McInnes and Kreiling, *J.A.C.S.*, 1917, **39**, 2350; Hicks-Bruun, *Bur. Stand. J. Res.*, 1930, **5**, 575. For an accurate apparatus, see von Weber, *Angew. Chem.*, 1939, **52**, 34.
8 Biltz, *Ber.*, 1888, **21**, 2013, 2772; V. Meyer, *ibid.*, 1888, **21**, 2018; Demuth and V. Meyer, *ibid.*, 1890, **23**, 311; Krause and V. Meyer, *Z. phys. Chem.*, 1890, **6**, 5.
9 Smith, *J.C.S.*, 1880, **37**, 491.
10 *J.A.C.S.*, 1929, **51**, 674; this method had been used for ether by Dalton, *Manch. Mem.* 1819, **3**, 446, who used an almost vacuous globe.

substance in a small capsule was put in the extension B and could be dropped into the bulb by pulling back magnetically the piece of iron in C, this being attached to a thin rod supporting the capsule. The displaced hydrogen passed into D over mercury. A volumeter method (§ 3) for reduced pressures has also been used.[1] A variety of modifications of the Victor Meyer method [2] are adapted to special purposes. A semi-micro Victor Meyer apparatus is described.[3]

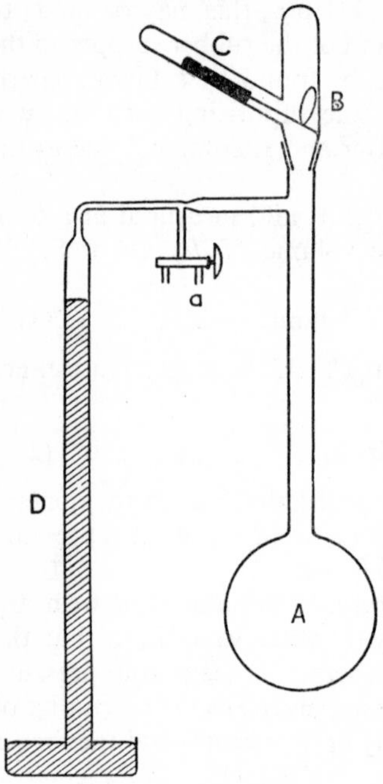

FIG. 11.VII D. Apparatus of Matheson and Maass

By using platinum or porcelain bulbs, the method can be used at high temperatures.[4] The bulb can then be heated inside two graphite crucibles in a furnace burning hard gas carbon in an air blast, or in a Perrot's gas furnace (§ 1.VI B).

Meyer and Mensching used a cylindrical porcelain bulb A (Fig. 12.VII D), the outlet tube B being connected with a glass tube similar to the upper part of a Victor Meyer apparatus. The bulb was filled with pure nitrogen through the platinum capillary C, and after the experiment this gas was displaced by hydrogen chloride and collected over water, which absorbed the displacing gas. From the volume of nitrogen collected, the temperature of the bulb could be calculated; if V is the volume of nitrogen in the bulb, v the volume displaced (both reduced to S.T.P.), the temperature is $t=(V-v)/(\alpha v-\alpha' V)$, where α is the coefficient of expansion of nitrogen, and α' (approximately 0·000027) that of the porcelain bulb. The uncertainty that the tube B projecting from the furnace contains gas at varying temperature was obviated by using an exactly similar compensating tube D alongside B, the nitrogen from which was driven out by hydrogen chloride under the conditions of the experiment, and the volume subtracted from the volume displaced from the main apparatus.

[1] Giguère and Rundle, *J.A.C.S.*, 1941, **63**, 1135.

[2] V. and C. Meyer, *Ber.*, 1879, **12**, 609, 1112; V. Meyer, *ibid.*, 1880, **13**, 401, 1721, 2019; 1882, **15**, 2775; Meier and Crafts, *ibid.*, 1880, **13**, 851; L. Meyer, *ibid.*, 1880, **13**, 991; Piccard, *ibid.*, 1880, **13**, 1079; Goldschmidt and V. Meyer, *ibid.*, 1882, **15**, 137, 1161; Langer and V. Meyer, *ibid.*, 1882, **15**, 2769; Schwarz, *ibid.*, 1883, **16**, 1051; Henderson, *J.A.C.S.*, 1912, **34**, 553; Gil, *An. Fis. Quim.*, 1912, **10**, 82; Chapin, *Ind. Eng. Chem.*, 1912, **4**, 684; Weiser, *J. Phys. Chem.*, 1916, **20**, 532.

[3] Niederl, *Z. anal. Chem.*, 1929, **77**, 169; Lakshminarayan and Mayak, *J. Indian Chem. Soc.*, 1931, **8**, 599; Niederl and Saschek, *Mikrochemie*, 1932, **11**, 237; de Causter, *Natuurw. Tijdschr.*, 1933, **15**, 189.

[4] V. and C. Meyer, *Ber.*, 1879, **12**, 1112, 1246; V. Meyer, *ibid.*, 1880, **13**, 1721; Crafts, *Compt. Rend.*, 1880, **90**, 183; 1884, **98**, 1259; Meier and Crafts, *Ber.*, 1880, **13**, 851, 1316; 1883, **16**, 457; Langer and V. Meyer, *ibid.*, 1882, **15**, 2769; Nilson and Pettersson, *Ber.*, 1884, **17**, 987; *J. prakt. Chem.*, 1886, **33**, 1; *Ann. Chim.*, 1886, **9**, 554; *Z. phys. Chem.*, 1889, **4**, 206; Meunier, *Compt. Rend.*, 1884, **98**, 1268; von Klobukoff, *Ann. Phys.*, 1884, **22**, 465, 493; V. Meyer and Langer, "Pyrochemische Untersuchungen," Brunswick, 1885, 25, 46; Dewar and Scott, *Proc. Roy. Soc. Edin.*, 1887, **14**, 410; Mensching and V. Meyer, *Z. phys. Chem.*, 1887, **1**, 145; Biltz and Meyer, *Ber.*, 1889, **22**, 725, 1116; *Z. phys. Chem.*, 1889, **4**, 249; Thiele, *Z. anorg. Chem.*, 1892, **1**, 277; Biltz, *Z. phys. Chem.*, 1896, **19**, 385; V. Meyer and Recklinghausen, *Ber*, 1897, **30**, 1926; Reinganum, *Phys. Z.*, 1905, **6**, 514; Löwenstein, *Z. phys. Chem.*, 1906, **54**, 707.

Vapour densities at very high temperatures have been determined by a micro-apparatus of the Victor Meyer type.[1] This has an iridium bulb of 3 ml. capacity, painted outside with zirconia and heated electrically to 2000° in a small iridium tube furnace. The substance (usually a fraction of a milligram) was weighed on a microbalance, and the displacement measured by the movement of a drop of mercury in a horizontal graduated glass side tube (Fig. 13.VII D).

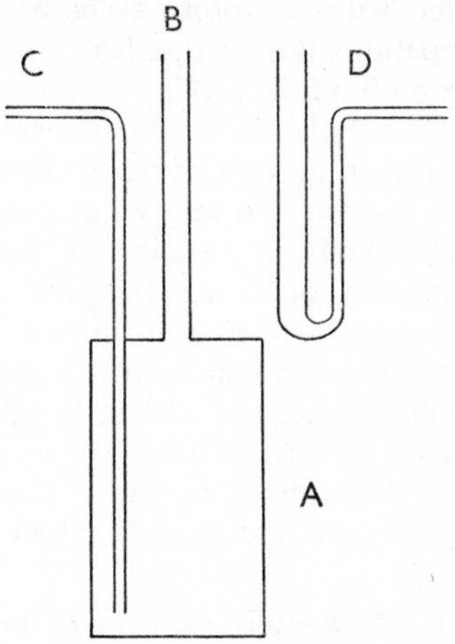

FIG. 12.VII D. Apparatus of Mensching and Meyer

A displacement method for permanent gases has been used.[2] Determinations of vapour density under reduced pressure can be made with substances which decompose on heating.[3] A modification of Victor Meyer's method consists in evaporating a known weight of liquid in a vessel filled with air (or other gas) and measuring the increase in pressure.[4] If v_0= volume of bulb in ml. at 0° C., α'=coefficient of expansion of glass, α=coefficient of expansion of air (or other gas), p_0=initial pressure, p=final pressure, t=temperature of evaporation, and m=mass of substance, the vapour density (g./ml.) is:

$$\rho=(760/V_0)[m(1+\alpha t)]/[(p-p_0)(1+\alpha' t)] \quad . \quad . \quad . \quad . \quad (3)$$

The vaporisation bulb and tube is similar to that of the Victor Meyer apparatus but much shorter. It is fitted through a split rubber bung into a wide boiling tube with a spiral condenser fitted to a side tube, serving as a vapour heating jacket. The outlet from the bulb is connected with a mercury manometer tube having a fixed mark and connected by pressure tubing with a graduated levelling tube. A tap on the inlet side of the manometer allows the level to be adjusted at the mark before the small bulb of substance is dropped into the heated large bulb by means of a device mentioned above for use with the Victor Meyer apparatus. Other modifications of the Victor Meyer and other vapour density apparatus have been described.[5]

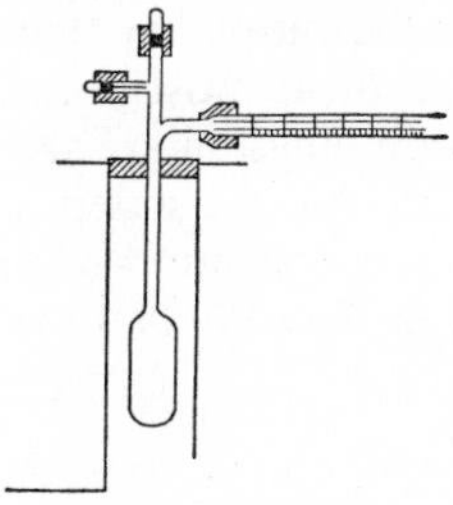
FIG. 13.VII D. Nernst's Vapour Density Apparatus

[1] Nernst, *Z. Elektrochem.*, 1903, **9**, 622; von Wartenberg, *Z. anorg. Chem.*, 1908, **56**, 320; *Ber.*, 1906, **39**, 381; Peak and Robinson, *J. Phys. Chem.*, 1934, **30**, 941.

[2] Goldschmidt and V. Meyer, *Ber.*, 1882, **15**, 137, 1161.

[3] La Coste, *Ber.*, 1885, **18**, 2122; Schall, *ibid.*, 1887, **20**, 2127; 1888, **21**, 100, 1435, 1759, 1827; 1889, **22**, 140, 919; 1890, **23**, 919, 1701; *J. prakt. Chem.*, 1892, **45**, 134; Malfatti and Schoop, *Z. phys. Chem.*, 1887, **1**, 159; Eykman, *Ber.*, 1889, **22**, 2754; Demuth and V. Meyer, *Ber.* 1890, **23**, 311; Biltz, *Z. phys. Chem.*, 1892, **10**, 354; Erdmann, *Z. anorg. Chem.*, 1902, **32**, 425.

[4] Dalton, *Manch. Mem.*, 1819, **3**, 446; Harker, *Chem. News*, 1890, **62**, 180; Bleier and Kohn, *Monatsh.*, 1899, **20**, 505, 909 (to 2–3 mm.); Lumsden, *J.C.S.*, 1903, **83**, 342, 349; Haupt, *Z. phys. Chem.*, 1904, **48**, 713; Menzies, *J.A.C.S.*, 1910, **32**, 1264; Chapin, *J. Phys. Chem.*, 1918, **22**, 337; Coolidge, *J.A.C.S.*, 1928, **50**, 2166; Linhorst, *ibid.*, 1929, **51**, 1165; Eucken and Meyer, *Z. phys. Chem.*, 1929, **5** B, 452; with spiral manometer, Johnson, *Z. phys. Chem.*, 1908, **61**, 457; Matheson and Maass, *J.A.C.S.*, 1929, **51**, 674; Braune and Knoke, *Z. phys. Chem.*, 1931, **152**, 409; Findlay, "Practical Physical Chemistry," 1941, 57.

[5] Pfaundler, *Ber.*, 1879, **12**, 165; Bott and Macnair, *ibid.*, 1887, **20**, 916; Dyson, *Chem. News*, 1887, **55**, 88; Anschütz and Evans, *Ann.*, 1889, **253**, 95; Richards, *Chem. News*, 1889, **59**, 39, 87; Young, *J.C.S.*, 1891, **59**, 911; Lunge and Neuberg, *Ber.*, 1891, **24**, 729; Hirsch,

The micro-apparatus of Blackman [1] consists of a capillary tube closed at one end, containing air enclosed by a thread of mercury, and placed in a closed tube with a stoppered bulb containing a weighed amount of liquid. The apparatus is heated, when the liquid evaporates and the increase of pressure is read off on the capillary manometer.

Although the vapour density of a dissociating gas will be dealt with later, reference may be made to the case of formic acid, which has been rather fully worked on.[2] It may be assumed to polymerise to double molecules, present in the vapour in equilibrium with single molecules, $(H.COOH)_2 \rightleftharpoons 2H.COOH$. Coolidge found that the pressure developed by the vapour was approximately the same as that of a mixture of single and double molecules, each deviating from the ideal state to the same extent as a monatomic vapour of the same molecular weight. Since formic acid is quite unstable, it seems an unfortunate choice for such work. The vapour densities of acetic acid at low pressures have been determined by the McLeod gauge.[3] Hydrocyanic acid was investigated by Sinosaki and Hara.[4] The vapour density of water is normal.[5]

§ 11. Gay-Lussac's Law of Volumes

When Alexander von Humboldt (1769–1859), the great explorer, brought back samples of air from different parts of the world, he and Gay-Lussac [6] analysed them in 1805 by explosion with hydrogen and established that " 100 volumes of oxygen absorb 199·89 volumes of hydrogen, or finally, in round numbers, 100 of oxygen require for saturation 200 of hydrogen." This simplicity of combining volume ratio was extended by Gay-Lussac [7] to a number of other gases, and in 1808 he announced that: " the compounds of gaseous substances with each other are always formed in very simple ratios, so that, representing one of the terms by unity, the other is 1, or 2, or at most 3. . . . The apparent contractions in volume suffered by gases on combination are also very simply related to the volume of one of them." The law may be stated in the form that, the temperature and pressure being supposed constant: *when gases take part in chemical change the reacting volumes are in the ratio of small whole numbers.*

Ann. Phys., 1899, **69**, 456; Cooke, *Z. phys. Chem.*, 1906, **55**, 537; Menzies, *J.A.C.S.*, 1910, **32**, 1264; Weiser, *J. Phys. Chem.*, 1916, **20**, 532; MacInnes and Kreiling, *J.A.C.S.*, 1917, **39**, 2350; Shirai, *Bull. Chem. Soc. Japan*, 1927, **2**, 37; Findlay, " Practical Physical Chemistry," 1941, 55.

[1] *J. Phys. Chem.*, 1908, **12**, 661; 1909, **13**, 138, 426; *Z. phys. Chem.*, 1908, **63**, 48, 381, 635; 1909, **65**, 549, 745; and several papers in *Chem. News*, 1907–16.

[2] Bineau, *Ann. Chim.*, 1846, **18**, 226; Pettersson and Ekstrand, *Ber.*, 1880, **13**, 1191; Ramsperger and Porter, *J.A.C.S.*, 1926, **48**, 1267; 1928, **50**, 3036; Coolidge, *ibid.*, 1928, **50**, 2166; 1930, **52**, 1874; Wrewsky and Glagoleva, *Z. phys. Chem.*, 1928, **133**, 370; Alexander and Lambert, *Trans. Faraday Soc.*, 1941, **37**, 421 (acetaldehyde); for elaborate calculations see Halford, *J. Chem. Phys.*, 1942, **10**, 582; for HF, see Benesi and Smyth, *ibid.*, 1947, **15**, 337. For calculations of dissociation from vapour density, see Gibbs, " Scientific Papers," 1906, **1**, 372.

[3] MacDougall, *J.A.C.S.*, 1936, **58**, 2585; 1941, **63**, 3420 (propionic acid); 1929, **8**, 297; cf. Faucon, *Compt. Rend.*, 1908, **146**, 691.

[4] *Techn. Rep. Tôhoku Imp. Univ.*, 1924, **4**, 145; 1927, **6**, 157.

[5] Levy, *Verhl. d. D. Phys. Ges.*, 1909, **11**, 328; Nernst, *ibid.*, 1909, **11**, 313, 336; criticised by von Steinwehr, *Z. Phys.*, 1920, **3**, 466; Oddo, *Gazz.*, 1915, **45**, i, 319; Menzies, *J.A.C.S.*, 1921, **43**, 851; Shirai, *Bull. Chem. Soc. Japan*, 1927, **2**, 37; Dorsey, " Properties of Ordinary Water Substance," New York, 1940, 54 (bibl.).

[6] Humboldt and Gay-Lussac, *J. de Phys.*, 1805, **60**, 129; Partington, "The Composition of Water," 1928, 57.

[7] *Mém. Soc. Arcueil*, 1809, **2**, 207 (read 31st December, 1808); *Alembic Club Reprint*, 1899, **4**; Ostwald's *Klassiker*, 1893, **42**.

Some accurate combining or reacting volumes at S.T.P. are:

2 vols. of hydrogen chloride give 1·0079 vols. of hydrogen; [1]
1 vol. of nitrogen combines with 3·00172 vols. of hydrogen; [2]
2·00288 vols. of hydrogen combine with 1 vol of oxygen.[3]

The law is only approximate, since different gases have somewhat different compressibilities at the same temperature and pressure.

Berzelius [4] commented on the fact that Gay-Lussac did not draw any conclusion about the combining or atomic weights from the simplicity of the combining volumes (probably because of the influence of Berthollet, who did not believe in fixed combining weights). The simplest assumption would, he said, be that equal volumes of elementary gases contain equal numbers of atoms, and by this so-called " volume theory " Berzelius was able to find the correct formulae for water, H_2O, ammonia, NH_3, and hydrogen chloride, HCl, and the correct atomic weights of hydrogen, nitrogen, and chlorine. There is, however, a difficulty in extending the volume theory to compound gases, which was pointed out by Dalton [5] (who also thought Gay-Lussac's experimental results were inaccurate, as they did not agree with his own, less accurate, determinations). Nitrogen and oxygen, he said, combine in nearly equal volumes (he found 100 nitrogen to 120 oxygen) to form nitric oxide, and without change in total volume. Hence " the number of ultimate particles could at most be one half that before the union. No two elastic fluids, probably, therefore, have the same number of particles either in the same volume or the same weight." If equal volumes contain equal numbers of atoms, the atoms of nitrogen and oxygen must have been divided into two, which is impossible, since an atom is the smallest particle of an element which takes part in chemical change.

This difficulty was resolved in an extremely simple way by the Italian physicist Amedeo Avogadro (1776–1856), who propounded what is now called *Avogadro's hypothesis.*[6]

1 Gray and Burt, *J.C.S.*, 1909, **95**, 1633.

2 Guye and Pintza, *Compt. Rend.*, 1908, **147**, 925.

3 Burt and Edgar, *Phil. Trans.*, 1916, **216**, 393; cf. Guye, *J. Chim. Phys.*, 1917, **15**, 208; Scott, *Phil. Trans.*, 1893, **184**, 543; Morley, *Z. phys. Chem.*, 1896, **20**, 417; Moles, *ibid.*, 1925, **115**, 161; 1925, **117**, 157.

4 " Essai sur la Théorie des Proportions Chimiques," Paris, 1819, 14. Many authors incorrectly attribute the volume theory to Gay-Lussac, so, e.g. Muir, " Principles of Chemistry," Cambridge, 1889, 12, 17.

5 " New System of Chemical Philosophy," 1808, **1**, i, 70; 1810, **1**, ii, 559; *Alembic Club Reprint*, 1899, **4**. He said in 1810: " The truth is, I believe, that gases do not unite in equal or exact measures in any one instance; when they appear to do so, it is owing to the inaccuracy of our experiments." He thought the nearest to a whole number ratio was his own value for H_2 and O_2, 1·97:1.

6 Careful authors of the last century call the statement " Avogadro's hypothesis," e.g. Lothar Meyer, " Modern Theories of Chemistry," 1888, 8; others, e.g. Muir, " Principles of Chemistry," 1889, 30, speak of " Avogadro's law." Maxwell, " Theory of Heat," 1875, 315, called it, by mistake, " Gay-Lussac's law." Nernst, in Dammer, " Handbuch der anorganischen Chemie," Stuttgart, 1892, **1**, 21; " Theoretical Chemistry from the Standpoint of Avogadro's Rule and Thermodynamics," 1904, called it " Avogadro's rule"; Berry, " Modern Chemistry," Cambridge, 1946, 6, calls it " Avogadro's theorem." Maxwell, who deduced Avogadro's hypothesis by a dubious argument from the kinetic theory of gases, says: " This law of volumes [Gay-Lussac's] has now been raised from the rank of an empirical fact to that of a deduction from our theory." The distinction between " hypothesis " on the one hand, and " law " on the other is often overlooked, but is important; Larmor, *Manch. Mem.*, 1908, **52**, No. 10; Benrath, *Chem. Ztg.*, 1908, **32**, 201, 219. Intermediate between " hypothesis " and " law " is the " theory " or " theorem," which usually has a place rather nearer the second.

§ 12. Avogadro's Hypothesis

Avogadro,[1] who says his hypothesis was devised to explain Gay-Lussac's law of volumes (not, as is often said, to explain the equal expansion of gases by heat), pointed out that the difficulty of reconciling this with Dalton's theory is resolved if it is assumed that the smallest particles of elementary gases are not usually the atoms, but are associations of two or more atoms. He gave the name *molecule* (a diminutive of the Latin *moles*, a mass) to the smallest particle of a substance which normally exists in the free state.[2] Maxwell [3] says that a molecule is " that minute portion of a substance which moves about as a whole, so that its parts, if it has any, do not part company during the motion of agitation of the gas." Avogadro called the molecules of elements " molécules constituantes," and those of compounds " molécules intégrantes," and the atoms (a name he does not use) he called " molécules élémentaires." Dalton had confused the latter with the gaseous molecules, but these " are made up of a certain number of these elementary molecules [atoms] united by attraction to form a single constituent molecule [molecule]."

Avogadro then assumed that *equal volumes of all gases, at the same temperature and pressure, contain equal numbers of molecules.* This is called *Avogadro's hypothesis.* Avogadro's words are: "le nombre des molécules intégrantes dans les gaz quelconques, est toujours le même à volume égal . . . les rapports des masses des molécules sont alors les mêmes que ceux des densités des différents gaz, à pression et température égales."

If it is assumed that each nitrogen and oxygen molecule contains two atoms, then in the formation of nitric oxide these molecules are divided into atoms and double the number of nitric oxide molecules, each containing one atom each of nitrogen and oxygen, are formed, which meets Dalton's criticism. Such results are clearly represented by volume diagrams, used by Gaudin [4] in 1832, whose actual diagrams (with modern symbols added) for three cases are:

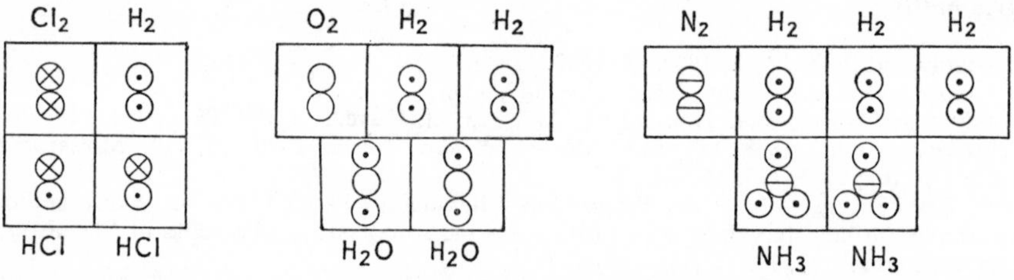

Gaudin, who mentions Ampère but not Avogadro, and speaks of Berzelius

[1] Essay on a manner of determining the relative masses of the elementary molecules of bodies, and the proportions according to which they enter into these compounds [ces combinations]: *J. de Phys.*, 1811, **73**, 58; *Alembic Club Reprint*, 1899, **4**; Ostwald's *Klassiker*, 1889, **8**; "Opere scelte di Amedeo Avogadro," Turin, 1911, 1 f.

[2] According to Ostwald, *Z. phys. Chem.*, 1899, **29**, 573, this definition " has no actual sense," but it seems generally satisfactory.

[3] "Theory of Heat," 1875, 305; "Ency. Brit.," 9th edit., 1877, art. "Atom"; "Scientific Papers," 1890, **2**, 445.

[4] *Ann. Chim.*, 1833, **52**, 113; Dumas, *Phil. Mag.*, 1869, **37**, 93 (who is favourably mentioned in Gaudin's memoir) said: " It would be unjust to omit the mention of M. Gaudin's name by the side of that of Ampère." Dumas, *Ann. Chim.*, 1826, **33**, 337, was practically the only chemist to mention Avogadro by name until Cannizzaro in 1858. Berzelius, *Jahres-Ber.*, 1835, **14**, 84, gave a long and favourable account of Gaudin's paper, saying that: " die Idee von gruppierten Atomen auch in den Gasen der einfachen Körper hat etwas lockendes." On Gaudin, see Delépine, *Bull. Soc. Chim.*, 1935, **2**, 1; Urbain, *ibid.*, 1935, **2**, 16.

with respect, used the names " atom " and " molecule " in the modern sense, and speaks of " monatomic," " biatomic," " triatomic," etc., molecules, composed of 1, 2, 3, etc., atoms. He recognised that mercury vapour is monatomic. He defined the " molécule " as " un group *isolé* d'atomes, en nombre quelconque et de nature quelconque."

In a letter to Berthollet, Ampère [1] again put forward Avogadro's hypothesis (he mentions Avogadro), but he supposed that the number of atoms (" molecules ") in the molecule (" integrant particle ") of an element is four (not usually two as Avogadro supposed), and also attempted to extend the hypothesis to crystalline solids, so that his speculations are more complicated, less general, and less accurate than Avogadro's.

Avogadro's hypothesis was almost completely ignored by chemists, who failed to appreciate that it provided a method of fixing atomic weights.[2] Prout [3] used Avogadro's hypothesis in 1834 (without mentioning Avogadro), and in reply to a criticism by W. C. Henry [4] says his hypothesis of atomic weights as whole multiples of that of hydrogen, proposed [5] anonymously in 1815–16, was actually founded on Avogadro's hypothesis, although this is not expressed.

Cannizzaro in 1858 revived Avogadro's hypothesis and defined an atom as *the smallest weight of an element occurring in the molecular weight of any of its compounds* (see p. 787).

§ 13. Gas or Vapour Density and Molar Weight

The relation between density and molecular weight was introduced by Cannizzaro as follows. The *relative density* of a gas or vapour is the *weight of any volume of the gas or vapour divided by the weight of an equal volume of hydrogen at the same temperature and pressure.* If the atomic weight of hydrogen is taken as 1, the hydrogen molecule H_2 has the molecular weight 2. By Avogadro's hypothesis, at the same temperature and pressure:

$$\text{relative density} = \frac{\text{wt. of any vol. of gas or vapour}}{\text{wt. of equal vol. of hydrogen}} = \frac{\text{wt. of } n \text{ molecules of gas or vapour}}{\text{wt. of } n \text{ molecules of hydrogen}}$$

$$= \frac{\text{wt. of 1 molecule of gas or vapour}}{\text{wt. of 1 molecule of hydrogen}} = \frac{\text{mol. wt. of gas or vapour}}{\text{mol. wt. of hydrogen}}$$

$$= \frac{\text{mol. wt. of gas or vapour}}{2};$$

$$\therefore \textit{molecular weight} = \textit{relative density} \times 2.$$

On the standard O=16, H=1·008 and the factor is 2·016. If the volume occupied by 1 g. of hydrogen is taken as unit, the weight of " two volumes " of any gas or vapour at the same temperature and pressure is the molecular weight.[6] Hofmann [7] called the weight of 1 lit. of hydrogen at S.T.P. a *crith*

1 On the determination of the proportions in which bodies combine according to the number and relative arrangement of the molecules of which their integrant particles are composed: *Ann. Chim.*, 1814, **90**, 45; Ostwald's *Klassiker*, 1889, **8**.

2 Odling, q. by Hartley, *Chem. and Ind.*, 1945, 398.

3 " Chemistry, Meteorology, and the Function of Digestion," 1834, 144, 152–5; Meldrum, " Avogadro and Dalton," Edinburgh, 1906, 40; Dobbin, *Chem. News*, 1916, **113**, 85.

4 *Phil. Mag.*, 1834, **5**, 33; Prout, *ibid.*, 1834, **5**, 132.

5 *Ann. Phil.*, 1815, **6**, 321; 1816, **7**, 111; *Alembic Club Reprint*, 1932, **20**. See § 25.

6 Gerhardt, *Ann. Chim.*, 1843, **7**, 129; 1843, **8**, 238; Laurent, " Méthode de Chimie," 1854, 82, transl. Odling, " Chemical Method," 1855, 80; Mendeléeff, " Principles of Chemistry," 1905, **1**, 319 f. The suggestion to refer gas densities to that of hydrogen as 1 was made by Davy, " Elements of Chemical Philosophy," 1812, 192; " Works," 1840, **4**, 140.

7 " Introduction to Modern Chemistry," 1865, 131.

(Greek κριθή, a barleycorn), and the weight of the same volume of any gas or vapour in crith units is half the molecular weight.

Formerly, dry air, freed from carbon dioxide by alkali, was used as the standard of relative density of gases, but the use of air as a standard in accurate determinations has been discontinued, since the composition of the atmosphere is slightly variable at different times, the weight of a litre of air varying by 0·5 mg. or more.[1] The value 1·2930 g./lit. for the normal density of air is probably the best, and may be used in converting data given relative to air=1 to normal densities (g./lit.) by multiplication by this figure. If the values are not at S.T.P., a knowledge of the compressibilities and coefficients of expansion of air and of the gas is necessary, but as values relative to air are not usually of a high order of accuracy, the assumption of Boyle's law and the known coefficients of expansion are usually sufficient.

When the weight of any quantity of a gas is compared with the weight of an equal volume of a standard gas at the same temperature and pressure, the ratio depends only on the nature of the gases, and (with ideal gases) Avogadro's hypothesis shows that this ratio is equal to the ratio of the molecular weights M of the two gases, $w_1/w_2=M_1/M_2$. If the molecular weight of oxygen is taken as $M_2=32$, the standard gas will be an imaginary gas with 1/32 the density of oxygen, and the molecular weight of a given gas is found by multiplying by 32 the ratio of the weight w_1 of the gas to the weight w_2 of an equal volume of oxygen at the same temperature and pressure, $M_1=32(w_1/w_2)$. The weight of 1 ml. of oxygen at S.T.P. is 0·001429 g. and at t° C. and p cm. Hg it is $0{\cdot}001429\times 273p/76(273+t)$. If w_1 g. is the weight of 1 ml. of any other gas or vapour calculated for the same conditions, the molar (g. mol. wt.) weight is:[2]

$$M_1=32w_1\times 76(273+t)/0{\cdot}001429\times 273p=6233w_1(273+t)/p \quad . \quad (1)$$

According to Avogadro's hypothesis, the volume occupied by one mol of any gas or vapour, calculated for S.T.P., is a constant, V_m, called the *molar volume.* Hence if M=molar weight, D=normal density=weight in g. of 1 lit. at S.T.P., then:[3]

$$M/D=\text{const.}=V_m \quad . \quad . \quad . \quad . \quad . \quad . \quad . \quad . \quad . \quad (2)$$

§ 14. The Molar Volume

The molar volume V_m can be calculated from the values of M and D for any gas. Oxygen, the standard gas, may be chosen; in this case $M/D=32/1{\cdot}4290=22{\cdot}4$. Hence, for approximate purposes, $M=22{\cdot}4D$. Since oxygen is not quite an ideal gas, this value requires a small correction which can be calculated from the compressibility coefficient of oxygen (§ 15), giving the ideal molar volume V_{m0} as 22·415 lit.

It is important to notice that the value of V_{m0}, the molar volume of an ideal

[1] Morley, *Amer. J. Sci.*, 1879, **18**, 168; 1881, **22**, 417; *Amer. Chem. J.*, 1882, **3**, 275; Guye, Kovacs, and Wourtzel, *J. Chim. Phys.*, 1912, **10**, 333; Tower, *ibid.*, 1913, **11**, 249 (bibl.); Guye, *ibid.*, 1917, **15**, 560; Jaquerod and Borel, *ibid.*, 1921, **19**, 11; Stock and Ritter, *Z. angew. Chem.*, 1926, **39**, 1463 (0·13 per cent.); Moles, *Gazz.*, 1926, **56**, 915; Moles, Paya, and Batuecas, *Rev. Acad. Cienc. Madrid*, 1930, **25**, 95; Stock, Ramser, and Eyber, *Z. phys. Chem.*, 1933, **163**, 80 (oxygen volume percentage 20·81–21·07); Paneth, *Nature*, 1937, **139**, 181; Carpenter, *J.A.C.S.*, 1937, **59**, 358 (who found the volume percentages of oxygen and carbon dioxide in dry uncontaminated air very constant).

[2] Mendeléeff, "Principles of Chemistry," 1905, **1**, 345.

[3] Mendeléeff, "Principles of Chemistry," 1905, **1**, 319, who calls this "the law of Avogadro-Gerhardt." Debus (see § 212) supposed that this was the form in which Dalton arrived at his atomic theory.

gas at S.T.P., should have the same value when calculated by the above method for all gases, and the following table, given by Berthelot,[1] shows that this is very nearly the case. The column headed $1-v_1/v_0$ gives the compressibility correction, v_1 and v_0 being the actual and ideal volumes at 1 atm. pressure.

Gas	D	M	$1-v_1/v_0$	V_m	V_{m0}
H_2 ...	0·08982	2·016	1·00064	22·445	22·4308
CO ...	1·25010	28·00	0·99954	22·406	22·4084
O_2 ...	1·42876	32·00	0·99924	22·397	22·4140
CO_2 ...	1·97625	44·00	0·99326	22·269	22·4146
C_2H_2 ...	1·17070	26·016	0·99160	22·231	22·4109
HCl ...	1·64073	36·458	0·99210	22·221	22·3983
SO_2 ...	2·92661	64·06	0·97642	21·889	22·4174
					22·4135

Berthelot adopted the best average value as $V_{m0}=22{\cdot}412$ lit./mol. More recent experimental values of densities and compressibilities indicate the value $V_{m0}=22{\cdot}415$ lit./mol, which is adopted in this book.[2]

§ 15. Accurate Molar Weights from Limiting Gas Densities

Since actual gases do not obey Boyle's law, they cannot agree exactly with Avogadro's hypothesis. Equal volumes of two gases may contain equal numbers of molecules at one pressure, but (owing to deviations from Boyle's law) these two equal volumes become two unequal volumes at another pressure whilst still containing equal numbers of molecules.

Suppose unit volume of a gas at a given temperature and pressure p contains N molecules in the *ideal* state and N' in the *actual* state, and let it contain N in the actual state when the pressure is $p+\delta p$, where δp is the deviation from Boyle's law. Since δp is small Boyle's law can be assumed in connecting N and N', giving[3] $N'/N=p/(p+\delta p)=1/(1+\delta p/p)$, therefore $N=N'(1+\delta p/p)$ or $N'=N/(1+\delta p/p)\simeq N(1-\delta p/p)$. Since Avogadro's hypothesis should hold strictly for an *ideal* gas, and since Boyle's law was shown experimentally by Rayleigh[4] to hold exactly at very small pressures (§ 11.VII A), it may be assumed with some confidence that *the ratio of the densities of two gases at very low pressures gives the exact ratio of the molar weights.*[5]

If a mass W g. of gas occupies a volume V lit. at 0° C. under a pressure p atm., W/pV is the *density* (W/V) *at unit pressure* ($p=1$). Owing to deviations from Boyle's law, pV is not quite constant at different pressures. When $p=p_1=1$, W/pV is the *normal density*, $D=W/p_1V=W/V$ when $p_1=1$. As p approaches zero W/pV approaches the value for the ideal gas, and the ratio

[1] *Z. Elektrochem.*, 1904, **10**, 620.

[2] Holborn, *Z. Phys.*, 1921, **6**, 69 (22·414); Baxter and Starkweather, *Proc. Nat. Acad.*, 1924, **10**, 479 (22·415); Moles, *Z. anorg. Chem.*, 1927, **167**, 40 (22·4148±0·0007); Clark, *Phil. Mag.*, 1938, **18**, 80; the difference between the alternative values given by Birge, *Rep. Progr. Phys.*, 1942, **8**, 90, 22·4151 for $g=980{\cdot}616$, and 22·4140 for $g=980{\cdot}665$, is within the limits of experimental error in this field.

[3] J. J. Thomson, in Watts' "Dictionary of Chemistry," edit. Morley and Muir, 1890, **1**, 88.

[4] *Phil. Trans.*, 1902, **198**, 417; *Proc. Roy. Soc.*, 1904, **73**, 153.

[5] Little, *Sci. Progr.*, 1913, **7**, 504; Young, "Stoichiometry," 1918, 44; Baxter, *J.A.C.S.*, 1922, **44**, 595.

$D_0=W/p_0V_0$ is called the *limiting density* (by Rankine[1] the "theoretical density"). This gives Rayleigh's equation:[2]

$$D_0=(p_1V_1/p_0V_0)D \quad . \quad . \quad . \quad . \quad . \quad . \quad . \quad . \quad (1)$$

Since D_0 is the weight of 1 lit. of the gas in the ideal state at S.T.P. and as the mol M is the weight of 22·415 lit. at S.T.P.,

$$M=22{\cdot}415D_0 \quad . \quad . \quad . \quad . \quad . \quad . \quad . \quad . \quad . \quad (2)$$

The first use of a limiting density seems to have been by Wrede,[3] who found that the density (air=1) of carbon dioxide is represented by $D=1{\cdot}5201(1+0{\cdot}0049p)/(1+\alpha t)$, where α is the coefficient of expansion. Hence the "true" density was taken as 1·52037. He found no dependence of pressure with oxygen and carbon monoxide.

By plotting pV against p a straight line is found for a given mass of most gases for values of p less than 1 atm., and hence by extrapolation to $p=0$ the value of p_0V_0 in (1) is found. This linear relation between pV and p holds strictly only for permanent gases; for more easily liquefiable gases the pV–p isothermals are probably slightly curved,[4] the slope decreasing somewhat at low pressures, but the curvature is quite small even for carbon dioxide. The accurate equation is:

$$pV=p_0V_0+Bp+Cp^2+\ldots \quad . \quad . \quad . \quad . \quad . \quad . \quad (3)$$

in which B, C, etc., are functions of temperature, but C and later coefficients are very small, and the corresponding terms are usually negligible at pressures below atmospheric.

D. Berthelot[5] defined the *compressibility coefficient* of a gas between 1 atm. (p_1) and a low pressure (p_0) as:

$$A_0^1=(p_0V_0-p_1V_1)/p_0V_0(p_1-p_0) \quad . \quad . \quad . \quad . \quad . \quad (4)$$

When $p_1=1$ and $p_0\to 0$, this becomes:

$$A_0^1=1-p_1V_1/p_0V_0 \quad . \quad . \quad . \quad . \quad . \quad . \quad . \quad . \quad (5)$$

From equations (1) and (5):

$$D_0=D(1-A_0^1) \quad . \quad . \quad . \quad . \quad . \quad . \quad . \quad . \quad . \quad (6)$$

Since the compressibility coefficient of oxygen is 0·000964, i.e. $1-p_1v_1/p_0v_0=0{\cdot}000964$, the volume at 1 atm. pressure which any volume of oxygen, v_1, would occupy if it were an ideal gas, v_0, is given by $1-v_1/v_0=0{\cdot}000964$. For 1 g. of oxygen at S.T.P., $v_1=1/1{\cdot}4290$ lit., and for 32 g., the molar weight, the ideal molar volume is:

$$V_{m0}=32/[1{\cdot}4290\times(1-0{\cdot}000964)]=22{\cdot}414 \text{ lit.}$$

Guye[6] found V_{m0} from the equation $V_{m0}=M/D(1-A_0^1)$ as 22·410 lit./mol.

1 *Phil. Mag.*, 1851, **2**, 509 (527).

2 Porter, in Gray and Burt, *J.C.S.*, 1909, **95**, 1633.

3 Berzelius, *Jahres-Ber.*, 1842, **22**, 72; Ostwald, "Lehrbuch," 1910, **1**, 82; Berthelot, *Compt. Rend.*, 1907, **144**, 76, says the idea is due to Regnault, 1842; Clarke, *Phil. Mag.*, 1881, **12**, 101, had used Regnault's gas densities at 1 atm. pressure to calculate atomic weights, but Thiesen, *Ann. Phys.*, 1885, **24**, 467, pointed out that they should be extrapolated to zero pressure and showed how this could be done. Blaserna, *Compt. Rend.*, 1869, **69**, 132, 134, pointed out that Regnault's value for carbon dioxide at 100° is not (as Regnault thought) equal to the ideal value.

4 Gray and Burt, *J.C.S.*, 1909, **95**, 1633.

5 *Compt. Rend.*, 1898, **126**, 954, 1030, 1415, 1501; 1907, **145**, 317; *J. de Phys.*, 1899, **8**, 263; *Z. Elektrochem.*, 1904, **10**, 620; *Trav. et Mém. Bur. Internat. Poids et Mésures*, 1907, **13**; see §29.VII C.

6 *Compt. Rend.*, 1907, **144**, 976, 1360.

He calculated A_0^1 from the critical data and thought there was a variation of V_{m0} with critical temperature t_c° C. according to the formula $22{\cdot}410+1{\cdot}5\times10^{-7}t_c^2$, but this is improbable.[1]

Guye [2] and his school used a different compressibility coefficient λ:

$$\lambda=(p_0V_0-p_1V_1)/p_1V_1(p_1-p_0) \quad . \quad . \quad . \quad . \quad . \quad . \quad (7)$$

or, for $p_1=1$, $p_0\to0$,

$$1+\lambda=p_0V_0/p_1V_1 \quad . \quad . \quad . \quad . \quad . \quad . \quad . \quad . \quad (8)$$

$$\therefore\ D_0=D/(1+\lambda) \quad . \quad . \quad . \quad . \quad . \quad . \quad . \quad . \quad (9)$$

The relation between A_0^1 and λ is given by (6) and (9) as:

$$A_0^1=\lambda/(1+\lambda) \quad . \quad . \quad . \quad . \quad . \quad . \quad . \quad . \quad (10)$$

$(1-A_0^1)$ and $(1+\lambda)$ are both nearly unity but have opposite signs, A_0^1 being usually positive (except for hydrogen) and λ negative (except for hydrogen); equations (6) and (9), although they give almost the same results, are not identical. For two gases of molecular weights M_1 and M_2:

$$\frac{M_1}{M_2}=\frac{D_1(1-A_0^1)_1}{D_2(1-A_0^1)_2}=\frac{D_1(1+\lambda_2)}{D_2(1+\lambda_1)} \quad . \quad . \quad . \quad . \quad . \quad . \quad (11)$$

For hydrogen $D=0{\cdot}089873$, $A_0^1=-0{\cdot}00054$; for oxygen $D=1{\cdot}42900$, $A_0^1=+0{\cdot}000964$. Hence:

$$\frac{\text{mol. wt. of } H_2}{\text{mol. wt. of } O_2}=\frac{0{\cdot}089873(1+0{\cdot}00054)}{1{\cdot}42900(1-0{\cdot}000964)}=\frac{1}{15{\cdot}876}=\frac{1{\cdot}0078}{16}.$$

The normal density of hydrogen chloride is 1·63915. For an arbitrary mass of gas $p_1V_1=54{,}803$, and the value of p_0V_0 found by graphical extrapolation from the slightly curved plot of pV against p to $p=0$ was 55,213 (Gray and Burt). Hence D_0 for $HCl=1{\cdot}63915\times54803/55213=1{\cdot}62698$.

The normal density of oxygen is 1·42900 and the following values of p_1v_1 and p_0v_0 (extrapolated) were found, the limiting densities shown being calculated in the same way as for HCl:

p_1V_1	p_0V_0 (extrap.)	D_0 for oxygen
139,628	139,769	1·42756
138,959	139,087	1·42768
56,256	56,311	1·42760
		mean 1·42762

$\therefore$ molecular wt. of $HCl=32\times1{\cdot}62698/1{\cdot}42762=36{\cdot}469$.

Guye [3] proposed the extended equation:

$$p_1v_1=[(1+\lambda)-\lambda(p-1)]p_0v_0 \quad . \quad . \quad . \quad . \quad . \quad . \quad (12)$$

[1] Wells, *Amer. Chem. Abstr.*, 1907, **1**, 2529.

[2] Guye, *J. Chim. Phys.*, 1905, **3**, 321; 1906, **4**, 174; 1908, **6**, 769; 1913, **11**, 275; 1919, **17**, 141; *Compt. Rend.*, 1907, **144**, 976, 1360; Baume and Wourtzel, *J. Chim. Phys.*, 1912, **10**, 520; see the papers by Baume, Cardoso, Jaquerod, Ter Gazarian, Moles, and Wourtzel, quoted in § 6; Henning and Jaeger, in Geiger and Scheel, "Handbuch der Physik," 1926, **2**, 493; Birge, *Rev. Mod. Phys.*, 1929, **1**, 1; Batuecas, *J. Chim. Phys.*, 1932, **29**, 26; Birge and Jenkins, *J. Chem. Phys.*, 1934, **2**, 167; Moles, *J. Chim. Phys.*, 1937, **34**, 49.

[3] Quoted by Wourtzel, *J. Chim. Phys.*, 1919, **17**, 143.

for more easily liquefiable gases, and Baume [1] used:

$$pv=1+a(1-D/D_1) \quad . \quad . \quad . \quad . \quad . \quad . \quad . \quad . \quad (13)$$

where D=wt. of 1 lit. under pressure p, D, do. under 1 atm. pressure. This corresponds [2] with $A_0^1=a/(1+a)=a-a^2+a^3$.

Leduc [3] used the equation

$$Mpv=RT\phi \quad . \quad . \quad . \quad . \quad . \quad . \quad . \quad . \quad . \quad . \quad (14)$$

where v=sp. vol., R=gas const. per g., ϕ is a function of temperature. At low pressures $Mp_0v_0=RT\phi_0$ ($\phi_0\rightarrow 1$ for $p\rightarrow 0$)

$$\therefore\ pv/p_0v_0=\phi/\phi_0\simeq\phi \quad . \quad . \quad . \quad . \quad . \quad . \quad . \quad . \quad (15)$$

where

$$\phi=1-mp-np^2=1-mp_c\pi-np_c^2\pi^2=1-mp_ce-np_c^2e^2 \quad . \quad . \quad (16)$$

where p_c=crit. press., π=reduced pressure (p/p_c) and e is expressed as the ratio p cm./p_c atm. He then found m and n as functions of temperature. The fundamental equation later used by Leduc (in 1923) was ($k=T_c/T$, and b is a constant):

$$p=(RT/M)\{v/(v-b)^2-3{\cdot}16[b/(v+b)^2](4^k-1)\} \quad . \quad . \quad . \quad (17)$$

It has been demonstrated several times [4] that the methods of Berthelot, Guye, and Leduc are the same in principle, and give almost identical results. Sinosaki and Hara [5] for hydrogen cyanide, found:

$$pV/W=R-bp-cp^2 \quad . \quad . \quad . \quad . \quad . \quad . \quad . \quad . \quad (18)$$

where W=weight of the gas, b and c are constants.

In a method used by Batuecas [6] the values of pV found at 1, $\frac{2}{3}$, $\frac{1}{2}$, and $\frac{1}{3}$ atm. were extrapolated to zero pressure to find p_0V_0. The densities at unit pressure (W/pV) of nitrous oxide at different pressures (p atm.) and the values of pV found were:

p	1·00	0·667	0·50	0·333
W/pV	1·9804	1·9746	1·9722	1·9694
pV	1·00000	1·00294	1·00416	1·00559

Extrapolation of the pV–p curve gave p_0V_0, and $1+\lambda=1{\cdot}0085$,

$$\therefore\ D_0=D_1/(1+\lambda)=1{\cdot}9804/1{\cdot}0085=1{\cdot}9637 \text{ g./lit.}$$

$$\therefore\ M=1{\cdot}9637\times 22{\cdot}415=44{\cdot}016,$$

$$\therefore\ \text{atom. wt. N}=\tfrac{1}{2}(44{\cdot}016-16)=14{\cdot}008.$$

1 *J. Chim. Phys.*, 1908, **6**, 52.

2 Baume and Wourtzel, *J. Chim. Phys.*, 1912, **10**, 520.

3 *Compt. Rend.*, 1896, **123**, 743; 1897, **124**, 285; 1897, **125**, 571, 646, 703; 1909, **148**, 407; 1912, **155**, 206; 1923, **176**, 1132; Leduc and Sacerdote, *ibid.*, 1897, **125**, 297, 299, 768; Leduc, *J. de Phys.*, 1898, **7**, 5, 189; 1899, **8**, 585; *Ann. Chim.*, 1898, **15**, 5, 90; 1899, **17**, 173; 1910, **19**, 441; " Volumes moléculaires: Applications," Paris, 1923.

4 Van Laar, *Verslag. K. Akad. Wetens. Amsterdam*, 1899, **7**, 350; *Proc. K. Akad. Wetens. Amsterdam*, 1899, **1**, 273; *Z. phys. Chem.*, 1899, **32**, 158; Burt and Howard, *Trans. Faraday Soc.*, 1924, **20**, 544; Wild, *Phil. Mag.*, 1931, **12**, 41; Boutaric, *J. Chim. Phys.*, 1931, **28**, 174; Cawood and Patterson, *J.C.S.*, 1933, 619; Dietrichson, Orleman, and Rubin, *J.A.C.S.*, 1933, **55**, 14; Keyes and Felsing, *ibid.*, 1946, **68**, 1883 (methylamines).

5 *Techn. Rep. Tôhoku Imp. Univ.*, 1929, **8**, 297.

6 *J. Chim. Phys.*, 1931, **28**, 572; *Arch. Sci. Phys. Nat.*, 1938, **20**, 59; *Z. anorg. Chem.*, 1941, **246**, 158; cf. Dietrichson *et al.*, *J.A.C.S.*, 1933, **55**, 1, 14 (NH_3, density at 1, $\frac{2}{3}$ and $\frac{1}{3}$ atm., 0·77126, 0·51161, 0·25458).

Moles [1] found that if allowance is made for adsorption on the glass globe the *density* (weight of 1 lit. at S.T.P.) of any gas is a linear function of pressure below 1 atm.:

$$D=D_0+ap \quad \text{. . . . .} \quad \textbf{(19)}$$

(This is a different relation from $pV=p_0V_0+Bp$.) The adsorption is expressed, for unit surface, by the equation $a=kp^m$ where p is the pressure, the constants k and m (=0·25 to 0·70 for different gases) being determined by experiment; m shows a tendency to decrease with increasing pressures. The *total* adsorption for a spherical bulb of volume v is:

$$a=kv^{2/3}(p^m-p_r^m)$$

where p_r is the residual pressure. If $1/D_p$ is a linear function of pressure and the uncorrected normal density is D_p', then:

$$1/D_p'=(1/D_0)(1-A_p)(1-a/g),$$

where a is the quantity of gas adsorbed and g is the weight of gas contained in the globe of volume v under the pressure p. Thus:

$$1/D_p'=(1/D_0)(1-A_p)[1-(k/g)v^{2/3}(p^m-p_r^m)] \quad \text{. . .} \quad \textbf{(20)}$$

Moles determined D_0 by measuring the density at 1, $\frac{3}{4}$, $\frac{2}{3}$, and $\frac{1}{2}$ atm., and extrapolating to zero pressure.

The micro-balance method for the comparison of densities (§ 4) is readily adapted to the determination of the ratio of limiting densities, i.e. the ratio of the molecular weights. From (4) ($p_0 \to 0$)

$$pV=p_0V_0(1-Ap) \quad \text{. . . . .} \quad \textbf{(21)}$$

But $p_0V_0=RT(W/M)$ for the ideal gas, since $W/M=n$, the number of mols, and $(W/V)=D$, hence:

$$p=(RTD/M)(1-Ap) \quad \text{. . . . .} \quad \textbf{(22)}$$

The densities of two gases are equal (equilibrium of the micro-balance) when:

$$\frac{p_1}{p_2}=r=\frac{M_2(1-A_1p_1)}{M_1(1-A_2p_2)} \quad \therefore \quad \frac{M_2}{M_1}=r\frac{(1-A_2p_2)}{(1-A_1p_1)} \quad \text{. . .} \quad \textbf{(23)}$$

When r, the observed pressure ratio, is extrapolated to the limiting value r_0 for zero pressures ($p_1 \to 0$ and $p_2 \to 0$):

$$M_2/M_1=r_0 \quad \text{. . . . .} \quad \textbf{(24)}$$

If the compressibility coefficient of one gas, A_1, is known, that of the other may be calculated from the values of r at two pressures below 1 atm., since:

$$\frac{r'}{r''}\cdot\frac{(1-p'_2A_2)}{(1-p''_2A_2)}=\frac{(1-p'_1A_1)}{(1-p''_1A_1)} \quad \text{. . . . . . .} \quad \textbf{(25)}$$

The micro-balance method was used by Woodhead and Whytlaw-Gray [2] in

[1] Moles and Clavera, *Z. anorg. Chem.*, 1927, **167**, 49 (N_2); Moles, *Rec. Trav. Chim.*, 1929, **48**, 864; Moles and Salazar, *An. Fis. Quim.*, 1932, **30**, 182; Moles, *ibid.*, 1937, **35**, 134; *Compt. Rend.*, 1937, **205**, 1391; *J. Chim. Phys.*, 1937, **34**, 49; in Les Déterminations physico-chimiques des Poids Moléculaires et Atomiques des Gaz, *Institut Internationale Coopération Intellectuelle*, Paris, 1938, 1, 116, and bibl. of other papers by Moles and collaborators; Moles and Toral, *Z. anorg. Chem.*, 1938, **236**, 225 (SiF_4).

[2] *J.C.S.*, 1933, 846.

finding the atomic weight of carbon from the determination of the limiting density of carbon monoxide. The temperature was 19·8° C.

Approximate balancing pressures, mm. Hg O_2	Approximate balancing pressures, mm. Hg CO	Uncorrected pressure ratio r'	Corrected pressure ratio r	Limiting pressure ratio $p \to 0$ r_0	Mol. wt. of CO M_2
181·9	207·8	0·87535	0·87523	0·87533	28·010(6)
361·9	413·5	0·87524	0·87514	0·87534	28·011(0)
572·3	654·0	0·87509	0·87500	0·87537	28·011(8)

§ 16. Table of Compressibility Coefficients

Some values of the compressibility coefficients at 0° are:

	$1+\lambda$	$A_0^1 \times 10^5$
Hydrogen H_2	0·99935 [15] *	−52 [18]
	0·99922 [16]	
Helium He	0·99955 [16]	−60 [18]
	1·0000 [9]	−86 [15]
Neon Ne	0·99895 [9]	−105 [9]
	0·99941 [7, 21]	−65·9 [21]
Nitrogen N_2	1·00045 [4]	+43 [11, 21]
	1·00043 [21]	
	1·0006 [6]	
	1·00074 [16]	
	1·00117 [18]	
Carbon monoxide CO... ...	1·00048 [6]	+81 [25]
	1·00040 [21]	+40 [21]
	1·00050 [30]	
Oxygen O_2	1·000926 [21]	+97 [18]
	1·00085 [15]	+92·5 [21]
	1·00097 [18]	+113 [15]
	1·00093 [7]	
	1·00087 [5]	
	1·000942 [29]	
Argon A	1·00104 [7]	+82 [25]
	1·00090 [21]	+90 [21]
Nitric oxide NO	1·00112 [3]	+117 [18]
Ethylene C_2H_4	1·0074[3]	
	1·0073 [21]	
	1·0078 [33]	+102 [33]
Acetylene C_2H_2	1·00884 [17]	
Carbon dioxide CO_2	1·00706 [15]	+691 [21]
	1·0068 [4]	+676 [11]
	1·0067 [10]	+663 [27]
	1·00702 [12]	+922 [15]
	1·00694 [21]	
Phosphine PH_3	1·0097 [26]	
Hydrogen sulphide H_2S ...	1·0104 [19]	
Nitrous oxide N_2O	1·0088 [1]	+739 [25]
	1·0073 [4]	+733 [21]
	1·00737 [21]	+700 [27]
Silicon fluoride SiF_4	1·01004 [21]	+1003 [21]

* See page 777 for footnotes.

	$1+\lambda$	$A_0^1 \times 10^5$
Hydrogen chloride HCl ...	1·00737 [18]	+736 [13]
Hydrogen bromide HBr ...	1·00934 [14]	+931 [20]
	1·00931 [20]	
Hydrogen iodide HI	1·01491 [23]	
Methyl oxide $(CH_3)_2O$ ...	1·0254 [3]	+2656 [8]
	1·027 [4]	
	1·02656 [8]	
Ammonia NH_3	1·01499 [18]	+1521 [18]
	1·01553 [24]	+1502 [21]
	1·01526 [21]	+1480 [27]
Methyl chloride CH_3Cl ...	1·02215 [8]	+2215 [8]
	1·0247 [31, 32]	
Sulphur dioxide SO_2	1·02341 [18]	+2380 [8, 18]
	1·0239 [22]	
	1·02410 [21]	
Propane C_3H_8	1·0204 [2]	
Nitrosyl chloride NOCl ...	1·02395 [28]	

[1] Batuecas, *J. Chim. Phys.*, 1931, **28**, 572.
[2] Batuecas, *J. Chim. Phys.*, 1934, **31**, 165.
[3] Batuecas, *J. Chim. Phys.*, 1925, **22**, 101.
[4] Batuecas, *J. Chim. Phys.*, 1934, **31**, 65.
[5] Batuecas, Maverick, and Schlatter, *J. Chim. Phys.*, 1925, **22**, 130.
[6] Batuecas, Schlatter, and Maverick, *J. Chim. Phys.*, 1929, **26**, 548 (chose 1·0006).
[7] Baxter and Starkweather, *Proc. Nat. Acad.*, 1928, **14**, 50; 1929, **15**, 441.
[8] Baume, *J. Chim. Phys.*, 1908, **6**, 1.
[9] Burt, *Trans. Faraday Soc.*, 1910, **6**, 19.
[10] Cawood and Patterson, *J.C.S.*, 1933, 619.
[11] Chappuis, *Trav. et Mém. Bur. Internat. Poids et Més.*, 1907, **13**.
[12] Deshusses, *Thesis*, Geneva, 1922; Landolt-Börnstein, " Tabellen," 1927, Ergzb. **1**, 163.
[13] Gray and Burt, *J.C.S.*, 1909, **95**, 1633.
[14] Guye, *J. Chim. Phys.*, 1919, **17**, 141.
[15] Guye and Batuecas, *Helv. Chim. Acta*, 1922, **5**, 532; *J. Chim. Phys.*, 1923, **20**, 308; cf. Addingley and Whytlaw-Gray, *Trans. Faraday Soc.*, 1928, **24**, 378.
[16] Henning and Heuse, *Z. Phys.*, 1921, **5**, 285.
[17] Howarth and Burt, *Trans. Faraday Soc.*, 1925, **20**, 544; cf. Sameshima, *Bull. Chem. Soc. Japan*, 1926, **1**, 41.
[18] Jaquerod and Scheuer, *Mém. Soc. Phys. Nat.* (Geneva), 1907, **35**, 659.
[19] Maverick, *Thesis*, Geneva, 1922.
[20] Moles, *J. Chim. Phys.*, 1916, **14**, 369; 1921–2, **19**, 135.
[21] Moles, Poids Moléculaires des Gaz, *Institut Internationale de Coopération Intellectulle*, Paris, 1938, 47, 191.
[22] Moles, *Rec. Trav. Chim.*, 1929, **48**, 864.
[23] Moles and Miravalles, Landolt-Börnstein, " Tabellen," 1927, Ergzbd. **1**, 163.
[24] Moles, *An. Fis. Quim.*, 1926, **24**, 717; Moles and Batuecas, Landolt-Börnstein, " Tabellen," 1931, Ergzb. **2**, 205.
[25] Rayleigh, *Phil. Trans.*, 1905, **204**, 351.
[26] Ritchie, *Nature*, 1929, **123**, 838.
[27] Whytlaw-Gray and Cawood, Poids Moléculaires des Gaz, *Institut Internationale de Coopération Intellectuelle*, Paris, 1938, 88.
[28] Wourtzel, *J. Chim. Phys.*, 1913, **11**, 29.
[29] Moles and Roquero, *An. Fis. Quim.*, 1937, **35**, 263.
[30] Pire and Moles, *An. Fis. Quim.*, 1929, **27**, 267.
[31] Batuecas, *An. Fis. Quim.*, 1925, **23**, 343.
[32] Bodareu, *Atti R. Accad. Lincei*, 1914, **23**, i, 491.
[33] Batuecas, *Helv. Chim. Acta*, 1922, **5**, 544.

§ 17. Calculation and Determination of Compressibility Coefficients

Instead of using a measured value of the compressibility coefficient, a value may be calculated from a characteristic equation. The simplest is van der Waals's equation,[1] $(p+a/v^2)(v-b)=RT$. If v_0 is the ideal volume, $pv_0=RT$,

$$\therefore\ pv_0=(p+a/v^2)(v-b)=(p+a/v^2)(1-b/v)v \quad . \quad . \quad . \quad (1)$$

If $p=1$ atm., then, since b/v is small:

$$v_0=v(1+a/v^2)(1-b/v)\simeq v(1+a/v^2-b/v)=v\phi \quad . \quad . \quad . \quad (2)$$

If D, D_0 are the normal and limiting densities:

$$D/D_0=v_0/v=\phi \quad \therefore\ D_0=D/\phi=M/22{\cdot}415 \quad . \quad . \quad . \quad (3)$$

from which M may be calculated from D, a and b, since v in ϕ may, with sufficient approximation, be replaced by $v_0=22{\cdot}415$ lit.

Van der Waals [2] used the equation:

$$\frac{D_0}{D}=1-0{\cdot}001645\frac{T_c}{T}\left(\frac{27}{8}\frac{T_c}{T}-1\right)=\frac{1}{(1+a)(1-b)} \quad . \quad . \quad . \quad . \quad (4)$$

A more accurate equation is that of D. Berthelot (§ 29.VII C):

$$pV=RT\left[1+\frac{9}{128}p\frac{(T^2-6T_c^2)T_c}{p_cT^3}\right] \quad . \quad . \quad . \quad . \quad . \quad . \quad (5)$$

Since $V=M/D$, and the expression in square brackets in (5) may be written $(1+Ap)$ at a given temperature:

$$M=(DRT/p)(1-Ap) \quad . \quad . \quad . \quad . \quad . \quad . \quad . \quad . \quad (6)$$

$$A=-(9/128)(T^2-6T_c^2)T_c/p_cT^3 \quad . \quad . \quad . \quad . \quad . \quad . \quad . \quad (7)$$

For hydrogen chloride $D=1{\cdot}63915$, $T_c=273{\cdot}09+51{\cdot}45$, $p_c=81{\cdot}55$ atm. Thus $A=+0{\cdot}007582$, and since $R=0{\cdot}08208$ lit. atm./1° C., therefore $M=1{\cdot}63915\times 0{\cdot}08208\times 273{\cdot}09\times 0{\cdot}992418=36{\cdot}466$.

Beattie and Bridgeman's [3] equation gives the simple result:

$$(1+\lambda)_{T_1}=1-\beta_1/(R^2T_1{}^2+\beta_1) \quad . \quad . \quad . \quad . \quad . \quad . \quad . \quad (8)$$

where $\beta=RTB_0-A_0-Rc/T^2$, A_0, B_0 and c being constants.

The apparatus used by Guye [4] and the Geneva workers for measuring compressibility coefficients is shown diagrammatically[5] in Fig. 14.VII D. Three bulbs A, B, and C, of 177 ml. capacity, are connected by capillaries 7 cm. long and 1·74 mm. diam., the capillaries having marks *a*, *b*, *c*, and *d*. The bulbs are

[1] Van der Waals, *Proc. K. Akad. Wetens. Amsterdam*, 1898, **1**, 198; D. Berthelot, *J. de Phys.*, 1899, **8**, 263; Guye and Friderich, *Arch. Sci. Phys. Nat.*, 1900, **9**, 505; Guye, *Compt. Rend.*, 1905, **140**, 1241; *J. Chim. Phys.*, 1905, **3**, 321; criticised by Kohnstamm, *J. Chim. Phys.*, 1905, **3**, 665; 1906, **4**, 102. For easily liquefiable gases Guye used " limiting values " of a and b given by $a_0=a(T_c/T)^{3/2}$, $b_0=b/[1-(T_c-T)/T_c](1-0{\cdot}0032229\ p_c/p)$.

[2] *Proc. K. Akad. Wetens. Amsterdam*, 1898, **1**, 198.

[3] See (4), § 38.VII C; Coppock, *J. Phys. Chem.*, 1933, **37**, 995; *Phil. Mag.*, 1935, **19**, 446; Roper, *J. Phys. Chem.*, 1940, **44**, 834; 1941, **45**, 321; used the virial equation (§ 10.VII A) $pv=RT+A/v+B/v^2+c/v^4$ for hydrocarbon gases.

[4] *J. Chim. Phys.*, 1927, **20**, 308.

[5] Important air-traps on the mercury connections, etc., are shown in the original, and must be used in accurate work; see Batuecas' criticism, *J. Chim. Phys.*, 1933, **30**, 482; 1935, **32**, 58; of the work of Klemenc and Bankowski, *Z. anorg. Chem.*, 1932, **208**, 348; 1934, **217**, 62.

contained in an ice-bath K, two horizontal tinned-iron tubes *ef* and *gh*, with glass windows, keeping parts clear of ice so that the marks can be observed through the windows (wire gauze tubes would be better). The lower tube D is connected with a mercury levelling reservoir (with an air-trap), and the upper tube E leads to a mercury gauge F with a fixed levelling point and a vertical pressure-tube G connected at the top H with a vacuum pump. By filling the tubes with gas at low pressure and raising the mercury level in succession past the marks *d*, *c*, *b*, and *a*, at the same time reading the pressures in FG, two (or three) values of pv for different pressures below atmospheric are found, from which $1+\lambda$ can be calculated. Values of pv at low pressures found by Rayleigh's method (§ 11.VII A), or in other ways, may be used.

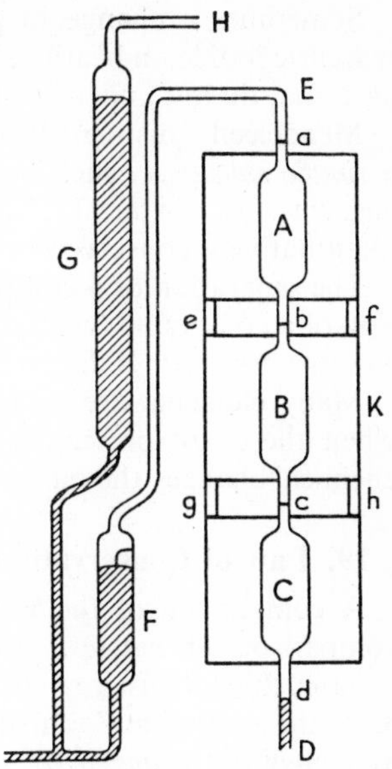

FIG. 14.VII D. Apparatus for Determination of Gas Compressibility

§ 18. Elements and Compounds

"In Chemistry, bodies are regarded as equal when their properties, apart from arbitrary size and shape, are completely identical. In order that two bodies shall be equal in this sense, it is necessary that for each body all the parts shall also be identical. Bodies considered without reference to size and shape are called *substances*, and those which satisfy the above conditions are called *homogeneous*. Experience shows that from homogeneous substances, in many circumstances, other homogeneous substances, with essentially different properties, can be produced. These changes usually occur discontinuously, so that a continuous change of substance does not occur in any ascertainable way. Such changes are called *chemical changes*."[1]

Homogeneous bodies may either have a constant composition, however prepared, when they are called *pure substances*, or they can be prepared with different compositions, when they are called *solutions*. Solutions can always be separated by suitable means (e.g. evaporation or distillation) into two or more pure substances.

A homogeneous pure substance may undergo a complete chemical change in different ways according to its composition:[2]

(i) It forms products of greater weight than itself in all changes, or *combines* with other substances, when it is called an *element*.

(ii) It forms products each of less weight than itself, or *decomposes*, when it is called a *compound*.

(iii) It remains unchanged in weight, when it is said to have undergone an *allotropic change* if it is an element, or an *isomeric change* if it is a compound.

[1] Ostwald, "Lehrbuch der allgemeinen Chemie," Leipzig, 1910, **1**, 1; "The Principles of Inorganic Chemistry," 1904, 1 f; *J.C.S.*, 1904, **85**, 506.

[2] Duhem, "Le Mixte et la Combinaison Chimique," Paris, 1902; Ostwald, "Outlines of General Chemistry," 1912, 109 f.; on the distinction between compounds and solutions, see Timmermans, "La Notion d'Espèces en Chimie," Paris, 1928; "Chemical Species," New York, 1940; on the definition of element, see Paneth, *Z. phys. Chem.*, 1916, **91**, 171; 1918, **92**, 677; 1918, **93**, 87; *Scientia*, 1935, 219, 272; Fajans, *Jahrb. Radioakt. Elektronik.*, 1917, **14**, 314; Wegscheider, *Z. phys. Chem.*, 1918, **92**, 741; 1919, **93**, 380; Fierz, *Scientia*, 1942, **71**, 67; Partington, *Chymia*, 1948, **1**, 109.

Sometimes a change in physical state of a *compound*, e.g. red into yellow mercuric iodide on heating, is called an allotropic change. A few elements, such as argon, do not undergo chemical changes.[1]

Mendeléeff[2] distinguished between a chemical *element*, such as carbon, and a *simple substance*, such as diamond, graphite, and charcoal, composed of the element. In chemical changes it is the element which is qualitatively and quantitatively conserved.[3]

The separation of a compound into its elements is called *analysis*; the formation of a compound from elements is called *synthesis*, although both these terms are also used with different meanings.

Many elements are mixtures of two or more varieties called *isotopes*, but when these are present in constant ratios and are inseparable by ordinary chemical changes the particular mixture behaves as a simple element.

§ 19. Law of Conservation of Mass

A comparison of the *weights* of bodies by an ordinary balance is really a comparison of *masses*. In all chemical changes, as was first categorically asserted by Lavoisier:[4] " an equal quantity of matter exists both before and after the operation." In its modern form, this runs:[5] *the total mass of any system is not changed by any process which takes place in the system.* The introduction of the concept of " matter " adds a metaphysical element to the law which is quite unnecessary.[6]

The law of conservation of mass can be established only by experiment. Heydweiller[7] noticed small changes in weight in some chemical reactions carried out in sealed glass tubes, e.g. $Fe+CuSO_4Aq=Cu+FeSO_4Aq$, a maximum *loss* of 0·217 mg. being found. Although lo Surdo[8] found no real changes amounting to 1 part in 10^7 to 10^8, Landolt[9] in a long series of experiments at first always found small losses (maximum 0·199 mg.), as did Sanford and Ray[10] in the reduction of ammoniacal silver nitrate with grape sugar (0·03–0·08 mg.). This might be due to the penetration of glass by gases and vapours, which Zenghelis[11] claimed to have detected by such experiments as one in which silver foil in a sealed vacuous tube was attacked at the ordinary temperature by iodine vapour outside the tube; but other experimenters[12] could not confirm

1 Compounds of argon with boron trifluoride were reported by Booth and Willson, *J.A.C.S.*, 1935, **57**, 2273.

2 " The Principles of Chemistry," 1905, **1**, 20 f., 362.

3 Mallet, *J.C.S.*, 1893, **63**, 1; Hooykaas, *Chem. Weekbl.*, 1947, **43**, 526 (54 refs.); Partington, *Chymia*, 1948, **1**, 109.

4 " Traité Élémentaire de Chimie," Paris, 1789, 140; reprint (incomplete), Paris, 1937, 82; the principle had been taken for granted long before this.

5 Ostwald, " Principles of Inorganic Chemistry," 1904, 18; Mellor, " Treatise on Inorganic and Theoretical Chemistry," 1922, **1**, 100, called this the law of " the perdurability of matter."

6 Stallo, " The Concepts and Theories of Modern Physics," 1882, 25, 86.

7 *Phys. Z.*, 1900, **1**, 527; 1902, **3**, 425; *Ann. Phys.*, 1901, **5**, 394; for older experiments on losses of weight in chemical and physical changes, see Partington and McKie, *Annals of Science*, 1937, **2**, 261; 1938, **3**, 1.

8 *Nuov. Cim.*, 1904, **8**, 45; cf. Kahlbaum, *Verhl. d. Naturforsch. Ges. Basel*, 1903, **16**, 441.

9 *Z. phys. Chem.*, 1893, **12**, 1; 1906, **55**, 589; 1908, **64**, 581; *Berlin Ber.*, 1893, 301; 1906, 266; Über die Erhaltung der Masse bei chemischen Umsetzungen, *Abhl. d. D. Bunsen Ges.*, Halle, 1909, **1**; Ostwald, *Z. phys. Chem.*, 1911, 77, 252.

10 *Phys. Rev.*, 1897, **5**, 247.

11 *Z. phys. Chem.*, 1909, **65**, 341; 1910, **72**, 425; on the supposed evaporation of solids at room temperature, *ibid.*, 1904, **50**, 219; 1906, **57**, 90.

12 Landolt, *Z. phys. Chem.*, 1909, **68**, 169; Stock and Heynemann, *Ber.*, 1909, **42**, 1800; Tollens, *ibid.*, 1909, **42**, 2013; Elsden, *Proc. Chem. Soc.*, 1910, **26**, 7; Firth, *ibid.*, 1913, **29**, 111.

these results. The small losses of weight at first found by Landolt were later traced by him to a slight increase in volume of the vessel by expansion (leading to increased air displacement), and the driving off of a film of moisture on the vessel. By using silica tubes coated with wax they did not occur. Joly [1] used a torsion balance sensitive to 0·04 dynes; no changes in weight were detectable when copper sulphate was dissolved in water or dilute sulphuric acid. Manley [2] reduced the observed change to 1 in 100,000,000 with the reaction between barium chloride and sodium sulphate. Poynting and Phillips [3] found a very small loss of weight when a brass cylinder was heated, but the supposed loss in weight of a lead sphere when a radioactive preparation was put underneath,[4] was due to experimental error.[5]

The distinction between "mass" and "weight," and whether it is more correct to speak of "atomic masses" or "atomic weights,"[6] need not detain us.

A result [7] pointed out by Hinrichs, that an atomic weight depends on the weight of substance used to determine it, was shown by Guye and Moles to be due, probably, to adsorption of air by the solids, especially if they are powders. This also causes an error on reducing the weight of a powder in air to the weight in vacuum; Zintl and Goubeau found that the weight of potassium nitrate in air corrected to vacuum is greater than the actual weight in vacuum, while that of potassium chloride is less. Ruer and Kuschmann found that cupric oxide ignited at 850° adsorbs only 0·00086 per cent. of its weight of air, whilst ferric oxide ignited at 700° takes up 0·0025 per cent. Many other powders, especially silica, adsorb air as well as moisture.

For all ordinary chemical experiments the law of conservation of mass may be considered to be exact. Einstein,[8] from the special theory of relativity, deduced that a loss of energy ΔE by a system leads to a loss of mass $\Delta m = \Delta E/c^2$, where c=velocity of light; this is significant only in natural or artificial radioactive changes.[9]

The construction and use of a sensitive *balance* and the technique of weighing,[10]

1 *Trans. Roy. Dublin Soc.*, 1903, **8**, 23.

2 *Phil. Trans.*, 1912, **212**, 227; *Proc. Roy. Soc.*, 1912, **86**, 591; *Proc. Phys. Soc.*, 1927, **39**, 441.

3 *Proc. Roy. Soc.*, 1905, **76**, 445.

4 Geigl, *Ann. Phys.*, 1903, **10**, 429.

5 Kaufmann, *Ann. Phys.*, 1903, **10**, 894.

6 Ostwald, "Lehrbuch der allgemeinen Chemie," 1910, **1**, **2**; "Outlines of General Chemistry," 3rd edit., 1912, 16; Meyer and Auerbach, *Z. Elektrochem.*, 1914, **20**, 225.

7 Turner, *Phil. Trans.*, 1833, **133**, 523; Marignac, *Bibl. Univ.*, 1843, **46**, 350 (372); "Oeuvres," Geneva, [1902], **1**, 94; Stas, *Mém. Acad. Roy. Belg.* (quarto), 1865, **35**, No. 1; "Oeuvres," Brussels, 1894, **1**, 477; Guye and Zachariades, *Compt. Rend.*, 1909, **149**, 593, 1122; Thorpe, *Proc. Chem. Soc.*, 1909, **25**, 285; Scott, *ibid.*, 1909, **25**, 286; Richards, Köthner, and Tiede, *Z. anorg. Chem.*, 1909, **61**, 320 (confirmed Stas's result); Richards and Baxter, *J.A.C.S.*, 1910, **32**, 507; *Z. anorg. Chem.*, 1910, **66**, 418; Guye, *J. Chim. Phys.*, 1916, **14**, 54, 83; Guye and Moles, *ibid.*, 1917, **15**, 360; Ruer and Kuschmann, *Z. anorg. Chem.*, 1926, **154**, 69; 1926, **166**, 257; 1928, **173**, 233; Zintl and Goubeau, *ibid.*, 1927, **163**, 105.

8 *Ann. Phys.*, 1906, **20**, 627; 1907, **23**, 197, 371.

9 Maxted, "Modern Advances in Inorganic Chemistry," Oxford, 1947, 3, 20, 41.

10 Manley, *Phil. Trans.*, 1910, **210**, 387; 1912, **212**, 227; *Proc. Roy. Soc.*, 1912, **86**, 591; *Proc. Phys. Soc.*, 1927, **39**, 444; 1945, **57**, 97; art. Balance in Thorpe and Whiteley, "Dict. of Applied Chem.," 1937, **1**, 587; Guye, *J. Chim. Phys.*, 1913, **11**, 319; 1916, **14**, 25, 54, 83, 195; 1917, **15**, 360, 405; 1918, **16**, 46; Shakespear, *Phil. Mag.*, 1914, **27**, 990 (rider apparatus); Rae and Reilly, *Chem. News*, 1916, **114**, 187, 200; Blount, *J.C.S.*, 1917, **111**, 1035; Guichard, *Bull. Soc. Chim.*, 1917, **21**, 233 (hints on exact weighing); Porritt, *J.S.C.I.*, **37**, 85 T (illumination of balance); Brinton, *J.A.C.S.*, 1919, **41**, 1151 (single swing method); Dean, *J.C.S.*, 1919, **115**, 826; Wells, *J.A.C.S.*, 1920, **42**, 411; Conrady, *Proc. Roy. Soc.*, 1922, **101**, 211; Petrie, *J. Sci.*

and the *calibration of weights*,[1] must be sought in the appropriate literature; the *vacuum balance*[2] has some special uses. Dean[3] found only very slight changes of zero of a balance over a long period (0·00006 g. in 10 months), probably due to the displacement of the knife edges. The air displacement correction in weighing is considered in § 20; it should be noted that it applies also to the weights, and that if the platinum fraction weights have been adjusted in air by counterpoising with brass weights, they must be given the density of brass in calculating the air displacement.[4] The use of what Leduc called " ornamental decimals " is as much out of place in weighings as in other work, and attempts to weight to 0·01 mg. are useless with ordinary gravimetric balances.[5]

The so-called *bottling apparatus* used by Richards[6] is used in preventing the access of moist air to a substance prepared in a dry state. A hard glass or quartz tube is fitted by a ground joint to a soft glass tube with a pocket. A platinum boat containing the substance is heated in the hard glass tube in a current of gas, the weighing bottle being put into the soft glass tube, with the stopper in the pocket. After cooling, the gas is displaced by dry air and the boat pushed (e.g. by a platinum wire) into the weighing bottle, after which the apparatus is rotated and the stopper similarly inserted. The bottle is then transferred to the balance. The apparatus of Hönigschmid[7] is similar, but the boat and stopper are moved by the action of a magnet on a bulb containing iron.

§ 20. Correction of Weights to Vacuum

An important correction necessary in all accurate weighings is for the buoyancy of the air in which the object is weighed. The true weight (in vacuum) is greater than that in air by the weight of the volume of air displaced by the body in the actual conditions of the experiment, and the same applies to the weights in the other pan of the balance. Turner[8] corrected for air displacement by adding to the weights of the object and the weights in air, the weights of air which they displaced; he says the method was used by Clark, of Glasgow, but Fahrenheit[9] had so corrected the densities of liquids determined by the specific gravity bottle, taking the density of air as 0·001. Berzelius[10] said Turner's correction was like " straining at a gnat and swallowing a camel," but Faraday[11] was fully aware of the need for the correction, including the case of the determination of gas densities.

Instr., 1923, **1**, 29 (chain balance); Guthrie, *Nature*, 1928, **121**, 745; Ramberg, *Svensk. Kem. Tidskr.*, 1929, **41**, 106; Buchan, *J. Sci. Instr.*, 1936, **13**, 1; Bond, *Analyst*, 1936, **61**, 85 (air-damped); Mellor and Thompson, " Treatise on Quantitative Analysis," 2nd edit., 1938, 3.

[1] Richards, *J.A.C.S.*, 1900, **22**, 144; *Z. phys. Chem.*, 1900, **33**, 605; Hopkins, Zinn, and Rogers, *J.A.C.S.*, 1920, **42**, 2528; Eaton, *ibid.*, 1932, **54**, 1; Hurley, *Ind. Eng. Chem. Anal.*, 1937, **9**, 239; Schmidt, *Deutsch. Apothek. Ztg.*, 1937, **52**, 811; Blade, *Ind. Eng. Chem. Anal.*, 1939, **11**, 498.

[2] Crookes, *Phil. Trans.*, 1873, **163**, 277; Blount and Woodcock, *J.C.S.*, 1918, **113**, 81; Meyer-Cords, *Ann. Phys.*, 1939, **36**, 651; Monk, *J. Appl. Phys.*, 1948, **19**, 485.

[3] *J.C.S.*, 1919, **115**, 826; differing from Blount, *ibid.*, 1917, **111**, 1035.

[4] Gray and Burt, *J.C.S.*, 1909, **95**, 1633; Guye, *J. Chim. Phys.*, 1913, **11**, 319.

[5] Guye, *J. Chim. Phys.*, 1917, **15**, 360.

[6] *Z. anorg. Chem.*, 1895, **8**, 253; *J.C.S.*, 1911, **99**, 1201; Partington, " General and Inorganic Chemistry," 1947, 25.

[7] *Z. anorg. Chem.*, 1929, **178**, 1; Emeléus and Anderson, " Modern Aspects of Inorganic Chemistry," 1938, 43.

[8] *Phil. Trans.*, 1833, **123**, 523.

[9] *Phil. Trans.*, 1724, **33**, 114; abrgd. edit., 1809, **7**, 32.

[10] Quoted by Brauner, *Ber.*, 1889, **22**, 1186.

[11] " Chemical Manipulation," 1842, 47, 395.

Let the force exerted on a mass of 1 g. in vacuum be called a " vacuum gram," and that exerted in air an " air gram." Let m, M be the weights of the empty vessel and the vessel containing the substance, respectively, ρ_1 the mean density of air (0·0012 g./ml.), ρ the density of the substance, x the weight of the substance in vacuum expressed in air grams; then in air x will decrease by $x\rho_1/\rho$, or become $x(1-\rho_1/\rho)$. Hence [1] $x(1-\rho_1/\rho)+m=M$, therefore:

$$x=(M-m)/(1-\rho_1/\rho)\simeq(M-m)(1+\rho_1/\rho) \quad \text{(1)}$$

If w' g. is the apparent weight of an object weighed in laboratory air, of density ρ_1 g./ml., with weights of density ρ_2 (e.g. brass, $\rho_2=8{\cdot}4$), and if ρ is the density of the object weighed, the true weight in vacuum is:

$$w=w'+w'\rho_1(1/\rho-1/\rho_2) \quad \text{(2)}$$

If the object consists of parts of different densities (e.g. liquid in a glass pyknometer) the formula must be modified in an obvious way.[2] It is usually sufficient to take $\rho_1=0{\cdot}0012$ g./ml., but in accurate work the actual density of the (moist) air must be used. In this case: [3]

$$\rho_1=0{\cdot}001293(P-p')/(1+0{\cdot}00367t)760 \quad \text{(3)}$$

where P=barometric pressure in mm. Hg, t=temperature ° C., $p'=0{\cdot}0038Hp$, where H=humidity in percentage of saturation at $t°$ and p=saturation vapour pressure in mm. at $t°$.

The apparent specific gravity s' of a substance is corrected by *adding* the value of δ given in the following table (density of air taken as 0·0012):

s'	δ	s'	δ	s'	δ	s'	δ
0·7	−0·00036	1·7	+0·00084	5·5	+0·0054	10·5	+0·0114
0·8	−0·00024	1·8	+0·00096	6·0	+0·0060	11·0	+0·0120
0·9	−0·00012	1·9	+0·00108	6·5	+0·0066	11·5	+0·0126
1·0	0·00000	2·0	+0·0012	7·0	+0·0072	12·0	+0·0132
1·1	+0·00012	2·5	+0·0018	7·5	+0·0078	13·0	+0·0144
1·2	+0·00024	3·0	+0·0024	8·0	+0·0084	14·0	+0·0156
1·3	+0·00036	3·5	+0·0030	8·5	+0·0090	15·0	+0·0168
1·4	+0·00048	4·0	+0·0036	9·0	+0·0096	16·0	+0·0180
1·5	+0·00060	4·5	+0·0042	9·5	+0·0102	17·0	+0·0192
1·6	+0·00072	5·0	+0·0048	10·0	+0·0108	18·0	+0·0204

If p is the weight in air, w is the weight of an equal volume of water, and Δ the weight of air displaced, the specific gravity is:

$$s=(p-\Delta)/(w-\Delta) \quad \text{(4)}$$

The weights p and w must be corrected for the air displacements of the weights in the opposite pan by adding the weights of air these displace, i.e.

1 Schottländer, *Z. phys. Chem.*, 1895, **16**, 459.

2 Meyer and Seubert, " Die Atomgewichte der Elemente," Leipzig, 1883, 7; Mendeléeff, *Ber.*, 1884, **17**, 2536; Schottländer, *Z. phys. Chem.*, 1895, **16**, 459; Watson, " Practical Physics," 1908, 76; Guye and Zachariades, *Compt. Rend.*, 1909, **149**, 1122; Ostwald, " Lehrbuch der allgemeinen Chemie," 1910, **1**, 285; Kuhn, *Chem. Ztg.*, 1910, **34**, 1097, 1108; Saar, *ibid.*, 1922, **46**, 433; 1924, **48**, 285 (correction tables for pyknometers); Hutchinson, *Mineral. Mag.*, 1924, **20**, 198; Felgentrager, in Geiger and Scheel, " Handbuch der Physik," 1926, **2**, 132; Bayley, " Chemists' Pocket Book," edit. Ensoll, 1929, 338; Ashley, Lips, and Tschudy, in Van Nostrand's " Chemical Annual," New York, 1935, 873; Mellor and Thompson, " Treatise on Quantitative Analysis," 2nd edit., 1938, 15.

3 Weatherill and Brundage, *J.A.C.S.*, 1932, **54**, 3932 (method of graphing ρ_1 against $P-p$); Bauer, in Weissberger, " Physical Methods of Organic Chemistry," New York, 1945, **1**, 86 f.

$\Sigma x \times 0{\cdot}0012/\rho_2$, where x=weight value and ρ_2=density of the material of the weight. Some sets of weights are already corrected for air displacement.

§ 21. The Laws of Chemical Combination

The following laws (sometimes called the laws of *stoichiometry*) [1] relating to the combination of elements by weight are established by experiment:

(1) *The law of fixed proportions* (Proust, 1797): [2] elements combine in definite ratios by weight and the composition of a pure chemical compound is independent of the way in which it is prepared.

This law was implicitly recognised in quantitative analyses in the eighteenth century,[3] but Proust first established it by special experiments. Berthollet [4] stated (1803) that the composition of compounds could vary within limits. Proust showed that variability occurred only with mixtures or solutions.[5]

(2) *The law of multiple proportions* (Dalton, 1803): [6] when two elements combine to form more than one compound, the weights of one element which combine separately with identical weights of the other are in the ratio of whole numbers, usually small.

(3) *The law of equivalent* (or *reciprocal*) *proportions* (J. B. Richter, 1792): [7] the weights of two elements A and B which combine separately with identical weights of another element C are either the weights in which A and B combine together, or are related to them in the ratio of whole numbers, usually small. (This applies also to the reacting weights of compounds, and was first applied by Richter to acids and bases.)

The law of equivalent proportions shows that *it is possible to assign to every element an* equivalent weight, *or* equivalent [8] *or* combining weight, *representing*

[1] Greek, *στοιχεῖον*, a first principle, or element; *μέτρον*, a measure; the name was introduced by Richter for "the art of measuring (Messkunst] the chemical elements," i.e. of their combining proportions by mass; see reference [7].

[2] *Ann. Chim.*, 1797, **23**, 85; 1799, **32**, 26; *J. de Phys.*, 1801, **53**, 89; 1802, **54**, 89; 1802, **55**, 325; 1804, **59**, 260, 265, 321, 343, 350, 403; 1806, **63**, 364, 421; Kopp, "Die Entwickelung der Chemie in der neueren Zeit," Munich, 1873, 249 f.; Mallet, *J.C.S.*, 1893, **63**, 1; Hartog, *Nature*, 1894, **50**, 149; Duhem, "Le Mixte et la Combinaison Chimique," Paris, 1902, 52; Evans, *Trans. Faraday Soc.*, 1923, **19**, 420. The distinction between a compound and a solution was clearly stated by Proust in 1806; see Partington, "Short History of Chemistry," 1948, 157.

[3] Walden, Mass, Zahl, und Gewicht in der Chemie der Vergangenheit, *Samml. chem.-und chem. techn. Vorträge*, Stuttgart, 1931, **8**, 93.

[4] "Essai de Statique Chimique," 2 vols, Paris, 1803; *J. de Phys.*, 1805, **60**, 284, 347; *Mém. de l'Inst.*, 1806, **7**, i, 229.

[5] Meldrum, *Manch. Mem.*, 1910, **54**, No. 7, showed that the decision between constant and variable proportions really resulted mainly from the adoption of Dalton's atomic theory, which was compatible only with the former; Partington, *Chymia*, 1948, **1**, 109.

[6] "New System of Chemical Philosophy," Manchester, 1808, **1**, i, 211 f.; the law was never explicitly stated by Dalton, but regarded as implied in his atomic theory: see Muir, "Principles of Chemistry," Cambridge, 1889, 8; *idem* in Watts, "Dict. of Chemistry," 1890, **1**, 336; Duhem, "Le Mixte et la Combinaison Chimique," Paris, 1902, 69; Puxeddu, *Gazz.*, 1919, **49**, i, 203; 1923, **53**, 202. The law was *explicitly* stated by Berzelius, *Ann. Phys.*, 1811, **37**, 249. In a conversation with W. C. Henry, q. by Meldrum, "Avogadro and Dalton," Edinburgh, 1906, 58, Dalton spoke of "the principle of multiple proportion."

[7] "Ueber die neuern Gegenstände der Chemie," Breslau and Hirschberg, 1791–1802; "Aufangsgründe der Stöchyometrie oder Messkunst chymischer Elemente," 3 vols., Breslau and Hirschberg, 1792–94; R. A. Smith, *Manch. Mem.*, 1856, **13**, 186. The law was erroneously attributed to Wenzel, "Lehre von der Verwandtschaft der Körper," 1777, owing to a slip by Berzelius, "Théorie des Proportions Chimiques," 1819, 2, 16; this was corrected by Hess, *J. prakt. Chem.*, 1841, **24**, 420, but is still regularly repeated in textbooks.

[8] The idea, and name, of "equivalent" were first used by Cavendish, *Phil. Trans.*, 1767, **57**, 92 (102); 1788, **78**, 166 (178).

the relative proportion in which it combines with other elements. Hydrogen with the smallest combining weight was taken by Dalton as the standard element and its equivalent as unity, but oxygen was used by Thomson,[1] Wollaston[2] and Berzelius,[3] and is at present [4] the standard element, with an equivalent of 8·000, on which basis the equivalent of hydrogen is 1·008. The *equivalent* of an element is the number of parts by weight of it which combine with or replace 8 parts by weight of oxygen or the equivalent of any other element.

The law of multiple proportions shows that if an element has more than one equivalent, these must be in the ratio of whole numbers, usually small (1:2, 2:3, 3:5, etc.).

§ 22. The Atomic Theory

The laws of chemical combination are observed facts independent of any hypothesis, but they are very simply explained by the *atomic theory*. The idea that matter consists of very small indivisible particles called atoms, separated by void and in constant motion, is very old, and was especially taught by the Greek

[1] " System of Chemistry," Edinburgh, 1807, **3**, 425, etc.; *Ann. Phil.*, 1813, **2**, 32 (42), 167; " An Attempt to Establish the First Principles of Chemistry by Experiment," **2** vols, 1825; Thomson used the standard oxygen=1.

[2] *Phil. Trans.*, 1814, **104**, 1; Scott, *J.C.S.*, 1917, **111**, 288. Wollaston used oxygen=10. He also invented a slide-rule of chemical equivalents; see Faraday, " Chemical Manipulation," 1842, 564.

[3] " Théorie des Proportions Chimiques," Paris, 1819, 2nd edit., 1835; Essay on the Cause of Chemical Proportions, *Ann. Phil.*, 1813, **2**, 443; 1814, **3**, 51, 93, 244, 353; Berzelius used oxygen=100. On Gmelin's atomic weight system, see Meldrum, " Avogadro and Dalton," Edinburgh, 1906, 76.

[4] Dalton's standard, H=1, was used by Lothar Meyer and Seubert, " Die Atomgewichte der Elemente aus den Originalzahlen neu berechnet," Leipzig, 1883. The ratio O:H was assumed by Ostwald, " Lehrbuch der allgemeinen Chemie," 1885, **1**, 44, to be really 16:1, and he re-calculated atomic weights on this basis. This ratio was found not to be exact (the value O=15·96, H=1, had been long in use), but Ostwald proposed to retain the standard O=16; Erdmann, *Z. angew. Chem.*, 1899, **12**, 571; *Z. anorg. Chem.*, 1901, **27**, 127. The standard O=16 was favoured by Marignac, *Arch. Sci. Phys. Nat.*, 1883, **10**, 3; *Ann. Chim.*, 1884, **1**, 289; Brauner, *Chem. News*, 1888, **58**, 307; *Ber.*, 1889, **22**, 1186; *Z. anorg. Chem.*, 1897, **14**, 256; 1901, **26**, 186; Ostwald, *Ber.*, 1889, **22**, 1021; Noyes, *Ber.*, 1891, **24**, 238; Küster, *Z. anorg. Chem.*, 1897, **14**, 251; and Richards, *ibid.*, 1901, **28**, 355. Fresenius, *Z. angew. Chem.*, 1899, **12**, 361, 570, was at first neutral, but later, *Ber.*, 1900, **33**, 1847, preferred H=1; Erdmann, *Z. angew. Chem.*, 1899, **12**, 424, 571, 648; *Z. anorg. Chem.*, 1901, **27**, 127; and Fischer, *Z. angew. Chem.*, 1899, **12**, 57, preferred (with reasons) H=1; Lothar Meyer and Seubert, *Ber.*, 1889, **22**, 872, 1161, 1392, and Seubert, *Z. anorg. Chem.*, 1897, **13**, 229, retained this standard. The matter was referred to an international commission, the prime mover being Ostwald (*Ber.*, 1898, **31**, 2949), and this resulted (*Ber.*, 1900, **33**, 1847) in a majority in favour of O=16, seven voting for H=1, two for both H=1 and O=16, and twenty-five for O=16, of whom seven pointed out the advantage of H=1 for teaching. As Bancroft, *J. Phys. Chem.*, 1902, **6**, 198, said: " If there is one thing that is absolutely certain in this world, it is that an appeal to authority is out of place in scientific matters." Oddo, *Gazz.*, 1921, **51**, ii, 161 (full bibl.), and Partington, " Text Book of Inorganic Chemistry," 1921, pref. v, proposed to retain H=1, O=15·88. The discovery of the isotopes of oxygen, of masses 16, 17, and 18 by Giauque and Johnston, *J.A.C.S.*, 1929, **51**, 1436, 3528, clouded the issue, and Meyer, *Phys. Z.*, 1932, **33**, 301, suggested the helium standard He=4·0000, cf. Meyer, *Naturwiss.*, 1922, **10**, 911 (historical); Aston, *Nature*, 1930, **126**, 953. The " oxygen standard " seems to have become unsuitable with the discovery that the atomic weight of atmospheric oxygen is about 0·00008 units greater than that of water oxygen: Dole, *J.A.C.S.*, 1935, **57**, 2731; Jones and Hall, *ibid.*, 1937, **59**, 259; Alexander and Hall, *ibid.*, 1940, **62**, 3462. The factor for converting chemical (O=16) to mass spectrograph (^{16}O=16) values is 1·000275: Smythe, *Phys. Rev.*, 1934, **45**, 299; Murphey, *ibid.*, 1941, **59**, 320, based on a ratio ^{16}O:^{18}O=500±15:1 in water. The atomic weight (O=16) of hydrogen is 1·0080: Swartout and Dole, *J.A.C.S.*, 1939, **61**, 2025, which is probably more accurate than 1·0081; Moles, *An. Fis. Quim.*, 1935, **33**, 721 (1·00806). There are two isotopes of hydrogen, which may exist in a slightly varying ratio in different specimens.

philosophers Leukippos and Demokritos (about 450 B.C.). Many applications of the atomic theory were made before the time of Dalton, especially by Newton.[1]

There was an unbroken tradition of the theory through Epikouros (341–270 B.C.) and Lucretius, whose long poem *De Rerum Natura* (57 B.C.) gives a faithful account of the classical atomic theory. The theory was revived by Gassend,[2] from whom it passed, by way of Boyle, to Newton. Bryan and William Higgins in 1786 and 1789, respectively, made notable use of Newton's form of the atomic theory,[1] but it was Dalton [3] who first established it in Chemistry. He arrived at the theory by considerations about mixed gases on Newtonian lines.[4] Dalton recognised that:

(1) *Every kind of atom has a definite weight.*

(2) *Different elements have atoms differing in weight.*

(3) *Atoms combine to form compounds in definite ratios of whole numbers, usually small.*

The *atomic weight* of an element is the ratio of the mass (or weight) of its atom with reference to the mass of the atom of some standard element which is arbitrarily assigned. If the mass of the oxygen atom is arbitrarily chosen as 16·000, that of the hydrogen atom is 1·008.

Atomic weights can be found from combining ratios only if the numbers of atoms combining together is known. If w_A and w_B are the weights of two elements A and B combining in the ratio of x atoms of A and y atoms of B to form a compound A_xB_y, the ratio of the atomic weights is yw_A/xw_B, and unless x and y are known this cannot be found from w_A and w_B.

The laws of chemical combination find a remarkably simple explanation in the atomic theory, but it should not be forgotten that they are experimental results independent of theory. The discovery of *isotopes*, i.e. elements with somewhat varying combining weights, makes it difficult, if not impossible, to frame accurate statements of the laws without introducing the language of the atomic theory.[5]

The most sustained attempt to deduce the laws of stoichiometry on the basis of the phase rule and without the atomic theory was made by F. Wald,[6] and

[1] For a full statement of the origins of the atomic theory, see Giua, *Gazz.*, 1919, **49**, ii, 1; Gregory, *Sci. Progr.*, 1927, **22**, 293; "A Short History of Atomism," 1931; Partington, *Annals of Science*, 1939, **4**, 245; Duchesne, *Scientia*, 1947, **82**, 37; Hooykaas, *Chem. Weekbl.*, 1948, **44**, 229, 407.

[2] *Syntagma Philosophiae Epicuri*, in his "Animadversiones in Decimvm Librvm Diogenis Laertii," Lyons, 1649; full account in *Syntagma Philosophium*, in vols. 1 and 2 of "Opera," Lyons, 1658.

[3] "New System of Chemical Philosophy," Manchester, 1808–10, **1**, i and ii. The theory was first published, from information supplied by Dalton, by Thomson, "System of Chemistry," Edinburgh, 1807, **3**, 425, and later sections. For excellent historical accounts of the development of the atomic and molecular theories, see Ida Freund, "The Study of Chemical Composition," Cambridge, 1904, 226 f.; Lowry, "Historical Introduction to Chemistry," 1915, 291 f.

[4] This was first elucidated by Roscoe and Harden, "A New View of the Origin of Dalton's Atomic Theory," 1894; an alternative view put forward by Debus, *Phil. Mag.*, 1896, **42**, 350; *Z. phys. Chem.*, 1896, **20**, 359; 1897, **24**, 325; 1899, **29**, 266; 1899, **30**, 556, was shown to be improbable by Roscoe and Harden, *Z. phys. Chem.*, 1897, **22**, 241; *Phil. Mag.*, 1897, **43**, 153; Kahlbaum, *J. Phys. Chem.*, 1896–7, **1**, 187, 736; *Z. phys. Chem.*, 1899, **29**, 700.

[5] Baborowsky, *Coll. Czech. Comm.*, 1931, **3**, 3; Šimek, *ibid.*, 1931, **3**, 5; Křiž, *ibid.*, 1931, **3**, 9; *Chem. Listy*, 1931, **25**, 5; Partington, *Chymia*, 1948, **1**, 109.

[6] *Z. phys. Chem.*, 1895, **18**, 337; 1896, **19**, 607; 1897, **22**, 253; 1897, **23**, 78; 1897, **24**, 315, 633; 1898, **25**, 524; 1898, **26**, 77; 1899, **28**, 12; 1908, **63**, 307; *J. Phys. Chem.*, 1896, **1**, 21; *Chem. Ztg.*, 1906, **30**, 963, 978; 1907, **31**, 756, 769; Baborowsky, *Chem. Ztg.*, 1930, **54**, 905; Druce, "Two Czech Chemists," 1944, 45 f.

his views were supported by Ostwald [1] (who emphasised the importance of energy), but were criticised by others.[2] Wald started from a very general conception of a "phase," and a rule that if various substances are brought together under ordinary conditions, the number of independent pure substances present is equal to the number of phases together with the number of possible independent changes of composition. Another attempt to connect chemical formulae with the mathematical invariant theory [3] is no more attractive. These suggestions were, in their time, helpful in disturbing a too conservative attitude in chemistry. Ostwald's thesis that "matter is merely a manifestation of energy" is sanctioned by modern theory dependent on the principle of relativity (§ 19), and the conversion of matter into energy, and of energy into matter,[4] is now a commonplace in nuclear transformations.

§ 23. Choice of Atomic Weights

The atomic weight of an element may be regarded as the smallest weight contained in a molecular weight of any of its compounds. This statement, which may be called [5] *Cannizzaro's principle*,[6] is the primary definition.[7] The so-called chemical methods [8] for determining which multiple of the equivalent is equal to the atomic weight, are not really satisfactory.[9] A check on the accuracy of the value found by Cannizzaro's principle, which is really a maximum value,[10] is given by the ratio of specific heats of a gas, the atomic heat and isomorphism for solids, and the position of the element in the periodic table.[11] The values so found are in general agreement,[12] and there is no longer any doubt as to the multiple of the equivalent which must be taken as the atomic weight of any element.[13]

1 *J.C.S.*, 1904, **85**, 506; *J. Chim. Phys.*, 1904, **2**, 398; *Z. Elektrochem.*, 1904, **10**, 572; *Z. phys. Chem.*, 1909, **69**, 506; "The Fundamental Principles of Chemistry," transl. Morse, 1909; cf. Arrhenius, "Theories of Chemistry," 1907, 39; Kenrick, "An Introduction to Chemistry," Toronto, 1932. Ideas similar to Ostwald's were proposed by E. J. Mills, *Phil. Mag.*, 1876, **1**, 1.

2 Benedicks, *Z. anorg. Chem.*, 1906, **49**, 284; Nasini, *Gazz.*, 1906, **36**, i, 540; 1907, **37**, ii, 137; Baur, *Z. anorg. Chem.*, 1906, **50**, 199 (supporting Ostwald); *Z. phys. Chem.*, 1908, **62**, 760; Kuhn, *Chem. Ztg.*, 1907, **31**, 688; 1908, **32**, 55; De Vries, *Z. phys. Chem.*, 1908, **62**, 308.

3 Gordon and Alexejeff, *Z. phys. Chem.*, 1900, **35**, 610; 1901, **36**, 741; 1901, **38**, 750; Study, *ibid.*, 1901, **37**, 546; for connexion with group theory, see Kurnakow, *Z. anorg. Chem.*, 1925, **146**, 69.

4 Cf. Houtermans and Jensen, *Z. Naturforsch.*, 1947, **2** A, 146.

5 Partington, "College Course of Inorganic Chemistry," 1939, 88; a good pedagogic survey of the whole subject is given by Waddell, *Chem., News*, 1915, **112**, 50.

6 Cannizzaro, Sunto di un Corso di Filosofia Chimica, in *Nuov. Cim.*, 1858, **7**, 321; *J.C.S.*, 1872, **25**, 945 (Faraday Lecture); Ostwald's *Klassiker*, 1891, **30**; *Alembic Club Reprint*, 1910, **18**; *Gazz.*, 1871, **1**, 1, 213, 293, 389, 567, 629; transl. as Historische Notizen und Betrachtungen über die Anwendung der Atomtheorie in der Chemie und über die Systeme der Konstitutionsformeln von Verbindungen, *Samml. chem.-und chem.-techn. Vorträge*, Stuttgart, 1913, **20**. Cannizzaro's views were made known generally by Lothar Meyer's book, "Die modernen Theorien der Chemie," 1862, and later editions and translations, e.g. "Modern Theories of Chemistry," by Bedson and Williams, 1888, 7 f.; see also Lothar Meyer's "Outlines, of Theoretical Chemistry," transl. Bedson and Williams, 2nd edit., 1899, 31 f.

7 Meldrum, "Avogadro and Dalton," Edinburgh, 1906, 43, 95.

8 Williamson, *J.C.S.*, 1869, **22**, 328; Odling, in Watts, "Dictionary of Chemistry," 1874 **1**, 457.

9 Meldrum "Avogadro and Dalton," Edinburgh, 1906, 43; Perrin, "Les Atomes," 1914, 41.

10 Muir, in Watts, "Dictionary of Chemistry," 1890, **1**, 336.

11 Partington, "General and Inorganic Chemistry," 1947, 22.

12 L. Meyer, "Modern Theories of Chemistry," transl. Bedson and Williams, 1888, 37 f.

13 Muir, "Principles of Chemistry," Cambridge, 1889, 39 f., 86, gives a table of values showing how the atomic weight was found in each case. A fuller account is given by Ostwald, "Lehrbuch der allgemeinen Chemie," 1910, **1**, 43 f.; see also Lowry, "Historical Introduction to Chemistry," 1915, 360.

§ 24. Determination of Atomic Weights

The various methods used in the determination of atomic weights cannot be considered in detail.[1] The *gravimetric method*, depending on the determination of the weight ratios of substances undergoing direct and complete chemical changes, was first accurately applied by Berzelius;[2] it was notably improved by Turner,[3] Penny,[4] and Marignac,[5] and brought to great accuracy by Stas.[6] More recently, T. W. Richards,[1] and his pupils Baxter and Hönigschmid (see below), made notable advances in the method.

The so-called *physico-chemical methods* depend on (*a*) the determination of limiting densities (§ 15), and (*b*) the analysis of gases by methods which partly involve accurate pressure determinations; these were especially developed by Guye and collaborators in Geneva,[7] and later by Whytlaw-Gray and collaborators in England, and by Moles and collaborators in Madrid.

The real standard used by Stas was silver, which, he says,[8] was "the pivot of my researches." He purified it carefully and finally distilled it by the oxy-hydrogen blowpipe in a quicklime apparatus.[9] Dumas[10] and Mallet[11] found, respectively, that silver so distilled contains 0·008 per cent. and 0·005 per cent. of oxygen, and Richards and Wells[12] (who criticised Stas's work) finally melted the silver on quicklime in hydrogen. Although this metal is free from oxygen, Baxter and Lundstedt[13] found that it contains a trace of calcium, formed by reduction of the lime. The silver-halogen method is one of the oldest precision methods of quantitative analysis;[14] it passed by way of Berzelius to Marignac and Stas,[15]

[1] Cleve, *J.C.S.*, 1895, **67**, 468 (on Marignac); Mallet, *J.C.S.*, 1893, **63**, 1 (on Stas); Guye and Bogdan, *J. Chim. Phys.*, 1905, **3**, 537; Brauner, in Abegg, "Handbuch der anorganischen Chemie," 1908, **1**, 4, 9, 155; 1907, **3**, iii, 6; Ostwald, "Lehrbuch der allgemeinen Chemie," 1910, **1**, 1; Richards, *J.C.S.*, 1911, **99**, 1201; 1930, 1937; J. N. Friend, "Text-Book of Inorganic Chemistry," 1917, **1**, 241; Meyer, *Naturwiss.*, 1922, **10**, 911; for earlier work, see Freund, "The Study of Chemical Composition," Cambridge, 1904 (to Stas). A summary is given in Partington, "General and Inorganic Chemistry," 1947, 21; for values, see Landolt-Börnstein, "Tabellen," 1923, **1**, 2; and the annual reports of the International Committee on Atomic Weights, in *J.C.S.* and *J.A.C.S.*

[2] Hisinger and Berzelius, *Afhandlingar i Fysik, Kemi och Mineralogi*, Stockholm, 1811, **5**; *Ann. Phys.*, 1811, **37**, 249, 415; Suppl. in *ibid.*, 1811, **38**, 161; 1812, **40**, 162, 235; Ostwald's *Klassiker*, 1892, **35**.

[3] *Phil. Trans.*, 1833, **133**, 523.

[4] *Phil. Trans.*, 1839, **129**, 13; Berry, *J.S.C.I.*, 1932, **51**, 453.

[5] "Oeuvres Complètes," Geneva, [1902]; Cleve, *J.C.S.*, 1895, **67**, 468; *Memorial Lectures,* Chemical Society," 1900, **1**, 468.

[6] "Oeuvres Complètes," 3 vols., Brussels, 1894 f.; *Memorial Lectures*, Chemical Society, London, 1900, **1**, 1.

[7] Guye and Bogdan, *J. Chim. Phys.*, 1905, **3**, 537 (N_2O); Jaquerod and Bogdan, *ibid.*, 1905, **3**, 562 (NO); Guye and Fluss, *ibid.*, 1908, **6**, 732 (NOCl); Guye, *Z. phys. Chem.*, 1909, **69**, 315; *Z. anorg. Chem.*, 1909, **64**, 1; Guye and Druginine, *J. Chim. Phys.*, 1910, **8**, 472 (NO_2); Batuecas, *ibid.*, 1932, **29**, 269; 1934, **31**, 65 (CH_3F).

[8] Recherches sur les Rapports réciproques des Poids Atomiques, *Bull. Acad. Roy. Belg.*, 1860, **10**, 208; "Oeuvres," Brussels, 1894, **1**, 325.

[9] Nouvelles Recherches sur les Lois des Proportions Chimiques, *Mém. Acad. Roy. Belg.* (quarto), 1865, **35**, No. 1; "Oeuvres," 1894, **1**, 455.

[10] *Ann. Chim.*, 1878, **14**, 289.

[11] *Phil. Trans.*, 1880, **171**, 1003.

[12] *J.A.C.S.*, 1905, **27**, 459; *Z. anorg. Chem.*, 1905, **47**, 56.

[13] *J.A.C.S.*, 1940, **62**, 1829; cf. Baxter and Parsons, *ibid.*, 1922, **44**, 577, 591.

[14] Walden, Mass, Zahl, und Gewicht in der Chemie der Vergangenheit, *Samml. chem.-und chem.-techn. Vorträge*, Stuttgart, 1931, **8**, 36 f.

[15] Marignac, *Bibl. Univ.*, 1842, **40**, 145; 1843, **45**, 346; 1843, **46**, 350; for Stas, see refs. 1 and 6.

and it has rightly been emphasised [1] that practically all accurate gravimetric atomic weight determinations rest on the value taken for silver. The ratio Ag:O, however, cannot be found directly, since it is impossible to prepare silver oxide in a condition of purity,[2] and the link between silver and oxygen, until recently, involved [3] the atomic weight of nitrogen through the ratio $Ag:AgNO_3$. Finally, Hönigschmid and Sachtleben,[4] by converting barium perchlorate, $Ba(ClO_4)_2$, to barium chloride, $BaCl_2$, by heating in hydrogen chloride gas, found the ratio $BaCl_2$:8O, and then by precipitating the barium chloride as silver chloride found the ratio $BaCl_2$:2AgCl. From these two ratios they calculated Ag:O=107·880:16·000. Since the value Ag=107·880 from the $AgNO_3$:Ag ratio requires N=14·008, a value found by physico-chemical methods with gases, the latter value is also confirmed.

An incomplete but representative list of papers by Baxter and collaborators is given in the reference.[5]

A representative list of papers by Hönigschmid and collaborators [6] (names given in brackets) on atomic weights gives a course of reading on the methods used in the Munich laboratory.

1 Erdmann, *Z. anorg. Chem.*, 1901, **27**, 127; Guye, *J. Chim. Phys.*, 1916, **14**, 204; Moles, *Z. phys. Chem.*, 1925, **115**, 61; 1925, **117**, 157; *Rec. Trav. Chim.*, 1929, **48**, 864; Moles and Clavera, *Z. anorg. Chem.*, 1927, **167**, 49.

2 Baker and Riley, *J.C.S.*, 1926, 2510.

3 Stas, *Bull. Acad. Roy. Belg.*, 1860, **10**, 208; *Mém. Acad. Roy. Belg.* (quarto), 1865, **35**, No. 1; " Oeuvres," 1894, **1**, 342, 717; Richards and Forbes, *J.A.C.S.*, 1905, **27**, 5; *Z. anorg. Chem.*, 1907, **55**, 34; Hönigschmid, *Z. anorg. Chem.*, 1927, **163**, 65.

4 *Z. anorg. Chem.*, 1929, **178**, 1.

5 Sn: *J.A.C.S.*, 1920, **42**, 905; Cd: *ibid.*, 1921, **43**, 1230; La: *ibid.*, 1921, **43**, 1080; B: *Science*, 1921, **54**, 524; Si: *Proc. Amer. Acad.*, 1923, **58**, 245; Ti: *J.A.C.S.*, 1923, **45**, 1228; 1926, **48**, 3117; 1928, **50**, 408; Co: *ibid.*, 1924, **46**, 357; Ge: *Proc. Amer. Acad.*, 1924, **59**, 235; He: *Proc. Nat. Acad.*, 1925, **11**, 231; 1926, **12**, 20; O: *ibid.*, 1924, **10**, 479; 1926, **12**, 699; normal density 1·42897; Ne: *ibid.*, 1928, **14**, 50; A: *ibid.*, 1928, **14**, 57; N: *ibid.*, 1926, **12**, 703 (low value, 14·007, by density); 1931, **53**, 604; As: *J.A.C.S.*, 1933, **55**, 1054, 1957; 1935, **57**, 851; Tl: *ibid.*, 1933, **55**, 2384; Cs: *ibid.*, 1933, **55**, 858; 1934, **56**, 1108; In: *ibid.*, 1933, **55**, 1943, K, Cl: *ibid.*, 1933, **55**, 3185; *Ann. Rep. Chem. Soc.*, 1933, **30**, 85; Na, I, C: *J.A.C.S.*, 1934, **56**, 615; C: *ibid.*, 1936, **58**, 510; 1937, **59**, 506; Scott and Hurley, *ibid.*, 1937, **59**, 1905, 2078; Eu: *ibid.*, 1938, **60**, 602; on Baxter, see Forbes, *J. Chem. Educ.*, 1934, **11**, 444.

6 Bi: *Z. Elektrochem.*, 1920, **26**, 403; *Ber.*, 1921, **54**, 1873 (Birckenbach); Be: *Ber.*, 1922, **55**, 4 (Birckenbach); B: *ibid.*, 1923, **56**, 1467 (Birckenbach); Fe: *ibid.*, 1923, **56**, 1473 (Birckenbach and Zeiss); Hg: *ibid.*, 1923, **56**, 1212 (Birckenbach and Steinheil); Br: *Ann.*, 1923, **433**, 201 (Zintl); Y: *Z. anorg. Chem.*, 1924, **140**, 341 (Meuwsen); 1927, **165**, 284 (von Welsbach); Dy: *ibid.*, 1927, **165**, 289 (von Welsbach); Sb: *ibid.*, 1924, **136**, 257 (Zintl and Linhard); Si: *ibid.*, 1924, **141**, 101 (Steinheil); Hf: *ibid.*, 1924, **140**, 335; *Ber.*, 1925, **58**, 453 (Zintl); K: *Z. anorg. Chem.*, 1927, **163**, 93; 1928, **177**, 102 (Goubeau); 1933, **213**, 365 (Sachtleben); Ag: *ibid.*, 1927, **163**, 65 (Zintl and Thilo); 1927, **163**, 315 (Chan and Birckenbach); *Z. Elektrochem.*, 1928, **34**, 625; *Z. anorg. Chem.*, 1929, **178**, 1 (Sachtleben); U: *Z. Elektrochem.*, 1914, **20**, 319, 452; *Z. anorg. Chem.*, 1928, **170**, 145 (Schilz); 1936, **226**, 289 (Wittner); Cl: *Z. anorg. Chem.*, 1927, **163**, 315 (Chan and Birckenbach); Te: *ibid.*, 1933, **212**, 242 (Sachtleben and Wintersberger); Re: *ibid.*, 1930, **191**, 309 (Sachtleben); S: *ibid.*, 1931, **195**, 207 (Sachtleben); Ca: *ibid.*, 1931, **195**, 1 (Kempter); Er: *ibid.*, 1933, **214**, 97 (Kappenberger); Se: *ibid.*, 1933, **212**, 198 (Kappenberger); *Naturwiss.*, 1944, **32**, 68 (Görnhardt); Yb: *Z. anorg. Chem.*, 1933, **212**, 385 (Striebel); I: 1932, **208**, 53; *Z. phys. Chem.*, 1931, *Bodenstein Festb.*, 283 (Striebel); Er: *Z. anorg. Chem.*, 1937, **232**, 113 (Wittner); Nb: *ibid.*, 1934, **219**, 161 (Wintersberger); Ta: *ibid.*, 1934, **221**, 129; 1935, **225**, 64 (Schlee); Ra: *ibid.*, 1934, **221**, 65 (Sachtleben); Cd: *ibid.*, 1936, **227**, 184 (Schlee); Ge: *ibid.*, 1936, **225**, 81 (Wintersberger and Wittner); 1936, **227**, 17 (Wintersberger); Mo: *ibid.*, 1936, **229**, 65 (Wittmann); W: *ibid.*, 1936, **229**, 49 (Menn); Se: *ibid.*, 1933, **212**, 198 (Kappenberger); Nd: *ibid.*, 1938, **235**, 220 (Hirschbold-Wittner); P: *ibid.*, 1937, **235**, 129 (Menn); 1939–40, **243**, 355 (Hirschbold-Wittner); Lu: *ibid.*, 1939, **240**, 284 (Hirschbold-Wittner); Ho: *ibid.*, 1940, **244**, 63 (Hirschbold-Wittner); Yb: *ibid.*, 1941, **248**, 72 (Hirschbold-Wittner); $AgNO_3$:AgCl: *Angew. Chem.*, 1936, **49**, 464; Zn: *Z. anorg. Chem.*, 1941, **246**, 363 (v. Mack); Cu: *ibid.*, 1944, **25**, 364 (Johannsen); N: *Z. Naturforsch.*,

The *nephelometer* (Greek νεφέλη, a cloud)[1] determines traces of sparingly soluble substances such as silver chloride dissolved in the washings of precipitates. In this case excess of silver nitrate is added, when (owing to the common ion effect) a small amount of silver chloride is precipitated from the solution and an opalescence develops, which is compared with a standard in the nephelometer. This consists of two test-tubes containing the liquids and inclined in an inverted V, partly screened from bright light by two shutters, one moving over a scale. If the screen over the standard covers half the tube when the same appearance is seen from above, viewed through two flat prisms, then a new standard about half as concentrated is put in, and a new comparison made. In this way the amount of suspended substance is accurately determined and a correction applied. Greene's apparatus used a photronic arrangement. Scott and Hurley found that the nephelometer end-point was affected by temperature and was not strictly proportional to the silver and chloride ion concentrations in the solution, and Briscoe and co-workers abandoned the nephelometric method as unreliable, and used a different procedure.

§ 25. Prout's Hypothesis

The idea that all elements are formed from one primary substance is found in old Greek philosophy. Davy[2] suggested that the "undecompounded substances" are compounds of hydrogen "with another principle as yet unknown in the separate form," and that "the same ponderable matter in different electrical states, or in different arrangements, may constitute substances chemically different." Dr. William Prout[3] in 1815 concluded that *the atomic weights of the elements are whole multiples of that of hydrogen*, and in 1816 he suggested[4] that *the atoms of all elements are formed by the condensation of atoms of hydrogen*, so that hydrogen is the primary substance or *protyle* (Greek πρῶτη, first, ὕλη, matter). Meinecke[5] also said "the numbers of all simple bodies, and hence of all compound bodies, represent a multiple of the value for hydrogen according to a whole number."

1946, **1**, 656 (Johannsen-Gröhling); Be: *ibid.*, 1946, **1**, 650 (Johannsen); Se: *ibid.*, 1946, **1**, 661 (Görnhardt); for a complete list of papers (with portrait), *Z. anorg. Chem.*, 1938, **236**, 1; on thirty years of atomic weight research, Hönigschmid, *Angew. Chem.*, 1940, **53**, 177; on Otto Hönigschmid, b. 1878, Horovitz (Bohemia), d. 1945, see Whytlaw-Gray, *Nature*, 1946, **158**, 543. For work of a similar character, see Zintl and Meuwsen, *Z. anorg. Chem.*, 1924, **136**, 223; Zintl and Goubeau, *ibid.*, 1927, **163**, 302.

[1] Richards, *Z. anorg. Chem.*, 1895, **8**, 253; *J.C.S.*, 1911, **99**, 1201; Richards and Wells, *Amer. Chem. J.*, 1904, **31**, 235; Dienert, *Compt. Rend.*, 1914, **158**, 1117; Vlès, de Watteville, and Lambert, *Compt. Rend.*, 1919, **168**, 797; Chéneveau and Audubert, *ibid.*, 1919, **168**, 553, 684, 766; 1920, **170**, 728; *J. de Phys.*, 1921, **2**, 19; Kleinmann, *Biochem. Z.*, 1919, **99**, 115; 1926, **179**, 301; Wells, *J.A.C.S.*, 1922, **44**, 266 (theory); *Chem. Rev.*, 1927, **3**, 331; Scott and Moilliet, *J.A.C.S.*, 1932, **54**, 205 (theory); Kugelmass, *Compt. Rend.*, 1922, **175**, 343; Kingslake, *Trans. Optical Soc. Amer.*, 1924–5, **26**, 53; Yoe and Kleinmann, "Photometric Chemical Analysis," New York, 1929, **2**; Briscoe *et al.*, *Proc. Roy. Soc.*, 1931, **133**, 440; Greene, *J.A.C.S.*, 1934, **56**, 1269; Furman and Low, *ibid.*, 1935, **57**, 1588; Scott and Hurley, *ibid.*, 1937, **59**, 1297; Kipp, *J. Sci. Instr.*, 1937, **14**, 213; Singh and Rao, *Proc. Indian Acad.*, 1939, **9** A, 78 (photoelectric); Davis and Parke, *J.A.C.S.*, 1942, **64**, 101.

[2] "Elements of Chemical Philosophy," 1812, 488; "Works," 1840, **4**, 359, 364.

[3] Anon., *Annals of Philosophy*, 1815, **6**, 321; *Ann. Chim.*, 1816, **1**, 411.

[4] Anon., *Annals of Philosophy*, 1816, **7**, 111; Prout, "Chemistry, Meteorology, and the Functions of Digestion," Bridgewater Treatise, 1834, 160; *Alembic Club Reprint*, 1932, **20**, with a summary of later developments.

[5] *J. der Pharmacie*, 1816, **25**, ii, 72, 200; *Ann. Phys.*, 1816, **24**, 159; "Erläuterungen zur chemischen Messkunst," Halle, 1817; *J. Chem. Phys.* (Schweigger), 1818, **22**, 137; 1819, **27**, 39; Prout is not mentioned.

Although Prout's hypothesis of whole multiple ratios was soon disproved by more accurate atomic weight determinations of Berzelius,[1] Turner [2] and others, it still fascinated chemists. Dumas and Stas[3] in 1841 showed that the atomic weight of carbon was almost exactly 12 and that Berzelius's value was 2·5 per cent. in error, and in 1842 they found that the atomic weight of oxygen (on the standard H=1) is almost exactly 16, which again seemed to support Prout's hypothesis. The general accuracy of Berzelius's other results was later confirmed and it was clear that Prout's hypothesis was unacceptable in its original form.

The atomic weight of chlorine is close to 35·5, so that Marignac [4] suggested that atomic weights are multiples of half the atomic weight of hydrogen, and Dumas [5] later reduced this to a quarter for aluminium, strontium and zinc, but this was obviously very arbitrary. Stas, beginning with " an almost complete confidence in the exactness of the law of Prout," was led by his exact researches to assert [6] in 1860 that it is " a pure illusion," a hypothesis definitely contradicted by experiment, and it was also rejected by Mendeléeff.[7] Marignac,[8] in a comment on Stas's paper, however, suggested that " while preserving the fundamental principle of . . . the hypothesis of the unity of matter," we might " suppose that the cause which has determined certain groupings of the atoms of the sole primordial substance " may have exercised an influence such that " the weight of each group might not be exactly the sum of the weights of the primordial atoms composing it." In many cases also the atomic weights are so nearly whole numbers " that it is impossible to consider this fact as accidental."

Hinrichs [9] argued that all atomic weights are whole number multiples of 0·5, or $\frac{1}{24}$ of the atomic weight of carbon taken as 12·000. To get this result it was necessary to exclude values determined by silver halide precipitation in solution, which were regarded as vitiated by errors, and the examples given by Hinrichs are mostly values determined before Stas's work, which is based on the method he rejected. The deduction from the theory of probabilities [10] that atomic weights " tend to approximate to whole numbers far more closely than can reasonably be accounted for by any accidental coincidence," although probably correct, was weakened by the discovery of isotopes which showed that many of the elements are mixtures. A very detailed discussion of Stas's atomic weights was given by Dubreuil.[11]

Witmer [12] proposed to take $m_p/6\times 861=1$ *prout* as the unit of mass or energy, m_p being the mass of the proton. The masses of all stable nuclei in the ground states are integral numbers of prouts.

1 See ref. 2, § 24; Ostwald's *Klassiker*, 1892, **35**; Berzelius, *Jahres-Ber.*, 1843, **23**, 11.
2 *Phil. Trans.*, 1833, **133**, 523.
3 *Ann. Chim.*, 1841, **1**, 5; 1843, **8**, 189; Stas, " Oeuvres," Brussels, 1894, **1**, 235 (sur le véritable poids atomique du carbone).
4 *Bibl. Univ.*, 1843, **46**, 350 (370); Dumas, *Compt. Rend.*, 1857, **45**, 709; *Ann.*, 1858, **105**, 74; Mallet, *J.C.S.*, 1893, **63**, 1.
5 *Compt. Rend.*, 1858, **46**, 951; *Ann. Chim.*, 1859, **55**, 129; *Ann.*, 1858, **108**, 324.
6 *Bull. Acad. Roy. Belg.*, 1860, **10**, 208; " Oeuvres," Brussels, 1894, **1**, 418.
7 " Principles of Chemistry," 1905, **2**, 459.
8 *Arch. Sci. Phys. Nat.*, 1860, **9**, 97; *J. Chim. Phys.*, 1920, **18**, 261; *Alembic Club Reprint*, 1932, **30**, 48.
9 " The True Atomic Weights of the Chemical Elements and the Unity of Matter," St. Louis, 1894; " The Absolute Weights of the Chemical Elements," New York, 1901; Bancroft, *J. Phys. Chem.*, 1902, **6**, 577.
10 Strutt, *Phil. Mag.*, 1901, **1**, 311: the chance of accidental coincidence is 1 in 1000.
11 *Bull. Soc. Chim.*, 1909, **5**, 172, 175, 260, 313, 341, 604, 610, 660, 708, 715, 852, 860, 1049, 1053.
12 *Proc. Nat. Acad.*, 1946, **32**, 283.

E. SPECIFIC HEATS OF GASES

§ 1. The Specific Heats of Gases

The true and mean specific (and molecular) heats of gases [1] are defined by the general equations of § 1.II, and the value at constant volume for unit mass:

$$c_v=(dE/dT)_v \quad \ldots \quad (1)$$

and that at constant pressure (§§ 3, 17.II) for unit mass:

$$c_p=(dH/dT)_p \quad \ldots \quad (2)$$

must be distinguished. The difference between the two values is (§ 21.II):

$$c_p-c_v=[(dE/dV)_T+p](dV/dT)_p \quad \ldots \quad (3)$$

and it is *only in the case of ideal gases*, for which $(dE/dV)_T=0$ (§ 54.II), that this difference, per mol, is equal to the gas constant:

$$C_p-C_v=R \quad \ldots \quad (4)$$

In other cases c_p-c_v (or C_p-C_v) must be calculated from the characteristic equation (see § 47.II, and §§ 11, 30, 31.VII C).[1]

Herz [2] found the empirical equations:

$$c_p-c_v=R/M=0{\cdot}0_487/\rho_c p_c=0{\cdot}0935 l_e/T_b=0{\cdot}0935 p_c/T_c\rho_c \quad \ldots \quad (5)$$

where M=mol. wt., p_c, ρ_c, T_c are the critical pressure, density, and temperature, l_e=latent heat of evaporation, T_b=b.p. abs. He also [3] connected $c_p-c_v=R/M$ with the Eötvös constant (see § 7.VIII G, Vol. II), $(M^{2/3}/\rho^{2/3})[\sigma/(T_c-T)]=2{\cdot}1$, where σ=surface tension, finding:

$$c_p-c_v=\sigma/M^{1/3}\rho^{2/3}(T_c-1) \quad \ldots \quad (6)$$

and from Lorenz's equation [4] $\rho_b/\rho_c=2{\cdot}66$, for the ratio of the densities of the liquid at the b.p. and critical point, he found:

$$c_p-c_v=0{\cdot}75\rho_b/\rho_c M \quad \ldots \quad (7)$$

For a *mixture* of gases the c_v values are nearly additive; according to Glansdorff [5] the value of mc_v is the sum of the values for the components in the same volume at the same temperature as the mixture:

$$Mc_v=c_v\Sigma m_1=m_1c_{v1}+m_2c_{v2}+\ldots \quad \ldots \quad (8)$$

The two specific heats are, in general, functions of temperature and pressure; in the case of ideal gases there is no dependence on pressure, but the specific heats may still be functions of temperature. The specific heat of hydrogen, for example, which is almost an ideal gas, varies with temperature over a considerable range much more than those of oxygen or nitrogen.

The first rough measurement of the specific heats of some gases at constant volume was made by Crawford,[6] who used two identical thin sheet brass vessels,

[1] Cf. Bachinski, *Z. Phys.*, 1927, **45**, 892.
[2] *Z. Elektrochem.*, 1921, **27**, 125.
[3] *Z. Elektrochem.*, 1921, **27**, 474.
[4] *Z. anorg. Chem.*, 1916, **94**, 240.
[5] *J. Chim. Phys.*, 1937, **34**, 96.
[6] "Experiments and Observations on Animal Heat," etc., London, 1779, 2nd edit., 1788, 177; Haycraft, *Trans. Roy. Soc. Edin.*, 1823 (1826), **10**, 195; de la Rive and Marcet, *Ann. Chim.*, 1840, **75**, 113; 1841, **2**, 121 (method of cooling); see Muncke, in Gehler's "Physikalisches Wörterbuch," 1841, **10**, 683.

one vacuous and the other filled with the gas, which he heated in boiling water and then cooled in two identical water calorimeters. The difference in temperature between the two calorimeters was supposed to correspond with the heat capacity of the gas. The results were considerably too high, e.g. the specific heat of air was found to be 1·79, nearly twice that of water. Experiments with the ice calorimeter and a flow method made by Lavoisier and Laplace [1] gave better results (air 0·3303, oxygen 0·65), but these were still too high.

Dalton [2] discussed hypotheses regarding the quantities of heat in various gases, and decided in favour of that which asserts that " the quantity of heat belonging to the ultimate particles of all elastic fluids must be the same under the same pressure and temperature "; and hence " the specific heats of equal weights of any two elastic fluids are inversely proportional to the weights of their atoms or molecules."

§ 2. Specific Heats at Constant Pressure

The so-called " method of mixture " in calorimetry (see § 2.IX M, Vol. II) was modified and first satisfactorily used in the determination of the mean specific heat of a gas at constant pressure by Delaroche and Bérard; [3] its accuracy was greatly increased in the classical work of Regnault.[4] The principle of the method is as follows. A mass m g. of the pure dry gas passed from a large reservoir A through a pressure regulator V at constant pressure through a metal [5] spiral tube S heated in an oil bath at a constant temperature t_2, measured by a mercury thermometer T_2. The gas then passed into a calorimeter C. In Regnault's apparatus this consisted of a thin brass box containing an inner spiral of sheet brass, and three flat brass boxes, all immersed in water (Fig. 1.VII E). The tube leading from the heater to the calorimeter was as short as possible and was enclosed in an air jacket. The calorimeter was also enclosed in an air jacket. The temperature in the calorimeter was measured by an accurate mercury thermometer T_3 divided in $\frac{1}{20}°$ and was read to $\frac{1}{200}°$. If w is the water value of the calorimeter, i.e. the heat in g.cal. required to raise the temperature of the water, calorimeter vessel, internal boxes, stirrer, and thermometer, through 1°, t_1 is the mean temperature of the gas leaving the calorimeter, and Δt is the rise in temperature in the calorimeter, then:

$$\bar{c}_p = w\Delta t / m(t_2 - t_1) \quad \ldots\ldots\ldots \quad (1)$$

where $\bar{c}_p$ is the mean specific heat of the gas at constant pressure between t_1 and t_2. The numerator in (1) is the quantity of heat q given to a mass m of gas to raise the temperature through $(t_2 - t_1)$, and hence this divided by m and $(t_2 - t_1)$ gives the mean specific heat. The value of m was found from the change of pressure in the reservoir A.

The principal difficulty in this method is the correct determination of the

1 Lavoisier, " Œuvres," Paris, 1862, **2**, 724, from Lavoisier, " Mémoires de Chimie," [1805], **1**, 121.

2 " New System of Chemical Philosophy," Manchester, 1808, **1**, i, 70 f.

3 *Ann. Chim.*, 1813, **85**, 72, 113; *Ann. Phil.*, 1813, **2**, 134, 211, 369, 426; a historical review is given by Regnault, *Mém. Acad. Sci.*, 1862, **26**, 3; Preston, " Theory of Heat," 1894, 243 f.; Haber, " Thermodynamics of Technical Gas Reactions," 1908, 208 f.; and Partington and Shilling, " The Specific Heats of Gases," 1924, 45 f.; cf. Eucken, in Stähler, " Arbeitsmethoden der anorganischen Chemie," 1913, **3**, i, 659; and in Wien-Harms, " Handbuch der Experimentalphysik," 1929, **8**, 360 f.

4 *Mém. Acad. Sci.*, 1862, **26**, 3; Partington and Shilling, " The Specific Heats of Gases," 1924, 58; for theory see Searle, *Proc. Cambr. Phil. Soc.*, 1906, **13**, 241.

5 Usually brass, but platinum with corrosive gases such as chlorine.

temperature t_2 at which the gas enters the calorimeter. This is not exactly equal to the temperature of the heating bath, since some heat loss occurs in the connecting tube between the heater and calorimeter. If an attempt is made to minimise this by having the tube short, then an error due to conduction of heat through the metal tube from the heater to the calorimeter is introduced. Regnault assumed that, if the velocity of the gas flow is sufficiently high, the temperature of the gas entering the calorimeter is the same as that of the heater, t_2, and then applied a correction for the transmission of heat from the heater to the calorimeter.

Before the gas was passed through the apparatus the rate of cooling of the calorimeter was observed. If θ_0 and τ_0 are the temperatures of the calorimeter

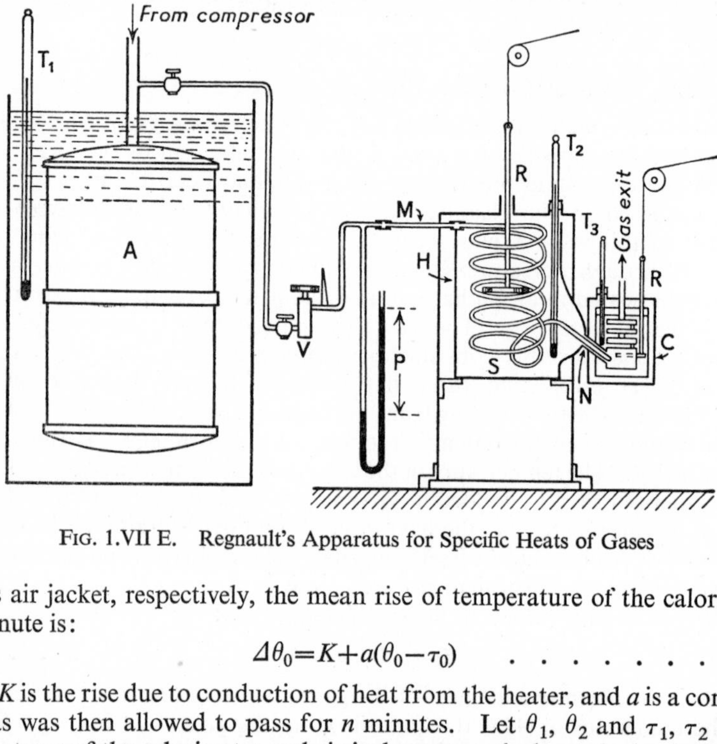

FIG. 1.VII E. Regnault's Apparatus for Specific Heats of Gases

and its air jacket, respectively, the mean rise of temperature of the calorimeter per minute is:

$$\varDelta\theta_0 = K + a(\theta_0 - \tau_0) \quad . \quad . \quad . \quad . \quad . \quad . \quad . \quad . \quad (2)$$

where K is the rise due to conduction of heat from the heater, and a is a constant. The gas was then allowed to pass for n minutes. Let θ_1, θ_2 and τ_1, τ_2 be the temperatures of the calorimeter and air jacket, respectively, at the beginning and end of the gas flow. The gas was again shut off and the cooling rate of the calorimeter again observed. If the mean temperatures are now θ_0' and τ_0', the mean temperature change per minute is:

$$\varDelta\theta_0' = K + a(\theta_0' - \tau_0') \quad . \quad . \quad . \quad . \quad . \quad . \quad . \quad . \quad (3)$$

and from (2) and (3) the values of K and a may be calculated. The rise in temperature of the calorimeter during the n minutes which is not due to heat carried in by the gas was then assumed to be:

$$\Sigma\varDelta\theta_0'' = n\left[K + a\left(\frac{\theta_1+\theta_2}{2} - \frac{\tau_1+\tau_2}{2}\right)\right] \quad . \quad . \quad . \quad . \quad . \quad (4)$$

This assumes that K remains the same whether gas is passing or not, which is not really true, since the heat transfer along the connecting tube by conduction, convection, and radiation is not quite the same in the two cases. There is no possibility of applying a correction to Regnault's results for this small error.[1] A correction for the expansion of the gas in passing from the heater to the calorimeter was applied by Leduc; [2] this changed Regnault's value of c_p for air, 0·2375, to the same value as Wiedemann's, 0·239, but Searle [2] showed that this correction is mistaken.

If w is the water value of the calorimeter, the heat given up by the gas is $w(\theta_2-\theta_1-\Sigma\Delta\theta_0'')$ and the mean specific heat of the gas, $\bar{c}_p$, is given by the equation:

$$m\bar{c}_p[t_2-\tfrac{1}{2}(\theta_1+\theta_2)]=w(\theta_2-\theta_1-\Sigma\Delta\theta_0'') \quad . \quad . \quad . \quad . \quad (5)$$

where $\frac{1}{2}(\theta_1+\theta_2)$ corresponds with t_1 in (1); hence:

$$\bar{c}_p=(2w/m)(\theta_2-\theta_1-\Sigma\Delta\theta_0'')/(2t_2-\theta_1-\theta_2) \quad . \quad . \quad . \quad . \quad (6)$$

Regnault's values of $\bar{c}_p$ cover the temperature range $-30°$ to $+270°$ and pressures of 1 to 12 atm., and have a general accuracy of about 1 per cent., so that in default of other data they are still of value.[3] He found that the specific heats of air, oxygen, and hydrogen were constant within these limits of temperature and pressure, but that of carbon dioxide increased with temperature.

Regnault's apparatus was much simplified without any loss of accuracy by E. Wiedemann,[4] who obtained practically the same results. Regnault's large metal gas reservoir was replaced by a rubber bag from which the gas was displaced by compressing the bag outside by water; the spiral heater was replaced by a short wide copper tube filled with copper turnings, and the metal boxes in the calorimeter by a silver vessel filled with silver turnings. The temperature interval was 0° to 200°. Both Regnault and Wiedemann determined the specific heats of a number of vapours as well as permanent gases.

Regnault's method was later modified [5] so as to give a *true* specific heat at a given temperature. A stream of gas at a constant temperature θ is passed through a spiral tube immersed in a bath at a temperature $\theta+\Delta\theta$. The slightly cooler gas takes heat from the bath, and to keep the temperature constant, heat q is added to the bath by an electric heater, q being measured by the electrical energy supplied, $I^2Rt/4{\cdot}185$ g.cal., where I=current in amp., R=resistance in ohms, t=time in sec. If n mols of gas are passed through, the true molecular heat is:

$$C_p=Mc_p=q/n\Delta\theta=I^2Rt/4{\cdot}185n\Delta\theta \quad . \quad . \quad . \quad . \quad . \quad (7)$$

A correction was applied for heat lost by conduction through the spiral tube and stirrer; this was estimated by stopping the gas flow and adjusting I. The chief difficulty in the method is in maintaining a constant gas flow.

§ 3. Specific Heats at Constant Pressure at High Temperatures

Some careful measurements of the mean specific heats of gases up to 800° were made in the Reichsanstalt by Holborn and Austin [6] and up to 1400° by

1 Gill, *Phil. Mag.*, 1868, **35**, 439; Searle, *Proc. Cambr. Phil. Soc.*, 1906, **13**, 241; Swann, *Engineering*, 1912, **94**, 516; *Phil. Mag.*, 1913, **25**, 109; Scheel and Heuse, *Berlin Ber.*, 1913, 44; Hoare, *Phil. Mag.*, 1940, **29**, 52.

2 *Compt Rend.*, 1898, **126**, 1860; Searle, *Proc. Cambr. Phil. Soc.*, 1906, **13**, 241.

3 See the table in Partington and Shilling, "The Specific Heats of Gases," 1924, 190.

4 *Ann. Phys.*, 1876, **157**, 1; 1877, **2**, 195; *Phil. Mag.*, 1876, **2**, 81; Thibaut, *Ann. Phys.*, 1911, **35**, 347; Escher, *ibid.*, 1913, **42**, 761; Partington and Shilling, "The Specific Heats of Gases," 1924, 60.

5 McCollum, *J.A.C.S.*, 1927, **49**, 28.

6 Holborn and Austin, *Berlin Ber.*, 1905, 175; *Abhl. Phys. Techn. Reichsanstalt*, 1905, **4**, 131; Nernst, *Z. Elektrochem.*, 1910, **16**, 96; Partington and Shilling, "The Specific Heats of Gases," 1924, 103.

Holborn and Henning.[1] They used electric heating and measured the temperatures with thermocouples. The gas first passed through a platinum spiral A heated in an electric furnace, then through a heated platinum tube B, then between the concentric electrically heated platinum tubes C, inside which was a thermocouple P_2, and then into the calorimeter. This was a silver vessel M containing three silver tubes filled with silver turnings (two of which DD are shown in Fig. 2.VII E), through which the gas (compressed in a steel cylinder)

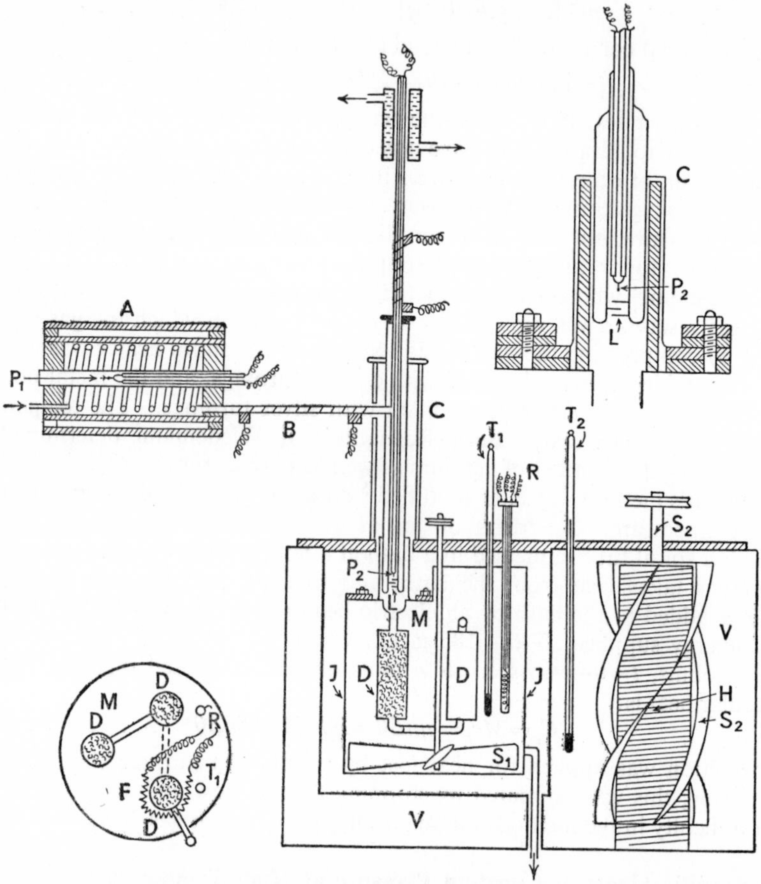

FIG. 2.VII E. Apparatus of Holborn and Henning for Determination of Specific Heats of Gases

passed on its way to a measuring apparatus. The calorimeter was provided with a stirrer S_1, a mercury thermometer T_1, and a platinum resistance thermometer R, and was contained in a jacket J containing paraffin oil enclosed in a large vessel containing vegetable oil kept at a constant temperature by an electric resistance heater H, a thermometer T_2, and a stirrer S_2. The temperature of the entering gas was measured by using thermocouples of different thicknesses and extrapolating to zero thickness to eliminate conduction and radiation errors. Radiation from the thermocouple P_2 was cut off by baffle-plates L.

[1] Holborn and Henning, *Ann. Phys.*, 1905, **18**, 739; 1907, **23**, 809; Callendar, *B. A. Rep.*, 1908, 334.

The results are probably accurate to about 1 per cent. except at the higher temperatures. They are given by the equations [1] for the *mean* specific heats $\bar{c}_p$ at 1 atm. between 0° C. (100° C. for steam) and t° C. in g.cal. per g.:

$$N_2 \; \bar{c}_p=0{\cdot}2491+0{\cdot}0_595t$$

$$\text{Air} \; \bar{c}_p=0{\cdot}2405+0{\cdot}0_595t$$

$$CO_2 \; \bar{c}_p=0{\cdot}1971+0{\cdot}0_31283t-0{\cdot}0_39908\times10^{-4}t^2+0{\cdot}0_43136\times10^{-6}t^3$$

$$H_2O \; \bar{c}_p=0{\cdot}4574+0{\cdot}0_4461t.$$

The temperature coefficient for steam is only half that found by Langen by a different method (§ 7).

Holborn and Henning in 1907 gave the equations for $\bar{c}_p$:

$$N_2 \; \bar{c}_{0,t}=0{\cdot}2350+0{\cdot}0_419t$$

$$CO_2 \; \bar{c}_{0,t}=0{\cdot}2010+0{\cdot}0_4742t-0{\cdot}0_718t^2$$

$$H_2O \; \bar{c}_{100,t}=0{\cdot}4669-0{\cdot}0_4168t+0{\cdot}0_744t^2$$

$$\text{or } =0{\cdot}4544+0{\cdot}0_26925\times10^{0{\cdot}0_37513t}.$$

A different type of formula was proposed by Faggiani: [2]

$$C_p=\alpha(1+\ln T)$$

for nitrogen ($\alpha=0{\cdot}993$), carbon monoxide ($\alpha=1{\cdot}002$), and air ($\alpha=1{\cdot}048$) from 400°–3500° K.; for hydrogen:

$$C_p=4{\cdot}965+0{\cdot}28(1+\ln T).$$

§ 4. Effect of Pressure on Specific Heat

The effect of pressure on the specific heat is given by equation (2), § 49.II:

$$(\mathrm{d}c_p/\mathrm{d}p)_T=-T(\mathrm{d}^2v/\mathrm{d}T^2)_p \quad . \; . \; . \; . \; . \; . \; . \; . \quad (1)$$

and since $(\mathrm{d}v/\mathrm{d}T)_p=\boldsymbol{R}/p$ per mol is constant for an ideal gas (§ 54.II) at constant pressure, c_p is independent of pressure in that case; for actual gases c_p depends on pressure but only slightly except at high pressures.[3] Regnault was unable to find any change in the specific heats of air, hydrogen, and carbon dioxide between 1 and 12 atm. pressure, but Lussana [4] found a dependence on pressure for air, hydrogen, carbon dioxide, nitric oxide, methane, and ethylene between 1 and 45 atm. and 10° and 90° C., which he represented by the equation (p in atm.):

$$c_p=a+b(p-1) \quad . \; . \; . \; . \; . \; . \; . \; . \; . \quad (2)$$

where a ($=c_p$ at 1 atm. pressure) and b are constants; or at higher pressures (30–100 atm.):

$$c_p=a+b(p-1)+c(p-1)^2 \quad . \; . \; . \; . \; . \; . \; . \; . \quad (3)$$

where c is another constant which is negative for air:

$$c_p=0{\cdot}23702+0{\cdot}0015504(p-1)-0{\cdot}0_519591(p-1)^2.$$

[1] Holborn *et al.*, "Wärmetabellen P.T.R.," Brunswick, 1919, 58; Schüle, "Technische Thermodynamik," Berlin, 1922–3, **2**, 29, 97.

[2] *Energia Termica*, 1942, **10**, 119, 128; *Amer. Chem. Abstr.*, 1944, **38**, 5703.

[3] Witkowski, *Bull. Acad. Polon.*, 1895, 290; *Z. phys. Chem.*, 1896, **21**, 168; *Phil. Mag.*, 1896, **42**, 1; Amagat, *Compt. Rend.*, 1895, **121**, 863; 1896, **122**, 66, 120; 1900, **130**, 1443 (CO_2); Meyer, *Phys. Z.*, 1899, **1**, 146; Koch, *Ann. Phys.*, 1908, **26**, 551; 1908, **27**, 311; Partington and Shilling, "The Specific Heats of Gases," 1924, 150; Hoxton, *Phys. Rev.*, 1930, **36**, 1091; Workman, *ibid.*, 1930, **36**, 1083; 1931, **37**, 1345; Dodge, *Ind. Eng. Chem.*, 1932, **24**, 1353 (review).

[4] *Nuov. Cim.*, 1894, **36**, 5, 70, 130; 1895, **1**, 327; 1896, **3**, 92; 1897, **6**, 81; 1898, **7**, 365; 1905, **10**, 192; 1908, **16**, 456; *Z. phys. Chem.*, 1895, **16**, 166; Peczalski, *Ann. de Phys.*, 1916, **5**, 113.

Gas	H_2	Air	N_2	CH_4	C_2H_4
a	3·4025	0·23707	0·22480	0·5915	0·40387
b	0·01330	0·001498	0·0018364	0·003463	0·0016022

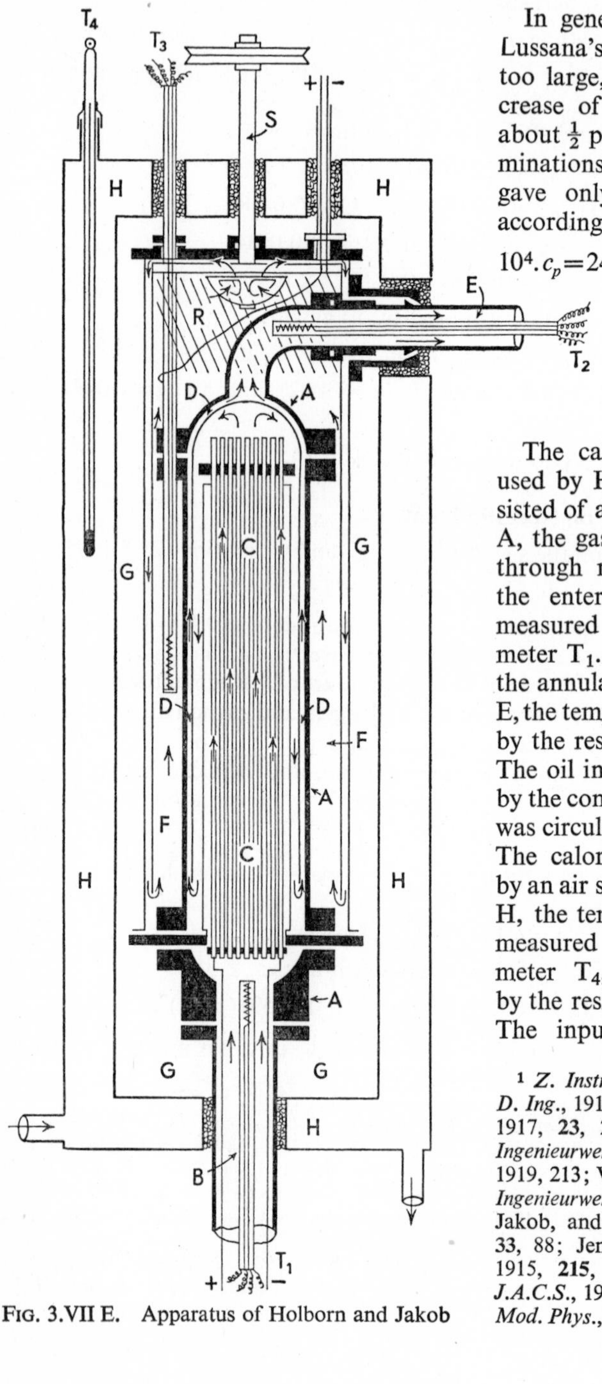

FIG. 3.VII E. Apparatus of Holborn and Jakob

In general, *b* increases with *a*. Lussana's values of *b* are probably too large, since they give an increase of c_p for air per atm. of about $\frac{1}{2}$ per cent., whilst the determinations of Holborn and Jakob[1] gave only about 0·1 per cent., according to the formula:

$$10^4 . c_p = 2414 + 2{\cdot}86p + 0{\cdot}0_3 5p^2 - 0{\cdot}0_4 106p^3 \quad . \quad (4)$$

which holds at 60°. There should be a maximum, 0·3033, at 316 atm.

The calorimeter (Fig. 3.VII E) used by Holborn and Jakob consisted of a strong nickel steel tube A, the gas entering which passed through narrow nickel tubes C, the entering temperature being measured by a resistance thermometer T_1. After passing through the annular space D the gas left at E, the temperature being measured by the resistance thermometer T_2. The oil in the bath F was heated by the constantan resistance R and was circulated by the centrifuge S. The calorimeter was surrounded by an air space G and steam jacket H, the temperature in which was measured by the mercury thermometer T_4, that of the oil bath by the resistance thermometer T_3. The input of electrical energy

[1] *Z. Instr.*, 1911, **31**, 116; *Z. Verein D. Ing.*, 1917, **61**, 146; *Z. Elektrochem.*, 1917, **23**, 287; *Forschungsarb. Gebiet Ingenieurwes.*, 1918, **187–8**; *Berlin Ber.*, 1919, 213; Vogel, *Forschungsarb. Gebiet Ingenieurwes.*, 1911, **108–9**; Holborn, Jakob, and Baumann, *Z. Instr.*, 1913, **33**, 88; Jenkin and Pye, *Phil. Trans.*, 1915, **215**, 353; Krase and Mackey, *J.A.C.S.*, 1930, **52**, 108; Bridgman, *Rev. Mod. Phys.*, 1946, **18**, 1 (bibl.).

was measured. The apparatus was standardised with air at 1 atm. pressure. The heat loss correction was independent of the flow velocity, was equivalent to 10 per cent. of the smallest heating current used, and was eliminated by using various flow velocities with the energy input adjusted to maintain the same temperature in each case.

The effect of pressure on the specific heat of steam was measured by Knoblauch and collaborators [1] (120° to 550° and 2 to 30 atm.; the results were represented graphically), and on the specific heat of ammonia by Osborne, Stimson, Sligh, and Cragoe.[2] The effect of pressure on c_p for air was calculated by Witkowski [3] from formula (1) from the measured coefficients of expansion, and he also found c_p at 1 atm. pressure to be independent of temperature from $-144°$ to $0°$ ($c_p=0{\cdot}2372$). The effect of pressure on c_v is considered in § 6.

The complicated apparatus used by Lussana, and Holborn and Jakob, is described by Partington and Shilling. Krase and Mackey used a simpler apparatus. The gas passed through a spiral steel tube round which a copper block was cast, and this was contained in a large Dewar vessel (Fig. 4.VII E). The rise of temperature of the block was measured and a correction applied for heat lost by conduction along the inlet and outlet tubes. The results were found to be independent of the flow rate. At 500 atm. pressure the values of C_p for nitrogen were:

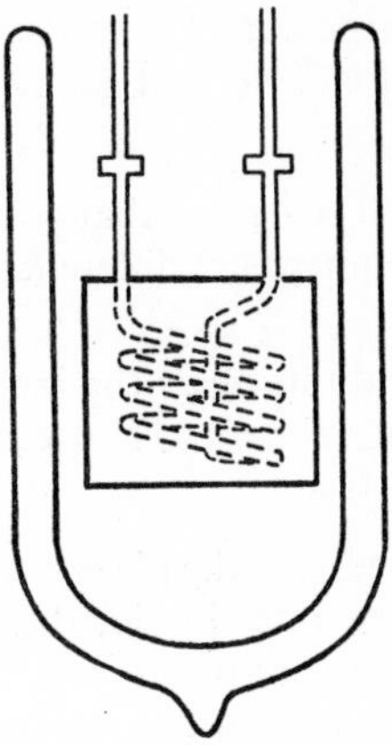

FIG. 4.VII E. Apparatus of Krase and Mackey

30°	50°	100°	150°
9·12	8·85	8·39	8·13

Amagat [4] doubted if the values of d^2p/dT^2 were known accurately enough to give reliable values of dc_v/dp by (1), § 49.II, or even to decide if it differed from zero. Some rough experiments [5] with unpurified gases, with a supersonic method (§ 24), showed an increase of the velocity of sound with pressure in the case of air, nitrogen, neon, and hydrogen, and a decrease with carbon dioxide. For air, a change of $c_p/c_v=\gamma$ from 1·406 to 1·580 was found [5] on changing the pressure from 1 to 100 atm., and for nitrogen from 1·403 to 1·56. For carbon dioxide γ was supposed to change from 1·304 at 1 atm. to 3·524 at 60 atm.

A temperature-entropy diagram for air to 300 atm. and 500° was calculated by Schlegel,[6] and Mollier charts for hydrogen, nitrogen, carbon monoxide, and mixtures by Guelpérine and Naiditch.[7]

1 Knoblauch and Jakob, *Forschungsarb. Gebiet Ingenieurwes.*, 1906, **35–36**, 109; Griessmann, *ibid.*, 1904, **13**; Knoblauch *et al.*, *Z. Verein D. Ing.*, 1907, **51**, 81; 1911, **55**, 665; 1912, **56**, 1980; 1915, **59**, 376; 1922, **66**, 418; Knoblauch and Mollier, *Forschungsarb. Gebiet Ingenieurwes.*, 1911, **108–9**, 79; *Engineering*, 1913, **96**, 627 (figure); Knoblauch and Winkhaus, *Forschungsarb. Gebiet Ingenieurwes.*, 1917, **195**; Partington and Shilling, "The Specific Heats of Gases," 1924, 175.

2 *Refrig. Eng.*, 1923, **10**, 145; *Bur. Stand. Bull.*, 1925, **20**, 65, 119; Cragoe, *Refrig. Eng.*, 1925, **12**, 131; for SO_2, Landsberg, *Z. ges. Kälte-Ind.*, 1925, **32**, 176.

3 *Phil. Mag.*, 1896, **41**, 288; 1896, **42**, 1; cf. Margules, *Wien Ber.*, 1888, **97**, IIA, 1385; Amagat, *J. de Phys.*, 1896, **5**, 114; Plank, *Phys. Z.*, 1910, **11**, 633; *Z. ges. Kälte-Ind.*, 1910, **17**, 81, 129 (N_2).

4 Quoted by Dieterici, *Ann. Phys.*, 1903, **12**, 144; Johnston and Weimer, *J.A.C.S.*, 1934, **56**, 625.

5 Hodge, *J. Chem. Phys.*, 1937, **5**, 974; Hubbard and Hodge, *ibid.*, 1937, **5**, 978.

6 *Forschungsarb. Gebiet Ingenieurwes.*, 1932, **3**, 297.

7 *Chim. et Ind.*, 1935, **34**, 1011, 1279.

§ 5. The Continuous Flow Method

The method of "continuous flow calorimetry" used by Callendar [1] and Barnes [2] for liquids (specific heat of water; see § 12.II, and § 1.VIII H, Vol. II) was applied to gases by Swann [3] and improved by Scheel and Heuse.[4] It has been much used, but seems to give results always slightly different from those found by other methods, except with hydrogen, so that some concealed defect seems to be inherent in it.[5]

A stream of gas flowing at a constant rate of m g. per sec. through a glass tube is heated by an electrically heated wire in the axis of the tube. If the electrical energy supplied per sec. is E g.cal. (volts × amps. × 0·2387) and if all this except a part e lost to the surroundings is used to heat the gas, the temperature of the exit gas will be $\Delta T°$ higher than that of the entering gas and:

$$c_p=(E-e)/m\Delta T \quad . \quad . \quad . \quad . \quad . \quad . \quad . \quad . \quad . \quad (1)$$

The heat exchange between the heated and incoming gas is proportional to the temperature difference:

$$e'=k_1\Delta T=k_2E/m,$$

and this heats the incoming gas by $\Delta T'=e'/m$. The heat loss to the surroundings is $e=k_3\Delta T'=k_3e'/m=k_4E/m^2$, therefore by substitution in (1):

$$c_p=(E/m\Delta T)(1-k_4/m^2)=c_p'(1-k/m^2) \quad . \quad . \quad . \quad . \quad (2)$$

A plot of the observed specific heats c_p' against the reciprocal of the square of the flow rate should, therefore, be a straight line, and the extrapolation to infinite flow rate $((1/m^2\rightarrow 0)$ gives the corrected specific heat.[6] The effect of pressure was considered by Workman.[7]

In Scheel and Heuse's apparatus (Fig. 5.VII E) the gas entered below, passed the platinum resistance thermometer T_1, and after flowing through the spiral passed through the two glass jackets into the inner tube containing the heater. The heated gas then passed the platinum resistance thermometer T_2 and left the apparatus. The apparatus was enclosed in a vacuum jacket silvered inside, and the heating of the gas was as far as possible adiabatic. The heat loss e was found by an empirical method; for high rates of flow (5 lit. per min.) e was small compared with E, but there was some uncertainty in this part of the experiment. The continuous flow method has been used in several cases and at low and high temperatures.[8]

[1] *Phil. Trans.*, 1902, **199**, 55.

[2] *Phil. Trans.*, 1902, **199**, 149.

[3] *Proc. Roy. Soc.*, 1909, **82**, 147; *Phil. Trans.*, 1910, **210**, 199; cf. Brinkworth, *ibid.*, 1915, **215**, 383.

[4] *Ann. Phys.*, 1912, **37**, 79; 1913, **40**, 473; 1919, **59**, 86; *Berlin Ber.*, 1913, 44; *Z. Instr.*, 1912, **32**, 244.

[5] Partington and Shilling, "The Specific Heats of Gases," 1924, 106.

[6] Partington and Shilling, "Specific Heats of Gases," 1924, 46; de Vries and Collins, *J.A.C.S.*, 1941, **63**, 1343.

[7] *Phys. Rev.*, 1930, **36**, 1083; 1931, **37**, 1345 (O_2, N_2, H_2).

[8] Knoblauch and Jakob, *Z. Verein D. Ing.*, 1907, **51**, 81; Nernst, *Z. Elektrochem.*, 1910, **16**, 96; Thibaut, *Ann. Phys.*, 1911, **35**, 347; Knoblauch and Mollier, *Z. Verein D. Ing.*, 1911, **55**, 665; Haber *et al.*, *Z. Elektrochem.*, 1914, **20**, 597; 1915, **21**, 228; Brinkworth, *Phil. Trans.*, 1915, **215**, 383; Knoblauch and Winkhaus, *Z. Verein D. Ing.*, 1915, **59**, 376; Eucken and Bartels, *Z. phys. Chem.*, 1921, **98**, 70; Knoblauch and Raisch, *Z. Verein D. Ing.*, 1922, **66**, 418; Millar, *J.A.C.S.*, 1923, **45**, 874; Schreiner, *Z. phys. Chem.*, 1924, **112**, 1; Krase and Mackey, *J.A.C.S.*, 1930, **52**, 108 (high pressure); Thayer and Stegeman, *J. Phys. Chem.*, 1931, **35**, 1505 (C_2H_6); Haas and Stegeman, *ibid.*, 1932, **36**, 2127 (CH_4); Haas, *Sci. Abstr.*, 1933, **36** A, 479; Felsing and Jessen, *J.A.C.S.*, 1933, **55**, 4418; Jennings and Bixler, *J. Phys. Chem.*, 1934, **38**, 747 (vapours; ether $C_p=23{\cdot}3833-14{\cdot}7\times10^{-3}t-5{\cdot}929\times10^{-4}t^2$); Felsing and Drake,

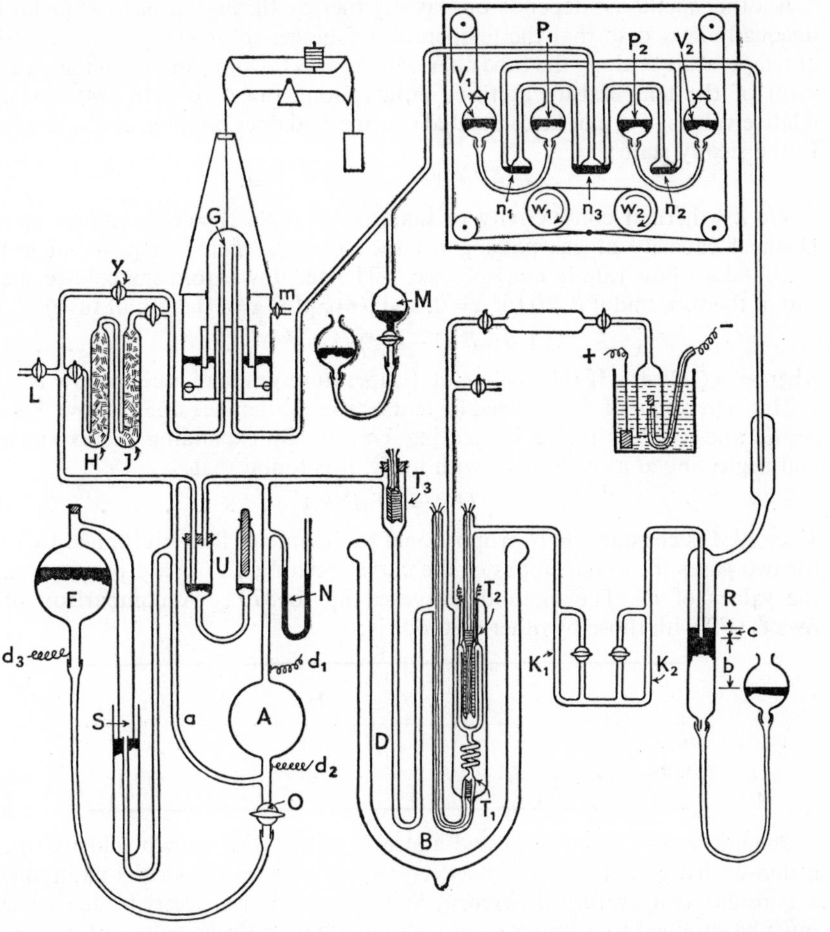

FIG. 5.VII E. Apparatus of Scheel and Heuse. The gas entered the bulb A through a, passed through the resistance thermometer T_3 and after attaining the temperature of the bath B in the tube D entered the calorimeter in the Dewar vessel. It passed from the calorimeter through the capillary tubes K_1K_2, regulating the rate of flow, and entered the regulator R, in which the suction was equal to the difference between the barometric height and the column of mercury b. By way of the mercury seals n_1n_2 it was drawn by a pumping action on the reservoirs V_1V_2 actuated by slow rotation of the pulley wheels w_1w_2, into the reservoirs P_1P_2, from which the gas passed to the balanced gas holder G over mercury. From G the gas passed back to a. H and J, normally shut off, contained charcoal and were immersed in liquid air, for adsorption of gas. The whole apparatus was first exhausted through L. The quantity of gas delivered was found by shutting off a, opening O, and raising F, so that the pressure in N remained constant. A chronograph marking the times of contact at the points d_1d_2 gave the time of passage of gas. U was a by-pass, S a sliding mercury seal. The value of the constant k in equation (2) varied somewhat with m, and was determined with several values of m. The amount of gas required was 5 litres.

J.A.C.S., 1936, **58**, 1714 (H_2S, HCN); Bennewitz and Rossner, *Z. phys. Chem.*, 1938, **39** B, 126 Fugassi and Rudy, *Ind. Eng. Chem.*, 1938, **30**, 1029; Pitzer, *J.A.C.S.*, 1941, **63**, 2413; de Vries and Collins, *ibid.*, 1941, **63**, 1343; 1942, **64**, 1224; Kiperash and Parks, *ibid.*, 1942, **64**, 179 (a 10 per cent. error in Bennewitz and Rossner's results); Montgomery and de Vries, *ibid.*, 1942, **64**, 2372, 2375; Pitzer and Scott, *ibid.*, 1943, **65**, 803; Waddington, Todd, and Huffman, *ibid.*, 1947, **69**, 22; Waddington and Douslin, *ibid.*, 1947, **69**, 2275; Wacker, Cheney, and Scott, *Bur. Stand. J. Res.*, 1947, **38**, 651.

Another method [1] depends on passing the gas through a narrow metal tube unequally heated so that the temperature is higher in one place. The gradient of temperature ϑ along the tube alters when gas is flowing, and from the measurement of the temperature at three points along the tube with two gases, the relative values of c_p can be calculated (the method does not give absolute values). In the steady state:

$$kA(d^2\vartheta/dx^2)-Q(d\vartheta/dx)=0 \quad \ldots \quad (3)$$

where k=thermal conductivity of material of tube, A=cross-section of tube, Q=heat capacity of gas passing per sec., $Q=cq$, where c=sp. ht. of gas per cm.³ and q=flow rate in cm.³ per sec. The gas flows from the cold to the hot end of the tube and if $\vartheta=0$ for $x=0$, and $\vartheta=\vartheta_1$ for $x=l$ (length of tube):

$$\vartheta=\vartheta_1(1-e^{2\alpha x})/(1-e^{2\alpha l}) \quad \ldots \quad (4)$$

where $\alpha=Q/2kA$. If the change of temperature gradient due to flow is small, $\alpha \ll 1$. The value of Θ=change of temperature difference due to flow, between $x=l/2$ and $x=0$, is found by putting $x=l/2$. By expanding the exponentials and neglecting αl as compared with unity, it is found that:

$$\Theta/\vartheta=-cql/8kA \quad \ldots \quad (5)$$

Since l/kA is constant, Θ is proportional to the rate of flow multiplied by c, and for two gases the *initial* slopes of the curves relating q to Θ are proportional to the values of c. The method was used up to 370°. A comparison of the results (F.) with those by other methods is:

	He	H_2	CO_2
F.	0·717	0·986	1·264
Other	0·716	0·987	1·268

Bennewitz and Schulze [2] passed a stream of gas with known velocity through a thin-walled glass tube fixed between two massive metal blocks maintained at a constant temperature difference, and measured the electrical energy which must be supplied to a heater in order to maintain a linear temperature gradient along the glass tube, as measured by a differential thermopile. The molecular heat is given by:

$$C_p=0{\cdot}239\Delta E/\Delta T(dn/dt) \quad \ldots \quad (1)$$

where ΔE=electrical energy supplied per sec. by the heater, ΔT=difference of temperature between the metal blocks, and dn/dt=rate of flow of the gas in mols per sec. The accuracy is of the order of 1 per cent.

Chopin [3] used a method depending on the flow of gas through two orifices, finding at 312°–1042°:

$$N_2,\ \bar{C}_p=6{\cdot}82+0{\cdot}00058t;\quad CO_2,\ \bar{C}_p=8{\cdot}9+0{\cdot}61(t/100)^{0{\cdot}673}.$$

[1] Blackett, Henry, and Rideal, *Proc. Roy. Soc.*, 1930, **126**, 319; 1931, **133**, 492; *Nature*, 1932, **129**, 200; the method is really the same as that proposed by Callendar, "Ency. Brit.," 11th edit., 1910, **6**, 890, for measuring the thermal conductivity of the material of the tube. It has never been used at high temperatures. See also Chapman, *Proc. Roy. Soc.*, 1930, **126**, 675; Okamura, *Sci. Rep. Tôhoku Imp. Univ.*, 1933, **22**, 519; Potop, *Compt. Rend.*, 1937, **205**, 1047; Roberts, " Heat and Thermodynamics," 1940, 133; Eucken and Sarstedt, *Z. phys. Chem.*, 1941, **50** B, 143 (vapours), whose results disagree with values calculated by Pitzer, § 29.IV, and experiments by Waddington and Douslin, *J.A.C.S.*, 1947, **69**, 2275.

[2] *Z. phys. Chem.*, 1940, **186**, 299; Dailey and Felsing, *J.A.C.S.*, 1943, **65**, 42, 44; Templeton, Davies, and Felsing, *ibid.*, 1944, **66**, 2033; 1945, **67**, 2279.

[3] *Compt. Rend.*, 1928, **186**, 1830; 1929, **188**, 1660.

§ 6. Specific Heat at Constant Volume

An ingenious method of measuring the specific heat of a gas at constant volume uses the *differential steam calorimeter* of Joly.[1] In this, two exactly similar copper globes A and B, about 6·7 cm. diameter, of equal weights, were suspended by wires from the ends of the beam of a sensitive balance inside two metal steam jackets. Below each globe was suspended a conical receiver for water condensed on the globe. Condensation of water on the parts of the wires outside the jackets was prevented by surrounding them with electrically heated spirals. One globe was vacuous and the other contained the gas, compressed to 30 atm. at the steam temperature.

The difference between the weights of water condensed on the two globes was found by adding weights to the side of the vacuous globe so as to balance the globes again. If the steam is passed in too quickly, a cloud is formed and drops fall on the globes; the steam supply must be cut down during weighing, otherwise the draught will tend to move the globe. Unless the collecting cones are exactly equal, a correction must be applied for the water condensed on these. A correction is also applied for the expansion of the globe on heating (when external work is done by the gas) and for the effect on c_v of the increase of pressure on heating the gas. If m is the mass of gas, t the initial temperature, m' the mass of water condensed (corrected to vacuum), l_e the latent heat of evaporation of water:

$$mc_v(100-t)=m'l_e \quad \text{(1)}$$

if the b.p. of water is 100°. Since less than 2 mg. of water are condensed per g.cal., very accurate weighing is necessary. The method was used by Carlton-Sutton [2] to determine the latent heat of steam. Keyes [3] corrected Joly's value for air by allowing for the expansion of the copper globe (changing c_v by pressure), finding $c_v=0{\cdot}1712$, independent of pressure to 27 atm.

Joly's experiments give the effect of density, $\rho=1/v$, on c_v, which is represented by the thermodynamic formula [4] (§ 49.II):

$$(\mathrm{d}c_v/\mathrm{d}v)_T=T(\mathrm{d}^2p/\mathrm{d}T^2)_v \quad \text{(2)}$$

In the case of air and carbon dioxide the specific heat was found to increase with the density, but with hydrogen it appeared to decrease. The values for carbon dioxide were:

p atm.	Density g./ml.	c_v
7·20	0·011530	0·16841
12·20	0·019950	0·17054
16·87	0·028498	0·17141
20·90	0·036529	0·17305
21·66	0·037802	0·17386

[1] Joly, *Proc. Roy. Soc.*, 1880, **41**, 352; 1888, **45**, 33; 1889, **47**, 218; 1890, **48**, 440; 1894, **55**, 390; *Chem. News*, 1888, **58**, 271; *Phil. Trans.*, 1891, **182**, 73; 1894, **185**, 943, 961; Bunsen, *Ann. Phys.*, 1887, **31**, 1; Neesen, *ibid.*, 1890, **39**, 131; Wirtz, *ibid.*, 1890, **40**, 438; Schükarew, *ibid.*, 1896, **59**, 229; Rudge, *Proc. Cambr. Phil. Soc.*, 1906, **14**, 85 (high pressures); Griffiths, in Glazebrook, " Dict. of Applied Physics," 1922, **1**, 50.

[2] *Proc. Roy. Soc.*, 1917, **93**, 155.

[3] *J.A.C.S.*, 1921, **43**, 1452; 1924, **46**, 1584.

[4] See also Beckman, *Arkiv Mat. Astron. Fys.*, 1911, **7**, No. 27; Godnev, *J. Gen. Chem. U.S.S.R.*, 1931, **1**, 684; Shpakovskij, *Compt. Rend. U.R.S.S.*, 1934, **3**, 26 (31) (small increase of c_v for CO_2 with pressure); Godnev and Sverdlin, *Khimstroi*, 1934, **6**, 8; Gusak, *Sow. Phys. Z.*, 1937, **11**, 60 (N_2 at 60–200 atm.).

In a method [1] in which a known amount of heat q is given to a large volume (30–80 lit.) of gas by means of a platinum wire through which a momentary current is passed, the increase in pressure Δp is measured before the convection from the heated gas reaches the top of the cylindrical vessel. The increase of pressure is the same as if the whole mass, n mols, of the gas had been warmed through a temperature difference ΔT:

$$\Delta p=(n\boldsymbol{R}/V)\Delta T=(n\boldsymbol{R}/V)(q/nC_v)=q\boldsymbol{R}/VC_v \quad . \quad . \quad . \quad . \quad (3)$$

since ΔT is inversely proportional to the mass of gas heated, i.e. $n\Delta T$ is constant. This has been used as a relative method by working with two bottles, one containing air and the other the gas, connected by an oil manometer. The volume of air is altered from V to V' by admitting oil until, on passing an equal momentary current through the two equal heating wires, the pressure increases are equal, i.e. the manometer does not move. Then:

$$C_v(\text{gas})=C_v(\text{air}) . (V'/V) \quad . \quad . \quad . \quad . \quad . \quad . \quad . \quad (4)$$

Although an accuracy of 1 per cent. is claimed, this is doubtful. Trautz and Hebbel found for C_v at room temperature, CO_2 6·925, H_2 4·83, N_2 4·975.

The value of C_v can be measured [2] *at low temperatures* by using an electrically heated steel cylinder suspended by a very narrow metal tube in a vacuous vessel, and determining the heat capacity by electric heating when empty and filled with compressed gas. At low temperatures (below −100°) the thermal capacity of the solid container becomes small compared with that of the gas. The accuracy is not very great.

§ 7. The Explosion Method

A method often used for the determination of the mean specific heat of a gas at constant volume up to high temperatures is the explosion method. In this, a known volume of explosive mixture (e.g. $2H_2+O_2$) is mixed with a known volume of inert gas (which may, for example, be an excess of H_2 or O_2), the specific heat of which is to be measured. The explosion (usually initiated by an electric spark) liberates a large amount of heat, which brings the burnt gas and the inert gas to a high temperature. It is assumed that no heat is lost by conduction to the walls or by radiation during the short time of duration of the explosion. If steam is produced, a correction must be applied for its latent heat of condensation in the subsequent cooling. Let t_2 be the highest temperature reached and t_1 the final temperature (room temperature) of the cooled products. The heat evolved is $(t_2-t_1)(m\bar{C}_{vr}+n\bar{C}_{vi})$, where m mols of reaction product of mean molecular heat $\bar{C}_{vr}$ and n mols of inert gas of mean molecular heat $\bar{C}_{vi}$ are present. This must be equal to the heat of reaction mq_v at the temperature t_1, which is supposed to be known from thermochemical results; hence if $n/m=r$:

$$q_v=(t_2-t_1)(\bar{C}_{vr}+r\bar{C}_{vi}) \quad . \quad . \quad . \quad . \quad . \quad . \quad . \quad . \quad (1)$$

1 Jamin and Richard, *Compt. Rend.*, 1870, **71**, 336; Voller, *Dissert.*, Berlin, 1909; Trautz and Grossinsky, *Ann. Phys.*, 1922, **67**, 462; Trautz and Hebbel, *ibid.*, 1924, **74**, 285; Trautz, *ibid.*, 1927, **83**, 457; 1928, **86**, 1; Trautz and Gürsching, *ibid.*, 1930, **4**, 985; Trautz and Kaufmann, *ibid.*, 1930, **5**, 581; Trautz and Blum, *ibid.*, 1933, **16**, 362; Trautz and Reichle, *ibid.*, 1935, **23**, 513; Giacomini, *Phil. Mag.*, 1925, **50**, 146.

2 Eucken, *Berlin Ber.*, 1912, 141; 1914, 682; *Verhl. d. D. Phys. Ges.*, 1916, **18**, 4; *Naturwiss.*, 1943, **31**, 314.

If P is the maximum pressure reached in the explosion, then:[1]

$$t_2=[P(t_1+273)/p_1]-273 \quad . \quad . \quad . \quad . \quad . \quad . \quad . \quad (2)$$

If there is no change in the number of molecules, $p_1=p_i$, the initial pressure of the mixture at t_1. The value of $\bar{C}_{vr}$ may be determined by exploding with argon (the value of C_{vi} for which is 3 g.cal. and constant). Then $\bar{C}_{vi}$ for any other gas can be found from (1).

The older experiments[2] by this method gave more or less unsatisfactory results, mainly on account of the loss of heat to the walls and the lag and oscillations of the manometers. The first really satisfactory method was developed by Pier,[3] who used a light steel diaphragm manometer.

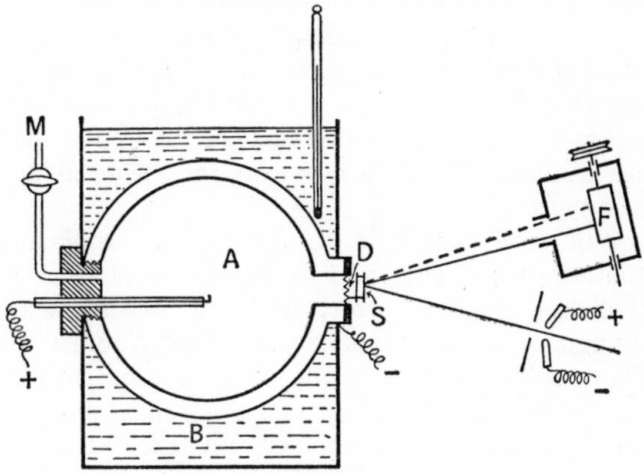

FIG. 6.VII E. Pier's Apparatus

A corrugated circular steel membrane D of 0·1 mm. thickness was clamped for 1 cm. round its edge over an opening of 3 cm. diam. in a spherical steel explosion bomb with a capacity of 35 lit. (Fig. 6.VII E). A small concave mirror S, 6 mm. diam. and 1 m. focal length, was attached by a rod to one side of the

1 For calculations, see Flamm and Mache, *Wien Ber.*, 1917, **126**, IIA, 9.

2 Bunsen, *Ann. Phys.*, 1867, **131**, 161; Mallard and Le Chatelier, *Compt. Rend.*, 1881, **93**, 1014; *Ann. des Mines*, 1883, **4**, 379; *Bull. Soc. Chim.*, 1883, **29**, 2, 98, 268; 1887, **48**, 122; Vieille, *Compt. Rend.*, 1882, **95**, 1280; 1883, **96**, 116; Sarrau and Vieille, *Compt. Rend.*, 1882, **95**, 26, 130, 180; 1886, **102**, 1054; 1887, **104**, 1759; Berthelot and Vieille, *ibid.*, 1884, **98**, 545, 601, 646, 770, 852; *Bull. Soc. Chim.*, 1884, **41**, 554; Berthelot, " Sur la Force des Matières Explosives," 1883, **2**, 149; Langen, *Forschungsarb. Gebiet Ingenieurwes.*, 1903, **8**, 1; *Z. Verein D. Ing.*, 1903, **47**, 622; for summaries and criticism, see Mellor, " Chemical Statics and Dynamics," 1904, 471; Haber, " Thermodynamics of Technical Gas Reactions," 1908, 224; Jellinek, " Physikalische Chemie der Gasreaktionen," 1913, 645; Muraour, *Compt. Rend.* 1919, **169**, 723; Partington and Shilling, " The Specific Heats of Gases," 1924, 112.

3 *Z. phys. Chem.*, 1908, **62**, 385; 1909, **66**, 759; *Z. Elektrochem.*, 1909, **15**, 536; 1910, **16**, 897; Bjerrum, *Z. phys. Chem.*, 1912, **79**, 513, 537; 1912, **81**, 281; *Z. Elektrochem.*, 1911, **17**, 731; 1912, **18**, 101; Budde, *Z. anorg. Chem.*, 1912, **78**, 159, 169; Siegel, *Z. phys. Chem.*, 1914, **87**, 641; Nernst, *Berlin Ber.*, 1915, 896; Wohl, *Z. Elektrochem.*, 1924, **30**, 36, 49; *Z. phys Chem.*, 1925, **118**, 460; for other measurements see Hopkinson, *Proc. Roy. Soc.*, 1906, **77**, 387; 1907, **79**, 138; 1910, **84**, 155; *B.A. Report*, 1908, 308; David *et al.*, *Phil. Trans.*, 1911, **211**, 375; *Phil. Mag.*, 1913, **25**, 256; 1920, **39**, 84; 1930, **9**, 390; 1932, **14**, 764; 1933, **15**, 177; 1934, **18**, 307; 1937, **23**, 345 (bibl.); *Engineer*, 1941, **171**, 268; *Nature*, 1942, **150**, 291, 320, 521; 1943, **151**, 392; 1947, **159**, 407 (crit. by Zeise, *Z. Elektrochem.*, 1941, **47**, 172); Bone, *Phil. Trans.*, 1915, **215**, 275; *Proc. Roy. Soc.*, 1921, **100**, 67, using the manometer of Petavel, *Phil. Trans.*, 1905, **205**, 357; Womersley, *Proc. Roy. Soc.*, 1922, **100**, 483; *Nature*, 1922, **100**, 483; 1923, **103**, 183; crit. by Glazebrook, *Nature*, 1922, **101**, 112; Thorp, *Phil. Mag.*, 1929, **8**, 813, 824; Wohl and von Elbe, *Z. phys. Chem.*, 1929, **5** B, 241; Wohl and Magat, *ibid.*, 1932, **19** B, 117; Lewis and von Elbe, *J.A.C.S.*, 1933, **55**, 504, 511; Campbell, Littler, and Whitworth, *J.C.S.*, 1932, 339 (rate of pressure rise in theoretical mixtures of O_2 with H_2, CH_4, C_2H_4, and CO very violent, except with CO); Maxwell and Wheeler, *ibid.*, 1933, 882; Burlot, *Mém. Poudres*, 1932–3, **25**, 314 (sp. hts. at high temp. and press. in explosions); Dorsey, " Properties of Ordinary Water Substance," New York, 1940, 107 (bibl.); Gaydon, *Nature*, 1942, **150**, 481; Walker, *Phil. Mag.*, 1943, **34**, 486; Corner. *Proc. Phys. Soc.*, 1946, **58**, 737; Leah, *Phil. Mag.*, 1947, **38**, 657.

diaphragm, and its deflexion was recorded by a beam of light from an arc reflected on a revolving photographic film F. The maximum pressure was recorded in somewhat less than 0·01 sec. and no cooling correction was considered necessary. The membrane was calibrated by applying oil pressure in a small vessel to which the membrane was fitted. The pressure-time curves [1] obtained with various types of manometer show that Pier's manometer gives a higher (instantaneous) maximum pressure than the older types.

The velocities of burning gas mixtures were studied by Nusselt.[2] Lees [3] concluded that the inequalities in temperature in different parts of a burning gas are negligible, and Stewart [4] that the time-lag in the distribution of molecular energy is negligible. The radiation emitted in the combustion of a gas mixture has a maximum frequency near the infra-red border, the other wave-lengths being negligible.[5]

Wohl and von Elbe [6] determined the specific heat of steam by explosion of a mixture of $2H_2+O_2$ and found the peculiar result that, whereas C_v found by exploding initially dry mixtures does not agree with that calculated by Einstein's formula (§ 30), C_v found by exploding a moist mixture is in closer agreement. They point out the difficulty of correlating the older measurements of Bjerrum and Siegel from this point of view, and as an explanation of their results, they surmise a heat loss with the dry mixture in the form of luminescence radiation, amounting to several per cent. of the heat of reaction, whilst in the moist mixture, even with 15 mm. partial pressure of water vapour, this loss is supposed to be less than 1 per cent. Absorption of radiant heat by water vapour will not account for the difference. No experimental proof of this hypothesis was given beyond the better agreement of the results with the moist mixture with theory, but reference was made to measurements by Garner and Johnson [7] with dry and moist carbon monoxide-oxygen explosions in which the *measured* radiant energy from the mixture dried with P_2O_5 amounted to 10 per cent. of the heat of combustion (" chemical energy set free "), whilst with gas containing 1·9 per cent. of water vapour it was only 2·5 per cent.

Nernst and Wohl [8] considered that Henning's experimental values for specific heats at high temperatures (§ 3) are 2 to 3 per cent. in error, but Henning [9] did not agree with this supposition, which is based on theoretical values only.

Wohl and Magat [10] confirmed Wohl and von Elbe's results with dry and moist gas, and by explosion measurements they obtained values for the specific heats of hydrogen and steam agreeing with theory, but the values for oxygen and nitrogen were somewhat too low; this was explained by assuming that the vibrational energy of the molecules was not fully excited in the small time of duration of the explosion. Lewis and von Elbe,[11] however, found just the opposite result from Wohl and Magat, i.e. values higher than the theoretical,

[1] Partington and Shilling, " The Specific Heats of Gases," 1924, 123, Fig. 21.
[2] *Z. Verein D. Ing.*, 1915, **59**, 872; *Ann. Phys. Beibl.*, 1916, **40**, 414.
[3] *Proc. Cambr. Phil. Soc.*, 1921, **20**, 285.
[4] *Phil. Mag.*, 1914, **28**, 748; Shtandel, *J. Phys. Chem. U.S.S.R.*, 1948, **22**, 289.
[5] Hopkinson, *Proc. Roy. Soc.*, 1906, **77**, 387; 1907, **79**, 138; 1910, **84**, 155; Wohlenberg, *Mech. Eng.*, 1930, **52**, 852, 915, 981, 1075.
[6] *Z. phys. Chem.*, 1929, **5** B, 241.
[7] *Phil. Mag.*, 1927, **3**, 97; 1928, **5**, 301; *J.C.S.*, 1928, 280; Garner, *Ind. Eng. Chem.*, 1928, **20**, 1008.
[8] *Z. techn. Phys.*, 1929, **10**, 608.
[9] *Z. techn. Phys.*, 1930, **11**, 191.
[10] *Z. phys. Chem.*, 1932, **19** B, 117.
[11] *J.A.C.S.*, 1933, **55**, 511.

by the explosion of ozone, which they attributed to a $^1\Delta$ metastable energy level in the neutral oxygen molecule. They gave empirical formulae to represent their results, from which they calculated: [1]

T° K.	200	300	500	800	1000	1500	2000	2500	3000
C_p	6·951	7·016	7·434	8·072	8·356	8·840	9·208	9·500	9·725

In view of these discrepancies, the newer explosion values for oxygen are doubtful.

Johnston and Walker [2] also calculated the theoretical specific heat of oxygen at high temperatures with the assumption of a $^1\Delta$ term which is supposed to add an insignificant contribution below 3000° K. and only a maximum of 0·36 g.cal to C_v at 4500° K. They considered Wohl and Magat's experimental results much too low, and Lewis and von Elbe's too high. Lewis and von Elbe,[3] however, by another manipulation of a $^1\Delta$ term [4] of 0·97 volt, managed to bring their results into agreement with theory, and adopted Wohl and Magat's explanation of the low experimental values in hydrogen-oxygen explosions. It cannot be said that the procedure is convincing, and the repeated errors in the calculations are disturbing.

§ 8. Numerical Values of Specific Heats of Gases

The following equations for the true specific heat of 1 mol at t° C., based on experimental results, are given by Partington and Shilling: [5]

$$O_2, N_2, CO, \text{air} \quad C_v=4{\cdot}970+0{\cdot}00017t+0{\cdot}0_631t^2$$
$$H_2 \quad C_v=4{\cdot}850+0{\cdot}00070t$$
$$CO_2 \quad C_v=6{\cdot}700+0{\cdot}0045t-0{\cdot}0_5102t^2$$
$$H_2O\ (0°\text{–}1700°) \quad C_v=6{\cdot}750-0{\cdot}00119t+0{\cdot}0_5234t^2$$
$$H_2O\ (1700°\text{–}2500°) \quad C_v=-12{\cdot}652+0{\cdot}02214t-0{\cdot}0_54671t^2.$$

Values of C_v (true) given by Nernst,[6] partly based on experiments, are:

t° C.	0°	100°	200°	500°	1200°	2000°
A	2·98	2·98	2·98	2·98	3·0	3·0
N_2, O_2, CO ...	4·99	5·05	5·15	5·26	5·75	6·3
H_2	4·87	4·93	5·05	5·16	5·67	6·28
HCl	5·00	5·09	5·27	5·46	6·13	6·9
Cl_2	5·95	6·3	6·7	6·9	7·1	7·2
H_2O	5·93	6·00	6·60	7·00	8·4	11·0
CO_2	6·68	7·69	9·04	9·75	10·6	11·1
SO_2	7·2	8·1	(9·2)	(9·8)	(10·6)	(11·1)
NH_3	6·62	7·05	8·3	9·5	11·4	—

1 The second and third decimals are quite superfluous.
2 *J.A.C.S.*, 1935, **57**, 682.
3 *J.A.C.S.*, 1935, **57**, 1399, 2737.
4 Herzberg, *Nature*, 1934, **133**, 759; Ellis and Kneser, *Phys. Rev.*, 1934, **45**, 133; see also the correction by Wilson, *J. Chem. Phys.*, 1936, **4**, 526, and Giauque, *J.A.C.S.*, 1937, **59**, 1158, of the theoretical calculation of the specific heat of steam by Gordon, *J. Chem. Phys.*, 1934, **2**, 65.
5 "The Specific Heats of Gases," 1924, 202 f.; some of the equations in terms of the absolute temperature T on p. 209 are mis-printed and should read: for O_2, N_2, CO, air, $4{\cdot}947+0{\cdot}0_631T^2$; CO_2, $5{\cdot}396+0{\cdot}00506T-0{\cdot}0_5102T^2$; H_2O (0°−1700°), $7{\cdot}249-0{\cdot}00247T+0{\cdot}0_5234T^2$. See Bryant, *Ind. Eng. Chem.*, 1931, **23**, 1019; 1932, **24**, 591; Partington and Shilling, *ibid.*, 1932, **24**, 591; *J.S.C.I.*, 1932, **51**, 82 T.
6 "Theoretische Chemie," 11th–15th edit., 1926, 287.

The following values of C_p (true), mostly from theoretical calculations, are given by Ulich:[1]

$T°$ K.	300°	600°	900°	1200°	1500°	1800°	2000°	2500°	3000°
H_2	6·90	7·01	7·14	7·41	7·72	8·01	8·18	8·53	8·80
O_2	7·02	7·68	8·22	8·53	8·74	8·92	9·03	9·31	9·52
H_2O	8·00	8·64	9·50	10·38	11·15	11·76	12·09	12·7	13·1
N_2	6·96	7·20	7·68	8·07	8·33	8·52	8·60	8·76	8·86
NO	7·14	7·48	8·00	8·34	8·56	8·71	8·77	8·90	8·98
Cl_2	8·07	8·66	8·81	8·87	8·91	8·92	8·92	—	—
HCl	6·95	7·07	7·41	7·78	8·06	8·28	8·38	—	—
H_2S	8·13	9·23	10·49	11·46	12·13	12·58	—	—	—
SO_2	9·53	11·67	12·70	13·17	13·42	13·56	—	—	—
CH_4	8·54	12·50	15·91	18·43	—	—	—	—	—
CO	6·96	7·28	7·79	8·17	8·42	8·59	8·67	8·81	8·90
CO_2	8·91	11·32	12·69	13·50	14·00	14·3	14·5	14·8	15·0

Values of the *mean* molecular heats at constant volume $\bar{C}_v$ between 273° and $T°$ abs., *calculated* from theory by Nernst and Wohl,[2] are:

$T°$ K.	273	373	473	573	800	1200	1600	2000	2400	2800
H_2	4·82	4·91	4·93	4·94	4·97	5·06	5·21	5·36	5·52	5·66
N_2	4·97	4·97	4·99	5·03	5·16	5·43	5·67	5·85	6·0	6·1
CO	4·97	4·98	5·00	5·06	5·22	5·52	5·76	5·9	6·1	6·2
O_2	5·01	5·08	5·18	5·29	5·54	5·89	6·12	6·29	6·41	—
CO_2	6·63	7·18	7·67	8·08	8·84	9·77	10·37	10·8	11·1	11·4
H_2O	5·99	6·05	6·14	6·24	6·53	7·09	7·61	8	8·5	8·8

The *true* molecular heats at constant pressure C_p at the absolute temperature T collected from miscellaneous sources, some experimental and some theoretical, are given, according to Kelley,[3] by the following equations (temperature range in brackets):

A, He, Ne, Kr, Xe	4·97	
CH_4	$5·34+11·5\times10^{-3}T$	(273–1200)
Cl_2	$8·28+0·56\times10^{-3}T$	(273–2000)
CO	$6·60+1·20\times10^{-3}T$	(273–2500)
CO_2	$10·34+2·74\times10^{-3}T-1·995\times10^5T^{-2}$	(273–1200)
H_2	$6·62+0·81\times10^{-3}T$	(273–2500)
HCl	$6·70+0·84\times10^{-3}T$	(273–2000)
HI	$6·93+0·83\times10^{-3}T$	(273–2000)
H_2S	$7·20+3·60\times10^{-3}T$	(300–600)
N_2	$6·50+1·00\times10^{-3}T$	(300–3000)
NH_3	$6·70+6·3\times10^{-3}T$	(300–800)
NO	$8·05+0·233\times10^{-3}T-1·563\times10^5T^{-2}$	(273–5000)
O_2	$8·27+0·258\times10^{-3}T-1·877\times10^5T^{-2}$	(300–5000)
SO_2	$7·70+5·30\times10^{-3}T-0·83\times10^{-5}T^2$	(300–2500)

[1] "Kurzes Lehrbuch der physikalischen Chemie," 1938, 301; cf. Schelest, "Die spezifischen Wärmen der Gase und Dämpfe," Leipzig and Vienna, 1922; Doczekal, "Absolute thermische Daten und Gleichgewichtskonstante," Vienna, 1935.

[2] *Z. techn. Phys.*, 1929, **10**, 608; see David and Leah, *Phil. Mag.*, 1934, **18**, 307.

[3] *U.S. Bureau of Mines Bull.*, 1934, **371**; Kelley and Anderson, *ibid.*, 1935, **384**. It should be noted that many specific heats of gases have been calculated from spectroscopic data and have no direct experimental foundation; Kelley included some old values which had been

Empirical specific heat equations of the form:

$$C_p = a + bT + cT^2$$

with the values of the constants tabulated below were given by Spencer and Justice,[1] the average and maximum percentage deviations from values calculated from *theoretical* equations by Johnston *et al.*—some later found to contain arithmetical errors—are also given:

	a	$b \times 10^3$	$c \times 10^7$	Maximum percentage	Average percentage
H_2 ...	6·9469	−0·1999	4·808	0·49	0·19
O_2 ...	6·0954	3·2533	−10·171	0·57	0·23
Cl_2 ...	7·5755	2·4244	−9·650	1·13	0·59
Br_2 ...	8·4228	0·9739	−3·555	0·71	0·25
N_2 ...	6·4492	1·4125	−0·807	1·35	0·54
CO ...	6·3424	1·8363	−2·801	1·38	0·47
HCl ...	6·7319	0·4325	3·697	0·98	0·48
HBr ...	6·5776	0·9549	1·581	1·23	0·54
H_2O ...	7·1873	2·3733	2·084	1·05	0·38
CO_2 ...	6·3957	10·1933	−35·333	2·17	0·76

Quite a different set of values for the same formula, from the same theoretical spectroscopic basis, are given by Bryant [2] and Taylor: [3]

	a	$b \times 10^6$	$-c \times 10^9$	a	$b \times 10^6$	$-c \times 10^9$
H_2	6·88	66	−279 *			
O_2	6·26	2746	770			
N_2	6·30	1819	345			
CO	6·25	2091	459			
CO_2	6·85	8533	2475	5·166	15177	9578
H_2O	6·89	3283	343	7·219	2374	−267*
CH_4	3·38	17905	4188	3·422	17845	4165
C_2H_2	8·28	10501	2644			
SO_2	8·12	6825	2103			
NH_3	5·92	8963	1764	6·189	7887	728

* All $-c$ values, except for H_2 and H_2O, are positive.

Other theoretical tables given by Lewis and von Elbe,[4] Spencer and Flannagan,[5] and Thompson,[6] are different from the above and from one another.[7]

selected in a very arbitrary way by Eastman, *U.S. Bur. Mines Techn. Paper*, 1929, No. **445**; Eastman and Rollefson, "Physical Chemistry," New York, 1947, 141, and should not appear in modern tables.

1 *J.A.C.S.*, 1934, **56**, 2311; Crawford and Parr, *J. Chem. Phys.*, 1948, **16**, 233.

2 *Ind. Eng. Chem.*, 1933, **25**, 820.

3 *Ind. Eng. Chem.*, 1934, **26**, 470.

4 *J.A.C.S.*, 1935, **57**, 612; corrected in *ibid.*, 1935, **57**, 2737.

5 *J.A.C.S.*, 1942, **64**, 2511; corrected by Spencer, *ibid.*, 1945, **67**, 1858.

6 *Trans. Amer. Electrochem. Soc.*, 1942, **82**, 397.

7 For appreciable discrepancies between observed and calculated values, see Darken and Gurry, *J.A.C.S.*, 1945, **67**, 1398; Katz, *J. Chem. Phys.*, 1943, **11**, 493, remarked that the specific heats of carbon dioxide found by *all* experimenters (Eucken is overlooked, however) are consistently higher than the calculated spectroscopic values.

Davis and Johnston's [1] *theoretical* values for hydrogen (ideal state at 1 atm.) are:

T°K.	250	500	700	1000	1500	2000	2500
C_p°	6·772	6·992	7·035	7·220	7·718	8·181	8·531

The *calculated* specific heats of steam at 1 atm. pressure, *actual* state (from ideal by Berthelot's equation) given by Fritz and Koch [2] are (c_p in g.cal./g.):

100°	0·464	160°	0·465
120°	0·463	180°	0·466
140°	0·464	200°	0·468

Theoretical values for *hydrocarbons* have been calculated,[3] and there are several collections of experimental and theoretical data for other gases.[4]

In view of the statement [5] that " the so-called [!] experimental values are of no use," it seems necessary to direct attention to some aspects of the alternative procedure. Many new theoretical specific heats are based on what has been well called a " guided guess," [6] and in cases where experimental values are presented, " it is suggested that thermochemists should check their methods so that the accuracy assigned to the experimental results will have a real significance." [7]

Some idea of the reliability of these theoretical specific heats may be gathered from the following. Johnston and Davis [8] pointed out that all Kassel's [9] figures are in error because of the use of wrong signs for two sets of terms in the expressions for the rotational energy (§ 25.IV). Witmer [10] then showed that Johnston and Chapman's figures [11] for nitric oxide are erroneous for the

1 *J.A.C.S.*, 1934, **56**, 1045 (entropies and free energies also given).

2 *Wärme-und Kälte-Techn.*, 1940, **42**, 65; *Amer. Chem. Abstr.*, 1942, **36**, 5685.

3 Sage, Webster, and Lacey, *Ind. Eng. Chem.*, 1937, **29**, 1309; Edminster, *ibid.*, 1938, **30**, 352; 1940, **32**, 373; Maron and Turnbull, *ibid.*, 1942, **34**, 544; Halcomb and Brown, *ibid.*, 1942, **34**, 590; Aston, *ibid.*, 1942, **34**, 514; Sage and Olds, *ibid.*, 1942, **34**, 526; Glockler and Edgell, *ibid.*, 1942, **34**, 532; all theoretical values. For nomogram of heat contents of hydrocarbons, see Scheibel and Jenny, *Ind. Eng. Chem.*, 1945, **37**, 990.

4 Peake, *Proc. Roy. Soc.*, 1905, **76**, 185 (superheated steam); Schreber, " Der Ölmotor," 1915 (12 pp.); *Ann. Phys. Beibl.*, 1916, **40**, 321; Eichelberg, *Z. Verein D. Ing.*, 1917, **61**, 750 (c_v superheated steam); Neumann, *Z. angew. Chem.*, 1919, **32**, i, 141 (air, O_2, N_2, H_2, CO_2, SO_2, and CH_4, 0°–3000°); Knoblauch, *Z. techn. Phys.*, 1922, **3**, 39; Knoblauch and Raisch, *Z. Verein D. Ing.*, 1922, **66**, 418 (superheated steam); Mewes, *Z. Sauerstoff Stickstoff Ind.*, 1922, **14**, 26; Jakob, *Z. techn. Phys.*, 1923, **4**, 460 (air −80° to 250°, 0 to 200 atm.); Fischer, *ibid.*, 1924, **5**, 17, 39, 83 (air, CO_2, H_2O); Plank, *ibid.*, 1924, **5**, 397 (superheated steam); Seligmann, *ibid.*, 1925, **6**, 237 (air at low temps.); Everett, *Mech. Eng.*, 1926, **48**, 1329 (air, O_2, N_2, CO_2 at 500°–5500° F. abs.); Yamaga, *Proc. Imp. Acad. Japan*, 1928, **4**, 102; Schmidt and Schnell, *Z. techn. Phys.*, 1928, **9**, 81 (to 3000° K.); Millar and Sullivan, *Bur. Mines Techn. Pap.*, 1928, **424** (Mollier charts for O_2 and N_2); Weydanz, *Z. techn. Phys.*, 1932, **13**, 233 (N_2—100° to 800°, 0 to 200 atm.); Schlegel, *Forschungsarb. Gebiet Ingenieuwes.*, 1932, **3**, 297 (entropy of air to 500° and 300 atm.); Justi, *Ann. Phys.*, 1937, **29**, 302; Kelley, *Bur. Mines Rep. Invest.*, 1937, **3341** (metal vapours); Schmidt, *Forschungsarb. Gebiet Ingenieurwes.*, 1937, **8**, 91; Dorsey, " Properties of Ordinary Water Substance," New York, 1940, 92 (steam); Krichevsky, Kazarnovsky, and Levchenko, *J. Phys. Chem. U.S.S.R.*, 1945, **19**, 314; Geyer, *Engineering*, 1945, **159**, 381, 423; Finnecome, *Proc. Inst. Mech. Eng.*, 1946, **155**, 117 (total heat-entropy charts for gases with variable specific heats); Manson, *Compt. Rend.*, 1947, **224**, 1548, 1816 (mixtures).

5 Gordon and Barnes, *J. Phys. Chem.*, 1932, **36**, 1143.

6 Aston, Kennedy, and Schumann, *J.A.C.S.*, 1940, **62**, 2059

7 Guthrie and Huffman, *J.A.C.S.*, 1943, **65**, 1139.

8 *J.A.C.S.*, 1934, **56**, 271.

9 *J. Chem. Phys.*, 1933, **1**, 576.

10 *J.A.C.S.*, 1934, **56**, 2229.

11 *J.A.C.S.*, 1933, **55**, 153.

same reason. All Johnston's figures are given to three places of decimals, and in the case of hydrogen [1] are given for temperatures over 4000° C., when H_2 would practically be non-existent. Such data are, in fact, misleading, and as the calculations are so involved that only experts can check them, the ordinary user would be well advised to leave them alone. The theoretical specific heats of steam calculated by Gordon [2] are also in error.[3]

Even more doubtful than the specific heats found solely by the calculating machine, are those surmised from large extrapolations of approximations reached from experimental results in quite different fields. A particularly grotesque example of this type of procedure is Bäckström's [4] calculation of the specific heats of carbon dioxide at high temperatures from a small number of not very accurate measurements of the small *differences* in solubilities of calcite and aragonite at room temperature.

§ 9. Ratio of the Specific Heats

The ratio of the specific heats at constant pressure and at constant volume, usually denoted by γ (sometimes κ), $c_p/c_v = C_p/C_v = \gamma$, is an important quantity. If γ and the difference of the specific heats, $c_p - c_v$ or $C_p - C_v$, are known, the two specific heats themselves may be calculated. In the measurement of γ two methods have generally been used; the first (due originally to Clement and Desormes) depends on *adiabatic expansion*, and the second on the measurement of the *velocity of sound* in the gas.

The heating and cooling of a gas by sudden compression and expansion was noticed by Cullen and by Erasmus Darwin; [5] the changes of temperature were more accurately studied by Dalton,[6] who concluded that on compressing air to half its volume there is a rise of temperature of 50° F., and a similar cooling when the air is expanded to double the volume. Dulong [7] found that equal volumes of all gases at the same temperature and pressure evolve or absorb the same amount of heat when suddenly compressed or expanded, respectively, by the same amount.

§ 10. Desormes and Clement's Method

In the Desormes and Clement experiment [8] the gas is contained in a large bottle (e.g. a carboy), fitted with a large-bore stopcock and a manometer, at an initial pressure p_1 somewhat above atmospheric pressure P. The tap

[1] Davis and Johnston, *J.A.C.S.*, 1934, **56**, 1045.

[2] *J. Chem. Phys.*, 1934, **2**, 65.

[3] Wilson, *J. Chem. Phys.*, 1936, **4**, 526; Giauque, *J.A.C.S.*, 1937, **59**, 1158.

[4] *J.A.C.S.*, 1925, **47**, 2443.

[5] Cullen, *Essays and Obs. Phys. and Lit.*, Edinburgh, 1756, **2**, 145; Darwin, *Phil. Trans.*, 1788, **78**, 43 (experiments made about 1775 with the assistance of Warltire); Joule, *Phil. Mag.*, 1845, **26**, 369.

[6] *Manch. Mem.*, 1800, **5**, 515.

[7] *Ann. Chim.*, 1828, **41**, 113.

[8] *J. de Phys.*, 1819, **89**, 321, 428 ("Par MM. Desormes et Clément, Manufacturiers"); they used initial pressures *below* atmospheric, the use of excess pressures being due to Gay-Lussac and Welter, q. by Laplace, *Ann. Chim.*, 1822, **20**, 266; "Mécanique Céleste," 1823, **5**, 123; "Oeuvres," 1882, **5**, 38; Poisson, "Traité de Mécanique," 1833, **2**, 637, 646; Donkin, *Phil. Mag.*, 1864, **28**, 458; Swyngedauw, *J. de Phys.*, 1897, **6**, 129; Guglielmo, *Atti R. Accad. Lincei*, 1913, **23**, i, 698; Rüchardt, *Phys. Z.*, 1929, **30**, 58; for modified apparatus, see Watson, "A Text Book of Practical Physics," 1908, 269; Foà, *Nuov. Cim.*, 1926, **3**, 101; Mohr, *Z. techn Phys.*, 1934, **15**, 284.

is opened and the gas allowed to expand rapidly and very nearly adiabatically to atmospheric pressure, when the tap is closed again. The gas is allowed to warm up to the atmospheric temperature and the final pressure p_2 is read on the manometer. The value of γ is caclulated from the three measured pressures, p_1, P, and p_2, as follows.

Let v_1 be the specific volume of the gas under the pressure p_1 and v_2 the specific volume under the pressure P after adiabatic expansion, which is also the specific volume under the pressure p_2 at the original temperature. Then:

$$p_1/P=(v_2/v_1)^\gamma \text{ (adiabatic expansion)}$$

$$\text{and } p_1/p_2=v_2/v_1 \text{ (temperature constant)}$$

$$\therefore p_1/P=(p_1/p_2)^\gamma$$

$$\therefore \gamma(\log p_1-\log p_2)=(\log p_1-\log P)$$

$$\therefore \gamma=(\log p_1-\log P)/(\log p_1-\log p_2) \quad . \quad . \quad . \quad . \quad (1)$$

If natural logarithms are used in (1) and if $p_1=P+h_1$, therefore $P=p_1-h_1$, and $p_2=P+h_2$, therefore $p_2=p_1-h_1+h_2$, where h_1 and h_2 are the manometer readings (excess pressures above atmospheric) in the same units as P, then:

$$\gamma=\ln[p_1/(p_1-h_1)]/\ln[p_1/(p_1-h_1+h_2)]$$

$$=\ln(1-h_1/p_1)/\ln[1-(h_1-h_2)/p_1]$$

$$\simeq(h_1/p_1)\div[(h_1-h_2)/p_1]\simeq h_1/(h_1-h_2) \quad . \quad . \quad . \quad . \quad (2)$$

since h_1/p_1 and $(h_1-h_2)/p_1$ are small compared with unity, and the logarithms may be expanded according to formula (3), § 34.I, $\ln(1-x)\simeq -x$. If only an approximate value of γ is required (which is all the method so carried out can give), it is, therefore, not necessary to know the atmospheric pressure P, and only the manometer readings are required.[1]

Owing to errors caused by rapid heat exchange between the gas and the walls of the vessel during the adiabatic expansion, and the difficulty of closing the tap at the exact moment when the inside and outside pressures are equalised (oscillations of pressure occur if too high an initial pressure is used, the gas surging in and out through the tap),[2] it is not possible to obtain accurate results by this method, the values of γ being always too low.[3] The theory of these errors is very involved and uncertain. Rayleigh [4] discussed the heat exchange in a 35-cm. diam. spherical vessel in a Desormes and Clement experiment. With 20 mm. water pressure the time of half recovery of the initial temperature was 15 secs., and with 3–4 mm. of water it was 26 secs. The time of half recovery is $t=0{\cdot}184\gamma a^2/\pi^2\nu$, where a=radius of sphere, $\gamma=c_p/c_v$, ν=thermometric conductivity=$k/\rho c_v$ (k=thermal conductivity, ρ=density), and γ/ν= thermal capacity of unit volume at constant pressure=$0{\cdot}00128\times0{\cdot}239$. Hence if $k=0{\cdot}000056$, $\nu=0{\cdot}258$, and $\nu/\gamma=0{\cdot}183$, then $t=0{\cdot}102a^2$. If $a=16{\cdot}4$ cm., $t=27{\cdot}4$ sec.

[1] Brillouin, *Ann. Chim.*, 1909, **18**, 191; Leduc, *Compt. Rend.*, 1912, **155**, 909; *J. de Phys.*, 1916, **6**, 5; Bérard, *Bull. Soc. Chim.*, 1947, 225; Spitzer, *J. Chem. Educ.*, 1947, **24**, 251.

[2] Bauschinger, *Z. Math. Phys.* (Schlömilch), 1863, **8**, 81, 153; Rayleigh, "Theory of Sound," 1896, **2**, 264.

[3] Cazin, *Ann. Chim.*, 1862, **66**, 206 (bibl.); 1870, **20**, 251; Swyngedauw, *J. de Phys.*, 1897, **6**, 129; Chapman, *Phys. Rev.*, 1911, **32**, 561.

[4] Rayleigh, *Phil. Mag.*, 1899, **47**, 308, 314; "Scientific Papers," Cambridge, 1903, **4**, 379, 382; Aichi, *Proc. Phys. Math. Soc. Japan*, 1919, **1**, 164.

The method was improved by Röntgen,[1] who measured the pressures by a metal membrane manometer closing a hole in the side of the vessel, and attempted to apply a correction for the exchange of heat between the gas and the walls of the 70-litre vessel by measuring the pressures at different times after expansion. With hydrogen, with a high thermal conductivity, this did not give satisfactory results, and it is almost impossible to eliminate this effect in this type of experiment, especially if small vessels are used. With a 7-litre vessel Röntgen was unable, even after correction, to get a value of γ for air higher than 1·370, the true value being 1·403. A method depending on rapid compression by a piston was used by Maneuvrier [2] and by Worthing [3] (at higher pressures).

§ 11. Assmann's Method

In a method used by Assmann,[4] the oscillations of mercury in a U-tube containing the gas and closed at one end were observed. This method was most carefully tested by Hartmann,[5] who concluded that it could not give accurate results, because of heat exchange, particularly by convection, occurring in the gas; nothing has since modified this judgment. Hartmann, with different tubes, found for γ, air 1·41–1·42, CO_2 1·304–1·310, H_2 1·418–1·422. The value found by Hartmann for air is the same as that (1·421) found in Assmann's crude experiments, and is 2 per cent. too large, corresponding with about 20 per cent. error in c_p. A revival of the method [6] is claimed to have given better results.

Chopin [7] from the pressure drop in a gas passing through a perforation in a plate found C_p for nitrogen $6{\cdot}82+0{\cdot}00058t$ and for carbon dioxide $8{\cdot}9+0{\cdot}62(t/100)^{0{\cdot}68}$. An "impact tube" method, depending on adiabatic expansion into a closed-end tube, has been used.[8]

§ 12. Lummer and Pringsheim's Method

A great improvement in the adiabatic expansion method was introduced by Lummer and Pringsheim,[9] who used the equation [10] (17), § 4.II, $Tv^{\gamma-1}$=const., therefore $T_1/T_2=(v_2/v_1)^{\gamma-1}=(p_1/p_2)^{(\gamma-1)/\gamma}$, since pv^γ=const. It can then be shown by simple algebra that:

$$\gamma=(\log p_1-\log p_2)/[(\log p_1-\log p_2)-(\log T_1-\log T_2)] \quad . \quad (1)$$

This equation holds only for an ideal gas, in which case the experiment will also

[1] *Ann. Phys.*, 1870, **141**, 552; 1873, **148**, 580; 1894, **51**, 414. A full description of Röntgen's work and of other methods for the determination of γ by adiabatic expansion, is given in Partington and Shilling, "The Specific Heats of Gases," 1924, 65 f; the results are recalculated on modern standards and suitably corrected, *ibid.*, 190 f.

[2] *J. de Phys.*, 1895, **4**, 341, 445; *Ann. Chim.*, 1895, **6**, 321; cf. Amagat, *Compt. Rend.*, 1873, **77**, 1325.

[3] *Phys. Rev.*, 1911, **32**, 243; 1911, **33**, 217. The writer could not obtain accurate results by this method in experiments made in 1912.

[4] *Ann. Phys.*, 1852, **85**, 1; *Jahresb.*, 1852, 30; Müller, *Ann. Phys.*, 1883, **18**, 94.

[5] *Ann. Phys.*, 1905, **18**, 253.

[6] Clark and Katz, *Canad. J. Res.*, 1941, **19** A, 111; 1943, **21** A, 1; Parodi, *Compt. Rend.*, 1944, **218**, 311.

[7] *Ann. de Phys.*, 1931, **16**, 101.

[8] Kantrowitz, *J. Chem. Phys.*, 1946, **14**, 150; Huber and Kantrowitz, *ibid.*, 1947, **15**, 275.

[9] *B.A. Rep.*, 1894, 564; *Smithsonian Contributions to Knowledge*, 1898, No. 1126; *Ann. Phys.*, 1898, **64**, 555.

[10] For the use of Helmholtz's so-called "potential temperature," see Bauer, *Phys. Rev.*, 1908, **26**, 177.

give directly a value of C_p, the molecular heat (assumed constant) at constant pressure.

For, from § 3.II, $dS=c_p dT/T$, and from Maxwell's equation (2), § 48.II:

$$(dT/dp)_S=(dV/dS)_p=(T/c_p)(dV/dT)_p$$

$$\therefore\ c_p=T(dV/dT)_p/(dT/dp)_S$$

$$\therefore\ (dp/dT)_S=(dp/dT)_q=(c_p/T)(dT/dV)_p \quad . \quad . \quad . \quad . \quad (2)$$

For 1 mol of ideal gas, $pV=\boldsymbol{R}T$, therefore $(dT/dV)_p=p/\boldsymbol{R}$,

$$\therefore\ (T/p)(dp/dT)_q=(d\ln p/d\ln T)_q=C_p/\boldsymbol{R} \quad . \quad . \quad . \quad . \quad (3)$$

$$\therefore\ C_p=\boldsymbol{R}(\ln p_1-\ln p_2)/(\ln T_1-\ln T_2) \quad . \quad . \quad . \quad . \quad (4)$$

In this method the final pressure p_2 is the atmospheric pressure P, and as the tap may be left open after expansion, one source of error in Desormes and Clement's method is eliminated. The other source of error, due to heat exchange with the walls, can be eliminated by using a large vessel, and measuring the temperature at the centre by means of a fine platinum wire resistance thermometer, or a thermocouple of thin wires, of small heat capacity, which follows the changes of temperature of the gas very quickly. An error due to the relatively slow heat conduction from the thicker leads to the fine measuring wire is eliminated by a device introduced by Makower,[1] viz. by using *compensating leads*. A small piece of the same thin wire is soldered to a second pair of leads and placed near the main measuring wire in the vessel. This pair of compensating leads is connected in series with the variable resistance arm of the Wheatstone bridge (see Fig. 7.VII E), when all changes of resistance occurring in the leads solderings in the main system are compensated by similar ones in the second system, and only the temperature change of a portion of the long wire, which is not in contact with the leads, is measured.

Lummer and Pringsheim used a 70-litre vessel with a resistance thermometer (" bolometer ") of very thin platinum strip, 7 cm. long, 0·2 cm. wide, and 0·0006 mm. thick, hung in the centre of the vessel. A galvanometer of 4 sec. period was used as a null instrument, the variable arm of the Wheatstone bridge being so adjusted before expansion that the bridge was balanced *after* the strip had been cooled by the expansion of the gas. The temperature immediately after expansion was found by cooling the water surrounding the globe until the bridge was again balanced (when the bolometer had the temperature it possessed just after expansion), and then determining the temperature of the water by a mercury thermometer. In accurate experiments by this method, it was found that a direct measurement of temperature from the resistance of the thin platinum wire or strip itself does not give satisfactory results.[2]

An error due to radiation from the warmer walls of the vessel to the platinum bolometer was eliminated by repeating the experiment with the platinum blackened, when if γ_1 and γ_2 are the values found with bright and black platinum, respectively, the corrected value is given [3] by $\gamma=\gamma_1+(\gamma_1-\gamma_2)/14$, the absorbing powers of black and bright platinum being in the ratio 15 : 1.

[1] *Phil. Mag.*, 1903, **5**, 226.

[2] Partington, *Z. Phys.*, 1930, **60**, 420.

[3] Lummer and Pringsheim, *Ann. Phys.*, 1898, **64**, 555; Brinkworth, *Proc. Roy. Soc.*, 1925, **107**, 510; 1926, **111**, 124; *Proc. Phys. Soc.*, 1925, **38**, 68, thought a correction for the thermal conductivity of the gas is necessary if the radiation correction has been determined in air. Since in Partington's experiments the temperature of the wire and gas were always equal for an appreciable time, this does not seem necessary, but further experiments on this point are

A thermocouple of 0·025 mm. diameter copper and constantan wires in a 60-lit. vessel was used by Moody,[1] but the results are probably somewhat less

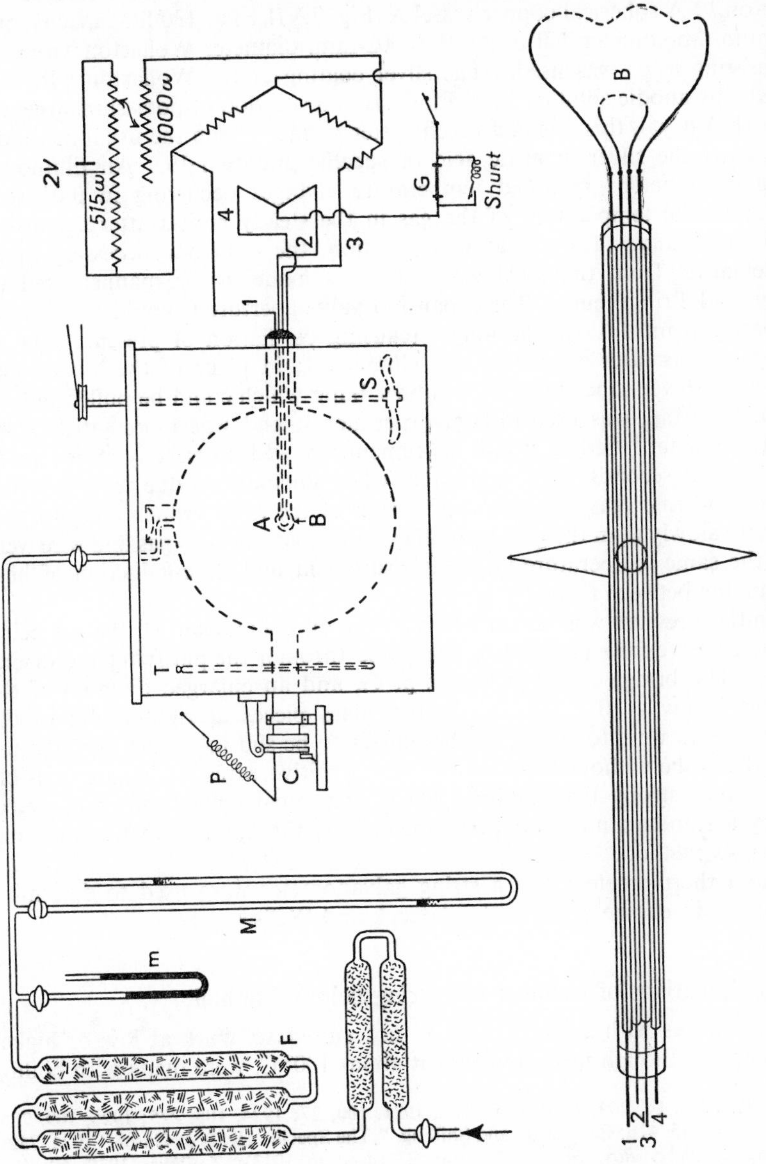

FIG. 7.VII E. Partington's Apparatus for determination of the Ratio of the Specific Heats of Gases by Adiabatic Expansion

accurate than Lummer and Pringsheim's. The very thin (1–4 μ) thermocouple foils used for radiation apparatus by Moll and Burgers [2] could probably be used in such work.

desirable. There may be large errors in the measurement of the temperature of a *flowing* gas by a thermocouple: Haslam and Chappell, *Ind. Eng. Chem.*, 1925, **17**, 402; Mandell, *Proc. Phys. Soc.*, 1925, **38**, 47.

1 *Phys. Z.*, 1912, **13**, 383; *Phys. Rev.*, 1912, **34**, 275; Shields, *Phys. Rev.*, 1917, **10**, 525 (1-lit. vessel, γ for air 1·4029, γ for H_2 at 18°=1·4012, which is much too low).

2 *Z. Phys.*, 1925, **32**, 575.

§ 13. Partington's Method

A modification of the method of Lummer and Pringsheim was used by Partington.[1] A spherical copper vessel A (Fig. 7.VII E) of 130 lit. capacity, and a platinum " bolometer " B of 0·001–0·002-mm. diameter Wollaston wire with compensating leads was used. The silver coating of the Wollaston wire was removed [2] by anodic solution by electrolysis in a solution of potassium argento-cyanide ($KAgCy_2$), this giving a much better surface [3] than the usual method [4] of dissolving the silver in nitric acid of specific gravity 1·19. An Einthoven string galvanometer [5] recorded temperature changes occurring in 0·01 sec., and so gave the temperature of the gas in the steady period after expansion without ambiguity. The radiation correction, the only one necessary apart from deviation from the ideal gas state, was made in the manner used by Lummer and Pringsheim. The expansion valve aperture C could be adjusted by diaphragms until " overshooting " (causing oscillation of pressure) due to the surge of gas after expansion was eliminated; in place of the hinged flap shown, a narrower tube closed by a rubber bung which could be pulled out, or a 3-mm. bore tap, was used in later experiments, and was more satisfactory. The galvanometer, used as a null instrument, showed a perfectly steady reading for several seconds after expansion, when fluctuations due to convection currents of warmer gas rising from the walls of the vessel (which cooled down much more slowly than the gas) made their appearance. The gas and wire were thus at the same temperature in the measurement and no conduction of heat was occurring between them.

The initial pressure was measured on a long oil manometer M, the gas being admitted under excess pressure to the globe through the purifying and drying tubes F. The bridge circuit is shown at G, and an enlarged diagram of the bolometer below at B. The star-shaped glass pieces at right-angles to the bolometer leads were to enable the bolometer to be slid into place through the neck of the globe without breaking the very sensitive wires (which are invisible except in very strong light under a lens). The final temperature was determined by a standard mercury thermometer T in the bath, as in Lummer and Pringsheim's method.

Platinum thermometers and a string galvanometer were used to determine temperatures in engine cylinders by Adcock and Wells.[6]

§ 14. Modifications of Lummer and Pringsheim's Method

This apparatus with a large globe is not suited to work at low or higher temperatures, although measurements at about 100° C. were made with boiling

[1] *Phys. Z.*, 1913, **14**, 969; *Proc. Roy. Soc.*, 1921, **100**, 27; 1924, **105**, 225; 1925, **109**, 286; *Phil. Mag.*, 1923, **45**, 416; Partington and Shilling, " The Specific Heats of Gases," 1924, 75.

[2] Partington, *Proc. Roy. Soc.*, 1921, **100**, 27 (used in 1913); *Z. Phys.*, 1930, **60**, 420; Waetzmann, Gnielinski, and Heisig, *ibid.*, 1929, **58**, 449. The wire must be annealed before solution.

[3] Friese and Waetzmann, *Z. Phys.*, 1925, **34**, 131; in Partington's experiments, the platinum was brilliant under a lens.

[4] Benedicks, *Phys. Z.*, 1916, **17**, 319 (annealed at 200°–400° and used warm concentrated nitric acid); Brüning, *Z. Instr.*, 1926, **46**, 29; *Amer. Chem. Abstr.*, 1926, **20**, 2098 (0·001 mm. wire visible on black velvet).

[5] Einthoven, *Ann. Phys.*, 1903, **12**, 1059; 1904, **14**, 182; 1905, **16**, 20; 1906, **21**, 483, 665; on string galvanometers, see also Apthorpe, *Electrician*, 1914, **74**, 111; Salomonson, *Proc. K. Akad. Wetens. Amsterdam*, 1918, **21**, 235 (Al string).

[6] *Phil. Mag.*, 1923, **45**, 532, with the theory of the unbalanced Wheatstone bridge.

water used in the bath. Small vessels have been used at low and higher temperatures.[1] The older workers [2] found much too low values of C_p/C_v with small vessels. When no actual measurements were made, but only comparisons with air (which was assumed to behave normally in small vessels), as in Eucken's experiments, the results are unconvincing, but the failures in early work were probably due to insensitive and slow methods of measuring temperatures. Brinkworth used small vessels successfully at low temperatures.

Eucken and von Lüde [3] used a small expansion vessel and an 8-μ thick wire, and did not determine its radiation correction but attempted to correct for it by comparing results with the platinum and a gold wire, on the basis of emissivities taken from the literature. They remarked that their platinum wire had a " fairly rough " surface, which does not agree with the experience of previous workers with Wollaston wires. They thought much thicker wires could be used. Although they gave a long theoretical discussion (partly with the object of discrediting previous work) of the radiation correction, they applied this, in the end, in the normal way. Instead of using a null method, they measured galvanometer *deflexions*, and by comparing them with the deflexions with air as a standard gas, attempted to calculate the temperature changes, amounting to 3° to 10°, by ratios of deflexions. No direct temperature measurements at all were made. The resistance changes were of the order of 5 ohms, and (although no wire lengths are given) it was claimed that heating of the wire by the current passing was negligible. The criticism that heating occurred in previous experiments is erroneous, since most earlier workers used a null method, when no current was passing at all through the wire when the galvanometer was read. Only one to three measurements were made with each gas at a given temperature. The results showed that only carbon monoxide agreed with the theoretical C_v (see § 8), but here the agreement was " almost exact "; " no great weight," however, was attached to this " not unpleasing " result. The apparatus failed to give satisfactory results above 220°. A similar method was used with an iridium wire in chlorine by Eucken and Hoffmann,[4] whose results disagreed with those of all previous workers.[5]

Eucken and Mücke [6] then found it possible to work the apparatus in a modified form up to 600°, still using the comparative deflexion method, which had now been so much improved that agreement with theory was obtained with all the gases used, except (curiously enough) now carbon dioxide. The authors, therefore, considered that further measurements were superfluous, and that specific heats of gases are best calculated from theory. Eucken and Mücke's results with hydrogen, however, have now come to lie well off the latest theoretical curve,[7] some older experimental values [8] being much nearer the latter.

[1] Lower temperatures, see Mercer, *Proc. Phys. Soc.*, 1914, **26**, 155; Shields, *Phys. Rev.*, 1917, **10**, 525; Selle, *Z. phys. Chem.*, 1923, **104**, 1; Brinkworth, *Proc. Roy. Soc.*, 1925, **107**, 510; 1926, **111**, 124; for higher temperatures see Eucken *et al.*, in references following.

[2] Kohlrausch, *Ann. Phys.*, 1869, **136**, 618; Witte, *ibid.*, 1869, **138**, 155; Röntgen, *ibid.*, 1870, **141**, 552; Boltzmann, *ibid.*, 1870, **141**, 473; " Wiss. Abhl.," 1909, **1**, 157; Partington and Shilling, " The Specific Heats of Gases," 1924, 67.

[3] *Z. phys. Chem.*, 1929, **5** B, 413; a similar apparatus, with 3·75-μ wire, was used by Sage, Webster, and Lacy, *Ind. Eng. Chem.*, 1937, **29**, 1309; see also Kistiakowski and Rice, *J. Chem. Phys.*, 1939, **7**, 281.

[4] *Z. phys. Chem.*, 1929, **5** B, 442.

[5] See Partington, *Z. phys. Chem.*, 1930, **7** B, 319, and Eucken's reply, not dealing with specific heats, *ibid.*, 1930, **7** B, 324.

[6] *Z. phys. Chem.*, 1932, **18** B, 167.

[7] Davis and Johnston, *J.A.C.S.*, 1934, **56**, 1045.

[8] Partington and Howe, *Proc. Roy. Soc.*, 1925, **109**, 286.

Eucken and Parts,[1] and Eucken and d'Or,[2] however, continued experiments with the type of apparatus described, obtaining remarkably good agreement with theoretical values current at the time.

§ 15. Calculation of C_p/C_v from Experiments with Non-Ideal Gases

It must be emphasised that most of the equations given above apply only to ideal gases. Van der Waals [3] substituted $(dp/dT)_v = R/(v-b)$ from his characteristic equation $(p+a/v^2)(v-b)=RT$, in the general equation $c_v dT + T(dp/dT)_v dv = 0$, which follows from (2a), § 3.II, and (5), § 41.II, finding after integration (with $R = C_p - C_v = (\gamma-1)C_v$, which is not general; see § 54.II), $T(v-b)^{\gamma-1} = \text{const.}$, or:

$$(p+a/v^2)(v-b)^\gamma = \text{const.} \quad \ldots \ldots \quad (1)$$

an equation used by Boynton.[4]

For experiments about room temperature and atmospheric pressure a better correction is obtained from Berthelot's equation (§ 30.VII C) as follows.[5] The temperature change in adiabatic expansion may be equated to that due to external work only (ideal gas) and that, dT', due to internal work only (Joule effect, § 23.VII A):

$$dT = -p dv/C_v + dT' = RT dp'/pC_v + dT'$$

since $dv = -RT dp'/p^2$, where dp' is the pressure change required to produce the change dv isothermally and p is the initial pressure. From (14), § 30.VII C:

$$dT' = \frac{RT_c}{C_v}\frac{dp'}{p_c}\tfrac{27}{32}\tau^2$$

$$\therefore\ dT = \frac{RT}{C_v}\cdot\frac{dp'}{p}(1+\tfrac{27}{32}\pi\tau^3)$$

where [6] $\pi = p/p_c$ and $\tau = T_c/T$; hence:

$$C_v = R\frac{d \ln p'}{d \ln T}(1+\tfrac{27}{32}\pi\tau^3) \quad \ldots \ldots \quad (2)$$

If dp_v is the increase of pressure due to the increase of temperature dT at constant volume, (5), § 30.VII C, gives:

$$(d \ln p/dT)_v = (1+\tfrac{27}{32}\pi\tau^3)/T$$

$$d \ln p_v = (1+\tfrac{27}{32}\pi\tau^3) d \ln T \quad \ldots \ldots \quad (2a)$$

$$\therefore\ C_v = R\frac{d \ln p'}{d \ln p_v}(1+\tfrac{27}{16}\pi\tau^3) \quad \ldots \ldots \quad (3)$$

since $(1+x)^2 \simeq 1+2x$ when x is small compared with 1. But from (9), § 30.VII C:

$$C_p - C_v = R(1+\tfrac{27}{16}\pi\tau^3).$$

[1] *Gött. Nachr.*, 1932, 274; *Z. phys. Chem.*, 1933, **20** B, 184 (C_2H_6, C_2H_4).
[2] *Gött. Nachr.*, 1932, 107 (NO).
[3] "Continuität," 2nd edit., 1898, **1**, 130.
[4] *Phys. Rev.*, 1901, **12**, 353; Olson and Brittain, *J.A.C.S.*, 1933, **55**, 4063.
[5] Partington, "Chemical Thermodynamics," 1924, 89; Kistiakowski and Rice, *J. Chem. Phys.*, 1939, **7**, 281; for other empirical equations, see Moreau, *Compt. Rend.*, 1901, **133**, 732; Eucken, *Z. phys. Chem.*, 1930, **7** B, 319, used Callendar's equation (§ 32.VII C); Honigmann, *Z. Phys.*, 1934, **31**, 659; Ribaud and Gaudry, *Compt. Rend.*, 1945, **220**, 909 (calc. $(dT/T)/(dp/p) = (\gamma-1)/\gamma$ at high temperatures); Bérard, *Bull. Soc. Chim.*, 1947, 225, gave $c_p/c_v = (\alpha+\theta)/\theta$, where α = coefficient of expansion, $\theta = -(1/v)(dv/dT)_q$, adiabatic.
[6] Great care should be used to take $\tau = T_c/T$ correctly, not T/T_c.

Therefore, from (3):

$$C_v=\frac{\mathrm{d}\ln p'}{\mathrm{d}\ln p_v}(C_p-C_v)\quad\therefore\quad\frac{\mathrm{d}\ln p'}{\mathrm{d}\ln p_v}(\gamma-1)=1\quad\therefore\ \gamma-1=\frac{\mathrm{d}\ln p_v}{\mathrm{d}\ln p'}\quad .\quad (4)$$

The pressure change for an adiabatic change of volume ($\mathrm{d}p_q$) is equal to the pressure change due to change of volume at constant temperature ($\mathrm{d}p'$) plus that due to change of temperature at constant volume ($\mathrm{d}p_v$):

$$\mathrm{d}p_q=\mathrm{d}p'+\mathrm{d}p_v.$$

Divide by p, then (if the pressure changes are small) $\mathrm{d}\ln p_q=\mathrm{d}\ln p'+\mathrm{d}\ln p_v$. Therefore from (4):

$$\gamma=1+\frac{\mathrm{d}\ln p_v}{\mathrm{d}\ln p'}=\frac{\mathrm{d}\ln p'+\mathrm{d}\ln p_v}{\mathrm{d}\ln p'}$$

$$\simeq\frac{\mathrm{d}\ln p_q}{\mathrm{d}\ln p'}=\frac{\log p_1-\log P}{\log p_1-\log p_2}\quad .\ .\ .\ .\ .\ .\ .\ .\quad (5)$$

with the notation used in (1), § 10, so that this equation requires no correction if the pressure change is small.

To find the correction for the Lummer and Pringsheim equation (1), § 12, integrate (2a). The temperature T_1 corresponds with p_1 and T_2 with P. If the volume remained constant after expansion and the temperature changed to T_1, the pressure would become p_2,

$$\mathrm{d}\ln p_v/\mathrm{d}\ln T=1+\tfrac{27}{32}\pi\tau^3$$

$$\therefore\ \ln\frac{p_2}{P}=\int_{T_2}^{T_1}(1+\tfrac{27}{32}\pi\tau^3)\mathrm{d}\ln T.$$

The integration cannot be effected exactly, but by putting $\pi=(p_1+P)/2p_c$, and $1/\tau=(T_1+T_2)/2T_c$,

$$\ln\frac{p_2}{P}\simeq(1+\tfrac{27}{32}\pi\tau^3)\ln\frac{T_1}{T_2}.$$

Substitute $\ln p_2$ in (5), then:

$$\gamma=\frac{\ln(p_1/P)}{\ln(p_1/P)-(1+\tfrac{27}{32}\pi\tau^3)\ln(T_1/T_2)},$$

and by comparison with (1), § 12, and rearrangement:

$$\gamma=\gamma'[1+(\gamma'-1)\tfrac{27}{32}\pi\tau^3]\quad .\ .\ .\ .\ .\ .\ .\ .\quad (6)$$

where γ' is the ideal gas value calculated by (1), § 12. Equation (4), § 12, may be corrected as follows. From the general equation (2), § 12:

$$(\mathrm{d}p/\mathrm{d}T)_q=(C_p/T)(\mathrm{d}T/\mathrm{d}V)_p.$$

If C_p' is the value calculated for the ideal gas, $(C_p/T)(\mathrm{d}T/\mathrm{d}V)_p=(C_p'/T)(p/R)$, hence:

$$C_p=C_p'(p/R)(\mathrm{d}V/\mathrm{d}T)_p\quad .\ .\ .\ .\ .\ .\ .\ .\quad (7)$$

the value of $(\mathrm{d}V/\mathrm{d}T)_p$ being given by (8), § 30.VII C.

If the behaviour of an actual gas is represented by

$$pV=RT+Bp\quad .\ .\ .\ .\ .\ .\ .\ .\ .\ .\quad (8)$$

where B is the second virial coefficient (§ 6.VII C), $V=RT/p+B$, and $(\mathrm{d}V/\mathrm{d}T)_p=R/p+(\mathrm{d}B/\mathrm{d}T)_p$; hence, from (7):

$$C_p=\frac{C_p'p}{R}\left[\frac{R}{p}+\left(\frac{\mathrm{d}B}{\mathrm{d}T}\right)_p\right]$$

$$=C_p'[1+(p/R)(\mathrm{d}B/\mathrm{d}T)_p]\quad .\ .\ .\ .\ .\ .\quad (9)$$

From (2), § 49.II, $(dC_p/dp)_T = -T(d^2V/dT^2)_p$, and since $(d^2V/dT^2)_p = (d^2B/dT^2)_p$, therefore: [1]

$$(dC_p/dp)_T = -T(d^2B/dT^2)_p$$
$$\therefore\ dC_p = -T(d^2B/dT^2)_p dp$$
$$\therefore\ C_p = -T(d^2B/dT^2)p + \text{const.}$$

For $p=1$, $C_p=C_{p1}$, and for $p\to 0$, $C_p=C_{p0}$; hence:

$$C_{p0} = C_{p1} + T(d^2B/dT^2)_p \quad \ldots\ldots\ (10)$$

Similarly, from (1), § 49.II, $(dC_v/dV)_T = T(d^2p/dT^2)_v$, and:

$$C_{v0} = C_{v1} + 2(dB/dT)_v + T(d^2B/dT^2) + (1/R)(dB/dT)_v^2 \quad \ldots\ (11)$$

For, from (8):

$$V(dp/dT)_v = R + B(dp/dT)_v + p(dB/dT)_v$$
$$(V-B)(d^2p/dT^2)_v = p(d^2B/dT^2)_v + 2(dp/dT)_v(dB/dT)_v.$$

By substitution in (1), § 49.II:

$$\frac{V-B}{T}\left(\frac{dC_v}{dV}\right)_T = \frac{RT}{V-B}\left(\frac{d^2B}{dT^2}\right)_v + 2\left(\frac{dB}{dT}\right)_v\left[\frac{R}{V-B} + \frac{RT}{(V-B)^2}\left(\frac{dB}{dT}\right)_v\right]$$

Put $dV = -[(V-B)/p]dp$ and integrate, when (11) follows. The last term is usually negligible.

Nesselmann [2] used the characteristic equation $p = RT/(v-b) - a/v^2$, where $a = a_0/T^n$, and found for air:

$$c_p = c_{p0} + (4{\cdot}76\beta - 2{\cdot}84)/(vT^{1{\cdot}5} - 4{\cdot}34) \quad \ldots\ldots\ (12)$$

where $vT^{n+1} = (v-b)/v = \beta$.

The extensive use made by the Eucken school of the second derivative of the second virial coefficient of Callendar's equation (§ 32.VII C), with their criticism of the use of Berthelot's equation by other workers, is unfortunate. The experimental results on *compressibilities* can be represented quite well with a Callendar virial coefficient B, but the choice of n in the equation is subject to rather a wide latitude. When the second temperature derivative of B is used to calculate or correct *specific heats*, the case is quite different, and even a small error in the choice of n can now lead to serious error. The use of Berthelot's equation is, therefore, generally preferable; [3] its use by the author [4] for chlorine, which was criticised by Eucken,[5] has been fully justified by later work,[6] which has disclosed numerous errors in Eucken's experimental results.

§ 16. The Velocity of Sound

The formula for the velocity of sound in a fluid (gas or liquid, or a longitudinal compression wave in a solid rod) was deduced by Newton; [7] it is very

[1] Amagat, *Compt. Rend.*, 1900, **130**, 1443; Schulze, *Ann. Phys.*, 1916, **49**, 569.

[2] *Z. techn. Phys.*, 1925, **6**, 151; for nomograms for the adiabatic compression and expansion of hydrocarbon gases, see Scheibel and Othmer, *Ind. Eng. Chem.*, 1944, **36**, 580.

[3] Vold, *J.A.C.S.*, 1935, **57**, 1192; Long and Gulbransen, *ibid.*, 1936, **58**, 203; Aston and Messerly, *ibid.*, 1940, **62**, 1917; and many other papers by Giauque, etc., see § 29.IV; Foz, Gazulla and Vidal, *An. Fis. Quim.*, 1947, **43**, 842.

[4] *Phys. Z.*, 1914, **15**, 601, 775.

[5] *Z. phys. Chem.*, 1929, **5 B**, 442; Partington, *ibid.*, 1930, **7 B**, 319.

[6] Schulze, *Ann. Phys.*, 1938, **34**, 41; Giauque and Powell, *J.A.C.S.*, 1939, **61**, 1970.

[7] "Principia" (1687), II, sect. viii, theorem 38, prop. 48; edit. Amsterdam, 1723, 340; see Whewell, "History of the Inductive Sciences," 1857, **2**, 246 f.; Rosenberger, "Geschichte der Physik," Brunswick, 1884, **2**, 233; 1887, **3**, 133.

easily obtained by the following elementary method.[1] Consider the fluid in a tube of unit cross-section and take an imaginary fixed plane X at right angles to the length (Fig. 8.VII E). If the wave travelling along the tube is of permanent type, no change in the properties of the fluid is seen by an observer moving with the velocity of the wave.

If u is the velocity of the substance at X, a volume u cm.³ passes per sec. through X, and if m is the mass of the substance passing and v its specific volume $(1/\rho)$, $u=mv$. If the plane is not fixed but moves from left to right with a velocity U, this equation is true if the relative velocity $(U-u)$ is substituted for u, where U is the velocity of the wave. Hence, for two planes A and B moving with velocity U the masses of substance crossing them from right to left are:

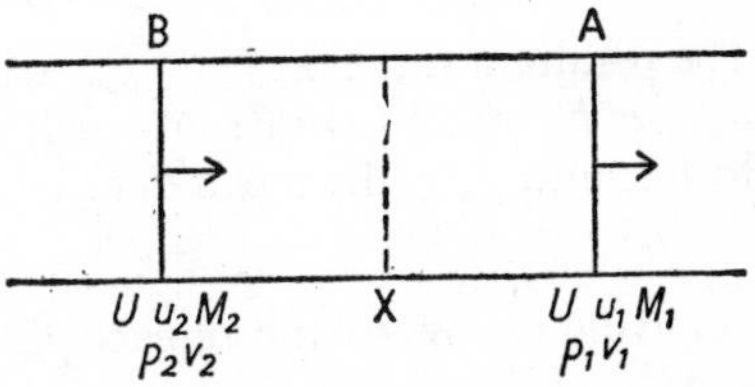

FIG. 8.VII E. Wave Velocity in a Gas

$$U-u_1=m_1v_1 \quad \text{and} \quad U-u_2=m_2v_2 \quad . \quad . \quad . \quad . \quad . \quad (1)$$

Since A and B move with the same velocity the distance and volume between them are constant, and hence the density of the substance in corresponding parts of the wave also remains constant; the mass of substance entering at A is thus equal to that leaving at B, or $m_1=m_2=m$, say, hence:

$$u_1=U-mv_1 \quad \text{and} \quad u_2=U-mv_2 \quad . \quad . \quad . \quad . \quad . \quad (2)$$

If p_1 is the pressure at A and p_2 that at B, the force from left to right is p_2-p_1. The momentum entering per sec. at A is mu_1 and that leaving at B is mu_2, hence from (2):

$$p_1-p_2=m(u_1-u_2)=m^2(v_2-v_1) \quad . \quad . \quad . \quad . \quad . \quad (3)$$

Hence the quantity $p+m^2v$ remains constant in the wave.

For small changes, $p_1-p_2=\delta p$ and $v_1-v_2=\delta v$, hence from (3):

$$-v(dp/dv)=\epsilon=m^2v \quad . \quad (4)$$

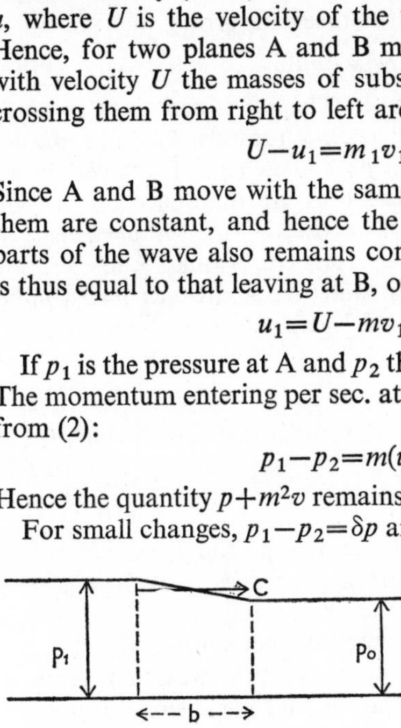

FIG. 9.VII E. Sound Wave in a Gas

where ϵ is the elasticity (§ 4.II) and v is the mean specific volume. If v and $\rho=1/v$ refer to the fluid at rest $(u=0)$, (2) and (4) give Newton's equation: [2]

$$U=mv=\sqrt{(\epsilon v)}=\sqrt{(\epsilon/\rho)} \quad (5)$$

The deduction may be put into a slightly different form as follows.[3] Assume that a pressure distribution moves to the right with a wave velocity c without change of form. As the gas is compressed, a part left behind the wave is moving to the right (Fig. 9.VII E).

1 Rankine, *Phil. Trans.*, 1870, **160**, 277; " Misc. Sci. Papers," 1881, 530; Maxwell, " Theory of Heat," 1897, 223.

2 For general accounts of acoustics, see: Whewell, " History of the Inductive Sciences," 1857, **2**, 231 f. (historical); Donkin, " Acoustics," Oxford, 1870; Tyndall, " On Sound," 1875; Rayleigh, " The Theory of Sound," 1896, **2**, 18 (velocity); Basset, " Elementary Treatise on Hydrodynamics and Sound," 2nd edit., Cambridge, 1900, 186; Poynting and Thomson, " Sound," 3rd edit., 1904; Klimpert, " Lehrbuch der Akustik," 3 vols., Bremerhaven, 1904–7; Lamb, " Dynamical Theory of Sound," 1910, 157, 162; Capstick, " Sound," Cambridge, 1913; Lübcke, in Geiger and Scheel, " Handbuch der Physik," 1927, **8**, 617; various authors in Wien-Harms, " Handbuch der Experimentalphysik," 1934, **17**, i and ii; Schimank, *Z. tech. Phys.*, 1936, **17**, 500 (historical). For an elementary account of waves in liquids and gases, see Coulson, " Waves," Edinburgh, 1941, 60, 87.

3 Ewald, Pöschl, and Prandtl, " The Physics of Solids and Fluids," 1936, 349.

Let p_1, p_0 be the pressures before and after the wave, p_1-p_0 and the corresponding density change $\rho_1-\rho_0$ being small. The transition region is of thickness b and the cross-section of the tube is a.

The condition of continuity requires that the increase of mass in the region per unit time, $ac(\rho_1-\rho_0)$, is equal to the mass flowing in, $au\rho_1$, where u is the mean mass-velocity. Hence

$$\rho_1 u = c(\rho_1-\rho_0) \quad \text{. . . . . (6)}$$

The resultant force is $a(p_1-p_0)$, equal to mass × acceleration $=\rho_m \times (ab) \times (u/t) = \rho_m \times uc/b$, where t=time in which velocity increases from 0 to u, which is equal to b/c, and ρ_m is the mean density. Hence:

$$\rho_m uc = p_1 - p_0 \quad \text{. . . . . (7)}$$

Divide (7) by (6) and replace ρ_m by ρ_1 (without serious error), then:

$$c^2 = (p_1-p_0)/(\rho_1-\rho_0) = \mathrm{d}p/\mathrm{d}\rho \quad \text{. . . . . . (8)}$$

A more symbolical derivation is as follows.[1] The gas is contained in a tube of unit cross-section. Let ϵ be the elasticity and p a pressure which produces a compression $\mathrm{d}u$ in a layer $\mathrm{d}x$ of gas. Then $p=\epsilon \mathrm{d}u/\mathrm{d}x$ (i). The layer $\mathrm{d}x$ will move backwards and forwards owing to the pressure difference $\mathrm{d}p$ on both sides. By differentiating p and $\mathrm{d}u$ in (i), $\mathrm{d}p=\epsilon \mathrm{d}^2u/\mathrm{d}x$ (ii). If ρ=density of gas in layer $\mathrm{d}x$, its mass is $m=\rho \mathrm{d}x$, and as force $(\mathrm{d}p)$=mass × acceleration, $\mathrm{d}p=m(\mathrm{d}^2u/\mathrm{d}t^2)=\rho \mathrm{d}x.(\mathrm{d}^2u/\mathrm{d}t^2)$ (iii). From (ii) and (iii), $\rho \mathrm{d}x(\mathrm{d}^2u/\mathrm{d}t^2)=\epsilon(\mathrm{d}^2u/\mathrm{d}x)$. Hence $\mathrm{d}^2u/\mathrm{d}t^2=(\epsilon/\rho)(\mathrm{d}^2u/\mathrm{d}x^2)$, and $(\mathrm{d}x/\mathrm{d}t)^2=U^2=\epsilon/\rho$.

§ 17. Velocity of Sound in Gases

Newton supposed that the elasticity ϵ was the *isothermal* value, which for an ideal gas is $\epsilon_T=p$ (see § 4.II), when:

$$U=\sqrt{(pv)} \quad \text{. . . . . (1)}$$

(p must be in absolute units, e.g. dynes/cm.^{2}). But some rough experiments he made in the cloisters of Trinity College, Cambridge, showed that the measured velocity of sound was distinctly higher than that calculated, which he explained by supposing that the sound travelled with a much higher velocity through dust particles suspended in the air. The correct explanation was first given by Laplace,[2] who pointed out that the compressions and expansions in a sound wave are so rapid that there is no time for an equalisation of temperature to occur, that the sudden compression produces a rise of temperature which increases the elasticity, and that the adiabatic elasticity must be used. In this case there is no exchange of heat between the heated and cooled parts of the fluid through which the wave is passing.

The temperature variations in a sound wave were measured by a thin Wollaston wire thermometer (§ 13) by Friese and Waetzmann.[3] They calculated that

[1] Weyrauch, *Ann. Phys.*, 1884, **23**, 147.

[2] *Ann. Chim.*, 1816, **3**, 238; 1822, **20**, 266; "Mécanique Céleste," 1823, **5**, 119; "Oeuvres," 1882, **5**, 109, 133; Poisson, *Ann. Chim.*, 1823, **23**, 337; "Traité de Mécanique," 1833, **2**, 637, 646; Simon, *Ann. Phys.*, 1830, **19**, 115; Stokes, *Phil. Mag.*, 1851, **1**, 305; Rankine, *ibid.*, 1851, **1**, 225; Stefan, *Ann. Phys.*, 1863, **118**, 494; Le Conte, *Phil. Mag.*, 1864, **27**, 1; Hoorweg, *Arch. Néerl.*, 1876, **11**, 131; *Ann. Phys. Beibl.*, 1877, **1**, 209; Tolver Preston, *Phil. Mag.*, 1877, **3**, 441; Rosenberger, "Geschichte der Physik," Brunswick, 1887, **3**, 133, 750; Brillouin, *Ann. Chim.*, 1909, **18**, 191; Rayleigh, "The Theory of Sound," 1896, **2**, 23, says the theory has always been "a stumbling block to those remarkable persons, called by de Morgan, 'paradoxers'": the reference is to de Morgan's "A Budget of Paradoxes," 1872.

[3] *Z. Phys*, 1925, **31**, 50; 1925, **34**, 131.

the period of temperature variation in the wire would be about half that in the gas.

The adiabatic elasticity is $\epsilon_q = \gamma p$, where $\gamma = c_p/c_v$ (see § 4.II):

$$\therefore \quad U = \sqrt{(\gamma p v)} = \sqrt{(\gamma p/\rho)} = \sqrt{(\gamma RT/M)} \quad . \quad . \quad . \quad . \quad (2)$$

where T is the absolute temperature of the undisturbed fluid, R is the gas constant, and M the molecular weight. Laplace's equation (2) gives very accurate results, except for waves of large amplitude (e.g. intense shock waves) to which (3), § 16, no longer applies.[1]

A measurement of the velocity of sound in a gas at a given temperature will give [2] a value of γ from equation (2). The velocity is independent of pressure (or density), since for an ideal gas pv is constant at a given temperature by Boyle's law. For actual gases (2) requires correction for deviation from the ideal state, as explained in § 22.

Very many experiments on the velocity of sound in free air have been made, the first reasonably accurate result (331 m. per sec. at 0°) being obtained by Goldhingham,[3] in Madras, in 1820–21. Many determinations have also been made in pipes, conduits, and sewers,[4] those of Violle and Vautier (at Grenoble) being perhaps the most accurate. The best value for the velocity of sound in free air is probably that found by Hebb,[5] who used repeated reflexion of sound waves from paraboloids, 15 in. diameter, 5 ft. apart. After suitable correction for moisture [6] the value $U = 331 \cdot 41$ m./sec. at 0° C. in dry CO_2-free air was found.

Kukkamäki,[7] with explosions in free air, found 330·8 m./sec. at 0°, but 331·7 m./sec. with higher frequencies. Such alleged variations with frequency [8] are probably spurious and due to rough surfaces; [9] Pan Tscheng Kao [10] found 331·85 m./sec. with ultrasonic waves with frequencies varying from 40,000 to a million, and neither Hebb nor Grüneisen and Merkel (see below) found any frequency effect. The latest reliable value [9] for the velocity of sound in dry air at 0° is $331 \cdot 60 \pm 0 \cdot 05$ m./sec., practically the same as Hebb's figure.

1 Earnshaw, *B.A. Rep.*, 1858, ii, 34; *Proc. Roy. Soc.*, 1858, **9**, 590; *Phil. Trans.*, 1860, **150**, 133; *Phil. Mag.*, 1860, **19**, 449; 1860, **20**, 186; Mach and Sommer, *Wien Ber.*, 1877, **75**, II, 101; Hugoniot, *J. de l'École Polytechn.*, 1887, **57**, 3; 1889, **58**, 1; Chapman, *Phil. Mag.*, 1899, **47**, 90; Jouguet, *J. de Math.*, 1905, **1**, 347; 1906, **2**, 5; Crussard, *Compt. Rend.*, 1907, **144**, 417; Crussard and Jouguet, *ibid.*, 1907, **144**, 560; 1908, **146**, 594; Crussard, *ibid.*, 1913, **156**, 447, 611; 1914, **158**, 125, 340; *Bull. Soc. Ind. Min.*, 1907, **6**, 257; Becker, *Z. Phys.*, 1922, **8**, 321; Klüsener, *ibid.*, 1927, **43**, 597; Ackert, in Geiger and Scheel, "Handbuch der Physik," 1927, **7**, 322 ; Caldirola, *J. Chem. Phys.*, 1946, **14**, 729; Staniukovitsch, *Compt. Rend. U.R.S.S.*, 1946, **52**, 589; Courant and Friedrichs, "Supersonic Flow and Shock Waves," New York, 1948; for a relativistic correction, Taub, *Phys. Rev.*, 1948, **74**, 328.

2 Rankine, *Trans. Roy. Soc. Edin.*, 1853, **20**, 147; "Misc. Scient. Papers," 1881, 256.

3 Auerbach, in Winkelmann, "Handbuch der Physik," 1909, **2**, 500; for a summary of earlier values, *ibid.*, 518, 529 f.; Partington and Shilling, "The Specific Heats of Gases," 1924, 79.

4 Regnault, *Phil. Mag.*, 1868, **35**, 161; Violle and Vautier, *Ann. Chim.*, 1890, **19**, 306; Violle, "Cours de Physique," 1888, **2**, i, 57 f., 64; *Congrès Internat. Phys.*, 1900, **1**, 228; Stevens, *Ann. Phys.*, 1902, **7**, 285; Partington and Shilling, "The Specific Heats of Gases," 1924, 79 f.

5 *Phys. Rev.*, 1905, **20**, 89; 1919, **14**, 74; *Trans. Roy. Soc. Canada*, 1919, **13**, III, 101.

6 Dorsey, "Properties of Ordinary Water Substance," New York, 1940, 70 (bibl.).

7 *Ann. Phys.*, 1938, **31**, 398.

8 Esclangon, *Compt. Rend.*, 1919, **168**, 165 (339·9 m./sec. at 15°); Barss and Bastille, *J. Math. Phys. Mass. Inst. Techn.*, 1923, **2**, 210; Grabau, *J. Acoust. Soc. Amer.*, 1933, **5**, 1 (344·48 m./sec. at 20° and 87 per cent. humidity, independent of frequency from 20,000 to 70,000); Parker, *Proc. Phys. Soc.*, 1937, **49**, 95 (331·7 m./sec. at 0°).

9 Kneser, *Ann. Phys.*, 1939, 34, 665.

10 *Compt. Rend.*, 1931, **193**, 21; very high frequencies were used by Koenig, *Ann. Phys.*, 1899, **69**, 626, 721.

In determinations made in tubes a correction applied by Kirchhoff and explained later (§ 23) must be made for the effect of the tube on the velocity, which is reduced below the value in the free gas. The most accurate value found by this method for air at 0° C. is probably that of Grüneisen and Merkel,[1] using a closed resonator method due to Thiesen; [2] they found 331·57 m./sec. at 0° C. (Thiesen found 331·92±0·05.) Measurements of velocities in tubes at high temperatures are described later (§ 20).

§ 18. Stationary Waves in Gases

In measuring the velocity of sound in tubes it is often more convenient to measure the *wave-length* λ and calculate the velocity from the equation (§ 49.I), $U=n\lambda$, where n is the frequency. This equation follows from the fact that the source makes n complete vibrations per sec., each corresponding with a complete wave-length λ cm., hence the disturbance travels a distance $n\lambda$ cm. per sec., and this is equal to the velocity. This equation and the fundamental equation (2), § 17, give: [3]

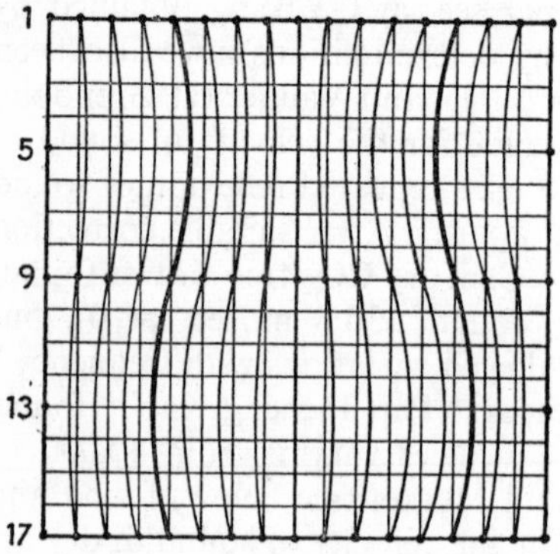

FIG. 10.VII E. Stationary Wave

$$U=n\lambda=\sqrt{(\gamma p/\rho)}, \quad \therefore \gamma=n^2\lambda^2\rho/p \quad (1)$$

When a sound wave travelling along a tube is reflected from a closed end, the incident and reflected waves interfere and, as is explained in works on sound, the column of gas is divided into portions separated by planes in which there is no motion (*nodes*), interposed between which are portions of gas where the motion is a maximum (*antinodes*). The distance between successive nodes or antinodes is half the wave-length, $\lambda/2$. Hence by measuring this distance, U can be calculated if the frequency n is known. If the wave-lengths are measured for two gases, with the same frequency, $U_1/U_2=\lambda_1/\lambda_2$, hence, at the same temperature, (2), § 17, gives:

$$\lambda_1^2/\lambda_2^2=\gamma_1 M_2/\gamma_2 M_1, \quad \therefore \gamma_1/\gamma_2=M_1\lambda_1^2/M_2\lambda_2^2 \quad . \quad . \quad . \quad (2)$$

If one gas (e.g. dry air, $\gamma=1{\cdot}403$) is taken as a standard, the values of γ for a series of other gases can be found from (2). The method requires corrections which are explained in § 22.

Fig. 10.VII E shows [4] the character of a stationary wave in a column of gas having a node at each end and one in the centre. The 17 particles shown as dots move first to the right and left (on opposite sides of the middle vertical) with an increasing amplitude, until the condition shown in row 5 is reached, when the

[1] *Z. Phys.*, 1920, **2**, 277; *Ann. Phys.*, 1921, **66**, 344; Partington and Shilling, "The Specific Heats of Gases," 1924, 81.

[2] *Z. Instr.*, 1905, **25**, 102; *Ann. Phys.*, 1907, **24**, 401; 1908, **25**, 506; for other experiments with resonator methods, see Dulong, *Mém. Acad. Sci.*, 1831, **10**, 147; Cornish and Eastman, *J.A.C.S.*, 1928, **50**, 627; Voelcker, *Ann. Phys.*, 1935, **24**, 361; Schulze, *ibid.*, 1938, **34**, 41 (Cl_2); Clark and Katz, *Canad. J. Res.*, 1940, **18** A, 23, 39; 1941, **19** A, 111; 1943, **21** A, 1; Tucker, *Phil. Mag.*, 1943, **34**, 217 (steam, etc.); Quigley, *Phys. Rev.*, 1945, **67**, 298 (330·6 m./sec. at 0°) for vapours, Neyreneuf, *Ann. Chim.*, 1886, **9**, 535; for theory of Helmholtz resonator, Jones, *Phys. Rev.*, 1925, **25**, 696.

[3] Shaha, *Indian J. Phys.*, 1931, **6**, 445.

[4] Auerbach, in Winkelmann, "Handbuch der Physik," 1909, **2**, 70.

compressions are a maximum. The particles then begin to move in opposite directions, and in row 9 are in the original positions but are moving in opposite directions to those in row 1 (half a period). In row 13 maximum compressions are again reached but in positions where in row 5 there were maximum dilatations. In row 17 the particles are in their original positions and are beginning to move again as in row 1 (a complete period). The horizontal rows correspond with equal intervals of time. The curves joining the points are sine curves representing the displacements of each point (§ 49.I).

Chladni [1] determined the velocities of sound in gases by the method of blowing an organ pipe, and found (with moist gases) in Paris feet per sec.:

	Air	O_2	N_2	H_2	CO_2	NO
1802	1038	950–960	990	2100–2500	840	980
1817	—	923	966	2070	857	—

Dulong [2] blew an organ pipe with a gas inside a large chest filled with the gas, and determined the frequency with a monochord. He calculated c_p/c_v from the velocities found. Lechner [3] used the method for vapours. A correction for the open end of a pipe must be applied.[4]

§ 19. Velocity of Sound by Kundt's Method

A simple method of determining the velocity of sound was devised by Kundt.[5] A glass tube A, 3–4 cm. diameter and over 1 m. long, provided with side tubes for filling with the gas (Fig. 11.VII E), was closed at one end by a cork through which passed a glass rod terminated inside the tube by a piston P_1 fitting loosely in the tube. A similar tube B contained air. The long sounding rod S, terminating

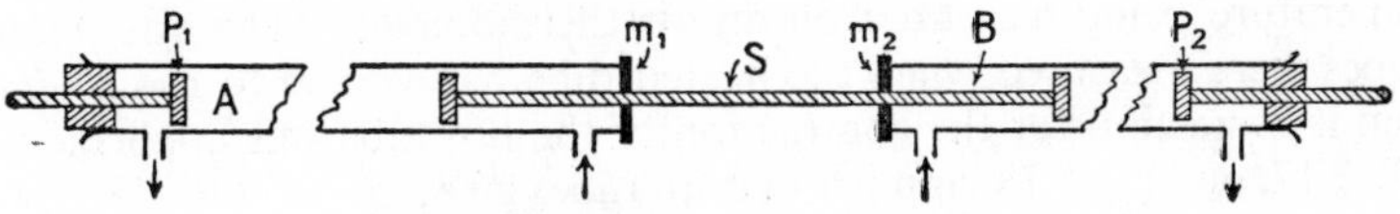

FIG. 11.VII E. Kundt's Apparatus

in pistons, passed through rubber sheets m_1 and m_2, and could be set in vibration by stroking the middle part with a damp cloth. Sound waves were produced in the gas by the vibrations of the pistons at the ends of the rod S, and by adjusting the positions of the pistons P_1 and P_2, the columns of gas and air divided into nodes and antinodes, which were made visible by lycopodium powder, cork dust, or fine sand in the tubes. The powder collects in small heaps at the nodes, where the gas is not moving, with clear spaces corresponding with

[1] "Die Akustik," Leipzig, 1802, 226 f. (new edit., Leipzig, 1830); "Neue Beyträge zur Akustik," Leipzig, 1817, 80.

[2] *Ann. Chim.*, 1829, **41**, 113.

[3] *Wien Ber.*, 1909, **118**, II A, 1035.

[4] Boehm, *Phys. Rev.*, 1910, **31**, 332.

[5] *Ann. Phys.*, 1866, **127**, 497; 1868, **135**, 337, 527; *Phil. Mag.*, 1868, **35**, 41; Oosting, *Ann. Phys.*, 1885, **24**, 319 (low frequencies); for experimental errors, etc., Leduc, *Ann. Chim.*, 1899, **17**, 484; *Compt. Rend.*, 1915, **160**, 601; 1924, **178**, 1148; *J. de Phys.*, 1916, **6**, 5; for lower pressures, Beckman, *Arkiv Mat. Astron. Fys.*, 1911, **7**, No. 27; general, see Partington and Shilling, "The Specific Heats of Gases," 1924, 84; on effect of moisture in the air in the comparison tube, see Dorsey, "Properties of Ordinary Water Substance." New York, 1940, 70.

the antinodes, where the powder is swept away by the motion of the gas. The wave-lengths in the gas and in air were then measured.

Jaeger,[1] working with vapours, said he found silica too heavy, and used charred cork dust, which had been used for halogens at high temperatures by Strecker.[2] The difficulty found with silica was probably due to the tube not having been well dried by baking in vacuum, which the writer [3] found essential. According to Shilling,[4] adsorbed moisture is removed from a glass tube on heating at 370°, and from a silica tube at 800°, in a current of air. Silica powder gives satisfactory results only when the powder and the walls of the tube have been *completely* dried by strong heating in vacuum, otherwise the powder sticks to the glass.

In calculating the average half wave-length, the arithmetic mean of the lengths along the tube reduces to $(x_n - x_0)/n$, only the first and last readings being effective. The average may be found from the formula: [5]

$$6[(n-1)(x_n - x_1) + (n-3)(x_{n-1} - x_2) + \ldots]/n(n^2-1) \quad . \; . \quad (1)$$

If n is odd, the middle reading does not appear, so that an even number of readings should be made.

A surprising amount of effort has been given to finding the cause of the peculiar ribbed and other forms assumed by the dust figures in the Kundt tube:[6] Müller says there are two main types, ribbed (sometimes curved) and heaps with clear spaces.

Raman [7] showed that the nodes of a vibrating string have a slight motion, chiefly longitudinal, differing in phase by a quarter of an oscillation from the rest of the string, serving to transmit the energy; something similar probably occurs in the Kundt tube.

Kundt's method was used at higher temperatures with mercury vapour by Kundt and Warburg.[8] The left-hand tube contained air as a comparison gas, the right-hand tube containing mercury was heated in an air bath at 275°–356°, the temperature being measured on an air thermometer. The dust figures in both tubes were measured when the heated tube had cooled to room temperature, and a correction for the contraction of the hot tube was applied. Equations (2), § 17, and (2), § 18, applied to both tubes give:

$$\gamma_1/\gamma_2 = (\lambda_1^2/\lambda_2^2)(T_2 M_1/T_1 M_2) \quad . \; . \; . \; . \; . \; . \quad (2)$$

The value $\gamma = 1{\cdot}666$ for mercury vapour under three different pressures was found, confirming that it is monatomic.

[1] *Ann. Phys.*, 1889, **36**, 165; Shaha, *Indian J. Phys.*, 1931, **6**, 445.

[2] *Ann. Phys.*, 1881, **13**, 544; 1883, **18**, 309.

[3] Partington, *Phys. Z.*, 1914, **15**, 601, 775.

[4] Quoted by Partington and Huntingford, *J.C.S.*, 1923, **123**, 163; Sherwood, *Phys. Rev.*, 1918, **12**, 448, gave 200° for glass; Ulrey, *ibid.*, 1919, **14**, 160.

[5] Mellor, " Higher Mathematics," 1931, 520.

[6] Rayleigh, *Phil. Trans.*, 1883, **175**, 1; " Scientific Papers," 1900, **2**, 239; Koenig, *Ann Phys.*, 1891, **42**, 353, 549; *Z. phys. chem. Unterricht*, 1895, **8**, 191; *Phys. Z.*, 1911, **12**, 991; Cook, *Phil. Mag.*, 1902, **3**, 471; Müller, *Ann. Phys.*, 1903, **11**, 331; Schulze, *ibid.*, 1904, **13**, 1067; Robinson, *Phil. Mag.*, 1909, **18**, 180; 1910, **19**, 476; *Proc. Phys. Soc.*, 1913, **25**, 256; Schweikert, *Ann. Phys.*, 1915, **48**, 593; 1917, **52**, 333; Irons, *Phil. Mag.*, 1929, **7**, 523; Hutchisson and Morgan, *Phys. Rev.*, 1931, **37**, 1155; Andrade, *Proc. Roy. Soc.*, 1931, **134**, 445; *Phil. Trans.*, 1932, **230**, 413; Brandt and Freund, *Z. Phys.*, 1934, **92**, 385; Howatson, *Phil. Mag.*, 1945, **36**, 20.

[7] *Nature*, 1909, **82**, 9; *Phys. Rev.*, 1911, **32**, 309.

[8] *Ann. Phys.*, 1876, **157**, 353; Leduc, *Compt. Rend.*, 1898, **127**, 659. For potassium vapour, see Wenz, *Ann. Phys.*, 1910, **33**, 951; sodium and potassium vapours, Robitzsch, *ibid.*, 1912 **38**, 1026.

Kundt's method has been used in several researches.[1] The modification of Kundt's method by Behn and Geiger [2] is more convenient. In this, the gas is contained in a sealed tube S (Fig. 12.VII E), which may be fitted with a stopcock in the centre, which is clamped at T. To bring the tube into resonance, so that a whole number of half wave-lengths occupy the exact length of the tube, the latter is weighted by cementing on the correct number of small metal discs d_1 and d_2 at each end. The dust (e.g. fine silica) is put into the tube before filling

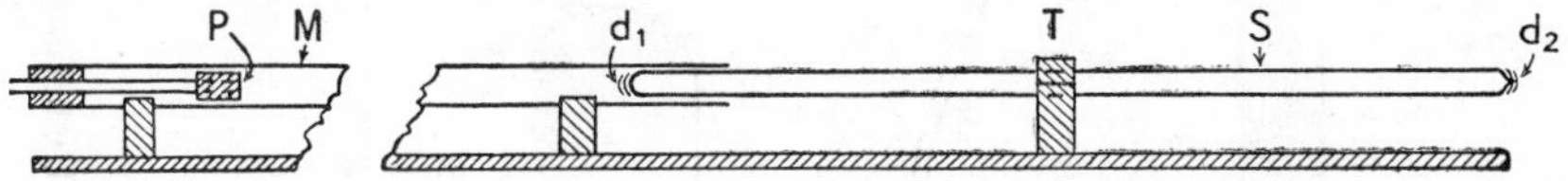

FIG. 12.VII E. Behn and Geiger's Apparatus

with gas, and careful drying by strong heating in vacuum is necessary. One end of the gas tube enters the open end of the air tube M containing lycopodium powder, the length of which is adjusted to resonance by a movable piston P.

The gas tube is caused to sound by rubbing with a damp or resined cloth, and dust figures are formed in both T and M. The half wave-lengths are measured as before and equation (2) is used. With suitable precautions this is a very straightforward and accurate method at room temperature, but it is not very suitable at other temperatures.

§ 20. Velocity of Sound at High Temperatures

Measurements of the velocity of sound in gases at high temperatures (up to 1000° C.) were made by Dixon, Campbell, and Parker.[3] A sound wave consisting of a single impulse was set off by striking a steel membrane with an electrically controlled hammer at one end of a long coiled lead, steel, or silica tube, the latter heated electrically by a platinum strip winding. The impulse lifted a small trap at this end of the tube, breaking an electrical contact with a chronograph, and the arrival of the sound wave at the other end of the tube was similarly recorded. Suitable corrections were applied,[4] including a tube correction (see § 23).

Another group of researches made use of an interference method devised by Quincke,[5] which can be adapted to high-temperature conditions. A column

[1] Wüllner, *Ann. Phys.*, 1878, **4**, 321; "Handbuch der Experimentalphysik," 5th edit., 1896, **2**, 552; Strecker, *Ann. Phys.*, 1881, **13**, 20; 1882, **17**, 85; Cohen, *ibid.*, 1889, **37**, 629; Capstick, *Phil. Trans.*, 1894, **185**, 1; *Proc. Roy. Soc.*, 1895, **57**, 322; Ramsay *et al.*, *J.C.S.*, 1895, **67**, 684; *Phil. Trans.*, 1895, **186**, 228; *Proc. Roy. Soc.*, 1911, **86**, 100; Leduc, *Compt. Rend.*, 1898, **127**, 659; Valentiner, *Ann. Phys.*, 1904, **15**, 74; Thibaut, *ibid.*, 1911, **35**, 347; Schweikert, *ibid.*, 1915, **48**, 593 (full bibl.); 1916, **49**, 433 (bibl.); Schulze and Rathgen, *ibid.*, 1916, **49**, 457; Trautz, *Z. Elektrochem.*, 1917, **22**, 206; *idem*, "Praktische Einführung in die allgemeine Chemie," Leipzig, 1917, 145; Partington and Shilling, "The Specific Heats of Gases," 1924, 86 (bibl.).

[2] *Verhl. d. D. Phys. Ges.*, 1907, **9**, 657; Keutel, *Dissert.*, Berlin, 1910; Schöler, *Ann. Phys.*, 1914, **45**, 913; Partington *et al.*, *Phys. Z.*, 1914, **15**, 601, 775; *Phil. Mag.*, 1922, **43**, 369; 1923, **45**, 416; 1925, **49**, 665; *J.C.S.*, 1922, **121**, 1604; Partington and Shilling, "The Specific Heats of Gases," 1924, 88; Bredig and Teichmann, *Z. Elektrochem.*, 1925, **31**, 449.

[3] *Proc. Roy. Soc.*, 1921, **100**, 1; Dixon and Greenwood, *ibid.*, 1924, **105**, 199 (vapours); Partington and Shilling, "The Specific Heats of Gases," 1924, 139.

[4] Dixon, *Phil. Trans.*, 1893, **184**, 97.

[5] *Ann. Phys.*, 1866, **128**, 177; 1897, **63**, 66; Webster Low, *ibid.*, 1894, **52**, 641; Stevens, *ibid.*, 1902, **7**, 285; Kalähne, *ibid.*, 1903, **11**, 225; 1906, **20**, 398; Handke and Martens, *Verhl. d. D. Phys. Ges.*, 1907, **9**, 121; Fürstenau, *Ann. Phys.*, 1908, **27**, 735; Partington and Shilling, *op. cit.*, 135 f.; on Stevens' and Kalähne's temperature scales, see *Ann. Phys.*, 1903, **12**, 447, 666.

of gas in a tube of glass, metal, or porcelain, which can be suitably heated, was set in vibration by a tuning fork or telephone near to, and outside, the open end of the tube, the length of the gas column being adjusted by a piston in the tube.

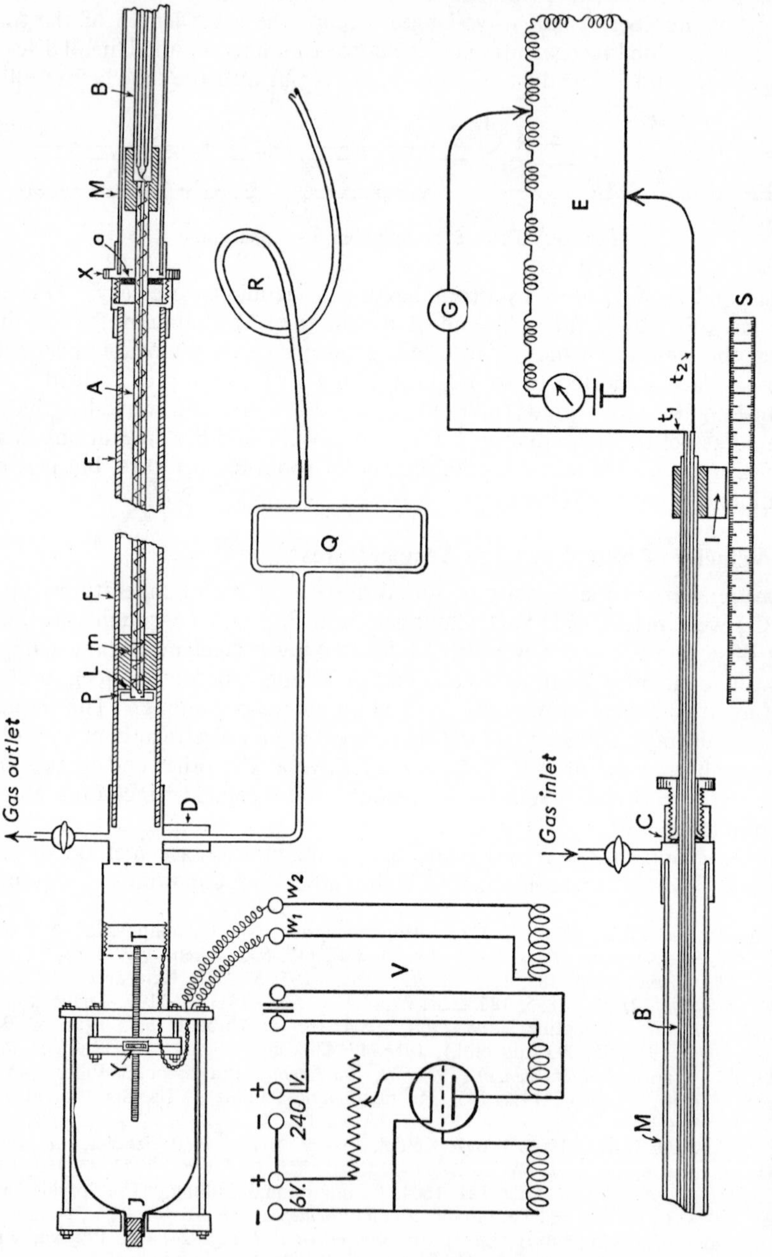

FIG. 13. VII E. Partington and Shilling's Apparatus for Determination of the Velocity of Sound in Gases at High Temperatures

A side tube attached to a rubber tube passing to the ear enabled the position of a node (minimum sound) or antinode (maximum sound) at the position of the side tube to be found. By moving the piston a succession of nodes or antinodes was brought to this place, the distances through which the piston is moved (read off by a pointer attached to the piston rod moving over a graduated scale) giving the half or full wave-length (node to antinode, or antinode to antinode, etc.).

This method was improved by Partington and Shilling,[1] who used it for air, nitrogen, oxygen, carbon dioxide, and steam to over 1000° C. Since silica tubes are not suitable for the highest temperatures, tubes of Alundum and Pythagoras mass (§ 2.VI B) were used. A diagram of the apparatus is shown in Fig. 13.VII E. The tube FF, about 4 cm. diam. and 230 cm. long, was wound for 200 cm. of its length with nichrome wire or platinum strip, subsidiary heating coils at each end serving to maintain uniformity of temperature. The furnace tube was placed inside a wider fireclay tube, the intervening space being packed with granular Alundum, and this outer tube was in turn heat-insulated by packing it round with calcined bauxite. At X a glass tube of similar diameter and 150 cm. long was attached by a screwed joint. Inside the tube F was a piston P of refractory material carried by a tube or rod A. When a platinum and platinum-rhodium thermocouple was used, the junction was at L, immediately behind the piston. Higher temperatures were measured optically by sighting on the back of the piston through the hollow piston-rod by a disappearing filament optical pyrometer, the apparatus being then suitably modified.

The piston diameter was slightly less than the bore of the tube and it was prevented from touching the tube by mica plates *m* strapped on with platinum wire. An asbestos disc *a* prevented radiation and convection into the tube M. A steel tube B prolonged the piston tube and passed through a gland at C. The free end of B carried a saddle I with a glass scale riding along the edge of an accurate steel scale S divided in mm.

The sound was produced by a telephone T excited to a constant frequency of about 3000 vibrations per sec. by a valve oscillator [2] V. A screw adjustment Y enabled the telephone diaphragm, which formed a reflecting surface at this end, to be moved relative to the side tube D, which carried the listening tube QR. The screw adjustment was enclosed in a gas-tight bell-jar J. The adjustment of the telephone position at each temperature was found essential to good working.

The hearing tube R enabled sharp maxima of sound to be located, and a series of 10–25 half wave-lengths could be measured. The temperature slope from the zero point, selected well within the uniformly heated part of the tube, to the telephone diaphragm varied with each temperature, but, provided equilibrium had been attained, this slope is immaterial, since no measurements were taken within its range. A tube correction was applied as explained later (§ 23).

The upper limit of frequency suitable for auditory detection is limited. According to Despretz [3] and Koenig,[4] the upper limit of audibility is 37,000

[1] *Trans. Faraday Soc.*, 1923, **18**, 386; " The Specific Heats of Gases," 1924, 142; *Phil. Mag.*, 1927, **3**, 273; 1928, **6**, 920; Partington and King, *ibid.*, 1930, **9**, 1020; Buss, *Ann. Phys.*, 1930, **7**, 601; Rechel, *ibid.*, 1931, **10**, 1; Shaha, *Indian J. Phys.*, 1931, **6**, 445; Felsing and Jessen, *J.A.C.S.*, 1933, **55**, 4418; Felsing and Drake, *ibid.*, 1936, **58**, 1714 (H_2S, HCN); Bilharz and Bishop, *J. Acoust. Soc. Amer.*, 1936, **7**, 225; Dorsey, " Properties of Ordinary Substance," New York, 1940, 68 (bibl.).

[2] This seems to have been first used by Grüneisen and Merkel, *Z. Phys.*, 1920, **2**, 277; another type, Giebe and Alberti, *Z. techn. Phys.*, 1925, **6**, 92, 135. The technical radio-apparatus used by Cornish and Eastman, *J.A.C.S.*, 1928, **50**, 627, is not sufficiently accurate for precision work. On the theory of sound waves from membranes, see Backhaus, *Ann. Phys.*, 1930, **5**, 1; Stenzel, *ibid.*, 1930, **7**, 947.

[3] *Compt. Rend.*, 1845, **20**, 794; *Ann. Phys.*, 1845, **65**, 400.

[4] *Ann. Phys.*, 1899, **69**, 626, 721 (gives 43,691).

complete (or 74,000 single) vibrations per sec., but this is probably much too high, 20,000 being nearer the mark.[1] With hydrogen, the intensity of sound is much weaker than in denser gases.[2] An important detail in the use of a resonator must be geometrically accurate planes,[3] and the sending and reflecting discs must fill the aperture of the tube.[4] The apparatus used by Eucken and Nümann[5] was unsuitable for accurate work.

Measurements at higher temperatures were made by Strecker,[6] Fürstenau,[7] and others,[8] using Kundt's method or modifications, and the effect of *pressure* was investigated by Koch [9] and Schöler,[10] and calculated by Benedict,[11] who gave for nitrogen at 30°:

p atm.	1	1000	2000	3000	4000	5000	6000
u m./sec.	354·8	813	1170	1393	1560	1697	1811

§ 21. Velocity of Sound at Low Temperatures

Measurements of the velocities of sound in gases at low temperatures were made by Valentiner [12] and Koch,[9] and by the resonator method in the Leyden laboratory.[13] They confirmed the validity of the tube correction used by Partington and Shilling (§ 23), and since this has also been confirmed at high temperatures,[14] the criticism of it by Cornish and Eastman [15] is invalid. It is noteworthy that the latter observed no dispersion effect in their measurements (§ 24). A compact apparatus for low temperatures was used by Himstedt and Widder.[16]

§ 22. Velocity of Sound in Non-Ideal Gases

As stated, many of the equations given in §§ 17–19 hold only for *ideal* gases. A suitable correction for actual gases is given by Berthelot's equation

[1] Schulze, *Ann. Phys.*, 1907, **24**, 785 (bibl.); cf. Tirunarayanchar, *Rev. Sci. Instr.*, 1932, **3**, 766; on the minimum perceptible amount of sound energy, see de Vries, *Nature*, 1948, **161**, 63.

[2] Leslie, *Trans. Cambr. Phil. Soc.*, 1822, **1**, 167; *Ann. Chim.*, 1822, **21**, 94.

[3] Thiesen, *Ann. Phys.*, 1907, **24**, 401; 1908, **25**, 506.

[4] Partington and Shilling, " The Specific Heats of Gases," 1924, 137, 144.

[5] *Z. phys. Chem.*, 1937, **36** B, 163.

[6] *Ann. Phys.*, 1881, **13**, 544; 1883, **18**, 309.

[7] *Ann. Phys.*, 1908, **27**, 735.

[8] See Partington and Shilling, " The Specific Heats of Gases," 1924, 85 f.

[9] *Ann. Phys.*, 1908, **26**, 551; 1908, **27**, 311; *Abhl. Akad. Munich* (Math. Phys. Kl.), 1909, **23**, 377; Shpakovskij, *Compt. Rend. U.R.S.S.*, 1934, **3**, 26, 31.

[10] *Ann. Phys.*, 1914, **45**, 913.

[11] *J.A.C.S.*, 1937, **59**, 2233; Clark and Katz, *Canad. J. Res.*, 1940, **18** A, 23, 39; 1941, **19** A, 111; 1943, **21** A, 1; Rundle, *J.A.C.S.*, 1944, **66**, 1797.

[12] *Ann. Phys.*, 1905, **15**, 74.

[13] Keesom and van Itterbeek, *Proc. K. Akad. Wetens. Amsterdam*, 1930, **23**, 440 (*Comm. Leiden* **209***a*, *c*); 1931, **34**, 204 (*Comm. Leiden* **213***b*); van Itterbeek and Keesom, *ibid.*, 1931, **34**, 988 (*Comm. Leiden* **216***c*; H_2, $\gamma=1{\cdot}667$ at 19° K.); Keesom, van Itterbeek, and van Lammeren, *ibid.*, 1931, **34**, 996 (*Comm. Leiden* **216***d*; O_2, $\gamma=1{\cdot}408$ at liq. air temp.); Keesom and van Lammeren, *ibid.*, 1932, **35**, 727 (*Comm. Leiden* **221***c*); 1934, **37**, 614; van Itterbeek, *Comm. Leiden*, 1932, Suppl. **70***b* (H_2), **70***c* (He at 4° K.); van Lammeren, *Physica*, 1935, **2**, 833 (O_2); van Itterbeek and Thys, *ibid.*, 1938, **5**, 888; van Itterbeek and Mariëns, *ibid.*, 1938, **5**, 153 (CO_2); van Itterbeek and Vandoninck, *ibid.*, 1943, **10**, 481; *Ann. de Phys.*, 1944, **19**, 88 (C_{v0} for H_2 at 90·2° K.=3·3); *Proc. Phys. Soc.*, 1946, **58**, 615 (He, A, H_2); van Itterbeek and Lauwers, *Physica*, 1946, **12**, 241 (NH_3; γ 1·333 at −30°); Walstra, *ibid.*, 1947, **13**, 643 (He).

[14] Kaye and Sherratt, *Proc. Roy. Soc.*, 1933, **141**, 123; Sherratt and Griffiths, *ibid.*, 1934, **147**, 292; 1936, **156**, 504.

[15] *J.A.C.S.*, 1928, **50**, 627; this paper contains a number of misleading and inaccurate statements, which have been uncritically copied into later publications.

[16] *Z. Phys.*, 1921, **4**, 355.

(§ 30.VII C). This gives for the density ρ and *specific* volume v:

$$\rho=1/v=Mp/RT[1-(9/128)\pi\tau(1-6\tau^2)] \quad . \quad . \quad . \quad . \quad (1)$$

where $\pi=p/p_c$, $\tau=T_c/T$, M=mol. wt., and R is in suitable units.

Equation (2), § 17, gives:

$$U^2=\epsilon/\rho=-v^2(\mathrm{d}p/\mathrm{d}v)_q=(\mathrm{d}p/\mathrm{d}\rho)_q=\gamma(\mathrm{d}p/\mathrm{d}\rho)_T \quad . \quad . \quad . \quad (2)$$

from (14), § 4.II. Hence:

$$\gamma=U^2\left(\frac{\mathrm{d}\rho}{\mathrm{d}p}\right)_T \text{ and } \left(\frac{\mathrm{d}\rho}{\mathrm{d}p}\right)_T=\frac{\mathrm{d}}{\mathrm{d}p}\left(\frac{Mp}{RT}\right)-\frac{\mathrm{d}}{\mathrm{d}p}\left[\frac{9p^2M\tau}{128RTp_c}(1-6\tau^2)\right]$$

$$\therefore \gamma=(U^2M/RT)[1-(9/64)\pi\tau(1-6\tau^2)] \quad . \quad . \quad . \quad . \quad (3)$$

Put

$$1-(9/64)\pi\tau(1-6\tau^2)=\phi \quad . \quad . \quad . \quad . \quad . \quad . \quad . \quad . \quad (4)$$

then (2), § 17, and (3) show that:

$$\gamma=\gamma'\phi \quad . \quad . \quad . \quad . \quad . \quad . \quad . \quad . \quad . \quad . \quad (5)$$

where γ' is the value calculated by (2), § 17. Hence (2), § 18, becomes:

$$\gamma_2/\gamma_1=(M_2\lambda_2{}^2/M_1\lambda_1{}^2)(\phi_2/\phi_1) \quad . \quad . \quad . \quad . \quad . \quad . \quad (6)$$

Values of ϕ and of C_p-C_v (from which C_v and C_p may be calculated from γ) are tabulated by Partington and Shilling [1] for several gases.

Bakker [2] used the equations $\gamma=(\mathrm{d}p/\mathrm{d}v)_q/(\mathrm{d}p/\mathrm{d}v)_T$, and $pv^{\gamma'}$=const., therefore $\gamma=-\gamma'(p/v)(\mathrm{d}v/\mathrm{d}p)_T$. But $\mathrm{d}(pv)/\mathrm{d}p=p\mathrm{d}v/\mathrm{d}p+v$, hence:

$$\gamma=\gamma'\{1-(1/v)[\mathrm{d}(pv)/\mathrm{d}p]_T\},$$

where $v=1/\rho$=specific volume. Chappius [3] found for CO_2 at 20°, $\mathrm{d}(pv)/\mathrm{d}p=-0{\cdot}00541$, with p in atm. and unit vol. that of 1 mol of ideal gas at S.T.P., hence $1/v=273/293=0{\cdot}93$, therefore $\gamma=\gamma'(1+0{\cdot}00541\times0{\cdot}93)=1{\cdot}005\gamma'$, whilst Berthelot's equation gives $1{\cdot}004\gamma'$. Schulze [4] used the equation:

$$(p+a/T^{1\cdot348}v^2)(v-b)=RT,$$

for air. The effects of temperature and pressure on γ were considered in a series of papers by Leduc.[5] Beckman [6] calculated γ from velocity of sound measurements by the characteristic equation $pv=a-bp$, where a, b are constants at a given temperature.

§ 23. The Tube Correction

In the measurement of the velocity of sound in tubes or resonators a number of corrections are necessary before the velocity in a free gas is found. Some of these depend on the geometry of the apparatus, such as the effect of the ends of tubes, etc., and these are discussed in the papers referred to.[7] An important

1 " The Specific Heats of Gases," 1924, 28; Boynton, *Phys. Rev.*, 1901, **12**, 353, and Olson and Brittain, *J.A.C.S.*, 1933, **55**, 4063, used van der Waals's equation (§ 15).

2 *Phys. Rev.*, 1910, **31**, 589.

3 *Trav. et Mém. Bur. Internat. Poids et Més.*, 1907, **13**.

4 *Ann. Phys.*, 1916, **49**, 569; cf. Magyar, *Z. techn. Phys.*, 1924, **5**, 404.

5 *Compt. Rend.*, 1897, **125**, 1089 (velocity of sound); 1898, **127**, 659; *Ann. Chim.*, 1899, **17** 484.

6 *Arkiv Mat. Astron. Fys.*, 1912, **7**, No. 27.

7 See also Rayleigh, " The Theory of Sound," 1896, **2**, 312; Auerbach, in Winkelmann, " Handbuch der Physik," 1909, **2**, 494, 508; Lamb, " The Dynamical Theory of Sound," 1910, 183, 187; " Hydrodynamics," 4th edit., Cambridge, 1932, 646; Partington and Shilling, *Phil. Mag.*, 1923, **45**, 426; " The Specific Heats of Gases," 1924, 51, 96; Lübcke, in Scheel and Heuse, " Handbuch der Physik," 1927, **8**, 627.

correction is for the effect of the walls of the tube. Regnault[1] and Kundt[2] had shown experimentally that the velocity of sound in a gas in a tube is less than that in the free gas, and had applied corrections.

A theory of this damping effect was worked out by Helmholtz[3] and more completely by Kirchhoff.[4] If U_∞, U_r are the velocities of sound in the free gas and in a tube of radius r, respectively, Kirchhoff found:

$$U_\infty = U_r[1 + c/2r\sqrt{(\pi n)}] \quad . \quad . \quad . \quad . \quad . \quad . \quad . \quad . \quad (1)$$

where n is the frequency and:

$$c = \sqrt{\mu} + (U_\infty/b - b/U_\infty)\sqrt{\nu} \quad . \quad . \quad . \quad . \quad . \quad . \quad . \quad . \quad (2)$$

where $\mu = \eta/\rho$ = viscosity/density, of the gas, $\nu = \kappa/\rho c_v$, where κ = thermal conductivity, c_v = specific heat at constant volume, and b = Newtonian velocity of sound in the gas $= \sqrt{(p/\rho)}$ (§ 17).

Thiesen[5] deduced Kirchhoff's equations for the motion of sound in a viscous, heat-conducting gas on more general assumptions, and solved them for a sphere and cylinder, showing how to apply the corrections for viscosity and thermal conductivity in certain experimental arrangements. Second order terms were considered by Kohler[6] and Bechert.[7]

The Helmholtz-Kirchhoff equation was confirmed by Schneebeli,[8] Seebeck,[9] Kayser,[10] Blaikley,[11] Stevens[12] (who found it to hold at high temperatures, except perhaps in very narrow tubes), Müller,[13] and Waetzmann and Keibs.[14] Sturm[15] did not confirm the dependence on radius. Koenig[16] confirmed it for very high frequencies, except in very narrow tubes. As a basis for all tube corrections, the formula has, therefore, abundant experimental verification.[17] Only the numerical constant c has been found to be somewhat different from that calculated by (2).

The value of Kirchhoff's constant c (sometimes denoted by γ) was given by Fürstenau[18] in a form which combines the Sutherland equation (§ 5.VII F) for the viscosity η of the gas, and the usual equation for the variation of density ρ with temperature (§ 21.VII A):

$$c = \sqrt{\left[\frac{\eta_0 T(1 + C/273)\sqrt{(1 + T/273)}}{273\rho_0(1 + C/T)}\right]} \cdot [1 + \sqrt{(\kappa/\eta c_v)}(\gamma - 1)/\sqrt{\gamma}] \quad . \quad (3)$$

where C is Sutherland's constant and $\gamma = c_p/c_v$. The value of $\kappa/\eta c_v$ is (§ 1.VII G)

[1] *Phil. Mag.*, 1868, **35**, 161.

[2] *Ann. Phys.*, 1868, **135**, 337, 527.

[3] *J. reine angew. Math.* (Crelle), 1860, **57**, 1; " Wiss. Abhl.," 1882, **1**, 383 (correction for viscosity).

[4] *Ann. Phys.*, 1868, **134**, 177; " Ges. Abhl.," 1882, 540 (correction for heat conduction).

[5] *Ann. Phys.*, 1907, **24**, 401; 1908, **25**, 506.

[6] *Ann. Phys.*, 1941, **39**, 209.

[7] *Ann. Phys.*, 1941, **40**, 207; Possio, *Atti Accad. Torino*, 1942–3, **78**, 274; Eckart, *Phys. Rev.*, 1948, **73**, 68.

[8] *Ann. Phys.*, 1869, **136**, 296.

[9] *Ann. Phys.*, 1870, **139**, 104.

[10] *Ann. Phys.*, 1877, **2**, 218.

[11] *Proc. Phys. Soc.*, 1883, **5**, 319; 1884, **6**, 228.

[12] *Ann. Phys.*, 1902, **7**, 285.

[13] *Ann. Phys.*, 1903, **11**, 331.

[14] *Ann. Phys.*, 1935, **22**, 247.

[15] *Ann. Phys.*, 1904, **14**, 823.

[16] *Ann. Phys.*, 1899, **69**, 626, 721.

[17] Wüllner, " Lehrbuch der Experimentalphysik," Leipzig, 1895, **1**, 944; Partington and Shilling, " The Specific Heats of Gases," 1924, 51 f., 142.

[18] *Ann. Phys.*, 1908, **27**, 735.

taken as 1·53 or 1·6027 by O. E. Meyer, 1·497 by Jeans, and $\frac{1}{4}(9\gamma-5)$ by Eucken; the approximate value 1·5 is sufficient. If values of η and ρ for the gas are known at the temperature concerned they may be substituted directly:

$$c=\sqrt{(\eta_t/\rho_t)}[1+\sqrt{(1\cdot5)}(\gamma-1)/\sqrt{\gamma}] \quad . \quad . \quad . \quad . \quad . \quad (4)$$

Much experimental work [1] has shown that the observed value of Kirchhoff's constant is always somewhat higher than the theoretical; the latter ignores the effects of friction and heat exchange with the walls of the tube; the rougher the walls and the greater their thermal conductivity, the greater the retardation. Attempts to eliminate the correction by the use of tubes of different radii are rather uncertain, and the best procedure seems to be the following.[2] The apparent velocity of sound U_r in a tube is determined for a gas for which the true velocity U_∞ is known. If c is the Kirchhoff constant, then:

$$U_r=U_\infty(1-kc) \quad . \quad . \quad . \quad . \quad . \quad . \quad . \quad . \quad . \quad (5)$$

where k is the so-called *tube correction*, which depends on the radius, thickness of wall, nature of surface, thermal conductivity, and perhaps other factors, but not on the gas. When k is so determined for one gas, equation (5) can be used for other gases *in the same tube.*

Buss [3] and Rechel [4] also found the Kirchhoff constant higher than the theoretical value for air, and for air, oxygen, nitrogen, carbon dioxide and ammonia at 20°–900°, respectively. Rechel's values are in agreement with those of other workers; no explanation is given of the effect of temperature on the Kirchhoff constant. Buss represented the velocity by (1) and determined the variation of c.

§ 24. Time-lag of Energy Distribution in Sound Waves

Another important correction, only recently fully recognised, is required for the time lag in the *internal* energy changes of a molecule when the temperature changes in adiabatic compressions and expansions occur rapidly in the sound wave. The adiabatic changes of volume first change the translational energy (to which the temperature corresponds; see § 3.III). This is then transferred by collisions to the rotational and vibrational energies until a state of equilibrium is reached. The effect will obviously depend on the frequency and it is supposed that the time-lag may reach 0·1 sec.

The possibility of the effect was predicted by Boltzmann [5] and Jeans,[6] and it has been esperimentally established,[7] especially for very high frequency

[1] Summarised in Partington and Shilling, " The Specific Heats of Gases," 1924, 53; Zwikker, van der Eijk, and Kosten, *Physica*, 1941, **8**, 1094.

[2] Dixon, *Proc. Roy. Soc.*, 1921, **100**, 1; Partington and Shilling, " The Specific Heats of Gases," 1924, 53, 141; *Phil. Mag.*, 1928, **6**, 920; Henry, *Proc. Phys. Soc.*, 1931, **43**, 340.

[3] *Ann. Phys.*, 1930, **7**, 601.

[4] *Ann. Phys.*, 1931, **10**, 1; Rocard, *J. de Phys.*, 1930, **1**, 426; Kohler, *Ann. Phys.*, 1941, **39**, 209; *Naturwiss.*, 1946, **33**, 251; Damköhler, *Z. Elektrochem.*, 1942, **48**, 62, 116.

[5] *Ann. Phys.*, 1870, **141**, 473; " Wiss. Abhl.," 1909, **1**, 157, who says, for adiabatic expansions: " es ist zwar nicht wahrscheinlich, aber immerhin nicht ausserhalb des Bereiches der Möglichkeit, dass diese Umsetzung eine längere Zeit beanspruche "; Jeans, *Phil. Mag.*, 1901, **2**, 638, predicted the lag in the case of sound waves; cf. Stewart, *Phil. Mag.*, 1914, **28**, 748.

[6] *Phil. Mag.*, 1901, **2**, 638; " Dynamical Theory of Gases," Cambridge, 1904, 228, 302; later predictions by Herzfeld and Rice, *Phys. Rev.*, 1928, **31**, 691; Henry, *Nature*, 1932, **129**, 200; Herzfeld, *Ann. Phys.*, 1935, **23**, 465.

[7] In an exuberant literature see, e.g.: Pierce, *Proc. Amer. Acad.*, 1925, **60**, 271 ($1\cdot5\times10^6$ cycles/sec.); Abello, *Proc. Nat. Acad.*, 1927, **13**, 699; *Phys. Rev.*, 1928, **31**, 1083; Pielmeier, *Phys. Rev.*, 1929, **34**, 1184; 1930, **36**, 1005; 1931, **38**, 1236; 1932, **41**, 833; *J. Acoust. Soc. Amer.*, 1935, **7**, 37; 1937, **9**, 212; Rocard, *J. de Phys.*, 1930, **1**, 426; Kneser, *Ann. Phys.*, 1931,

(*supersonic waves*). The *vibrational* energy of the molecule is mainly affected.[1] The values of C_v found by the velocity of sound method may be appreciably lower than those calculated from the quantum theory (§ 30).[2] By making determinations with different frequencies and extrapolating to zero frequency, the effect appears to be eliminated.[3]

For nitric oxide Kneser [4] found no delay in the assumption of thermal equilibrium in the frequency range of 300–3000 cycles per sec., and if any lag occurs it is less than 10^{-6} sec. Heil [5] thought Kneser's positive results with carbon dioxide were due to an accidental relation between the vibrational quantum number and the temperature for that gas.

Mokhtar and Richardson [6] found the velocity in dry air independent of supersonic frequency from 42 to 700 kilocycles/sec., the absorption coefficient being several times greater than that predicted by Kirchhoff's theory. In moist air, the absorption coefficient rose to a maximum which was 2–3 times the value

11, 761, 777; 1932, **12**, 1015; 1933, **16**, 337, 360; 1941, **39**, 261; 1943, **43**, 465; *Phys. Z.*, 1931, **32**, 179; *Nature*, 1932, **129**, 729; *Phys. Rev.*, 1933, **43**, 1015; *J. Acoust. Soc. Amer.*, 1933, **5**, 122; *Z. techn. Phys.*, 1938, **19**, 486; Kneser and Zühlke, *Z. Phys.*, 1932, **77**, 649; Kneser and Knudsen, *Ann. Phys.*, 1934, **20**, 682; Knudsen, *J. Acoust. Soc. Amer.*, 1933, **5**, 112; Heil, *Z. Phys.*, 1932, **74**, 31; Eucken *et al.*, *Naturwiss.*, 1932, **20**, 85; *Z. phys. Chem.*, 1932, **18** B, 167; 1933, **20** B, 460, 467; 1934, **21** B, 219, 235; 1935, **20** B, 85; 1940, **46** B, 195; *Z. techn. Phys.*, 1938, **19**, 517; *Die Chemie*, 1943, **56**, 129; Rutgers, *Ann. Phys.*, 1933, **16**, 350; Teeter, *J. Chem. Phys.*, 1933, **1**, 251; Wallmann, *Ann. Phys.*, 1934, **20**, 671; Grossmann, in Wien-Harms, " Handbuch der Experimentalphysik," 1934, **17**, i, 463; *Ann. Phys.*, 1932, **13**, 681; Railstone and Richardson, *Proc. Phys. Soc.*, 1935, **47**, 533; Penman, *ibid.*, 1935, **47**, 543; Knudsen and Obert, *J. Acoust. Soc. Amer.*, 1936, **7**, 249; Sinness and Roseveare, *J. Chem. Phys.*, 1936, **4**, 427; Brandt, *Koll. Z.*, 1937, **81**, 2 (absorption in fogs); Metter, *Sow. Phys. Z.*, 1937, **12**, 233; Jatkar, *J. Indian Inst. Sci.*, 1938, **21** A, 245; 1939, **22** A, ii, 19, 39; Jatkar and Lakshminarayanan, *ibid.*, 1946, **28** A, 1, 17; Schulze, *Ann. Phys.*, 1938, **34**, 41; Saxton, *J. Chem. Phys.*, 1938, **6**, 30; Dwyer, *ibid.*, 1939, **7**, 40; Pumper, *J. Phys. U.S.S.R.*, 1939, **1**, 411; Thys, *Physica*, 1938, **5**, 888; Richards, *Rev. Mod. Phys.*, 1939, **11**, 36; Keller, *Phys. Z.*, 1940, **41**, 386; Pielmeier, Saxton, and Telfair, *J. Chem. Phys.*, 1940, **8**, 106; Gemant, *J. Appl. Phys.*, 1941, **12**, 718; Bender, *Ann. Phys.*, 1940, **38**, 199; Van Itterbeek, *Medd. K. Vlaam. Akad. Wet.*, 1940, No. **2**; Mariëns, *ibid.*, 1940, No. **11**; Van Itterbeek and Mariëns, *Physica*, 1940, **7**, 909, 938; Schäfer, *Z. phys. Chem.*, 1940, **46** B, 212; Anderson and Lambert, *Proc. Roy. Soc.*, 1941–2, **179**, 499; Kohler, *Ann. Phys.*, 1941, **39**, 209; Buschmann and Schäfer, *Z. phys. Chem.*, 1941, **50** B, 73; Ganse, *Wis. Natuurkd. Tijdschr.*, 1941, **10**, 95; Oberbeck and Kendall, *J. Acoust. Soc. Amer.*, 1941, **13**, 26; Damköhler, *Z. Elektrochem.*, 1942, **48**, 62, 116; *Naturwiss.*, 1943, **31**, 305; Telfair and Pielmeier, *Rev. Sci. Instr.*, 1942, **13**, 122; Kantrowitz, *J. Chem. Phys.*, 1942, **10**, 145; Telfair, *ibid.*, 1942, **10**, 167; Tisza, *Phys. Rev.*, 1942, **61**, 531; Van Itterbeek and Vermaelen, *Physica*, 1942, **9**, 345, 356 (H_2, D_2); Pielmeier and Byers, *J. Acoust. Soc. Amer.*, 1943, **15**, 17; Pielmeier, *ibid.*, 1943, **15**, 22; Byers, *J. Chem. Phys.*, 1943, **11**, 348; Meixner, *Ann. Phys.*, 1943, **43**, 470; Kudryavtsev, *Amer. Chem. Abstr.*, 1943, **37**, 1068; *J. Expt. Theor. Phys. U.S.S.R.*, 1947, **17**, 294 (gas mixture); Stewart, *Phys. Rev.*, 1946, **69**, 632; Richardson, *Nature*, 1946, **158**, 296; Rhodes, *Phys. Rev.*, 1946, **70**, 91, 932 (normal and pH_2); Kantrowitz, *J. Chem. Phys.*, 1946, **14**, 150; Huber and Kantrowitz, *ibid.*, 1947, **15**, 275; Van Itterbeek and Lauwers, *Physica*, 1946, **12**, 241 (NH_3, γ ultrasonic $>1{\cdot}333$, probably a dispersion effect); Gorélik, *Compt. Rend. U.R.S.S.*, 1946, **54**, 779; Kohler, *Naturwiss.*, 1946, **33**, 251 (relation to *volume* viscosity); Van Vleck, *Phys. Rev.*, 1947, **71**, 413, 425; King, Hainer, and Cross, *ibid.*, 1947, **71**, 433 (micro-waves; formulae); Kittel, *Rep. Progr. Phys.*, 1948, **11**, 205.

[1] Although Richards and Reid, *J. Chem. Phys.*, 1934, **2**, 206, found that the *rotational* energy of hydrogen was not fully excited by ultrasonic waves, this was not confirmed by Kneser and Wallman, *Naturwiss.*, 1934, **22**, 510.

[2] Zeise, *Z. Elektrochem.*, 1933, **39**, 895.

[3] Kaye and Sherratt, *Proc. Roy. Soc.*, 1933, **141**, 123; Sherratt and Griffiths, *ibid.*, 1934, **147**, 292; 1936, **156**, 504.

[4] *Ann. Phys.*, 1941, **39**, 261.

[5] *Z. Phys.*, 1932, **74**, 31.

[6] *Proc. Roy. Soc.*, 1945, **184**, 117; Parker, *Proc. Phys. Soc.*, 1937, **49**, 95, had found no change in the range 92–801.

in dry air. A method [1] depending on the impedance of a vibrating source gave too low values of γ.

Olson and Brittain,[2] who used a frequency of 100 kc., did not find any abnormal effect with dichloroethylene, and Cornish and Eastman's results [3] also do not seem to have been affected; it would seem, curiously enough, that only some experimenters' results are so vitiated. The experiments and calculations of Richards [4] seem to be affected by serious errors.

Relaxation times, in which half the unquantised translational and (except for H_2 and D_2) slightly quantised rotational energy given to a gas by sound waves is transformed into vibrational (and rotational with H_2 and D_2) modes, were calculated and observed by van Paemel and Mariëns [5] as follows:

	O_2 290° K.	H_2 290° K.	D_2 290° K.	H_2 90° K.	D_2 90° K.
Calc. ...	$2{\cdot}1\times10^{-6}$ sec.	$1{\cdot}3\times10^{-9}$ sec.	$6{\cdot}6\times10^{-10}$ sec.	$3{\cdot}9\times10^{-9}$ sec.	$5{\cdot}1\times10^{-10}$ sec.
Obs. ...	$1{\cdot}6\times10^{-6}$ sec.	$2{\cdot}1\times10^{-8}$ sec.	$1{\cdot}5\times10^{-8}$ sec.	$2{\cdot}8\times10^{-8}$ sec.	$0{\cdot}5\times10^{-8}$ sec.

Bömmel [6] found the ultrasonic velocities at 0° C. (taking air 331·5 m./sec.): A 307·8, O_2 316·6, N_2 336·6, CO_2 268·3, m./sec. Specific heats found from the velocity of sound are tabulated by Lourié.[7]

§ 25. Theory of Time-lag in Energy Distribution

The equation deduced by Rutgers [8] for the velocity of sound of frequency ν and period $\tau=2\pi\nu$ in an ideal gas of pressure p and density ρ is:

$$U_\nu^2=\frac{p}{\rho}\left(1+R\frac{C_{vst}+\tau^2\beta^2C_{v\infty}}{C^2_{vst}+\tau^2\beta^2C_{v\infty}{}^2}\right) \quad . \; . \; . \; . \; . \; . \; . \quad (1)$$

where C_{vst} is the fully excited molecular heat at constant volume, $C_{v\infty}$ the molecular heat at constant volume which would be measured with sound waves of very high frequency, and β is a period defined by the equation:

$$C_s^t=C_s^{st}(1-\mathrm{e}^{-t/\beta}) \quad . \; . \; . \; . \; . \; . \; . \; . \quad (2)$$

where t=time, C_s^{st} is the fully excited vibrational molecular heat and C_s^t the vibrational molecular heat which is excited in a temperature change occurring in a time t. Equation (2), which is analogous to that for the amplitude of an oscillation in a very viscous medium (§ 65.I), may be regarded as fundamental. By differentiation of (2):

$$\mathrm{d}C_s^t/\mathrm{d}t=(C_s^{st}/\beta)\mathrm{e}^{-t/\beta}=(1/\beta)(C_s^{st}-C_s^t) \quad . \; . \; . \; . \quad (3)$$

For an adiabatic change, $C_v\mathrm{d}T+p\mathrm{d}V=0$ (ideal gas, see § 55.II):

$$\therefore\ (C_{v\infty}+C_s^t)\mathrm{d}T+p\mathrm{d}V=0 \; . \; . \; . \; . \; . \; . \; . \; . \quad (4)$$

1 Bouchard, *Compt. Rend.*, 1948, **226**, 1434.
2 *J.A.C.S.*, 1933, **55**, 4063.
3 *J.A.C.S.*, 1928, **50**, 627.
4 *Nature*, 1932, **130**, 739; *J.A.C.S.*, 1932, **54**, 3014; *J. Chem. Phys.*, 1933, **1**, 114; 1934, **2**, 206; 1936, **4**, 561; see, e.g., Teeter, *J.A.C.S.*, 1932, **54**, 4111.
5 *Amer. Chem. Abstr.*, 1944, **38**, 6145.
6 *Helv. Phys. Acta.*, 1945, **18**, 3.
7 *Chaleur et Ind.*, 1930, **11**, 423.
8 *Ann. Phys.*, 1933, **16**, 350; Bourgin, *Phys. Rev.*, 1933, **42**, 721; Eucken and Becker, *Z. phys. Chem.*, 1934, **27** B, 235; Saxton, *J. Chem. Phys.*, 1938, **6**, 30; Leontowitsch, *Bull. Acad. Sci. U.R.S.S.*, 1936, 633 (Phys.); Schäfer, *Z. phys. Chem.*, 1940, **46** B, 212; Eucken, *Naturwiss.*, 1943, **31**, 314.

In a periodic change of state of period τ (§ 64.I):

$$C_s^t = C_s^{st} e^{i\tau t} \quad \therefore \ dC_s^t/dt = i\tau C_s^t \quad . \quad . \quad . \quad . \quad . \quad . \quad (5)$$

$$\therefore \ C_s^t = C_s^{st}/(1+i\tau\beta) \quad . \quad . \quad . \quad . \quad . \quad . \quad . \quad . \quad (6)$$

by equating (3) and (5). Substitute (6) in (4) and put $C_{v\infty}+C_s^{st}=C_{vst}$, then:

$$\left(\frac{dT}{dV}\right)_q = \left(\frac{dT}{dV}\right)_S = -\frac{p(1+i\tau\beta)}{C_{v\infty}(1+i\tau\beta)+C_s^t} = -\frac{p(1+i\tau\beta)}{C_{vst}+i\tau\beta C_{v\infty}} \quad . \quad . \quad (7)$$

The equation for the velocity of sound of frequency ν is (§ 17):

$$U_\nu^2 = (p/\rho)(C_p/C_v) = (p/\rho)[(C_v+\boldsymbol{R})/C_v] = (p/\rho)(1+\boldsymbol{R}/C_v) \quad . \quad . \quad (8)$$

Also, from Maxwell's equation (1), § 48.II:

$$(dV/dT)_S = -(dS/dp)_V = -(dS/dT)_V(dT/dp)_V = -(C_v/T)(V/\boldsymbol{R}) = -C_v/p$$

with $T=pV/\boldsymbol{R}$. Hence:

$$\boldsymbol{R}/C_v = -(\boldsymbol{R}/p)(dT/dV)_S \quad . \quad . \quad . \quad . \quad . \quad . \quad . \quad (9)$$

Substitute (9) in (8) and introduce $(dT/dV)_S$ from (7), then:

$$U_\nu^2 = \frac{p}{\rho}\left(1+\boldsymbol{R}\frac{1+i\tau\beta}{C_{vst}+i\tau\beta C_{v\infty}}\right) \quad . \quad . \quad . \quad . \quad . \quad . \quad (10)$$

Multiply numerator and denominator of the complex term in the bracket by $(C_{vst}-i\tau\beta C_{v\infty})$ and reject imaginary quantities,[1] when (1) results. Since C_p/C_v in (8) may be written γ^0, the ratio for the ideal gas state:

$$\therefore \ \gamma_\nu^0 = 1+\boldsymbol{R}\frac{C_{vst}+\tau^2\beta^2 C_{v\infty}}{C_{vst}^2+\tau^2\beta^2 C_{v\infty}^2} \quad . \quad . \quad . \quad . \quad . \quad . \quad (11)$$

When $\tau=0$, i.e. infinitely long waves, this goes over into the simple limiting equation:

$$\gamma^0 = 1+\boldsymbol{R}/C_v \quad . \quad . \quad . \quad . \quad . \quad . \quad . \quad . \quad . \quad (12)$$

A more detailed deduction of Rutgers' equation [2] does not alter it essentially, but adds some refinement to (2).

The conversion of translational (collision) into vibrational energy, as determined by the degree of agreement of observed and theoretical specific heats found by sound velocity (frequency about 10^5 hertz), is said [3] to be facilitated, in the cases of chlorine and carbon dioxide, by addition of an indifferent gas.

Attempts to determine relative values of specific heats by comparing the values of the thermal conductivities [4] and making use of equation (11), § 1.VII G,

[1] Steil, *Z. phys. Chem.*, 1935, **31** B, 343.

[2] Eucken and Jaacks, *Z. phys. Chem.*, 1935, **30** B, 85; Eucken, *ibid.*, 1936, **32** B, 404; Landau and Teller, *Sow. Phys. Z.*, 1936, **10**, 34, Hardy, *J. Acoust. Soc. Amer.*, 1943, **15**, 91.

[3] Eucken and Becker, *Z. phys. Chem.*, 1933, **20** B, 467; Eucken and Jaacks, *ibid.*, 1935, **30** B, 85; Patat and Bartholomé, *ibid.*, 1936, **32** B, 396; Eucken and Veith, *ibid.*, 1936, **34** B, 275 (corrected by Maue, *Ann. Phys.*, 1937, **30**, 555); Eucken and Veith, *Z. phys. Chem.*, 1937, **38** B, 393; Eucken and Nümann, *ibid.*, 1937, **36** B, 163 (faulty apparatus); Küchler, *ibid.*, 1938, **41** B, 199.

[4] Schreiner, *Z. phys. Chem.*, 1924, **112**, 1; Eucken and Weigert, *ibid.*, 1933, **23** B, 265 (corrected by Kistiakowski and Nazmi, *J. Chem. Phys.*, 1938, **6**, 18; and Roper, *J. Phys. Chem.*, 1941, **45**, 321); Eucken and Bertram, *Z. phys. Chem.*, 1935, **31** B, 361; Hunsmann, *ibid.*, 1938, **39** B, 23 (critical; defects of method); Kistiakowsky and Nazmi, *J. Chem. Phys.*, 1938, **6**, 18 (disagreeing with Hunsmann with the same method and gas, C_2H_6); Witt and Kemp, *J.A.C.S.*, 1937, **59**, 273; Eucken and Krome, *Z. phys. Chem.*, 1940, **45** B, 175 (corrected by Giguère and Rundle, *J.A.C.S.*, 1941, **63**, 1135); see the earlier criticism of the method by Eucken, in Wien-Harms, " Handbuch der Experimentalphysik," 1929, **8**, i, 426, where other sources of error are mentioned.

do not seem attractive, and (for reasons mentioned in § 4.VII G) must be regarded as crude; the accommodation coefficient, for example, was assumed equal in the various gases. The equation for the heat lost per cm.² per sec. per 1° temperature difference:

$$\Delta q/\Delta t = c\bar{v}\alpha(C_v+\tfrac{1}{2}R)/\sqrt{(6\pi)} \quad \ldots\ldots\ldots (13)$$

where c=concentration of gas in mol/ml., $\bar{v}$=mean molecular velocity, α= accommodation coefficient, gives:

$$\frac{(\Delta q/\Delta t)_1}{(\Delta q/\Delta t)_2} = \frac{c_1\bar{v}_1\alpha_1}{c_2\bar{v}_2\alpha_2}\frac{(C_{v1}+\tfrac{1}{2}R)}{(C_{v2}+\tfrac{1}{2}R)} \quad \ldots\ldots\ldots (14)$$

§ 26. Velocity of Sound in a Dissociating Gas

E. and L. Natanson [1] and Pochettino,[2] by Kundt's method, determined γ for nitrogen peroxide at temperatures from 4·2° to 150° and found it to change to 1·296 at 150°, the latter value corresponding with a triatomic molecule (NO_2). E. and L. Natanson had calculated the density from the velocity of sound by Kundt's method and found it to agree with the experimental density. The theory of the specific heat of a dissociating gas was given by Bell and Trevor,[3] and the specific heat (c_p) of nitrogen peroxide was determined by Regnault's method (§ 2) by McCollum.[4] The theory of the velocity of sound in a dissociating gas was worked out by Einstein,[5] and Damköhler [6] studied the adiabatic equation pv^n=const. for this case.

Einstein's formula [7] for the velocity of sound in a dissociating gas applies when the absorption coefficient is sufficiently small. The extrapolated value for zero frequency ($\tilde{\omega}=0$) is:

$$U_{\tilde{\omega}=0} = \sqrt{[(P/\rho)(1+A/B)]} \quad \ldots\ldots\ldots (1)$$

and for infinite frequency ($\tilde{\omega}=\infty$):

$$U_{\tilde{\omega}=\infty} = \sqrt{[(P/\rho)(1+R/\bar{C}_v)]} \quad \ldots\ldots\ldots (2)$$

and for an intermediate frequency ($\tilde{\omega}=\tilde{\omega}$)

$$U_{\tilde{\omega}} = \sqrt{\left[\frac{P}{\rho}\left(1+\frac{k^2AB+R\bar{C}_v\tilde{\omega}^2}{k^2B^2+\bar{C}_v{}^2\tilde{\omega}^2}\right)\right]} \quad \ldots\ldots\ldots (3)$$

where $\tilde{\omega}$=frequency, P=pressure, ρ=density, R=molar gas constant, $\bar{C}_v$=mean mol. ht. of mixture at const. vol., k=dissociation velocity constant,

$$A = (2q_D/T - \bar{C}_v)n_1/(n_1+n_2) + R[1-4(n_1/n_2)] \quad \ldots (4)$$

$$B = (q_D{}^2/RT^2)n_1/(n_1+n_2) + \bar{C}_v[1-4(n_1/n_2)] \quad \ldots (5)$$

where q_D=heat of dissociation at constant volume, T=abs. temperature, n_1 and

[1] *Ann. Phys.*, 1885, **24**, 454.
[2] *Nuov. Cim.*, 1899, **9**, 450; *Atti R. Accad. Lincei*, 1899, **8**, i, 183.
[3] *J. Phys. Chem.*, 1905, **9**, 179; Partington, " Text Book of Thermodynamics," 1913, 349.
[4] *J.A.C.S.*, 1927, **49**, 28.
[5] *Berlin Ber.*, 1920, 380; Luck, *Phys. Rev.*, 1932, **40**, 440; Kneser and Gauler, *Phys. Z.*, 1936, **37**, 677; for a dissociating gas in a temperature gradient, see Dirac, *Proc. Cambr. Phil. Soc.*, 1924, **22**, 132.
[6] *Z. Elektrochem.*, 1942, **48**, 62, 116.
[7] *Berlin Ber.*, 1920, 380; Selle, *Z. phys. Chem.*, 1923, **104**, 1; Grüneisen and Goens, *Ann. Phys.*, 1923, **72**, 193; Kistiakowsky and Richards, *J.A.C.S.*, 1930, **52**, 4661; Verhoek and Daniels, *ibid.*, 1931, **53**, 1186.

n_2 are the numbers of molecules of the undissociated substance X and of its product of dissociation Y, respectively, where $X \rightleftharpoons 2Y$.

Grüneisen and Goens gave the equations:

$$U_0 = \sqrt{\left[\frac{P}{\rho}\left(1 - A + \frac{(1+AB)^2}{AB^2 + \bar{C}_v/R}\right)\right]}; \quad U_\infty = \sqrt{[(P/\rho)(1 + R/\bar{C}_v)]} \quad . \quad (6)$$

where (α=degree of dissociation):

$$A = \alpha(1-\alpha)/[2+\alpha(1-\alpha)], \quad B = q_D/RT \quad . \quad . \quad . \quad . \quad (7)$$

Kistiakowsky and Richards used a magnetostriction oscillator devised by Pierce,[1] consisting of a chrome-steel rod; three rods had frequencies of 10, 41·5, and 80 kilocycles. The reaction was $N_2O_4 \rightleftharpoons 2NO_2$. The curve of U corresponded, for all three frequencies, almost with the theoretical curve for $\tilde{\omega}=0$, which shows that the velocity of dissociation is very large; the attempts to calculate it seem of doubtful interest in view of the uncertainty of most of the data used, and the probable interference of the Kneser effect (§ 24).

Brass and Tolman,[2] by a method depending on measuring the change of temperature on rapid flow through a perforated diaphragm, claimed to have obtained a figure of $k \simeq 15$ sec.$^{-1}$ for the velocity coefficient of dissociation of N_2O_4. Richards and Reid's [3] experiments and calculations, which are said to verify Einstein's equation, seem to be erroneous; the gas was found by Teeter [4] to show strong absorption at higher frequencies, and an equation deduced by Luck [5] for a real gas showing absorption should have been used. The subject is in an unsatisfactory state.

§ 27. Velocity of Sound in Gas Mixtures

The velocity of sound in a mixture of gases was considered by Laplace,[6] and was treated theoretically by Richarz,[7] Leduc,[8] and Powell.[9] The calculation, which involves the critical constants, is rather complicated. It shows, for example, that the value of γ for air containing 15 mm. partial pressure of water vapour is reduced from the value for dry air by about 0·01 unit, so that in wave-length measurements it is essential to use dry air in the comparison tube (§ 19).[10] Some experiments with mixtures of gases made by Dixon and Greenwood [11] are available for comparison with theories. Brillouin [12] showed theoretically that some local changes of composition may occur in a sound wave passing through a mixture of gases.

1 *Proc. Amer. Acad.*, 1928, **63**, 1.
2 *J.A.C.S.*, 1932, **54**, 1003.
3 *J.A.C.S.*, 1932, **54**, 3014; cf. Richards *et al.*, *Nature*, 1932, **130**, 739; *J. Chem. Phys.*, 1933, **1**, 114; 1934, **2**, 193, 206; 1936, **4**, 561; see the criticism by Rose, *ibid.*, 1934, **2**, 260; Wansbrough-Jones, *Sci. Progr.*, 1934, **29**, 110.
4 *J.A.C.S.*, 1932, **54**, 4111.
5 *Phys. Rev.*, 1932, **40**, 440.
6 " Oeuvres," 1882, **5**, 148.
7 *Ann. Phys.*, 1906, **19**, 639.
8 *Compt. Rend.*, 1898, **126**, 218; 1915, **160**, 338 516,; Kotovic, *J. Russ. Phys. Chem. Soc.*, 1908, **40**, 16 (P); see the summary in Partington and Shilling, " The Specific Heats of Gases," 1924, 99.
9 *Proc. Roy. Soc.*, 1928, **119**, 553; Bourgin, *Phil. Mag.*, 1929, **7**, 821; *Phys. Rev.*, 1929, **34**, 521.
10 Partington and Shilling, *op. cit.*, 101; Ivanescu. *Ann. Sci. Univ. Jassy.* 1941, **27**, i, 167.
11 *Proc. Roy. Soc.*, 1925, **109**, 561.
12 *Ann. Chim.*, 1899, **18**, 433.

The influence of radiation on the velocity of sound has been examined.[1] Okamura [2] found no influence of a magnetic field on c_p for air, O_2, N_2, and CO_2 as measured by a flow method.

§ 28. Specific Heat and Molecular Structure

The following are some values of $\gamma = c_p/c_v$ found by modifications of the Desormes and Clement method (C.D.) or from the velocity of sound (V.): [3]

A	1·667 (V.)	H_2	1·4092 (24°, C.D.) [5]	NH_3	1·308 (14·5°, V.)
Air	1·4034 (17°, C.D.)	Cl_2	1·353 (16°, V.)	HCN	1·281 (21°, V.) [4]
N_2	1·405 (20°, C.D.)	H_2S	1·340 (18°, V.)	SO_2	1·290 (13°, V.)
CO	1·404 (10°, V.) [4]	CO_2	1·3025 (18°, C.D., V.) [6]	C_2H_2	1·280 (20°, V.)
O_2	1·395 (18°, C.D., V.)	N_2O	1·303 (12°, V.)	C_2N_2	1·256 (0°, V.)
NO	1·400 (7·6°, V.)	H_2O	1·305 (108°, C.D.)	C_2H_4	1·250 (12°, V.)
HCl	1·404 (0°, V.)	CH_4	1·307 (0°, V.)	C_2H_6	1·232 (10°, V.)

The value $\gamma = 1{\cdot}40$ was deduced by Boltzmann [7] for a *rigid* diatomic molecule and this is seen to be approximately true for many diatomic gases. Chlorine and iodine vapour show [8] a much smaller value and this is certainly due to the vibration of the two atoms in the molecule, which increases the internal energy and hence reduces the value of γ. The values for the halogen hydracids HCl, HBr, and HI are normal, but that for iodine chloride ICl is 1·315 at 100°. The value 1·667 for argon (and other inert gases) was used by Rayleigh and Ramsay [9] to prove that the molecule is monatomic. Schweikert,[10] from a peculiar characteristic equation, deduced the obviously incorrect result that the maximum value of γ is 1·424, not 1·667. Press [11] found for gases and vapours $(\gamma-1)c_vM = \text{const.} \simeq 2$ (M=mol. wt.); since $\gamma - 1 = (c_p - c_v)/c_v$, this is equivalent to $(c_p - c_v)M \simeq R$, which is approximately 2!. A strong dependence on temperature among diatomic gases is found only for hydrogen and deuterium; at low temperatures γ approaches that for a monatomic gas (for the reason, see § 23.IV). Brinkworth [12] found γ for H_2:

17° C.	... 1·4070	−78° C.	... 1·4427
0° C.	... 1·4099	−118° C.	... 1·4800
−21° C.	... 1·4200	−183° C.	... 1·6054

[1] Küpper, *Ann. Phys.*, 1914, **43**, 905; Westphal, *Verhl. d. D. Phys. Ges.*, 1914, **16**, 613; Streider, *ibid.*, 1914, **16**, 615 (X-rays have no effect). Campetti, *Nuov. Cim.*, 1919, **17**, i, 143, found no change in specific heat of chlorine illuminated by light from a mercury lamp filtered through copper sulphate solution; the change of wave-length was shown to be due to temperature rise.

[2] *Sci. Rep. Tôhoku Imp. Univ.*, 1933, **22**, 519.

[3] Partington and Shilling, " The Specific Heats of Gases," 1924, 190 f.

[4] Partington and Carroll, *Phil. Mag.*, 1925, **49**, 665.

[5] Partington and Howe, *Proc. Roy. Soc.*, 1925, **109**, 286.

[6] Partington, *Phys. Z.*, 1913, **14**, 969; Beckman, *Arkiv Mat. Astron. Fys.*, 1912, **7**, No 27, found 1·3045 (V.) at 15° and examined the effect of pressure.

[7] *Wien Ber.*, 1876, **74**, II, 553; *Ann. Phys.*, 1877, **160**, 175; 1883, **18**, 309; *Z. phys. Chem.*, 1893, **11**, 751; " Vorlesungen über Gastheorie," 1898, **2**, 128.

[8] Strecker, *Ann. Phys.*, 1881, **13**, 20 (Cl_2, I_2); 1882, **17**, 85 (HCl, HBr, HI, ICl).

[9] *Phil. Trans.*, 1895, **186**, 187 (228); the value 1·667 was predicted for a monatomic molecule by Naumann, *Ann.*, 1867, **142**, 265.

[10] *Z. Phys.*, 1934, **90**, 355; the " proof " by Burton, *Phil. Mag.*, 1887, **24**, 166, that $\gamma = 5/3$ for all gases is falacious.

[11] *Phil. Mag.*, 1928, **5**, 832; the specific heat involved is $(dE/dT)_p$, which is *approximately* equal to c_v (§ 54.II); the con stant varied from 0·98 to 3·0.

[12] *Proc. Roy. Soc.*, 1925, **107**, 510.

Lewis and McAdams [1] found for the molecular heats of paraffin hydrocarbon vapours:

$$C_p=4{\cdot}4+4{\cdot}4n+(0{\cdot}012+0{\cdot}006n)t \quad \text{(1)}$$

where n=no. of carbon atoms. For ozone, O_3, Jacobs [2] calculated $\gamma=1{\cdot}29$ by extrapolation.

Clausius [3] assumed that the internal energy is a constant fraction β of the translational kinetic energy K, so that the total energy is:

$$E=K(1+\beta)=\tfrac{3}{2}RT(1+\beta) \quad \text{(2)}$$

hence $C_v=\frac{3}{2}R(1+\beta)$, $C_p=\frac{3}{2}R(1+\beta)+R$, and hence:

$$C_p/C_v=\gamma=1+\tfrac{2}{3}[1/(1+\beta)] \quad \text{(3)}$$

and

$$K/E=1/(1+\beta)=\tfrac{3}{2}(\gamma-1) \quad \text{(4)}$$

Thus the value of β can be found from the measured value of γ.

Trautz [4] gave an empirical formula for the specific heat of a gas or vapour:

$$(C_v-\tfrac{3}{2}R)/M^{2/3}z=k/z=0{\cdot}0912\sqrt{\vartheta} \quad \text{(5)}$$

where M=mol. wt., z=no. of valency bonds in molecule, ϑ=reduced temperature=T/T_c. For example, for a value $\vartheta=0{\cdot}5$, multiply the sum of the valency bonds by $M^{2/3}$ and add $\frac{3}{2}R$ to the product. He believed that the ratios T_c/M for gases are in simple whole number ratios.

Petrini [5] and Kolossowski [6] deduced the equation:

$$\gamma=(2n+3)/(2n+1) \quad \text{(6)}$$

where n=no. of atoms in the molecule, and Kolossowski also deduced:

$$U/c=0{\cdot}627\sqrt{[(2n+3)/(2n+1)]}=K \quad \text{(7)}$$

where U=velocity of sound, c=translational velocity of the molecules, and K is a constant for any gas with a given value of n (the observed values of U he used are old ones):

n	2	3	4	5	6	9	15
K ...	0·741	0·711	0·693	0·682	0·673	0·659	0·647
U/c obs.	0·744	0·701	0·699	0·712	0·696	0·651	0·641

Capstick [7] found that the chlorine derivatives of methane, all having five

[1] *Chem. Met. Eng.*, 1929, **36**, 336.

[2] *Dissert.*, Marburg, 1904; *Ann. Phys. Beibl.*, 1905, **29**, 951.

[3] *Ann. Phys.*, 1857, **100**, 353; *Phil. Mag.*, 1857, **14**, 108; Kekulé, *Compt. Rend.*, 1865, **60**, 174; Lothar Meyer, *Z. f. Chem.*, 1865, **1**, 250; J. J. Thomson, in Watts, " Dictionary of Chemistry," edit. Morley and Muir, 1890, **1**, 87; Clausius, Die kinetische Theorie der Gase, " Die mechanische Wärmetheorie," 2nd edit., Brunswick, 1891, **3**, 35; Cornelius, *Z. phys. Chem.*, 1893, **11**, 403; van Laar, *ibid.*, 1893, **11**, 665; Kirchhoff, " Vorlesungen über die Theorie der Wärme," Leipzig, 1894, 168; Wüllner, " Lehrbuch der Experimentalphysik," 5th edit., 1896, **2**, 533; Girtler, *Wien Ber.*, 1907, **116**, II A, 759; Bose, *Ann. Phys.*, 1905, **16**, 155; Wassmuth, *ibid.*, 1909, **30**, 381; Jankowsky, *Z. Elektrochem.*, 1917, **23**, 368; Drucker, *ibid.*, 1918, **24**, 83.

[4] *Ann. Phys.*, 1931, **8**, 267, 433; 1931, **9**, 465 (paraffins).

[5] *Z. phys. Chem.*, 1895, **16**, 97.

[6] *J. Chim. Phys.*, 1925, **22**, 79.

[7] *Phil. Trans.*, 1894, **185**, 1; 1895, **186**, 567 (also vapours); Peters, *Z. Elektrochem.*, 1907, **13**, 657.

atoms in the molecule, had different values of γ, and this disproved the deduction of J. J. Thomson [1] that if the molecule is very symmetrical, the molecular heat is equal to a constant β, the ratio of the total kinetic energy to the translatory energy of the centre of gravity, multiplied by the number of atoms in the molecule, β being supposed to be a constant for different simple and compound gases: deviations were supposed to be due to the heat absorbed in breaking up molecular clusters.

Trautz [2] believed that the *internal* heat capacity ($C_v - \frac{3}{2}R$) for a mol of gas is additively composed of atomic values, and the same extension of Kopp's rule for solids (see § 16.IX M, Vol. II) was made for the values of C_{v0} (at zero pressure) for many organic vapours by Bennewitz and Rossner [3] at 137° C., who also calculated them from Raman and vibration spectra: in g.cal./mol.:

	Benzene	Toluene	Cyclohexane	Acetone	Ethyl alcohol	Ethyl acetate
C_p obs. ...	27·3	33·6	37·3	22·5	19·8	33·7
C_{v0}	25·1	31·2	35·0	20·3	17·6	31·4

Cohen [4] found values of γ for steam by Kundt's method ranging from 1·252 at 144° to 1·320 at 300° (air=1·4053).

Naumann,[5] by subtracting from C_v the energy $\frac{3}{2}R \simeq 3$ g.cal. for the translatory motion, obtained the value of the *internal energy* of the molecule, due to the motion of the atoms. He assumed that this is equally divided among the atoms, and for H_2, NO, CO, HCl, H_2S, NH_3, CH_4, and C_2H_4 it was found to be 0·90–1·09, or 0·98 in the average. For a gas containing n atoms he wrote $C_v = (3+n) \times 0{\cdot}98$, and $C_p = (5+n) \times 0{\cdot}98$, therefore:

$$\gamma = C_p/C_v = (5+n)/(3+n),$$

which for $n=1$ gives $\gamma = 1{\cdot}667$, for $n=2$, $\gamma = 1{\cdot}400$, and for $n=3$, $\gamma = 1{\cdot}333$. These are in general agreement with the observed values.

Some values of γ for vapours at the b.p. found by Lechner [6] were:

C_2H_5OH 1·15, $(C_2H_5)_2O$ 1·10, $C_5H_{11}OH$ 1·24, C_6H_6 1·14, $C_4H_9COOH(n)$ 1·20, $C_4H_9OH(n)$ 1·36, CCl_4 1·17, CH_3OH 1·28, CS_2 1·26, I_2 1·35.

Calculations of C_p/C_v for vapours, based on the change of latent heat with temperature (see § 9.VIII L, Vol. II), gave: [7]

$(C_2H_5)O$ 1·06 C_6H_6 1·12 $CHCl_3$ 1·136 H_2O 1·46 (!).

Olson and Brittain,[8] by the velocity of sound method, found the same specific

1 Watts, "Dictionary of Chemistry," edit. Morley and Muir, 1890, **1**, 90; Jankowsky, *Z. Elektrochem.*, 1917, **23**, 368.

2 *Z. anorg. Chem.*, 1915, **93**, 177; 1916, **95**, 79; 1916, **96**, 1; 1916, **97**, 113, 127, 241; 1918, **102**, 81, 149; 1920, **110**, 1; *Elster und Geitel Festschr.*, 1915, 333; *Z. Elektrochem.*, 1916, **22**, 104; 1917, **23**, 206.

3 *Z. phys. Chem.*, 1938, **39** B, 126; reduction to zero pressure by Berthelot's equation.

4 *Ann. Phys.*, 1889, **37**, 629; Amagat, *J. de Phys.*, 1896, **5**, 114.

5 *Ann.*, 1867, **142**, 265.

6 *Wien Ber.*, 1909, **118**, II A, 1035 (organ pipe method).

7 Leduc, *Compt. Rend.*, 1911, **152**, 1752; 1911, **153**, 51; Déjardin, *ibid.*, 1919, **168**, 161; *Ann. de Phys.*, 1919, **11**, 253 (benzene 1·106 at 20°, cyclohexane 1·077 at 20°–90°).

8 *J.A.C.S.*, 1933, **55**, 4063.

heat (C_p=12·14 at 20°–140°, independent of temperature) for *cis*- and *trans*-dichloroethylenes:

```
H·C·Cl        H·C·Cl
  ||            ||
H·C·Cl        Cl·C·H
```

The kinetic energy of translation of a molecule as a whole is equal to $\frac{3}{2}RT$ per mol (§ 3.III) and hence that part of the molecular heat at constant volume due to the translational energy is $dE/dT=\frac{3}{2}R\simeq 3$ g.cal., which is independent of temperature. This value of C_v is shown only by monatomic gases;[1] for gases containing more than one atom in the molecule C_v is always greater than $\frac{3}{2}R$ and increases with the complexity of the molecule[2] and with the temperature.

For diatomic molecules C_v about room temperature is approximately $\frac{5}{2}R\simeq 5$, although such gases really fall into three groups.[3] (*a*) One gas, hydrogen,[4] having C_v appreciably lower than 5 at room temperature and decreasing with fall of temperature fairly rapidly from 4·87 at 0° C. to 2·98 (approximately 3) at −200° C., remaining constant at this value to the lowest temperature investigated (about −240° C.). (*b*) A group of diatomic gases (O_2, N_2, CO, NO, HCl, HBr, HI) for which C_v is very nearly 5 over a wide range of temperature; the members of this group show small but well-established differences in C_v. (*c*) The halogen gases Cl_2, Br_2, and I_2 (vapour) which have higher values of C_v, about 6 at ordinary temperature and more dependent on temperature than those of group (*b*).[5] The effect of the introduction of a second atom of halogen into a molecule, exemplified by HX and X_2, is also found in organic substitution products.[6]

§ 29. Boltzmann's Theory of Specific Heats of Gases

The behaviour of diatomic molecules of type (*b*), for which $C_v\simeq 5$ g.cal., was ingeniously explained by Boltzmann,[7] and since his results are still the basis of the modern theory, they will be explained in detail. Boltzmann followed up some earlier work on similar lines.[8]

The capability of motion of a body depends on the number of *degrees of*

[1] A supposed decrease of C_v for helium at low temperatures found by Eucken, *Verhl. d. D. Phys. Ges.*, 1916, **18**, 4, 18, is certainly due to experimental error.

[2] Berthelot, "Thermochimie," 1897, **1**, 47.

[3] Partington, *Nature*, 1921, **107**, 172; *Trans. Faraday Soc.*, 1922, **17**, 734; Rankine, *Nature*, 1921, **107**, 203.

[4] The case of deuterium is similar.

[5] Strecker, *Ann. Phys.*, 1881, **13**, 20; 1882, **17**, 85; Partington, *Phys. Z.*, 1914, **15**, 601, 775.

[6] Capstick, *Phil. Trans.*, 1894, **185**, 1.

[7] *Wien Ber.*, 1876, **74**, II, 553; *Ann. Phys.*, 1877, **160**, 175; "Vorlesungen über Gastheorie," 1898, **2**, 128; Kirchhoff, "Vorlesungen über die Theorie der Wärme," Leipzig, 1894, 168; a simple exposition is given by Ramsay, "Gases of the Atmosphere," 3rd edit., 1905, 211.

[8] Maxwell, *J.C.S.*, 1875, **13**, 493; *Nature*, 1875, **11**, 357; 1877, **16**, 242; "Scientific Papers," Cambridge, 1890, **2**, 418; Watson, "Kinetic Theory of Gases," Oxford, 1876, 27, 37; 2nd edit., Oxford, 1893, 82; Roiti, *Mem. Accad. Lincei*, 1877, **1**, ii, 762; *Nuov. Cim.*, 1877, **2**, 42; Viola, *Mem. Accad. Lincei*, 1883, **7**, 112; *Nuov. Cim.*, 1883, **14**, 183, 207; Petrini, *Z. phys. Chem.*, 1895, **16**, 97; Staigmüller, *Ann. Phys.*, 1898, **65**, 655, 670; Richarz, *ibid.*, 1899, **67**, 702; Leduc, *Compt. Rend.*, 1898, **127**, 659; Meyer, "Kinetic Theory of Gases," 1899, 139; Jeans, *Phil. Mag.*, 1901, **2**, 638; Ensrud, *Z. phys. Chem.*, 1907, **58**, 257; Crompton, *ibid.*, 1907, **59**, 635; Girtler, *Wien Ber.*, 1907, **116**, II A, 759; Drucker, *Z. Elektrochem.*, 1911, **17**, 466; Thornton, *Electrician*, 1915, **75**, 948; Ewing, *Engineering*, 1920, **109**, 842; Rocard, *Compt. Rend.*, 1924, **178**, 2068. Van der Waals, junr., *Verslag. K. Akad. Wetens. Amsterdam*, 1914, **22**, 1131, argued that a diatomic molecule has 7, not 5, degrees of freedom.

freedom,[1] f (Waterston, and Maxwell). A particle regarded as a point may move in three directions in space (x, y, z) and any motion may be specified in terms of these; it has three degrees of freedom. Boltzmann assumed that a monatomic molecule may be pictured as a small *smooth* sphere; any rotation it might have could not then be changed by collisions[2] and it has only three degrees of freedom ($f=3$).

A *rigid* diatomic molecule may be regarded as two smooth spheres at a fixed distance apart, like a small dumb-bell. This has three degrees of freedom for the translational motion of its centre of gravity; rotation about the axis could not be affected by collisions and is not effective, but the two rotations of the molecule about its centre of gravity in two planes at right angles (Fig. 14.VII E) can be changed by collisions, and hence the molecule has two effective rotational degrees of freedom. Such a rigid diatomic molecule has, therefore, *five* effective degrees of freedom ($f=5$). Rotation about axis (1) is constant and ineffective; rotation about axis (2) is in the plane of the paper; rotation about axis (3) is at right angles to the plane of the paper.

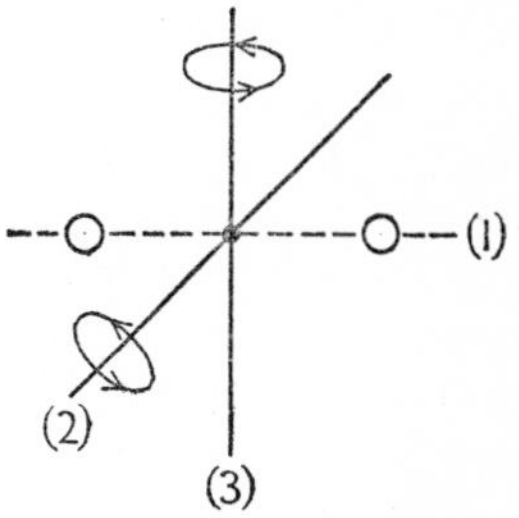

FIG. 14.VII E. Axes of Rotation of a Rigid Diatomic Molecule

A rigid molecule containing more than two atoms[3] will have an additional effective rotational degree of freedom about the axis (1), making six degrees in all ($f=6$).

Boltzmann assumed that the *kinetic energy* is shared equally among all the degrees of freedom, which is an extension of Maxwell's theorem of equipartition of energy (§ 20.IV). Since in the above cases, all the energy is kinetic, the theorem is directly applicable. The energy of a monatomic gas being (from the kinetic theory, § 3.III) $\frac{3}{2}RT$ per mol, the kinetic energy per degree of freedom for all molecules will be $\frac{1}{3}\times\frac{3}{2}RT=\frac{1}{2}RT$; hence the contribution to C_v per degree of freedom will be $\frac{1}{2}R\simeq 1$ g.cal., and $C_v=\frac{1}{2}Rf$ g.cal. per mol.

Molecule	f transl.	f rotational	$\frac{1}{2}Rf$	C_v obs.
monatomic ...	3	0	$\frac{3}{2}R=3$	3
diatomic rigid ...	3	2	$\frac{5}{2}R=5$	5
polyatomic rigid	3	3	$\frac{6}{2}R=6$	>5

Most polyatomic gases have C_v values greater than 6:

CO_2 (17°) ...	6·76	NH_3 (14·5°) ...	6·71
SO_2 (13°) ...	7·27	N_2O (12°) ...	6·76

and diatomic gases of group (c) (§ 28) have C_v greater than 5. The abnormally small value for hydrogen cannot be explained on Boltzmann's theory, but cases

[1] This must not be confused with the number of degrees of freedom of a system as considered by the Phase Rule. For a different definition see Roberts, " Heat and Thermodynamics," 1940, 147. Staigmüller (*op. cit.*) called $6(n-1)$, for a molecule having $3n$ coordinates (degrees of freedom), the " heat dimension "; $3(n-1)$ is the number of non-translational coordinates, and as Staigmüller assumed that the kinetic and potential energies are equal in these, the total energy due to them will be $6(n-1)\bar{\epsilon}$, where $\bar{\epsilon}$ is the mean kinetic energy per degree of freedom.

[2] For the mechanical vibrations of *atoms*, see Sutherland, *Phil. Mag.*, 1910, **20**, 657.

[3] Sackur, *Ann. Phys.*, 1913, **40**, 87.

where C_v is abnormally large (Cl_2, Br_2, and I_2 vapours) can be explained by assuming that the molecules are not rigid but the atoms are vibrating, the molecule will then have *vibrational energy* as well as translational and rotational.

For a simple harmonic motion, in which the restoring force is proportional to the displacement (Hooke's law) and the frequency is independent of the amplitude (for small displacements), the classical theory (§ 52.I) shows that the *average* kinetic and potential energies are equal, so that the total energy (kinetic+potential) is twice the average kinetic energy, i.e. $2\times\frac{1}{2}RT$ per mol. If it is assumed that in the chlorine molecule the two atoms are vibrating, the total energy will be $\frac{3}{2}RT$ (transl.)+$\frac{2}{2}RT$ (rotl.)+$\frac{2}{2}RT$ (kinetic and potential of vibr.)=$\frac{7}{2}RT$, and hence $C_v=\frac{7}{2}R\simeq 7$ g.cal. This is higher than the observed value, 6 g.cal. By assuming that $f=3$ at low temperatures, a theoretical value of df/dT may be found on the basis of classical theory which will explain qualitatively the variation of C_v with temperature.[1] The necessity of assuming motions of translation, rotation, and vibration, in general, in the case of polyatomic molecules was pointed out by Clausius.[2] Bateman [3] proposed the rule that the number of degrees of freedom of an atom is equal to the sum of 3 and its valency, and the number of degrees of freedom of a molecule is the sum of the numbers for the atoms, less the number of conditions which must be satisfied in order that the geometrical relations peculiar to a stable configuration or state of motion may remain permanent.

Boltzmann's theory encountered considerable opposition in Britain,[4] but it is now recognised as essentially correct for classical conditions, and the apparently arbitrary assumptions about constancy of rotation about the axis of diatomic molecules, etc., are now explicable by the quantum theory. For particles in Brownian movement, the theorem of equipartition as applied to translation and rotation was experimentally verified by Perrin.[5]

When Strecker [6] showed that C_v for chlorine and for bromine and iodine vapours is abnormally high for a diatomic gas, and concluded that " neither Maxwell's [7] nor Boltzmann's assumption about the kind of motion of the atoms in the gas molecule have a general validity," Boltzmann [8] remarked that spectra show that even monatomic atoms (e.g. Hg) " are not material points but must be complex (zusammengesetzt); " his assumptions were only approximate, " and in default of a better founded hypothesis." The halogen *atom* might be an ellipsoid of revolution, which would lead to the value $\gamma=1{\cdot}333$ found.

[1] Todd, *Phil. Mag.*, 1920, **40**, 357; cf. Todd and Owen, *ibid.*, 1919, **37**, 224; 1919, **38**, 655.

[2] *Phil. Mag.*, 1857, **14**, 108.

[3] *Manch. Mem.*, 1908, **53**, No. 3.

[4] At the British Association meeting at Aberdeen in 1885, Crum Brown, Lord Kelvin, J. J. Thomson, Liveing, Hicks, and Osborne Reynolds, all urged objections against it; see *Nature*, 1885, **32**, 352, 533; J. J. Thomson, Watts " Dictionary of Chemistry," edit. Morley and Muir, 1890, **1**, 89; Stoney, *Proc. Roy. Soc.*, 1895, **58**, 177; Lord Kelvin, " Baltimore Lectures," 1904, Appendix *B*; Peddie, *Proc. Roy. Soc. Edin.*, 1906, **26**, 130; 1907, **27**, 181; Magie, *Science*, 1906, **23**, 161; Ehrenfest, *Proc. Roy. Soc. Edin.*, 1907, **27**, 195; Brillouin, *J. de Phys.*, 1907, **6**, 32. This attitude persisted till quite recent times; see, e.g. *Trans. Faraday Soc.*, 1922, **17**, 734.

[5] *Compt. Rend.*, 1909, **149**, 549; *Ann. Chim.*, 1909, **18**, 5; " Les Atomes," 1914, 93, 163.

[6] *Ann. Phys.*, 1881, **13**, 20.

[7] *J.C.S.*, 1875, **13**, 493; Maxwell assumed that all the a atoms in the molecule were mobile, which gives $\gamma=1+2/(3a+i)$, where i is the internal energy, whilst Boltzmann assumed that $\gamma=1+2/n$, where n=3, 5, 6; see Jeans, *Phil. Mag.*, 1901, **2**, 638.

[8] *Ann. Phys.*, 1881, **13**, 544; 1883, **18**, 309.

§ 30. Quantum Theory of Specific Heats of Gases

Although, as mentioned above, the variation of C_v with temperature may be explained, at least qualitatively, on the basis of the acquisition of additional degrees of freedom, this is not generally successful, and in the case of hydrogen it is necessary to assume that the two degrees of *rotational* freedom disappear at lower temperatures, a result quite incompatible with the classical theory. It is only by abandoning the *general* validity of the theorem of equipartition that the specific heats of gases can be satisfactorily explained; it must be replaced by the quantum theory.

In lecturing in 1900, Lord Kelvin [1] said that " the beauty and clearness of the dynamical theory which asserts heat and light to be modes of motion, is at present obscured by two clouds," which he called " nineteenth-century clouds over the dynamical theory of heat." One of these concerned radiation (§ 12.VI B), the other was concerned with the theory of equipartition of energy, which Lord Kelvin did not accept. Both clouds were dissipated by the quantum theory, which came into being in the same year as Lord Kelvin's lecture (§ 15.IV).

Planck [2] in 1900 concluded that the energy of a linear resonator, consisting of a mobile electric charge which may be set in vibration, is a whole multiple of a quantum $\epsilon = h\nu$, where h is a universal constant ($6{\cdot}61 \times 10^{-27}$ erg sec.) and ν the frequency of vibration. The theory was extended by Einstein [3] to vibrating ponderable charged atoms (ions), and by Nernst [4] to vibrating or rotating neutral atoms and molecules.

It is assumed that the material particles contain linear oscillators of frequency ν, so that the energy of any particle is $nh\nu$, where n is an integer. Calculation (§ 16.IV) then shows that the mean energy of the oscillator (omitting zero-point energy) is:

$$\bar{\epsilon} = h\nu/(e^x - 1) \quad \text{. . . . .} \quad (1)$$

where $x = h\nu/kT$, k=Boltzmann's constant, R/N; or by multiplying by Avogadro's number N, the energy per g. atom or mol is:

$$N\bar{\epsilon} = E = Nh\nu/(e^x - 1) \quad \text{. . . . .} \quad (2)$$

which is Einstein's formula. Nernst put $h/k = \beta$, $Nk = R$,

$$\therefore \; E = Nk\beta\nu/(e^{\beta\nu/T} - 1) = R\beta\nu/(e^{\beta\nu/T} - 1) \quad \text{. . . .} \quad (3)$$

The heat capacity per mol for one degree of freedom is found by differentiating (3) with respect to T:

$$C_v = dE/dT = R(\beta\nu/T)^2[e^{\beta\nu/T}/(e^{\beta\nu/T} - 1)^2] \quad \text{. . . .} \quad (4)$$

These equations may be applied to calculate the *vibrational energy*. The *rotational energy* is also quantised (§ 18.IV), but deviations from the equipartition value $\frac{1}{2}RT$ per degree of freedom are very small at and above room temperature for all gases except hydrogen and deuterium; the last case can be dealt with only by the use of wave mechanics (§ 23.IV).

For a diatomic ideal gas with fully excited translational and rotational

[1] Royal Institution lecture, Friday, April 27, 1900; *Phil. Mag.*, 1901, **2**, 1; " Baltimore Lectures," 1904, 486 f.; Jeans, " Dynamical Theory of Gases," 3rd edit., 1921, 13.

[2] *Verhl. d. D. Phys. Ges.*, 1900, **2**, 202, 237; *Ann. Phys.*, 1901, **4**, 553, 564; 1901, **6**, 818; 1902, **9**, 629.

[3] *Ann. Phys.*, 1907, **23**, 197; Jeans, " Dynamical Theory of Gases," 3rd edit., 1921, 371.

[4] *Z. Elektrochem.*, 1911, **17**, 265.

energies (i.e. the equipartition or maximum values) the true molecular heat at constant volume is:

$$C_v=\tfrac{3}{2}R+\tfrac{2}{2}R+\mathrm{E}(\Theta/T)=4{\cdot}963+\mathrm{E}(\Theta/T) \quad . \quad . \quad . \quad . \quad (5)$$

where E denotes the Einstein function (3), and $\Theta=\beta\nu$. Values of E may be obtained from tables.[1] Formulae involving Einstein functions are not very convenient in practice, and Fugassi and Rudy [2] found that the experimental and calculated results can be represented with sufficient approximation by a power series (§ 1.II), $C_p=a+bT+cT^2+dT^3+\ldots$.

The mean molecular heat is:

$$\bar{C}_v=(1/T)\int_0^T C_v \mathrm{d}T=4{\cdot}963+E_T/T \quad . \quad . \quad . \quad . \quad . \quad (6)$$

where E_T is the vibrational energy given by (3) for the temperature T. The following table gives some observed and calculated values of $\bar{C}_v$ for hydrogen chloride: [3]

$$\bar{C}_v=4{\cdot}963+(E_T-E_{291})/(T-291); \quad \Theta=3420.$$

T	$\bar{C}_v$ obs.	$\bar{C}_v$ for $\Theta=3420$	$\bar{C}_v$ for $\Theta=4220$
1955	5·808	5·818	5·623
2115	5·898	5·881	5·688
2135	5·916	5·890	5·696
2318	5·943	5·953	5·764

The values calculated with $\Theta=3420$ (found by trial) are moderately good; the value found from the infra-red spectrum [4] is $\Theta=4220$, for which the calculated $\bar{C}_v$ values are not so good.

Some *approximate* values of Θ for diatomic gases are: [5]

H_2 ...	5000 (6140)	CO ...	3100 (3120)	Br_2 ...	510 (470)
N_2 ...	3800 (3380)	NO ...	2720 (2740)	I_2 ...	350 (310)
O_2 ...	3300 (2260)	Cl_2 ...	830 (810)	HCl ...	4150 (4300)

Godnev [6] used the empirical formula:

$$C_p=C_{p0}+\Sigma\mathrm{E}(\Theta/T)+aT+bT^2 \quad . \quad . \quad . \quad . \quad . \quad . \quad (7)$$

where E is an Einstein function for two degrees of freedom, and a and b are constants. Usually b may be taken as zero. For example, for nitrogen:

$$C_p=\tfrac{7}{2}R+\mathrm{E}(3360/T)+0{\cdot}4\times10^{-4}T.$$

For triatomic and more complex molecules, coupling occurs between the

[1] Nernst, "The New Heat Theorem," 1926, 246 f.; Simon, in Geiger and Scheel, "Handbuch der Physik," 1926, **10**, 364.

[2] *Ind. Eng. Chem.*, 1938, **30**, 1029.

[3] Wohl, *Z. Elektrochem.*, 1924, **30**, 47; Wohl and Kadow, *Z. phys. Chem.*, 1925, **118**, 460; no more recent experimental values at high temperatures are available.

[4] Hettner, *Z. Phys.*, 1920, **1**, 345; Hicks and Mitchell, *J.A.C.S.*, 1926, **48**, 1520; Giauque and Overstreet, *ibid.*, 1932, **54**, 1731.

[5] Eucken, in Wien-Harms, "Handbuch der Experimentalphysik," 1929, **8**, 422; Eucken and Fried, *Z. Phys.*, 1924, **29**, 36; quite different values (in brackets) are given by Slater, "Introduction to Chemical Physics," New York, 1939, 142; for several equations of this type see Yamaga, *Proc. Imp. Acad. Japan*, 1928, **4**, 102.

[6] *J.A.C.S.*, 1936, **58**, 180.

atomic vibrations, and the theory becomes more complicated. The first attempt to deal with such molecules was by Bjerrum.[1] For a triangular molecule (Fig. 15.VII E) three kinds of vibrations were assumed: (i) the vibration of the atom A at right angles to the line BC, with the frequency ν_1, (ii) symmetrical vibrations of B and C along AB and AC (ν_2); (iii) an unsymmetrical vibration of A in the direction of AC (ν_3). The problem was dealt with in greater detail by Hund.[2] In cases where overtones and combination vibrations occur, e.g. with ammonia,[3] the problem is more difficult.[4]

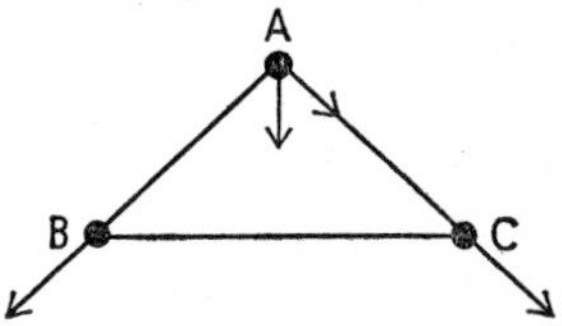

FIG. 15.VII E. Modes of Vibration of Triangular Triatomic Molecule

The quantum theory gives an explanation for the ineffective rotation of monatomic molecules and of diatomic molecules about the axis, assumed in Boltzmann's theory, since on account of the small moment of inertia the rotational quantum is very large and practically no energy is taken up.

Linear triatomic molecules such as OCO and NNO have been considered, the fundamental frequencies being known.[5]

The number of vibrational degrees of freedom of a molecule containing N atoms is calculated as follows. If all the atoms were free the number would be $3N$; from this is subtracted the translational degrees of freedom (3) for the molecule as a whole, and the rotational degrees of freedom (0 for $N=1$, 2 for $N=2$, and 3 when N is 3 or more):

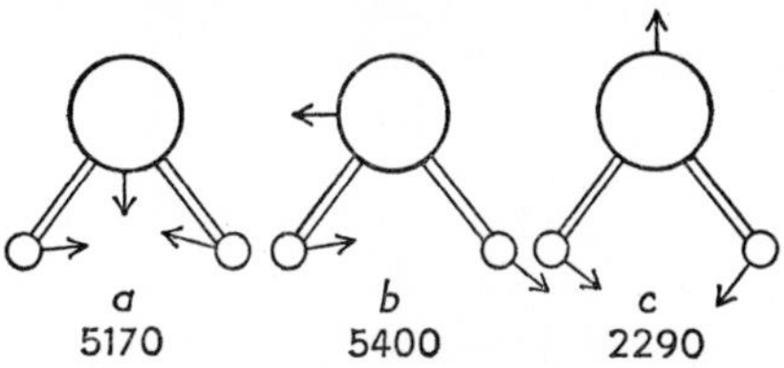

FIG. 16.VII E. Modes of Vibration of Water Molecule

f_v for monatomic gas $=3\times1-3-0=0$

" diatomic " $=3\times2-3-2=1$

" triatomic " $=3\times3-3-3=3$

" N-atomic " $=3N-6$.

The water molecule has three modes of vibration, shown[6] in Fig. 16.VII E, the characteristic temperatures Θ for the Einstein functions $E(\Theta/T)$ being given below them. The contributions to the value of C_v due to these three vibrations are shown in the table; to these are added the value 7·95 for $\boldsymbol{R}$ and the translational and (fully excited) rotational motions, and the total C_p (not C_v) calculated is shown. The last column gives the value of C_p calculated with small corrections (not discussed here), which include interaction

[1] *Z. Elektrochem.*, 1911, **17**, 731; 1912, **18**, 101; *Nernst Festschrift*, 1912, 90; *Verhl. d. D. Phys. Ges.*, 1914, **16**, 737; Eucken, *Z. Elektrochem.*, 1920, **26**, 377.

[2] *Z. Phys.*, 1925, **31**, 81.

[3] Stuart, " Molekülstruktur," Berlin, 1934, 249; Slater, " Introduction to Chemical Physics," 1939, 145.

[4] See Teller, *Hand u.- Jahrb. d. chem. Phys.*, 1934, **9**, II, 43; a summary of the modes of vibration of polyatomic molecules was given by Bartholomé, *Z. Elektrochem.*, 1936, **42**, 341; see also Dennison, *Rev. Mod. Phys.*, 1931, **3**, 280; Penney and Sutherland, *Proc. Roy. Soc.*, 1936, **156**, 654, 678 (vibration frequency, force constant and angles of triatomic molecules and groups); Wu, " Vibrational Spectra and Structure of Polyatomic Molecules," Kun-Ming, China, 1939, Ann Arbor, Mich., 1946; El'yashevich, *J. Exptl. Theor. Phys. U.S.S.R.*, 1943, **13**, 65; Herzberg, " Infra-red and Raman Spectra of Polyatomic Molecules," New York, 1945; a brief, highly abstract, summary is given by Margenau and Murphy, " The Mathematics of Physics and Chemistry," New York, 1943, 280 f.

[5] Plyler and Barker, *Phys. Rev.*, 1931, **38**, 1827; Herzberg, *Z. phys. Chem.*, 1932, **17** B, 68.

[6] Mecke, *Z. phys. Chem.*, 1932, **16** B, 409, 421; 1932, **17** B, 1; Stull and Mayfield, *Ind. Eng. Chem.*, 1943, **35**, 639.

between vibration and rotation and (at high temperatures) electronic excitation (§ 21.IV):

T	a	b	c	C_p calc.	C_p corr.
300	0·00	0·00	0·10	8·05	8·00
400	0·00	0·00	0·25	8·20	8·16
500	0·00	0·00	0·40	8·35	8·38
600	0·02	0·02	0·66	8·63	8·64
800	0·16	0·15	1·05	9·31	9·20
1000	0·31	0·30	1·30	9·86	9·80
1500	0·80	0·78	1·65	11·18	11·15
2000	1·18	1·15	1·79	12·07	12·09
3000	1·58	1·52	1·90	12·90	13·10

F. VISCOSITIES OF GASES

§ 1. Viscosity of Gases

The kinetic theory of the viscosity of gases was first worked out by Maxwell.[1] The following simplified treatment is based on that given by Stefan.[2]

Consider two large plates, parallel to the xy plane in the coordinate system x, y, z and at a distance z apart, and with gas between them (Fig. 1.VII F). One plate is supposed fixed and the other moves from left to right with a constant velocity U. It is assumed that the gas in contact with the fixed plate is at rest, and that in contact with the moving plate is moving with it with a mass velocity U parallel to the x axis. This assumption of the absence of " slip " requires modification at low pressures (see § 12). The velocity gradient in the gas is assumed to be linear, and hence is U/z per unit length, and the force of resistance, R, to the motion of the upper plate caused by the viscosity of the gas is assumed to be proportional to this:

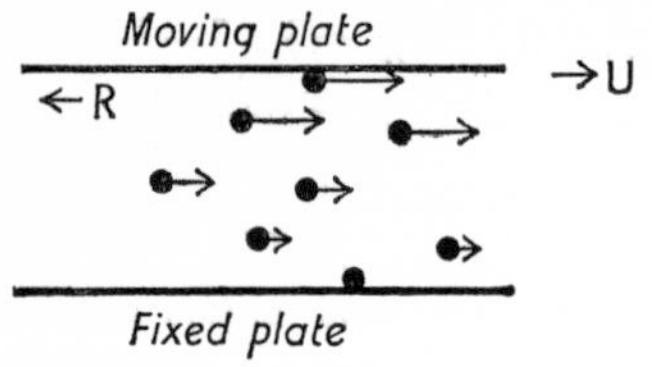

FIG. 1.VII F. Origin of a Velocity Gradient leading to a Viscous Force

$$R = -\eta(U/z) \text{ per cm.}^2 \quad . \quad . \quad . \quad . \quad . \quad . \quad . \quad (1)$$

where η is the *coefficient of viscosity* (or simply *viscosity*), a constant at a given temperature. The dimensions of η in c.g.s. units are g.cm.$^{-1}$sec.$^{-1}$. The negative sign in (1) indicates that the force exerted by the gas on the plate is

[1] *Phil. Mag.*, 1860, **19**, 19; 1868, **35**, 129, 185; *Phil. Trans.*, 1866, **156**, 249; 1867, **157**, 49; " Scientific Papers," 1890, **1**, 377; **2**, 1, 26; Clausius, Die kinetische Theorie der Gase, " Die mechanische Wärmetheorie," Brunswick, 1889–91, **3**, 84; Kitsler, *J. Franklin Inst.*, 1929, **207**, 389; Kimball, *Phil. Mag.*, 1935, **20**, 97, 355; Smith, *ibid.*, 1942, **33**, 775.

[2] *Wien Ber.*, 1872, **65**, II, 323 (360); cf. O. E. Meyer, *Ann. Phys.*, 1865, **125**, 564; " Kinetic Theory of Gases," 1899, 174; von Lang, *Wien Ber.*, 1871, **64**, II, 485; *Ann. Phys.*, 1879, **145**, 290 (simple deduction); Boltzmann, *Wien Ber.*, 1872, **66**, II, 275; 1880, **81**, II, 117; 1881, **84**, II, 40, 1230; 1887, **96**, II, 891; " Wiss. Abhl.," 1909, **1**, 316; **2**, 388, 431, 523; **3**, 293; Gemant, *J. Appl. Phys.*, 1941, **12**, 626. For the general theory of viscosity, see Stokes, *Trans. Cambr. Phil. Soc.*, 1845, **8**, 107, 287; " Math. and Phys. Papers," Cambridge, 1880, **1**, 75; Tisza, *Phys. Rev.*, 1942, **61**, 531; on a supposed volume viscosity, see § 1.VIII E, Vol. II, and for gases, Kohler, *Naturwiss.*, 1946, **33**, 251.

in the opposite direction to the motion of the plate. Cox [1] developed a theory of fluid flow in which the velocity is assumed to increase exponentially (not linearly) with the distance from the wall or fixed plate. A theory of the viscosity and thermal conductivity of dense gases and liquids was developed [2] from Born and Green's theory of liquids (see § 1.VIII A, Vol. II).

Suppose the gas between the plates divided into imaginary layers each of thickness dz, and assume that each layer offers a resistance to the adjoining layers of moving gas, all the layers being in motion with different velocities except the one at rest in contact with the fixed plate. The force per cm.^{2} between any two layers such as shown in Fig. 1.VII F is, from (1):

$$R = -\eta(\mathrm{d}U/\mathrm{d}z) \quad \ldots\ldots\ldots \quad (2)$$

Gas molecules are leaving and entering each layer. If the gas is at rest, the velocities are uniformly distributed in all directions, but if it is moving, the velocity component of each molecule is greater in the direction of the mass motion of the gas than in the opposite direction. Molecules enter the *faster* layers, and by collisions with the molecules there, the velocity component U of the entering molecules is increased. Thus, momentum is taken from the molecules in the faster layers.

The velocity component in a plane parallel to the xy plane and distant z from it is:

$$U = U_0 + (\mathrm{d}U/\mathrm{d}z)z \quad \ldots\ldots\ldots \quad (3)$$

where U_0 is the velocity in the xy plane. Since $\mathrm{d}U/\mathrm{d}z > 0$ (the upper plate is moving) every layer of gas experiences a retardation from the layer below it, and this lower layer receives an acceleration from the layer above it. These accelerations give rise to the viscous forces, and thus the viscosity, a non-dynamical phenomenon in bulk, is explained molecularly by ordinary dynamics.

The internal friction in the gas is equal to the momentum transmitted per sec. through 1 cm.^{2} of the xy plane. If there are n molecules per cm.^{3} with a velocity component w parallel to the vertical z axis, and having a total velocity component (mass+molecular) u' parallel to the x axis, then of these molecules, the number nw pass through 1 cm.^{2} of the xy plane in a direction parallel to the z axis per second. Hence the momentum transported parallel to the x axis per sec. is $nw \cdot mu'$, and the total momentum transported parallel to the x axis per sec. is:

$$R = \Sigma nmwu'$$

where u' can vary from $-\infty$ to $+\infty$. If u is the component of molecular velocity parallel to the x axis, then $u' = u + U$, and hence:

$$R = \Sigma nmwu + \Sigma nmwU \quad \ldots\ldots\ldots \quad (4)$$

The term $\Sigma nmwu$ is obviously zero, since on an average there will be as many molecules moving with a velocity u *in a given direction* as with a velocity $-u$ in the opposite direction in the gas, hence:

$$R = \Sigma nmwU = \Sigma nmwU_0 + \Sigma nmwz(\mathrm{d}U/\mathrm{d}z) \quad \ldots\ldots \quad (5)$$

The term $\Sigma nmwU_0$ is again zero, for the same reason as before, and hence:

$$R = m(\mathrm{d}U/\mathrm{d}z)\Sigma nwz \quad \ldots\ldots\ldots \quad (6)$$

Now consider a molecule having a velocity c making an angle θ with the

[1] *J. Franklin Inst.*, 1924, **198**, 769.
[2] Yang, *Nature*, 1948, **161**, 523.

z axis (Fig. 2.VII F), then $w=c\cos\theta$. Assume that every molecule has, on the average, the mass motion of the layer in which it *last* made a collision, then $z=-\lambda\cos\theta$, where λ is the free path of the molecule; hence

$$R=-m(\mathrm{d}U/\mathrm{d}z)\Sigma nc\lambda\cos^2\theta \quad . \quad . \quad . \quad . \quad . \quad . \quad . \quad (7)$$

In (7) n is the number of molecules with a velocity c making an angle θ with the axis of z which, after collision, have traversed a distance λ before crossing the xy plane. First sum over all possible angles θ, with c and λ fixed. Suppose the directions of the velocities are drawn from a fixed point and pass through the surface of a sphere drawn around this point as centre. The number of these lines making an angle with the z axis between θ and $\theta+\mathrm{d}\theta$ is equal to the total number multiplied by $\frac{1}{2}\sin\theta\mathrm{d}\theta$ (see (4), § 8.III); hence:

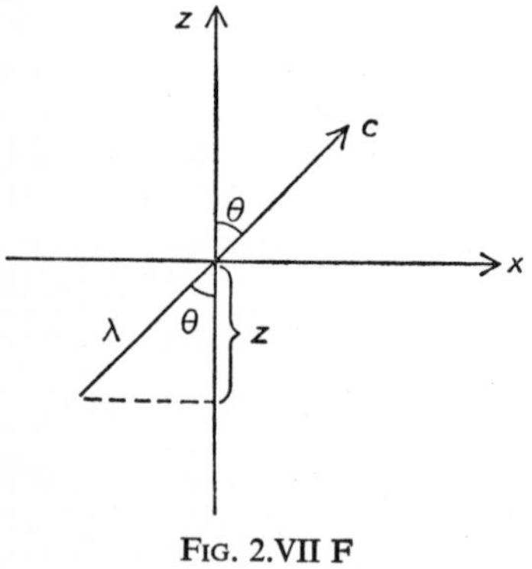

FIG. 2.VII F

$$\delta R=-(m/2)(\mathrm{d}U/\mathrm{d}z)\Sigma nc\lambda \cos^2\theta\sin\theta\mathrm{d}\theta \quad . \quad (8)$$

To find the total force, integrate between $\theta=0$ and $\theta=\pi$, when (see § 8.III):

$$R=-(m/2)(\mathrm{d}U/\mathrm{d}z)\Sigma nc\lambda\int_0^\pi\cos^2\theta\sin\theta\mathrm{d}\theta$$
$$=-(m/2)(dU/\mathrm{d}z)\Sigma nc\lambda[-\cos^3\theta/3]_0^\pi$$
$$=-(m/3)(\mathrm{d}U/\mathrm{d}z)\Sigma nc\lambda \quad . \quad . \quad . \quad . \quad (9)$$

In $\Sigma nc\lambda$, n is the number of molecules per cm.[3] which have travelled a distance λ since the last collision before passing the xy plane, and λ can have all values from 0 to ∞. Hence $\Sigma nc\lambda$ should be found by summing over all values of λ from 0 to ∞ for each value of c, and then summing over all values of c from 0 to ∞. The value of λ for a given value of c will not, of course, be the ordinary "free path" (§ 20.III), which varies with c, but as a first approximation n may be equated to N, the total number of molecules per cm.[3], λ to l, the mean free path,[1] and c to $\bar{c}$, the average velocity of the molecules; the summation sign is then omitted, and if $Nm=\rho=$density:

$$\Sigma nc\lambda=N\bar{c}l \quad . \quad . \quad . \quad . \quad . \quad . \quad . \quad . \quad . \quad . \quad (10)$$

$$\therefore\ R=-\tfrac{1}{3}Nm\bar{c}l(\mathrm{d}U/\mathrm{d}z)=-\eta(\mathrm{d}U/\mathrm{d}z)$$

$$\therefore\ \eta=\tfrac{1}{3}Nm\bar{c}l=\tfrac{1}{3}\rho\bar{c}l \quad . \quad . \quad . \quad . \quad . \quad . \quad . \quad (11)$$

Equation (11) may be written in various other forms, e.g. by taking $N=N'/V$, where N'=total number of molecules in a volume V, giving:

$$\eta=(N'/3V)m\bar{c}l=\tfrac{1}{3}M\xi\bar{c}l \quad . \quad . \quad . \quad . \quad . \quad . \quad (11a)$$

where M=molecular weight and ξ=concentration in mols per cm.[3] (or per lit. if V is in litres).

A more exact calculation, in which the average value of λ is found, gives:

$$\eta=k\rho\bar{c}l \quad . \quad . \quad . \quad . \quad . \quad . \quad . \quad . \quad . \quad . \quad . \quad (12)$$

where k is a numerical factor. This has been differently evaluated; O. E.

[1] Jäger, *Wien Ber.*, 1900, **109**, II A, 74, took λ as the mean free path plus half the diameter of the molecule.

Meyer [1] gave $k=0{\cdot}30967$, Boltzmann,[2] $k=0{\cdot}350271$, Jäger,[3] $\frac{5}{12}=0{\cdot}4166$, Jeans,[4] $k=0{\cdot}461$, and Chapman,[5] for elastic spheres, $k=0{\cdot}491$ to $0{\cdot}499$, perhaps $0{\cdot}500$ (see below). Since Chapman's value seems most probable:

$$\eta=0{\cdot}499\rho\bar{c}l \quad . \quad . \quad . \quad . \quad . \quad . \quad . \quad . \quad . \quad . \quad (13)$$

will be taken as the definitive equation in this section.

If a typical molecule describes a free path with a momentum mu parallel to the x axis, and if the projection of the free path on the z axis is λ', the increase in momentum at the end of the path will be $m\lambda'(\mathrm{d}\bar{u}/\mathrm{d}z)$. If there are N molecules per cm.^{3} with an average velocity $\bar{c}$, the number of molecules crossing one cm.^{2} of the plane $z=0$ per sec. is $N\bar{c}$, and hence the transfer of momentum is:

$$N\bar{c} \,.\, m\lambda'(\mathrm{d}\bar{u}/\mathrm{d}z)=\rho\bar{c}\lambda'(\mathrm{d}\bar{u}/\mathrm{d}z)$$

if each free path has the same projection λ' on the z axis. If the free paths are distributed equally in all directions at random, and are of average length λ, the average value of λ' is $\frac{1}{2}\lambda$, and hence the transfer of momentum is:

$$\tfrac{1}{2}\rho\bar{c}\lambda(\mathrm{d}\bar{u}/\mathrm{d}z).$$

But this is equal to $\eta(\mathrm{d}\bar{u}/\mathrm{d}z)$, where η is the coefficient of viscosity; hence:

$$\eta=\tfrac{1}{2}\rho\bar{c}\lambda \quad . \quad . \quad . \quad . \quad . \quad . \quad . \quad . \quad . \quad . \quad (14)$$

which is practically the same as (13).[6]

By substituting l and $\bar{c}$ from (18), § 21.III, and (35), § 10.III, the equation (13) may be written in a form giving the molecular diameter σ from the measured values of η:

$$\eta=0{\cdot}499Nm\bar{c}l, \quad l=1/\sqrt{(2N\pi\sigma^2)},$$

$$\bar{c}=2\sqrt{(2RT/\pi M)}, \quad m=M/N,$$

$$\therefore \; \eta=2{\cdot}715\times10^{-21}\sqrt{(MT)}/\sigma^2 \quad . \quad . \quad . \quad . \quad . \quad . \quad . \quad (15)$$

where N is Avogadro's number, $6{\cdot}02\times10^{23}$, and $\boldsymbol{R}=83{\cdot}15\times10^6$ c.g.s. units. With Tait's free path (44), § 22.III:

$$\eta=1{\cdot}051(\tfrac{1}{3}\rho\bar{c}l)=0{\cdot}350\rho\bar{c}l \quad . \quad . \quad . \quad . \quad . \quad . \quad . \quad (16)$$

§ 2. Effect of Pressure on Gaseous Viscosity

Substitution of l in (12), § 1, from (18), § 21.III, gives:

$$\eta=kNm\bar{c}/\sqrt{(2)}N\pi\sigma^2=km\bar{c}/\sqrt{(2)}\pi\sigma^2 \quad . \quad . \quad . \quad . \quad . \quad (1)$$

which shows that η is proportional to $\sqrt{m}$ (since $\bar{c}$ is proportional to $1/\sqrt{m}$) but is independent of the pressure, and depends only on the temperature (through $\bar{c}$) and the molecular diameter σ. The surprising independence of

[1] "Kinetic Theory of Gases," 1899, 176, 189, 451.

[2] "Vorlesungen über Gastheorie," 1896, **1**, 79; Dushman, "Production and Measurement of High Vacuum," Schenectady, 1922, 16, prefers this value; Clausius, Die kinetische Theorie der Gase, "Die mechanische Wärmetheorie," Brunswick, 1889–91, **3**, 101, gave 0·3501.

[3] *Wien Ber.*, 1899, **108**, II A, 447.

[4] "Dynamical Theory of Gases," 3rd edit., 1921, 248, 287, 299, 316; "Kinetic Theory of Gases," 1940, 163.

[5] *Phil. Trans.*, 1916, **217**, 115–197; Chapman and Hainsworth, *Phil. Mag.*, 1924, **48**, 593; Chapman and Cowling, "The Mathematical Theory of Non-Uniform Gases," Cambridge, 1939, 151 f.; Herzfeld, "Weglänge und Transporterscheinungen in Gasen," Leipzig, 1939; Kirkwood, *J. Chem. Phys.*, 1947, **15**, 72, 155; Hirschfelder, Bird, and Spotz, *ibid.*, 1948, **16**, 968.

[6] Jeans, "Kinetic Theory of Gases," 1940, 46.

pressure was confirmed by experiment and became one of the best arguments for the truth of the kinetic theory.[1]

The figures below [2] give the *relative* viscosities (η' at 750 mm. Hg pressure=1) of air at 15° C. as measured by the oscillating disc method (§ 8; distance between plates=1·967 mm.), and the mean free paths l. The *apparent* decrease at low pressures is due to slip (§ 12):

p mm. Hg	750	380	20·5	2·4	1·53	0·63
η/η'	1	1·01	1·004	0·978	0·956	0·908
l mm.	6×10^{-5}	$1{\cdot}2\times10^{-4}$	$2{\cdot}2\times10^{-3}$	$1{\cdot}9\times10^{-2}$	0·030	0·073

A " commonsense " view would have led one to think that the viscosity should increase with density, because the viscosity of liquids is much greater than that of gases. Another curious result is that for gases the viscosity *increases* with temperature, whilst for liquids it *decreases*. The reason for such differences may be *roughly* stated as a consequence of the negligible value of cohesive forces between gas molecules, and their large value in the case of liquids. Viscosity in liquids is largely determined by cohesive forces, which are weakened by rise of temperature, and it shows little dependence on molecular velocity or free path.

Some consequences of the independence of viscosity on density are surprising. Stokes's law [3] for the velocity of fall, u, of a sphere of radius a and mass m in a fluid of viscosity η is (g=acceleration of gravity):

$$u=g(m-m_0)/6\pi\eta a \qquad \text{(2)}$$

where m_0 is the weight of fluid displaced. Since m_0 for gases is very small compared with m it may be neglected, so that the steady velocity of fall will be the same at all pressures. Similarly, the air-resistance of a pendulum should be independent of the density of the air, so that the oscillations should die out at the same rate at low pressure as at high, as was found experimentally by Boyle [4] in 1660. Maxwell [5] found that when three movable discs oscillate between four fixed parallel discs on a torsion thread, the oscillations die away at the same rate whether the air between is at atmospheric or lower pressure. For very small spheres (e.g. oil drops), still large in comparison with the mean free path, falling in a gas, Stokes's law no longer holds. Cunningham [6] then found that the denominator in (2) must be replaced by $6\pi\eta a/(1+A/a)$, where A is an empirical constant, found by Millikan to be 0·864. This is important in the determination of the electronic charge by Millikan's oil-drop method, probably one of the most exact methods.[7] The question of the validity of

[1] O. E. Meyer, *Ann. Phys.*, 1865, **125**, 177; 1866, **127**, 253, 353; 1873, **148**, 1; Maxwell, *Phil. Trans.*, 1866, **156**, 249; Crookes, *ibid.*, 1881, **172**, 387; for laboratory demonstration apparatus, Piwnikiewicz, *Phys. Z.*, 1913, **14**, 305.

[2] Quoted by Herzfeld, in H. S. Taylor, " Physical Chemistry," 1931, **1**, 155.

[3] *Trans. Cambr. Phil. Soc.*, 1850, **9**, 8 (equation (126), p. 51); " Math. and Phys. Papers," Cambridge, 1901, **3**, 1 (59).

[4] " Works," 1744, **1**, 40. Quoted by Tomlinson, *Phil. Trans.*, 1886, **177**, 767.

[5] *Phil. Trans.*, 1866, **156**, 249; " Scientific Papers," 1890, **2**, 1; Stokes, *Phil. Trans.*, 1886, **177**, 786.

[6] *Proc. Roy. Soc.*, 1910, **83**, 357; McKeehan, *Phys. Rev.*, 1911, **33**, 153; *Phys. Z.*, 1911, **12**, 707; Millikan, *Phys. Rev.*, 1913, **2**, 109; 1923, **21**, 217; *Proc. Nat. Acad.*, 1923, **9**, 67; Sexl, *Ann. Phys.*, 1926, **81**, 855; Herzfeld, in H. S. Taylor, " Physical Chemistry," 1931, **1**, 183.

[7] It is amusing to find Cunningham saying that the method cannot give a reliable value of ***e***, " as at first sight seemed not impossible." Some papers dealing with the use of Stokes's law in calculating the electronic charge in Millikan's method are: McKeehan, *Phys. Rev.*, 1911, **33**, 153; *Phys. Z.*, 1911, **12**, 707 (finds $A\simeq1$); Roux, *Compt. Rend.*, 1912, **155**, 1490;

Stokes's law in cases where the particles are in Brownian movement was discussed by Weyssenhoff.[1]

At higher pressures the viscosity is no longer independent of the density of the gas. Some values for carbon dioxide at 40° C. are: [2]

p atm.	1	24	100
$\eta\times10^4$	1·57	1·69	4·83

At 100 atm. η is nearly proportional to the density. At very low pressures, when molecular collisions are infrequent, the viscosity should again be proportional to the density. In this case a molecule between two parallel plates at a distance apart which is small compared with the mean free path makes no collisions in the space between them. If one plate is fixed and the other moving with a constant velocity u, each molecule after striking one plate moves with constant velocity until it strikes the other. If the plates are rough the force on a plate per unit area is $up/\surd(2\pi RT/M)$ (see (1), § 1.VII J). The coefficient multiplying u has been called the free-molecule viscosity.[3] The effect of density on viscosity at higher pressures was considered by Enskog,[4] who used a method which is a generalisation of the one used in Lorentz's electron theory of metallic conduction. He took account of the transport of momentum in collisions, assuming that a transport over the molecular diameter σ occurs with practically infinite velocity. The transport for the free path should therefore refer to a distance $\lambda+\sigma\cos\theta$ instead of λ (§ 1), where θ is the angle between the free path and the normal to the xy plane. The correction is expressed in terms of van der Waals's equation (see § 1.VII C):

$$(p+a/v^2)(v-b)\simeq p(v-b)=RT$$

and takes the form:

$$\eta/\eta_0=1/H+\tfrac{4}{5}b\rho+0{\cdot}7614b^2\rho^2H \quad . \quad . \quad . \quad . \quad . \quad (3)$$

where ρ=density, η_0=viscosity of ideal gas$=1{\cdot}016(5/16\sigma^2)\surd(mkT/\pi)$, $b=\tfrac{2}{3}\pi\sigma^3$, the molecular diameter σ being calculated from η_0, and H is a coefficient for the probability of one molecule being near another. Clausius and Boltzmann found:

$$H=1+\tfrac{5}{8}b\rho+0{\cdot}287b^2\rho^2+\ldots \quad . \quad . \quad . \quad . \quad . \quad (4)$$

and when substituted in (1) this gives:

$$\eta/\eta_0=1+0{\cdot}175b\rho+0{\cdot}86b^2\rho^2+\ldots \quad . \quad . \quad . \quad . \quad . \quad (5)$$

The equation may also be written in the form:

$$2{\cdot}545(\eta/\rho)=(\eta/\rho)_0(v/b+0{\cdot}8000+0{\cdot}7614b/v) \quad . \quad . \quad . \quad (6)$$

where $(\eta/\rho)_0$ is the minimum value of η/ρ reached when $v=0{\cdot}8726b$. This formula gives satisfactory results at high densities, as is seen in a comparison

Schidlof and Murzynowska, *ibid.*, 1913, **156**, 304; Shakespear, *Phil. Mag.*, 1914, **28**, 728; Parankiewicz, *Phys. Z.*, 1917, **18**, 567; 1918, **19**, 280; Lassalle, *Phys. Rev.*, 1921, **17**, 354 (A=0·8249); Ishida, *ibid.*, 1923, **21**, 550; Eglin, *ibid.*, 1923, **22**, 161; Epstein, *ibid.*, 1924, **23**, 710; Breit, *ibid.*, 1924, **23**, 608.

[1] *Bull. Acad. Polon.*, 1925, **7** A, 219.

[2] Warburg and Babo, *Ann. Phys.*, 1882, **17**, 390; Phillips, *Proc. Roy. Soc.*, 1912, **87**, 48; Wildhagen, *Z. angew. Math. Mech.*, 1923, **3**, 181; Speyerer, *Forschungsarb. Gebiet Ingenieurwes.*, 1925, **273** (steam); Kennard, " Kinetic Theory of Gases," 1938, 150.

[3] Kennard, " Kinetic Theory of Gases," 1938, 301.

[4] *K. Svensk. Vet. Akad. Handl.*, 1922, **63**, No. 4 (in German); *Arkiv Mat. Astron. Fys.*, 1922, **16**, No. 16; 1928, **21** A, No. 13; Chapman and Cowling, " The Mathematical Theory of Non-Uniform Gases," Cambridge, 1939, 273 f.

of the calculated values with the experimental figures (by the capillary method) of Michels and Gibson [1] for nitrogen at 50° C. given in the table (values at 25° and 75° were also found); a minimum value of η/ρ is shown and the value $v=0{\cdot}8726b$ at which it should occur is reached at about 580 atm.

p atm.	η/ρ obs. $\times 10^5$	$\eta \times 10^6$ obs.	$\eta \times 10^6$ calc.
15·37	1179	191·3	181
57·60	327·4	198·1	190
104·5	192·8	208·8	205
212·4	114·8	237·3	224
320·4	95·2	273·7	266
430·2	88·7	312·9	308
541·7	86·6	350·9	348
630·4	85·9	378·6	380
742·1	87·0	416·5	418
854·1	88·9	455·0	455
965·8	90·9	491·3	492

Jäger [2] used the equation:

$$\eta=\eta_0[(1+\tfrac{5}{2}\beta+\ldots)^{-1}+4\beta] \quad \ldots\ldots \quad (7)$$

where $\beta=b/v$, and also introduced a correction for the intermolecular forces depending on the van der Waals a constant, $2a/v\boldsymbol{R}T=27\beta T_c/4T$:

$$\eta=\eta_0[1+\tfrac{3}{2}(1+9kT_c/2T)\beta] \quad \ldots\ldots \quad (8)$$

Dubief [3] connected the viscosity η of an actual gas with that, η_0, of the gas in the ideal state by the equation $\eta=\eta_0V/(V-b)$, where b is van der Waals's co-volume for the total volume V, and $b=b_0-[d^2/(V^2+c)]$, where c and d are constants.

The results of Warburg and von Babo [4] for carbon dioxide at 77·2 atm. and $\rho=0{\cdot}450$ g./cm.^{3} agree with Enskog's formula. Trautz [5] considered the effect of pressure on viscosity and the reduction to zero pressure. He assumed that by collision, two molecules may form a pair (dimer) and if A_{22}/A_{11} is the ratio of the cross-sections of the dimer and simple molecule (approximately 5:3), P the total pressure in atm., a the van der Waals-van Laar constant (§ 34.VII C), $\boldsymbol{R}=0{\cdot}0036618$, and η_m and η_i the measured viscosity and that in the ideal state, respectively, then:

$$\eta_m=\eta_i+[2aP/(\boldsymbol{R}T)^2](A_{22}/A_{11})(\eta_{12}-\eta_m) \quad \ldots \quad (9)$$

where η_{12} is the value for collisions between dimeric and monomeric molecules. Thus, η_m is a linear function of pressure.

Schröer and Becker [6] found that the temperature coefficient of η for ether vapour at various temperatures above the critical point changes with increasing pressure from a positive value, characteristic of a gas, to a negative value,

[1] *Proc. Roy. Soc.*, 1931, **134**, 288.
[2] *Wien Ber.*, 1899, **108**, II A, 447.
[3] *Compt. Rend.*, 1925, **180**, 1164; 1926, **182**, 688; *J. de Phys.*, 1926, **7**, 402.
[4] *Berlin Ber.*, 1882, 509; *Ann. Phys.*, 1882, **17**, 390; corrected by Brillouin, "Leçons sur la Viscosité," 1907, **2**, 49; Graetz, in Winkelmann, "Handbuch der Physik," 1908, **1**, ii, 1399, 1406. Warburg and von Babo used temperatures above the critical point.
[5] *Ann. Phys.*, 1931, **8**, 797.
[6] *Z. phys. Chem.*, 1935, **173**, 178.

characteristic of a liquid (Fig. 3.VII F). Leipunsky[1] found that, at high densities, the viscosity calculated by Enskog's formula is higher than the observed, and connected this with the change of b with pressure. For mixtures, Enskog's formula still gave satisfactory results, the value of b being calculated from:

$$b=1{\cdot}872\times10^{-7}T^{3/4}/\eta_0{}^{3/2}M^{1/4} \quad (M=\text{mol. wt.}).$$

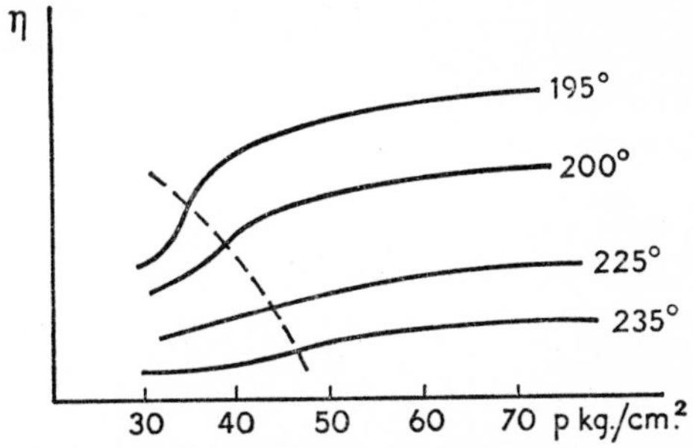

FIG. 3.VII F. Effect of Pressure and Temperature on the Viscosity of Ether Vapour

Measurements of viscosities of steam at high pressures (to 300 atm.) and temperatures (600°) by the capillary method[2] gave values higher than those extrapolated by Sigwart.[3] The pressure effect followed the equation given by Shirokov,[4] $\eta=\alpha(p+a/v^2)[v^2/(v-b)]$. Air at high pressures was investigated by Nasini and Pastonesi.[5] Shugajew[2] found η for steam independent of pressure up to 93 atm.:

t° C.	100	200	300	350	400
η dynes sec. cm.$^{-1}\times10^6$	125·5	163·5	202·4	221·4	241·2

There is no effect of an electric field on the viscosity of a gas.[6] The effect of a magnetic field on the viscosities of the paramagnetic nitric oxide and oxygen is to produce an apparent decrease of mean free path.[7] The viscosity of fog is nearly independent of the size of the droplets of water (5×10^{-5} to 10^{-3} cm. diam.) and is given at 0° by $\eta=0{\cdot}000171+1{\cdot}59w$, where w=weight of water per cm.³ ($1{\cdot}5\times10^{-6}$ to $1{\cdot}5\times10^{-5}$ g.).[8]

§ 3. Persistence of Velocities

The simple viscosity equation (11), § 1, $\eta=\frac{1}{3}\rho\bar{c}l$, found by Maxwell (1860), is obviously in need of correction owing to over-simplification in the assumptions. The corrections modify the numerical factor $\frac{1}{3}$, as stated in § 1.

One apparent correction is really non-existent. It might be thought that the mean free path from the *last* collision to the plane should not be l, as assumed,

[1] *Acta Physicochim. U.R.S.S.*, 1943, **18**, 172; Gonikberg, *J. Phys. Chem. U.S.S.R.*, 1947, **21**, 811.
[2] Speyerer, *Forschungsarb. Gebiet Ingenieurwes.*, 1925, **273**; Shirokov, *J. Phys. Chem. U.S.S.R.*, 1932, **3**, 175; *J. Exptl. Theor. Phys. U.S.S.R.*, 1933, **3**, 237; Shugajew, *J. Exptl. Theor. Phys. U.S.S.R.*, 1933, **3**, 247; *Sow. Phys. Z.*, 1934, **5**, 659; Timrot, *J. Phys. U.S.S.R.*, 1940, **2**, 419; Dorsey, "Properties of Ordinary Water Substance," New York, 1940, 61 (bibl.).
[3] *Forschungsarb. Gebiet. Ingenieurwes.*, 1936, **7 B**, 125; Rudorff, *Eng. and Boiler House Rev.*, 1946, **60**, 100.
[4] *J. Exptl. Theor. Phys. U.S.S.R.*, 1933, **3**, 237; Sage and Lacey, *Amer. Inst. Min. Met. Eng. Techn. Publ.*, 1937, **845**.
[5] *Gazz.*, 1933, **63**, 821 (200 atm.).
[6] Ray, *Phil. Mag.*, 1922, **43**, 1129; Sirk, *Z. Phys.*, 1923, **13**, 35; *Phil. Mag.*, 1923, **45**, 640 (<1 in 10^9).
[7] Engelhardt and Sack, *Phys. Z.*, 1932, **33**, 724 (O_2); Sack, *Helv. Phys. Acta*, 1934, **7**, 639; Trautz and Fröschl, *Ann. Phys.*, 1935, **22**, 223 (O_2, NO); von Laue, *ibid.*, 1935, **23**, 1; Senftleben and Gladisch, *ibid.*, 1937, **30**, 713; 1938, **33**, 471; van Itterbeek and Claes, *J. de Phys.*, 1938, **9**, 457.
[8] Mokrzycki, *J. de Phys.*, 1926, **7**, 188.

but $l/2$, leaving $l/2$ for the path from the plane to the next collision. A detailed consideration [1] shows that long free paths have a greater chance of crossing the plane than short ones, and with Maxwellian distribution the mean free path of molecules crossing the plane with velocity $\bar{c}$ is just double the mean free path for all molecules in the gas with that velocity; in all cases, regardless of velocity, the mean distance to the plane and the mean distance beyond it are each half the mean free path. The assumption, therefore, stands.

The assumption that the mean free path is the same for all velocities requires correction, but Boltzmann [2] showed that this changes $\frac{1}{3}$ only to 0·35, or by 5 per cent., which is negligible. A further correction [3] for the change of collision rate because of the change in mass velocity of the gas through which the molecule is passing, changes 0·35 to 0·31, which still leaves the coefficient practically equal to $\frac{1}{3}$.

Actually, the most important correction is for the fundamental assumption that the velocity distribution of the molecules which have just collided is a Maxwellian distribution, and this correction requires a completely new method of deduction, already foreshadowed by Maxwell, but first carried through by Chapman; [4] another line of approach, opened out by Boltzmann, was elaborated by Enskog.[5] Both lead to the final equation, (13), § 1, for hard elastic spheres: $\eta=0{\cdot}499\rho\bar{c}l$. The main cause for the large change of coefficient from 0·333 to 0·499 is the *persistence of velocities* after collision, which was taken into account by Jeans.[6] Molecules show a tendency to continue to move in their original direction after a collision, and in the case of elastic spheres the average component of velocity in the original direction after collision is found to be about 40 per cent. of the velocity before collision. This results in an apparent increase in l.

Jeans calculated for two hard elastic spherical molecules of equal mass colliding with velocities c and c', the " expectation " α of velocity in the direction of motion of the first molecule, and showed that the persistence of velocity α/c of the first molecule depends only on the ratio $c/c'=\kappa$ according to the formulae:

$$\left.\begin{aligned} \alpha/c&=(15\kappa^4+1)/10\kappa^2(3\kappa^2+1) \quad \text{when } \kappa>1\\ \text{and } \alpha/c&=(3\kappa^2+5)/5(\kappa^2+3) \quad \text{when } \kappa<1 \end{aligned}\right\} \quad . \quad . \quad . \quad (1)$$

c/c'	∞	4	2	1	0·66	0·5	0·25	0
α/c	0·500	0·492	0·473	0·400	0·368	0·354	0·339	0·333

For two molecules of unequal masses m_1, m_2, the value of α/c depends on the masses, and if $(\alpha/c)_e$ is the value for equal masses, its value for the first molecule is:

$$\alpha/c=(m_1-m_2)/(m_1+m_2)+[2m_2/(m_1+m_2)](\alpha/c)_e \quad . \quad . \quad . \quad (2)$$

m_2/m_1	0	0·1	0·2	0·5	1	2	5	10	∞
average $\overline{(\alpha/c)}$	1·000	0·879	0·779	0·573	0·406	0·243	0·152	0·086	0·000

[1] Kennard, " Kinetic Theory of Gases," 1938, 141.
[2] " Gastheorie," 1896, **1**, 79.
[3] O. E. Meyer, " Kinetic Theory of Gases," 1899, 446.
[4] *Phil. Trans.*, 1912, **211**, 433; 1916, **216**, 279; 1917, **217**, 115; Jones, *ibid.*, 1922, **223**, 1; for the integrals involved, see Jones, *Manch. Mem.*, 1922, **66**, No. 1; Hirschfelder, Bird, and Spotz, *J. Chem. Phys.*, 1948, **16**, 968.
[5] *Phys. Z.*, 1911, **12**, 56, 533; *Dissert.*, Uppsala, 1917; *Arkiv Mat. Astron. Fys.*, 1922, **16**, No. 16.
[6] Jeans, *Phil. Mag.*, 1904, **8**, 700; " Dynamical Theory of Gases," 3rd edit., 1921, 260; " Kinetic Theory of Gases," 1940, 148; Kuenen, *Verslag. K. Akad. Wetens. Amsterdam*, 1913, **21**, 1088; *Proc. K. Akad. Wetens. Amsterdam*, 1913, **15**, 1152; 1915, **17**, 1068 (correction).

The persistence is positive, but it can have any value whatever, according to the ratio of the masses of the molecules. Jäger [1] obtained a somewhat different numerical coefficient, a factor 1·051 in his equation being omitted by Jeans.

Since (35), § 10.III shows that $\bar{c}$ is proportional to $\sqrt{T}$ it follows from (11), § 1, that the viscosity should be proportional to the square root of the absolute temperature. This result is not confirmed by experiment, the viscosity increasing with temperature more rapidly than $\sqrt{T}$. This indicates that the mean free path must really be a function of temperature, and hence the hypothesis that the molecules are hard elastic spheres must be given up. Since the viscosity is proportional to the mean free path in the simple formula, it appears that the free path increases somewhat with temperature, i.e. the molecular centres approach more closely than they would if the molecules remained hard elastic spheres. This matter is taken up again in § 5.

§ 4. Numerical Values of the Viscosities of Gases

The following table [2] gives some values of η at 15° C., the values of l calculated from equation (13), § 1, $\eta=0{\cdot}499\rho\bar{c}l$, the molecular " diameters " σ calculated on the assumption of elastic spheres by (18), § 21.III, $l=1/\sqrt{(2)}\pi N_L\sigma^2$, and the coefficient n of temperature variation of η from $\eta=kT^n$, where k is a constant. The units are η dyne sec. cm.$^{-1}$, l cm., σ cm. Calculations of molecular diameters by four methods were given by Wheeler [3] (density of liquid, critical volume, viscosity, van der Waals's equation).

	$\eta\times10^7$	$l\times10^6$	$\sigma\times10^8$	n		$\eta\times10^7$	$l\times10^6$	$\sigma\times10^8$	n
H_2	871	11·77	2·74	0·69	O_2	2003	6·79	3·61	0·81
D_2	1231	11·77	2·74	0·69(?)	HCl	1397	4·44	4·46	(1·07)
He	1943	18·62	2·18	0·64	A	2196	6·66	3·64	0·86
CH_4	1077	5·16	4·14	0·88	CO_2	1448	4·19	4·59	0·95
NH_3	970	4·51	4·43	1·09	Kr	2431	5·12	4·16	(0·85)
H_2O	926	4·18	4·60	(1·07)	CH_3Br	1310	2·58	5·85	1·10
Ne	3095	13·22	2·59	0·67	Xe	2236	3·76	4·85	0·92
N_2	1734	6·28	3·75	0·77	Hg (219·4°)	4700	8·32	4·26	—
C_2H_4	998	3·61	4·95	0·95	Air	1796	6·40	3·72	0·79
C_2H_6	900	3·15	5·30	0·97					

Much attention has been given to the absolute viscosity of air at 23° C., which is important in the calculation of the electronic charge e from Millikan's oil-drop method and is also used as a standard in the determination of gas viscosities. Millikan [4] took this as 1824×10^{-7}. A critical survey of earlier values [5] gave $\eta_{23}=1825\times10^{-7}$; more recent determinations show a tendency to raise this value, the reason not being clearly understood, and a weighted mean

(For continuation of text, see p. 863)

[1] *Wien Ber.*, 1899, **108**, II A, 447; 1918, **127**, II A, 849; see § 1.

[2] Kennard, " Kinetic Theory of Gases," 1938, 149; the figure for deuterium is from Van Cleave and Maass, *Canad. J. Res.*, 1935, **12**, 57, who found $\eta\times10^7$ equal to 1181 at 0°, 1240 at 20°, and 1242·5 at 22°, equal to $\sqrt{(\rho_{H_2}/\rho_{D_2})}$ times the values for H_2, a result confirmed by Admur, *J.A.C.S.*, 1935, **57**, 588; the value for air is from Kjellström, *Nature*, 1935, **136**, 682 (see ref. 1, p. 863); see Jeans, *Phil. Mag.*, 1904, **8**, 692.

[3] *Rec. Trav. Chim.*, 1932, **51**, 1204.

[4] *Ann. Phys.*, 1913, **41**, 759; 1938, **32**, 34, 520; *Phys. Rev.*, 1923, **21**, 217; 1923, **22**, 1; Rapp, *Phys. Rev.*, 1913, **2**, 363 ($1837{\cdot}5\times10^{-7}$ at 29°).

[5] Anfilogoff, *Thesis*, London, 1932, 387.

Viscosity Data for Inorganic Substances

	Viscosity $\eta \times 10^7$ at various temperatures, C							$\eta_c \times 10^7$	Sutherland's C	Remarks	References (see page 862)
	0°	20°	50°	100°	150°	200°	250°				
Air...	1708	1807	—	2171	—	2569	2751	—	112	Obeys Sutherland's law.	1, 8, 9, 12, 14, 15, 16, 17, 19, 20, 25, 40, 41, 43, 50
Ammonia, NH_3	[916]	982	1092	1278	1463	1645	1813	1380	503	C constant from 20–300° C.	10, 26, 31, 35, 52
Argon, A	[2114]	2217	—	2695	—	3223	3444	1209	142	C constant up to 800° C.	2, 3, 19, 20, 23, 31, 52
Bromine, Br_2	[1464]	(19) 1526	(25) 1528	(94) 1921	—	(190) 2369	—	2958	533	C increases with temp. Value 533 holds above 460° C.	5, 36
Carbon monoxide, CO ...	[1659]	1763	1864	2083	2276	2463	2632	878	101·2	Obeys Sutherland's law.	1, 16, 19, 22, 31, 52
Carbon dioxide, CO_2 ...	[1375]	(26·9) 1493	(76·9) 1725	—	(126·9) 2160	(226·9) 2354	(276·9) 2556	1510	254	C constant above 300° C., when its value is 213.	1, 23, 24, 31, 45, 52
Carbon disulphide, CS_2 ...	[886]	—	—	(114·3) 1303	(152·5) 1434	(190·2) 1561	(267·3) 1830	—	499·5	—	10, 39
Chlorine, Cl_2	[1227]	1312	(55·1) 1470	(99·4) 1651	(145·4) 1845	(199·5) 2081	2244	1839	330	C=350 from 100–250° C.	4, 27, 52
Cyanogen, C_2N_2 ...	928	(17) 987	—	1271	—	—	—	—	330	—	7, 10
Helium, He	1885	1941	—	2281	—	2672	2853	97·1	80	—	1, 20, 31, 46, 52
Hydrogen, H_2	835	876	937	1032	1126	1212	1297	153	84·4	$\eta \propto (T)^{0\cdot675}$	1, 14, 15, 16, 17, 18, 19, 20, 21, [illegible]

Hydrogen sulphide, H_2S...	1166	(17) 1241	—	1587	—	—	—	—	331	—	10, 22, 23, 25, 40
Hydrogen bromide, HBr	[1697]	(18·7) 1819	—	(100·2) 2344	—	—	—	2305	357	—	10, 47
Hydrogen chloride, HCl	[1313]	(21) 1434	(54) 1600	(99) 1832	(154) 2093	2303	2530	1581	362	—	15, 41, 47
Hydrogen Iodide, HI ...	[1726]	(20·5) 1857	—	(96·6) 2310	(149·4) 2631	(198·6) 2922	(251) 3228	2640	331	C=355 between 100–200° C.	27, 47
Iodine, I_2	[1228]	—	—	(102·2) 1785	—	(232·2) 2319	(319·2) 2561	3615	568	—	6, 35
Krypton, Kr	2327	(15) 2460	—	—	—	—	—	1780	188	—	2, 3
Neon, Ne	[2962]	3111	—	3646	(184·5) 4177	4248	4532	705	56	—	2, 3, 11, 20, 31, 52
Nitrogen, N_2	[1652]	(16·1) 1728	(51·6) 1880	2084	(151·9) 2287	2461	2929	835	104	C constant up to 830° C.	1, 16, 22, 23, 52
Nitrous oxide, N_2O ...	1381	(26·9) 1488	(76·9) 1723	(126·9) 1943	(176·9) 2158	(226·9) 2355	(276·9) 2555	1536	260	—	24, 52
Nitric oxide, NO	1777	1876	2036	2272	2474	2682	2870	1208	128	—	1, 30, 31, 33, 49, 52
Oxygen, O_2	[1911]	(14·8) 1985	—	(127·7) 2568	—	3017	3220	1154	125	C constant up to 830° C.	1, 22, 23, 46, 52
Sulphur dioxide, SO_2 ...	1158	1266	(40) 1352	1612	(120) 1716	2038	—	1884	416	—	1, 14, 27, 38, 40, 52
Water, H_2O	861	937	—	1255	1445	1635	1827	—	650	η independent of pressure up to 94 atm.	35, 42, 48, 51
Xenon, Xe	2107	(16·5) 2250	—	(99·4) 2871	—	—	—	2249	252	—	31

VISCOSITY DATA FOR ORGANIC SUBSTANCES

	Viscosity $\eta \times 10^7$ at various temperatures, C							$\eta_c \times 10^7$	Sutherland's C	Remarks	References (see page 862)
	0°	20°	50°	100°	150°	200°	250°				
Methane, CH_4	[1022]	1087	1182	1331	1471	1603	1725	726	164	—	1, 10, 25, 31, 52
Methyl alcohol, CH_3OH	[865]	—	—	(111·3) 1259	(153·9) 1408	(188·8) 1527	1725	—	487	—	38
Methyl chloride, CH_3Cl...	[981]	1061	1175	1357	—	(219·4) 1769	—	1512	454	—	1, 35, 38
Methylene chloride, CH_2Cl_2	[910]	(22·1) 991	—	1267	—	(219·1) 1667	—	1752	395	C computed graphically.	31
Chloroform, $CHCl_3$ ...	[929]	1001	—	1267	(161·3) 1491	(189·1) 1579	1776	1780	373	—	1, 31, 35, 38
Carbon tetrachloride, CCl_4	[898]	—	—	(127·9) 1334	(169·3) 1463	1562	(282·2) 1808	1750	365	—	31, 38
Methyl bromide, CH_3Br...	[1229]	1327	1457	(120) 1797	—	—	—	2115	402	C computed graphically.	1, 31, 38
Methyl ether, $(CH_3)_2O$ ...	[846]	(19·5) 909	(60) 1044	1167	(120) 1228	—	—	1255	426	—	31, 38
Ethane, C_2H_6	[851]	909	998	1142	1278	1408	1525	935	252	—	1, 25, 31, 38
Ethyl alcohol, C_2H_5OH ...	[752]	—	—	(130·2) 1173	(170·7) 1293	(191·8) 1355	(251·7) 1519	—	407	—	38
Ethyl chloride, C_2H_5Cl ...	937	—	—	—	—	—	—	—	411	C computed from T_c	1
Ethylene, C_2H_4	[944]	1008	1103	1256	1403	1541	1666	962	241	—	17, 22, 26, 31, 38

Acetone, $(CH_3)_2CO$ ...	[660]	—	—	(119) 991	(159·5) 1101	(190·4) 1186	(247·7) 1334	—	541	—	38
Acetylene, C_2H_2 ...	[955]	1020	1113	1254	(120) 1318	—	—	1073	215	—	1, 38, 52
Propane, C_3H_8	[746]	801	880	1008	1132	1253	1362	990	278	—	24, 25, 44, 52
n-Propyl alcohol, C_3H_7OH	[682]	—	—	(121·7) 1025	(149) 1102	(209·7) 1267	(243·2) 1350	—	515·6	—	38
Iso-Propylalcohol, C_3H_7OH	[698]	—	—	(119·2) 1028	(149·2) 1112	(198·4) 1248	(251·0) 1382	—	459·9	—	38
Propylene, C_3H_6 ...	[775]	835	(60) 959	1071	(120) 1122	—	—	1045	362	—	31, 38
Ether, $(C_2H_5)_2O$	[679]	—	—	955	(159·4) 1079	(217·7) 1222	(251·0) 1300	—	404	—	1, 38
n-Butane, C_4H_{10} ...	[686]	739	(40) 787	947	(120·0) 998	—	—	—	358	—	38, 52
Iso-butane, C_4H_{10} ...	[692]	744	(40) 792	947	(120·0) 995	—	—	—	330	—	38
n-Pentane, C_5H_{12} ...	[621]	—	—	(121·6) 911	(158·9) 995	(219·1) 1126	(249·5) 1191	—	383	—	38
Benzene, C_6H_6	[677]	738	918	(131·3) 1031	(161·3) 1110	(194·6) 1198	(252·5) 1343	1423	447·5	—	38
n-Hexane	[586]	—	—	(120·7) 866	(160·8) 958	(188·9) 1021	(248·0) 1144	—	436·1	—	38

[1] Vogel, *Ann. Phys.*, 1914, **43**, 1235 (air, CO, CO_2, He, H_2, N_2, CH_4, C_2H_6, C_2H_2, CH_3Cl $CHCl_3$, CH_3Br, $(C_2H_5)_2O$, C_2H_5Cl).
[2] Rankine, *Proc. Roy. Soc.*, 1910, **83**, 265, 516 (air, He, Ne, A, Kr, Xe).
[3] Rankine, *Proc. Roy. Soc.*, 1911, **84**, 181 (air, He, Ne, A, Kr, Xe).
[4] Rankine, *Proc. Roy. Soc.*, 1912, **86**, 162 (Cl_2, Br_2); for fluorine, F_2, see Aoyama and Kanda, *J. Chem. Soc. Japan*, 1937, **58**, 804 ($\sigma = 3\cdot02 \times 10^{-8}$ cm.).
[5] Rankine, *Proc. Roy. Soc.*, 1913, **88**, 575 (Br_2).
[6] Rankine, *Proc. Roy. Soc.*, 1915, **91**, 201 (I_2).
[7] Rankine, *Proc. Roy. Soc.*, 1921, **99**, 331 (C_2N_2).
[8] Rankine, *Proc. Roy. Soc.*, 1926, **111**, 219 (air).
[9] Rankine and Edwards, *Proc. Roy. Soc.*, 1927, **117**, 245 (air).
[10] Rankine and Smith, *Phil. Mag.*, 1921, **42**, 601, 615 (NH_3, PH_3, AsH_3; CH_4, H_2S, C_2N_2 COS, CS_2).
[11] Edwards, *Proc. Roy. Soc.*, 1928, **119**, 578 (Ne).
[12] Williams, *Proc. Roy. Soc.*, 1926, **110**, 141 (air).
[13] Nasini, *Proc. Roy. Soc.*, 1929, **123**, 692 (C_6H_6, $C_6H_5CH_3$, cyclohexane).
[14] Trautz and Weizel, *Ann. Phys.*, 1925, **78**, 305 (SO_2 and mixtures with H_2).
[15] Trautz and Narath, *Ann. Phys.*, 1926, **79**, 637 (H_2, HCl and mixtures).
[16] Trautz and Baumann, *Ann. Phys.*, 1929, **2**, 733 (H_2, N_2, CO).
[17] Trautz and Stauf, *Ann. Phys.*, 1929, **2**, 737 (H_2, C_2H_4).
[18] Trautz and Kipphan, *Ann. Phys.*, 1929, **2**, 743 (He, Ne, A).
[19] Trautz and Ludewigs, *Ann. Phys.*, 1929, **3**, 409.
[20] Trautz and Binkele, *Ann. Phys.*, 1930, **5**, 561 (H_2, He, Ne, A, and mixtures).
[21] Keesom and Macwood, *Physica*, 1938, **5**, 749.
[22] Trautz and Melster, *Ann. Phys.*, 1930, **7**, 409 (H_2, N_2, O_2, CO, C_2H_4, and mixtures).
[23] Trautz and Zink, *Ann. Phys.*, 1930, **1**, 427 (air, H_2, N_2, O_2, SO_2, CO_2, CH_4, He, Ne, A).
[24] Trautz and Kurz, *Ann. Phys.*, 1931, **9**, 981 (H_2, N_2O, CO_2, C_3H_8, and mixtures).
[25] Trautz and Sorg, *Ann. Phys.*, 1931, **10**, 81 (H_2, CH_4, C_2H_6, C_3H_8, and mixtures).
[26] Trautz and Heberling, *Ann. Phys.*, 1931, **10**, 155 (NH_3, H_2 ,N_2, O_2, C_2H_4, and mixtures).
[27] Trautz and Winterkorn, *Ann. Phys.*, 1931, **10**, 511 (Cl_2, HI); Trautz and Freytag, *ibid.*, 1934, **20**, 135 (Cl_2, NO, NOCl); Trautz and Ruf, *ibid.*, 1934, **20**, 127 (Cl_2, HI).
[28] Trautz, *Ann. Phys.*, 1931, **10**, 263 (theoretical).
[29] Trautz, *Ann. Phys.*, 1931, **11**, 190 (theoretical).
[30] Trautz and Gabriel, *Ann. Phys.*, 1931, **11**, 606 (N_2, NO, and mixtures).
[31] Trautz, *Ann. Phys.*, 1932, **15**, 198 (η_c, theory; calc. of σ); Trautz and Heberling, *ibid.*, 1934, **20**, 118 (Xe, and H_2+Xe).
[32] Trautz, *Ann. Phys.*, 1933, **16**, 751 (theory; calc. of σ).
[33] Trautz and Freytag, *Ann. Phys.*, 1934, **20**, 135 (Cl_2, NO, NOCl).
[34] Trautz and Zimmerman, *Ann. Phys.*, 1935, **22**, 189 (H_2, He, Ne and mixtures at low temperatures).
[35] Smith, *Proc. Roy. Soc.*, 1924, **106**, 83; Braune and Linke, *Z. phys. Chem.*, 1930, **148**, 195.
[36] Braune, Basch, and Wentzel, *Z. phys. Chem.*, 1928, **137**, 176, 447 (Zn, Cd, Hg).
[37] Binkele, *Ann. Phys.*, 1931, **9**, 839; 1932, **15**, 729 (calc. σ).
[38] Titani, *Bull. Chem. Soc. Japan*, 1929, **4**, 277 (air); 1930, **5**, 98; 1933, **8**, 255 (many organic vapours); Trautz and Ishaq Husseini, *Ann. Phys.*, 1934, **20**, 121 (butylene).
[39] Sutherland and Maass, *Canad. J. Res.*, 1932, **6**, 428 (air, H_2, CO_2).
[40] Stewart and Maass, *Canad. J. Res.*, 1932, **6**, 453 (SO_2).
[41] Anfilogoff, *Thesis*, London, 1932 (air, A, HCl); Partington, *Phys. Z.*, 1933, **34**, 289.
[42] Schugajew, *Sow. Phys. Z.*, 1934, **5**, 659 (H_2O vap. under pressure).
[43] Győző Zemplén, *Ann. Phys.*, 1905, **19**, 783 (η for air at $20\cdot4° = 0\cdot0_31794$).
[44] Sage and Lacey, *Ind. Eng. Chem.*, 1938, **30**, 829. See also Landolt-Börnstein, " Tabellen," 5th edit., 1923, 171; 1931, *Ergzb.*, **2**, i, 137; Schudel, *Schweiz. Verein Gas- u. Wasserfach.*, 1942, **22**, 112.
[45] Lassalle, *Phys. Rev.*, 1921, **17**, 354 (η CO_2 at $23° = 1\cdot490 \times 10^{-4}$ by falling oil drop).
[46] States, *Phys. Rev.*, 1923, **21**, 662 (He, O_2, rotating cylinder).
[47] Harle, *Proc. Roy. Soc.*, 1922, **100**, 429 (capillary).
[48] Speyerer, *Z. techn. Phys.*, 1923, **4**, 430 (H_2O, capillary, 100°–350°, $\eta \times 10^8 = 127\cdot92 + 0\cdot3785(t-100)$ in kg. sec. m.^{2} units).
[49] Klemenc and Remi, *Monatsh.*, 1924, **44**, 307.
[50] Carvalho, *An. Assoc. Quim. Brasil*, 1945, **4**, 5.
[51] Dorsey, " Properties of Ordinary Water Substance," New York, 1940, 61 (bibl.); Hawkins, Sibbitt, and Solberg, *Trans. Amer. Soc. Mech. Eng.*, 1948, **70**, No. 1, 19.
[52] Wobser and Müller, *Koll. Beih.*, 1941, **52**, 165.

of values for air ranging from $1822 \cdot 6 \times 10^{-7}$ to $1838 \cdot 8 \times 10^{-7}$ was given [1] as $\eta_{23} = (1830 \cdot 0 \pm 2 \cdot 5) \times 10^{-7}$. Hopper and Laby [1] showed that $e = (4 \cdot 8044 \pm 0 \cdot 0007) \times 10^{-10}$, from the X-ray results, requires a value of $\eta_{23} = (1830 \cdot 9 \pm 0 \cdot 5) \times 10^{-7}$ for agreement with the oil-drop results.

The table on pages 858–61 gives values of η for several gases and vapours, and some values of Sutherland's constant C (§ 5) are included.[2]

Some viscosity values at lower temperatures (1 atm. pressure) found by Sutherland and Maass [3] are (η air at $20 \cdot 8° = 1811 \cdot 6 \times 10^{-7}$):

	t° C.	$\eta \times 10^7$	t° C.	$\eta \times 10^7$	t° C.	$\eta \times 10^7$
H_2	20·7	876·4	−62·6	700·6	−113·5	571·5
	0	835·1	−97·5	615·2	−123·7	547·5
	−31·6	766·9	−112·6	576·9	−183·4	388·4
					−198·4	336·0
CO_2	21·8	1470·8	−19·4	1259·9	−60·0	1060·8
	1·3	1361·1	−40·2	1154·5	−78·2	971·6
					−97·8	895·8

Stewart and Maass [4] found for sulphur dioxide (η air$=1824 \cdot 0 \times 10^{-7} - 4 \cdot 93 \times 10^{-7}(23-t)$):

t° C. ...	29·8	20·5	0	−6·2	−17·9	−19·2	−35·6	−75
p mm. ...	760	760	760	733	474	450	105	8
$\eta \times 10^7$ ...	1298·0	1255·0	1158·0	1132·0	1083·9	1080·6	1013·6	858·1

Day [5] found at 25° C. for pentane gas $\eta = (677 \cdot 2 - 0 \cdot 0084 p_{mm}) \times 10^{-7}$, and

[1] Kaye and Laby, "Tables of Physical and Chemical Constants," 9th edit., 1941, 40; 10th edit., 1948, 136; including values from Kjellström, *Nature*, 1935, **136**, 682; Bond, *Phil. Mag.*, 1936, **22**, 624; *Proc. Phys. Soc.*, 1937, **49**, 205; Houston, *Phys. Rev.*, 1937, **52**, 751; Rigden, *Phil. Mag.*, 1938, **25**, 961; Bearden, *Phys. Rev.*, 1939, **56**, 1023; see also Hogg, *Proc. Amer. Acad.*, 1905, **40**, 611 (method of oscillating spheres, $\eta = 0 \cdot 0001713$ for air at 0°); Markwell, *Phys. Rev.*, 1916, **8**, 479 (capillary tube method, $\eta = 0 \cdot 00018273$ for air at 23°); Harrington, *ibid.*, 1916, **8**, 738 ($\eta = 0 \cdot 00018226$ for air at 23° by Gilchrist's method, § 8); Fortier, *Compt. Rend.*, 1935, **201**, 1330; 1936, **203**, 711; 1939, **208**, 506, by a new capillary method found $\eta = 1834 \cdot 1 \times 10^{-7}$ for air at 23°; Majumdar and Vajifdar, *Proc. Indian Acad.*, 1938, **8** A, 171 ($1834 \cdot 38 \times 10^{-7}$ at 23°; capillary method); Banerjea and Plattanaik, *Z. Phys.*, 1938, **110**, 676 ($1833 \cdot 3 \times 10^{-7}$ at 23°; capillary method); for a discussion of values, see Harrington, *Phys. Rev.*, 1939, **55**, 230; Hopper and Laby, *Proc. Roy. Soc.*, 1941, **178**, 243.

[2] Older values, see Fisher, *Phys. Rev.*, 1907, **24**, 385; Kuenen, "Die Eigenschaften der Gase" (Ostwald-Drucker, "Handbuch der allgemeinen Chemie," **3**), Leipzig, 1919, 105; Anfilogoff, *Thesis*, London, 1932; Schuil, *Phil. Mag.*, 1939, **28**, 679; Kaye and Laby, "Tables," 9th edit., 1941, 41; values in square brackets were computed by Schuil; viscosities not measured at the temperature at the head of the table were measured at temperatures shown in round brackets above the values. η_c is the viscosity at the critical temperature.

[3] *Canad. J. Res.*, 1932, **6**, 428; for viscosity of O_2 and N_2 at low temperatures (oscillating disc method) see Van Itterbeek and Claes, *Physica*, 1936, **3**, 275; *J. de Phys.*, 1938, **9**, 457; for H_2 and D_2, *idem*, *Physica*, 1938, **5**, 938; Keesom and Macwood, *ibid.*, 1938, **5**, 749; for oxygen, Van Itterbeek and Keesom, *ibid.*, 1935, **2**, 97; *Proc. K. Akad. Wetens. Amsterdam*, 1935, **38**, 11; CH_4 and CD_4, Van Itterbeek, *Physica*, 1940, **7**, 831 (η_{CD_4}/η_{CH_4} independent of temperature). Van Itterbeek and Claes, *Nature*, 1938, **142**, 793, found:

T° K.	293	90	75	20	17	14
η_{D_2}/η_{H_2}	1·39	1·34	1·35	1·24	1·24	1·25

Viallard, *Comp. Rend.*, 1946, **223**, 1128, found $\eta_{D_2}/\eta_{H_2} = 1 \cdot 368$ at −200°; the value at −30° to +25° is 1·395; this shows that the H_2 and D_2 molecules have different diameters.

[4] *Canad. J. Res.*, 1932, **6**, 453.

[5] *Phys. Rev.*, 1932, **40**, 281.

for *iso*pentane gas $\eta=(696{\cdot}5-0{\cdot}0077p_{mm})\times 10^{-7}$. Yen [1] found at 23°, H_2 882·16×10⁻⁷, O_2 2142·35×10⁻⁷, N_2 1764·80×10⁻⁷. Aoyama and Kanda [2] determined the viscosity of fluorine by the oscillating disc method from 86·8° to 273° K. Höfsass [3] used the viscosity (by a capillary method) to find the composition of coal gas.

O. E. Meyer [4] concluded that there is a relation between η and the molecular weight; in certain groups of gases η first rises with the molecular weight to a maximum and then falls; gases with a large number of atoms in the molecule have nearly equal viscosities. The following are values of $\eta\times 10^4$:

He	1·65	A	2·08	Hg	1·62	NO	1·68	O_2	1·91
H_2	0·84	CO	1·67	N_2	1·67	N_2O	1·44	HCl	1·41
H_2O	0·97	H_2S	1·18	CO_2	1·45	SO_2	1·25	Cl_2	1·28

Weinstein [5] also pointed out a periodic dependence on molecular weight. Onnes,[6] from considerations of the law of corresponding states (§ 25.VII C), concluded that $\eta(T_c/M^3p_c^4)^{1/6}$ should have the same value for all substances in corresponding states; if $\vartheta=T/T_c$ and $\pi=p/p_c$ are the reduced temperature and pressure, then $\eta/\sqrt{M}=\mathrm{f}(\vartheta,\pi)$. Onnes and Weber concluded that $-\frac{1}{2}\log\eta/\sqrt{(TM)}=\log r-\log c$, where r=mean (collision) radius of the molecule and c is a constant for all substances. Smith and Brown [7] concluded that $\log(\eta/\sqrt{M})$ is a linear function of the reduced temperature for gases and vapours at normal pressure, a result based on the theorem of corresponding states. Nernst [8] deduced that *at very low temperatures*, $\eta=0{\cdot}47(MT)^{3/2}\times 10^{-7}$, a relation which is not even approximately followed at room temperature.

§ 5. Effect of Temperature on Gaseous Viscosity

Many formulae for the effect of temperature on gas viscosity have been proposed; Stöcke [9] lists fourteen. A commonly used formula was deduced by Sutherland,[10] who assumed that the mean free path l increases somewhat with temperature. Since the number of collisions is larger the smaller the mean free path, this means that, for a fixed density, the collision number is larger at the lower temperatures than for the ideal case. Sutherland's theory postulates forces between the molecules. The deduction of the equation is essentially by the method of planetary theory,[11] and will not be repeated in full.

1 *Phil. Mag.*, 1919, **38**, 582.
2 *J. Chem. Soc. Japan*, 1937, **58**, 804.
3 *J. Gasbeleucht.*, 1919, **62**, 776.
4 "Kinetic Theory of Gases," 1899, 191 f., 195.
5 "Thermodynamik und Kinetik der Körper," 1901, **1**, 331; see also Sutherland, *Phil. Mag.*, 1893, **36**, 507; Smith, *Proc. Phys. Soc.*, 1922, **34**, 155; Schulz, *Z. Elektrochem.*, 1944, **50**, 122; on relation of σ to van der Waals's b, see Binkele, *Ann. Phys.*, 1932, **15**, 729.
6 Onnes and Weber, *Proc. K. Akad. Wetens. Amsterdam*, 1913, **15**, 1399 (*Comm. Leiden* **134** *c*); Trautz, *J. prakt. Chem.*, 1943, **162**, 218.
7 *Ind. Eng. Chem.*, 1943, **35**, 705; Licht and Stechert, *J. Phys. Chem.*, 1944, **48**, 23.
8 *Berlin Ber.*, 1919, 118.
9 Landolt-Börnstein, "Tabellen," 5th edit., 1923, 178.
10 *Phil. Mag.*, 1893, **36**, 507; cf. O. E. Meyer, "Kinetic Theory of Gases," 1899, 166, 218, 425. Reinganum, *Ann. Phys.*, 1908, **28**, 142, pointed out that similar ideas were proposed qualitatively by Lothar Meyer, *Ann. Phys.*, 1879, **7**, 497 (533); 1882, **16**, 394 (distance of closest approach decreases with rise of temperature).
11 See the deductions by Jäger, "Fortschritte der kinetischen Gastheorie," 1906, 93; and Herzfeld, in H. S. Taylor, "Physical Chemistry," 1931, **1**, 127. Keyes, *J.A.C.S.*, 1928, **50**, 930, considered that the basis of Sutherland's theory is "rather illusory."

Consider two molecules approaching one another in a gas. It can be supposed that one is at rest at O (Fig. 4.VII F) and the other approaching this with the relative velocity r. Let the second molecule describe the orbit ACB and let the asymptotes to this be drawn. Let there be an attractive force acting between the two particles which is some function of the distance ρ, represented by $F(\rho)$. For simplicity let the mass of the molecule be taken as unity. The x and y components of the force are (force=mass × acceleration):

$$d^2x/dt^2=-F(\rho)(x/\rho)$$

$$d^2y/dt^2=-F(\rho)(y/\rho).$$

The integration of these equations leads to a general equation (*Principle of Surfaces*) which holds for all central forces of this type:[1] $d\phi/dt=h/\rho^2$, where ϕ is the surface swept out and h is a constant. For large values of ρ, when the attractive force is practically zero, $h=rb$, and r is equal to the relative velocity c along the asymptote before the " encounter " begins. Then it is shown that:

$$d^2\rho/dt^2=b^2r^2/\rho^3-F(\rho).$$

The smallest distance $OC=\rho_0$ at which the second molecule passes the first has the radius vector ρ at right angles to the path (since ρ is passing through a minimum value), hence $d\rho/dt=0$, and this leads to the equation:

$$b^2=\rho_0^2\left[1+\frac{2}{r^2}\int_{\rho_0}^{\infty}F(\rho)d\rho\right] \quad . \quad (1)$$

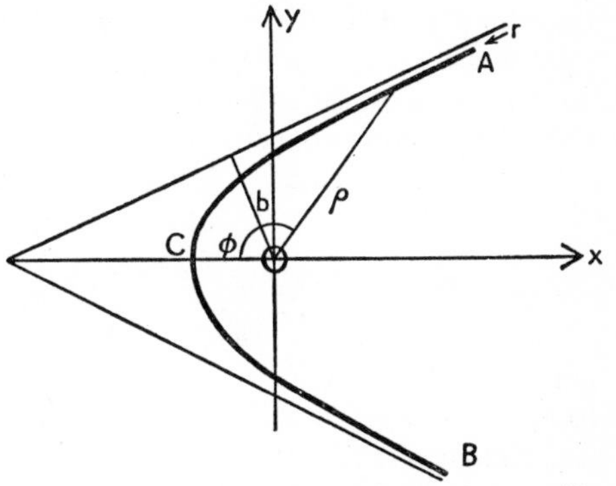

FIG. 4.VII F. Path of a Molecule Approaching a Centre of Attraction

There will be a " collision " when $\rho_0=\sigma_\infty$, the fictitious " molecular diameter," i.e. when:

$$b_0^2=\sigma_\infty^2\left[1+\frac{2}{r^2}\int_{\sigma_\infty}^{\infty}F(\rho)d\rho\right] \quad . \quad . \quad . \quad . \quad . \quad . \quad . \quad (2)$$

The effect is the same as if there were no central force, and the real molecular diameter were b_0 instead of σ_∞ ($b_0>\sigma_\infty$).

This value b_0^2 may be substituted for σ^2 in Maxwell's equation (18), § 21.III, $l=1/\sqrt{(2)}N\pi\sigma^2$.

Since $F(\rho)$ has been assumed independent of temperature, and since r is proportional to $\sqrt{T}$ (from (36), § 10.III), it follows that:

$$(2/r^2)\int_{\sigma_\infty}^{\infty}F(\rho)d\rho=C/T \quad . \quad . \quad . \quad . \quad . \quad . \quad . \quad . \quad . \quad (3)$$

where C is called *Sutherland's constant.* Hence:

$$l=[1/\sqrt{(2)}N\pi\sigma_\infty^2](1+C/T) \quad . \quad . \quad . \quad . \quad . \quad . \quad . \quad (4)$$

According to Clausius:

$$l=[1/\sqrt{(2)}\pi N\sigma^2]/[1+(5/8)(b/v)] \quad . \quad . \quad . \quad . \quad . \quad . \quad (5)$$

where b=van der Waals's volume correction.[2]

[1] Gruner, *Ann. Phys.*, 1911, **35**, 381.
[2] See Jellinek, " Lehrbuch der physikalischen Chemie," 1914, **1**, 381; 1915, **2**, 151.

The introduction of Keyes' characteristic equation (§ 37.VII C) into viscosity calculations was considered by Phillips,[1] and the Beattie-Bridgeman equation (§ 38.VII C) by Boyd.[2]

From (12), § 1:

$$\eta = kp\bar{c}l = kp\bar{c}/\sqrt{(2)}N\pi\sigma^2$$

$$\therefore\ \sigma^2 = kp\bar{c}/\sqrt{(2)}N\pi\eta$$

and with $\sigma = b_0$ from (2) and (3):

$$\sigma^2 = \sigma_\infty{}^2(1 + C/T) \quad \text{(6)}$$

$$\pi\sigma_\infty{}^2 = kp\bar{c}/\sqrt{(2)}N\eta(1 + C/T) \quad \text{(7)}$$

If $\sigma'_\infty = \frac{1}{2}\sigma_\infty$ = molecular *radius*, then:

$$4\pi\sigma_\infty{}'^2 = kp\bar{c}/\sqrt{(2)}N\eta(1 + C/T) \quad \text{(8)}$$

and $\pi\sigma_\infty{}'^2$ is the area of cross-section for a spherical molecule. Chapman's value of k (equation (13), § 1) is $k = 0{\cdot}499$. For ellipsoidal molecules the calculations [3] of the collision areas involve gamma functions (§ 54.I), but it is doubtful if these calculations have much significance in relation to the fundamental equation connecting η and σ.

Sutherland's formula, therefore, gives:

$$\eta = kp\bar{c}/[\sqrt{(2)}N\pi\sigma_\infty{}^2(1 + C/T)] \quad \text{(9)}$$

$$\therefore\ \frac{\eta}{\eta_0} = \frac{\bar{c}}{\bar{c}_0} \cdot \frac{1 + C/T_0}{1 + C/T} = \sqrt{(T/T_0)} \cdot \frac{1 + C/T_0}{1 + C/T} \quad \text{(10)}$$

(since ρ/N is constant). Sutherland's equation may also (since $\bar{c}$ is proportional to $\sqrt{T}$) be written in a form very convenient for the graphical treatment of experimental results: [4]

$$T = KT^{3/2}/\eta - C \quad \text{(11)}$$

where K is a constant. A plot of $T^{3/2}\eta$ against T then gives a straight line, from which K and C can be found.

The experimental results are often in very good agreement with (11) over certain temperature ranges, so that Sutherland's formula is much used in the study of the viscosities of gases. Zimmer [5] found good agreement with Sutherland's equation at low temperatures with carbon monoxide, except a slight deviation at the lowest temperatures, but with ethylene the observed viscosity was greater than the calculated below −20°. Fortier [6] found that C for air depends on temperature.

Maxwell [7] considered a model of a gas consisting of elastic molecules with a repulsive force varying as the inverse power s of the distance r between the molecular centres:

$$F = \mu r^{-s} \quad \text{(12)}$$

[1] *J. Math. Phys. Mass. Inst. Techn.*, 1921, **1**, 42.

[2] *Phys. Rev.*, 1930, **35**, 1284.

[3] Rankine, *Proc. Roy. Soc.*, 1920–1, **98**, 369; 1921, **99**, 331; Edwards, *ibid.*, 1927, **117**, 245; Rankine and Smith, *Phil. Mag.*, 1921, **42**, 601, 615; Smith, *Proc. Phys. Soc.*, 1922, **34**, 155; on molecular models based on target areas, see Mack, *J.A.C.S.*, 1925, **47**, 2468; Melaven and Mack, *ibid.*, 1932, **54**, 888 (highly speculative); Hare and Mack, *ibid.*, 1932, **54**, 4272; on calculation of σ by Sutherland's equation, see Sutherland, *Phil. Mag.*, 1909, **17**, 320; 1910, **19**, 25; Binkele, *Ann. Phys.*, 1931, **9**, 839; Müller, *Wiss. Veröffl. Siemens-Werke*, 1938, **17**, No. iv, 33.

[4] Fisher, *Phys. Rev.*, 1907, **24**, 385; 1909, **28**, 73.

[5] *Verhl. d. D. Phys. Ges.*, 1912, **14**, 471.

[6] *Compt. Rend.*, 1936, **203**, 711.

[7] *Phil. Trans.*, 1867, **157**, 49; "Scientific Papers," 1890, **2**, 26.

where μ is a constant. It follows from this that the distance of closest approach of the molecular centres is: [1]

$$\sigma=\left[\frac{\mu}{kT(s-1)}\right]^{1/(s-1)} \quad \ldots \ldots \ldots (13)$$

Such molecules can be regarded as elastic spheres in the calculation of the pressure (§ 8.III) if σ is given by (13) multiplied by a factor $\sqrt[3]{\{\Gamma[1-3/(s-1)]\}}$, where Γ denotes the gamma function of the expression in square brackets.[1] This is equivalent to a change of diameter for the two calculations (viscosity and pressure), except where the molecules are truly spherical. The divergence may be considerable when s is small; for the lowest probable value $s=5$ for any gas the factor is 1·5363, and for carbon dioxide ($s=5·6$) the divergence reaches 50 per cent. According to Jeans: [1]

$$\eta=kT^n \quad \ldots \ldots \ldots \ldots (14)$$

$$n=\tfrac{1}{2}+2/(s-1) \quad \ldots \ldots \ldots (15)$$

and k is a constant; for some gases, especially helium, the simple formula:

$$\eta=\eta_0(T/273\cdot 1)^n \quad \ldots \ldots \ldots (16)$$

where η_0 is the viscosity at 0° C. and n is an empirical constant, gives very satisfactory results. Some values of n are: [1]

Gas	H_2	D_2	He	Ne	N_2	CO	Air	O_2	HCl	A	N_2O	CO_2	Cl_2
n	0·695	0·699	0·647	0·657	0·756	0·758	0·768	0·814	1·03	0·823	0·89	0·935	1·0

Rayleigh,[2] who deduced from (12) a proportionality of η to T^x, where $x=(n+3)/(2n-2)$, found that this does not agree with the results with argon.

Since η is proportional to $\sqrt{(mkT)}/\sigma^2$, if σ is given by (13) it follows that:

$$\eta=A\sqrt{(mkT)}[kT(s-1)/\mu]^{2/(s-1)} \quad \ldots \ldots \ldots (17)$$

where A is a numerical constant.

For elastic spheres *attracting* according to the law μr^{-s}, Sutherland's constant becomes:

$$C=(217/615)\mu\beta/k(s-1)\sigma^{s-1} \quad \ldots \ldots \ldots (18)$$

where β has the values:

s	3	4	5	7	9
β	0·701	0·636	0·587	0·517	0·467

The " target area " for collision of two rigid ellipsoids of semi-axes a_0 and $b_0(a_0>b_0)$ has been worked out [3] as:

$$\overline{\overline{D^2}}=a\,.\,\frac{\frac{\pi}{8}\cdot\frac{a+b_0}{a}[2(a+b_0)^2+(a-b_0)^2]+\frac{1}{3}E[4(a-b_0)^2+11ab_0]+\frac{1}{3}Fb_0^2}{\pi(a+b_0)/4+aE} \quad (19)$$

where a=mean semi-axis, $a^2=\frac{1}{3}(2a_0^2+b_0^2)$, and E and F are elliptic normal

1 Jeans, " Kinetic Theory of Gases," 1940, 76, 172.

2 Rayleigh, *Proc. Roy. Soc.*, 1900, **66**, 68; 1900, **67**, 137; Onnes, Dorsman, and Weber, *Proc. K. Akad. Wetens. Amsterdam*, 1913, **15**, 1386 (*Comm. Leiden*, **134***a*); Onnes and Weber, *ibid.*, 1913, **15**, 1396 (*Comm. Leiden*, **134***b*); Jeans, " Kinetic Theory of Gases," 1940, 172; n is related to the critical pressure p_c atm. by the empirical equation $n=0\cdot642+0\cdot00116p_c+0\cdot0_4399p_c^2$, Partington, *Trans. Faraday Soc.*, 1922, **17**, 734.

3 Eirich and Simha *Z. phys. Chem.*, 1937, **180**, 447.

integrals of the first (I) and second (II) kind: [1]

$$\text{(I) } E=\int_0^{\pi/2} d\phi\sqrt{(1-\epsilon^2\sin^2\phi)} \qquad \text{(II) } F=\int_0^{\pi/2} d\phi/\sqrt{(1-\epsilon^2\sin^2\phi)}$$

ϵ being the ellipticity modulus.

Chapman [2] gave for the effective collision radius σ of rigid spherical molecules:

$$\sigma^2=0{\cdot}491(1+\epsilon)\rho_0\bar{c}/4\sqrt{(2)}\pi N\eta(1+C/T) \quad . \; . \; . \; . \; (20)$$

which is equivalent to a mean collision area:

$$\bar{A}=0{\cdot}0868\rho_0\bar{c}(1+\epsilon)/N\eta(1+C/T) \quad . \; . \; . \; . \; . \; (21)$$

where ρ_0=density at S.T.P., $\bar{c}$=mean velocity of molecules at absolute temperature T, N=no. of molecules per cm.^{3} at S.T.P., η=viscosity at T, C=Sutherland's constant, and $(1+\epsilon)$ is a correction factor, ϵ being usually small (0·001–0·006). The results are in good agreement with the molecular diameters calculated by van der Waals's equation. The applicability of this formula to non-spherical molecules is very problematical. Another equation was deduced by Enskog.[3]

Uehling and Hellund [4] found that the elastic sphere model was not satisfactory for helium.

Maxwell,[5] in a mathematical investigation which is classical, had found that the equations for rigid spheres become simpler when an inverse fifth power repulsive force ($s=5$) is assumed; the decrease of effective cross-section with increasing velocity is then exactly compensated by the increased collision frequency resulting from the increasing relative velocity; on this theory the mean free path is proportional to $\sqrt{T}$, which is not in agreement with experiment.

Reinganum [6] assumed that molecular clustering occurs, the increased density in a region towards which attractive forces act being given by Boltzmann's equation (§ 19.III), i.e. by a factor $e^{-\epsilon_p/kT}$, where ϵ_p is the potential energy. With rise in temperature this decreases. The average density ρ_0 of the molecules in the gas is replaced by the density in the cluster:

$$\rho=\rho_0 e^{-\epsilon_p/kT}=\rho_0 e^{-C'/T} \quad . \; . \; . \; . \; . \; . \; . \; . \; (22)$$

and the collision frequency is then given by a modification of Maxwell's formula (20), § 21.III, as

$$Z=\sqrt{(2)}N\pi\sigma^2\bar{c}(\rho/\rho_0)=\sqrt{(2)}N\pi\sigma^2\bar{c}e^{-C'/T} \quad . \; . \; . \; . \; (23)$$

[1] See bibliography to Section I; tables of E and F elliptic integrals, Nagaoka and Sakarai, *Sci. Pap. Inst. Phys. Chem. Res. Tokyo*, 1925, **2**, suppl.; Burington, "Handbook of Mathematical Tables and Formulas," Sandusky (Ohio), 1941, 263, where F is denoted by K.

[2] *Phil. Trans.*, 1912, **211**, 433; 1916, **211**, 279 (347); James, *Proc. Cambr. Phil. Soc.*, 1921, **20**, 447; Lennard-Jones, *Proc. Roy. Soc.*, 1924, **106**, 441. Cf. Melaven and Mack, *J.A.C.S.*, 1932, **54**, 888; Sperry and Mack, *ibid.*, 1932, **54**, 904 (CCl_4; C=335); Eberhart, Hare, and Mack, *ibid.*, 1933, **55**, 4894 (hydrocarbons); Kotani, *Proc. Phys. Math. Soc. Japan*, 1942, **24**, 76.

[3] *Phys. Z.*, 1911, **12**, 56, 533; *Dissert.*, Uppsala, 1917; *Arkiv Mat. Astron. Fys.*, 1922, **16**, No. 16; Chapman and Cowling, "The Mathematical Theory of Non-Uniform Gases," Cambridge, 1939, 151 f.; Amdur, *J. Chem. Phys.*, 1947, **15**, 482 (He at low temps.); for a statistical deduction of the Chapman-Enskog transport equations, see Kirkwood, *J. Chem. Phys.*, 1947, **15**, 72; for calculation of molecular diameter from viscosity, see Magat, *Z. phys. Chem.*, 1932, **16** B, 1; Vaillard, *Compt. Rend.*, 1946, **223**, 1128.

[4] *Phys. Rev.*, 1938, **54**, 479.

[5] *Phil. Mag.*, 1866, **32**, 390; 1868, **35**, 129, 185; *Phil. Trans.*, 1867, **157**, 49; "Scientific Papers," 1890, **2**, 26; Boltzmann, *Ann. Phys.*, 1885, **24**, 37; Jäger, *ibid.*, 1907, **24**, 607; Boltzmann, "Gastheorie," 1896, **1**, 153; Jeans, "Dynamical Theory of Gases," 3rd edit., 1921, 231; "Kinetic Theory of Gases," 1940, 225; Condon and van Amringe, *Phil. Mag.*, 1927, **3**, 604.

[6] *Phys. Z.*, 1901, **2**, 241; *Ann. Phys.*, 1902, **10**, 334; 1909, **28**, 142.

If the ideal collision frequency is $Z_0=\sqrt{(2)}N\pi\sigma^2\bar{c}$, then:

$$Z/Z_0=l_0/l=e^{-C'/T} \qquad (24)$$

By expanding in a series of terms in C'/T and neglecting squares and higher powers, Sutherland's equation (4) is again obtained. Even for large intervals of temperature (4) and (24) give similar results.[1] Licht and Stechert [2] wrote Reinganum's viscosity equation in the form (C' and K are constants):

$$\log (T^{1/2}/\eta)=C'/2\cdot303T-\log K' \qquad (25)$$

At low temperatures (20° K.) a modification of Sutherland's formula given by Chapman [3] holds; this is equivalent to:

$$\frac{\eta_0}{\eta_T}=\left(\frac{T_0}{T}\right)^{1/2}\frac{1+C/T-(C'/T)^2}{1+C/T_0-(C'/T_0)^2} \qquad (26)$$

Kassel [4] found that the collision number in a non-ideal gas is increased in the ratio $(1+C/T)$:1, but the meaning of C is " quite different from Sutherland's ": his paper should be consulted for details.

The applicability of Sutherland's equation (10) may be illustrated by the results of Breitenbach [5] for two gases:

Ethylene, $\eta_0=961\cdot3\times10^{-7}$, $C=225\cdot9$					
t° C.	−21·2	+15·0	99·3	182·4	302·0
$10^7 . \eta$ obs.	891	1006	1278	1530	1826
$10^7 . \eta$ calc.	890	1012	1278	1519	1833
Carbon dioxide, $\eta_0=1387\cdot9\times10^{-7}$, $C=239\cdot7$					
t° C.	−20·7	+15·0	99·1	182·4	302·0
$10^7 . \eta$ obs.	1294	1457	1861	2221	2682
$10^7 . \eta$ calc.	1284	1462	1857	2216	2686

Hydrogen also agreed, with $\eta_0=857\cdot4\times10^{-7}$, and $C=71\cdot7$. Some values of Sutherland's constant C collected by Jeans [6] from more recent experimental researches are:

He	Ne	A	Kr	Xe	H_2	N_2	CO	Air	NO	O_2
78·2 70 80·3 (72·9)	56 (64·1)	174·6 169·9 142 (148)	188	252	83 79 72·2 71·7 (66·8)	102·7 118 (104)	100 118 (102)	113 119·4 111·3 (113)	128 (133)	138 (127)
Cl_2	**N_2O**	**CO_2**	**C_2H_4**	**CH_3Cl**	**NH_3**	**SO_2**	**C_2H_2**	**CH_4**	**C_3H_8**	**n-C_4H_{10}**
325 (345)	274 260 (263)	274 277 239·7 (253)	225·9 272	454	(505)	(404)	(320)	(169)	(288)	(309)

[1] Rappenecker, *Z. phys. Chem.*, 1910, **72**, 695.
[2] *J. Phys. Chem.*, 1944, **48**, 23.
[3] *Phil. Trans.*, 1912, **211**, 433 (459).
[4] *J. Phys. Chem.*, 1930, **34**, 1777.
[5] *Ann. Phys.*, 1901, **5**, 166.
[6] " Kinetic Theory of Gases," 1940, 178; see Anfilogoff, *Thesis*, London, 1932, 307, 387; the values in brackets are from Wobser and Müller, *Koll. Beih.*, 1941, **52**, 165.

The following table [1] shows the superiority for helium of equation (16) with $n=0\cdot647$ over Sutherland's formula at low temperatures.

$t°$ C.	183·7	18·7	−22·8	−70	−102·6	−197·6	−253	−258·1
$10^7 . \eta$ obs. ...	2681	1980	1788	1564	1392	817·6	349·8	294·6
$10^7 . \eta$ (16) ...	2632	1970	1783	1558	1389	821·3	348·9	288·7
$10^7 . \eta$ (Suth.)	2682	1979	1771	1513	1317	628	135	92

§ 6. Viscosity Equations

Sutherland's formula, although it holds very well for argon over a wide range of temperature,[2] fails for helium at low temperatures, and applies only over limited ranges of temperature for most gases.[3] Trautz and Binkele [4] replaced it by the empirical formula:

$$\eta=aT^n/(1+C/T) \quad . \ . \ . \ . \ . \ . \ . \ . \ . \quad (1)$$

containing three constants, a, n, and C. This can be fitted within about 1 per cent. over the whole range of temperature for helium, neon, hydrogen, and nitrogen, but not for argon and carbon dioxide.

Nernst [5] suggested that, at *very low temperatures*, $\eta=(1/9)m^3\bar{c}^3/\boldsymbol{h}^2$, where m=mass of molecule, $\bar{c}$=velocity of molecule, $\boldsymbol{h}$=Planck's constant. This gives:

$$\eta_1/\eta_2=(T_1/T_2)^{3/2} \quad . \ . \ . \ . \ . \ . \ . \ . \ . \quad (2)$$

Van Cleave and Maass [6] proposed:

$$\eta=AT^{1/2}e^{BT} \quad . \ . \ . \ . \ . \ . \ . \ . \ . \ . \quad (3)$$

where A and B are constants. A four-constant formula was deduced by Lennard-Jones [7] on the assumption of a molecular force field (§ 42.VII C):

$$F=\lambda_n/r^n-\lambda_m/r^m \quad . \ . \ . \ . \ . \ . \ . \ . \ . \quad (4)$$

[1] Jeans, *op. cit.*, 179, where other temperatures are also given. For earlier values, see Sutherland, *Phil. Mag.*, 1909, **17**, 320; 1910, **19**, 25; for plots of η and temperature, see Genereaux, *Ind. Eng. Chem.*, 1930, **22**, 1382; for other gases, see Müller, *Wiss. Veröffl. Siemens-Werke*, 1938, **17**, No. iv, 33; Wobser and Müller, *Koll. Beih.*, 1941, **52**, 165.

[2] Anfilogoff, *Thesis*, London, 1932; Partington, *Phys. Z.*, 1933, **34**, 289; Brémond, *Compt. Rend.*, 1933, **196**, 1472; Vasilesco, *Ann. de Phys.*, 1945, **20**, 137, 292, found an increase in C for air, nitrogen, argon, and carbon dioxide with rise of temperature up to 1600°:

	0° C.	1627° C.
air	113	124
N_2	110	120
A	142·3	168
CO_2 ...	254	307 (1427° C.)

[3] Vogel, *Ann. Phys.*, 1914, **43**, 1235 (fails for H_2 at 21° K.); Günther, *Z. phys. Chem.*, 1924, **110**, 626 (fails at low temps.); Erk, *Z. ges. Kälte-Ind.*, 1924, **31**, 49.

[4] *Ann. Phys.*, 1930, **5**, 561; Trautz, *ibid.*, 1930, **5**, 919; 1931, **11**, 190; Trautz and Sorg, *ibid.*, 1931, **10**, 81; Licht and Stechert, *J. Phys. Chem.*, 1944, **48**, 23.

[5] *Berlin Ber.*, 1919, 118; Günther, *ibid.*, 1920, 720 (H_2); *Z. phys. Chem.*, 1924, **110**, 626.

[6] *Canad. J. Res.*, 1935, **13** B, 140.

[7] *Proc. Roy. Soc.*, 1924, **106**, 441; 1925, **107**, 157; Hassé and Cook, *Phil. Mag.*, 1927, **3**, 977; *Proc. Roy. Soc.*, 1929, **125**, 196; Shames, *Phys. Z.*, 1928, **29**, 91, found $m=n=8$ for helium; Burnett, *Proc. Cambr. Phil. Soc.*, 1937, **33**, 363. A detailed critical discussion of the formula is given by Anfilogoff, *Thesis*, London, 1932, 327 f.; Kichara and Kotani, *Proc. Phys. Math. Soc. Japan*, 1943, **25**, 602.

With $m=3$ for mathematical convenience this gives for a relatively weak attracting field:

$$\eta=aT^{1/2}/(T^{-2/(n-1)}+B/T) \quad . \quad . \quad . \quad . \quad . \quad . \quad . \quad . \quad (5)$$

where B is a constant. This gave good results with argon, but the fit was equally good with $n=21$ and $B=62{\cdot}45$, and with $n=14\frac{1}{3}$ and $B=38{\cdot}62$. The virial coefficients (§ 6.VII C) calculated from viscosities, however, do not agree very well with those calculated from compressibilities.[1]

Van Itterbeek and Van Paemel [2] found that the viscosity of argon, which follows Sutherland's equation at high temperatures,[3] can be represented by (16), § 5, in the form $\eta=\eta_{90}(T/90)^{0{\cdot}883}$, with η_{90} (at 90° K.)$=759{\cdot}2\times10^{-7}$, but not by any of Lennard-Jones's potential functions. The viscosity of helium at 1·6° K. and above [4] agrees with a quantum theory of temperature dependence based on Bose-Einstein statistics (§ 36.IV).[5]

Trautz [6] concluded that the viscosity of a gas at the critical temperature is related to the temperature by the formula:

$$(\mathrm{d}\ln\eta/\mathrm{d}\ln T)_{T_c}=1 \quad . \quad . \quad . \quad . \quad . \quad . \quad . \quad . \quad (6)$$

Licht and Stechert [7] deduced from this the formula:

$$\eta=bT(\vartheta^{3/4}+\vartheta^{-3/4})^{-c} \quad . \quad . \quad . \quad . \quad . \quad . \quad . \quad . \quad (7)$$

where b and c are constants, and $\vartheta=T/T_c$. Another form is

$$\eta/\eta_c=2^c\vartheta(\vartheta^{3/4}-\vartheta^{-3/4})^{-c} \quad . \quad . \quad . \quad . \quad . \quad . \quad . \quad . \quad (8)$$

which they call Trautz's equation.

Dutta [8] found that the plots of η/η_b against T/T_b, where η_b is the viscosity at the b.p. T_b (abs.) for several gases, give a single " universal " curve, as previously found for liquids.[9] A relation between viscosity and vapour pressure [10] is, therefore, not unexpected. Rankine [11] found that Sutherland's constant C is related to the critical temperature by the empirical equation:

$$T_c/C=1{\cdot}12 \text{ to } 1{\cdot}14 \text{ (or } 0{\cdot}45 \text{ for hydrogen)} \quad . \quad . \quad . \quad . \quad (9)$$

Vogel,[12] from the relation between T_c and abs. b.p., $T_b/T_c=\frac{2}{3}$ (§ 7.VII B), concluded that:

$$C=1{\cdot}47T_b \quad \text{or} \quad C/T_c=0{\cdot}98 \quad . \quad . \quad . \quad . \quad . \quad . \quad . \quad (10)$$

Keyes [13] found that Sutherland's constant C is (except for He) approximately a linear function of the polarisation:

$$P_e=V_m(D-1)/(D+1) \quad . \quad . \quad . \quad . \quad . \quad . \quad . \quad . \quad (11)$$

1 Massey and Buckingham, *Proc. Roy. Soc.*, 1938, **168**, 378; Buckingham, Hamilton, and Massey, *ibid.*, 1941, **179**, 103.

2 *Physica*, 1938, **5**, 1009; 1940, **7**, 273; the agreement is better with the energy value $E=-ar^{-6}+be^{-pr}$ (§ 46.VII C) used by Herzfeld, *Phys. Rev.*, 1937, **52**, 374.

3 Anfilogoff, *Thesis*, London, 1932; Partington, *Phys. Z.*, 1933, **34**, 289.

4 Van Itterbeek and Keesom, *Physica*, 1938, **5**, 257 (*Comm. Leiden*, **252***a*).

5 Uehling and Uhlenbeek, *Phys. Rev.*, 1933, **43**, 552; Uehling, *ibid.*, 1934, **45**, 766; 1934, **46**, 917; Kahn and Uhlenbeek, *Physica*, 1938, **5**, 399.

6 *Ann. Phys.*, 1931, **10**, 263; 1931, **11**, 190; 1932, **15**, 198; 1933, **16**, 751; A. W. Müller, *Wiss. Veröffl. Siemens-Werke*, 1938, **17**, No. iv, 33.

7 *J. Phys. Chem.*, 1944, **48**, 23.

8 *Nature*, 1943, **152**, 445.

9 Nissan, *Nature*, 1943, **152**, 630.

10 Trautz, *Ber.*, 1943, **75**, 1750.

11 *Proc. Roy. Soc.*, 1910, **84**, 181; Cuthbertson, *Phil. Mag.*, 1911, **21**, 69; Porter, *Trans. Faraday Soc.*, 1928, **24**, 108 ($C\simeq T_c$); Arnold, *Ind. Eng. Chem.*, 1930, **22**, 1091; Melaven and Mack, *J.A.C.S.*, 1932, **54**, 888.

12 *Ann. Phys.*, 1914, **43**, 1235; Arnold, *J. Chem. Phys.*, 1933, **1**, 170.

13 *Z. phys. Chem.*, 1927, **130**, 709.

where D=dielectric constant, V_m=molar vol. Braune, Basch, and Wentzel[1] found that the mean electric moment of inertia of a molecule, Θ, related to Sutherland's constant C in Debye's[2] theory of quadrupole attraction (§ 43.VII C), is proportional to the volume of the atom for monatomic gases:

$$C=0{\cdot}118\frac{P_e\Theta^2}{R\sigma^3}=0{\cdot}118\frac{R\Theta^2}{\boldsymbol{R}\sigma^3};\ \Theta/\sigma^3=\text{const.} \quad . \quad . \quad . \quad . \quad (12)$$

where σ=atomic diameter, R=molecular refraction for long waves, equal to the electron polarisation P_e, and $\boldsymbol{R}$=gas constant.

Hirota[3] used the quantum-mechanical method of Massey and Mohr[4] to calculate the viscosity cross-section for a rigid elastic sphere molecule; he found the agreement with helium and neon over a wide range of temperature was not good, but better than that with the classical method. Agreement was better if a Sutherland factor was introduced to take into account the inter-molecular potential. The Sutherland constant as calculated by quantum mechanics agreed with the Rankine and Vogel rules, (9) and (10), even for substances of low mol. wt., and the disagreement in the Debye formula between electric moment and Sutherland constant also disappeared.

If the value of (d ln η/d ln T) is unity at the critical temperature, and is m at any other temperature, Trautz[5] found that the limiting value of m is:

$$m_g=[m-(2-m)(T_c/T)^{3/2}]/[1-(T_c/T)^{3/2}] \quad . \quad . \quad . \quad . \quad (13)$$

and is identical with the value of n in the equation $\eta=aT^n$, the constant a being η_c/T_c. He called $\eta_c/\sqrt{T_c}$ the "specific critical viscosity." Müller,[6] with a "reduced viscosity" $\eta_r=\eta/\eta_c$, found a linear relation between $\sqrt{(\eta_r/\vartheta)}$ and $\sqrt{(1/\vartheta)}$, where $\vartheta=T/T_c$.

Trautz regarded the apparent molecular diameter σ as variable with temperature, and calculated[7] it by using the formula $\eta=aT^n$ and the Enskog-Chapman formula. He found d ln σ/dT=1−2m, where m is d ln η/d ln T. A calculation[8] of critical volume from the relation of η to the vapour-pressure curve, assuming proportionality between v_c and the "viscosity volume" $b_{c\eta}$ is on similar lines. Trautz[9] also found:

$$\eta_c(T_c/m^3p_c^4)^{1/6}=\text{const.} \quad . \quad . \quad . \quad . \quad . \quad . \quad . \quad . \quad (14)$$

and with Chapman's equation (13), § 1, and the equation of Weber:[10]

$$\log(\sigma/2)=-\tfrac{1}{2}\log[\eta/\sqrt{(MT)}] \quad . \quad . \quad . \quad . \quad . \quad . \quad (15)$$

this gives the reduced value (where $c^2=2{\cdot}7\times10^{-21}$):

$$\log(\sigma/c)_r=-\tfrac{1}{2}\log\{[\eta/\sqrt{(MT)}](T_c/p_c)^{2/3}\} \quad . \quad . \quad . \quad . \quad (16)$$

Weng Wen Po[11] found that $\eta/\sqrt{T}$ is a linear function of L_e/T, where L_e=molar heat of evaporation. Rankine,[12] for monatomic gases of atomic weight A, found:

$$\eta_c^2/A=3{\cdot}93\times10^{-10} \quad . \quad . \quad . \quad . \quad . \quad . \quad . \quad . \quad (17)$$

1 *Z. phys. Chem.*, 1928, **138**, 447.
2 *Phys. Z.*, 1920, **21**, 178.
3 *Bull. Chem. Soc. Japan*, 1944, **19**, 102, 109.
4 *Proc. Roy. Soc.*, 1933, **141**, 434; 1934, **144**, 188.
5 *Ann. Phys.*, 1931, **10**, 263; 1931, **11**, 190; 1932, **15**, 198; 1933, **16**, 751.
6 *Wiss. Veröffl. Siemens Werke*, 1938, **17**, 395.
7 *Ann. Phys.*, 1933, **16**, 751, 865.
8 Trautz, *Ann. Phys.*, 1934, **20**, 313.
9 *J. prakt. Chem.*, 1943, **162**, 218.
10 *Physica*, 1939, **6**, 551.
11 *Phil. Mag.*, 1938, **25**, 865.
12 *Proc. Roy. Soc.*, 1913, **88**, 575.

A so-called " general viscosity curve " was devised by Van Itterbeek and Van Paemel.[1]

Fisher [2] found for Sutherland's constant:

$$C=0{\cdot}058M^2+74 \quad . \quad . \quad . \quad . \quad . \quad . \quad . \quad . \quad . \quad (18)$$

where M=mol. wt. Rankine [3] found the ratio of Sutherland's constants for the following pairs of gases and vapours is constant, $Cl_2/A(325/142=2{\cdot}3)$, $Br_2/Kr(460/188=2{\cdot}4)$, $I_2/Xe(590/252=2{\cdot}3)$. A supposed relation [4] between Sutherland's constant and the van der Waals constant b has been criticised.[5] Bradford [6] considered viscosity and thermal conductivity from the point of view of molecular attraction. Othmer and Josefowitz [7] represented viscosities by:

$$\log \eta=A \log p+C \quad . \quad . \quad . \quad . \quad . \quad . \quad . \quad . \quad (19)$$

where A and C are constants, and p is the vapour pressure at the temperature of a reference substance. They gave a nomographic treatment.

Cooper and Maass [8] used the formula for dependence of viscosity on temperature (K=constant):

$$\eta=\sqrt{T}(1+KT) \quad . \quad . \quad . \quad . \quad . \quad . \quad . \quad . \quad . \quad (20)$$

Licht and Stechert [9] tested Sutherland's, Reinganum's, and Trautz's equations, and the exponential equation (14), § 5, with data for 24 gases and vapours, and found that the general overall percentage error is as follows:

Exponential 1·8, Sutherland 1·3, Reinganum 2·6, Trautz 1·4.

Hydrogen and helium do not agree at all with Sutherland's equation, but do with Trautz's; if they are omitted, Sutherland's equation is decidedly better, the overall percentage errors being:

Exponential 1·7, Sutherland 0·8, Reinganum 1·8, Trautz 1·4.

Licht and Stechert recommended that Sutherland's equation be used for gases except hydrogen and helium, for which Trautz's equation should be used. They gave the following as the best values of the constants C and K of Sutherland's equation (11), § 5:

	C	$K\times10^6$		C	$K\times10^6$
Acetone	530	11·79	Helium	97·6	15·13
Acetylene	206	10·07	Hydrogen	70·6	6·48
Ammonia	472	15·42	Hydrogen chloride	359	18·66
Argon	133	19·00	Mercuric chloride	996	31·29
Benzene	403	10·33	Mercury	996	63·00
Bromine	517	23·33	Methane	155	9·82
Carbon dioxide ...	233	15·52	Methyl chloride ...	390	14·45
Carbon tetrachloride	335	12·17	Nitrogen	102	13·85
Cyclohexane ...	319	8·41	Nitrous oxide ...	273	16·36
Ethyl acetate ...	425	10·60	Oxygen	110	16·49
Ethyl alcohol ...	400	11·67	Sulphur dioxide ...	362	16·53
Ethyl ether	349	9·43	Toluene	365	9·09
Ethylene	232	10·54	Water	659	18·31

1 *Physica*, 1940, **7**, 265; Viallard, *Compt. Rend.*, 1946, **223**, 1128.
2 *Phys. Rev.*, 1907, **24**, 385.
3 *Phil. Mag.*, 1915, **29**, 552.
4 Fowler, *Phil. Mag.*, 1922, **43**, 785.
5 Core, *Phil. Mag.*, 1923, **45**, 622.
6 *Phil. Mag.*, 1943, **34**, 433.
7 *Ind. Eng. Chem.*, 1946, **38**, 110.
8 *Canad. J. Res.*, 1932, **6**, 596.
9 *J. Phys. Chem.*, 1944, **48**, 23; for data for many vapours of organic compounds, see Titani, *Bull. Chem. Soc. Japan*, 1929, **4**, 277; 1930, **5**, 98; 1933, **8**, 255; Bleakney, *Physics*, 1932, **3**, 123 (pentanes, pentenes, CCl_4).

Since hydrogen and helium do not follow Sutherland's equation, the constants of Trautz's equation (7) are given: hydrogen $b=0{\cdot}653\times10^{-6}$, $c=0{\cdot}464$; helium $b=2{\cdot}790\times10^{-6}$, $c=0{\cdot}470$.

They proposed a general viscosity-temperature equation for estimating the viscosity when no experimental data are available. The data required are critical temperature, critical pressure (p_c atm.), and molecular weight of the gas, and in general the experimental results are reproduced within 2 to 10 per cent. A nomograph is given for the evaluation of viscosity based on this equation:

$$\eta=6{\cdot}30\times10^{-6}[\vartheta^{3/2}/(\vartheta+0{\cdot}8)](M^3p_c^4/T_c)^{1/6} \quad . \quad . \quad . \quad . \quad (21)$$

§ 7. Viscosity of Gas Mixtures

The viscosity of a mixture of gases varies with the composition. Graham [1] found that the change may not be continuous, and for a certain composition the viscosity η_{12} of a mixture of two gases may be greater than either of the viscosities η_1 and η_2 of the pure gases.

As a first approximation an additive relation [2] based on (11), § 1, may be assumed:

$$\eta=\tfrac{1}{3}(\rho_1\bar{c}_1l_1+\rho_2\bar{c}_2l_2+\rho_3\bar{c}_3l_3+\ldots) \quad . \quad . \quad . \quad . \quad . \quad . \quad (1)$$

or for a binary mixture:

$$\eta_{12}=\tfrac{1}{3}\rho_1\bar{c}_1l_1+\tfrac{1}{3}\rho_2\bar{c}_2l_2 \quad . \quad . \quad . \quad . \quad . \quad . \quad . \quad . \quad (2)$$

By substituting for l_1 and l_2 from (37) and (38) of § 22.III, the equation [3] due to Sutherland and Thiesen:

$$\eta_{12}=\eta_1/(1+\kappa_{12}n_2/n_1)+\eta_2/(1+\kappa_{21}n_1/n_2) \quad . \quad . \quad . \quad . \quad (3)$$

is found, where n_1, n_2 are the concentrations in mols per cm.^{3}, and κ_{12}, κ_{21} are constants depending on the molecular weights and diameters:

$$\kappa_{12}=\frac{(\sigma_1+\sigma_2)^2}{4\sqrt{(2)}\sigma_1^2}\bigg/\sqrt{\left(\frac{M_1+M_2}{M_2}\right)};\quad \kappa_{21}=\frac{(\sigma_1+\sigma_2)^2}{4\sqrt{(2)}\sigma_2^2}\bigg/\sqrt{\left(\frac{M_1+M_2}{M_1}\right)}.$$

When n_2/n_1 is small this reduces to:

$$\eta_{12}=\eta_1+(n_2/n_1)[(\eta_2/\kappa_{21})-\eta_1\kappa_{12}] \quad . \quad . \quad . \quad . \quad . \quad . \quad (4)$$

and if $\eta_2>\eta_1\kappa_{12}\kappa_{21}$, a small addition of the second gas (even if $\eta_2<\eta_1$) increases the viscosity. If η_2 is also less than η_1 the value of η_{12} must first increase to a maximum as n_2/n_1 is increased and then fall to its final value η_2.

Schmick used the formula:

$$\eta_{12}=\eta_1/(1+Ap_2/p_1)+\eta_2/(1+Bp_1/p_2) \quad . \quad . \quad . \quad . \quad (5)$$

[1] *Phil. Trans.*, 1846, **136**, 573; "Researches," 1876, 145; Schmitt, *Ann. Phys.*, 1909, **30**, 393 (He and A).

[2] Graham, *loc. cit.*; O. E. Meyer, *Ann. Phys.*, 1861, **113**, 383; Puluj, *Wien Ber.*, 1879, **79**, II, 97, 745; O. E. Meyer, "Kinetic Theory of Gases," 1899, 201; for a *dissociating* gas, see *ibid.*, 230.

[3] Sutherland, *Phil. Mag.*, 1895, **40**, 421; Thiesen, *Verhl. d. D. Phys. Ges.*, 1902, **4**, 348; 1906, **8**, 236; Kleint, *ibid.*, 1905, **7**, 146; Tänzler, *ibid.*, 1906, **8**, 222; Schmitt, *Ann. Phys.*, 1909, **30**, 393; Thomsen, *ibid.*, 1911, **36**, 815; Gille, *ibid.*, 1915, **48**, 799 (H_2+He); Kuenen, "Die Eigenschaften der Gase" (Ostwald-Drucker, "Handbuch der allgemeinen Chemie," 3), Leipzig, 1919, 110; Schmick, *Phys. Z.*, 1928, **29**, 633; Drucker, *Z. Elektrochem.*, 1929, **35**, 640; Nasini and Rossi, *Gazz.*, 1929, **58**, 898, 912; Jung and Schmick, *Z. phys. Chem.*, 1930, **7** B, 130; Herzfeld, in H. S. Taylor, "Physical Chemistry," 1931, **1**, 157; Trautz, *Ann. Phys.*, 1931, **8**, 797; 1933, **18**, 816, 833; Azumi, *Sci. Pap. Inst. Phys. Chem. Res. Tokyo*, 1932, **19**, Suppl. 119; *Bull Inst. Phys. Chem. Res. Tokyo*, 1932, **11**, 1103; Schröer, *Z. phys. Chem.*, 1936, **34** B, 161.

where p_1, p_2 are the partial pressures, and A and B are complicated expressions given later in § 5.VII G.

Another formula, deduced by Puluj:[1]

$$\eta=\eta_1 \cdot \frac{\sqrt{[p_1+(M_2/M_1)p_2]}}{\left[p_1+\left(\frac{\eta_1}{\eta_2}\Big/\sqrt{\frac{M_2}{M_1}}\right)^{3/2} p_2\right]^{2/3}} \quad . \quad . \quad . \quad . \quad . \quad (6)$$

where p_1, p_2 are the partial pressures ($p_1+p_2=1$) of two gases of mol. wts. M_1, M_2 and viscosities η_1, η_2, was found by Schmitt[2] to give less satisfactory results than Thiesen's (3), whilst Klemenc and Remi[3] found it to give results within 2 to 3 per cent. for mixtures of nitric oxide and hydrogen. Equation (3) gives fairly satisfactory results for most binary mixtures, but a theoretically more exact formula deduced by Chapman[4] was confirmed experimentally by Trautz and co-workers,[5] who also used ternary mixtures:

$$\eta_{12}=\frac{a_1n_1^2\eta_1+a_{12}n_1n_2+a_2n_2^2\eta_2}{a_1n_1^2+bn_1n_2+a_2n_2^2} \quad . \quad . \quad . \quad . \quad . \quad (7)$$

where a_1, a_{12}, a_2 and b are constants depending on the molecular weights, the law of force, and the temperature. A similar equation had been given by Maxwell.[6]

Enskog,[7] by a generalisation of Maxwell's equation, found:

$$\eta_{12}=\frac{\eta_1(1+\beta_2n_1/n_2)+\eta_2(1+\beta_1n_2/n_1)+A}{(1+\beta_2n_1/n_2)(1+\beta_1n_2/n_1)-A^2/4\eta_1\eta_2} \quad . \quad . \quad . \quad (8)$$

which differs from Maxwell's only by the term $-A^2/4\eta_1\eta_2$ in the denominator. For elastic spheres without attractive forces:

$$\beta_1=\tfrac{1}{12}[(\sigma_1+\sigma_2)/\sigma_1]^2[2m_2/(m_1+m_2)]^{1/2}(5m_1+3m_2)/(m_1+m_2)$$

$$\beta_2=\tfrac{1}{12}[(\sigma_1+\sigma_2)/\sigma_2]^2[2m_1/(m_1+m_2)]^{1/2}(3m_1+5m_2)/(m_1+m_2)$$

$$A^2=16\eta_1\eta_2\beta_1\beta_2m_1m_2/(15m_1^2+34m_1m_2+15m_2^2).$$

Jung and Schmick allowed for persistence of velocities (§ 3). They found a maximum viscosity in mixtures of methane and ammonia with about 25 per cent. of ammonia (a maximum in mixtures of ethylene and ammonia with 40 per cent. of ammonia was previously known). They concluded from theoretical considerations that the Sutherland constant of a binary mixture of gases is given by $C=0{\cdot}733\sqrt{(C_1C_2)}$, which is of the same form as the van der Waals a equation (§ 35.VII C), $a=\sqrt{(a_1a_2)}$, and for similar reasons, but Schröer found from London's wave-mechanical theory of van der Waals forces

[1] *Wien Ber.*, 1879, **79**, II, 97, 745.
[2] *Ann. Phys.*, 1909, **30**, 393.
[3] *Monatsh.*, 1924, **44**, 307.
[4] *Phil. Trans.*, 1912, **211**, 433; 1916, **216**, 279; 1916, **217**, 115; *Proc. Roy. Soc.*, 1916, **93**, 1.
[5] Trautz, *Heidelberg Ber.*, 1929, No. 12 (bibl.); Trautz *et al.*, *Ann. Phys.*, 1925, **78**, 305; 1926, **79**, 637; 1926, **80**, 637; 1927, **82**, 227; 1929, **2**, 733, 737, 743; 1929, **3**, 409; 1930, **5**, 561; 1930, **7**, 409; 1931, **8**, 797; 1931, **9**, 981; 1931, **10**, 81, 155; 1931, **11**, 606; 1932, **15**, 198; 1933, **18**, 816, 833; 1934, **20**, 118, 121; 1935, **22**, 189; Ishikawa, *Bull. Chem. Soc. Japan*, 1929, **4**, 288.
[6] Maxwell, *Phil. Mag.*, 1868, **35**, 185 (212); "Scientific Papers," 1890, **2**, 72.
[7] Enskog, *Phys. Z.*, 1911, **12**, 56, 533; *Dissert.*, Uppsala, 1917; *Arkiv Mat. Astron. Fys.*, 1922, **16**, No. 16; for review, see Schudel, *Schweiz. Verein Gas- u. Wasserfach. Monats-Bull.*, 1942, **22**, 21; for relation to diffusion coefficient, see Kuenen, *Proc. K. Akad. Wetens. Amsterdam*, 1914, **16**, 1162 (*Comm. Leiden*, Suppl., 36*a*); for binary mixtures of hydrogen and hydrocarbons, Adzumi, *Bull. Chem. Soc. Japan*, 1937, **12**, 199.

(§ 44.VII C) that the numerical factor is 0·95, i.e. $C=0{\cdot}95\sqrt{(C_1C_2)}$. He found qualitative, and sometimes quantitative, agreement with (7).

§ 8. Determination of Gaseous Viscosity

The experimental methods for the determination of the viscosities of gases [1] fall mainly into two groups. In the first, a solid disc, cylinder, or sphere is moved in the gas, in most cases very close to a fixed disc, cylinder, or concentric sphere, and the force exerted is measured in a suitable way. In the second method, the gas is forced through a capillary tube and the pressure difference between the ends of the tube is measured. The two methods are here called the viscous reaction and transpiration methods, respectively.

The *viscous reaction* method was first used for gases by O. E. Meyer,[2] with three parallel horizontal oscillating discs. Maxwell [3] interposed four fixed discs very close to the three moving ones, and his apparatus was improved and used by Kundt and Warburg.[4] Allan [5] reports that Poynting in 1901 had used parallel discs, the upper disc being surrounded by a guard-ring (like the disc in a Thomson's absolute electrometer) to eliminate the edge-effect. Győző Zemplén [6] used concentric spheres (which avoid some end and side corrections), and other modifications of the method have been devised, some with quartz apparatus for use at high temperatures.[7]

The oscillating disc method can also be used at low temperatures,[8] when it has the advantages that only small quantities of pure gas are required and the apparatus can be accommodated in a constant-temperature bath of moderate dimensions. Oscillating cylinders have also been used.[9] Gilchrist, in Millikan's laboratory, used a rotating cylinder, inside which (protected at the top and bottom by short fixed guard-cylinders) was a cylinder suspended from a bifilar phosphor-bronze strip carrying a mirror, the deflexion of which was measured (Fig. 5.VII F). If ϕ=deflexion angle, I=moment of inertia of inner moving

[1] Summary by Graetz in Winkelmann, " Handbuch der Physik," 1908, **1**, ii, 1399 f.; Brillouin, " Leçons sur la Viscosité des Liquides et des Gaz," 2 vols., 1907; Eucken, in Stähler, " Arbeitsmethoden der anorganischen Chemie," Leipzig, 1913, **3**, i, 546; Kuenen, " Die Eigenschaften der Gase " (Ostwald-Drucker, " Handbuch der allgemeinen Chemie," **3**), Leipzig, 1919, 89; Barr, " Monograph of Viscometry," 1931; Anfilogoff, *Thesis*, London, 1932 (from the author's laboratory) gave a critical review of the whole subject; Wobser and Müller, *Koll. Beih.*, 1941, **52**, 165.

[2] *Ann. Phys.*, 1865, **125**, 177; 1866, **127**, 253, 353; 1887, **32**, 642; *Munich Ber.*, 1887, **17**, 343.

[3] *Phil. Trans.*, 1866, **156**, 249; *Proc. Roy. Soc.*, 1866, **15**, 14.

[4] *Ann. Phys.*, 1875, **155**, 337, 525; 1876, **159**, 399; Grossmann, *ibid.*, 1882, **16**, 619; Schumann, *ibid.*, 1884, **23**, 353.

[5] *Phys. Z.*, 1909, **10**, 961 (equations for calculation of η).

[6] *Ann. Phys.*, 1906, **19**, 783; 1909, **29**, 869; 1912, **38**, 71; 1916, **49**, 39; Allan, *Phys. Z.*, 1909, **10**, 961.

[7] Hogg, *Proc. Amer. Acad.*, 1905, **40**, 611; 1906, **42**, 115; 1909, **45**, 1; *Phil. Mag.*, 1910, **19**, 376; Braune, Basch, and Wentzel, *Z. phys. Chem.*, 1928, **137**, 176, 447.

[8] Vogel, *Dissert.*, Berlin, 1913; *Ann. Phys.*, 1914, **43**, 1235; Günther, *Z. phys. Chem.*, 1924, **110**, 626; Braune, Basch, and Wentzel, *ibid.*, 1928, **137**, 176, 447; Sutherland and Maass, *Canad. J. Res.*, 1932, **6**, 428; van Itterbeek and Keesom, *Physica*, 1938, **5**, 257; Weber, *ibid.*, 1939, **6**, 551; Johnston and McClosky, *J. Phys. Chem.*, 1940, **44**, 1038; Johnston and Grilly, *ibid.*, 1942, **46**, 948; van Paemel, *Verhl. K. Vlaam. Acad. Wet.*, 1941, **3**, No. 3; van Itterbeek, van Paemel, and van Lierde, *Physica*, 1947, **13**, 88.

[9] Tomlinson, *Phil. Trans.*, 1887, **177**, 767; Gilchrist, *Phys. Z.*, 1913, **14**, 160; *Phys. Rev.*, 1913, **1**, 124; Timiriazev, *Ann. Phys.*, 1913, **40**, 971; States, *Phys. Rev.*, 1923, **21**, 662; Day, *ibid.*, 1932, **40**, 281; Kjellström, *Phil. Mag.*, 1937, **23**, 313 (bibl.); Müller, *Ann. Phys.*, 1942, **41**, 335.

cylinder, τ=period of oscillation, a=radius of inner moving cylinder, b=radius of outer fixed cylinder, l=length of inner moving cylinder, ω=angular velocity of inner moving cylinder, then: [1]

$$\eta=\pi\phi I(b^2-a^2)/a^2b^2\tau^2\omega l \quad . \quad . \quad (1)$$

Weissweiler [2] compared the viscosities of gases and vapours by measuring the deflexion of a quartz fibre in a stream of the gas. Chella [3] used an oscillating cylinder between two fixed cylinders.

The *transpiration method* was used as a comparative method by Faraday, [4] and later by Graham [5] in some remarkably accurate researches. It was improved by O. E. Meyer [6] and Warburg,[7] and was applied to steam and to mercury vapour by Puluj and by Koch [8] respectively. It was used by Lothar Meyer [9] and his pupils Schumann and Steudel, for vapours of organic compounds (esters, acids) and steam. Important researches on the effect of temperature on viscosity were made by this method by Holman [10] and Bestelmeyer,[11] and very high temperatures (up to 1340°) (with a platinum spiral capillary heated in an Argand petroleum lamp chimney) were used by Barus.[12] The transpiration method was brought to a much more advanced stage by Breitenbach,[13] whose apparatus, with some modifications, was

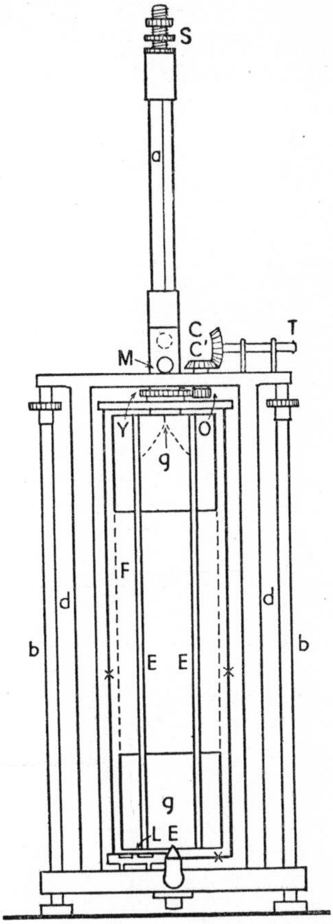

FIG. 5.VII F. Rotating Cylinder Viscosity Apparatus of Gilchrist. XX rotating cylinder pivoted at E; gg guard cylinders fixed by brass rods EE and also fixed to tube carrying torsion-head S; F inner cylinder nearly filling space between g and g and suspended by bifilar strip a with mirror M

1 Poynting and Thomson, "Properties of Matter," 1903, 213; Newman and Searle, "General Properties of Matter," 1928, 204; for Millikan's deduction, see Yen, *Phil. Mag.*, 1919, **38**, 582.

2 *Phys. Z.*, 1929, **30**, 364.

3 *Atti R. Accad. Lincei*, 1905, **14**, ii, 23; 1906, **15**, i, 119 (low temperatures).

4 *Quart. J. Sci.*, 1817, **3**, 354; 1819, **7**, 106; "Experimental Researches in Chemistry and Physics," 1859, 5, 6.

5 *Phil. Trans.*, 1846, **136**, 573; 1849, **139**, 349; "Elements of Chemistry," 1850, **1**, 82; "Researches," 1876, 88, 162.

6 *Ann. Phys.*, 1866, **127**, 253, 353; 1873, **148**, 1, 203, 526.

7 *Ann. Phys.*, 1876, **159**, 399.

8 Puluj, *Wien Ber.*, 1878, **78**, II, 279 (steam); Koch, *Ann. Phys.*, 1883, **19**, 857; for other vapours, see Noyes and Goodwin, *Z. phys. Chem.*, 1896, **21**, 671; *Phys. Rev.*, 1896, **4**, 207; Pedersen, *Phys. Rev.*, 1907, **25**, 225; Rappenecker, *Dissert*, Freiburg i. B., 1909; *Z. phys. Chem.*, 1910, **72**, 695.

9 *Ann. Phys.*, 1879, **7**, 497; 1881, **13**, 1; 1882, **16**, 369, 394; 1884, **23**, 353.

10 *Proc. Amer. Acad.*, 1877, **12**, 41; 1886, **21**, 1; *Phil. Mag.*, 1886, **21**, 199 (bibl.); Schall, *Ber.*, 1885, **18**, 2052; Schneebeli, *Arch. Sci. Phys. Nat.*, 1885, **14**, 197.

11 *Dissert.*, Munich, 1903; *Ann. Phys.*, 1904, **13**, 944; Fisher, *Phys. Rev.*, 1907, **24**, 385; 1909, **28**, 73 (air and CO_2 to 500°); 1909, **29**, 147.

12 *Amer. J. Sci.*, 1888, **35**, 407; *Ann. Phys.*, 1889, **36**, 358; full account in *U.S. Geol. Survey Bull.*, 1889, **8**, No. 54, 242.

13 *Dissert.*, Erlangen, 1898; *Ann. Phys.*, 1899, **67**, 803; 1901, **5**, 166.

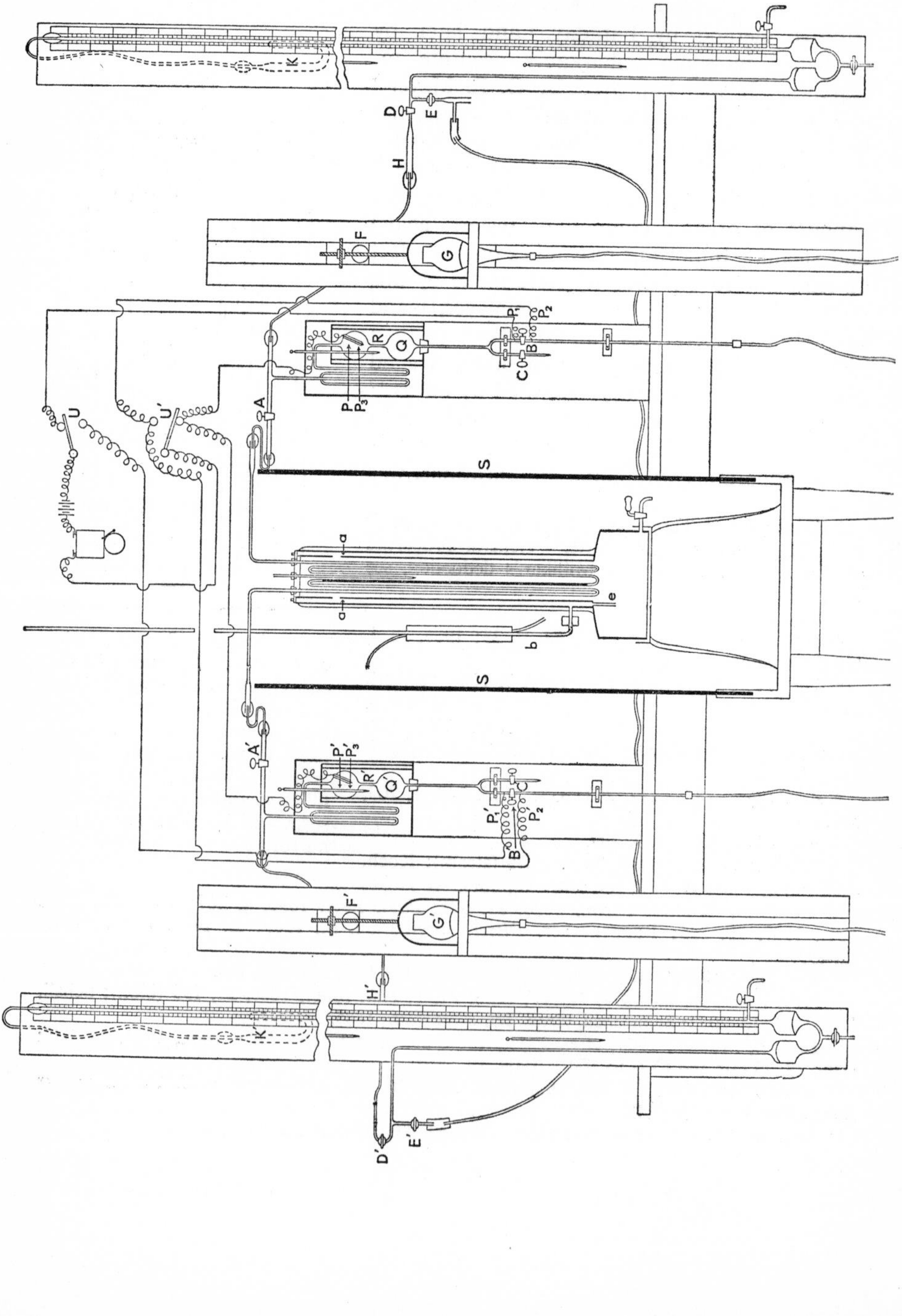

FIG. 6.VII F. Apparatus of Schultze for Measurement of the Viscosity of a Gas by the Transpiration Method. PQ, P′Q′, gas reservoirs, G, G′ mercury bulbs connected by pressure-tubing with PQ and P′Q′, by raising and lowering which gas is passed from the reservoirs first through bent pre-heating tubes in the baths and then through the pre-heating tubes and the capillary (shown black) in a constant temperature (e.g. vapour) bath. The pressures on the two sides of the capillary are measured by water or mercury manometers K, K′. The passage of the mercury between the platinum points P_1 and P_3, or $P_1′$ and $P_3′$, is indicated by electrical contacts ringing a bell, U and U′ being commutators

used in a series of very accurate researches [1] on the inert gases in Professor Dorn's laboratory at Halle. Until recently, these represented the last word in the experimental technique of the transpiration method. A typical arrangement of the apparatus (from Schultze, 1901) is shown in Fig. 6.VII F.

More recent measurements by the transpiration method, some at high temperatures, have been made by Anfilogoff [2] and by Trautz and collaborators; [3] low temperature measurements were made by workers in the Leyden Laboratory.[4] A crude apparatus for comparing viscosities by the transpiration method is described by Ubbelohde and Hofsäss.[5] Measurements at high pressures are mentioned in § 2.

In the apparatus used by Anfilogoff and Partington, which was a modification of that used by Shilling and Laxton, the capillary, of clear fused silica κ (Fig. 7.VII F), 1 m. long and of very uniform bore of 0·026 cm. radius, was wound by the Thermal Syndicate into a close helix [6] without affecting the bore. This was fused on one side to a silica bulb β with a baffle-plate inside, and on the other side to a silica tube fitted by a ground joint to the gas exit X. The whole unit was fused together by silica bracing rods and discs, so that it could be inserted into the electrically heated tube furnace, the temperature of which could be closely controlled. The measured volume of gas, under a pressure measured by the manometer μ, was displaced from the bulb B by mercury run in from M by way of a constant level J, and electrical contacts indicated the arrival of the mercury surface just below the inlet tube H. The temperature of the capillary was measured by thermocouples. The mercury was raised from the vessel D to the upper vessel M by an air-lift K, and could be returned from AB to D by way of Q, attached to a vacuum line.

Piwnikiewicz [7] used a capillary joining two vessels containing gas at different pressures. Searle [8] measured the time t taken for the pressure in a vessel

[1] Schultze, *Dissert.*, Halle, 1901; *Ann. Phys.*, 1901, **5**, 140; 1901, **6**, 302 (He); Markowski, *Dissert.*, Halle, 1903; *Ann. Phys.*, 1904, **14**, 742; Kleint, *Dissert.*, Halle, 1904; *Verhl. d. D. Phys. Ges.*, 1905, **7**, 146; Taenzler, *Dissert.*, Halle, 1906; *Verhl. d. D. Phys. Ges.*, 1906, **8**, 222; Schierloch, *Dissert.*, Halle, 1908; Schmitt, *Dissert.*, Halle, 1909; *Ann. Phys.*, 1909, **30**, 393; Kopsch, *Dissert.*, Halle, 1909; Völker, *Dissert.*, Halle, 1910; Zimmer, *Dissert.*, Halle, 1911; *Verhl. d. D. Phys. Ges.*, 1912, **14**, 471; for simpler apparatus see Rapp, *Phys. Rev.*, 1913, **2**, 363; Smith, *Proc. Roy. Soc.*, 1924, **106**, 83 (steam); Edwards and Worswick, *Proc. Phys. Soc.*, 1925, **38**, 16.

[2] *Thesis*, London, 1932; Partington, *Phys. Z.*, 1933, **34**, 289.

[3] For a list of the numerous papers, see § 4, and Schuil, *Phil. Mag.*, 1939, **28**, 679. See also Pedersen, *Phys. Rev.*, 1907, **25**, 225 (bibl.); Grindley and Gibson, *Proc. Roy. Soc.*, 1908, **80**, 114; Fisher, *Phys. Rev.*, 1910, **30**, 269; Roberts, *Phil. Mag.*, 1912, **23**, 250; Piwnikiewicz, *Phys. Z.*, 1913, **14**, 305; Pochettino, *Nuov. Cim.*, 1914, **8**, 5; Clark, *Trans. Roy. Soc. Canada*, 1919, **13**, III, 177; Harle, *Proc. Roy. Soc.*, 1922, **100**, 429; Mack, *J.A.C.S.*, 1925, **47**, 2468; Williams, *Proc. Roy. Soc.*, 1926, **110**, 141; 1927, **113**, 233; recalculated by Braune, Basch, and Wentzel, *Z. phys. Chem.*, 1928, **137**, 176; Nasini, *Phil. Mag.*, 1929, **8**, 596, 601 (vapours); Shilling and Laxton, *Phil. Mag.*, 1930, **10**, 721; Boyd, *Phys. Rev.*, 1930, **35**, 1284 (high pressures); Melaven and Mack, *J.A.C.S.*, 1932, **54**, 888; Brémond, *Compt. Rend.*, 1933, **196**, 1472 (porcelain capillary); Comings and Egly, *Ind. Eng. Chem.*, 1940, **32**, 714 (high pressure); Schmid, *Gas- u. Wasserfach*, 1942, **85**, 92; Sibbitt, Hawkins, and Solberg, *Trans. Amer. Soc. Mech. Eng.*, 1943, **65**, 401 (high temp. and press.); Comings and Mayland, *Chem. Met. Eng.*, 1945, **52**, No. 3, 115 (high temps.); Vasilesco, *Ann. de Phys.*, 1945, **20**, 137, 292 (air, A, N_2, CO_2).

[4] Onnes, Dorsman, and Weber, *Proc. K. Akad. Wetens. Amsterdam*, 1913, **15**, 1386 (*Comm. Leiden*, **134***a*); Onnes and Weber, *ibid.*, 1913, **15**, 1399 (*Comm. Leiden*, **134***b*); van Itterbeek and Keesom, *Physica*, 1938, **5**, 257; Weber, *ibid.*, 1939, **6**, 551.

[5] *Z. Elektrochem.*, 1913, **19**, 32.

[6] A spiral copper tube was used for steam by Speyerer, *Z. techn. Phys.*, 1923, **4**, 430.

[7] *Phys. Z.*, 1913, **14**, 305.

[8] *Proc. Cambr. Phil. Soc.*, 1913, **17**, 183.

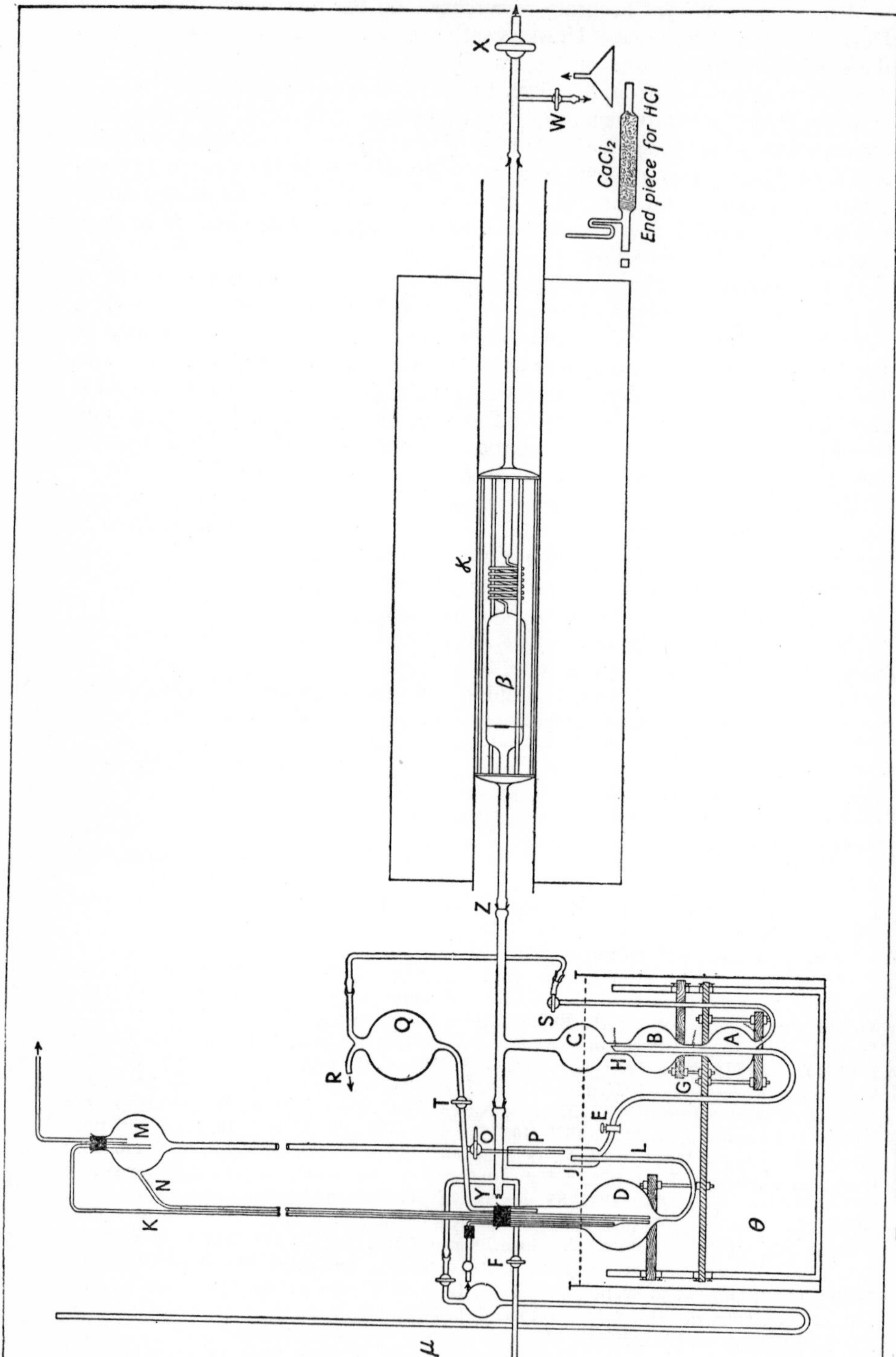

FIG. 7.VII F. Apparatus of Anfilogoff and Partington for Measuring the Viscosities of Gases at High Temperatures

of volume V (c. 10 lit.) to fall from p_1 to p_2 by escape of gas through a capillary of length l and radius r into the atmosphere of pressure p_0, when $\eta=(\pi r^4 p_0/8lV)(t/\lambda)$, where $\lambda=\ln[(p_1-p_0)/(p_2-p_0)]\,.\,[(p_2+p_0)/(p_1+p_0)]$.

A simple comparative method depending on the fall of a pellet of mercury in a tube, driving the gas through a capillary sealed above and below the tube,[1] is liable to error owing to leakage of gas past the mercury pellet, and the correction for the effect of the surface tension of the mercury is also irregular.[2] This method cannot be regarded as satisfactory; the accuracy claimed is about 0·5 per cent. West [3] found that the pressure required to drive a mercury thread of length l upwards in a capillary of radius a, is given by:

$$P=2\sigma(\cos\alpha_2-\cos\alpha_1)/a+8l\eta v/a^2$$

where v is the velocity of motion, α_1 and α_2 are the lower and upper contact angles (independent of the velocity), σ the surface tension, and η the viscosity of mercury. For a 0·35-mm. tube, $P=0{\cdot}038/a+8l\eta v/a^2$.

In the rolling ball method [4] a steel ball is allowed to roll down inside a slightly inclined steel tube of polished bore (e.g. 10 in. long and 0·3 in. bore), the time taken being recorded electrically, and the tube rotated by trunnions in a thermostat. The theory will be mentioned in the section on liquid viscosity (see § 4.VIII E, Vol. II).

§ 9. Poiseuille's Law

The principle of the transpiration method depends on Poiseuille's law: [5]

$$v=(\pi/8\eta)(p_1-p_2)(r^4/l)t \quad . \quad . \quad . \quad . \quad . \quad . \quad . \quad (1)$$

where v is the volume of gas in cm.^{3}, measured at the given temperature and under the mean pressure $\frac{1}{2}(p_1+p_2)$, which flows in t secs. through a straight capillary tube of length l cm. and radius r cm. when the pressures at the beginning and end of the capillary, respectively, are p_1 and p_2 dynes/cm.^{2}. Poiseulle's equation (1) is easily deduced for an *incompressible fluid* as follows. In a tube of length l and circular cross-section of radius r let the fluid at a distance $r=x$ from the axis, and measured at right angles to this, move with a velocity u. The cylinder of fluid of radius x coaxial with the tube experiences a viscous drag $-\eta(\mathrm{d}u/\mathrm{d}x)$ per cm.^{2} over its whole surface, i.e. for its total area a drag of $-2\pi xl\eta\,.\,\mathrm{d}u/\mathrm{d}x$.

In steady flow with uniform velocity, there is no resultant force on the fluid,

1 Pedersen, *Phys. Rev.*, 1907, **25**, 225 (vapours); Rankine, *Phys. Z.*, 1910, **11**, 497, 745; *Proc. Roy. Soc.*, 1910, **83**, 265, 516; 1911, **84**, 181; 1912, **86**, 162; 1913, **88**, 575; 1915, **91**, 201; *Phil. Mag.*, 1911, **21**, 45; 1921, **42**, 601, 615; *J. Sci. Instr.*, 1924, **1**, 105; Klemenc and Remi, *Monatsh.*, 1923, **44**, 307; Nasini and Rossi, *Gazz.*, 1928, **58**, 433; Titani, *Bull. Chem. Soc. Japan*, 1929, **4**, 277; 1930, **5**, 98; 1933, **8**, 255; Eyring and van Valkenburg, *J.A.C.S.*, 1930, **52**, 2619; Nasini and Pastonesi, *Gazz.*, 1933, **63**, 821 (air at high press.); Adzumi, *Bull. Chem. Soc. Japan*, 1937, **12**, 199; Comings and Egly, *Ind. Eng. Chem.*, 1941, **33**, 1224 (under pressure).

2 Kuenen and Visser, *Proc. K. Akad. Wetens. Amsterdam*, 1913, **16**, 355 (*Comm. Leiden*, **138**); Roller and Woolridge, *Proc. Oklahoma Acad. Sci.*, 1932, **12**, 73 (error 2 per cent.); Shugajew, *Sow. Phys. Z.*, 1934, **5**, 659.

3 *Proc. Roy. Soc.*, 1911, **86**, 20; Yarnold, *Proc. Phys. Soc.*, 1938, **50**, 540; 1940, **52**, 191.

4 Flowers, *Proc. Amer. Soc. Testing Mater.*, 1914, **14**, 565; Sage, *Ind. Eng. Chem. Anal.*, 1933, **5**, 261; Schröer and Becker, *Z. phys. Chem.*, 1935, **173**, 178; Wobser and Müller, *Koll. Beih.*, 1941, **52**, 165; Hubbard and Brown, *Ind. Eng. Chem. Anal.*, 1943, **15**, 212; Smith and Brown, *Ind. Eng. Chem.*, 1943, **35**, 705; Bicher and Katz, *ibid.*, 1943, **35**, 754.

5 Poiseuille, *Compt. Rend.*, 1840, **11**, 961, 1041; 1841, **12**, 112; 1842, **15**, 1167; *Ann. Chim.*, 1843, **7**, 50; 1847, **21**, 76; *Mém. div. Sav.*, 1846, **9**, 433; see § 2.VIII E, Vol. II. Jean Léon Marie Poiseuille, 1799–1869, a practising physician in Paris.

so that the viscous drag is equal and opposite to the force due to the pressure difference between the ends of the tube, $\pi x^2(p_1-p_2)$, and hence:

$$-2\pi x l\eta \, . \, du/dx = \pi x^2(p_1-p_2).$$

Divide by $-2\pi x l\eta$ and integrate with respect to x:

$$u = -\frac{p_1-p_2}{4l\eta}x^2 + C$$

where C is the integration constant. If there is no slip (§ 12), $u=0$ when $x=r$ (on the walls of the tube), hence:

$$0 = -\frac{p_1-p_2}{4l\eta}r^2 + C$$

$$\therefore \; C = [(p_1-p_2)/4l\eta]r^2 \quad . \; . \; . \; . \; . \; . \; . \; . \; . \quad (2)$$

$$u = [(p_1-p_2)/4l\eta](r^2-x^2).$$

The total volume of incompressible fluid flowing through the tube per sec. is:

$$v = \int_0^r 2\pi x u \mathrm{d}x = \frac{\pi(p_1-p_2)}{8l\eta}r^4 = \frac{\pi(p_1-p_2)d^4}{128l\eta} \quad . \; . \; . \; . \quad (3)$$

where d=diameter of tube=$2r$.

In the case of a *gas*,[1] v varies with the pressure along the tube and also changes with temperature, being different for isothermal and adiabatic flow.[2] For a very small pressure difference $\mathrm{d}p$, (3) can be written as $\mathrm{d}v=(\pi r^4/8l\eta)\mathrm{d}p$. Also $p\mathrm{d}v=\mathrm{d}nRT$, where $\mathrm{d}n$=number of mols in the volume $\mathrm{d}v$, therefore $\mathrm{d}v=\mathrm{d}nRT/p$,

$$\therefore \; \mathrm{d}n = \pi r^4 p \mathrm{d}p/8l\eta RT$$

$$\therefore \; n = \frac{\pi r^4}{8lR}\int\frac{p\mathrm{d}p}{\eta T}.$$

If T is constant (isothermal flow), η is also constant, hence:

$$n = \frac{\pi r^4}{8l\eta RT}\int_{p_2}^{p_1} p\mathrm{d}p = \frac{\pi r^4}{8l\eta RT}\cdot\frac{p_1^2-p_2^2}{2} = \frac{\pi r^4(p_1-p_2)}{8l\eta RT}\cdot\frac{p_1+p_2}{2} \quad . \quad (4)$$

If $(p_1+p_2)/2=\bar{p}$=average pressure:

$$nRT/\bar{p} = v = \pi r^4(p_1-p_2)/8l\eta,$$

showing that (1) applies also to this case [3] if v is the volume measured under the *average* pressure $(p_1+p_2)/2$.

For a given pressure difference (4) shows that the flow in g. per sec. is

$$Mn = \text{const.} \times [(p_1+p_2)/2RT]M = \text{const.} \times \bar{\rho} \quad . \; . \; . \quad (5)$$

where $\bar{\rho}=\bar{p}M/RT$ is the mean density, M being the mol. wt. This was confirmed experimentally by Graham [4] and Bunsen.[5]

A method of determining viscosity depending on the optical measurement of the rate of approach of two parallel plates by an interferometer was used by

[1] Jellinek, "Lehrbuch der physikalischen Chemie," 1928, **1**, 244.

[2] Fisher, *Phys. Rev.*, 1909, **29**, 147; 1910, **30**, 269; 1910, **31**, 586; 1911, **32**, 216, 433; Holm, *Ann. Phys.*, 1914, **44**, 81; 1914, **45**, 1165.

[3] On supposed deviations from Poiseuille's law for gases, see Knodel, *Ann. Phys.*, 1926, **80**, 533; Schiller, *ibid.*, 1926, **81**, 866.

[4] *Phil. Trans.*, 1849, **139**, 349; "Researches," 1876, 88.

[5] "Gasometry," transl. Roscoe, 1857, 122.

Fabry and Perot;[1] the amount of gas streaming out from between the plates per 1 cm. length per sec. is

$$n=(d^3/12\eta RT)\,.\,[(p_1^2-p_2^2)/2] \quad . \; . \; . \; . \; . \; . \; . \quad (6)$$

where d is the distance between the plates. If $d \simeq 10^{-4}$ cm., the volume of air measured at 1 atm. pressure flowing per sec. per 1 mm. Hg/cm. pressure gradient is only $0{\cdot}6 \times 10^{-6}$ cm.^{3}.

§ 10. Corrections to Poiseuille's Law

Poiseuille's law holds only for so-called *stream-line flow*[2] through the tube; this is conditioned by the dimensions of the tube, the pressure difference, and the viscosity η of the fluid, all of which regulate the linear velocity of the fluid flowing through the tube. If this velocity exceeds a certain value, *turbulent flow* sets in, and the equation breaks down. According to Osborne Reynolds,[3] turbulent flow of a gas or liquid sets in when the linear velocity V exceeds the value given by:

$$d\rho V/\eta=2000 \quad . \; . \; . \; . \; . \; . \; . \; . \; . \; . \quad (1)$$

where d=diameter of circular tube, ρ=density. This value of V is called the *Reynolds number*, and equation (1) gives the criterion for streamline flow, $v<V$. The equation applies also to gases.[4] Dowling[5] found the Reynolds number for gases higher than for liquids. There is also a correction for the *slip* of the gas along the wall of the tube (see § 12):

$$v_{\text{corr.}}=v_{\text{obs.}}(1+4\zeta/r) \quad . \; . \; . \; . \; . \; . \; . \; . \quad (2)$$

where ζ=coefficient of slip; and a correction for the kinetic energy of the moving fluid (*Hagenbach correction*);[6] if η' is the viscosity calculated from Poiseuille's law, the value corrected for kinetic energy is:

$$\eta=\eta'-1{\cdot}10v\rho/8\pi lt \quad . \; . \; . \; . \; . \; . \; . \; . \quad (3)$$

For long and narrow tubes (t large) the Hagenbach correction is negligible.

At the ends of the capillary, and particularly at the entry end, it is possible that the motion of the fluid is not streamline or parallel to the wall. The result will be the same as if, on account of the greater resistance, the gas has traversed a greater length of capillary than is actually the case, and the effect depends on

[1] *Ann. Chim.*, 1898, **13**, 275; Gaede, *Ann. Phys.*, 1915, **46**, 357; Barus, *Proc. Nat. Acad.*, 1923, **9**, 71.

[2] In this, the velocity of flow along a cylindrical tube is constant for a given distance from the axis, and the velocity gradient is constant. On " linear " flow, see Villey, *J. de Phys.*, 1942, **3**, 79.

[3] *Phil. Trans.*, 1883, **174**, 935; 1886, **177**, 157; 1895, **186**, 123; "Papers," Cambridge, 1900–03, **1**, 257; **2**, 51, 535; Stanton and Pannell, *Phil. Trans.*, 1914, **214**, 199; Lees, *Proc. Roy. Soc.*, 1914, **91**, 46. On *turbulent flow*, see, e.g., Wildhagen, *Z. angew. Math.*, 1923, **3**, 181; Taimni, *J. Phys. Chem.*, 1929, **33**, 52; Trubridge, *Sci. Progr.*, 1934, **29**, 61; Ewald, Pöschl, and Prandtl, " The Physics of Solids and Fluids," 1936, 250; Goldstein (edit.), " Modern Developments in Fluid Dynamics " (Aeronautical Res. Committee), Oxford, 1938, **1**, 319; for flow through packed aggregates (e.g. catalyst masses, and absorption towers) see Burke and Plummer, *Ind. Eng. Chem.*, 1928, **20**, 1196; Chilton and Colburn, *ibid.*, 1931, **23**, 913 (bibl.); Damköhler and Delcker, *Z. Elektrochem.*, 1938, **44**, 193. For literature from 1819–1907, see Fritzsche, *Z. Verein D. Ing.*, 1908, **52**, 81.

[4] Ruckes, *Ann. Phys.*, 1908, **25**, 983; Satterly, *Trans. Roy. Soc. Canada*, 1924, **18**, III, 261; Anfilogoff, *Thesis*, London, 1932, 224.

[5] *Proc. Roy. Dublin Soc.*, 1912, **13**, 375.

[6] Hagenbach, *Ann. Phys.*, 1860, **109**, 385; Couette, *Ann. Chim.*, 1890, **21**, 433; *J. de Phys.*, 1890, **9**, 560; Wilberforce, *Phil. Mag.*, 1891, **31**, 407; Knibbs, *Proc. Roy. Soc. N.S. Wales*, 1895, **24**, 77; see § 2.VIII E, Vol. II.

the form of the ends. Couette, to correct for this, added to the actual length l of the tube a fictitious length λ, which he found was approximately three times the diameter of the tube, $\lambda=3d$.

Especially in the case of liquids, a jet leaving an orifice does not preserve the diameter of this, but contracts, the narrowest part being called the *vena contracta.*

The end-correction for capillaries was discussed by Benton,[1] who found Fisher's method unsatisfactory and used a modification of a method proposed by Brillouin.[2] The total resistance is $H=k_1\eta lM/\rho R^4+k_2CM^2/\rho R^4$, where l=length of tube, M=mass transpired per sec., R=radius of tube, ρ=density of fluid, C=(radius of tube)/(*vena contracta*), and k_1 and k_2 are constants:

$$\rho HR^4=2{\cdot}580\eta lM+0{\cdot}1248M^2.$$

§ 11. Curved-pipe Flow

An important correction, formerly overlooked, is involved when a spiral, as contrasted with a straight, capillary is used, and is due to an increased resistance caused by *curved-pipe flow.*[3] The more rapidly flowing central parts of the fluid are forced outwards by centrifugal force, and the slower parts along the wall are driven inwards towards the axis of the tube. The resistance to flow in a curved pipe is f(D) times that in a straight pipe of the same length and bore, f(D) being a function of:

$$D=(qr/\nu)\sqrt{(r/R)} \quad . \quad . \quad . \quad . \quad . \quad . \quad . \quad . \quad (1)$$

where q=average velocity of flow, r=radius of bore, R=radius of curvature of bent pipe (e.g. of a circle for a circular spiral coil), and ν is the kinematic viscosity, $\nu=\eta/\rho$, η being the viscosity and ρ the density. The correction is applied by a graphical method. For $D<20$, f(D) is approximately unity; for $20<D<1000$, $f(D)=0{\cdot}37D^{0{\cdot}36}$. This correction also depends on the linear velocity of the fluid through the tube, and it is desirable to arrange the apparatus so that it becomes negligible. If measurements with gases at various temperatures are involved, this effect may come in at lower temperatures in an apparatus which does not show it at higher temperatures.

Definite indications of curved-pipe flow of gases in spiral capillaries were found by Eger,[4] Williams,[5] Satterly,[6] and Shilling and Laxton,[7] but its importance in viscosity measurements was first pointed out, on the basis of experiments, by Anfilogoff. If G is the ratio of the resistance to motion in a curved tube of internal radius r coiled into a circular helix of radius R, to the resistance in a straight tube of the same length and internal radius, the gas being under the same pressure head and at the same temperature, then:

$$\log G=\log f[(r\rho V/\eta)(r/R)^{1/2}]$$

1 *Phys. Rev.*, 1919, **14**, 403.

2 " Leçons sur la Viscosité," 1907, **1**, 133; **2**, 37.

3 Eustice, *Proc. Roy. Soc.*, 1910, **84**, 107; 1911, **85**, 119; Lechner, *Ann. Phys.*, 1913, **42**, 614; Dean, *Phil. Mag.*, 1927, **3**, 912; 1927, **4**, 208; 1928, **5**, 673; White, *Proc. Roy. Soc.*, 1929, **123**, 645; Anfilogoff and Partington, *B.A. Rep.*, 1931, 348; Anfilogoff, *Thesis*, London, 1932, 78 f., 222 f.; Partington, *Phys. Z.*, 1933, **34**, 289; Ewald, Pöschl, and Prandtl, " The Physics of Solids and Fluids," 1936, 280; Goldstein (edit.), " Modern Developments in Fluid Dynamics " (Aeronautical Res. Committee), Oxford, 1938, **1**, 312.

4 *Ann. Phys.*, 1908, **27**, 819 (attributed effect to centrifugal force).

5 *Proc. Roy. Soc.*, 1926, **110**, 141; 1927, **113**, 233.

6 *Trans. Roy. Soc. Canada*, 1924, **18**, III, 261.

7 *Phil. Mag.*, 1930, **10**, 721.

where $2r\rho V/\eta$ is the Reynolds number, and f is a function of the argument in square brackets. If the Reynolds number is denoted by n, then experiments show that a value of $2n^2r/R$ greater than 280–300 causes an increased resistance due to curved-pipe flow. According to Anfilogoff and White a limiting value of log G of about 0·95, corresponding with a value of $2n^2r/R$ of 158, corresponds with the onset of curved-pipe flow.

Vasilesco,[1] using a coiled platinum tube, confirmed Dean's and White's results up to 1600°, but found an increase in Sutherland's constant for air, argon, and carbon dioxide with rise of temperature.

§ 12. Slip

Experiment shows that the flow of gas in very narrow tubes exceeds that predicted by Poiseuille's formula, and this would be explained if the gas " slipped " in contact with the walls, instead of being anchored there with zero velocity, as was assumed in the deduction. Such a slip was shown to occur with liquids by Helmholtz and Piotrowski,[2] and with gases by O. E. Meyer [3] and Kundt and Warburg.[4] The theory was investigated by Maxwell.[5]

If u_0 is the velocity with which the gas slips along the walls of the tube, there will be a viscous drag on the gas which is proportional to u_0 and to the area $2\pi rl$ $(x=r)$ over which slip occurs, i.e. the total drag will be $2\pi rl\epsilon u_0$, where ϵ is a constant. This drag is equal to the driving force $\pi r^2(p_1-p_2)$, therefore $2\pi rl\epsilon u_0=\pi r^2(p_1-p_2)$, hence:

$$u_0=(p_1-p_2)r/2l\epsilon \quad . \quad . \quad . \quad . \quad . \quad . \quad . \quad . \quad (1)$$

The integration constant C in equation (2), § 9, must therefore be adjusted to give u_0 when $x=r$, instead of zero, and the result shows that:

$$u=[(p_1-p_2)/4l\eta](r^2-x^2+2r\eta/\epsilon).$$

Hence, by integration as before, the streamline flow per sec. is found to be:

$$v=\frac{\pi r^4(p_1-p_2)}{8l\eta}\left(1+\frac{4\eta}{\epsilon r}\right) \quad . \quad . \quad . \quad . \quad . \quad . \quad . \quad . \quad (2)$$

Thus, the flow is increased by slip by the fraction $4\eta/\epsilon r$, which is generally known as the *Kundt and Warburg correction.* It is negligible when r is large compared with η/ϵ, but becomes important with tubes of small radii; when r is very small the flow is largely controlled by slip, becoming proportional to r^3 instead of r^4 as in slip-free flow. The fraction η/ϵ is called the *coefficient of slip*, and is denoted by ζ. It has the dimension of length, and the motion is the same as if the wall were moved back a distance ζ and the velocity gradient continued uniformly to zero in contact with the wall.

Maxwell, in his discussion of slip, assumed that a fraction $(1-f)$ of the molecules impinging on a surface is " specularly " reflected (angle of incidence=

[1] *Ann. de Phys.*, 1945, **20**, 137, 292.
[2] *Wien Ber.*, 1860, **40**, 607; Stacy, *Phys. Rev.*, 1923, **21**, 239.
[3] *Ann. Phys.*, 1866, **127**, 253.
[4] *Ann. Phys.*, 1875, **155**, 337.
[5] *Phil. Trans.*, 1879, **170**, 231; " Scientific Papers," Cambridge, 1890, **2**, 703; Hogg, *Proc. Amer. Acad.*, 1905, **40**, 611; 1906, **42**, 115; *Phil. Mag.*, 1910, **19**, 376; Brillouin, *Compt. Rend.*, 1928, **186**, 553; on the whole subject, see Bingham, *J.A.C.S.*, 1914, **36**, 1393; Anfilogoff, *Thesis*, London, 1932; Loeb, " Kinetic Theory of Gases," 2nd edit., 1934, 285 f.; Kennard, " Kinetic Theory of Gases," 1938, 291 f.; a good brief treatment is given by Dushman, " Production and Measurement of High Vacuum," Schenectady, 1922, 30 f., and Gemant, *J. Appl. Phys.*, 1941, **12**, 626, 718.

angle of reflexion), and the fraction f of the molecules leave at random angles independent of the previous motions (the so-called " cosine law "). He considered that Kundt and Warburg's experiments indicated that $f=\frac{1}{2}$, approximately. Knudsen,[1] however, concluded that f may often approach unity, i.e. nearly all the molecules fly off at random angles. Knudsen says: " a gas molecule on striking the surface is repelled in a direction which is completely independent of the angle of incidence, and the distribution of directions of an infinitely large number of molecules after reflexion from a surface follows Lambert's cosine law for the reflexion of light from a glowing body." The measurements of Blankenstein [2] also showed that for helium, hydrogen, oxygen, and air, reflected from polished oxidised silver, f is 1·00, 1·00, 0·99, and 0·98, respectively, whilst for other solids it may be appreciably smaller. Millikan [3] gave the following values for f:

air or CO_2 on machined brass, old shellac, and mercury	1·00
air on oil	0·895
CO_2 on oil	0·92
air on glass	0·89
air on fresh shellac	0·79

If the gas flows through a tube at such a low pressure that the free path of the molecules is of the same order as, or greater than, the diameter of the tube, the rate of flow is independent of the viscosity and density.[4] If the streaming velocity is small compared with the molecular velocities, and the latter conform to Maxwell's law for a gas with mass velocity equal to the velocity of flow, the mass of gas striking 1 cm.² of tube per sec. is (see § 14.III) $\frac{1}{4}\rho\bar{c}$. The average velocity along the tube is u_0, the same for all points of the gas, and the total momentum given to the walls per sec. is $2\pi rl\times(\frac{1}{4}\rho\bar{c}u_0)$. This, as before, must be equal to $\pi r^2(p_1-p_2)$, so that:

$$u_0=2r(p_1-p_2)/l\rho\bar{c} \quad . \quad . \quad . \quad . \quad . \quad . \quad . \quad . \quad (3)$$

The total mass of gas flowing in 1 sec. is then: [5]

$$\pi r^2\rho u_0=2\pi r^3(p_1-p_2)/l\bar{c} \quad . \quad . \quad . \quad . \quad . \quad . \quad . \quad . \quad (4)$$

independent of η and ρ, and proportional to r^3 instead of r^4. This agrees well with experiment, according to Knudsen.

When gas streams slowly through a tube the number of molecules striking 1 cm.² of wall is (§ 14.III) $\frac{1}{4}N\bar{c}$, where N=number of molecules per cm.³, and $\bar{c}$ is the mean velocity of the molecules due to thermal motion in the gas. If the impinging molecules have a mass velocity u parallel to the surface, which is small compared with $\bar{c}$, and if a fraction f of the impinging molecules are adsorbed and later re-emitted, the momentum given per sec. to the wall is $\frac{1}{4}mN\bar{c}f\bar{u}$, where $\bar{u}$ is the average tangential velocity of the impinging molecules.[6]

[1] *Ann. Phys.*, 1909, **28**, 75, 999; 1915, **48**, 1113; " Kinetic Theory of Gases," 1934, 26 f.; Timiriazeff, *Ann. Phys.*, 1913, **40**, 971; Knudsen's results for flow through tubes at low pressures are further considered in § 2.VII J.

[2] *Phys. Rev.*, 1923, **22**, 582; cf. Stacy, *ibid.*, 1923, **21**, 239; Van Dyke, *ibid.*, 1923, **21**, 250.

[3] *Phys. Rev.*, 1923, **21**, 217; the following text is mainly based on this important paper, which greatly simplified the whole theory of the subject; see also Ishida, *Phys. Rev.*, 1923, **21**, 550; Epstein, *ibid.*, 1924, **23**, 710; Brown, de Nardo, Cheng, and Sherwood, *J. Appl. Phys.*, 1947, **17**, 802.

[4] Knudsen, *Ann. Phys.*, 1909, **28**, 75, 999; 1910, **32**, 809; 1911, **34**, 593; " Kinetic Theory of Gases," 1934, 21 f.

[5] Jeans, " Kinetic Theory of Gases," 1940, 170, omitting a factor $8\pi/3$ given (erroneously?) by Knudsen; experiments agree with (4).

[6] Langmuir, *J.A.C.S.*, 1915, **37**, 417, 1139.

The average tangential velocity of the *surface* layer of molecules is u_0. This surface layer is made up of $\frac{1}{4}N\bar{c}$ impinging molecules with tangential velocity u, of $\frac{1}{4}N\bar{c}(1-f)$ returning molecules also with tangential velocity u, and $\frac{1}{4}N\bar{c}f$ returning molecules with zero tangential velocity. The total number of molecules in this layer is the sum of those entering and leaving, viz. $\frac{1}{2}N\bar{c}$, therefore:

$$\tfrac{1}{2}N\bar{c}u_0=[\tfrac{1}{4}N\bar{c}+\tfrac{1}{4}N\bar{c}(1-f)]u+\tfrac{1}{4}N\bar{c}f\times 0$$

$$\therefore\ u=u_0/(1-\tfrac{1}{2}f) \quad . \quad . \quad . \quad . \quad . \quad . \quad . \quad . \quad (5)$$

If $f=1$ (complete adsorption and re-emission) $u=2u_0$, i.e. the surface layer is made up half of molecules entering the surface with tangential velocity u, and half of molecules leaving with tangential velocity zero. The tangential momentum given to 1 cm.^{2} of wall per sec. is then $\frac{1}{2}Nm\bar{c}u_0$ dynes per cm.^{2}, and this divided by u_0 gives the *coefficient of external friction* ϵ:

$$\epsilon=\tfrac{1}{2}Nm\bar{c} \quad . \quad . \quad . \quad . \quad . \quad . \quad . \quad . \quad . \quad . \quad (6)$$

If f is not unity the average tangential momentum of the impinging molecules is (as shown above) $\frac{1}{4}Nm\bar{c}fu$, hence on substituting for u:

$$\tfrac{1}{4}Nm\bar{c}f\,.\,u_0/(1-\tfrac{1}{2}f)=\epsilon u_0,$$

and by using equation (12), § 1, for η with Boltzmann's value for k, if l=mean free path:

$$\zeta=\frac{\eta}{\epsilon}=\frac{0{\cdot}3502Nm\bar{c}l}{\frac{1}{4}Nm\bar{c}f/(1-\frac{1}{2}f)}=0{\cdot}7004l(2/f-1) \quad . \quad . \quad . \quad . \quad (7)$$

The factor 0·3502 is $\frac{1}{3}\times 1{\cdot}051$, derived from an integral evaluated by Tait.[1] Apart from the factor 0·7004 instead of $\frac{2}{3}=0{\cdot}667$, this equation is the same as the one given by Maxwell,[2] who inferred from Kundt and Warburg's experiments that for air and glass, $\zeta=2l$, or $f=\frac{1}{2}$ (with his constant). Maxwell's equation for the coefficient of slip is:

$$\zeta=\tfrac{1}{2}\eta\sqrt{(2\pi/p\rho)}(2/f-1) \quad . \quad . \quad . \quad . \quad . \quad . \quad . \quad . \quad (8)$$

where a fraction f of molecules is reflected diffusely, and $1-f$ specularly. O. E. Meyer [3] deduced that $\zeta=l$ (mean free path), and Knudsen [4] that:

$$\zeta=0{\cdot}81(8\sqrt{2}/3\sqrt{\pi})[\eta/\sqrt{(p\rho)}] \quad . \quad . \quad . \quad . \quad . \quad . \quad (9)$$

Experiments show that cadmium and mercury atoms are specularly reflected from clean rock salt, but sodium atoms are not reflected at all,[5] and that hydrogen atoms are diffusely reflected from various crystal surfaces maintained at a sufficiently high temperature.[6]

The effect of slip transforms the formula (1), § 8, for rotating cylinders into: [7]

$$\eta=[1/a^2-1/b^2+2\zeta(1/a^3+1/b^3)](I\pi\phi/\tau^2\omega l) \quad . \quad . \quad . \quad (10)$$

States,[8] with a rotating cylinder, found low slip values as compared with those calculated from Maxwell's equation.

[1] *Trans. Roy. Soc. Edin.*, 1887, **33**, 251; " Papers," edit. Knott, 2 vols, Cambridge, 1898–1900, **2**, 153.
[2] *Phil. Trans.*, 1879, **170**, 231; " Scientific Papers," Cambridge, 1890, **2**, 703.
[3] " Kinetic Theory of Gases," 1899, 211.
[4] *Ann. Phys.*, 1908, **28**, 75; Darbord, *J. de Phys.*, 1932, **3**, 345.
[5] Ellett and Olson, *Phys. Rev.*, 1928, **31**, 643.
[6] Johnson, *J. Franklin Inst.*, 1928, **206**, 301.
[7] Warburg, " Über Wärmeleitung und andere Ausgleichende Vorgänge," Berlin, 1924, **99**.
[8] *Phys. Rev.*, 1923, **21**, 662.

G. CONDUCTION OF HEAT IN GASES

§ 1. Theory of the Conduction of Heat in Gases

The unusually large thermal conductivity of hydrogen was noticed by Priestley [1] in 1781; whilst Achard [2] found that a body cools more slowly in hydrogen than in air. It is elegantly shown by an experiment due to Andrews,[3] who found that a platinum wire heated to redness by an electric current in a tube which is exhausted or filled with air, has its glow either greatly diminished, or even removed, when the tube is filled with hydrogen. Magnus [4] observed the effect in very narrow (1 mm.) tubes, so that it is not due to convection. Andrews gave comparative values for the currents required to maintain the same brightness in gases or vapours, that in air being taken as 1·00, and this is really the basis of Schleiermacher's method for the determination of the thermal conductivities of gases (§ 4). Andrews gave: SO_2 0·967, N_2O 0·995, CO_2 1·010, O_2 1·109, NH_3 1·118, H_2 1·382.

Dalton [5] measured the times taken by a heated thermometer to cool the same number of degrees in different gases. Leslie [6] also found that a hot body cools more rapidly in hydrogen than in air. The experiments of Magnus,[4] Peclet,[7] and Buff [8] gave unsatisfactory results; Magnus used a gas at low pressure (15 mm. or less) and arranged the apparatus so that the heat was propagated downwards, so minimising convection.

The kinetic theory of heat conduction in a gas, first worked out by Maxwell,[9] and later by Clausius,[10] Stefan,[11] von Lang,[12] Boltzmann,[13] and O. E. Meyer,[14] removed an apparent objection to the kinetic theory, viz. that the very swift molecules, either by unhindered motion or by the transfer of kinetic energy by head-on collisions with other molecules, might be expected to transfer heat rapidly through a gas.[15] The following treatment is based on that of Jäger.[16]

[1] "Experiments and Observations on Natural Philosophy," 1781, **2**, 375; "Experiments and Observations on Air," Birmingham, 1790, **2**, 457.

[2] *Nouv. Mém. Acad. Berlin*, 1783 (1785), 84.

[3] *Proc. Roy. Irish Acad.*, 1840, **1**, 465; "Scientific Papers," 1889, 66; Grove, *Phil. Mag.*, 1845, **27**, 442; *Phil. Trans.*, 1847, **137**, 1.

[4] *Ann. Phys.*, 1861, **112**, 351, 497; *Phil. Mag.*, 1861, **22**, 1.

[5] "New System of Chemical Philosophy," 1808 (2nd edit., 1842), **1**, 117.

[6] "Experimental Inquiry into the Nature and Propagation of Heat," 1804, 484.

[7] "Traité de la Chaleur," 3rd edit., 1861, **3**, 418.

[8] *Ann. Phys.*, 1876, **158**, 177.

[9] *Phil. Mag.*, 1860, **20**, 21; 1868, **35**, 185; *Phil. Trans.*, 1867, **157**, 49; "Scientific Papers," Cambridge, 1890, **1**, 377 (403); **2**, 26 (74); Kirkwood, *J. Chem. Phys.*, 1946, **14**, 180.

[10] *Ann. Phys.*, 1862, **115**, 1; *Phil. Mag.*, 1862, **23**, 417, 512; Die kinetische Theorie der Gase, "Die mechanische Wärmetheorie," Brunswick, 1889–91, **3**, 105.

[11] *Wien Ber.*, 1863, **47**, II, 81; 1875, **72**, II, 69.

[12] *Wien Ber.*, 1871, **64**, II, 485; 1872, **65**, II, 415; *Ann. Phys.*, 1872, **145**, 290.

[13] *Wien Ber.*, 1872, **66**, II, 275; 1875, **72**, II, 458; 1887, **94**, II, 891; "Wiss. Abhl.," 1909, **1**, 316; **2**, 31; **3**, 293; "Vorlesungen über Gastheorie," Leipzig, 1896, **1**, 86.

[14] "Kinetic Theory of Gases," 1899, 277, 461.

[15] See Clausius, Die kinetische Theorie der Gase, "Die mechanische Warmetheorie," Brunswick, 1889–91, **3**, 105; on a "paradox" in the usual theory, see Jaffé, *Phys. Rev.*, 1942, **61**, 643; on the thermal conductivity of a moving gas, see Natanson, *Bull. Acad. Polon.*, 1902, 137.

[16] "Fortschritte der kinetischen Gastheorie," Brunswick, 1906, 43; *idem*, in Winkelmann, "Handbuch der Physik," 1906, **3**, 747; Kuenen, "Die Eigenschaften der Gase" (Ostwald-Drucker, "Handbuch der allgemeinen Chemie," 3), Leipzig, 1919, 112; Warburg, "Über

In considering the viscosity of a gas, the total momentum which a molecule transports through the xy plane per sec. was found (§ 1.VII H) to be given by:

$$m[U_0+z(\mathrm{d}U/\mathrm{d}z)] \quad . \quad . \quad . \quad (1)$$

When a gas is conducting heat along a temperature gradient, it may be assumed that in each plane parallel to the xy plane the temperature T is constant, and the change of temperature occurs only in the direction of the z axis; i.e. T is a function of z only. It is further assumed that T is a linear function of z, so that the temperature at any point distant z above the xy plane ($z=0$; $T=T_0$) is (since $\mathrm{d}T/\mathrm{d}z$ is constant) given by:

$$T=T_0+z(\mathrm{d}T/\mathrm{d}z) \quad . \quad . \quad . \quad (2)$$

If m is the mass of a molecule and c_v the specific heat of the gas at constant volume per unit mass, then if z is the height of the layer in which the molecule made its last collision:

$$mc_v(T_0+z\,.\,\mathrm{d}T/\mathrm{d}z) \quad . \quad . \quad . \quad (3)$$

is the average heat content transported by this molecule in passing through the xy plane.[1]

A comparison of (3) with (1) shows that if U is replaced by T, and m by mc_v, an equation is found which replaces the viscosity equation (12), § 1.VII F ($\rho=Nm$, $k=K$):

$$\eta=KNm\bar{c}l \quad . \quad . \quad . \quad (4)$$

by one giving the coefficient of heat transport, i.e. the *thermal conductivity coefficient* k:

$$k=KNmc_v\bar{c}l \quad . \quad . \quad . \quad (5)$$

since, just as the viscosity η is defined by (2), § 1.VII F:

$$R=-\eta\,.\,\mathrm{d}U/\mathrm{d}z \quad . \quad . \quad . \quad (6)$$

so the thermal conductivity is defined by:

$$q=-k\,.\,\mathrm{d}T/\mathrm{d}z \quad . \quad . \quad . \quad (7)$$

where q=heat transport (corresponding with momentum transport R) per sec. per cm.^{2}. The dimensions of k are cal. cm.$^{-1}$ sec.$^{-1}$ degree^{-1}. Since Nm=density ρ, (5) can be written as:

$$k=K\rho\bar{c}lc_v \quad . \quad . \quad . \quad (8)$$

A comparison of (4) and (5) shows that

$$k=\eta c_v \quad . \quad . \quad . \quad (9)$$

Equation (9) is not accurately in agreement with the experimental results and according to O. E. Meyer [2] the equation:

$$k=1{\cdot}6027\eta c_v \quad . \quad . \quad . \quad (10)$$

Wärmeleitung und andere ausgleichende Vorgänge," Berlin, 1924; for some refinements, see Kimball, *Phil. Mag.*, 1935, **20**, 97, 355; Smith, *ibid.*, 1942, **33**, 775. For a treatment by Gentile statistics (§ 37.IV), see Salvetti, *Atti Accad. Ital. R. Sci. fis. mat. nat.*, 1942, **13**, 651.

[1] Maxwell calculated the coefficients of viscosity, thermal conductivity, and diffusion from a general "equation of transport"; see also Brillouin, *Ann. Chim.*, 1900, **20**, 440; Jeans, "Kinetic Theory of Gases," 1940, 230; Schäfer, *Naturwiss.*, 1947, **34**, 104.

[2] "Kinetic Theory of Gases," 1899, 284, 466; in the first edition (1877) Meyer used the factor 1·537. Jeans, "Dynamical Theory of Gases," 3rd edit., 1921, 299, pointed out that the constant in equation (10), 1·6027, given by Meyer is incorrect and appears to be the result of a faulty calculation, since the value of an integral correctly calculated for Meyer by Conrau gives the constant as 1·395. Cf. Smoluchowsky, *Ann. Phys.*, 1911, **35**, 983; Haag, *Compt. Rend.*, 1922, **176**, 32.

which he deduced from theory, gives better results. A combination of (10) and (5) enables the mean free path to be deduced from a measurement of the coefficient of thermal conductivity. In theory, also, a measurement of c_v is possible from (9), $c_v=k/\eta$, but this probably holds only for a monatomic gas (see below).

A more general equation is:

$$k=K\eta c_v \quad \text{. . . . . (11)}$$

where K is a constant which is found empirically to be independent of temperature and pressure over a wide range, and seems to depend principally on the number of atoms in the molecule.[1] For molecules repelling one another with a force inversely proportional to the fifth power of the distance between their centres ($F=\mu r^{-5}$) Maxwell[2] found $K=2{\cdot}5$. For monatomic gases Chapman[3] found for a law of force $F=\mu r^{-s}$ the value 2·500 as a first approximation (for $s=5$ this is exact); further approximations alter this by only about 1 per cent., the greatest deviation being for elastic spheres, for which $K=2{\cdot}522$. Enskog[4] also obtained a general formula which gives $K=2{\cdot}500$ for $s=5$; he gave the following values of K, and the theoretical value 2·5 is seen to decrease at low temperatures:

He	0° C. 2·40	−191·6° C. 2·33	−252.1° C. 2·02
A	0° C. 2·49	182·5° C. 2·57	
Ne	10° C. 2·501		

Eucken[1] suggested that $K=1$ for the transport of the *internal* (non-translational) energy of molecules.

Jeans[5] suggested that the simple equation (9), $k=\eta c_v$, might apply to the *rotational* energy, and Maxwell's equation $k=\frac{5}{2}\eta c_v$ to the *translational* energy. If n is the total number of degrees of freedom, the specific heats are given (see § 29.VII E) by $C_v=\frac{1}{2}n\boldsymbol{R}$ and $C_p=\frac{1}{2}(n+2)\boldsymbol{R}$ per mol, hence $C_p/C_v=\gamma=(n+2)/n$. The factor K for the thermal conductivity equation, on the above assumption, is:

$$[3\times\tfrac{5}{2}+(n-3)]/n=[9(n+2)-5n]/4n=\tfrac{1}{4}(9\gamma-5),$$

an equation given by Eucken.[6]

	H_2	He	O_2	A	CO	CO_2	N_2O	C_2H_4
$k/\eta c_v$ obs.	1·89	2·38	1·93	2·49	1·88	1·52	1·72	1·55
$\frac{1}{4}(9\gamma-5)$	1·90	2·44	1·90	2·44	1·91	1·72	1·73	1·55

1 Eucken, *Phys. Z.*, 1911, **12**, 1101; 1913, **14**, 324; Brüche and Littwin, *Z. Phys.*, 1931, **67**, 362.

2 *Phil. Trans.*, 1867, **157**, 49; "Scientific Papers," Cambridge, 1890, **2**, 26; Boltzmann, "Vorlesungen über Gastheorie," Leipzig, 1896, **1**, 176. By an arithmetical error, Maxwell gave 5/3 instead of 5/2=2·5 for K. Schleiermacher, *Ann. Phys.*, 1889, **36**, 346, found 3·15 for mercury vapour. Pidduck, *Proc. Roy. Soc.*, 1922, **101**, 101, concluded that $k/\eta c_v \simeq 2{\cdot}5$ for monatomic or non-rotating molecules; for deviations from 2·5 with dipole molecules, see Chapman and Hainsworth, *Phil. Mag.*, 1924, **48**, 593; Schäfer, *Z. phys. Chem.*, 1943, **53** B, 149. Trautz and Zündel, *Ann. Phys.*, 1933, **17**, 345, found $K=5/3$ for propane.

3 *Phil. Trans.*, 1912, **211**, 433; 1915, **216**, 279; Jones, *ibid.*, 1923, **223**, 1; Herzfeld, *Ann. Phys.*, 1935, **23**, 476.

4 *Phys. Z.*, 1911, **12**, 56, 353; *Dissert.*, Uppsala, 1917; Ubbink, *Physica*, 1947, **13**, 629, 659; 1948, **14**, 165; Amdur, *J. Chem. Phys.*, 1947, **15**, 482; 1948, **16**, 190; Hirschfelder, Bird and Spotz, *ibid.*, 1948, **16**, 968.

5 "Kinetic Theory of Gases," 1940, 190.

6 *Phys. Z.*, 1911, **12**, 1101; 1913, **14**, 324; the equation was not confirmed by Ubbink, *Physica*, 1948, **14**, 165.

Hercus and Laby [1] gave the following table:

Gas	$k \times 10^5$ at 0° C.	c_p	γ	c_v	$\eta \times 10^4$ at 0° C.	K
He	32·7	1·255	1·667	0·753	1·883	2·31
A	3·85	0·123	1·667	0·0744	2·108	2·47
H_2	36·3	3·407	1·399	2·406	0·852	1·76
N_2	5·14	0·244	1·401	0·175	1·673	1·76
O_2	5·35	0·218	1·401	0·1531	1·925	1·79
Air	5·22	0·239	1·402	0·1715	1·733	1·76
NO	4·93	0·231	1·397	0·1654	1·737	1·73
CO	5·05	0·246	1·405	0·1751	1·677	1·72
CO_2	3·25	0·2015	1·300	0·160	1·428	1·45
N_2O	3·34	0·220	1·317	0·1751	1·364	1·47
H_2S	2·81	0·2389	1·317	0·1814	1·154	1·34
SO_2	1·80	0·1527	1·258	0·1061	1·204	1·35

Eucken,[2] taking k for air as 0·0000566 at 0° C. and 1 atm., found the following values of k (which later measurements by Weber, quoted in § 4, show are often quite inaccurate); the other columns give the values for the viscosity (η), specific heat (c_v), and the constant K of equation (11).

	$k \times 10^7$	$\eta \times 10^7$	c_v	K
He	3360	1876	0·746	2·40
A	390	2102	0·0745	2·49
H_2	3970	850	2·38	1·965
N_2	566	1676	0·177	1·905
O_2	570	1922	0·155	1·913
CO	542·5	1672	0·177	1·835
NO	555	1794	0·1655	1·870
Cl_2	182·9	1237	0·082	1·803
SO_2	195·0	1183	0·103	1·601
CO_2	337·0	1380	0·1500	1·628
N_2O	351·5	1362	0·1575	1·640
CS_2	161·5	924	0·11	1·59
H_2S	304·5	1184	0·180	1·435
H_2O	429	1006	0·342	1·25
C_2H_2	440	943	0·295	1·58
NH_3	513·5	926	0·388	1·429
CH_4	714·5	1029	0·405	1·715
C_2H_4	407	906·6	0·293	1·53
C_2H_6	426	855	0·33	1·51

The high thermal conductivities of hydrogen and helium are noteworthy. Equation (9) shows that k should be independent of pressure to the same degree

[1] *Proc. Roy. Soc.*, 1919, **95**, 190; Hercus and Sutherland, *ibid.*, 1934, **145**, 599; for other values, see Kuenen, "Die Eigenschaften der Gase" (Ostwald-Drucker, "Handbuch der allgemeinen Chemie," **3**), Leipzig, 1919, 115; Landolt-Börnstein, "Tabellen," 5th edit., 1923, **2**, 1304; Laby and Nelson, "Internat. Crit. Tables," 1929, **5**, 213; Guareschi, *Atti R. Accad. Lincei*, 1936, **23**, 603, 690; 1938, **27**, 92.

[2] *Phys. Z.*, 1911, **12**, 1101; 1913, **14**, 324.

as the viscosity (since c_v is practically independent of pressure), and this is confirmed experimentally.[1] For actual gases and vapours there is some dependence of k on pressure.[2] Schäfer and Foz Gazulla [3] regarded pressure dependence of k as indicating dissociation of molecular aggregates. Schäfer, Rating, and Eucken [4] explained the decrease of k for carbon dioxide at lower pressure as due to limitation of exchange of translational and vibrational energy. Ubbink [5] found 1·1 per cent. increase in k for 100 cm. Hg pressure increase for hydrogen at 20° K.; for helium, k was independent of pressure at 20° K. but increased by 5·2 per cent. at 4° K. between 0 and 100 cm. Hg pressure.

Comings and Nathan [6] assumed that the correlation of viscosity data could be used as a first approximation to correlate conductivity data at high pressures by assuming that $k_p/k_1=\eta_p/\eta_1$, although this assumption (derived from transport theory based on the kinetic theory of gases) will not hold exactly for non-ideal gases. Enskog's equation of state was used, $p+a\rho^2=(\boldsymbol{R}T/M)\rho(1+b\rho x)$, where ρ=density, and $k_p/k_1=b\rho(1/b\rho x+1{\cdot}2+0{\cdot}7574b\rho x)$, a and b being constants. If x is a function of density only, $b\rho x=(M/\boldsymbol{R}\rho)(dp/dT)_v-1$. Plots against reduced pressure were used, the graphs resembling those for viscosities (Fig. 2.VII F).

Curie and Lepape,[7] with results from the rate of cooling method (§ 4) found:

	He	Ne	A	Kr	Xe
$k\times10^5$	33·63	10·92	4·06	2·12	1·24
$k_0/\eta c_v$	2·42	2·49	2·59	2·54	2·58

Sherratt and Griffiths [8] found that $k/\eta c_v$ increased in the interval 0°–300° only from 1·68 to 1·70 for carbon dioxide, whilst for air it increased from 1·96 to 2·06. Gregory and Dock [9] found that $k/\eta c_v$ for hydrogen increased from 2·0 at room temperature to 2·27 at liquid oxygen temperature. The value of $k/\eta c_v$ for steam [10] at 70°–250° depends somewhat on temperature; at 288°–476° the dependence is greater, the value rising from 1·416 at 288·8° to 1·546 at 476·7°.

Pollock,[11] using Eucken's results, found $K=7{\cdot}32(\gamma-1)/\gamma^{1\cdot3}$, where $\gamma=c_p/c_v$, and K is the constant in (11). Laby and Hercus,[12] using better experimental data, found a linear plot of K against $1/\gamma$, and Pollock [13] then gave the improved formula $K=6{\cdot}15(1-\gamma)/\gamma$.

[1] Gregory and Archer, *Phil. Mag.*, 1926, **1**, 593; 1933, **15**, 301; Gregory and Dock, *ibid.*, 1938, **25**, 129; Varghaftik, *Techn. Phys. U.S.S.R.*, 1937, **4**, No. 5, 341; *Amer. Chem. Abstr.*, 1937, **31**, 6958; Jeans, " Kinetic Theory of Gases," 1940, 189.

[2] Enskog, *K. Svensk. Vet. Akad. Handl.*, 1922, **63**, No. 4; *Arkiv Mat. Astron. Fys.*, 1922. **16**, No. 16; for steam, see Milverton, *Proc. Roy. Soc.*, 1935, **150**, 287; Varghaftik, *Techn, Phys. U.S.S.R.*, 1937, No. 5, **4**, 341; *Amer. Chem. Abstr.*, 1937, **31**, 6958.

[3] *An. Fis. Quim.*, 1942, **38**, 316; Foz Gazulla and Senet, *ibid.*, 1943, **39**, 399; Foz Gazulla and Schäfer, *Z. phys. Chem.*, 1942, **52** B, 299; Foz Gazulla and Pérez, *ibid.*, 1944, **193**, 162 (SO_2).

[4] *Ann. Phys.*, 1942, **42**, 176.

[5] *Physica*, 1948, **14**, 165 ; cf. de Boer, *ibid.*, 1943, **10**, 348.

[6] *Ind. Eng. Chem.*, 1947, **39**, 964 (bibl.).

[7] *Compt. Rend.*, 1931, **193**, 842; *J. de Phys.*, 1931, **2**, 392.

[8] *Phil. Mag.*, 1939, **28**, 68.

[9] *Phil. Mag.*, 1938, **25**, 129.

[10] Varghaftik, *Amer. Chem. Abstr.*, 1937, **31**, 6957; Rudorff, *Eng. and Boiler House Rev.*, 1946, **60**, 100; cf. Dorsey, " Properties of Ordinary Water Substance," New York, 1940, 121.

[11] *J. Roy. Soc. N.S. Wales*, 1915, **49**, 249.

[12] *Proc. Roy. Soc.*, 1918, **95**, 209.

[13] *Proc. Roy. Soc. N.S. Wales*, 1919, **53**, 116.

§ 2. Values of Thermal Conductivities

The following values are all in g.cal. cm.$^{-1}$ sec.$^{-1}$ deg. C.$^{-1}$.

Air	0°	0·0000568 [1]	A	0°	0·0000385 [3]
		0·0000566 [6]			0·00003961 [6]
		0·00005777 [5]	D_2	0°	0·0003031 [5]
	−59°	0·00003678 [2]	O_2	0°	0·00005889 [5]
	−149·5°	0·00002146 [2]			0·00005768 [3]
H_2	0°	0·0004245 [5]	CO_2	0°	0·00003393 [3]
		0·0004165 [3]			0·00003375 [6]
	−59°	0·0002393 [2]			0·0000347 [8]
	−150°	0·0001175 [2]		−59°	0·00002645 [2]
		$(2{\cdot}14\times10^{-6})T^{0{\cdot}938}$ [7]	N_2O	0°	0·0000353 [3]
He	0°	0·0003438 [3]	CH_4	0°	0·0000770 [3]
Ne	0°	0·0001087 [3]			0·00007205 [6]
		0·0001091 [4]	C_3H_8	0°	0·00003549 [5]
	−74·37°	0·0000879 [3]	CO	0°	0·00005399 [6]
	−181·43°	0·0000499 [3]			

Mann and Dickins [9] by the Schleiermacher method (§ 4), found the following values of $k\times10^5$ at 0°, and the temperature coefficients α, where $k_t=k_0(1+\alpha t)$:

	$k\times10^5$	α		$k\times10^5$	α
Air	5·79	0·0028	*n*-butane	3·22	0·0074
Methane	7·21	0·0049	*Iso*-butane	3·32	—
Ethane	4·36	0·0066	*n*-pentane	3·12	—
Propane	3·60	0·0074	*n*-hexane	2·96	—

Both values appear to approach a limit with increasing number of carbon atoms. Ulsamer [10] gave the following selected values of $k\times10^5$ at 0°:

Air	H_2	O_2	N_2	CO_2
5·74	41·39	5·83	5·73	3·44

Dickins,[11] by the Schleiermacher method, found the following values at 0° C., all higher than the average of previous values but in better agreement with these if only the Schleiermacher values are included; the values are $\times10^6$ and the second figure is the temperature coefficient $\alpha\times10^4$:

He	351·0	21	CO	55·8	29	N_2	58·1	29	SO_2	20·6	39
A	39·8	25	O_2	59·0	30	N_2O	36·4	47	NH_3	52·2	48
H_2	417	28	Air	58·4	29	CO_2	35·1	47			

1 Winkelmann, *Ann. Phys.*, 1893, **48**, 180.
2 Eckerlein, *Ann. Phys.*, 1900, **3**, 120.
3 Weber, *Ann. Phys.*, 1917, **54**, 325, 437, 481; *Proc. K. Akad. Wetens. Amsterdam*, 1919, **21**, 342 (*Comm. Leiden* Suppl. **42***b*).
4 Bennewitz, *Ann. Phys.*, 1915, **48**, 577.
5 Nothdurft, *Ann. Phys.*, 1937, **28**, 137, 157.
6 Trautz and Zündel, *Ann. Phys.*, 1933, **17**, 345.
7 Gregory and Dock, *Phil. Mag.*, 1938, **25**, 129.
8 Archer, *Phil. Mag.*, 1935, **19**, 901.
9 *Proc. Roy. Soc.*, 1931, **134**, 77; for hydrocarbons, see Delaplace, *Compt. Rend.*, 1936, **203**, 1505; 1937, **204**, 263; 1938, **206**, 1646.
10 *Z. Verein D. Ing.*, 1936, **80**, 537.
11 *Proc. Roy. Soc.*, 1934, **143**, 517; Milverton, *Phil. Mag.*, 1934, **17**, 347, found 0·0000581 for air by this method.

Shushpanov[1] found the molar thermal conductivities ($k \times$ mol. wt. M) of vapours of normal aliphatic alcohols from methyl to amyl to be linear functions of the number n of CH_2 groups in the molecule, $Mk=an+b$. Values of $k \times 10^7$ for dialkyl ether vapours found by Gribkova[2] at 100° are: $CH_3OC_2H_5$ 582, $CH_3OC_3H_7$ 539, $CH_3OC_4H_9$ 500, $C_2H_5OC_2H_5$ 562, $C_2H_5OC_3H_7$ 504, $C_2H_5OC_4H_9$ 470, $C_3H_7OC_3H_7$ 464, (*iso*-$C_3H_7)_2O$ 483, $C_3H_7OC_4H_9$ 425, $C_4H_9OC_4H_9$ 401. From 50° to 130° the value of k increases linearly in all cases by about 45 per cent.; k decreases with increasing mol. wt. and is greater for *iso*- than for *n*-compounds.

Gregory and Marshall[3] found for O_2 $k=5{\cdot}89\times10^{-5}$, $\alpha=0{\cdot}00289$; N_2 $k=5{\cdot}80\times10^{-5}$, $\alpha=0{\cdot}00293$. The results of Gregory and Archer[4] require correction for the temperature discontinuity between the hot wire and gas[5] (§ 4.VII J); this changes the values they found for air and hydrogen from 0·0000585 and 0·000406 to 0·0000533 and 0·000379, respectively. Müller[6] found that the thermal conductivity of air increased with temperature more slowly than the viscosity.

§ 3. Effect of Temperature on Thermal Conductivities of Gases

The investigations of the effect of temperature on the thermal conductivity of gases at first gave contradictory results. Graetz,[7] Winkelmann,[8] and Christiansen[9] found a much smaller increase with temperature than was the case with the viscosity, k being approximately proportional to $\sqrt{T}$. Schleiermacher,[10] on the contrary, found a much larger dependence of k on the temperature, the coefficient being approximately the same as for the viscosity. Eucken[11] found at the absolute temperatures stated, η_0 and k_0 being the values at 273° K.:

	T° K.	k/k_0	η/η_0	$k\eta_0/k_0\eta$
He	81·5	0·441	0·474	0·930
	21	0·155	0·184	0·843
A	90·6	0·364	0·352	1·034
H_2	194·6	0·774	0·790	0·980
	81·5	0·335	0·444	0·754
	21	0·0813	0·107	0·760
N_2	81·6	0·322	0·333	0·965
O_2	194·6	0·745	0·754	0·988
	81·6	0·302	0·335	0·900
CO	194·6	0·730	0·764	0·957
	81·6	0·302	0·337	0·896
CO_2	194·6	0·656	0·745	0·88
NH_3	215·5	0·764	0·817	0·936
CH_4	194·6	0·702	0·770	0·912
	91·5	0·314	0·340	0·924

1 *J. Exptl. Theor. Phys. U.S.S.R.*, 1939, **9**, 875; 1940, **10**, 674.
2 *J. Exptl. Theor. Phys. U.S.S.R.*, 1941, **11**, 364.
3 *Proc. Roy. Soc.*, 1927, **114**, 354; 1928, **118**, 594.
4 *Phil. Mag.*, 1926, **1**, 593.
5 Hercus and Laby, *Phil. Mag.*, 1927, **3**, 1061.
6 *Phys. Z.*, 1900, **2**, 161.
7 *Ann. Phys.*, 1892, **45**, 298; in Winkelmann, "Handbuch der Physik," 1906, **3**, 528.
8 *Ann. Phys.*, 1883, **19**, 649; 1892, **46**, 322; 1893, **48**, 180.
9 *Ann. Phys.*, 1881, **14**, 23; Eichhorn, *ibid.*, 1890, **40**, 697; Eckerlein, *ibid.*, 1900, **3**, 120; Pauli, *ibid.*, 1907, **23**, 907 (gases and vapours).
10 See § 4.
11 *Phys. Z.*, 1911, **12**, 1101; 1913, **14**, 324.

These figures show that the temperature coefficients of the thermal conductivity and viscosity are not very different, but the first (except for argon) is less than the second. The accuracy of these results is not very high.

Two theoretical equations for the temperature dependence of k make it proportional to $\sqrt{T}$ (Clausius),[1] and proportional to T (Maxwell).[2] Eckerlein's [3] experiments with carbon dioxide favoured Maxwell's formula, and most modern results give a linear dependence on temperature. Gregory and Dock [4] found for hydrogen, $k=(2\cdot14\times10^{-6})T^{0\cdot938}$. The theory of the thermal conductivity of a dissociating gas ($N_2O_4 \rightleftharpoons 2NO_2$) was developed by Nernst.[5]

§ 4. Determination of Thermal Conductivity of Gases

The experimental methods [6] for the determination of the thermal conductivity of a gas are principally two. The first or *plate method* was developed by Stefan.[7] Fig. 1.VII G shows Winkelmann's modification of Stefan's apparatus. An inner massive copper cylinder a, of mass m and specific heat c, was drilled at the top to receive a thermocouple t_1t_2, and cemented by sealing wax into a supporting glass tube d, fixed by a rubber stopper covered by a screwed plate hi into the cover of an outer copper cylinder b, closed by a screwed lid fg and provided with an inlet tube for the gas, which filled the space between the two cylinders at low pressure (to avoid convection).[8] The apparatus was plunged into ice-water and the rate of fall of the temperature of the inner cylinder determined.

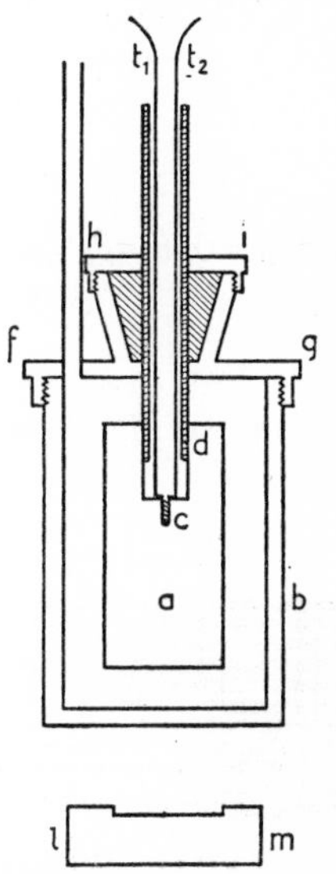

FIG. 1.VII G. Winkelmann's Apparatus for the Determination of the Thermal Conductivity of a Gas

If A=mean of the areas of the two cylindrical surfaces,

1 *Ann. Phys.*, 1862, **115**, 1.
2 *Phil. Mag.*, 1860, **19**, 19; 1860, **20**, **21**; "Scientific Papers," Cambridge, 1890, **2**, 377 (403).
3 See note 9 on p. 894.
4 *Phil. Mag.*, 1938, **25**, 129.
5 *Ann. Phys.*, *Boltzmann Festschr.*, 1904, 904; Riewe and Rompe, *Z. Phys.*, 1937, **105**, 478.
6 Graetz, in Winkelmann, "Handbuch der Physik," 1906, **3**, 526; Eucken, in Stähler, "Arbeitsmethoden der anorganischen Chemie," Leipzig, 1913, **3**, i, 581; Kuenen, "Die Eigenschaften der Gase" (Ostwald-Drucker, "Handbuch der allgemeinen Chemie," **3**), Leipzig, 1919, 112; Trautz and Zündel, *Z. techn. Phys.*, 1931, **12**, 273 (bibl., 204 refs.).
7 Dulong and Petit, *Ann. Chim.*, 1818, **7**, 113, 225, 337; Magnus, *Ann. Phys.*, 1861, **112**, 351; Narr, *ibid.*, 1871, **142**, 123; Stefan, *Wien Ber.*, 1875, **72**, II, 69; Plank, *ibid.*, 1875, **72**, II, 269; 1876, **74**, II, 215; Kundt and Warburg, *Ann. Phys.*, 1875, **156**, 177; Winkelmann, *ibid.*, 1875, **156**, 497; 1876, **157**, 497; 1876, **159**, 177; 1881, **14**, 534; 1883, **19**, 649; 1883, **20**, 350; 1886, **29**, 68; 1891, **44**, 177, 429; 1893, **48**, 180; Graetz, *ibid.*, 1881, **14**, 232, 541; Eichhorn, *ibid.*, 1890, **40**, 697; Müller, *ibid.*, 1897, **60**, 82; Rayleigh, *Phil. Mag.*, 1899, **47**, 314; Eckerlein. *Ann. Phys.*, 1900, **3**, 120; Pauli, *ibid.*, 1907, **23**, 907; Todd, *Proc. Roy. Soc.*, 1909, **83**, 19; Giacomini, *Verhl. d. D. Phys. Ges.*, 1918, **20**, 94; Hercus and Laby, *Proc. Roy. Soc.*, 1919, **95**, 190; Hercus and Sutherland, *ibid.*, 1934, **145**, 599; Henderson, *Phys. Rev.*, 1920, **15**, 46; Ubbink, *Physica*, 1947, **13**, 629, 659; 1948, **14**, 165 (low temperatures). For an elegant theory of the apparatus, based on conformal representation, see Kutta, *Ann. Phys.*, 1895, **54**, 104.
8 Wassiljewa, *Dissert.*, Göttingen, 1905; *Phys. Z.*, 1904, **5**, 737; Langmuir, *Phys. Rev.*, 1912, **34**, 401; below 150 mm. the effects of convection are small; Kundt and Warburg found the following figures for the times of equal cooling in air: 19·5 mm., 277 sec.; 9 mm., 277 sec.; 4 mm., 278 sec.; 0·5 mm., 280 sec.

d=thickness of layer of gas, then the heat given up in a time element dt by the inner cylinder is

$$-mc\mathrm{d}\theta=kA(\theta/d)\mathrm{d}t \quad . \quad . \quad . \quad . \quad . \quad . \quad . \quad . \quad (1)$$

(since the temperature of the inner cylinder is $\theta°$ and that of the outer cylinder 0°), this equation expressing the law that the loss of heat is proportional to the area of the surface, the time, and the temperature difference (θ–0), and inversely proportional to the thickness of the conductor (the gas). Put:

$$kA/mcd=\text{const.}=\alpha \quad . \quad . \quad . \quad . \quad . \quad . \quad . \quad . \quad (2)$$

$$\therefore \ (1/\theta)(\mathrm{d}\theta/\mathrm{d}t)=-\alpha \quad . \quad . \quad . \quad . \quad . \quad . \quad . \quad . \quad (3)$$

$$\therefore \ \ln\theta=-\alpha t+\text{const.} \quad . \quad . \quad . \quad . \quad . \quad . \quad . \quad . \quad (4)$$

For t=0, $\theta=\theta_0$=initial temperature of inner cylinder,

$$\therefore \ \ln\theta=\ln\theta_0-\alpha t \quad . \quad . \quad . \quad . \quad . \quad . \quad . \quad . \quad (5)$$

$$\text{or} \quad \theta=\theta_0 e^{-\alpha t} \quad . \quad . \quad . \quad . \quad . \quad . \quad . \quad . \quad . \quad (6)$$

By measuring the rate of fall of temperature of the inner cylinder, the constant α is calculated from (5) or (6), and thence k is calculated by (2). If relative values only are required, α need not be determined in terms of equation (2), since for the same apparatus and two different gases:

$$\alpha_1/\alpha_2=k_1/k_2 \quad (7)$$

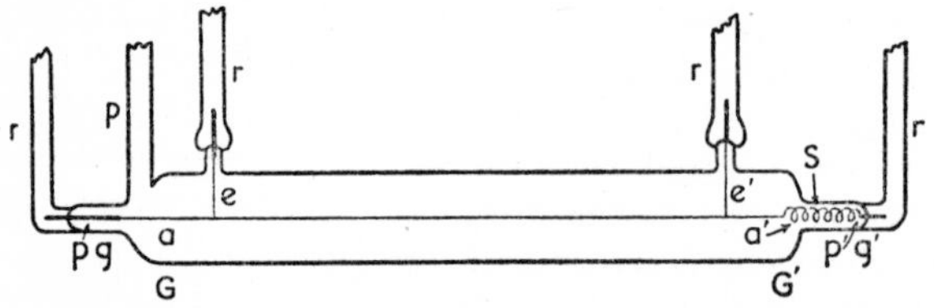

FIG. 2.VII G. Schleiermacher's Apparatus for the Determination of the Thermal Conductivity of a Gas. (The representation of the spring at S is simplified, the thin platinum wire being attached to the thicker platinum leads pg and p′g′, and the stretched spiral spring being anchored at one end and attached to the wire at the other.)

A correction for the conduction along the tube d, and one for heat transmitted by radiation, are necessary in the absolute determinations; the second is determined with the apparatus vacuous, since then heat is transmitted by radiation alone, and this is subtracted from the observed transfer when the apparatus contains gas. Curie and Lepape,[1] by Dulong and Petit's method of the rate of cooling of a thermometer in the gas, found the conductivities of the inert gases.

Hercus and Laby used two plates of silvered copper with a guard ring, accurately separated horizontally by ivory spacers. The upper plate was electrically heated, and the lower cooled by flowing water, a temperature difference of about 28° being used. The distance between the plates was 6·28 mm. The temperatures were measured by thermocouples. The heat flow downwards (to avoid convection) was measured by the input of electrical heating energy and a correction for radiation was applied.

The second general method is the *hot-wire* method, generally called Schleiermacher's method, although the principle goes back to Andrews [2] and the method was used for determination of thermal conductivity by Bottomley.[3] The apparatus used is shown in Fig. 2.VII G (Wachsmuth, 1907). The glass tube GG′

1 *Compt. Rend.*, 1931, **193**, 842.

2 *Proc. Roy. Irish Acad.*, 1840, **1**, 465; " Scientific Papers," 1889, 66.

3 *Proc. Roy. Soc.*, 1884, **37**, 177; Schleiermacher, *Ann. Phys.*, 1885, **26**, 287; 1888, **34**, 623; 1889, **36**, 346; Eichhorn, *ibid.*, 1890, **40**, 697; Graetz, *ibid.*, 1892, **45**, 298; dissertations from Dorn's laboratory (Halle) by Schwarze (1902), *Ann. Phys.*, 1903, **11**, 303; *Phys. Z.*, 1903, **4**,

contains a thin platinum wire aa′ stretched along the axis by a steel spring at S, and heated electrically by a current. The wire is sealed into the tubes rr through thicker platinum wires at the ends, and contact is made by mercury to the heating current. The thin platinum wires ee′ communicate through the mercury contacts rr to a Wheatstone's bridge, where the resistance of the defined part of aa′ is measured. The gas is admitted through p at reduced pressure, and the tube is immersed in a water bath at a constant temperature. A stationary state is reached when as much heat is lost by conduction and radiation from the wire as is supplied by the heating current, the radiation loss being separately determined with the apparatus vacuous. No heat is lost by conduction through the thin wires ee′, as these are at the same temperature as the axial wire.

If R is the resistance of the axial wire (from which the temperature θ_1 is calculated by the platinum resistance thermometer formula, § 7.VI A) and I the heating current, the Joule heat generated per sec. in the wire is $\dot{q}=I^2R$. Let l be the length of the wire, r_1 its radius, r_2 the radius of the outer tube, and θ_2 the temperature of the bath. The temperature gradient is radial, and $\mathrm{d}\theta/\mathrm{d}x$ can be put equal to $\mathrm{d}\theta/\mathrm{d}r$. The surface of an imaginary cylinder of length l and radius r with the wire as axis is $2\pi lr$. The heat passing by conduction only per sec. through this surface is $\dot{q}'=-k\,.\,2\pi rl\,.\,\mathrm{d}\theta/\mathrm{d}r$, therefore $\dot{q}'\mathrm{d}r/r=-2\pi kl\mathrm{d}\theta$. Integrate on the left side from $r=r_1$ to $r=r_2$ and on the right from $\theta=\theta_1$ to $\theta=\theta_2$, then $\dot{q}'(\ln r_2-\ln r_1)=-2\pi kl(\theta_2-\theta_1)$, hence $\dot{q}'=2\pi kl(\theta_1-\theta_2)/(\ln r_2-\ln r_1)$, and:

$$\dot{q}=2\pi kl(\theta_1-\theta_2)/(\ln r_2-\ln r_1)+S \quad . \quad . \quad . \quad . \quad . \quad (8)$$

where S is the radiation loss, from which k may be calculated.[1] The apparatus may be used to find relative values of k, in which case the value of $2\pi l/(\ln r_2-\ln r_1)$ is constant. The method requires careful attention to detail.[2]

Dickins [3] used the equation for heat transport:

$$\dot{q}=2\pi kl(\theta_1-\theta_2)/[\ln (r_2/r_1)+X/p],$$

229; Gunther (1906); Wachsmuth (1907); and Krey (1912); Goldschmidt, *Phys. Z.*, 1911, **12**, 417; Eucken, *ibid.*, 1911, **12**, 1101; 1913, **14**, 324; Vogel, *Dissert.*, Berlin, 1913; *Ann. Phys.*, 1914, **43**, 1235; Langmuir, *J.A.C.S.*, 1912, **34**, 860; Isnardi, *Z. Elektrochem.*, 1915, **21**, 405; Weber, *Ann. Phys.*, 1917, **54**, 325, 437, 481; 1927, **82**, 479 (values 1 per cent. higher than previous); *idem*, *Proc. K. Akad. Wetens. Amsterdam*, 1919, **21**, 342; Moeller, *Wiss. Abhl. Siemens-Konzern*, 1920, **1**, 147; Busch, *Ann. Phys.*, 1921, **64**, 401; Hurst and Rideal, *J.C.S.*, 1924, **25**, 694; Schneider, *Ann. Phys.*, 1926, **79**, 177; 1926, **80**, 215; Hercus and Laby, *Phil. Mag.*, 1927, **3**, 1061; Gregory and Marshall, *Proc. Roy. Soc.*, 1927, **114**, 354; 1928, **118**, 594; Gregory and Archer, *Proc. Roy. Soc.*, 1928, **118**, 594; Eucken and Suhrmann, " Physikalisch-chemische Praktikumsaufgaben," Leipzig, 1928, 95; Bonhoeffer and Harteck, *Z. phys. Chem.*, 1929, **4** B, 113; Wilner and Borelius, *Ann. Phys.*, 1930, **4**, 316 (N_2 at 500°); Jenckel, *Z. phys. Chem.*, 1931, **155**, 100; Kannuluik and Martin, *Proc. Roy. Soc.*, 1934, **144**, 496; Laby, *ibid.*, 1934, **144**, 494; Dickins, *ibid.*, 1934, **143**, 517; Sachsse and Bratzler, *Z. phys. Chem.*, 1934, **171**, 331; Milverton, *Phil. Mag.*, 1934, **17**, 397; Gregory, *Proc. Roy. Soc.*, 1935, **149**, 35; Farkas and Farkas, " Orthohydrogen, Parahydrogen, and Heavy Hydrogen," Cambridge, 1935; Gregory and Dock, *Phil. Mag.*, 1938, **25**, 129; Sherratt and Griffiths, *ibid.*, 1939, **27**, 68; Munch, *Ind. Eng. Chem.*, 1945, **37**, No. 8, 85; Taylor and Johnston, *J. Chem. Phys.*, 1946, **14**, 219; Johnston and Grilly, *ibid.*, 1946, **14**, 233.

[1] Preston, " Theory of Heat," 1894, 546; Wüllner, " Lehrbuch der Experimentalphysik," Leipzig, 1896, **2**, 341; Christiansen, " Elements of Theoretical Physics," 1897, 301; for corrections for leads, see Busch, *Ann. Phys.*, 1926, **80**, 33; other corrections, Weber, *ibid.*, 1926, **82**, 479.

[2] Sherratt and Griffiths, *Phil. Mag.*, 1939, **27**, 68; for a modified method, see Delaplace, *Compt. Rend.*, 1936, **203**, 1505; 1937, **204**, 263; 1938, **206**, 1646; for low temperatures, Ubbink and de Haas, *Physica*, 1943, **10**, 451.

[3] *Proc. Roy. Soc.*, 1934, **143**, 517.

where X/p is the correction for accommodation coefficient (§ 5.VII J) and temperature discontinuity. By plotting $1/\dot{q}$ against $1/p$ a straight line was obtained below certain values of p (when convection was negligible), and by extrapolation k could be found from the intercept.

Trautz and Zündel [1] found that the Schleiermacher apparatus used by Eucken gave unsatisfactory results, but they devised a form (" block apparatus ") which they claimed gave results accurate to 0·1 per cent. Fischer [2] also found that Eucken's apparatus left much to be desired in accuracy.

Thermal conductivity methods have been used in gas analysis.[3] The Schleiermacher method has been used to determine the concentrations of ortho- and para-hydrogen, and of deuterium, in hydrogen,[4] but very much more careful work is necessary than was at first used,[5] and earlier results found by rather crude apparatus are of little value. One rather unexpected source of error [6] is that, in certain circumstances, especially at low pressures, the temperature gradient along an electrically heated wire in hydrogen may suddenly become unstable, and different parts of the wire then have different temperatures; some spots may even become red-hot. This effect is not found in vacuum or in other gases, but only in hydrogen—the gas which, it may be noted, is the one generally used with the method. The apparatus must be pumped out at 400° for some hours between each experiment.

The thermal conductivity of a paramagnetic gas (like its viscosity, § 2.VII F) is slightly affected by a magnetic field.[7]

§ 5. Thermal Conductivity of Gas Mixtures

Deviation from additivity of thermal conductivity in gas mixtures is to be expected when there are differences in the attractive forces (or attractive potentials),[8] or in the masses,[9] of the molecules of the components. The simple kinetic theory [10] gives for a mixture of gases of conductivities k_1, k_2, and with

[1] *Ann. Phys.*, 1933, **17**, 345.

[2] *Ann. Phys.*, 1939, **34**, 669.

[3] Daynes, " Gas Analysis by Measurement of Thermal Conductivity," Cambridge, 1933; Smith, *Bur. Mines. Rep. Invest.*, 1934, **3250** (He in natural gas); Pieters, *Chem. Weekbl.*, 1940, **37**, 316; Minter, *J. Chem. Educ.*, 1947, **23**, 237.

[4] Senftleben, *Z. phys. Chem.*, 1929, **4** B, 169; Farkas, *ibid.*, 1933, **22** B, 344; *Proc. Roy. Soc.*, 1934, **144**, 467; Gross and Steiner, *Mikrochemie*, 1935, **17**, 43 (micro-app.); Eley and Tuck, *Trans. Faraday Soc.*, 1936, **32**, 1425; Bolland and Melville, *ibid.*, 1937, **33**, 1316; *Nature*, 1937, **140**, 63; Twigg, *Trans. Faraday Soc.*, 1937, **33**, 1329; Burshtein, *J. Phys. Chem. U.S.S.R.*, 1937, **9**, 870; *Acta Physicochim. U.R.S.S.*, 1937, **6**, 815; Trenner, *J. Chem. Phys.*, 1937, **5**, 382; Gregory and Archer, *Proc. Roy. Soc.*, 1938, **165**, 474 (D_2).

[5] Farkas *et al.*, *Proc. Roy. Soc.*, 1935, **152**, 124; *Nature*, 1936, **137**, 315; Fajans, *Z. phys. Chem.*, 1935, **28** B, 239; Newell *et al.*, *Nature*, 1936, **137**, 69; Wirtz, *Z. phys. Chem.*, 1936, **32** B, 334.

[6] Busch, *Ann. Phys.*, 1921, **64**, 401; 1926, **80**, 33; Lenher and Taylor, *J.A.C.S.*, 1929, **51**, 2741; Farkas and Rowley, *Z. phys. Chem.*, 1933, **22** B, 335; Walton, *Trans. Faraday Soc.*, 1938, **34**, 450.

[7] Senftleben, *Phys. Z.*, 1930, **31**, 961; Bonwitt and Groetzinger, *Z. Phys.*, 1931, **72**, 600; Senftleben and Pietzner, *Ann. Phys.*, 1933, **16**, 907; 1936, **27**, 108, 117; 1937, **30**, 541; *Phys. Z.*, 1934, **35**, 986; von Laue, *Ann. Phys.*, 1935, **23**, 1; 1936, **26**, 474; Rieger, *ibid.*, 1938, **31**, 453; Torwegge, *ibid.*, 1938, **33**, 459; Becker, *Z. Naturforsch.*, 1947, **2** A, 297.

[8] Schmick, *Phys. Z.*, 1928, **29**, 633; Gruss and Schmick, *Wiss. Veroffl. Siemens-Konzern*, 1928, **7**, 202; Kornfeld and Hilferding, *Z. phys. Chem.*, 1931, *Bodenstein Festb.*, 792.

[9] Weber, *Ann. Phys.*, 1917, **54**, 481; Ibbs and Hirst, *Proc. Roy. Soc.*, 1929, **123**, 134; Sachsse and Bratzler, *Z. phys. Chem.*, 1934, **171**, 331; Riechemeier, Senftleben, and Pastorff, *Ann. Phys.*, 1934, **19**, 218.

[10] Wassiljewa, *Phys. Z.*, 1904, **5**, 737; Wachsmuth, *ibid.*, 1908, **9**, 235; Enskog, *Arkiv Mat. Astron. Fys.*, 1922, **16**, No. 16; Schmick, *Phys. Z.*, 1928, **29**, 633.

partial pressures p_1, p_2:

$$k=\frac{k_1}{1+A(p_2/p_1)}+\frac{k_2}{1+B(p_1/p_2)} \quad . \; . \; . \; . \; . \; . \; (1)$$

$$A=\tfrac{1}{4}\sqrt{\left[\tfrac{1}{2}\left(1+\frac{m_1}{m_2}\right)\right]\left[1+\left(\frac{\eta_1}{\eta_2}\right)^{1/2}\left(\frac{m_2}{m_1}\right)^{1/4}\right]^2}; \quad B=\eta_2 A/\eta_1 \quad . \; (2)$$

where m_1, m_2 are the masses of the molecules, and η_1, η_2 the viscosities. Weber [1] found, however, that the experimental A and B values could be either greater or less than the theoretical, and varied with the proportions in the mixture. For example, with hydrogen and oxygen, A was 3·06 and 2·37 with one mixture, and 1·38 and 0·92 with another; with argon and helium, values for one mixture were 0·38 and 1·62, and with another 2·92 and 1·16; for hydrogen and carbon dioxide, A=1·01, B=2·56 (theor.), A=2·70, B=0·40 (obs.).

Ishikawa and Yagi [2] found a rapid increase in thermal conductivity in mixtures of CO and CO_2 as compared with the separate gases, at low pressures, reaching a maximum value.

In Schmick's formula, the coefficients A and B in (1) are:

$$\left.\begin{aligned} A&=(\sigma/d_1)^2\frac{1-m_1\Theta_1/(m_1+m_2)}{0{\cdot}797}\sqrt{[(m_1+m_2)/2m_2]}\frac{(1+C_{12}/T)}{(1+C_1/T)} \\ B&=(\sigma/d_2)^2\frac{1-m_2\Theta_2/(m_1+m_2)}{0{\cdot}797}\sqrt{[(m_1+m_2)/2m_1]}\frac{(1+C_{12}/T)}{(1+C_2/T)} \end{aligned}\right\} \quad . \; (3)$$

where d_1, d_2 are the molecular diameters, $\sigma=\frac{1}{2}(d_1+d_2)$,

$$\left.\begin{aligned} \Theta_1&=\frac{m_1}{2(m_1+m_2)}+\frac{1}{4}\frac{m_1^2}{m_2^{1/2}(m_1+m_2)^{3/2}}\ln\frac{\sqrt{(m_1+m_2)}+\sqrt{m_2}}{\sqrt{(m_1+m_2)}-\sqrt{m_2}} \\ \Theta_2&=\frac{m_2}{2(m_1+m_2)}+\frac{1}{4}\frac{m_2^2}{m_1^{1/2}(m_1+m_2)^{3/2}}\ln\frac{\sqrt{(m_1+m_2)}+\sqrt{m_1}}{\sqrt{(m_1+m_2)}-\sqrt{m_1}} \end{aligned}\right\} \quad . \; (4)$$

C_1, C_2, and C_{12} are the Sutherland constants (§ 5.VII F), where C_{12} may be taken as $\sqrt{(C_1C_2)}$. If $d_1=d_2$, the equation (1) can be used with the constants A and B as given. The same constants are to be used in the formula for the viscosity of a gas mixture (§ 7.VII F).

For most practical purposes the simpler quadratic formula

$$k=k_1(n_1/n)^2+k_{12}(n_1n_2/n^2)+k_2(n_2/n)^2 \quad . \; . \; . \; . \; (5)$$

can be used, where k_1, k_2 are the conductivities of the component gases, k_{12} is an empirical constant; n_1/n and n_2/n are the fractional concentrations in mols or volumes ($n=n_1+n_2$).[3] Sometimes, but not always, the mixture rule applies:

$$k=k_1(n_1/n)+k_2(n_2/n) \quad . \; . \; . \; . \; . \; . \; . \; . \; (6)$$

1 See note 9 on p. 898.
2 *Bull. Inst. Phys. Chem. Res. Tokyo*, 1943, **22**, 12.
3 Kennard, " Kinetic Theory of Gases," New York, 1938, 183.

H. DIFFUSION OF GASES

§ 1. Diffusion

One apparent objection to the kinetic theory was the slowness of the diffusion of one gas into another when the molecules are supposed to be moving with high speeds approximating to a mile a second. This was answered by Clausius,[1] who showed that the moving molecules are constantly deflected by collisions, so that the free path is very short and zig-zags about in the gas; a molecule has to make an enormous number of collisions before it can move appreciably forward. At very low pressures, diffusion should be much faster.

The kinetic theory of diffusion is one of the more complicated parts of the theory; Tait [2] said that " the higher parts of the theory of this subject are very complex and difficult, and cannot yet be considered as at all satisfactorily developed." In what follows the fairly straightforward treatment due essentially to O. E. Meyer [3] is given, but the subject still bristles with difficulties. Other more accurate treatments are given by Maxwell,[4] Boltzmann,[5] Jeans,[6] Langevin,[7] and Chapman; [8] a brief statement of some of their main results is given at the end of this section.

Consider [9] a non-uniform mixture of two gases containing N_1 molecules of one gas and N_2 molecules of the other per cm.^{3}; at constant temperature and total pressure the total number $N=N_1+N_2$ per cm.^{3} is constant (Avogadro's hypothesis) throughout the diffusion. The ratio N_1/N_2 varies along the vertical z axis, but since N_1+N_2 is constant, $\mathrm{d}(N_1+N_2)=0$ and hence:

$$\mathrm{d}N_1/\mathrm{d}z=-\mathrm{d}N_2/\mathrm{d}z \quad . \quad . \quad . \quad . \quad . \quad . \quad . \quad (1)$$

Let the molecules have mean velocities $\overline{c_1}$ and $\overline{c_2}$ distributed at random as to direction, and a component w_0 along the z axis corresponding to the diffusion. Let the mean free paths be λ_1 and λ_2 (the symbol l being used below for length in general). Consider a plane perpendicular to the direction of flow at the point $z=z_0$ and itself moving with a velocity w_0. The number of molecules of the first gas crossing this plane will be proportional to (i) the solid angle

[1] *Ann. Phys.*, 1858, **105**, 239; *Phil. Mag.*, 1859, **17**, 81.

[2] " Properties of Matter," 4th edit., 1899, 280.

[3] " Kinetic Theory of Gases," 1899, 247; criticised by Chapman, *Phil. Mag.*, 1928, **5**, 630; for an improved elementary treatment, see Frankel, *Phys. Rev.*, 1941, **57**, 660; Furry, *Amer. J. Phys.*, 1948, **16**, 63.

[4] *Phil. Mag.*, 1860, **20**, 21; 1868, **35**, 129, 185; *Phil. Trans.*, 1867, **157**, 49; *Nature*, 1873, **8**, 298; " Scientific Papers," Cambridge, 1890, **1**, 377; **2**, 26, 343, 501.

[5] *Wien Ber.*, 1872, **66**, II, 324; 1878, **78**, II, 733; 1882, **86**, II, 63; 1883, **88**, II, 835; *Ann. Phys.*, 1894, **53**, 959; " Ges. Abhl.," 1909, **3**, 3, 38, 504, 598; " Vorlesungen über Gastheorie," Leipzig, 1896, **1**, 89, 194; Burbury, *Phil. Mag.*, 1890, **30**, 298; 1907, **14**, 122; Gross, *Ann. Phys.*, 1890, **40**, 424; Sutherland, *Phil. Mag.*, 1894, **38**, 1; Nabl, *Phys. Z.*, 1906, **7**, 240.

[6] " Dynamical Theory of Gases," 4th edit., Cambridge, 1925, ch. xiii; " Kinetic Theory of Gases," Cambridge, 1940, 199.

[7] *Ann. Chim.*, 1905, **5**, 245; see also Brillouin, *ibid.*, 1899, **18**, 433; 1900, **20**, 440; Thiesen, *Verhl. d. D. Phys. Ges.*, 1902, **4**, 348; 1903, **5**, 130; Nabl, *Phys. Z.*, 1906, **7**, 240.

[8] *Phil. Mag.*, 1917, **34**, 146; Chapman and Dootson, *ibid.*, 1917, **33**, 248; Ibbs, *Proc. Roy. Soc.*, 1921, **99**, 385; 1925, **107**, 470; Elliott and Masson, *ibid.*, 1925, **108**, 378; Ibbs and Underwood, *Proc. Phys. Soc.*, 1927, **39**, 227; Chapman and Cowling, *Proc. Roy. Soc.*, 1941, **179**, 159.

[9] Brillouin, *Ann. Chim.*, 1899, **18**, 433; Jäger, in Winkelmann, " Handbuch der Physik," 1906, **3**, 753; " Fortschritte der kinetischen Gastheorie," 1906, 45; Kuenen, *Proc. K. Akad. Wetens. Amsterdam*, 1913, **15**, 1152 (*Comm. Leiden*, Suppl. **28**); " Die Eigenschaften der Gase " (Ostwald-Drucker, " Handbuch der allgemeinen Chemie," **3**), Leipzig, 1919, 121.

$2\pi \sin\theta d\theta$ in which the direction of motion must lie, (ii) the component velocity parallel to the z axis, $\bar{c_1} \cos\theta$, and (iii) the number of molecules per cm.[3], $N_1 \pm \lambda_1 \cos\theta (dN_1/dz)$ at the average distance $\pm\lambda_1 \cos\theta$ from which they have come since their last collision (see Fig. 1.VII H). The net number of molecules passing per cm.[2] per sec. in the direction of increasing values of z will be:

$$dZ_1 = (2\pi \sin\theta d\theta/4\pi)\, \bar{c_1} \cos\theta \,.\, 2\lambda_1 \cos\theta\, (dN_1/dz) \quad . \quad . \quad . \quad . \quad (2)$$

This, when integrated for all possible values of θ from 0 to $\pi/2$, gives:

$$Z_1 = -\tfrac{1}{3}\bar{c_1}\lambda_1(dN_1/dz) \quad . \quad . \quad . \quad . \quad . \quad . \quad . \quad . \quad (3)$$

(see (9), § 8.III), which is the number of molecules crossing the plane moving with a velocity w_0 in the z direction.

The corresponding number crossing a fixed plane is:

$$Z_1' = N_1 w_0 - \tfrac{1}{3}\bar{c_1}\lambda_1(dN_1/dz) \quad (4)$$

Similarly, for molecules of the second gas:

$$Z_2' = N_2 w_0 - \tfrac{1}{3}\bar{c_2}\lambda_2(dN_2/dz) \quad (5)$$

The constancy of the total number of molecules on each side gives:

$$Z_1' = -Z_2' \quad . \quad . \quad (6)$$

$$\therefore\ w_0 = [\bar{c_1}\lambda_1(dN_1/dz) + \bar{c_2}\lambda_2(dN_2/dz)]/3(N_1+N_2) \quad (7)$$

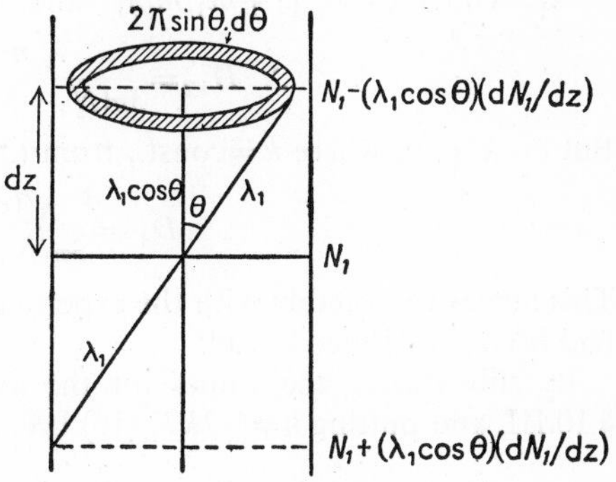

FIG. 1.VII H

Equations (4)–(7), and (1), give: [1]

$$\left.\begin{aligned} Z_1' &= -\frac{N_1\lambda_2\bar{c_2} + N_2\lambda_1\bar{c_1}}{3(N_1+N_2)} \cdot \frac{dN_1}{dz} \\ Z_2' &= -\frac{N_1\lambda_2\bar{c_2} + N_2\lambda_1\bar{c_1}}{3(N_1+N_2)} \cdot \frac{dN_2}{dz} \end{aligned}\right\} \quad . \quad . \quad . \quad . \quad . \quad (8)$$

Fick's Law of Diffusion (see § 2) states that the mass of substance diffusing through 1 cm.[2] per sec. is related to the concentration gradient in the direction of diffusion by the equation:

$$dM/dt = -D(dc/dt) \quad . \quad . \quad . \quad . \quad . \quad . \quad . \quad . \quad . \quad (9)$$

where D is the *coefficient of diffusion* (or the *diffusivity*). Its dimensions are cm.^{2} sec.$^{-1}$. By definition then, the coefficient of the concentration gradient in (8) is the diffusion coefficient D_{12} of the first gas into the second:

$$\therefore\ D_{12} = \frac{N_1\bar{c_2}\lambda_2 + N_2\bar{c_1}\lambda_1}{3(N_1+N_2)} \quad . \quad . \quad . \quad . \quad . \quad . \quad . \quad (10)$$

This must be the same for both gases in the mixture, since the constancy of N_1+N_2 per cm.[3] implies that the molecules of one diffusing gas must have their places taken by an equal number of molecules of the other gas, hence $D_{12}=D_{21}$. Since $N_1/(N_1+N_2)=n_1$ and $N_2/(N_1+N_2)=n_2=1-n_1$ are the *mol fractions* of the two gases in the mixture, (10) may be written:

$$D_{12} = \tfrac{1}{3}(n_1\bar{c_2}\lambda_2 + n_2\bar{c_1}\lambda_1) \quad . \quad . \quad . \quad . \quad . \quad . \quad . \quad (11)$$

[1] In O. E. Meyer's equation, "Kinetic Theory of Gases," 1899, 255, 458, the factor $\frac{1}{3}$ is replaced by $3\pi/8$, since an attempt was made to correct for the variation of λ with velocity, but this is not claimed to be exact; see Winkelmann, *Ann. Phys.*, 1885, **24**, 1; Weinstein, "Thermodynamik und Kinetik der Körper," 1901, **1**, 341, found $\pi/16$, as the factor.

If λ is identified with Maxwell's mean free path l, $\eta=\frac{1}{3}\rho\bar{c}l$ (§ 1.VII F),

$$D_{12}=n_2(\eta_1/\rho_1)+n_1(\eta_2/\rho_2) \quad . \quad . \quad . \quad . \quad . \quad . \quad . \quad (12)$$

If $n_1=n_2=\frac{1}{2}$, $D_{12}=\frac{1}{2}(\eta_1/\rho_1+\eta_2/\rho_2)$, an equation given by Maxwell. The interpretation of λ, however, requires consideration. Maxwell's equation (37), § 22.III, for the free path of one gas in a mixture of two gases gives:

$$\lambda_1=1/[\sqrt{(2)}\pi N_1\sigma_{11}^2+\pi N_2\sigma_{12}^2\sqrt{(1+m_1/m_2)}] \quad . \quad . \quad . \quad (13)$$

Since diffusion is not hindered by collisions of molecules of the *same* kind, which leaves the total momentum in the z direction unchanged, Stefan and Maxwell put $N_1=0$ in (13) and $N_2=0$ in the corresponding equation for λ_2. Hence:

$$\lambda_1=1/[\pi N_2\sigma_{12}^2\sqrt{(1+m_1/m_2)}] \quad \text{and} \quad \lambda_2=1/[\pi N_1\sigma_{12}^2\sqrt{(1+m_2/m_1)}] \quad (14)$$

$$\therefore\ D_{12}=\frac{\sqrt{m_1}\bar{c}_2+\sqrt{m_2}\bar{c}_1}{3\pi(N_1+N_2)\sigma_{12}^2\sqrt{(m_1+m_2)}} \quad . \quad . \quad . \quad . \quad (15)$$

But $\bar{c}=k/\sqrt{m}$, where k=const., from (35), § 10.III, hence:

$$D_{12}=\frac{\sqrt{(\bar{c}_1^2+\bar{c}_2^2)}}{3\pi(N_1+N_2)\sigma_{12}^2} \quad . \quad . \quad . \quad . \quad . \quad . \quad . \quad . \quad (16)$$

This agrees reasonably with the experimental data, and better than if λ_1 and λ_2 had been substituted in full.

By substituting the values for the average velocities $\bar{c}_1$ and $\bar{c}_2$ from (35), § 10.III, and putting $h=1/2kT$, (16) becomes: [1]

$$D_{12}=\frac{2}{3\pi(N_1+N_2)\sigma_{12}^2}\sqrt{\left[\frac{1}{\pi h}\left(\frac{1}{m_1}+\frac{1}{m_2}\right)\right]} \quad . \quad . \quad . \quad . \quad (17)$$

Langevin [2] by a different calculation, found the factor $\frac{3}{16}$ instead of $\frac{2}{3}$ in (17). If $m_1=m_2$, and $\sigma_1=\sigma_2$, i.e. the molecules have identical (or nearly identical) masses and diameters, (16) gives:

$$D=\tfrac{1}{3}\bar{c}/\sqrt{(2)}N\pi\sigma^2=\tfrac{1}{3}\bar{c}l=\eta/\rho \quad . \quad . \quad . \quad . \quad . \quad . \quad . \quad (18)$$

for the *coefficient of self-diffusion*, this giving the rate of diffusion of a gas into itself,[3] or of a gas into another of the same molecular weight and molecular diameter (e.g. N_2 and CO) Winn and Ney [4] for self-diffusion of $^{13}CH_4$ into $^{12}CH_4$ found $\rho D/\eta=\epsilon=1{\cdot}33$ instead of (18)

Equation (10) shows that the diffusion coefficient D_{12} should vary with the composition (N_1 and N_2) of the gas mixture to a comparatively large extent.[5] Earlier experiments seemed to disagree with this, and Stefan [6] deduced a formula not involving the composition, but by an assumption not depending on molecular theory and of questionably validity. Gross [7] deduced another formula which gave a dependence on composition but in the opposite direction to that predicted by O. E. Meyer's formula (10). Careful experiments [8] show a dependence on composition in the direction predicted by (10) but much smaller, and the observed value is *numerically* of the order predicted by Gross's

[1] Boltzmann, " Gastheorie," 1896, **1**, 96; Jeans, " Kinetic Theory of Gases," 1940, 208.
[2] *Compt. Rend.*, 1905, **140**, 35.
[3] The formula has been applied to the diffusion of *para*-hydrogen into normal hydrogen by Harteck and Schmidt, *Z. phys. Chem.*, 1933, **21** B, 447; and of carbon monoxide and nitrogen by Boardman and Wild, *Proc. Roy. Soc.*, 1937, **162**, 511.
[4] *Phys. Rev.*, 1947, **72**, 77.
[5] Cf. Tait, *Proc. Roy. Soc. Edin.*, 1887, **33**, 266; *Phil. Mag.*, 1887, **23**, 141.
[6] *Wien Ber.*, 1871, **63**, II, 63; 1872, **65**, II, 323.
[7] *Ann. Phys.*, 1890, **40**, 424; Stanzel, *Wien Ber.*, 1901, **110**, II A, 1038.
[8] Lonius, *Ann. Phys.*, 1909, **29**, 664.

formula. An approximate calculation by the method of Enskog,[1] which is similar to Chapman's,[2] gives no dependence on composition; a second approximation gives such a dependence, and the resulting very complicated equation represents the experimental results moderately well. The correcting coefficients have been worked out both for two different gases, and for self-diffusion. For the latter, Chapman gives instead of (18):

$$D=1{\cdot}017\times\tfrac{1}{3}\bar{c}l \quad . \quad . \quad . \quad . \quad . \quad . \quad . \quad . \quad (19)$$

A correction for persistence of velocities (§ 3.VII F) was applied to Meyer's calculation by Kuenen.[3]

If (12) is true, the dependence of D on temperature would be expected to follow that of η, and the dependence of D for one gas diffusing into a second has been represented [4] by a Sutherland viscosity formula (§ 5.VII F):

$$D=D_0[(T_0+C)/(T+C)](T/T_0)^{5/2} \quad . \quad . \quad . \quad . \quad . \quad (20)$$

for CO_2 diffusing into air from 17° to 1260°, and H_2O into air from 100° to 1200°. The experimental values lie below the theoretical curve $D=D_0(T/T_0)^n$ if $n=1{\cdot}96$ and above it if $n=1{\cdot}5$, whilst the above equation, with C between those of the pure gases (CO_2–air 125–130; H_2O–air 305–323) agrees very well. The value of C can be found from the empirical formula $C_{12}=M_{12}(C_1/M_1+C_2/M_2)$ where M=mol. wt. ($M_2>M_1$).

It is possible to calculate the size of molecules from diffusion coefficients,[5] but this method is probably less accurate than those depending on viscosity.[6]

The elementary result, due to Graham,[7] that the rates of diffusion of gases are inversely proportional to the square roots of the densities, was successfully used by Soret [8] in deciding the formula O_3 for ozone (interdiffusion through a small hole), but it should be clear from the preceding discussion that it is only quite approximate. Ethylene (C_2H_4) and nitrogen (N_2), with the same density, have coefficients of diffusion into hydrogen of 0·486 and 0·674, respectively. The correct equations, derived from Maxwell's theory, are complicated, but must be used in accurate work.[9] For two gases, if σ_{12}=sum of radii of molecules, $N_1+N_2=N$:

$$D_{12}=\frac{1}{3\pi N}\left[\frac{\bar{c}_1}{\sigma_{12}^2\sqrt{(1+m_1/m_2)}}+\frac{\bar{c}_2}{\sigma_{12}^2\sqrt{(1+m_2/m_1)}}\right] \quad . \quad . \quad (21)$$

1 *Phys. Z.*, 1911, **12**, 56, 533; *Dissert.*, Uppsala, 1917; *Arkiv Mat. Astron. Fys.*, 1922, **16**, No. 16; *K. Svensk. Vetensk. Handl.*, 1922, **63**, No. 4.

2 *Phil. Trans.*, 1912, **211**, 433; 1916, **217**, 115; *Proc. Roy. Soc.*, 1928, **119**, 34, 55; Chapman and Hainsworth, *Phil. Mag.*, 1924, **48**, 593; Chapman and Cowling, *Proc. Roy. Soc.*, 1941, **179**, 159; cf. Jeans, "Kinetic Theory of Gases," 1940, 210; Hirschfelder, Bird, and Spotz, *J. Chem. Phys.*, 1948, **16**, 968.

3 *Verslag. K. Akad. Wetens. Amsterdam*, 1913, **21**, 1088; 1914, **22**, 1158; 1915, **23**, 1049; *Proc. K. Akad. Wetens. Amsterdam*, 1913, **15**, 1152; 1915, **17**, 1068 (correction).

4 Pochettino, *Nuov. Cim.*, 1914, **8**, 5; Klibanova, Pomerantsev, and Frank-Kamenetsky, *J. Techn. Phys. U.S.S.R.*, 1942, **12**, 14; *Amer. Chem. Abstr.*, 1943, **37**, 1310.

5 Pochettino, *Nuov. Cim.*, 1914, **8**, 5; Mack, *J.A.C.S.*, 1925, **47**, 2468; Melaven and Mack, *ibid.*, 1932, **54**, 888.

6 Pochettino, *Nuov. Cim.*, 1914, **8**, 5.

7 *Quart. J. Sci.*, 1829, **28**, 74; *Ann. Phys.*, 1829, **17**, 341; *Phil. Mag.*, 1833, **2**, 175, 269, 351.

8 *Ann. Chim.*, 1868, **13**, 247; Maxwell, *Phil. Mag.*, 1868, **35**, 185; Partington, "General and Inorganic Chemistry," 1945, 661.

9 Voss, *Ann. de Phys.*, 1923, **20**, 66; Barter and Beckham, *J.A.C.S.*, 1933, **55**, 3926, who give full examples of the calculations as applied to hydrocarbon mixtures. On diffusion theory generally, see Ricketts and Colbertson, *J.A.C.S.*, 1931, **53**, 4002. Lonius, *Ann. Phys.*, 1909, **29**, 664, concluded that Maxwell's theory gave wrong results and O. E. Meyer's was nearer the truth, but the diffusion coefficient is a function of composition; for the diffusion of *mixtures*

in which m_1/m_2 and m_2/m_1 can be replaced by the ratios of the molecular weights M_1/M_2 and M_2/M_1. For s gases, one of which is supposed to be diffusing in one direction and $s-1$ in the opposite direction:

$$D_{mk}=(1/3\pi N)[\bar{c}_m/\mathrm{f}(m, s)+\bar{c}_k/\mathrm{f}(k, s)] \quad . \quad . \quad . \quad . \quad (22)$$

$$\mathrm{f}(m, s)=\sum_1^{s-1}[\alpha_s\sigma_{ms}^2\sqrt{(1+M_m/M_s)}+\alpha_k\sigma_{mk}^2\sqrt{(1+M_m/M_k)}] \quad . \quad . \quad (23)$$

$$\mathrm{f}(k, s)=\sum_1^{s-1}[\beta_s\sigma_{ks}^2\sqrt{(1+M_k/M_s)}+\beta_m\sigma_{km}^2\sqrt{(1+M_k/M_m)} \quad . \quad . \quad (24)$$

the subscript s referring to the gas diffusing in one direction, and the subscript k to the gas diffusing in the opposite direction, and m refers to the particular one of the s gases of which the diffusion coefficient is to be calculated; α_s is the mol fraction of the gas s calculated by omitting the gas m, β_s the mol fraction of the gas s calculated by omitting the gas k, α_k the mol fraction of the gas k calculated by omitting the gas m, and β_m the mol fraction of the gas m calculated by omitting the gas k, these mol fractions being average values taken over the whole diffusion column.

The effect of a magnetic field on the diffusion of a paramagnetic gas (O_2) is so small as to be doubtful.[1] Changes of temperature may occur locally in diffusion.[2]

§ 2. Methods of Measurement of Diffusion of Gases

The earliest experiments on gaseous diffusion were made by Priestley.[3] Dalton [4] and Berthollet [5] used a lighter gas and a heavier gas in two bottles joined by a vertical tube, the lighter gas being in the upper bottle; the gases were found to have mixed on standing. Quantitative measurements by Graham [6] led to the well-known law of diffusion that the rates of diffusion of two gases are inversely proportional to the square roots of the densities (§ 2.III). In Graham's apparatus the gases were separated by a porous partition of plaster of Paris or graphite, and this apparatus is not adapted to the determination of the diffusion coefficient.

The general law of diffusion was first stated by Fick,[7] by analogy with the law of conduction of heat previously given by Fourier: [8]

$$\mathrm{d}M=-DA\,.\,(\mathrm{d}c/\mathrm{d}x)\,.\,\mathrm{d}t \quad . \quad . \quad . \quad . \quad . \quad . \quad . \quad . \quad (1)$$

of gases, see Kuenen, *Proc. K. Akad. Wetens. Amsterdam*, 1913, **15**, 1152 (important); Trautz and Ries, *Ann. Phys.*, 1931, **8**, 163; for *three* gases, Wretschko, *Wien Ber.*, 1870, **62**, II, 575; Benigar, *ibid.*, 1870, **62**, II, 687.

1 Senftleben, *Phys. Z.*, 1933, **34**, 835.

2 Géhéniau, *Bull. Acad. Roy. Belge*, 1942, **28**, 283; Kramers and Kistemaker, *Physica*, 1943, **10**, 699 (*Comm. Leiden*, **268***a*) (slip of diffusing gas mixture along wall); Waldmann, *Z. Naturforsch.*, 1946, **1**, 59; 1947, **2** A, 358 (change of sign of thermal diffusion coefficient with temperature).

3 " Experiments and Observations on Natural Philosophy," Birmingham, 1786, **3**, 390; " Experiments and Observations on Air," Birmingham, 1790, **2**, 441; he found that air and carbon dioxide, and air and hydrogen, etc., in a cylinder became " equally diffused " on standing for a day.

4 *Manch. Mem.*, 1805, **1**, 244 (" On the tendency of elastic fluids to diffusion through each other "); *Ann. Phys.*, 1803, **13**, 25, 122, 197; 1807, **27**, 388.

5 *Mém. Soc. Arcueil*, 1809, **2**, 463 (" Sur le mélange réciproque des gaz "); the results are tabulated by Thomson, " System of Chemistry," 5th edit., 1817, **3**, 33.

6 *Quart. J. Sci.*, 1829, **28**, 74; *Ann. Phys.*, 1829, **17**, 341; *Phil. Mag.*, 1833, **2**, 175, 269, 351; " Researches," 1876, 28, 44.

7 *Ann. Phys.*, 1855, **94**, 59.

8 " Théorie Analytique de la Chaleur," Paris, 1822; " Analytical Theory of Heat," transl. Freeman, Cambridge, 1878, 55; see § 73.I.

where dM=mass of substance diffusing in time dt through an area A in the direction of x (c constant over the area A), when the concentration gradient is dc/dx; D is the *diffusion coefficient* or *diffusivity*. The minus sign shows that diffusion occurs in the direction of diminishing concentration; dM and c must be in the same units of quantity, e.g. grams or mols, and if x is in cm., c must be in grams or mols per cm.^{3}. Equation (1) applies both to gaseous and liquid diffusion. Since diffusion is a slow process, the unit of time is usually the hour. The c.g.s. dimensions of D are cm.^{2} sec.$^{-1}$.

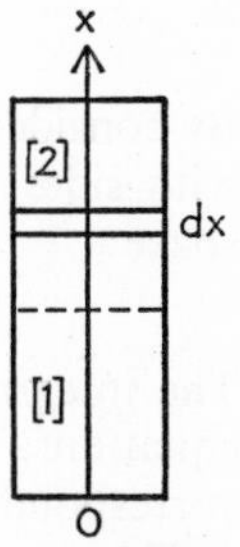

FIG. 2.VII H. Diffusion of one Gas into another

The theory of diffusion on the basis of the kinetic theory was developed by Maxwell,[1] who defined the diffusion coefficient D as " the volume of gas, reduced to unit of pressure, which passes in unit of time through unit of area when the total pressure is uniform and equal to p, and the pressure of either gas increases or diminishes by unity in unit of distance." He says D " varies directly as the square of the absolute temperature and inversely as the total pressure p." There has been some discussion on the meaning of Maxwell's definition and especially on the effect of total pressure,[2] and the relation between Maxwell's equation and Fick's; the two are actually identical.[3]

In Fig. 2.VII H the gas [2] is shown stratified over an equal volume of the heavier gas [1], and diffusion occurs in the direction of the x axis. Let A be the cross-section of the vertical cylinder and consider a volume Adx between two imaginary horizontal planes at x and $x+dx$ above the base (x=0). Let dc_1/dx be the concentration gradient at the section x; that at the section $x+dx$ will be:

$$dc_1/dx+(d/dx)(dc_1/dx)dx \quad . \quad . \quad . \quad . \quad . \quad . \quad (2)$$

The mass of gas [1] diffusing through the section x *into* the volume element Adx in time dt will be, by (1):

$$dM_1=-DA(dc_1/dx)dt \quad . \quad . \quad . \quad . \quad . \quad . \quad . \quad (3)$$

and the mass of gas [1] diffusing *out* of the volume element through the section $x+dx$ in time dt will be:

$$dM_1'=-A\left[D\frac{dc_1}{dx}+\frac{d}{dx}\left(D\frac{dc_1}{dx}\right)dx\right]dt \quad . \quad . \quad . \quad . \quad (4)$$

The diffusion coefficient D may depend on the composition of the mixture of gases, i.e. on x, hence it must follow the symbol d/dx. The mass of [1] added to the volume element in time dt is thus, by subtraction:

$$dM_1''=dM_1-dM_1'=Adt\frac{d}{dx}\left(D\frac{dc_1}{dx}\right)dx \quad . \quad . \quad . \quad . \quad (5)$$

This is obviously also given by:

$$dM_1''=Adx(dc_1/dt)dt \quad . \quad . \quad . \quad . \quad . \quad . \quad . \quad . \quad (6)$$

Equating (5) and (6), and simplifying, gives:

$$\frac{dc_1}{dt}=\frac{d}{dx}\left(D\frac{dc_1}{dx}\right) \quad . \quad . \quad . \quad . \quad . \quad . \quad . \quad . \quad . \quad (7)$$

1 *Phil. Mag.*, 1860, **19**, 19; 1860, **20**, 21; 1868, **35**, 129, 185; *Phil. Trans.*, 1867, **157**, 49.
2 Trautz and Müller, *Ann. Phys.*, 1935, **22**, 313, 329, 333, 353.
3 Kuusinen, *Ann. Phys.*, 1935, **24**, 445, 447, 752; see also Brillouin, *Congrès Internat. Phys.*, 1901, **1**, 512.

or, by replacing concentration by partial pressure, $p_1 = c_1 RT$:

$$\frac{dp_1}{dt} = \frac{d}{dx}\left(D\frac{dp_1}{dx}\right) \quad \text{(7a)}$$

If D is constant, these equations become:

$$dc_1/dt = D(d^2c_1/dx^2) \quad \text{(8)}$$

$$dp_1/dt = D(d^2p_1/dx^2) \quad \text{(8a)}$$

By considering the three pairs of opposite faces of a small rectangular element with sides dx, dy, and dz, it is easy to show, similarly, that, for diffusion in space:

$$\partial c_1/\partial t = D(\partial^2 c_1/\partial x^2 + \partial^2 c_1/\partial y^2 + \partial^2 c_1/\partial z^2) = D\nabla^2 c_1 \quad \text{(9)}$$

The integration of (8), and especially (9), can lead to some very complicated equations, sometimes involving Fourier's series (§ 73, I), as in the case of the corresponding equations for the conduction of heat.

The concentrations in (9) may, in the case of gaseous mixtures, be replaced by the partial pressures, $p_1 = c_1 RT$ and $p_2 = p - p_1$, where p=total pressure; or (perhaps most conveniently) by the mol fractions $n_1 = N_1/(N_1 + N_2)$ and $n_2 = 1 - n_1$; then $c_1 = \text{const.} \times n$, and hence:

$$dn_1/dt = D(d^2n_1/dx^2) \quad \text{(10)}$$

If the diffusion tube of length l (97·5 cm. and 2·6 cm. diam. in Loschmidt's experiments, see below) is divided into two equal parts $l/2$, each initially filled with one of the pure gases, the differential equation (10) (involving *two* independent variables, x and t) applied to one gas satisfies the following conditions:

(i) $n_1 = 1$ for $t = 0$ and x from 0 to $l/2$;

(ii) $n_1 = 0$ for $t = 0$ and x from $l/2$ to l;

(iii) $dn_1/dx = 0$ for $x = 0$ and $x = l$, for all values of t.

In order to indicate that in differentiating with respect to x, the time t is held constant, and *vice versa*, partial differential coefficients, $\partial n_1/\partial t$ and $\partial^2 n_1/\partial x^2$ may be used.

§ 3. General Equations for Diffusion

Since the mathematics applies to other problems, it will first be carried through generally, n_1 in (10), § 2, being replaced by v, called by Lord Kelvin [1] a *quality* at a time t and at a distance x from a fixed plane of reference, the conditions in each of the planes parallel to this being uniform, and change taking place only in the direction of x. The constant D is the *diffusivity*. The equation applies e.g. to (i) one of the three components of velocity, relative to rectangular coordinates, of the viscous motion of a fluid; (ii) the density of an electric current per unit area perpendicular to the direction of flow; (iii) the temperature in heat conduction; (iv) the electric potential at any point of an isolated conductor; or (v) (as at present) the concentration (or its difference from some standard value) in a solution, including a gas mixture. The general equation to be solved is then:

$$\partial v/\partial t = D(\partial^2 v/\partial x^2) \quad \text{(1)}$$

[1] "Math. and Phys. Papers," 1884, **2**, 41; 1890, **3**, 428; on the integrals, see also Simmler and Wild, *Ann. Phys.*, 1857, **100**, 217.

Two important cases will be considered. The cross-section of the tubes is supposed to be unit area in both.

(1) A tube A of solution [1] of uniform initial concentration v_0 is immersed vertically in a large jar of pure solvent B, the open end of the tube, of length h, being just under the solvent surface (Fig. 3.VII H). The solution at the bottom of the tube A is supposed to remain constant in composition (e.g. it may be kept saturated with solid). The boundary (or limiting) conditions are:

(i) when $x=0$, $\partial v/\partial x=0$, for all values of t;

(ii) when $x=h$, $v=0$ (the solvent only) [2] for all values of t;

(iii) when $t=0$, $v=v_0$ for all values of x from 0 to h. (Note that $v=v_0$ for $x=h$ now refers to the solution in the tube.)

A particular solution of (1) is (§ 70.I):

$$v=e^{\alpha x+\beta t} \quad . \quad . \quad . \quad . \quad . \quad . \quad (2)$$

where α and β are constants. Substitution in (1) gives:

$$\beta=D\alpha^2 \quad . \quad . \quad . \quad . \quad . \quad . \quad (3)$$

for all values of α. Put $\alpha=i\mu$, where $i=\sqrt{-1}$, then:

$$v=e^{i\mu x+D\alpha^2 t}=e^{i\mu x-D\mu^2 t} \quad \text{or} \quad v=e^{-i\mu x-D\mu^2 t},$$

corresponding with the two roots of (3). The sum or difference of these values of v will also satisfy (1), hence:

$$v=\tfrac{1}{2}e^{-D\mu^2 t}(e^{i\mu x}\pm e^{-i\mu x}).$$

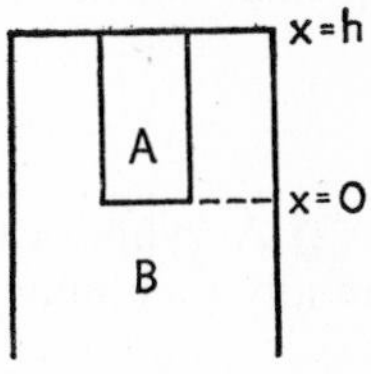

FIG. 3.VII H. Diffusion from a Solution in A into Solvent in B

De Moivre's theorem (§ 46.I) gives:

$$\tfrac{1}{2}(e^{iz}-e^{-iz})=i\sin z \quad \text{and} \quad \tfrac{1}{2}(e^{iz}+e^{-iz})=\cos z,$$

hence the solution:

$$v=ae^{-D\mu^2 t}\cos\mu x+be^{-D\mu^2 t}\sin\mu x=e^{-D\mu^2 t}(a\cos\mu x+b\sin\mu x) \quad . \quad (4)$$

where a and b are constants, will satisfy (1). The constants a and b are determined by the boundary conditions. Differentiate (4) with respect to x:

$$\partial v/\partial x=(-\mu a\sin\mu x+\mu b\cos\mu x)e^{-D\mu^2 t}.$$

When $x=0$, $\partial v/\partial x=0$, and since $\sin 0=0$ and $\cos 0=1$, it follows that $b=0$. When $x=h$, $v=0$, therefore from (4), with the condition $b=0$, $a\cos\mu h=0$, or $\cos\mu h=0$. If n is any integer, $\cos\frac{1}{2}(2n-1)\pi=0$, this being the cosine of every *odd* multiple of $\frac{1}{2}\pi$. Hence μh must have the values $\pi/2$, $3\pi/2$. $5\pi/2$, . . . $(2n-1)\pi/2$, and μ the values $\pi/2h$, $3\pi/2h$, $5\pi/2h$, . . . $(2n-1)\pi/2h$.

If these values are substituted in the cosine of (4) and the results added (since *each* multiplied by a constant satisfies the equation, their sum will do so):

$$v=a_1e^{-(\pi/2h)^2 Dt}\cos(\pi x/2h)+a_2e^{-(3\pi/2h)^2 Dt}\cos(3\pi x/2h)+\dots \quad . \quad (5)$$

is an infinite series satisfying boundary conditions (i) and (ii).

1 A liquid solution, or a mixture of two gases, may be considered: in the second case, one gas is regarded as the solvent. Case (1) usually applies only to liquids, because of the boundary condition $\partial v/\partial x=0$ when $x=0$.

2 The diffusate is supposed to be so dispersed into the *large* mass of pure solvent, that this remains practically pure solvent over the mouth of the tube: on this boundary condition, see Somers, *Proc. Phys. Soc.*, 1913, **25**, 74; de Groot, *Physica*, 1928, **8**, 23; and for general diffusion calculations, Eversole and Doughty, *J. Phys. Chem.*, 1935, **39**, 289; 1937, **41**, 663; Eversole, Peterson, and Kindsvater, *ibid.*, 1941, **45**, 1398; Dobrowsky, *Koll. Z.*, 1944, **109**, 137; Longsworth *et al.*, *Annals New York Acad. Sci.*, 1945, **46**, 209; Crisp, *Trans. Faraday Soc.*, 1946, **42**, 619 (two dimensions); Harned and Nuttall, *J.A.C.S.*, 1947, **69**, 736; Lamm, *J. Phys. Chem.*, 1947, **51**, 1063.

To satisfy condition (iii) the values of $a_1, a_2, \ldots$ in (5) must be such that when $t=0$, $v=v_0$. Hence:

$$v_0=a_1 \cos (\pi x/2h)+a_2 \cos (3\pi x/2h)+ \ldots +a_n \cos [(2n-1)\pi x/2h]+ \ldots$$

for all values of x from 0 to h. The coefficients are evaluated as for a Fourier's series of cosines, and by § 73.I (with $f(x)=v_0=\text{const.}$):

$$a_1=\frac{2v_0}{h}\int_0^h \cos\frac{\pi x}{2h}dx, \quad a_2=\frac{2v_0}{h}\int_0^h \cos\frac{3\pi x}{2h}dx \ldots$$

$$a_n=\frac{2v_0}{h}\int_0^h \cos\frac{(2n-1)\pi x}{2h}dx=\frac{2v_0}{h}\left[\frac{2h}{(2n-1)\pi}\sin\frac{(2n-1)\pi x}{2h}\right]_0^h=\frac{4v_0}{(2n-1)\pi} \quad . \quad (6)$$

By substituting in (5), and summing over all positive values of n from 0 to ∞, the final solution is found to be:

$$v=\frac{4v_0}{\pi}\sum_0^\infty \frac{1}{2n-1}e^{-[(2n-1)\pi/2h]^2Dt}\cos\frac{2n-1}{2h}\pi x \quad . \quad . \quad . \quad (7)$$

(2) A cylindrical vessel of total height H and unit cross-section contains initially a column of solution of concentration v_0 of height h covered with a layer of pure solvent (Fig. 4.VII H).

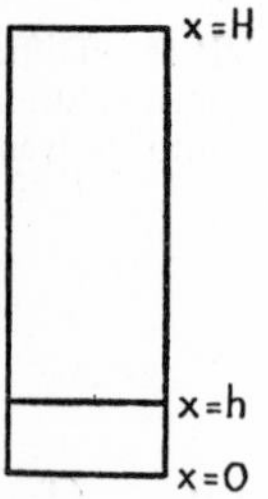

FIG. 4.VII H

The boundary conditions are :

(i) when $x=0$, $\partial v/\partial x=0$ for all values of t;

(ii) when $x=H$, $\partial v/\partial x=0$ for all values of t;

(iii) when $t=0$, $v=v_0$ for all values of x between 0 and h;

(iv) when $t=0$, $v=0$ for all values of x between h and H.

The particular integral is again assumed to be:

$$v=e^{\alpha x+\beta t},$$

giving

$$v=(a \cos \mu x+b \sin \mu x)e^{-D\mu^2 t},$$

and on differentiation with respect to x, it is found again that condition (i) requires $b=0$. To satisfy condition (ii) with $b=0$, $-a\mu \sin \mu H \, . \, e^{-D\mu^2 t}=0$ for all values of t, therefore $\sin \mu H=0$, therefore $\mu H=n\pi$, where n is a positive integer including zero, therefore $\mu=n\pi/H$. By summing the particular integrals:

$$v_0=a_0+a_1 \cos\frac{\pi x}{H}e^{-(\pi/H)^2Dt}+a_2 \cos\frac{2\pi x}{H}e^{-(2\pi/H)^2Dt}+ \ldots .$$

From condition (iii) $v=v_0$ for $t=0$ for $x=0$ to $x=h$, hence:

$$v_0=a_0+a_1 \cos (\pi x/H)+a_2 \cos (2\pi x/H)+ \ldots +a_n \cos (n\pi x/H)+ \ldots .$$

To find the coefficients, the results for the Fourier's series are used, the integrals being from 0 to h and from h to H (§ 21.I):

$$a_0=\frac{1}{H}\int_0^H v_0 dx=\frac{1}{H}\left(\int_h^H 0 \, . \, dx+\int_0^h v_0 dx\right)=\frac{v_0 h}{H}$$

$$a_n=\frac{2}{H}\int_0^H v_0 \cos\frac{n\pi x}{H}dx=\frac{2v_0}{H}\int_0^h \cos\frac{n\pi x}{H}dx=\frac{2v_0}{n\pi}\int_0^h \cos\frac{n\pi x}{H}d\left(\frac{n\pi x}{H}\right)=\frac{2v_0}{n\pi}\sin\frac{n\pi h}{H}.$$

The general solution is

$$v=\frac{v_0 h}{H}+\frac{2v_0}{\pi}\sum_1^\infty \frac{1}{n}\sin\frac{n\pi h}{H}\cos\frac{n\pi x}{H}e^{-(n\pi/H)^2Dt} \quad . \quad . \quad . \quad (8)$$

In Loschmidt's experiment (see below), $v=n_1$, $v_0=1$, and the boundary conditions are the same as before if $h=\frac{1}{2}l$, $H=l$, hence the solution is [1] seen to be:

$$n_1=\tfrac{1}{2}+\frac{2}{\pi}\sum_{1}^{\infty}\frac{1}{n}\sin\frac{n\pi}{2}\cos\frac{n\pi x}{l}\mathrm{e}^{-Dt(n\pi/l)^2} \quad . \quad . \quad . \quad . \quad . \quad . \quad (9)$$

where n is a positive integer varying from 1 to ∞. In the experiments the diffusion is interrupted after a time t, the gases in each half of the tube are thoroughly mixed, and the *average* mol fraction $\bar{n}_1$ of the first gas determined in the upper (U) and lower (L) parts, respectively:

$$(\bar{n}_1)_U=\frac{2}{l}\int_{l/2}^{l}n_1\mathrm{d}x=\tfrac{1}{2}-\frac{4}{\pi^2}\sum_{1}^{\infty}\frac{1}{n^2}\sin^2\frac{n\pi}{2}\mathrm{e}^{-Dt(n\pi/l)^2} \quad . \quad . \quad . \quad (10)$$

$$(\bar{n}_1)_L=\frac{2}{l}\int_{0}^{l/2}n_1\mathrm{d}x=\tfrac{1}{2}+\frac{4}{\pi^2}\sum_{1}^{\infty}\frac{1}{n^2}\sin^2\frac{n\pi}{2}\mathrm{e}^{-Dt(n\pi/l)^2} \quad . \quad . \quad . \quad (11)$$

$$\therefore\ (\bar{n}_1)_L-(\bar{n}_1)_U=\frac{8}{\pi^2}\sum_{1}^{\infty}\frac{1}{n^2}\sin^2\frac{n\pi}{2}\mathrm{e}^{-Dt(n\pi/l)^2}$$

$$=\frac{8}{\pi^2}(\mathrm{e}^{-\alpha}+\tfrac{1}{9}\mathrm{e}^{-9\alpha}+\tfrac{1}{25}\mathrm{e}^{-25\alpha}+\ldots) \quad . \quad (12)$$

where $\alpha=\pi^2Dt/l^2$.

Obermayer (see § 4) gave a table of values of the series in (12) for various values of Dt. By comparison of the entries with the measured values of $(\bar{n}_1)_L-(\bar{n}_1)_U$ the values of Dt can be found, and hence, by dividing by the appropriate values of t, the values of D. The accuracy is about $\frac{1}{2}$ per cent. To complete the discussion of diffusion for later purposes, the following solutions are needed.

(3) To find the amount Q of diffusate passing any horizontal section A in a time t, note that $-DA(\partial v/\partial x)\mathrm{d}t$ is the transport in time $\mathrm{d}t$; $\partial v/\partial x$ is found from (5), and $-DA(\partial v/\partial x)\mathrm{d}t$ is integrated from $t=0$ to $t=t$:

$$\partial v/\partial x=\frac{a_1\pi}{2h}\mathrm{e}^{-(\pi/2h)^2Dt}\sin\frac{\pi x}{2h}+\frac{3a_2\pi}{2h}\mathrm{e}^{-(3\pi/2h)^2Dt}\sin\frac{3\pi x}{2h}+\ldots$$

$$\therefore\ Q/A=-D\int_0^t(\partial v/\partial x)\mathrm{d}t$$

$$=-\frac{a_1\pi D}{2h}\sin\frac{\pi x}{2h}\int_0^t\mathrm{e}^{-(\pi/2h)^2Dt}\mathrm{d}t-\frac{3a_2\pi D}{2h}\sin\frac{3\pi x}{2h}\int_0^t\mathrm{e}^{-(3\pi/2h)^2Dt}\mathrm{d}t-\ldots$$

$$=\frac{2a_1h}{\pi}\sin\frac{\pi x}{2h}[1-\mathrm{e}^{-(\pi/2h)^2Dt}]+\frac{2a_2h}{3\pi}\sin\frac{3\pi x}{2h}[1-\mathrm{e}^{-(3\pi/2h)^2Dt}]+\ldots \quad (13)$$

(4) To find the amount of substance diffusing out of the tube in case (1) in a time t, put $x=h$ in (13). Then $\sin(\pi/2)=1$, $\sin(3\pi/2)=-1$, etc.,

$$\therefore\ Q_1/A=\frac{2a_1h}{\pi}[1-\mathrm{e}^{-(\pi/2h)^2Dt}]-\frac{2a_2h}{3\pi}[1-\mathrm{e}^{-(3\pi/2h)^2Dt}]+\ldots \quad . \quad (14)$$

(5) To find the diffusion coefficient D. Since the series (14) converges rapidly, the higher terms may usually be neglected. If measurements are

[1] Schulze, *Dissert.*, Berlin, 1897; *Z. phys. Chem.*, 1899, **28**, 743; Thovert, *Compt. Rend.*, 1905, **141**, 717; Lemonde, *Ann. de Phys.*, 1938, **9**, 539; Liebhafsky, *J. Appl. Phys.*, 1941, **12**, 707; for tables of functions used in diffusion calculations, see McKay, *Proc. Phys. Soc.*, 1930, **42**, 547.

made at $x=h$, $x=\frac{1}{3}h$, $x=\frac{1}{5}h$, . . ., the values of $\sin(\pi x/2h)$, . . . then become unity. Since $Q\pi/2ha_1A=1-e^{-Dt\pi^2/4h^2}$

$$D=\frac{4h^2}{t\pi^2}\ln(Q\pi/2ha_1A-1)$$

$$a_1=\frac{2v_0}{h}\cdot\frac{2h}{\pi}\int_0^h\cos\frac{\pi x}{2h}\mathrm{d}\left(\frac{\pi x}{2h}\right)=\frac{4v_0}{\pi}$$

$$\therefore\ D=(4h^2/t\pi^2)\ln(Q\pi^2/8hv_0A-1) \quad . \ . \ . \ . \ . \ (15)$$

§ 4. Measurement of Diffusion Coefficients

The first accurate measurements of diffusion coefficients of gases [1] were made by Loschmidt,[2] whose method was used by many later experimenters.[3] In this method the arrangement is essentially that described above; the two gases are contained in a vertical steel tube AB (Fig. 5.VII H) of uniform bore, separated into two parts by a three-way steel stopcock D of equal bore. The gases are filled through stopcocks O, U, and M, and after diffusion the gas in each half is displaced through M and O, respectively, by mercury from R. The apparatus is maintained at a constant temperature, and after diffusion has gone on for a measured time, the stopcock is closed and the contents of the two parts of the tube analysed. The diffusion coefficient of hydrogen into air found by Barnes [4] is larger than the usual value.

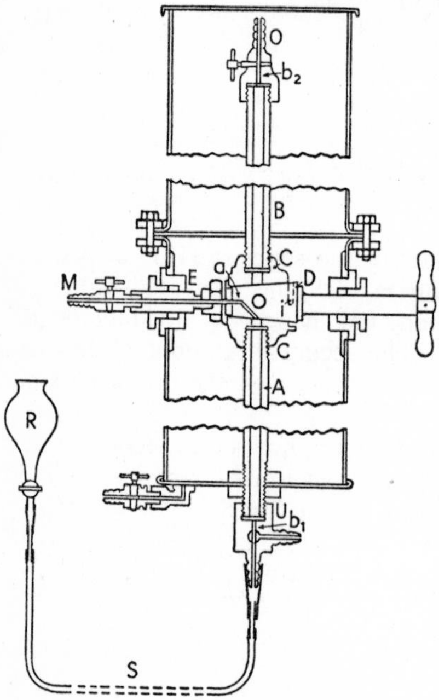

FIG. 5.VII H. Schmidt's Diffusion Apparatus

The *diffusion of vapours* can be investigated by a method due to Stefan.[5]

1 Waitz, in Winkelmann, "Handbuch der Physik," 1908, **1**, ii, 1415; Eucken, in Stähler, "Arbeitsmethoden der anorganischen Chemie," Leipzig, 1913, **3**, i, 564; Kuenen, in "Die Eigenschaften der Gase" (Ostwald and Drucker, "Handbuch der allgemeinen Chemie," 1919, 3), 121.

2 *Wien Ber.*, 1870, **61**, II, 367; 1870, **62**, II, 468; Smith, *Ind. Eng. Chem.*, 1934, **26**, 1167.

3 Wretschko, *Wien Ber.*, 1870, **62**, II, 575; Benigar, *ibid.*, 1870, **62**, II, 687; von Obermayer, *ibid.*, 1880, **81**, II, 1102; 1882, **85**, II, 147, 748; 1883, **87**, II, 188; 1887, **96**, II, 546; Waitz, *Ann. Phys.*, 1882, **17**, 201, 351 (optical method); Hausmaniger, *Wien Ber.*, 1882, **86**, II, 1073; Winkelmann, *Ann. Phys.*, 1884, **22**, 1, 152; 1884, **23**, 203; 1885, **26**, 105; 1886, **27**, 479; Toepler and Hennig, *ibid.*, 1888, **34**, 790; Toepler, *ibid.*, 1896, **58**, 599; Brillouin, *Congrès Internat. Phys.*, 1901, **1**, 512; Schmidt, *Dissert.*, Halle, 1904; *Ann. Phys.*, 1904, **14**, 801; Jackmann, *Dissert.*, Halle, 1906; Deutsch, *Dissert.*, Halle, 1907; Lonius, *Dissert.*, Halle, 1909; *Ann. Phys.*, 1909, **29**, 664 (summarising results found in Dorn's laboratory at Halle); Foch, *Ann. Chim.*, 1913, **29**, 597; McKenzie and Melville, *Proc. Roy. Soc. Edin.*, 1932, **52**, 337; 1933, **53**, 225 (Br_2 vap. in various gases); Trautz and Müller, *Ann. Phys.*, 1935, **22**, 313, 329, 333, 353 (bibl.); Coward and Georgeson, *J.C.S.*, 1937, 1085 (CH_4 in air: $D^{0°}_{760}=0{\cdot}196$ cm.^{2} sec.$^{-1}$).

4 *Proc. Nat. Acad.*, 1924, **10**, 153, 447.

5 *Wien Ber.*, 1871, **63**, II, 63; 1872, **65**, II, 323; 1874, **68**, II, 385; 1889, **98**, II, 1418; *Ann. Phys.*, 1882, **17**, 551; 1890, **41**, 725; Winkelmann, *Ann. Phys.*, 1884, **22**, 1, 152; 1884, **23**, 203;

The liquid is contained in a small graduated glass tube, 90 mm. long and 6 mm. diam., supported in the lower constricted part of a wider tube 200 mm. high and 20 mm. diam., fitted with tubes *g* and *l* for passing a slow stream of an indifferent gas (Fig. 6.VII H). Just above the liquid meniscus the vapour is saturated at the given temperature, whilst at the mouth of the small tube the partial pressure of the vapour is reduced by the stream of gas practically to zero. The velocity of evaporation of the liquid, measured by observing the change of height of the meniscus through a reading microscope, depends on the rate of diffusion of the vapour through the length *h* of the inner tube which does not contain liquid, and a stationary state is set up. This part of the tube contains both vapour and the indifferent gas. Consider two sections of the tube, of area *A* and d*x* apart (Fig. 7.VII H). At the liquid surface O the vapour concentration c_v corresponds with saturation, $c_v=c_s$. The amount of vapour in mols (concentration c_1 mols/cm.^{3}) diffusing upwards in time d*t* is:

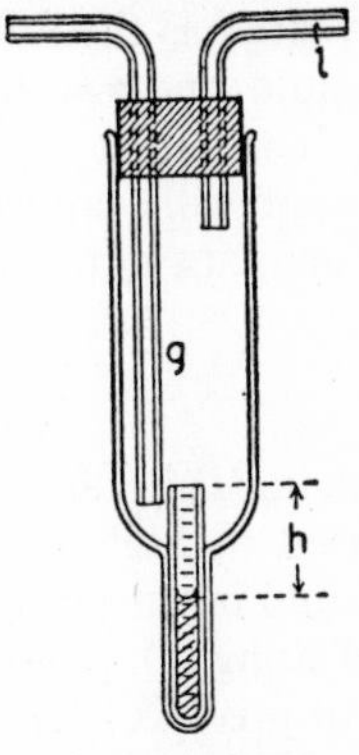

FIG. 6.VII H. Stefan's Diffusion Apparatus

$$dM_1=-DA(dc_1/dx)dt \quad . \quad . \quad . \quad (1)$$

The mass of indifferent gas (concentration c_2) diffusing downwards through *A* in time d*t* is (since $c_1+c_2=$const., therefore $dc_2=-dc_1$):

$$dM_2=-DA(dc_2/dx)dt=DA(dc_1/dx)dt \quad . \quad . \quad . \quad . \quad (2)$$

This indifferent gas is blocked by the liquid surface and unless there is compensation its concentration would increase in the lower volume element (1) and so would upset the stationary state. Thus an amount of gas-vapour *mixture* containing the amount (2) of indifferent gas must diffuse upwards in the time d*t*, this containing the amount of vapour:

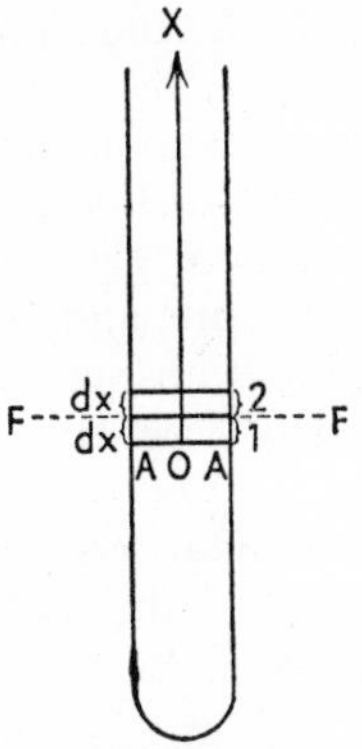

FIG. 7.VII H

$$dm=-(c_1/c_2)DA(dc_1/dx)dt.$$

Hence the total mass of vapour rising through *A* in the time d*t* is:

$$dM_1+dm=-DA[(c_1+c_2)/c_2](dc_1/dx)dt \quad . \quad (3)$$

and since the state is stationary, the total mass diffusing in a finite time *t* is:

$$M_1=-DAt[(c_1+c_2)/c_2](dc_1/dx) \quad . \quad . \quad (4)$$

The value of dc_1/dx varies along the tube (since the indifferent gas is at rest), and d^2c_1/dx^2 is not zero, although dc_1/dt is zero. It follows from (4) that $(1/c_2)(dc_1/dx)=-(1/c_2)(dc_2/dx)=$const, therefore $\ln c_2=kx+C$, where *k* and *C* are constants, *k* being $M_1/DAt(c_1+c_2)$. When $x=0$, $c_1=c_s$ (the concentration of the

1885, **26**, 105; 1888, **33**, 445; 1888, **35**, 401; 1889, **36**, 93; Phookan, *Z. anorg. Chem.*, 1893, **5**, 69; Naccari, *Atti Accad. Torino*, 1909, **44**, 791; *Ann. Phys. Beibl.*, 1910, **34**, 182; Wuppermann, *Dissert.*, Leipzig, 1910; Vaillant, *J. de Phys.*, 1911, **1**, 877; Pochettino, *Nuov. Cim.*, 1914, **8**, 5; Le Blanc and Wuppermann, *Z. phys. Chem.*, 1916, **91**, 143; Mack, *J.A.C.S.*, 1925, **47**, 2468; Arnold, *Ind. Eng. Chem.*, 1930, **22**, 1091; Trautz and Ludwig, *Ann. Phys.*, 1930, **5**, 887; Trautz and Müller, *ibid.*, 1935, **22**, 329, 333, 353; Spier, *Physica*, 1940, **7**, 381 (Hg vap. in N_2); Klotz and Miller, *J.A.C.S.*, 1947, **69**, 2557; Brookfield, Fitzpatrick, Jackson, Matthews, and Moelwyn-Hughes, *Proc. Roy. Soc.*, 1947, **190**, 59.

saturated vapour), and when $x=h$, $c_1=0$. Hence, if $c_1+c_2=c$:

$$k=(1/h)\ln[c/(c-c_s)]$$

$$\therefore\ M_1=(DAtc/h)\ln[c/(c-c_s)]$$

$$D=(M_1h/cAt)/\ln[c/(c-c_s)]=(M_1hRT/Atp)/\ln[p/(p-p_s)] \quad . \quad (5)$$

where p is the total pressure and p_s the saturation pressure of the vapour of the liquid, and $p=cRT$.

The height h will not remain quite constant during the interval t, since some liquid will evaporate and a mean value is to be used. Now let δh be the fall of the meniscus, ρ_1 the density of the liquid and M the mol. wt. of the vapour. Then

$$M_1=A\,.\,\delta h\,.\,\rho_1/M \quad . \quad . \quad . \quad . \quad . \quad . \quad . \quad . \quad (6)$$

$$\therefore\ D=(h\,.\,\delta h\,.\,\rho_1\,.\,RT/Mpt)/2{\cdot}3026\log[p/(p-p_s)] \quad . \quad . \quad (7)$$

giving D in terms of the observed heights h and δh, and known quantities. As used by Stefan, this method gave an accuracy of only 1 to 2 per cent., but it could be modified, e.g. by absorbing and weighing the vapour carried off instead of using (6), to give more accurate results. A similar method was used for gases but it is less accurate than Loschmidt's method.

Winkelmann, and others, found an increase in diffusion coefficient with increasing height of the diffusion column, but Le Blanc and Wuppermann [1] found that this was due to the temperature drop at the liquid surface. When this was avoided, the diffusion coefficient remained constant. A hot-wire method of measuring diffusibilities was investigated by So; [2] the change of temperature is greater the greater the diffusibility.

§ 5. Values of Diffusion Coefficients

The experimental results show that the diffusion coefficient D depends on the nature of both gases diffusing, the total pressure of the mixture, the temperature, and to a small extent on the relative proportions of the two components in the mixture. The units are generally cm.^{2}/sec. but sometimes m.^{2}/hour; to convert D (m.^{2}/hour) into D (cm.^{2}/sec.) it is multiplied by $60\times60/100\times100=0{\cdot}36$. The results indicate that D varies inversely as the total pressure, and as a power of the absolute temperature between 1·75 and 2, at about atmospheric temperature and pressure. The variation with composition is about 8 per cent. of the mean value.

The following table gives the experimental results for D as summarised by Lonius,[3] and the calculated values from the formula of Chapman; [4] the mol ratio N_1/N_2 gives the composition in the order of the gases as stated.

H_2–CO_2	N_1/N_2	3	1	$\frac{1}{3}$			
	D obs.	0·21351	0·21774	0·22772			
	D calc.	0·212	0·222	0·226			
He–A	N_1/N_2	2·65	2·26	1·66	1	0·477	0·311
	D obs.	0·24418	0·24965	0·25040	0·25405	0·25626	0·26312
	D calc.	0·248	0·250	0·251	0·254	0·257	0·259

[1] *Z. phys. Chem.*, 1916, **91**, 143.

[2] *Proc. Phys. Math. Soc. Japan*, 1920, **2**, 118.

[3] *Ann. Phys.*, 1909, **29**, 664; Landolt-Börnstein, "Tabellen," 5th edit., 1923, 249; Loeb, "Kinetic Theory of Gases," New York, 1934, 272; for NH_3 in air, see Wintergerst, *Ann. Phys.*, 1930, **4**, 323 (bibl); H_2 and D_2, Harteck and Schmidt, *Z. phys. Chem.*, 1933, **21 B**, 447; Kr and Xe, Groth and Harteck, *Z. Elektrochem.*, 1941, **47**, 167; for water vapour in gases, Dorsey, "Properties of Ordinary Water Substance," New York, 1940, 73.

[4] *Phil. Trans.*, 1912, **211**, 433.

Values given by Lonius in which the composition is expressed in terms of the mol fraction $n_1=N_1/(N_1+N_2)$ of the first named gas are:

O_2–H_2	n_1	0·5	0·252	0·25	0·5	0·75
	D	0·27335	0·27609	0·27616	0·28003	0·28934

(the first two and the last three are by different experimenters).

O_2–N_2	n_1	0·5	0·467	N_2–H_2	n_1	0·5	0·235
	D	0·07304	0·07333		D	0·26565	0·26830

The *coefficient of self-diffusion* of a gas into itself may be calculated [1] as follows. Three gases are taken for which the mutual coefficients of diffusion are D_{12}, D_{23}, D_{31}. From these, the values of σ_{12}, σ_{23}, and σ_{31} are calculated by (16), § 1, and hence σ_1, σ_2, and σ_3 are known, since $\sigma_{12}=\frac{1}{2}(\sigma_1+\sigma_2)$, etc. These values inserted in (18), § 1 gave consistent results. In the table, the gases are numbered as follows: $H_2=1$, $O_2=2$, $CO=3$, $CO_2=4$; e.g. 12 means hydrogen diffusing into oxygen, giving D_{12}, etc.

	D_{11}		D_{22}
(12, 13, 23)	1·32	(12, 13, 23)	0·193
(12, 14, 24)	1·35	(12, 14, 24)	0·190
(13, 14, 34)	1·26	(23, 24, 34)	0·183
	D_{33}		D_{44}
(12, 13, 23)	0·169	(12, 14, 24)	0·106
(13, 14, 34)	0·175	(13, 14, 34)	0·111
(23, 24, 34)	0·178	(23, 24, 34)	0·109

Boardman and Wild [2] found at 15° C. H_2 1·43, N_2 0·203, CO 0·211, N_2O 0·107, CO_2 0·121, but the results were not completely consistent. Chapman, Enskog, and Pidduck [3] gave the theoretical equation $D=1{\cdot}200\eta/\rho$ (η=viscosity) for elastic spheres; Maxwell, for the repulsion law μr^{-5}, found $D=1{\cdot}543\eta/\rho$. Jeans gave this as $1{\cdot}504\eta/\rho$, but according to Kennard [4] the correct figure is 1·543; Chapman's value is 1·550. The observed values are intermediate between the extreme values for the constant.

§ 6. Rate of Evaporation of Liquids

The rate of evaporation of a liquid from a free surface was studied by Stefan [5] and Winkelmann.[6] Stefan deduced the equation:

$$w=4DR \ln [(P-p'')/(P-p')] \quad . \quad . \quad . \quad . \quad . \quad . \quad (1)$$

[1] Stanzel, *Wien Ber.*, 1901, **110**, II A, 1038; Lord Kelvin, "Baltimore Lectures," Cambridge, 1904, 294; Jeans, "Kinetic Theory of Gases," 1940, 214.

[2] *Proc. Roy. Soc.*, 1937, **162**, 511; Wall and Kidder, *J. Phys. Chem.*, 1946, **50**, 235.

[3] Quoted by Jeans, "Kinetic Theory of Gases," 1940, 211.

[4] "Kinetic Theory of Gases," 1938, 195; for self-diffusion of UF_6, Ney and Armistead, *Phys. Rev.*, 1947, **71**, 14; Hutchinson, *Phys. Rev.*, 1947, **72**, 1256 (argon, ^{41}A in ^{40}A); Amdur, *J. Chem. Phys.*, 1947, **15**, 482; 1948, **16**, 190; Winn and Ney, *Phys. Rev.*, 1948, **72**, 77 (CH_4).

[5] *Wien Ber.*, 1874, **68**, II, 385; 1881, **83**, II, 545, 943; 1889, **98**, II, 1418; *Ann. Phys.*, 1882, **17**, 551; 1890, **41**, 725; *J. de Phys.*, 1882, **1**, 202.

[6] *Ann. Phys.*, 1888, **33**, 445; 1888, **35**, 401; 1889, **36**, 93; see also Laval, *J. de Phys.*, 1882, **1**, 560; Sresnewsky and Schuck, *J. Russ. Phys. Chem. Soc.* (P), 1882, **14**, 420, 487; 1883, **15**, 1; Phookan, *Z. anorg. Chem.*, 1892, **2**, 7; 1894, **5**, 69; Trabert, *Meteorol. Z.*, 1896, **13**, 261; von Pallich, *Wien Ber.*, 1897, **106**, II A, 384; Jablczynski and Przemyski, *J. Chim. Phys.*, 1912, **10**, 241; on evaporation and diffusion into gas bubbles passing through a liquid see Luther and MacDougall, *Z. phys. Chem.*, 1908, **62**, 206.

where w=weight of liquid evaporating per sec. in a circular dish of radius R, D=the diffusion coefficient, P=total atmospheric pressure (air+vapour), p' and p''=vapour pressures of the liquid at the surface and at a great distance from it, respectively. It should be noted that w is proportional to the *radius* of the surface and not (as was assumed by Dalton) [1] to its area. The rate of evaporation of a drop of liquid is also proportional to the radius rather than the surface.[2]

According to Schall,[3] the velocities of evaporation of two liquids in contact with their own vapours are inversely proportional to their molecular weights, the velocities at equal pressures being nearly inversely proportional to the vapour densities; [4] and the times of evaporation are inversely proportional to the latent heats of evaporation.[5]

Trumbull [6] found the rates of evaporation of water into different gases inversely proportional to the square of the density of the gas, and proposed to compare the molar weights of gases by this rule. A slow evaporation of drops of mercury in air saturated with mercury vapour was attributed to the displacement of mercury atoms in an adsorbed layer by colliding air molecules; if this is so, the effect should increase with increasing air pressure.[7]

Thomas and Ferguson [8] found the rate of evaporation from a circular surface of radius r proportional to r^n, where n is a constant, and Burger [9] found $n=5/3$. The rate of evaporation from a rectangular surface in the plane $z=0$ with the flow in the direction of the y axis was found by Burger to be proportional to $A^{1/3} D^{2/3} y^{2/3}$, where A=area and D=diffusion coefficient. Morse's [10] observations on the evaporation of small *solid* spheres in air were calculated by Langmuir.[11] Vaillant [12] found the quantity of liquid evaporating per sec. in 10^{-6} g. is given by $q=aMp^{4/3}$, where M=mol. wt., p=maximum vapour presssure, and a is a constant. Weber [13] found the rate of evaporation of a metal in a gas inversely proportional to the square root of the pressure of the gas.

The explanation that deviations from the theoretical Stefan equation value were due to local lowering of temperature at the evaporating surface was disproved experimentally by Mache.[14] Sutton [15] had found that the rate of

[1] *Ann. Phys.*, 1803, **15**, 25, 122, 197; this may hold for evaporation in a *draught* of air.

[2] Morse, *Proc. Amer. Acad.*, 1910, **45**, 362; Langmuir, *Phys. Rev.*, 1918, **12**, 368; Topley and Whytlaw-Gray, *Phil. Mag.*, 1927, **4**, 873; Woodland and Mack, *J.A.C.S.*, 1933, **55**, 3149; Fuchs, *Sow. Phys. Z.*, 1934, **6**, 224; Stern, *J. Techn. Phys. U.S.S.R.*, 1935, **5**, 812; Bradley, Evans, and Whytlaw-Gray, *Proc. Roy. Soc.*, 1946, **186**, 368 (wide departure from Langmuir's formula, but agreement with Fuchs); for summary and bibliography, Dorsey, " Properties of Ordinary Water Substance," New York, 1940, 622; for a maximum rate of evaporation in vacuum, Penner, *J. Phys. Chem.*, 1948, **52**, 367.

[3] *Ber.*, 1883, **16**, 3011; 1884, **17**, 1044, 2199; 1885, **18**, 2032, 2042; *Z. phys. Chem.*, 1891, **8**, 158, 241.

[4] Despretz, *Ann. Chim.*, 1823, **24**, 323.

[5] Schall, *Ber.*, 1884, **17**, 2199; Sperber, " Versuch eines allgemeinen Gesetz über die specifische Wärme," Zürich, 1884, had deduced this theoretically.

[6] *J.A.C.S.*, 1915, **37**, 2662; Stefan, and Laval, *J. de Phys.*, 1882, **1**, 560, found the rate to vary with the gas.

[7] Schidlof, *Arch. Sci. Phys. Nat.*, 1917, **43**, 217; Targonski, *ibid.*, 1917, **43**, 295, 389.

[8] *Phil. Mag.*, 1917, **34**, 308.

[9] *Proc. K. Akad. Wetens. Amsterdam*, 1919, **21**, 271; cf. Jeffreys, *Phil. Mag.*, 1918, **35**, 270.

[10] *Proc. Amer. Acad.*, 1910, **45**, 361.

[11] *Phys. Rev.*, 1918, **12**, 368.

[12] *Compt. Rend.*, 1910, **150**, 213, 689, 1048.

[13] *K. Dansk. Vidensk. Selsk. Meddel. Mat. fys.*, 1920, **3**, No. 3.

[14] *Z. Phys.*, 1937, **107**, 310.

[15] *Proc. Roy. Dublin Soc.*, 1907, **11**, 137 (bibl.).

evaporation of water does not follow the equations of Stefan or of Fitzgerald.[1] He found that electrifying the surface had no effect.

Lurie and Michailoff[2] found the rate of evaporation from a free water surface in a current of air of velocity V m./sec. to be $(22+16\cdot8V)\Delta p$ kg. hour^{-1} m.$^{-2}$, where Δp is the partial pressure difference in mm. Hg from saturation. Alty[3] found the rate of evaporation of water only 0·04 that predicted by Knudsen's equation (§ 3.VII J).

De Heen[4] gave for the velocity of evaporation in a current of dry air $v=7\cdot19\sqrt{V}$, where V=air current (reduced to dry air) in centilit. per min., and v is the velocity referred to 100 for $V=200$. In moist air of percentage humidity f, $v=100$ (dry air)$-0\cdot88f$. This gives $v=12$ per cent. even for saturated air ($f=1$), which de Heen claimed to have found. Similar results were found for solutions.

Sklyarenko and Baranaev,[5] who pointed out that the velocity depends on the nature of the gas,[6] found three empirical equations:

(i) in moving air:

$$v_1/v_2=(P_1/P_2)\sqrt{(D_1b_2/D_2b_1)} \quad . \quad . \quad . \quad . \quad . \quad . \quad (2)$$

where P_1, P_2 are the vapour pressures, and D_1, D_2 the diffusion coefficients of two liquids, and $b=B-P/2$, where B=barometric pressure;

(ii) for a vapour heavier than the gas streaming over the liquid surface:

$$v_1/v_0=\sqrt{(D_1/D_0)} \quad . \quad . \quad . \quad . \quad . \quad . \quad . \quad . \quad . \quad (3)$$

where v_0=velocity in air, v_1=velocity in gas;

(iii) for components of a mixture:

$$v_1/v_2=(p_1/p_2)\sqrt{(D_1/D_2)} \quad . \quad . \quad . \quad . \quad . \quad . \quad . \quad . \quad (4)$$

where p=partial pressure.

The general aspects of *air conditioning* cannot be considered, but mention

1 *Trans. Amer. Soc. Civ. Eng.*, 1886, **15**, 581; $E=0\cdot0166\ (V-v)(1+w/2)$, symbols not defined.

2 *Ind. Eng. Chem.*, 1936, **28**, 345; see also Schierbeck, *Ov. K. Dansk. Vidensk. Selskab. Forhl.*, 1896, No. **1**; Trabert, *Meteorol. Z.*, 1896, **13**, 261; Coffey and Horn, *J. Amer. Soc. Refrig. Eng.*, 1916, **3**, No. 3, 32; Carrier, *Ind. Eng. Chem.*, 1921, **13**, 432; Allen, *Proc. Nat. Acad.*, 1924, **10**, 88; Himus and Hinchley, *J.S.C.I.*, 1924, **43**, 840 R; Carrier and Lindsay, *Refrig. Eng.*, 1925, **11**, 241; *Mech. Eng.*, 1925, **47**, 327; Thiesenhusen, *Gesundh. Ing.*, 1930, **53**, 113; Rohwer, *U.S. Dept. Agric. Techn. Bull.*, 1931, **271**; Chakravorty, *J. Imp. Coll. Chem. Eng. Soc.*, 1947, **3**, 46; Marwedel and Hauser, *Farbe u. Lack*, 1948, **54**, 115, 175 (organic solvents).

3 *Phil. Mag.*, 1933, **15**, 82; Naccari, *Atti Accad. Torino*, 1908–9, **44**, 791 (electrification has no effect); Vaillant, *Compt. Rend.*, 1908, **146**, 582, 811; 1909, **148**, 1099 (solutions); 1910, **150**, 213, 689, 1048; *J. de Phys.*, 1911, **1**, 877; Mache, *Wien Ber.*, 1910, **119**, II, A, 1399; Marcelin, *Compt. Rend.*, 1912, **154**, 587 (superheated liquid); *Ann. de Phys.*, 1915, **3**, 120; Schultze, *Koll. Z.*, 1925, **36**, 65; 1926, **39**, 362 (from capillaries); Cummings and Richardson, *Phys. Rev.*, 1927, **30**, 527; Quilez, *An. Fis. Quim.*, 1932, **30**, 492; Starokadomskaya, *J. Exptl. Theor. Phys. U.S.S.R.*, 1933, **3**, 189 (in moving air); Quint, *Compt. Rend.*, 1934, **199**, 1023; Khudyakov, *Bull. Acad. Sci. U.R.S.S.* (*Sci. Tech.*), 1946, 533; Turrell, *Science*, 1947, **105**, 434 (sulphur); Blet and Blet, *Compt. Rend.*, 1947, **225**, 379.

4 *Bull. Acad. Roy. Belg.*, 1891, **21**, 11, 214, 798; 1892, **23**, 136; *J. Chim. Phys.*, 1913, **11**, 204; Hine, *Phys. Rev.*, 1924, **24**, 79; Himus and Hinchley, *J.S.C.I.*, 1924, **43**, 840 R (air current); Sharpley and Boetter, *Ind. Eng. Chem.*, 1938, **30**, 1125; Ingels, *ibid.*, 1938, **30**, 980; Molstad, Farevaag, and Farrell, *ibid.*, 1938, **30**, 1131.

5 *Z. phys. Chem.*, 1935, **175**, 195, 203, 214; *J. Phys. Chem. U.S.S.R.*, 1936, **8**, 51; Mache, *Z. Phys.*, 1937, **107**, 310.

6 Centnerszwer, *Bull. Acad. Polon.*, 1932 A, 369; Preston, *Trans. Faraday Soc.*, 1933, **29**, 1188.

may be made of a few books and papers dealing with its more scientific aspects.[1] The rate of evaporation of salt solutions in air is, apparently, always less than that of pure water, some cases of greater rates given by Babington being due to experimental errors.[2] The effect of a thin insoluble film on a liquid is to retard the rate of evaporation; [3] the action is specific.

§ 7. Separation of Gases by Diffusion

The theory of the separation of gases by diffusion through a porous septum (which has been applied in the separation of isotopes) was given by Rayleigh.[4] If the gases diffuse into a vacuum and if x, y are the quantities in the residue at a given time, and $-dx$ and $-dy$ the further losses in a time dt, then $dy/dx=\nu y/\mu x$, where μ and ν are the diffusion rates. Integration gives $y^{1/\nu}=Cx^{1/\mu}$, or $y/x=Cx^{-1+\nu/\mu}$, where C is a constant. If X, Y are the initial amounts, then:

$$(y/x)\div(Y/X)=(x/X)^{-1+\nu/\mu} \qquad (1)$$

$$x=X[(y/x)/(Y/X)]^{\mu/(\nu-\mu)} \qquad (2)$$

$$y=Y[(x/y)/(X/Y)]^{\nu/(\mu-\nu)} \qquad (3)$$

If $(y/x)/(Y/X)=r$, the enrichment ratio, (2) and (3) give:

$$(x+y)/(X+Y)=[X/(X+Y)]r^{\mu/(\nu-\mu)}+[Y/(X+Y)]r^{\nu/(\nu-\mu)} \qquad (4)$$

Equation (1) shows that as x decreases with time the enrichment tends to zero or infinity, indicating that the residue becomes purer without limit. If the vacuum is replaced by an atmosphere of fixed composition and the inside volume is given, then if x, y, and α, β, are the partial pressures inside and outside the given volume, and C, D, and E are constants:

$$dx=\mu(\alpha-x)dt \quad \text{and} \quad dy=\nu(\beta-y)dt,$$

$$\therefore\ x=\alpha+Ce^{-\mu t} \quad \text{and} \quad y=\beta+De^{-\nu t},$$

$$\therefore\ y-\beta=E(x-\alpha)^{\nu/\mu} \qquad (5)$$

The effect of diffusing half the mixture, and repeating with the residue, was considered and other useful formulae given.

[1] Obermiller, *Z. phys. Chem.*, 1923, **106**, 178; 1924, **109**, 145; Gilliland, *Ind. Eng. Chem.*, 1938, **30**, 506; Downs, *ibid.*, 1939, **31**, 134; Carrier, Cherne, and Grant, "Modern Air Conditioning, etc.", New York, 1940; Jennings and Lewis, "Air Conditioning and Refrigeration," 2nd edit., New York, 1944; Allen, Walker, and James, "Heating and Air Conditioning," 2nd edit., New York, 1946; H. and H. Herkimer, "Air Conditioning," New York, 1947; S. P. Brown, "Air Conditioning and Elements of Refrigeration," New York, 1947; O'Brien, *J. Sci. Instr.*, 1948, **25**, 73; see special journals, and *Science Abstracts, B.*

[2] Babington, *Proc. Roy. Soc.*, 1859, **10**, 127; Weiser and Porter, *J. Phys. Chem.*, 1920, **24**, 333.

[3] Adam, *J. Phys. Chem.*, 1925, **29**, 610; Rideal, *ibid.*, 1925, **29**, 1585; contradicting Hedestrand, *ibid.*, 1924, **28**, 1245; Baranaev, *J. Phys. Chem. U.S.S.R.*, 1937, **9**, 69; Sklyarenko and Baranaev, *ibid.*, 1938, **12**, 271; Sklyarenko, Baranaev, and Mazhueva *ibid.*, 1940, **14**, 839; Sebba and Briscoe, *J.C.S.*, 1940, 106; Powell, *Trans. Faraday Soc.*, 1943, **39**, 311; Alexander, Kitchiner, and Briscoe *ibid.*, 1944, **40**, 10; Tovbin and Schlosberg, *J. Phys. Chem. U.S.S.R.*, 1948, **22**, 379.

[4] *Phil. Mag.*, 1896, **42**, 493; "Scientific Papers," Cambridge, 1903, **4**, 261; abstr. in *J. Phys. Chem.*, 1897, **1**, 518; results of calculations do not agree with experimental results of Graham, *Phil. Trans.*, 1863, **153**, 385; see also Mulliken and Harkins, *J.A.C.S.*, 1922, **44**, 37; Hertz, *Phys. Z.*, 1922, **23**, 433; *Z. Phys.*, 1932, **79**, 108; *Proc. K. Akad. Wetens. Amsterdam*, 1923, **45**, 434; Wussow, *Brennstoff Chem.*, 1924, **5**, 65; Riesenfeld and Chang, *Arkiv Kem. Min. Geol.*, 1937, **12** A, No. 19; Kammermeyer and Ward, *Ind Eng. Chem.*, 1941, **33**, 474; Braune and Zehle, *Z. phys. Chem.*, 1941, **49** B, 247 (HCl and DCl, and HBr and DBr).

The rate of diffusion of a gas through a small opening in a thin diaphragm into another gas, which was used by Soret [1] in finding the density of ozone, and is of interest in the passage of carbon dioxide through the stomata of green leaves,[2] is proportional, not to the area of the aperture (as might be expected) but to its diameter. The lines of flow in the stationary state converge towards the opening; adjacent openings influence one another, and there is a certain arrangement of openings of given diameter for which the diffusion is a maximum.

The passage of gases by diffusion through porous solids was called *diffusion* or *atmolysis* by Graham,[3] who was led to its study by some observations by Döbereiner [4] that hydrogen confined in a cracked flask escaped faster than air passed in. Bunsen [5] showed that the velocity of diffusion within certain limits is proportional to the difference of pressure on the two sides of the porous plate; Graham that the volumes of two gases diffusing through a porous (gypsum) plate are inversely proportional to the square roots of the densities. If δ=density referred to air=1 and the diffusion volume V is relative to 1 vol. of air, then Graham found the figures in the table. He used a glass tube, closed at one end by a thin plate of plaster of Paris, containing the gas and inverted over water or mercury in a cylinder, the tube being moved so as to keep the levels inside and outside equal; when no further change of volume occurred the volume of air (which alone was present) in the tube was read off, and by dividing this into the original volume of gas, V was found.

Gas	δ (air=1)	$\sqrt{(1/\delta)}$	V
H_2	0·0694	3·7947	3·83
CH_4	0·555	1·3414	1·344
C_2H_4	0·972	1·0140	1·0191
CO	0·972	1·0140	1·0149
N_2	0·972	1·0140	1·0143
O_2	1·111	0·9487	0·9487
H_2S	1·1805	0·9204	0·95
N_2O	1·527	0·8091	0·82
CO_2	1·527	0·8091	0·812
SO_2	2·222	0·6708	0·68

The results were not confirmed for a plaster plug by Bunsen in more accurate experiments. Graham also used an apparatus he called a *diffusiometer*, in which a current of air was passed over the outside of the plug by a T-tube, and he also failed to confirm the square-root law. The latter was, however, found by Graham [6] to apply with a plug of compressed powdered graphite, and it

[1] *Ann. Chim.*, 1868, **13**, 247; theory by Maxwell, *Phil. Mag.*, 1868, **35**, 185.

[2] Brown, *Chem. News.*, 1900, **82**, 161; *Nature*, 1901, **64**, 171, 193; *J.C.S.*, 1918, **113**, 559; Brown and Escombe, *Phil. Trans.*, 1900, **193** B, 223.

[3] *Quart. J. Sci.*, 1829, **28**, 74; *Ann. Phys.*, 1829, **17**, 341; 1833, **28**, 331; 1863, **120**, 415; *Phil. Mag.*, 1833, **2**, 175, 269; *Phil. Trans.*, 1846, **136**, 573; 1849, **139**, 349; "Researches," 1876, 28, 44, 88, 162; Winkelmann, "Handbuch der Physik," 1908, **1**, ii, 1431; Barrer, "Diffusion in and through Solids," Cambridge, 1941, 65.

[4] "Über eine neu entdeckte, höchst merkwürdige Eigenschaft des Platins und die pneumatisch kapillare Tätigkeit gesprungener Gläser," Jena, 1823; *Ann. Chim.*, 1823, **24**, 332; Faraday, *Ann. Phys.*, 1826, **8**, 124; Magnus, *ibid.*, 1827, **10**, 153.

[5] "Gasometry," 1857, 198; Reusch, *Ann. Phys.*, 1865, **124**, 431; Stefan, *Wien Ber.*, 1871, **63, II**, 63; Dufour, *Arch. Sci. Phys. Nat.*, 1872, **45**, 9; 1874, **49**, 103; 1875, **53**, 177; Hüfner, *Ann. Phys.*, 1882, **16**, 253; Hansemann, *ibid.*, 1884, **21**, 545; Christiansen, *ibid.*, 1890, **41**, 565; Rasmussen, *ibid.*, 1937, **29**, 665

[6] *Phil. Trans.*, 1863, **153**, 385; "Researches," 1876, 210.

probably holds fairly accurately for a finely porous body,[1] but not with a solid containing capillary holes, such as a plaster plug.

The theory of diffusion through porous bodies was developed by Stefan [2] on the basis of free diffusion, but the results of Hansemann were not in good agreement with it. Other experiments with porous cells, etc., were made by von Lang,[3] Puluj,[4] and Prytz.[5]

Graham [6] distinguished three types of septa: (i) those behaving as assemblies of diffusion plates, with holes of molecular dimensions (compressed graphite; unglazed porcelain), (ii) those with relatively large interstices (most compressed powders), (iii) those with fine capillaries of large ratio length/diameter (plaster of Paris). Only (i) gave the square-root law. Compressed powdered graphite forms a suitable diffusion plug.[7]

Brémond [8] also found disagreement with Graham's law in the diffusion of gases through a porous septum at 17°–700°. Diffusion through paper and similar porous materials has been investigated.[9]

Sameshima [10] used the formula:

$$t=k\eta^n M^{(1-n)/2} \quad \ldots\ldots\ldots \quad (6)$$

for flow of gas through a porous plate, where t is the time of flow for a given volume of gas of viscosity η and molecular weight M, and n and k are constants, k depending on the nature of the plate and the pressure, and n is less than 1. For a very thin wall $n \to 0$ and $t=kM^{1/2}$ (Graham's law); for a very thick wall $n \to 1$ and $t=k\eta$. A more complicated formula was used by Adzumi.[11]

The free energy change on the isothermal mixing of gases (§ 28.II) was calculated by Rayleigh [12] and Boltzmann; [13] for n_1 mols of gas [1] and n_2 mols of gas [2] at a temperature T it is:

$$-\Delta F=n_1 RT \ln [(v_1+v_2)/v_1]+n_2 RT \ln [(v_1+v_2)/v_2] \quad . \; . \quad (7)$$

where the volumes v_1 and v_2 are those of the unmixed gases at the same pressure, and v_1+v_2 is the volume of the mixture. If the final volume is V, not v_1+v_2, this replaces v_1+v_2 in the formula.

The well-known porous pot experiment for illustrating diffusion is due originally to Wöhler; [14] a neat apparatus in which the change in weight of a beaker containing CO_2 or (inverted) H_2 is shown by the change of level of a Nicholson's hydrometer supporting it, is described by Röntgen.[15] The *atmolyser* of Graham, used for separating mixtures of gases, consisted of a porous clay

[1] Reusch, *Ann. Phys.*, 1865, **124**, 431; Hüfner, *ibid.*, 1882, **16**, 253.

[2] *Wien Ber.*, 1871, **63**, II, 63; Kirchhoff, *Ann. Phys.*, 1884, **21**, 563, who does not compare his equations with experiment.

[3] *Wien Ber.*, 1870, **61**, II, 288; Bellamy, *Compt. Rend.*, 1876, **83**, 669.

[4] Carl's *Repert. d. Phys.*, 1877, **13**, 469, 533 (vapours); Graham's $1/\sqrt{\delta}$ law was approximately found.

[5] *Ann. Phys.*, 1905, **18**, 617.

[6] *Phil. Trans.*, 1863, **153**, 385; " Researches," 1876, 210.

[7] Palmer, " Experimental Physical Chemistry," Cambridge, 1941, 27.

[8] *Compt. Rend.*, 1933, **196**, 1651.

[9] Carson, *Bur. Stand. J. Res.*, 1934, **12**, 567 (bibl.).

[10] *J. Chem. Soc. Japan*, 1923, **44**, 671 (in Japanese); *Bull. Chem. Soc. Japan*, 1926, **1**, 5.

[11] *Bull. Chem. Soc. Japan*, 1937, **12**, 304.

[12] *Phil. Mag.*, 1875, **49**, 311; 1896, **42**, 493; Woodward, *ibid.*, 1883, **16**, 375.

[13] *Wien Ber.*, 1878, **78**, II, 733; Maxwell, " Scientific Papers," 1890, **2**, 644; Manson, *Compt. Rend.*, 1947, **224**, 1548, 1816.

[14] *Ber.*, 1871, **4**, 10; for modifications, see e.g. Roscoe and Schorlemmer, "Treatise on Chemistry," 1920, **1**, 95; Viswanthan, *J. Indian Chem. Soc.*, 1934, **11**, 79.

[15] *Ann. Phys.*, 1890, **40**, 110.

churchwarden tobacco-pipe stem enclosed in a vacuous glass jacket, the lighter gas passing out through the pipe. The pipes made in Scotland are said by Harkins and Jenkins [1] to have the finest grain and to be most suitable. The separation of gaseous mixtures by diffusion or atmolysis was used by Graham, and frequently since.[1] Christiansen [2] found a continuous gradation from transpiration to diffusion; mixed gases can separate to some extent by streaming through narrow slits or tubes.

§ 8. Diffusion of Gases through Films and Solids

Diffusion of gases through *thin liquid films*, such as soap-bubbles, was observed by Draper [3] and Marianini,[4] and quantitatively investigated by Exner,[5] who observed the movement of a film in a wide vertical glass tube open at one end and closed and filled with the gas at the other. If G and L are the gas and air volumes passing through, α the absorption coefficient of the gas in the soap solution, and δ the density of the gas, then G/L was found to be proportional to $\alpha/\sqrt{\delta}$.

The theory for diffusion through *thick liquid laminae* was developed by Stefan [6] and tested by Hüfner; [7] the amount w of gas passing should be proportional to the square root of the time:

$$w=2\rho_0 A\sqrt{(Dt/\pi)} \quad . \quad . \quad . \quad . \quad . \quad . \quad . \quad . \quad (1)$$

where ρ_0 is the constant density of the diffusing gas on one side, A the area, and D the diffusion coefficient. For CO_2, Stefan calculated D for water as 0·000016 cm.^{2}/sec., and for alcohol 0·000031 cm.^{2}/sec., at 16°–17°.

The literature on the passage of gases through metals, glass, silica, rubber, etc., is very extensive, and only a small selection can be given here.[8] The permeation

1 Rayleigh and Ramsay, *Phil. Trans.*, 1895, **186**, 187 (206); Urbain and Urbain, *Compt. Rend.*, 1923, **176**, 166, 304; Lorenz and Magnus, *Z. anorg. Chem.*, 1924, **136**, 97; Harkins and Jenkins, *J.A.C.S.*, 1926, **48**, 58; Maier, *Bur. Mines Bull.*, 1940, **431**; Wicke and Kallenbach, *Koll. Z.*, 1941, **97**, 135; Grunberg and Nissan, *J. Inst. Petrol.*, 1943, **29**, 193.

2 *Ann. Phys.*, 1890, **41**, 565.

3 *Phil. Mag.*, 1837, **11**, 559; "Scientific Memoirs," 1878, 342; Waitz, in Winkelmann, "Handbuch der Physik," 1908, **1**, ii, 1439.

4 *Ann. Chim.*, 1843, **9**, 382.

5 *Wien Ber.*, 1875, **70**, II, 465; 1877, **75**, II, 263; *Ann. Phys.*, 1875, **155**, 321, 443; Pranghe, *Dissert.*, Bonn, 1877; *Ann. Phys. Beibl.*, 1878, **2**, 202; Wroblewski, *Ann. Phys.*, 1877, **2**, 481; 1878, **4**, 268; 1879, **7**, 11; 1879, **8**, 29.

6 *Wien Ber.*, 1878, **77**, II, 371.

7 *Ann. Phys.*, 1897, **60**, 134; *Z. phys. Chem.*, 1898, **27**, 227; cf. Müller, *Ann. Phys.*, 1891, **43**, 554; Hagenbach, *ibid.*, 1898, **65**, 673 (moist gelatin); Ardelt, *Dissert.*, Münster, 1904; *Ann. Phys. Beibl.*, 1904, **28**, 905.

8 See Barrer, "Diffusion in and through Solids," Cambridge, 1941 (copious bibliography), 117 (glass), 144 (metals); Jost and Widmann, *Z. phys. Chem.*, 1935, **29** B, 247; 1940, **45** B, 285; Fast, *Chem. Weekbl.*, 1940, **37**, 342; 1941, **38**, 2, 19 (metals; review); Kostitzin, *Compt. Rend.*, 1940, **211**, 62. Some selected individual researches are:
(i) *Rubber and fabrics*: Mitchell, *J. Roy. Inst.*, 1831, **2**, 101, 307; Graham, *Phil. Trans.*, 1863, **153**, 385; 1866, **156**, 399; "Researches," 1876, 210, 235; *Ann. Phys.* 1866, **129**, 549; *J.C.S.*, 1867, **20**, 235; Wroblewski, *Ann. Phys.*, 1876, **158**, 539; 1877, **2**, 481; 1879, **8**, 29; Hüfner, *ibid.*, 1888, **34**, 1; Kayser, *ibid.*, 1891, **43**, 544; Rayleigh, *Phil. Mag.*, 1903, **49**, 220 (argon); Grunmach, *Verhl. d. D. Phys. Ges.*, 1905, **7**, 355; *Phys. Z.*, 1905, **6**, 795; Rodt, *Chem. Ztg.*, 1914, **38**, 1249; Dewar, *Proc. Roy. Inst.*, 1916, **21**, 813; Elworthy and Murray, *Trans. Roy. Soc. Canada*, 1919, **13**, III, 37; McLennan and Shaver, *Phil. Mag.*, 1920, **40**, 272 (H_2, He; fabrics); Daynes, *Proc. Roy. Soc.*, 1920, **97**, 286; Edwards and Pickering, *Bur. Stand. Bull.*, 1920, **16**, 327; *Chem. Met. Eng.*, 1920, **23**, 17; Venable and Fuwa, *Ind. Eng. Chem.*, 1922, **14**, 139; Schumacher and Ferguson, *J.A.C.S.*, 1927, **49**, 427 (various membranes); Alexejeff and Matalsky, *J. Chim. Phys.*, 1927, **24**, 737; Hill, *Science*, 1928, **67**, 374; Kanata,

of metals (palladium, platinum, iron) by hydrogen almost certainly occurs in the form of atoms or hydrogen nuclei (protons), as was inferred by Winkelmann [2] from the fact that the rate of permeation is proportional to the square-root of the hydrogen gas pressure, i.e. to the concentration of hydrogen atoms. Helium, which passes through silica glass even at room temperature, does not permeate metals, although its molecules are smaller than H_2 molecules. The passage of oxygen through silver behaves similarly, being proportional to the square-root of the gas pressure.[3] Richardson found the rate given by:

$$X=(C/d)p^{1/2}T^{1/2}e^{-q/4T} \quad . \ . \ . \ . \ . \ . \ . \ . \quad (2)$$

where C=constant, d=thickness, p=pressure, T=abs. temp., and q=heat of dissociation of the gas in the metal; Johnson and Larose for oxygen and silver found:

$$X \text{ (cm.}^3 \text{ per m.}^2 \text{ per hour)}=(1{\cdot}71\sqrt{p_{mm}}/10^{43}h)T^{14{\cdot}62} \quad . \ . \quad (3)$$

Bull. Chem. Soc. Japan, 1928, **3**, 183 (various); Sandri, *Wien Ber.*, 1932, **141**, II A, 81; Dorsey, "Properties of Ordinary Water Substance," New York, 1940, 75 (bibl.); Riehl, *Koll. Z.*, 1944, **106**, 201; Todd, *Paper Trade J.*, 1944, **118**, No. 10, 32; Cartwright, *Ind. Eng. Chem. Anal.*, 1947, **19**, 393.

(ii) *Metals*: Deville and Troost, *Compt. Rend.*, 1863, **57**, 897; Graham, *Phil. Trans.*, 1866, **156**, 399; *Proc. Roy. Soc.*, 1868, **16**, 422; 1868, **17**, 212, 500; "Researches," 1876, 253; Dorn, *Phys. Z.*, 1906, **7**, 312; Sieverts, *Z. phys. Chem.*, 1907, **60**, 129 (bibl.); Charpy and Bonnerot, *Compt. Rend.*, 1912, **154**, 592; Deming and Hendricks, *J.A.C.S.*, 1923, **45**, 2857; Spencer, *J.C.S.*, 1923, **123**, 2124 (O_2 through Ag); Lombard, *Compt. Rend.*, 1923, **177**, 116; 1926, **182**, 463; 1927, **184**, 1327 (Ni), 1557 (Pd); *J. Chim. Phys.*, 1928, **25**, 501, 587; Borelius and Lindblom, *Ann. Phys.*, 1927, **82**, 201 (H_2); Lombard and Eichner, *Bull. Soc. Chim.*, 1932, **51**, 1462; 1933, **53**, 1176; 1934, **1**, 945, 954; 1935, **2**, 1555 (Pd); *Compt. Rend.*, 1932, **195**, 322 (Pd); Ham, *J. Chem. Phys.*, 1933, **1**, 476; *Trans. Amer. Soc. Metals*, 1937, **25**, 536 (H in Fe, Ni); Smith and Derge, *Trans. Amer. Electrochem. Soc.*, 1934, **66**, 253 (H through Pd); Duhm, *Z. Phys.*, 1935, **94**, 434 (H in Pd; bibl.); Lombard, Eichner, and Albert, *Compt. Rend.*, 1936, **202**, 1777 (Pd); *Bull. Soc. Chim.*, 1936, **3**, 2203; Jouan, *J. de Phys.*, 1936, **7**, 101 (H_2 and D_2 through Pt); Smithells and Ransley, *Proc. Roy. Soc.*, 1936, **155**, 195 (CO through Ni); de Boer and Fast, *Rec. Trav. Chim.*, 1939, **58**, 984 (H through Fe); Betz, *Z. phys.*, 1940, **117**, 100 (H in Fe); Chaudron and Moreau, *Compt. Rend.*, 1941, **213**, 790 (H in Fe); Fast, *Chem. Weekbl.*, 1941, **38**, 2, 19 (theory, bibl.); Michel, Bénard, and Chaudron, *Bull. Soc. Chim.*, 1945, **12**, 336 (H in Pd); Sutra and Darmois, *Compt. Rend.*, 1948, **226**, 177 (H in Fe).

(iii) *Glass and quartz*: Villard, *Compt. Rend.*, 1900, **130**, 1752 (H_2 and silica); Richardson and Ditto, *Phil. Mag.*, 1911, **22**, 704 (glass and quartz; bibl.); Mayer, *Phys. Rev.*, 1915, **6**, 283; Johnson and Burt, *J. Opt. Soc. Amer.*, 1922, **6**, 734 (H_2, quartz glass); Williams and Ferguson, *J.A.C.S.*, 1922, **44**, 2160 (bibl.); 1924, **46**, 635 (He through silica glass); Boggio-Lera, *Rend. Accad. Fis. Mat. Napoli*, 1923, **29**, 111; *Mem. Accad. Lincei*, 1923, **14**, 125; *Atti R. Accad. Lincei*, 1924, **33**, ii, 532; Voorhis, *Phys. Rev.*, 1924, **23**, 557 (He and glasses); Elsey, *J.A.C.S.*, 1926, **48**, 1600 (He permeates quartz glass at room temperature); Paneth *et al.*, *Z. phys. Chem.*, 1928, **134**, 353; 1931, **152**, 110; 1928, **1 B**, 170. 253; *Ber.*, 1929, **62**, 801; Baxter, Starkweather, and Ellestad, *Science*, 1928, **68**, 316; Baxter and Starkweather, *ibid.*, 1931, **73**, 618; McLennan and Wilhelm, *Trans. Roy. Soc. Canada*, 1932, **26**, III, 119; Urry, *J.A.C.S.*, 1932, **54**, 3887; 1933, **55**, 3243; Liu Sheng T'sai and Hogness, *J. Phys. Chem.*, 1932, **36**, 2595; Burton, Braaten, and Wilhelm, *Canad. J. Res.*, 1933, **8**, 463; Alty, *Phil. Mag.*, 1933, **15**, 1035; Barrer, *J.C.S.*, 1934, 378; Rayleigh, *Proc. Roy. Soc.*, 1936, **156**, 350; Wang, *Trans. Cambr. Phil. Soc.*, 1936, **32**, 657; Braaten and Clark, *J.A.C.S.*, 1936, **57**, 2714; Taylor and Rast, *J. Chem. Phys.*, 1938, **6**, 612; Ledoux, *J. École Polytechn.*, 1938, **36**, 1; Baxter, *J.A.C.S.*, 1939, **61**, 1597; Smith and Taylor, *J. Amer. Ceram. Soc.*, 1940, **23**, 139; Kondratiev, *J. Exptl. Theor. Phys. U.S.S.R.*, 1943, **13**, 59; Giauque, *Rev. Sci. Instr.*, 1947, **18**, 852 (Jena glass less permeable than Pyrex to He); Levi, *Trans. Faraday Soc.*, 1946, **42**, 152 (organic resins, etc.; theory only).

[2] *Ann. Phys.*, 1901, **6**, 104; 1902, **8**, 388 (Pt); 1905, **16**, 773 (Pd); 1905, **19**, 1045 (Pt); Schmidt, *ibid.*, 1904, **13**, 747 (Pd).

[3] Richardson, *Phil. Mag.*, 1904, **7**, 266; Richardson, Nicol, and Parnell, *ibid.*, 1904, **8**, 1: Spencer, *J.C.S.*, 1923, **123**, 2124; Lombard, *Compt. Rend.*, 1923, **177**, 116 (Ni); Johnson and Larose, *J.A.C.S.*, 1924, **46**, 1377; 1927, **49**, 313; Sieverts, Baukloh, and Hofmann, *Metallwirtsch.*, 1938, **17**, 655 (H_2 in Fe).

where h=thickness of metal in mm., though they found Richardson's equation approximately valid. Hendricks and Raiston [1] also verified it for hydrogen passing through hot zinc, copper, and nickel. Smithells [2] gave the following figures for the rate of diffusion of hydrogen in cm.³ per cm.² per sec. at 760 mm. Hg pressure through a 1-mm. thick plate of the metal at the given temperature ° C.:

	1000°	500°	0°
Iron	1×10^{-3}	1×10^{-4}	6×10^{-6}
Nickel	2×10^{-3}	3×10^{-6}	1×10^{-11}
Molybdenum ...	4×10^{-3}	5×10^{-6}	2×10^{-16}
Platinum	1×10^{-4}	1×10^{-5}	5×10^{-15}
Copper	1×10^{-4}	1×10^{-6}	4×10^{-15}
Aluminium	—	1×10^{-7}	2×10^{-23}

Borelius and Lindblom [3] found for the diffusate m of hydrogen per dcm.² per hour:

$$m=(A/d)(\sqrt{p}-\sqrt{p_t})e^{-b/T} \quad . \quad . \quad . \quad . \quad . \quad . \quad . \quad . \quad (4)$$

where d=thickness in mm., A and b are constants, p=pressure, and p_t is a threshold value, of importance only for iron. Post and Ham [4] found the rate of diffusion of hydrogen through iron and nickel equal to:

$$AT^z p^y e^{-b/T} \quad . \quad . \quad . \quad . \quad . \quad . \quad . \quad . \quad . \quad . \quad (5)$$

where A, z, y, and b are constants. The theory of degassing of metals by heating in vacuum [5] also involves the rate of diffusion.

The general trend of recent theory is to assume that some kind of energy of activation is necessary to enable the gas molecules to pass through minute pores or fissures in the solid; this theory is considered in relation to diffusion through solids in § 4.IX A, Vol. II.

A theory of diffusion of a gas through metals, developed by Lennard-Jones [6] did not agree with experiments on silica glass and was modified by Alty,[7] who gave the equation:

$$M=Bpe^{-(W_0+E_0)/kT} \quad . \quad . \quad . \quad . \quad . \quad . \quad . \quad . \quad (6)$$

where M=mass of gas diffusing through the solid per sec., B is a constant, W_0=energy of entry of gas molecule into a crack or pore which is sufficient to overcome the protective barrier of two overlapping fields of force at the entrance,[8] E_0=a small energy increment necessary for the diffusion of the atom along the crack or pore, i.e. for mobilising an adsorbed atom.[9]

1 *J.A.C.S.*, 1929, **51**, 3278; also verified by Khitrin, *J. Exptl. Theor. Phys. U.S.S.R.*, 1934, **4**, 160.
2 Smithells and Ransley, *Proc. Roy. Soc.*, 1935, **152**, 706 (Al); Smithells, *Nature*, 1937, **139**, 1113.
3 *Tekn. Tidskr.* (*Kem.*), 1926, **56**, 41.
4 *J. Chem. Phys.*, 1937, **5**, 913 (Fe); 1938, **6**, 598 (Ni); Ham, *ibid.*, 1933, **1**, 476; *Trans. Amer. Soc. Metals*, 1937, **25**, 536; see Jost and Widmann, *Z. phys. Chem.*, 1935, **29** B, 285; 1940, **45** B, 247 (H_2 and D_2 in Pd); Rast and Ham, *Phys. Rev.*, 1937, **51**, 1015 (Fe).
5 Van Liempt, *Rec. Trav. Chim.*, 1938, **57**, 871.
6 *Trans. Faraday Soc.*, 1928, **28**, 333.
7 *Phil. Mag.*, 1933, **15**, 1035; Braaten and Clark, *J.A.C.S.*, 1935, **57**, 2714.
8 Lennard-Jones assumed non-overlapping fields.
9 Barrer, *Trans. Faraday Soc.*, 1944, **40**, 374.

Rayleigh [1] found that helium does not pass through *single* crystals, e.g. very thin sheets of mica up to 415°; Piutti and Boggio-Lera [2] had previously found that helium, which passes through vitreous silica, does not penetrate crystalline quartz at 480°.

J. GASES AT LOW PRESSURES

§ 1. Knudsen's Absolute Manometer

Before leaving the special treatment of gases a brief account will be given of some important results which apply to gases at very low pressures.[3] The first of these concerns the measurement of low pressures.

A low-pressure manometer used by Knudsen [4] and by Dushman [5] for pressures of the order of 10^{-8} mm. Hg, comprises a rotating disc with another disc suspended above it by a quartz fibre acting on the torsion balance principle. The torque (twisting couple) on the upper disc is measured. If the gas between the two discs, distant d cm. apart, is at such a low pressure that the molecules make hardly any collisions with one another between the plates in the short distance d, and if $\bar{c}$ is the mean molecular velocity, the mean velocity towards *one* disc is $\bar{c}/2$, and a molecule makes $\bar{c}/4d$ return journeys per second between the plates; hence the total number of return journeys per sec. between one cm.² of area of the plates will be:

$$Nd(\bar{c}/4d)=N\bar{c}/4,$$

where N=no. of molecules per cm.³ (Nd=no. of molecules in the volume $d\times 1$ cm.³ between 1 cm.² area on each plate.)

If u is the velocity of the moving plate, it may be supposed that each molecule striking this plate acquires a tangential velocity u and a momentum mu, and gives up this momentum to the fixed plate on striking it. Hence the momentum given per sec. to one cm.² of fixed plate is $\frac{1}{4}N\bar{c}mu$. This is the force exerted on the fixed plate per cm.². Substitution of $\bar{c}$ from (35), § 10.III:

$$\bar{c}=\sqrt{(8kT/\pi m)}$$

gives for the force per cm.² which must be applied to the fixed plate to prevent it from moving:

$$F=(Nmu/4)\sqrt{(8kT/\pi m)}=up\sqrt{(m/2\pi kT)} \quad . \quad . \quad . \quad . \quad (1)$$

since $p=NkT$; hence the torque is proportional to:

$$up\sqrt{(m/kT)} \quad . \quad . \quad . \quad . \quad . \quad . \quad . \quad . \quad . \quad (2)$$

[1] *Nature*, 1935, **135**, 30; *Proc. Roy. Soc.*, 1937, **163**, 376.

[2] *Mem. Accad. Lincei*, 1923, **14**, 125; *Atti R. Accad. Lincei*, 1924, **33**, ii, 532; *R. Accad. Napoli* (*Fis. Mat.*), 1923, **29**, 111.

[3] A fuller account of the subject (which is rather involved and tedious) must be sought in the original papers quoted in the references. Summaries are given by Jellinek, "Lehrbuch der physikalischen Chemie," 1928, **1**, 261 f.; Knudsen, "Kinetic Theory of Gases," 1934; Loeb, "Kinetic Theory of Gases," 1934, 278; Kennard, "Kinetic Theory of Gases," 1938, 291; Dushman, "Scientific Foundations of Vacuum Technique," New York, 1949.

[4] *Ann. Phys.*, 1910, **32**, 809; 1914, **44**, 525 (oscillating sphere); 1930, **6**, 129; Fredlund, *ibid.*, 1932, **13**, 802; 1932, **14**, 617.

[5] *Phys. Rev.*, 1915, **5**, 212; "Production and Measurement of High Vacuum," Schenectady, 1922, 101; cf. Dewar, *Chem. News*, 1907, **96**, 97 (radiometer gauge); Langmuir, *Phys. Rev.*, 1913, **1**, 337; Rutherford, *Engineering*, 1924, **117**, 365; Lockenvitz, *Rev. Sci. Instr.*, 1938, **9**, 417 (radiometer gauge); Klumb and Schwarz, *Z. Phys.*, 1944, **122**, 418 (radiometer type, bibl.); Weber, *Kgl. Dansk. Vidensk. Selsk. Mat. fys. Medd.*, 1947, **24**, No. 4.

In the *absolute manometer* devised by Knudsen,[1] which has a different construction, two plates are at two slightly different temperatures T_1 and T_2. In this case the force on one plate, suspended very close to a fixed plate is:

$$F=\tfrac{1}{2}Ap[\sqrt{(T_1/T_2)}-1] \quad . \quad . \quad . \quad . \quad . \quad . \quad . \quad (3)$$

In the simplified deduction of Knudsen's equation (3) given by Smoluchowski it was assumed that the mean free path is large compared with the dimensions of the vessel, so that the gas may be treated like black-body radiation in an enclosure (an idea due to Maxwell). The molecules are assumed to have two velocities c_1 and c_2 (really $\sqrt{(\overline{c_1^2})}$ and $\sqrt{(\overline{c_2^2})}$), and in each category n_1 and n_2 per cm.[3] are supposed to move from below to above, and n_1' and n_2' from above to below. It is then assumed that:

$$n_2c_2=n_1'c_1, \quad \text{and} \quad n_1c_1=n_2'c_2.$$

The number of collisions ν per sec. on the under side of the upper plate is equal to the number on the upper side. The upper plate is opposite to a constant temperature wall, and in the upper space all the molecules have a velocity c_2 corresponding with the temperature T_2. Hence, if N is the number of molecules per cm.^{3} moving both up and down in the upper space, $n_1c_1+n_2c_2=\tfrac{1}{2}Nc_2$. The excess pressure from inside to outside per cm.^{2} of upper plate is:

$$\tfrac{1}{3}m(n_1c_1^2+n_2c_2^2+n_1'c_1^2+n_2'c_2^2-Nc_2^2)$$

which, with the previous equations, gives Knudsen's formula ($A=1$):

$$F=\tfrac{1}{6}mNc_2^2(c_1/c_2-1)=(p/2)[\sqrt{(T_1/T_2)}-1].$$

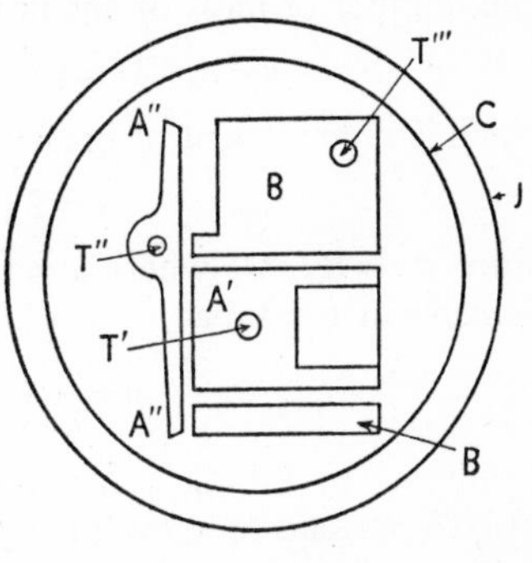

FIG. 1.VII J. Knudsen's Absolute Manometer

A section of Knudsen's absolute manometer is shown in Fig. 1.VII J. A copper cylinder A′ 1·63 cm. diam., with a boring for a thermometer T′, is contained in a blackened metal tube C, surrounded by an evacuated bell-jar J. The polished base of A′ is heated electrically. The cylinder A′ is surrounded by a copper guard-ring block B, with a clearance of 0·174 mm., and having an inserted thermometer T‴. A copper plate A″, with a thermometer T″, is hung from a platinum wire of 0·1 mm. diam. The distance between A′ and A″ is 0·12 mm., the effective area is 2·1 cm.^{2}, and the distance from the supporting wire to the central point of the hot base of A′ is 1·2 cm. The angular displacement of the suspended plate A″ is measured. With a temperature difference of 46° in hydrogen at 0·002 mm. Hg pressure, a deflexion of a beam of light from a mirror on A″ was 4 mm. Deviations from the formula (3) began at 0·006 mm. Hg pressure.

Gaede [2] used a " molvacuum meter " depending on the thermal repulsion

[1] *Ann. Phys.*, 1910, **32**, 809; Smoluchowski, *ibid.*, 1911, **34**, 182; von Angerer, *ibid.*, 1913, **41**, 1; Woodrow, *Phys. Rev.*, 1914, **4**, 491; *Phys. Z.*, 1914, **15**, 868; Schrader and Sherwood, *Phys. Rev.*, 1918, **11**, 134; 1918, **12**, 70; Sherwood, *ibid.*, 1918, **11**, 241; Todd, *Phil. Mag.*, 1919, **38**, 381; Richardson, *Proc. Phys. Soc.*, 1919, **31**, 270; Martin, *Phil. Mag.*, 1930, **9**, 97; Spiwak, *Sow. Phys. Z.*, 1932, **2**, 101; Fredlund, *Ann. Phys.*, 1932, **13**, 802; 1914, **14**, 617; Hughes, *Rev. Sci. Instr.*, 1937, **8**, 409; Weber, *K. Danske Videns. Selsk. Mat. Fys. Medd.*, 1937, **14**, No. 13; *Physica*, 1939, **6**, 551; Werner, *Z. techn. Phys.*, 1939, **20**, 13; Williams, *J. Sci. Instr.*, 1946, **23**, 144 (10^{-4}–10^{-6} mm.).

[2] *Z. techn. Phys.*, 1934, **15**, 664; Paranjpe, *Proc. Indian Acad. Sci.*, 1946, **23** A, 233.

principle. A modified Knudsen gauge was described by Du Mond and Pickels.[1] Murman [2] used a "hot wire" manometer, the pressure being determined from the length of the wire.

§ 2. The Flow of Gases at Very Low Pressure

The flow of gas through a circular capillary tube of length L and radius r *at very low pressure* can be derived from equation (2), § 12.VII F ($\eta/\epsilon=\zeta$):

$$v=(\pi r^4/8\eta L)(p_1-p_2)(1+4\zeta/r) \quad . \quad . \quad . \quad . \quad . \quad . \quad (1)$$

where L is now used for the length of the tube.

In this equation unity can be neglected in comparison with $4\zeta/r$, hence:

$$v=(\pi\zeta r^3/2\eta L)(p_1-p_2) \quad . \quad . \quad . \quad . \quad . \quad . \quad . \quad (2)$$

Substitute $\eta=0{\cdot}350\rho\bar{c}l$ from Boltzmann's formula (12), § 1.VII F, and $\zeta=0{\cdot}700l(2-f)/f$ from (7), § 12.VII F, giving:

$$v=(\pi r^3/\rho\bar{c}L)(p_1-p_2)[(2-f)/f] \quad . \quad . \quad . \quad . \quad . \quad . \quad (3)$$

The number of mols of gas flowing per sec. is:

$$n=pv/RT=(\pi r^3/\bar{c}L)(p_1-p_2)[(2-f)/f](p/\rho)(1/RT) \quad . \quad . \quad . \quad (4)$$

which is independent of pressure (p/ρ=const.). From (35), § 10.III:

$$\bar{c}=2\surd(2RT/\pi M)=\surd(8p/\pi\rho) \quad . \quad . \quad . \quad . \quad . \quad . \quad (5)$$

(since $pv=RT/M$, where v=vol. of 1 g., and $v=1/\rho$), and if $d=2r$ is the *diameter* of the tube:

$$n=\sqrt{\left(\frac{\pi^3}{512}\right)}\frac{\sqrt{p}}{\sqrt{\rho}}\frac{d^3}{RT}\frac{p_1-p_2}{L}\frac{2-f}{f}.$$

Knudsen,[3] by taking account of Maxwell's distribution law, found the factor $\surd(\pi/18)$ instead of $\surd(\pi^3/512)$, hence he gave:

$$n=\sqrt{\left(\frac{\pi}{18}\right)}\frac{1}{\sqrt{\rho_0}}\frac{d^3}{RT}\frac{p_1-p_2}{L}\frac{2-f}{f} \quad . \quad . \quad . \quad . \quad . \quad (6)$$

where $\rho/p=\rho_0$=density in g. per cm.^{3} under a pressure p=1 dyne/cm.^{2}.

Knudsen's formula for the mass Q in g. of gas flowing per sec. is obtained from (6) by putting $f=1$, $d=2r$, $Q=Mn$, where M=mol. wt. Since v=specific volume, $p(Mv)=RT$, $1/v=\rho=Mp/RT$, $\rho_0=\rho/p=M/RT$. By substitution in (6) it follows that:

$$Q=(8/3)\surd(\pi/2)r^3\surd\rho_0[(p_1-p_2)/L] \quad . \quad . \quad . \quad . \quad . \quad (7)$$

The transition between Poiseuille's law, when the amount of gas passing is proportional to the pressure, and the case of very low pressures, when the amount is independent of the pressure, is represented by Knudsen by the formula:

$$Q=ap+b(1+c_1p)/(1+c_2p) \quad . \quad . \quad . \quad . \quad . \quad . \quad (8)$$

[1] *Rev. Sci. Instr.*, 1935, **6**, 362.

[2] *Z. techn. Phys.*, 1933, **14**, 538.

[3] *Ann. Phys.*, 1908–9, **28**, 75, 999; Fisher, *Phys. Rev.*, 1909, **29**, 325; Knudsen and Fisher, *ibid.*, 1910, **31**, 586; cf. Hogg, *Proc. Amer. Acad.*, 1905, **40**, 611; 1906, **42**, 115; *Phil. Mag.*, 1910, **19**, 376; Bolza, Born, and von Kármán, *Gött. Nachr.*, 1913, 221; Onnes and Weber, *Verslag. K. Akad. Wetens. Amsterdam*, 1931, **21**, 1530 (*Comm. Leiden*, **134** c); Dodd, *Phys. Rev.*, 1918, **11**, 242 (verified); Dushman, "Production and Measurement of High Vacuum," Schenectady, 1922, 30; Jellinek, "Lehrbuch der physikalischen Chemie," 1928, **1**, 275; Krase, *Ann. Phys.*, 1931, **11**, 73; Darbord, *J. de Phys.*, 1932, **3**, 345; Loeb, "Kinetic Theory of Gases," 1934, 290; Jeans, "Kinetic Theory of Gases," Cambridge, 1940, 170; Brown, de Nardo, Cheng, and Sherwood, *J. Appl. Phys.*, 1947, **17**, 802.

in which Q is now the quantity of gas which, when divided by RT, gives the number of mols of gas passing at the mean pressure p and a pressure difference (p_1-p_2) of 1 dyne per cm.^{2} between the ends of the capillary, and a, b, c_1, and c_2 are constants. At high pressures (of the order of atmospheric) the second term is negligible, and the constant a is Poiseuille's constant $(\pi d^4/128\eta L)$. At very small pressures $(p\to 0)$ Q approaches b, which is Knudsen's constant $\sqrt{(\pi/18)}(d^3/L)(1/\sqrt{\rho_0})$. At moderate pressures, unity is small compared with $c_1 p$ and $c_2 p$ in (8); hence, by comparison with (1) with $Q=pv$:

$$Q=ap+b(c_1/c_2)=ap(1+8\zeta/d) \quad . \quad . \quad . \quad . \quad . \quad . \quad (9)$$

$$\therefore \ \zeta=db(c_1/c_2)/(8ap) \quad . \quad . \quad . \quad . \quad . \quad . \quad . \quad (10)$$

For *low pressures* Weber [1] proposed to vary the viscosity according to the law $\eta=\eta_0 p/(p+a\eta_0)$, where η_0 is the constant limiting value at higher pressures. The constant a is found for an oscillating disc apparatus to be: [2]

$$a=k_1\sqrt{(2\pi)}[(d_1+d_2)/d_1 d_2](1/\sqrt{{}_1\rho_T}) \quad . \quad . \quad . \quad . \quad . \quad (11)$$

where d_1, d_2 are the distances of the oscillating from two fixed discs, ${}_1\rho_T$ is the density of the gas at T° K. and 1 dyne/cm.^{2} pressure, and k_1 is slightly less than 4/3.

The equation:

$$Q/(p_1-p_2)=(0{\cdot}1472r/l+Z)\times(30{\cdot}48r^3\sqrt{T}/L\sqrt{M}) \quad . \quad . \quad . \quad (12)$$

where p_1-p_2=pressure difference in microns (10^{-3} mm. Hg) between the ends of a cylindrical tube of length L and radius r cm., l=mean free path at the average pressure $\frac{1}{2}(p_1+p_2)$, Q=flow in micron litres (pv units) per sec., Z=a function of r/l which increases from $Z=0{\cdot}81$ for $r/l>100$ to $1{\cdot}0$ for $r/l\leqq 0{\cdot}1$, is given by Dushman [3] for the whole range of pressure.

At very low pressures the viscosity coefficient of a gas becomes abnormally small, since the molecules have not space available in the apparatus to describe free paths by collisions. If the mean free path l is less than some value l_0, then $\eta=\frac{1}{3}\rho\bar{c}l$ cannot be greater than $\frac{1}{3}\rho\bar{c}l_0$, and should vanish along with ρ. Crookes [4] had found abnormally low viscosities at pressures of the order of 10^{-3} mm. Hg which tended to vanish as the density of the gas vanished.

A practical point is the marked slowness of passage of a gas at low pressure through narrow tubes; Knudsen connected two $2\frac{3}{4}$-lit. flasks, one containing hydrogen at 0·01 mm. Hg pressure and the other highly vacuous, by a tube 30 cm. long and 0·1 mm. diam., and found that it took about 15 hours for one-third of the gas to pass from one flask to the other. For this reason, all connecting tubes in high-vacuum apparatus must be of wide bore. The slow flow through small openings at very low pressures is utilised in the *molecular pump* of Gaede,[5] consisting of a metal cylinder rotating inside a fixed cylinder with a small clearance, and with a fixed deflecting vane on the latter; the inlet and outlet tubes are on opposite sides of the vane. This pump has been superseded by vapour pumps (see § 12.VII A).

Knudsen expressed his equation in the form:

$$Q=(1/\sqrt{\rho_0})[(p_1-p_2)/W] \quad . \quad . \quad . \quad . \quad . \quad . \quad . \quad (13)$$

1 *Physica*, 1939, **6**, 551.
2 Miyako, *Proc. Phys. Math. Soc. Japan*, 1942, **24**, 852 (η and second virial coefficient of H_2 at low temperature); van Itterbeek, van Paemel, and van Lierde, *Physica*, 1947, **13**, 88.
3 *Ind. Eng. Chem.*, 1948, **40**, 778.
4 *Phil. Trans.*, 1881, **172**, 387.
5 *Ann. Phys.*, 1913, **41**, 337; Dunoyer, "Vacuum Practice," transl. Smith, New York, 1928, 36.

where W is the resistance to flow, given by:

$$W=(3/8)\sqrt{(\pi/2)}\int_0^L (O/A^2)\mathrm{d}L \quad . \quad . \quad . \quad . \quad . \quad . \quad . \quad (14)$$

where O=circumference of tube, L=length of tube, A=area of nominal section at a distance L (in the integral) from the end. The Knudsen flow for gaseous mixtures is additive.[1]

Todd [2] proposed the general equation (d=diameter of tube):

$$\eta_p=\eta_\infty(1-\mathrm{e}^{-kpd}) \quad . \quad . \quad . \quad . \quad . \quad . \quad . \quad . \quad . \quad (15)$$

which for small pressures gives $\eta=\eta_\infty kpd$, agreeing with Knudsen's formula if, in the equivalent form of the latter, $v_2(\mathrm{d}p_2/\mathrm{d}t)=c(d^3/l)(p_1-p_2)$, the constant $c=\pi/k\eta_\infty$; and at high pressures $\eta=\eta_\infty$.

The flow characteristics of a vacuum line may be expressed [3] by

$$Q=C(p_1-p_2) \quad . \quad . \quad . \quad . \quad . \quad . \quad . \quad . \quad . \quad (16)$$

where Q=quantity of gas in pv units passing any point per sec. and C=conductance of the line. For parts in series, $1/C=\Sigma(1/C_1)$, and for parts in parallel, $C=\Sigma C_1$. The speed of pumping S of a pump, defined as the volume of gas, measured at inlet pressure, entering the pump per sec., is related to the rate S' of removal of gas from an attached chamber by the equation:

$$1/S'=1/S+1/C \quad . \quad . \quad . \quad . \quad . \quad . \quad . \quad . \quad . \quad (17)$$

From (7):

$$C=\tfrac{4}{3}\sqrt{(2\pi)}\sqrt{(RT/M)}(r^3/L) \quad . \quad . \quad . \quad . \quad . \quad . \quad . \quad . \quad (18)$$

The conditions of application at various pressures and with various types of pipes, including bends, etc., and semi-empirical formulae for transition cases, are given by Normand.[3]

§ 3. Effusion at Low Pressures

The case of effusion through a very small hole of area A (e.g. 5×10^{-6} cm.^{2}), in a plate separating two parts of a gas at the very low pressures p_1 and p_2, was treated by Knudsen [4] as follows. Since there are practically no collisions, the numbers of molecules passing through the hole per cm.^{2} per sec. are, from (8), § 8.III, $N_1\bar{c}/4$ and $N_2\bar{c}/4$, where N_1 and N_2 are the numbers per cm.^{3}; hence the number of molecules passing through the hole per sec. from the pressure p_1 to the pressure p_2 is:

$$\nu=A\bar{c}(N_1-N_2)/4 \quad . \quad . \quad . \quad . \quad . \quad . \quad . \quad . \quad . \quad (1)$$

If m=mass of a molecule, $N_1m=\rho_1$, $N_2m=\rho_2$, and $\nu m=Q$=mass of gas passing per sec., then:

$$Q=A\bar{c}(\rho_1-\rho_2)/4 \quad . \quad . \quad . \quad . \quad . \quad . \quad . \quad . \quad . \quad (2)$$

Put $\rho_1=p_1\rho_0$, and $\rho_2=p_2\rho_0$, where ρ_0=density at unit pressure (1 dyne per cm.^{2}), and substitute $\bar{c}=\sqrt{(8/\pi\rho_0)}$, then:

$$Q=[A/\sqrt{(2\pi)}]\sqrt{\rho_0}(p_1-p_2) \quad . \quad . \quad . \quad . \quad . \quad . \quad . \quad . \quad (3)$$

Equation (3) was verified experimentally by Knudsen.

[1] Adzuni, *Bull. Chem. Soc. Japan*, 1937, **12**, 199, 285, 292.
[2] *Proc. Durham Phil. Soc.*, 1920, **6**, 8.
[3] Normand, *Ind. Eng. Chem.*, 1948, **40**, 780.
[4] *Ann. Phys.*, 1909, **28**, 75, 999; 1909, **29**, 179; 1911, **34**, 823; 1911, **35**, 389; 1914, **44**, 525; Smoluchowski, *ibid.*, 1910, **33**, 1559; Gaede, *ibid.*, 1913, **41**, 289; Clausing, *Dissert.*, Amsterdam, 1918; *Verslag. K. Akad. Wetens. Amsterdam*, 1926, **35**, 1023; *Physica*, 1929, **9**, 65; *Ann. Phys.*, 1930, **7**, 533, 567; 1930, **7**, 569; 1932, **12**, 961; 1932, **14**, 129, 134.

Clausing found for a low-pressure gas passing through a short or long round *tube* into a vacuous space:

$$\nu = WAN_1 \quad . \quad . \quad . \quad . \quad . \quad . \quad . \quad . \quad . \quad . \quad (4)$$

where ν=no. of molecules passing per sec., A=area of section of tube, N_1=no. of molecules striking unit area of the gas-containing vessel per sec., and W is a probability coefficient calculated by Clausing.

§ 4. Heat Conduction at Low Pressures.

Kundt and Warburg [1] found that whilst, at suitably reduced gas pressures when convection is minimised, the thermal conductivity is independent of pressure, this is not the case at very low pressures, so small that the mean free path of the molecules is larger than the linear dimensions of the apparatus, when the molecules " transport heat across the whole apparatus at a single bound." [2] There is no temperature gradient and the whole gas is at a uniform temperature, which is different from that of the solid wall. This case was investigated by Knudsen.[3]

For such a " molecular conduction " between two parallel plates of area A at temperatures T_1 and T_2, he found for the quantity of heat passing in t secs.:

$$q = At(T_1 - T_2)p\epsilon \quad . \quad . \quad . \quad . \quad . \quad . \quad . \quad (1)$$

where, for a complete exchange of energy on collisions of gas molecules with the plates (" absolutely rough " surfaces):

$$\epsilon = \tfrac{1}{4}\sqrt{\left(\frac{2}{273\pi\rho_0 T}\right)} \cdot \frac{c_p + c_v}{c_p - c_v} \quad . \quad . \quad . \quad . \quad . \quad . \quad (2)$$

If the observed heat transfer is $q' = Kq$, then K is a constant for the same gas and plates, but varies with the gas and the degree of roughness of the plates. The fact that K is not unity shows that the exchange of energy is not usually complete with a single collision. If $\overline{c^2}$ is the mean square velocity of the molecules in the gas in temperature equilibrium with the solid, $\overline{c_1{}^2}$ the value for molecules approaching the solid, and $\overline{c_2{}^2}$ for molecules leaving the solid, then the *accommodation coefficient* is defined as:

$$a = \frac{\overline{c_2{}^2} - \overline{c_1{}^2}}{\overline{c^2} - \overline{c_1{}^2}} = \frac{T_2 - T_1}{T - T_1} \quad . \quad . \quad . \quad . \quad . \quad . \quad . \quad (3)$$

For hydrogen, Knudsen found this to vary from 0·26 for bright platinum or glass to 0·71 for platinised platinum [4] (see § 5).

Knudsen deduced the above equations as follows. Call A_1 and A_2 the plates at absolute temperatures T_1 and T_2. The molecules leaving A_1 have a velocity c_1 and those leaving A_2 a velocity c_2. If there are dN_1 molecules per cm.[3] with velocity components between c_1 and $c_1 + dc_1$ directed away from A_1,

[1] *Ann. Phys.*, 1875, **156**, 177; Crookes, *Proc. Roy. Soc.*, 1881, **31**, 239.

[2] Jeans, " Kinetic Theory of Gases," 1940, 190.

[3] *Ann. Phys.*, 1910, **31**, 205; 1910, **33**, 1435; 1911, **34**, 593, 823; 1911, **35**, 389; 1911, **36**, 871; 1927, **83**, 385, 797; 1930, **6**, 129; " The Kinetic Theory of Gases," 1934, 46; Smoluchowski, *Ann. Phys.*, 1910, **33**, 1559; 1911, **35**, 983; Trowbridge, *Phys. Rev.*, 1913, **2**, 58 (air at 0·001 mm.); Bolza, Born, and von Kármán, *Gött. Nachr.*, 1913, 221; Loeb, " Kinetic Theory of Gases," 1927, 265, 2nd edit., 1934, 310; Gregory, *Phil. Mag.*, 1936, **22**, 257; 1943, **34**, 120; Fredlund, *Ann. Phys.*, 1937, **28**, 319.

[4] Marcelin, *Compt. Rend.*, 1914, **158**, 1674; Knudsen, *Ann. Phys.*, 1915, **47**, 697; 1916, **50**, 472; Bennewitz, *Ann. Phys.*, 1919, **59**, 193; Volmer and Estermann, *Z. Phys.*, 1921, **7**, 1; *Z. phys. Chem.*, 1921, **99**, 383; Czerny and Hettner, *Z. Phys.*, 1924, **27**, 12; 1924, **30**, 258.

these will strike one cm.^{2} of A_2, and if there are dN molecules per cm.^{3} having velocities in all directions, then $\frac{1}{4}dNc_1$ of these strike one cm.^{2} of A_2 per sec. Since the dN_1 molecules move only in all directions in a hemisphere, but dN in all directions in a sphere, $dN_1=\frac{1}{2}dN$; hence $\frac{1}{2}dN_1c_1$ molecules strike one cm.^{2} of A_2 per sec. Similarly, if there are dN_2 molecules per cm.^{3} with velocities between c_2 and c_2+dc_2, directed away from A_2, the number $\frac{1}{2}dN_2c_2$ of these will strike one cm.^{2} of A_1 per sec.

Knudsen first assumed the plates absolutely rough, i.e. that each molecule striking a plate adheres to it but can afterwards re-evaporate with a temperature appropriate to the plate it leaves. The plate A_2 thus gains energy $dE_1=\frac{1}{2}dN_1.c_1.\frac{1}{2}mc_1^2$ from the group of molecules striking it, and, from Maxwell's distribution law (29), § 10.III:

$$dN_1=\frac{4N_1}{\sqrt{\pi}}\frac{c_1^2}{\alpha_1^3}e^{-c_1^2/\alpha_1^2}dc_1,$$

it follows that the total gain of energy per cm.^{2} per sec. is:

$$E_1=\tfrac{1}{4}m\int_0^\infty c_1^3dN_1=\tfrac{1}{4}m\frac{4N_1}{\sqrt{(\pi)}\alpha_1^3}\int_0^\infty c_1^5e^{-c_1^2/\alpha_1^2}dc_1$$
$$=\frac{N_1m}{\sqrt{(\pi)}\alpha_1^3}\int_0^\infty c_1^5e^{-c_1^2/\alpha_1^2}dc_1$$
$$=\frac{\rho_1}{\sqrt{(\pi)}\alpha_1^3}\int_0^\infty c_1^5e^{-c_1^2/\alpha_1^2}dc_1 \quad . \quad . \quad . \quad (4)$$

where $\rho_1=N_1m=$density. By integration by parts (§ 19.I):

$$\int_0^\infty c_1^5e^{-c_1^2/\alpha_1^2}dc_1=\Big[-c_1^4(\alpha_1^2/2)e^{-c_1^2/\alpha_1^2}\Big]_0^\infty-\int_0^\infty-(\alpha_1^2/2)e^{-c_1^2/\alpha_1^2}\,.\,4c_1^3dc_1$$
$$=2\alpha_1^2\int_0^\infty c_1^3e^{-c_1^2/\alpha_1^2}dc_1=\alpha_1^6 \quad . \quad (5)$$

since, from (23), § 10.III, the last integral is equal to $\frac{1}{2}\alpha_1^4$. Hence, from (4) and (5), and the result from (24), § 10.III, $\alpha_1=\frac{1}{2}\sqrt{(\pi)}\bar{c}_1$,

$$E_1=(\rho_1\alpha_1^3/\sqrt{\pi})=(\pi/8)\rho_1\bar{c}_1^3=(\pi/8)N_1m\bar{c}_1^3 \quad . \quad . \quad . \quad (6)$$

Similarly:

$$E_2=(\pi/8)\rho_2\bar{c}_2^3=(\pi/8)N_2m\bar{c}_2^3 \quad . \quad . \quad . \quad (6a)$$

Since E_1 is received by A_2, and E_2 given up by A_2 to A_1, the net gain of translational energy per cm.^{2} of A_2 per sec. is:

$$E_1-E_2=(\pi/8)m(N_1\bar{c}_1^3-N_2\bar{c}_2^3) \quad . \quad . \quad . \quad (7)$$

The number of molecules striking one cm.^{2} of A_2 per sec. is $\frac{1}{2}N_1\bar{c}_1$, and the number striking A_1 is $\frac{1}{2}N_2\bar{c}_2$, and as the numbers arriving and leaving each surface per sec. are equal in equilibrium, and no molecules escape from between the plates, it follows that:

$$\tfrac{1}{2}N_1\bar{c}_1=\tfrac{1}{2}N_2\bar{c}_2 \quad . \quad . \quad . \quad (8)$$

If the plates are surrounded by gas of density N molecules per cm.^{3} of average velocity $\bar{c}$, the constancy of pressure implies that the number passing out per sec. per cm.^{2} between the edges is equal to the number entering; hence from (8), § 8.III:

$$\tfrac{1}{4}N_1\bar{c}_1+\tfrac{1}{4}N_2\bar{c}_2=\tfrac{1}{4}N\bar{c},$$

$\therefore$ from (8),

$$N_1\bar{c}_1=N_2\bar{c}_2=\tfrac{1}{2}N\bar{c} \quad . \quad . \quad . \quad (9)$$

$\therefore$ from (7) and (9):

$$E_1-E_2=(\pi/16)Nm\bar{c}(\overline{c_1^2}-\overline{c_2^2}) \quad \ldots \ldots \quad (10)$$

From (5), § 2, $\bar{c}=2\sqrt{(2RT/\pi M)}=\sqrt{(8p/\pi\rho)}$, and if ρ_0 is the density at 0° C. for unit pressure of one dyne per cm.^{2}, $\rho=\rho_0(273p/T)$, hence:

$$\bar{c}=\sqrt{(8/\pi)}\sqrt{(T/273)}\,.\,(1/\sqrt{\rho_0}) \quad \ldots \ldots \quad (11)$$

$$\bar{c}^2=(8/\pi)(p/\rho) \quad \ldots \ldots \quad (12)$$

and substitution in (10), with $Nm=\rho$, gives:

$$E_1-E_2=\frac{\pi}{16}\rho\sqrt{\frac{8}{\pi}}\sqrt{\frac{T}{273}}\frac{1}{\sqrt{\rho_0}}\left(\frac{8}{\pi}\frac{p_1}{\rho_1}-\frac{8}{\pi}\frac{p_2}{\rho_2}\right)$$

$$=\frac{\rho}{2}\sqrt{\frac{8}{\pi}}\sqrt{\frac{T}{273}}\frac{1}{\sqrt{\rho_0}}\frac{\boldsymbol{R}}{M}(T_1-T_2)$$

$$=\frac{pM}{2\boldsymbol{R}T}\sqrt{\frac{8}{\pi}}\sqrt{\frac{T}{273}}\frac{1}{\sqrt{\rho_0}}\frac{\boldsymbol{R}}{M}(T_1-T_2)$$

$$=\frac{p}{2T}\sqrt{\frac{8}{\pi}}\sqrt{\frac{T}{273}}\frac{1}{\sqrt{\rho_0}}(T_1-T_2);$$

hence the translational energy transferred, E_1-E_2, is:

$$E_t=\sqrt{\left(\frac{2}{\pi}\right)}p\frac{1}{\sqrt{\rho_0}}\frac{T_1-T_2}{\sqrt{(273T)}} \quad \ldots \ldots \quad (13)$$

Equation (13) is equivalent to (1), except for the factor ϵ. This enters the equation when a polyatomic gas is considered instead of a monatomic gas. Knudsen assumed in this case that if E_i is the internal energy of rotation, etc., the ratio k of the total energy $E=E_t+E_i$ to the translational energy E_t is given by the equipartition theorem, (4), § 28.VII E:

$$k=E/E_t=\tfrac{2}{3}c_v/(c_p-c_v)=\tfrac{2}{3}/(\gamma-1) \quad \ldots \ldots \quad (14)$$

where $\gamma=c_p/c_v$. The average internal energy is $(k-1)$ times the translational energy.

The internal energy taken per sec. per cm.^{2} between the plates is thus:

$$E_i=(k-1)(\tfrac{1}{2}N_1\bar{c}_1\,.\,\tfrac{1}{2}m\overline{c_1^2}-\tfrac{1}{2}N_2\bar{c}_2\,.\,\tfrac{1}{2}m_2\overline{c_2^2}),$$

or, from (9), if $\bar{c}$ is the average velocity in *all* directions:

$$E_i=\tfrac{1}{8}mN\bar{c}(k-1)(\overline{c_1^2}-\overline{c_2^2}) \quad \ldots \ldots \quad (15)$$

From (11), (13), (14), and (15), § 8.III, $\overline{c^2}=3\boldsymbol{R}T/M=3T/273\rho_0$, it follows that the total energy transported per sec. per cm.^{2} is:

$$E=E_t+E_i=\sqrt{(2/\pi)}[1+\tfrac{3}{4}(k-1)](p/\sqrt{\rho_0})[(T_1-T_2)/\sqrt{(273T)}]$$

$$=\frac{1}{4}\,.\,\frac{c_p/c_v+1}{c_p/c_v-1}\sqrt{\frac{2}{\pi}}p\frac{1}{\sqrt{\rho_0}}\frac{T_1-T_2}{\sqrt{(273T)}}$$

$$=\tfrac{1}{4}\sqrt{(2/273\pi\rho_0 T)}[(c_p+c_v)/(c_p-c_v)](T_1-T_2)p \quad \ldots \quad (16)$$

which is now equivalent to (1). The actual value of ϵ is less than the theoretical, because of the intervention of the accommodation coefficient. Equation (16) was verified for hydrogen, nitrogen, helium, and neon at low pressures at 12°–20° K. by Keesom and Schmidt,[1] who found an accommodation coefficient of approximately unity.

[1] *Physica*, 1936, 3, 590, 1085; 1937, **4**, 825 (*Comm. Leiden*, **250***a*); Weber, Keesom, and Schmidt, *Comm. Leiden*, 1936, **246***a–b*.

§ 5. The Accommodation Coefficient

The possible existence of a discontinuity of temperature between the wall of a vessel and a gas at a different temperature, analogous to slip in viscous flow (§ 12.VII F), was suggested by Poisson,[1] but was first experimentally demonstrated, at Warburg's suggestion, by Smoluchowski.[2] He explained it as due to the decreased length of the free paths in the immediate neighbourhood of the walls, and to the imperfect equalisation of temperature on collisions between gas molecules and the molecules of the solid, of very different masses. The second effect seemed to be confirmed by the much larger effect found with hydrogen as compared with other gases with heavier molecules.

The effect is now specified in terms of the so-called *accommodation coefficient a*, introduced by Knudsen,[3] and defined in (3), § 4. If T_w is the wall temperature and T_K the *extrapolated* temperature of the gas at the wall on the assumption that the temperature gradient $\mathrm{d}T/\mathrm{d}z$ along the z axis normal to the wall continues uniform up to the wall, Poisson [1] suggested that:

$$T_K - T_w = g(\mathrm{d}T/\mathrm{d}z) \quad . \quad . \quad . \quad . \quad . \quad . \quad . \quad . \quad (1)$$

where the coefficient g is a length giving the temperature-spring distance. It was shown [4] that:

$$g = \frac{(2-a)}{a} \frac{4K}{(\gamma+1)} \frac{k}{\eta c_v} l \quad . \quad . \quad . \quad . \quad . \quad . \quad . \quad . \quad (2)$$

where K is a constant (approximately $\frac{1}{2}$), $\gamma = c_p/c_v$, k=thermal conductivity, η=viscosity, and l is the mean free path. If $a=1$, then g is a little larger than l.

Pioneer measurements of the accommodation coefficient a were made by Soddy and Berry,[5] and by Knudsen,[6] and the results recalculated by Smoluchowski;[7] the determinations were refined by later experimenters,[8] using the same method.

[1] " Théorie mathématique de la Chaleur," 1835, 119.

[2] *Ann. Phys.*, 1898, **64**, 101; *Wien Ber.*, 1898, **107**, II A, 304; 1899, **108**, II A, 5; *Phil. Mag.*, 1898, **46**, 192; Brush, *ibid.*, 1898, **45**, 31; Gehrcke, *Ann. Phys.*, 1900, **2**, 102 (introd. by Warburg); Langmuir, *Z. Elektrochem.*, 1917, **23**, 16.

[3] *Ann. Phys.*, 1911, **34**, 593.

[4] Kennard, " Kinetic Theory of Gases," 1938, 314.

[5] *Proc. Roy. Soc.*, 1910, **83**, 254; 1911, **84**, 576; 1915, **46**, 641.

[6] *Ann. Phys.*, 1911, **34**, 593; 1911, **36**, 871.

[7] *Ann. Phys.*, 1911, **35**, 983; *Phil. Mag.*, 1911, **21**, 11.

[8] Lasareff, *Ann. Phys.*, 1912, **37**, 233; Weber, *ibid.*, 1927, **82**, 479; Clausing, *ibid.*, 1930, **4**, 533; Knudsen, *ibid.*, 1930, **6**, 129; Roberts, *Proc. Roy. Soc.*. 1930, **129**, 146; 1932, **135**, 192; 1933, **142**, 518; Blodgett and Langmuir, *Phys. Rev.*, 1932, **40**, 78; Michels, *ibid.*, 1932, **40**, 472 (He and A on W; etc.); Zener, *ibid.*, 1932, **40**, 335 (theory); Dickins, *Proc. Roy. Soc.*, 1933, **143**, 517; Jackson and Howarth, *ibid.*, 1933, **142**, 447; Rowley and Bonhoeffer, *Z. phys. Chem.*, 1933, **21** B, 84; Mann, *Proc. Roy. Soc.*, 1934, **146**, 776; Loeb, " Kinetic Theory of Gases," 1934, 321; Archer, *Phil. Mag.*, 1935, **19**, 901; *Proc. Roy. Soc.*, 1938, **165**, 474; Gregory, *Proc. Roy. Soc.*, 1935, **149**, 35; Eucken and Bertram, *Z. phys. Chem.*, 1935, **31** B, 361; Keesom and Schmidt, *Proc. K. Akad. Wetens. Amsterdam*, 1936, **39**, 1048; *Physica*, 1936, **3**, 590, 1085; 1937, **4**, 828; Weber, *Comm. Leiden*, 1937, **246***b*; Michels, *Phys. Rev.*, 1937, **52**, 1067 (He and A on W, etc.); Mann and Newell, *Proc. Roy. Soc.*, 1937, **158**, 397; Gregory and Stephens, *Nature*, 1937, **139**, 28; Gregory and Dock, *Phil. Mag.*, 1938, **25**, 129; Kennard, " Kinetic Theory of Gases," 1938, 322; Kistiakowski and Nazmi, *J. Chem. Phys.*, 1938, **6**, 18; Kistiakowski, Lacher, and Stitt, *ibid.*, 1939, **7**, 289; Roberts, " Some Problems in Adsorption," Cambridge, 1939; " Heat and Thermodynamics," 1940, 228; Weber, *K. Dansk. Vidensk. Selskab. Mat. Fys. Meddel.*, 1942, **19**, No. 11; Thomas and Olmer, *J.A.C.S.*, 1942, **64**, 2190; 1943, **65**, 1036; Amdur, Jones, and Pearlman, *J. Chem. Phys.*, 1944, **12**, 159; Amdur, *ibid.*, 1946, **14**, 339; Klumb and Schwarz, *Z. Phys.*, 1944, **122**, 418; Rolf, *Phys. Rev.*, 1944, **65**, 185; Grilly, Taylor, and Johnston, *J. Chem. Phys.*, 1946, **14**, 435; Morrison, *ibid.*, 1946, **14**, 466; Paranjpe, *Proc. Indian Acad. Sci.*, 1946, **23** A, 233; Baranaev, *J. Phys. Chem., U.S.S.R.*, 1946, **20**, 399 (on liquids and solids); Bosworth, *J. Proc. Roy. Soc. N.S. Wales*, 1946, **79**, 166, 190 (N_2, O_2 on tungsten).

This depends on the measurement of the loss of heat from a wire, stretched along the axis of a cylinder kept at a constant temperature. Recent work indicates the need for a uniform temperature throughout the wire. The electrical resistance of the wire measures its temperature; the power expenditure measures the heat loss from the wire which is compared with the loss in high vacuum. The pressure of the gas is so low that the mean free path is at least six times the diameter of the wire. The temperature of the molecules impinging on the wire was assumed by Roberts to be that of the cylinder, but Blodgett and Langmuir took it as the mean temperature of the gas at a distance of one mean free path from the wire, the temperature drop from this point to the cylinder being calculated by the ordinary equation for mass heat conduction; this makes a difference of 5 to 10 per cent. The results should be extrapolated to a temperature difference of zero.

The results show, as might be expected, a great dependence on the state of the solid surface. Blodgett and Langmuir, with a tungsten filament 0·00779 cm. diam. and 40 cm. long in hydrogen at 0·2 mm. Hg pressure, in a tube 6·4 cm. diam. cooled in liquid air, found $a=0\cdot54$ above 1000° C., when the surface was supposed to be clean, but at lower temperatures a was as low as 0·14, when the wire was supposed to be covered with a film of adsorbed hydrogen. In presence of some oxygen, a was lowered to 0·2 to 0·1, when an oxide film was supposed to be formed. The *lowering* of a by an adsorbed gas film is hard to understand, and in experiments by Michels,[1] and by Roberts,[2] the effect was in the opposite direction, a being smallest for a clean tungsten surface, and increasing slowly with time (more rapidly at first). In the case of helium and tungsten an initial difference was also found between fresh tungsten and that after prolonged heating. This was found to persist, and was attributed by Roberts to fine-grained roughening of the metal surface caused by evaporation. Dickins used platinum and much higher pressures. The accommodation coefficients of hydrogen and deuterium are different.[3]

Baule,[4] on the basis of classical kinetic theory, deduced for elastic spherical gas molecules with random directions of motion:

$$a=2m_1m_2/(m_1+m_2)^2 \quad . \quad . \quad . \quad . \quad . \quad . \quad . \quad (3)$$

where m_1 and m_2 are the masses of the molecules of the gas and of the solid surface respectively; the assumption was made that only translational energy is concerned, and that a gas molecule makes only one collision with the solid before returning to the gas. This gives a maximum value $a=\frac{1}{2}$ when $m_1=m_2$; larger values would indicate multiple collisions.

Knudsen claimed to have established that the internal energy of the gas molecule also has an accommodation coefficient, which seems to be about the same as that for the translational energy.

A semi-classical theory of accommodation coefficients (using Compton's theory of specific heats; see § 1.IX N, Vol. II) was developed by Michels,[5] who postulated a heat of adsorption. The theory was also developed [6] on the basis

[1] *Phys. Rev.*, 1937, **52**, 1067.

[2] *Proc. Roy. Soc.*, 1930, **129**, 146; 1932, **135**, 192; 1933, **142**, 518; "Some Problems in Adsorption," Cambridge, 1939.

[3] Weber, *K. Dansk. Vidensk. Selskab. Mat. fys. Meddel.*, 1947, **24**, No. 4.

[4] *Ann. Phys.*, 1914, **44**, 145; Smoluchowski, *ibid.*, 1914, **45**, 623; Sexl, *ibid.*, 1926, **80**, 515; Polanyi and Wigner, *Z. phys. Chem.*, 1928, **139**, 439.

[5] *Phys. Rev.*, 1937, **52**, 1067.

[6] Zener, *Phys. Rev.*, 1931, **37**, 556; 1932, **40**, 178, 335; Jackson, *Proc. Cambr. Phil. Soc.*, 1932, **28**, 136; Jackson and Mott, *Proc. Roy. Soc.*, 1932, **137**, 703; Jackson and Howarth,

of wave mechanics; for details, reference must be made to the originals. Beeck [1] found for the accommodation coefficient of gaseous paraffin hydrocarbons on nickel:

$$a=(C_{v0}+R/2)/M=\text{const.}=0\cdot352 \quad . \quad . \quad . \quad . \quad . \quad (4)$$

where M=mol. wt., C_{v0}=ideal state mol. ht. at const. vol.$=1\cdot80+0\cdot352M$.

Soddy and Berry found $a=0\cdot37$ for hydrogen on platinum at 110°, and Rowley and Bonhoeffer 0·22 at room temperature. Some values for the accommodation coefficient of various gases on platinum for pressures below 5×10^{-2} mm. found by Thomas and Olmer in the first line, and by Amdur, Jones, and Pearlman in the second, are:

H_2	D_2	He	Ne	A	Hg	O_2	CO_2	CO	H_2O	N_2
0·220	0·295	0·238	0·57	0·89	1·00	0·74	0·76	0·75	0·72	—
0·313	—	—	0·403	0·847	—	0·782	—	—	—	0·769

Previous results are tabulated by these authors. At low temperatures the accommodation coefficient increases, and Keesom and Schmidt suggested that it may become unity at the critical temperature. Spivak [2] found that the accommodation coefficient on metals when an adsorbed film is present is related to temperature by the equation:

$$a=be^{c/T}+\alpha(T-p) \quad . \quad . \quad . \quad . \quad . \quad . \quad . \quad . \quad (5)$$

The first term depends on the fraction of surface covered by the film and the second on the temperature. For helium, the equation of Landau: [3]

$$a=kT^n \quad . \quad . \quad . \quad . \quad . \quad . \quad . \quad . \quad . \quad . \quad . \quad (6)$$

with $n=1\cdot5$, holds approximately.

It is clear that the accommodation coefficient is sensitive to small changes in the nature of the solid surface, and may give valuable information as to the changes of state of a surface in many types of experiment; it thus promises to be a valuable adjunct to experiment in many lines of research, e.g. on contact catalysis.

§ 6. Pirani and Ionisation Pressure Gauges

Equation (1), § 4, shows that, at very low pressures, the heat transport is proportional to the pressure, and this has been applied in the measurement of low pressures. In the *Pirani gauge*,[4] the heat conducted away from an electrically

ibid., 1933, **142**, 447; 1935, **152**, 515; Lennard-Jones and Strachan, *ibid.*, 1935, **150**, 442; Strachan, *ibid.*, 1935, **150**, 456; Landau, *Sow. Phys. Z.*, 1935, **8**, 489; Lennard-Jones and Devonshire, *Proc. Roy. Soc.*, 1936, **156**, 6; 1937, **158**, 242; Devonshire, *ibid.*, 1937, **158**, 269; Jackson and Tyson, *Manch. Mem.*, 1936–7, **81**, 87; Mann, *Proc. Roy. Soc.*, 1937, **161**, 236.

[1] *J. Chem. Phys.*, 1936, **4**, 680, 743; 1937, **5**, 268.

[2] *Amer. Chem. Abstr.*, 1942, **36**, 3995.

[3] *Sow. Phys. Z.*, 1935, **8**, 489 (classical theory).

[4] Pirani, *Verhl. d. D. Phys. Ges.*, 1906, **8**, 685; Hale, *Trans. Amer. Electrochem. Soc.*, 1911, **20**, 243; Campbell, *Proc. Phys. Soc.*, 1921, **33**, 287; Daudt, *Z. phys. Chem.*, 1923, **106**, 255 (bibl.); Schreiner, *ibid.*, 1924, **112**, 1; King, *Proc. Phys. Soc.*, 1925, **38**, 80; Knudsen, *Ann. Phys.*, 1927, **83**, 385; Skellett, *J. Opt. Soc. Amer.*, 1927, **15**, 56; de Vries, *ibid.*, 1929, **18**, 333; Stanley, *Proc. Phys. Soc.*, 1929, **41**, 194; Anderson, *Ind. Eng. Chem.*, 1929, **21**, 795 (0·25μ–1 atm.); Tanner, *J. Phys. Chem.*, 1930, **34**, 1113; Paneth and Urry, *Z. phys. Chem.*, 1930, **152**, 110; Ellett and Zabel, *Phys. Rev.*, 1931, **37**, 1102 (theory), 1112 (very sensitive gauge); Murmann, *Z. Phys.*, 1933, **86**, 14; Lannung, *Z. phys. Chem.*, 1934, **170**, 134; *Z. anorg. Chem.*,

heated wire in a gas at low pressure is measured by the input of electrical energy. Campbell [1] found that at low pressures, if the temperature of the Pirani gauge filament is kept constant by varying the potential across the bridge circuit:

$$p=k(V^2-V_0^2)/V_0^2=f(V) \quad . \quad . \quad . \quad . \quad . \quad . \quad . \quad . \quad (1)$$

where V_0, V are the balancing potentials at zero pressure and pressure p. This holds only at such low pressures that the thermal conductivity of the gas is proportional to the pressure. At higher pressures, the thermal conductivity is independent of pressure, and the plot of $1/f(V)$ against $1/p$ is found [2] to be linear at pressures of 0·05 to 0·5 mm. This relation can, as Foster showed, be used in calibrating the gauge, and is particularly useful in the region between 0·1 and 1 mm.

Nickel is said [3] to be better than tungsten wire in the Pirani gauge, and a narrow thread of mercury in a thin-walled glass capillary tube has been used.[4] A Wollaston hot-wire manometer was used by Weber [5] in measuring the vapour presssure of ice. The heat loss from a metal strip,[6] the change of temperature of a heated bimetallic strip due to the change of pressure in the surrounding gas,[7] and the bending of a bimetallic electrically heated strip owing to temperature changes caused by varying heat loss in a surrounding gas with variations of pressure,[8] have been used to measure low pressures. A manometer for 10^{-3}–10^{-5} mm. depends on an electric glow discharge in a magnetic field.[9]

The latest type of high-vacuum gauge is the *ionisation gauge*,[10] depending on

1936, **228**, 1; Bolland and Melville, *Trans. Faraday Soc.*, 1937, **33**, 1316; Twigg, *ibid.*, 1937, **33**, 1329; Rogers, Robertson, and Davis, *Gen. Elec. Rev.*, 1938, **41**, 534; Fawcett, *J.S.C.I.*, 1939, **58**, 43 T; Thomas and Olmer, *J.A.C.S.*, 1942, **64**, 2190; Rittner, *Rev. Sci. Instr.*, 1946, **17**, 113. A different (thermocouple) type of gauge was described by Rohn, *Z. Elektrochem.*, 1914, **20**, 539; Rumpf, *Z. techn. Phys.*, 1926, **7**, 224; Bartholomeyczyk, *ibid.*, 1941, **22**, 25; Berraz, *Amer. Chem. Abstr.*, 1943, **37**, 803; Smiley, *Ind. Eng. Chem. Anal.*, 1946, **18**, 800; Picard, Smith, and Zollers, *Rev. Sci. Instr.*, 1946, **17**, 125; Mellen, *Ind. Eng. Chem.*, 1948, **40**, 787.

1 *Proc. Phys. Soc.*, 1921, **33**, 287.

2 Dickins, *Proc. Roy. Soc.*, 1934, **143**, 517; Foster, *ibid.*, 1934, **147**, 128; *J.C.S.*, 1945, 360; Gregory, *Proc. Roy. Soc.*, 1935, **149**, 35; *Phil. Mag.*, 1936, **22**, 257; Archer, *ibid.*, 1935, **19**, 446, 901.

3 Ellett and Zabel, *Phys. Rev.*, 1931, **37**, 1102.

4 King, *Proc. Phys. Soc.*, 1925, **38**, 80; Rollefson, *J.A.C.S.*, 1929, **51**, 804.

5 *Oversigt K. Danske Vidensk. Selskab. Forhl.*, 1915, 459.

6 Haase, Klages, and Klumb, *Phys. Z.*, 1936, **37**, 440.

7 Klumb and Haase, *Phys. Z.*, 1936, **37**, 27.

8 Michelson, *Phys. Z.*, 1908, **9**, 18; Klumb and Haase, *ibid.*, 1936, **37**, 27.

9 Penning, *Physica*, 1937, **4**, 71.

10 Buckley, *Proc. Nat. Acad.*, 1916, **2**, 683; Masamichi So, *Proc. Phys. Math. Soc. Japan*, 1919, **1**, 76; Dushman and Found, *Phys. Rev.*, 1920, **15**, 133, 134; 1921, **17**, 7; 1924, **23**, 734; Dushman, *Gen. Elec. Rev.*, 1920, **23**, 731, 847; Kaufmann and Serowy, *Z. Phys.*, 1921, **5**, 319; Simon, *Z. techn. Phys.*, 1924, **5**, 221 (bibl.); Perucca, *Nuov. Cim.*, 1925, **2**, 287; Poindexter, *Phys. Rev.*, 1925, **26**, 859; 1926, **28**, 208; Found and Reynolds, *J. Opt. Soc. Amer.*, 1926, **13**, 217; Teichmann, *Z. techn. Phys.*, 1928, **9**, 22; Veil, *Rev. Gén. Sci.*, 1928, **39**, 10; Simon and Feher, *Z. Elektrochem.*, 1929, **35**, 162; Molthan, *Z. techn. Phys.*, 1930, **11**, 522; Jaycox and Weinhart, *Rev. Sci. Instr.*, 1931, **2**, 401; Morgulis, *J. Techn. Phys. U.S.S.R.*, 1931, **1**, 51 (theory); *Sow. Phys. Z.*, 1934, **5**, 407; Oberbeck and Meyer, *Rev. Sci. Instr.*, 1934, **5**, 287; Hoag and Smith, *ibid.*, 1936, **7**, 497; Huntoon and Ellett, *Phys. Rev.*, 1936, **49**, 381 (3×10^{-11} mm.); Ridenour and Lampson, *Rev. Sci. Instr.*, 1937, **8**, 162; Montgomery and Montgomery, *ibid.*, 1938, **9**, 58; Nelson and Wing, *ibid.*, 1942, **13**, 215; Zielinski, *Electronics*, 1944, July, 112 (also other methods); Dushman and Young, *Phys. Rev.*, 1945, **68**, 278; Van Valkenberg, *Gen. Elec. Rev.*, 1946, **49**, No. vi, 38 ($<10^{-7}$ atm.); Picard, Smith, and Zollers, *Rev. Sci. Instr.*, 1946, **17**, 125 (thermocouple type); Downing and Mellen, *ibid.*, 1946, **17**, 218; Dushman, *Instruments*, 1947, **20**, 234 (review); von Ubisch, *Arkiv Mat. Astron. Fys.*, 1947, **34** A, No. 14; 1948, **35** A, No. 28; Krusser, *J. Techn. Phys. U.S.S.R.*, 1947, **17**, 63; Roy-Pochon, *Le Vide*, 1947, **2**, 333; Dayton, *Ind. Eng. Chem.*, 1948, **40**, 795 (calibration errors); Apker, *ibid.*, 1948, **40**, 846.

the positive ionisation of a gas at low pressure produced by a stream of electrons. This gauge comprises a diode or triode tube, the ion current in which is a definite function of the gas pressure. If the grid current is I_G and the anode current I_A, the gas pressure is:

$$p=KI_G/I_A \quad . \quad . \quad . \quad . \quad . \quad . \quad . \quad . \quad . \quad . \quad (2)$$

where the proportionality factor K depends on the tube, the applied voltage, and the gas, so that relative measurements are used. The measurable pressure goes down to 10^{-8} mm. Hg. The radium source ionisation gauge [1] depends on the use of a radio-active source to produce the ion current, an amplifier [2] being used. The *thermoelectric valve manometer* depends on a different principle, a resistance or capacity change brought about by a pressure difference being transmitted to the grid of the valve.

§ 7. The Radiometer

The so-called radiometer effect is demonstrated in Crookes's radiometer,[3] consisting of light metal vanes polished on one side and blackened on the other, mounted on an axis in an evacuated glass bulb and rotating on exposure to light. It may be used to measure radiant energy,[4] but the theory is difficult and still not fully understood.[5] The effect is almost certainly due to the thermal creep of residual gas over the unequally heated solid. Calculation of molecular diameters from the radiometer effect is possible.[6] Brüche and Littwin [7] confirmed that at very low pressures the radiometer effect is a surface effect, and at higher pressures an edge effect. A modified radiometer has been used as a low-pressure gauge.[8] The thermal repulsion of droplets in air is a radiometer effect.[9]

1 Downing and Mellen, *Rev. Sci. Instr.*, 1946 ,**17**, 218; Mellen, *Ind. Eng. Chem.*, 1948, **40**, 787.

2 Roberts, *Rev. Sci. Instr.*, 1939, **10**, 181.

3 *Phil. Trans.*, 1874, **164**, 501; 1876, **166**, 325; 1879, **170**, 87.

4 Nichols, *Ann. Phys.*, 1897, **60**, 401; *Phys. Rev.*, 1923, **21**, 587; Spence, *J. Opt. Soc. Amer.*, 1922, **6**, 625; Marsh, Condon, and Loeb, *ibid.*, 1925, **11**, 257; Marsh, *ibid.*, 1926, **12**, 135; Sandvik, *ibid.*, 1926, **12**, 355.

5 Einstein, *Z. Phys.*, 1924, **27**, 1; cf. Laski and Zerner, *ibid.*, 1920, **3**, 224; Rutherford, *Engineering*, 1929, **127**, 319, 347, 381, 449; Herzfeld, in Taylor, " Physical Chemistry," 1931, **1**, 204; Loeb, " Kinetic Theory of Gases," 2nd edit., 1934, 364; Weber, *Comm. Leiden*, 1937, **246***b*; Kennard, " Kinetic Theory of Gases," 1938, 333.

6 Brillouin, *Ann. Chim.*, 1900, **20**, 440; Debye, *Phys. Z.*, 1910, **11**, 1115; Czerny and Hettner, *Z. Phys.*, 1924, **27**, 12; 1924, **30**, 258; Fredlund, *Ann. Phys.*, 1937, **30**, 99.

7 *Z. Phys.*, 1928, **52**, 318.

8 Klumb and Schwarz, *Z. Phys.*, 1944, **122**, 418.

9 Rosenblatt and La Mer, *Phys. Rev.*, 1946, **70**, 385 (bibl.); Paranjpe, *Proc. Indian Acad. Sci.*, 1946, **23 A**, 233.

INDEX[1]

[1] To save space, cross-references are not usually given, and in using the index alternative entries should be consulted. For example, for " zero-point energy " see " energy, zero-point."